Small Business Sourcebook

ISSN 0883-3397

Small Business Sourcebook

The Entrepreneur's Resource

FORTY-SECOND EDITION

Volume 3

General Small Business Topics

(Entries 16530-26478)

Holly M. Selden
Project Editor

Small Business Sourcebook, 42nd edition

Project Editor: Holly M. Selden

Editorial Support Services: Pranav Kokate

Composition and Electronic Prepress: Carolyn Roney

Manufacturing: Rita Wimberley

© 2025 Gale, a Cengage Company

ALL RIGHTS RESERVED. No part of this work covered by the copyright herein may be reproduced, transmitted, stored, or used in any form or by any means graphic, electronic, or mechanical, including but not limited to photocopying, recording, scanning, digitizing, taping, Web distribution, information networks, or information storage and retrieval systems, except as permitted under Section 107 or 108 of the 1976 United States Copyright Act, without the prior written permission of the publisher.

This publication is a creative work fully protected by all applicable copyright laws, as well as by misappropriation, trade secret, unfair competition, and other applicable laws. The authors and editors of this work have added value to the underlying factual material herein through one or more of the following: unique and original selection, coordination, expression, arrangement, and classification of the information.

For product information and technology assistance, contact us at
Gale Customer Support, 1-800-877-4253.
For permission to use material from this text or product,
submit all requests online at **www.cengage.com/permissions**.
Further permissions questions can be emailed to
permissionrequest@cengage.com.

While every effort has been made to ensure the reliability of the information presented in this publication, Gale, part of Cengage Group, does not guarantee the accuracy of the data contained herein. Gale accepts no payment for listing and inclusion in the publication of any organization, agency, institution, publication, service, or individual does not imply endorsement of the editors or publisher. Errors brought to the attention of the publisher and verified to the satisfaction of the publisher will be corrected in future editions.

Gale, part of Cengage Group
5191 Natorp Blvd.
Mason, OH 45040

978-1-5358-7663-6 (set)
978-1-5358-7664-3 (vol. 1)
978-1-5358-7665-0 (vol. 2)
978-1-5358-7666-7 (vol. 3)
978-1-5358-7667-4 (vol. 4)
978-1-5358-7668-1 (vol. 5)
978-1-5358-7669-8 (vol. 6)

ISSN 0883-3397

This title is also available as an e-book.
978-1-5358-7670-4
Contact your Gale sales representative for ordering information.

Contents

Volume 1
Introduction vii
User's Guide. ix
List of Small Business Profiles xv
Standard Industrial Classification (SIC) Codes for
 Profiled Small Businesses xix
Licensing Assistance Programs xxxiii
Guide to Publishers. xxxvii
Glossary. lxxxix

Small Business Profiles 1

Provides start-up information, associations and other organizations, educational programs, directories of educational programs, reference works, sources of supply, statistical sources, trade periodicals, video/audio media, trade shows and conventions, consultants, franchises and business opportunities, computerized databases, computer systems/software, libraries, and research centers.

Volume 2
Introduction vii
User's Guide ix
List of Small Business Profiles xv
Standard Industrial Classification (SIC) Codes for
 Profiled Small Businesses xix

Small Business Profiles 623

Volume 3
Introduction vii
User's Guide ix
List of General Small Business Topics xv

General Small Business Topics. 1253

Includes associations and other organizations, educational programs, directories of educational programs, reference works, sources of supply, statistical sources, trade periodicals, video/audio media, trade shows and conventions, consultants, computerized databases, computer systems/software, libraries, and research centers.

Volume 4
Introduction vii
User's Guide ix
List of General Small Business Topics xv

General Small Business Topics. 1827

Volume 5
Introduction vii
User's Guide ix

State Listings. 2393

Offers sources of small business assistance by state, territory, and Canadian province, including small business development centers, small business assistance programs, SCORE offices, better business bureaus, chambers of commerce, minority business assistance programs, financing and loan programs, procurement assistance programs, incubators/research and technology parks, educational programs, legislative assistance, small business development consultants, and publications.

Volume 6
Introduction vii
User's Guide ix

State Listings. 2951

Federal Government Assistance 3111

Lists U.S. federal government agencies and offices, including regional, branch, and district offices, which focus on small business issues, programs, assistance, and policy.

Master Index 3167

Introduction

The appeal of small business ownership remains perpetually entrenched in American culture as one of the most viable avenues for achieving the American Dream. To many entrepreneurs, going into business for themselves represents financial independence, an increased sense of identity and self-worth, and the fulfillment of personal goals. Small business owners strive to make their mark in today's competitive marketplace by establishing healthy businesses that can, over time, become legacies handed down from one generation to the next. Entrepreneurs from each generation tackle the obstacles and adversities of the current business and economic climate to test their business savvy and generate opportunities. Today's entrepreneurs face many of the problems of their predecessors, as well as some distinctly new challenges.

With the rightsizing, downsizing, and reorganization of corporate America, many individuals have decided to confront the risks of developing and operating their own businesses. Small business ownership is rapidly becoming a viable alternative to what is perceived as an equally unstable corporate environment. These entrepreneurs, many of whom have firsthand experience with the problems and inefficiencies inherent in today's large corporations, seek to improve upon an archaic business model and to capitalize on their own ingenuity and strengths. Led by their zeal, many would-be entrepreneurs let their desire, drive, and determination overshadow the need for business knowledge and skill. Ironically, aids in obtaining these components of entrepreneurial success are widely available, easily accessible, and often free of charge.

Small Business Sourcebook (*SBS*) is a six-volume annotated guide to nearly 17,000 listings of live and print sources of information designed to facilitate the start-up, development, and growth of specific small businesses, as well as more than 19,500 similar listings on general small business topics. An additional 12,500 state-specific listings and nearly 1,100 U.S. federal government agencies and offices specializing in small business issues, programs, and assistance are also included. *SBS* covers more than 300 specific small business profiles more than 100 general small business topics.

Features of This Edition

This edition of *Small Business Sourcebook* has been revised and updated, incorporating thousands of changes to names, addresses, contacts, and descriptions of listings from the previous edition. We have also added several hundred podcasts that will help users better understand topics on entrepreneurship and small business ownership.

Contents and Arrangement

The geographical scope of *SBS* encompasses the United States and Canada, with expanded coverage for resources pertaining to international trade and for resources that have a U.S. or Canadian distributor or contact. Internet sites that are maintained outside of the U.S. and Canada are also included if they contain relevant information for North American small businesses. Resources that do not relate specifically to small businesses are generally not included.

The information presented in *SBS* is grouped within four sections: Specific Small Business Profiles, General Small Business Topics, State Listings, and Federal Government Assistance. Detailed outlines of these sections may be found in the Users' Guide following this Introduction. Also included is a Master Index to Volumes 1 through 6.

Specific Small Business Profiles This section includes the following types of resources: start-up information, associations and other organizations, educational programs, directories of educational programs, reference works, sources of supply, statistical sources, trade periodicals, videos and podcasts, trade shows and conventions, consultants, franchises, and business opportunities, computerized databases, computer systems/software, Internet databases, libraries, and research centers. All resources are arranged by business type. Entries range from Accounting Service to Word Processing Service, and include such businesses as Cannabis Dispensaries, Computer Consulting, Food Trucks, and Web Site Design.

General Small Business Topics This section offers such resources as associations, books, periodicals, articles, pamphlets, educational programs, directories of educational

INTRODUCTION

programs, trade shows and conventions, consultants, computerized databases, Internet databases, software, libraries, and research centers. All resources in this section are arranged alphabetically by business topic.

State Listings Entries include government, academic, and commercial agencies and organizations, as well as select coverage of relevant state-specific publications. Listings are arranged alphabetically by state, territory, and Canadian province. Some examples include small business development consultants, SCORE offices, financing and loan programs, better business bureaus, and chambers of commerce.

Federal Government Assistance Listings Entries include federal organizations and agencies specializing in small business issues, programs, assistance, and policy. Listings are arranged alphabetically by U.S. government agency or office; regional or branch offices are listed alphabetically by state.

Master Index All entries in Volumes 1 through 6 are arranged in one alphabetic index for convenience.

Entries in SBS include (as appropriate and available):

- Organization, institution, or product name
- Contact information, including contact name, address and phone, toll-free, and fax numbers
- Author/editor, date(s), and frequency
- Availability, including price
- Brief description of purpose, services, or content
- Company and/or personal E-mail addresses
- Web site addresses

SBS also features the following:

Guide to Publishers—An alphabetic listing of nearly 1,000 companies, associations, institutions, and individuals that publish the periodicals, directories, guidebooks, and other publications noted in the Small Business Profiles and General Topics sections. Users are provided with full contact information, including address, phone, fax, and e-mail and URL when available. The Guide to Publishers facilitates contact with publishers and provides a one-stop resource for valuable information.

Method of Compilation

SBS was compiled by consulting small business experts and entrepreneurs, as well as a variety of resources, including direct contact with the associations, organizations, and agencies through Internet research or materials provided by those listees; government resources; and data obtained from other relevant Gale directories. *SBS* was reviewed by a team of small business advisors, all of whom have numerous years of expertise in small business counseling and identification of small business information resources. The last and perhaps most important resource we utilize is direct contact with our readers, who provide valuable comments and suggestions to improve our publication. *SBS* relies on these comprehensive market contacts to provide today's entrepreneurs with relevant, current, and accurate information on all aspects of small business.

Available in Electronic Formats

Licensing. Small Business Sourcebook is available for licensing. The complete database is provided in a fielded format and is deliverable on various forms of media. For more information, contact Gale's Business Development Group at 1-800-877-GALE, or visit our website at www.gale.com.

Comments and Suggestions Welcome

Associations, agencies, business firms, publishers, and other organizations that provide assistance and information to the small business community are encouraged to submit material about their programs, activities, services, or products. Comments and suggestions from users of this directory are also welcomed and appreciated. Please contact:

Project Editor
Small Business Sourcebook
27555 Executive Dr., Ste. 270
Farmington Hills, MI 48331
Gale, part of Cengage Group
URL: www.gale.com

User's Guide

Small Business Sourcebook (*SBS*) provides information in a variety of forms and presentations for comprehensive coverage and ease of use. The directory contains four parts within six volumes:

- Specific Small Business Profiles
- General Small Business Topics
- State Listings
- Federal Government Assistance

Information on specific businesses is arranged by type of business; the many general topics that are of interest to the owners, operators, or managers of all small businesses are grouped in a separate section for added convenience. Users should consult the various sections to benefit fully from the information *SBS* offers. For example, an entrepreneur with a talent or interest in the culinary arts could peruse a number of specific small business profiles, such as Restaurant, Catering Service, Cooking School, Specialty/Gourmet Food/Wine Shop, Food Truck, Healthy Restaurant, or Candy/Chocolate Shop. Secondly, the General Small Business Topics section could be consulted for any applicable subjects, such as Service Industry, Retailing, Franchising, and other relevant topics. Then, the appropriate state within the State Listings section would offer area programs and offices providing information and support to small businesses, including venture capital firms and small business development consultants. Finally, the Federal Government Assistance section could supply relevant government offices, such as procurement contacts.

Features Included in Volumes 1 and 2

List of Small Business Profiles. This list provides an alphabetic outline of the small businesses profiled. The page number for the beginning of each profile is indicated.

Standard Industrial Classification (SIC) Codes for Profiled Small Businesses. This section lists four-digit SIC codes and corresponding classification descriptions for the small businesses profiled in this edition. The SIC system, which organizes businesses by type, is a product of the Statistical Policy Division of the U.S. Office of Management and Budget. Statistical data produced by government, public, and private organizations is usually categorized according to SIC codes, thereby facilitating the collection, comparison, and analysis of data as well as providing a uniform method for presenting statistical information. Hence, knowing the SIC code for a particular small business increases access and the use of a variety of statistical data from many sources.

Guide to Publishers. This resource lists alphabetically the companies, associations, institutions, and individuals that publish the periodicals, directories, guidebooks, and other publications noted in the "Small Business Profiles" and "General Topics" sections. Users are provided with full contact information, including address, phone, fax, and e-mail and URL when available. The "Guide" facilitates contact with publishers and provides a one-stop resource for valuable information.

Glossary of Small Business Terms. This glossary defines nearly 400 small business terms, including financial, governmental, insurance, procurement, technical, and general business definitions. Cross-references and acronyms are also provided.

Small Business Profiles A-Z. More than 300 small business profiles are represented in volumes 1 and 2. Profiles are listed alphabetically by business type. Each profile may contain up to sixteen subheadings that correlate to a resource type; entries within are listed alphabetically. These resource types are detailed below:

- **Start-up Information**—Includes periodical articles, books, manuals, book excerpts, kits, and other sources of information. Entries offer title; publisher; address; phone, fax, toll-free numbers; company e-mail and URL addresses; and a description. Bibliographic data is provided for cited periodical articles whenever possible.

- **Associations and Other Organizations**—Includes trade and professional associations whose members gather and disseminate information of interest to small business owners. Entries offer the association's name; address; phone, toll-free and fax numbers; company e-mail address; contact name; purpose and objective; a description of membership; telecommunication services; and a listing of its publications, including publishing frequency.

- **Educational Programs**—Includes university and college programs, schools, training opportunities, association seminars, correspondence courses, and other educational programs. Entries offer name of program or institution, sponsor name, address, phone, toll-free and fax numbers, e-mail and URL addresses; and description of program.

- **Directories of Educational Programs**—Includes directories and other publications that list educational programs. Entries offer name of publication; publisher name, address, and phone, toll-free and fax numbers; editor; frequency or date of publication; price; and description of contents, including directory arrangement and indexes.

- **Reference Works**—Includes handbooks, manuals, textbooks, guides, directories, dictionaries, encyclopedias, and other published reference materials. Entries offer name of publication; publisher name, address, and phone, toll-free and fax numbers; e-mail and URL addresses; and, when available, name of author or editor, publication year or frequency, and price. A brief description is often featured.

- **Sources of Supply**—Includes buyer's guides, directories, special issues of periodicals, and other publications that list sources of equipment, supplies, and services related to the operation of the profiled small business. Entries offer publication name; publisher name, address, and phone, toll-free and fax numbers; e-mail and URL addresses; and, when available, editor's name, frequency or publication year, and price. A brief description of the publication, including directory arrangement and indexes, is often provided.

- **Statistical Sources**—Includes books, reports, pamphlets, and other sources of statistical data of interest to an owner, operator or manager of the profiled small business, such as wage, salary, and compensation data; financial and operating ratios; prices and costs; demographics; and other statistical information. Entries offer publication/data source name; publisher (if applicable); address; phone, toll-free and fax numbers of data source; publication date or frequency; and price. A brief description of the publication/data source is often provided.

- **Trade Periodicals**—Includes trade journals, newsletters, magazines, and other serials that offer information about the management and operation of the profiled small business. Such periodicals often contain industry news; trends and developments; reviews; articles about new equipment and supplies; and other information related to business operations. Entries offer publication name; publisher name, address, phone, toll-free and fax numbers, and e-mail and URL addresses; editor name; publication frequency; and price. A brief description of the publication's content is also included, when known.

- **Video/Audio Media**—Includes videos, podcasts, and other audiovisual media offering information on the profiled small business. Entries offer program title; creator or distributor name, address, phone, toll-free and fax numbers, and e-mail and URL addresses; description of program; price; and format(s).

- **Trade Shows and Conventions**—Includes tradeshows, exhibitions, expositions, conventions, and other industry meetings that provide prospective and existing business owners with the opportunity to meet and exchange information with their peers, review commercial exhibits, establish business or sales contacts, and attend educational programs. Entries offer event name; sponsor or management company name, address, phone, toll-free and fax numbers, and e-mail and URL addresses; a description of the event, including audience, frequency, principal exhibits, and dates and locations of event for as many years ahead as provided by the event's sponsor.

- **Consultants**—Includes consultants and consulting organizations that provide services specifically related to the profiled small business. Entries offer individual consultant or consulting organization name, address, and phone, toll-free and fax numbers; company and individual e-mail addresses; and a brief description of consulting services. (For e-mail and URL addresses, see the Small Business Development Consultants subheadings in the State Listings section in Volume 2.)

- **Franchises and Business Opportunities**—Includes companies granting franchise licenses for enterprises falling within the scope of the profiled small business, as well as other non-franchised business opportunities that operate within a given network or system. Entries offer franchise name, address, phone, toll-free and fax numbers, and e-mail and URL addresses, as well as a description of the franchise or business opportunity, which has been expanded whenever possible to include the number of existing franchises, the founding date of the franchise, franchise fees, equity capital requirements, royalty fees, any managerial assistance offered, and available training.

- **Computerized Databases**—Includes diskettes, magnetic tapes, CD-ROMs, online systems, and other computer-readable databases. Entries offer database name; producer name, address, phone, toll-free and fax numbers, e-mail and URL addresses; description; and available format(s), including vendor name.

(Many university and public libraries offer online information retrieval services that provide searches of databases, including those listed in this category.)

- *Computer Systems/Software*—Includes software and computerized business systems designed to assist in the operation of the profiled small business. Entries offer name of the software or system; publisher name, address, phone, toll-free and fax numbers; price; and description.

- *Libraries*—Includes libraries and special collections that contain material especially applicable to the profiled small business. Entries offer library or collection name; parent organization (where applicable); address; phone, toll-free and fax numbers; e-mail and URL addresses; contact name and title; scope of collection; and description of holdings, subscriptions, and services.

- *Research Centers*—Includes university-related and independently operated research institutes and information centers that generate, through their research programs, data related to the operation of the profiled small business. Also listed are associations and other business-related organizations that conduct research programs. Entries offer name of organization; address; phone, toll-free and fax numbers; company web site address; contact name and personal e-mail; a description of principal fields of research or services; publications, including title and frequency; and related conferences.

Features Included in Volumes 3 and 4

General Small Business Topics. This section offers chapters on different topics in the operation of any small business, for example, venture capital and other funding, or compensation. Chapters are listed alphabetically by small business topic; entries within each chapter are arranged alphabetically, within up to 14 subheadings, by resource type:

- *Associations and Other Organizations*—Includes trade and professional associations that gather and disseminate information of interest to small business owners. Entries offer the association's name; address; phone, toll-free and fax numbers; organization e-mail and URL addresses; contact name; purpose and objectives; a description of membership; telecommunication services; and a listing of its publications, including publishing frequency.

- *Educational Programs*—Includes university and college programs, schools, training opportunities, association seminars, correspondence courses, and other educational programs. Entries offer name of program or institution, sponsor name, address, phone, toll-free and fax numbers, e-mail and URL addresses, and description of program.

- *Directories of Educational Programs*—Includes directories and other publications that list educational programs. Entries offer name of publication; publisher name, address, phone, toll-free and fax numbers, and e-mail and URL addresses; editor; frequency or date of publication; price; and description of contents, including arrangement and indexes.

- *Reference Works*—Includes articles, handbooks, manuals, textbooks, guides, directories, dictionaries, encyclopedias, and other published reference materials. Entries offer title of article, including bibliographic information; name of publication; publisher name, address, phone, toll-free and fax numbers, and e-mail and URL addresses; and, when available, name of author or editor, publication year or frequency, and price. A brief description is often featured.

- *Sources of Supply*—Includes buyer's guides, directories, special issues of periodicals, and other publications that list sources of equipment, supplies, and services. Entries offer publication name; publisher name, address, phone, toll-free and fax numbers, and e-mail and URL addresses; editor's name, frequency or publication year, price, and a brief description of the publication, when available.

- *Statistical Sources*—Includes books, reports, pamphlets, and other sources of statistical data of interest to an owner, operator, or manager of a small business, such as wage, salary, and compensation data; financial and operating ratios; prices and costs; demographics; and other statistical information. Entries offer publication/data source name; publisher (if applicable); address; phone, toll-free and fax numbers of data source; publication date or frequency; and price. A brief description is often provided.

- *Trade Periodicals*—Includes journals, newsletters, magazines, and other serials. Entries offer name of publication; publisher name, address, phone, toll-free and fax numbers, and e-mail and URL addresses; and name of editor, frequency, and price. A brief description of the periodical's content is included when known.

- *Video/Audio Media*—Includes videos, podcasts, and other audiovisual media. Entries offer program title; distributor name, address, phone, toll-free and fax numbers, and e-mail and URL addresses; price; description of program; and format(s).

- *Trade Shows and Conventions*—Includes tradeshows, exhibitions, expositions, seminars, and conventions. Entries offer event name; sponsor or management company name, address, phone, toll-free and fax numbers, and e-mail and URL addresses; frequency of event; and dates and locations of the event for as many years ahead as known.

USER'S GUIDE

- **Consultants**—Includes consultants and consulting organizations. Entries offer individual consultant or consulting organization name, address, and phone, toll-free and fax numbers; company and individual e-mail addresses; and a brief description of consulting services. (See also Consultants in the State Listings section.)

- **Computerized Databases**—Includes diskettes, CD-ROMs, magnetic tape, online systems and other computer-readable databases. Entries offer database name; producer, address, phone, toll-free and fax numbers, and e-mail and URL addresses; description; and available format(s), including vendor name. (Many university and public libraries offer online information retrieval services that provide searches of databases, including those listed in this category.)

- **Computer Systems/Software**—Includes software and computerized business systems. Entries offer name of the software or system; publisher name, address, phone, toll-free and fax numbers, and e-mail and URL addresses; price; and description.

- **Libraries**—Includes libraries and special collections that contain material applicable to the small business topic. Entries offer library or collection name, parent organization (where applicable), address, phone and fax numbers, e-mail and URL addresses, scope of collection, and description of holdings and services.

- **Research Centers**—Includes university-related and independently operated research institutes and information centers that generate, through their research programs, data related to specific small business topics. Entries offer name of organization, address, phone, toll-free and fax numbers, e-mail and URL addresses, a description of principal fields of research or services, and related conferences.

Features Included in Volumes 5 and 6

State Listings. This section lists various sources of information and assistance available within given states, territories, and Canadian provinces; entries include governmental, academic, and commercial agencies, and are arranged alphabetically within up to 15 subheadings by resource type:

- **Small Business Development Center Lead Office**— Includes the lead small business development center (SBDC) for each state.

- **Small Business Development Centers**—Includes any additional small business development centers (SBDC) in the state, territory, or province. SBDCs provide support services to small businesses, including individual counseling, seminars, conferences, and learning center activities.

- **Small Business Assistance Programs**—Includes state small business development offices and other programs offering assistance to small businesses.

- **SCORE Offices**—Includes SCORE office(s) for each state. The Service Corps of Retired Executives Association (SCORE), a volunteer program sponsored by the Small Business Administration, offers counseling, workshops, and seminars across the U.S. for small business entrepreneurs.

- **Better Business Bureaus**—Includes various better business bureaus within each state. By becoming a member of the local Better Business Bureau, a small business owner can increase the prestige and credibility of his or her business within the community, as well as make valuable business contacts.

- **Chambers of Commerce**—Includes various chambers of commerce within each state. Chambers of Commerce are valuable sources of small business advice and information; often, local chambers sponsor SCORE counseling several times per month for a small fee, seminars, conferences, and other workshops to its members. Also, by becoming a member of the local Chamber of Commerce, a small business owner can increase the prestige and credibility of his or her business within the community, as well as make valuable business contacts.

- **Minority Business Assistance Programs**—Includes minority business development centers and other sources of assistance for minority-owned business.

- **Financing and Loan Programs**—Includes venture capital firms, small business investment companies (SBIC), minority enterprise small business investment companies (MESBIC), and other programs that provide funding to qualified small businesses.

- **Procurement Assistance Programs**—Includes state services such as counseling, set-asides, and sheltered-market bidding, which are designed to aid small businesses in bidding on government contracts.

- **Incubators/Research and Technology Parks**— Includes small business incubators, which provide newly established small business owners with work sites, business services, training, and consultation; also includes research and technology parks, which sponsor research and facilitate commercialization of new technologies.

- **Educational Programs**—Includes university and college programs, as well as those sponsored by other organizations that offer degree, nondegree, certificate, and correspondence programs in entrepreneurship and in small business development.

- **Legislative Assistance**—Includes committees, subcommittees, and joint committees of each state's senate and house of representatives that are concerned with small business issues and regulations.

- **Consultants**—Includes consultants and consulting firms offering expertise in small business development.
- **Publications**—Includes publications related to small business operations within the profiled state.
- **Publishers**—Includes publishers operating in or for the small business arena within the profiled state.
- **Early Stage Financing**—Includes organizations offering early-stage capital needed to launch and grow new businesses.
- **Venture Capital Firm**—Includes organizations offering financial support to small, early-stage and emerging firms.

Federal Government Assistance. This section lists federal government agencies and offices, many with additional listings for specific offices, as well as regional or district branches. Main agencies or offices are listed alphabetically; regional, branch, or district offices are listed after each main office or agency.

Master Index. This index provides an alphabetic listing of all entries contained in Volumes 1 through 6. Citations are referenced by their entry numbers. Publication titles are rendered in italics.

List of General Small Business Topics

This section covers sources of assistance applicable to a variety of small businesses. Resources are arranged by topic and include associations, educational programs, directories of educational programs, reference works, sources of supply, statistical sources, periodicals, videocassettes/audiocassettes, trade shows and conventions, consultants, computerized databases, computer systems/software, Internet databases, libraries, and research centers.

General Small Business Topics 1253	Family-Owned Business 1659	Payroll Tax 2125
Accounting 1262	Financial Management 1666	Pricing 2127
Advertising 1273	Franchising 1698	Public Administration 2128
Agribusiness 1274	General Business 1710	Public Relations 2135
Bartering 1294	Government Assistance 1730	Publicity/Advertising 2140
Benefits 1296	Government Procurement 1740	Purchasing 2146
Brand Image/Branding 1306	Government Regulations 1745	Remediation 2148
Budgets/Budgeting 1309	Healthcare and Social Assistance 1771	Research and Development 2150
Business Communications 1312	High-Tech Business 1809	Retailing 2159
Business Correspondence 1331	Hiring 1827	Risk Management 2175
Business Growth and Statistics 1337	Home-Based Business 1840	S Corporations 2177
Business Law 1366	Human Resource Management 1845	Sales Techniques 2179
Business Networks	Incorporation 1865	Scientific and Technical
(Social Groups) 1385	Incubators 1867	Research/Development 2194
Business Planning 1388	Insurance 1868	Seasonal Business 2209
Business Relocation 1403	International Trade 1878	Selecting Business Services 2211
Business Sale 1407	Internet Marketing 1901	Self-Employment 2212
Business to Business Market 1408	Intrapreneurship 1902	Selling a Business 2213
Business Scams (How to Avoid) 1409	Inventions, Licensing, and Patents ...1903	Senior-Owned Business 2216
Business Travel 1411	Inventory 1912	Service Industry 2218
Business Vision/Goals 1419	Knowledge Management/	Site Selection 2230
Buying a Business 1432	Competitive Intelligence 1915	Small Business Development 2236
Cash Flow 1436	Loans 1918	Small Business Software 2255
Compensation 1438	Management 1929	Small Business Trends 2267
Competition 1441	Manufacturing 1981	Social Security Taxes 2283
Competitive Pricing 1453	Market Research 2003	Socially Responsible
Consultants 1458	Market Strategy 2005	Business Practices 2284
Credit and Collection 1470	Marketing 2007	Sole Proprietorships 2295
Customer Service 1477	Minority-Owned Business 2043	Startups 2297
Discrimination/Sexual Harassment ...1488	Mobile Business 2055	Substance Abuse in
Distributing 1491	Multicultural Workforce 2058	the Workplace 2305
Economic Development 1496	Multilevel/Network Marketing	Target Marketing 2309
Education and Training 1529	Business 2068	Taxation 2310
Electronic Commerce/E-Business 1560	New Product Development 2069	Time Management 2323
Employee Motivation/	Nonmanufacturing 2080	Trade Shows/Exhibiting 2328
Team Building 1574	Nontraditional Financing 2082	Unions and Labor Relations 2336
Employee Theft 1593	Occupational Safety and Health 2085	Venture Capital and Other Funding ...2342
Entrepreneurial Traits/Skills 1595	Office Automation 2086	Wages and Salaries 2356
Entrepreneurship on the Web 1624	Outfitting the Business/Workspace ...2091	Wholesaling 2357
Environmentally Responsible	Outsourcing 2097	Women-Owned Business 2359
Business Practices 1629	Part-Time Business 2099	Workplace Safety 2383
Ethics 1652	Partnerships/Mergers 2100	Young Adult-Owned Business 2389

Small Business Sourcebook • 42nd Edition

General Small Business Topics

START-UP INFORMATION

16530 ■ *"Venturing Into New Territory: Career Experiences of Corporate Venture Capital Managers and Practice Variation"* in Academy of Management Journal (Vol. 55, June 1, 2012, No. 3, pp. 563)
Pub: Academy of Management
Contact: Sharon Alvarez, President
Ed: Gina Dokko, Vibha Gaba. **Description:** The role of venture capital managers' experiences in information technology firms' practice variation is investigated. Findings reveal that firms with managers who have practice-specific experience invest more in diverse industries and early-stage startups. The firm's goal orientation also tend to change from financial to strategic when venture capital managers have firm-specific experience and engineering experience. **Availability:** Electronic publishing; Download; PDF; Online.

ASSOCIATIONS AND OTHER ORGANIZATIONS

16531 ■ **Small Business and Entrepreneurship Council (SBEC)**
800 Connecticut Ave. NW, Ste. 300
Washington, DC 20006
Ph: (703)242-5840
Co. E-mail: info@sbecouncil.org
URL: http://sbecouncil.org
Contact: Karen Kerrigan, President
Facebook: www.facebook.com/sbecouncil
X (Twitter): x.com/SBECouncil
YouTube: www.youtube.com/TheSBECouncil
Description: Works to protect small business and sustain entrepreneurship. **Founded:** 1994. **Geographic Preference:** National.

SMALL BUSINESS ASSISTANCE PROGRAMS

16532 ■ **Small Unites**
URL: http://smallunites.org
Facebook: www.facebook.com/SmallUnites
X (Twitter): twitter.com/smallunites
Instagram: www.instagram.com/smallunites
YouTube: www.youtube.com/channel/UCFK0_hUDLfsAeVUDimXwk1A
Description: Provides resources and funds to small businesses facing economic challenges.

REFERENCE WORKS

16533 ■ *"7 Tips for Managing Your Business While on Vacation"* in Legal Zoom (March 17, 2023)
URL(s): www.legalzoom.com/articles/7-tips-for-managing-your-business-while-on-vacation
Ed: Jane Haskins, Esq. **Released:** March 17, 2023. **Description:** Small business owners have a lot to take care of on a day-to-day basis, and that doesn't end even for a vacation! However, there are steps you can take to get away for some much needed rest while keeping your business running. **Availability:** Online.

16534 ■ *"10 Tips for Adjusting Your Business Strategies to Meet the Demands of Modern Consumers"* in Small Business Trends (January 22, 2022)
URL(s): smallbiztrends.com/2022/01/adjusting-your-small-business-strategies.html
Ed: Annie Pilon. **Released:** January 22, 2022. **Description:** Provides a list of tips for small business owners to follow to help them meet customer expectations. **Availability:** Online.

16535 ■ *"15 Amazing Small Business Owner Titles: Which One is Right for You?"* in Small Business Trends (May 14, 2018)
URL(s): smallbiztrends.com/2018/05/small-business-owner-titles.html
Ed: Annie Pilon. **Released:** May 14, 2018. **Description:** Defines and discusses the various titles available for small business owners. **Availability:** Online.

16536 ■ *"16 Venmo Scams to Watch Out For"* in Small Business Trends (February 7, 2023)
URL(s): smallbiztrends.com/2023/02/venmo-scams.html
Ed: Rob Starr. **Released:** February 07, 2023. **Description:** The popular online payment method, Venmo, does attract it's share of scammers. This articles discusses how to recognize them so your business doesn't become their next victim. **Availability:** Online.

16537 ■ *"19 Best Books for Starting a Business"* in Legal Zoom (March 14, 2023)
URL(s): www.legalzoom.com/articles/19-best-books-for-starting-a-business
Released: March 14, 2023. **Description:** Looking for inspiration before you start a new business? Perhaps you want to learn about the finer points in business ownership. If so, the books on this list can help guide you. Includes a Key Takeaway on each book. **Availability:** Online.

16538 ■ *"The 20 Best Jobs for Flexibility"* in Business News Daily (March 17, 2023)
URL(s): www.businessnewsdaily.com/9705-best-jobs-for-flexibility.html
Ed: Bassam Kaado. **Released:** March 17, 2023. **Description:** If you are looking for a career with more flexibility, these jobs may serve your needs. Included are descriptions of what these jobs are and what makes them flexible. **Availability:** Online.

16539 ■ *"25 Cybersecurity Statistics Small Businesses Should Know"* in Small Business Trends (December 06, 2022)
URL(s): smallbiztrends.com/2022/08/cybersecurity-statistics.html
Ed: Sandeep Babu. **Released:** December 06, 2022. **Description:** Small businesses may not have IT teams to deal with cybersecurity issues, so becoming educated on the topic can save a lot of time and effort down the road. Listed are the top cybersecurity statistics small business owners should know. **Availability:** Online.

16540 ■ *"30 New Year Greetings for Business Owners"* in Small Business Trends (September 21, 2022)
URL(s): smallbiztrends.com/2019/12/new-year-greetings-for-business.html
Ed: Annie Pilon. **Released:** September 21, 2022. **Description:** The New Year is often a good time to thank those who helped with making your business a success during the previous year. Includes exact phrasing on what to say depending on your audience. **Availability:** Online.

16541 ■ *"30 Office Desk Plants to Brighten Your Business"* in Small Business Trends (July 18, 2022)
URL(s): smallbiztrends.com/2017/05/office-desk-plants.html
Ed: Annie Pilon. **Description:** A list and descriptions of plants that can be used in your office or on your desk to brighten up the space and bring enjoyment without taking up too much space or requiring specialized care. **Availability:** Online.

16542 ■ *"The Advantage: Why Organizational Health Trumps Everything Else in Business (J-B Lencioni Series)"*
Pub: Jossey-Bass
Released: February 01, 2012. **Price:** $28.95, hardcover. **Description:** A comprehensive examination of the unique advantage organizational health provides any small business and sets them apart from their competition. A healthy organization is whole, consistent and complete, is free of politics and confusion, and provides an environment where star performers want to stay. **Availability:** E-book; Print.

16543 ■ *"Anthem Becomes First to Penalize Small-Business Employees for Smoking"* in Denver Business Journal (Vol. 64, August 17, 2012, No. 13, pp. 1)
Pub: Baltimore Business Journal
Contact: Rhonda Pringle, President
E-mail: rpringle@bizjournals.com
Description: Health insurance companies Anthem Blue Cross and Blue Shield of Colorado are first to impose higher premiums on employee smokers who are under their small-group policies. The premiums may increase up to 15 percent starting September, to be paid by the smoking employees or the company. The law aims to help reduce tobacco-related health problems, as well as health care costs.

16544 ■ *"Are You Ready for a Four-Day Workweek?"* in Business News Daily (March 22, 2023)
URL(s): www.businessnewsdaily.com/four-day-workweek

Ed: Ross Mudrick. **Released:** March 22, 2023. **Description:** The idea of a four-day workweek is gaining steam, but how would a business implement that policy?. **Availability:** Online.

16545 ■ *The Art of Business Valuation: Accurately Valuing a Small Business*
URL(s): www.wiley.com/en-us/The+Art+of+Business+Valuation%3A+Accurately+Valuing+a+Small+Business-p-9781119605997

Released: August 2020. **Price:** $48, e-book; $60, hardcover. **Description:** Teaches what you need to know to become a small business valuator and how to work with financial statements that are not up to par with bigger businesses. **Availability:** E-book; Print.

16546 ■ *"Top 25 Engineering Firms" in South Florida Business Journal (Vol. 34, February 14, 2014, No. 30, pp. 12)*
Pub: American City Business Journals, Inc.
Contact: Mike Olivieri, Executive Vice President

Released: Weekly. **Price:** $25, Print. **Description:** Rankings of the companies within the engineering services in South Florida are presented. Rankings are based on the number of licensed engineers in the region. **Availability:** Print; Online.

16547 ■ *"Best Business Books of All Time" in Small Business Trends(November 23, 2020)*
URL(s): smallbiztrends.com/2020/11/best-business-books.html

Ed: Ivana Taylor. **Released:** November 23, 2020. **Description:** A list containing descriptions of the best business books of all time. These are must-reads for anyone just starting out on running a small business or looking to become an entrepreneur. **Availability:** Online.

16548 ■ *"Big Tax Breaks for Small Businesses" in Legal Zoom (March 23, 2023)*
URL(s): www.legalzoom.com/articles/big-tax-breaks-for-small-businesses

Ed: Sandra Beckwith. **Released:** March 23, 2023. **Description:** Discusses the changes made to the business tax codes, so you can be informed of the opportunities given to benefit your small business. **Availability:** Online.

16549 ■ *Built to Sell: Creating a Business That Can Thrive Without You*
Contact: John Warrillow
URL(s): www.amazon.com/Built-Sell-Creating-Business-Without/dp/1591845823?source=ps-sl-shoppingads-lpcontext&ref_=fplfs&psc=1&smid=ATVPDKIKX0DER

Price: $15, Paperback.; $14.99, E-book. **Description:** Gives tips to business owners on how not to micro-manage the business and how to effectively step away while keeping the company profitable. **Availability:** E-book; Print.

16550 ■ *"Business Books for Women" in Small Business Trends(October 31, 2022)*
URL(s): smallbiztrends.com/2020/10/business-books-for-women.html?utm_content=vc-true

Ed: Ivana Taylor. **Released:** October 31, 2022. **Description:** Includes a list and descriptions about business books that women entrepreneurs and small business owners would benefit from reading. **Availability:** Online.

16551 ■ *Business Psychology and Organizational Behaviour*
URL(s): www.routledge.com/Business-Psychology-and-Organizational-Behaviour/McKenna/p/book/9781138182646#

Ed: Eugene McKenna. **Released:** May 27, 2020. **Price:** $70.95, Paperback; $63.85, eBook. **Description:** A graduate and undergraduate textbook discussing theories and research findings on behaviors exhibited within a work environment. **Availability:** E-book; Print.

16552 ■ *"Congresswoman Aimed at Improving Small Business Exports" in Small Business Trends (September 23, 2022)*
URL(s): smallbiztrends.com/2022/09/congresswoman-aimed-at-improving-small-business-exports.html

Ed: Gabrielle Pickard-Whitehead. **Released:** September 23, 2022. **Description:** Intending to improve on small business exports, the House Small Business Committee recently held a meeting where Chairwoman Nydia M. Velazquez spoke out about improving programs from the Small Business Association. **Availability:** Online.

16553 ■ *"The Definitive Office Supplies Checklist for Small Businesses" in Small Business Trends(January 27, 2023)*
URL(s): smallbiztrends.com/2018/12/office-supplies-checklist-small-business.html

Ed: Annie Pilon. **Released:** January 27, 2023. **Description:** Small businesses need supplies and equipment just as much as much larger offices. Included here is a list of basic supplies plus lists of needed technology, furniture, and other items to help your business thrive. **Availability:** Online.

16554 ■ *"Do Small Businesses Need NDAs?" in Legal Zoom (March 27, 2023)*
URL(s): www.legalzoom.com/articles/do-small-businesses-need-ndas

Ed: Michelle Kaminsky, Esq. **Released:** March 27, 2023. **Description:** Nondisclosure agreements, or NDAs, are used to help keep business information private, which is helpful in protecting proprietary information. Explains what is involved in a NDA and how to apply one to your business. **Availability:** Online.

16555 ■ *"Eight Common Loan Scams – Don't Fall for Them" in Small Business Trends (February 8, 2023)*
URL(s): smallbiztrends.com/2023/02/loan-scams.html

Ed: Lisa Price. **Released:** February 08, 2023. **Description:** A guide on how to tell the difference between a legitimate loan broker and one who is trying to scam your small business. **Availability:** Online.

16556 ■ *"Etsy Says Payment Delays from SVB Collapse are Resolved" in Small Business Trends (March 17, 2023)*
URL(s): smallbiztrends.com/2023/03/etsy-says-payment-delays-from-svb-collapse-have-been-resolved.html

Ed: Gabrielle Pickard-Whitehead. **Released:** March 17, 2023. **Description:** There were payment delays to Etsy vendors due to the collapse of the Silicon Valley Bank (SVB). However, those issues have been resolved. Details about the collapse and the affects on Etsy are discussed. **Availability:** Online.

16557 ■ *"Evolutionary Psychology in the Business Sciences"*
Pub: Springer Publishing Co.
Contact: Bernhard Springer, Founder

Released: First edition. **Description:** All individuals operating in the business sphere share a common biological heritage, including consumers, employers, employees, entrepreneurs, or financial traders, to name a few. The evolutionary behavioral sciences and specific business contexts including marketing, consumer behavior, advertising, innovation and creativity and invention, intertemporal choice, negotiations, competition and cooperation in organizational settings, sex differences in workplace patterns, executive leadership, business ethics, store and office design, behavioral decision making, and electronic communications and commerce are all addressed. **Availability:** E-book; Print.

16558 ■ *"The Financial Illiteracy Problem Among Small Business Owners" in Small Business Trends (September 12, 2022)*
URL(s): smallbiztrends.com/2022/09/financial-illiteracy-problem-among-small-business-owners.html

Released: September 12, 2022. **Description:** Interview with Lisa L. Baker who discusses small business owners and their financial illiteracy. **Availability:** Online.

16559 ■ *"Free Versus Paid Apps—when Upgrades Make Sense for Small Businesses" in Legal Zoom (February 15, 2023)*
URL(s): www.legalzoom.com/articles/free-versus-paid-apps-when-upgrades-make-sense-for-small-businesses

Ed: Sandra Beckwith. **Released:** February 15, 2023. **Description:** Discusses the pros and cons of free versus paid apps that your business uses. **Availability:** Online.

16560 ■ *"Great Breakroom Snacks for Your Business" in Small Business Trends(May 7, 2023)*
URL(s): smallbiztrends.com/2021/04/breakroom-snacks.html

Ed: Michael Guta. **Released:** May 07, 2023. **Description:** Having breakroom snacks on hand can be a great way to give your employees a boost of energy during the day, and these snacks are more on the healthy side in order to keep people from having that sugar slump in the middle of their workday. **Availability:** Online.

16561 ■ *"Highly Effective Cybersecurity Practices That Require Little to No Investment" in Minority Business Entrepreneur (Vol. 39, Fall, 2022, No. 4, pp. 40-41)*
URL(s): digital.mbemag.com/?m=53732&i=769780&p=40&ver=html5

Ed: Oliver Noble. **Price:** $7.95. **Description:** Tips on securing your small business from cyber-attacks. **Availability:** Print; Online.

16562 ■ *"House Subcommittee to Hear from Small Business Owners on Right to Repair" in Small Business Trends (September 13, 2022)*
URL(s): smallbiztrends.com/2022/09/small-business-committee-hearing-right-to-repair-testimony-small-business-owners.html

Ed: Samson Haileyesus. **Released:** September 13, 2022. **Description:** The House Committee on Small Business Subcommittee on Underserved, Agricultural, and Rural Business Development is going to listen to a right-to-repair group as they discuss their concerns. **Availability:** Online.

16563 ■ *"How to Conduct a Financial Stress Test for Small Business Owners" in Legal Zoom (November 10, 2022)*
URL(s): www.legalzoom.com/articles/how-to-conduct-a-financial-stress-test-for-small-business-owners

Ed: Marcia Layton Turner. **Released:** November 10, 2022. **Description:** Provides details on how to perform a small business stress test to make sure your company will be able to survive tough financial situations. **Availability:** Online.

16564 ■ *"How to Get Government Contracts" in Small Business Trends (January 14, 2022)*
URL(s): smallbiztrends.com/2022/01/how-to-get-government-contracts.html

Ed: Rob Starr. **Released:** January 14, 2022. **Description:** Well-paying government contract jobs are available to small business owners. This article discusses how to seek them out from local, state, and federal level. **Availability:** Online.

16565 ■ *"How to Know if You Really Classify as a Small Business" in Business News Daily (February 21, 2023)*
URL(s): www.businessnewsdaily.com/295-sba-size-standards-small-business.html

Ed: Max Freedman. **Released:** February 21, 2023. **Description:** This article explains the Small Business Administration's classification on business size, which small business owners should be familiar with. Being classified as a true small business has some advantages, which are discussed. **Availability:** Online.

16566 ■ *"How to Make the Business World Sane Again" in Small Business Trends (October 17, 2022)*
URL(s): smallbiztrends.com/2022/10/making-the-business-world-sane-again.html

GENERAL SMALL BUSINESS TOPICS

Released: October 17, 2022. **Description:** The world and with it, the business world, went through some severe events such as COVID and the supply chain shortage that resulted from the pandemic. The article discusses ways businesses can get back to normal. **Availability:** Online.

16567 ■ *"How to Pay Yourself from Your Small Business"* in Legal Zoom (February 10, 2023)
URL(s): www.legalzoom.com/articles/how-to-pay-yourself-from-your-small-business
Ed: Jane Haskins, Esq. **Released:** February 10, 2023. **Description:** Getting a small business off the ground is not easy and it can even come with a financial cost to your personal funds. However, consider the given ideas in this article and see if there is a better way so you can pay yourself from money earned through all your hard work. **Availability:** Online.

16568 ■ *"How to Report a Scam"* in Small Business Trends (March 6, 2023)
URL(s): smallbiztrends.com/2023/03/how-to-report-a-scam.html
Ed: Rob Starr. **Released:** March 06, 2023. **Description:** Fraud against small businesses are prevalent. This article explains what to do if you become a victim and need to report a scamming issue. **Availability:** Online.

16569 ■ *"How to Retain That 'Small Business' Feel as Your Company Grows"* in Small Business Trends (December 9, 2021)
URL(s): smallbiztrends.com/2021/12/small-business-feel-while-company-grows.html
Released: December 09, 2021. **Description:** Many businesses thrive when their culture is based on a small business feel. However, how does a business retain that concept when the business starts expanding and becoming more corporate? Included are tips to make sure the culture that made your business successful is retained. **Availability:** Online.

16570 ■ *"How Small Business Can Negotiate with Landlords and Vendors during a Crisis"* in Legal Zoom (March 9, 2023)
URL(s): www.legalzoom.com/articles/how-small-business-can-negotiate-with-landlords-and-vendors-during-a-crisis
Ed: Jenn Morson. **Released:** March 09, 2023. **Description:** It's not always smooth sailing when running a business and sometimes situations arise which can affect your bottom line in a negative way. Learning to negotiate with a landlord and even your vendors for stock could save the business and give you some breathing room. **Availability:** Online.

16571 ■ *"How Will Small Businesses Address Cleanliness and Decontamination in a Post-Coronavirus World"* in Legal Zoom (February 21, 2023)
URL(s): www.legalzoom.com/articles/how-will-small-businesses-address-cleanliness-and-decontamination-in-a-post-coronavirus
Ed: Gwen Moran. **Released:** February 21, 2023. **Description:** Business owners everywhere are becoming more aware of cleaning and sanitation due to the necessity of killing the COVID-19 germ that affected the world. Disinfectants, barriers, and other cleansing and precautions are discussed. **Availability:** Online.

16572 ■ *"Improve Passwords and More during Cybersecurity Awareness Month"* in Small Business Trends (September 29, 2022)
URL(s): smallbiztrends.com/2022/09/cybersecurity-awareness-month.html
Ed: Annie Pilon. **Released:** September 29, 2022. **Description:** Cybersecurity Month is in October and that is a great reminder to have your IT department check over password management. **Availability:** Online.

16573 ■ *Innovation and Export: The Joint Challenge of the Small Company*
Pub: John Wiley & Sons, Inc.
Contact: Christina Van Tassell, Executive Vice President Chief Financial Officer
URL(s): www.wiley.com/en-us/Innovation+and+Export%3A+The+Joint+Challenge+of+the+Small+Company-p-9781786306203
Ed: Manon Enjolras. **Released:** volume 37. **Price:** $132, e-book; $165, hardcover. **Description:** Discusses how innovation and export can be joined to achieve company success. **Availability:** E-book; Print.

16574 ■ *"Interesting Stats on Too Many Virtual Meetings"* in Small Business Trends (October 17, 2022)
URL(s): smallbiztrends.com/2022/07/stats-on-virtual-meetings.html
Ed: Gabrielle Pickard-Whitehead. **Released:** October 17, 2022. **Description:** Since remote work has become so popular among office workers, meeting online has become the new normal. However, when does it become too much?. **Availability:** Online.

16575 ■ *"Is Your Business Protecting Its Classified Documents?"* in Small Business Trends (February 12, 2023)
URL(s): smallbiztrends.com/2023/02/protecting-classified-documents.html
Ed: Rob Starr. **Released:** February 12, 2023. **Description:** Discusses how small businesses can protect their most valuable documents. **Availability:** Online.

16576 ■ *"Jobs for the Future Asks Congress to Help Promote Youth Apprenticeship and Workforce Development"* in Small Business Trends (September 22, 2022)
URL(s): smallbiztrends.com/2022/09/jff-has-called-on-the-us-congress-to-expand-youth-workforce-development.html
Ed: Samson Haileyesus. **Released:** September 22, 2022. **Description:** Discusses how Jobs for the Future (JFF) is asking the U.S. congress to expand youth workforce development. **Availability:** Online.

16577 ■ *"Local Community Revitalization Business Grants Available Across the US"* in Small Business Trends (January 25, 2023)
URL(s): smallbiztrends.com/2023/01/community-revitalization-small-business-grants.html
Ed: Annie Pilon. **Released:** January 25, 2023. **Description:** Details on community grants for small businesses. **Availability:** Online.

16578 ■ *"Mileage Reimbursement: What You Need to Know"* in Business News Daily (March 8, 2023)
URL(s): www.businessnewsdaily.com/15891-mileage-reimbursement-laws-policies.html
Ed: Adam Uzialko. **Released:** March 08, 2023. **Description:** There are various state for federal regulations when it comes to mileage reimbursement. Small business owners should become familiar with these laws, especially fleet owners. **Availability:** Online.

16579 ■ *"Most Americans Expect to Keep Working in Retirement"* in Business News Daily (March 20, 2023)
URL(s): www.businessnewsdaily.com/15330-retired-americans-to-keep-working.html
Ed: Andrew Martins. **Released:** March 20, 2023. **Description:** Americans are redefining retirement and adjusting its parameters after decades. Many are planning on working even after they can officially retire, due to economic necessity, but others plan to keep working to stay mentally sharp. **Availability:** Online.

16580 ■ *"Network Detection and Response Explained"* in Small Business Trends (March 23, 2023)
Pub: Small Business Trends, LLC
Contact: Anita Campbell, Chief Executive Officer
URL(s): smallbiztrends.com/2023/03/network-detection-and-response.html
Ed: Gabrielle Pickard-Whitehead. **Released:** March 23, 2023. **Description:** Explains network detection and response in terms of cybersecurity for your small business. **Availability:** Online.

16581 ■ *"New Data Reveals the Best Dog Breeds for Remote Workers"* in Small Business Trends (June 2, 2021)
URL(s): smallbiztrends.com/2021/05/shih-tzu-best-dog-remote-workers.html
Ed: Gabrielle Pickard-Whitehead. **Released:** June 02, 2021. **Description:** With the uptick in remote work due to the COVID pandemic, many people have turned to adopting dogs to help with isolation issues. The top breed is revealed in the article. **Availability:** Online.

16582 ■ *"The New Free Apple Business Connect Tool – What Is It?"* in Small Business Trends (January 18, 2023)
URL(s): smallbiztrends.com/2023/01/apple-business-connect-tool.html
Ed: Gabrielle Pickard-Whitehead. **Released:** January 18, 2023. **Description:** Small businesses can use Apple Business Connect, which is a free tool that allows users to control how their information about their business appears across all of Apple's products. **Availability:** Online.

16583 ■ *"New Gmail Design Integrates Workspace and Chat Features"* in Small Business Trends (August 10, 2022)
URL(s): smallbiztrends.com/2022/08/the-new-gmail-design-update.html
Ed: Gabrielle Pickard-Whitehead. **Released:** August 10, 2022. **Description:** Gmail recently launched a new design on its platform, which lets users jump between various aspects within the layout. **Availability:** Online.

16584 ■ *"No Charlotte Tax Hike, But Plenty of Challenges"* in Charlotte Business Journal (Vol. 27, June 29, 2012, No. 15, pp. 1)
Pub: American City Business Journals, Inc.
Contact: Mike Olivieri, Executive Vice President
Ed: Erik Spanberg. **Released:** Weekly. **Price:** $20, Introductory 12-week offer(Digital & Print). **Description:** Charlotte, North Carolina City Council has rejected a proposed tax increase. The move halted investments in roads, business hubs, and major transportation projects. Comments from officials are included. **Availability:** Print; Online.

16585 ■ *"Not Normal: Inflation Taking Its Toll on Small Business"* in Small Business Trends (February 19, 2023)
URL(s): smallbiztrends.com/2023/02/inflation-taking-its-toll-on-small-business.html
Ed: Gabrielle Pickard-Whitehead. **Released:** February 19, 2023. **Description:** Prices have risen across the board for goods and services, which not only has affected consumers, but small businesses as well. **Availability:** Online.

16586 ■ *"Now You Can Sign Docs in Real Time on Microsoft Teams Meetings"* in Small Business Trends (September 25, 2022)
URL(s): smallbiztrends.com/2022/09/now-you-can-sign-docs-in-real-time-on-microsoft-teams.html
Ed: Gabrielle Pickard-Whitehead. **Released:** October 17, 2022. **Description:** Microsoft Teams is developing a proof of concept allowing signatures on documents during virtual meetings. **Availability:** Online.

16587 ■ *"PNC Study Highlights Small Business Gloom"* in Pittsburgh Business Times (Vol. 33, April 11, 2014, No. 39, pp. 5)
Pub: American City Business Journals, Inc.
Contact: Mike Olivieri, Executive Vice President
Released: April 11, 2014. **Price:** $4, Introductory 4-week offer(Digital & Print). **Description:** PNC Financial Services Group Inc. economist, Kurth Rankin, offers insights into the perspective of local small business owners in Pennsylvania. Rankin explains

that the mixed results of their semi-annual survey in the local area showed that small business owners are dealing with a difficult economy. **Availability:** Print; Online.

16588 ■ *Presence: Bringing Your Boldest Self to Your Biggest Challenges*
Ed: Amy Cuddy. **Released:** January 30, 2018. **Price:** $11.99, e-book; $14.49, paperback. **Description:** Explains how to use our physical experiences to tap into our emotional states in order to succeed in important tasks, such as a job interview, a business presentation, or any other challenge. **Availability:** E-book; Print.

16589 ■ *"SAIC To Be Honored For Supporting Veteran-Owned Businesses" in News Bites US (June 13, 2012)*
Description: Science Applications International Corporation (SAIC) was recognized by the National Veteran Small Business Coalition at the Veteran Entrepreneur Training Symposium (VETS2012) 'Champions of Veteran Enterprise' luncheon held in Reno, Nevada in June. SAIC is honored for its work with veteran-owned and service-disabled veteran owned small businesses. Statistical data included. **Availability:** Print; Online.

16590 ■ *"Should My Business Get a Toll-Free Number?" in Business News Daily (February 21, 2023)*
URL(s): www.businessnewsdaily.com/29-should-my-business-get-a-toll-free-number.html
Ed: Adam Uzialko. **Released:** February 21, 2023. **Description:** Discusses the pros and cons of obtaining a toll-free number for your small business. **Availability:** Online.

16591 ■ *"Signs of the Times" in Harvard Business Review (Vol. 92, May 2014, No. 5, pp. 36)*
Pub: Harvard Business Publishing
Contact: Diane Belcher, Managing Director
Price: $6. **Description:** A history is presented of modern symbols used in business, including the "at" swirl, the command icon, firewire, USB, and power. Anachronisms include the old telephone handset to indicate "call" and the manila file folder to indicate "storage". **Availability:** Online; PDF.

16592 ■ *"A Skimmer's Guide to the Latest Business Books" in Inc. (Volume 32, December 2010, No. 10, pp. 34)*
Pub: Inc. Magazine
Description: A list of new books published covering all aspects of small business is offered. **Availability:** Online.

16593 ■ *Small Business: Creating Value through Entrepreneurship*
URL(s): www.wiley.com/en-us/Small+Business%3A+Creating+Value+Through+Entrepreneurship%2C+1st+Edition-p-9781119791430
Ed: Vishal K. Gupta. **Released:** July 2021. **Price:** $26, e-book; $85, paperback. **Description:** A textbook for undergraduates about the concepts of starting and running a small business. **Availability:** E-book; Print.

16594 ■ *Small Business Optimism Index*
URL(s): www.nfib.com/surveys/small-business-economic-trends
Description: Index maintained by NFIB that details the results from surveys about the optimism associated with small businesses in the 2021 economy. **Availability:** Download.

16595 ■ *"Small Business Owners Share Their Best Advice" in Legal Zoom (February 16, 2023)*
URL(s): www.legalzoom.com/articles/small-business-owners-share-their-best-advice
Ed: Jenn Morson. **Released:** February 16, 2023. **Description:** Some well-regarded advice from current small business owners is given. **Availability:** Online.

16596 ■ *"Small Businesses Dealing with Higher Gas Prices" in Small Business Trends (October 31, 2022)*
Ed: Holly Chavez. **Released:** October 31, 2022. **Description:** The trend of higher gas prices is here to stay for the time being and it's having an impact on small businesses. **Availability:** Online.

16597 ■ *"Spate of Recent Eagle Ford Deals Shows Big Success of Small Operators" in San Antonio Business Journal (Vol. 28, May 30, 2014, No. 16, pp. 8)*
Pub: American City Business Journals, Inc.
Contact: Mike Olivieri, Executive Vice President
Released: Weekly. **Price:** $4, introductory 4-week offer(Digital only). **Description:** Smaller oil and gas exploration and production companies in Texas secured some deals at the Eagle Ford Shale Formation while major oil companies were looking to sell. Industry experts attribute such trend to the different business model of smaller companies compared to large companies that focus on offshore drilling. **Availability:** Print; Online.

16598 ■ *"Spring Cleaning: Getting Your Business in Order" in Legal Zoom (March 20, 2023)*
URL(s): www.legalzoom.com/articles/spring-cleaning-getting-your-business-in-order
Ed: Jane Haskins. **Released:** March 20, 2023. **Description:** The spring is a good time to get in the mindset to go over all of your small business documentation and make sure you are in compliance tax-wise. **Availability:** Online.

16599 ■ *"The State of Boomer-Owned Small Business" in Small Business Trends (November 6, 2022)*
URL(s): smallbiztrends.com/2022/11/boomer-owned-small-business.html
Ed: Gabrielle Pickard-Whitehead. **Released:** November 06, 2022. **Description:** An update on the state of small businesses being run by older generations and what the business landscape looks like as they retire. **Availability:** Online.

16600 ■ *State & Territories Small Business Profiles*
URL(s): advocacy.sba.gov/category/research/state-profiles
Released: Annual **Description:** Contains analysis of each state's small business activities. **Availability:** Print; PDF; Online.

16601 ■ *"Supply Chain Management: What Small Businesses Need to Know" in Business News Daily (February 21, 2023)*
URL(s): www.businessnewsdaily.com/4804-supply-chain-management.html
Ed: Jill Bowers. **Released:** February 21, 2023. **Description:** Small businesses need to consider how and when they receive goods to run their business. The supply chain the main component in that process and when disruptions hit it can be a disaster for a store in need of their supplies. **Availability:** Online.

16602 ■ *"Trouble Getting Customers to Pay?" in Legal Zoom (March 22, 2023)*
URL(s): www.legalzoom.com/articles/trouble-getting-customers-to-pay
Ed: Heleigh Botswick. **Released:** March 22, 2023. **Description:** There may come a time when your small business gets taken advantage of by a customer who refuses to pay for your goods or services. What are your options in a situation like this? Advice is given to deal with these customers. **Availability:** Online.

16603 ■ *"Using the SBA to Help Your Business Grow" in Legal Zoom (February 10, 2023)*
URL(s): www.legalzoom.com/articles/using-the-sba-to-help-your-business-grow

Ed: Brette Sember, J.D. **Released:** February 10, 2023. **Description:** The Small Business Association is full of resources for your small business. Everything from funding, classes, and even certifications are available to help your business. **Availability:** Online.

16604 ■ *"Venmo Reaches Small Business Milestone" in Small Business Trends (August 22, 2022)*
URL(s): smallbiztrends.com/2022/08/venmo-reaches-new-small-business-milestone.html
Ed: Samson Haileyesus. **Released:** August 22, 2022. **Description:** The payment services provider used by consumers and small businesses, Venmo, has grown by 50% and has about 90 million accounts. **Availability:** Online.

16605 ■ *"What is C2C?" in Business News Daily (February 21, 2023)*
URL(s): www.businessnewsdaily.com/5084-what-is-c2c.html
Ed: Andreas Rivera. **Released:** February 21, 2023. **Description:** Discusses C2C, which means either customer to customer or consumer to consumer, and how this business model can be used within your business. **Availability:** Online.

16606 ■ *"What Does the Secretary of State Do?" in Legal Zoom (March 15, 2023)*
URL(s): www.legalzoom.com/articles/what-does-the-secretary-of-state-do
Ed: Heather R. Johnson. **Released:** March 15, 2023. **Description:** Describes the role the Secretary of State provides on a state and federal level. **Availability:** Online.

16607 ■ *"What Is B2B, and How Does It Differ From B2C and DTC?" in Business News Daily (February 21, 2023)*
URL(s): www.businessnewsdaily.com/5000-what-is-b2b.html
Released: February 21, 2023. **Description:** An in-depth article discussing the B2B business model. **Availability:** Online.

16608 ■ *"What Is the Difference Between an App and a Mobile Website?" in Business News Daily (March 8, 2023)*
URL(s): www.businessnewsdaily.com/6783-mobile-website-vs-mobile-app.html
Ed: Mona Bushnell. **Released:** March 08, 2023. **Description:** Small business owners should understand the difference between an app and mobile websites and then choose which one would be most beneficial for their business practices. **Availability:** Online.

16609 ■ *"What You Should Know about Zoning Laws" in Legal Zoom (March 15, 2023)*
URL(s): www.legalzoom.com/articles/what-you-should-know-about-zoning-laws
Ed: Stephanie Vozza. **Released:** March 15, 2023. **Description:** Make sure your small business is not breaking the law by not being zoned properly. Discusses zoning laws and what you need to know before forming your small business. **Availability:** Online.

16610 ■ *"When You Need to Find outside Help for Your Business" in Legal Zoom (March 21, 2023)*
URL(s): www.legalzoom.com/articles/when-you-need-to-find-outside-help-for-your-business
Ed: Jane Haskins, Esq. **Released:** March 21, 2023. **Description:** What many people fail to realize is that there is a lot of background work that needs to be done while running a small business and a lot of it takes special knowledge. Having a lawyer, accountant, bookkeeper, and even a business coach is often very beneficial. **Availability:** Online.

16611 ■ *"Why Every Business Owner Needs a Trust" in Legal Zoom (March 24, 2023)*
URL(s): www.legalzoom.com/articles/why-every-business-owner-needs-a-trust

GENERAL SMALL BUSINESS TOPICS

Ed: Candice Lapin. **Released:** March 24, 2023. **Description:** Discusses the financial security small business owners receive when creating a trust. **Availability:** Online.

16612 ■ *"Why Your Employees Aren't Working the Way They Used To" in Small Business Trends(March 6, 2023)*
URL(s): smallbiztrends.com/2023/03/why-employees-arent-working-the-way-they-used-to.html
Released: March 06, 2022. **Description:** Discusses how employers need to acknowledge employees' mental health. **Availability:** Online.

16613 ■ *"Women Are Crushing the Gender Pay Gap" in Legal Zoom (March 16, 2023)*
URL(s): www.legalzoom.com/articles/women-are-crushing-the-gender-pay-gap
Ed: Gwen Moran. **Released:** March 16, 2023. **Description:** A report on the state of the Gender Pay Gap and discusses the disparity that is still happening. **Availability:** Online.

16614 ■ *"WordPress May NOT Be Right for This Type of Business" in Small Business Trends(January 10, 2023)*
URL(s): smallbiztrends.com/2023/01/why-use-wordpress.html
Ed: Holly Chavez. **Released:** January 10, 2023. **Description:** While WordPress is a great option for many small businesses to present an online presence, it is not a good option for those that rely on e-commerce. **Availability:** Online.

16615 ■ *"Your First Commercial Lease: How to Prepare and What to Expect" in Business News Daily (February 21, 2023)*
URL(s): www.businessnewsdaily.com/7619-negotiate-commercial-lease.html
Ed: Dock Treece. **Released:** February 21, 2023. **Description:** Many small businesses look for a commercial space to occupy. What do you need to know before signing that contract? This article takes a look at what should be included in the contract and what you need to understand in terms of finance and real estate. **Availability:** Online.

STATISTICAL SOURCES

16616 ■ *Small Business Sentiment Index*
URL(s): tradingeconomics.com/country-list/small-business-sentiment
Description: An index of small business sentiment for select countries. **Availability:** Online.

VIDEO/AUDIO MEDIA

16617 ■ *12 Tools I Can't Run My Business Without*
URL(s): www.makinggoodpodcast.com/episodes/187
Ed: Lauren Tilden. **Released:** July 19, 2023. **Description:** Podcast dicsusses tools for design, email, and productivity.

16618 ■ *Be a Profitable Badass Small Business Owner: 5 Mistakes Small Business Owners Make*
URL(s): traffic.libsyn.com/secure/localsmallbusinessownercoach/607_5_mistakes.mp3
Ed: Tammy Adams. **Released:** July 08, 2024. **Description:** Podcast suggests assessing your small business.

16619 ■ *Be a Profitable Badass Small Business Owner: 7 Key Pillars of a Strong Business Foundation*
URL(s): traffic.libsyn.com/secure/localsmallbusinessownercoach/588_building_a_strong_foundation_podcast.mp3
Ed: Tammy Adams. **Released:** January 15, 2024. **Description:** Podcast discusses seven areas of a small business that need to be solid.

16620 ■ *The Best Small Business Show: 4 Things to Keep in Mind When Starting Your Own Business*
URL(s): richgee.libsyn.com/225-4-things-to-keep-in-mind-when-starting-your-own-business
Ed: Rich Gee. **Released:** January 10, 2022. **Description:** Podcast offers four actionable steps when starting your own business.

16621 ■ *The Best Small Business Show: Enhancing Your Lead Generation*
URL(s): richgee.libsyn.com/309-enhancing-your-lead-generation
Ed: Rich Gee. **Released:** August 21, 2023. **Description:** Podcast discusses better lead generation.

16622 ■ *The Best Small Business Show: Fortified Bytes - Cybersecurity on a Small Business Budget*
URL(s): richgee.libsyn.com/317-fortified-bytes-cybersecurity-on-a-small-budget
Ed: Rich Gee. **Released:** October 16, 2023. **Description:** Podcast offers cybersecurity budgeting tips.

16623 ■ *The Best Small Business Show: How to Hire Your First Employee*
URL(s): richgee.libsyn.com/230-how-to-hire-your-first-employee
Released: February 14, 2022. **Description:** Podcast reflects on some the questions around hiring your first employee, including how to know if you're ready, where to start, how much to pay, what if you can't afford to pay them, and what if you don't have enough work for them.

16624 ■ *The Best Small Business Show: Six Books That Will Explode Your Business*
URL(s): richgee.libsyn.com/239-6-books-that-will-explode-your-business
Ed: Rich Gee. **Released:** April 18, 2022. **Description:** Podcast offers a list of their most requested books.

16625 ■ *BS-Free Service Business Show: 5 Questions Every Micro Agency Owner Needs to Ask*
URL(s): bsfreebusiness.com/micro-agency-questions
Ed: Maggie Patterson. **Released:** November 14, 2022. **Description:** Podcast outlines questions to ask as the owner of a micro agency, including how much (of if) you want to expand and if it supports your values.

16626 ■ *BS-Free Service Business Show: Agency or Solo: What's Right for You?*
URL(s): bsfreebusiness.com/agency-or-solo
Ed: Maggie Patterson. **Released:** October 16, 2023. **Description:** Podcast outlines what to consider when deciding whether to start an agency or remain solo.

16627 ■ *BS-Free Service Business Show: Building a Business by Blending Products and Services with Zoe Linda*
URL(s): bsfreebusiness.com/products-and-services
Ed: Maggie Patterson. **Released:** April 15, 2024. **Description:** Podcast discusses how to adapt offerings to meet customer needs.

16628 ■ *BS-Free Service Business Show: Exits and Evolutions: Navigating Change in Your Service Business*
URL(s): bsfreebusiness.com/exits-and-evolutions
Ed: Maggie Patterson. **Released:** April 25, 2024. **Description:** Podcast offers tips on when to adapt, whether by keeping up with trends, using new tech, or meeting changing needs.

16629 ■ *BS-Free Service Business Show: Keeping Your Business Simple and Sustainable (A Check-In)*
URL(s): bsfreebusiness.com/simple-and-sustainable-business
Ed: Maggie Patterson. **Released:** November 13, 2023. **Description:** Podcast offers six items to check on, with a focus on simplicity and sustainability, before starting a business.

16630 ■ *BS-Free Service Business Show: Leadership Fundamentals for a Successful Agency*
URL(s): bsfreebusiness.com/successful-agency
Ed: Maggie Patterson. **Released:** November 06, 2023. **Description:** Podcast discusses top six leadership skills for micro agencies.

16631 ■ *BS-Free Service Business Show: Staying Solo: Ditching Busy Work for Systems*
URL(s): insidescoop.libsyn.com/staying-solo-ditching-busy-work-with-systems
Ed: Maggie Patterson. **Released:** September 18, 2023. **Description:** Podcast examines the use of systems to remain a solo entrepreneur.

16632 ■ *BS-Free Service Business Show: Staying Solo: Rethinking Planning to Focus on Seasons*
URL(s): bsfreebusiness.com/rethining-planning
Ed: Maggie Patterson. **Released:** August 28, 2023. **Description:** Podcast outlines the benefits of quarterly planning.

16633 ■ *BS-Free Service Business Show: Staying Solo: Using Strategy to Break the Income Ceiling*
URL(s): bsfreebusiness.com/income-ceiling
Ed: Maggie Patterson. **Released:** September 11, 2023. **Description:** Podcast offers advice on breaking the income ceiling for solo agency owners.

16634 ■ *BS-Free Service Business Show: Staying Solo: What Support Do You Really Need?*
URL(s): bsfreebusiness.com/solo-support
Ed: Maggie Patterson. **Released:** September 04, 2023. **Description:** Podcast offers advice for making intentional and strategic decisions about why, when, and how to get support as a solo business owner.

16635 ■ *BS-Free Service Business Show: Staying Solo: Your Framework for a Simple, Sustainable Service Business*
URL(s): bsfreebusiness.com/staying-solo
Ed: Maggie Patterson. **Released:** August 07, 2023. **Description:** Podcast discusses the framework for a solo business.

16636 ■ *BS-Free Service Business Show: The Art of Reinvention with AdeOla Fadumiye*
URL(s): bsfreebusiness.com/art-of-reinvention
Ed: Maggie Patterson. **Released:** April 22, 2024. **Description:** Podcast offers a conversation with someone who walked away from a thriving business.

16637 ■ *BS-Free Service Business Show: The Different Types of Support for Entrepreneurs*
URL(s): insidescoop.libsyn.com/the-different-types-of-support-for-entrepreneurs
Ed: Maggie Patterson. **Released:** November 20, 2023. **Description:** Podcast offers suggestions for entreprenurial support, from hiring a business coach to getting a massage.

16638 ■ *BS-Free Service Business Show: The Growth Path for Micro Agency Owners*
URL(s): bsfreebusiness.com/growth-path-for-micro-agency
Ed: Maggie Patterson. **Released:** October 30, 2023. **Description:** Podcast discusses the non-linear growth path of micro agencies.

16639 ■ *BS-Free Service Business Show: The Power of Retainer Clients*
URL(s): bsfreebusiness.com/retainer-clients
Ed: Maggie Patterson. **Released:** March 27, 2023. **Description:** Podcast explains how a retainer with the proper structure can be incredibly effective.

16640 ■ *BS-Free Service Business Show: The Real Cost of Bad Boundaries with Clients*
URL(s): bsfreebusiness.com/boundaries-with-clients

Ed: Maggie Patterson. **Released:** March 11, 2024. **Description:** Podcast discusses client boundaries and how to build more sustainable relationships with them. .

16641 ■ *BS-Free Service Business Show: The Real Cost of Content Creation*
URL(s): bsfreebusiness.com/cost-of-content-creation
Ed: Maggie Patterson. **Released:** March 04, 2024. **Description:** Podcast discusses the value of blogging, podcasting and posting on social media and how to determine if it's right for your agency.

16642 ■ *BS-Free Service Business Show: The Real Cost of Tech and Tools for Solopreneurs*
URL(s): bsfreebusiness.com/tools-for-solopreneurs
Ed: Maggie Patterson. **Released:** February 12, 2024. **Description:** Podcasts highlights what tech tools are essential, what's extravagant, and red flags to notice. Also discusses yearly costs for different tech stacks.

16643 ■ *BS-Free Service Business Show: The Summer Slowdown*
URL(s): insidescoop.libsyn.com/the-summer-slow-down
Ed: Maggie Patterson. **Released:** June 05, 2023. **Description:** Podcast offers practical ideas for a summer slowdown.

16644 ■ *BS-Free Service Business Show: What No One Tells You About Running a Micro Agency*
URL(s): bsfreebusiness.com/running-a-micro-agency
Ed: Maggie Patterson. **Released:** October 31, 2022. **Description:** Podcast offers some considerations if you're thinking about shifting into a micro agency model.

16645 ■ *Build, Buy or Franchise? The Best Way to Jumpstart Your Entrepreneurial Journey with Tim Vogel*
URL(s): www.eofire.com/podcast/timvogel
Released: August 29, 2023. **Description:** Podcast discusses different ways to start a business,.

16646 ■ *The Client Lifecycle*
URL(s): bizchix.com/586-the-client-lifecycle
Ed: Natalie Eckdahl. **Released:** July 27, 2023. **Description:** Discusses the client journey from getting seen to the signed contract and payment.

16647 ■ *Competition and Financials - Back of the Napkin to Business Plan in 11 Slides with Brandon White*
URL(s): podcasts.apple.com/us/podcast/competition-and-financials-back-of-the-napkin-id1377276636?i=1000619363880
Released: July 05, 2023. **Description:** Podcast discusses funding options, including venture capital, angel investments, loans, or trading stocks.

16648 ■ *Elevated Entrepreneurship: Ashley Alderson: Connecting in the Chaos*
URL(s): mikemichalowicz.com/podcast/18613
Ed: Mike Michalowiicz. **Released:** June 15, 2020. **Description:** Podcast shares how to build community to help a small business survive.

16649 ■ *Elevated Entrepreneurship: Geoff Woods: Finding Your One Thing*
URL(s): mikemichalowicz.com/podcast/geoff-woods
Ed: Mike Michalowiicz. **Released:** July 06, 2020. **Description:** Podcast discusses how to find one thing to make everything else easier.

16650 ■ *Failure Is Your Trampoline to Success with Rich Moyer*
URL(s): www.eofire.com/podcast/richmoyer
Ed: John Lee Dumas. **Released:** July 31, 2023. **Description:** Podcast discusses failure as an impetus for success.

16651 ■ *How to Avoid the Pitfalls that Make You Hate Your Business with Eric Bandholz*
URL(s): www.eofire.com/podcast/ericbandholz2
Ed: Jon Lee Dumas. **Released:** October 15, 2024. **Description:** Podcast explains that owners define what success and how to be intentional about the products sold: determine if it's worthy of your time, will bring you joy, and is sustainable for your desired life direction.

16652 ■ *The How of Business: Delegation*
URL(s): www.thehowofbusiness.com/episode-026-delegation
Ed: Henry Lopez. **Released:** July 25, 2016. **Description:** Podcast discusses how to delegate effectively in your small business.

16653 ■ *The How of Business: Donata Kalnenaite - Legal Insights*
URL(s): www.thehowofbusiness.com/episode-095-donata-kalnenaite
Ed: Henry Lopez. **Released:** March 27, 2017. **Description:** Podcasts shares legal advice for small business owners.

16654 ■ *The How of Business: Matt Ruedlinger - Launching a Small Business*
URL(s): www.thehowofbusiness.com/episode-057-matt-ruedlinger
Ed: Henry Lopez. **Released:** November 21, 2016. **Description:** Podcast offers anecdotes and tips on starting a small business.

16655 ■ *The How of Business: Randy Long - Business Exit*
URL(s): www.thehowofbusiness.com/episode-040-randy-long
Ed: Henry Lopez. **Released:** September 09, 2016. **Description:** Podcast discusses exit strategies for your small business.

16656 ■ *The How of Business: Shahara Wright - Legal and Business Growth Strategies*
URL(s): www.thehowofbusiness.com/episode-094-shahara-wright
Ed: Henry Lopez. **Released:** March 20, 2017. **Description:** Podcast shares legal guidance and growth strategies for small businesses.

16657 ■ *The How of Business: Small Business Failure*
URL(s): www.thehowofbusiness.com/episode-035-small-business-failure
Ed: Henry Lopez. **Released:** August 29, 2016. **Description:** Podcast discusses preparing for and dealing with small business failure.

16658 ■ *The How of Business: Small Business Ownership Readiness Assessment*
URL(s): www.thehowofbusiness.com/440-business-ownership-readiness-assessment
Ed: Henry Lopez. **Released:** September 19, 2022. **Description:** Podcast offers tips to determine if you're ready to own a small business. Criteria include purpose, mental/emotional readiness, time, personal characteristics, money, business knowledge, and effort.

16659 ■ *The How of Business: Steve Hoffman - Surviving a Start-Up*
URL(s): www.thehowofbusiness.com/381-steve-hoffman-surviving-startup
Ed: Henry Lopez. **Released:** July 19, 2021. **Description:** Podcast offers tips on how to avoid common mistakes and have a better chance of achieving success with a small business start-up.

16660 ■ *The How of Business: Top 5 Reasons Small Businesses Fail*
URL(s): www.thehowofbusiness.com/524-5-reasons-businesses-fail
Ed: Henry Lopez. **Released:** June 10, 2024. **Description:** Podcast outlines why small businesses fail.

16661 ■ *How Entrepreneurs Are Scaling Disruptive Consumer Businesses with Steve Berg*
URL(s): www.eofire.com/podcast/steveberg
Ed: John Lee Dumas. **Description:** Podcast discusses consumer loyalty and founders with compelling stories.

16662 ■ *How to Find Your Zone of Genius to Grow Your Impact and Income with Cait Scudder: An EOFire Classic from 2021*
URL(s): www.eofire.com/podcast/caitscudder
Ed: Jon Lee Dumas. **Released:** September 07, 2024. **Description:** Podcast explains how to find your center point in business--the place where interest and skillsets intersect with a need in the world. Also discusses cultivating a relationship with risk.

16663 ■ *How I Built This: Advice Line with Tony Lamb of Kona Ice*
URL(s): wondery.com/shows/how-i-built-this/episode/10386-advice-line-with-tony-lamb-of-kona-ice
Ed: Guy Raz. **Released:** July 25, 2024. **Description:** Podcast answers questions about franchising and social media marketing from early-stage founders with a candy store and home decor brands.

16664 ■ *How Tech Debt Hurts Your Small Business with Corey Winter*
URL(s): beingboss.club/podcast/how-tech-debt-hurts-your-small-business
Ed: Emily Thompson. **Released:** January 24, 2023. **Description:** Podcasta explains tech debt, how it shows up in your business, and problems it can cause.

16665 ■ *How to Translate Your Passion into Purpose*
URL(s): ducttapemarketing.com/translate-passion-into-purpose
Released: September 14, 2023. **Description:** Podcast discusses how to set goals with deadlines, embrace constant innovation, and empower women to lead to billion-dollar success with Liz Elting, the CEO of TransPerfect.

16666 ■ *How to Trust a Coach Again (After You Have Been Burned)*
URL(s): bizchix.com/592-how-to-trust-a-coach-again-after-you-have-been-burned
Ed: Natalie Eckdahl. **Released:** September 07, 2023. **Description:** Podcast offers what to look for in a coaching program and the questions you should ask.

16667 ■ *The Key to Real Business Sucess May Surprise You with Penny Sansevieri*
URL(s): www.eofire.com/podcast/pennysansevieri2
Ed: Jon Lee Dumas. **Released:** September 30, 2024. **Description:** Podast explains why consistency and finding your lane are crucial for business success.

16668 ■ *Legal Basics for Small Businesses with Larissa Bodniowycz*
URL(s): www.makinggoodpodcast.com/episodes/160
Ed: Lauren Tilden. **Released:** February 07, 2023. **Description:** Podcast discusses legal consideration for small businesses, trademark and copyright basics, how to manage legal matters with a budget, and legal mistakes small business owners make.

16669 ■ *Main Street Business Insights: Janet Hurn, Future Ready Consulting*
URL(s): mainstreet.org/resources/knowledge-hub/podcast/janet-hurn-future-ready-consulting
Ed: Matt Wagner. **Released:** March 21, 2024. **Description:** Podcast features a conversation with a small business consultant on how to use technology to streamline processes, adapt marketing strategy, and save time and money.

16670 ■ *Marketplace: For This Michigan Business Owner, Wage Hikes Are Tied to Price Hikes*
URL(s): www.marketplace.org/2021/10/16/for-this-michigan-business-owner-wage-hikes-are-tied-to-price-hikes
Ed: Sean McHenry. **Released:** October 16, 2023. **Description:** Podcast explains how a stationery-store business owner correlates employee raises with price hikes.

16671 ■ Midwest Moxie: Computer Engineering and Biological Products: Nancy Benovich Gilby and Katie Thompson
URL(s): www.wuwm.com/podcast/midwest-moxie/2023-03-26/computer-engineering-and-bilogical-prodcucts-nancy-benovich-gilby-and-katie-thompson
Ed: Kathleen Gallagher. **Released:** March 26, 2023. **Description:** Podcast discusses how entrepreneurs took different paths to bring unique products to market.

16672 ■ Navigating Entrepreneurship with Ashley Menzies Babatunde
URL(s): beingboss.club/podcast/navigating-entrepreneurship
Ed: Emily Thompson. **Released:** September 27, 2022. **Description:** Podcast discusses how removing expectations and adopting curiosity can help embrace your entreprenurial experiences.

16673 ■ Networking Strategies for Introverts with Matthew Pollard: An EOFire Classic from 2021
URL(s): www.eofire.com/podcast/matthewpollard2
Ed: Jon Lee Dumas. **Description:** Podcast explains that networking is a system and can be learned like anything else.

16674 ■ Planet Money Summer School: MBA 1: Planet Money Goes to Business School
URL(s): www.npr.org/2023/07/20/1189029188/summer-school-1-planet-money-goes-to-business-school
Ed: Robert Smith. **Released:** July 20, 2023. **Description:** Outlines what goes into starting a small business.

16675 ■ Planet Money Summer School: MBA 2: Competition and the Cheaper Sneaker
URL(s): www.npr.org/2023/07/20/1189034915/summer-school-2-competition-and-the-cheaper-sneaker
Ed: Robert Smith. **Released:** July 20, 2023. **Description:** Discusses competition in a crowded market.

16676 ■ Professional on the Go: Can I Use Venmo for My Business?
URL(s): www.spreaker.com/user/11226745/venmo-for-business
Ed: Chinwe Onyeagoro. **Released:** July 16, 2019. **Description:** Podcast discusses mobile payment processing solutions.

16677 ■ Professional on the Go: Who Are the Top Paid Freelancers?
URL(s): www.spreaker.com/user/11226756/top-paid-freelancers
Ed: Chinwe Onyeagoro. **Released:** September 24, 2019. **Description:** Podcast discusses fastest growing freelance job categories, the top paid freelancers, and reasons to join a group like the Freelancers Union.

16678 ■ Profit First Nation: Relish Your Ownership
URL(s): www.profitfirstnation.com/episodes/ep-151-relish-your-ownership
Ed: Danielle Mulvey. **Released:** December 19, 2023. **Description:** Podcast discusses the importance of enjoying business ownership while maintaining financial responsibility. Also outlines five key areas of ownership.

16679 ■ Profit First Nation: The Switzerland Structure
URL(s): www.profitfirstnation.com/episodes/ep-147-switzerland-structure
Ed: Danielle Mulvey. **Released:** November 21, 2023. **Description:** Podcast explains the "Switzerland structure," where you avoid dependence on any one customer, employee, or vendor to ensure long-term success. Also discusses diversification, vendor audits, and employee cross-training.

16680 ■ Raising Capital in Saturated Markets
URL(s): omny.fm/shows/startup-hustle/raising-capital-in-saturated-markets

Ed: Matt DeCoursey. **Released:** August 18, 2023. **Description:** Podcast discusses the saturated AI startup scene, keys to fundraising in that environment, and how to educate the market. Features Jon Ricketts, CEO of Writerly.

16681 ■ Side Hustle to Small Business: Knowing Your Worth After Transitioning to Self-Employment
URL(s): www.hiscox.com/side-hustle-to-small-business/hannah-smolinksi-podcast-season-3
Ed: Sanjay Parekh. **Released:** August 02, 2023. **Description:** Podcast discusses knowing your worth as an entrepreneur, managing cash flow, and handling burnout.

16682 ■ Side Hustle to Small Business: Overcoming Your Fears and Achieving Your Dreams
URL(s): www.hiscox.com/side-hustle-to-small-business/brooke-monaghan-air-date-podcast-season-3
Ed: Sanjay Parekh. **Released:** December 27, 2023. **Description:** Podcast discusses overcoming the fear of starting your own business.

16683 ■ Small Biz 101: Hidden Treasures: Unveiling Small Business Resources at Your Public Library
URL(s): podcasts.apple.com/us/podcast/hidden-treasures-unveiling-small-business-resources/id1179203265?i=1000620964491
Ed: Connie Whitesell. **Released:** July 12, 2023. **Description:** Podcast suggest tools, materials, and expertise available to small business owners through the public library.

16684 ■ Small Biz 101: Unlocking Business Growth and Financial Freedom
URL(s): scatteredtostreamlined.com/money-moves-unlocking-business-growth-and-financail-freedom
Ed: Connie Whitesell. **Released:** March 13, 2024. **Description:** Podcast discusses challenges to business growth, including overcoming resistance to raising rates, hating selling, neglecting to give yourself credit, and feeling incapable.

16685 ■ Small Business, Big Mindset: The 4 Critical Steps to Starting a Business
URL(s): podcast.musclecreative.com/924061/episodes/8738144-the-4-critical-steps-to-starting-a-business
Ed: Erin Geiger. **Released:** June 22, 2021. **Description:** Podcast explains how to come up with a business idea, find clarity on vison, validate your business idea, and identify ideal clients or customers.

16686 ■ Small Business Growth: Buidling a Freepreneur Lifestyle
URL(s): smallbusinessgrowthpodcast.podbean.com/e/building-a-freepreneur-lifestyle-what-it-is-how-to-start-building-it
Released: October 17, 2023. **Description:** Podcast explains how to run a small business with freedom and balance in mind. .

16687 ■ Small Business Rundown: Advocacy - From Grassroots to Elections
URL(s): podcasts.apple.com/us/podcast/advocacy-from-grassroots-to-elections/id1669051104?i=1000630261516
Ed: Adam Temple. **Released:** October 05, 2023. **Description:** Podcast explains how NFIB advocates for small businesses and helps them get involved in pro-small business laws and regulations.

16688 ■ Small Business Rundown: Essential Tips to Grow Your Small Business
URL(s): podcasts.apple.com/us/podcast/essential-tips-to-grow-your-small-business/id1669051104?i=1000622473225
Released: July 27, 2023. **Description:** Podcast offers a toolkit for owners looking to expand their small businesses.

16689 ■ The Small Business School Podcast: Choosing the Perfect Business Location
URL(s): podcasts.apple.com/us/podcast/choosing-the-perfect-business-location/id1695210366?i=1000651166665
Ed: Staci Millard. **Released:** April 02, 2024. **Description:** Podcast discusses finding the right location. Includes considering the space the business requires, whether it relies on foot traffic, evaluating noise level, understanding cost analysis, and assessing growth projections.

16690 ■ Small Business Sessions: Erika Robinson: Small Businesses Have a Superpower that Big Companies Don't Have
URL(s): www.enterprisenation.com/learn-something/small-business-sessions-podcast-erika-robinson
Ed: Dan Martin. **Released:** October 23, 2024. **Description:** Podcast explains the superpowers of small businesses.

16691 ■ Small Business Startup Checklist
URL(s): www.thehowofbusiness.com/408-small-business-startup-checklist
Ed: Henry Lopez. **Released:** February 07, 2022. **Description:** Podcast outlines the primary steps for starting a small business.

16692 ■ Startups for the Rest of Us: Founder Regrets, DIY vs. Hiring, Defining Your ICP, and More Later Stage Listener Questions
URL(s): www.startupsfortherestofus.com/epidoses/episode-736-founder-regrets-diy-vs-hiring-defining-your-icp-and-more-later-stage-listener-questions
Ed: Rob Walling. **Released:** October 16, 2024. **Description:** Podcast discusses common pitfalls in delegation, transitioning to SaaS models, and when to target multiple ICPs.

16693 ■ Startups for the Rest of Us: Make Ever-Increasing and Manageably-Sized Mistakes (A Rob Solo Adventure)
URL(s): www.startupsfortherestofus.com/epidoses/episode-660-make-ever-increasing-and-manageably-sized-mistakes-a-rob-solo-adventure
Ed: Rob Walling. **Released:** May 09, 2023. **Description:** Podcast discusses the tradeoffs of hiring a team vs. contractors, when to raise funding as a bootstrapper, and the importance of knowing what you're bad at.

16694 ■ Startups for the Rest of Us: Why Launching a Second Product Is Usually a Bad Idea
URL(s): www.startupsfortherestofus.com/epidoses/episode-681-why-launching-a-second-product-is-usually-a-bad-idea
Ed: Rob Walling. **Released:** October 03, 2023. **Description:** Podcast disusses the drawbacks of launching a second product.

16695 ■ The Strategy Hour: 9 Critically Important Lessons I've Learned from 9 Years in Business
URL(s): bossproject.com/podcast/9-critically-important-lessons-ive-learned-from-9-years-in-business
Ed: Abagail Pumphrey. **Released:** March 07, 2024. **Description:** Podcast offers important lessons for new businesses.

16696 ■ Team, Funding, and Summary - Back of the Napkin to Business Plan in 11 Slides with Brandon White
URL(s): podcasts.apple.com/us/podcast/team-funding-and-summary-back-of-the-napkin-id137736636?i=1000620890993
Released: July 12, 2023. **Description:** Podcast discusses the importance of a strong team to scale your business. Also references market size, competitive landscape, and financials. .

16697 ■ Think Business with Tyler: Business Owners, You're the Problem and Solution - A Talk with Michael Morrison
URL(s): thinktyler.com/podcast_episode/business-owners-michael-morrison

Ed: Tyler Martin. **Released:** May 29, 2023. **Description:** Podcast discusses taking responsibility for your business, the importance of planning, and the benefits of having a mission statement.

16698 ■ *Think Business with Tyler: Cash Flow Secrets: Uncover the Lifeblood of Small Business with Jason Kruger*
URL(s): thinktyler.com/podcast_episode/cash-flow
-secrets-jason-kruger

Ed: Tyler Martin. **Released:** July 24, 2023. **Description:** Podcast discusses the benefits of knowing your financial records, why cash flow is essential for small businesses, and understanding every aspect of your business.

16699 ■ *Think Business with Tyler: Navigating Rapid Business Growth without Sacrifices - Kim Walsh Phillips*
URL(s): thinktyler.com/podcast_episode/business
-growth-kim-walsh-phillips

Ed: Tyler Martin. **Released:** September 11, 2023. **Description:** Podcast explains how to scale your company without sacrificing yourself.

16700 ■ *Think Business with Tyler: Surviving and Thriving after a Career Crisis with Bruce Weinstein*
URL(s): thinktyler.com/podcast_episode/career-crisis
-bruce-weinstein

Ed: Tyler Martin. **Released:** July 31, 2023. **Description:** Podcast discusses the "octopus style" business strategy, different insurance policies for different types of businesses, and the importance of living your purpose.

16701 ■ *Think Business with Tyler: Taking Control of Your Business Finances with Financial Coach Alex Engar*
URL(s): thinktyler.com/podcast_episode/business
-finances-alex-engar

Ed: Tyler Martin. **Released:** April 03, 2023. **Description:** Podcast discusses the importance of examining your business's finances.

16702 ■ *Think Business with Tyler: The Real Game-Changers in Business Growth - Carl Gould*
URL(s): thinktyler.com/podcast_episode/mentors-carl
-gould

Ed: Tyler Martin. **Released:** August 14, 2023. **Description:** Podcast discusses the value of professional business coaching.

16703 ■ *Think Business with Tyler: Unleashing the True Value of Your Company with Tony Cotrupe*
URL(s): thinktyler.com/podcast_episode/value-com-
pany-with-tony-cotrupe

Ed: Tyler Martin. **Released:** July 03, 2023. **Description:** Podcast discusses the importance of driving value to your business, why business owners shouldn't do everything, and why to avoid relying solely on financial statements.

16704 ■ *Think Business with Tyler: Why Uniqueness is the Only Survival Strategy for Your Business - Dustin Bogle*
URL(s): thinktyler.com/podcast_episode/uniqueness
-survival-dustin-bogle

Ed: Tyler Martin. **Released:** May 22, 2023. **Description:** Podcast discusses being unique in business, how to hustle, hot to create an emotional connection with customers, and the importance of communication.

16705 ■ *Think Business with Tyler: Why Your Business Isn't Meant for Everyone with Glenn Gardone*
URL(s): thinktyler.com/podcast_episode/meant-ev-
eryone-with-glenn-gardone

Ed: Tyler Martin. **Released:** March 06, 2023. **Description:** Podcast offers tips on earing your customer's passion, discovering their buying motive, and why your target audience isn't everyone.

16706 ■ *This Is Small Business: Entrepreneurial Wisdom: Mastering Marketing, Networking, and Audience Building*
URL(s): www.smallbusiness.amazon/podcast-episo
des/ep-61-entrepreneurial-wisdom-mastering
-marketing-networking-and-audience-building

Ed: Andrea Marquez. **Released:** June 30, 2024. **Description:** Podcast discusses mindset, target audience, networking, and social media.

16707 ■ *This Is Small Business: Justin Tackles the Top 3 Steps to Start a Business*
URL(s): www.smallbusiness.amazon/podcast-episo
des/ep-13-justin-tackles-the-top-3-steps-to-start-a
-business

Ed: Andrea Marquez. **Released:** February 07, 2023. **Description:** Podcast discusses how to get your business off the ground.

16708 ■ *This Is Small Business: Renee Aces Achievable Goals*
URL(s): www.smallbusiness.amazon/podcast-episo
des/ep-17-renee-aces-achievable-goals

Ed: Andrea Marquez. **Released:** March 07, 2023. **Description:** Podcast discusses how to set goals, mechanisms to set, and often overlooked steps that can make a big impact.

16709 ■ *This Is Small Business: Small Business Fun Facts: What to Know Before Starting a Small Business*
URL(s): www.smallbusiness.amazon/podcast-episo
des/ep-54-business-fun-facts-what-to-know
-before-starting-a-small-business

Ed: Andrea Marquez. **Released:** April 23, 2024. **Description:** Podcast discusses how small businesses drive innovation, aid the economy, and benefit the community.

16710 ■ *This Is Small Business: Top 3 Small Business Mistakes to Avoid*
URL(s): www.smallbusiness.amazon/podcast-episo
des/ep-14-top-3-small-business-mistakes-to-avoid

Ed: Andrea Marquez. **Released:** February 14, 2023. **Description:** Podcast discusses common mistakes early-stage entrepreneurs make.

16711 ■ *Ty Crandall - Small Business Credit*
URL(s): www.thehowofbusiness.com/episode-056-ty
-crandall

Ed: Henry Lopez. **Description:** Podcast outlines how to build credit for your small business.

PUBLICATIONS

16712 ■ *101 Business Problems: Diagnosis and Remedy*
826 Riviera Dr.
Mansfield, TX 76063
Free: 800-990-4273
URL: http://www.americancpe.com
Contact: Dennis Gatlin, President
URL(s): www.americancpe.com/CPE-Courses/24-10
1-Business-Problems---Diagnosis-and-Remedy
.html

Price: $55, for additional exams; $134, for printed text; $124, for searchable CD-ROM; $109, for download searchable text and exam for apple computers or download searchable text and exam. **Description:** Contains detailed training information covering causes and solutions to more than 100 common business problems. **Availability:** CD-ROM; Print; Download. **Type:** Full-text.

16713 ■ *Choosing the Right Business Entity*
826 Riviera Dr.
Mansfield, TX 76063
Free: 800-990-4273
URL: http://www.americancpe.com
Contact: Dennis Gatlin, President
URL(s): www.americancpe.com/CPE-Courses/
25-Choosing-the-Right-Business-Entity.html

Price: $159, for Download Searchable Text and Exam; $159, for Download Searchable Text and Exam for Apple Computers; $194, for Printed Text; $79, for Additional Exams. **Description:** Contains detailed training information covering methods and factors involved in selecting the most advantageous type of business entity for a new venture. **Availability:** Print; Online; Download. **Type:** Full-text.

16714 ■ *Getting Cash Out of Your Business*
826 Riviera Dr.
Mansfield, TX 76063
Free: 800-990-4273
URL: http://www.americancpe.com
Contact: Dennis Gatlin, President
URL(s): www.americancpe.com/CPE-Courses/24-Ge
tting-Cash-Out-of-Your-Business.html

Price: $79, for additional; $189, for printed text; $159, for download searchable text and exam for apple computers; $159, for download searchable text and exam. **Description:** Contains detailed training information covering methods of minimizing tax burdens and maximizing owner benefits and opportunities to draw cash from businesses. **Availability:** Print; Online; Download. **Type:** Full-text.

16715 ■ *Handbook of Business Finance*
URL(s): uentrepreneurs.com/handbook-business-fi-
nance/

Description: $38. Offers detailed information about 11 types of equity financing, six types of debt financing, six other financial sources that offer unique types of financing, two types of equity instruments, 21 types of debt and leasing instruments, six other types of financial instruments, and numerous types of local, state and federal financial sources. The book also offers details about how to raise money via private placements or public offerings so you can select the right option for you. **Availability:** Print.

16716 ■ *How to Organize and Run a Small Business*
826 Riviera Dr.
Mansfield, TX 76063
Free: 800-990-4273
URL: http://www.americancpe.com
Contact: Dennis Gatlin, President
URL(s): www.americancpe.com/CPE-Courses/
24-How-to-Organize-and-Run-a-Small-Business
.html

Price: $79, for download searchable text and exam; $79, for download searchable text and exam for apple computers; $99, for printed text; $35, for additional exams. **Description:** Contains detailed training information covering the basics of creating, organizing, and running a small business. **Availability:** Print; Download. **Type:** Full-text.

16717 ■ *Journal of Small Business & Entrepreneurship*
6382 Young St.
Halifax, NS, Canada B3L 2A1
URL: http://ccsbe.org
Contact: John MacRitchie, President
URL(s): www.tandfonline.com/journals/rsbe20

Released: Bimonthly **Price:** $601, Institutions for print & online; $493, Institutions for online only. **Description:** Contains studies that seek to improve the knowledge and understanding of entrepreneurship and small business management and, eventually, shape these fields of research. **Availability:** Print; Download; PDF; Online.

16718 ■ *Journal of Small Business and Entrepreneurship Development (JSBED)*
3942 Tulane Ave.
Madison, WI 53714
Co. E-mail: editor@aripd.org
URL: http://aripd.net
URL(s): jsbednet.com

Released: Semiannual **Price:** $50, for PhD/M.Phil. candidates/graduate students (print copy only); $45, for aair members (print copy only); $45, for authors of the journal (print copy only); $60, Institutions for library, institution, government and association (print copy only); $30, Single issue for single issue print. **Description:** Contains articles in focusing on theoretical, empirical, policy, and practitioner issues within the fields of small business and entrepreneurship. **Availability:** Print; PDF; Online.

GENERAL SMALL BUSINESS TOPICS

16719 ◾ *Journal of Small Business Management (JSBM)*
530 Walnut St., Ste. 850
Philadelphia, PA 19106
Ph: (215)625-8900
Fax: (215)207-0050
URL: http://taylorandfrancis.com/journals
Contact: Annie Callanan, Chief Executive Officer
URL(s): www.tandfonline.com/journals/ujbm20
Released: 6/year **Price:** $695, Institutions for online only; $887, Institutions for print and online; $1,983, Institutions for print and online; $246, Individuals for print +online; $1,626, Institutions for online only. **Description:** Magazine dedicated to the development of entrepreneurship and small business management through education, research, and the free exchange of ideas. **Availability:** Print; Download; PDF; Online.

16720 ◾ **Phoenix Business Journal**
101 N First Ave., Ste. 2300
Phoenix, AZ 85003
Ph: (602)230-8400
Fax: (602)230-0955
Co. E-mail: phoenix@bizjournals.com
URL: http://www.bizjournals.com/phoenix
Contact: Alex McAlister, Director
E-mail: amcalister@bizjournals.com
Facebook: www.facebook.com/phxbizjournal
Linkedin: www.linkedin.com/company/phoenix-business-journal
X (Twitter): x.com/phxbizjournal
Description: Publisher of journal covering business news, business events, residential real estate and commercial real estate. **Founded:** 1980.

16721 ◾ *Small Business Economics: An Entrepreneurship Journal*
233 Spring St.
New York, NY 10013
Free: 866-839-0194
Fax: (212)460-1700
Co. E-mail: customerservice@springernature.com
URL: http://www.springer.com
Contact: Derk Haank, Chief Executive Officer
URL(s): link.springer.com/journal/11187
Released: 8/year **Description:** Journal covering research on entrepreneurship, self-employment, family firms, small and medium-sized firms, and new venture creation. **Availability:** Print; PDF; Download; Online.

16722 ◾ *Small Business Investment Company Directory and Handbook*
PO Box 186
Merrick, NY 11566-0186
Ph: (516)766-5850
Free: 800-323-0548
Fax: (516)766-5919
URL: http://www.iwsmoney.com
Contact: Tyler G. Hicks, Contact
URL(s): iwealthsuccess.com/product/iws-2-small-business-investment-company-directory-handbook
Price: $24, Single issue. **Description:** Gives tips from the U.S. Small Business Administration (SBA) on obtaining financing and on small business financial management and explains how SBICs work. Covers over 400 small business investment companies interested in investing in various businesses. **Arrangement:** Geographical. **Availability:** E-book; PDF.

16723 ◾ *"Small Businesses Support Expansive Tax Reforms Needed to Level the Playing Field and Offset the Costs of 'Build Back Better' Plan" in Business2Community (November 3, 2021)*
URL(s): www.business2community.com/small-business/small-businesses-support-expansive-tax-reforms-needed-to-level-the-playing-field-and-offset-the-costs-of-build-back-better-plan-02438911
Ed: John Arensmeyer. **Released:** November 02, 2021. **Description:** Discusses the tax reforms for small businesses within the Build Back Better plan.

16724 ◾ *Starting a Successful Business*
45 Gee St., 2nd Fl.
London EC1V 3RS, United Kingdom
Ph: 44 20 7278-0433
Co. E-mail: kpinfo@koganpage.com
URL: http://www.koganpage.com
Contact: Christina Lindeholm, Manager, Sales
URL(s): www.koganpage.com/general-business-interest/starting-a-successful-business-9780749480868
Price: $19.99, for eBook; $19.99, for paperback + eBook; $19.99, for paperback. **Description:** Covers topics such as franchises, marketing, publicity, e-business, financial management, business law, recruitment, taxation, insurance, business planning and development. **Availability:** E-book; Print.

INTERNET DATABASES

16725 ◾ *Small Business Source*
10 Estes St.
Ipswich, MA 01938
Ph: (978)356-6500
Free: 800-653-2726
Co. E-mail: information@ebsco.com
URL: http://www.ebsco.com
Contact: Tim Collins, Chief Executive Officer
URL(s): www.ebsco.com/products/research-databases/small-business-source

Description: A collection of state-specific resources supported with demographic data and other local information. Completing the database are business videos that provide critical information for business owners including interviews, "lessons learned" features, lectures and "how to" videos to help foster success in all aspects of managing a business. **Availability:** PDF; Online. **Type:** Full-text; Video.

RESEARCH CENTERS

16726 ◾ **Yale University - Center for Business and the Environment (CBEY)**
195 Prospect St.
New Haven, CT 06511
Ph: (203)432-3736
Co. E-mail: cbey@yale.edu
URL: http://cbey.yale.edu
Contact: Stuart DeCew, Executive Director
E-mail: stuart.decew@yale.edu
Facebook: www.facebook.com/Yale-Center-for-Business-and-the-Environment-276871215670694/info
Linkedin: www.linkedin.com/showcase/yale-center-for-business-and-environment
X (Twitter): x.com/YaleCBEY
Instagram: www.instagram.com/yalecbey
YouTube: www.youtube.com/channel/UCPqZCejv5zOfuMr3prALzVA
Description: Conducts research in management and products, finance and markets, and entrepreneurship and innovation. **Scope:** Conducts research in management and products, finance and markets, and entrepreneurship and innovation. **Founded:** 2004.

Accounting

START-UP INFORMATION

16727 ■ *The Small Business Start-Up Kit*
Pub: Nolo
Contact: Chris Braun, President
Ed: Peri Pakroo. **Released:** 12th edition. **Price:** $20.99, E-book. **Description:** Entrepreneurial advice for launching a new business. Topics include compliance with state regulations, sole proprietorships, partnerships, corporations, limited liability companies, as well as accounting and tax information. **Availability:** E-book; Print; Electronic publishing; PDF.

ASSOCIATIONS AND OTHER ORGANIZATIONS

16728 ■ **Accountants Association of Iowa (AAI)**
PO Box 63
Creston, IA 50801
Ph: (641)782-2401
Fax: (641)782-2401
Co. E-mail: aai_iowa@iowatelecom.net
URL: http://www.aaiiowa.com
Contact: Donald Keast, President
Facebook: www.facebook.com/aaofiowa

Description: Represents and supports individuals licensed by the State of Iowa or another state as a Certified Public Accountant (CPA), a Licensed Public Accountant (LPA), or the equivalent. Promotes a high standard of conduct for members, and seeks to instill in members an appreciation of responsibilities to their clients and the importance of rendering prompt, faithful, and efficient service. **Founded:** 1945. **Geographic Preference:** State.

16729 ■ **Accounting & Financial Women's Alliance (AFWA)**
2365 Harrodsburg Rd., Ste. A325
Lexington, KY 40504
Ph: (859)219-3532
URL: http://www.afwa.org
Contact: Wendi Christian, President
Facebook: www.facebook.com/AFWANational
Linkedin: www.linkedin.com/company/accounting-&-financial-women%27s-alliance
X (Twitter): x.com/afwanational
Instagram: www.instagram.com/afwanational

Description: Works to enable women in all accounting and finance fields to achieve their full potential and to contribute to their profession.

16730 ■ **Accounting and Financial Women's Alliance - Mesa East Valley Chapter**
PO Box 2216
Gilbert, AZ 85299
Co. E-mail: chapter@mesaeastvalleyafwa.org
URL: http://www.mesaeastvalleyafwa.org
Contact: Diane Hanson, President
Facebook: www.facebook.com/afwamev
X (Twitter): x.com/afwa_mev

Description: Aims to increase opportunities and professional growth for women working on all facets of accounting and finance. **Geographic Preference:** Local.

16731 ■ **Accounting and Financial Women's Alliance - Springfield Chapter**
Springfield, MO
Co. E-mail: springfieldafwa@gmail.com
URL: http://www.afwa.org/springfield
Contact: Megan Cannon, President
E-mail: megan@brscpa.biz
Facebook: www.facebook.com/Springmoafwa

Description: Aims to increase opportunities and professional growth for women working on all facets of accounting and finance. **Geographic Preference:** Local.

16732 ■ **American Association of Finance & Accounting, Inc. (AAFA)**
URL: http://aafa.com
Facebook: www.facebook.com/pg/AAFANetwork
Linkedin: www.linkedin.com/company/american-association-of-finance-&-accounting-aafa-
X (Twitter): twitter.com/aafanetwork

Description: An alliance of executive search firms specializing in the recruitment of finance & accounting professionals. **Founded:** 1978.

16733 ■ **Association of International Certified Public Accountants (AICPA)**
100 Princeton S, Ste. 200
Ewing, NJ 08628
Ph: (609)671-2902
Free: 888-777-7077
Co. E-mail: service@aicpa.org
URL: http://www.aicpa.org/home
Contact: Mary Grace Davenport, Contact

Description: Represents members in the accounting profession around the world. **Founded:** 2017.

16734 ■ **Auto Dealers CPAs**
818 18th Ave. 10th Fl.
Nashville, TN 37203
Ph: (615)373-9880
Co. E-mail: info@autodealercpas.com
URL: http://autodealercpas.com
Contact: Angie Grissom, Owner
Facebook: www.facebook.com/Rainmakercompanies
X (Twitter): twitter.com/RainmakerCPAs

Description: Certified Public Accounting (CPA) firms providing financial and consulting services to automobile dealers. Seeks to advance CPA services to automobile dealers. Sponsors continuing education and training courses; conducts industry and member surveys; facilitates formation of joint ventures; makes available marketing assistance; facilitates resource sharing among members. **Founded:** 1996. **Publications:** *Auto Focus* (Quarterly). **Geographic Preference:** National.

16735 ■ **Construction Industry CPAs/Consultants Association (CICPAC)**
4531 Bohemia Dr.
Pensacola, FL 32504
Ph: (850)723-0372
Co. E-mail: info@cicpac.com
URL: http://cicpac.com
Contact: Christina Chifici, President
E-mail: cchifici@laporte.com
Facebook: www.facebook.com/CICPAC
Linkedin: www.linkedin.com/company/cicpac

Description: Certified Public Accounting (CPA) firms providing financial and consulting services to construction companies. Seeks to advance CPA services to the construction industries. Sponsors continuing education and training courses; conducts industry and member surveys; facilitates formation of joint ventures; makes available marketing assistance; facilitates resource sharing among members. **Founded:** 1989. **Educational Activities:** CICPAC Annual Conference (Annual); American Association of Attorney-Certified Public Accountants Annual Meeting and Educational Conference (Annual). **Geographic Preference:** National.

16736 ■ *Dialogue Magazine*
250 Bloor St. E, Ste. 1600
Toronto, ON, Canada M4W 1E6
Ph: (416)487-3380
Free: 800-387-4693
Fax: (416)487-3384
Co. E-mail: infoline@payroll.ca
URL: http://payroll.ca
Contact: Peter Tzanetakis, President
URL(s): payroll.ca/dialogue-magazine

Released: Quarterly **Availability:** Print; PDF; Download; Online.

16737 ■ **International Budget Partnership (IBP)**
750 First St. NE, Ste. 700
Washington, DC 20002
Ph: (202)792-6833
Fax: (202)792-6833
Co. E-mail: info@internationalbudget.org
URL: http://internationalbudget.org
Contact: Warren Krafchik, Executive Director
E-mail: wkrafchik@international.com
Facebook: www.facebook.com/InternationalBudgetPartnership
Linkedin: www.linkedin.com/company/international-budget-partnership
YouTube: www.youtube.com/user/IntBudgetPartnership/playlists

Description: Works to assist civil society organizations globally to improve budget policies and decision-making processes and reduce poverty. **Publications:** *A Guide to Budget Work for NGOs*; *IBP Newsletter* (Monthly). **Educational Activities:** IBP Conferences. **Geographic Preference:** Multinational.

16738 ■ **Manufacturing CPAs**
188 Front St., Ste. 116-90
Franklin, TN 37064
Ph: (615)373-9880
Co. E-mail: info@manufacturingcpas.com
URL: http://manufacturingcpas.com

GENERAL SMALL BUSINESS TOPICS

Accounting ■ 16752

Description: Provides accountants in the manufacturing industry a forum for information exchange, technical expertise, and resources. Sponsors continuing education and training courses; conducts industry and member surveys; facilitates formation of joint ventures; makes available marketing assistance; facilitates resource sharing among members. **Publications:** Client (Periodic). **Geographic Preference:** National.

16739 ■ Maryland Association of Certified Public Accountants (MACPA)
901 Dulaney Valley Rd., Ste. 800
Towson, MD 21204
Ph: (410)296-6250
Free: 800-782-2036
Co. E-mail: team@macpa.org
URL: http://www.macpa.org
Contact: Tom Hood, President
Facebook: www.facebook.com/macpa
Linkedin: www.linkedin.com/company/maryland-association-of-cpas
X (Twitter): x.com/macpa
YouTube: www.youtube.com/user/macpapro
Description: Helps guide CPAs to to achieve their professional growth. **Founded:** 1901. **Awards:** MACPA Scholarships (Annual). **Geographic Preference:** State.

16740 ■ Michigan Association of Certified Public Accountants (MICPA)
888 W Big Beaver Rd., Ste. 550
Troy, MI 48084
Ph: (248)267-3700
URL: http://www.micpa.org
Contact: Robert Doyle, President
E-mail: bdoyle@micpa.org
Facebook: www.facebook.com/MichiganCPAs
Linkedin: www.linkedin.com/company/micpa
X (Twitter): x.com/MichiganCPAs
YouTube: www.youtube.com/user/MichiganCPAs
Description: Dedicated to promoting and enhancing the value of the CPA profession and working in corporate finance, education, government, and public accounting. **Founded:** 1901. **Publications:** Leader's Edge (Bimonthly); Leader's Edge; Leaders' Edge (Bimonthly); The Michigan CPA (Quarterly). **Awards:** MICPA Accounting Teaching Excellence Award (Annual); Outstanding CPA in Government Impact Award (Annual); Michigan Accountancy Foundation Final Year Accounting Scholarship (Annual). **Geographic Preference:** State.

16741 ■ National Association of Forensic Accountants (NAFA)
6635 W Commercial Blvd., Ste. 217
Tamarac, FL 33319
Free: 844-217-6975
Fax: (954)537-4942
Co. E-mail: mail@nafanet.com
URL: http://www.nafanet.com
Description: Professional investigative accounting firms providing claims support to the insurance industry and claims litigation clients. **Founded:** 1991. **Publications:** Accounting and Claims. **Geographic Preference:** National.

16742 ■ National Association of Professional Accountants (NAPA)
162 W Baer Creek Dr.
Kaysville, UT 84037
Contact: David Bybee, Contact
Description: Serves bookkeepers who provide bookkeeping services to the public. Members are owners or employees of bookkeeping or accounting businesses.

16743 ■ National Payroll Institute [Association canadienne de la paie (ACP)]
250 Bloor St. E, Ste. 1600
Toronto, ON, Canada M4W 1E6
Ph: (416)487-3380
Free: 800-387-4693
Fax: (416)487-3384
Co. E-mail: infoline@payroll.ca
URL: http://payroll.ca
Contact: Peter Tzanetakis, President

Facebook: www.facebook.com/nationalpayrollinstitute
Linkedin: www.linkedin.com/company/national-payroll-institute
X (Twitter): x.com/NatPayrollInst
YouTube: www.youtube.com/c/nationalpayrollinstitute
Description: Represents the payroll community in Canada; offers education programs, advocacy efforts, products and services to help members enhance and adapt payroll operations. **Founded:** 1978. **Publications:** Dialogue Magazine (Quarterly); CPA E-Source (Bimonthly). **Awards:** Diana Ferguson Award (Annual); The CPA Partner Award (Annual); CPA Board of Directors Award (Annual). **Geographic Preference:** National.

16744 ■ North Carolina Association of Certified Public Accountants (NCACPA)
3100 Gateway Centre Blvd.
Morrisville, NC 27560
Ph: (919)469-1040
Free: 800-722-2836
Fax: (919)378-2000
Co. E-mail: experiencesupport@ncacpa.org
URL: http://www.ncacpa.org
Contact: Arleen Thomas, Chairman
Facebook: www.facebook.com/NCACPA
Linkedin: www.linkedin.com/company/north-carolina-association-of-cpas-ncacpa-
X (Twitter): x.com/NCACPA
Instagram: www.instagram.com/ncacpa
YouTube: www.youtube.com/user/NCACPAtv
Description: Represents the interests of Certified Public Accountants (CPAs) in North Carolina. Provides access to professional news, including real-time updates on our enhanced advocacy efforts, and to the online resource members utilize the most. **Founded:** 1919. **Awards:** North Carolina CPA Foundation Scholarships (Annual); NCACPA Outstanding Minority Accounting Student Scholarships (Annual). **Geographic Preference:** State.

16745 ■ Pennsylvania Society of Tax and Accounting Professionals - Buxmont Chapter
c/o Tamatha Polichetti, President
82 Annawanda Rd.
Ottsville, PA 18942
Ph: (215)795-0212
Fax: (215)795-0445
URL: http://www.pstap.org/about-us/chapters
Contact: Aaron Perriello, Co-President
Description: Represents certified public accountants (CPAs), public accountants, enrolled agents, and tax practitioners. Protects the interests of public accountants and small accounting firms to become visible and establish integrity of public accounting profession. **Geographic Preference:** Local.

16746 ■ Pennsylvania Society of Tax and Accounting Professionals - Lehigh Valley Chapter
c/o Deborah Mininger Lahneman, President
528 W Broad St.
Quakertown, PA 18951-1216
Ph: (215)536-6829
Fax: (215)536-8781
URL: http://www.pstap.org/about-us/chapters
Contact: Aaron Perriello, Co-President
Description: Represents certified public accountants (CPAs), public accountants, enrolled agents, and tax practitioners. Protects the interests of public accountants and small accounting firms to become visible and establish integrity of public accounting profession. **Geographic Preference:** Local.

16747 ■ Pennsylvania Society of Tax and Accounting Professionals - Northeast Chapter
c/o Philip Reid, President
1130 Twin Stacks Dr.
Dallas, PA 18612
Ph: (570)991-0551
URL: http://pstap.org/about-us/chapters
Contact: Philip Reid, President

Description: Represents certified public accountants (CPAs), public accountants, enrolled agents, and tax practitioners. Protects the interests of public accountants and small accounting firms to become visible and establish integrity of public accounting profession. **Geographic Preference:** Local.

16748 ■ Pennsylvania Society of Tax and Accounting Professionals - Philadelphia Tri-County Chapter
c/o Margaret Rovinski, President
139 Scenic Rd.
Springfield, PA 19064
Ph: (610)256-3416
Fax: (610)543-8295
Co. E-mail: info@pstap.org
URL: http://pstap.org/about-us/chapters/?fsubpg=chapterdetails&chapterid=6
Contact: Margaret Rovinski, President
Description: Represents certified public accountants (CPAs), public accountants, enrolled agents, and tax practitioners. Protects the interests of public accountants and small accounting firms to become visible and establish integrity of public accounting profession. **Geographic Preference:** Local.

16749 ■ Pennsylvania Society of Tax and Accounting Professionals - South Central Chapter
c/o Celestine Henderson, President
2032 Green St.
Harrisburg, PA 17102
Ph: (717)238-3332
Fax: (717)238-8153
URL: http://pstap.org/about-us/chapters
Contact: Aaron Perriello, Co-President
Description: Represents Certified Public Accountants (CPAs), public accountants, enrolled agents, and tax practitioners. Protects the interests of public accountants and small accounting firms to become visible and establish integrity of public accounting profession. **Geographic Preference:** Local.

16750 ■ Pennsylvania Society of Tax and Accounting Professionals - Southeast Chapter
c/o Richard Kelly, President
2 W Pennsbury Way
Chadds Ford, PA 19317
Ph: (610)388-9700
Fax: (610)388-9537
URL: http://www.pstap.org/about-us/chapters
Contact: Richard B. Kelly, President
Description: Represents certified public accountants (CPAs), public accountants, enrolled agents, and tax practitioners. Protects the interests of public accountants and small accounting firms to become visible and establish integrity of public accounting profession. **Founded:** 1946. **Geographic Preference:** Local.

16751 ■ Pennsylvania Society of Tax and Accounting Professionals - West Central Chapter
20 Erford Rd., Ste. 200A
Lemoyne, PA 17043
Ph: (717)737-6847
Free: 800-270-3352
Co. E-mail: info@pstap.org
URL: http://www.pstap.org/about-us/chapters/?fsubpg=chapterdetails&chapterid=3
Contact: James S. Frederick, President
Description: Represents certified public accountants (CPAs), public accountants, enrolled agents, and tax practitioners. Protects the interests of public accountants and small accounting firms to become visible and establish integrity of public accounting profession. **Founded:** 1946. **Geographic Preference:** Local.

16752 ■ Pennsylvania Society of Tax and Accounting Professionals - Western Pennsylvania Chapter
701 Mill St., Ste. 4
Manorville, PA 16238
Ph: (724)763-3049
Fax: (724)763-1108

URL: http://pstap.org
Contact: Aaron Perriello, Co-President
Description: Represents certified public accountants (CPAs), public accountants, enrolled agents, and tax practitioners. Protects the interests of public accountants and small accounting firms to become visible and establish integrity of public accounting profession. **Geographic Preference:** Local.

16753 ■ PrimeGlobal
PrimeGlobal
3235 Satellite Blvd., Bldg. 400, Ste. 300
Duluth, GA 30096
Ph: (678)417-7730
Fax: (678)999-3959
Co. E-mail: communications@primeglobal.net
URL: http://www.primeglobal.net
Contact: Katie O'Bryan, Executive Director
E-mail: kobryan@primeglobal.net
Facebook: www.facebook.com/PrimeGlobalAccts
Linkedin: www.linkedin.com/company/primeglobalacct
X (Twitter): x.com/PrimeGlobalAcct
YouTube: www.youtube.com/channel/UCRVCVsNrjHhlQe5IBJ89m9Q
Description: Ensures that accounting, auditing, and management services standards are maintained. **Founded:** 1977. **Publications:** *Polaris International*. **Geographic Preference:** Multinational.

16754 ■ Society of Depreciation Professionals (SDP)
12110 N Pecos St., Ste. 220
Westminster, CO 80234
Ph: (303)254-6496
Co. E-mail: admin@depr.org
URL: http://www.depr.org
Contact: Rebecca Richards, President
Linkedin: www.linkedin.com/company/depr
Description: Accountants and other individuals with an interest in the depreciation of assets. Promotes "professionalism and ethics within the art of depreciation." Serves as a forum for the discussion of issues affecting depreciation; sponsors continuing professional development courses for members. **Founded:** 1987. **Publications:** *The Journal of the Society of Depreciation Professionals* (Annual). **Geographic Preference:** National.

16755 ■ South Carolina Association of Certified Public Accountants (SCACPA)
1300 12th St., Ste. D
West Columbia, SC 29033
Ph: (803)791-4181
Fax: (803)791-4196
Co. E-mail: communications@scacpa.org
URL: http://www.scacpa.org
Contact: Lesley Kelly, Chairman
Facebook: www.facebook.com/SCACPA
Linkedin: www.linkedin.com/company/south-carolina-association-of-cpas
X (Twitter): x.com/scacpa
Instagram: www.instagram.com/scacpa
YouTube: www.youtube.com/user/scacpa
Description: Aims for the advancement of the accounting profession through assistance to its members in their efforts to maintain and develop professional competence, integrity and objectivity. **Founded:** 1915. **Geographic Preference:** State.

16756 ■ Utah Association of Certified Public Accountants (UACPA)
136 S Main St., Ste. 510
Salt Lake City, UT 84101
Ph: (801)466-8022
Co. E-mail: mail@uacpa.org
URL: http://www.uacpa.org
Contact: Ray Langhaim, President
Facebook: www.facebook.com/UtahAssociationofCPAs
Linkedin: www.linkedin.com/in/uacpa
X (Twitter): x.com/UACPA
Description: Certified public accountants. Offers continuing education programs, conferences, free CPA referral service, student and non-CPA professional affiliate services, and other member services.

Founded: 1920. **Publications:** *The Journal Entry* (Quarterly); *Resource and Membership Directory* (Annual). **Geographic Preference:** State.

16757 ■ Virginia Society of Tax & Accounting Professionals (VSTAP)
11 Main St., Ste. D
Warrenton, VA 20186
Free: 800-927-2731
Fax: (888)403-0920
Co. E-mail: asv@virginia-accountants.org
URL: http://www.virginia-accountants.org
Contact: William R. Silzer, President
E-mail: wrsilzer@verizon.net
X (Twitter): x.com/VA_Accountants
Description: Dedicated to providing rigorous educational opportunities, elevating high standards of proficiency and integrity, and promoting and protecting the interests of tax preparers, accountants, and bookkeepers across Virginia. **Founded:** 1948. **Geographic Preference:** State.

16758 ■ Wisconsin Association of Accountants (WAA)
1124 17th Ave.
Monroe, WI 53566
Ph: (608)325-5250
Co. E-mail: office@waainc.org
URL: http://www.waainc.org
Contact: Harlan Rose, President
Description: Promotes high professional and ethical standards; seeks to safeguard and defend the professional and legal rights of attorney-CPAs. Conducts research on dual licensing and dual practice; maintains speakers' bureau, placement service, and a collection of published and unpublished articles on these subjects. **Founded:** 1955. **Geographic Preference:** State.

EDUCATIONAL PROGRAMS

16759 ■ Accounting's New Guidelines: From GAAP to IFRS (Onsite)
URL(s): www.amanet.org
Description: Understand the complexities of the coming GAAP-to-IFRS changeover in this two-day course. **Audience:** Financial managers and executives, professionals. **Principal Exhibits:** Understand the complexities of the coming GAAP-to-IFRS changeover in this two-day course.

16760 ■ AMA Fixed Asset Accounting (Onsite)
URL(s): www.amanet.org
Description: Covers tax benefits, transitioning to a computerized system, and getting started with paperwork. **Audience:** Controllers, accountants, fixed asset managers, fixed asset accountants, and line managers. **Principal Exhibits:** Covers tax benefits, transitioning to a computerized system, and getting started with paperwork. **Telecommunication Services:** customerservice@amanet.org.

16761 ■ AMA Fundamentals of Cost Accounting (Onsite)
American Management Association (AMA)
1601 Broadway
New York, NY 10019
Ph: (212)586-8100
Free: 800-262-9699
Fax: (212)903-8168
Co. E-mail: customerservice@amanet.org
URL: http://www.amanet.org
Contact: Manny Avramidis, President
URL(s): www.amanet.org/training/seminars/onsite/Fundamentals-of-Cost-Accounting.aspx
Description: Covers the use of cost accounting, analyzing reports, choosing a cost system, and measuring results. **Audience:** Accountants, accounting managers, cost accountants, cost analysts, budget analysts, systems analysts, auditors and financial planners. **Principal Exhibits:** Covers the use of cost accounting, analyzing reports, choosing a cost system, and measuring results.

16762 ■ AMA Fundamentals of Finance and Accounting for Administrative Professionals (Onsite)
URL(s): www.amanet.org
Description: Covers basic accounting principles, cash flow accounting, and learning to understand various financial documents. **Audience:** Administrative professionals. **Principal Exhibits:** Covers basic accounting principles, cash flow accounting, and learning to understand various financial documents. **Telecommunication Services:** customerservice@amanet.org.

16763 ■ AMA's Comprehensive Budgeting Workshop
American Management Association (AMA)
1601 Broadway
New York, NY 10019
Ph: (212)586-8100
Free: 800-262-9699
Fax: (212)903-8168
Co. E-mail: customerservice@amanet.org
URL: http://www.amanet.org
Contact: Manny Avramidis, President
URL(s): www.amanet.org/comprehensive-budgeting-workshop
Price: $2,345, Non-members; $2,095, Members AMA; $1,984, Members GSA. **Frequency:** Continuous. **Description:** Two-day seminar covering the budgeting process from fundamentals through development and how to measure performance. **Audience:** Managers and anyone with budget responsibilities. **Principal Exhibits:** Two-day seminar covering the budgeting process from fundamentals through development and how to measure performance.

16764 ■ Budgeting for Publications
URL(s): www.eeicom.com
Description: Seminar that covers the basics of developing and monitoring budgets for the publications department, including types of publications departments, profit and cost centers, defining profit, margins, revenues, and analysis, budgeting traps, and what you can and cannot control. **Audience:** Industry professionals. **Principal Exhibits:** Seminar that covers the basics of developing and monitoring budgets for the publications department, including types of publications departments, profit and cost centers, defining profit, margins, revenues, and analysis, budgeting traps, and what you can and cannot control.

16765 ■ CMC's Course on Financial Analysis
URL(s): cmcoutperform.com
Description: Two-day seminar for managers with budget responsibilities; covers corporate planning, capital investments, cash flow, balance sheets, mergers and acquisitions, and other financial aspects of business. **Audience:** Industry professionals. **Principal Exhibits:** Two-day seminar for managers with budget responsibilities; covers corporate planning, capital investments, cash flow, balance sheets, mergers and acquisitions, and other financial aspects of business. **Telecommunication Services:** cmcinfo@cmcoutperform.com.

16766 ■ Discover the Power of Crystal Reports
Fred Pryor Seminars & CareerTrack
5700 Broadmoor, Ste. 300
Mission, KS 66202
Free: 800-780-8476
Fax: (913)967-8849
Co. E-mail: customerservice@pryor.com
URL: http://www.pryor.com
Contact: Janet Turner, Contact
E-mail: dmca@pryor.com
URL(s): www.pryor.com/training-seminars/discover-power-crystal-reports
Frequency: Irregular. **Description:** Learn effective data management, including financial, sales, and personal presentation and distribution. **Audience:** Industry professionals. **Principal Exhibits:** Learn effective data management, including financial, sales, and personal presentation and distribution.

GENERAL SMALL BUSINESS TOPICS   Accounting ■ 16786

16767 ■ Government Contract Accounting (Onsite)
Seminar Information Service Inc. (SIS)
 250 El Camino Real., Ste. 112
 Tustin, CA 92780
Ph: (714)508-0340
Free: 877-736-4636
Fax: (714)734-8027
Co. E-mail: info@seminarinformation.com
URL: http://www.seminarinformation.com
Contact: Catherine Bellizzi, President
URL(s): www.seminarinformation.com
Description: Accounting principles as they relate to procurement activities with the Federal Government, with focus on Government forms and formats, direct and indirect cost rate submissions, cost principles, dealing with Government auditors, changes and delay claims and terminations. **Audience:** Purchasing professionals. **Principal Exhibits:** Accounting principles as they relate to procurement activities with the Federal Government, with focus on Government forms and formats, direct and indirect cost rate submissions, cost principles, dealing with Government auditors, changes and delay claims and terminations.

16768 ■ How to Develop and Administer a Budget (Onsite)
URL(s): www.pryor.com/mkt_info/products/budget.asp
Description: Covers the benefits of budgeting, budgeting concepts, templates, and methods for evaluating budgets. **Audience:** Managers, supervisors, and business owners. **Principal Exhibits:** Covers the benefits of budgeting, budgeting concepts, templates, and methods for evaluating budgets. **Telecommunication Services:** customerservice@pryor.com.

16769 ■ How to Use QuickBooks
Fred Pryor Seminars & CareerTrack
 5700 Broadmoor, Ste. 300
 Mission, KS 66202
Free: 800-780-8476
Fax: (913)967-8849
Co. E-mail: customerservice@pryor.com
URL: http://www.pryor.com
Contact: Janet Turner, Contact
E-mail: dmca@pryor.com
URL(s): www.pryor.com/training-seminars/how-to-use-quickbooks
Description: Learn how to manage your inventory, track costs of your business, generate professional invoices and purchase orders, manage accounts payables and receivables and more. **Audience:** Business professionals. **Principal Exhibits:** Learn how to manage your inventory, track costs of your business, generate professional invoices and purchase orders, manage accounts payables and receivables and more.

16770 ■ Organizing and Managing Accounts Payable (Onsite)
National Seminars Training L.L.C. (NST)
 14502 W 105th St.
 Lenexa, KS 66215
Free: 800-349-1935
Co. E-mail: info@findaseminar.com
URL: http://www.findaseminar.com/tpd/Padgett-Thompson-Seminars.asp
URL(s): www.findaseminar.com
Description: Seminar promotes the latest proven techniques and best practices to improve accuracy and save money for your company. **Audience:** Accounting, finance and accounts payable professionals. **Principal Exhibits:** Seminar promotes the latest proven techniques and best practices to improve accuracy and save money for your company.

16771 ■ Project Cost Management: Estimating, Budgeting and Earned Value Analysis (Onsite)
URL(s): cmcoutperform.com
Description: Learn how to apply proven methods, tools, and techniques to prepare estimates, develop and monitor budgets, manage cash flow, and use earned value analysis. **Audience:** Accountants and professionals. **Principal Exhibits:** Learn how to apply proven methods, tools, and techniques to prepare estimates, develop and monitor budgets, manage cash flow, and use earned value analysis.

16772 ■ The Sales And Use Tax Seminar (Onsite)
Seminar Information Service Inc. (SIS)
 250 El Camino Real., Ste. 112
 Tustin, CA 92780
Ph: (714)508-0340
Free: 877-736-4636
Fax: (714)734-8027
Co. E-mail: info@seminarinformation.com
URL: http://www.seminarinformation.com
Contact: Catherine Bellizzi, President
URL(s): www.seminarinformation.com/details.cfm?qc=qqaask
Description: Learn how to determine which transactions are taxable, find exemptions you may not be aware of, and handle business partners who aren't in compliance with new tax laws. **Audience:** Accounting and purchasing professionals. **Principal Exhibits:** Learn how to determine which transactions are taxable, find exemptions you may not be aware of, and handle business partners who aren't in compliance with new tax laws.

REFERENCE WORKS

16773 ■ "6 Best Accounts Receivable Software for Small Businesses" in FreshBooks Hub
URL(s): www.freshbooks.com/hub/accounting/accounts-receivable-software
Description: Covers the six best accounts receivable software to help your small business reduce the number of days it takes to get paid. **Availability:** Online.

16774 ■ "6 Lessons from Audit Experts Who Adopted AI Early" in Journal of Accountancy (November 23, 2021)
Ed: Andrew Kenney. **Released:** November 23, 2021. **Description:** With the advance of AI, the best thing those in the accountancy industries can do is learn about various AI platforms and how to incorporate them into their businesses. The technology is still evolving, but tips are given on how to use AI to benefit customers. **Availability:** Online.

16775 ■ "The 8 Most Common Small Business Accounting Mistakes" in Bplans
URL(s): articles.bplans.com/the-8-most-common-small-business-accounting-mistakes/
Ed: Ivan Lavelle. **Description:** Examines eight of the most common small business accounting errors and explains how they can create issues for your business. **Availability:** Online.

16776 ■ "11 Accounting Tips All Small Businesses Should Know" in business.com (Feb. 3, 2022)
URL(s): www.business.com/articles/small-business-accounting/
Ed: Rashan Dixon. **Released:** February 03, 2022. **Description:** Provides eleven accounting tips all small business owners should follow. **Availability:** Online.

16777 ■ "18 Best Small-Business Apps" in NerdWallet (Jan. 19, 2022)
URL(s): www.nerdwallet.com/article/small-business/20-apps-small-business-owners
Ed: Claire Tsosie, Alex Rosenberg. **Released:** January 19, 2022. **Description:** Explores how small business apps can help you run your company more efficiently, saving time and money. Provides top picks for accounting, point-of-sale payroll, and invoicing apps. **Availability:** Online.

16778 ■ "2011 Tax Information of Interest" in Business Owner (Vol. 35, November-December 2011, No. 6, pp. 10)
Description: Compilation of 2011 tax information to help small business take advantage of all tax incentives. **Availability:** Print; Online.

16779 ■ "Accountants Get the Hook" in Canadian Business (Vol. 80, October 22, 2007, No. 21, pp. 19)
Description: Chartered Accountants of Ontario handed down the decision on Douglas Barrington, Anthony Power and Claudio Russo's professional misconduct case. The three accountants of Deloitte & Touche LLP must pay C$100,000 in fines and C$417,000 in costs. Details of the disciplinary case are presented. **Availability:** Print; Online.

16780 ■ "Accounting Lags Behind: Profession Trails Others in Recruiting and Retaining Minorities" in Philadelphia Business Journal (Vol. 28, June 29, 2012, No. 20, pp. 1)
Pub: Baltimore Business Journal
Contact: Rhonda Pringle, President
E-mail: rpringle@bizjournals.com
Description: Accounting firms in the US had a low number of ethnic minorities in their talent pool, particularly African Americans and Hispanic accountants. A survey by the Pennsylvania Institute of CPAs found that 71 percent of their members do not believe their organization has a diversity recruitment and retention strategy in place. **Availability:** Print; Online.

16781 ■ Accounting Workbook for Dummies
URL(s): www.wiley.com/en-us/Accounting+Workbook+For+Dummies%2C+2nd+Edition-p-9781119897651
Ed: Tage C. Tracy. **Released:** 2nd edition. **Price:** $15, e-book; $24.99, paperback. **Description:** Increase your accounting knowledge with this guide. Includes worksheets, spreadsheets, and examples to work through. **Availability:** E-book; Print.

16782 ■ "Accrual vs. Cash Accounting, Explained" in Business Owner (Vol. 35, July-August 2011, No. 4, pp. 13)
Description: Cash method versus accrual accounting methods are examined, using hypothetical situations.

16783 ■ "At-Home Tax Prep Trend Likely to Grow After Pandemic's Boost" in Bloomberg Tax (July 10, 2020)
Released: July 10, 2020. **Description:** With many businesses closed or people wanting to avoid closed-spaces in an accountant's office during the COVID-19 pandemic, the do-it-yourself tax industry grew. Many people also took advantage of the extra three months given by the government to file taxes and learned how to do so.

16784 ■ "Auditing the Auditors" in Barron's (Vol. 92, September 17, 2012, No. 38, pp. 16)
Description: The Public Company Accounting Oversight Board banned Michael T. Studer, president of the accounting firm Studer Group, because he failed to comply with auditing standards in his audits involving hinese reverse mergers. **Availability:** Online.

16785 ■ "Best Accounting Software for Small Business" in The Balance Small Business (Dec. 8, 2021)
URL(s): www.thebalancesmb.com/best-accounting-software-for-small-business-3967626
Ed: Allison Bethell. **Released:** December 08, 2021. **Description:** Provides research and information on eight top accounting software applications based on the features and specifically designed for small business owners. **Availability:** Online.

16786 ■ "The Best Business Accounting Software Services of 2023" in Business News Daily (March 9, 2023)
URL(s): www.businessnewsdaily.com/7543-best-accounting-software.html
Ed: Erica Sandberg. **Released:** March 09, 2023. **Description:** A review of the best business accounting software out there along with a comparison guide. **Availability:** Online.

GENERAL SMALL BUSINESS TOPICS

16787 ■ *"Bookkeeping Options for Time-Starved Startups" in Legal Zoom (February 21, 2023)*
URL(s): www.legalzoom.com/articles/bookkeeping-options-for-time-starved-startups
Ed: Sandra Beckwith. **Released:** February 21, 2023. **Description:** Bookkeeping is an essential part of any business and not everyone has the skills to manage the books. Listed are several options that would work well with startups. **Availability:** Online.

16788 ■ *Bookkeeping Practices for Digital Marketers*
URL(s): bookkeepwithus.com/bookkeeping-practices-for-digital-marketers
Ed: Chris Groote. **Description:** Explores the value of professional bookkeeping; includes bookkeeping practices. **Availability:** Online.

16789 ■ *"Budgeting vs. Forecasting: What's the Difference Between the Two?" in FreshBooks Hub*
URL(s): www.freshbooks.com/hub/accounting/budgeting-forecasting
Description: Explains the difference between budgeting and forecasting and how to create accurate budgets and forecasts for your small business. **Availability:** Online.

16790 ■ *"Cautions on Loans with Your Business" in Business Owner (Vol. 35, July-August 2011, No. 4, pp. 5)*
Description: Caution must be used when borrowing from or lending to any small business. Tax guidelines for the borrowing and lending practice are also included. **Availability:** Print; Online.

16791 ■ *"Changing the Rules of the Accounting Game" in Canadian Business (Vol. 81, December 8, 2008, No. 21, pp. 19)*
Description: Interference from world politicians in developing accounting standards is believed to have resulted in untested rules that are inferior to current standards. European lawmakers have recently asked to change International Financial Reporting Standards. **Availability:** Online.

16792 ■ *"Convergence Collaboration: Revising Revenue Recognition" in Management Accounting Quarterly (Vol. 12, Spring 2011, No. 3, pp. 18)*
Pub: Management Accounting Quarterly
Contact: Mike DePrisco, President
Ed: Jack T. Ciesielski, Thomas R. Weirich. **Description:** While revenue recognition is critical, regulations have been developed on an ad hoc basis until now. The joint FASB/IASB proposed accounting standard on revenue recognition is a meaningful convergence of standards that will require a major adjustment for financial statement preparers. The proposal is a radical departure from the way revenue has been recognized by the U.S. GAAP. For industries such as consulting, engineering, construction, and technology, it could dramatically change revenue recognition, impacting the top line. The new proposed standard, its potential impact, and the critical role that contracts play is examined thoroughly. **Availability:** PDF; Online.

16793 ■ *"Crucible: Battling Back from Betrayal" in Harvard Business Review (Vol. 88, December 2010, No. 12, pp. 130)*
Pub: Harvard Business Publishing
Contact: Diane Belcher, Managing Director
Ed: Daniel McGinn. **Price:** $8.95, PDF. **Description:** Stephen Greer's scrap metal firm, Hartwell Pacific, lost several million dollars due to a lack of efficient and appropriate inventory audits, accounting procedures, and new-hire reference checks for his foreign operations. Greer believes that balancing growth with control is a key component of success. **Availability:** Print; PDF.

16794 ■ *Deduct It! Lower Your Small Business Taxes*
Pub: Nolo
Contact: Chris Braun, President
Ed: Stephen Fishman. **Released:** 19th edition. **Price:** $17.99, e-book; $19.99, book and e-book; $17.99, E-Book; $19.99, book and e-book; $17.99, e-book. **Description:** Information is provided to help small companies maximize taxable deductions. **Availability:** Handheld; E-book; Print; Electronic publishing; PDF.

16795 ■ *Determining Your Small Business Break Even Point*
URL(s): bookkeepwithus.com/break-even-point
Ed: Chris Groote. **Description:** Discusses the importance of understanding where profitability will begin in a new small business venture. Explains the importance of doing a break-even analysis and how to perform that analysis. **Availability:** Online.

16796 ■ *"Develop the Finance and Accounting Skills Every Entrepreneur Needs" in Entrepreneur (Feb. 9, 2022)*
URL(s): www.entrepreneur.com/article/417111
Released: February 09, 2022. **Description:** Provides information on the importance of understanding how to balance your small business finances and keep your business compliant. **Availability:** Online.

16797 ■ *"Do Fair Value Adjustments Influence Dividend Policy?" in Accounting and Business Research (Vol. 41, Spring 2011, No. 2, pp. 51)*
Ed: Igor Goncharov, Sander van Triest. **Description:** The impact of positive fair value adjustments on corporate distributions is examined using a Russian setting that requires disclosure of unrealized fair value adjustments in income. It was found that there is no rise in dividends due to positive fair value adjustments and that on the contrary, a negative relationship exists between adjustments and dividend changes.

16798 ■ *Don't Run Out Off Cash! Manage Your Accounts Receivable (A/R) Properly*
URL(s): bookkeepwithus.com/accounts-receivable-tampa-business
Ed: Chris Groote. **Description:** Explains accounts receiveable monies, how to establish policies to manage accounts receivable, and suggests software to manage accounts receivables. **Availability:** Online.

16799 ■ *EBay Income: How ANYONE of Any Age, Location, and/or Background Can Build a Highly Profitable Online Business with eBay*
Pub: Atlantic Publishing Co.
Contact: Dr. Heather L. Johnson, Contact
Description: A complete overview of eBay is given and guides any small company through the entire process of creating the auction and auction strategies, photography, writing copy, text and formatting, multiple sales, programming tricks, PayPal, accounting, creating marketing, merchandising, managing email lists, advertising plans, taxes and sales tax, best time to list items and for how long, sniping programs, international customers, opening a storefront, electronic commerce, buy-it now pricing, keywords, Google marketing and eBay secrets.

16800 ■ *"Economic Crisis and Accounting Evolution" in Accounting and Business Research (Vol. 41, Summer 2011, No. 3, pp. 2159)*
Pub: Routledge, Taylor & Francis Group
Ed: Gregory Waymire, Sudipta Basu. **Description:** Financial reporting changes at the face of economic crises are studied using a punctuated equilibrium evolution. Findings show that financial reporting has a minor impact but may amplify economic crises. Attempts to enhance accounting and economic crises may not be as beneficial as planned. **Availability:** PDF; Online; Download.

16801 ■ *Employer Legal Forms Simplified*
Released: First edition. **Description:** Business reference containing the following forms needed to handle employees in any small business environment: application, notice, confidentiality, absence, federal employer forms and notices, and many payroll forms. All forms are included on a CD that comes in both PDF and text formats. Adobe Acrobat Reader software is also included on the CD. The forms are valid in all fifty states and Washington, DC. **Availability:** Print.

16802 ■ *Finance & Accounting: How to Keep Your Books and Manage Your Finances with an MBA, a CPA, or a Ph.D*

16803 ■ *"Finding the Right Accountant for Your Small Business" Business News Daily (February 21, 2023)*
URL(s): www.businessnewsdaily.com/8039-find-small-business-accountant.html
Ed: Simone Johnson. **Released:** February 21, 2023. **Description:** Filing your small business taxes can be daunting, especially if you don't have a background in accounting. This article explains what to look for when choosing an accountant. **Availability:** Online.

16804 ■ *"Five Essential Finance and Accounting Strategies for Small Businesses" in Forbes (July 9, 2021)*
URL(s): www.forbes.com/sites/forbesbusinesscouncil/2021/07/09/five-essential-finance-and-accounting-strategies-for-small-businesses/?sh=71d0945e3e46
Ed: Sagar Tarawade. **Released:** July 09, 2021. **Description:** Explores finance and accounting strategies for small businesses that can help you to manage operations and plan ahead to achieve your business goals. **Availability:** Online.

16805 ■ *The Flaw of Averages: Why We Underestimate Risk in the Face of Uncertainty*
Pub: John Wiley & Sons, Inc.
Contact: Christina Van Tassell, Executive Vice President Chief Financial Officer
Ed: Sam L. Savage. **Released:** March 26, 2012. **Price:** $19.95, paperback; $27.95, hardcover; $12.99, E-Book. **Description:** Personal and business plans are based on uncertainties on a daily basis. The common avoidable mistake individuals make in assessing risk in the face of uncertainty is defined. The explains why plans based on average assumptions are wrong, on average, in areas as diverse as finance, healthcare, accounting, the war on terror, and climate change. **Availability:** E-book; Print.

16806 ■ *"How Accountants Break the Bad News about Tax Refunds: with Chocolate and Tissues" in The Wall Street Journal (March 4, 2019)*
URL(s): www.wsj.com/articles/tax-preparers-stock-up-on-tissues-to-deliver-bad-news-about-your-refund-11551715931
Ed: Laura Saunders. **Released:** March 04, 2019. **Description:** Changes in the Treasury Department rules have made it a difficult tax season because many Americans are either getting a lower tax refund, none at all, or are having to pay the IRS. Accountants are preparing to break the bad news as gently as possible and have found ways to soften the blow by offering treats or even just a kind and sympathetic ear. **Availability:** Online.

16807 ■ *How to Start an Internet Sales Business Without Making the Government Mad*
Pub: Lulu Press Inc.
Ed: Dan Davis. **Released:** October 01, 2011. **Price:** $19.95, paperback; $14.38, PDF; $14.38, e-book. **Description:** Small business guide for launching an Internet sales company. Topics include business structure, licenses, and taxes. **Availability:** E-book; Print; PDF.

16808 ■ *"How To: Manage Your Cash Better" in Inc. (Volume 32, December 2010, No. 10, pp. 69)*
Pub: Mansueto Ventures L.L.C.
Contact: Stephanie Mehta, Chief Executive Officer

GENERAL SMALL BUSINESS TOPICS

Released: December 01, 2010. **Description:** A monthly guide to policies, procedures and practices for managing cash for a small business. **Availability:** Online.

16809 ■ *"The Impact of Organizational Context on the Failure of Key and Strategic Account Management Programs"* in *Journal of Business & Industrial Marketing (Vol. 29, June 2014, No. 5)*
Pub: Emerald Group Publishing Limited
Contact: Erika Valenti, President
Description: Examination of how organizational context affects the failure of various account management programs. Two key factors directing the organizational context include formal or hard elements supporting K/SAM programs, and informal and partly cultural or soft elements moderating the implementation. The relationship between organizational elements in K/SAM is illustrated and vital implications for managers are underscored. **Availability:** Download; Online.

16810 ■ *"Internal Auditor Wants Ethics Review of City's Billy Casper Golf Contract"* in *Business Courier (Vol. 27, September 10, 2010, No. 19, pp. 1)*
Pub: Business Courier
Ed: Dan Monk. **Description:** Mark Ashworth, an internal auditor for Cincinnati, Ohio is pushing for an ethics review of management contract for seven city-owned golf courses. Ashworth wants the Ohio Ethics Commission to investigate family ties between a superintendent for the Cincinnati Recreation Commission and Billy Casper Golf. **Availability:** Print; Online.

16811 ■ *"IRS Announces New Standards for Tax Preparers"* in *Bellingham Business Journal (Vol. February 2010, pp. 9)*
Pub: Sound Publishing Inc.
Contact: Josh O'Connor, President
Ed: Isaac Bonnell. **Description:** A new oversight plan was announced by the Internal Revenue Services (IRS) that will require tax professionals to pass a competency test and register with the government in order to ensure greater accountability in the industry.

16812 ■ *"Is Your Tax Pro Worth the Money?"* in *U.S. News & World Report (February 15, 2018)*
URL(s): money.usnews.com/money/personal-finance/taxes/articles/2018-02-15/is-your-tax-pro-worth-the-money
Ed: Maryalene LaPonsie. **Released:** February 15, 2018. **Description:** Although it may be easier to pay someone to do your taxes, how do you know you are not being taken advantage of? Experts advise doing some research to see what kind of tax professional you need and to meet in person. Set expectations and learn what kind of services will be provided and what price. It's also advisable to look up industry standards for pricing and compare. **Availability:** Online.

16813 ■ *"Kaboom!"* in *Canadian Business (Vol. 81, November 10, 2008, No. 19, pp. 18)*
Description: International Financial Reporting Standards (IFRS) is a good idea in theory but was implemented in a hurry and had poor quality standards from the beginning. **Availability:** Print; Online.

16814 ■ *"Lifesavers"* in *Black Enterprise (Vol. 41, December 2010, No. 5, pp. 38)*
Pub: Earl G. Graves Ltd.
Contact: Earl Graves, Jr., President
Ed: Tamara E. Holmes. **Description:** Profile of Interventional Nephrology Specialists Access Center and founders Dr. Omar Davis and Dr. Natarsha Grant; the center generated $5.5 million in revenue for 2009. Details on how they run their successful center are included. **Availability:** Online.

16815 ■ *"Living in a 'Goldfish Bowl'"* in *WorkingUSA (Vol. 11, June 2008, No. 2, pp. 277)*
Description: Recent changes in laws, regulations and even the reporting format of labor organization annual financial reports in both the U.S. and Australia have received surprisingly little attention, yet they have significantly increased the amount of information available both to union members and the public in general, as reports in both countries are available via government Websites. While such financial reporting laws are extremely rare in European countries, with the exception of the UK and Ireland, the U.S. and Australian reporting systems have become among the most detailed in the world. After reviewing these changes in financial reporting and the availability of these reports, as well as comparing and contrasting the specific reporting requirements of each country, this paper then examines the cost-benefit impact of more detailed financial reporting. **Availability:** Print; Online.

16816 ■ *Mergers and Acquisitions from A to Z*
Pub: HarperCollins Leadership
Contact: Donald Miller, Chief Executive Officer
Released: 2nd edition. **Price:** $19.99, Paperback. **Description:** Guide for the entire process of mergers and acquisitions, including taxes, accounting, laws, and projected financial gain. **Availability:** E-book; Print.

16817 ■ *"Michael Daszkal On Going Beyond the Role of CPA"* in *South Florida Business Journal (Vol. 34, April 25, 2014, No. 40)*
Pub: American City Business Journals, Inc.
Contact: Mike Olivieri, Executive Vice President
Released: Weekly. **Price:** $8, Introductory 4-week offer(Digital & Print). **Description:** Michael Daszkal launched his CPA firm, Daszkal Bolton CPAs in 1994. It has grown from two people to a staff of 115, with 2013 net revenue pegged at $16 million. **Availability:** Print; Online.

16818 ■ *Minding Her Own Business, 4th Ed.*
Released: 4th edition. **Description:** A guide to taxes and financial records for women entrepreneurs is presented. **Availability:** E-book; Print.

16819 ■ *"My Favorite Tool for Managing Expenses"* in *Inc. (Volume 32, December 2010, No. 10, pp. 60)*
Pub: Inc. Magazine
Ed: J.J. McCorvey. **Description:** Web-based service called Expensify is outlined. The service allows companies to log expenses while away from the office using the service's iPhone application. **Availability:** Online.

16820 ■ *"New Institutional Accounting and IFRS"* in *Accounting and Business Research (Vol. 41, Summer 2011, No. 3, pp. 309)*
Pub: Routledge, Taylor & Francis Group
Ed: Peter Wysocki. **Description:** A new framework for institutional accounting research is presented. It has five fundamental components: efficient versus inefficient results, interdependencies, causation, level of analysis, and institutional structure. The use of the framework for evaluation accounting institutions such as the international financial reports standards (IFRS) is discussed. **Availability:** PDF; Online; Download.

16821 ■ *Nonprofit Management All-in-One for Dummies*
URL(s): www.wiley.com/en-us/Nonprofit+Management+All+in+One+For+Dummies-p-9781394172436
Ed: Beverly A. Browining, Sharon Farris, Maire Loughran. **Released:** May 2023. **Price:** $49.99, paperback. **Description:** A thorough guide on how to handle the accounting for nonprofits and general business practices for these organizations. **Availability:** Print.

16822 ■ *"Olympus is Urged to Revise Board"* in *Wall Street Journal Eastern Edition (November 28, 2011, pp. B3)*
Pub: Dow Jones & Company Inc.
Contact: Almar Latour, Chief Executive Officer
Ed: Phred Dvorak. **Description:** Koji Miyata, once a director on the board of troubled Japanese photographic equipment company, is urging the company to reorganize its board, saying the present group should resign their board seats but keep their management positions. The company has come under scrutiny for its accounting practices and costly acquisitions. **Availability:** Online.

16823 ■ *"Place Restrictions on Your Stock Shares"* in *Business Owner (Vol. 35, July-August 2011, No. 4, pp. 14)*
Description: It is critical for any small business owner to be certain that the buyer or recipient of any part of the company represents that the stock is being acquired or given for investment purposes only. **Availability:** Online.

16824 ■ *"Proposed Accounting Changes Could Complicate Tenants' Leases"* in *Baltimore Business Journal (Vol. 28, July 2, 2010, No. 8, pp. 1)*
Pub: Baltimore Business Journal
Contact: Rhonda Pringle, President
E-mail: rpringle@bizjournals.com
Ed: Daniel J. Sernovitz. **Description:** The Financial Accounting Standards Board has proposed that companies must indicate the value of real estate leases as assets and liabilities on balance sheets instead of expenses. The proposals could cause some companies to document millions of dollars in charges on their books or find difficulty in getting loans. **Availability:** Print.

16825 ■ *QuickBooks 2014 on Demand*
Pub: Que Publishing
Ed: Gail Perry. **Released:** 1st edition. **Price:** $22.39, Members, e-book. **Description:** Step-by-step training for using various small business financial software programs; includes illustrated, full color explanations. **Availability:** watermarked; E-book; Print; Electronic publishing; PDF.

16826 ■ *QuickBooks for the New Bean Counter: Business Owner's Guide 2006*
Description: Profile of QuickBooks software, offering insight into using the software's accounting and bookkeeping functions.

16827 ■ *QuickBooks Online for Dummies*
Pub: John Wiley & Sons, Inc.
Contact: Christina Van Tassell, Executive Vice President Chief Financial Officer
URL(s): www.wiley.com/en-us/QuickBooks+Online+For+Dummies%2C+2023+Edition-p-9781119910015
Ed: David H. Ringstrom. **Released:** October 2022. **Price:** $18, e-book; $29.99, paperback. **Description:** Get help right here with learning about QuickBooks for your small business. **Availability:** E-book; Print.

16828 ■ *"Quicken Starter Edition 2008"* in *Black Enterprise (Vol. 38, March 1, 2008, No. 8, pp. 54)*
Pub: Earl G. Graves Ltd.
Contact: Earl Graves, Jr., President
Ed: Dale Coachman. **Description:** Profile of Quicken Starter Edition 2008 offering programs that track spending; it will also categorize tax deductible expenses. **Availability:** Online.

16829 ■ *Reading Financial Reports for Dummies*
Pub: John Wiley & Sons, Inc.
Contact: Christina Van Tassell, Executive Vice President Chief Financial Officer
URL(s): www.amazon.com/gp/product/1119871360/ref=as_li_tl?ie=UTF8&tag=wiley01-20
Ed: Lita Epstein. **Released:** 4th Edition. **Price:** $27.18, paperback; $18, e-book. **Description:** The fourth edition contains more new and updated information. This book is meant as a guide to help the reader interpret and understand financial reports, annual reports, balance sheets, income statements, statements of cash flow and consolidated statements. Real-world examples are given. . **Availability:** E-book; Print.

16830 ■ *Schaum's Outline of Financial Management*
Pub: McGraw-Hill Professional

Ed: Jae K. Shim, Joel G. Siegel. **Released:** Third edition. **Description:** Rules and regulations governing corporate finance, including the Sarbanes-Oxley Act are discussed. **Availability:** E-book; Print; Download.

16831 ■ *Selecting the Right CPA Firm*
URL(s): bookkeepwithus.com/selecting-the-right-cpa-accounting-firm
Ed: Chris Groote. **Description:** Explores questions to ask and things to consider when choosing the right CPA or accounting firm to help you handle financials for your growing business. **Availability:** Online.

16832 ■ *Self-Employed Tax Solutions: Quick, Simple, Money-Saving, Audit-Proof Tax and Recordkeeping Basics*
Released: Second edition. **Description:** A simple system for maintaining tax records and filing tax forms for any small business is explored.

16833 ■ *"Small Business Accounting 101: How to Set Up and Manage Your Books" in Shopify Blog (Oct. 1, 2021)*
URL(s): www.shopify.com/blog/15334373-small-business-accounting-101-ten-steps-to-get-your-startup-on-track
Ed: Kendra Murphy. **Released:** October 01, 2021. **Description:** Covers accounting basics for small business, the best small business accounting software, the importance of knowing your numbers to grow your business, and small business accounting FAQ. **Availability:** Online.

16834 ■ *The Small Business Bible: Everything You Need to Know to Succeed in Your Small Business*
Pub: John Wiley & Sons, Inc.
Contact: Christina Van Tassell, Executive Vice President Chief Financial Officer
Ed: Steven D. Strauss. **Released:** Third edition. **Price:** $22.95, paperback; $14.99, E-book. **Description:** Comprehensive guide to starting and running a successful small business. Topics include bookkeeping and financial management, marketing, publicity, and advertising. **Availability:** E-book; Print.

16835 ■ *Small Business for Dummies*
Pub: John Wiley & Sons, Inc.
Contact: Christina Van Tassell, Executive Vice President Chief Financial Officer
Ed: Eric Tyson, Jim Schell. **Released:** 5th Edition. **Price:** $24.99, paperback; $16.99, E-book. **Description:** Guidebook for anyone wanting to start or grow a small business; topics include information financing, budgeting, marketing, management and more. **Availability:** E-book; Print.

16836 ■ *Small Business Survival Guide*
Released: First edition. **Description:** Small business expert provides strategies to start a company and survive in the 21st Century. He shows small business owners how to succeed despite challenges that can defeat any firm. His advice covers suppliers; customers and contractors; competitors and creditors; spouses, family and friends; as well as the ways lawyers, accountants and other can steal an entrepreneur's success. Ennico also describes how startups can comply with local regulations. **Availability:** E-book; Print.

16837 ■ *"Small Is Bountiful for Intuit" in Barron's (Vol. 90, September 13, 2010, No. 37, pp. 22)*
Pub: Barron's Editorial & Corporate Headquarters
Ed: Mark Veverka. **Description:** Finance software maker Intuit wants to tap the underserved small business market. One analyst sees Intuit's shares rising 25 percent to 55 percent in the next 12 months from September 2010. **Availability:** Online.

16838 ■ *"Smart Year-End Tax Moves" in Business Owner (Vol. 35, November-December 2011, No. 6, pp. 8)*
Description: Managing small business and individual taxes is more important in a bad economy. It is imperative to seek all tax incentives that apply to your business.

16839 ■ *"Spotlight on Pensions" in Business Horizons (Vol. 51, March-April 2008, No. 2, pp. 105)*
Pub: Elsevier Advanced Technology Publications
Ed: Laureen A. Maines. **Description:** Perceptions of pension burden and risk among financial statement users is likely to increase with changes in pension accounting. These perceptions might affect decisions on pension commitments and investments. **Availability:** Online.

16840 ■ *Streetwise Finance and Accounting for Entrepreneurs: Set Budgets, Manage Costs, Keep Your Business Profitable*
Description: Book offers a basic understanding of accounting and finance for small businesses, including financial statements, credits and debits, as well as establishing a budget. Strategies for small companies in financial distress are included.

16841 ■ *Streetwise Small Business Book of Lists: Hundreds of Lists to Help You Reduce Costs, Increase Revenues, and Boost Your Profits!*
Price: Paperback. **Description:** Strategies to help small business owners locate services, increase sales, and lower expenses. **Availability:** Print.

16842 ■ *"Take Control of Your Company's Finances" in Green Industry Pro (Vol. 23, March 2011, No. 3, pp. 24)*
Ed: Gregg Wartgow. **Description:** Understanding that when certain leading indicators that affect the outcome of certain lagging indicators are aligned, companies will be able to take control of their firm's finances. Ways to improve the processes that drive financial performance for landscape firms are outlined. **Availability:** Online.

16843 ■ *"Throughput Metrics Meet Six Sigma" in Management Accounting Quarterly (Vol. 12, Spring 2011, No. 3, pp. 12)*
Pub: Management Accounting Quarterly
Contact: Mike DePrisco, President
Ed: Shaun Aghili. **Description:** Throughput accounting (TA) metrics can be combined with six sigma's DMAIC methodology and various time-tested analysis and measurement tools for added effectiveness in resolving resource constraint issues. The goal is to optimize not only the output of a specific department but that of the entire system, by implementing a cost accounting system that is conducive to system optimization while increasing product quality, process integrity, or ideally, both. **Availability:** Print; PDF; Online.

16844 ■ *Top 15 Small Business and Startup Accounting Tips*
URL(s): www.netsuite.com/portal/resource/articles/accounting/small-business-accounting-tips.shtml
Ed: Scott Beaver. **Released:** November 17, 2020. **Description:** Proper management of a business's finances is a crucial component of success for small businesses and startups. This article provides fifteen basic accounting processes to ensure strong financial management practices. **Availability:** Online.

16845 ■ *"The Unbanking of America"*
Ed: Lisa Servon. **Released:** January 10, 2017. **Price:** $15.99, hardcover; $9.99, e-book. **Description:** With nearly half of Americans living paycheck to paycheck, consumers are finding alternatives to traditional banking. Banks often have high monthly fees and overdraft charges are pushing more and more to seek out check-cashers, payday lenders, and even informal lending clubs. This book examines how middle class Americans are operating without banks. **Availability:** E-book; Print.

16846 ■ *"UPMC Develops Own Billing Solutions" in Pittsburgh Business Times (Vol. 33, January 17, 2014, No. 27, pp. 6)*
Pub: American City Business Journals, Inc.
Contact: Mike Olivieri, Executive Vice President
Description: How University of Pittsburgh Medical Center (UPMC) Health System transformed its accounts payable department by passing its process to a subsidiary, Prodigo Solutions, is discussed. UPMC moved suppliers and purchasers to a shared electronic platform and created a digital marketplace. The system's no purchase order, no pay policy has reduced the number of rogue purchases. **Availability:** Online.

16847 ■ *"What Franchises Need From an Accountant" in Entrepreneur (May 5, 2020)*
URL(s): www.entrepreneur.com/franchise/what-franchises-need-from-an-accountant/348616
Ed: Hayden Field. **Released:** May 05, 2020. **Description:** Provides a checklist for franchisors to follow when looking for an account for their business. **Availability:** Online.

16848 ■ *"What Is Negative Cash Flow & How to Manage It?" in FreshBooks Hub*
URL(s): www.freshbooks.com/hub/accounting/negative-cash-flow
Description: Looks at the best ways to manage cash flow deficits in your small business. **Availability:** Online.

16849 ■ *"What Should You Look For in a Business Bank Account" in Business News Daily (February 21, 2023)*
URL(s): www.businessnewsdaily.com/15768-how-to-choose-a-business-bank-account.html
Ed: Julie Ross. **Released:** February 21, 2023. **Description:** Discusses the benefits of opening up a separate business bank account, which will make tax time a lot easier. **Availability:** Online.

16850 ■ *"Why Is Accounting Important for the Start Up of a Business?" in Chron*
URL(s): smallbusiness.chron.com/accounting-important-start-up-business-52.html
Ed: Osmond Vitez. **Description:** Supplies information for small businesses that are transitioning from small cash transactions to the accrual accounting method. **Availability:** Online.

16851 ■ *"Why Is Accounting Important?" in FreshBooks Article Hub*
URL(s): www.freshbooks.com/hub/accounting/why-is-accounting-important
Description: Discusses the vital information that accounting provides for your small business, including cost and earnings, profit and loss, liabilities and assets, etc. Talks about the purpose, the usefulness, and the importance of accounting for your small business. **Availability:** Online.

16852 ■ *Why Outsourcing Your Accounting Could Be the Right Solution for Your Small Business*
URL(s): bookkeepwithus.com/outsourcing-your-accounting
Ed: Chris Groote. **Description:** Discusses benefits to outsourcing accounting tasks for your small business. **Availability:** Online.

TRADE PERIODICALS

16853 ■ *Keep Up to Date on Accounts Payable*
Pub: American Future Systems Inc.
Contact: Edward G. Rendell, Governor
URL(s): www.pbp.com/divisions/publishing/newsletters/financial-management/keep-up-to-date-on-accounts-payable
Released: Semimonthly **Description:** Supplies updates on state and local sales use taxes, plus IRS 1099 regulations and best practices in accounts payable. Recurring features include interviews, news of research, a calendar of events, and a column titled Sharpen Your Judgment. **Availability:** Online.

VIDEO/AUDIO MEDIA

16854 ■ *The How of Business: Matt Chiappetta - Year-End Tax Considerations*
URL(s): www.thehowofbusiness.com/501-matt-chiappetta-tax-considerations

Ed: Henry Lopez. **Released:** December 11, 2023. **Description:** Podcast discusses year-end tax considerations for small businesses.

16855 ■ *The Perfect Profit and Loss Statement with Adam Rundle*
URL(s): www.eofire.com/podcast/adamrundle
Ed: John Lee Duma. **Released:** September 07, 2023. **Description:** Podcast discusses profit and loss statements.

16856 ■ *Planet Money Summer School: MBA 3: Accounting and the Last Supper*
URL(s): www.npr.org/2023/07/26/1190300217/summer-school-accounting-last-supper
Ed: Robert Smith. **Released:** July 26, 2023. **Description:** Discusses the basics and origins of accounting.

16857 ■ *The Practical Applications of Impact Accounting with Angel Lance*
URL(s): www.awarepreneurs.com/podcast/328-impact-accounting
Ed: Paul Zelizer. **Released:** April 02, 2024. **Description:** Podcast discusses impact accounting.

16858 ■ *Professional on the Go: Using Excel for Small Business Accounting*
URL(s): www.spreaker.com/user/11226745/using-excel-for-small-business-accounting
Ed: Chinwe Onyeagoro. **Description:** Podcast asks is Excel is the best way to manage business finances.

16859 ■ *Profit First Nation: Total Revenue Minus Materials, Subs, and More*
URL(s): www.profitfirstnation.com/episodes/ep-154-total-revenue-minus-materials-subs-more
Ed: Danielle Mulvey. **Released:** November 07, 2023. **Description:** Podcast discusses above-the-line expenses, including materials, subcontractor costs, and franchise fees.

16860 ■ *This Week in Startups: Avoiding Accidental Tax Fraud*
URL(s): thisweekinstartups.com/episodes/bWZZYo6rRaD
Ed: Jason Calacanis. **Released:** November 16, 2023. **Description:** Podcast explains how to navigate potential ERC fraud, expected year-one expenses for startups, and the importance of accounting.

TRADE SHOWS AND CONVENTIONS

16861 ■ **Florida Accounting and Business Expo**
Florida Institute of Certified Public Accountants (FICPA)
3800 Esplanade Way, Ste. 210
Tallahassee, FL 32311
Ph: (850)224-2727
Free: 800-342-3197
Co. E-mail: msc@ficpa.org
URL: http://www.ficpa.org
Contact: Shelly Weir, President
E-mail: shelly@ficpa.org
URL(s): www.ficpa.org/learning/conferences
Description: Accounting equipment, supplies, and services. **Audience:** Accounting and business professionals. **Principal Exhibits:** Accounting equipment, supplies, and services.

16862 ■ **IASA Annual Conferences**
Majesco
412 Mt. Kemble Ave., Ste. 110C
Morristown, NJ 07960
Ph: (973)461-5200
Free: 833-977-1950
Fax: (973)496-9126
Co. E-mail: info@majesco.com
URL: http://www.majesco.com
Contact: Manish Shah, President
URL(s): my.iasa.org/s/community-event?id=a1YPa000001VS4NMAW
Frequency: Annual. **Audience:** Industry professionals, accountants, auditors, and solution providers.

16863 ■ **NABA National Convention & Expo**
National Association of Black Accountants, Inc. (NABA)
7474 Greenway Center Dr., Ste. 1120
Greenbelt, MD 20770
Ph: (301)474-6222
Co. E-mail: customerservice@nabainc.org
URL: http://nabainc.org
Contact: Guylaine Saint Juste, President
URL(s): nabainc.org/2024-convention-expo
Frequency: Annual. **Description:** Exhibits relating to accounting. **Audience:** Accounting professionals. **Principal Exhibits:** Exhibits relating to accounting. **Telecommunication Services:** info@nabainc.org.

16864 ■ **National Association of Tax Professionals Convention**
URL(s): www.natptax.com/EventsAndEducation/Conferences/NationalConference/Pages/default.aspx
Frequency: Annual. **Description:** Provides forums, education, and seminars on current tax preparation information. **Audience:** Tax preparers. **Principal Exhibits:** Provides forums, education, and seminars on current tax preparation information.

CONSULTANTS

16865 ■ **AccountantsWorld L.L.C.**
IRIS Software Group Ltd.
1412 Broadway, Ste.1200
New York, NY 10018
Ph: 44 344 815 5555
Co. E-mail: support@iris.co.uk
URL: http://www.iris.co.uk
Contact: Chandra Bhansali, Chief Executive Officer
E-mail: cbhansali@accountantsworld.com
Facebook: www.facebook.com/accountantsworld
Linkedin: www.linkedin.com/company/accountantsworld
X (Twitter): twitter.com/PowerAccountant
YouTube: www.youtube.com/accountantsworld
Description: Firm provides accountant-centric cloud solutions. It offers services for cloud-based payroll, document management, and billing functions. **Founded:** 2003. **Publications:** *Website Relief*.

16866 ■ **Accounting and Finance Personnel Inc.**
2390 E Camelback, Ste. 130
Phoenix, AZ 85016
Ph: (602)277-3700
URL: http://www.afpersonnel.com
Contact: Mike Nolan, President
X (Twitter): x.com/AFPersonnel
Description: Provider of professional staffing services in the accounting and finance fields in Arizona. **Founded:** 1990.

16867 ■ **Arnold S. Goldin & Associates Inc.**
PO Box 276158
Boca Raton, FL 33427
Ph: (561)994-5810
Fax: (561)431-3102
URL: http://www.arnoldgoldin.com
Description: An accounting and management consulting firm. Serves clients worldwide. Provides management services. Handles monthly write-ups and tax returns. **Scope:** An accounting and management consulting firm. Serves clients worldwide. Provides management services. Handles monthly write-ups and tax returns.

16868 ■ **Avery, Cooper & Co.**
4918-50th St.
Yellowknife, NT, Canada X1A 2P2
Ph: (867)873-3441
Free: 800-661-0787
Fax: (867)873-2353
URL: http://averycooper.com
Contact: William Senfuma, Manager
E-mail: william.senfuma@averycooper.com
Facebook: www.facebook.com/averycooperandco

Description: Provider of public accounting and auditing services. **Scope:** Provider of public accounting and auditing services. **Founded:** 1969. **Training:** Sage Software Training. **Special Services:** ACCPAC Plus; Sage Accpac ERP.

16869 ■ **A Bigger Bottom Line LLC**
4470 W Sunset Blvd., Unit No 90599
Los Angeles, CA 90027
Free: 855-752-6886
Co. E-mail: info@abiggerbottom-line.com
URL: http://www.abiggerbottomline.com
Contact: Sandra Menjivar, Contact
Facebook: www.facebook.com/abiggerbottomline
Linkedin: www.linkedin.com/in/andria-radmacher-68612b95
Instagram: www.instagram.com/abiggerbottomline
Description: Provides a variety of business services including bookkeeping and accounting, payables and receivables, payroll support, cash flow forecasting, Quickbooks setup/training, system integration, remote working, tax planning, start-up consulting, business consulting, forensic accounting, and PPP and bank loans. **Scope:** Provides a variety of business services including bookkeeping and accounting, payables and receivables, payroll support, cash flow forecasting, Quickbooks setup/training, system integration, remote working, tax planning, start-up consulting, business consulting, forensic accounting, and PPP and bank loans.

16870 ■ **Business Computer Consultants, Inc. (BCCI)**
2741 N 81st St.
Lincoln, NE 68507
Ph: (402)466-5954
Fax: (402)466-1371
URL: http://www.bccine.com
Contact: Jerome J. Clinch, President
Description: Provider of accounting solutions such as hardware, networking, internet, and much more. **Scope:** Provider of accounting solutions such as hardware, networking, internet, and much more. **Founded:** 1989. **Special Services:** Traverse®; OSAS®.

16871 ■ **Business Financial Consultants Inc. (BFC)**
4468 Walton Blvd., Ste. B
Waterford, MI 48329
Contact: Jennifer Spiers, President
Description: Provider of services such as taxation and other business matters including accounting and corporate finance. **Scope:** Provider of services such as taxation and other business matters including accounting and corporate finance. **Publications:** "Year End Tax Planning," Nov, 2002; "New Year's Resolution! - Financial Planning & Budgeting," Dec, 2001; "The Tax Relief Act of 2001," Jul, 2001; "Tax Benefits for Graduate Students," The Chicago Business; "B School Tax Deductions after TRA 1997," The Wharton Journal; "The Cost of an MBA may be Tax Deductible," The Wharton Journal; "The 1997 Tax Act Benefits Students and MBA," The Wharton Journal; "Educational Expenses"; "R O I of an MBA is in the TAX," Career Central; "Can I Deduct My MBA Expenses," Wharton Journal. **Training:** Potential for tax deductions for temporary living expenses.

16872 ■ **Business Learning Center (BLC)**
7830 SW Oleson Rd.
Portland, OR 97223
Description: Firm offers business management, financial analysis and strategic planning to small and medium-sized businesses and provides customized accounting and bookkeeping, consultation, payroll, and special support services and its capabilities also include tax planning and audit preparation.

16873 ■ **CapActix Business Solutions**
347 5th Ave., Ste. 1402-227
New York, NY 10016
Ph: (201)778-0509
Co. E-mail: biz@capactix.com
URL: http://www.capactix.com
Contact: Chirag Koshti, Chief Executive Officer
Facebook: www.facebook.com/Capactix

Linkedin: www.linkedin.com/company/capactix-business-solutions
X (Twitter): x.com/CapActix
YouTube: www.youtube.com/channel/UC6UZOg0dy7FZYMC9Mf9159A

Description: A business solutions company providing services in accounting and bookkeeping, CFO services, business analysis, and accounting software consulting. **Scope:** A business solutions company providing services in accounting and bookkeeping, CFO services, business analysis, and accounting software consulting. **Founded:** 2015.

16874 ■ CBIZ, Inc.
CBIZ, Inc.
5959 Rockside Woods Blvd. N, Ste. 600
Independence, OH 44131
Ph: (216)447-9000
Fax: (216)447-9007
Co. E-mail: cbizwomensadvantage@cbiz.com
URL: http://www.cbiz.com
Contact: Jerome P. Grisko, Jr., President
Facebook: facebook.com/cbizmhmcareers
Linkedin: www.linkedin.com/company/cbiz
X (Twitter): twitter.com/cbz
YouTube: www.youtube.com/user/CBIZSolutions

Description: Diversified services company is engaged in providing an array of professional business services which include accounting and tax, healthcare and health benefits consulting, financial advisory, valuation, risk and advisory services, payroll, property and casualty insurance, retirement planning, managed networking and hardware services primarily to small and medium-sized businesses, as well as individuals, government agencies, and not-for-profit enterprises. **Founded:** 1996. **Training:** Health Care - What the Future Holds; Consumer Driven Health Plans; Executive Plans; Health Savings Accounts; Healthy Wealthy and Wise; Legislative Update; Medicare Part D; Retirement Plans.

16875 ■ Charles A. Krueger
1908 Innsbrooke Dr.
Sun Prairie, WI 53590-3515
Contact: Charles A. Krueger, Contact

Description: Financial management consultant specializing in professional education programs for managers and executives. Programs include: Finance and accounting for nonfinancial executives, financial management for executives and developing and using financial information for decision making. Major industries served include manufacturing, service, healthcare and insurance. **Scope:** Financial management consultant specializing in professional education programs for managers and executives. Programs include: Finance and accounting for nonfinancial executives, financial management for executives and developing and using financial information for decision making. Major industries served include manufacturing, service, healthcare and insurance. **Publications:** "Monitoring Financial Results, chapter in Corporate Controllers Manual," Warren Gorham and Lamont. **Training:** Finance and Accounting for Nonfinancial Executives; Financial Management for Health Care Executives; Financial Management for Insurance Executives; Direct Costing; Flexible Budgeting; Contribution Reporting; Building Value and Driving Profits - A Business Simulation.

16876 ■ CheckMark Software Inc.
323 W Drake Rd., Ste. 100
Fort Collins, CO 80526
Free: 800-444-9922
Fax: (970)225-0611
Co. E-mail: sales@checkmark.com
URL: http://www.checkmark.com
Contact: Mohammed A. Ghani, Contact
X (Twitter): x.com/CheckMark_Inc
YouTube: www.youtube.com/channel/UCpJam_8CH-fjiC4eUG--wSA

Description: Developer of accounting and payroll software. **Scope:** Developer of accounting software tools for small businesses and provides fast, easy to use, affordable accounting and payroll solutions to small and medium sized businesses. Provides payroll software and multiledger integrated accounting software. **Founded:** 1984. **Special Services:** MultiLedger; Payroll.

16877 ■ Clearview Business Solutions Inc.
27-1300 King St., E Ste. No. 202
Oshawa, ON, Canada L1H 8J4
Ph: (905)743-0651
Co. E-mail: info@cbsonline.ca
URL: http://cbsonline.ca

Description: Services: Provides business controllership and computerized accounting consulting solutions. **Scope:** Services: Provides business controllership and computerized accounting consulting solutions. **Founded:** 2001. **Special Services:** INFOtrac; Sage BusinessVision Accounting.

16878 ■ Crowe Horwath International
Crowe Horwath International
485 Lexington Ave., 11th Fl.
New York, NY 10017-2619
Ph: (212)572-5500
Fax: (212)572-5572
Co. E-mail: mail@crowe.com.kw
URL: http://www.crowe.com
Contact: James L. Powers, Chairman
Linkedin: www.linkedin.com/company/crowe

Description: Services include accounting, auditing, tax, and management consulting provides innovative business solutions in the area of assurance, business services, consulting, corporate finance, risk management, tax and technology. **Scope:** Services include accounting, auditing, tax, and management consulting provides innovative business solutions in the area of assurance, business services, consulting, corporate finance, risk management, tax and technology. **Founded:** 1991. **Publications:** "Does Your Business Have an E-Commerce Strategy"; "Americas Tax Facts," 2007; "Caring Sharing Investing Growing: The Story of Horwath International," Nov, 2006; "How To Franchise Internationally"; "International Tax Planning Manual: Expatriates and Migrants"; "Americas Tax Facts 2007"; "European and Middle East Tax Facts 2008"; "International Offshore Financial Services"; "International Tax Planning Manual: Corporations"; "Asia or Pacific Tax News 2008: Issue 2"; "FOMB: A Quiz for Business Owners". **Training:** Demand Creation Training, Dec, 2006; Marketing, Dec, 2006.

16879 ■ Focus On Your Business Inc.
3237 Greenfield Dr.
Marietta, GA 30068
Contact: Mike Williford, Chief Executive Officer

Description: Helps small businesses deploy and maximize QuickBooks and peachtree accounting software. Focus is on sales and installation and customized one-on-one problem solving consulting. **Scope:** Helps small businesses deploy and maximize QuickBooks and peachtree accounting software. Focus is on sales and installation and customized one-on-one problem solving consulting. **Publications:** "Click! Now I Understand Accounting"; "The Accounting Software School"; "Professor Peevy Teaches". **Special Services:** Peachtree® 7.0; QuickBooks®.

16880 ■ Franchise Business Systems Inc. (FBS)
2319 N Andrews Ave.
Fort Lauderdale, FL 33311
Free: 800-382-1040
URL: http://www.franchiseaccounting.com
Contact: Steven J. Weil, President
E-mail: steve@franchiseaccounting.com

Description: National business consulting and accounting firm provides accounting and financial systems development, support and training to franchisors for use by their franchisee, accounting, bookkeeping, tax, business consulting and SBA loan packaging services to franchisees. **Scope:** National business consulting and accounting firm provides accounting and financial systems development, support and training to franchisors for use by their franchisee, accounting, bookkeeping, tax, business consulting and SBA loan packaging services to franchisees. **Founded:** 1998. **Training:** Tax planning for business owners; The dos and don'ts of S-corporations; Don't let the tax tail wag the dog; Cash is king; Business budgeting and living your budget; Working with your spouse; Employee incentives, how to get what you pay for; Who to turn to when the IRS comes calling; How to protect your family assets in estate planning; Elder care: what is it and who needs it; Tax planning for seniors; When to run - not walk - away from a financial professional; Year-end tax planning; So you want to start a business; Wealth care for the new millennium.

16881 ■ Hallden Business Services
c/o Hallden Of America Inc
290 Reynolds Bridge Rd.
Thomaston, CT 06787
Ph: (860)283-4386
Fax: (860)283-5784
Co. E-mail: email@hallden.com
URL: http://hallden.com

Description: Firm provides accounting and bookkeeping, IT support, business administration, human resources support for small businesses and self-employed individuals and other services such as slitting shears and lines, automated inspection systems, stretch-bend and tension levelers and lines. **Scope:** Firm provides accounting and bookkeeping, IT support, business administration, human resources support for small businesses and self-employed individuals and other services such as slitting shears and lines, automated inspection systems, stretch-bend and tension levelers and lines.

16882 ■ I-Business Network L.L.C.
2617 Sandy Plains Rd.
Marietta, GA 30066
Ph: (678)627-0646
Fax: (678)627-0688
Co. E-mail: ibn@i-bn.net
URL: http://i-bn.com
Contact: Gary J. Feldman, Contact

Description: Firm provides accounting software and related services for small and medium sized business. Provides wide area network capability, accounting systems, ERP software and other technology services. **Scope:** Firm provides accounting software and related services for small and medium sized business. Provides wide area network capability, accounting systems, ERP software and other technology services. **Founded:** 1999. **Training:** Competitive landscape for application hosting and the impact on there seller sales cycle, Sage Insights reseller conference.

16883 ■ Mitchell and Titus L.L.P.
80 Pine St., 32th Fl.
New York, NY 10005
Ph: (212)709-4500
Fax: (212)709-4680
Co. E-mail: info@mitchelltitus.com
URL: http://www.mitchelltitus.com
Contact: Anthony S. Kendall, Chief Executive Officer
Facebook: www.facebook.com/mitchelltitusllp
Linkedin: www.linkedin.com/company/mitchell-&-titus-llp
X (Twitter): x.com/Mitchell_Titus

Description: Firm provides public accounting, auditing, tax preparation and management consulting. **Scope:** Firm provides assurance, advisory business services, transaction support and tax services. Specializes in auditing and accounting services, tax planning and preparation services management and business advisory services. **Founded:** 1974. **Publications:** "ITEM Club Budget preview report," 2010; "Year end personal planning," 2010; "Steering towards the future using the Pre Budget Report to help the UK rebound," 2009; "Be careful what you wish for," 2009; "Year end personal planning," 2009. **Training:** Budget Seminar 2010, Mar, 2010.

16884 ■ Penny & Associates Inc. (PA)
2748 Bur Oak Ave., Ste. 2
Markham, ON, Canada L6B 1K4
Ph: (416)907-7158
Free: 866-370-0703
Co. E-mail: info@pennyinc.com
URL: http://www.pennyinc.com
Contact: Betty Penny, Contact

Description: Firm is an accounting and management firm that offers accounting and business solutions. **Scope:** Firm is an accounting and management firm that offers accounting and business solutions. **Founded:** 1994. **Training:** Quick Books, Aug, 2001; How to Stand Up to People Without Being a Jerk; How to Build Influence and Rapport With Almost Anyone; Dealing With Dissatisfied, Different and Difficult People; Effective Public Speaking; How to Incorporate Yourself; Company Perks: Attracting & Retaining Good People; FIRST AID. **Special Services:** Quickbooks®.

16885 ■ PYA GatesMoore
Resurgens Plz., Ste. 2100, 945 E Paces Ferry Rd. NE
Atlanta, GA 30326
Ph: (404)266-9876
Free: 800-270-9629
Co. E-mail: info@pyapc.com
URL: http://www.pyapc.com
Contact: Marty Brown, President
E-mail: mbrown@pyapc.com
Facebook: www.facebook.com/pyapc
Linkedin: www.linkedin.com/company/pyapc
Description: Firm provides healthcare consulting, audit and accounting and valuation services. **Scope:** Firm provides healthcare consulting, audit and accounting and valuation services. **Founded:** 1982. **Publications:** "Practicing Medicine in the 21st Century"; "Physicians, Dentists and Veterinarians"; "Insurance Portability and Accountability Act Privacy Manual"; "How To Guide for your Medical Practice and Health Insurance Portability and Accountability Act Security Manual"; "A How To Guide for your Medical Practice"; "Cost Analysis Made Simple: A Step by Step Guide to Using Cost Accounting to Ensure Practice Profitability"; "Cost Cutting Strategies for Medical Practices"; "Cost Cutting Strategies for Medical Practices"; "Getting the Jump on Year-End Tax Planning"; "New 401(k) Safe Harbor Option: Increased Opportunities for the Physician and Practice"; "Not All Tax News is Bad News"; "Shareholder Agreements: Identifying and Addressing Five Risk Areas"; "Surprise - Your Practice has a Deferred Income Tax Liability". **Training:** Documenting and Billing High Risk Codes, 2010; Current Challenges in Ob/Gyn Recruiting, 2010; Planning for Physician Wind-down & Retirement, 2010; HITECH "How To" - Opportunities & Risks, 2010; Pediatric Coding and Audits; Recruiting and Retaining Physicians; How to Prepare for the Recovery Audit Contractors - RAC, 2010; Meaningful Use Rule, 2010; The Revenue Stream in Practice, Apr, 2008; Improving Efficiencies in a Small Family Medicine Practice, Oct, 2007; Using Compensation Models to Improve Performance, Sep, 2007; The Financial Side of Personnel Management, Sep, 2007; Pay for Performance-Is it Really Contracting for Quality?, New York State Ophthalmological Society, Sep, 2007; Beyond the Class Action Settlement Payments-Looking Prospectively at Managed Care Companies Behavior, New York State Ophthalmological Society, Sep, 2007; Protecting your clients from Embezzlement, Jun, 2007; What P4P Means to Your Medical Practice, May, 2007; Finance for the Practicing Physician, May, 2007; Trashing, Dipping and Ghosts in Medical Practices: Protecting your clients from Embezzlement, Apr, 2006.

16886 ■ Stillwater Insurance Group
6800 S point Pkwy, Ste. 700
Jacksonville, FL 32216
Free: 800-220-1351
Fax: (800)491-7683
Co. E-mail: ins@stillwater.com
URL: http://stillwaterinsurance.com
Contact: Mark Davey, President
Facebook: www.facebook.com/Stillwater.Insurance.Company
Linkedin: www.linkedin.com/company/stillwater-insurance-group

Description: Provides strategic planning, budget and financial management, process improvement, organizational design and assessment and college student services operations. **Scope:** Provides strategic planning, budget and financial management, process improvement, organizational design and assessment and college student services operations. **Founded:** 2000. **Publications:** "Integrated Resource Planning (Irp)," Business Officer Magazine, 2005; "The Economic Risk Conundrum," University Business Magazine; "Revenue Analysis and Tuition Strategy"; "Managing Advancement Services: Processes and Paper".

16887 ■ Unique Business Services Inc. (UBS)
26622 Woodward Ave., Ste. 250
Royal Oak, MI 48067
Ph: (248)542-1198
Free: 888-438-8271
Co. E-mail: sales@uniquebusiness.services
URL: http://www.uniquebusiness.services
Contact: Chris Hall, President
X (Twitter): x.com/ubs_50
YouTube: www.youtube.com/user/SAGE50UBS
Description: Developer of accounting software. **Scope:** Developer of accounting software. **Founded:** 2005. **Training:** Peachtree Training, Beginner; Peachtree Training, Advanced.

PUBLICATIONS

16888 ■ Accounting and Business Research (ABR)
530 Walnut St., Ste. 850
Philadelphia, PA 19106
Ph: (215)625-8900
Fax: (215)207-0050
URL: http://taylorandfrancis.com/journals
Contact: Annie Callanan, Chief Executive Officer
URL(s): www.tandfonline.com/journals/rabr20
Ed: Juan Manuel Garcia Lara, Edward Lee, Mark Clatworthy. **Released:** 7/year **Price:** $1,167, Institutions for print and online; $957, Institutions for online only; $321, Individuals for print only. **Description:** Peer-reviewed journal covering all areas of accounting in business, including financial reporting, auditing, tax, corporate governance, and public sector. **Availability:** Print; Download; PDF; Online.

16889 ■ The CPA Journal
URL(s): www.cpajournal.com
Released: Monthly. **Description:** Provides analysis, perspective, and debate on the issues that affect the CPA profession. **Availability:** Print; Online.

16890 ■ CPA Magazine
1705 W NW Hwy., Ste. 170
Grapevine, TX 76051
URL: http://www.cpataxmag.net
Description: Publication that covers accounting, taxation, and other business-related news. **Publications:** CPA Magazine (Weekly).

COMPUTERIZED DATABASES

16891 ■ Accounting & Auditing Resource Guide
URL(s): guides.loc.gov/accounting-and-auditing
Description: An online database of current accounting and auditing research. **Availability:** Online.

COMPUTER SYSTEMS/ SOFTWARE

16892 ■ Aatrix Top Pay™
Aatrix Software Inc.
2617 S Columbia Rd.
Grand Forks, ND 58201
Ph: (701)746-6017
Free: 800-426-0854
Co. E-mail: sales@aatrix.com
URL: http://www.aatrix.com
URL(s): www.aatrix.com/solutions/mac/top-pay
Price: $259.95, for annual. **Description:** Handles payroll calculations and tax deductions for both salaried and hourly employees. **Availability:** Download; Online.

16893 ■ Argos Software / ABECAS Insight
Argos Software
8770 W Bryn Mawr Ave., Ste. 1300
Chicago, IL 60631
Ph: (559)227-1000
Free: 888-253-5353
Co. E-mail: info@argosoftware.com
URL: http://www.argosoftware.com
Contact: Sean Sullivan, President
URL(s): www.argosoftware.com/request-a-demo
Description: Available for MS-DOS operating system. Payroll system for agricultural employees. **Availability:** Online.

INTERNET DATABASES

16894 ■ Arithmetic, Numeracy, Literacy & Imagination: A Research Guide
URL(s): guides.loc.gov/arithmetic-numeracy-literacy-imagination
Description: An online guide listing print and electronic resources on arithmetic and how it relates to business applications. **Availability:** Online.

16895 ■ History of Accounting: A Resource Guide
URL(s): guides.loc.gov/history-of-accounting
Description: Provides links to guide the user towards the history of accounting, which includes print materials in the Library of Congress plus other internet sources. **Availability:** Online.

LIBRARIES

16896 ■ Buffalo & Erie County Public Library-Business, Science & Technology
1 Lafayette Sq.
Buffalo, NY 14203
URL: http://www.buffalolib.org
Scope: Investments, real estate, economics, marketing, engineering, computer science, technology, medical information for laymen, consumer information, automotive repair. **Services:** Interlibrary loan; copying; library open to the public. **Founded:** 1952. **Holdings:** 312,916 books; 60,516 bound periodical volumes; 600 periodical.

16897 ■ Carnegie Library of Pittsburgh Downtown & Business
612 Smithfield St.
Pittsburgh, PA 15222
Ph: (412)281-7141
URL: http://www.carnegielibrary.org/clp_location/downtown-business
Contact: Andrew Medlar, President
Scope: Local history. **Services:** Library open to the public. **Founded:** 1924. **Holdings:** Books; magazines; CD-ROMs; videos.

16898 ■ Edinburgh Napier University - Craiglockhart Campus Library
219 Colinton Rd.
Edinburgh EH14 1DJ, United Kingdom
Ph: 44 131 455 4260
Co. E-mail: library@napier.ac.uk
URL: http://my.napier.ac.uk/library/about-the-library/craiglockhart
Description: Library of the University Business School situated at the center. of the stunning Craiglockhart Campus. **Scope:** Accounting; entrepreneurship; financial; human resource management; law; marketing; economics; tourism. **Services:** Printing;

copying; scanning; library open to the public for reference use only;photocopying; WiFi. **Holdings:** Figures not available.

16899 ■ Nichols College - Conant Library
121 Center Rd.
  Dudley, MA 01571
Ph: (508)213-2334
Co. E-mail: circulation@nichols.edu
URL: http://www.nichols.edu/offices/conant-library
Contact: Carrie Grimshaw, Director
E-mail: carrie.grimshaw@nichols.edu
Scope: Sports management and education. **Services:** Interlibrary loan; copying; information service to groups; document delivery; library open to Dudley and Webster residents. **Founded:** 1962. **Holdings:** Figures not available.

16900 ■ University of Kentucky - Business & Economics Information Center
105 Main Bldg.
  Lexington, KY 40506-0132
URL: http://gatton.uky.edu
Description: Center that provides various programs involving business strategies and ideas about the economy. **Scope:** Business, economics, business management, marketing, finance, accounting. **Services:** Library open to the public for reference use only. **Founded:** 1993.

Advertising

ASSOCIATIONS AND OTHER ORGANIZATIONS

16901 ■ **Hispanic Marketing Council (HMC)**
PO Box 3915
Merrifield, VA 22116-3915
Ph: (703)745-5531
Co. E-mail: info@hispanicmarketingcouncil.org
URL: http://hispanicmarketingcouncil.org
Contact: Isabella Sanchez, Chairman of the Board
E-mail: isanchez@zubiad.com
Linkedin: www.linkedin.com/company/hispanicmarketingcouncil
X (Twitter): x.com/hmchispanic
Instagram: www.instagram.com/hmchispanic
YouTube: www.youtube.com/channel/UC-o4XUedP-ObuCyqsOoiW1Q
Description: Advertising and marketing firms targeting Hispanic consumers. Promotes professional advancement of advertising and marketing personnel working with Hispanic markets. Conducts educational programs to raise awareness of Hispanic markets in the United States in the advertising industry. **Founded:** 1996. **Publications:** *The AHAA Red Book* (Annual); *Conexion AHAA* (Monthly). **Educational Activities:** Association of Hispanic Advertising Agencies Conference (Annual). **Awards:** HMC Strategic Excellence Awards (Annual). **Geographic Preference:** National.

REFERENCE WORKS

16902 ■ *"5 Tips to Attract New Online Customers"* in Legal Zoom (March 9, 2023)
URL(s): www.legalzoom.com/articles/5-tips-to-attract-new-online-customers
Ed: Sandra Beckwith. **Released:** March 09, 2023. **Availability:** Online.

16903 ■ *"7 Ways to Advertise Your Home-Based Small Business for Free"* in Citizens General blog (Dec. 7, 2018)
URL(s): citizensgeneral.com/business-insurance-news/postid/130/7-ways-to-advertise-your-home-based-small-business-for-free
Released: December 07, 2018. **Description:** Maximizing the return-on-investment for a home-based business is crucial. This article takes a look at some of the best ways to advertise your business for free. **Availability:** Online.

16904 ■ *"In-House Agencies Grew During COVID-19"* in AdAge (November 23, 2021)
Ed: Keira Wingate. **Released:** November 23, 2021. **Description:** Discusses the growth of in-house advertising opportunities while businesses were on lockdown due to the COVID-19 pandemic. **Availability:** Online.

16905 ■ *"Location-Based Advertising: Convenience and Personalization vs. Data Privacy"* in Business News Daily (March 20, 2023)
URL(s): www.businessnewsdaily.com/15049-survey-location-based-advertising.html
Ed: Andrew Martins. **Released:** March 20, 2023. **Description:** Location-based advertising can be a very useful tool for small businesses, but many consumers are against it for data privacy reasons. This article explores this concept in depth. **Availability:** Online.

16906 ■ *"Snapchat for Business: Everything You Need to Know"* in Business News Daily (March 17, 2023)
URL(s): www.businessnewsdaily.com/9860-snapchat-for-business.html
Ed: Saige Driver. **Released:** March 17, 2023. **Description:** Explains how small businesses can utilize Snapchat to advertise. **Availability:** Online.

16907 ■ *"The Value of Social Media Advertising Strategies on Tourist Behavior: A Game-Changer for Small Rural Businesses"* in Journal of Small Business Strategy (Vol. 31, December 1, 2021, No. 4, 64-75)
URL(s): libjournals.mtsu.edu/index.php/jsbs/article/view/2136
Ed: Nory B. Jones, Patti Miles, Tanya Beaulieu. **Released:** November 16, 2021. **Description:** Discusses the research done on the affects social media has on the tourism industry within rural communities. **Availability:** PDF; Online.

16908 ■ *"What Is the Best Way to Promote My New Company?"* in Legal Zoom (March 9, 2023)
URL(s): www.legalzoom.com/articles/what-is-the-best-way-to-promote-my-new-company
Ed: Kylie Ora Lobell. **Released:** March 09, 2023. **Description:** There are several really good options for getting the word out about your new business including hiring an advertising company to handle the details or by using social media and other online options yourself. **Availability:** Online.

STATISTICAL SOURCES

16909 ■ *Advertising Agencies Industry in the US - Market Research report*
URL(s): www.ibisworld.com/united-states/market-research-reports/advertising-agencies-industry/
Price: $925. **Description:** Downloadable report analyzing the current and future trends in the advertising agency industry. **Availability:** Download.

16910 ■ *Advertising in Gaming - US - 2021*
URL(s): store.mintel.com/report/advertising-in-gaming-us-2021
Price: $4,366.35. **Description:** Downloadable report examining digital advertising in the video game industry. Discusses strategies along with player reactions and preferences. Report includes an executive summary, interactive databook, PowerPoint presentation, infographic overview, report PDF, and previous years data. **Availability:** PDF.

16911 ■ *US Digital Advertising Market Report 2021*
URL(s): store.mintel.com/report/us-digital-advertising-market-report
Price: $4,366.35. **Description:** Downloadable report examining recent trends in digital advertising, especially with the impact the Covid-19 pandemic has had on the way people consume advertising. Includes an executive summary, interactive databook, PowerPoint Presentation, Infographic Overview, report PDF, and previous years data. **Availability:** PDF.

VIDEO/AUDIO MEDIA

16912 ■ *Side Hustle to Small Business: Exploring the Ins and Outs of Freelancing in Today's World*
URL(s): www.hiscox.com/side-hustle-to-small-business/josh-bernstein-josh-bernstein-media-podcast-season-3
Ed: Sanjay Parekh. **Released:** June 27, 2023. **Description:** Podcast debunks myths about freelancing and offers tips on starting out.

16913 ■ *Tech's Impact on Modern Sales*
URL(s): www.startuphustlepodcast.com/techs-impact-on-modern-sales
Ed: Matt Watson. **Released:** March 05, 2024. **Description:** Podcast explains how Ai can craft ads and automate ad-buying management.

TRADE SHOWS AND CONVENTIONS

16914 ■ **ASI Show Orlando 2022 - Advertising Specialty Institute**
URL(s): www.asishow.com/shows/2022/orlando
Facebook: www.facebook.com/asishow
Linkedin: www.linkedin.com/company/asi-show
X (Twitter): twitter.com/TheASIShow
Instagram: www.instagram.com/theasishow
Description: Tradeshow showcasing suppliers with new products for the advertising industry. **Principal Exhibits:** Tradeshow showcasing suppliers with new products for the advertising industry.

INTERNET DATABASES

16915 ■ *Marketing Industry: A Resource Guide*
URL(s): guides.loc.gov/marketing-industry
Description: Provides links to online resources covering the topics of marketing, public relations, and advertising. Users can obtain links to books, academic journals, trade publications, marketing associations, agencies, rankings and awards, brands and advertisements, manufacturers and wholesalers, regulations and ethics, and subscription databases. **Availability:** Online.

Agribusiness

START-UP INFORMATION

16916 ■ *"Fixing Up the Area: Leo Piatz Opens General Repair Business"* in *The Dickinson Press (November 16, 2010)*
Pub: The Dickinson Press
Contact: Joy Schoch, Business Manager
Description: Profile of Leo Piatz, owner of Leo's Repair in Dickinson, North Dakota; Piatz provides welding and fabricating services to farmers and ranchers in the area.

16917 ■ *"No. 373: Back To the Roots"* in *Inc. (Vol. 36, September 2014, No. 7, pp. 82)*
Pub: Mansueto Ventures L.L.C.
Contact: Stephanie Mehta, Chief Executive Officer
Released: September 2014. **Description:** AquaFarm uses a technique called aquaponics which combines fish and plant cultivation by using fish waste to fertilize vegetation. The startup company prides itself on being part fish tank, part herb garden and sells a $60 kit for growing mushrooms. **Availability:** Print; Online.

16918 ■ *Starting & Running Your Own Horse Business*
Pub: Storey Publishing L.L.C.
Contact: Maribeth Casey, Director
E-mail: maribeth.casey@storey.com
Ed: Mary Ashby McDonald. **Released:** Second edition. **Price:** $19.95, trade paper. **Description:** Insight into starting and running a successful equestrian business is given. The book covers safety, tips for operating a riding school or horse camp, strategies for launching a carriage business, along with tax and insurance advice. **Availability:** E-book; Print.

16919 ■ *"Urban Organics Launches Aquaponic Farm in Old Hamm's Brewery"* in *Business Journal (Vol. 31, April 11, 2014, No. 46, pp. 4)*
Pub: American City Business Journals, Inc.
Contact: Mike Olivieri, Executive Vice President
Price: $4, Introductory 4-Week Offer(Digital & Print). **Description:** Urban Organics launched its new aquaponics farm at the old site of Hamm's Brewery in St. Paul, Minnesota. The facility has four 3,000 gallon fish tanks that hold 1,000 fish which Urban Organics uses to grow fresh and healthy tilapia and vegetable produce. **Availability:** Print; Online.

ASSOCIATIONS AND OTHER ORGANIZATIONS

16920 ■ **ACDI/VOCA**
50 F St. NW, Ste. 1000
Washington, DC 20001
Ph: (202)469-6000
Fax: (202)469-6257
Co. E-mail: acdivocainfo@acdivoca.org
URL: http://www.acdivoca.org
Contact: Morgan Mercer, Director
Facebook: www.facebook.com/acdivoca
Linkedin: www.linkedin.com/company/acdivoca
X (Twitter): x.com/acdivoca
YouTube: www.youtube.com/user/acdivocaDC
Description: Assists in organizing and providing technical assistance for cooperatives and agribusinesses in developing countries, usually under contract with the Agency for International Development. Advises governmental and other agencies in agricultural marketing, supply, and credit; carries out feasibility studies for specific agribusiness ventures; arranges formal and on-the-job training in cooperative practices for government officials, cooperative functionaries, and rural leaders; conducts short- and long-term technical assistance programs. **Scope:** Promotes economic opportunities for cooperatives, enterprises and communities through the application of sound business practice. **Founded:** 1997. **Publications:** *ACDI/VOCA World Report* (Semiannual). **Geographic Preference:** National; Regional.

16921 ■ **Agri-Energy Roundtable (AER)**
PO Box 5565
Washington, DC 20016
Ph: (202)296-4563
Co. E-mail: agenergy@aol.com
URL: http://www.agribusinesscouncil.org/aer.htm
Contact: Nicholas Hollis, Executive Director
Description: Serves as an information clearinghouse to improve dialogue on cooperative energy-agricultural development among the industrialized and developing nations. **Founded:** 1980. **Publications:** *Agri-Energy Report* (Quarterly); *Regional Africa Bulletin*. **Geographic Preference:** National.

16922 ■ **AgriBusiness Association of Kentucky (ABAK)**
340 Democrat Dr.
Frankfort, KY 40601
Ph: (502)226-1122
Fax: (502)875-1595
URL: http://www.kyagbusiness.org
Contact: Jeff Pendleton, President
Facebook: www.facebook.com/kyagbusiness
X (Twitter): x.com/KyAgBusiness
Description: Represents professionals engaged in business of supplying inputs for agriculture production throughout the state of Kentucky. Provides support, resources, and opportunities in Kentucky agriculture. **Founded:** 1962. **Geographic Preference:** State.

16923 ■ **Agribusiness Council (ABC)**
PO Box 5565
Washington, DC 20016
Ph: (202)296-4563
Co. E-mail: info@agribusinesscouncil.org
URL: http://agribusinesscouncil.org
Contact: Nicholas E. Hollis, President
Description: Business organizations, universities and foundations, and individuals interested in stimulating agribusiness in cooperation with the public sector, domestic and international. Aids in relieving the problems of world food supply. Supports coordinated agribusiness in the developing nations by identifying opportunities for investment of U.S. private-sector technology management and financial resources. Brings potential investment opportunities to the attention of U.S. agribusiness firms; coordinates informal network of state agribusiness councils and grassroots organization; encourages companies to make investment feasibility studies in agribusiness; provides liaison and information exchange between agribusiness firms, governments, international organizations, universities, foundations, and other groups with the objective of identifying areas of cooperation and mutual interest. **Founded:** 1967. **Geographic Preference:** National.

16924 ■ **American Brahmousin Council (ABC)**
PO Box 88
Whitesboro, TX 76273
Ph: (903)815-0321
Co. E-mail: rsopbc@gmail.com
URL: http://www.americanbrahmousincouncil.org
Contact: Dewon Rankin, President
Description: Breeders of Brahmousin cattle. **Geographic Preference:** National.

16925 ■ **American Feed Industry Association (AFIA)**
2101 Wilson Blvd., Ste. 810
Arlington, VA 22201
Ph: (703)524-0810
Fax: (703)524-1921
Co. E-mail: afia@afia.org
URL: http://www.afia.org
Contact: Constance Cullman, President
Facebook: www.facebook.com/AmericanFeedIndustryAssociation
X (Twitter): x.com/FeedFolks
Instagram: www.instagram.com/afiafeed
YouTube: www.youtube.com/channel/UCOjJK0EQC-Qv0gbzkisa0VA
Description: Manufacturers of formula feed and pet food; suppliers to feed manufacturers; other trade related associations. Maintains Equipment Manufacturing Council. **Founded:** 1909. **Publications:** *National Feed Ingredients Association--Directory* (Annual); *American Feed Industry Association--Software Directory* (Irregular); *Publications Catalog*; *Safety-Gram* (Monthly); *American Feed Industry Association--Membership Directory and Buyer's Guide*. **Educational Activities:** International Fair/San Salvador (Biennial); International Feed Expo (Annual); Liquid Feed Symposium (LFS) (Annual); Equipment Manufacturers Conference (EMC) (Annual). **Awards:** American Feed Industry Association Poultry Nutrition Research Award (Annual); Food Safety Innovation Award (Annual); Food Safety Innovation Awards (Annual); AFIA Distinguished Service Award (Annual); Member of the Year (Annual); AFIA Liquid Feed Hall of Fame (Annual); AFIA/KSU Feed Manufacturing Lifetime Achievement Award (Annual); AFIA Feed Facility of the Year (Annual); AFIA Ruminant Animal Nutrition Award (Annual); AFIA and Federa-

GENERAL SMALL BUSINESS TOPICS

tion of Animal Science Societies New Frontiers in Animal Nutrition Award (Annual). **Geographic Preference:** National.

16926 ■ American Hereford Association (AHA)
11500 NW Ambassador Dr., Ste. 410
Kansas City, MO 64153
Ph: (816)842-3757
Fax: (816)842-6931
Co. E-mail: aha@hereford.org
URL: http://hereford.org
Contact: Amari Seiferman, President
E-mail: aseiferman@herefordbeef.org
Facebook: www.facebook.com/americanherf
X (Twitter): x.com/americanherf
YouTube: www.youtube.com/channel/UC
_UwWbkCpshc5hrTNOSlfqQ
Description: Breeders of purebred Hereford cattle. Maintains registry, pedigree, and performance records; provides fieldman assistance and guidance; conducts research programs; maintains hall of fame and museum; sponsors competitions; compiles statistics. **Founded:** 1881. **Publications:** *American Hereford Association Annual Report* (Annual); *Polled Hereford World--Directory of Polled Hereford Associations Issue* (Annual). **Geographic Preference:** National.

16927 ■ American Jersey Cattle Association (AJCA)
6486 E Main St.
Reynoldsburg, OH 43068-2362
Ph: (614)861-3636
Fax: (614)861-8040
Co. E-mail: info@usjersey.com
URL: http://www.usjersey.com
Contact: Neal Smith, Executive Secretary
Facebook: www.facebook.com/USJersey
Description: Owners and breeders of Jersey cattle. Promotes sale and use of Jersey milk through National All-Jersey, Inc., a marketing affiliate. **Scope:** Jersey dairy cattle. **Founded:** 1868. **Publications:** *Jersey Directory*; *Jersey Journal* (Monthly). **Awards:** Cedarcrest Farms Scholarships (Annual); Reuben R. Cowles Youth Educational Award (Annual); Cedarcrest Farms Scholarship (Annual); AJCA Distinguished Service Award (Annual); AJCA Master Breeder Award (Annual); Reuben R. Cowles Jersey Youth Award (Annual); AJCA Young Jersey Breeder Award (Annual). **Geographic Preference:** National.

16928 ■ American Junior Brahman Association (AJBA)
1920 W Villa Maria Rd., No. 302
Bryan, TX 77807
Ph: (979)485-5528
URL: http://brahman.org/ajba
Contact: Ty Hebert, President
Description: Individuals less than 21 years of age who are interested in Brahman cattle. **Founded:** 1980. **Educational Activities:** All-American Junior Brahman Show (Annual). **Geographic Preference:** National.

16929 ■ American Junior Shorthorn Association (AJSA)
7607 NW Prairie View Rd.
Kansas City, MO 64151
Ph: (816)599-7777
Fax: (816)599-7782
Co. E-mail: info@shorthorn.org
URL: http://juniorshorthorn.org
Contact: Faye Smith, President
Facebook: www.facebook.com/americanjuniorshor
thornassociation
Description: Young people involved in the U.S. beef industry. Aims to educate and interest young people in Shorthorn and Polled Shorthorn cattle. **Founded:** 1968. **Geographic Preference:** National.

16930 ■ American Society of Agricultural Consultants (ASAC)
126 W Main St.
New Prague, MN 56071
Contact: Keith Dickinson, President
Description: Independent, full-time consultants in specialty areas serving agribusiness interests throughout the world. **Scope:** Association of agricultural consultants serving its membership through ethics, networking, strong continuing education. Maintains directory of members who provide a variety of agricultural consulting services. **Publications:** *American Society of Agricultural Consultants--Membership Directory*. **Training:** Leading Edge Consulting; Communications for Ag Professionals; Seven Habits of Highly Effective People; Ethics. **Geographic Preference:** National.

16931 ■ American Soybean Association (ASA)
12647 Olive Blvd., Ste. 410
Saint Louis, MO 63141
Ph: (314)576-1770
Free: 800-688-7692
Co. E-mail: info@soy.org
URL: http://soygrowers.com
Contact: Ron Moore, President
E-mail: rmoore@speednet.com
Facebook: www.facebook.com/
AmericanSoybeanAssociation
X (Twitter): x.com/ASA_Soybeans
YouTube: www.youtube.com/user/
americansoybeanassoc
Description: Develops and implements policies to increase the profitability of its members and the entire soybean industry. **Founded:** 1920. **Publications:** *Soybean Digest--Marketing Guide Issue*; *Soya & Oilseed Bluebook: Annual Directory of the World Oilseed Industry* (Annual). **Educational Activities:** ASA Commodity Classic (Annual). **Geographic Preference:** National.

16932 ■ California Canning Peach Association (CCPA)
2600 River Plz. Dr., Ste. 200
Sacramento, CA 95833
Ph: (916)925-9131
Fax: (916)925-9030
Co. E-mail: ccpa@calpeach.com
URL: http://www.calpeach.com
Contact: Rich Hudgins, President
Description: California cling peach growers. Works to market members' production and obtain a reasonable return for cling peach growers' raw product. Conducts research on breeding new varieties of cling peaches. Compiles statistics on the cling peach industry. **Founded:** 1922. **Geographic Preference:** National.

16933 ■ *Canadian Biosystems Engineering*
E2-376 EITC Bldg.
75A Chancellor Cir.
Winnipeg, MB, Canada R3T 5V6
Ph: (204)479-4084
URL: http://csbe-scgab.ca
Contact: Jan Adamowski, President
E-mail: jan.adamowski@mcgill.ca
URL(s): csbe-scgab.ca/publications/cbe-journal
Ed: Dr. Ranjan Sri Ranjan. **Released:** Annual **Description:** Scientific engineering journal. **Availability:** PDF.

16934 ■ Communicating for America (CA)
403 S Union
Fergus Falls, MN 56537
Ph: (218)739-3241
Free: 800-432-3276
Fax: (218)739-3832
URL: http://www.communicatingforamerica.org
Contact: Stephen Rufer, Chairman General Counsel
Description: Promotes the general health, well being and advancement of people in agriculture and agribusiness. Participates in federal and state issues that affect the quality of life in rural America and provides members with a variety of money-saving benefit programs. Conducts grants program, research on rural issues, and international exchange programs with an agricultural focus. **Founded:** 1972. **Publications:** *CA Highlights*; *CAEP In Touch* (Quarterly); *Smart Choices*. **Geographic Preference:** National.

Agribusiness ■ 16939

16935 ■ Farm and Food Care Ontario [Farm & Food Care]
660 Speedvale Avenue W, Unit 302
Guelph, ON, Canada N1K 1E5
Ph: (519)837-1326
Co. E-mail: info@farmfoodcare.org
URL: http://www.farmfoodcareon.org
Contact: Kelly Daynard, Executive Director
Facebook: www.facebook.com/FarmFoodCare
X (Twitter): x.com/FarmFoodCareON
Instagram: www.instagram.com/farmfoodcare
YouTube: www.youtube.com/user/FarmandFoodCare
Description: Promotes environmentally sustainable food production. Facilitates communication among members; serves as a clearinghouse on sustainable agriculture. **Founded:** 1987. **Publications:** *AGCare Update* (Quarterly); *Project Report* (Periodic). **Geographic Preference:** National.

16936 ■ Fresh Produce Association of the Americas (FPAA)
590 E Frontage Rd.
Nogales, AZ 85621
Ph: (520)287-2707
Fax: (520)287-2948
Co. E-mail: info@freshfrommexico.com
URL: http://www.freshfrommexico.com
Contact: Lance Jungmeyer, President
E-mail: lance@freshfrommexico.com
Facebook: www.facebook.com/FreshProduceAA
X (Twitter): x.com/FreshProduceAA
Description: Importers, brokers, and related industry stakeholders for Mexican fruits and vegetables. Ensures market access of high quality produce throughout the world. Facilitates international trade by working with government officials, retailers, purchasers, growers, and consumer groups. Provides information on the safety of imported produce. **Founded:** 1944. **Geographic Preference:** National.

16937 ■ Georgia Agribusiness Council (GAC)
1655 S Elm St.
Commerce, GA 30529
Ph: (706)336-6830
Fax: (706)336-6898
URL: http://www.ga-agribusiness.org
Contact: Will Bentley, President
E-mail: wbentley@ga-agribusiness.org
Facebook: www.facebook.com/GAagribusiness
X (Twitter): x.com/GAagribusiness
YouTube: www.youtube.com/user/GAagribusiness
Description: Advances the business of agriculture through economic development, environmental stewardship and education to improve the quality of life. **Founded:** 1966. **Publications:** *AgOutlook* (Monthly). **Geographic Preference:** State.

16938 ■ International Dairy Foods Association (IDFA)
1250 H St. NW, Ste. 900
Washington, DC 20005
Ph: (202)737-4332
Fax: (202)331-7820
Co. E-mail: membership@idfa.org
URL: http://www.idfa.org
Contact: Michael Dykes, President
Linkedin: www.linkedin.com/company/idfa
X (Twitter): x.com/dairyidfa
YouTube: www.youtube.com/user/dairyIDFA
Description: Umbrella organization providing services such as government relations, regulatory affairs monitoring, marketing, public relations, seminars, and general management for the dairy industry. **Founded:** 1908. **Publications:** *International Dairy Foods Association Membership Directory* (Annual); *Dairy Facts* (Annual). **Educational Activities:** Worldwide Food Expo; Dairy Forum (Annual). **Awards:** GrassRoots Action Network for Dairy Pioneer Award; IDFA Innovative Dairy Farmer of the Year (Annual); IDFA Safety Recognition Awards (Annual); IDFA Soaring Eagle Award (Annual). **Geographic Preference:** Multinational.

16939 ■ International Food and Agribusiness Management Association (IFAMA)
922 NW Cir., Blvd., Ste. 160, No. 234
Corvallis, OR 97330

Ph: (541)368-5545
Co. E-mail: ifama@ifama.org
URL: http://www.ifama.org
Contact: Raj Vardhan, President
Facebook: www.facebook.com/IFAMA-163452890485145
Linkedin: www.linkedin.com/company/ifama
X (Twitter): x.com/IFAMAintl
YouTube: www.youtube.com/user/IFAMA2013
Description: Stimulates strategic thinking across the food and fiber systems. Serves as a forum for people involved in the food and agribusiness management. **Founded:** 1993. **Publications:** *ChainLetter* (Quarterly). **Geographic Preference:** Multinational.

16940 ■ MBG Marketing - The Blueberry People
PO Box 322
Grand Junction, MI 49056
Ph: (269)434-6791
Co. E-mail: contact@blueberries.com
URL: http://www.blueberries.com
Contact: Larry Ensfield, Chief Executive Officer
Description: Represents the interests of blueberry growers in Michigan. **Founded:** 1936. **Educational Activities:** The National Blueberry Conference & Exposition.

16941 ■ Michigan Bean Commission (MBC)
516 South Main St., Ste. D
Frankenmuth, MI 48734
Ph: (989)262-8550
Co. E-mail: jcramer@michiganbean.com
URL: http://michiganbean.com
Contact: Joe Cramer, Chairman
E-mail: jcramer@michiganbean.com
Facebook: www.facebook.com/MichiganBeanCommission
X (Twitter): x.com/michbeans
YouTube: www.youtube.com/channel/UC7m9bCRMzZ71cs5SgN7GhFQ
Pinterest: www.pinterest.com/michbeans/nutrient-dense-bean-dishes
Description: Represents Michigan's dry bean farmers and processors. Dedicated to educating the public about the benefits of Michigan beans. **Founded:** 1966. **Publications:** *Bean Commission News* (Monthly). **Geographic Preference:** State.

16942 ■ Michigan Beef Industry Commission (MBIC)
2145 University Pk. Dr., Ste. 300
Okemos, MI 48864
Ph: (517)347-0911
URL: http://www.mibeef.org
Contact: George Quackenbush, Executive Director
Facebook: www.facebook.com/michiganbeef
X (Twitter): x.com/Beef
YouTube: www.youtube.com/user/BeefForDinner
Pinterest: www.pinterest.com/beeffordinner
Description: Aims to promote beef industry in Michigan. **Founded:** 1972. **Geographic Preference:** State.

16943 ■ Michigan Corn Growers Association (MCGA)
13750 S Sedona Pky., Ste. 5
Lansing, MI 48906
Ph: (517)668-2676
Free: 888-323-6601
Fax: (517)668-2670
Co. E-mail: corninfo@micorn.org
URL: http://micorn.org
Contact: Jim Zook, Executive Director
E-mail: jzook@micorn.org
Facebook: www.facebook.com/michigancorn
X (Twitter): x.com/MI_Corn
Instagram: www.instagram.com/mi_corn
YouTube: www.youtube.com/user/MichiganCorn
Description: Seeks to increase the profitability of corn production in Michigan. Offers marketing seminars, educational meetings, research plots, political action, tradeshows, and advocacy at the state and national level to enhance the economic viability of corn farmers through fair and just regulations, trade agreements, and legislation. **Founded:** 1972. **Geographic Preference:** State.

16944 ■ Michigan Emu Growers Association (MEGA)
c/o Dennis E Homant, President
2147 Thorntree Ln.
Ortonville, MI 48462
Ph: (248)324-2687
Co. E-mail: dhomant@mi.rr.com
URL: http://michemu.tripod.com
Contact: Dennis E. Homant, President
E-mail: dhomant@mi.rr.com
Description: Association of emu growers in Michigan. **Geographic Preference:** State.

16945 ■ Michigan Milk Producers Association (MMPA)
41310 Bridge St.
Novi, MI 48376
Ph: (248)474-6672
URL: http://www.mimilk.com
Contact: Joe Diglio, President
Facebook: www.facebook.com/MichiganMilkProducersAssociation
Linkedin: www.linkedin.com/company/michigan-milk-producers-association
X (Twitter): x.com/michiganmilk
Instagram: www.instagram.com/michiganmilk
Description: Association of milk producers in Michigan. **Founded:** 1916. **Geographic Preference:** State.

16946 ■ Michigan Sheep Producers Association (MSBA)
c/o Maury Kaercher, Executive Director
5859 E E Ave.
Kalamazoo, MI 49004
Ph: (269)569-9592
Co. E-mail: kaercher@msu.edu
URL: http://misheep.org
Contact: Maury Kaercher, Executive Director
E-mail: kaercher@msu.edu
Facebook: www.facebook.com/MichiganSheep
Description: Represents and supports Michigan's sheep industry. Provides information and activities to new and small producers. Encourages the development of wool and related skills such as spinning, weaving, knitting, felting, and tanning through workshops, information, and other events. **Geographic Preference:** State.

16947 ■ Michigan Soybean Association (MSA)
3055 W M-21
Saint Johns, MI 48879
Ph: (989)652-3294
Co. E-mail: soyinfo@michigansoybean.org
URL: http://www.misoy.org
Contact: Heather Feuerstein, President
Facebook: www.facebook.com/michigansoybean
X (Twitter): x.com/michigansoybean
Instagram: www.instagram.com/michigansoybean
YouTube: www.youtube.com/channel/UCLRQvSSSeAopPsHwGdNa5Dw
Pinterest: www.pinterest.com/michigansoybean
Description: Represents Michigan's soybean producers through lobbying, advocacy, and other legislative activities at the state and national level. **Founded:** 1976. **Geographic Preference:** State.

16948 ■ Michigan Vegetable Council
6835 S Krepps Rd., St. Johns
Saint Johns, MI 48879
Ph: (517)663-6725
Fax: (517)663-6725
URL: http://www.michiganvegetablecouncil.org
Contact: Greg Bird, Executive Director
E-mail: gbird@michiganvegetablecouncil.org
Description: Seeks to represent and support the vegetable industry of Michigan. Funds research and education beneficial to vegetable growers. Co-sponsors the Great Lakes Fruit, Vegetable and Farm Market EXPO. Represents the interests of vegetable growers at government, industry, and university meetings, hearings, and planning sessions. **Founded:** 1964. **Publications:** *The Vegetable Growers News* (Monthly). **Educational Activities:** Great Lakes Fruit, Vegetable and Farm Market Expo (Annual); Great Lakes Vegetable Growers Convention and Farm Market Show (Annual). **Awards:** MVC Master Farmer Associate Award (Annual); MVC Master Farmer Award (Annual). **Geographic Preference:** State.

16949 ■ Missouri Agribusiness Association (MO-AG)
410 Madison St.
Jefferson City, MO 65101
Ph: (573)636-6130
Fax: (573)636-3299
Co. E-mail: info@mo-ag.com
URL: http://www.mo-ag.com
Contact: Steve Taylor, Executive Director
E-mail: staylor@mo-ag.com
Facebook: www.facebook.com/moagribusiness
X (Twitter): x.com/MOAGBIZ
Description: Seeks to strengthen the U.S. agricultural sectors. Facilitates American agribusiness participation in agricultural trade and development programs. Raises public awareness of agriculture's vital importance in national and global economic health. **Founded:** 1969. **Geographic Preference:** State.

16950 ■ Montana Agricultural Business Association (MABA)
PO Box 7325
Helena, MT 59604
Ph: (406)227-3523
Fax: (406)227-3745
Co. E-mail: mabamgea@gmail.com
URL: http://www.mtagbiz.org
Contact: Jake Yates, President
Facebook: www.facebook.com/MontanaAgriculturalBusinessAssociation
X (Twitter): x.com/maba_ag
Description: Seeks to strengthen the U.S. agricultural sectors. Facilitates American agribusiness participation in agricultural trade and development programs. Raises public awareness of agriculture's vital importance in national and global economic health. **Geographic Preference:** State.

16951 ■ National Association of Institutional Agribusiness (NAIA)
URL: http://www.naiaweb.com
Description: Sponsors discussion of mutual problems, exchange of ideas, development of organized studies and other activities designed for the contributions of institutional farms to both the treatment of inmates and the economy of their respective agencies. **Founded:** 1951. **Geographic Preference:** National.

16952 ■ National Association of Wheat Growers (NAWG)
25 Massachusetts Ave. NW, Ste. 500B
Washington, DC 20001
Ph: (202)547-7800
Co. E-mail: wheatworld@wheatworld.org
URL: http://wheatworld.org
Contact: Chandler Goule, Chief Executive Officer
Facebook: www.facebook.com/wheatworld
Linkedin: www.linkedin.com/company/national-association-of-wheat-growers-nawg
X (Twitter): x.com/wheatworld
Instagram: www.instagram.com/wheatgrowers
Description: Federation of 20 state wheat growers associations. Represents wheat grower interest in educational, legislative, and regulatory projects and issues for wheat farmers in Washington, DC. Sponsors research and transportation, and leadership conferences; conducts seminars. Conducts charitable programs. **Founded:** 1950. **Publications:** *The Wheat Grower*. **Educational Activities:** National Association of Wheat Growers Convention (Annual). **Geographic Preference:** National.

16953 ■ National Council of Agricultural Employers (NCAE)
525 9th St. NW, Ste. 800
Washington, DC 20004
Ph: (202)629-9320

GENERAL SMALL BUSINESS TOPICS

URL: http://www.ncaeonline.org
Contact: Michael Marsh, President
Facebook: www.facebook.com/ncaeonline/timeline
Linkedin: www.linkedin.com/company/national-council-of-agricultural-employers
X (Twitter): x.com/NCAEonline
Description: Growers of agricultural commodities who employ hand labor for field crops; processors and handlers, farm and commodity organizations, and others whose business is related to labor-intensive farming in the U.S. Aims to improve the position and image of U.S. agriculture as an employer of labor and to facilitate and encourage the establishment and maintenance of an adequate force of agricultural employees. Serves as clearinghouse for exchange of information on labor supply, length of employment, and other conditions of work. Does not engage in recruitment, housing, supplying, or employment of agricultural workers, and does not represent its members or others in negotiating with labor unions or other organizations, or in agreeing to any contract relating to hours, wages, or working conditions. Keeps member abreast of national legislation affecting agricultural labor. **Founded:** 1964. **Geographic Preference:** National.

16954 ■ National Farm and Ranch Business Management Education Association (NFRBMEA)
6540 65th St. NE
Rochester, MN 55906-1911
Ph: (507)951-3610
Fax: (888)255-9735
URL: http://www.nfrbmea.org
Contact: Pauline Van Nurden, President
E-mail: pvannurd@umn.edu
Facebook: www.facebook.com/nfrbmea
X (Twitter): x.com/nfrbmea
Description: Works to bring ideas and techniques in farm and ranch business management education to its members. **Founded:** 1973. **Geographic Preference:** Multinational.

16955 ■ National Hay Association (NHA)
4735 Massillon Rd., Unit 769
Green, OH 44232
Ph: (615)854-5574
Fax: (330)408-7128
Co. E-mail: nhaexecoffice@gmail.com
URL: http://www.nationalhay.org
Contact: John Russell, President
Facebook: www.facebook.com/NationalHayAssociation
X (Twitter): x.com/NatlHayAssoc
YouTube: www.youtube.com/results
Description: Hay shippers, dealers, brokers, producers, and others interested in the hay industry. Publishes information to keep members aware of supplies of hay products, shortage areas and legislative issues concerning members. Accepts unsolicited manuscripts. Reaches market through direct mail. **Founded:** 1895. **Publications:** *National Hay Association--News Release* (Periodic); *National Hay Association--Yearbook and Membership Directory* (Annual). **Awards:** NHA Haymaker of the Year (Annual). **Geographic Preference:** National.

16956 ■ National Junior Hereford Association (NJHA)
11500 NW Ambassador Dr., Ste. 410
Kansas City, MO 64153
Ph: (816)842-3757
Fax: (816)243-1314
Co. E-mail: aha@hereford.org
URL: http://hereford.org/youth/njha
Contact: Whitey Hunt, Chairman
Facebook: www.facebook.com/americanherf
X (Twitter): x.com/americanherf
YouTube: www.youtube.com/channel/UC_UwWBkCpshc5hrTNOSIfqQ
Description: Members of state junior Hereford associations under 22 years of age seeking to assist in the education and training of youth in leadership and the production and handling of beef cattle. Holds educational meetings, field days, and demonstrations to familiarize rural youth with the latest techniques.

Sponsors competitions. **Founded:** 1965. **Awards:** B.C. Snidow Award (Annual); NJHA Golden Bull Achievement Award (Annual); NJHA National Junior Merit Award (Annual); Walter and Joe Lewis Memorial Award (Annual). **Geographic Preference:** National.

16957 ■ National Onion Association (NOA)
218 Oak Ave.
Eaton, CO 80615
Ph: (970)353-5895
Co. E-mail: info@onions-usa.org
URL: http://www.onions-usa.org
Contact: Doug Bulgrin, President
Facebook: www.facebook.com/NationalOnion
X (Twitter): x.com/Onionista
Instagram: www.instagram.com/nationalonionassociation
YouTube: www.youtube.com/channel/UCMIvVXINAHvTxQ1t-mh7dcQ
Pinterest: www.pinterest.com/NationalOnion
Description: Growers, brokers, grower-shippers, shippers, suppliers, and support professionals engaged in the onion industry. Promotes the onion industry. Compiles monthly statistical report of stocks-on-hand, acreage, yield, and production of onions in the U.S. Lobbies issues of importance to national onion industry. **Founded:** 1913. **Publications:** *National Onion Association--Newsletter* (Monthly). **Geographic Preference:** National.

16958 ■ National Sunflower Association (NSA)
2401 46th Ave. SE, Ste. 206
Mandan, ND 58554-4829
Ph: (701)328-5100
Free: 888-718-7033
Co. E-mail: info@sunflowernsa.com
URL: http://www.sunflowernsa.com
Contact: John Sandbakken, Executive Director
E-mail: johns@sunflowernsa.com
Facebook: www.facebook.com/sunflowernsa
X (Twitter): x.com/NatlSunflower
YouTube: www.youtube.com/user/sunflower58554
Description: Growers, firms, and organizations associated with the sunflower and its products, including growers' councils, seed companies, processors, exporters, researchers, chemical firms, and merchandisers. Promotes the development of the sunflower industry. Seeks to improve sunflower production through research and education and to expand markets for sunflower products in the U.S. and abroad. Sponsors educational events; provides financial support for scientific research projects; disseminates information. **Founded:** 1978. **Publications:** *Sunflower Directory*; *The Sunflower* (Monthly). **Geographic Preference:** National.

16959 ■ National Watermelon Association (NWA)
190 Fitzgerald Rd., Ste. 3
Lakeland, FL 33813
Ph: (863)619-7575
Co. E-mail: communications@nwawatermelon.com
URL: http://www.watermelon.ag
Contact: Hamilton Dicks, President
Facebook: www.facebook.com/nwawatermelonag
Linkedin: www.linkedin.com/in/national-watermelon-association-6669721b1
Instagram: www.instagram.com/nwawatermelon
Pinterest: www.pinterest.com/watermelonag
Description: Individuals involved in the production, marketing, and sales of watermelon. Maintains files of clippings and business records. Maintains speakers' bureau and conducts educational programs. **Founded:** 1914. **Publications:** *Annual Convention Proceedings* (Annual). **Educational Activities:** National Watermelon Association's National Convention (Annual). **Awards:** National Watermelon Association's National Watermelon Queen (Annual). **Geographic Preference:** National.

16960 ■ Nebraska Agri-Business Association, Inc.
8700 Executive Woods Dr., Ste. 400
Lincoln, NE 68512-9612
Ph: (402)476-1528

Co. E-mail: info@na-ba.com
URL: http://na-ba.com
Contact: Scott Merritt, Director
Description: Represents individuals involved in the agricultural chemical and fertilizer industry. **Founded:** 1955. **Publications:** *The Fertilizer and Ag-Chemical Digest* (Quarterly). **Educational Activities:** Nebraska Agri-Business Exposition (Annual). **Geographic Preference:** State.

16961 ■ New York State Agribusiness Association (NYSABA)
PO Box 268
Macedon, NY 14502
Ph: (315)986-9320
Fax: (315)986-8534
Co. E-mail: nysaba@rochester.rr.com
URL: http://www.nysaba.com
Contact: Gregg Sargis, Director
Description: Promotes educational, research, legislative and regulatory activities, which will provide sound business practices and working environment for its members. Works to improve agricultural production efficiency through scientifically sound agronomic practices. **Geographic Preference:** State.

16962 ■ North American Millers' Association (NAMA)
1400 Crystal Dr., Ste. 650
Arlington, VA 22202
Ph: (202)484-2200
Co. E-mail: generalinfo@namamillers.org
URL: http://namamillers.org
Contact: Jane DeMarchi, President
E-mail: jdemarchi@namamillers.org
Facebook: www.facebook.com/NAMAmillers
Linkedin: www.linkedin.com/company/north-american-millers'-association
X (Twitter): x.com/NAMAmillers
Description: Grain milling companies that are processors of specially blended corn, wheat, and sorghum foods that are used primarily for overseas feeding programs. Millers of wheat, corn, oats, durum, and rye flour; members' mill 95% of total U.S. capacity. **Founded:** 1998. **Publications:** *News*. **Educational Activities:** NAMA Annual Meeting (Annual); NAMA Annual Meeting (Annual). **Geographic Preference:** National.

16963 ■ North American Olive Oil Association (NAOOA)
3301 Rte. 66, Ste. 205, Bldg. C
Neptune, NJ 07753
Ph: (732)922-3008
Co. E-mail: info@naooa.org
URL: http://www.aboutoliveoil.org
Contact: Samantha Dorsey, President
Facebook: www.facebook.com/NorthAmericanOliveOilAssociationnaooa
X (Twitter): x.com/about_oliveoil
Instagram: www.instagram.com/about_oliveoil
YouTube: www.youtube.com/channel/UCCIGB_KDsBYLLWKuAfmG-3Q
Description: A division of Association of Food Industries. Represents importers, processors, and distributors of olive oil. **Founded:** 1989. **Publications:** *Association of Food Industries* (Annual); *Import Report* (Monthly). **Geographic Preference:** Multinational.

16964 ■ North Carolina Agribusiness Council (NCAg)
2500 Regency Pkwy.
Cary, NC 27518
Ph: (919)782-4063
Co. E-mail: info@ncagribusiness.com
URL: http://ncagribusiness.com
Contact: Leon Troutman, President
Description: Agricultural production, processing, and marketing firms and suppliers of goods and services to the industry. Promotes agribusiness advancement and development. Supports research, education, and extension. Represents industry before the public.

Founded: 1969. Publications: *AgNews* (Weekly). Educational Activities: North Carolina Agribusiness Council Conference (Annual). Geographic Preference: State.

16965 ■ Organization for Competitive Markets (OCM)
PO Box 6486
Lincoln, NE 68506
Ph: (402)327-8390
Co. E-mail: info@competitivemarkets.com
URL: http://competitivemarkets.com
Contact: Taylor Haynes, President
Facebook: www.facebook.com/CompetitiveMarkets
X (Twitter): x.com/ocm_tweets
YouTube: www.youtube.com/user/ocmchannel
Description: Works for increased competition and protection for the agricultural marketplace. Works against "abuse of corporate power and consolidation of the agricultural market". Founded: 1998. Publications: *OCM Newsletter* (Quarterly). Geographic Preference: National.

16966 ■ Pacific Northwest Grain and Feed Association (PNWGFA)
147 SE 102nd Ave.
Portland, OR 97216
Ph: (503)227-0234
Fax: (503)253-9172
Co. E-mail: margerie@pnwgfa.org
URL: http://www.pnwgfa.org
Contact: Scott Zuger, President
Description: Represents firms involved in the grain business; suppliers; retired grain executives. Conducts seminars and workshops. Offers honorary memberships. Founded: 1917. Publications: *Pacific Northwest Grain and Feed Association--Official Directory* (Annual). Geographic Preference: National.

16967 ■ *Perspectives*
E2-376 EITC Bldg.
75A Chancellor Cir.
Winnipeg, MB, Canada R3T 5V6
Ph: (204)479-4084
URL: http://csbe-scgab.ca
Contact: Jan Adamowski, President
E-mail: jan.adamowski@mcgill.ca
URL(s): www.csbe-scgab.ca/perspectives-newsletter-spring-2024
Released: Quarterly; Fall, Sapring, Summer, Winter.
Description: Contains news, reports, awards, coming events and editorials. Availability: Print.

16968 ■ Potato Association of America (PAA)
37637 Five Mile Rd, No. 399
Livonia, MI 48154
Ph: (734)239-8022
Fax: (734)677-2407
Co. E-mail: paaoffice@potatoassociation.org
URL: http://potatoassociation.org
Contact: Samuel Essah, Editor-in-Chief
E-mail: samuel.essah@colostate.edu
Facebook: www.facebook.com/potatoamerica
Description: Represents breeders, entomologists, horticulturists, plant pathologists, soil and fertilizer specialists, food technologists, producers, and handlers. Founded: 1913. Publications: *American Journal of Potato Research* (Bimonthly). Awards: Frank L Haynes Graduate Student Research Award Competition (Annual). Geographic Preference: Multinational.

16969 ■ *Project Report*
Arthur van Schendelstraat 752
3511 Utrecht, Netherlands
Co. E-mail: femconsult@fairandsustainable.nl
URL: http://www.femconsult.org
Released: Periodic Availability: Print; PDF.

16970 ■ Rocky Mountain Agribusiness Association (RMAA)
12110 N Pecos St., Ste. 220
Westminster, CO 80234
Ph: (303)280-5208
Co. E-mail: info@rmagbiz.org
URL: http://rmagbiz.org
Contact: Gary Leeper, Executive Director
E-mail: gary@imigroup.org
Facebook: www.facebook.com/RockyMountainAgribusinessAssociation
X (Twitter): x.com/RMAgBiz
Description: Serves as an advocate for agribusiness across the Rocky Mountain region. Provides information and programs to develop environmental concerns in the agribusiness industries in Colorado and adjoining states. Geographic Preference: Local.

16971 ■ Societe Canadienne de Genie Agroalimentaire et de Bioingenierie (SCGAB)
E2-376 EITC Bldg.
75A Chancellor Cir.
Winnipeg, MB, Canada R3T 5V6
Ph: (204)479-4084
URL: http://csbe-scgab.ca
Contact: Jan Adamowski, President
E-mail: jan.adamowski@mcgill.ca
Description: Individuals engaged in the practice of agricultural and biosystems engineering; agricultural and biosystems engineering educators and students. Seeks to advance the study and practice of agricultural engineering and bioengineering. Conducts research; makes available continuing professional development programs for members. Founded: 1958. Publications: *Canadian Biosystems Engineering* (Annual); *Perspectives* (Quarterly). Awards: Jim Beamish Award (Annual); CSBE Young Eng of the Year Award (Annual); John Clark Award (Annual); John Turnbull Award (Annual); CSBE Maple Leaf Award (Annual); Glenn Downing Award (Annual); CSAE-SCGAB Fellow Awards (Annual). Geographic Preference: National.

16972 ■ South Carolina Young Farmer and Agribusiness Association (SCYFAA)
c/o Jennifer Lyda
PO Box 1746
Clemson, SC 29633
Ph: (864)656-8668
Co. E-mail: jrlyda@clemson.edu
URL: http://www.clemson.edu/extension/scaged/SC-Farmer-Agribusiness-Association/membership-application.html
Contact: Jennifer Lyda, Administrative Assistant
E-mail: jrlyda@clemson.edu
Description: Young farmers in South Carolina over 16 years of age who are out of school and enrolled in an Adult Agricultural Education class. Aims to assist young farmers through educational programs to become satisfactorily established in farming or agribusiness occupations. Founded: 1947. Publications: *South Carolina Young Farmer and Agribusiness Association* (Bimonthly).

16973 ■ South Dakota Agri-Business Association (SDABA)
320 E Capitol Ave.
Pierre, SD 57501
Ph: (605)224-2445
Fax: (605)224-9913
Co. E-mail: info@sdaba.org
URL: http://www.sdaba.org
Contact: Dave Clark, President
Facebook: www.facebook.com/sdagribusiness
Description: Works as a trade association of agricultural chemical and fertilizer dealers, associate members are companies and sales representatives in the agricultural chemical and fertilizer industry. Conducts lobbying activities. Founded: 1962. Publications: *Legislative Report* (Weekly). Educational Activities: SDABA Ag Expo (Annual). Geographic Preference: State.

16974 ■ Southwest Council of Agribusiness (SWCA)
8303 Aberdeen
Lubbock, TX 79424
Ph: (806)792-4904
URL: http://southwest-council.org
Contact: Jim Sugarek, President
X (Twitter): x.com/SWCouncilofAg
Description: Strives to represent and promote broad-based agriculture and business interests and increase economic opportunity in the Southwest region. Promotes value-added agribusiness and other enterprises. Geographic Preference: Regional.

16975 ■ Texas Longhorn Breeders Association of America (TLBAA)
221 W Exchange, Ste. 210
Fort Worth, TX 76164
Ph: (817)625-6241
Fax: (817)625-1388
Co. E-mail: tlbaa@tlbaa.org
URL: http://www.tlbaa.org
Contact: Keith Du Bose, Chairman of the Board
Description: Individuals, firms, and organizations interested in the Texas Longhorn breed of cattle. Promotes public awareness of the Texas Longhorn, its link with history, and its role in modern beef production. Founded: 1964. Geographic Preference: National.

16976 ■ United Fresh Produce Association (UFPA)
1901 Pennsylvania Ave. NW, Ste. 1100
Washington, DC 20006
Ph: (202)303-3400
Co. E-mail: united@unitedfresh.org
URL: http://www.freshproduce.com
Contact: Tom Brugato, President
Facebook: www.facebook.com/UnitedFreshProduceAssociation
X (Twitter): x.com/unitedfresh
Description: Promotes the growth and success of produce companies and their partners. Represents interests of growers, shippers, processors, brokers, wholesalers and distributors of produce, working together with their customers at retail and food service, suppliers at every step in the distribution chain, and international partners. Provides leadership to shape business, trade and public policies that drive the industry. Founded: 1904. Publications: *Outlook--International Trade Directory Issue*; *United Fresh Fruit and Vegetable Association--Membership Directory* (Annual). Educational Activities: United FreshTec Expo (Annual); Washington Public Policy Conference (Annual). Geographic Preference: National.

16977 ■ U.S. Poultry & Egg Association
1530 Cooledge Rd.
Tucker, GA 30084-7303
Ph: (770)493-9401
Fax: (770)493-9257
Co. E-mail: info@uspoultry.org
URL: http://www.uspoultry.org
Contact: John Starkey, President
E-mail: jstarkey@uspoultry.org
X (Twitter): x.com/USPOULTRY1947
YouTube: www.youtube.com/USPOULTRY
Pinterest: www.pinterest.com/uspoultry
Description: Producers, hatcherymen, feed millers, processors, packagers, manufacturers and suppliers of products and services used in the production cycle of poultry products. Identifies problem areas and needs of the membership and concentrates industry efforts toward solutions. Founded: 1947. Educational Activities: International Production & Processing Expo (IPPE) (Annual). Geographic Preference: National.

16978 ■ UnitedAg
54 Corporate Pk.
Irvine, CA 92606
Free: 800-223-4590
Co. E-mail: membership@unitedag.org
URL: http://www.unitedag.org
Contact: Kirti Mutatkar, President
E-mail: kmutatkar@unitedag.org
Facebook: www.facebook.com/UnitedAgOrg
Linkedin: www.linkedin.com/company/unitedag
X (Twitter): x.com/UnitedAgOrg
Instagram: www.instagram.com/unitedagorg
Description: Agricultural industries and businesses. Promotes the development and common interest of the agricultural industry. Works to coordinate members' activities to advance agribusiness in general;

provides services and benefits to enable members to realize greater productive efficiency. Serves as a clearinghouse on international agribusiness. Provides employee health care plans and other insurance to agribusinesses. **Founded:** 1980. **Publications:** *Healthy Times* (Monthly); *Ag Crime Prevention Brochures*; *Crime Prevention* (Quarterly). **Awards:** UnitedAg Vocational Scholarships (Annual); UnitedAg Educational Scholarships (Annual). **Geographic Preference:** National.

16979 ■ **Wisconsin Agri-Business Association (WABA)**
2801 International Ln., Ste. 105
Madison, WI 53704
Ph: (608)223-1111
Fax: (608)223-1147
Co. E-mail: info@wiagribusiness.org
URL: http://wiagribusiness.org
Contact: Howard Hartmann, President
Facebook: www.facebook.com/WIAgBusiness
Description: Provider of programs, services and representation for diverse crop production industry. Leverages legislation and monitors action that directly influences all levels of business. **Founded:** 1971. **Geographic Preference:** State.

INCUBATORS/RESEARCH AND TECHNOLOGY PARKS

16980 ■ **Square Roots**
630 Flushing Ave.
Brooklyn, NY 11206
Co. E-mail: hello@squarerootsgrow.com
URL: http://www.squarerootsgrow.com
Contact: Gianna Costa, Manager
X (Twitter): twitter.com/squarerootsgrow
Instagram: www.instagram.com/squarerootsgrow
Description: Urban farming incubator supporting real food entrepreneurs.

REFERENCE WORKS

16981 ■ *"4 Financing Options for Agriculture Business Owners"* in FORA Financial (Jan. 30, 2020)
URL(s): www.forafinancial.com/blog/industries-we-serve/agriculture-business/
Released: January 30, 2020. **Description:** Discusses what an agribusiness is, the pros and cons of starting an agribusiness, and options for financing your agribusiness. **Availability:** Online.

16982 ■ *10 Most Profitable Agricultural Business Ideas in 2021*
URL(s): www.yahoo.com/video/10-most-profitable-agricultural-business-071053845.html
Ed: Trish Novicio. **Released:** March 30, 2021. **Description:** Discusses the ten most profitable agricultural business ideas. **Availability:** Online.

16983 ■ *"14 Tips to Tune Up Your Self-Propelled Sprayer"* in Farm Industry News (November 3, 2010)
Pub: Informa Business Media, Inc.
Contact: Charlie McCurdy, President
Ed: Jodie Wehrspann. **Description:** Tips for maintaining a self-propelled sprayer used to apply farm chemicals and fertilizers are listed. **Availability:** Online.

16984 ■ *"50 Small Agricultural Business Ideas"* in Small Business Trends (July 5, 2021)
URL(s): smallbiztrends.com/2016/12/agricultural-business-ideas.html
Ed: Annie Pilon. **Released:** July 05, 2021. **Description:** Lists 50 small agricultural business ideas that entrepreneurs might consider. **Availability:** Online.

16985 ■ *"100 Percent Equipment Tax Deduction Deadline Nears"* in Farm Industry News (December 1, 2010)
Pub: Informa Business Media, Inc.
Contact: Charlie McCurdy, President
Ed: Karen McMahon. **Description:** Farmers and small business owners are warned that the first deadline for taking advantage of the tax code provision that allows them to deduct the full purchase price of qualified capital expenditures up to $500,000 during the tax year is nearing. **Availability:** Print; Online.

16986 ■ *"$550 Cash Rent on 330 Acres in Iowa"* in Farm Industry News (November 30, 2011)
Pub: Informa Business Media, Inc.
Contact: Charlie McCurdy, President
Ed: Karen McMahon. **Description:** A farmer in Iowa accepted a bid for $550/acre for his 330-acre farm for one year. The next closest bid was $350/acre. This rent will amount to more than the farmer paid for all of his land in the 1960s and 1970s. High rents are not alarming because of the high profitability farmers are currently receiving from crops. **Availability:** Online.

16987 ■ *"2011 FinOvation Awards"* in Farm Industry News (January 19, 2011)
Pub: Informa Business Media, Inc.
Contact: Charlie McCurdy, President
Ed: Karen McMahon, Jodie Wehrspann. **Description:** The 2011 FinOvation Award winners are announced, covering new products that growers need for corn and soybean crops. Winners range from small turbines and a fuel-efficient pickup to a Class 10 combine and drought-tolerant hybrids. **Availability:** Online.

16988 ■ *"Ag Firms Harvest Revenue Growth"* in The Business Journal-Serving Metropolitan Kansas City (Vol. 26, July 18, 2008, No. 45, pp. 1)
Description: Five of the biggest agricultural companies in the Kansas City area, except one, reported multibillion-dollar revenue increases in 2007. The companies, which include Lansing Trade Group, posted a combined $9.5 billion revenue growth. The factors that affected the revenue increase in the area's agricultural companies, such as prices and high demand, are also examined. **Availability:** Print; Online.

16989 ■ *"AgraQuest Deal Signals Growth for Biopesticide Makers"* in Sacramento Business Journal (Vol. 29, July 13, 2012, No. 20, pp. 1)
Pub: Baltimore Business Journal
Contact: Rhonda Pringle, President
E-mail: rpringle@bizjournals.com
Description: Industry observes claim that biotechnology irm Bayer CropScience's upcoming acquisition of AgraQuest Inc. could signal the growth of biopesticide manufacturing chemical methods for agricultural crop protection could then be complemented with environmentally friendly approaches allowed by biopesticides. **Availability:** Print; Online.

16990 ■ *"Agribusiness and Value Chains"* in The World Bank
URL(s): www.worldbank.org/en/topic/agribusiness
Description: Explores how to increase access for small agribusiness enterprises to strengthen food value chains. **Availability:** Online.

16991 ■ *"Agricharts Launches New Mobile App for Ag Market"* in Farm Industry News (December 1, 2011)
Pub: Informa Business Media, Inc.
Contact: Charlie McCurdy, President
Description: AgriCharts provides market data, agribusiness Website hosting and technology solutions for the agricultural industry. AgriCharts is a division of Barchart.com Inc. and announced the release of a new mobile applications that offers real-time or delayed platform for viewing quotes, charts and analysis of grains, livestock and other commodity markets. **Availability:** Print; Online.

16992 ■ *"Agriculture Law 'Infoline' Available for Maryland Farmers"* in Ecology, Environment & Conservation Business (June 21, 2014, pp. 3)
Pub: NewsRX LLC.
Contact: Kalani Rosell, Contact
Description: The Agriculture Law Education Initiative created an Infoline phone number for the agricultural community to call for legal information resources related to their agricultural operation. The Infoline is answered by staff at the University of Maryland Francis King Carey School of Law and aims to assist in the preservation of family farms. The Infoline will connect family farmers with resources to further this goal. **Availability:** Online.

16993 ■ *Agritech Sprouts Start-Ups*
URL(s): www.businesstoday.in/magazine/the-hub/story/agritech-sprouts-start-ups-117925-2018-12-10
Ed: K T P Radhika. **Released:** December 30, 2018. **Description:** Discusses the growing agri-tech business sector and how they are attracting investors. **Availability:** Online.

16994 ■ *Agritech Startups, Innovations & Facts*
URL(s): apiumhub.com/tech-blog-barcelona/agritech-startups-innovations-facts/
Ed: Ekaterina Novoseltseva. **Released:** September 19, 2019. **Description:** Discusses agri-tech innovations and eight agri-tech startups to follow. **Availability:** Online.

16995 ■ *"Allowing Ethanol Tax Incentive to Expire Would Risk Jobs, RFA's Dinneen Says"* in Farm Industry News (November 3, 2010)
Pub: Informa Business Media, Inc.
Contact: Charlie McCurdy, President
Ed: Lynn Grooms. **Price:** $4, Print and Online; Special Offers only for 4 weeks. **Description:** Jobs would be at risk if the ethanol tax incentive expires. **Availability:** Print; Online.

16996 ■ *"Alternative Energy Is a Major Topic at Agritechnica 2011"* in Farm Industry News (November 16, 2011)
Pub: Informa Business Media, Inc.
Contact: Charlie McCurdy, President
Ed: Mark Moore. **Description:** Sustainable agricultural systems were a hot topic at this year's Agritechnia 2011, held in Germany. Germany is a leader in the development of on-farm biogas systems. **Availability:** Online.

16997 ■ *"Ambitious Horse Center Is In the Works for Southeastern Idaho"* in Idaho Business Review (August 25, 2014)
Pub: BridgeTower Media
Contact: Adam Reinebach, President
Price: $99, Digital & Mobile Only(1 Year); $11.99, Print, Digital & Mobile(1 Month); $149, Print, Digital & Mobile(1 Year); $99, Digital & Mobile Only(For 1 Year); $11.99, Print, Digital & Mobile (For 1 Month Intro Rate); $149, Print, Digital & Mobile (For 1 Year). **Description:** Ernest Bleinberger is planning to develop a 167-acre mixed-use project called Horse Station and will be located in Cache Valley, Idaho. Horse Station will include stables for about 250 horses and an arena, along with medical facilities, a hotel, retail shopping center, and a farmers market. **Availability:** Print; Online.

16998 ■ *"American Farmland Trust Profiles In Stewardship, How California Farmers and Ranchers are Producing a Better Environment"* in Ecology, Environment & Conservation Business (January 4, 2014, pp. 2)
Pub: PR Newswire Association LLC.
Description: Forty-five Profiles In Stewardship were presented by the American Farmland Trust showing how farmers and ranchers in 25 California counties are improving the environment by adopting conservation practices that serve examples for others to follow in order to promote sound farming practices and improve the environment by protecting land, air and water.

16999 ■ *"American Farmland Trust, The Culinary Institute of America, Fabulous Beekman Boys Hold Special Event to Raise Awareness in Culinary Students"* in Ecology, Environment & Conservation Business (April 19, 2014, pp. 3)
Pub: NewsRX LLC.
Contact: Kalani Rosell, Contact

Description: American Farmland Trust and The Culinary Institute of American were joined by the Fabulous Beekman Boys, Brent Ridge and Josh Kilmer-Purcell of Beekman 1802, to host a screening of The First Season, a documentary film about dairy farming in New York. The event was held to raise awareness in culinary arts students about the issues faced by farmers today. **Availability:** Online.

17000 ■ *"American Indian College Fund to Support Environmental Science and Sustainability Programs, Fellowships, and Internships"* in *Ecology, Environment & Conservation Business (April 12, 2014, pp. 21)*
Pub: NewsRX LLC.
Contact: Kalani Rosell, Contact

Description: Tribal colleges serve communities facing environmental issues, such as water quality, energy development, depletion of natural resources, and agricultural management. The American Indian College Fund has created a new Environmental Science and Sustainability Project of $1.35 million grant money to support tribal colleges and universities in select states that underwrite environmental science and sustainability programs of studies. Details of the project are included. **Availability:** Online.

17001 ■ *"Apples, Decoded: WSU Scientist Unraveling the Fruit's Genetics"* in *Puget Sound Business Journal (Vol. 29, September 5, 2008, No. 20)*

Description: Washington State University researcher is working to map the apple's genome in order to gain information about how the fruit grows, looks and tastes. His work, funded by a research grant from the US Department of Agriculture and the Washington Apple Commission is crucial to improving the state's position as an apple-producing region. **Availability:** Print; Online.

17002 ■ *"Art of the Online Deal"* in *Farm Industry News (March 25, 2011)*
Pub: Informa Business Media, Inc.
Contact: Charlie McCurdy, President

Description: Farmers share advice for shopping online for machinery; photos, clean equipment, the price, equipment details, and online sources topped their list. **Availability:** Print; Online.

17003 ■ *"Autumn Rat Control Essential for Poultry Units"* in *Poultry World (Vol. 165, September 2011, No. 9, pp. 32)*

Description: Dr. Alan Buckle discusses the use of rodenticides control, focusing on poultry units. **Availability:** Online.

17004 ■ *"Beep Fruit Drink Makes Comeback: Prodded by Fans, a Maritime Dairy Brings Back Retro Drink Beep"* in *Canadian Business (Vol. 85, August 13, 2012, No. 13, pp. 9)*

Ed: Matthew McClearn. **Description:** Farmers Co-Operative Dairy temporarily resumed production of the Beep fruit drink in response to customers' call to bring back the product that the company has been selling since 1962. As part of the relaunch, the company replicated the original 1960s packaging and used social media to connect with customers. **Availability:** Print; Online.

17005 ■ *"Bertha's Birth Stirs Juice"* in *Barron's (Vol. 88, July 14, 2008, No. 28, pp. M11)*
Pub: Dow Jones & Company Inc.
Contact: Almar Latour, Chief Executive Officer

Ed: Tom Sellen. **Description:** Price of frozen concentrated orange juice, which has risen to four-month highs of $1.3620 in July 2008 is due, in part, to the hurricane season that has come earlier than normal in the far eastern Atlantic thereby possibly harming the 2008-2009 Florida orange crop. Future tropical-storm development will affect the prices of this commodity. **Availability:** Online.

17006 ■ *"Biodiesel Poised to Regain Growth"* in *Farm Industry News (January 21, 2011)*
Pub: Informa Business Media, Inc.
Contact: Charlie McCurdy, President

Ed: Lynn Grooms. **Description:** According to Gary Haer, vice president of sales and marketing for Renewable Energy Group, the biodiesel industry is positioned to regain growth in 2011 with the reinstatement of the biodiesel blendersa tax credit of $1 per gallon. **Availability:** Print; Online.

17007 ■ *"Brazil's New King of Food"* in *Barron's (Vol. 89, July 13, 2009, No. 28, pp. 28)*
Pub: Dow Jones & Company Inc.
Contact: Almar Latour, Chief Executive Officer

Ed: Kenneth Rapoza. **Description:** Perdigao and Sadia's merger has resulted in the creation of Brasil Foods and the shares of Brasil Foods provides a play on both Brazil's newly energized consumer economy and its role as a major commodities exporter. Brasil Foods shares could climb as much as 36 percent. **Availability:** Online.

17008 ■ *"Buhler Versatile Launches Next Generation of Equipment"* in *Farm Industry News (November 23, 2011)*
Pub: Informa Business Media, Inc.
Contact: Charlie McCurdy, President

Ed: Jodie Wehrspann. **Description:** Canadian owned Versatile is expanding its four-wheel drive tractor division with sprayers, tillage, and seeding equipment. **Availability:** Online.

17009 ■ *"Building a Sustainable Business"* developed by the Minnesota Institute for Sustainable Agriculture; published by Sustainable Agriculture Research and Education.
URL(s): www.sare.org/wp-content/uploads/Building-a-Sustainable-Business.pdf
Ed: Gigi DiGiacomo, Robert King, Dale Nordquist. **Description:** A guide to developing a business plan for farms and rural businesses. **Availability:** Online.

17010 ■ *Business Management for Tropical Dairy Farmers*
Pub: CSIRO Publishing
Contact: Dr. Stefan Doerr, Editor-in-Chief
E-mail: s.doerr@swansea.ac.uk

Ed: John Moran. **Description:** Business management skills required for dairy farmers are addressed, focusing on financial management and ways to improve cattle housing and feeding systems. **Availability:** Print; PDF; Download.

17011 ■ *"Buzz Kill"* in *Canadian Business (Vol. 83, August 17, 2010, No. 13-14, pp. 24)*

Description: Beekeeping industry has been plagued by a massive wave of honeybee deaths since 2006, which pushed upward the cost of per hive-rental. The death of honeybees has put the food supply at risk since it jeopardized the growth of pumpkins, as well as other crops in large acreage. Insights on the Colony Collapse Disorder are outlined. **Availability:** Online.

17012 ■ *"California Wines Nab 64 Percent of U.S. Sales"* in *Sacramento Business Journal (Vol. 31, April 25, 2014, No. 9)*
Pub: American City Business Journals, Inc.
Contact: Mike Olivieri, Executive Vice President

Released: Weekly. **Description:** California wine sales represented 64 percent of all wine sales in the U.S. in 2013. This totaled $23.1 billion in sales at the retail level. California has held this level of market share in the U.S. wine market for some time. In 2003, the state shipped 65 percent of all wine in the country. **Availability:** Print; Online.

17013 ■ *"Careers in Organic Food Production"* in *Occupational Outlook Quarterly (Vol. 54, Fall 2010, No. 3, pp. 3)*
Pub: U.S. Department of Labor Bureau of Labor Statistics
Contact: Amrit Kohli, Director
E-mail: kohli.amrit@bls.gov

Ed: Adam Bibler. **Description:** Organic methods of food production, including methods that combine science with traditional farming practices, are outlined. Facts regarding careers in organic food preparation are presented. **Availability:** Online; PDF.

17014 ■ *"Case IH Announces Strategy to Meet 2014 Clean Air Standards"* in *Farm Industry News (September 15, 2011)*
Pub: Informa Business Media, Inc.
Contact: Charlie McCurdy, President

Ed: Jodie Wehrspann. **Description:** Case IH will meet EPA's stringent engine emissions limits imposed in 2014, called Tier 4. The limits call for a 90 percent reduction in particulate matter and nitrogen oxides (NOx) over the Tier 3 requirements from a few years ago. **Availability:** Print; Online.

17015 ■ *"Cash Rents Reach Sky-High Levels"* in *Farm Industry News (November 23, 2011)*
Pub: Informa Business Media, Inc.
Contact: Charlie McCurdy, President

Ed: Karen McMahon. **Description:** Strong commodity prices are driving land values creating a hot rental market for farm land. Highest rents occur when farmers compete head-to-head for land. **Availability:** Online.

17016 ■ *"The CEO Poll: Potash Sale Must Be Blocked"* in *Canadian Business (Vol. 83, October 12, 2010, No. 17, pp. 24)*
Pub: Rogers Media Inc.
Contact: Neil Spivak, Chief Executive Officer

Ed: Kasey Coholan. **Description:** Chief executive officers (CEOs) and corporate leaders in Canada are concerned about the possible sale of Potash Corporation to foreign buyers. A Compas Inc. poll recently asked CEOs whether the Canadian Government should step in to block the sale of the country's largest fertilizer firm. **Availability:** Print; Online.

17017 ■ *"CGB Purchases Illinois Grain-Fertilizer Firm"* in *Farm Industry News (December 2, 2011)*
Pub: Informa Business Media, Inc.
Contact: Charlie McCurdy, President

Description: CGB Enterprises Inc. bought Twomey Company's grain and fertilizer assets. The purchase includes eight locations and a barge loading terminal near Gladstone, Illinois and storage capacity of 51 million bushels and 18,000 tons of liquid fertilizer. **Availability:** Online.

17018 ■ *"Cheese Is Now Idaho's Largest Export"* in *Idaho Business Review (August 28, 2014)*
Pub: BridgeTower Media
Contact: Adam Reinebach, President

Description: According to the Southern Idaho Economic Development Organization, cheese topped whey and dry milk powders for being the leading export for the state. Statistical details included.

17019 ■ *"Chopping Option Added to Calmer Corn Head Kits"* in *Farm Industry News (January 16, 2011)*
Pub: Informa Business Media, Inc.
Contact: Charlie McCurdy, President

Ed: Karen McMahon. **Description:** New equipment for combines, called the BT Chopper option for Calmer Corn Heads, will chop and crust BT corn stalks into confetti-sized pieces for easier decomposition in the field.

17020 ■ *"Click Your Chicken"* in *Canadian Business (Vol. 87, October 2014, No. 10, pp. 11)*

Released: October 2014. **Description:** A number of business ideas, products and strategies are ranked from the ingenious to the extremely bizarre. A mobile Web startup called FarmLogs helps farmers track everything from soil conditions to weather to profit forecasts. Kentucky Fried Chicken restaurants awards top Twitter fans in Japan with USB drive, a mouse and a keyboard designed with chicken parts.

GENERAL SMALL BUSINESS TOPICS   Agribusiness ■ 17042

17021 ■ *"Co-Op Launches Revolving Loan Program for Farmers"* in Bellingham Business Journal (Vol. February 2010, pp. 3)
Pub: Sound Publishing Inc.
Contact: Josh O'Connor, President
Ed: Lance Henderson. **Description:** Community Food Co-op's Farm Fund received a $12,000 matching grant from the Sustainable Whatcom Fund of the Whatcom Community Foundation. The Farm Fund will create a new revolving loan program for local farmers committed to using sustainable practices.

17022 ■ *"Colorado's Ag Industry Grows Despite Flooding"* in Denver Business Journal (Vol. 65, January 10, 2014, No. 35, pp. A6)
Pub: American City Business Journals, Inc.
Contact: Mike Olivieri, Executive Vice President
Description: Colorado's net farm income for 2013 has fallen slightly to $1.6 billion from the record $1.7 billion in 2012 in spite of the damaging floods that affected an estimated 4,500 square miles of land. However, exports of agricultural products from Colorado to other countries are expected to hit $2 billion in 2013. Insights into the flood damage are also offered. **Availability:** Online.

17023 ■ *"Coming Soon: Electric Tractors"* in Farm Industry News (November 21, 2011)
Pub: Informa Business Media, Inc.
Contact: Charlie McCurdy, President
Ed: Jodie Wehrspann. **Description:** The agricultural industry is taking another look at electric farm vehicles. John Deere Product Engineering Center said that farmers can expect to see more diesel-electric systems in farm tractors, sprayers, and implements. **Availability:** Online.

17024 ■ *"Company Severs Ties with Chiquita, Starts Own Brand"* in Business Journal-Serving Phoenix and the Valley of the Sun (October 4, 2007)
Pub: Phoenix Business Journal
Contact: Alex McAlister, Director
E-mail: amcalister@bizjournals.com
Ed: Mike Sunnucks. **Description:** Melones International is ending a deal with Chiquita Brands International Inc. Melones will now distribute its produce in the U.S. under its own brand, called Plain Jane. Alejandro N. Canelos Jr., head of the firm, stated their relationship with Chiquita was good, but wants to promote the Plain Jane brand name. **Availability:** Print; Online.

17025 ■ *"Corn Belt Farmland Prices Hit Record Levels"* in Farm Industry News (December 1, 2011)
Pub: Informa Business Media, Inc.
Contact: Charlie McCurdy, President
Ed: David Hest. **Description:** Farmland prices have set records over the last six months in Iowa. Farmland broker and auction company owner, Murray Wise, believes this is not a bubble, that the economics of this market are solid. **Availability:** Print; Online.

17026 ■ *"Crop Insurance Harvest Prices in 2011"* in Farm Industry News (November 9, 2011)
Pub: Informa Business Media, Inc.
Contact: Charlie McCurdy, President
Ed: Gary Schnitkey. **Description:** Risk Management Agency (RMA) reported harvest prices for corn and soybean grown in the Midwest with corn at $6.32 per bushel, 31 cents higher than the project $6.01; soybeans were at $12.14 per bushel, down $1.35 from the projected price of $13.49. **Availability:** Print; Online.

17027 ■ *"Deere to Open Technology Center in Germany"* in Chicago Tribune (September 3, 2008)
Description: Deere & Co. plans to open a technology and innovation center in Germany; details of the company's expansion plans are discussed. **Availability:** Print; Online.

17028 ■ *"Delivering the Milk"* in Barron's (Vol. 92, July 23, 2012, No. 30, pp. M7)
Pub: Dow Jones & Company Inc.
Contact: Almar Latour, Chief Executive Officer
Ed: Kopin Tan. **Description:** The stocks of China Mengniu Dairy could continue losing value in the short term but could gain value in the long term. The company's revenue growth and profit margins face downward pressure due to aggressive pricing after food safety scandals. **Availability:** Online.

17029 ■ *"Despite Higher Prices, Organic Food Gains"* in MMR (Vol. 29, February 20, 2012, No. 4, pp. 39)
Description: Despite higher prices, consumers are buying organic food products at a high rate. Total sales of organic products rose 15 to 20 percent due to shoppers increasing the number and variety of organic products they bought. Statistical data included. **Availability:** Print; Online.

17030 ■ *"Dow AgroSciences Buys Wheat-Breeding Firm in Pacific Northwest"* in Farm Industry News (July 29, 2011)
Pub: Informa Business Media, Inc.
Contact: Charlie McCurdy, President
Description: Dow AgroSciences purchased Northwest Plant Breeding Company, a cereals breeding station in Washington in 2011. The acquisition will help Dow expand its Hyland Seeds certified wheat seed program foundation in the Pacific Northwest. Financial terms of the deal were not disclosed. **Availability:** Online.

17031 ■ *"Drought Takes Toll on Farmers, Restaurants"* in Saint Louis Business Journal (Vol. 31, August 12, 2011, No. 51, pp. 1)
Pub: Saint Louis Business Journal
Contact: Robert Bobroff, President
E-mail: rbobroff@bizjournals.com
Ed: E.B. Solomont. **Description:** The drought in St. Louis, Missouri has adversely impacted farmers and restaurants in the areas. Diners can expect to lose some ingredients from their menus. **Availability:** Online.

17032 ■ *"DuPont's Pioneer Hi-Bred, Evogene to Develop Rust-Resistant Soybean Varieties"* in Farm Industry News (November 22, 2011)
Pub: Informa Business Media, Inc.
Contact: Charlie McCurdy, President
Ed: Karen McMahon. **Description:** DuPont and Evogene have signed a new contract to work together to develop resistance in soybeans to rust. Financial terms of the agreement were not disclosed. **Availability:** Online.

17033 ■ *"Eco-Preneuring"* in Small Business Opportunities (Feb. 6, 2012)
Pub: Harris Publishing, Inc.
Contact: Janet Chase, Contact
Description: Iceland Naturally is a joint marketing effort among tourism and business interests hoping to increase demand for Icelandic products including frozen seafood, bottled water, agriculture, and tourism in North America.

17034 ■ *"Egg Fight: The Yolk's on the Shorts"* in Barron's (Vol. 88, July 7, 2008, No. 27, pp. 20)
Pub: Dow Jones & Company Inc.
Contact: Almar Latour, Chief Executive Officer
Ed: Christopher C. Williams. **Description:** Shares of Cal-Maine Foods, the largest egg producer and distributor in the US, are due for a huge rise because of the increase in egg prices. Short sellers, however, continue betting that the stock, priced at $31.84 each, will eventually go down. **Availability:** Online.

17035 ■ *"EPA Grants E15 Waiver for 2001-2006 Vehicles"* in Farm Industry News (January 21, 2011)
Pub: Informa Business Media, Inc.
Contact: Charlie McCurdy, President
Ed: Lynn Grooms. **Description:** U.S. Environmental Protection Agency waived a limitation on selling gasoline that contains more than 10 percent ethanol for model year 2001-2006 cars and light trucks, allowing fuel to contain up to 15 percent ethanol (E15) for these vehicles. **Availability:** Online.

17036 ■ *Equipment Marketing and Distribution Association--Membership Directory*
Pub: Equipment Marketing and Distribution Association
Contact: Bob Doran, II, President
Released: Annual **Description:** Listings for all EMDA member firms and associate member firms. **Entries include:** Names and photos of their officers and key managers; business profile paragraph; branch office information; sales territory quick reference listing; product code listing indicating product types currently distributed by each EMDA member; product code quick reference listing. **Arrangement:** Alphabetical. **Availability:** Print; PDF; Online.

17037 ■ *"Experts Discuss New Tax Rules in Webinar to Help Farmers With Year-End Tax Planning"* in Farm Industry News (November 22, 2011)
Pub: Informa Business Media, Inc.
Contact: Charlie McCurdy, President
Description: Section 179 deductions and Bonus Depreciation tax rules for years 2011 and 2012 and how they impact farming operations are available at TractorLife.com. The Website helps farmers maintain and extend the operating lives of their tractors. **Availability:** Print; Online.

17038 ■ *"Farm to Table Distribution Getting Boost"* in Philadelphia Business Journal (Vol. 28, May 11, 2012, No. 13, pp. 1)
Pub: Baltimore Business Journal
Contact: Rhonda Pringle, President
E-mail: rpringle@bizjournals.com
Price: $4, Introductory 4-Week Offer(Digital & Print).
Description: The farm-to-table movement has changed the distribution network of food and the offerings on many restaurants in Philadelphia. A new range of companies has emerged due to the demand for local food. Green Meadow Farms and Lancaster Farm Fresh are two of the businesses that found the niche in supplying restaurants with local produce. **Availability:** Print; Online.

17039 ■ *"Farming Starts in December; High-Priced Embryos"* in Farm Industry News (November 29, 2011)
Pub: Informa Business Media, Inc.
Contact: Charlie McCurdy, President
Ed: Kent Lock. **Description:** One farmer suggests the season starts in December because one third of his seed and fertilizer for the following year has already been bought and paid for and his cropping mix changes little from one year to another. **Availability:** Print; Online.

17040 ■ *"A Few Points of Contention"* in Barron's (Vol. 88, July 14, 2008, No. 28, pp. 3)
Pub: Dow Jones & Company Inc.
Contact: Almar Latour, Chief Executive Officer
Ed: Michael Santoli. **Description:** Headline inflation tends to revert to the lower core inflation, which excludes food and energy in its calculation over long periods. Prominent private equity figures believe that regulators should allow more than the de facto 10 percent to 25 percent limit of commercial banks to hasten the refunding of the financial sector. **Availability:** Online.

17041 ■ *"FinOvation 2009"* in Farm Industry News (Vol. 42, January 1, 2009, No. 1)
Ed: Karen McMahon, Mark Moore, David Hest. **Description:** New and innovative products and technologies are presented.

17042 ■ *"First Impressions of Robotic Farming Systems"* in Farm Industry News (September 30, 2011)
Pub: Informa Business Media, Inc.
Contact: Charlie McCurdy, President

Small Business Sourcebook • 42nd Edition   1281

Ed: Jodie Wehrspann. **Description:** Farm Science Review featured tillage tools and land rollers, including John Deere's GPS system where a cart tractor is automatically controlled as well as a new line of Kinze's carts and a video of their robotic system for a driver-less cart tractor. **Availability:** Print; Online.

17043 ■ *"Five Ways to Make RTK Pay" in Farm Industry News (March 25, 2011)*
Pub: Informa Business Media, Inc.
Contact: Charlie McCurdy, President
Ed: David Hest. **Description:** It is important for farmers to decide whether they are seeking greater accuracy or faster payback when upgrading navigation systems. The trend towards higher accuracy continues to grow. **Availability:** Print; Online.

17044 ■ *"Florida Harvest Power Converting Organic Biz Waste to Electricity" in Orlando Business Journal (Vol. 30, March 21, 2014, No. 39, pp. 3)*
Pub: American City Business Journals, Inc.
Contact: Mike Olivieri, Executive Vice President
Released: Weekly. **Price:** $8, introductory 4-week offer(Digital & Print). **Description:** Florida Harvest Power is converting organic waste from local businesses into natural fertilizer and electricity in a new $30 million facility called the Central Florida Energy Garden. Regional vice president, Chris Peters, predicts that the facility will have 6,000 tons of fertilizer to sell annually. **Availability:** Print; Online.

17045 ■ *"Fossil Fuel, Renewable Fuel Shares Expected to Flip Flop" in Farm Industry News (April 29, 2011)*
Pub: Informa Business Media, Inc.
Contact: Charlie McCurdy, President
Ed: Lynn Grooms. **Description:** Total energy use of fossil fuels is predicted to fall 5 percent by the year 2035, with renewable fuel picking it up. **Availability:** Online.

17046 ■ *"Fuel King: The Most Fuel-Efficient Tractor of the Decade is the John Deere 8295R" in Farm Industry News (November 10, 2011)*
Pub: Informa Business Media, Inc.
Contact: Charlie McCurdy, President
Description: Farm Industry News compiled a list of the most fuel-efficient tractors with help from the Nebraska Tractor Test Lab, with the John Deere 8295R PTO winner of the most fuel-efficient tractor of the decade. **Availability:** Print; Online.

17047 ■ *"General Clark Stresses Ethanol's Role In National Security At AgConnect" in Farm Industry News (January 11, 2011)*
Pub: Informa Business Media, Inc.
Contact: Charlie McCurdy, President
Ed: Lynn Grooms. **Description:** General Clark stressed the role of ethanols in national security at the AgConnect. **Availability:** Online.

17048 ■ *Getting Expert Advice When Starting a Farm Business*
URL(s): farms.extension.wisc.edu/articles/getting-expert-advice-when-starting-a-farm-business/
Ed: Leigh Presley. **Description:** Provides information on organizations in Wisconsin specifically devoted to helping farm and food-related businesses get started and grow. **Availability:** Online.

17049 ■ *Gift from Farm Credit Groups Supports Rural Entrepreneurship*
URL(s): extension.umn.edu/news/gift-farm-credit-groups-supports-rural-entrepreneurship
Released: January 24, 2022. **Description:** Explains a gift from farm credit groups that supports rural entrepreneurship in Wisconsin and Minnesota. **Availability:** Online.

17050 ■ *"GIV Mobile Announces New Partnership with American Forests, the Oldest National Nonprofit Conservation Organization in the Country" in Ecology, Environment & Conservation Business (January 25, 2014, pp. 34)*
Pub: PR Newswire Association LLC.
Description: GIV Mobile has partnered with American Forests to restore and protect urban and rural forests in the nation. GIV is the first consumer conscious wireless network and operates on the 4G network of T-Mobile USA cellular service. **Availability:** Online.

17051 ■ *"Global Organic Food" in Investment Weekly News (January 21, 2012, pp. 272)*
Description: Research and Markets has added 'Global Organic Food' to its reporting of industry profiles. The report will offer top-line qualitative and quantitative summary information including, market size, description of leading players with key financial metrics and analysis of competitive pressures within the market covering the global organic food market. Market size and segmentation data, textual and graphical analysis of market growth trends, leading companies and macroeconomic information will be provided. **Availability:** Online.

17052 ■ *A Golden Opportunity in Crisis? Decoding Agri-Tech Post Pandemic*
URL(s): economictimes.indiatimes.com/small-biz/startups/newsbuzz/a-golden-opportunity-in-crisis-decoding-agri-tech-post-pandemic/articleshow/75499858.cms?from=mdr
Ed: Pankajj Ghode. **Released:** May 02, 2020. **Description:** Discusses the need for agribusiness to transition from traditional methods to incorporating technology to ensure healthy food production as well as continued revenue. **Availability:** Online.

17053 ■ *"'Gregory Cunningham on Taking on Farm Credit of Florida" in South Florida Business Journal (Vol. 34, July 18, 2014, No. 52, pp. 11)*
Pub: American City Business Journals, Inc.
Contact: Mike Olivieri, Executive Vice President
Released: Weekly. **Price:** $8, introductory 4-week offer(Digital only). **Description:** Gregory Cunningham, president and CEO of Farm Credit of Florida, shares the lessons he learned from his military background that he applies to managing a company. He explains why he decided to take on the challenge of helping the agricultural credit group deal with its regulatory order. **Availability:** Print; Online.

17054 ■ *"Growing Food and Protecting Nature Don't Have to Conflict – Here's How They Can Work Together" in The Conversation (March 9, 2021)*
URL(s): theconversation.com/growing-food-and-protecting-nature-dont-have-to-conflict-heres-how-they-can-work-together-146069
Ed: Thomas Hertel. **Released:** March 09, 2021. **Description:** Explores how agribusiness owners can grow food in a sustainable, environmentally friendly way, while also producing enough of their product. **Availability:** Online.

17055 ■ *"Half Empty or Half Full" in Crain's Chicago Business (Vol. 31, March 24, 2008, No. 12, pp. 4)*
Pub: Crain Communications Inc.
Contact: Barry Asin, President
Ed: Meghan Streit. **Description:** Lifeway Foods Inc., the health food company which manufactures a yogurt-like drink called kefir, is being negatively affected by the soaring price of milk; however, the fact that probiotics are picking up in the market may mean that Lifeway stands a good chance of bouncing back and the company's lower share price could be an opportunity for long-term investors who have a tolerance for risk. **Availability:** Online.

17056 ■ *Heart: Building a Great Brand in the Digital Age*
Pub: CreateSpace
Released: September 29, 2014. **Price:** $3.70, paperback. **Description:** Business leader and consultant who works with designers, contractors and service providers in the green industry helps business owners develop and implement company systems and increase revenue. His is a third-generation horticulturist and small business owner and share the challenges of being an entrepreneur. **Availability:** Print.

17057 ■ *"How Agritech Startups Are Boosting Agricultural Economy by Employing AI and Data Science - Expert Explains" in Zee Business (Nov. 12, 2021)*
URL(s): www.zeebiz.com/small-business/news-how-agritech-startups-are-boosting-agricultural-economy-by-employing-ai-and-data-science-expert-explains-170613
Ed: Prashant Singh. **Released:** November 12, 2021. **Description:** Explores the need for agritech startups to shift their operations from legacy structures to technology-driven solutions. **Availability:** Online.

17058 ■ *"How Growers Buy" in Farm Industry News (Vol. 42, January 1, 2009, No. 1)*
Pub: Informa USA, Inc.
Contact: Stephen A. Carter, Chief Executive Officer
Ed: Karen McMahon. **Description:** According to a survey regarding the buying habits among large commercial growers, most prefer to purchase from local retailers, customer service is important concerning their decision on who to buy products from, and price and convenience seem to be more important then brand.

17059 ■ *"How High Can Soybeans Fly?" in Barron's (Vol. 88, March 10, 2008, No. 10, pp. M14)*
Pub: Dow Jones & Company Inc.
Contact: Almar Latour, Chief Executive Officer
Ed: Kenneth Rapoza. **Description:** Prices of soybeans have risen to $14.0875 a bushel, up 8.3 percent for the week. Increased demand, such as in China and in other developing economies, and the investment-driven commodities boom are boosting prices. **Availability:** Online.

17060 ■ *"How Sweet It Will Be" in Barron's (Vol. 89, July 13, 2009, No. 28, pp. M13)*
Pub: Dow Jones & Company Inc.
Contact: Almar Latour, Chief Executive Officer
Ed: Debbie Carlson. **Description:** Raw sugar experienced a rally in the first half of 2009 and the long term outlook for sugar prices is still good. However, there is a likely near-term correction due to the onset of Brazilian harvest that could be 20.7 percent higher for 2009 as compared to the previous year and October contracts could fall to 15.61 cents per pound. **Availability:** Online.

17061 ■ *"IBR Breakfast Series: Idaho's Dairy Industry Quietly Grows" in Idaho Business Review (August 15, 2014)*
Pub: BridgeTower Media
Contact: Adam Reinebach, President
Description: Several dairy industry members were called to a breakfast to discuss the past, present and future of the Idaho dairy farms and products. The impact of technology changes and rising foreign market demands as well as creating more and different products was addressed.

17062 ■ *"Ill Winds; Cuba's Economy" in The Economist (Vol. 390, January 3, 2009, No. 8612, pp. 20)*
Description: Cuba's long-term economic prospects remain poor with the economy forecasted to grow only 4.3 percent for the year, about half of the original forecast, due in part to Hurricane Gustav which caused $10 billion in damage and disrupted the food-supply network and devastated farms across the region; President Raul Castro made raising agricultural production a national priority and the rise in global commodity prices hit the country hard. The only bright spot has been the rise in tourism which is up 9.3 percent over 2007. **Availability:** Online.

17063 ■ *"Illinois Farmland Tops $11,000 Per Acre" in Farm Industry News (June 27, 2011)*
Pub: Informa Business Media, Inc.
Contact: Charlie McCurdy, President

Ed: Karen McMahon. **Description:** Farmland property in Illinois continues to grow in value, selling for $11,000 per acre. Statistical data included. **Availability:** Online.

17064 ■ *"Investment Bank Predicts Shakeup in Farm Equipment Industry"* in *Farm Industry News (November 16, 2011)*
Pub: Informa Business Media, Inc.
Contact: Charlie McCurdy, President
Ed: Jodie Wehrspann. **Description:** Farming can expect to see more mergers and acquisitions in the agricultural equipment industry, as it appears to be in the early stages of growth over the next few years. **Availability:** Online.

17065 ■ *"Investment In Israel Is Investment in the Future of Georgia"* in *Atlanta Business Chronicle (May 30, 2014, pp. 22A)*
Pub: American City Business Journals, Inc.
Contact: Mike Olivieri, Executive Vice President
Description: Georgia Governor Nathan Deal will travel to Israel to lead an economic and trade mission and consolidate Georgia's trade ties with Israel. Israel and the State of Georgia are already collaborating in the fields of health information technology, agrotechnology, homeland security, defense, aerospace and cybersecurity, and microelectronics and nanotechnology. The proposed visit by the Governor will build on this particular partnership from which both parties will benefit. **Availability:** Print; Online.

17066 ■ *"It's Here: the New World of $3+ Corn"* in *Farm Journal (Vol. 138, September 2014, No. 8, pp. 6)*
Pub: Farm Journal Media Inc.
Released: August 26, 2014. **Description:** Record corn prices have leveled out pushing prices down to levels seen in 2009. Hard times can also present opportunities for the best farmers. The impacts of corn prices on the agricultural industry are highlighted. **Availability:** Print; Online.

17067 ■ *"Kraft Taps Cheese Head; Jordan Charged With Fixing Foodmaker's Signature Product"* in *Crain's Chicago Business (April 14, 2008)*
Pub: Crain Communications Inc.
Contact: Barry Asin, President
Ed: David Sterrett. **Description:** Kraft Foods Inc. has assigned Rhonda Jordan, a company veteran, to take charge of the cheese and dairy division which has been losing market shares to cheaper store-brand cheese among cost-sensitive shoppers as Kraft and its competitors raise prices to offset soaring dairy costs. **Availability:** Online.

17068 ■ *"The Latin Beat Goes On"* in *Barron's (Vol. 88, July 7, 2008, No. 27, pp. L5)*
Pub: Dow Jones & Company Inc.
Contact: Almar Latour, Chief Executive Officer
Ed: Tom Sullivan. **Description:** Latin American stocks have outperformed other regional markets due to rising commodities prices and favorable economic climate. Countries such as Brazil, Mexico, Chile, and Peru provide investment opportunities, while Argentina and Venezuela are tougher places to invest. **Availability:** Online.

17069 ■ *"Leica Beefs Up Steering Options, Steering Display Features"* in *Farm Industry News (January 10, 2011)*
Pub: Informa Business Media, Inc.
Contact: Charlie McCurdy, President
Ed: David Hest. **Description:** Leica Geosystems is offering a new hydraulic steering kit for older tractors, along with new steering patterns and other features on its Leica mojo3C and mojoMINI displays. **Availability:** Online.

17070 ■ *"Marketer Bets Big on U.S.'s Growing Canine Obsession"* in *Advertising Age (Vol. 79, April 14, 2008, No. 15, pp. 14)*
Pub: Crain Communications, Inc.
Contact: Jessica Botos, Manager, Marketing
E-mail: jessica.botos@crainsnewyork.com

Ed: Emily Bryson York. **Description:** Overview of FreshPet, a New Jersey company that began marketing two brands of refrigerated dog food-Deli Fresh and FreshPet Select-which are made from fresh ingredients such as beef, rice and carrots. The company projects continued success due to the amount of money consumers spend on their pets as well as fears derived from the 2007 recalls that inspired consumers to look for smaller, independent manufacturers that are less likely to source ingredients from China. **Availability:** Online.

17071 ■ *"Markets Defy the Doomsayers"* in *Barron's (Vol. 88, March 24, 2008, No. 12, pp. M5)*
Pub: Dow Jones & Company Inc.
Contact: Almar Latour, Chief Executive Officer
Ed: Leslie P. Norton. **Description:** US stock markets registered strong gains, with the Dow Jones Industrial Average rising 3.43 percent on the week to close at 12,361.32, in a rally that may be seen as short-covering. Shares of Hansen Natural are poised for further drops with a slowdown in the energy drink market. **Availability:** Online.

17072 ■ *"Mary Kramer: Good Things Happen When We Buy Local"* in *Crain's Detroit Business (Vol. 24, October 6, 2008, No. 40, pp. 7)*
Pub: Crain Communications Inc.
Contact: Barry Asin, President
Description: Michigan is facing incredibly difficult economic times. One way in which each one of us can help the state and the businesses located here is by purchasing our goods and services from local vendors. The state Agriculture Department projected that if Michigan households earmarked $10 per week in their grocery purchases to made-in-Michigan products, this would generate $30 million a week in economic impact. **Availability:** Online.

17073 ■ *"McCormick Focuses on Customer, Dealer Service"* in *Farm Industry News (September 17, 2010)*
Pub: Informa Business Media, Inc.
Contact: Charlie McCurdy, President
Price: $4, Print and Online; Special Offers only for 4 weeks. **Description:** McCormick has developed a new plan that focuses on fast and complete service to both customers and dealers. **Availability:** Print; Online.

17074 ■ *"Melamine Analytical Methods Released"* in *Feedstuffs (Vol. 80, October 6, 2008, No. 41, pp. 2)*
Pub: Miller Publishing Company
Description: Romer Labs has released new validations for its AgraQuant Melamine enzyme-linked immunosorbent assay. The test kit screens for melamine in feed and diary products, including pet foods, milk and milk powder. Melamine by itself is nontoxic in low doses, but when combined with cyanuric acid it can cause fatal kidney stones. The Chinese dairy industry is in the midst of a huge melamine crisis; melamine-contaminated dairy and food products from China have been found in more than 20 countries. **Availability:** Print; Online.

17075 ■ *"Midwest Drought Hurts Agriculture in California"* in *Sacramento Business Journal (Vol. 29, August 24, 2012, No. 26, pp. 1)*
Pub: Baltimore Business Journal
Contact: Rhonda Pringle, President
E-mail: rpringle@bizjournals.com
Ed: Melanie Turner. **Description:** The Midwest drought has adversely affected California's agricultural sector. Consumers are seen to face increased beef, pork and poultry prices. **Availability:** Print; Online.

17076 ■ *"Monsanto's Next Single-Bag Refuge Product Approved"* in *Farm Industry News (December 5, 2011)*
Pub: Informa Business Media, Inc.
Contact: Charlie McCurdy, President

Description: Monsanto's refuge-in-a-bag (RIB) product was approved for commercialization in 2012. The Genuity VT Double Pro RIB Complete is a blend of 95 percent Genuity VT Double Pro and 5 percent refuge (non-Bt) seed and provides above-ground pest control and not corn rootworm protection. **Availability:** Print; Online.

17077 ■ *National Agri-Marketing Association--Membership Directory*
Pub: National Agri-Marketing Association
Contact: John Rozum, President
URL(s): web.nama.org/Portal/PortalLogin.aspx?ReturnURL=%2fsearch
Price: Included in membership. **Description:** Covers 2,500 persons active in agricultural advertising and marketing for manufacturers, advertising agencies, and media. Published as part of the Agri-Marketing Marketing Services Guide. **Entries include:** Member name and position, company name, address, phone. **Arrangement:** Geographical, alphabetical. **Availability:** Print.

17078 ■ *"National Cattlemen's Beef Association"* in *Retail Merchandiser (Vol. 51, September-October 2011, No. 5, pp. 77)*
Pub: Phoenix Media Corp.
Description: National Cattlemen's Beef Association offers a wide range of tools and information to keep its members informed regarding the state of the beef industry. Their Website provides tools to help cattle producers improve operations. **Availability:** Online.

17079 ■ *"The New Alchemists"* in *Canadian Business (Vol. 81, October 27, 2008, No. 18, pp. 22)*
Description: Ethanol industry expects second-generation ethanol or cellulosic biofuels to provide ecologically friendly technologies than the ethanol made from food crops. Government and industries are investing on producing cellulosic biofuels. **Availability:** Print; Online.

17080 ■ *"New Crop Protection Products from Monsanto, Valent, DuPont, FMC, BASF"* in *Farm Industry News (December 17, 2010)*
Pub: Informa Business Media, Inc.
Contact: Charlie McCurdy, President
Ed: Mark Moore. **Price:** $4, Print and Online; Special Offers only for 4 weeks. **Description:** Glyphosate-dominated herbicides are declining because a more diversified market for corn and soybeans is available. New crop care includes old chemistries, new formulations and unique combinations of both giving farmers more choices to protect the yield potential of their corn and soybean crops. Profiles of new products are included. **Availability:** Print; Online.

17081 ■ *"New Ethanol Plant, Planned for Nevada, IA, Will Use Corn Stover"* in *Farm Industry News (June 27, 2011)*
Pub: Informa Business Media, Inc.
Contact: Charlie McCurdy, President
Ed: Lynn Grooms. **Description:** DuPont Danisco Cellulosic Ethanol (DDCE) will buy land next to the Lincolnway Energy corn-based ethanol plant in Nevada, Iowa in order to produce ethanol from corn stover at the location. **Availability:** Online.

17082 ■ *"New No. 1 at Element 8: Angel Group Brings on New Executive Director"* in *Puget Sound Business Journal (Vol. 35, September 19, 2014, No. 22, pp. 6)*
Pub: American City Business Journals, Inc.
Contact: Mike Olivieri, Executive Vice President
Description: Element 8 executive director, Kristi Growdon, says the company continues to find investment opportunities in the Pacific Northwest's clean technology sector. She also said the agricultural sector is a potentially lucrative investment destination. Growdon added that the company bases decisions on clean technology. **Availability:** Online.

17083 ■ *"New Yetter Stubble Solution Prevents Tire, Track Damage"* in *Farm Industry News (November 21, 2011)*
Pub: Informa Business Media, Inc.
Contact: Charlie McCurdy, President

Description: The new Yetter 5000 Stalk Devastator helps prevent premature tire and track wear and damage caused by crop stubble. **Availability:** Print; Online.

17084 ■ *"Nonstop Round Baler Earns Top International Award for Krone"* in *Farm Industry News (November 18, 2011)*
Pub: Informa Business Media, Inc.
Contact: Charlie McCurdy, President

Ed: Karen McMahon. **Description:** The new Ultima baler from Krone can make and net a bale in 40 seconds without stopping, thus producing 90 bales an hour. The new baler, still in test stage, won top honors at the Agritechnica farm equipment show in Hannover, Germany. **Availability:** Online.

17085 ■ *"Numerous Changes Made to Crop Production and Consumption Forecasts"* in *Farm Industry News (November 9, 2011)*
Pub: Informa Business Media, Inc.
Contact: Charlie McCurdy, President

Ed: Darrel Good. **Description:** USDA November Crop Production and WASDE reports contained various changes in production and consumption forecasts for corn, soybeans, and what for the current marketing year. A brief summary for each crop is included. **Availability:** Online.

17086 ■ *"Opinion: Prison Farms are Closing, but the Manure Remains"* in *Canadian Business (Vol. 83, August 17, 2010, No. 13-14, pp. 9)*
Pub: Rogers Media Inc.
Contact: Neil Spivak, Chief Executive Officer

Ed: Steve Maich. **Description:** The explanation given by Canada's government ministers on planned closure of the prison farms and scrapping of the long form census are designed by mixing of spin, argument and transparent justification. The defense should have been plausible but the ministers could not handle the simple questions about statistics and prison job training with pretense. **Availability:** Online.

17087 ■ *"Organic Food Industry Goes to College"* in *USA Today (April 9, 2012)*
Ed: Chuck Raasch. **Description:** With the organic food industry growing the US Department of Agriculture is has pumped $117 million into organic research in the last three years. According to a recent report by the Organic Farming Research Foundation (OFRF), the number of states committing land for organic research has nearly doubled from 2003 to 2011. Universities offering academic programs in organic farming rose from none to nine. The OFRF supports organic farmers and producers. **Availability:** Online.

17088 ■ *"OSHA Begins Process of Creating Standard to Protect Workers From Hazardous Heat"* in *GardenCenter (October 26, 2021)*
Ed: Chris Markham. **Released:** October 26, 2021. **Description:** With the warming temperatures spreading around the globe, workers are routinely exposed to extreme heat, which can prove to be fatal. OSHA is publishing an Advance Notice in order to deal with the situation and make it less hazardous for workers in fields. **Availability:** Online.

17089 ■ *"Outlook for Montana Agriculture"* in *Montana Business Quarterly (Vol. 49, Spring 2011, No. 1, pp. 26)*
Pub: University of Montana Bureau of Business and Economic Research
Contact: Patrick Barkey, Director
E-mail: patrick.barkey@business.umt.edu

Ed: George Haynes. **Released:** Quarterly. **Description:** Montana farmers and ranchers are rebounding from lower prices and production to higher prices and record production in 2010. The state has limited dairy and hog production, but farm income is still likely rise between 15 to 25 percent in 2010 over previous year. **Availability:** Online.

17090 ■ *"People Want Organic Food Because of What Isn't On It, Local Producers Say"* in *Republican & Herald (September 24, 2012)*
Released: September 24, 2012. **Description:** Local producers believe that people want organically grown food because it is free of pesticides and toxins, thus making it healthier. **Availability:** Print; Online.

17091 ■ *"Perry's Goes Organic"* in *Ice Cream Reporter (Vol. 22, December 20, 2008, No. 1, pp. 1)*
Description: Family-owned Perry's Ice Cream is starting a new line of organic ice cream in both vanilla and chocolate flavors. All Perry's products are made with milk and cream from local dairy farmers. **Availability:** Print; Online.

17092 ■ *"Pioneer Unveils Drought-Tolerant Hybrids"* in *Farm Industry News (January 6, 2011)*
Pub: Informa Business Media, Inc.
Contact: Charlie McCurdy, President

Ed: Mark Moore. **Description:** Eight new drought-tolerant hybrids are now available across five genetic platforms from Pioneer. The new hybrids, marketed under the Optimum AQUAmax brand name (previously announced as Drought Tolerant 1 Hybrids), contain a collection of native corn traits that improve water access and utilization. **Availability:** Print; Online.

17093 ■ *"Precision Crop Control with Valley Irrigation/CropMetrics Partnership"* in *Farm Industry News (January 6, 2011)*
Pub: Informa Business Media, Inc.
Contact: Charlie McCurdy, President

Ed: Karen McMahon. **Description:** Irrigation systems have become a precision farming tool since partnering with agronomic software systems to apply products across the field by prescription. Valley Irrigation and CropMetrics have partnered in order to variably control water, fertilizer and other crop management products through a center pivot irrigation system. **Availability:** Print; Online.

17094 ■ *"Precision Fertilizer Spreading Shown at Agritechnica"* in *Farm Industry News (November 23, 2011)*
Pub: Informa Business Media, Inc.
Contact: Charlie McCurdy, President

Ed: Karen McMahon. **Description:** Rauch, the German firm, introduced a new system that precisely spreads fertilizer on crops. The new product was shown at Agritechnica. **Availability:** Online.

17095 ■ *"Presidential Address: Innovation in Retrospect and Prospect"* in *Canadian Journal of Electronics (Vol. 43, November 2010, No. 4)*
Pub: Journal of the Canadian Economics Association

Ed: James A. Brander. **Description:** Has innovation slowed in recent decades? While there has been progress in information and communications technology, the recent record of innovation in agriculture, energy, transportation and healthcare sectors is cause for concern. **Availability:** PDF; Online.

17096 ■ *"Press Release: New Corn Hybrid from Seed Consultants"* in *Farm Industry News (January 6, 2011)*
Description: Seed Consultants Inc. is releasing its first proprietary corn line called SC 1101. The product was developed, bred, and tested for the eastern Corn Belt diseases, soils, and growing conditions.

17097 ■ *"Press Release: Trimble Introduces CFX-750 Display"* in *Farm Industry News (January 4, 2011)*
Description: Trimble is offering a touch screen display called the CFX-750. The new 8-inch full-color display allows farmers to choose the specific guidance, steering and precision agriculture capabilities that best fit their farm's particular needs. The display can be upgraded as business needs change, including the addition of GLONASS capabilities, or the addition of section and rate control for crop inputs such as seed, chemicals and fertilizer. **Availability:** Print; Online.

17098 ■ *"Pro Livestock Launches Most Comprehensive Virtual Sales Barn for Livestock and Breed Stock"* in *Benzinga.com (October 29, 2011)*
Description: Pro Livestock Marketing launched the first online sales portal for livestock and breed stock. The firm has designed a virtual sales barn allowing individuals to purchase and sell cattle, swine, sheep, goats, horses, rodeo stock, show animals, specialty animals, semen and embryos globally. It is like an eBay for livestock and will help ranchers and farmers grow. **Availability:** Print; PDF; Online.

17099 ■ *"The Pumpkin Plan: A Simple Strategy to Grow a Remarkable Business in Any Field"*
Pub: Portfolio Hardcover
Contact: Adrian Zackheim, President

Released: September 22, 2022. **Price:** $17.95, paperback. **Description:** One million new businesses are started every year in America and nearly 80 percent of them fail within the first five years. Entrepreneur, Mike Michalowicz discovered the inspiration he needed to successfully grow his business when reading an article about a pumpkin farmer who was committed to growing giant pumpkins. Michalowicz applied the same process to his small business and transformed his company into a multimillion dollar success. The pumpkin plan includes: planting the right seeds, wedding out the losers, and nurturing the winners. **Availability:** Print.

17100 ■ *"Purdue Agronomist: Consider Costs Before Tilling"* in *Farm Industry News (November 8, 2011)*
Pub: Informa Business Media, Inc.
Contact: Charlie McCurdy, President

Ed: Lisa Schluttenhofer. **Description:** Farmers consider soil drainage, fertilizer and planting needs as well as economic thresholds before making tillage decisions, according to a Purdue extension agronomist. **Availability:** Online.

17101 ■ *"Recipe for Disaster?"* in *Sacramento Business Journal (Vol. 25, July 4, 2008, No. 18, pp. 1)*
Pub: American City Business Journals, Inc.
Contact: Mike Olivieri, Executive Vice President

Ed: Mark Anderson. **Description:** Restaurateurs are challenged with balancing rising operating costs and what customers are willing to pay for their services. Flour prices in 2008 have increased by 46 percent from April 2007. Other views on the situation, as well as trends, forecasts and statistics on sales, outlook on economic conditions, consumer price index, and the typical split of restaurant revenue, are presented. **Availability:** Online.

17102 ■ *"Report: McD's Pepsi Score Best With Young Hispanics"* in *Brandweek (Vol. 49, April 21, 2008, No. 16, pp. 8)*
Description: According to a new report, in order to reach Hispanic Gen Yers, marketing strategists need to understand this demographic's "bi-dentity," something which has proved an elusive task to many marketers. Another trend is the emergence of Latinas who have careers, as opposed to just jobs. There is an opportunity to tap this new, young and empowered female market with innovative messaging. Statistical data included. **Availability:** Online.

17103 ■ *"Roll Your Own"* in *Business North Carolina (Vol. 28, March 2008, No. 3, pp. 66)*
Description: Profile of U.S. Flue-Cured Tobacco Growers who process tobacco and make cigarettes. Details of the program are outlined. **Availability:** Online.

17104 ■ *"Roseville Investing Big in Downtown"* in *Sacramento Business Journal (Vol. 28, September 2, 2011, No. 27, pp. 1)*
Pub: Sacramento Business Journal
Contact: Stephanie Fretwell, Director

GENERAL SMALL BUSINESS TOPICS
Agribusiness ■ 17125

E-mail: sfretwell@bizjournals.com
Ed: Michael Shaw. **Price:** $4, Digital introductory 4-week offer; $4, Print & Digital introductory 4-week offer. **Description:** The city of Roseville, California is planning to invest in downtown development projects. The plan includes a new town square, a venue for a farmers market and an interactive water fountain. **Availability:** Print; Online.

17105 ■ *"Russian Renaissance"* in *Chicago Tribune* **(September 22, 2008)**
Pub: Tribune News Service
Contact: Jack Barry, Vice President, Operations
E-mail: jbarry@tribpub.com
Ed: Alex Rodriguez. **Description:** Winemakers from Russia are returning to the craft and quality of winemaking now that they are free from Soviet restraints. **Availability:** Print; Online.

17106 ■ *"Santa Clara Wineries at Odds with County Over Regulations"* in *Silicon Valley/San Jose Business Journal* **(Vol. 30, September 7, 2012, No. 24, pp. 1)**
Pub: Baltimore Business Journal
Contact: Rhonda Pringle, President
E-mail: rpringle@bizjournals.com
Description: A proposed ordinance in Santa Clara County, California will change existing winery regulations and implement a sliding fee system for event permits. Officials believe that the government ordinance will improve agricultural tourism, but winery owners claim that it would force them to choose between canceling events and footing the bill for certain costs. **Availability:** Print; Online.

17107 ■ *"SCPA Members Seek Senate Support for H.R. 872"* in *Farm Industry News* **(May 26, 2011)**
Pub: Informa Business Media, Inc.
Contact: Charlie McCurdy, President
Ed: Forrest Laws. **Description:** U.S. House of Representatives passed legislation, H.R. 872 the Reducing Regulatory Burdens Act that frees pesticide applicators from having to obtain NPDES permits for applications over or near water. **Availability:** Online.

17108 ■ *"The Second Most Fuel-Efficient Tractor of the Decade: John Deere 8320R"* in *Farm Industry News* **(November 10, 2011)**
Pub: Informa Business Media, Inc.
Contact: Charlie McCurdy, President
Description: John Deere's 8320R Tractor was ranked second in the Farm Industry News listing of the top 40 most fuel-efficient tractors of the decade, following the winner, John Deere's 8295R PTO tractor. **Availability:** Online.

17109 ■ *"Seed-Count Labeling"* in *Farm Industry News* **(October 20, 2010)**
Pub: Informa Business Media, Inc.
Contact: Charlie McCurdy, President
Ed: Mark Moore. **Price:** $4, Print and Online; Special Offers only for 4 weeks. **Description:** National Conference on Weights and Measures voted to standardize testing methods and procedures that will verify seed-count labeling. **Availability:** Print; Online.

17110 ■ *"Self-Employment in the United States"* in *Montly Labor Review* **(Vol. 133, September 2010, No. 9, pp. 17)**
Pub: U.S. Department of Labor Bureau of Labor Statistics
Contact: Amrit Kohli, Director
E-mail: kohli.amrit@bls.gov
Description: Self employment in 2009 in the U.S. continued to be more common among men, Whites, Asians, and older workers and in the agriculture, construction, and services industries. **Availability:** PDF; Online.

17111 ■ *"Shear Profit"* in *Crain's Cleveland Business* **(Vol. 28, October 29, 2007, No. 43, pp. 3)**
Pub: Crain Communications Inc.
Contact: K. C. Crain, President

Ed: David Bennett. **Description:** Alpaca farms are becoming a very profitable business for a number of Northeast Ohio entrepreneurs due to the high return on initial investments, tax incentives and the rise in demand for the animals. Ohio leads the country in the number of alpaca farms with roughly one-third located in Northeast Ohio. **Availability:** Online.

17112 ■ *"A Simple Old Reg that Needs Dusting Off"* in *Barron's* **(Vol. 88, June 30, 2008, No. 26, pp. 35)**
Pub: Dow Jones & Company Inc.
Contact: Almar Latour, Chief Executive Officer
Ed: Gene Epstein. **Description:** Senator Joe Lieberman has a point when he accused speculators of inflating the prices of food and fuel futures but introducing legislation to address speculation has an alternative. The senator's committee should instead demand that the Commodity Futures Trading Commission enforce position limits on the maximum number of contracts in a given market per speculative entity. **Availability:** Online.

17113 ■ *"Sleep It Off In a Silo B&B"* in *Chicago Tribune* **(December 14, 2008)**
Pub: Tribune News Service
Contact: Jack Barry, Vice President, Operations
E-mail: jbarry@tribpub.com
Ed: Bill Daley. **Description:** Profile of Oregon's Abbey Road Farm bed-and-breakfast which is located on an 82-acre working farm; guests stay in shiny metal farm silos which have been converted into luxury rooms with views of the farm.

17114 ■ *"Social Networking: Growing Pains"* in *Canadian Business* **(Vol. 81, July 22, 2008, No. 12-13, pp. 35)**
Pub: Rogers Media Inc.
Contact: Neil Spivak, Chief Executive Officer
Ed: Alex Mlynek. **Description:** Laughing Stock Vineyards' Cynthia Enns and David Enns plan to target young buyers by using social media. The Enns however, are concerned that targeting younger buyers may affect Laughing Stock's image as a premium brand. Additional information regarding the company's future plans is presented. **Availability:** Print; Online.

17115 ■ *"A Soggy Harvest"* in *Business Journal-Portland* **(Vol. 24, October 5, 2007, No. 32, pp. 1)**
Pub: Portland Business Journal
Contact: Andy Giegerich, Managing Editor
E-mail: agiegerich@bizjournals.com
Ed: Robin J. Moody. **Description:** Vintners in Willamette Valley are facing a tough challenge with a rainy wine harvest season and a delay in the ripening of grapes due to a cool spring and August. Rain decreased the sugar content of grapes and poses a danger with molds. The economic impact of the rainy harvest season in wine making is discussed. **Availability:** Print; Online.

17116 ■ *"Sole Proprietorship Returns, 2008 Part 2"* in *SOI Bulletin* **(Vol. 30, Summer 2010, No. 1, pp. 27)**
Description: Table of Nonfarm Sole Proprietorships is presented. Statistics are broken down by sector reporting all nonfarm industries as well as agriculture, forestry, hunting and fishing. **Availability:** PDF; Online.

17117 ■ *"Starting a Sustainable Agriculture Business"* in *Texas A&M Forest Service*
URL(s): agrilifeextension.tamu.edu/library/agricultural-business/starting-a-sustainable-agriculture-business/
Ed: Megan Clayton, Amanda Corso Krause, Parker Creek Ranch, John Smith. **Description:** Discusses sustainable vs. traditional agriculture methods and provides steps to help your sustainable agriculture venture get off to a good start. **Availability:** Online.

17118 ■ *"State Investment Goes Sour"* in *Business Journal Portland* **(Vol. 26, December 4, 2009, No. 39, pp. 1)**
Pub: Portland Business Journal
Contact: Andy Giegerich, Managing Editor

E-mail: agiegerich@bizjournals.com
Ed: Erik Siemers. **Description:** Oregon might recoup only $500,000 of a $20 million loan to Vancouver-based Cascade Grain Products LLC. Cascade Grain's ethanol plant in Clatskanie, OR will be put into auction under the supervision of a bankruptcy court. **Availability:** Print; Online.

17119 ■ *"A Stock Worth Trading Down To"* in *Barron's* **(Vol. 88, July 14, 2008, No. 28, pp. 36)**
Pub: Dow Jones & Company Inc.
Contact: Almar Latour, Chief Executive Officer
Ed: Alexander Eule. **Description:** Shares of Ralcorp Holdings are cheap at around $49.95 after slipping 20 percent prior to their acquisition of Post cereals from Kraft. Some analysts believe its shares could climb over 60 percent to $80 as value-seeking consumers buy more private label products. **Availability:** Print; Online.

17120 ■ *"Stronger Corn? Take It Off Steroids, Make It All Female"* in *Farm Industry News* **(December 5, 2011)**
Pub: Informa Business Media, Inc.
Contact: Charlie McCurdy, President
Ed: Brian Wallheimer. **Description:** Purdue University researcher found that higher improvements in corn crops, and possibly other crops, were yielded when steroids were discontinued. **Availability:** Print; Online.

17121 ■ *"Survey: Ag Lenders Less Optimistic"* in *Idaho Business Review* **(June 27, 2014)**
Pub: BridgeTower Media
Contact: Adam Reinebach, President
Price: $11.99, Print, Digital & Mobile (For 1 Month Intro Rate); $149, Print, Digital & Mobile (For 1 Year); $99, Digital & Mobile Only(For 1 Year). **Description:** According to a survey conducted by Kansas State University, agricultural lenders are showing less optimism than previously felt last fall. Lenders are expecting interest rates to rise, while the spread over cost of funds is expected to increase in the long term. Statistical data included. **Availability:** Print; Online.

17122 ■ *"Tabs Says Organic Food Sales Hit Record in 2011. Sales Jump 15-20 Percent"* in *Entertainment Close-Up* **(February 21, 2012)**
Description: Tabs Group reported it found an increase in American consumers reporting they purchased organic products along with a rise in overall sales in its Annual Organic Product Survey. Statistical data included.

17123 ■ *"Tax Relief Available for Livestock Sold Due to Drought"* in *Southeast Farm Press* **(October 4, 2012)**
Description: Designated areas have been identified for farmers and ranchers who were forced to sell draft animals, breeding livestock or dairy animals becuase of drought, flood or other weather relate conditions. These farmers and ranchers have been give more time to defer payment of capital gains taxes on replacement animals. Details of the program are examined.

17124 ■ *"Time to Leave the Party? Re-Evaluating Commodities"* in *Barron's* **(Vol. 88, March 24, 2008, No. 12, pp. M16)**
Pub: Dow Jones & Company Inc.
Contact: Almar Latour, Chief Executive Officer
Ed: Andrea Hotter. **Description:** Prices of commodities such as gold, copper, crude oil, sugar, cocoa, and wheat have fallen from their all-time highs set in the middle of March 2008. Analysts, however, caution that this decline in prices may be temporary, and that a banking crisis may trigger new price rises in commodities. **Availability:** Online.

17125 ■ *"Too Much Precaution About Biotech Corn"* in *Barron's* **(Vol. 88, March 17, 2008, No. 11, pp. 54)**
Pub: Dow Jones & Company Inc.
Contact: Almar Latour, Chief Executive Officer

Ed: Mark I. Schwartz. **Description:** In the U.S., 90 percent of cultivated soybeans are biotech varietals as well as 60 percent of the corn. Farmers have significantly reduced their reliance on pesticides in the growing of biotech corn. Biotech cotton cultivation has brought hundreds of millions of dollars in net financial gains to farmers. The European Union has precluded the cultivation or sale of biotech crops within its border. **Availability:** Online.

17126 ■ *"Top Design Award for Massey Ferguson 7624 Dyna-VT" in Farm Industry News (November 14, 2011)*
Pub: Informa Business Media, Inc.
Contact: Charlie McCurdy, President
Description: Massey Ferguson won top honors for its MF 7624 Dyna-VT as the Golden Tractor for Design award in the 2012 Tractor of the Year competition. The award is presented annually by journalists from 22 leading farming magazines in Europe and manufacturers have to be nominated to enter. **Availability:** Online.

17127 ■ *"Top Worst Weeds in Corn" in Farm Industry News (November 29, 2011)*
Pub: Informa Business Media, Inc.
Contact: Charlie McCurdy, President
Ed: John Pocock. **Description:** Effective weed control for profitable crops is discussed with information from leading weed scientists from the University of Illinois Extension. It is important for farmers to know what their worst weed is in order to choose the best product, or mix of products, to control them. **Availability:** Print; Online.

17128 ■ *"Transgenerational Trend: New Fans for Fresh Fare" in Barron's (Vol. 92, July 7, 2012, No. 28, pp. 15)*
Pub: Dow Jones And Co.
Contact: Almar Latour, Chief Executive Officer
Ed: Robin Goldwyn Blumenthal. **Description:** The preference for natural and organic food is shared by baby boomers and millennials. Spending on natural and organic food is projected to rise along with rising food spending. **Availability:** Online.

17129 ■ *"Tri-State to Get New Headquarters" in Business Courier (Vol. 27, October 22, 2010, No. 25, pp. 1)*
Description: Hong Kong-based corn processing firm Global Bio-Chem Technology is set to choose Greater Cincinnati, Ohio as a location of its North American headquarters. The interstate access, central location, and low labor and property costs might have enticed Global Bio-Chem to invest in the region. Statistics on Chinese direct investment in U.S. are also presented. **Availability:** Online; PDF.

17130 ■ *"The Trouble With $150,000 Wine" in Barron's (Vol. 88, July 7, 2008, No. 27, pp. 33)*
Pub: Dow Jones & Company Inc.
Contact: Almar Latour, Chief Executive Officer
Ed: Jay Palmer. **Description:** Review of the book, "The Billionaire's Vinegar: The Mystery of the World's Most Expensive Bottle of Wine," which discusses vintners along with the marketing and distribution of wine as well as the winemaking industry as a whole. **Availability:** Online.

17131 ■ *"Up On The Farm" in Canadian Business (Vol. 81, March 31, 2008, No. 5, pp. 23)*
Description: Agricultural products have outperformed both energy and metal and even the prospect of a global economic slowdown does not seem to hinder its prospects. The Organization for Economic Cooperation and Development sees prices above historic equilibrium levels during the next ten years given that fuel and fertilizers remain high and greater demand from India and China remain steady. **Availability:** Print; Online.

17132 ■ *"Updated LGMA Website Provides Food Safety News, Resources" in Western Farm Press (October 14, 2014)*
Description: California's Leafy Greens Marketing Agreement (LGMA) updated its Website to include easier access to news, information, and resources involving leafy greens food safety and the program developed in 2007. The site offers a blog featuring three key topic areas: Food Safety Modernization Act; LGMA's comprehensive training program, called LGMA Tech; and resources for members.

17133 ■ *"Weather Jitters Boost Coffee" in Barron's (Vol. 92, July 23, 2012, No. 30, pp. M12)*
Pub: Dow Jones & Company Inc.
Contact: Almar Latour, Chief Executive Officer
Ed: Alexandra Wexler. **Description:** Coffee futures prices rose by 20 percent as rains in Brazil sparked concerns about the crop's size and quality. Arabica futures for September 2012 delivery rose to $1.8695/pound and could exceed $2/pound by the end of the summer. **Availability:** Online.

17134 ■ *"We're Ignoring the Only Industry We Can't Do Without" in Entrepreneur (Apr 11, 2019)*
URL(s): www.entrepreneur.com/article/331120
Ed: Kim Walsh. **Released:** April 11, 2019. **Description:** Discusses the need for agricultural practices to make significant advances to support growing agribusiness needs -- agritech. **Availability:** Online.

17135 ■ *"What Is Agribusiness?" in The Balance Small Business (Dec. 18, 2020)*
URL(s): www.thebalancesmb.com/what-is-agribusiness-2538209
Ed: Jennifer Chait. **Released:** December 18, 2020. **Description:** Explains what agribusiness is, types of agribusiness companies, and provides information on agribusiness vs. organic farming. **Availability:** Online.

17136 ■ *"Which Direction are Herbicides Heading?" in Farm Industry News (October 11, 2011)*
Pub: Informa Business Media, Inc.
Contact: Charlie McCurdy, President
Ed: Jennifer Shike. **Description:** Currently, one of the best solutions for growers fighting weed resistance may be 2,4-D or other auxin herbicides. **Availability:** Print; Online.

17137 ■ *"Why Nestle Should Sell Alcon" in Barron's (Vol. 88, March 17, 2008, No. 11, pp. M12)*
Pub: Dow Jones & Company Inc.
Contact: Almar Latour, Chief Executive Officer
Ed: Sean Walters. **Description:** Nestle should sell Alcon because Nestle can't afford to be complacent as its peers have made changes to their portfolios to boost competitiveness. Nestle's stake in Alcon and L'Oreal have been ignored by investors and Nestle could realize better value by strengthening its nutrition division through acquisitions. **Availability:** Online.

17138 ■ *"Wind Farm Is Planned for Yolo Farmland" in Sacramento Business Journal (Vol. 29, September 21, 2012, No. 30, pp. 1)*
Pub: Baltimore Business Journal
Contact: Rhonda Pringle, President
E-mail: rpringle@bizjournals.com
Ed: Melanie Turner. **Description:** Austin, Texas-based Pioneer Green Energy LLC has been planning to build as many as 400 wind turbines in Yolo County, California that could potentially generate up to 600 megawatts. The company has already raised $20 and it is expected to formally propose the project in early 2013. The economic impact on the farmers and landowners in the region is explored. **Availability:** Online.

17139 ■ *"Women Up: Kathleen Ligocki of Harvest Power Inc." in Boston Business Journal (Vol.. 34, April 11, 2014, No. 10)*
Pub: American City Business Journals, Inc.
Contact: Mike Olivieri, Executive Vice President
Released: Weekly. **Price:** $4, introductory 4-week offer(Digital & Print). **Description:** Kathleen Ligocki is the CEO of Harvest Power Inc. of Massachusetts. The company diverts organic waste destined for landfills and produces green energy and soil enrichment products. The company was founded in 2008 and reported sales of over $130 million in 2013. **Availability:** Print; Online.

TRADE PERIODICALS

17140 ■ *Agribusiness: An International Journal*
Pub: Wiley Periodicals Inc.
Contact: Brian Napack, Chief Executive Officer
URL(s): www.wiley.com/en-jp/Agribusiness-p-978047 1541684onlinelibrary.wiley.com/journal/15206297
X (Twitter): x.com/AgribusinessJrn
Ed: Monika Hartmann, Nobuhiro Suzuki, Rigoberto A. Lopez. **Released:** Quarterly; Winter, Spring, Summer and Fall. **Price:** $3,714, Institutions for print and online US, Canada and India; $3,307, Institutions for online US, Canada and India; $3,449, Institutions for print US, Canada and India. **Description:** International journal covering the application of economic analysis to the organization and performance of firms and markets in industrial food systems. **Availability:** Print; PDF; Download; Online.

17141 ■ *American Journal of Agricultural Economics (AJAE)*
Pub: Wiley-Blackwell
URL(s): onlinelibrary.wiley.com/journal/14678276
Released: 5/year **Price:** $759, Institutions for print and online Canada, US, India; $676, Institutions for online Canada, US, India; $705, Institutions for print Canada, US, India. **Description:** Scholarly journal focused on the economics of agriculture and food, natural resources and the environment, and rural and community development throughout the world. Published by Wiley on behalf of the Agricultural & Applied Economics Association. **Availability:** Print; PDF; Download; Online.

17142 ■ *Canola Digest*
Pub: Canola Council of Canada
Contact: Jim Everson, President
E-mail: eversonj@canolacouncil.org
URL(s): canoladigest.ca
Released: Quarterly **Description:** Provides information on canola and related interests. Recurring features include on farm articles, market reports analysis, news of research, a calendar of events, reports of meetings, and news of educational opportunities, industry news and issues. **Availability:** Print; PDF; Download; Online.

17143 ■ *Composting News*
Pub: McEntee Media Corp.
URL(s): compostingnews.com
Facebook: www.facebook.com/CompostingNews
X (Twitter): x.com/CompostingNews
Released: Monthly **Price:** $83, Individuals for one year; $140, Individuals for two years. **Description:** Covers news and trends in the composting industry. Also reports on compost product prices. Recurring features include letters to the editor, interviews, news of research, a calendar of events, reports of meetings, and notices of publications available. **Availability:** Print; Download; Online.

17144 ■ *Farm Bureau News*
Pub: American Farm Bureau Federation
Contact: Zippy Duvall, President
URL(s): www.fb.org/news
Ed: Lynne Finnerty. **Description:** Discusses current legislation, court decisions, trade issues, and the use of innovative production methods. Recurring features include editorials, commentaries and the President's Column. **Availability:** Print.

17145 ■ *Farm Industry News*
Pub: Southwest Farm Press - Agribusiness Div.
Contact: Willie Vogt, Executive Director
E-mail: willie.vogt@farmprogress.com
URL(s): www.farmprogress.com/farm-industry-news
Facebook: www.facebook.com/FarmIndustryNews
Released: Monthly **Description:** Agriculture trade magazine covering new products and technology. **Availability:** Print; Online.

GENERAL SMALL BUSINESS TOPICS

17146 ■ Fastline
Pub: Fastline
Description: Illustrated buying guide for the farming industry. Availability: Print; Online.

17147 ■ Fastline--Indiana Farm Edition
Pub: Fastline
URL(s): www.fastline.com/digital-editions/indiana-farm/2024/11
Released: Annual Description: Illustrated buying guide for the farming industry. Availability: Print; PDF; Download; Online.

17148 ■ Fastline--Kentucky Farm Edition
Pub: Fastline
Released: 17 Times Per Year. Price: $45, Two years; $30, for one year print; $1.17, for per edition; $60, for three years. Description: Illustrated buying guide for the farming industry. Availability: PDF; Online; Download.

17149 ■ Fastline--Mid-South Farm Edition
Pub: Fastline
URL(s): www.fastline.com/digital-editions/mid-south-farm/2021/03www.fastline.com/digital-editions/mid-south-farm/2016/13
Description: Illustrated buying guide for the farming industry. Availability: Print; PDF; Online.

17150 ■ Fastline--Missouri Farm Edition
Pub: Fastline
URL(s): www.fastline.com/catalogs
Released: Latest edition 2024. Description: Illustrated buying guide for the farming industry. Availability: Print; Online.

17151 ■ Fastline--Oklahoma Farm Edition
Pub: Fastline
URL(s): www.fastline.com/catalogs
Released: Last edition 2024. Description: Illustrated buying guide for the farming industry. Availability: Online.

17152 ■ Fastline--Tennessee Farm Edition
Pub: Fastline
URL(s): www.fastline.com/catalogs
Description: Illustrated buying guide for the farming industry. Availability: Online.

17153 ■ Fastline --Texas Farm Edition
Pub: Fastline
Released: 17/year. Price: $45, Two years; $1.17, for per edition; $60, for three years; $30, for 1 year. Description: Illustrated buying guide for the farming industry. Availability: Print; PDF; Download; Online.

17154 ■ Fastline--Wisconsin Farm Edition
Pub: Fastline
URL(s): www.fastline.com/digital-editions/wisconsin-farm/2024/10
Released: 17 Times Per Year. Price: $1.17, Single issue for per edition; $45, for 2 years; $60, for 3 years; $30, for 1 year. Description: Illustrated buying guide for the farming industry. Availability: PDF; Download; Online.

17155 ■ Journal of International Food & Agribusiness Marketing
Pub: Taylor And Francis Group
Contact: Annie Callanan, Chief Executive Officer
URL(s): www.tandfonline.com/journals/wifa20
Released: 5/year; vol.36, 2024. Price: $1,504, Institutions for print and online; $331, Individuals for print and online; $1,233, Institutions for online only; $307, Individuals for online only. Description: Journal studying food and agribusiness marketing systems in a variety of socioeconomic and political systems around the world. Availability: Print; PDF; Download; Online.

VIDEO/AUDIO MEDIA

17156 ■ Disruptors for Good: Creating an Entrepreneurial Blueprint for the Next Generation of Farmers
URL(s): share.transistor.fm/s/36df69bd
Description: Podcast offers tips on an entrepreneurial blueprint for regenerative farmers.

17157 ■ How I Built This: A Climate-Resilient Ancient Grain with Pierre Thiam of Yolélé
URL(s): wondery.com/shows/how-i-built-this/episode/10386-a-climate-resilient-ancient-grain-with-pierre-thiam-of-yolele-2022
Ed: Guy Raz. Released: September 21, 2023. Description: Podcast offers a discussion with Pierre Thiam, the co-founder of Yolélé, a company introducing a West African grain built for climate change.

17158 ■ Innovating with the Grain World's First Bulk Solids Locomotion Devices
URL(s): www.startuphustlepodcast.com/innovating-with-the-grain-worlds-first-bulk-solids-locomotion-device
Ed: Matt Watson. Released: February 29, 2024. Description: Podcast explores automation and grain production.

TRADE SHOWS AND CONVENTIONS

17159 ■ The 3i Show
URL(s): 3ishow.com/3ishow
Frequency: Annual. Description: Industry show for agribusiness products. Principal Exhibits: Industry show for agribusiness products.

17160 ■ AAEA Annual Meeting
Agricultural and Applied Economics Association (AAEA)
555 E Wells St., Ste. 1100
Milwaukee, WI 53202
Ph: (414)918-3190
Fax: (414)276-3349
Co. E-mail: info@aaea.org
URL: http://www.aaea.org
Contact: Norbert Wilson, President
E-mail: norbert.wilson@duke.edu
URL(s): www.aaea.org/meetings/2024-aaea-annual-meeting
Frequency: Annual. Description: Agricultural economics software, hardware, teaching texts, tools, equipment, supplies, and services. Audience: Agricultural economists, professionals and students. Principal Exhibits: Agricultural economics software, hardware, teaching texts, tools, equipment, supplies, and services. Dates and Locations: 2025 Jul 27-29 Denver, CO; 2026 Jul 26-28 Kansas City, MO; 2027 Jul 25-27 Philadelphia, PA; 2028 Jul 23-25 San Antonio, TX; 2029 Jul 22-24 Washington, DC. Telecommunication Services: info@aaea.org.

17161 ■ AAEA Annual Meeting
Agricultural and Applied Economics Association (AAEA)
555 E Wells St., Ste. 1100
Milwaukee, WI 53202
Ph: (414)918-3190
Fax: (414)276-3349
Co. E-mail: info@aaea.org
URL: http://www.aaea.org
Contact: Norbert Wilson, President
E-mail: norbert.wilson@duke.edu
URL(s): www.aaea.org/meetings/2024-aaea-annual-meeting
Frequency: Annual. Description: Teaching on topics related to agricultural and applied economics, including climate change, biofuels, regional and behavioral economics, linkages between food and health. Audience: Professionals and students in the field of agricultural and applied economics. Principal Exhibits: Teaching on topics related to agricultural and applied economics, including climate change, biofuels, regional and behavioral economics, linkages between food and health. Dates and Locations: 2025 Jul 27-29 Denver, CO; 2026 Jul 26-28 Kansas City, MO; 2027 Jul 25-27 Philadelphia, PA; 2028 Jul 23-25 San Antonio, TX; 2029 Jul 22-24 Washington, DC. Telecommunication Services: info@aaea.org.

17162 ■ Agri Marketing Conference
Readex
5801 Pelican Bay Blvd., Ste. 600
Naples, FL 34108-2734
Free: 800-762-8182
Fax: (802)875-2904
Co. E-mail: sales@readex.com
URL: http://www.readex.com
URL(s): www.nama.org/bright_horizons.html
Description: Agricultural business and marketing equipment, supplies, and services. Event includes sessions, keynote speakers, and networking opportunities. Audience: Professionals in marketing and agribusiness. Principal Exhibits: Agricultural business and marketing equipment, supplies, and services. Event includes sessions, keynote speakers, and networking opportunities. Dates and Locations: 2025 Apr 09-11 Kansas City, MO; 2026 Apr 15-17 Saint Louis, MO. Telecommunication Services: jennyp@nama.org.

17163 ■ Agricultural Publications Summit
URL(s): www.ageditors.com/index.php/events/ag-media-summit
Frequency: Annual. Description: Editors and editorial staff members of farm publications, affiliate members are agricultural public relations and advertising personnel, and state and national agricultural officials. Audience: Editors, writers, photographers, and communication professionals. Principal Exhibits: Editors and editorial staff members of farm publications, affiliate members are agricultural public relations and advertising personnel, and state and national agricultural officials.

17164 ■ Commodity Classic
National Corn Growers Association (NCGA)
632 Cepi Dr.
Chesterfield, MO 63005
Ph: (636)733-9004
Fax: (636)733-9005
Co. E-mail: corninfo@ncga.com
URL: http://www.ncga.com
Contact: Tom Haag, President
URL(s): commodityclassic.com
Facebook: www.facebook.com/CommodityClassic
X (Twitter): twitter.com/comclassic
Frequency: Annual. Description: Corn, soybeans, wheat, sorghum, agricultural equipment, seeds, chemicals, and services. Audience: Farmers, growers, and government officials. Principal Exhibits: Corn, soybeans, wheat, sorghum, agricultural equipment, seeds, chemicals, and services. Dates and Locations: 2025 Mar 02-04 Denver, CO; 2026 Feb 26-28 San Antonio, TX; 2027 Mar 04-06 New Orleans, LA; 2028 Mar 02-04 Atlanta, GA; 2029 Mar 01-03 San Antonio, TX; 2030 Feb 02-28 Orlando, FL. Telecommunication Services: tradeshow@commodityclassic.com.

17165 ■ CPMA Convention and Tradeshow
Canadian Produce Marketing Association (CPMA)
162 Cleopatra Dr.
Ottawa, ON, Canada K2G 5X2
Ph: (613)226-4187
Fax: (613)226-2984
Co. E-mail: question@cpma.ca
URL: http://www.cpma.ca
Contact: Colin Chapdelaine, Chairperson
URL(s): convention.cpma.ca
Frequency: Annual. Description: Includes exhibits, and reception. Audience: Industry professionals. Principal Exhibits: Includes exhibits, and reception. Dates and Locations: 2025 Apr 08-10 Palais des congrès de Montréal, Montreal, QC; 2026 Apr 28-30 Toronto, ON.

17166 ■ EcoFarm Conference
Concentric
19548 Chardonnay Ct
Saratoga, CA 95070
URL: http://www.concentric.ai
Contact: Karthik Krishnan, Chief Executive Officer
URL(s): www.eco-farm.org/ecofarm-2025
Facebook: www.facebook.com/EcoFarm
X (Twitter): twitter.com/Eco_Farm

Description: Organic farmers; wholesalers and retailers of natural foods; university level researchers and educators; consumers concerned with food safety, environmental, and land use issues. **Audience:** Farmers, ranchers, and food system advocates. **Principal Exhibits:** Organic farmers; wholesalers and retailers of natural foods; university level researchers and educators; consumers concerned with food safety, environmental, and land use issues. Dates and Locations: 2025 Jan 22-25; 2025 Jan 22-25; 2026. Asilomar State Beach & Conference Grounds, Pacific Grove, CA. **Telecommunication Services:** sponsors@eco-farm.org.

17167 ■ Farm Science Review
Ohio State University (OSU)
281 W In. Ave.
Columbus, OH 43210
Ph: (614)292-6446
Co. E-mail: askabuckeye@osu.edu
URL: http://www.osu.edu
Contact: Molly Ranz Calhoun, President
E-mail: calhoun.1@osu.edu
URL(s): fsr.osu.edu/about

Frequency: Annual; held on September. **Audience:** Producers, agribusiness professionals, and general public. Dates and Locations: 2025 Sep 16-18 135 State Route 38 NE, London; 2026 Sep 22-24 135 State Route 38 NE, London; 2027 Sep 21-23 135 State Route 38 NE, London; 2028 Sep 19-21 135 State Route 38 NE, London; 2029 Sep 18-20 135 State Route 38 NE, London; 2030 Sep 17-19 135 State Route 38 NE, London. **Telecommunication Services:** fsrinfo@osu.edu.

17168 ■ Florida Citrrus Show
URL(s): www.citrusshow.com

Description: Exhibits, products, and professional talks about citrus growing. **Principal Exhibits:** Exhibits, products, and professional talks about citrus growing.

17169 ■ IDEAg Dakotafest
URL(s): www.ideaggroup.com/dakotafest

Frequency: Annual. **Description:** Networking and educational opportunities for farmers and livestock owners residing in the northern plains of the US. **Audience:** Farmers and livestock owners in the northern plains region. **Principal Exhibits:** Networking and educational opportunities for farmers and livestock owners residing in the northern plains of the US.

17170 ■ Illinois Fertilizer and Chemical Association Annual Convention
Illinois Fertilizer & Chemical Association (IFCA)
14171 Carole Dr.
Bloomington, IL 61705
Ph: (309)827-2774
Co. E-mail: leslief@ifca.com
URL: http://www.ifca.com
Contact: Kevin Johnson, President
E-mail: kj@ifca.com
URL(s): www.ifca.com/convention

Frequency: Annual. **Description:** Providing education for suppliers in agribusiness. **Audience:** Agri Industry professionals. **Principal Exhibits:** Providing education for suppliers in agribusiness. Dates and Locations: 2025 Jan 21-23 Peoria Civic Center, Peoria, IL. **Telecommunication Services:** leslief@ifca.com.

17171 ■ Kansas Agri Business Expo
D.E. Bondurant Grain Company Inc.
223 S Iowa Ave.
Ness City, KS 67560
Ph: (785)798-3322
URL: http://bondurantgrain.com
Contact: Robert F. Gantz, Contact
URL(s): www.ksabe.org/about-us/

Frequency: Annual; each November. **Description:** Fertilizer and chemical manufacturers equipment, distributors, grain and feed related equipment, related service firms, and agriculture software companies. Event includes keynote speakers, scholarship auction, reception, and entertainment. **Audience:** Industry professionals from the agribusiness industry. **Principal Exhibits:** Fertilizer and chemical manufacturers equipment, distributors, grain and feed related equipment, related service firms, and agriculture software companies. Event includes keynote speakers, scholarship auction, reception, and entertainment. **Telecommunication Services:** sidney@kansasag.org.

17172 ■ Michigan Agri-Business Association Outlook Conference
Michigan Agri Business Association (MABA)
2500 Kerry St., Ste. 102
Lansing, MI 48912
Ph: (517)336-0223
Fax: (866)829-3786
Co. E-mail: maba@miagbiz.org
URL: http://miagbiz.org
Contact: Chuck Lippstreu, President
URL(s): maba.swoogo.com/2024outlookconference/5536253

Frequency: Annual. **Description:** Agribusiness equipment, supplies, and services. **Audience:** Agricultural professionals. **Principal Exhibits:** Agribusiness equipment, supplies, and services. **Telecommunication Services:** maba@miagbiz.org.

17173 ■ Mid-South Farm & Gin Show
Southern Cotton Ginners Association (SCGA)
874 Cotton Gin Pl.
Memphis, TN 38106
Ph: (901)947-3104
Fax: (901)947-3103
URL: http://www.southerncottonginners.org
Contact: William E. Lindamood, Jr., Director
URL(s): www.farmandginshow.com
Facebook: www.facebook.com/farmandginshow

Frequency: Annual. **Description:** Agricultural equipment, supplies and services. **Audience:** Agricultural scientists and professionals, and public. **Principal Exhibits:** Agricultural equipment, supplies and services. Dates and Locations: 2025 Feb 28-Mar 01 Renasant Convention Center, Memphis, TN.

17174 ■ Midwest Organic and Sustainable Education Service Organic Farming Conference
URL(s): mosesorganic.org/conference

Price: $120. **Frequency:** Annual. **Description:** Provides workshops, keynote speakers, roundtables, and an exhibit hall for organic and sustainable farming. **Principal Exhibits:** Provides workshops, keynote speakers, roundtables, and an exhibit hall for organic and sustainable farming.

17175 ■ NACAA Annual Meeting and Professional Improvement Conference (NACAA AM/PIC)
National Association of County Agricultural Agents (NACAA)
6584 W Duroc Rd.
Maroa, IL 61756
Ph: (217)794-3700
Fax: (217)794-5901
Co. E-mail: exec-dir@nacaa.com
URL: http://www.nacaa.com
Contact: Adm. (Ret.) J. Craig Craig Williams, President
E-mail: jcw17@psu.edu

Frequency: Annual. **Description:** Exhibits for county agricultural agents and extension workers. **Audience:** Educators and professionals. **Principal Exhibits:** Exhibits for county agricultural agents and extension workers. Dates and Locations: 2025 Jun 29-Jul 02 Billings, MT; 2026 Jul 08-12 Denver, CO; 2027 Sep 12-17 St. Paul, MN; 2028. **Telecommunication Services:** nacaaemail@aol.com.

17176 ■ National Alliance of Independent Crop Consultants - AG PRO EXPO
URL(s): naicc.org/meetings

Frequency: Annual. **Description:** Meeting, networking, and vendor show for agricultural professionals. **Audience:** Agricultural professionals. **Principal Exhibits:** Meeting, networking, and vendor show for agricultural professionals.

17177 ■ New York Farm Show (NYFS)
New York Farm Show Inc. (NYFS)
581 State Fair Blvd
Syracuse, NY 13209
Ph: (315)457-8205
URL: http://www.newyorkfarmshow.com/en/home.html
Contact: Scott Grigor, Manager
E-mail: sgrigor@ne-equip.com
URL(s): www.newyorkfarmshow.com/en/home.html

Frequency: Annual. **Description:** Agricultural equipment, supplies, and services. **Audience:** Farmers, business owners, and decision-makers. **Principal Exhibits:** Agricultural equipment, supplies, and services. Dates and Locations: 2025 Feb 20-22 New York State Fairgrounds, Syracuse, NY; 2026 Feb 26-28 New York State Fairgrounds, Syracuse, NY; 2027 Feb 25-27 New York State Fairgrounds, Syracuse, NY. **Telecommunication Services:** sgrigor@ne-equip.com.

17178 ■ North American Farm and Power Show
Minnesota-South Dakota Equipment Dealers Association (MSDEDA)
121 E Park Sq.
Owatonna, MN 55060
Ph: (507)455-5318
Fax: (507)455-5909
Co. E-mail: office@msdeda.com
URL: http://www.msdeda.com
Contact: Rich Strom, President (Acting)
E-mail: office@msdeda.com
URL(s): www.tradexpos.com/north-american-farm-and-power-show

Frequency: Annual. **Audience:** Farmers and industry professionals.

17179 ■ Organic Produce Summit
URL(s): www.organicproducesummit.com
Facebook: www.facebook.com/organicproducesummit
X (Twitter): twitter.com/OrgProduceSum

Frequency: Annual. **Description:** Networking and education opportunities for those involved in the fresh organic produce industry. **Audience:** Farmers, handlers, distributors, processors, retailers, and co-ops. **Principal Exhibits:** Networking and education opportunities for those involved in the fresh organic produce industry. **Telecommunication Services:** info@organicproducesummit.com.

17180 ■ Southern Exposure - Southeast Produce Council
URL(s): seproducecouncil.com/events-networking/southern-exposure

Description: Annual conference for produce farmers, suppliers, buyers, and consumers in the Southeast. **Principal Exhibits:** Annual conference for produce farmers, suppliers, buyers, and consumers in the Southeast.

17181 ■ Southwest Horticulture Annual Day of Education
Arizona Nursery Association (ANA)
1710 W Ranch Rd, Ste. 202
Tempe, AZ 85284
Ph: (480)966-1610
Fax: (480)966-0923
Co. E-mail: info@azna.org
URL: http://azna.org
Contact: Cheryl Koury, Executive Director
URL(s): azna.org/event-5693215

Frequency: Annual. **Description:** Horticultural equipment, supplies, and services; plant material. **Audience:** Retail and wholesale nursery professionals, including landscape architects, contractors, maintenance workers, arborists, and florists. **Principal Exhibits:** Horticultural equipment, supplies, and services; plant material. **Telecommunication Services:** info@azna.org.

17182 ■ Spokane Ag Expo
Oxarc
11 N 4th Ave.
Walla Walla, WA 99362
Ph: (509)529-3060

Free: 800-765-9055
Co. E-mail: oxarc@oxarc.com
URL: http://www.oxarc.com
Contact: Steve Barer, Manager
URL(s): www.agshow.org
Frequency: Annual. **Description:** Farm machinery, technology, and services. **Audience:** Industry Professionals. **Principal Exhibits:** Farm machinery, technology, and services. **Telecommunication Services:** agshow@greaterspokane.com

17183 ■ Unified Wine & Grape Symposium
Saxco International L.L.C.
 100 S Spring St.
 Louisville, KY 40216
Free: 877-641-4003
Co. E-mail: sales@saxco.com
URL: http://www.saxco.com
Contact: John Berry, Chief Executive Officer
URL(s): www.unifiedsymposium.org
Facebook: www.facebook.com/unifiedsymposium
X (Twitter): twitter.com/theunified
Frequency: Annual. **Description:** The program features sessions and a two-day trade show. **Audience:** Industry suppliers, marketing executives, vineyard managers and owners, winemakers, and winery managers. **Principal Exhibits:** The program features sessions and a two-day trade show. Dates and Locations: 2025 Jan 28-30; 2026 Jan 27-29; 2027 Jan 26-28; 2028 Jan 25-27; 2029 Jan 23-25; 2030 Jan 22-24. SAFE Credit Union Convention Center, Sacramento, CA. **Telecommunication Services:** jenny@cawg.org.

CONSULTANTS

17184 ■ Agpro Inc.
859 Airport Rd.
 Paris, TX 75462
Free: 800-527-1030
Fax: (903)784-7895
Co. E-mail: info@agprousa.com
URL: http://agprousa.com
Facebook: www.facebook.com/AgproInc
YouTube: www.youtube.com/channel/UCqq-DbK tHAMiOiBmleX6ceQ
Description: Firm offers agricultural engineering design consultation for animal raising facilities including dairies, beef feedlots, swine operations and embryo transplant facilities. **Scope:** Firm offers agricultural engineering design consultation for animal raising facilities including dairies, beef feedlots, swine operations and embryo transplant facilities. **Founded:** 1962. **Publications:** "PD Exclusive: Progressivedairy.com," Jul, 2008; "ANM: Industry Insights," Mar, 2007.

17185 ■ Agri-Business Consultants Inc.
911 Edison Ave.
 Lansing, MI 48910-3339
Ph: (517)243-5292
Fax: (517)482-7506
URL: http://www.agri-businessconsultants.com
Contact: Mark A. Otto, President
Description: Firm provides integrated crop management and related services. **Scope:** Firm provides integrated crop management and related services. **Founded:** 1983.

17186 ■ Agribusiness Development Partners
1570 E Tomahawk Dr.
 Salt Lake City, UT 84103
Contact: David C. Hamblin, Contact
Description: Consultancy firm that specializes in the development, management, and financing of modern food and fiber systems throughout the world and expertise includes knowledge in the organization and growth of private enterprise agribusiness, management of farms, projects and technology transfer, analysis of business strategy and the competitive environment, appropriate resources and operating procedures. **Scope:** Consultancy firm that specializes in the development, management, and financing of modern food and fiber systems throughout the world and expertise includes knowledge in the organization and growth of private enterprise agribusiness, management of farms, projects and technology transfer, analysis of business strategy and the competitive environment, appropriate resources and operating procedures.

17187 ■ Agricultural Consulting Services, Inc. (ACS)
730 Warren Rd.
 Ithaca, NY 14850
Ph: (607)252-2002
Co. E-mail: info@acscrops.com
URL: http://acscrops.com
Contact: Brian Boerman, Contact
E-mail: brian.boerman@acscrops.com
Facebook: www.facebook.com/acscrops
Description: Provider of farm business management services including economic analysis, computer hardware, software installation, training, enterprise budgets and analysis. **Scope:** Provider of farm business management services including economic analysis, computer hardware, software installation, training, enterprise budgets and analysis. **Publications:** "Forage - Timing of First Cutting," May, 2009.

17188 ■ Agricultural Engineering Associates (AEA)
1000 Promontory Dr.
 Uniontown, KS 66779
Free: 800-499-5893
URL: http://www.agengineering.com
Contact: John A. George, President
Facebook: www.facebook.com/Agricul turalEngineeringAssociates
Description: Firm provides independent, objective and technical engineering services at the production agriculture grassroots as well as sophisticated research, demonstration, test facilities, in both domestic and international projects. **Scope:** Firm provides independent, objective and technical engineering services at the production agriculture grassroots as well as sophisticated research, demonstration, test facilities, in both domestic and international projects. **Founded:** 1974.

17189 ■ Agricultural Investment Associates, Inc.
1000 Skokie Blvd., Ste. 358
 Wilmette, IL 60091
Contact: John C. Cottingham, President
Description: Investment consultant to domestic and foreign institutions, corporations and individuals covering investments in farms, ranches and agri businesses. Services include feasibility studies, appraisals, management, analysis and negotiations. **Scope:** Investment consultant to domestic and foreign institutions, corporations and individuals covering investments in farms, ranches and agri businesses. Services include feasibility studies, appraisals, management, analysis and negotiations.

17190 ■ Agvise Laboratories Inc.
804 Hwy. 15 W
 Northwood, ND 58267
Ph: (701)587-6010
Fax: (701)587-6013
URL: http://www.agvise.com
Contact: Amber Storey, Director
Linkedin: com.linkedin.com/company/agvise-labora tories-inc
X (Twitter): x.com/AGVISE
Description: Provider of agricultural testing services and technical support services. **Scope:** Provides agriculture testing services such as soil testing and plant analysis including, GLP and Non-GLP analysis to crop consultants, fertilizer retailers, producers, engineering firms and pesticide registration companies. **Founded:** 1976. **Publications:** "Manure and Nematode Test Results on the Internet"; "Sampling and Submitting Livestock Waste for Analysis"; "Precision Ag Helpers"; "New Minnesota Corn Nitrogen Fertilizer Guidelines"; "Zone Nutrient Management in Sugar beet Production"; "Reducing Soybean Cyst Nematode with Crop Rotation"; "Fall Strip Tillage: More and More Each Year"; "High Soil Nitrates Following Drought!"; "High Soil pH-Can we Fix this Problem?". **Training:** Precision Ag-Update 2009, 2009; Rock Rolling-Is It For You?, 2009; Seed Placed Fertilizer Limits, 2009; Precision Soil Testing, 2008; Soil Fertility Seminars; Tornado Tale; Compaction Update; Delta Yield; Phosphorus for Soybean; Soil Amendments; Strip Tillage Update; Sulfur for Corn.

17191 ■ The Canada Co.
4141 S 87th E Ave.
 Tulsa, OK 74145
Ph: (918)622-5400
Fax: (918)660-0913
Co. E-mail: info@canadaco.com
URL: http://www.canadaco.com
Contact: W. Deke Canada, Contact
Description: Distributor of process control instrumentation for oil and gas industry and manufacturers. **Scope:** Distributor of process control instrumentation for oil and gas industry and manufacturers. **Founded:** 1947.

17192 ■ ConsulAgr Inc.
2269 DeWindt Rd.
 Newark, NY 14513-8803
Contact: James R. Peck, Chief Executive Officer
Description: Firm provides agricultural consulting for soils, crop production, animal husbandry and farm business management. **Scope:** Firm provides agricultural consulting for soils, crop production, animal husbandry and farm business management. **Training:** Farm scout training.

17193 ■ Custom Forestry Inc.
16798 Claridon-Troy Rd.
 Burton, OH 44021
Contact: Ralph Elton Hershberger, II, Contact
Description: Offers forestry consulting services that include forest management, timber sales, valuations, timber trespass valuations and litigation, advice on federal assistance programs, Christmas tree plantation management, multiple use land management, shelter-belts, silviculture and insect management. **Scope:** Offers forestry consulting services that include forest management, timber sales, valuations, timber trespass valuations and litigation, advice on federal assistance programs, Christmas tree plantation management, multiple use land management, shelter-belts, silviculture and insect management.

17194 ■ DPRA Inc.
121 S 4th St., Ste. 202
 Manhattan, KS 66502
Ph: (865)777-3772
Co. E-mail: info@dpra.com
URL: http://www.dpra.com
Contact: Mark Heinrich, Chief Executive Officer
Linkedin: www.linkedin.com/company/dpra
Description: Firm specializes in environmental problems and situations, their experience includes agriculture, agribusiness, water pollution control, hazardous and municipal waste management, their activities emphasize litigation support, data management and information services, as well as international programs and serves private industries as well as government agencies. **Scope:** Firm specializes in environmental problems and situations, their experience includes agriculture, agribusiness, water pollution control, hazardous and municipal waste management, their activities emphasize litigation support, data management and information services, as well as international programs and serves private industries as well as government agencies. **Founded:** 1961. **Special Services:** TALIRA.

17195 ■ Eastern Laboratory Service Associates
517 N George St.
 York, PA 17404
Description: Provider of technical counsel on chemical and microbiological testing, evaluation and quality control services primarily for environmental, agribusiness, feed industry and food manufacturing. Offers consultation, advisory services, research and development on technical problems, new product formulation and product or process improvement. **Scope:** Provider of technical counsel on chemical and microbiological testing, evaluation and quality control services primarily for environmental, agribusiness, feed industry and food manufacturing. Offers consul-

17196 ■ Agribusiness

tation, advisory services, research and development on technical problems, new product formulation and product or process improvement.

17196 ■ **Indiana Design Consortium Inc. (IDC)**
1281 Win Hentschel Blvd.
West Lafayette, IN 47906
Ph: (765)423-5469
Co. E-mail: idc@idc-marketing.com
URL: http://idc-marketing.com
Contact: Patrick Nycz, President
E-mail: patrick@idc-marketing.com
Linkedin: www.linkedin.com/company/indiana-design-consortium
Description: Provider of online marketing programs, websites, social media management, print, display, video and streaming media in the form of integrated marketing plans. **Scope:** Provider of online marketing programs, websites, social media management, print, display, video and streaming media in the form of integrated marketing plans. **Founded:** 1972.

17197 ■ **J.H. Hare & Associates Ltd.**
1-270 Roslyn Rd.
Winnipeg, MB, Canada R3L 0H3
Ph: (204)955-8495
URL: http://immunade.com
Description: A distributor of animal nutrition, feed formulation. **Founded:** 1970. **Special Services:** X-CEL; X-Change; X-Change Plus.

17198 ■ **Micro-Macro International Inc. (MMI)**
183 Paradise Blvd., Ste. 108
Athens, GA 30607
Ph: (706)548-4557
Fax: (706)548-4891
Co. E-mail: info@mmilabs.com
URL: http://www.mmilabs.com
Contact: Josh Bryson, Manager
E-mail: josh@mmilabs.com
Facebook: www.facebook.com/mmilabs
X (Twitter): x.com/mmi_labs
Description: Provider of analytical services for analysis of water, waste water, soil, plant tissue and other biological substances for their element content for agricultural producers, research institutes and individuals, fertilizer manufacturers and government agencies. **Scope:** Provider of analytical services for analysis of water, waste water, soil, plant tissue and other biological substances for their element content for agricultural producers, research institutes and individuals, fertilizer manufacturers and government agencies. **Founded:** 1988. **Publications:** "Plant Analysis Handbook," 1991; "Diagnosis and Recommendation Integrated Systems (Dris)"; "Kjeldahl Method for Nitrogen Determination"; "Plant Nutrition Manual". **Training:** Techniques of soil testing and plant analysis; Laboratory instruction on methods of analysis.

17199 ■ **Southern Plantations Group Inc. (SPG)**
PO Box 70967
Albany, GA 31708-0967
Ph: (229)894-7415
Co. E-mail: info@splantations.com
URL: http://www.splantations.com
Contact: Jeff Peterson, President
E-mail: jpeterson@splantations.com
Description: Firm provides consulting services for real estate, appraisals, farm management, and timberland. **Scope:** Firm provides consulting services for real estate, appraisals, farm management, and timberland. **Founded:** 1978.

PUBLICATIONS

17200 ■ *Business Farmer*
211 Hwy. 38
Rochelle, IL 61068
Ph: (815)562-4171
Co. E-mail: info@newsmediacorp.com
URL: http://www.newsmediacorporation.com
URL(s): thebusinessfarmer.com

Ed: Andrew D. Brosig. **Released:** Weekly (Fri.) **Price:** $32.99, Out of area for 3 month; $77.99, for 1 year (outside delivery area); $57.99, for 1 year (inside delivery area); $49.99, for online only 1 year; $19.99, for 3 month (in area); $5.99, for online 1 month. **Description:** Trade newspaper covering farm news. **Availability:** Print; Online.

17201 ■ *The Delmarva Farmer: The Agribusiness Newspaper of the Mid-Atlantic Region*
PO Box 2026
Easton, MD 21601
Ph: (410)822-3965
Free: 800-634-5021
Fax: (410)822-5068
URL: http://americanfarmpublications.com
Contact: Jonathan Cribbs, Editor
E-mail: jonathan@americanfarm.com
URL(s): americanfarm.com/category/delmarvafarmer
Facebook: www.facebook.com/delmarvafarmer
Released: Weekly **Price:** $44.52, for one year; $72.08, for 2 years; $85.86, for 3 years; $42, Out of state for 1 year; $68, Out of state for 2 year; $81, Out of state for 3 year. **Description:** Newspaper (tabloid) featuring news of interest to agricultural concerns in Maryland, Delaware, Virginia, New Jersey, and Pennsylvania. **Availability:** Print; Online.

17202 ■ *Meat and Poultry: The Business Journal of the Meat and Poultry Industry*
4801 Main St., Ste. 650
Kansas City, MO 64112-2513
Ph: (816)756-1000
Free: 800-338-6201
URL: http://www.sosland.com
Contact: Joshua Sosland, President
URL(s): www.meatpoultry.com
Facebook: www.facebook.com/MeatPoultry
Linkedin: www.linkedin.com/showcase/meat-poultry
X (Twitter): x.com/meatpoultry
Instagram: www.instagram.com/meatpoultry
Released: Monthly **Description:** Provides industry info to industry professionals. **Availability:** Print; Online.

COMPUTERIZED DATABASES

17203 ■ *AGRICOLA Database*
U.S. Department of Agriculture - National Agricultural Library
10301 Baltimore Ave.
Beltsville, MD 20705
Ph: (301)504-5755
URL: http://www.nal.usda.gov
Contact: Paul Wester, Director
E-mail: paul.wester@usda.gov
URL(s): search.nal.usda.gov/discovery/search?vid=0 1NAL_INST:MAIN
Availability: Online. **Type:** Bibliographic.

LIBRARIES

17204 ■ **Alberta Agriculture and Forestry-Crop Diversification Centre South Library**
301 Horticultural Station Rd. E
Brooks, AB, Canada T1R 1E6
Ph: (403)362-1346
Fax: (403)362-1326
URL: http://www1.agric.gov.ab.ca/$department/dep tdocs.nsf/all/opp4386
Contact: Shelley Barkley, Contact
Scope: Plants; pathology; entomology and special crops. **Holdings:** Figures not available.

17205 ■ **Booz Allen Hamilton - Research Services and Information Center**
8283 Greensboro Dr.
Hamilton Bldg.
McLean, VA 22102
Ph: (703)902-5000
URL: http://www.boozallen.com
Contact: Horacio D. Rozanski, President
Facebook: www.facebook.com/boozallen

GENERAL SMALL BUSINESS TOPICS

Linkedin: www.linkedin.com/company/booz-allen-hamilton
X (Twitter): x.com/BoozAllen
Instagram: www.instagram.com/boozallen
Description: Business advisors. **Scope:** Management, agribusiness, finance, marketing, manufacturing, retailing, information management, consumer products, healthcare, telecommunications, food retailing, consulting, electronic commerce. **Services:** Interlibrary loan; center not open to the public. **Founded:** 1914. **Holdings:** Serials.; 5000 books; client reports; company Annual reports.

17206 ■ **Canada Agriculture and Agri-Food - Dairy and Swine Research and Development Centre Lennoxville - Canadian Agriculture Library**
1341 Baseline Rd., Twr 6., Fl 1
Ottawa, ON, Canada K1A 0C5
Co. E-mail: aafc.library-bibliotheque.aac@agr.gc.ca
URL: http://science-libraries.canada.ca/eng/agriculture
URL(s): agriculture.canada.ca/en/department/library-agriculture
Description: Research and development center. **Scope:** Agricultural; food sciences; research and innovation. **Services:** Interlibrary loan; copying; library provides limited on-site consultation to the public. **Founded:** 1910. **Holdings:** 5,000 books; 6,000 e-books.

17207 ■ **Canadian Grain Commission Library (CGC)**
303 Main St., Ste. 600
Winnipeg, MB, Canada R3C 3G8
URL: http://www.grainscanada.gc.ca/en/transparency/info/info-eng.html
Description: Canadian grain commission library. **Scope:** Grain producers. **Founded:** 1972. **Holdings:** Historical reports.

17208 ■ **Cargill, Incorporated - Library**
Cargill, Incorporated
15407 McGinty Rd. W
Wayzata, MN 55391
Ph: (952)742-6000
Free: 800-227-4455
Co. E-mail: cis_customerservice@cargill.com
URL: http://www.cargill.com
Contact: Brian Sikes, President
Facebook: www.facebook.com/Cargill
Linkedin: www.linkedin.com/company/cargill
X (Twitter): twitter.com/Cargill
Instagram: www.instagram.com/cargill/
YouTube: www.youtube.com/user/Cargill
Description: Provider of food as well as agricultural, financial, and industrial products and services. **Founded:** 1865. **Educational Activities:** AOCS Annual Meeting & Expo (Annual); Kansas Agri Business Expo (Annual); USEA Annual Meeting and Convention (Annual).

17209 ■ **Delaware Valley University - Joseph Krauskopf Memorial Library**
700 E Butler Ave.
Doylestown, PA 18901
URL: http://delval.edu/joseph-krauskopf-memorial-library
Contact: Peter Kupersmith, Director
E-mail: peter.kupersmith@delval.edu
Scope: Agribusiness, agronomy, large animal science, biology, communication, computer and business information systems, criminal justice administration, dairy science, English literature, equine science, food industry, horticulture, ornamental horticulture, chemistry, business administration, small animal science, turf management, wildlife conservation, zoo biology. **Services:** Interlibrary loan; copying; open to the public for reference use only. **Founded:** 1924. **Subscriptions:** 13,000 journals.

17210 ■ **DuPont Pioneer - Library Resources Group**
Pioneer Hi-Bred International, Inc.
Resource Connection
PO Box 1000
Johnston, IA 50131-0184

Ph: (515)535-3200
URL: http://www.pioneer.com/home/site/about/news-media/media-library
Linkedin: www.linkedin.com/company/dupont-pioneer
X (Twitter): twitter.com/pioneerseeds
YouTube: www.youtube.com/user/PioneerHB
Scope: Plant genetics, agriculture, agribusiness, law, taxation, business. **Services:** Interlibrary loan; library not open to the public. **Holdings:** 1,480 books.

17211 ■ Hartness Library System
124 Admin Dr.
Randolph Center, VT 05061
Free: 800-431-0025
Co. E-mail: hartness@vsc.edu
URL: http://www.vtc.edu/office/hartness-library
Contact: Susan Currier, Librarian
E-mail: scurrier@vtc.edu
Facebook: www.facebook.com/HartnessLibrary
Description: The Hartness Library, located in Randolph Center, VT, serves both the Community College of Vermont and Vermont Tech. **Scope:** General reference. **Services:** Library not open to the public. **Founded:** 1964. **Subscriptions:** 58,000 journals and other serials 42,000 books; 200,000 e-books; 24,000 online films and documentaries; 6,000 audio materials and DVDs.

17212 ■ Illinois Farm Bureau Information Research Center (IFB)
PO Box 2901
Bloomington, IL 61702-2901
URL: http://www.ilfb.org/legal/member-information-drive-rules
Scope: Agriculture; environment. **Services:** Interlibrary loan; copying; subscriptions; Internet training; abstracting; library open to the public for reference use only. **Holdings:** Figures not available.

17213 ■ International Fertilizer Development Center (IFDC) - Library
46 David Lilienthal Dr.
Muscle Shoals, AL 35661
Ph: (256)381-6600
URL: http://ifdc.org
Contact: Henk van Duijn, President
Facebook: www.facebook.com/IFDCGlobal
Linkedin: www.linkedin.com/company/ifdc
X (Twitter): x.com/ifdcglobal
Instagram: www.instagram.com/ifdcglobal
YouTube: www.youtube.com/ifdcmuscleshoals
Description: Innovative and economically viable solutions to environmental problems. **Scope:** Publishes papers and scientific reports on environmental subjects. **Founded:** 1974. **Holdings:** Figures not available. **Publications:** *IFDC: An International Center for Soil Fertility and Agricultural Development Annual report* (Annual); *IFDC Corporate Report* (Annual); *Perspectives* (Semiannual); *North American Fertilizer Capacity Data* (Annual). **Training:** Improving Agricultural Productivity and Net Returns Among Smallholder Farmers Through Efficient Use of Nutrients and Water in Partnership with the Agricultural Research Organization (ARO) Volcani Center, 2012; Decision Support Tools for Agricultural Production, Fertilizer Recommendations and Climatic Variability, 2012; Designing and Implementing Agro-Input Marketing Strategies in Developed and Developing Countries, 2012; Increasing Agricultural Input and Output Trade Through Innovative Market Information Systems in Africa, 2012; Technology Advances in Agricultural Production and Fertilization, 2012; Granular Fertilizers Production, 2012; Developing and Managing Profitable Agro-Input Business Through Sustainable Value Chains. **Educational Activities:** IFDC Annual Board of Directors meetings (Annual). **Geographic Preference:** Multinational.

17214 ■ International Food Policy Research Institute (IFPRI) - Library
1201 Eye St., NW
Washington, DC 20005-3915
Ph: (202)862-5600
Fax: (202)862-5606
Co. E-mail: ifpri@cgiar.org
URL: http://www.ifpri.org
Contact: Johan Swinnen, Director General
E-mail: j.swinnen@cgiar.org
Facebook: www.facebook.com/ifpri.org
Linkedin: www.linkedin.com/company/ifpri
X (Twitter): x.com/ifpri
Instagram: www.instagram.com/ifpri
YouTube: www.youtube.com/user/IFPRI
Description: Research center established to analyze alternative national and international strategies and policies for meeting the food needs in developing countries with a view toward reducing hunger and malnutrition. **Scope:** Alternative international, national, and local policies for improved food security and nutrition, with an emphasis on low-income countries and poor people. **Services:** Interlibrary loan; copying; library open to the public by appointment. **Founded:** 1975. **Holdings:** Books; journals; articles. **Publications:** *IFPRI at a Glance*; *IFPRI Forum*; *2020 Focus Briefs*; *Food Policy Reports, Reviews and Statements*; *IFPRI/Johns Hopkins University Press Books* (Annual); *Occasional Series*; *Policy/Research/Issue Briefs*; *IFPRI Research Reports* (Quarterly); *Working Paper Series*. **Educational Activities:** CAER-IFPRI Annual Conference (Annual); Policy Seminars (Weekly). **Geographic Preference:** Multinational.

17215 ■ Mississippi State University - Agricultural & Forestry Experiment Station - Delta Research and Extension Center (DREC)
82 Stoneville Rd.
Stoneville, MS 38776
Ph: (662)686-9311
Fax: (662)686-7336
URL: http://extension.msstate.edu/delta-research-and-extension-center
Contact: Dr. Jimmy L. Avery, Director
E-mail: jimmy.avery@msstate.edu
Scope: Agriculture. **Services:** Interlibrary loan; copying; library open to the public. **Founded:** 1966. **Holdings:** 14,500 books; 6,000 bound periodical volumes; 348 reels of microfilm; 50,000 pamphlets.

17216 ■ Purdue University - Roland G. Parrish Library of Management and Economics
Krannert Building - 2nd Fl. 403 Mitch Daniels Blvd.
West Lafayette, IN 47907-2058
Ph: (765)494-2920
Co. E-mail: parrlib@purdue.edu
URL: http://www.lib.purdue.edu/libraries/mgmt
Scope: Business management; economics; accounting and tax; entrepreneurship; finance; marketing; food and agribusiness management; hospitality & tourism management and more. **Services:** Interlibrary loan;Copying;Library open to the public. **Founded:** 1998. **Holdings:** Figures not available.

17217 ■ Tennessee Valley Authority (TVA) - Environmental Research Center - Research Library
1101 Market St.
Chattanooga, TN 37402
URL: http://www.tva.com/careers/benefits-quality-of-life
Contact: Jeffrey J. Lyash, President
Scope: Environmental sciences; biomass; chemistry; chemical engineering; competitive business marketing; waste management. **Services:** Interlibrary loan. **Founded:** 1935. **Holdings:** 600 volumes; government documents.

17218 ■ U.S.D.A. Economic Research Service Reference Center (USDA ERS)
1400 Independence Ave. SW
Washington, DC 20250-0002
URL: http://www.ers.usda.gov
Contact: Jennifer Smits, Director, Communications
E-mail: jennifer.smits@ers.usda.gov
X (Twitter): x.com/USDA_ERS
Scope: Agriculture. **Founded:** 1982. **Holdings:** Figures not available.

17219 ■ University of California, Berkeley - Giannini Foundation of Agricultural Economics Reference/Reading Room
248 Giannini Hall No 3310
Berkeley, CA 94720-3310
Co. E-mail: gflibrary@berkeley.edu
URL: http://are.berkeley.edu/library
Scope: Agricultural and environmental economics. **Services:** Only available to members of the Agricultural & Resource Economics department with ID. **Founded:** 1930. **Holdings:** 40,000 records; digital publications.

17220 ■ University of California, Davis - Agricultural and Resource Economics Library
One Shields Ave.
Davis, CA 95616-8512
Ph: (530)752-9286
Co. E-mail: arel@primal.ucdavis.edu
URL: http://are.ucdavis.edu/department/library
Contact: Tiffany Denman, Library Associate
E-mail: tndenman@ucdavis.edu
Facebook: www.facebook.com/UCDavisARE
X (Twitter): x.com/UCDavisARE
Description: Department administers the popular managerial economics undergraduate major. **Scope:** Agricultural economics; agricultural business. **Services:** Interlibrary loan; document delivery; copying; library open to the public for reference use only. **Founded:** 1951. **Holdings:** 7,000 books; 150,000 pamphlets and government documents; 2,600 serial publications; e-journals.

17221 ■ University of Illinois at Urbana-Champaign - Isaac Funk Family Library of Agricultural, Consumer and Environmental Sciences
ACES Library, Information & Alumni Center
1101 S Goodwin Ave.
Urbana, IL 61801
Co. E-mail: illiarch@illinois.edu
URL: http://www.library.illinois.edu/funkaces
Scope: Agricultural economics; animal science; agricultural engineering; crops; biotechnology; family and consumer economics; foods and nutrition; human development and family ecology; textiles; horticulture; food science and technology; environmental science; agricultural history; forestry; soils. **Services:** Interlibrary loan; copying. **Founded:** 1915. **Holdings:** Books.

17222 ■ University of Minnesota, St. Paul - Magrath Library
1984 Buford Ave.
Saint Paul, MN 55108
Ph: (612)624-2233
URL: http://www.lib.umn.edu/spaces/magrath
Description: Library serves students and faculties of University of Minnesota. **Scope:** Agriculture; food science; life sciences; design and social work. **Services:** Interlibrary loan; copying; document delivery; library open to the public for reference use only. **Founded:** 1890. **Holdings:** 7.7 million print volumes; 1.97 million eBooks; 120,000 serials; 130,000 linear feet of archival materials.

17223 ■ University of Wisconsin-Madison-Land Tenure Center Collection (LTC)
122 Science Hall
550 N Pk. St.
Madison, WI 53706
URL: http://minds.wisconsin.edu/handle/1793/21862
Contact: J. David Stanfield, Author
Scope: Land tenure and land use; agrarian reform; land markets; legislative drafting; land registration and titling; institutional dimensions of rural development; environmental management and natural resource management. **Founded:** 1962. **Holdings:** Figures not available.

17224 ■ University of Wisconsin, Madison - Steenbock Memorial Library
550 Babcock Dr.
Madison, WI 53706
Ph: (608)262-9635
Co. E-mail: libraries@wisc.edu
URL: http://www.library.wisc.edu/steenbock
Contact: Jean Ruenger-Hanson, Head
E-mail: jean.ruengerhanson@wisc.edu
Facebook: www.facebook.com/asksteenbock
X (Twitter): x.com/AskSteenbock

17225 ■ Agribusiness

Instagram: www.instagram.com/asksteenbock
Pinterest: www.pinterest.com/asksteenbock
Scope: Agriculture; biology; botany; chemistry; computer science; environmental studies; engineering; life sciences; natural resources; primatology; veterinary medicine; and zoology. **Services:** Interlibrary loan; copying; document delivery; library open to the public appointment required. **Founded:** 1888. **Holdings:** Figures not available.

17225 ■ Western Maryland Regional Library (WMRL)
100 S Potomac St.
Hagerstown, MD 21740
Ph: (301)739-3250
Co. E-mail: whilbr@washcolibrary.org
URL: http://www.wmrl.info
Contact: Jenny Bakos, Executive Director
E-mail: wcfl@washcolibrary.org
Facebook: www.facebook.com/whilbr
Scope: History. **Services:** Interlibrary loan; copying; library open to the public with restrictions. **Founded:** 1967. **Holdings:** Figures not available.

RESEARCH CENTERS

17226 ■ Agricultural Utilization Research Institute (AURI)
510 County Rd. 71, Ste. 120
Crookston, MN 56716
Ph: (218)281-7600
Co. E-mail: news@auri.org
URL: http://auri.org
Contact: Shannon Schlecht, Executive Director
E-mail: sschlecht@auri.org
Facebook: www.facebook.com/AgriculturalUtilizationResearchInstitute
Linkedin: www.linkedin.com/company/agricultural-utilization-research-institute
X (Twitter): x.com/AURIcomm
YouTube: www.youtube.com/channel/UCCcVs1DBEmiYrjscq8WHWNw
Description: Developer of produce new uses for agricultural products through science and technology, partnering with businesses and entrepreneurs. Offers technical assistance to farmers, agribusinesses, and producer groups: new product development, feasibility testing, technology development (daily). **Scope:** Agriculture products from state, including research projects to convert corn to ethanol and biodegradable plastics, and to pelletize soybeans for export. Seeks to identify and create new markets and expand existing markets for new or existing commodities, ingredients, and products; develop energy efficient, natural resource-saving production practice; and develop alternative crops and products for emerging markets. **Founded:** 1989. **Publications:** *Ag Innovation News* (Quarterly).

17227 ■ AgriInstitute
72 W Main St.
Danville, IN 46122
Ph: (317)745-0947
Fax: (317)745-0956
URL: http://www.agriinstitute.org
Contact: Beth Archer, Executive Director
E-mail: beth@agriinstitute.org
Facebook: www.facebook.com/AgriInstitute-152956248090039
Linkedin: www.linkedin.com/company/agriinstitute
X (Twitter): x.com/agriinstitute
Description: Independent, nonprofit organization. **Scope:** Offers Agricultural Leadership Development Program and Resource for Developing Community Leadership Program. **Founded:** 1982. **Publications:** *AgriInstitute* (10/year). **Educational Activities:** IALI Indiana Agricultural Forum; IALI Annual meetings and focus forums.

17228 ■ American Seed Research Foundation (ASRF)
1701 Duke St., Ste. 275
Alexandria, VA 22314
Ph: (703)837-8140
Co. E-mail: ajorss@betterseed.org
URL: http://www.seedresearch.org
Description: Breeders, producers, and distributors of seeds. Seeks to advance seed technology by supporting research on seeds. **Scope:** Seeds, including technology advancement in the seed industry. **Founded:** 1959. **Geographic Preference:** National.

17229 ■ Arizona State University Department of Economics - W. P. Carey School of Business (CEESP) - Center for Environmental Economics and Sustainability Policy
PO Box 879801
Tempe, AZ 85287-9801
Ph: (480)965-0352
Fax: (480)965-0748
Co. E-mail: ceesp@asu.edu
URL: http://ceesp.wpcarey.asu.edu
Contact: W. Michael Hanemann, Director
Description: Integral unit of Arizona State University. **Scope:** Environmental economics policy studies, including topics such as water management, food safety, Medicare, ecosystems, and natural disasters. **Founded:** 1885. **Publications:** *Center for Environmental Economics and Sustainability Policy Working Papers*.

17230 ■ California Institute for Rural Studies (CIRS) - Library
5960 S Land Pk., No. 840
Sacramento, CA 95822
Co. E-mail: info@cirsinc.org
URL: http://cirsinc.org
Contact: Megan Beaman Jacinto, President
Facebook: www.facebook.com/CIRSINC
X (Twitter): x.com/CARuralStudies
Instagram: www.instagram.com/cali_institute_rural_studies
Description: Research center provides sustainable agriculture, farmworker safety and immigrant welfare. Offers consulting on a contract basis. **Scope:** Rural community ethnography and demographics; rural justice; rural poverty; hired farm labor; labor contractors; pesticide use and sustainable agriculture; land ownership and farm structure; water law, transfers, and distribution; COVID-19 and farm workers; various agricultural health and safety topics. **Founded:** 1977. **Holdings:** Figures not available. **Publications:** *Rural California Report* (Weekly). **Educational Activities:** Rural Justice Summit (Annual), A space for community members, students, organizers, artists, advocates, and researchers to explore common challenges on rural livelihood and seek solutions.

17231 ■ California State University, Fresno - Institute for Food and Agriculture (IFA)
6014 N Cedar Ave.
Fresno, CA 93710
Ph: (559)278-4405
Fax: (559)278-6032
URL: http://www.fresnostate.edu/jcast/ifa
Contact: Dr. Susan Pheasant, Director
E-mail: spheasant@csufresno.edu
Facebook: www.facebook.com/InstituteforFoodandAg
Linkedin: www.linkedin.com/in/institute-for-food-and-agriculture-fresno-state-1394a6183
X (Twitter): twitter.com/FresnoState_IFA
Description: Integral unit of College of Agricultural Sciences and Technology of California State University, Fresno and operating under the umbrella of California Agricultural Technology Institute (CATI). **Scope:** Agribusiness in California, especially the San Joaquin Valley. Studies concentrate on farm business planning and other related labor issues. **Founded:** 1985. **Publications:** *CAB Conference proceedings*.

17232 ■ Institute for Agriculture and Trade Policy (IATP) - Library
1700 Second St. NE Ste. 200
Minneapolis, MN 55413
Ph: (612)870-0453
Co. E-mail: info@iatp.org
URL: http://www.iatp.org
Contact: Patti Landres, Librarian
E-mail: plandres@iatp.org
Facebook: www.facebook.com/IATPiatp
Linkedin: www.linkedin.com/company/institute-for-agriculture-and-trade-policy
X (Twitter): x.com/iatp

YouTube: www.youtube.com/c/IatpOrg
Description: Individuals concerned with the current plight of the small farm in the U.S. Seeks to educate voters about federal farm legislation and efforts to expand sustainable and local food systems. Conducts research and disseminates information on government farm policies. Provides funds for lobbying farm issues. Promotes adoption of U.S. farm policies that will benefit the international farming community as well as domestic farmers. Maintains speakers' bureau. **Scope:** Food, trade, agriculture, land, rural affairs, environmental issues, and sustainable development. **Founded:** 1971. **Holdings:** Figures not available. **Publications:** *Food Safety and Health* (Monthly); *Global Food Watch* (Biweekly); *IATP News* (Monthly); *Intellectual Property and Biodiversity News* (Weekly). **Geographic Preference:** National.

17233 ■ New Mexico State University - College of Agricultural, Consumer and Environmental Sciences - Agricultural Experiment Station (AES)
Gerald Thomas Hall, Rm. 220
Las Cruces, NM 88003
Ph: (575)646-3125
Fax: (575)646-2816
Co. E-mail: agresearch@nmsu.edu
URL: http://aes.nmsu.edu
Contact: Brooke Boren, Director
E-mail: brookeb@nmsu.edu
Description: Integral unit of College of Agricultural, Consumer and Environmental Sciences, New Mexico State University. Offers science-based information service to citizens of New Mexico, via the Cooperative Extension Service. **Scope:** Conducts studies in agricultural economics, agricultural business, economic development, agricultural and extension education, agronomy, animal science, clothing/textile/fashion marketing. **Founded:** 1889. **Publications:** *Agricultural Experiment Station Research Bulletins*.

17234 ■ North Carolina Department of Agriculture and Consumer Services - Research Stations Div.
2 W Edenton St.
Raleigh, NC 27601
Ph: (919)707-3236
Fax: (919)733-1754
Co. E-mail: teresa.herman@ncagr.gov
URL: http://www.ncagr.gov/research
Contact: Brandon Herring, Manager, Marketing
Description: Cooperative research effort of the North Carolina Department of Agriculture and Consumer Services and North Carolina State University. **Scope:** Crops, forestry, aquaculture, livestock, and poultry. **Founded:** 1877.

17235 ■ Prairie Agricultural Machinery Institute (PAMI) - Library
Hwy. 5 W
2215 - 8th Ave.
Humboldt, SK, Canada S0K 2A0
Ph: (306)682-5033
Free: 800-567-7264
Fax: (306)682-5080
Co. E-mail: pami@pami.ca
URL: http://pami.ca
Contact: Leah Olson, President
Facebook: www.facebook.com/PAMIMachinery
X (Twitter): x.com/PAMI_Machinery
YouTube: www.youtube.com/channel/UCSZABIP1FGkD29IdlSdv59Q
Description: Independent, nonprofit research organization, supported by the provincial governments of Saskatchewan and Manitoba, Canada. **Scope:** Component machinery testing. **Services:** Interlibrary loan; copying; SDI; library open to the public. **Founded:** 1975. **Holdings:** 2,283 books; 80 bound periodical volumes; 20,000 technical papers. **Publications:** *PAMI Research reports*.

17236 ■ Purdue University - Center for Food and Agricultural Business (CFAB)
403 W State St.
West Lafayette, IN 47907-2056
Ph: (765)494-4247

Co. E-mail: agbusinessinfo@purdue.edu
URL: http://agribusiness.purdue.edu
Contact: Dave Downey, Professor
Facebook: www.facebook.com/purdueagribusiness
Linkedin: www.linkedin.com/company/purdue-university-center-for-food-and-agricultural-business
X (Twitter): x.com/PurdueAgBiz
YouTube: www.youtube.com/user/foodandagbusiness/feed

Description: Integral unit of Purdue University. **Scope:** Agribusiness, including the use of operations research techniques for solving agribusiness problems; analysis of the specialized marketing, management and finance problems of agricultural businesses; buying behaviors of agricultural producers; risk management strategies of food and agribusiness firms; and evaluation of agribusiness marketing strategies. **Founded:** 1986. **Publications:** *Center for Food and Agricultural Business Articles* (Quarterly). **Educational Activities:** Food and agribusiness management education programs, Focus on specific functional management areas such as marketing, finance, personnel management, sales management, and relationship marketing.

17237 ■ University of Florida - Institute of Food and Agricultural Sciences (IFAS)
1008 McCarty Hall
  Gainesville, FL 32611-0180
Ph: (352)392-1971
Fax: (352)392-6932
URL: http://www.ifas.ufl.edu
Facebook: www.facebook.com/UFIFASNews
Linkedin: www.linkedin.com/school/ufifas
X (Twitter): x.com/UF_IFAS
Instagram: www.instagram.com/ufifas_solutions
YouTube: www.youtube.com/c/IFASVideo

Description: Integral unit of University of Florida. **Scope:** Food and agriculture sciences, natural resources, and renewable resources. **Founded:** 1964. **Publications:** *Faculty Directory* (Semiannual); *Impact Magazine* (Irregular); *Inside IFAS Newsletter* (Monthly); *Newsline Newsletter* (Semiannual).

Bartering

ASSOCIATIONS AND OTHER ORGANIZATIONS

17238 ■ International Reciprocal Trade Association (IRTA) - Library
c/o Ron Whitney, President & CEO
524 Middle St.
Portsmouth, VA 23704
Ph: (757)393-2292
Fax: (757)257-4014
Co. E-mail: ron@irta.com
URL: http://www.irta.com
Contact: Ron Whitney, President
E-mail: ron@irta.com
Facebook: www.facebook.com/IrtaBarter
Linkedin: www.linkedin.com/company/international-reciprocal-trade-association
X (Twitter): x.com/irtabarter
YouTube: www.youtube.com/irtabarter
Description: Works to foster and promote the interests of the commercial barter industry through the establishment of ethical standards and self-regulation; to represent members before government agencies in matters affecting the industry; to introduce firms engaged in bartering activities; to resolve disputes between members; influence public laws and regulations affecting the industry; disseminate information and conduct public relations programs. **Scope:** Modern trade and barter. **Holdings:** Fact sheets. **Educational Activities:** Barter Congress. **Awards:** IRTA Hall of Fame (Irregular). **Geographic Preference:** Multinational.

17239 ■ The Waterfront Center (TWC)
The Waterfront Ctr.
Washington, DC 20009
Ph: (202)337-0356
Fax: (202)337-0356
Co. E-mail: mail@waterfrontcenter.org
URL: http://www.waterfrontcenter.org
Contact: Dick Rigby, Director
Facebook: www.facebook.com/The-Waterfront-Center-335672479708
X (Twitter): twitter.com/TheWaterfrontC1
Instagram: www.instagram.com/waterfrontcenter1
YouTube: www.youtube.com/channel/UC4KklvxSTbX6ns-MHRJfB0A
Description: Conducts forums that address problems and opportunities in a particular community; provides onsite analyses and consulting; offers slide presentations; conducts research. **Founded:** 1981. **Publications:** Urban Waterfront Resource List (Periodic); Waterfront World Spotlight (Monthly). **Awards:** WFC Excellence on the Waterfront Award (Annual). **Geographic Preference:** National.

REFERENCE WORKS

17240 ■ "6 Tips on Using Bartering Services in Your Small Business" in Tech Funnel (Jan. 6, 2020)
URL(s): www.techfunnel.com/information-technology/6-tips-on-using-bartering-services-in-your-small-business/
Ed: Marianne Chrisos. **Released:** January 06, 2020. **Description:** While bartering is not the traditional way that businesses secure products and services, it remains a legitimate way, particularly in small business circles. This article offers six tips on successful bartering. **Availability:** Online.

17241 ■ "Area Small Businesses Enjoy Benefits of Bartering Group" in News-Herald (August 22, 2010)
Pub: The News Herald
Contact: Tricia Ambrose, Executive Editor
E-mail: tambrose@news-herald.com
Ed: Brandon C. Baker. **Description:** ITEX is a publicly traded firm that spurs cashless, business-to-business transactions within its own marketplace. Details of the bartering of goods and services within the company are outlined. **Availability:** Online.

17242 ■ "Barter: A Strategic Tool for the New Economy" in Zen Business (Aug. 11, 2021)
URL(s): www.zenbusiness.com/blog/barter/
Ed: Richard Cravatts. **Released:** August 11, 2021. **Description:** Explores the advantages of bartering for things like office furniture, phone systems, and advertising as you begin your startup. Includes specific tips on things that you can use to barter. **Availability:** Online.

17243 ■ "Barter Exchanges and How They Work" in The Balance Small Business (Aug 2, 2019)
URL(s): www.thebalancesmb.com/what-is-barter-exchange-398141
Ed: Jean Murray. **Released:** August 02, 2019. **Description:** Explores modern bartering, barter exchanges, and how they work for small businesses. **Availability:** Online.

17244 ■ "Barter in Small Business" in Business Practical Knowledge
URL(s): businesspracticalknowledge.wordpress.com/financial-resources/barter-in-small-business/
Description: Provides current statistics on business bartering, discusses advantages and disadvantages of bartering, and explains tax implications of bartering. **Availability:** Online.

17245 ■ The Barter System - Is It for You?
URL(s): www.1stsource.com/advice/business/sbr_template.cfm?docnumber=pl08_0080.htm
Description: Explores how utilizing a barter system can preserve working capital to apply to your small business venture. Includes information on benefits, timing, and process of bartering as well as details on barter exchanges, establishing trading partnerships, and protecting your interests. **Availability:** Online.

17246 ■ "Bartering is Local Club's Stock in Trade" in Pueblo Chieftain (September 6, 2010)
Description: As the economy waivers, a barter club in Pueblo, Colorado thrives. An examination of the club and the way it operates is included. **Availability:** Print; Online.

17247 ■ "Bartering Trades on Talents" in Reading Eagle (June 20, 2010)
Description: Bartering is not just a way of trading goods and services, it can be an essential tool for small business to survive in a bad economy.

17248 ■ "Beat the Buck: Bartering Tips from In-The-Know Authors" in (June 23, 2010)
Pub: The Telegraph
Contact: Don Cherry, District Manager
E-mail: dcherry@thetelegraph.com
Description: The Art of Barter is a new book to help small businesses learn this art form in order to expand customer base and reserve cash flow. **Availability:** Online.

17249 ■ "Benefits of Bartering" in Mail Tribune (November 22, 2010)
Ed: Damian Mann. **Description:** Various people discuss the use of bartering for their small companies in order to improve business. **Availability:** Online.

17250 ■ "Bartering Takes Businesses Back to Basics" in Buffalo News (July 9, 2010)
Pub: The Buffalo News, Inc.
Contact: Tom Wiley, President
E-mail: twiley@buffnews.com
Ed: Dino Grandoni. **Description:** Bartering clubs can help small businesses reach new customers and to expand their business. **Availability:** Print; Online.

17251 ■ "Everything You Need to Know About...Bartering" in Courier Workshop Newsletter (Oct. 28, 2021)
URL(s): mailchimp.com/courier/article/bartering/
Released: October 28, 2021. **Description:** Discusses the usefulness of bartering in the modern business world, particularly for startups. **Availability:** Online.

17252 ■ "Examples of Barter Transactions?" in Investopedia (May 5, 2021)
URL(s): www.investopedia.com/ask/answers/101314/what-are-some-examples-barter-transactions.asp
Ed: Brian Beers. **Released:** May 05, 2021. **Description:** Provides examples of bartering for goods and services along with a common contemporary barter exchange. **Availability:** Online.

17253 ■ "A Family's Fortune" in Canadian Business (Vol. 80, Winter 2007, No. 24, pp. 103)
Price: $23. **Description:** James Richardson started as a tailor before moving into the grain business because his clients paid him in sacks of wheat and barley. The James Richardson and Sons Ltd. entered the radio business in 1927 but later sold it off in 1951. **Availability:** Print; Online.

17254 ■ "How B2B Bartering Can Boost Your Small Business" in KC Source Link Blog (Aug. 24, 2016)
URL(s): www.kcsourcelink.com/blog/post/blog/2016/08/24/how-b2b-bartering-can-boost-your-small-business

GENERAL SMALL BUSINESS TOPICS

Ed: Tommy Leslie. **Released:** August 24, 2016. **Description:** Explores how modern businesses can take advantage of bartering and trading to help them run their enterprises more effectively. **Availability:** Online.

17255 ■ *"Poor Economy Inspires Rich Alternatives In a Modern, and Tax-Free, Twist on Bartering" in Houston Chronicle (June 7, 2010)*

Pub: Houston Chronicle

Ed: Michael Rubinkam. **Description:** Time banking helps individuals and firms receive goods or services by depositing time dollars into a bank reserved for receipt of goods and services.

17256 ■ *Recordkeeping for Business Barter Transactions*

URL(s): www.taxproplus-la.com/10772/Recordkeeping-for-Business-Barter-Transactions/

Description: Discusses appropriate tax reporting and recordkeeping practices when bartering is a part of your small business. **Availability:** Online.

17257 ■ *Small Business Bartering Increased During the Pandemic. Is It Right for You?*

URL(s): www.fool.com/the-blueprint/small-business-bartering-increased-during-pandemic-is-it-right-for-you/

Ed: Maurie Backman. **Released:** February 01, 2021. **Description:** Discusses how bartering - swapping services and skills - increased during the pandemic. Explores the upside of continued bartering. **Availability:** Online.

Benefits

ASSOCIATIONS AND OTHER ORGANIZATIONS

17258 ■ American Mutual Life Association (AMLA)
19424 S Waterloo Rd.
Cleveland, OH 44119
Ph: (216)531-1900
Co. E-mail: amla@americanmutual.org
URL: http://americanmutual.org
Facebook: www.facebook.com/AmericanMutualLifeAssociation
Linkedin: www.linkedin.com/company/american-mutual-life-association
X (Twitter): x.com/AMLA_SDZ
YouTube: www.youtube.com/channel/UC2FaKy7QV7TIoGfYcwCUyNg
Description: Fraternal benefit society which operates through the sale of life insurance and annuity products. **Founded:** 1910. **Publications:** *Our Voice* (Biweekly). **Geographic Preference:** National.

17259 ■ American Society of Pension Professionals and Actuaries (ASPPA)
4401 N Fairfax Dr., Ste. 600
Arlington, VA 22203
Ph: (703)516-9300
Fax: (703)516-9308
Co. E-mail: customercare@asppa-net.org
URL: http://www.asppa.org
Contact: Natalie R. E. Wyatt, President
X (Twitter): x.com/asppa
Description: Educates pension actuaries, consultants, administrators, and other benefits professionals. Seeks to enhance the private pension system as part of the development of a cohesive and coherent national retirement income policy. **Founded:** 1966. **Publications:** *ASPPA Yearbook* (Annual). **Awards:** ASPPA Educator's Award (Annual); Harry T. Eidson Founder's Award (Annual); Martin Rosenberg Academic Achievement Award (Annual); Presidential Scholarship (Annual). **Geographic Preference:** National.

17260 ■ Council on Employee Benefits (CEB)
64 Walker St., Ste. 2
Lenox, MA 01240
Ph: (413)644-6034
Fax: (202)861-6027
Co. E-mail: info@ceb.org
URL: http://www.ceb.org
Contact: Lisa Woods, President
X (Twitter): x.com/FollowCEB
Description: Employers seeking informal exchange of experiences and information on the design, financing, and administration of employee benefit programs, both domestic and international. Provides a medium for the exchange of ideas, information, and statistics; sponsors or conducts research projects on benefits; makes known its views on legislative matters affecting employee benefits. **Founded:** 1946. **Geographic Preference:** National.

17261 ■ Employee Benefit Research Institute (EBRI) - Library
901 D St., SW Ste. 802
Washington, DC 20024
Ph: (202)659-0670
Fax: (202)775-6360
Co. E-mail: info@ebri.org
URL: http://www.ebri.org
Contact: Lori Lucas, Chief Executive Officer
Description: Corporations, consulting firms, banks, insurance companies, unions, and others with an interest in the future of employee benefit programs. Seeks to contribute to the development of effective and responsible public policy in the field of employee benefits through research, publications, educational programs, seminars, and direct communication. Sponsors studies on retirement income, health, disability, and other benefit programs; disseminates study results. **Scope:** A public policy research organization serving as an employee benefits information source on health, welfare and retirement issues. Services include: basic benefit program descriptions, legislation analysis, media coverage and interpretation and long-range planning. Specializes in research on pensions, social security, health care, Medicare, long-term care and flexible benefits. Serves government, academic consumers, consultants, banks, insurance companies, investment managers, law and accounting firms, corporations and individuals. **Founded:** 1978. **Holdings:** Figures not available. **Publications:** Dedicated to providing unbiased, fact-based research on employee benefits. **Training:** Policy Forums, Congressional Briefings. **Awards:** EBRI Lillywhite Award (Annual). **Geographic Preference:** National.

17262 ■ Employers Council on Flexible Compensation (ECFC)
1802 Vernon St. NW, No. 1035
Washington, DC 20009
Ph: (202)659-4300
Fax: (202)618-6060
URL: http://ecfc.org
Contact: Christa Day, Executive Director
E-mail: cday@ecfc.org
Linkedin: www.linkedin.com/company/go-ecfc
X (Twitter): x.com/GoECFC
YouTube: www.youtube.com/channel/UCKeDNB97ZKHywpHFNz7a1Bw
Description: Employers and service providers who have implemented or are interested in flexible compensation plans. Promotes flexible compensation plans including cafeteria plans, health reimbursement arrangements, cash-or-deferred plans and other defined contribution plans. Monitors legislation and represents member's interests before Congress. Lobbies to preserve and simplify the flexible compensation provisions of the Internal Revenue Code. **Founded:** 1979. **Educational Activities:** ECFC Annual Symposium (Annual). **Geographic Preference:** National.

17263 ■ ERISA Industry Committee (ERIC)
701 8th St. NW, Ste. 610
Washington, DC 20001
Ph: (202)789-1400
Fax: (202)789-1120
Co. E-mail: memberservices@eric.org
URL: http://www.eric.org
Contact: James Gelfand, President
E-mail: jgelfand@eric.org
Linkedin: www.linkedin.com/company/the-erisa-industry-committee
X (Twitter): x.com/erisaindcmte
Description: Large corporations that sponsor employee pension, health, and other benefit programs. Represents the concerns of major employers regarding policy, legislative, judicial, and regulatory matters involving the administration of private retirement, health, and other employee benefit plans. Issues briefings to members' congressional representatives. (ERISA is an acronym for the Employee Retirement Income Security Act of 1974). **Founded:** 1976. **Geographic Preference:** National.

17264 ■ International Foundation of Employee Benefit Plans (IFEBP) - Library
18700 W Bluemound Rd.
Brookfield, WI 53045
Ph: (262)786-6700
Free: 888-334-3327
Co. E-mail: infocenter@ifebp.org
URL: http://www.ifebp.org/home
Contact: Donald D. Crosatto, President
Facebook: www.facebook.com/IFEBP
Linkedin: www.linkedin.com/company/international-foundation-of-employee-benefit-plans
X (Twitter): x.com/ifebp
Instagram: www.instagram.com/international.foundation
YouTube: www.youtube.com/user/IFEBP
Description: Provides sources for employee benefits and compensation information and education, including seminars and conferences, books and an information center, CEBS and Certificate Series. Conducts more than 100 educational programs. Provides Internet job and resume posting service. **Scope:** Employee benefits and compensation. **Founded:** 1954. **Holdings:** Figures not available. **Publications:** *Benefits Magazine* (Monthly); *InfoQuick*; *Employee Benefits Journal* (Quarterly); *Benefits & Compensation Digest*; *Legal-Legislative Reporter* (Monthly); *Employee Benefits Infosource*. **Educational Activities:** Annual Employee Benefits Conference (Annual). **Geographic Preference:** National.

17265 ■ International Society of Certified Employee Benefit Specialists (ISCEBS)
18700 W Bluemound Rd.
Brookfield, WI 53045-2936
Ph: (262)786-8771
Fax: (262)786-8670
Co. E-mail: iscebs@iscebs.org
URL: http://www.iscebs.org/home
Contact: John Eshleman, President
X (Twitter): x.com/ISCEBS
Description: Graduates of the Certified Employee Benefit Specialist Program, co-sponsored by the International Foundation of Employee Benefit Plans

and the Wharton School of the University of Pennsylvania. Promotes continuing education and professional development of employee benefit practitioners through courses and seminars. **Founded:** 1981. **Publications:** *International Society of Certified Employee Benefit Specialists--Membership Directory*; *Benefits Quarterly* (Quarterly). **Geographic Preference:** National.

17266 ■ **National Coordinating Committee for Multiemployer Plans (NCCMP)**
815 16th St. NW
Washington, DC 20006
Ph: (202)737-5315
Fax: (202)737-1308
Co. E-mail: nccmp@nccmp.org
URL: http://nccmp.org
Contact: Michael D. Scott, Executive Director

Description: International trade unions and jointly administered employee benefit trust funds. Promotes the interests of organizations that provide retirement security, health, and other welfare benefits to individuals working in industries that, due to their structure, would not otherwise provide sufficient pension and welfare benefits. Lobbies before Congress and federal regulatory agencies and participates in judicial proceedings affecting multiemployer plans and participants. **Founded:** 1974. **Awards:** John L. Lewis Award (Annual). **Geographic Preference:** National.

17267 ■ **National Institute of Pension Administrators (NIPA)**
330 N Wabash Ave., Ste. 2000
Chicago, IL 60611-7621
Free: 800-999-6472
Fax: (312)673-6609
Co. E-mail: nipa@nipa.org
URL: http://www.nipa.org
Contact: Shayna Osborne, President

Description: Individuals with at least a year of experience in pension administration, full-time pension administration employees, and interested individuals. Sponsors educational program for the accreditation of pension administrators and a series of regional programs relative to pension/profit-sharing programs and administration. **Founded:** 1983. **Publications:** *PLAN Horizons* (Quarterly). **Educational Activities:** Business Management Conference (BMC) (Annual). **Geographic Preference:** National.

17268 ■ **Woman's Life Insurance Society**
1338 Military St.
Port Huron, MI 48061-5020
Ph: (810)985-5191
Free: 800-521-9292
Fax: (810)985-6970
Co. E-mail: info@womanslife.org
URL: http://www.womanslife.org
Facebook: www.facebook.com/WomansLife
Linkedin: www.linkedin.com/company/woman's-life-insurance-society
YouTube: www.youtube.com/channel/UCcXg8HWw0TGP7PBCJBiC4WA

Description: Fraternal benefit life insurance society focusing on the needs of women. Each review or local club engages in local charitable community projects. **Founded:** 1892. **Publications:** *Woman's Life Magazine* (Quarterly). **Awards:** Woman's Life Woman of Distinction Award (Annual). **Geographic Preference:** National.

17269 ■ **Workmen's Benefit Fund of the U.S.A. (WBF)**
399 Conklin St., Ste. 310
Farmingdale, NY 11735-2614
Ph: (516)938-6060
Fax: (516)706-9020
Co. E-mail: info@wbfusa.org
URL: http://www.wbfusa.org

Description: Serves as a fraternal benefit life insurance society. **Founded:** 1884. **Publications:** *WBF in Action*. **Awards:** WBF Foundation Community Service Scholarship Awards (Annual). **Geographic Preference:** National.

REFERENCE WORKS

17270 ■ *"9 Competitive Benefits for Small Businesses"* in *CareerBuilder*
URL(s): resources.careerbuilder.com/small-business/9-competitive-benefits-for-small-businesses
Ed: Ray Roache. **Description:** Benefits and perks are among the top things job seekers consider when deciding on a new job. This article provides a list of modern benefits that will make any team feel happier, healthier, and more engaged at your small business. **Availability:** Online.

17271 ■ *"16 Creative and Cheap Ways to Say 'Thank You"* in *HR Specialist (Vol. 8, September 2010, No. 9, pp. 8)*
Pub: Capitol Information Group Inc.
Contact: Allie Ash, Chief Executive Officer
Released: October 14, 2010. **Description:** Tips for starting an employee appreciation program for a small company are presented. **Availability:** Print; PDF; Online.

17272 ■ *"17 Employee Benefits That Are Actually Worth the Investment"* in *gusto Blog (Oct. 19, 2020)*
URL(s): gusto.com/blog/benefits/creative-employee-benefits
Ed: Susan Shain. **Released:** October 19, 2020. **Description:** Explains unique employee benefits that matter to your employees. Also looks at commonly overlooked benefits and their costs to help you build the best package for your team. **Availability:** Online.

17273 ■ *"401(k) Keys to Stable Value"* in *Barron's (Vol. 88, March 10, 2008, No. 10, pp. 40)*
Pub: Dow Jones & Company Inc.
Contact: Almar Latour, Chief Executive Officer
Ed: Tom Sullivan. **Description:** Stable-value funds offer investors stability in a period of volatility in financial markets, attracting $888 million in funds. The Securities and Exchange Commission approved the launch of actively managed exchange-traded funds. **Availability:** Online.

17274 ■ *"The Annual Entitlement Lecture Medicare Elephantiasis"* in *Barron's (March 31, 2008)*
Pub: Dow Jones & Company Inc.
Contact: Almar Latour, Chief Executive Officer
Ed: Thomas G. Donlan. **Description:** Expenditures on Medicare hospital insurance and the revenues available to pay for it have led to a gap of capital valued at $38.6 trillion. Slashing the benefits or raising taxes will not solve the gap which exists unless the government saves the money and invests it in private markets. **Availability:** Online.

17275 ■ *"Are Prepaid Legal Services Worthwhile?"* in *Contractor (Vol. 56, December 2009, No. 12, pp. 31)*
Ed: Susan Linden McGreevy. **Description:** Companies' provision of legal insurance as an employee benefit in the United States is discussed. Stoppage of premium payment halts employee coverage. It also does not cover all kinds of personal issues. **Availability:** Print; Online.

17276 ■ *"Bank On It: New Year, New Estate Plan"* in *Hawaii Business (Vol. 53, February 2008, No. 8, pp. 54)*
Pub: PacificBasin Communications
Contact: Chuck Tindle, Director
E-mail: chuckt@pacificbasin.net
Ed: Antony M. Orme. **Description:** Discusses the start of the new year which can be a time to revise wills and estate plans as failure to do so may create problems of unequal inheritance and increase in estate tax exemption, which could disinherit beneficiaries. Other circumstances that can prompt changes in wills and estate plans are presented. **Availability:** Print; Online.

17277 ■ *The Basics of Employee Benefits*
URL(s): www.entrepreneur.com/article/80158
Description: Discusses the importance of offering a good benefits package to keep your small business employees on board. This article discusses benefits basics, legal matters, errors to avoid, health insurance, cost containment, retirement plans, incentive plans, etc. **Availability:** Online.

17278 ■ *"The Best Option for All"* in *American Executive (Vol. 7, September 2009, No. 5, pp. 170)*
Ed: Ashley McGown. **Description:** Plaza Associates, a collections agency that conducts business primarily in the accounts receivable management sector, is the first in the industry to purchase 100 percent of the company from the founders through the formation of a leveraged Employee Stock Ownership Plan (ESOP).

17279 ■ *"Best Practices: Developing a Rewards Program"* in *Franchising World (Vol. 42, September 2010, No. 9, pp. 13)*
Pub: International Franchise Association
Contact: Matthew Haller, President
E-mail: mhaller@franchise.org
Ed: Leah Templeton. **Description:** Rewards for a job well done are examined in order to recognize franchisees for outstanding performance. Ways to customize a rewards program are outlined. **Availability:** Online.

17280 ■ *"Bills Raise Blues Debate: An Unfair Edge or Level Playing Field?"* in *Crain's Detroit Business (Vol. 24, January 21, 2008, No. 3)*
Pub: Crain Communications Inc.
Contact: Barry Asin, President
Ed: Sherri Begin. **Description:** Changes in Michigan state law would change the way health insurance can be sold to individuals. Michigan Blue Cross Blue Shield is working to keep its tax-exempt status while staying competitive against for-profit insurers and nonprofit HMOs. **Availability:** Print; Online.

17281 ■ *"Bonuses In Bad Times: In a Recession, How Should a Supermarket Chain Acknowledge Its Employees' Extra Effort?"* in *Harvard Business Review (Vol. 90, July 2012, No. 7-8, pp. 153)*.
Pub: Harvard Business Review Press
Contact: Moderna V. Pfizer, Contact
Ed: Daniela Beyersdorfer, Vincent Dessain, Zeynep Ton. **Price:** $6, hardcopy black and white; $7.46, hardcopy and PDF. **Description:** A fictional case study offering advice on how to acknowledge efforts made by workers during a recession. **Availability:** Print; Online.

17282 ■ *"Boomers' Spending Hurts Retirement"* in *Employee Benefit News (Vol. 25, November 1, 2011, No. 14, pp. 18)*
Pub: SourceMedia LLC
Contact: Gemma Postlethwaite, Chief Executive Officer
Ed: Ann Marsh. **Description:** Financial planners and employers need to educate clients and employees about retirement planning. Boomers are spending money that should be saved for their retirement.

17283 ■ *"Builders Aim to Cut Costs: Pushing Changes to Regain Share of Residential Market; Seek Council's Help"* in *Crain's New York Business*
Pub: Crain Communications, Inc.
Contact: Jessica Botos, Manager, Marketing
E-mail: jessica.botos@crainsnewyork.com
Ed: Erik Engquist. **Description:** Union contractors and workers are worried about a decline in their market share for housing so they intend to ask the City Council to impose new safety and benefit standards on all contractors to avoid being undercut by nonunion competitors. **Availability:** Print; Online.

17284 ■ *"Business Builders: Tradeshow Attendance Incentives Add Up"* in *Pet Product News (Vol. 64, December 2010, No. 12, pp. 14)*
Ed: Mark E. Battersby. **Description:** Pointers on how pet specialty retailers can claim business travel tax and income tax deductions for expenses paid or

17285 ■ Benefits

incurred in participation at tradeshows, conventions, and meetings are presented. Incentives in form of these deductions could allow pet specialty retailers to gain business benefits, aside from the education and enjoyment involved with the travel. **Availability:** Online.

17285 ■ "Catch Up To Your Dream Retirement" in Canadian Business (Vol. 85, July 16, 2012, No. 11-12, pp. 46)
Ed: David Aston. **Description:** Tips on how to save for retirement during the early saving years, family years, and pre-retirement years are provided. Priority for those in their early saving years is to pay off debts first then consider employer pension plans and registered retirement savings plans. Those in their family years can save bonuses while those in pre-retirement should start by taking stock.

17286 ■ "CEO Pay: Best Bang for Buck" in Philadelphia Business Journal (Vol. 30, September 30, 2011, No. 33, pp. 1)
Pub: Philadelphia Business Journal
Contact: Sierra Quinn, Director
E-mail: squinn@bizjournals.com
Ed: Jeff Blumenthal. **Description:** A study by Strategic Research Solutions on the compensation of chief executive officers in Philadelphia, Pennsylvania-based public companies reveals that only a few of them performed according to expectations. These include Brian Roberts of Comcast, John Conway of Crown Holdings, and Frank Hermance of Ametek Inc. **Availability:** Online.

17287 ■ "CEO Pay: The Details" in Crain's Detroit Business (Vol. 25, June 22, 2009, No. 25)
Pub: Crain Communications Inc.
Contact: Barry Asin, President
Description: Total compensation packages for CEOs at area companies our outlined. These packages include salary, bonuses, stock awards, and options. **Availability:** Online.

17288 ■ "Column: Good Decisions. Bad Outcomes" in Harvard Business Review (Vol. 88, December 2010, No. 12, pp. 40)
Pub: Harvard Business Publishing
Contact: Diane Belcher, Managing Director
Ed: Dan Ariely. **Price:** $6, PDF. **Description:** Suggestions are provided for developing and implementing improved reward systems that in turn produce better decision-making processes. These include documenting critical assumptions and changing mind sets. **Availability:** Online; PDF.

17289 ■ "Consulting Firm Goes Shopping" in Crain's Chicago Business (Vol. 31, April 28, 2008, No. 17, pp. 45)
Pub: Crain Communications Inc.
Contact: Barry Asin, President
Ed: Phuong Ly. **Description:** Clark & Wamberg LLC was created last year after the merger of Clark Inc. to a Dutch insurance conglomerate. Clark Inc. was a life insurance and benefits consultancy which had been on a downslide, returning just 5.6 percent a year to shareholders. In contrast Clark & Wamberg posted first-year revenue of $106.8 million, fueled by business from its executive compensation and health care clients. **Availability:** Online.

17290 ■ "Corporate Canada Eyes Retiree Health Benefit Cuts" in Globe & Mail (March 8, 2006, pp. B3)
Ed: Virginia Galt. **Description:** A survey on Canadian companies reveals that due to rising health care costs and increasing number of baby boomer retirements, these companies are to cut down on health benefits they are providing to these retired employees. **Availability:** Online.

17291 ■ Cost Still the Main Hurdle for Small Business Employers Looking to Expand Benefits
URL(s): www.benefitspro.com/2021/09/01/cost-still-the-main-hurdle-for-small-business-employers-looking-to-expand-benefits/?slreturn=20220110155753
Ed: Scott Wooldridge. **Released:** September 01, 2021. **Description:** Discusses the expense hurdle that small businesses face as they look to expand benefits for their employees. **Availability:** Online.

17292 ■ "Covered California Adds Dental Benefits" in Sacramento Business Journal (Vol. 31, August 29, 2014, No. 27, pp. 8)
Pub: American City Business Journals, Inc.
Contact: Mike Olivieri, Executive Vice President
Released: Weekly. **Price:** $4, introductory 4-week offer(Digital only). **Description:** Health benefit exchange, Covered California, is introducing stand-alone family dental benefits for consumers who enroll in health insurance coverage for 2015. The Governor has yet to sign a bill that would establish a separate vision care marketplace linked to Covered California's Website. **Availability:** Print; Online.

17293 ■ Create Your Own Employee Handbook: A Legal & Practical Guide for Employers
Pub: Nolo
Contact: Chris Braun, President
Ed: Amy DelPo, Lisa Guerin. **Released:** 10th edition. **Price:** $39.99, book and e-book; $34.99, ebook (downloadable); $39.99, book and e-book. **Description:** Information for business owners to develop an employee handbook that covers company benefits, policies, procedures, and more. **Availability:** E-book; PDF.

17294 ■ "Crouching Tigers Spring to Life" in Globe & Mail (April 14, 2007, pp. B1)
Ed: Grant Robertson. **Description:** The prospects of the acquisition of BCE Inc, by Canadian pension funds are discussed. The effect of the growth of these pension funds on the Canadian economy is described. **Availability:** Online.

17295 ■ "Cutting Health Care Costs: the 3-Legged Stool" in HR Specialist (Vol. 8, September 2010, No. 9, pp. 1)
Pub: Capitol Information Group Inc.
Contact: Allie Ash, Chief Executive Officer
Description: Employer spending on health insurance benefits to employees is investigated. **Availability:** Print; Online; PDF.

17296 ■ "The Darwinian Workplace: New Technology Is Helping Employers Systematically Shift More Work To Their Best Employees" in Harvard Business Review (Vol. 90, May 2012, No. 5, pp. 25)
Pub: Harvard Business Review Press
Contact: Moderna V. Pfizer, Contact
Ed: Serguei Netessine, Valery Yakubovich. **Price:** $6. **Description:** The winners-take-all model is a productivity-based system that shifts work and incentives to a firm's most productive employees. Challenges such as unpredictable pay swings, excessive competition, and unfair comparisons are addressed. **Availability:** Online; PDF.

17297 ■ "Decent Termination: A Moral Case for Severance Pay" in Business Ethics Quarterly (Vol. 24, April 2014, No. 2, pp. 203)
Pub: Business Ethics Quarterly
Contact: Dawn Elm, Executive Director
E-mail: drelm@stthomas.edu
Description: People are often involuntarily laid off from their jobs through no fault of their own. Employees who are dismissed in this manner cannot always legitimately hold employers accountable for these miserable situations because the decision to implement layoffs is often the best possible outcome given the context. Even in circumstances in which layoffs qualify as 'necessary evils', morality demands that employers respect the dignity of those whose employment is involuntarily terminated. This paper argues that to preserve the dignity of the employees involuntarily terminated, in most cases employers have a substantial reason to offer a special unemployment benefit or severance pay. **Availability:** Online.

17298 ■ "Discovery Communications: Don't Sell, But Don't Buy" in Workforce Management (Vol. 88, December 14, 2009, No. 13, pp. 17)
Pub: Crain Communications Inc.
Contact: Barry Asin, President
Ed: Jeremy Smerd. **Description:** Discovery Communications provides its employees a wealth of free health services via a comprehensive work-site medical clinic that is available to its employees and their dependents. Overview of the company's innovative approach to healthcare is presented. **Availability:** Online.

17299 ■ "Do You Have A Retirement Parachute?" in Barron's (Vol. 88, July 7, 2008, No. 27, pp. 32)
Pub: Dow Jones & Company Inc.
Contact: Almar Latour, Chief Executive Officer
Ed: Jane White. **Description:** The idea that American companies should emulate the Australian retirement system which implements a forced contribution rate for all employers regarding an adequate retirement plan for their employees is discussed. **Availability:** Online.

17300 ■ "Employee Benefits Requirements As a Small Business Owner" in WeWork (Jan. 13, 2021)
URL(s): www.wework.com/ideas/professional-development/business-solutions/employee-benefits-requirements-as-a-small-business-owner
Ed: Julie Dower, Lizz Morse. **Released:** January 13, 2021. **Description:** Details what small business owners need to know about benefits. Provides information on what benefits are legally required, what benefits you should offer, additional perks you can offer, and how to build an employee benefits plan. **Availability:** Online.

17301 ■ "Executive Compensation: Both Eyes on the Prize" in Canadian Business (Vol. 83, September 14, 2010, No. 15, pp. 42)
Pub: Rogers Media Inc.
Contact: Neil Spivak, Chief Executive Officer
Ed: Jacqueline Nelson. **Description:** North American executive compensation has fundamentally shifted partly due to pressure from the US government and recent adjustments in the way CEO pay packages are structured. The changes have also become common practice in Canada and helped in scrutinizing the executive pay. **Availability:** Online.

17302 ■ "Facilitating and Rewarding Creativity During New Product Development" in Journal of Marketing (Vol. 75, July 2011, No. 4, pp. 53)
Pub: American Marketing Association
Contact: Bennie F. Johnson, Chief Executive Officer
Ed: James E. Burroughs, Darren W. Dahl, C. Page Moreau, Amitava Chattopadhay, Gerald J. Gorn. **Description:** A study to determine the effects of rewards to creativity in the process of new product development is presented. The findings show that the effect of rewards can be made positive if combined with appropriate creativity training. **Availability:** PDF.

17303 ■ "Falling Local Executive Pay Could Suggest a Trend" in Tampa Bay Business Journal (Vol. 30, January 15, 2010, No. 4, pp. 1)
Pub: Tampa Bay Business Journal
Contact: Ian Anderson, President
E-mail: ianderson@bizjournals.com
Ed: Margie Manning. **Description:** Tampa Bay, Florida-based Raymond James Financial Inc. and MarineMax Inc.'s proxy statements have shown the decreasing compensation of the companies' highest paid executives. The falling trend in executive compensation was a result of intensified shareholder scrutiny and the economy. **Availability:** Print; Online.

GENERAL SMALL BUSINESS TOPICS

17304 ■ *"Firms Bet On Games To Hike Wellness"* in *Business Journal* (Vol. 30, June 1, 2012, No. 1, pp. 1)
Pub: American City Business Journals, Inc.
Contact: Mike Olivieri, Executive Vice President
Ed: Katharine Grayson. **Released:** Weekly. **Price:** $4, introductory 4-week offer(Digital only). **Description:** Twin Cities-based firms providing corporate wellness services are integrating games into these programs. These games include friendly competitions between work teams or high-tech smartphone applications. **Availability:** Print; Online.

17305 ■ *"Four Ways to Fix Banks: A Wall Street Veteran Suggests How To Cut Through the Industry's Complexity"* in (Vol. 90, June 2012, No. 6, pp. 106)
Pub: Harvard Business Review Press
Contact: Moderna V. Pfizer, Contact
Ed: Sallie Krawcheck. **Description:** Despite new regulations in the post-global economic crisis of 2008, banks are sill too complex for effective management of their boards. Recommendations for improving governance include incorporating bank debt in executive compensation to increase their sensitivity to risk, and paying dividends as a percentage of company earnings to maintain capital.

17306 ■ *"Glossary of Health Benefit Terms"* in *HRMagazine* (Vol. 53, August 2008, No. 8, pp. 78)
Pub: Society for Human Resource Management
Contact: Johnny C. Taylor, Jr., President
E-mail: shrmceo@shrm.org
Description: Glossary of health benefit terms is presented to help when choosing a health benefits package. **Availability:** Print; Online.

17307 ■ *Greening Your Small Business: How to Improve Your Bottom Line, Grow Your Brand, Satisfy Your Customers and Save the Planet*
Price: $19.95. **Description:** A definitive resource for anyone who wants their small business to be cutting-edge, competitive, profitable, and eco-conscious. Stories from small business owners address every aspect of going green, from basics such as recycling waste, energy efficiency, and reducing information technology footprint, to more in-depth concerns such as green marketing and communications, green business travel, and green employee benefits.

17308 ■ *"Holiday Shopping Meets Social Media"* in *Employee Benefit News* (Vol. 25, December 1, 2011, No. 15)
Pub: SourceMedia LLC
Contact: Gemma Postlethwaite, Chief Executive Officer
Ed: Rob J. Thurston. **Description:** Offering employees access to discount shopping using social media sites for Christmas bonuses, could be the gift that keeps on giving.

17309 ■ *"How to Avoid Leave-Related Lawsuits"* in *Employee Benefit News* (Vol. 25, December 1, 2011, No. 15, pp. 12)
Pub: SourceMedia LLC
Contact: Gemma Postlethwaite, Chief Executive Officer
Ed: John F. Galvin. **Description:** Tips for employers when adding disability and maternity leave benefits to workers are outlined, with focus on ways to avoid leave-related lawsuits.

17310 ■ *"How to Avoid the Most Common and Costliest Mistakes in Retirement Portfolio Investing"* in *Barron's* (Vol. 88, March 10, 2008, No. 10, pp. 30)
Pub: Dow Jones & Company Inc.
Contact: Almar Latour, Chief Executive Officer
Ed: Karen Hube. **Description:** Investors, particularly those having retirement investments, are advised to diversify their investments, refrain from market timing, and minimize payments to maximize investment gains. An investor committing these mistakes could lose as much as $375,000 dollars over ten years. **Availability:** Online.

17311 ■ *"Handling New Health Insurance Regulations"* in *Baltimore Business Journal* (Vol. 31, April 25, 2014, No. 52, pp. 25)
Pub: American City Business Journals, Inc.
Contact: Mike Olivieri, Executive Vice President
Released: March 13, 2014. **Description:** Research and consulting firm, Mercer, surveyed businesses in January 2014 to examine their employer-sponsored health plans following enrollment in the Affordable Care Act-created exchanges. The survey found employers were taking advantage of a delay to a key regulation in the Act on offering insurance to employees who work at least 30 hours a week. **Availability:** Print; Online.

17312 ■ *"How to Retire: Do's and Don'ts"* in *Canadian Business* (Vol. 79, July 17, 2006, No. 14-15, pp. 29)
Pub: Rogers Media Inc.
Contact: Neil Spivak, Chief Executive Officer
Ed: Andy Holloway, Erin Pooley, Thomas Watson. **Description:** Strategic tips for planning systematic investments, in order to make life more enjoyable after retirement, are elucidated. **Availability:** Print; Online.

17313 ■ *How to Set Up an Employee Benefits Program in 6 Steps*
URL(s): fitsmallbusiness.com/setting-up-employee-benefits/
Ed: Charlette Beasley, Jennifer Hartman. **Description:** Includes six important steps for small businesses to follow to set up their employee benefits program. **Availability:** Online.

17314 ■ *How to Start and Run Your Own Corporation: S-Corporations For Small Business Owners*
Pub: HCM Publishing
Ed: Peter I. Hupalo. **Description:** Basics of corporate business structure are explained. Topics include discovering the best business structure for your company; how to decided between an S-Corporation and LLC; choosing the state in which to incorporate, how to form a corporation, angel investing, special issues for one-person corporations, the role of bylaws and corporate minutes, board of directors, taxes, workers' compensation issues, retirement plans, and more. **Availability:** Print.

17315 ■ *"The Incentive Bubble: Outsourcing Pay Decisions To Financial Markets Has Skewed Compensation and, With It, American Capitalism"* in *Harvard Business Review* (Vol. 90, March 2012, No. 3, pp. 124)
Pub: Harvard Business Review Press
Contact: Moderna V. Pfizer, Contact
Ed: Mihir A. Desai. **Price:** $8.95. **Description:** Basing incentive contracts and executive compensation on financial markets actually rewards luck rather than performance, and can promote dangerous risk taking. This has led to America's two main crises of capitalism: growing income inequality and governance failures. Boards of directors must focus on performance rather than stocks, and endowments and foundations must focus on incentives for long-term growth. **Availability:** Online; PDF.

17316 ■ *"International Benefits Roundup"* in *Employee Benefit News* (Vol. 25, December 1, 2011, No. 15)
Pub: SourceMedia LLC
Contact: Gemma Postlethwaite, Chief Executive Officer
Description: Employee contributions to an employer-sponsored defined contribution plan in Japan are allowed on a tax-deductible basis; however, currently employee contributions are not allowed. The defined contribution plan is outlined for better understanding.

17317 ■ *"Investing In Employee Health, Wellness"* in *South Florida Business Journal* (Vol. 34, June 6, 2014, No. 46, pp. 28)
Pub: American City Business Journals, Inc.
Contact: Mike Olivieri, Executive Vice President
Released: Weekly. **Price:** $8, introductory 4-week offer(Digital & Print). **Description:** Companies are investing in employee wellness programs as an employee benefit because health issues within the organization can lead to absenteeism and unproductive employees. The results of a study indicate that losses from absenteeism across all professions could reach $84 billion. **Availability:** Print; Online.

17318 ■ *"Is Raising CPP Premiums a Good Idea?"* in *Canadian Business* (Vol. 83, July 20, 2010, No. 11-12, pp. 37)
Description: Big labor is pushing for an increase in Canada Pension Plan premiums but pension consultants believe this system is not broken and that the government needs to focus on addressing the low rate of personal retirement savings. If the premiums go up, even those with high savings will be forced to pay more and it could block other plans that really address the real issue. **Availability:** Print; Online.

17319 ■ *"Is There a Doctor In the House?"* in *Black Enterprise* (Vol. 41, December 2010, No. 5, pp. 42)
Pub: Earl G. Graves Ltd.
Contact: Earl Graves, Jr., President
Ed: Renita Burns. **Description:** Health insurance premiums have increased between 15 percent and 20 percent for small business owners, making it one of the most expensive costs. Ways to evaluate a health plan's costs and effectiveness are examined. **Availability:** Online.

17320 ■ *"J.C. Penney Head Shops for Shares"* in *Barron's* (Vol. 88, July 7, 2008, No. 27, pp. 29)
Pub: Dow Jones & Company Inc.
Contact: Almar Latour, Chief Executive Officer
Ed: Teresa Rivas. **Description:** Myron Ullman III, chairman and chief executive officer of J.C. Penney, purchased $1 million worth of shares of the company. He now owns 393,140 shares of the company and an additional 1,282 on his 401(k) plan. **Availability:** Online.

17321 ■ *"Kids in Crisis"* in *Employee Benefit News* (Vol. 25, November 1, 2011, No. 14, pp. 26)
Pub: Comtex News Network Inc.
Contact: Kan Devnani, President
Ed: Lisa V. Gillespie. **Description:** Employers and vendor are taking more aggressive steps to help battle childhood obesity. **Availability:** Print; Online.

17322 ■ *"Labor Pains"* in *Canadian Business* (Vol. 79, August 14, 2006, No. 16-17, pp. 80)
Description: Canada's employment insurance is analyzed in view of the growing shortage of labor. **Availability:** Print; Online.

17323 ■ *"Legg Mason Compensation Committee Chair Defends CEO Fetting's Pay"* in *Baltimore Business Journal* (Vol. 29, July 22, 2011, No. 11, pp. 1)
Pub: Boston Business Journal
Contact: Carolyn M. Jones, President
E-mail: cmjones@bizjournals.com
Ed: Gary Haber. **Description:** Legg Mason Inc. CEO Mark R. Fetting has been awarded $5.9 million pay package and he expects to receive questions regarding it in the coming shareholders meeting. However, Baltimore, Maryland-based RKTL Associates chairman emeritus Harold R. Adams believes Fetting has done a tremendous job in bringing Legg's through a tough market. **Availability:** Print; Online.

17324 ■ *"Legislators Must Cut Cost of Government"* in *Crain's Detroit Business* (Vol. 24, October 6, 2008, No. 40, pp. 6)
Pub: Crain Communications Inc.
Contact: Barry Asin, President

Description: Southeast and West Michigan business leaders are setting aside their differences and have proposed clear agendas, ranging from eliminating the Michigan Business Tax to overhauling public employee and retiree benefits and pensions. Lawmakers must also come together to find solutions for the state's economy and discover an entirely new vision for the future of Michigan business. **Availability:** Print; Online.

17325 ■ *"Lowering Retirement System Barriers for Women" in Employee Benefit News (Vol. 25, December 1, 2011, No. 15)*
Pub: SourceMedia LLC
Contact: Gemma Postlethwaite, Chief Executive Officer

Ed: Mary Nell Billings. **Description:** Challenges faced by small business for lowering retirement benefits barriers for women and minorities, which is difficult to put into practice, is discussed.

17326 ■ *"The Massachusetts Mess" in Barron's (Vol. 89, July 27, 2009, No. 30, pp. 39)*
Pub: Dow Jones & Company Inc.
Contact: Almar Latour, Chief Executive Officer

Ed: Thomas G. Donlan. **Description:** Massachusetts' mandatory health insurance has produced the highest rate of insurance coverage among the states but the state is now unable to afford its dream of universal coverage just three years after they enacted it. This supposed model for federal health-care reform is turning out to be a joke. **Availability:** Online.

17327 ■ *"MCM Bulks Up by Merging With Maritime Insurer" in Puget Sound Business Journal (Vol. 33, June 1, 2012, No. 6, pp. 1)*
Pub: Baltimore Business Journal
Contact: Rhonda Pringle, President
E-mail: rpringle@bizjournals.com

Ed: Peter Neurath. **Description:** Seattle, Washington-based brokerage and benefits company MCM has formed a merger with Global Insurance Specialists that would strengthen its property-casualty insurance brokerage division. MCM has 2012 premium volume of $794.7 million, a total of 75 employees and provides service in areas such as employee benefits, executive benefits, and retirement plans. **Availability:** Print; Online.

17328 ■ *"Md. Pension System Tries to Recoup $73M from Actuary" in Baltimore Business Journal (Vol. 28, June 11, 2010, No. 5, pp. 1)*
Pub: Baltimore Business Journal
Contact: Rhonda Pringle, President
E-mail: rpringle@bizjournals.com

Ed: Gary Haber. **Description:** Maryland State Retirement and Pension System has won nearly $73 million in administrative ruling against Milliman Inc. over pension loss miscalculations. However, Milliman filed two court cases seeking to reverse the decision and to recoup to the state any money a court orders. **Availability:** Print; Online.

17329 ■ *"Medicare Plans Step Up Battle for Subscribers" in Sacramento Business Journal (Vol. 28, October 21, 2011, No. 34, pp. 1)*
Pub: Sacramento Business Journal
Contact: Stephanie Fretwell, Director
E-mail: sfretwell@bizjournals.com

Ed: Kathy Robertson. **Description:** California's market for health plans have become increasingly competitive as more than 313,000 seniors try to figure out the best plans to meet their needs for 2012. Health plans are rated on Medicare materials to help consumers distinguish among the Medicare health maintenance organizations (HMOs). **Availability:** Online.

17330 ■ *"More Small Businesses in Baltimore Willing to Fund Employees' Health Benefits" in Baltimore Business Journal (Vol. 28, June 18, 2010, No. 6, pp. 1)*
Pub: Baltimore Business Journal
Contact: Rhonda Pringle, President

E-mail: rpringle@bizjournals.com
Ed: Scott Graham. **Description:** An increasing number of small businesses in Maryland are tapping into potentially cheaper self-funded health plans instead of providing fully insured benefits to employees through traditional health plans. Self-funded health plans charge employers for health care up to a specified level. Economic implications of self-funded plans to small businesses are discussed.

17331 ■ *"Nobel Prize Winners Provide Insight on Outsourcing, Contract Work" in Workforce Management (Vol. 88, November 16, 2009, No. 12, pp. 11)*
Pub: Crain Communications Inc.
Contact: Barry Asin, President

Ed: Jeremy Smerd. **Description:** Insights into such workforce management issues as bonuses, employee contracts and outsourcing has been recognized by the Nobel Prize winners in economics whose research sheds a light on the way economic decisions are made outside markets. **Availability:** Online.

17332 ■ *"Oberg Industries' Initiative Offers Many Paths Down Wellness Road" in Pittsburgh Business Times (Vol. 33, June 6, 2014, No. 47, pp. 12)*
Pub: American City Business Journals, Inc.
Contact: Mike Olivieri, Executive Vice President
Released: Weekly. **Price:** $4, introductory 4-week offer(Digital only). **Description:** Oberg Industries, Category Winner in the 500 to 1,999 employee group in Healthiest Employers of Western Pennsylvania 2014, offers several awareness programs to help employees adopt a healthier lifestyle. Initiatives to increase employee participation in wellness programs include the National Walk at Lunch Day and providing free blood work services. **Availability:** Print; Online.

17333 ■ *"Open Enrollment: Staying Healthy During Enrollment Season" in Employee Benefit News (Vol. 25, November 1, 2011, No. 14, pp. 41)*
Pub: SourceMedia LLC
Contact: Gemma Postlethwaite, Chief Executive Officer

Ed: Shana Sweeney. **Description:** Tips for staying healthy during your benefit open enrollment period are outlined.

17334 ■ *"Orange County's Paid Sick Leave Initiative Draws Ire of Businesses" in Orlando Business Journal (Vol. 29, August 24, 2012, No. 10, pp. 1)*
Pub: Baltimore Business Journal
Contact: Rhonda Pringle, President
E-mail: rpringle@bizjournals.com

Ed: Anjali Fluker. **Description:** A proposed sick leave initiative has been opposed by businesses in Orange County, Florida. The regulation will require businesses with more than than 15 employees to provide workers with paid sick leave benefits. **Availability:** Print; Online.

17335 ■ *"Paychecks of Some Bank CEOs Have a Pre-Recession Look" in Boston Business Journal (Vol. 29, May 13, 2011, No. 1, pp. 1)*
Pub: Boston Business Journal
Contact: Carolyn M. Jones, President
E-mail: cmjones@bizjournals.com

Ed: Gary Haber. **Description:** The salaries of United States-based bank chief executive officers have increased to pre-recession levels. Wells Fargo and Company's John G. Stumpf received $17.6 million in 2010. Community bank executives, on the other hand, have seen minimal increases. **Availability:** Print; Online.

17336 ■ *"The People Puzzle; Re-Training America's Workers" in The Economist (Vol. 390, January 3, 2009, No. 8612, pp. 32)*
Description: With thousands of workers losing their jobs, America is now facing the task of getting them back to work. With an overall unemployment rate of 6.7 percent, the federal government has three main ways for leading workers back to employment: training them for new jobs, providing unemployment insurance in order to replace lost wages during the period of job-hunting; and matching employers who desire a skill with workers who have that skill. Specialized staffing agencies provide employers and potential employees with the help necessary to find a job in some of the more niche markets. **Availability:** Online.

17337 ■ *"Perks Still Popular: Jets May be Out, but CEO Benefits Abound" in Crain's Detroit Business (Vol. 25, June 22, 2009)*
Pub: Crain Communications Inc.
Contact: Barry Asin, President

Ed: Ryan Beene. **Description:** Benefits packages of local CEOs are outlined. Statistical data included. **Availability:** Online.

17338 ■ *PPC's Guide to Choosing Retirement Plans for Small Businesses*
Price: $190; $215. **Description:** Guide to evaluate and select retirement plans for small business. **Availability:** Online.

17339 ■ *PPC's Guide to Compensation Planning for Small Business*
Released: Annual. **Price:** $190, book volume 1; $215, online; $180. **Description:** Technical guide for developing a compensation system for small business. Forms and letters included. **Availability:** Online.

17340 ■ *"The Price of Citizenship" in Canadian Business (Vol. 79, August 14, 2006, No. 16-17, pp. 13)*
Description: Safety and insurance benefits provided by the Canadian government to Canadian passport holders returning from Lebanon, is discussed. **Availability:** Print; Online.

17341 ■ *"Providence Exec Explains Why the Deal with Boeing is the Way of the Future" in Puget Sound Business Journal (Vol. 35, June 27, 2014, No. 10, pp. 6)*
Pub: American City Business Journals, Inc.
Contact: Mike Olivieri, Executive Vice President

Description: Providence-Swedish Accountable Care Organization CEO, Joe Gifford, shares his views on the deal to provide health care to Boeing employees. Gifford says there is opportunity to grow the business if public image spreads showing they offer great quality and service in providing unique healthcare and benefits at a lower cost. Gifford believes meeting directly with the employer customer they create a direct loop of process improvement. **Availability:** Online.

17342 ■ *"Reforms Equal Smaller 401(k)s" in Employee Benefit News (Vol. 25, December 1, 2011, No. 15, pp. 19)*
Pub: SourceMedia LLC
Contact: Gemma Postlethwaite, Chief Executive Officer

Ed: Lisa V. Gillespie. **Description:** According to a new analysis by the Employee Benefit Research Institute, two recent proposals to change existing tax treatment of 401(k) retirement plans could cost workers because they would lower their account balances towards retirement.

17343 ■ *"Retirement Plan Disclosures: Prepare Now for Fiduciary Rules" in Employee Benefit News (Vol. 25, November 1, 2011, No. 14, pp. 24)*
Pub: SourceMedia LLC
Contact: Gemma Postlethwaite, Chief Executive Officer

Ed: Brian M. Pinheiro, Kurt R. Anderson. **Description:** Department of Labor has delayed the deadlines on new affirmative obligations for fiduciaries of retirement plans subject to the Employee Retirement Income Security Act. Details included. **Availability:** Online; PDF; Download.

GENERAL SMALL BUSINESS TOPICS

17344 ■ *"Retirement Plans in a Quandary"* in *Employee Benefit News* (Vol. 25, December 1, 2011, No. 15, pp. 18)
Pub: SourceMedia LLC
Contact: Gemma Postlethwaite, Chief Executive Officer
Ed: Terry Dunne. **Description:** Complex issues arise when employees don't cash their 401(k) balance checks. The US Department of Labor permits plans to cash out accounts of former employees with less than $1,000 to reduce the cost and time required to manage them.

17345 ■ *"RIM Rocks Out: Billionaire Bosses Sponsor a Free Concert for Deserving Staff"* in *Canadian Business* (Vol. 80, Winter 2007, No. 24)
Description: Jim Balsillie and Mike Lazaridis of Research in Motion Ltd. (RIM) rented out the Air Canada Centre in Toronto to give their employees a free concert that features performances by the Tragically Hip and Van Halen on November 15, 2007. RIM has sponsored concerts by Aerosmith, Tom Cochrane, and the Barenaked Ladies in past parties that only shows how far the company goes in terms of employee appreciation.

17346 ■ *"A Safety Net in Need of Repair"* in *The Economist* (Vol. 390, January 3, 2009, No. 8612, pp. 33)
Description: America's unemployment-insurance scheme is outdated and skimpy compared to other industrialized countries despite the fact that Americans tend to work harder at returning to the job market; the benefits are lower and available for a smaller amount of time and less unemployed workers are even able to collect these benefits. Statistical data included.

17347 ■ *"SECU's Tax Preparation Services Net Members More Than $86 Million in Refunds"* in *Economics Week* (May 11, 2012)
Description: State Employees' Credit Union (SECU) helped nearly 65,000 North Carolina members file their income taxes in 2012. SECU reports $86 million in refunds and saving members more than $8 million in preparation fees. The credit union promotes its tax preparation services so members can avoid the high fees paid to tax preparers. **Availability:** Print; Online.

17348 ■ *"Should You Choose a Lump-Sum Pension Payout? Here's How Entrepreneur Ramona Harper Decided"* in *Black Enterprise* (Vol. 44, June 2014, No. 10, pp. 27)
Pub: Earl G. Graves Ltd.
Contact: Earl Graves, Jr., President
Description: Entrepreneur, Ramona Harper, chose a lump sum payout of her pension in order to start a new business. She used $110,000 to start her accessories boutique and put the remaining money into a small business 401(k), which helped her avoid a large tax. Tips to help individuals decide the best way to collect their pension are provided. **Availability:** Online.

17349 ■ *"Small Biz Owners Are Tapping Into Health Savings Plans"* in *Small Business Opportunities* (Fall 2007)
Description: Health savings accounts were developed by Golden Rule, a United Healthcare company. Today, more than 40 percent of the company's customers are covered by health savings account plans.

17350 ■ *"Small Business Compensation"* in *Small Business Economic Trends* (February 2008, pp. 10)
Pub: National Federation of Independent Business
Contact: Brad Close, President
Ed: William C. Dunkelberg, Holly Wade. **Description:** Graphs and tables that present compensation plans and compensation changes of small businesses in the U.S. are provided. The figures include data from 1974 to 2008.

17351 ■ *Small Business Guide to Benefits That Attract and Retain Employees*
URL(s): www.benefitspro.com/2021/05/10/small-business-guide-to-benefits-that-attract-and-retain-employees/
Ed: Kristen Beckham. **Released:** May 10, 2021. **Description:** Provides information for growing small businesses to consider as they formulate the benefits that will be offered to their employees. **Availability:** Online.

17352 ■ *"Small Business Health Insurance Costs: What Can You Expect?"* in *PeopleKeep* (Oct. 17, 2021)
URL(s): www.peoplekeep.com/blog/small-business-health-insurance-costs-what-can-you-expect
Ed: Josh Miner. **Released:** October 17, 2021. **Description:** Discusses the costs small businesses can expect when offering group health insurance as well as how companies can control their costs by offering alternatives such as health reimbursement arrangements (HRA). **Availability:** Online.

17353 ■ *"Small, But Mighty"* in *Employee Benefit News* (Vol. 25, November 1, 2011, No. 14, pp. 32)
Pub: SourceMedia LLC
Contact: Gemma Postlethwaite, Chief Executive Officer
Ed: Andrea Davis. **Description:** Three consulting firms are facing the challenge of helping clients understand the new health care reform in a tight economy. **Availability:** Print; PDF; Online.

17354 ■ *"Spotlight on Pensions"* in *Business Horizons* (Vol. 51, March-April 2008, No. 2, pp. 105)
Pub: Elsevier Advanced Technology Publications
Ed: Laureen A. Maines. **Description:** Perceptions of pension burden and risk among financial statement users is likely to increase with changes in pension accounting. These perceptions might affect decisions on pension commitments and investments. **Availability:** Online.

17355 ■ *"Spouses, Health Coaching Added to Mix"* in *Pittsburgh Business Times* (Vol. 33, June 6, 2014, No. 47, pp. 5)
Pub: American City Business Journals, Inc.
Contact: Mike Olivieri, Executive Vice President
Released: Weekly. **Price:** $4, introductory 4-week offer (Digital & Print). **Description:** Hospital giant, UPMC, was the Category Winner in the 5,000+ employees group of Healthiest Employers in Western Pennsylvania, for its initiative in expanding its health assessment and wellness programs to the spouses and partners of all its employees, regardless of their health insurance carrier. In addition, UPMC Health Plan expanded its individual health coaching option for members as well as corporate clients. **Availability:** Print; Online.

17356 ■ *"Spreading Your Wings"* in *Canadian Business* (Vol. 81, March 17, 2008, No. 4, pp. 31)
Ed: Megan Harman. **Released:** February 09, 2017. **Description:** Financing from angel investors is one avenue that should be explored by startups. Angel investors are typically affluent individuals who invest their own money. Angel investors usually want at least 10 times their initial investment within eight years but they benefit the businesses through their help in decision-making and the industry expertise they provide. **Availability:** Download; Online.

17357 ■ *"A Stakeholder--Human Capital Perspective on the Link Between Social Performance and Executive Compensation"* in *Business Ethics Quarterly* (Vol. 24, January 2014, No. 1, pp. 1)
Pub: Business Ethics Quarterly
Contact: Dawn Elm, Executive Director
E-mail: drelm@stthomas.edu
Description: The link between firm corporate social performance (CSP) and executive compensation could be driven by a sorting effect (a firm's CSP is related to the initial levels of compensation of newly hired executives), or by an incentive effect (incumbent executives are rewarded for past firm CSP). An exploration of the sorting effect of firm CSP on the initial compensation of newly hired executives is discussed. **Availability:** Download; PDF; Online.

17358 ■ *"State of the States"* in *Barron's* (Vol. 92, August 27, 2012, No. 38, pp. 23)
Pub: Dow Jones & Company Inc.
Contact: Almar Latour, Chief Executive Officer
Ed: Andrew Bary. **Description:** The strength of finances of US states are ranked based on their debt ad unfunded pensions compared with their gross domestic products. South Dakota is considered to have the healthiest finances, while those of Connecticut are the weakest. **Availability:** Online.

17359 ■ *"Steeling for Battle"* in *Crain's Chicago Business* (Vol. 31, April 21, 2008, No. 16, pp. 3)
Pub: Crain Communications Inc.
Contact: Barry Asin, President
Ed: Bob Tita. **Description:** Discusses contract negotiations between the United Steelworkers union and ArcelorMittal USA Inc., the nation's largest steelmaker, and U.S. Steel Corp., the third-largest; the union sees these negotiations as the best chance in two decades to regain lost ground but industry experts predict the companies will try to reduce benefits, demand a separate, lower wage scale for new hires and look for relief from the rising costs for retirees' health insurance coverage. **Availability:** Online.

17360 ■ *"Surprise Package"* in *Business Courier* (Vol. 27, June 25, 2010, No. 8, pp. 1)
Pub: Business Courier
Ed: Dan Monk, Jon Newberry, Steve Watkins. **Description:** More than 60 percent of the chief executive officers (CEOs) in Greater Cincinnati's 35 public companies took a salary cut in 2009, but stock grants resulted in large paper gains for the CEOs. The salary cuts show efforts of boards of directors to observe austerity. Statistics on increased values of stock awards for CEOs, median pay for CEOs, and median shareholder return are also presented. **Availability:** Online.

17361 ■ *"Swinging For the Fences: The Effects of Ceo Stock Options on Company Risk Taking and Performance"* in *Academy of Management Journal* (Vol. 50, No. 5, October 1, 2007, pp. 1055)
Pub: Academy of Management
Contact: Sharon Alvarez, President
Ed: Gerard Sanders, Donald C. Hambrick. **Description:** Study examines managerial risk-taking vis-a-vis stock options of the company; results reveal that stock options instigate CEOs to take unwise risks that could bring huge losses to the company. **Availability:** Electronic publishing; PDF; Download; Online.

17362 ■ *"Taking Full Advantage: What You Need To Know During Open-Enrollment Season"* in *Black Enterprise* (Vol. 38, November 2007, No. 4)
Pub: Earl G. Graves Ltd.
Contact: Earl Graves, Jr., President
Ed: Donald Jay Korn. **Description:** Employees can change or enroll in new insurance benefits during the fall season. It is important to assess each plan offered and to determine your deductible. Statistical data included. **Availability:** Online.

17363 ■ *"Teachers, U.S. Fund Providence Made Moves On BCE Buyout"* in *Globe & Mail* (April 10, 2007, pp. B17)
Ed: Boyd Erman, Sinclair Stewart, Jacquie McNish. **Description:** The Ontario Teachers' Pension Plan, the largest shareholder of telecommunications firm BCE Inc., has called for a partnership with buyout firm Providence Equity Partners Inc. in order to acquire BCE Inc. **Availability:** Online.

17364 ■ "Top Pension Fund Sends a Warning" in Barron's (Vol. 92, July 23, 2012, No. 30, pp. M9)
Pub: Dow Jones & Company Inc.
Contact: Almar Latour, Chief Executive Officer
Ed: Michael Aneiro. Description: The California Public Employees' Retirement System reported a 1 percent return on investments for the fiscal year ended June 30, 2012. It lost 7.2 percent on stock investments, 11 percent on forest-land holdings and 2 percent on absolute-return assets, negating a 12.7 percent gain on its fixed-income investments. Availability: Online.

17365 ■ "TrendHR Changes Rockwall Landscape with $25M Office Tower" in Dallas Business Journal (Vol. 35, May 25, 2012, No. 37, pp. 1)
Pub: Baltimore Business Journal
Contact: Rhonda Pringle, President
E-mail: rpringle@bizjournals.com
Ed: Candace Carlisle. Description: TrendHR Services is planning to build an executive tower in Rockwall, Texas. The company provides human resource outsourcing, employee benefits, and consulting services. Availability: Print; Online.

17366 ■ "The Ultimate Guide to Employee Benefits for Small Businesses" in The Blueprint (July 30, 2020)
URL(s): www.fool.com/the-blueprint/employee-benefits/
Ed: Elizabeth Gonzalez. Released: July 30, 2020.
Description: Highlights benefits required nationwide as well as voluntary benefits small businesses can extend to employees. Availability: Online.

17367 ■ Understanding Workers Compensation: A Guide for Safety and Health Professionals
Contact: Kenneth Wolff, DC, Doctor
URL(s): rowman.com/ISBN/9780865874640
Price: $91, Individuals paperback. Description: Publication includes listing of state and provincial workers compensation administrators. Includes sample forms, checklists, U.S. Chamber of Commerce analysis. Entries include: Name, address, phone. Principal content of publication is explanation of the Workers Compensation System. Availability: Print.

17368 ■ Unique Employee Benefits: Perks Small Businesses Can Consider
URL(s): hires.shareable.com/blog/unique-employee-benefits
Ed: Andrea Collatz. Released: April 08, 2021.
Description: Discusses the importance of desirable employee benefits as it relates to employee retention. Includes several types of unique benefits to consider offering to your employees. Availability: Online.

17369 ■ "Use Benefits Checklist to Smooth New-Hire Onboarding" in HR Specialist (Vol. 8, September 2010, No. 9, pp. 4)
Pub: Capitol Information Group Inc.
Contact: Allie Ash, Chief Executive Officer
Description: Checklist to help employees enroll in a company's benefit offerings is provided, courtesy of Wayne State University in Detroit, Michigan. Availability: Print; Online.

17370 ■ "Vacation, All I Ever Wanted" in Entrepreneur (August 2014)
Pub: Entrepreneur Media Inc.
Contact: Dan Bova, Director
E-mail: dbova@entrepreneur.com
Description: Small business owners can maximize the value of spending time away from work. Paid vacations boost employee productivity and the same effect can also be experienced by owners. Vacation expenses can be managed with creativity and careful planning according to Matt Kepnes, author of 'How to Travel the World on $50 a Day: Travel Cheaper, Longer, Smarter'. The three main vacation expenses that business owners should carefully plan include lodging, transportation, and food and entertainment. Availability: Print; Online.

17371 ■ "A Well-Crafted Employee Handbook Can Make Work Run More Smoothly" in Idaho Business Review (September 17, 2014)
Pub: BridgeTower Media
Contact: Adam Reinebach, President
Description: An employee handbook will provide a complaint process, provide company management flexibility and clarity and keep a company out of legal problems. Training, compensation, benefits, security, health, performance appraisals, and safety issues must be covered. Human resource managers and other mangers should cover basics to help communicate with workers.

17372 ■ "Western & Southern to Trim Rich Retirement Plan" in Business Courier (Vol. 27, October 15, 2010, No. 24, pp. 1)
Pub: Business Courier
Ed: Dan Monk. Description: Insurance firm Western & Southern Financial Group announced that it will reduce the pension benefits of its 4,000 associates by more than 30 percent starting January 1, 2011. The move is expected to reduce annual retirement payments by several thousand dollars per associate. Western is a Fortune 500 company and has $34 billion in total assets. Availability: Print; Online.

17373 ■ "What Choice Did I Have?" in Entrepreneur (Vol. 37, October 2009, No. 10, pp. 88)
Pub: Entrepreneur Media Inc.
Contact: Dan Bova, Director
E-mail: dbova@entrepreneur.com
Ed: Craig Matsuda. Description: Profile of a worker at a financial services company who acquired first-hand knowledge concerning the relationship between health insurance costs and coverage. The worker's son got severely ill, forcing the worker to spend above what is covered by health insurance. Availability: Print; Online.

17374 ■ "Why His Merit Raise Is Bigger Than Hers" in Harvard Business Review (Vol. 90, April 2012, No. 4, pp. 26)
Pub: Harvard Business Review Press
Contact: Moderna V. Pfizer, Contact
Ed: Stephen Benard. Price: $6, hardcover. Description: Research indicates that companies that utilize meritocracy as their pay-for-performance system are paradoxically more likely to award pay on biases, and specifically, to give smaller increases to women. Tranparency and accountability are therefore key in the implementation of merit pay. Availability: PDF; Online.

17375 ■ "Why Loyalty Programs Alienate Great Customers" in Harvard Business Review (Vol. 90, July-August 2012, No. 7-8, pp. 38)
Pub: Harvard Business Review Press
Contact: Moderna V. Pfizer, Contact
Ed: Hal Brierley. Price: $6. Description: Airline loyalty programs should replace the mileage metric with money spent, and should also extend rewards to second-tier customers. Rewars should also be accessible sooner, and retirees should be granted emeritus status. Availability: Online; PDF.

17376 ■ "Why Taking a Vacation Is Your Patriotic Duty" in South Florida Business Journal (Vol. 34, June 27, 2014, No. 49, pp. 14)
Pub: American City Business Journals, Inc.
Contact: Mike Olivieri, Executive Vice President
Released: Weekly. Description: The negative impact on the U.S. economy of unused vacation days is explained. Tips that employees should follow before taking a paid vacation leave benefit are presented. Availability: Print; Online.

17377 ■ "Winners and Losers" in Crain's Detroit Business (Vol. 25, June 22, 2009, No. 25, pp. 18)
Pub: Crain Communications Inc.
Contact: Barry Asin, President
Description: Rankings for Detroit's 50 top-compensated CEOs has changed due to the economic recession. The biggest changes are discussed. Availability: Online.

17378 ■ "Winners & Losers" in Canadian Business (Vol. 85, July 16, 2012, No. 11-12, pp. 22)
Description: Canadian Pacific Railway's 4,800 locomotive engineers and conductors walked out in protest of the proposed work rules and pension cuts. Shareholders rejected a $25-million bonus and retention payout to Astral Media chief executive officer Ian Greenburg. The Dragon spacecraft of Space Exploration Technologies delivered supplies and experiments to the International Space Station. Availability: Print.

17379 ■ "Work/Life Balance" in Dallas Business Journal (Vol. 37, June 20, 2014, No. 41, pp. 4)
Pub: Routledge, Taylor & Francis Group
Description: Younger generations of corporate employees are increasingly looking for a more engaged workplace community. Research firm, Quantum Workplace, identifies several trends that help to attract and retain employees, including jobs that align with the workers' own values, growth opportunities within the firm, social interactions with co-workers, and employee health benefits. Availability: Print; Online.

STATISTICAL SOURCES

17380 ■ Human Resources & Benefits Administration Industry in the US - Market Research Report
URL(s): www.ibisworld.com/united-states/market-research-reports/human-resources-benefits-administration-industry/
Price: $925. Description: Downloadable report analyzing data about current and future trends in the human resources and benefits administration industries. Availability: Download.

TRADE PERIODICALS

17381 ■ Benefits Law Journal
Pub: Wolters Kluwer Law and Business
Contact: Linda Gharib, Director, Communications Director, Marketing
E-mail: linda.gharib@wolterskluwer.com
URL(s): law-store.wolterskluwer.com/s/product/benefits-law-journal-3-mo-subvitallaw/01t0f00000J3FBfAAN
Ed: Elaine Stattler, Joyce Anne Grabel. Description: Journal covering the welfare benefits field, including new types, delivery methods, and legal requirements. Availability: Print.

17382 ■ Benefits Quarterly
Pub: International Society of Certified Employee Benefit Specialists
Contact: John Eshleman, President
URL(s): www.iscebs.org/home/education---resources/benefits-quarterly
Ed: Jack L. VanDerhei, Jack L. VanDerhei, PhD.
Released: Quarterly Description: Journal for human resources professionals. Availability: Print; Online.

17383 ■ Employee Benefit Plan Review
Released: Monthly Price: $495, Single issue.
Description: Magazine serving decision-makers who administer, design, install, and service employee benefit plans. Availability: Print.

17384 ■ Journal of Compensation and Benefits
Contact: Jeffrey D. Mamorsky, Editor
URL(s): store.legal.thomsonreuters.com/law-products/Treatises/Journal-of-Compensation-and-Benefits/p/100000474

Ed: Jeffrey D. Mamorsky. **Released:** 6/year **Price:** $2,232, Individuals r 1 year subscription. **Description:** Magazine offering practical guidance on compensation and employee benefits issues. **Availability:** Print; Online.

17385 ■ What's New in Benefits & Compensation
Pub: American Future Systems Inc.
Contact: Edward G. Rendell, Governor
URL(s): www.pbp.com/divisions/publishing/newsletters/human-resources/whats-new-in-benefits-compensation

Released: Semimonthly **Description:** Communicates the latest legal, tax and policy developments that help benefits executives address cost concerns while meeting complex needs of employees. Recurring features include interviews, news of research, and a column titled Sharpen Your Judgment. **Availability:** Print.

CONSULTANTS

17386 ■ Aaron Deitsch, F.S.A.
107-23 71st Rd., Ste. 231
Forest Hills, NY 11375
Ph: (718)793-9885
URL: http://www.pensionconsultant.com
Contact: Aaron Deitsch, Contact

Description: Firm provides pension consulting and actuary consulting services in employee benefits and specializing in retirement plans. **Scope:** Firm provides pension consulting and actuary consulting services in employee benefits and specializing in retirement plans. **Founded:** 1978. **Publications:** "Retirement Plan Basics"; "Retirement Plan Tips, Retirement Plan Traps"; "Profit Sharing Plan Tips, Profit Sharing Plan Traps"; "Defined Benefit Pension Plan Tips, Defined Benefit Pension Plan Traps"; "401(K) Plan Tips, 401(K) Plan Traps"; "401(K) Plans-Tips on Controlling 401(K) Plan Costs". **Training:** Pension Plan Library; Pension Plan Tools/Applications; Pension Plan and Retirement Plan Assistance.

17387 ■ ABAX of RI, Inc.
55 Stamp Farm Rd.
Cranston, RI 02921
Contact: Robert Chin, President

Description: Firm provides financial advisor, investment platform, retirement plans, and strategic alliances. **Scope:** Firm provides financial advisor, investment platform, retirement plans, and strategic alliances.

17388 ■ Aldrich & Cox Inc. (A&C)
3075 SW Blvd.,Ste.,202
Orchard Park, NY 14127-1287
Contact: Daniel C. Buser, Executive Vice President
E-mail: buser@aldrichandcox.com

Description: Provider of independent, fee-based risk management, insurance and employee benefit consulting services.

17389 ■ Benefit Communications Inc. (BCI)
2977 Sidco Dr.
Nashville, TN 37204
Free: 800-489-3786
Fax: (615)383-7917
URL: http://benefitcommunications.com
Contact: Dale Nichols, Director

Description: Firm specializes in employee benefit communication services in three areas such as voluntary products, employee communications, and open enrollment outsourcing. **Founded:** 1981.

17390 ■ Benefit Partners Inc.
People Corporation Inc.
1-2140 Regent St.
Sudbury, ON, Canada P3E 5S8
Ph: (204)940-3900
Free: 866-940-3950
Co. E-mail: info@peoplecorporation.com
URL: http://www.peoplecorporation.com

Description: Firm provides employee benefits, pension and human resources management consulting services. **Scope:** Firm provides employee benefits, pension and human resources management consulting services.

17391 ■ Benetech Inc.
3841 N Fwy., Blvd., Ste. 280
Sacramento, CA 95834
Free: 800-285-7526
URL: http://benetechinc.com
Contact: Amy Brandon, President
E-mail: amyb@benetechinc.com

Description: An actuarial consulting and administration firm specializing in retirement plans for small and medium-size businesses. Offers plan design, record keeping and consulting services. Consulting services in plan design options for Profit Sharing, 401k, and Defined Benefit Plans. **Scope:** An actuarial consulting and administration firm specializing in retirement plans for small and medium-size businesses. Offers plan design, record keeping and consulting services. Consulting services in plan design options for Profit Sharing, 401k, and Defined Benefit Plans. **Founded:** 1974.

17392 ■ Business Benefits, Inc. (BBI)
2620 Regatta Dr., Ste. 102
Las Vegas, NV 89128
Ph: (702)252-0888
Fax: (702)252-0785
URL: http://bbblt.com
Contact: Tim deRosa, President
Facebook: www.facebook.com/BusinessBenefitsInc

Description: Firm provides professional and insurance services such as group benefits, individual, and commercial insurance coverage plans. **Scope:** Firm provides professional and insurance services such as group benefits, individual, and commercial insurance coverage plans. **Founded:** 1981. **Training:** Guardian Advantage product. **Special Services:** Guardian Advantage®; MyWave.

17393 ■ Business Planning Inc. (BPI)
2075 Columbiana Rd., Ste. 1
Birmingham, AL 35216
Ph: (205)824-8969
Free: 800-239-5135
Fax: (205)824-8939
URL: http://www.businessplanninginc.com
Contact: Scott Sutton, Contact
E-mail: scott@businessplanninginc.com

Description: Firm provides personalized planning, installation, administration, corporate retirement planning, and much more services. **Scope:** Firm provides personalized planning, installation, administration, corporate retirement planning, and much more services. **Founded:** 1974.

17394 ■ CF Services Group Inc.
9083 Shady Grove Ct.
Gaithersburg, MD 20877
Contact: David S. Yarn, Contact

Description: Provider of financial advices, personal services, tailored financial plans, and much more for individuals, families, and businesses. **Publications:** "Leading Economic Index Is Designed To Assess The U.S Economic Outlook"; "Whole Life Insurance"; "Term Life Insurance"; "Universal Life Insurance"; "Variable Life Insurance"; "Auto Insurance"; "Insurance Claims"; "Maximizing Insurance Benefits"; "Insuring Your Future"; "Assessing Disability Insurance"; "Types of Health Care"; "Protecting Your Home"; "Additional Liability Coverage"; "Planning Options"; "Future of Social Security"; "Social Security Income"; "Keogh Plans"; "Equity-Indexed Annuities"; "Retirement Plan Distributions"; "Cash Management Basics". **Training:** Hanging the Help Wanted Sign, 2011; Where The Jobs Are, How To Spruce Up Your Skills And Ready Your, Finances For The Change.

17395 ■ Chadler Solutions
100 Passaic Ave., Ste. 120.
Fairfield, NJ 07004
Ph: (973)227-0025
URL: http://chadlersolutions.com
Contact: Scott Rappoport, President

E-mail: srappoport@chadlersolutions.com
Description: Provider of business leaders and human resource professionals at emerging companies and established global corporations with a personalized multi-faceted approach to manage their employee benefit programs, the firm designs, implements, and administers employee benefit plans that are integrated into an employers compensation package. **Scope:** Provider of business leaders and human resource professionals at emerging companies and established global corporations with a personalized multi-faceted approach to manage their employee benefit programs, the firm designs, implements, and administers employee benefit plans that are integrated into an employers compensation package. **Founded:** 1960.

17396 ■ Counts Benefit Services Inc.
23246 Rainbow Arch Dr.
Clarksburg, MD 20871
Ph: (301)916-0100
Co. E-mail: jcounts@countsbenefits.us
URL: http://www.countsfinancial.com

Description: Consulting services include evaluation of employer benefit plans as to cost vs. benefits, self-insured benefits as well as fully insured welfare plans and defined contribution and defined benefit plans and also designs executive compensation programs and salary continuation benefits and active with a wide variety of industries. **Scope:** Consulting services include evaluation of employer benefit plans as to cost vs. benefits, self-insured benefits as well as fully insured welfare plans and defined contribution and defined benefit plans and also designs executive compensation programs and salary continuation benefits and active with a wide variety of industries. **Founded:** 1984. **Publications:** "Eighty percent of Americans agree they would benefit from having basic financial education and information". **Training:** The Financial Alternative to Success Seminar.

17397 ■ Employee Benefit Research Institute (EBRI) - Library
901 D St., SW Ste. 802
Washington, DC 20024
Ph: (202)659-0670
Fax: (202)775-6360
Co. E-mail: info@ebri.org
URL: http://www.ebri.org
Contact: Lori Lucas, Chief Executive Officer

Description: Corporations, consulting firms, banks, insurance companies, unions, and others with an interest in the future of employee benefit programs. Seeks to contribute to the development of effective and responsible public policy in the field of employee benefits through research, publications, educational programs, seminars, and direct communication. Sponsors studies on retirement income, health, disability, and other benefit programs; disseminates study results. **Scope:** A public policy research organization serving as an employee benefits information source on health, welfare and retirement issues. Services include: basic benefit program descriptions, legislation analysis, media coverage and interpretation and long-range planning. Specializes in research on pensions, social security, health care, Medicare, long-term care and flexible benefits. Serves government, academic consumers, consultants, banks, insurance companies, investment managers, law and accounting firms, corporations and individuals. **Founded:** 1978. **Holdings:** Figures not available. **Publications:** Dedicated to providing unbiased, fact-based research on employee benefits. **Training:** Policy Forums, Congressional Briefings. **Awards:** EBRI Lillywhite Award (Annual). **Geographic Preference:** National.

17398 ■ First Health Review Inc.
2755 S Decker Ln.,Ste.,8
Salt Lake City, UT 84119

Description: Firm provides retirement and savings plan design, administration, welfare plan design and employee benefit communication services. **Scope:** Firm provides retirement and savings plan design, administration, welfare plan design and employee benefit communication services.

17399 ■ Benefits

17399 ■ A Friend of the Family
Atlanta, GA
Ph: (770)725-2748
Co. E-mail: info@afriend.com
URL: http://afriend.com

Description: Firm provides family care staffing services for infants, children, adults, households, institutions, and families. **Scope:** Firm provides family care staffing services for infants, children, adults, households, institutions, and families. **Founded:** 1985.

17400 ■ Gallagher Benefit Services Inc.
Arthur J. Gallagher & Co. (AJG)
2850 Golf Rd.
Rolling Meadows, IL 60008
Ph: (630)773-3800
Co. E-mail: info@ajg.com
URL: http://www.ajg.com
Contact: Christopher E. Mead, Chief Marketing Officer
Facebook: www.facebook.com/GallagherGlobal
X (Twitter): x.com/GallagherGlobal
Instagram: www.instagram.com/gallagherglobal
YouTube: www.youtube.com/GallagherGlobal

Description: Provider of benefits planning, delivery and administration services. **Scope:** Offers consultation in areas of benefits planning, delivery, and administration. Services include executive benefits programs, health and welfare schemes, healthcare analytics, human resource services, international benefits services, retirement plan services and voluntary benefits services. Industries served: healthcare, higher education, hospitality and restaurant, transportation and non profit organizations. **Founded:** 1927. **Publications:** "Final HIPAA Nondiscrimination and Wellness Plan Rules Issued," 2007; "Using Electronic Media For Employee Benefit Elections and Notices," 2006. **Training:** Safety By Design, Marina Center, South Sioux City, NE, Nov, 2008; Hospitality Loss Prevention, DFW Radisson South Hotel, Irving, TX, Mar, 2006.

17401 ■ Health Insurance Specialists Inc. (HISI)
PO Box 5743
Derwood, MD 20855
Ph: (301)590-0006
Fax: (301)590-0661
Co. E-mail: info@his-inc.com
URL: http://his-inc.com
Facebook: www.facebook.com/HealthInsuranceSpecialistsInc

Description: Firm provides insurance and business financial planning solutions. **Scope:** Firm provides insurance and business financial planning solutions. **Founded:** 1982.

17402 ■ HealthChoice
583 D'Onofrio Dr., 101
Madison, WI 53719
Ph: (608)833-5823
Free: 800-833-5823
Co. E-mail: info@healthchoice.com
URL: http://healthchoice.com

Description: Firm provides employee assistance program for reducing employer productivity loses. **Scope:** Firm provides employee assistance program for reducing employer productivity loses. **Founded:** 1995. **Publications:** "Graduating From Child Care to Elder Care".

17403 ■ In Plain English
14501 Antigone Dr.
Gaithersburg, MD 20878-2484
Ph: (301)340-2821
Free: 800-274-9645
Fax: (301)279-0115
URL: http://www.inplainenglish.com

Description: Management consultants helping government and businesses research, design, write and produce user oriented management information for human resources, employee benefits, business process, corporate and marketing needs. Services include: GSA mob is schedule for consulting to the government; employee benefit communications, plain English business writing workshops for print and electronic media; communicating strategy and tactics; marketing research, business planning and communications; readability testing; usability testing and monitoring strategy. **Scope:** Management consultants helping government and businesses research, design, write and produce user oriented management information for human resources, employee benefits, business process, corporate and marketing needs. Services include: GSA mob is schedule for consulting to the government; employee benefit communications, plain English business writing workshops for print and electronic media; communicating strategy and tactics; marketing research, business planning and communications; readability testing; usability testing and monitoring strategy. **Founded:** 1977. **Publications:** "The Benefits Communication"; "The Employee Benefits Communication ToolKit," Commerce Clearinghouse; "Benefits Communication," Business and Legal Reports. **Training:** Plain English Writing Training; Summary Plan Description Compliance workshops; Re-Humanizing the Corporation, Human Resources and Employee Benefits Communication Workshop; 21 Writing Tips for the 21st Century; Make the Write Impression; Writing to Inform and Instruct; The Dreaded Nuts and Bolts; Writing to Persuade; Writing Policy and Procedure Manuals In Plain English; Writing for Accountants and Auditors In Plain English. **Special Services:** In Plain English®.

17404 ■ John Chute & Associates
150 Consumers Rd., Ste. 508
Toronto, ON, Canada M2J 1P9
Ph: (416)250-8600
Free: 800-565-2488
Fax: (416)250-8605
Co. E-mail: postmaster@jchute.com
URL: http://www.jchute.com
Contact: Jack Chute, President
E-mail: jack.chute@jchute.com

Description: Firm engages in design, costing, implementation and communication of employee benefit plans. **Scope:** Firm engages in design, costing, implementation and communication of employee benefit plans. **Founded:** 1982.

17405 ■ Money Source Financial Services Inc.
1310 S Main St., Ste. 15
Ann Arbor, MI 48104
Ph: (734)213-0300
URL: http://www.msfs.com
Contact: Glen Darmos, Contact

Description: Firm provides financial planning, residential and commercial mortgage services. **Scope:** Firm provides financial planning, residential and commercial mortgage services. **Founded:** 1994.

17406 ■ Navia Benefit Solutions Inc.
PO Box 53250
Bellevue, WA 98015
Ph: (425)452-3500
Free: 800-669-3539
Co. E-mail: customerservice@naviabenefits.com
URL: http://www.naviabenefits.com
Contact: Bob Camenzind, Chief Operating Officer
YouTube: www.youtube.com/user/FlexPlanServices

Description: Provider of flexible benefits plan design and administration for cafeteria-type plans, form 5500 preparation and employee benefit statements. **Scope:** Provider of flexible benefits plan design and administration for cafeteria-type plans, form 5500 preparation and employee benefit statements. **Founded:** 1989.

17407 ■ New Ways to Work [New Ways]
1012 West Beverly Blvd. No.377
Montebello, CA 90640
Ph: (707)824-4000
Co. E-mail: coyn@newwaystowork.org
URL: http://www.newwaystowork.org
Contact: Che Casul, Chief Executive Officer
Facebook: www.facebook.com/newwaystoworkfb
X (Twitter): x.com/NewWays2Work

Description: Helps communities build systems that connect schools, community organizations and businesses, and improve the services, educational programs and support the community provides for its youth. Engages and supports local communities in the invention and renewal of connected, comprehensive youth-serving systems. **Scope:** Focuses on improving the lives of the nations youth. helps communities build systems that connect schools, community organizations and businesses. Creates the environment and guides a process that brings the right people together with customized tools for powerful learning and dramatic change. **Founded:** 1972. **Publications:** "A Guide to Career Development Opportunities in California's High Schools". **Training:** Career pathways; building local intermediary organizations; strengthening youth councils; increasing youth involvement; creating quality work-based learning systems; All Youth-One Systems. **Educational Activities:** New Ways to Work Workshops, To educate employers and employees in work time options and policy issues. **Geographic Preference:** National.

17408 ■ Nyhart
FuturePlan
750 Castle Creek Pkwy., Ste. 245
Indianapolis, IN 46250
Ph: (817)563-3400
Free: 866-831-3526
Fax: (817)563-3445
URL: http://www.futureplan.com/transition/401k-plus
Contact: Carter Angell, Chief Executive Officer
E-mail: carter.angell@nyhart.com

Description: An employee-owned national actuarial and retirement firm. **Founded:** 1943.

17409 ■ Princeton Health Systems Inc. (PHS)
9 Mercer St.
Princeton, NJ 08540
Ph: (609)924-7799
URL: http://www.princetonhealthsystems.com
Contact: Beth Young, Contact

Description: Services: Health promotion and wellness programs. **Scope:** Services: Health promotion and wellness programs. **Founded:** 1987. **Publications:** "Certain Solutions Administrator's Guide," Johnson & Johnson Health Management Inc., 1992; "Sports Medicine Up-Date," New Jersey Medicine, 1991; "The Wrestlers' Nutrition Manual," Bucknell University, 1990.

17410 ■ Ralph Moss Ltd. (RML)
10520 Yonge St., Unit 35B, Ste. 143
Richmond Hill, ON, Canada L4C 3C7
Ph: (905)513-9868
Free: 888-667-7583
Fax: (905)513-9893
Co. E-mail: info@ralphmossltd.on.ca
URL: http://ralphmoss.ca

Description: Firm provides insurance services such as plan design including traditional and flexible benefits, utilization reviews, risk analysis, and much more. **Scope:** Firm provides insurance services such as plan design including traditional and flexible benefits, utilization reviews, risk analysis, and much more. **Publications:** "Financial Planning Report".

17411 ■ Segal Co.
333 W 34th St.
New York, NY 10001-2402
Ph: (212)251-5000
Fax: (646)365-3243
URL: http://www.segalco.com
Contact: Andrew Sherman, Director
E-mail: asherman@segalco.com
Linkedin: www.linkedin.com/company/segal-
X (Twitter): x.com/SegalCo

Description: A leading, independent firm of benefit, compensation and human resources consultants. In January 2002, Segal acquired Sibson Consulting, a human capital consulting firm. The combined organization, with more than 1, 000 employees is headquartered in New York and has offices throughout the United States, in Canada and the United Kingdom. Clients include corporations, non-profit organizations, professional service firms, state and local governments and joint boards of trustees administering pension, health and welfare plans under the Taft-Hartley Act. **Scope:** A leading, independent firm of benefit, compensation and human resources consultants. In January 2002, Segal acquired Sibson Consulting, a human capital consulting firm. The combined organization, with more than 1,000 employees is headquartered in New York and has offices throughout the United States, in Canada and the United Kingdom. Clients include corporations, non-profit organizations, professional service firms, state and local governments and joint boards of trustees administering pension, health and welfare plans under the Taft-Hartley Act. **Founded:** 1939.

17412 ■ Siebrand-Wilton Associates Inc. (S-WA)
PO Box 193
Rocky Hill, NJ 08553-0193
URL: http://www.s-wa.com
Contact: John S. Sturges, Principal
Description: Firm provides nationwide human resources consulting support and also offers executive coaching and counseling, benefit plan design, and other related services. **Founded:** 1986. **Publications:** "Should Government or Business Try to Save Medicare," HR News; "Executive Temping," HR Horizons; "When is an Employee Truly an Employee," HR Magazine; "Examining Your Insurance Carrier," HR Magazine.

17413 ■ The Stoller Co.
190 N Wiget Ln., Ste. 125
Walnut Creek, CA 94598
Ph: (925)932-1800
Fax: (925)932-1869
Co. E-mail: info@stollerco.com
URL: http://www.stollerco.com
Contact: Curtis J. Stoller, Contact
Description: Firm provides retirement plan consulting services and also provides 401k plan, 403b tax sheltered annuity plan, profit sharing, defined benefit, money purchase and cash balance plan. **Founded:** 1976.

17414 ■ Swartzbaugh-Farber & Associates, Inc.
Financial Plz.
9140 W Dodge Rd., Ste. 418
Omaha, NE 68114
Ph: (402)397-5800
Fax: (402)397-5424
URL: http://www.swartzbaugh.com
Contact: Bob Swartzbaugh, President
E-mail: bob.swartzbaugh@swartzbaugh.com
Facebook: www.facebook.com/SwartzbaughFarber
Linkedin: www.linkedin.com/company/swartzbaugh-farber-&-associates-inc-
X (Twitter): x.com/sfaibenefits
Instagram: www.instagram.com/swartzbaugh_farber
Description: Firm provides business related consulting services such as executive benefits, estate planning and business succession, and financial planning solutions. **Founded:** 1993. **Training:** Health care Boot Camp, Aug, 2007; Benchmarking Seminar, 2007; Understanding HIPAA Seminar, Mar, 2006; HR - Developing a Profit Center, Nov, 2005.

17415 ■ TRI-AD Actuaries, Inc.
221 W Crest St., Ste. 300
Escondido, CA 92025
Ph: (760)743-7555
Free: 800-743-7555
Fax: (760)489-9343
Co. E-mail: info@tri-ad.com
URL: http://www.tri-ad.com
Contact: Thad Hamilton, President
Linkedin: www.linkedin.com/companies/tri-ad
Description: Human resources consulting and administration firm specializing in outsourcing benefits administration, and designing comprehensive compensation. **Founded:** 1974. **Publications:** "A Complete Chart of the 2008 Cost of Living Adjustments," Oct, 2007; "Check the Rollover Chart to See Which Types of Plans Will Accept Your Rollover," Aug, 2006; "A Complete Chart of the 2006 Cost of Living Adjustments," Jan, 2006; "Valerie Gieseke in Compensation and Benefits Review: Automating Benefits Administration," Nov, 2005. **Training:** Beyond COBRA: Offering More Comprehensive Post-Employment Benefits, Aug, 2009; Primer on Providers: Who Does What for Your 401(k) Plan, Jul, 2009; Refresher Course on the Basics of FSA Plan Administration, Jun, 2009; Found Money in Your 401(k) Plans, May, 2009; Found Money in Your Health & Welfare Benefit Plans, Apr, 2009; 401(k) Loans: Deal or No Deal?, Apr, 2008; COBRA 101: What You Need to Know About COBRA, Apr, 2007; An Update on Automatic Enrollment, Mar, 2007; Preparing for COBRA Open Enrollment, Oct, 2006.

COMPUTERIZED DATABASES

17416 ■ *ABI/INFORM*
ProQuest LLC
789 E Eisenhower Pky.
Ann Arbor, MI 48108
Ph: (734)761-4700
Free: 800-521-0600
URL: http://www.proquest.com
Contact: Matti Shem Tov, Chief Executive Officer
URL(s): about.proquest.com/en/products-services/abi_inform_complete
Availability: Online. **Type:** Full-text; Bibliographic; Image.

17417 ■ *Business Insurance*
Crain Communications Inc.
1155 Gratiot Ave.
Detroit, MI 48207-2732
Ph: (313)446-6000
Co. E-mail: info@crain.com
URL: http://www.crain.com
Contact: Barry Asin, President
URL(s): www.businessinsurance.com
Facebook: www.facebook.com/BusInsMagazine
Linkedin: www.linkedin.com/company/business-insurance
X (Twitter): x.com/BusInsMagazine
Released: Biweekly **Description:** International newsweekly reporting on corporate risk and employee benefit management news. **Availability:** Print; Online. **Type:** Full-text.

17418 ■ *InfoQuick*
International Foundation of Employee Benefit Plans
18700 W Bluemound Rd.
Brookfield, WI 53045
Ph: (262)786-6700
Free: 888-334-3327
Co. E-mail: infocenter@ifebp.org
URL: http://www.ifebp.org/home
Contact: Donald D. Crosatto, President
URL(s): www.ifebp.org/resources---news
Availability: Online. **Type:** Bibliographic.

LIBRARIES

17419 ■ Ivins, Phillips, Barker Library (IPB)
1717 K St. NW, Ste. 600
Washington, DC 20006-5343
Ph: (202)393-7600
Fax: (202)393-7601
Co. E-mail: ipb@ipbtax.com
URL: http://www.ipbtax.com
Contact: Natanya H. Allan, Partner
E-mail: nallan@ipbtax.com
Linkedin: www.linkedin.com/company/ivins-phillips-&-barker
Description: Attorneys deals with tax and other benefits. **Scope:** Pensions; taxation. **Services:** Interlibrary loan; copying; library not open to the public. **Founded:** 1924. **Holdings:** 1,000 volumes; technical reports; CD-ROMs.

RESEARCH CENTERS

17420 ■ Pennsylvania State University - Risk Management Research Center (RMRC)
310F Business Bldg.
University Park, PA 16802
Ph: (814)865-3961
Fax: (814)865-6284
Co. E-mail: macc@smeal.psu.edu
URL: http://www.smeal.psu.edu/rmrc
Contact: Arnold F. Shapiro, Director
E-mail: afs1@psu.edu
Description: Integral unit of Division of Research, College of Business Administration, Pennsylvania State University. **Scope:** Encourages and conducts research on the design and funding of employee benefit plans, including pensions and group health insurance, and actuarial studies. **Founded:** 1985.

17421 ■ Pension Research Council (PRC)
The Wharton School of the University of Pennsylvania
3620 Locust Walk
3000 Steinberg Hall - Dietrich Hall
Philadelphia, PA 19104-6302
Ph: (215)898-7620
Fax: (215)573-3418
Co. E-mail: prc@wharton.upenn.edu
URL: http://pensionresearchcouncil.wharton.upenn.edu
Contact: Dr. Olivia S. Mitchell, Executive Director
E-mail: mitchelo@wharton.upenn.edu
Facebook: www.facebook.com/PRC.Boettner
Linkedin: www.linkedin.com/company/pension-research-council
X (Twitter): x.com/PensionResearch
YouTube: www.youtube.com/user/PRCoffice
Description: Sponsors interdisciplinary research on the entire range of private pension and social security programs. **Scope:** Seeks to strengthen institutional arrangements designed to provide financial resources for a secure old age through basic research into their social, economic, legal, actuarial, and financial foundations. **Founded:** 1954. **Publications:** *The Future of Pensions in the United States*; *Providing Health Care Benefits in Retirement*; *PRC Newsletter*; *Working paper series*. **Educational Activities:** PRC Symposium (Annual); PRC Symposium (Annual). **Geographic Preference:** National.

17422 ■ University of North Carolina at Chapel Hill - Cecil G. Sheps Center for Health Services Research
725 Martin Luther King Jr Blvd.
Chapel Hill, NC 27599-7590
Ph: (919)966-5011
Fax: (919)966-3811
Co. E-mail: contact@schsr.unc.edu
URL: http://www.shepscenter.unc.edu
Contact: Dr. Mark Holmes, Director
E-mail: mark_holmes@unc.edu
X (Twitter): x.com/uncsheps
Description: Firm engaged to improve health of individuals, families and populations by understanding problems, issues and alternatives in design and delivery of health care services. Offers technical assistance for a number of state agencies. **Scope:** Researches on aging, disability, and long-term care; child health services; health care economics and finance; health care organization; medical practice; mental health and substance abuse services and systems research. **Founded:** 1968. **Publications:** *North Carolina HCUP State Inpatient Database (SID)*; *North Carolina HCUP State Ambulatory Surgery Database (SASD)*; *Consensus in DHHS Region IV: Women and Infant Health Indicators for Planning and Evaluation*; *North Carolina Health Professions Data Book*; *North Carolina Health Professions Fact Sheet*. **Educational Activities:** Cecil G. Sheps Center for Health Services Research Seminars (Continuous); Cecil G. Sheps Center for Health Services Research Annual DHHS Region IV Conference on Maternal and Child Health, Family Planning, and Services for Children With Special Health Needs; Cecil G. Sheps Center for Health Services Research Annual DHHS Region IV Workshop on the Collection and Use of Data for MCH and Women's Health Planning and Evaluation. **Awards:** Cecil G. Sheps Center for Health Services Research Postdoctoral Fellowships (Annual); UNC-CH NRSA Predoctoral Training Fellowships in Health Services Research.

Brand Image/Branding

START-UP INFORMATION

17423 ■ *Branding Basics for Small Business*
Ed: Maria Ross. **Released:** March 23, 2014. **Price:** $7.95, paperback. **Description:** Readers will be able to comprehend and start creating a successful brand for their product after finishing the title. **Availability:** 2nd edition; Print.

ASSOCIATIONS AND OTHER ORGANIZATIONS

17424 ■ **American Branding Association (ABA)**
2704 W Dravus St.
Seattle, WA 98199
Ph: (206)234-5485
Co. E-mail: info@americanbranding.org
URL: http://www.americanbranding.org
Contact: Jeffrey Hamilton Smith, Founder
E-mail: jeffreys@americanbranding.org
X (Twitter): x.com/ABASeattle
Description: Organization devoted to the promotion of branding and developing American brands. **Founded:** 2003.

EDUCATIONAL PROGRAMS

17425 ■ **The Content Sales Funnel - Creating an Effective Social Media Content Strategy Series**
URL(s): cwewbc.ecenterdirect.com/events/977328
Description: This online course offered by the Center for Women and Enterprise discusses brand identity, sales funnel strategy, effective writing, and social media branding. **Audience:** Women who are small business owners. **Principal Exhibits:** This online course offered by the Center for Women and Enterprise discusses brand identity, sales funnel strategy, effective writing, and social media branding.

17426 ■ **Discovering Your Brand Identity**
URL(s): cwewbc.ecenterdirect.com/events/977303
Description: This online class offered by the Center for Women and Enterprise discusses how to develop brand identity, how to reach your audience, and how to use social media. **Audience:** Women who are small business owners. **Principal Exhibits:** This online class offered by the Center for Women and Enterprise discusses how to develop brand identity, how to reach your audience, and how to use social media.

REFERENCE WORKS

17427 ■ *"3 Ways a Strong Brand Identity Can Lead to Greater Success for Your Small Business"* in *Entrepreneur* (July 25, 2021)
URL(s): www.entrepreneur.com/article/375785
Ed: Christina-Lauren Pollack. **Released:** July 25, 2021. **Description:** Explores how a strong brand identity has the power to elevate and position a company for greater success. Discusses branding strategy and brand marketing. **Availability:** Online.

17428 ■ *"5 Inexpensive Branding Strategies for Small Businesses"* in *99designs* (2016)
Ed: Deanna deBara. **Released:** 2016. **Description:** Discusses five inexpensive branding strategies that will help take your small business to the next level. **Availability:** Online.

17429 ■ *"7 Ways to Build Customer Loyalty"* *Business News Daily* (March 17, 2023)
URL(s): www.businessnewsdaily.com/16017-build-customer-loyalty.html
Ed: Sean Peek. **Released:** March 17, 2023. **Description:** Small businesses can improve customer loyalty and bring in more business by implementing the factors discussed in this article. **Availability:** Online.

17430 ■ *"14 Stunning Examples of Small Business Branding"* in *ActiveCampaign* (March 7, 2018)
Ed: Benyamin Elias. **Released:** March 07, 2018. **Description:** Discusses how to build your brand on a small budget and how small businesses can create brands that stand out. Provides 14 examples of great small business branding. **Availability:** Online.

17431 ■ *"50+ Eye-Opening Branding Statistics"* in *smallbizgenius* (August 2, 2019)
Ed: Ivana Vojinovic. **Released:** August 02, 2019. **Description:** The primary purpose of branding is helping businesses stand out from the competition. This article details top branding statistics and describes how they are meaningful for small business owners. **Availability:** Online.

17432 ■ *"The Basics of Branding"* in *Entrepreneur*
URL(s): www.entrepreneur.com/article/77408
Ed: John Williams. **Description:** Explores what branding is and how it affects your small business. Provides detail on aspects including brand strategy, how to define your brand, and your logo. **Availability:** Online.

17433 ■ *"Best April Fools' Day Brand Pranks"* in *Business News Daily* (March 21, 2023)
URL(s): www.businessnewsdaily.com/4249-april-fools-pranks.html
Ed: Joyce Walsack. **Released:** March 21, 2023. **Description:** Over the years, some big brands fully embraced April Fools' Day pranks and listed are some examples from these companies over the years. **Availability:** Online.

17434 ■ *"Brand, Branding and Small Businesses"* in *The Economic Times* (Sept. 2, 2021)
URL(s): economictimes.indiatimes.com/small-biz/marketing-branding/branding/brand-branding-and-small-businesses/articleshow/85856875.cms
Ed: Harsh Verma. **Released:** September 02, 2021. **Description:** Explores the importance of brand and brand strategy and how the presence of vision is the reason why many small brands have become big. **Availability:** Online.

17435 ■ *:Branding in a Diverse Universe: Serving Both Sides of the Buy/Sell'* in *Minority Business Entrepreneur* (March 14, 2023)
URL(s): mbemag.com/articles/branding-in-a-diverse-universe-serving-both-sides-of-the-buy-sell/
Ed: Brooke Foley. **Description:** Discusses branding along with interviewing Jade Melvin, who served with the National Minority Supplier Development Council. **Availability:** Online.

17436 ■ *Buffalo, Barrels, & Bourbon: The Story of How Buffalo Trace Distillery Became The World's Most Awarded Distillery*
Pub: John Wiley & Sons, Inc.
Contact: Christina Van Tassell, Executive Vice President Chief Financial Officer
URL(s): www.wiley.com/en-us/Buffalo%2C+Barrels%2C+%26+Bourbon%3A+The+Story+of+How+Buffalo+Trace+Distillery+Became+The+World%27s+Most+Awarded+Distillery-p-9781119599913
Ed: F. Paul Pacult. **Released:** September 2021. **Price:** $16, e-book; $27, hardcover. **Description:** Conveys the history of Buffalo Trace Distillery and how the brand was developed and grown. **Availability:** E-book; Print.

17437 ■ *"A Comprehensive Guide to Branding for Small Businesses"* in *Small Biz Ahead Blog* (Feb. 4, 2022)
URL(s): sba.thehartford.com/business-management/marketing/small-business-branding/
Ed: Belle Wong. **Released:** February 04, 2022. **Description:** Discusses the importance of including branding in your priorities of running your small business. While it is sometimes not easy to measure the immediate impact of effective branding, it is actually crucial to long-term success. **Availability:** Online.

17438 ■ *"Cope with Unforseen Challenges at BrandSmart 2023"* in *Small Business Trends* (March 4, 2023)
URL(s): smallbiztrends.com/2023/03/event-post-ssmall-business-live-virtual-events-march-4-2023.html
Released: March 04, 2023. **Description:** An overview of the BrandSmart 2023 conference. **Availability:** Online.

17439 ■ *"Does Branding Really Matter for a Small Business?"* in *Forbes* (June 10, 2021)
URL(s): www.forbes.com/sites/forbesagencycouncil/2021/06/10/does-branding-really-matter-for-a-small-business/?sh=6f0cb1fe39e2
Ed: Brian Sullivan. **Released:** June 10, 2021. **Description:** Discusses the importance of branding regardless of the size of your business. This article explores what a brand is and how a small business can affect their brands. **Availability:** Online.

GENERAL SMALL BUSINESS TOPICS   Brand Image/Branding ■ 17464

17440 ■ *"Entenmann's Brings Back Classic Packaging after Rampant Customer Complaints" in Small Business Trends (March 12, 2023)*
URL(s): smallbiztrends.com/2023/03/entenmanns-brings-back-classic-packaging.html
Ed: Joshua Sophy. **Released:** March 12, 2023. **Description:** After receiving negative feedback about their new windowless packaging, Entenmann's has reverted back to their classic design so consumers can see the products before making a purchase. **Availability:** Online.

17441 ■ *The Four Steps to the Epiphany: Successful Strategies for Products that Win*
Pub: John Wiley & Sons, Inc.
Contact: Christina Van Tassell, Executive Vice President Chief Financial Officer
URL(s): www.wiley.com/en-us/The+Four+Steps+to+the+Epiphany%3A+Successful+Strategies+for+Products+that+Win-p-9781119690351
Ed: Steve Blank. **Released:** March 2020. **Price:** $24, e-book; $40, hardcover. **Description:** Helps entrepreneurs starting new businesses understand the four-step Customer Development process, which helps target what is necessary to achieve sales and marketing for your product. **Availability:** E-book; Print.

17442 ■ *"How to Create the Perfect Brand Image for Your Business" in Small Business Rainmaker (November 5, 2020)*
Ed: Andre Palko. **Released:** November 05, 2020. **Description:** Discusses the importance of brand identity, how to find your brand identity and brand personality. **Availability:** Online.

17443 ■ *"How to Create Superfans for Your Small Business" in Small Business Trends(January 30, 2023)*
URL(s): smallbiztrends.com/2023/01/creating-superfans-for-your-small-business.html
Released: January 30, 2023. **Description:** Learn how to turn your loyal customers into superfans, who will often promote your brand and business because they truly love the products or services. **Availability:** Online.

17444 ■ *"How to Create a Unique and Memorable Brand Identity in 2020" in Crowdspring (January 9, 2020)*
Ed: Ross Kimbarovsky. **Released:** January 09, 2020. **Description:** Discusses how brand identity is the best way a startup, small business, established business, agency, or nonprofit can gain a competitive advantage. Provides a guide with information on how to build a unique and memorable brand identity. **Availability:** Online.

17445 ■ *"How to Pick Gifts that Match Your Brand" in Small Business Trends*
URL(s): smallbiztrends.com/2023/02/corporate-gifting.html
Ed: Gabrielle Pickard-Whitehead. **Released:** February 12, 2023. **Description:** A guide on how to find your brand archetype when it comes to corporate gift giving. **Availability:** Online.

17446 ■ *"How to Register and Trademark a Brand Name" in Business News Daily (February 21, 2023)*
URL(s): www.businessnewsdaily.com/15762-how-to-register-trademark-brand-name.html
Ed: Marisa Sanfilippo. **Released:** February 21, 2023. **Description:** Tips on how to register any brands associated with your business. Your intellectual property should be protected and the process is outlined in the article. **Availability:** Online.

17447 ■ *"How Small Businesses Can Protect Themselves against Counterfeiters" in Legal Zoom (February 15, 2023)*
URL(s): www.legalzoom.com/articles/how-small-businesses-can-protect-themselves-against-counterfeiters
Ed: Katherine Gustafson. **Released:** February 15, 2023. **Description:** Discusses protecting your brand and merchandise from counterfeiters who steal product ideas and can ruin your business by selling cheaper and fake products that look like yours. **Availability:** Online.

17448 ■ *"It's Time to Strengthen Your Small Business Brand Identity" in Keap (November 7, 2019)*
Released: November 07, 2019. **Description:** Discusses the importance of forming brand identity early in developing your business as brand identity helps to cultivate emotional connections with your audiences through marketing, messaging, and engagement. Offers tips on how to create a brand identity, three of the most common branding myths, top brand listening tools, and tips on how to stand out. **Availability:** Online.

17449 ■ *Launching & Building a Brand for Dummies*
URL(s): www.wiley.com/en-us/Launching+%26+Building+a+Brand+For+Dummies-p-9781119748038
Ed: Amy Will. **Released:** December 2021. **Price:** $16, e-book; $26.99, paperback. **Description:** This handbook will guide the user through developing a strong brand and launch it in order to connect consumers to your product. Advice on using social media, creating viral campaigns and building up market share are all part of the book. **Availability:** e-book; E-book; Print.

17450 ■ *Oversubscribed: How to Get People Lining up to Do Business with You*
Pub: John Wiley & Sons, Inc.
Contact: Christina Van Tassell, Executive Vice President Chief Financial Officer
URL(s): www.wiley.com/en-us/Oversubscribed%3A+How+To+Get+People+Lining+Up+To+Do+Business+With+You%2C+2nd+Edition-p-9780857088253
Ed: Daniel Priestley. **Released:** 2nd edition. **Price:** $13, e-book; $22, paperback. **Description:** Discusses the principles used to achieve popularity with customers. **Availability:** E-book; Print.

17451 ■ *"The Role of Brand Image on Customer Loyalty" in Radiant Marketing Blog (April 4, 2020)*
Ed: Karen Cummings. **Released:** April 04, 2020. **Description:** Often, the brand image a small business creates acts as a powerful and often inexpensive 'tool' to compete against big businesses with big budgets. This blog discusses how to create a powerful brand image, brand loyalty, brand advocates, and branding strategy. **Availability:** Online.

17452 ■ *"Six Brand-Building Strategies for Small Businesses and Startups" in Forbes (February 20, 2019)*
Ed: Shane Barker. **Released:** February 20, 2019. **Description:** No matter how small your company might be, the key steps involved in brand building are to make your brand memorable and to maintain consistency. This article provides strategies small businesses and startups can use to help create a memorable identity. **Availability:** Online.

17453 ■ *"The Small Business Guide to Branding" in Foundr (June 16, 2021)*
URL(s): foundr.com/articles/marketing/small-business-branding
Ed: Kate Miller. **Released:** June 16, 2021. **Description:** Discusses the importance of branding as it relates to growth for your small business. Provides details on how to build your brand as well as your brand strategy. **Availability:** Online.

17454 ■ *Small Business Marketing Strategies Need Rethinking*
URL(s): www.yahoo.com/now/small-business-marketing-strategies-rethinking-200500272.html
Released: May 09, 2021. **Description:** Explores how and why small businesses need to adapt and rethink their marketing strategies. **Availability:** Online.

17455 ■ *What Is Brand Equity and What Does it Mean for Small Businesses?*
Ed: Lisa Furze. **Description:** Lisa Furze, a brand consultant and designer, defines brand equity, discusses the impact of a brand on business worth, and demonstrates why it is important to take control of your branding and the impact it has on your business. **Availability:** Online.

17456 ■ *"What Your Logo Design Says about Your Business and Why It Matters" in Legal Zoom (February 15, 2023)*
URL(s): www.legalzoom.com/articles/what-your-logo-design-says-about-your-business-and-why-it-matters
Ed: Diane Faulkner. **Released:** February 15, 2023. **Description:** A discussion about logos and branding for your business. **Availability:** Online.

17457 ■ *"Why Brand Image Is Important for a Small Business?" in appyple (August 5, 2020)*
Released: August 05, 2020. **Description:** Brand image is a general impression of a product held by real or potential consumers. This article discusses why branding is so important, why brand image is important, and how to build a strong brand image. **Availability:** Online.

17458 ■ *"Why Digital Marketing Is Important for Small Business" by Digital Marketing Institute (Nov. 3, 2021)*
URL(s): digitalmarketinginstitute.com/blog/why-digital-marketing-is-important-for-small-business
Released: November 03, 2021. **Description:** Discusses the benefits of stepping outside of traditional marketing and incorporating digital marketing to help grow your small business. **Availability:** Online.

VIDEO/AUDIO MEDIA

17459 ■ *The 4 Commitments to Grow Your Reach Online*
URL(s): ducttapemarketing.com/the-4-commitments-to-grow-your-reach-online
Ed: John Jantsch. **Released:** July 06, 2023. **Description:** Podcast discusses four commitments for a successful online brand: value, consistency, longevity, and generosity.

17460 ■ *The Best Small Business Show: Brand Awareness - Collaboration Is Key*
URL(s): richgee.libsyn.com/267-brand-awareness-collaboration-is-key
Ed: Rich Gee. **Released:** October 31, 2022. **Description:** Podcast discusses the importance of collaboration in branding.

17461 ■ *The Best Small Business Show: Content Is King - Delivering on Your Company's Message*
URL(s): richgee.libsyn.com/282-content-is-king-delivering-on-your-companys-message
Ed: Rich Gee. **Released:** February 13, 2023. **Description:** Podcast discusses the importance of content in company messaging.

17462 ■ *The Best Small Business Show: Increasing Your Brand Awareness*
URL(s): richgee.libsyn.com/306-increasing-brand-awareness
Ed: Rich Gee. **Released:** July 31, 2023. **Description:** Podcast discusses how to increase brand awareness.

17463 ■ *The Best Small Business Show: Take Charge of Your Brand CV*
URL(s): richgee.libsyn.com/283-take-charge-of-your-brand-cv
Ed: Rich Gee. **Released:** February 20, 2023.

17464 ■ *The Big Pitch: Professional, Concise, and Attention-Grabbing with Billion-Dollar Funder Suneera Madhan*
URL(s): theceoschool.co/242-the-big-pitch-professional-consice-attention-grabbing-with-billion-dollar-founder-suneera-madhani

Ed: Suneera Madhani. **Released:** May 22, 2023. **Description:** Podcast offers insider tips on making your brand shine and discusses how to harness the influence of publishing your own content.

17465 ■ *Community Building vs. Traditional Marketing*
URL(s): www.startuphustlepodcast.com/community-building-vs-traditional-marketing
Ed: Andrew Morgans. **Released:** December 12, 2023. **Description:** Podcast explores the symbiotic relationship between a brand and its community, particularly in fashion.

17466 ■ *Direct-to-Retail (DTR) Strategies that Win*
URL(s): omny.fm/shows/startup-hustle-direct-to-retail-dtr-strategies-that-win
Ed: Matt Decoursey. **Released:** September 23, 2023. **Description:** Podcast discusses the significance of compelling content, an authentic brand narrative, and why viral content may fall short. Features Benoit Vatere, CEO of Mammoth.

17467 ■ *Discover the New "I Wrote a Book" and How to Grow Your Brand with Carolina Flores*
URL(s): theceoschool.co/253-discover-the-new-i-wrote-a-book-and-how-to-grow-your-brand-with-carolina-flores/
Ed: Suneera Madhani. **Released:** August 07, 2023. **Description:** Podcast discusses how to turn a side hustle into a successful business, along with attracting the best-fit clients, building strong business relationships, and podcasts as tools for thought leadership and long-term vision.

17468 ■ *Diversifying Your Business Revenue*
URL(s): theceoschool.co/how-to-start-diversifying-your-revenue
Ed: Suneera Madhani. **Released:** October 12, 2022. **Description:** Podcast discusses diversifying your revenue streams by focusing on your core product or service, then adding on more services at different levels as you grow to achieve monthly recurring revenue.

17469 ■ *Finding a Product Market Fit*
URL(s): omny.fm/shows/startup-hustle/findng-a-product-market-fit
Ed: Matt DeCoursey. **Released:** September 14, 2023. **Description:** Podcast discusses the role of product-market fit, the signs of a well-aligned product, and the decision to pivot or persevere. Features Phil Alves, founder and CEO of DevSquad.

17470 ■ *Helping Sellers Expand Their Brands*
URL(s): www.startuphustlepodcast.com/helping-sellers-expand-their-brands
Ed: Andrew Morgans. **Released:** October 10, 2023. **Description:** Podcast discusses the value of feedback, understanding the nuances of each marketplace, and being cautious when expanding. .

17471 ■ *How to Be the Ambassador of Your Own Brand with Talyn Rahman-Figueroa*
URL(s): www.makinggoodpodcast.com/episodes/228
Ed: Lauren Tilden. **Released:** March 26, 2024. **Description:** Podcast discusses solo entrepreneurs into brand ambassadors.

17472 ■ *How to Create Branding You LOVE with Hollie Arnett*
URL(s): www.makinggoodpodcast.com/episodes/238
Ed: Lauren Tilden. **Released:** May 21, 2024. **Description:** Podcast explains branding in an accessible way; includes its stages, where to start, and current trends.

17473 ■ *How to Create a Personable Brand with Megan Dowd*
URL(s): www.makinggoodpodcast.com/episodes/230
Ed: Lauren Tilden. **Released:** April 09, 2024. **Description:** Podcast discusses branding strategies.

17474 ■ *How I Built This: Advice Line with Fawn Weaver of Uncle Nearest Premium Whiskey*
URL(s): wondery.com/shows/how-i-built-this/episode/10386-advice-line-with-fawn-weaver-of-nearest-premium-whiskey
Ed: Guy Raz. **Released:** April 25, 2024. **Description:** Podcast answers questions from entrepreneurs a jewelry maker, a coffee roaster, and a home baker) about branding .

17475 ■ *How I Built This: Advice Line with Holly Thaggard of Supergoop!*
URL(s): wondery.com/shows/how-i-built-this/episode/10386-advice-line-with-holly-thaggard-of-supergoop
Ed: Guy Raz. **Released:** August 15, 2024. **Description:** Podcast offers question from founders about finding the right audience and introducing their brands.

17476 ■ *How I Built This: Advice Line with Randy Goldberg of Bombas*
URL(s): wondery.com/shows/how-i-built-this/episode/10386-advice-line-with-randy-goldberg-of-bombas
Ed: Guy Raz. **Released:** June 13, 2024. **Description:** Podcast answers questions from early-stage founders (a clothing desiinger, a tabletop game developer, and a boutique owner) about building brands and reaching new communities.

17477 ■ *How I Built This: Advice Line with Tom Rinks of Sun Bum*
URL(s): wondery.com/shows/how-i-built-this/episode/10386-advice-line-with-tom-rinnks-of-sun-bum
Ed: Guy Raz. **Released:** May 23, 2024. **Description:** Podcast answers question from early-stage founders about refining their brand identity.

17478 ■ *How I Built This: Spikeball: Chris Ruder*
URL(s): wondery.com/shows/how-i-built-this/episode/10386-spikeball-chris-ruder
Ed: Guy Raz. **Released:** June 19, 2023. **Description:** Podcast explains how someone who wasn't into sports and had never run a business turned a childhood game into a thriving brand.

17479 ■ *How I Built This: Sun Bum: Tom Rinks*
URL(s): wondery.com/shows/how-i-built-this/episode/10386-sun-bum-tom-rinks
Ed: Guy Raz. **Released:** March 27, 2023. **Description:** Podcast discusses the art of branding from the Sun Bum founder.

17480 ■ *How to Make Your Brand Stand Out with Zuza Hicks*
URL(s): www.makinggoodpodcast.com/episodes/168
Ed: Lauren Tilden. **Released:** March 28, 2023. **Description:** Podcast discusses branding: from identity to strategic design to standing out through your brand.

17481 ■ *How Poppi Disrupted the Soda Industry: A Conversation with Steve Clements and Allison Ellsworth*
URL(s): theceoschool.co/259-how-poppi-disrupted-the-soda-industry-a-conversation-with-stevie-clements-and-allison-ellsworth
Ed: Suneera Madhani. **Released:** September 18, 2023. **Description:** Podcast discusses the building of a successful brand and disrupting the soda industry, including the challenges of rebranding, accepting feedback, and building a community around your brand.

17482 ■ *How Poppi Disrupted the Soda Industry: A Conversation with Stevie Clements and Allison Ellsworth*
URL(s): theceoschool.co/259-how-poppi-disrupted-the-soda-industry-a-conversation-with-stevie-clements-and-allison-ellsworth
Ed: Suneera Madhani. **Released:** September 18, 2023. **Description:** Podcast discusses the building of a successful brand and disrupting the soda industry, including the challenges of rebranding, accepting feedback, and building a community around your brand.

17483 ■ *This Is Small Business: How Good Design Can Help Increase Sales*
URL(s): www.smallbusiness.amazon/podcast-episodes/ep-60-how-good-design-can-help-increase-sales
Ed: Andrea Marquez. **Released:** June 04, 2024. **Description:** Podcast discusses whether a rebrand is worth the price.

17484 ■ *Values and Brand Messaging with Ashlee Sang*
URL(s): www.makinggoodpodcast.com/episodes/173
Ed: Andrea Marquez. **Released:** April 25, 2023. **Description:** Podcast discusses brand messaging: what, why, and how.

Budgets/Budgeting

ASSOCIATIONS AND OTHER ORGANIZATIONS

17485 ■ American Association for Budget and Program Analysis (AABPA)
PO Box 1157
Falls Church, VA 22041
Co. E-mail: aabpa@aabpa.org
URL: http://www.aabpa.org
Contact: Courtney Timberlake, President
Facebook: www.facebook.com/AABPA
Linkedin: www.linkedin.com/company/american-association-for-budget-and-program-analysis
X (Twitter): x.com/AABPA
Description: Seeks to advance knowledge in budgeting management and program analysis. Promotes the exchange of ideas and information. **Founded:** 1975. **Publications:** *Public Budgeting & Finance* (Quarterly); *Public Budgeting & Finance* (Quarterly). **Geographic Preference:** National.

17486 ■ International Budget Partnership (IBP)
750 First St. NE, Ste. 700
Washington, DC 20002
Ph: (202)792-6833
Fax: (202)792-6833
Co. E-mail: info@internationalbudget.org
URL: http://internationalbudget.org
Contact: Warren Krafchik, Executive Director
E-mail: wkrafchik@international.com
Facebook: www.facebook.com/InternationalBudgetPartnership
Linkedin: www.linkedin.com/company/international-budget-partnership
YouTube: www.youtube.com/user/IntBudgetPartnership/playlists
Description: Works to assist civil society organizations globally to improve budget policies and decision-making processes and reduce poverty. **Publications:** *A Guide to Budget Work for NGOs*; *IBP Newsletter* (Monthly). **Educational Activities:** IBP Conferences. **Geographic Preference:** Multinational.

EDUCATIONAL PROGRAMS

17487 ■ Project Scheduling and Budgeting - Achieving Cost-Effective and Timely Delivery (Onsite)
Seminar Information Service Inc. (SIS)
250 El Camino Real., Ste. 112
Tustin, CA 92780
Ph: (714)508-0340
Free: 877-736-4636
Fax: (714)734-8027
Co. E-mail: info@seminarinformation.com
URL: http://www.seminarinformation.com
Contact: Catherine Bellizzi, President
URL(s): www.seminarinformation.com
Description: Learn how to: Build schedules and budgets that transform project constraints into project success; Construct Work Breakdown Structures (WBS) and network diagrams and estimate task durations; Calculate Critical Path and optimize your project plan; Allocate costs and chart expected cash flow; Assign resources effectively and respond to end-date changes; Perform Earned Value Analysis (EVA) to keep the project on track. **Audience:** Industry professionals. **Principal Exhibits:** Learn how to: Build schedules and budgets that transform project constraints into project success; Construct Work Breakdown Structures (WBS) and network diagrams and estimate task durations; Calculate Critical Path and optimize your project plan; Allocate costs and chart expected cash flow; Assign resources effectively and respond to end-date changes; Perform Earned Value Analysis (EVA) to keep the project on track.

REFERENCE WORKS

17488 ■ "6 Steps to a Better Business Budget" in Investopedia (Jan. 6, 2020)
URL(s): www.investopedia.com/articles/pf/08/small-business-budget.asp
Ed: Brian Beers. **Released:** January 06, 2020. **Description:** Without a budget or a plan, a small business runs the risk of spending more money than it is taking in or not spending enough money to grow the business. This article explores how to get started with a budget for your small business. **Availability:** Online.

17489 ■ "7 Smart Budgeting Tips for Small Business Owners" in Business News Daily (Dec. 21, 2021)
URL(s): www.businessnewsdaily.com/8323-small-business-budget.html
Ed: Sammi Caramela. **Released:** December 21, 2021. **Description:** Outlines tips for small business owners to follow to create and maintain a reliable budget. **Availability:** Online.

17490 ■ "8 Tips for How to Successfully Manage a Business Budget" in TravelBank Blog
URL(s): travelbank.com/blog/expense-management/how-to-manage-a-business-budget/
Ed: Jessica Sillers. **Description:** While business budgets can sometimes feel constraining, there is a lot you can do to work effectively with your budget. This article discusses ways to track expenses and to keep your budget connected to your actual business operations. **Availability:** Online.

17491 ■ "10 Types of Business Budget to Consider at the Budget Planning Stage" in Finextra Blog (Sept. 14, 2021)
URL(s): www.finextra.com/blogposting/20894/10-types-of-business-budget-to-consider-at-the-budget-planning-stage
Released: September 14, 2021. **Description:** Explores 10 business budget types for mature businesses and startups. **Availability:** Online.

17492 ■ "Budgeting vs. Forecasting: What's the Difference Between the Two?" in FreshBooks Hub
URL(s): www.freshbooks.com/hub/accounting/budgeting-forecasting
Description: Explains the difference between budgeting and forecasting and how to create accurate budgets and forecasts for your small business. **Availability:** Online.

17493 ■ "Business Stands Firm for Reform: Battle Over 2011 Budget Expected" in Crain's Detroit Business (Vol. 26, January 4, 2010, No. 1, pp. 3)
Pub: Crain Communications Inc.
Contact: Barry Asin, President
Ed: Amy Lane. **Description:** As Michigan faces a new year of budgetary problems, many business groups are preparing to hold firm against tax increases and instead push for enacting spending reforms. **Availability:** Print; Online.

17494 ■ "The Difference Between Management and Project Management" in Contractor (Vol. 57, February 2010, No. 2, pp. 30)
Ed: H. Kent Craig. **Description:** There are differences when managing a two-man crew as a foreman and a 2,000 employee company as a corporate president. A project manager should have good skills in human psychology, accounting, and the knowledge of a mechanical engineer, architect, civil engineer, and also the meditative skills of a Zen master. **Availability:** Print; Online.

17495 ■ "Dream On" in Barron's (Vol. 89, July 27, 2009, No. 30, pp. 21)
Pub: Dow Jones & Company Inc.
Contact: Almar Latour, Chief Executive Officer
Ed: Jonathan R. Laing. **Description:** California's budget agreement which purports to eliminate a $26 billion deficit is discussed. The frequent budgetary dustups in the state calls for several reforms including a rainy day fund of 15 percent of any budget and a constitutional convention. Other reform suggestions are discussed.

17496 ■ *Entrepreneurial Finance*
Pub: Pearson Education Inc.
Contact: Andy Bird, Chief Executive Officer
Ed: Philip J. Adelman, Alan M. Marks. **Released:** Sixth edition. **Description:** Financial aspects of running a small business are covered; topics include sole proprietorships, partnerships, limited liability companies, and private corporations. **Availability:** Print; Download; Online.

17497 ■ "Facebook: A Promotional Budget's Best Friend" in Women Entrepreneur (February 1, 2009)
Description: Facebook began as a social networking website but has become a valuable marketing tool for all types of businesses, organizations and

17498 ■ Budgets/Budgeting

causes. Tips are provided for creating a Facebook account and growing one's network on Facebook. **Availability:** Online.

17498 ■ *"How to Create a Business Budget for Your Small Business"* in *NerdWallet (Oct. 30, 2020)*
URL(s): www.nerdwallet.com/article/small-business/how-to-create-a-business-budget
Ed: Meredith Turits. **Released:** October 30, 2020. **Description:** Discusses the importance of creating a budget for your small business and provides a 6-step guide to create it as well as information on how to make your budget efficient. **Availability:** Online.

17499 ■ *"How to Create a Social Media Budget for Every Size of Business"* in *Hootsuite Blog (Aug. 31, 2021)*
URL(s): blog.hootsuite.com/the-7-components-of-every-social-media-budget/
Ed: Christina Newberry. **Released:** August 31, 2021. **Description:** Explores incorporating social media marketing into your small business budget. Details how big your social media budget should be, what to include in your social media budget plan, and how to create the plan. **Availability:** Online.

17500 ■ *"How Do Small Businesses Approach the Budgeting Process?"* in *Clutch (May 12, 2021)*
URL(s): clutch.co/accounting/resources/why-small-businesses-need-budgets
Ed: Seamus Roddy. **Released:** May 12, 2021. **Description:** Discusses the varied approaches small businesses take to budgeting, including the fact that some businesses do not budget at all. **Availability:** Online.

17501 ■ *"How to Start Budget Planning for Your Business"* in *Business.com (Jan. 25, 2022)*
URL(s): www.business.com/articles/budget-planning/
Ed: Sean Peek. **Released:** January 25, 2022. **Description:** Explores how to forecast revenue and expenses to ensure profitability through budget planning. **Availability:** Online.

17502 ■ *A How-To Guide for Creating a Business Budget*
URL(s): bench.co/blog/accounting/business-budget/?blog=e6
Ed: Amanda Smith. **Released:** September 28, 2021. **Description:** A guide to what makes a good small business budget, different types of budgets for different types of companies, and budget templates. **Availability:** Online.

17503 ■ *"I Quit My Day Job 4 Months Ago to Become a Freelance Writer. Here's What My Family of 4 Spends in a Typical Week"* in *Business Insider (October 14, 2019)*
URL(s): www.businessinsider.com/spending-diary-family-freelance-income-daytona-beach-florida
Ed: Clint Proctor. **Released:** October 14, 2019. **Description:** An honest look at one family's budeting with the breadwinner working a freelance writing job. **Availability:** Online.

17504 ■ *"Insurers No Longer Paying Premium for Advertising"* in *Brandweek (Vol. 49, April 21, 2008, No. 16, pp. SR3)*
Description: Insurance companies are cutting their advertising budgets after years of accelerated double-digit growth in spending due to the economic downturn, five years of record-breaking ad spend and a need to cut expenditures as claims costs rise and a competitive market keeps premiums in place. Statistical data included. **Availability:** Print; Online.

17505 ■ *"Keith Crain: Business Must Stand Up And Be Counted"* in *Crain's Detroit Business (Vol. 24, October 6, 2008, No. 40, pp. 6)*
Pub: Crain Communications Inc.
Contact: Barry Asin, President

Description: Discusses the challenges that the new mayor of Detroit faces concerning business, the state of the economy and the exceptionally tight budget the city is running on, which includes a lot of red ink. It is very likely that the city is going to see tax revenues fall substantially in the next few months and business leaders may find it in their favor to lend their support to the new mayor as well as provide him with the executive talent necessary to overcome some of these crucial issues. **Availability:** Online.

17506 ■ *"Life's Work: Oliver Sacks"* in *Harvard Business Review (Vol. 88, November 2010, No. 11, pp. 152)*
Pub: Harvard Business Publishing
Contact: Diane Belcher, Managing Director
Ed: Lisa Burrell. **Price:** $8.95, PDF. **Description:** Neurologist and author Oliver Sacks discusses whether different types of minds tend toward certain skills, physician-patient communication, and his own perspectives from being a patient himself. **Availability:** Online; PDF.

17507 ■ *"Local Hotels Brace for Downturn"* in *Crain's Chicago Business (Vol. 31, March 31, 2008, No. 13, pp. 3)*
Pub: Crain Communications Inc.
Contact: Barry Asin, President
Ed: Bob Tita. **Description:** Chicago hotels are seeing a noticeable drop in business-related guests so far this year due to a slumping national economy, tighter corporate expense budgets and higher airfares. **Availability:** Online.

17508 ■ *Small Business for Dummies*
Pub: John Wiley & Sons, Inc.
Contact: Christina Van Tassell, Executive Vice President Chief Financial Officer
Ed: Eric Tyson, Jim Schell. **Released:** 5th Edition. **Price:** $24.99, paperback; $16.99, E-book. **Description:** Guidebook for anyone wanting to start or grow a small business; topics include information financing, budgeting, marketing, management and more. **Availability:** E-book; Print.

17509 ■ *Streetwise Finance and Accounting for Entrepreneurs: Set Budgets, Manage Costs, Keep Your Business Profitable*
Description: Book offers a basic understanding of accounting and finance for small businesses, including financial statements, credits and debits, as well as establishing a budget. Strategies for small companies in financial distress are included.

17510 ■ *Streetwise Small Business Book of Lists: Hundreds of Lists to Help You Reduce Costs, Increase Revenues, and Boost Your Profits!*
Price: Paperback. **Description:** Strategies to help small business owners locate services, increase sales, and lower expenses. **Availability:** Print.

17511 ■ *"Sweeten Your Bottom Line: How To Bring In Dollars When Times Are Tough"* in *Small Business Opportunities (November 2007)*
Description: Adding a new product or promoting a product in a new way can help any small business during hard economic times. **Availability:** Online.

17512 ■ *"Ten Ways to Save on Business Travel"* in *Women Entrepreneur (November 21, 2008)*
Description: Advice regarding ways in which to save money when traveling for business is given. **Availability:** Online.

17513 ■ *"Travel Leery"* in *Crain's Chicago Business (Vol. 31, March 31, 2008, No. 13, pp. 3)*
Pub: Crain Communications Inc.
Contact: Barry Asin, President
Ed: John Pletz. **Description:** Due to the rise in airline prices and a possible recession, many companies are starting to change their travel policies and limit travel spending. **Availability:** Online.

GENERAL SMALL BUSINESS TOPICS

17514 ■ *"Watchful Eye: Entrepreneur Protects Clients and His Bottom Line"* in *Black Enterprise (Vol. 38, March 1, 2008, No. 8, pp. 46)*
Pub: Earl G. Graves Ltd.
Contact: Earl Graves, Jr., President
Ed: Tennille M. Robinson. **Description:** Profile of Elijah Shaw, founder of Icon Services Corporation, a full service security and investigative service; Shaw shares his plans to protect clients while growing his business. **Availability:** Online.

17515 ■ *"Why Business Budget Planning Is So Important"* in *The Balance Small Business (March 9, 2021)*
URL(s): www.thebalancesmb.com/business-budget-planning-reasons-393029
Ed: Rosemary Carlson. **Released:** March 09, 2021. **Description:** Discusses the many things that go into building a budget for your small business. Includes information on budget planning, preparation, evaluation, financing, staffing, and software. **Availability:** Online.

TRADE PERIODICALS

17516 ■ *Public Budgeting & Finance*
Pub: John Wiley & Sons, Inc.
Contact: Christina Van Tassell, Executive Vice President Chief Financial Officer
URL(s): onlinelibrary.wiley.com/journal/15405850
X (Twitter): x.com/pbaf_journal
Ed: Justin Marlowe, Sharon Kioko. **Released:** Quarterly; Spring, Summer, Fall, Winter. **Price:** $119, Individuals for print + online US, Canada and India; $723, Institutions for print and online US, Canada; $643, Institutions for online only US, Canada; $671, Institutions for print only US, Canada; $1,108, Institutions for print and online; $986, Institutions for online India; $1,029, Institutions for print only; $119, Individuals for print + online US, Canada; $986, Institutions for online only India; $1,108, Institutions for print and online India; $1,029, Institutions for print only India; $119, Individuals for print + online India. **Description:** Journal covering research and experiences related to all facets of government finance and budgeting. Published by Wiley on behalf of Public Financial Publications, Inc. **Availability:** Print; PDF; Download; Online.

VIDEO/AUDIO MEDIA

17517 ■ *The How of Business: Budgeting Fundamentals for Small Business*
URL(s): www.thehowofbusiness.com/506-budgeting-fundamentals-small-business
Ed: Henry Lopez. **Released:** January 22, 2024. **Description:** Podcast explains how to create an operating budget for a small business. Includes planning, goal setting, and performance management.

17518 ■ *Nurture Small Business: Denise's Opinions: Mastering Your Business Financial Plan with Budgets, Forecasts, and a Vision*
URL(s): nurturesmallbusiness.buzzsprout.com/900445/episodes/1432015-denise-s-opinions-mastering-your-business-financial-plan-with-budgets-forecasts-and-a-vision
Ed: Denise Cagan. **Released:** January 22, 2024. **Description:** Podcast discusses the difference between budgeting and forecasting and how to use each effectively.

17519 ■ *This Is Small Business: Making It Work: How to Build a Business with a Small Budget*
URL(s): www.smallbusiness.amazon/podcast-episodes/ep-63-making-it-work-how-to-build-a-business-with-a-small-budget
Ed: Andrea Marquez. **Released:** August 13, 2024. **Description:** Podcast discusses how to reduce costs by building a strong network, coming up with creative solutions, building momentum, and understanding your target audience and conducting market research on a budget.

CONSULTANTS

17520 ■ Business Methods Corp. (BMC)
503 Rte. 10 E
 Randolph, NJ 07869
Ph: (973)703-2022
Fax: (973)328-4584
Co. E-mail: businessmethodscorp@gmail.com
URL: http://www.bmclogo.com
Contact: Dr. Kevin S. Chen, President
Description: Distributor of promotional products.
Scope: Distributor of promotional products.
Founded: 1995.

FRANCHISES AND BUSINESS OPPORTUNITIES

17521 ■ Leadership Management International Inc. (LMI)
4567 Lake Shore Dr.
 Waco, TX 76710
Ph: (254)776-7551
Free: 800-876-2389
Co. E-mail: info@lmi-inc.com
URL: http://www.lmi-world.com
Contact: Randy Slechta, President
Facebook: www.facebook.com/LMIWorld
Linkedin: www.linkedin.com/company/leadership
 -management-international-inc
X (Twitter): x.com/lmi_inc
Instagram: www.instagram.com/lmi.world
YouTube: www.youtube.com/channel/UCczBssCLU
 _RjOyeHXPZ0Rjw

Description: The franchise provides business aids and services. **Scope:** Executive, leadership and management development firm, sales division for marketing management and leadership development programs. Process development specialists set about developing a complete solution to organizational planning and development. **Founded:** 1966. **Royalty Fee:** 6%. **Publications:** "Believe Yourself to Success"; "Consider the Three Common Thread of Leadership"; "Do It Now"; "Enthusiastic Customers"; "Enthusiasm The Sixth Key to a Successful Future"; "Five Steps to Success"; "Helping Your Employees Change"; "Motivating Employees to Change Behavior"; "How to Write an Up-Front Management Agreement"; "Make Your Dreams Come True". **Financial Assistance:** Yes **Training:** Includes 2 days training at headquarters, 2 days at franchisee's location and ongoing support. **Special Services:** Leadership Management®; LMI Strategic Development Process™; Effective Personal Productivity®; Effective Personal Leadership®; Effective Motivational Leadership®; EffectiveSupervisory Management®; Effective Leadership Development®; Effective Communication®; Effective Team Dynamics®; Effective Selling Strategies®; Effective Strategic Leadership®.

COMPUTER SYSTEMS/ SOFTWARE

17522 ■ *Aatrix Top Pay*™
Aatrix Software Inc.
2617 S Columbia Rd.
 Grand Forks, ND 58201
Ph: (701)746-6017
Free: 800-426-0854
Co. E-mail: sales@aatrix.com
URL: http://www.aatrix.com
URL(s): www.aatrix.com/solutions/mac/top-pay
Price: $259.95, for annual. **Description:** Handles payroll calculations and tax deductions for both salaried and hourly employees. **Availability:** Download; Online.

17523 ■ *Argos Software / ABECAS Insight*
Argos Software
8770 W Bryn Mawr Ave., Ste. 1300
 Chicago, IL 60631
Ph: (559)227-1000
Free: 888-253-5353
Co. E-mail: info@argosoftware.com
URL: http://www.argosoftware.com
Contact: Sean Sullivan, President
URL(s): www.argosoftware.com/request-a-demo
Description: Available for MS-DOS operating system. Payroll system for agricultural employees. **Availability:** Online.

Business Communications

START-UP INFORMATION

17524 ■ *"Breaking Barriers" in Baltimore Business Journal (Vol. 30, June 29, 2012, No. 8, pp. 1)*
Ed: Jack Lambert. **Description:** Many Hispanic entrepreneurs have been struggling to start businesses in Baltimore, Maryland. Many necessary documents are available only in English. Hispanic businesses are seen to spark future economic growth in Baltimore. **Availability:** Print; Online.

ASSOCIATIONS AND OTHER ORGANIZATIONS

17525 ■ **Association for Business Communication (ABC)**
PO Box 304
Natural Bridge Station, VA 24579-0304
Co. E-mail: abcoffice@businesscommunication.org
URL: http://www.businesscommunication.org
Contact: D. Joel Whalen, President
X (Twitter): x.com/A4_BC
Description: College teachers of business communication; management consultants in business communications; training directors and correspondence supervisors of business firms, direct mail copywriters, public relations writers, and others interested in communication for business. **Founded:** 1935. **Publications:** *Video in the 90's: A Practical Guide to Professional Video*; *Association for Business Communication Bulletin--Membership Directory Issue*; *Making Communication Requirements More Explicit in the AACSB Standards for MBA Programs*; *International Journal of Business Communication (IJBC)* (Quarterly). **Educational Activities:** ABC Annual International Conference (Annual). **Awards:** Kitty O. Locker Outstanding Researcher Award (Annual); Meada Gibbs Outstanding Teacher-Scholar Award (Annual); ABC Outstanding Dissertation Award (Annual); ABC Distinguished Publication on Business Communication (Annual); ABC Outstanding Article in Business and Professional Communication Quarterly (Annual); ABC Outstanding Article in the International Journal of Business Communication (Annual). **Geographic Preference:** National.

17526 ■ **International Association of Business Communicators (IABC) - Library**
330 N Wabash Ave., Ste. 2000
Chicago, IL 60611
Ph: (312)321-6868
Free: 800-218-8097
Fax: (312)673-6708
Co. E-mail: news@iabc.com
URL: http://www.iabc.com
Contact: Peter Finn, Executive Director
E-mail: pfinn@iabc.com
Linkedin: www.linkedin.com/groups/international-association-business-communicators-iabc-58441/about
X (Twitter): x.com/iabc
Instagram: www.instagram.com/iabcsnaps
YouTube: www.youtube.com/user/IABClive
Description: Conducts research in the communication field and encourages establishment of college-level programs in organizational communication. Offers accreditation program; conducts surveys on employee communication effectiveness and media trends. **Scope:** Business communicators. **Founded:** 1970. **Holdings:** Figures not available. **Publications:** *World Book of IABC Communicators*; *World Book of IABC Communicators*; *Communication World: The Magazine for Communication Professionals* (Monthly). **Educational Activities:** IABC World Conference (Annual). **Awards:** IABC Gold Quill Awards (Annual); IABC Lifetime Foundation Friend Award (Annual); IABC Chapter Management Award (Annual); Excellence in Communication Leadership (EXCEL) Award (Annual); IABC Chair's Award (Annual); IABC Fellow (Annual). **Geographic Preference:** Multinational.

17527 ■ **Lochmueller Group Inc.**
6200 Vogel Rd.
Evansville, IN 47715
Ph: (812)479-6200
Free: 800-423-7411
Co. E-mail: info@lochgroup.com
URL: http://www.lochgroup.com
Contact: Carl Camacho, Chief Operating Officer
Facebook: www.facebook.com/lochgroup
Linkedin: www.linkedin.com/company/lochmueller-group
X (Twitter): x.com/lochgroup
Instagram: www.instagram.com/lochgroup
Description: Professional planning, engineering and environmental firm and services include air quality, civil engineering, economic development, environmental analysis, environmental engineering, land use planning, surveying, traffic engineering, traffic studies, transportation plans, and systems. **Scope:** Professional planning, engineering and environmental firm and services include air quality, civil engineering, economic development, environmental analysis, environmental engineering, land use planning, surveying, traffic engineering, traffic studies, transportation plans, and systems. **Founded:** 1980. **Publications:** *Technical Communication* (Quarterly); *Intercom: The Magazine of the Society for Technical Communication* (8/year); *Technical Communication--Special Issue/Membership Directory* (Annual). **Educational Activities:** STC Technical Communication Summit (Annual). **Awards:** STC Scholarships (Annual); Marian Norby Scholarships.

EDUCATIONAL PROGRAMS

17528 ■ **Advanced Leadership Communication Strategies (Onsite)**
URL(s): www.amanet.org/training/seminars/onsite/advanced-leadership-communication-strategies.aspx
Price: $2,745, Non-members; $2,495, Members AMA; $2,268, Members GSA. **Description:** Three-day seminar to build on current strong leadership skills and influence across the board. **Audience:** Professionals and Experienced Leaders. **Principal Exhibits:** Three-day seminar to build on current strong leadership skills and influence across the board.

17529 ■ **AMA Effective Technical Writing (Onsite)**
American Management Association (AMA)
1601 Broadway
New York, NY 10019
Ph: (212)586-8100
Free: 800-262-9699
Fax: (212)903-8168
Co. E-mail: customerservice@amanet.org
URL: http://www.amanet.org
Contact: Manny Avramidis, President
URL(s): www.amanet.org/training/seminars/onsite/Effective-Technical-Writing.aspx
Description: Covers the basics of writing technical documents such as reports, manuals, specifications, proposals, and instructions. **Audience:** Engineers, scientists, IT/computer personnel and people in R&D. **Principal Exhibits:** Covers the basics of writing technical documents such as reports, manuals, specifications, proposals, and instructions.

17530 ■ **AMA Managing Emotions in the Workplace: Strategies for Success (Onsite)**
American Management Association (AMA)
1601 Broadway
New York, NY 10019
Ph: (212)586-8100
Free: 800-262-9699
Fax: (212)903-8168
Co. E-mail: customerservice@amanet.org
URL: http://www.amanet.org
Contact: Manny Avramidis, President
URL(s): www.amanet.org/training/seminars/onsite/Managing-Emotions-in-the-Workplace-Strategies-for-Success.aspx
Description: Covers methods for effectively and professionally communicating emotion, creating positive work environments, and emotional control. **Audience:** Business professionals. **Principal Exhibits:** Covers methods for effectively and professionally communicating emotion, creating positive work environments, and emotional control.

17531 ■ **AMA Responding to Conflict: Strategies for Improved Communication**
American Management Association (AMA)
1601 Broadway
New York, NY 10019
Ph: (212)586-8100
Free: 800-262-9699
Fax: (212)903-8168
Co. E-mail: customerservice@amanet.org
URL: http://www.amanet.org
Contact: Manny Avramidis, President
URL(s): www.amanet.org/training/seminars/Responding-to-Conflict-Strategies-for-Improved-Communication.aspx

GENERAL SMALL BUSINESS TOPICS

Business Communications ■ 17544

Frequency: Continuous. **Description:** Covers effective communication, diffusing misunderstanding, creating open and honest work environments, dealing with conflict, and improving listening skills. **Audience:** Business professionals who want to expand their conflict management skills, understand their own emotions and behaviors when addressing conflict, and find productive ways to manage conflict. **Principal Exhibits:** Covers effective communication, diffusing misunderstanding, creating open and honest work environments, dealing with conflict, and improving listening skills. **Telecommunication Services:** customerservice@amanet.org.

17532 ■ AMA Strategies for Developing Effective Presentation Skills (Onsite)
American Management Association (AMA)
1601 Broadway
New York, NY 10019
Ph: (212)586-8100
Free: 800-262-9699
Fax: (212)903-8168
Co. E-mail: customerservice@amanet.org
URL: http://www.amanet.org
Contact: Manny Avramidis, President
URL(s): www.amanet.org/training/seminars/onsite/Strategies-for-Developing-Effective-Presentation-Skills.aspx
Description: Covers overcoming stage fright, various types of presentations, developing a full presentation, and techniques for delivering a presentation, including answering questions and interacting with the audience. **Audience:** Everyone who needs to develop their presentation skills, speak in front of groups or sell ideas to others and has little or no presentation experience. **Principal Exhibits:** Covers overcoming stage fright, various types of presentations, developing a full presentation, and techniques for delivering a presentation, including answering questions and interacting with the audience.

17533 ■ AMA Successful Meeting Planning (Onsite)
URL(s): www.amanet.org
Description: Covers all aspects of successfully planning a meeting, including objectives, budget, site selection, and working with vendors. **Audience:** Industry professionals. **Principal Exhibits:** Covers all aspects of successfully planning a meeting, including objectives, budget, site selection, and working with vendors. **Telecommunication Services:** customerservice@amanet.org.

17534 ■ Assertive Communication - Essential Skills for Successful Women (Onsite)
National Seminars Training L.L.C. (NST)
14502 W 105th St.
Lenexa, KS 66215
Free: 800-349-1935
Co. E-mail: info@findaseminar.com
URL: http://www.findaseminar.com/tpd/Padgett-Thompson-Seminars.asp
URL(s): www.findaseminar.com/event1.asp?eventID=9750
Price: $199. **Description:** Assertiveness training for today's business woman. **Audience:** Professionals. **Principal Exhibits:** Assertiveness training for today's business woman.

17535 ■ Assertiveness Skills: Communicating With Authority and Impact (Onsite)
Learning Tree International Inc.
13650 Dulles Technology Dr., Ste. 400
Herndon, VA 20171-6156
Free: 888-843-8733
Co. E-mail: info@learningtree.com
URL: http://www.learningtree.com
URL(s): www.learningtree.com/courses/244/assertiveness-skills-communicating-with-authority-impact
Description: Develop a positive, assertive style and build a skill set that will enable you to react positively in demanding situations. **Audience:** Business, nonprofit, government and educational professionals. **Principal Exhibits:** Develop a positive, assertive style and build a skill set that will enable you to react positively in demanding situations.

17536 ■ Assertiveness Training for Managers
Canadian Management Centre (CMC)
150 King St. W Ste. 271
Toronto, ON, Canada M5H 1J9
Ph: (416)214-5678
Free: 877-262-2519
Fax: (416)214-6047
Co. E-mail: cmcinfo@cmcoutperform.com
URL: http://cmcoutperform.com
Contact: Chris Peacock, Director
URL(s): cmcoutperform.com/manager-assertiveness-training
Price: C$2,095, Members; C$2,295, Non-members.
Description: Covers using assertive behavior professionally, requesting change, managing conflict, and defining objectives. Held in Toronto and Ottawa, ON. **Audience:** Professionals interested in adopting a more impactful and effective interpersonal management style. **Principal Exhibits:** Covers using assertive behavior professionally, requesting change, managing conflict, and defining objectives. Held in Toronto and Ottawa, ON.

17537 ■ Assertiveness Training for Women in Business
American Management Association (AMA)
1601 Broadway
New York, NY 10019
Ph: (212)586-8100
Free: 800-262-9699
Fax: (212)903-8168
Co. E-mail: customerservice@amanet.org
URL: http://www.amanet.org
Contact: Manny Avramidis, President
URL(s): www.amanet.org/training/seminars/Assertiveness-Training-for-Women-in-Business.aspx
Price: $2,345, Non-members; $2,095, Members; $1,794, Members General Services Administration (GSA). **Frequency:** Continuous. **Description:** Covers self-image, stress management, various communication techniques for assertiveness, and male and female workplace attitudes. Also available live online. **Audience:** Women in business. **Principal Exhibits:** Covers self-image, stress management, various communication techniques for assertiveness, and male and female workplace attitudes. Also available live online. **Telecommunication Services:** customerservice@amanet.org.

17538 ■ Assertiveness Training for Women in Business Canada
URL(s): cmcoutperform.com/business-women-assertiveness-training
Price: C$2,095, Members; C$2,295, Non-members.
Audience: All women professionals, managers and supervisors who want to improve and build on their communication, conflict resolution, delegation and action planning skills. **Telecommunication Services:** cmcinfo@cmcoutperform.com.

17539 ■ Bargaining With Vendors and Suppliers (Onsite)
National Seminars Training L.L.C. (NST)
14502 W 105th St.
Lenexa, KS 66215
Free: 800-349-1935
Co. E-mail: info@findaseminar.com
URL: http://www.findaseminar.com/tpd/Padgett-Thompson-Seminars.asp
URL(s): www.findaseminar.com/event1.asp?eventID=946
Description: A one-day seminar that teaches practical bargaining skills that will help a company come out of every negotiation a winner. **Audience:** Vendors, suppliers, and professionals. **Principal Exhibits:** A one-day seminar that teaches practical bargaining skills that will help a company come out of every negotiation a winner.

17540 ■ Business Conversation for Sales and Service (Onsite)
Seminar Information Service Inc. (SIS)
250 El Camino Real., Ste. 112
Tustin, CA 92780
Ph: (714)508-0340
Free: 877-736-4636
Fax: (714)734-8027
Co. E-mail: info@seminarinformation.com
URL: http://www.seminarinformation.com
Contact: Catherine Bellizzi, President
URL(s): www.seminarinformation.com/details.cfm?qc=qqbmve
Description: Participants will learn practical tips and practice conversation. Build common ground with colleagues, customers, and senior managers, including methods to develop a repertoire of topics, make skillful transitions, develop confidence and draw people to you. **Audience:** Business professionals. **Principal Exhibits:** Participants will learn practical tips and practice conversation. Build common ground with colleagues, customers, and senior managers, including methods to develop a repertoire of topics, make skillful transitions, develop confidence and draw people to you.

17541 ■ Business Conversation Skills for the Multilingual Professional (Onsite)
URL(s): www.amanet.org
Description: Comprehensive two-day workshop will improve your conversation skills on all levels to achieve your professional and organizational goals. **Audience:** Multilingual business professionals. **Principal Exhibits:** Comprehensive two-day workshop will improve your conversation skills on all levels to achieve your professional and organizational goals.

17542 ■ Communicating Change
URL(s): cmcoutperform.com
Description: Learn how to leverage communication as a critical vehicle for enabling change in an organization. **Audience:** Professionals, and managers. **Principal Exhibits:** Learn how to leverage communication as a critical vehicle for enabling change in an organization.

17543 ■ Communicating with Confidence (Onsite)
American Management Association (AMA)
1601 Broadway
New York, NY 10019
Ph: (212)586-8100
Free: 800-262-9699
Fax: (212)903-8168
Co. E-mail: customerservice@amanet.org
URL: http://www.amanet.org
Contact: Manny Avramidis, President
URL(s): www.amanet.org/communicating-with-confidence
Price: $2,345, Non-members; $2,095, Members AMA; $1,889, Members GSA. **Frequency:** Continuous. **Description:** Three-day seminar to assess your communication skills, develop listening competencies, increase cognitive skills, and roadmap for clearer communication. **Audience:** Early career professionals or anyone interested in enhancing their fundamental verbal communication skills, including coordinators, specialists, analyst, consultants, associate managers, project managers and leadership-track administrative professionals. **Principal Exhibits:** Three-day seminar to assess your communication skills, develop listening competencies, increase cognitive skills, and roadmap for clearer communication.

17544 ■ Communicating Effectively in Your Corporate Culture (Onsite)
Seminar Information Service Inc. (SIS)
250 El Camino Real., Ste. 112
Tustin, CA 92780
Ph: (714)508-0340
Free: 877-736-4636
Fax: (714)734-8027
Co. E-mail: info@seminarinformation.com
URL: http://www.seminarinformation.com
Contact: Catherine Bellizzi, President
URL(s): www.seminarinformation.com
Description: Gives participants a sound understanding of the principles of effective communication and the skill to recognize and resolve communication breakdowns in the workplace. Attendees learn the objectives of communication, gain active listening skills and how to give directions that get results. **Audience:** General public, industry professionals.

Principal Exhibits: Gives participants a sound understanding of the principles of effective communication and the skill to recognize and resolve communication breakdowns in the workplace. Attendees learn the objectives of communication, gain active listening skills and how to give directions that get results.

17545 ■ Communication and Interpersonal Skills: A Seminar for IT and Technical Professionals (Onsite)
American Management Association (AMA)
  1601 Broadway
  New York, NY 10019
Ph: (212)586-8100
Free: 800-262-9699
Fax: (212)903-8168
Co. E-mail: customerservice@amanet.org
URL: http://www.amanet.org
Contact: Manny Avramidis, President
URL(s): www.amanet.org/communication-and-in terpersonal-skills-for-technical-professionals
Price: $2,195, Non-members; $1,995, Members AMA; $1,795, Members GSA. **Frequency:** Continuous. **Description:** Learn how to combine your interpersonal communication skills effectively with your technical skills to get results. **Audience:** All technical and IT professionals who need to develop the interpersonal and communication skills necessary to effectively convey their knowledge to those around them. **Principal Exhibits:** Learn how to combine your interpersonal communication skills effectively with your technical skills to get results. **Telecommunication Services:** customerservice@amanet.org.

17546 ■ Communication and Interpersonal Skills for IT & Technical Professionals
URL(s): cmcoutperform.com/communication-and-in terpersonal-skills-for-technical-professionals
Price: C$1,845, Members; C$1,995, Non-members. **Description:** Covers effective communication skills, prioritizing, and dealing with various types of communication styles. **Audience:** Managers, supervisors and experienced technical professionals seeking to build stronger relationships with clients and customers in their workplaces. **Principal Exhibits:** Covers effective communication skills, prioritizing, and dealing with various types of communication styles.

17547 ■ Communication Skills: Results Through Collaboration (Onsite)
Seminar Information Service Inc. (SIS)
  250 El Camino Real., Ste. 112
  Tustin, CA 92780
Ph: (714)508-0340
Free: 877-736-4636
Fax: (714)734-8027
Co. E-mail: info@seminarinformation.com
URL: http://www.seminarinformation.com
Contact: Catherine Bellizzi, President
URL(s): www.seminarinformation.com/qqbdnd/ communication-skills-results-through-collaboration
Description: Learn how to: Achieve results in your communications with others; Build collaborative relationships that emphasize trust and respect; Communicate effectively using simple, concise and direct language; Enhance your active listening skills; Foster cross-cultural understanding in your workplace; Eliminate the roadblocks that undermine your ability to communicate effectively. **Audience:** Industry professionals. **Principal Exhibits:** Learn how to: Achieve results in your communications with others; Build collaborative relationships that emphasize trust and respect; Communicate effectively using simple, concise and direct language; Enhance your active listening skills; Foster cross-cultural understanding in your workplace; Eliminate the roadblocks that undermine your ability to communicate effectively.

17548 ■ Communication Skills: Results Through Collaboration (Onsite)
Learning Tree International Inc.
  13650 Dulles Technology Dr., Ste. 400
  Herndon, VA 20171-6156
Free: 888-843-8733
Co. E-mail: info@learningtree.com
URL: http://www.learningtree.com
URL(s): www.learningtree.com/courses/292/ communication-skills-results-through-collaboration/ #tab1
Description: Learn to achieve results in your communications with others and build collaborative relationships. **Audience:** Industry professionals. **Principal Exhibits:** Learn to achieve results in your communications with others and build collaborative relationships.

17549 ■ Communication Skills for Women
Fred Pryor Seminars & CareerTrack
  5700 Broadmoor, Ste. 300
  Mission, KS 66202
Free: 800-780-8476
Fax: (913)967-8849
Co. E-mail: customerservice@pryor.com
URL: http://www.pryor.com
Contact: Janet Turner, Contact
E-mail: dmca@pryor.com
URL(s): www.pryor.com/training-seminars/ communication-skills-for-women
Frequency: Irregular. **Description:** Covers valuable insights women can use to enhance their communication style while earning the respect and cooperation of others, including how to control your emotions and stay composed and effective while under pressure. **Audience:** Women. **Principal Exhibits:** Covers valuable insights women can use to enhance their communication style while earning the respect and cooperation of others, including how to control your emotions and stay composed and effective while under pressure.

17550 ■ Comprehensive Proofreading (Onsite)
URL(s): www.eeicom.com
Description: Covers creating proofreading checklists, using style guides, and proofreading electronic documents. **Audience:** Professional proofreaders. **Principal Exhibits:** Covers creating proofreading checklists, using style guides, and proofreading electronic documents.

17551 ■ Conflict Communications
URL(s): www.eeicom.com
Description: Learn to coach people through conflict, identify different levels and forms of conflict and why people react differently to conflict. **Audience:** Industry professionals, managers and administrative. **Principal Exhibits:** Learn to coach people through conflict, identify different levels and forms of conflict and why people react differently to conflict.

17552 ■ Conflict Management Skills for Women (Onsite)
Seminar Information Service Inc. (SIS)
  250 El Camino Real., Ste. 112
  Tustin, CA 92780
Ph: (714)508-0340
Free: 877-736-4636
Fax: (714)734-8027
Co. E-mail: info@seminarinformation.com
URL: http://www.seminarinformation.com
Contact: Catherine Bellizzi, President
URL(s): www.seminarinformation.com/details.cfm?qc =qqayxe
Description: Learn how to keep unmanaged conflicts, disagreements and out-of-control emotions from harming your important working and personal relationships. **Audience:** Women. **Principal Exhibits:** Learn how to keep unmanaged conflicts, disagreements and out-of-control emotions from harming your important working and personal relationships.

17553 ■ Critical Thinking and Out-of-the-Box Problem Solving (Onsite)
Seminar Information Service Inc. (SIS)
  250 El Camino Real., Ste. 112
  Tustin, CA 92780
Ph: (714)508-0340
Free: 877-736-4636
Fax: (714)734-8027
Co. E-mail: info@seminarinformation.com
URL: http://www.seminarinformation.com
Contact: Catherine Bellizzi, President
URL(s): www.seminarinformation.com/qqbtjz/critical -thinking-and-creative-problem-solving
Description: Learn how to: Make better decisions through critical thinking and creative problem solving; Adapt to different thinking styles in group and team environments; Foster an innovative environment in your workplace; Recognize and remove barriers to individual and group creativity; Systematically analyze a target problem; Present your ideas clearly and concisely for maximum stakeholder buy-in; Transform your creativity into practical business solutions. **Audience:** Industry professionals. **Principal Exhibits:** Learn how to: Make better decisions through critical thinking and creative problem solving; Adapt to different thinking styles in group and team environments; Foster an innovative environment in your workplace; Recognize and remove barriers to individual and group creativity; Systematically analyze a target problem; Present your ideas clearly and concisely for maximum stakeholder buy-in; Transform your creativity into practical business solutions.

17554 ■ Customer Focused Telephone Techniques (Onsite)
Seminar Information Service Inc. (SIS)
  250 El Camino Real., Ste. 112
  Tustin, CA 92780
Ph: (714)508-0340
Free: 877-736-4636
Fax: (714)734-8027
Co. E-mail: info@seminarinformation.com
URL: http://www.seminarinformation.com
Contact: Catherine Bellizzi, President
URL(s): www.seminarinformation.com
Description: Participants learn the importance of telephone and acquire professional skills for better business practice, including calming angry clients and projecting a confident business image. **Audience:** Employees who use the phone to do business with internal and external customers. **Principal Exhibits:** Participants learn the importance of telephone and acquire professional skills for better business practice, including calming angry clients and projecting a confident business image.

17555 ■ Developing Dynamic Presentation Skills
Seminar Information Service Inc. (SIS)
  250 El Camino Real., Ste. 112
  Tustin, CA 92780
Ph: (714)508-0340
Free: 877-736-4636
Fax: (714)734-8027
Co. E-mail: info@seminarinformation.com
URL: http://www.seminarinformation.com
Contact: Catherine Bellizzi, President
URL(s): www.seminarinformation.com
Description: Learn how to prepare an effective presentation by organizing key points into a coherent story; Capture and maintain audience interest and attention using interactive techniques. **Audience:** Industry professionals, IT. **Principal Exhibits:** Learn how to prepare an effective presentation by organizing key points into a coherent story; Capture and maintain audience interest and attention using interactive techniques.

17556 ■ Developing Effective Business Conversation Skills (Onsite)
American Management Association (AMA)
  1601 Broadway
  New York, NY 10019
Ph: (212)586-8100
Free: 800-262-9699
Fax: (212)903-8168
Co. E-mail: customerservice@amanet.org
URL: http://www.amanet.org
Contact: Manny Avramidis, President
URL(s): www.amanet.org/training/seminars/onsite/ Developing-Effective-Business-Conversation-Skills .aspx
Price: $2,195, Non-members; $1,995, Members AMA; $1,795, Members GSA. **Description:** Learn effective business communication skills. **Audience:**

Managers, supervisors, team leaders and business professionals. **Principal Exhibits:** Learn effective business communication skills.

17557 ■ Developing Effective Communications Skills (Onsite)
Seminar Information Service Inc. (SIS)
250 El Camino Real., Ste. 112
Tustin, CA 92780
Ph: (714)508-0340
Free: 877-736-4636
Fax: (714)734-8027
Co. E-mail: info@seminarinformation.com
URL: http://www.seminarinformation.com
Contact: Catherine Bellizzi, President
URL(s): www.seminarinformation.com
Description: learn skills for communicating powerfully, sending clear messages, and conducting challenging conversations while maintaining effective working relationships with supervisors and co-workers. **Audience:** Managers and supervisors. **Principal Exhibits:** learn skills for communicating powerfully, sending clear messages, and conducting challenging conversations while maintaining effective working relationships with supervisors and co-workers. **Telecommunication Services:** info@seminarinformation.com.

17558 ■ Dynamic Listening Skills for Successful Communication (Onsite)
URL(s): www.amanet.org
Description: Develop listening skills that encourage productive interactions. **Audience:** Administrative professional, entry-level staff and mid-level staff. **Principal Exhibits:** Develop listening skills that encourage productive interactions.

17559 ■ Editorial Skills for Non-Editors (Onsite)
URL(s): www.eeicom.com
Description: Covers punctuation and grammar, usage, and proofreading marks. **Audience:** Industry professionals. **Principal Exhibits:** Covers punctuation and grammar, usage, and proofreading marks.

17560 ■ EEI Communications Adobe Captivate 3
URL(s): www.eeicom.com
Description: Seminar that teaches how to create professional quality, interactive simulations and software demonstrations without any programming or multimedia knowledge, including basics, captions and timelines, images, pointer paths, buttons, and highlight boxes, movies, rollover captions and rollover images, slide labels and notes, audio, animation, and question slides. **Audience:** Industry professionals. **Principal Exhibits:** Seminar that teaches how to create professional quality, interactive simulations and software demonstrations without any programming or multimedia knowledge, including basics, captions and timelines, images, pointer paths, buttons, and highlight boxes, movies, rollover captions and rollover images, slide labels and notes, audio, animation, and question slides.

17561 ■ EEI Communications Advanced Editing
URL(s): www.eeicom.com
Description: Covers advanced editing techniques, including copyediting, substantive editing, style sheets, English grammar, and query lists. **Audience:** Content creators, editors, proofers, graphic designers, specialists, desktop publishers, recruiters, and sales team. **Principal Exhibits:** Covers advanced editing techniques, including copyediting, substantive editing, style sheets, English grammar, and query lists. **Telecommunication Services:** train@eeicom.com.

17562 ■ EEI Communications Designing for Diversity
URL(s): www.eeicom.com
Description: Workshop to help you connect with all your audiences utilizing the appropriate visual imagery and words, including when not to send ethnically targeted messages, and designing "one size fits all" publications when your budget won't permit targeted publications, and the effects of visual imagery on attitudes and behavior. **Audience:** Designers, programmers and production specialists. **Principal Exhibits:** Workshop to help you connect with all your audiences utilizing the appropriate visual imagery and words, including when not to send ethnically targeted messages, and designing "one size fits all" publications when your budget won't permit targeted publications, and the effects of visual imagery on attitudes and behavior.

17563 ■ EEI Communications Effective Briefings
URL(s): www.eeicom.com
Description: Hands-on course where you explore elements, principles, and guidelines of effective briefings, including how to deliver vocally, verbally, and visually, find the focus and the right tone, organize your message, create slides and handouts that support your message, and customize the message and delivery for your various audiences. **Audience:** Industry professionals, public. **Principal Exhibits:** Hands-on course where you explore elements, principles, and guidelines of effective briefings, including how to deliver vocally, verbally, and visually, find the focus and the right tone, organize your message, create slides and handouts that support your message, and customize the message and delivery for your various audiences.

17564 ■ EEI Communications Effective Business Writing (Onsite)
URL(s): www.eeicom.com
Description: Covers the basic elements of writing effective business letters, e-mails, and memos, including grammar, audience analysis, persuasion, and usage problems. **Audience:** Writers, editors, designers, and publication specialists. **Principal Exhibits:** Covers the basic elements of writing effective business letters, e-mails, and memos, including grammar, audience analysis, persuasion, and usage problems. **Telecommunication Services:** train@eeicom.com.

17565 ■ EEI Communications Effective Presentation Techniques: Public Speaking
URL(s): www.eeicom.com
Description: Covers assessing the audience, organizational skills, and effective delivery styles. **Audience:** Professionals. **Principal Exhibits:** Covers assessing the audience, organizational skills, and effective delivery styles. **Telecommunication Services:** train@eeicom.com.

17566 ■ EEI Communications Introduction to Information Design
URL(s): www.eeicom.com
Description: Topics include defining information design, understanding how users process information, techniques for information design, information graphics, and presenting Web information. **Audience:** Professional designers. **Principal Exhibits:** Topics include defining information design, understanding how users process information, techniques for information design, information graphics, and presenting Web information. **Telecommunication Services:** train@eeicom.com.

17567 ■ EEI Communications Strategies of Effective Writing (Onsite)
URL(s): www.eeicom.com
Description: Covers basic writing skills, including effective planning as a means of saving time, generating ideas, organizing ideas, writing concisely and clearly, and attracting and holding readers' interest. **Audience:** Writers, editors, designers, proofreaders, and publication specialists . **Principal Exhibits:** Covers basic writing skills, including effective planning as a means of saving time, generating ideas, organizing ideas, writing concisely and clearly, and attracting and holding readers' interest. **Telecommunication Services:** train@eeicom.com.

17568 ■ EEI Communications Substantive Editing I (Onsite)
URL(s): www.eeicom.com
Description: Covers editing for clarity and meaning, including reworking vague or inappropriate phrases, untangling muddled language, posing effective questions to the author, and revising with a purpose. **Audience:** Proofreaders, copyeditors and substantive editors . **Principal Exhibits:** Covers editing for clarity and meaning, including reworking vague or inappropriate phrases, untangling muddled language, posing effective questions to the author, and revising with a purpose. **Telecommunication Services:** train@eeicom.com.

17569 ■ EEI Communications Technical Writing (Onsite)
URL(s): www.eeicom.com
Description: Covers the technical writing process from analyzing an audience and developing a purpose to laying out a document with both text and graphics. **Audience:** Writers, editors, designers, proofreaders, and publication specialists. **Principal Exhibits:** Covers the technical writing process from analyzing an audience and developing a purpose to laying out a document with both text and graphics. **Telecommunication Services:** train@eeicom.com.

17570 ■ EEI Communications Writing for the Web II (Onsite)
URL(s): www.eeicom.com
Description: Seminar for persons with 3-5 years' experience as a Web writer or editor, or have completed Writing for the Web I, covering how to define your genre and audience, develop a structure for your Web content, working with subject matter experts who aren't writers, making the most of your writing project, giving and getting feedback, writing links that work for your client, how to write menus so clients can use them, and recasting a print article for the Web. **Audience:** Web writers and editors. **Principal Exhibits:** Seminar for persons with 3-5 years' experience as a Web writer or editor, or have completed Writing for the Web I, covering how to define your genre and audience, develop a structure for your Web content, working with subject matter experts who aren't writers, making the most of your writing project, giving and getting feedback, writing links that work for your client, how to write menus so clients can use them, and recasting a print article for the Web.

17571 ■ Effective Communication and Motivation (Onsite)
Seminar Information Service Inc. (SIS)
250 El Camino Real., Ste. 112
Tustin, CA 92780
Ph: (714)508-0340
Free: 877-736-4636
Fax: (714)734-8027
Co. E-mail: info@seminarinformation.com
URL: http://www.seminarinformation.com
Contact: Catherine Bellizzi, President
URL(s): www.seminarinformation.com
Description: Gives managerial personnel a sound understanding of the principles of effective communication and the skill to recognize and to resolve communication breakdowns in the workplace. Participants learn to apply communication skills to problem solving, employee relations and performance appraisal. **Audience:** General public, industry professionals. **Principal Exhibits:** Gives managerial personnel a sound understanding of the principles of effective communication and the skill to recognize and to resolve communication breakdowns in the workplace. Participants learn to apply communication skills to problem solving, employee relations and performance appraisal.

17572 ■ Effective Executive Speaking (Onsite)
American Management Association (AMA)
1601 Broadway
New York, NY 10019
Ph: (212)586-8100
Free: 800-262-9699
Fax: (212)903-8168
Co. E-mail: customerservice@amanet.org
URL: http://www.amanet.org
Contact: Manny Avramidis, President

17573 ■ Business Communications

URL(s): www.amanet.org/effective-executive-speaking
Price: $2,445, Non-members; $2,195, Members AMA; $1,984, Members GSA. **Frequency:** Continuous. **Description:** Learn to speak, present, and communicate effectively. **Audience:** This seminar is recommended for every executive with some prior public speaking experience who must speak in front of groups, make presentations, sell ideas to others or face cameras and microphones. **Principal Exhibits:** Learn to speak, present, and communicate effectively.

17573 ■ Effective Negotiating
Seminar Information Service Inc. (SIS)
250 El Camino Real., Ste. 112
Tustin, CA 92780
Ph: (714)508-0340
Free: 877-736-4636
Fax: (714)734-8027
Co. E-mail: info@seminarinformation.com
URL: http://www.seminarinformation.com
Contact: Catherine Bellizzi, President
URL(s): www.seminarinformation.com/details.cfm?qc=qqaccz
Description: Learn basic negotiation techniques by focusing on the dynamics of interpersonal and group conflict; differing styles and approaches to negotiation; the negotiation process; and negotiating to achieve mutual benefit. **Audience:** Managers, executives and those who must negotiate. **Principal Exhibits:** Learn basic negotiation techniques by focusing on the dynamics of interpersonal and group conflict; differing styles and approaches to negotiation; the negotiation process; and negotiating to achieve mutual benefit.

17574 ■ Enhancing Your People Skills
Seminar Information Service Inc. (SIS)
250 El Camino Real., Ste. 112
Tustin, CA 92780
Ph: (714)508-0340
Free: 877-736-4636
Fax: (714)734-8027
Co. E-mail: info@seminarinformation.com
URL: http://www.seminarinformation.com
Contact: Catherine Bellizzi, President
URL(s): www.seminarinformation.com
Description: Build awareness and skill in the areas of team dynamics, group problem solving, and group decision making. The critical structural and behavioral dimensions of building and leading an effective work team or task force are fully explored. You will develop leadership skills applicable to many areas, but especially suited to self-directed work teams, employee participation teams, interdepartmental task groups, and other group situations where combined efforts are needed to reach optimal performance levels. **Audience:** General public. **Principal Exhibits:** Build awareness and skill in the areas of team dynamics, group problem solving, and group decision making. The critical structural and behavioral dimensions of building and leading an effective work team or task force are fully explored. You will develop leadership skills applicable to many areas, but especially suited to self-directed work teams, employee participation teams, interdepartmental task groups, and other group situations where combined efforts are needed to reach optimal performance levels.

17575 ■ Essential Skills of Dynamic Public Speaking (Onsite)
National Seminars Training L.L.C. (NST)
14502 W 105th St.
Lenexa, KS 66215
Free: 800-349-1935
Co. E-mail: info@findaseminar.com
URL: http://www.findaseminar.com/tpd/Padgett-Thompson-Seminars.asp
URL(s): www.nationalseminarstraining.com/SeminarSearchResults/Essential_Skills_of_Dynamic_Public_Speaking/YPSK/index.html
Description: Workshop provides face-saving techniques that will make any business presentation easier. **Audience:** Business industry professionals. **Principal Exhibits:** Workshop provides face-saving techniques that will make any business presentation easier.

17576 ■ The Essentials of Communicating With Diplomacy and Professionalism (Onsite)
Seminar Information Service Inc. (SIS)
250 El Camino Real., Ste. 112
Tustin, CA 92780
Ph: (714)508-0340
Free: 877-736-4636
Fax: (714)734-8027
Co. E-mail: info@seminarinformation.com
URL: http://www.seminarinformation.com
Contact: Catherine Bellizzi, President
URL(s): www.seminarinformation.com/details.cfm?qc=qqbjfj
Description: Learn techniques to handle even the most difficult situations and difficult people with confidence. **Audience:** Managers and professionals. **Principal Exhibits:** Learn techniques to handle even the most difficult situations and difficult people with confidence.

17577 ■ The Essentials of Communication and Collaboration (Onsite)
National Seminars Training L.L.C. (NST)
14502 W 105th St.
Lenexa, KS 66215
Free: 800-349-1935
Co. E-mail: info@findaseminar.com
URL: http://www.findaseminar.com/tpd/Padgett-Thompson-Seminars.asp
URL(s): www.nationalseminarstraining.com/Onsite/OSP/YEECC.cfm
Description: Seminar teaches the essential communication techniques that facilitate cooperation and collaboration at work. **Audience:** Industry professionals. **Principal Exhibits:** Seminar teaches the essential communication techniques that facilitate cooperation and collaboration at work.

17578 ■ Exceptional Presentation Training
URL(s): www.bakercommunications.com/exceptional_presentations.htm
Description: This workshop will aid all participants in helping to deliver their intended message to both internal and external clients. Cloud-based training also available. **Audience:** Industry professionals. **Principal Exhibits:** This workshop will aid all participants in helping to deliver their intended message to both internal and external clients. Cloud-based training also available.

17579 ■ Fred Pryor Seminars Mistake-Free Grammar & Proofreading
Fred Pryor Seminars
5700 Broadmoor St., Ste. 300
Mission, KS 66202
Free: 800-780-8476
Co. E-mail: customerservice@pryor.com
URL: http://www.pryor.com
Contact: James R. Anderson, President
URL(s): www.pryor.com/training-seminars/mistake-free-grammar-proofreading
Frequency: Irregular. **Description:** Covers grammar and usage in business writing, including punctuation, capitalization, quotations, spelling, sentence structure, and related topics. **Audience:** Managers, secretaries, technical writers, editors, and proofreaders. **Principal Exhibits:** Covers grammar and usage in business writing, including punctuation, capitalization, quotations, spelling, sentence structure, and related topics.

17580 ■ Geometric Dimensioning and Tolerancing, Level 1 (Onsite)
Seminar Information Service Inc. (SIS)
250 El Camino Real., Ste. 112
Tustin, CA 92780
Ph: (714)508-0340
Free: 877-736-4636
Fax: (714)734-8027
Co. E-mail: info@seminarinformation.com
URL: http://www.seminarinformation.com
Contact: Catherine Bellizzi, President
URL(s): www.seminarinformation.com
Description: Learn how to improve your effectiveness at communicating and interpreting specifications on engineering drawings. **Audience:** Coordinating measuring machines professionals, IT. **Principal Exhibits:** Learn how to improve your effectiveness at communicating and interpreting specifications on engineering drawings.

17581 ■ High Performance Business Writing
URL(s): cmcoutperform.com/fr/high-performance-business-writing
Description: Covers improving business writing skills, focusing on documents, letters, e-mails, reports, and memos. Also offers course on request. Held in Toronto, ON; Montreal, PQ; Ottawa, ON; and Edmonton, AB. **Audience:** Writers and journalists. **Principal Exhibits:** Covers improving business writing skills, focusing on documents, letters, e-mails, reports, and memos. Also offers course on request. Held in Toronto, ON; Montreal, PQ; Ottawa, ON; and Edmonton, AB. **Telecommunication Services:** cmcinfo@cmcoutperform.com.

17582 ■ How to Be an Outstanding Communicator (Onsite)
National Seminars Training L.L.C. (NST)
14502 W 105th St.
Lenexa, KS 66215
Free: 800-349-1935
Co. E-mail: info@findaseminar.com
URL: http://www.findaseminar.com/tpd/Padgett-Thompson-Seminars.asp
URL(s): www.findaseminar.com/event1.asp?eventID=916#desc
Description: One-day seminar that teaches how to get support from employees and co-workers, project a confident image, and master the key communication skills that you will need to succeed in the workplace. **Audience:** Administrators, managers, supervisors, team leaders, project leaders, and members of a team. **Principal Exhibits:** One-day seminar that teaches how to get support from employees and co-workers, project a confident image, and master the key communication skills that you will need to succeed in the workplace.

17583 ■ How to Communicate with Tact & Professionalism
Fred Pryor Seminars & CareerTrack
5700 Broadmoor, Ste. 300
Mission, KS 66202
Free: 800-780-8476
Fax: (913)967-8849
Co. E-mail: customerservice@pryor.com
URL: http://www.pryor.com
Contact: Janet Turner, Contact
E-mail: dmca@pryor.com
URL(s): www.pryor.com/training-seminars/communicate-with-tact-professionalism
Description: Learn to become a polished, persuasive communicator and express your thoughts and ideas with clarity and diplomacy, including how to decode body language to understand what people are really saying. **Audience:** Industry professionals. **Principal Exhibits:** Learn to become a polished, persuasive communicator and express your thoughts and ideas with clarity and diplomacy, including how to decode body language to understand what people are really saying.

17584 ■ How to Deliver Presentations with Ease & Confidence
Fred Pryor Seminars & CareerTrack
5700 Broadmoor, Ste. 300
Mission, KS 66202
Free: 800-780-8476
Fax: (913)967-8849
Co. E-mail: customerservice@pryor.com
URL: http://www.pryor.com
Contact: Janet Turner, Contact
E-mail: dmca@pryor.com
URL(s): www.pryor.com/training-seminars/deliver-presentations-ease-confidence
Frequency: Irregular. **Description:** Improve and enhance your effectiveness in every speaking situation without fear and anxiety. **Audience:** Business professionals. **Principal Exhibits:** Improve and enhance your effectiveness in every speaking situation without fear and anxiety.

GENERAL SMALL BUSINESS TOPICS

17585 ■ How to Design Eye-Catching Brochures, Newspapers, Ads, Reports
URL(s): www.pryor.com/site/webinar-audio/great-layout-and-graphic-design-tips-tricks-and-latest-trends

Description: Covers basic design and layout skills for headlines, text, and graphics for printed documents. **Audience:** Graphic designers. **Principal Exhibits:** Covers basic design and layout skills for headlines, text, and graphics for printed documents. **Telecommunication Services:** customerservice@pryor.com.

17586 ■ How to Manage Conflict and Confrontation
Fred Pryor Seminars & CareerTrack
5700 Broadmoor, Ste. 300
Mission, KS 66202
Free: 800-780-8476
Fax: (913)967-8849
Co. E-mail: customerservice@pryor.com
URL: http://www.pryor.com
Contact: Janet Turner, Contact
E-mail: dmca@pryor.com
URL(s): www.pryor.com/training-seminars/how-to-manage-conflict-confrontation

Frequency: Irregular. **Description:** Learn practical and proven techniques for managing workplace conflict. **Audience:** Professionals. **Principal Exhibits:** Learn practical and proven techniques for managing workplace conflict.

17587 ■ How to Present Online: A Skills-Based Workshop
American Management Association (AMA)
1601 Broadway
New York, NY 10019
Ph: (212)586-8100
Free: 800-262-9699
Fax: (212)903-8168
Co. E-mail: customerservice@amanet.org
URL: http://www.amanet.org
Contact: Manny Avramidis, President
URL(s): www.amanet.org/training/webcasts/How-to-Present-Online-A-Skills-Based-Workshop.aspx

Description: Learn how to conduct presentations to online audiences with successful techniques. **Audience:** Anyone who wants to deliver effective and engaging online presentations, including trainers, facilitators, sales and marketing professionals, consultants and all others who present content to an online audience. **Principal Exhibits:** Learn how to conduct presentations to online audiences with successful techniques. **Telecommunication Services:** customerservice@amanet.org.

17588 ■ How to Work Most Effectively with Your Boss (Onsite)
URL(s): www.amanet.org

Description: Covers effective communication and problem solving teamwork skills. **Audience:** Industry professionals. **Principal Exhibits:** Covers effective communication and problem solving teamwork skills. **Telecommunication Services:** customerservice@amanet.org.

17589 ■ How to Work With Difficult, Demanding, and Inconsiderate People (Onsite)
National Seminars Training L.L.C. (NST)
14502 W 105th St.
Lenexa, KS 66215
Free: 800-349-1935
Co. E-mail: info@findaseminar.com
URL: http://www.findaseminar.com/tpd/Padgett-Thompson-Seminars.asp
URL(s): www.nationalseminarstraining.com/join/SeminarSearchResults/Working_With_Difficult_People/YWDDP/index.html

Description: Learn what it takes to defuse angry coworkers and how to keep emotions in check. **Audience:** Industry professionals. **Principal Exhibits:** Learn what it takes to defuse angry coworkers and how to keep emotions in check.

17590 ■ Improving Your Communication Skills for Success (Onsite)
Seminar Information Service Inc. (SIS)
250 El Camino Real., Ste. 112
Tustin, CA 92780
Ph: (714)508-0340
Free: 877-736-4636
Fax: (714)734-8027
Co. E-mail: info@seminarinformation.com
URL: http://www.seminarinformation.com
Contact: Catherine Bellizzi, President
URL(s): www.seminarinformation.com

Description: Learn the essential communication skills you need to handle any situation that arises with confidence. **Audience:** Business professionals. **Principal Exhibits:** Learn the essential communication skills you need to handle any situation that arises with confidence.

17591 ■ Indexing I (Onsite)
URL(s): www.eeicom.com

Description: Covers indexing for websites and books, including determining key words, categorizing information, and using cross-references. **Audience:** Industry professionals. **Principal Exhibits:** Covers indexing for websites and books, including determining key words, categorizing information, and using cross-references.

17592 ■ Indexing II (Onsite)
URL(s): www.eeicom.com

Description: Covers editing and evaluating indices. **Audience:** Industry professionals. **Principal Exhibits:** Covers editing and evaluating indices.

17593 ■ Influence Skills: Getting Results Without Direct Authority (Onsite)
Seminar Information Service Inc. (SIS)
250 El Camino Real., Ste. 112
Tustin, CA 92780
Ph: (714)508-0340
Free: 877-736-4636
Fax: (714)734-8027
Co. E-mail: info@seminarinformation.com
URL: http://www.seminarinformation.com
Contact: Catherine Bellizzi, President
URL(s): www.seminarinformation.com/qqabyr/influence-skills-getting-results-without-direct

Description: Learn how to: Apply influence strategies to gain commitment from others and foster collaboration; Define desired outcomes for win-win results; Dynamically adjust your approach to others to gain buy-in; Achieve goals by enhancing trust and cooperation; Deal effectively with challenging behaviors to overcome resistance and inertia in others; Use knowledge and competence rather than position and status to influence others. **Audience:** Managers, project managers and individual contributors. **Principal Exhibits:** Learn how to: Apply influence strategies to gain commitment from others and foster collaboration; Define desired outcomes for win-win results; Dynamically adjust your approach to others to gain buy-in; Achieve goals by enhancing trust and cooperation; Deal effectively with challenging behaviors to overcome resistance and inertia in others; Use knowledge and competence rather than position and status to influence others.

17594 ■ Influence Strategies
Seminar Information Service Inc. (SIS)
250 El Camino Real., Ste. 112
Tustin, CA 92780
Ph: (714)508-0340
Free: 877-736-4636
Fax: (714)734-8027
Co. E-mail: info@seminarinformation.com
URL: http://www.seminarinformation.com
Contact: Catherine Bellizzi, President
URL(s): www.seminarinformation.com

Description: Provides you with a greater understanding of your personal motive preferences, the preferences of others, and application of this dynamic toward becoming more effective in specific work situations. **Audience:** Industry professionals. **Principal Exhibits:** Provides you with a greater understanding of your personal motive preferences, the preferences of others, and application of this dynamic toward becoming more effective in specific work situations.

17595 ■ Interactive Training Techniques for the Classroom (Onsite)
Seminar Information Service Inc. (SIS)
250 El Camino Real., Ste. 112
Tustin, CA 92780
Ph: (714)508-0340
Free: 877-736-4636
Fax: (714)734-8027
Co. E-mail: info@seminarinformation.com
URL: http://www.seminarinformation.com
Contact: Catherine Bellizzi, President
URL(s): www.seminarinformation.com/details.cfm?qc=qqbrrn

Description: Participants prepare themselves to be both presenter and discussion leader. **Audience:** Trainers, supervisors and leaders. **Principal Exhibits:** Participants prepare themselves to be both presenter and discussion leader.

17596 ■ Interpersonal Skills for Managers
URL(s): cmcoutperform.com/interpersonal-skills-managers

Price: C$1,995, Members; C$2,195, Non-members. **Audience:** Managers, supervisors and team leaders who work in constant communication with others to achieve results. **Telecommunication Services:** cmcinfo@cmcoutperform.com.

17597 ■ Keeping the Team on Track (Onsite)
Seminar Information Service Inc. (SIS)
250 El Camino Real., Ste. 112
Tustin, CA 92780
Ph: (714)508-0340
Free: 877-736-4636
Fax: (714)734-8027
Co. E-mail: info@seminarinformation.com
URL: http://www.seminarinformation.com
Contact: Catherine Bellizzi, President
URL(s): www.seminarinformation.com/qqazew/keeping-the-team-on-track

Description: Learn to recognize the signs of ineffective meetings and learn the formal tools to accomplish expected results with particular focus on managing the meeting process and techniques to keep the team on track. **Audience:** Leaders. **Principal Exhibits:** Learn to recognize the signs of ineffective meetings and learn the formal tools to accomplish expected results with particular focus on managing the meeting process and techniques to keep the team on track.

17598 ■ Managing Emotions under Pressure
Fred Pryor Seminars & CareerTrack
5700 Broadmoor, Ste. 300
Mission, KS 66202
Free: 800-780-8476
Fax: (913)967-8849
Co. E-mail: customerservice@pryor.com
URL: http://www.pryor.com
Contact: Janet Turner, Contact
E-mail: dmca@pryor.com
URL(s): www.pryor.com/training-seminars/managing-emotions-under-pressure

Frequency: Irregular. **Description:** Learn to develop self-discipline and manage your emotions in the workplace. **Audience:** Industry professionals. **Principal Exhibits:** Learn to develop self-discipline and manage your emotions in the workplace.

17599 ■ Managing Emotions and Thriving Under Pressure (Onsite)
Seminar Information Service Inc. (SIS)
250 El Camino Real., Ste. 112
Tustin, CA 92780
Ph: (714)508-0340
Free: 877-736-4636
Fax: (714)734-8027
Co. E-mail: info@seminarinformation.com
URL: http://www.seminarinformation.com
Contact: Catherine Bellizzi, President
URL(s): www.seminarinformation.com/details.cfm?qc=qqbsfq

17600 ■ Business Communications

Description: Learn self-discipline skills and rid yourself of unproductive behaviors. **Audience:** Professionals and public. **Principal Exhibits:** Learn self-discipline skills and rid yourself of unproductive behaviors.

17600 ■ Managing Successful Negotiations (Onsite)
Seminar Information Service Inc. (SIS)
250 El Camino Real., Ste. 112
Tustin, CA 92780
Ph: (714)508-0340
Free: 877-736-4636
Fax: (714)734-8027
Co. E-mail: info@seminarinformation.com
URL: http://www.seminarinformation.com
Contact: Catherine Bellizzi, President
URL(s): www.seminarinformation.com/qqbecl/managing-successful-negotiations

Description: Design to help acquire the necessary concept, skills, and techniques to prepare for and to conduct successful negotiations. **Audience:** Anyone who wishes to enhance their negotiating skills. **Principal Exhibits:** Design to help acquire the necessary concept, skills, and techniques to prepare for and to conduct successful negotiations.

17601 ■ Negotiating to Win
American Management Association (AMA)
1601 Broadway
New York, NY 10019
Ph: (212)586-8100
Free: 800-262-9699
Fax: (212)903-8168
Co. E-mail: customerservice@amanet.org
URL: http://www.amanet.org
Contact: Manny Avramidis, President
URL(s): www.amanet.org/training/seminars/Negotiating-to-Win.aspx

Price: $2,345, Non-members; $2,095, Members; $1,794, Members General Services Administration (GSA). **Frequency:** Continuous. **Description:** Covers appropriate scenarios for negotiation, persuasion skills, and strategies for oral and written negotiations. Also available live online. **Audience:** Those responsible for negotiating the best possible terms of an agreement for their organization. **Principal Exhibits:** Covers appropriate scenarios for negotiation, persuasion skills, and strategies for oral and written negotiations. Also available live online. **Telecommunication Services:** customerservice@amanet.org.

17602 ■ Negotiating to Win
Canadian Management Centre (CMC)
150 King St. W Ste. 271
Toronto, ON, Canada M5H 1J9
Ph: (416)214-5678
Free: 877-262-2519
Fax: (416)214-6047
Co. E-mail: cmcinfo@cmcoutperform.com
URL: http://cmcoutperform.com
Contact: Chris Peacock, Director
URL(s): cmcoutperform.com/negotiating-to-win

Description: Covers techniques for successful negotiations, in every industry and at every level; includes the negotiation process, overcoming people problems, and improving negotiation strategies. Also offers course on request. Held in Calgary, AB; Ottawa, ON; Mississauga, ON; Vancouver, BC; and Toronto, ON. **Audience:** Industry professionals. **Principal Exhibits:** Covers techniques for successful negotiations, in every industry and at every level; includes the negotiation process, overcoming people problems, and improving negotiation strategies. Also offers course on request. Held in Calgary, AB; Ottawa, ON; Mississauga, ON; Vancouver, BC; and Toronto, ON.

17603 ■ Negotiation Skills: Achieving Successful Outcomes (Onsite)
Seminar Information Service Inc. (SIS)
250 El Camino Real., Ste. 112
Tustin, CA 92780
Ph: (714)508-0340
Free: 877-736-4636
Fax: (714)734-8027
Co. E-mail: info@seminarinformation.com
URL: http://www.seminarinformation.com
Contact: Catherine Bellizzi, President
URL(s): www.seminarinformation.com

Description: Learn how to: Conduct principled negotiations that result in wise agreements; Incorporate a process approach into your negotiation skill set; Formulate principled communication strategies and styles to deflect 'hardball' tactics; Apply psychology principles to negotiate effectively; Enhance your negotiation skills by applying best practices in a real-world setting. **Audience:** Industry professionals. **Principal Exhibits:** Learn how to: Conduct principled negotiations that result in wise agreements; Incorporate a process approach into your negotiation skill set; Formulate principled communication strategies and styles to deflect 'hardball' tactics; Apply psychology principles to negotiate effectively; Enhance your negotiation skills by applying best practices in a real-world setting.

17604 ■ The Outstanding Receptionist
Fred Pryor Seminars & CareerTrack
5700 Broadmoor, Ste. 300
Mission, KS 66202
Free: 800-780-8476
Fax: (913)967-8849
Co. E-mail: customerservice@pryor.com
URL: http://www.pryor.com
Contact: Janet Turner, Contact
E-mail: dmca@pryor.com
URL(s): www.pryor.com/training-seminars/outstanding-receptionist

Price: $79. **Frequency:** Irregular. **Description:** Learn how to improve your skills and better support everyone in your organization. **Audience:** Receptionists. **Principal Exhibits:** Learn how to improve your skills and better support everyone in your organization.

17605 ■ Performance Measurement Analysis (Onsite)
URL(s): www.eeicom.com

Description: Through communication, integration, and alignment with objectives, Performance Measurement can help employees realize the value of their contributions to the organization. **Audience:** Industry professionals, administrative. **Principal Exhibits:** Through communication, integration, and alignment with objectives, Performance Measurement can help employees realize the value of their contributions to the organization.

17606 ■ Persuasive Communications
URL(s): www.eeicom.com

Description: Course designed for department heads and project managers, as well as mid-level communications professionals who want to expand their public relations and marketing skills. **Audience:** Industry professionals, students. **Principal Exhibits:** Course designed for department heads and project managers, as well as mid-level communications professionals who want to expand their public relations and marketing skills.

17607 ■ Persuasive Leadership: Storytelling that Inspires (Onsite)
Seminar Information Service Inc. (SIS)
250 El Camino Real., Ste. 112
Tustin, CA 92780
Ph: (714)508-0340
Free: 877-736-4636
Fax: (714)734-8027
Co. E-mail: info@seminarinformation.com
URL: http://www.seminarinformation.com
Contact: Catherine Bellizzi, President
URL(s): www.seminarinformation.com/details.cfm?qc=qqbfng

Description: Participants develop their storytelling abilities and learn how to use humor to persuade and motivate others, as well as polish their existing speaking skills and develop powerful new ones. **Audience:** Executives, managers, others in positions of influence and experienced speakers. **Principal Exhibits:** Participants develop their storytelling abilities and learn how to use humor to persuade and motivate others, as well as polish their existing speaking skills and develop powerful new ones.

17608 ■ Powerful Communication Skills for Women (Onsite)
National Seminars Training L.L.C. (NST)
14502 W 105th St.
Lenexa, KS 66215
Free: 800-349-1935
Co. E-mail: info@findaseminar.com
URL: http://www.findaseminar.com/tpd/Padgett-Thompson-Seminars.asp
URL(s): www.findaseminar.com/event1.asp?eventID=917

Description: A workshop designed specifically for professional women. **Audience:** Managers, supervisors, team leaders, sales reps, HR professionals, and marketing professionals. **Principal Exhibits:** A workshop designed specifically for professional women.

17609 ■ Professional Communication: What Message Are You Sending?
Fred Pryor Seminars & CareerTrack
5700 Broadmoor, Ste. 300
Mission, KS 66202
Free: 800-780-8476
Fax: (913)967-8849
Co. E-mail: customerservice@pryor.com
URL: http://www.pryor.com
Contact: Janet Turner, Contact
E-mail: dmca@pryor.com
URL(s): www.pryor.com/training-seminars/professional-communication-what-message-are-you-sending

Frequency: Irregular. **Description:** Learn to communicate with confidence and credibility. **Audience:** Business communication professionals. **Principal Exhibits:** Learn to communicate with confidence and credibility.

17610 ■ Resolving Conflict (Onsite)
Seminar Information Service Inc. (SIS)
250 El Camino Real., Ste. 112
Tustin, CA 92780
Ph: (714)508-0340
Free: 877-736-4636
Fax: (714)734-8027
Co. E-mail: info@seminarinformation.com
URL: http://www.seminarinformation.com
Contact: Catherine Bellizzi, President
URL(s): www.seminarinformation.com/details.cfm?qc=qqayqy

Description: Provide you with an understanding of the nature of conflict in organizations, key approaches to managing conflict, and an insight into your style of handling conflict and ways to enhance your conflict resolution effectiveness. **Audience:** Managers and supervisors. **Principal Exhibits:** Provide you with an understanding of the nature of conflict in organizations, key approaches to managing conflict, and an insight into your style of handling conflict and ways to enhance your conflict resolution effectiveness.

17611 ■ Responding to Conflict: Strategies for Improved Communication
URL(s): cmcoutperform.com/strategies-improved-communication

Price: C$1,845, Members; C$1,995, Non-members. **Description:** Covers effective communication, diffusing misunderstanding, creating open and honest work environments, dealing with conflict, and improving listening skills. **Audience:** Business professionals who want to expand their conflict management skills, understand their own emotions and behaviors when addressing conflict, and find productive ways to manage conflict. **Principal Exhibits:** Covers effective communication, diffusing misunderstanding, creating open and honest work environments, dealing with conflict, and improving listening skills.

17612 ■ Sensitivity Skills in Working with Others (Onsite)
Seminar Information Service Inc. (SIS)
250 El Camino Real., Ste. 112
Tustin, CA 92780
Ph: (714)508-0340
Free: 877-736-4636
Fax: (714)734-8027

GENERAL SMALL BUSINESS TOPICS

Business Communications ■ 17627

Co. E-mail: info@seminarinformation.com
URL: http://www.seminarinformation.com
Contact: Catherine Bellizzi, President
URL(s): www.seminarinformation.com
Description: Learn the difference between behaviors that are appropriate, inappropriate, and perhaps illegal, and improve skills in communicating across cultures. **Audience:** Managers, supervisors, lead people and team leaders. **Principal Exhibits:** Learn the difference between behaviors that are appropriate, inappropriate, and perhaps illegal, and improve skills in communicating across cultures.

17613 ■ Speak! Present! Influence! (Onsite)
Seminar Information Service Inc. (SIS)
 250 El Camino Real., Ste. 112
 Tustin, CA 92780
Ph: (714)508-0340
Free: 877-736-4636
Fax: (714)734-8027
Co. E-mail: info@seminarinformation.com
URL: http://www.seminarinformation.com
Contact: Catherine Bellizzi, President
URL(s): www.seminarinformation.com/details.cfm?qc=qqanxp
Description: Participants learn to overcome fear and relax under pressure; to become more dynamic and persuasive; to improve voice quality and speak without strain; to organize material for clear, effective delivery; and to make a personal connection with the audience. **Audience:** Professionals and individuals who must guide, influence and persuade others, managers, salespeople and technologists. **Principal Exhibits:** Participants learn to overcome fear and relax under pressure; to become more dynamic and persuasive; to improve voice quality and speak without strain; to organize material for clear, effective delivery; and to make a personal connection with the audience.

17614 ■ Speaking Skills for Professionals (Onsite)
Seminar Information Service Inc. (SIS)
 250 El Camino Real., Ste. 112
 Tustin, CA 92780
Ph: (714)508-0340
Free: 877-736-4636
Fax: (714)734-8027
Co. E-mail: info@seminarinformation.com
URL: http://www.seminarinformation.com
Contact: Catherine Bellizzi, President
URL(s): www.seminarinformation.com
Description: Learn the techniques and practices of expert speakers. Participants will learn how to gain people's attention, how to project an image of authority and competence, and how to speak with confidence. **Audience:** General public, professionals, managers, executives. **Principal Exhibits:** Learn the techniques and practices of expert speakers. Participants will learn how to gain people's attention, how to project an image of authority and competence, and how to speak with confidence.

17615 ■ Strengthening Your People Skills in the Workplace (Onsite)
National Seminars Training L.L.C. (NST)
 14502 W 105th St.
 Lenexa, KS 66215
Free: 800-349-1935
Co. E-mail: info@findaseminar.com
URL: http://www.findaseminar.com/tpd/Padgett-Thompson-Seminars.asp
URL(s): www.nationalseminarstraining.com/Onsite/OSP/INTRP.cfm
Description: A one-day workshop to gain the essential people skills needed to push your career ahead. **Audience:** Professionals, managers, supervisors and employees. **Principal Exhibits:** A one-day workshop to gain the essential people skills needed to push your career ahead.

17616 ■ TechConnect (Onsite)
Seminar Information Service Inc. (SIS)
 250 El Camino Real., Ste. 112
 Tustin, CA 92780
Ph: (714)508-0340
Free: 877-736-4636

Fax: (714)734-8027
Co. E-mail: info@seminarinformation.com
URL: http://www.seminarinformation.com
Contact: Catherine Bellizzi, President
URL(s): www.seminarinformation.com/details.cfm?qc=qqbrqe
Description: Learn how to put technical information into language a lay audience can understand, including how to organize information so it flows smoothly and leads to action and how to deliver information at the appropriate level of audience understanding and to be concise, to the point, and eliminate data dump. **Audience:** Technical experts, business professionals. **Principal Exhibits:** Learn how to put technical information into language a lay audience can understand, including how to organize information so it flows smoothly and leads to action and how to deliver information at the appropriate level of audience understanding and to be concise, to the point, and eliminate data dump.

17617 ■ Training Difficult Issues in Diversity (Onsite)
Seminar Information Service Inc. (SIS)
 250 El Camino Real., Ste. 112
 Tustin, CA 92780
Ph: (714)508-0340
Free: 877-736-4636
Fax: (714)734-8027
Co. E-mail: info@seminarinformation.com
URL: http://www.seminarinformation.com
Contact: Catherine Bellizzi, President
URL(s): www.seminarinformation.com
Description: Provides trainers with a step-by-step curriculum for delivering training and education on the tougher issues, including racism, privilege, religion, sexual orientation, gender identity, and oppression. Explore training techniques and models that get diversity messages across. **Audience:** Diversity managers and consultants. **Principal Exhibits:** Provides trainers with a step-by-step curriculum for delivering training and education on the tougher issues, including racism, privilege, religion, sexual orientation, gender identity, and oppression. Explore training techniques and models that get diversity messages across.

17618 ■ Webinars with a WOW Factor: Creating Memorable Meeting Across the Globe (Onsite)
Seminar Information Service Inc. (SIS)
 250 El Camino Real., Ste. 112
 Tustin, CA 92780
Ph: (714)508-0340
Free: 877-736-4636
Fax: (714)734-8027
Co. E-mail: info@seminarinformation.com
URL: http://www.seminarinformation.com
Contact: Catherine Bellizzi, President
URL(s): www.seminarinformation.com/qqbvka/webinars-that-work
Description: Discover techniques that will make your material come to life on the screen and over the phone. **Audience:** Veteran and apprentice trainers. **Principal Exhibits:** Discover techniques that will make your material come to life on the screen and over the phone.

17619 ■ Writing Statements of Work: The Heart of Any Contract (Onsite)
Seminar Information Service Inc. (SIS)
 250 El Camino Real., Ste. 112
 Tustin, CA 92780
Ph: (714)508-0340
Free: 877-736-4636
Fax: (714)734-8027
Co. E-mail: info@seminarinformation.com
URL: http://www.seminarinformation.com
Contact: Catherine Bellizzi, President
URL(s): www.seminarinformation.com/qqbmxq/writing-statements-of-work-the-heart-of-any-contract
Description: Provides the essential information you'll need, including basic contract management concepts, to consistently develop and administer effective Statements of Work. **Audience:** In-house SOW team members, project managers, and contract managers

. **Principal Exhibits:** Provides the essential information you'll need, including basic contract management concepts, to consistently develop and administer effective Statements of Work.

17620 ■ XML Web Services (Onsite)
URL(s): www.eeicom.com
Description: Learn how Web services can enhance your Web site and communication with other companies. **Audience:** Web Designer, students. **Principal Exhibits:** Learn how Web services can enhance your Web site and communication with other companies.

REFERENCE WORKS

17621 ■ *"4 Small-Business Communication Trends (and How They Improve Customer Experience)"* **in CallRail Blog (Nov. 11, 2021)**
URL(s): www.callrail.com/blog/4-small-business-communication-trends/
Ed: Carly Cornforth. **Released:** November 11, 2021. **Description:** Discusses 4 trends in small business communications and how you can utilize them to improve customer experience and increase revenue. **Availability:** Online.

17622 ■ *"5 Ways To Improve Your Communication in Business and Why It's Important"* **in Indeed (Feb. 22, 2021)**
URL(s): www.indeed.com/career-advice/career-development/importance-of-business-communication
Released: February 22, 2021. **Description:** Details the four standard methods of business communication, why communication is important, and five ways to improve your business communication skills. **Availability:** Online.

17623 ■ *"10 Business Apology Letter Examples"* **in Small Business Trends (July 15, 2021)**
URL(s): smallbiztrends.com/2020/01/business-apology-letter.html
Ed: Annie Pilon. **Released:** July 15, 2021. **Description:** Provides a guide for small businesses to use while crafting an apology letter for any mistake that caused harm to a customer, vendor, or employee. **Availability:** Online.

17624 ■ 10 Make-or-Break Career Moments: Navigate, Negotiate, and Communicate for Success
Price: $13.99, paperback. **Description:** Communication consultant, Casey Hawley, provides a guide to smart communication for any business setting. **Availability:** Print.

17625 ■ *"10 Tips for Effectively Communicating with Clients, Prospects, Employees, and Other Business Stakeholders"* **in Small Business Trends (January 29, 2022)**
URL(s): smallbiztrends.com/2022/01/communicating-with-clients.html
Ed: Annie Pilon. **Released:** January 29, 2022. **Description:** Communicating clearly is a required skill when dealing with clients and stakeholders. Sharpen up those skills with the tips given in this article. **Availability:** Online.

17626 ■ *"The 11 Best Communication Tools for Business (By Category)"* **in DialPad Newsletter (July 27, 2021)**
URL(s): www.dialpad.com/blog/communication-tools/
Ed: Grace Lau. **Released:** July 27, 2021. **Description:** Offers a guide to communication tools in categories for small businesses to review as well as suggestions for how to pick the best online tools for your team. **Availability:** Online.

17627 ■ *"11 Reasons Why Business Communication Is Critical to Your Company's Success"* **in Smarp Blog (July 9, 2020)**
URL(s): blog.smarp.com/11-reasons-why-business-communication-is-crucial-for-companys-success

Released: July 09, 2020. **Description:** Emphasizes the importance of effective business communication for success and growth for your small business. Discusses the 4 main types of business communications and 11 reasons why effective business communication is so powerful. **Availability:** Online.

17628 ■ *"12 Helpful Tips for Communicating Bad News to Staff and Stakeholders" in Small Business Trends (October 16, 2022)*
URL(s): smallbiztrends.com/2022/10/communicating-bad-news-to-staff-and-stakeholders.html
Released: October 16, 2022. **Description:** Sharing bad news is a skill that needs to be developed because not all news is good. Included are tips to deliver news that may not be the best. **Availability:** Online.

17629 ■ *"14 Business Letter Templates Every Business Should Have" in Legal Zoom (February 15, 2023)*
URL(s): www.legalzoom.com/articles/14-business-letter-templates-every-business-should-have
Ed: Ronna L. DoLoe, Esq. **Released:** February 15, 2023. **Description:** Keep these templates on file for easy access when you need to write a particular letter for your small business. Includes items such as a cease and desist letter, demand letter, and a thank-you letter. **Availability:** Online.

17630 ■ *"14 Collaboration Tools for Small Business" in Business News Daily (Jan. 14, 2021)*
URL(s): www.businessnewsdaily.com/6176-communication-tools.html
Ed: Andreas Rivera. **Released:** January 14, 2021. **Description:** Includes information for small business owners who want to implement more collaborative digital tools in their company's daily operations. **Availability:** Online.

17631 ■ *"20 Communication Platforms for High-Growth Companies" in Nextiva Blog*
URL(s): www.nextiva.com/blog/communication-platforms.html
Ed: Devin Pickell. **Description:** Lists the five types of business communication platforms as well as a rundown of the top communications solutions you should consider for your small business.

17632 ■ *20 Ways to Communicate Effectively with Your Team" in Small Business Trends (November 24, 2021)*
URL(s): smallbiztrends.com/2013/11/20-ways-to-communicate-effectively-in-the-workplace.html
Ed: Valentine Belonwu. **Released:** November 24, 2021. **Description:** Describes best practices for team communication. **Availability:** Online.

17633 ■ *"74% of Consumers Prefer Texting with Businesses if a Real Person is Texting Back" in Small Business Trends (January 26, 2023)*
URL(s): smallbiztrends.com/2021/07/customers-prefer-texting-business-real-people.html
Ed: Gabrielle Pickard-Whitehead. **Released:** July 25, 2021. **Description:** As texting keeps growing in popularity as a means of communication, a recent poll found out that consumers prefer texting with company as long as they are interacting with a human. **Availability:** Online.

17634 ■ *"All Those Applications, and Phone Users Just Want to Talk" in Advertising Age (Vol. 79, August 11, 2008, No. 31, pp. 18)*
Pub: Crain Communications, Inc.
Contact: Jessica Botos, Manager, Marketing
E-mail: jessica.botos@crainsnewyork.com
Ed: Mike Vorhaus. **Description:** Although consumers are slowly coming to text messaging and other data applications, a majority of those Americans surveyed stated that they simply want to use their cell phones to talk and do not care about other activities. Statistical data included. **Availability:** Online.

17635 ■ *"The Americans Are Coming" in The Economist (Vol. 390, January 3, 2009, No. 8612, pp. 44)*
Description: Student recruitment consultancies, which help place international students at universities in other countries and offer services such as interpreting or translating guidelines, are discussed; American universities who have shunned these agencies in the past; the result has been that America underperforms in relation to its size with a mere 3.5 percent of students on its campuses that are from abroad. **Availability:** Print; Online.

17636 ■ *"The Art and Business of Motivational Speaking: Your Guide" in Inc. (Volume 32, December 2010, No. 10, pp. 124)*
Pub: Inc. Magazine
Description: Profile of Josh Shipp that discusses his career as a motivational speaker. **Availability:** Print; Online.

17637 ■ *Be a Brilliant Business Writer: Write Well, Write Fast, and Whip the Competition*
Released: October 05, 2010. **Price:** $14.99, paperback; $5.99. **Description:** Tools for mastering the art of persuasive writing in every document created, from email and client letters to reports and presentations, this book will help any writer convey their message with clarity and power, increase productivity by reducing rewrites, and provide the correct tone for navigating office politics. **Availability:** E-book; Print.

17638 ■ *"The Best Online Fax Services of 2023" in Business News Daily (March 17, 2023)*
URL(s): www.businessnewsdaily.com/5706-best-online-fax-services.html
Ed: Andrew Martins. **Released:** March 17, 2023. **Description:** Surprisingly, faxes are still a means of business communication. Discussed are the best online fax services that are available along with their pricing. **Availability:** Online.

17639 ■ *The Best Phone Systems for Small Business*
URL(s): www.businessnewsdaily.com/6780-best-business-phone-systems.html
Ed: Jeff Hale. **Released:** February 15, 2023. **Description:** Business phone systems are reviewed and discussed. **Availability:** Online.

17640 ■ *"The Best Text Message Marketing Services of 2023" in Business News Daily (March 22, 2023)*
URL(s): www.businessnewsdaily.com/15044-best-text-message-marketing-solutions.html
Ed: Max Freedman. **Released:** March 22, 2023. **Description:** Text message marketing is gaining popularity since it lets small businesses be able to send out communications directly to customers. This article discusses the best services available. **Availability:** Online.

17641 ■ *"Blog Buzz Heralds Arrival of IPhone 2.0" in Advertising Age (Vol. 79, June 9, 2008, No. 40, pp. 8)*
Pub: Crain Communications, Inc.
Contact: Jessica Botos, Manager, Marketing
E-mail: jessica.botos@crainsnewyork.com
Ed: Abbey Klaassen. **Description:** Predictions concerning the next version of the iPhone include a global-positioning-system technology as well as a configuration to run on a faster, 3G network. **Availability:** Online.

17642 ■ *"Brief: Make a Bigger Impact by Saying Less"*
Pub: John Wiley & Sons, Inc.
Contact: Christina Van Tassell, Executive Vice President Chief Financial Officer
Released: February 23, 2014. **Price:** $24, hardcover; $15.99, e-book. **Description:** Communication is key to any business success. Today, busy executives demand respect and manage their time more efficiently than ever. The author addresses the challenges of inattention, interruptions, and impatience faced by professionals and to help leaders gain the strength required to eliminate wasteful words and stand out from others when communicating. **Availability:** E-book; Print.

17643 ■ *Business Meeting & Event Planning for Dummies*
Pub: John Wiley & Sons, Inc.
Contact: Christina Van Tassell, Executive Vice President Chief Financial Officer
URL(s): www.wiley.com/en-us/Business+Meeting+%26+Event+Planning+For+Dummies%2C+2nd+Edition-p-9781119982838
Ed: Susan Friedmann. **Released:** 2nd edition. **Price:** $18, e-book; $29.99, paperback. **Description:** During the worldwide pandemic, many companies moved to an online working model. That meant many meetings were held online instead of face-to-face, and now virtual working conditions are here to stay on at least some level. This guide will take you through the steps to host successful virtual meetings, which will engage your attendees and maximize communication. **Availability:** E-book; Print.

17644 ■ *Business Psychology and Organizational Behaviour*
URL(s): www.routledge.com/Business-Psychology-and-Organizational-Behaviour/McKenna/p/book/9781138182646#
Ed: Eugene McKenna. **Released:** May 27, 2020. **Price:** $70.95, Paperback; $63.85, eBook. **Description:** A graduate and undergraduate textbook discussing theories and research findings on behaviors exhibited within a work environment. **Availability:** E-book; Print.

17645 ■ *"Can We Talk?" in Canadian Business (Vol. 79, September 11, 2006, No. 18, pp. 131)*
Ed: Sarah B. Hood. **Released:** September 08, 2015. **Description:** The importance of informal communications and steps to build strong social networks within the organizations are discussed. **Availability:** Online.

17646 ■ *"Can You Overcome Fear of Public Speaking? Y.E.S." in Idaho Business Review (August 22, 2014)*
Pub: BridgeTower Media
Contact: Adam Reinebach, President
Description: Three lessons learned about public speaking are shared. The list forms the acronym Y.E.S.: Year-Round Sport, speechmaking is like learning an instrument or foreign language. Exorbitance Bores: Picking an overly ambitious, technical topic distracts from focusing on delivery of a simple, memorable message. Sweat Not The Details, perfectionism will create a stiff sounding speech.

17647 ■ *"Candor, Criticism, Teamwork" in Harvard Business Review (Vol. 90, January-February 2012, No.1-2, pp. 40)*
Pub: Harvard Business Review Press
Contact: Moderna V. Pfizer, Contact
Ed: Keith Ferrazzi. **Price:** $6. **Description:** To ensure honest and effective feedback, meetings should be broken up into smaller groups. Individuals should be selected to be advocates of candor, and techniques for caring criticism should be taught, such as identifying a problem but then suggesting ways to correct it. **Availability:** Online; PDF.

17648 ■ *"Charlotte Pipe Launches Satirical Campaign" in Contractor (Vol. 57, January 2010, No. 1, pp. 6)*
Description: Charlotte Pipe and Foundry Co. launched an advertising campaign that uses social media and humor to make a point about how it can be nearly impossible to determine if imported cast iron pipes and fittings meet the same quality standards as what made in the U.S. The campaign features 'pipe whisperers' and also spoofs pipe sniffing dogs. **Availability:** Print; Online.

17649 ■ *"Conferencing Takes on High-Tech Futuristic Feel" in Crain's Cleveland Business (Vol. 28, October 29, 2007, No. 43, pp. 17)*
Pub: Crain Communications Inc.
Contact: K. C. Crain, President

Ed: Chuck Soder. **Description:** Overview of the newest technologies which are making local company's meetings more effective including: tele-presence, a videoconferencing technology, as well as virtual flip charts. **Availability:** Online.

17650 ■ *"Contagious: Why Things Catch On"*
Pub: Simon & Schuster, Inc.
Contact: Jonathan Karp, President

Released: March 2013. **Price:** $26, after_pricingtext. **Description:** Wharton marketing professor, Jonah Berger, reveals the science of successful word-of-mouth and social media marketing that provides greater results than traditional advertising. **Availability:** Print.

17651 ■ *"Conversations with Customers"* in Business Journal Serving Greater Tampa Bay (Vol. 31, December 31, 2010, No. 1, pp. 1)
Pub: Tampa Bay Business Journal
Contact: Ian Anderson, President
E-mail: ianderson@bizjournals.com

Description: Tampa Bay, Florida-based businesses have been using social media to interact with customers. Forty percent of businesses have been found to have at least one social media platform to reach customers and prospects. **Availability:** Print; Online.

17652 ■ *"The Copyright Evolution"* in Information Today (Vol. 28, November 2011, No. 10, pp. 1)
Pub: Information Today Inc.
Contact: Thomas H. Hogan, President

Ed: Nancy Davis Kho. **Description:** For information professionals, issues surrounding copyright compliance have traditionally been on the consumption side. However, today, content consumption is only half the program because blogging, tweeting, and commenting is a vital part of more standard duties for workers as corporations aim to create authentic communications with customers.

17653 ■ *"Crew Training Changes Tactics"* in Memphis Business Journal (Vol. 33, March 16, 2012, No. 49, pp. 1)
Pub: Baltimore Business Journal
Contact: Rhonda Pringle, President
E-mail: rpringle@bizjournals.com

Ed: Cole Epley. **Description:** Teamwork and communication training services firm Crew Training International Inc. has revamped its strategy and executive board as it moved from small to mid-tier status. The recalibration of strategy comes along with a renovation at the headquarters in southeast Memphis, Tennessee. **Availability:** Print; Online.

17654 ■ *"David Leonhardt on Hiring a Copywriter for Your Small Business"* in Small Business Trends(October 18, 2022)
URL(s): smallbiztrends.com/2022/10/how-to-hire-a-copywriter.html

Ed: Holly Chavez. **Released:** October 21, 2022. **Description:** David Leonhardt, President of The Happy Guy (THGM) Writing Services, discusses the benefits of small businesses hiring copywriters in order to communicate clearly to customers. **Availability:** Online.

17655 ■ *"Defend Your Research: I Can Make Your Brain Look Like Mine"* in Harvard Business Review (Vol. 88, December 2010, No. 12, pp. 32)
Pub: Harvard Business Publishing
Contact: Diane Belcher, Managing Director

Ed: Uri Hasson. **Price:** $6, PDF. **Description:** Psychology professor Uri Hasson discusses findings that the brain waves of a speaker and a listener become similar as the listener's comprehension increases. **Availability:** Online; PDF.

17656 ■ *"Defend Your Research: People Often Trust Eloquence More Than Honesty"* in Harvard Business Review (Vol. 88, November 2010, No. 11, pp. 36)
Pub: Harvard Business Publishing
Contact: Diane Belcher, Managing Director

Ed: Todd Rogers, Michael I. Norton. **Price:** $6, PDF. **Description:** The article shows how deftly sidestepping a question in an eloquent manner generates a more positive response in an audience than does a direct answer that is ineffectively delivered. Implications for both politics and business are discussed. **Availability:** Online; PDF.

17657 ■ *"Discipline In Your Business"* in South Florida Business Journal (Vol. 34, June 6, 2014, No. 46, pp. 10)
Pub: American City Business Journals, Inc.
Contact: Mike Olivieri, Executive Vice President

Released: Weekly. **Price:** $8, introductory 4-week offer(Digital only). **Description:** Ways a business can maintain a disciplined response to market conditions and achieve success are discussed. Organizations are advised to set clear goals, communicate these goals, and establish clear lines of accountability. The importance of compensation to motivate staff is also explained. **Availability:** Print; Online.

17658 ■ *"The Discomfort Zone: How Leaders Turn Difficult Conversations Into Breakthroughs"*
Released: October 13, 2014. **Price:** $21.95, Nonmembers, paperback; $19.76, Members, paperback; $18.95, paperback; $17.06, paperback; $18.95, Nonmembers, electronic publishing; $13.27, Members, electronic publishing; $18.95, Nonmembers, PDF e-book; $13.27, Members, PDF e-book. **Description:** Top leadership coach provides a model for using the Discomfort Zone, which leads people to think through problems, see situations more strategically, and transcend their limitations. The author draws on recent findings in the neuroscience of learning and provides exercises and case studies to use discomfort in business conversations and communication to create lasing changes and a more motivated workforce. **Availability:** E-book; Print; PDF; Electronic publishing.

17659 ■ *"Does Rudeness Really Matter? The Effects of Rudeness on Task Performance and Helpfulness"* in Academy of Management Journal (Vol. 50, No. 5, October 1, 2007, pp. 1181)
Pub: Academy of Management
Contact: Sharon Alvarez, President

Ed: Christine L. Porath, Amir Erez. **Description:** Study assessing the effect of impoliteness on performance and helpfulness showed rude behavior lowered performance levels and also decreased attitude of helpfulness. **Availability:** Electronic publishing; Download; PDF; Online.

17660 ■ *"Don't Ask To Get Married Before Courting Your Prospect"* in South Florida Business Journal (Vol. 34, June 13, 2014, No. 47, pp. 21)
Pub: American City Business Journals, Inc.
Contact: Mike Olivieri, Executive Vice President

Released: Weekly. **Price:** $8, introductory 4-week offer(Digital only). **Description:** Tips for salesmen when courting prospective buyers are presented. Courting prospects should not be done in haste. Salesmen should ask proper questions to get clients talking. **Availability:** Print; Online.

17661 ■ *"The Don't Do Lists"* in Inc. (Vol. 33, October 2011, No. 8, pp. 65)
Pub: Inc. Magazine

Ed: Jennifer Alsever, Adam Bluestein. **Description:** Ten business leaders and experts share their don't do lists, the things that should be avoided when going on sales calls, planning business lunches, motivating employees and more are presented. **Availability:** Online.

17662 ■ *"Don't Leave Employees on the Outside Looking In"* in Canadian Business (Vol. 83, July 20, 2010, No. 11-12, pp. 13)
Description: Managers should be careful with employee's tendencies to use the word 'they' when problems occur since this shows that employees are not associating themselves with their company. Employees should be involved in the development of the company and improving the flow of information is important in overcoming this communication challenge. **Availability:** Print; Online.

17663 ■ *"Eclectic Reading"* in Business Strategy Review (Vol. 23, Spring 2012, No. 1, pp. 68)
Released: March 06, 2012. **Description:** If ever a field of study was both science and art, marketing seems to fit the bill. Which may be why Nader Tavassoli has a keen interest in diverse subjects: branding, consumer cognition, communication effectiveness, consumer behavior across culturesand several others. What keeps his mind open to a constant flow of new possibilities? As you'll see by his suggested top ten list of books to read, Tavassoli believes strongly in delving into the arts and sciences. **Availability:** Print; PDF; Online.

17664 ■ *"Effective Networking"* in Women in Business (Vol. 64, Summer 2012, No. 2, pp. 50)
Ed: Diane Stafford. **Description:** Tips on effective networking at the 2012 American Business Women's Association National Women's Leadership Conference are suggested. The purpose of networking is to make contacts and build relationships so asking for too much free advice or selling personal services are not advisable. **Availability:** Online.

17665 ■ *Electronic Commerce*
Ed: Gary P. Schneider, Bryant Chrzan, Charles McCormick. **Released:** 12th edition. **Price:** $29.49, e-book. **Description:** E-commerce can open the door to more opportunities than ever before for small business. Packed with real-world examples and cases, the book delivers comprehensive coverage of emerging online technologies and trends and their influence on the electronic marketplace. It details how the landscape of online commerce is evolving, reflecting changes in the economy and how business and society are responding to those changes. Balancing technological issues with the strategic business aspects of successful e-commerce, the new edition includes expanded coverage of international issues, social networking, mobile commerce, Web 2.0 technologies, and updates on spam, phishing, and identity theft. **Availability:** Print.

17666 ■ *Emerging Business Online: Global Markets and the Power of B2B Internet Marketing*
Pub: FT Press

Ed: Lara Fawzy, Lucas Dworski. **Released:** First edition. **Price:** $39.99, Members, watermarked. **Description:** An introduction into ebocube (emerging business online), a comprehensive proven business model for Internet B2B marketing in emerging markets. **Availability:** E-book; Print; Online; PDF; Electronic publishing.

17667 ■ *"Evolutionary Psychology in the Business Sciences"*
Pub: Springer Publishing Co.
Contact: Bernhard Springer, Founder

Released: First edition. **Description:** All individuals operating in the business sphere share a common biological heritage, including consumers, employers, employees, entrepreneurs, or financial traders, to name a few. The evolutionary behavioral sciences and specific business contexts including marketing, consumer behavior, advertising, innovation and creativity and invention, intertemporal choice, negotiations, competition and cooperation in organizational settings, sex differences in workplace patterns, executive leadership, business ethics, store and office design, behavioral decision making, and electronic communications and commerce are all addressed. **Availability:** E-book; Print.

17668 ■ *"Executive Presence: The Missing Link Between Merit and Success"*
Pub: Harper Business
Contact: Hollis Heimbouch, Senior Vice President Publisher

Released: June 03, 2014. **Price:** $23.99, hardcover. **Description:** Ways to find out if you possess executive presence are discussed. Executive presence is a conglomeration of qualities exuded by true leaders, a presence that shows you are in charge. Executive presences is a dynamic, collective mix of appearance, communication and gravitas and leaders must know how to use them all to their advantage. **Availability:** E-book; Print; Audio.

17669 ■ *"Extreme Negotiations" in Harvard Business Review (Vol. 88, November 2010, No. 11, pp. 66)*
Pub: Harvard Business Publishing
Contact: Diane Belcher, Managing Director
Ed: Jeff Weiss, Aram Donigian, Jonathan Hughes. **Price:** $8.95, PDF. **Description:** Examination of military negotiation skills that are applicable in business situations. Skills include soliciting others' perspectives, developing and proposing multiple solutions, and inviting others to assess them. **Availability:** Online; PDF.

17670 ■ *"Facebook: A Promotional Budget's Best Friend" in Women Entrepreneur (February 1, 2009)*
Description: Facebook began as a social networking website but has become a valuable marketing tool for all types of businesses, organizations and causes. Tips are provided for creating a Facebook account and growing one's network on Facebook. **Availability:** Online.

17671 ■ *The Facebook Effect: The Inside Story of the Company That Is Connecting the World*
Ed: David Kirkpatrick. **Released:** 2011. **Price:** $18, paperback; $13.99, e-book. **Description:** There's never been a Website like Facebook: more than 350 million people have accounts, and if the growth rate continues, by 2013 every Internet user worldwide will have his or her own page. No one's had more access to the inner workings of the phenomenon than Kirkpatrick, a senior tech writer at Fortune magazine. Written with the full cooperation of founder Mark Zuckerberg, the book follows the company from its genesis in a Harvard dorm room through its successes over Friendster and MySpace, the expansion of the user base, and Zuckerberg's refusal to sell. **Availability:** E-book; Print.

17672 ■ *"The File On..Jenne Distributors" in Crain's Cleveland Business (Vol. 28, October 8, 2007, No. 40, pp. 26)*
Pub: Crain Communications Inc.
Contact: K. C. Crain, President
Ed: Kimberly Bonvissuto. **Description:** Overview of the telecommunications equipment company, Jenne Distributors, a firm that is projecting more than $125 million in revenue for 2007. **Availability:** Online.

17673 ■ *"Fiscal Cliff Notes" in Barron's (Vol. 92, September 15, 2012, No. 38, pp. 27)*
Pub: Dow Jones & Company Inc.
Contact: Almar Latour, Chief Executive Officer
Ed: Mike Hogan. **Description:** Websites and blogs dedicated to providing information on the economic effects of the 'fiscal cliff' are described. These sites discuss possible effects on the US economy, budget, and personal finances. **Availability:** Online.

17674 ■ *"Gen Z-Led Executive Communications and Strategic Engagement Agency Launches in DC" in Minority Business Entrepreneur (March 17, 2023)*
URL(s): mbemag.com/articles/gen-z-led-executive-communications-and-strategic-engagement-agency-launches-in-dc/
Ed: Gaby M. Rojas. **Description:** One of the first Black, Queer, and Gen Z-led agencies was launched by Words Normalize Behavior, which is a company dedicated to communications, coalition-building, and advice. **Availability:** Online.

17675 ■ *"Geo-Location Technology Linking Stores, Shoppers" in Providence Business News (Vol. 29, May 5, 2014, No. 5, pp. 1)*
Pub: American City Business Journals, Inc.
Contact: Mike Olivieri, Executive Vice President
Released: May 03, 2014. **Description:** Jewelry maker, Alex and Ani LLC of Cranston, Rhode Island, outfitted their 40 retail stores in the U.S. with Bluetooth Low Energy systems called iBeacons to communicate directly with customers' mobile phones when they are in or near the store. The company claims that its stores have not received any negative feedback on hyperlocal messaging since the program started in summer 2013. **Availability:** Online.

17676 ■ *"Getting Drowned Out by the Brainstorm" in Canadian Business (Vol. 83, June 15, 2010, No. 10, pp. 91)*
Pub: Rogers Media Inc.
Contact: Neil Spivak, Chief Executive Officer
Ed: Joe Castaldo. **Description:** A study reveals that people generate more ideas when they do it alone rather than as part of a brainstorming group. The limited range of ideas is due to the fixation of group members on the first idea that gets offered. **Availability:** Online.

17677 ■ *Getting More: How to Negotiate to Achieve Your Goals in the Real World*
Released: January 04, 2011. **Price:** $26. **Description:** When negotiating, people fail to meet their goals due to focusing on power and the 'win-win' instead of on relationships and perceptions, thus not finding enough things to trade. They think others should be rational when they are dealing with emotions and they get distracted from the real goal.

17678 ■ *Getting to Yes: Negotiating Agreement Without Giving In*
Pub: Penguin Publishing Group
Ed: Roger Fisher, William L. Ury, Bruce Patton. **Released:** May 03, 2011. **Price:** $17, paperback; $14.99, e-book; $11.55, paperback; $5.38, hardcover. **Description:** Strategies for negotiating mutually acceptable agreements in all types of conflict. **Availability:** E-book; Print.

17679 ■ *"Global Business Speaks English: Why You Need a Language Strategy Now" in Harvard Business Review (Vol. 90, May 2012, No. 5, pp. 116)*
Pub: Harvard Business Review Press
Contact: Moderna V. Pfizer, Contact
Ed: Tsedal Neeley. **Price:** $8.95. **Description:** English is rapidly becoming the language of businesses regardless of where they are located. To improve efficiency, the author advocates implementing an English-only policy. However, this must be conducted with sufficient training and support, and appropriate cultural sensitivity. **Availability:** PDF; Online.

17680 ■ *The Golden 120 Seconds of Every Sales Call: A Fresh Innovative Look at the Sales Process*
Pub: NorlightsPress.com
Contact: Dee Justesen, Co-Founder
Ed: Peter G. Dennis. **Released:** Second edition. **Description:** Salespeople who want to find their personal style, gain confidence, and avoid deal-killing mistakes must read this book. It will show both new and experienced sales professionals how to use key fundamentals with every call, every selling interaction, and every opportunity to make something happen. Anyone who sells for a living has experienced the magic moments that can make or break a sales. Advice is given to help recognize, and learn to cultivate, this vital part of the sales process. **Availability:** Print.

17681 ■ *"Grooming Your Online Persona" in Women In Business (Vol. 62, June 2010, No. 2, pp. 36)*
Description: Employees' use of online social networks could become a basis on how their employers, clients, or business partners would judge them. Personal details, pictures and other online data should be filtered to avoid inappropriate or uncomfortable situations and distinguish personal from professional or work life. **Availability:** Online.

17682 ■ *Groundswell: Winning in a World Transformed by Social Technologies*
Pub: Harvard Business Review Press
Contact: Moderna V. Pfizer, Contact
Ed: Charlene Li, Josh Bernoff. **Released:** June 09, 2011. **Price:** $22, paperback/softbound. **Description:** Individuals are using online social technologies such as blogs, social networking sites, YouTube, and podcasts to discuss products and companies, write their own news, and find their own deals. When consumers you've never met are rating your company's products in public forums with which you have no experience or influence, your company is vulnerable. This book teaches the tools and data necessary to turn this treat into an opportunity. **Availability:** E-book; Print.

17683 ■ *"Group Thinking" in Business Strategy Review (Vol. 23, Spring 2012, No. 1, pp. 48)*
Description: Conflicts and decision making in groups has long been a subject of fascination for Randall Peterson, Professor of Organizational Behavior at London Business School. He talks to Business Strategy Review about what ignited his interest and his latest research and thinking. **Availability:** Print; Online.

17684 ■ *"How Anger Poisons Decision Making" in Harvard Business Review (Vol. 88, September 2010, No. 9, pp. 26)*
Pub: Harvard Business Publishing
Contact: Diane Belcher, Managing Director
Ed: Jennifer S. Lerner, Katherine Shonk. **Price:** $6, PDF. **Description:** Importance of accountability in mitigating the negative effects of anger on the decision making process is stressed. **Availability:** Online; PDF.

17685 ■ *"How to Create a Communication Plan for Your Small Business" in Camino Financial Blog (Dec. 23, 2021)*
URL(s): www.caminofinancial.com/how-to-create-a-communications-plan-for-your-small-business/
Released: December 23, 2021. **Description:** A guide to creating an effective communication plan for your small business. **Availability:** Online.

17686 ■ *"How to Make a Mailing List in Gmail for Business Use" in Small Business Trends (February 8, 2023)*
URL(s): smallbiztrends.com/2017/05/how-to-make-a-mailing-list-in-gmail.html
Ed: Michael Guta. **Released:** February 08, 2023. **Description:** Email lists are a primary tool for many small business owners. This article explains how to use Gmail to create one for your business so you can run your company more efficiently. **Availability:** Online.

17687 ■ *How to Make Money with Social Media: An Insider's Guide to Using New and Emerging Media to Grow Your Business*
Ed: Jamie Turner, Reshma Shah, PhD. **Released:** 2nd edition. **Description:** Marketers, executives, entrepreneurs are shown more effective ways to utilize Internet social media to make money. This guide brings together both practical strategies and proven execution techniques for driving maximum value from social media marketing. **Availability:** E-book; Print.

17688 ■ *"How to Master Cold Calling (Scripts Included)" in Business News Daily (February 21, 2023)*
URL(s): www.businessnewsdaily.com/16057-cold-calling.html
Ed: Yara Simon. **Released:** February 21, 2023. **Description:** Small businesses sometimes need to participate in cold calling, which can be effective if

GENERAL SMALL BUSINESS TOPICS

done correctly. This article describes what is cold calling and gives examples on what to do. **Availability:** Online.

17689 ■ *How to Persuade and Influence People: Powerful Techniques to Get your Own Way More Often*
Pub: John Wiley & Sons, Inc.
Contact: Christina Van Tassell, Executive Vice President Chief Financial Officer
Ed: Philip Hesketh. **Released:** September 2010. **Price:** $26, paperback; $16.99, e-book. **Description:** Seven psychological reasons behind why and how people are persuaded and how to use these reasons to your advantage in both your personal and business life. **Availability:** E-book; Print.

17690 ■ *"How Small Businesses Should Adapt Their Customer Communication This Year"* in Forbes (Apr 14, 2021)
URL(s): www.forbes.com/sites/forbesbusinesscouncil/2021/04/14/how-small-businesses-should-adapt-their-customer-communication-this-year/?sh=6848c0a055e6
Ed: Corey Kelly. **Released:** April 14, 2021. **Description:** Discusses the importance of customer communication management and its reliance on flexibility, accommodation, and convenience. **Availability:** Online.

17691 ■ *How to Start an Internal Communications Department*
URL(s): www.legalzoom.com/articles/how-to-start-an-internal-communications-department
Ed: Sandra Beckwith. **Released:** February 15, 2023. **Description:** Keep your employees up to date on the business by forming an internal communications department. **Availability:** Online.

17692 ■ *"How To Be a Twitter Ninja"* in Canadian Business (Vol. 87, October 2014, No. 10, pp. 51)
Description: Robert Palmer, public relations manager at WestJet, shares some rules when it comes to customer engagement on Twitter. He emphasizes the importance of communication when dealing with customer complaints as quickly as possible. **Availability:** Print; Online.

17693 ■ *If You Have to Cry, Go Outside: And Other Things Your Mother Never Told You*
Pub: HarperCollins Publishers L.L.C.
Contact: Brian Murray, President
Ed: Kelly Cutrone, Meredith Bryan. **Released:** February 02, 2010. **Price:** $10.99, e-book; $7.24, e-book. **Description:** Women's mentor advices on how to make it in one of the most competitive industries in the world, fashion. She has kicked people out of fashion shows, forced some of reality television's shiny start to fire their friends, and built her own company which is one of the most powerful public relations firms in the fashion business. **Availability:** E-book; Print.

17694 ■ *I'm on LinkedIn - Now What?*
Pub: Happy About
Contact: Ric Vatner, Chief Executive Officer
Ed: Jason Alba. **Released:** Fourth edition. **Price:** $19.95, paperback; $14.95; $9.99. **Description:** Designed to help get the most out of LinkedIn, the popular business networking site and follows the first edition and includes the latest and great approaches using LinkedIn. With over 32 million members there is a lot of potential to find and develop relationships to help in your business and personal life, but many professionals find themselves wondering what to do once they sign up. This book explains the different benefits of the system and recommends best practices (including LinkedIn Groups) so that you get the most out of LinkedIn. **Availability:** E-book; Print; PDF; DVD; Electronic publishing; Download; Online.

17695 ■ *"Increasing Business-to-Business Buyer Word-of-Mouth and Share-of-Purchase"* in Journal of Business & Industrial Marketing (Vol. 29, June 2014, No. 5)
Pub: Emerald Group Publishing Limited
Contact: Erika Valenti, President

Description: The satisfaction-loyalty framework pertaining to word-of-mouth communications and share-of-purchases was examined for situations in which business-to-business buyers are associated with the salesperson as well as the selling firm. The results indicated that satisfaction, loyalty, and WOMC relating to the salesperson directly affect satisfaction, loyalty, and WOMC with the selling firm, and that buyer satisfaction and loyalty also influence their post purchase conduct. **Availability:** Download; Online.

17696 ■ *Information Technology for the Small Business: How to Make IT Work For Your Company*
Description: Basics of information technology to help small companies maximize benefits are covered. Topics include pitfalls to avoid, email and Internet use, data backup, recovery and overall IT organization.

17697 ■ *"Internet Marketing 2.0: Closing the Online Chat Gap"* in Agent's Sales Journal (November 2009, pp. 14)
Ed: Jeff Denenholz. **Description:** Advice regarding the implementation of an Internet marketing strategy for insurance agencies includes how and why to incorporate a chat feature in which a sales agent can communicate in real-time with potential or existing customers. It is important to understand if appropriate response mechanisms are in place to convert leads into actual sales. **Availability:** Print; Online.

17698 ■ *"An Introvert's Guide to Schmoozing"* in Canadian Business (Vol. 83, July 20, 2010, No. 11-12, pp. 73)
Pub: Rogers Media Inc.
Contact: Neil Spivak, Chief Executive Officer
Ed: Jasmine Budak. **Description:** Writer Nancy Ankowitz says that introverts seem to get grouped with social misfits but introverts are people who recharge by spending time alone. Ankowitz advises introverts to use their strengths in quiet strengths such as writing and listening as well as learning to speak in public. **Availability:** Print; Online.

17699 ■ *"Is It Time to Ban Swearing in the Workplace?"* in HR Specialist (Vol. 8, September 2010, No. 9, pp. 2)
Pub: Capitol Information Group Inc.
Contact: Allie Ash, Chief Executive Officer
Description: Screening software has been developed to identify profanity used in business correspondence. **Availability:** PDF; Online.

17700 ■ *"Israeli Spam Law May Have Global Impact"* in Information Today (Vol. 26, February 2009, No. 2, pp. 28)
Pub: Information Today Inc.
Contact: Thomas H. Hogan, President
Ed: David Mirchin. **Description:** Israels new law, called Amendment 40 of the Communications Law, will regulate commercial solicitations including those sent without permission via email, fax, automatic phone dialing systems, or short messaging technologies. **Availability:** PDF; Online.

17701 ■ *It's Not Just Who You Know: Transform Your Life (and Your Organization) by Turning Colleagues and Contacts into Lasting Relationships*
Released: August 10, 2010. **Price:** $11.99, hardcover; $29.57, paperback. **Description:** Tommy Spaulding teaches the reader how to reach out to others in order to create lasting relationships that go beyond superficial contacts. **Availability:** audiobook; E-book; Print.

17702 ■ *It's Not Who You Know - It's Who Knows You!: The Small Business Guide to Raising Your Profits by Raising Your Profile*
Pub: John Wiley & Sons, Inc.
Contact: Christina Van Tassell, Executive Vice President Chief Financial Officer
Ed: David Arvin. **Released:** 2nd edition. **Price:** $8.69, hardcover. **Description:** When it comes to promoting a small business or a brand, it is essential to know how valuable high-profile attention can be. But for most small companies, the cost of hiring an outside firm to increase attention can be too expensive. **Availability:** Print; Online.

17703 ■ *"Jab, Jab, Jab, Right Hook: How to Tell Your Story in a Noisy Social World"*
Pub: Harper Business
Contact: Hollis Heimbouch, Senior Vice President Publisher
Released: November 26, 2013. **Price:** $23.99, hardcover. **Description:** Author and social media expert shares advice on ways to connect with customers and beat the competition. Social media strategies for marketers and managers need to convert Internet traffic to sales. Communication is the key to online sales that are adapted to high quality social media platforms and mobile devices. **Availability:** E-book; Print.

17704 ■ *"Keys to Overcome Fear of Follow-Up"* in Agency Sales Magazine (Vol. 39, December 2009, No. 11, pp. 26)
Description: In order to be more successful at making follow-up calls, salespeople should not take rejection personally and never assume that they are going to annoy prospects if they follow-up. Those that follow-up with prospects stand out among others since few salespeople do this. **Availability:** Online.

17705 ■ *"Leadership Is a Conversation: How To Improve Employee Engagement and Alignment In Today's Flatter, More Networked Organizations"* in Harvard Business Review (Vol. 90, June 2012, No. 6, pp. 76)
Pub: Harvard Business Review Press
Contact: Moderna V. Pfizer, Contact
Ed: Boris Groysberg, Michael Slind. **Description:** A two-way flow of communication is essential in promoting and maintaining employee motivation. Key points are establishing intimacy through gaining trust, interactivity via dialogue, inclusion by expanding employee roles, and intentionality through establishing an agenda.

17706 ■ *"Learning Charisma: Transform Yourself Into the Person Others Want to Follow"* in Harvard Business Review (Vol. 90, June 2012, No. 6, pp. 127)
Pub: Harvard Business Review Press
Contact: Moderna V. Pfizer, Contact
Ed: John Antonakis, Marika Fenley, Sue Liechti. **Price:** $8.95, hardcopy black and white. **Description:** Chrismatic leadership tactics include gestures, facial expressions, and an animated voice, all of which can enhance the receptiveness of a given message. Tips include engaging listeners and distilling points, and demonstrating passion, authority, and integrity. **Availability:** Print; Online; PDF.

17707 ■ *"LIBOR's Hidden Lesson: Instant Messages Are Deadly"* in Canadian Business (Vol. 85, August 12, 2012, No. 14, pp. 75)
Ed: Vanessa Farquharson. **Description:** The appropriate use of instant messaging in the workplace is discussed. Employees involved in a business that deals with other people's finances or intellectual property are advised to keep all of their work and private email accounts separate. **Availability:** Print; Online.

17708 ■ *Liespotting: Proven Techniques to Detect Deception*
Pub: St. Martins Press/Macmillan
Ed: Pamela Meyer. **Released:** September 13, 2011. **Price:** $15.99, paperback; $25.99, hardcover. **Description:** Liespotting links three disciplines: facial recognition training, interrogation training, and a comprehensive survey of research in the field - into a specialized body of information developed specifically to help business leaders detect deception and get the information they need to successfully conduct their most important interactions and transactions. **Availability:** Paperback; E-book; Print.

17709 ■ *"Life's Work: Interview with Alain Ducasse"* in *Harvard Business Review* (Vol. 92, May 2014, No. 5, pp. 136)
Pub: Harvard Business Press
Contact: Gabriela Allmi, Regional Manager
E-mail: gabriela.allmi@hbsp.harvard.edu
Price: $8.95. **Description:** Alain Ducasse believes supervision is secondary to shared experience, and emphasizes the importance of communicating with employees to engage them and enable them to perform well. Job satisfaction is dependent on individual growth, appropriate compensation, and harmony. **Availability:** PDF; Online.

17710 ■ *"Listen Up: There's a Revolution in the Cubicle"* in *Barron's* (Vol. 89, July 27, 2009, No. 30, pp. 18)
Pub: Dow Jones & Company Inc.
Contact: Almar Latour, Chief Executive Officer
Ed: Jay Palmer. **Description:** Plantronics will be among the first beneficiaries when the unified communications revolution arrives in the office. Plantronics' shares could rise to around 30 in 2009 from the 20s as of July 2009. Unified communications could create a huge new multimillion-dollar market for Plantronics. **Availability:** Online.

17711 ■ *"Managing the Facebookers; Business"* in *The Economist* (Vol. 390, January 3, 2009, No. 8612, pp. 10)
Pub: Economist Newspaper Ltd.
Contact: Lara Boro, Chief Executive Officer
Description: According to a report from PricewaterhouseCoopers, a business consultancy, workers from Generation Y, also known as the Net Generation, are more difficult to recruit and integrate into companies that practice traditional business acumen. 61 percent of chief executive managers say that they have trouble with younger employees who tend to be more narcissistic and more interested in personal fulfillment with a need for frequent feedback and an over-precise set of objectives on the path to promotion which can be hard for managers who are used to a different relationship with their subordinates. Older bosses should prepare to make some concessions to their younger talent since some of the issues that make them happy include cheaper online ways to communicate and additional coaching, both of which are good for business. **Availability:** Online.

17712 ■ *"Marketers Push for Mobile Tuesday as the New Black Friday"* in *Advertising Age* (Vol. 79, December 1, 2008, No. 44, pp. 21)
Pub: Crain Communications, Inc.
Contact: Jessica Botos, Manager, Marketing
E-mail: jessica.botos@crainsnewyork.com
Ed: Natalie Zmuda. **Description:** Marketers are using an innovative approach in an attempt to stimulate business on the Tuesday following Thanksgiving by utilizing consumer's cell phones to alert them of sales or present them with coupons for this typically slow retail business day; with this campaign both advertisers and retailers are hoping to start Mobile Tuesday, another profitable shopping day in line with Black Friday and Cyber Monday. **Availability:** Online.

17713 ■ *"Marketing Scholarship 2.0"* in *Journal of Marketing* (Vol. 75, July 2011, No. 4, pp. 225)
Pub: American Marketing Association
Contact: Bennie F. Johnson, Chief Executive Officer
Ed: Richard J. Lutz. **Released:** Volume: 75 issue: 4. **Description:** A study of the implications of changing environment and newer collaborative models for marketing knowledge production and dissemination is presented. Crowdsourcing has become a frequently employed strategy in industry. Academic researchers should collaborate more as well as the academe and industry, to make sure that important problems are being investigated. **Availability:** PDF.

17714 ■ *"Mastering Business Negotiation: A Working Guide to Making Deals and Resolving Conflict"*
Pub: Jossey-Bass

Ed: Roy J. Lewicki, Alexander Hiam. **Released:** 2011. **Description:** Provides extensive insight into practical strategies and ideas for conducting business negotiations. **Availability:** Print; Electronic publishing; Online.

17715 ■ *"The Mobility Imperative"* in *Business Strategy Review* (Vol. 23, Spring 2012, No. 1, pp. 70)
Description: The founder of Sutton Trust, Sir Peter Lampl, explains his passion for social mobility. **Availability:** Print; Online.

17716 ■ *"Monique Johnson on the Pros and Cons of Hybrid Events"* in *Small Business Trends* (November 1, 2022)
URL(s): smallbiztrends.com/2022/11/hybrid-events.html
Ed: Holly Chavez. **Released:** November 01, 2022. **Description:** The founder of Live Video Lab goes over the basics about hybrid business events. **Availability:** Online.

17717 ■ *"More Power to Your Presentation"* in *Business Strategy Review* (Vol. 21, Spring 2010, No. 1, pp. 50)
Ed: Roly Grimshaw. **Released:** March 22, 2010. **Description:** You might wonder what similarities there can be between a Russian oligarch and an entrepreneur. When it comes to persuading people to invest, there are plenty. **Availability:** Online; Electronic publishing.

17718 ■ *"Mosaid Grants First Wireless Patent License To Matsushita"* in *Canadian Electronics* (Vol. 23, June-July 2008, No. 5, pp. 1)
Pub: Annex Buisness Media
Contact: Mike Fredericks, President
Description: Matsushita Electric Industrial Co. Ltd. has been granted a six-and-a-half-year license by Mosaid Technologies Inc. to manufacture the latter's products. The patent portfolio license agreement covers Mosaid's Wi-Fi, Wi-Max, CDMA-enabled notebook computers and other products.

17719 ■ *"Negotiating for Success: Essential Strategies and Skills"*
Released: October 04, 2014. **Price:** $5.81, paperback. **Description:** Negotiation is the key to business success. The book includes a Negotiation Planning Checklist and all the essential tools to perfect negotiation skills. **Availability:** Print.

17720 ■ *"Networking Web Sites: a Two-Edge Sword"* in *Contractor* (Vol. 56, October 2009, No. 10, pp. 52)
Ed: H. Kent Craig. **Description:** People need to be careful about the information that they share on social networking Web sites. They should realize that future bosses, coworkers, and those that might want to hire them might read those information. Posting on these sites can cost career opportunities and respect. **Availability:** Print; Online.

17721 ■ *"Never Eat Alone, Expanded and Updated: And Other Secrets to Success, One Relationship at a Time"*
Released: June 03, 2014. **Description:** The power of their relationships is what makes successful business leaders stand out from the rest. He lists specific steps to reach out and connect with colleagues, friends, and associates, along with successful ways to use social media to advance in business. **Availability:** Print.

17722 ■ *"New Sales. Simplified: The Essential Handbook for Prospecting and New Business Development"*
Pub: HarperCollins Leadership
Contact: Donald Miller, Chief Executive Officer
Released: September 04, 2012. **Price:** $19.99, Paperback. **Description:** The constant flow of new accounts is essential for any small business to grow and thrive. A proven formula for prospecting; customer-focused selling; proactive telephone calling that leads to face-to-face meetings; the use of email, voicemail, and social media; prevent the buyer's anti-salesperson response; build a rapport; winning sales; communicating with clients; plan time for business development activities; and more. **Availability:** E-book; Print; Audio; Download.

17723 ■ *"The New Science of Building Great Teams: The Chemistry of High-Performing Groups Is No Longer a Mystery"* in *Harvard Business Review* (Vol. 90, April 2012, No. 4, pp. 60)
Pub: Harvard Business Review Press
Contact: Moderna V. Pfizer, Contact
Ed: Alex Pentland. **Description:** Body language and tone of voice are key to the dynamics of a team that works well together. Face-to-face communication is the most valuable. Energy, engagement, and exploration delineate how team members contribute, communicate with other team members, and communicate with other teams respectively.

17724 ■ *"New Sprint Phone Whets Appetite for Applications, Brings Revenue for Handmark"* in *The Business Journal-Serving Metropolitan Kansas City* (Vol. 26, July 25, 2008)
Description: Firms supporting the applications of the new Samsung Instinct, which was introduced by Sprint Nextel Corp. in June 2008, have reported usage rates increase for their products. Handmark, whose mobile services Pocket Express comes loaded with Instinct, has redirected employees to meet the rising demand for the services. Other views and information on Instinct, are presented. **Availability:** Print; Online.

17725 ■ *"Next-Level Networking: You Know Who, But Does Who Know You?"* in *South Florida Business Journal* (Vol. 34, February 7, 2014, No. 29, pp. 10)
Pub: American City Business Journals, Inc.
Contact: Mike Olivieri, Executive Vice President
Released: Weekly. **Price:** $8, Introductory 4-week offer(Digital & Print). **Description:** Businesspeople are advised to focus on 'next-level-networking' by meeting new people and developing relationships with others. It is believed that contact management systems become a way of life when companies master this form of networking. **Availability:** Print; Online.

17726 ■ *"'No Snitch' Culture in American Business"* in *Business Owner* (Vol. 35, September-October 2011, No. 5, pp. 7)
Description: It is important to make known the fact that a businessman is performing unethical or illegal activities in his firm. **Availability:** Online.

17727 ■ *"Nortel Makes Customers Stars in New Campaign"* in *Brandweek* (Vol. 49, April 21, 2008, No. 16, pp. 8)
Description: Nortel has launched a new television advertising campaign in which the business-to-business communications technology provider cast senior executives in 30-second TV case studies that show how Nortel's technology helped their businesses innovate. **Availability:** Online.

17728 ■ *"Not Sales, But a Secret Sauce"* in *Memphis Business Journal* (Vol. 35, March 14, 2014, No. 49, pp. 15)
Pub: American City Business Journals, Inc.
Contact: Mike Olivieri, Executive Vice President
Released: Weekly. **Price:** $4, introductory 4-week offer(Digital only). **Description:** Farmhouse Marketing LLC creative director, Ben Fent, says businesses should focus on connections instead of sales. He added that businesses should use more visual language in selling. Fant also stated that the key to making a sale is making people see the benefit of a product. **Availability:** Print; Online.

17729 ■ *"On Technology: The Web Gets Real"* in *Canadian Business* (Vol. 79, July 17, 2006, No. 14-15, pp. 19)
Pub: Rogers Media Inc.
Contact: Neil Spivak, Chief Executive Officer

Ed: Andrew Wahl. **Description:** Ron Lake's efforts of bringing the virtual and physical worlds more closely together by using Geographic Markup Language (GML) are presented. **Availability:** Print; PDF; Online.

17730 ■ *"The One Thing You Must Get Right When Building a Brand" in Harvard Business Review (Vol. 88, December 2010, No. 12, pp. 80)*
Pub: Harvard Business Publishing
Contact: Diane Belcher, Managing Director

Ed: Patrick Barwise, Sean Meehan. **Price:** $8.95, PDF. **Description:** Four uses for new media include: communicating a clearly defined customer promise, creating trust via delivering on the promise, regularly improving on the promise, and innovating past what is familiar. **Availability:** Online; PDF.

17731 ■ *The Orange Revolution: How One Great Team Can Transform an Entire Organization*
Pub: Simon & Schuster, Inc.
Contact: Jonathan Karp, President

Ed: Adrian Gostick, Chester Elton. **Released:** September 2010. **Price:** $25, hardcover; $16.99. **Description:** Based on a 350,000-person study by the Best Companies Group, as well as research into exceptional teams at leading companies, including Zappos.com, Pepsi Beverages Company, and Madison Square Garden, the authors have determined a key set of characteristics displayed by members of breakthrough teams, and have identified a set of rules great teams live by, which generate a culture of positive teamwork and led to extraordinary results. Using specific stories from the teams they studied, they reveal in detail how these teams operate and how managers can transform their own teams into such high performers by fostering: stronger clarity of goals, greater trust among team members, more open and honest dialogue, stronger accountability for all team members, and purpose-based recognition of team member contributions. **Availability:** E-book; Print.

17732 ■ *Persuasive Business Proposals*
Pub: HarperCollins Leadership
Contact: Donald Miller, Chief Executive Officer

Ed: Tom Sant. **Released:** 3rd edition. **Price:** $22.99, Paperback. **Description:** Writing to win more customers, clients, and contracts. **Availability:** E-book; Print.

17733 ■ *"Pioneering Strategies for Entrepreneurial Success" in Business Horizons (Vol. 51, January-February 2008, No. 1, pp. 21)*
Pub: Elsevier Advanced Technology Publications

Ed: Candida G. Brush. **Price:** $8.95, hardcopy black and white. **Description:** Entrepreneurs are known for new products, services, processes, markets and industries. In order to achieve success, they have to develop a clear vision, creatively manage finances, and use social skills to persuade others to commit to the venture. Pioneering strategies and their implementation are examined. **Availability:** Print; PDF; Online.

17734 ■ *"Pitch Perfect: How to Say It Right the First Time, Every Time"*
Pub: Harper Business
Contact: Hollis Heimbouch, Senior Vice President Publisher

Released: April 01, 2014. **Price:** $3.34, kindle; $17.91, hardcover; $1.54, hardcover(74 used from $1.54); $11.95, hardcover(56 new from $11.95); $10.19, paperback; $4.48, paperback(57 used from $4.48); $9.47, paperback(63 new from $9.47). **Description:** Media guru and Emmy Award-winning correspondent, Bill McGowan, teaches how to overcome common communications pitfalls using his simple Principles of Persuasion. They will help harness the power of persuasion and have people listening closely and remembering you long after you've departed. **Availability:** E-book; Print; Online; Audio.

17735 ■ *"Power Cues: The Subtle Science of Leading Groups, Persuading Others, and Maximizing Your Personal Impact"*
Pub: Harvard Business Review Press
Contact: Moderna V. Pfizer, Contact

Released: May 13, 2014. **Price:** $30, hardcover. **Description:** Renowned speaking coach and communication expert, Nick Morgan, shows how humans are programmed to respond to the nonverbal cues of others. He teaches business leaders and entrepreneurs how to take control of their communications in order to communicate more effectively while commanding influence. **Availability:** E-book; Print.

17736 ■ *"The Power of Noticing: What the Best Leaders See"*
Pub: Simon & Schuster Adult Publishing Group
Contact: Jonathan Karp, President

Released: August 05, 2014. **Price:** $17.99, paperback, plus $1.55 shipping charges. **Description:** A guide to help entrepreneurs and managers gain the advantage in negotiations, decision making, and leadership skills. Instruction is given to see and evaluate information that others overlook. **Availability:** E-book; Print; Download; Audio.

17737 ■ *PPC's Guide to Small Business Consulting Engagements*
Released: Annual. **Price:** $365, book; $280, online. **Description:** Technical guide for conducting consulting engagements for small business. **Availability:** Print; Online.

17738 ■ *Reading Financial Reports for Dummies*
Pub: John Wiley & Sons, Inc.
Contact: Christina Van Tassell, Executive Vice President Chief Financial Officer
URL(s): www.amazon.com/gp/product/1119871360/ref=as_li_tl?ie=UTF8&tag=wiley01-20

Ed: Lita Epstein. **Released:** 4th Edition. **Price:** $27.18, paperback; $18, e-book. **Description:** The fourth edition contains more new and updated information. This book is meant as a guide to help the reader interpret and understand financial reports, annual reports, balance sheets, income statements, statements of cash flow and consolidated statements. Real-world examples are given. . **Availability:** E-book; Print.

17739 ■ *"Research and Markets Adds Report: The U.S. Mobile Web Market" in Entertainment Close-Up (December 10, 2009)*
Description: Highlights of the new Research and Markets report "The U.S. Mobile Web Market: Taking Advantage of the iPhone Phenomenon" include: mobile Internet marketing strategies; the growth of mobile web usage; the growth of revenue in the mobile web market; and a look at Internet business communications, social media and networking. **Availability:** Print; Online.

17740 ■ *"Rethinking the Organization" in Strategy & Leadership (Vol. 38, September-October 2010, No. 5, pp. 13-19)*
Pub: Emerald Inc.

Ed: Stephen Denning. **Description:** A study identifies the changes needed to be adopted by top managers to achieve game-changing innovation at an organization-wide level. Findings indicate that CEOs should practice pull management in order to nurture fruitful communication between employees and customers and achieve organizational involvement of customers. **Availability:** Print; PDF.

17741 ■ *"Rise Interactive, Internet Marketing Agency, Now Offers Social Media Services" in Marketwired (November 4, 2009)*
Pub: Comtex News Network Inc.
Contact: Kan Devnani, President

Description: Profile of Rise Interactive, a full-service Internet marketing agency which has recently added social media to its list of offerings; the agency touts that its newest service gives their clients the power to have ongoing communication with current and potential customers on the sites they are most actively visiting. **Availability:** Print; Online.

17742 ■ *"The Rise of Pompei" in Retail Merchandiser (Vol. 51, September-October 2011, No. 5, pp. 13)*

Description: Soho creative consulting group follows its C3 philosophy to create an invigorated brand experience that transforms customers from consumers to empowered buyers. Pompei AD is a leading creative consultancy that specializes in design and branding for retail, museum, hospitality, and other sectors. **Availability:** Print; Online.

17743 ■ *"Rogue Caller Infiltrates Cincinnati Firms' Analyst Calls: 'Mr. CEO, Please Do Elaborate On Your Firm's Metrics'" in Business Courier (Vol. 24, February 28, 2008, No. 47, pp. 1)*
Pub: American City Business Journals, Inc.
Contact: Mike Olivieri, Executive Vice President

Ed: Jon Newberry. **Description:** Discusses a rogue caller who goes by the name of Joe Herrick, Steven Nissan and Joe Harris has joined in over a dozen conference calls, asking chief executive officers on their plans and commenting on the companies' operations. The mystery caller attempts to pass himself off as a financial analyst. Transcripts of some conference calls, in which the rogue caller is involved, are provided. **Availability:** Online.

17744 ■ *The Savvy Gal's Guide to Online Networking: Or What Would Jane Austen Do?*
Pub: Booklocker.com Inc.

Ed: Diane K. Danielson, Lindsey Pollak. **Description:** It is a truth universally acknowledged that a woman in search of a fabulous career must be in want of networking opportunities. Or so Jane Austen would say if she were writing, or more likely, blogging today. So begins the must-read guide to networking in the 21st Century. Authors and networking experts share the nuts, bolts and savvy secrets that businesswomen need in order to use technology to build professional relationships. **Availability:** Print; Online; PDF.

17745 ■ *"Say Goodbye to Voicemail, Hello To Ribbit Mobile" in Agency Sales Magazine (Vol. 39, November 2009, No. 10, pp. 3)*

Description: Salespeople should think twice before leaving a voicemail. The emerging modern etiquette is to send a text message or to e-mail the customer or client. Communication suggestions for both salespeople and their principals are presented. **Availability:** Print; Online.

17746 ■ *"Scientific American Builds Novel Blog Network" in Information Today (Vol. 28, September 2011, No. 8, pp. 12)*
Pub: Information Today Inc.
Contact: Thomas H. Hogan, President

Ed: Kurt Schiller. **Description:** Scientific American launched a new blog network that joins a diverse lineup of bloggers cover various scientific topics under one banner. The blog network includes 60 bloggers providing insights into the ever-changing world of science and technology.

17747 ■ *"The Secret Strategy for Meaningful Sales Meetings" in Agency Sales Magazine (Vol. 39, December 2009, No. 11, pp. 40)*

Description: Sales meetings can be made more meaningful by focusing on the end results that the meeting seeks to achieve. Describing the changed behavior that is sought from the sales force and working backwards from there also help make a sales meeting more meaningful. **Availability:** Online.

17748 ■ *"Secrets To Trade Show Success" in Women Entrepreneur (September 12, 2008)*

Description: Trade shows require an enormous amount of work, but they are an investment that can pay off handsomely because they allow a business to get their product or service in front of their target market. Advice regarding trade shows is given including selecting the correct venue, researching the affair and following up on leads obtained at the event. **Availability:** Online.

17749 ■ Business Communications — GENERAL SMALL BUSINESS TOPICS

17749 ■ *"Seven Annoying People You'll Meet At Your Company Golf Day"* in Canadian Business (Vol. 85, August 29, 2012, No. 14, pp. 76)
Ed: Jeff Beer. **Description:** The characteristics of people one may meet on a company golf tournament are described. Tips on how to deal with negative attitudes are provided. **Availability:** Print; Online.

17750 ■ *"Shocks and Final Straws: Using Exit-Interview Data to Examine the Unfolding Model's Decision Paths"* in Human Resource Management (Vol. 51, January-February 2012, No. 1, pp. 25-46)
Pub: John Wiley & Sons, Inc.
Contact: Christina Van Tassell, Executive Vice President Chief Financial Officer
Ed: Carol T. Kulik, Gerry Treuren, Prashant Bordia. **Released:** January 26, 2012. **Description:** Employees leaving their organizations are examined according to the unfolding model using data from exit interviews. Results indicate that employees along the same exit path may experience different kinds and combinations of shocks, while some experience shock-like events. **Availability:** Print; PDF; Online.

17751 ■ *"Should I Stay or Should I Go?"* in Entrepreneur (August 2014)
Pub: Entrepreneur Media Inc.
Contact: Dan Bova, Director
E-mail: dbova@entrepreneur.com
Description: The timing of meeting clients in person is critical to the success of a business venture. Entrepreneurs can save time and money if they know when it is worth seeing the client in person. For Jackie Kimzey of the Institute for Innovation and Entrepreneurship, the best time for a face-to-face meeting with clients is when a business relationship is starting to flourish. Kimzey advises entrepreneurs to consider their budget, the amount of time they have been working together, and the importance of the client to the business. **Availability:** Print; Online.

17752 ■ *"Show and Tell: How Everybody Can Make Extraordinary Presentations"*
Pub: Portfolio Hardcover
Contact: Adrian Zackheim, President
Released: March 01, 2016. **Price:** $19, paperback. **Description:** Whether in a one-on-one meeting, a conference room with strangers, or a lecture hall in front of thousands, giving a presentation can be difficult. Even good speakers can learn from the tips presented. Understanding your audience, organizing your content, building a clear storyline, creating effective visual effects, and channeling fear into fun will help create effective and successful presentations. **Availability:** Print.

17753 ■ *"Signs of the Times"* in Harvard Business Review (Vol. 92, May 2014, No. 5, pp. 36)
Pub: Harvard Business Publishing
Contact: Diane Belcher, Managing Director
Price: $6. **Description:** A history is presented of modern symbols used in business, including the "at" swirl, the command icon, firewire, USB, and power. Anachronisms include the old telephone handset to indicate "call" and the manila file folder to indicate "storage". **Availability:** Online; PDF.

17754 ■ *"Slow but Steady into the Future"* in Barron's (Vol. 88, July 7, 2008, No. 27, pp. M)
Pub: Dow Jones & Company Inc.
Contact: Almar Latour, Chief Executive Officer
Ed: Mark Veverka. **Description:** Investors are advised to maintain their watch on the shares of business software company NetSuite. The company's chief executive officer, Zach Nelson, claims that the company has a 10-year lead on its competitors with the development of software-as a service. **Availability:** Online.

17755 ■ *The Social Media Bible: Tactics, Tools, and Strategies for Business Success*
Pub: John Wiley & Sons, Inc.
Contact: Christina Van Tassell, Executive Vice President Chief Financial Officer

Ed: Lon Safko. **Released:** Third edition. **Price:** $29.95, paperback; $19.99, E-Book. **Description:** Information is given to build or transform a business into social media, where customers, employees, and prospects connect, collaborate, and champion products and services in order to increase sales and to beat the competition. **Availability:** E-book; Print.

17756 ■ *"Social Media, E-Mail Remain Challenging for Employers"* in Workforce Management (Vol. 88, December 14, 2009, No. 13, pp. 4)
Pub: Crain Communications Inc.
Contact: Barry Asin, President
Ed: Ed Frauenheim. **Description:** Examining the impact of Internet social networking and the workplace; due to the power of these new technologies, it is important that companies begin to set clear policies regarding Internet use and employee privacy. **Availability:** Online.

17757 ■ *"Social Networks in the Workplace: The Risk and Opportunity of Business 2.0"* in Strategy & Leadership (Vol. 38, July-August 2010, No. 4, pp. 50-53)
Pub: Emerald Inc.
Ed: Daniel Burrus. **Description:** The opinions of futurist Daniel Burrus on a novel trend called 'Business 2.0', which involves the use of social networking applications as business tools, are presented. His suggestion that personal social networking technology can be used by businesses to improve collaboration, problem solving, and leadership communications to achieve continuous value innovation is discussed. **Availability:** Online.

17758 ■ *"The Solution Became the Problem"* in Barron's (Vol. 92, August 25, 2012, No. 35, pp. 45)
Pub: Dow Jones & Company Inc.
Contact: Almar Latour, Chief Executive Officer
Ed: John Steele Gordon. **Description:** Computers were seen as a solution to technology glitches affecting Wall Street during the 1960s. Telephones and paper proved inadequate in handling rising stock market volumes during the period. **Availability:** Online.

17759 ■ *"Sound Check"* in Agency Sales Magazine (Vol. 39, August 2009, No. 8, pp. 14)
Description: Most customers believe salespersons are unable to do well in terms of listening, which is one of the four fundamental competencies of a sales person. Listening is the primary tool to uncover deeper and more powerful needs and motivations of the customer. A guide on how to listen better and improve listening effectiveness is presented. **Availability:** Online.

17760 ■ *"Staying Engaged: Location, Location"* in Black Enterprise (Vol. 38, February 2008, No. 7, pp. 64)
Pub: Earl G. Graves Ltd.
Contact: Earl Graves, Jr., President
Ed: Marcia A. Reed-Woodard. **Description:** Rules to help business leaders construct networking contacts in order to maximize professional success are outlined. **Availability:** Online.

17761 ■ *"Study: Ineffective Customer Communications Can Cost Small Businesses Time, Money and Talent"* in Business Wire (Dec. 8, 2021)
URL(s): www.businesswire.com/news/home/20 211208005270/en/Study-Ineffective-Customer -Communications-Can-Cost-Small-Businesses -Time-Money-and-Talent
Released: December 08, 2021. **Description:** Presents information on how rapidly business communication is evolving and how technology is powering new ways for businesses to build customer relationships, remove inefficiencies, and retain employees. **Availability:** Online.

17762 ■ *Table Talk: The Savvy Girl's Alternative to Networking*
Pub: AuthorHouse Inc.
Contact: William Elliott, President
Ed: Diane Danielson. **Description:** Let's face it. Women and men are different. So why should we all have to network in the same way? And, why should women have to 'network' at all? Between family and work responsibilities, the idea of pressing flesh at some not-very-festive cocktail party is right up there in appeal with a root canal. But what if women could find a way to make career boosting connections that are actually fun? Enter 'table talk', a new way to network for time-pressed, professional women. **Availability:** Print.

17763 ■ *"Take the 'I' Out of Making Connections"* in Pittsburgh Business Times (Vol. 33, January 3, 2014, No. 25, pp. 3)
Pub: American City Business Journals, Inc.
Contact: Mike Olivieri, Executive Vice President
Released: January 03, 2014. **Price:** $4, Introductory 4-Week Offer(Digital & Print). **Description:** Ways to overcome the discomfort with networking is discussed. The awkwardness of first encounters with strangers can be avoided by focusing on making a connection to someone known and easing the conversation. A key factor to doing business is making personal connections, while also developing an individualized strategy that is suited for the business and the people involved. **Availability:** Print; Online.

17764 ■ *"Talk, Inc.: How Trusted Leaders Use Conversation to Power Their Organizations"* in Canadian Business (Vol. 85, August 13, 2012, No. 13, pp. 59)
Ed: Boris Groysberg, Michael Slind. **Price:** $32. **Description:** Review of the book entitled, "Talk, Inc.: How Trusted Leaders Use Conversation to Power Their Organizations". As the title states, this book will help business leaders deliver their messages concisely and effectively. **Availability:** E-book; Print; Online.

17765 ■ *"Thanks for the Feedback: The Science and Art of Receiving Feedback Well"*
Pub: Penguin Publishing Group
Released: March 31, 2015. **Price:** $26.11, audiobook; $16.20, paperback. **Description:** Feedback is an important part of communication, but is difficult to receive as it sits at the junction of two conflicting human desires. Feedback from bosses, colleagues, customers, family and friends is essential for healthy relationships and professional development. **Availability:** audiobook ; E-book; Print.

17766 ■ *"Three Megatrends to Help Your Business Compete in 2014"* in South Florida Business Journal (Vol. 34, January 3, 2014, No. 24, pp. 10)
Pub: American City Business Journals, Inc.
Contact: Mike Olivieri, Executive Vice President
Released: Weekly. **Price:** $8, Introductory 4-week offer(Digital & Print). **Description:** Businesses can improve their competitive edge in 2014 by adapting several mega small business trends in marketing and communications. Brands can use brand bridging to get customers attention, use wearable technology to increase their value, and adapt environmental sustainability and corporate social responsibility to keep their customers. **Availability:** Print; Online.

17767 ■ *"Tips for Better Email Inbox Management"* in Business News Daily (March 13, 2023)
URL(s): www.businessnewsdaily.com/10328-email -habits-inbox-management.html
Ed: Natalie Hamingson. **Released:** March 13, 2023. **Description:** Develop email management skills with these best practices. Business owners can often waste a lot of time dealing with unnecessary email issues, so adhering to these habits will help organize your work day. **Availability:** Online.

17768 ■ Top 10 Communication Apps for Your Small Business
URL(s): clariti.app/article/best-team-communication-apps/
Description: Discusses the significant impact that communication has on all aspects of small businesses and shares 10 top communication apps for your small business. Availability: Online.

17769 ■ "The Top Mistakes of Social Media Marketing" in Agency Sales Magazine (Vol. 39, November 2009, No. 9, pp. 42)
Description: One common mistake in social media marketing is having more than one image on the Internet because this ruins a business' credibility. Marketers need to put out messages that are useful to their readers and to keep messages consistent. Availability: Online.

17770 ■ "Tracking Your Fleet Can Increase Bottom Line" in Contractor (Vol. 56, November 2009, No. 11, pp. 26)
Ed: Candace Roulo. Description: GPS fleet management system can help boost a contractor's profits, employee productivity, and efficiency. These are available as a handheld device or a cell phone that employees carry around or as a piece of hardware installed in a vehicle. These lets managers track assets and communicate with employees about jobs. Availability: Online.

17771 ■ "The Ultimate Sales Letter: Attract New Customers. Boost Your Sales"
Released: February 2011. Description: With email and instant communication, sales copy is indispensable to closing a deal. Most sales letters end up in the junk file or wastebasket. Updated text and examples, great headline formulas, and new exercises to be innovative with sales copy along with ways to use graphics successfully from an expert in direct-response copywriting.

17772 ■ "Use Social Media to Enhance Brand, Business" in Contractor (Vol. 56, December 2009, No. 12, pp. 14)
Ed: Elton Rivas. Description: Advice on how plumbing contractors should use online social networks to increase sales is presented including such issues as clearly defining goals and target audience. An additional advantage to this medium is that advertisements can easily be shared with other users.

17773 ■ "The Value of Conversations With Employees; Talk Isn't Cheap" in Gallup Management Journal (June 30, 2011)
Ed: Jessica Tyler. Released: June 30, 2011. Description: When managers have meaningful exchanges with their employees, they don't only show they care, they also add value to their organization's bottom line. Availability: Print; Online.

17774 ■ "Vision Statement: Tired of PowerPoint? Try This Instead" in Harvard Business Review (Vol. 88, September 2010, No. 9, pp. 30)
Pub: Harvard Business Publishing
Contact: Diane Belcher, Managing Director
Ed: Daniel McGinn, Stephanie Crowley. Price: $6, PDF. Description: Usefulness of graphic recording, also known as storyboarding or visual facilitation, during client meetings is illustrated. Availability: Online; PDF.

17775 ■ "Vision Statement: Why Mumbai at 1 PM is the Center of the Business World" in Harvard Business Review (Vol. 88, October 2010, No. 10, pp. 38)
Pub: Harvard Business Publishing
Contact: Diane Belcher, Managing Director
Ed: Michael Segalla. Price: $6, PDF. Description: A time zone chart is presented for assisting in the planning of international conference calls. Availability: Online; PDF.

17776 ■ "Vistaprint Survey Indicates that Online Marketing Taking Hold Among Small Businesses" in Marketwired (December 10, 2009)
Pub: Comtex News Network Inc.
Contact: Kan Devnani, President
Description: According to a comprehensive survey from Vistaprint N.V., small businesses are very likely to increase their use of Internet marketing strategies such as paid and organic search, email marketing, social media networking and custom websites over the next year. Trends continue to show that more small businesses are indeed adapting to the changing marketplace and are more willing to diversify their marketing strategies than ever before. Availability: Print; Online.

17777 ■ "What's In Your Toolbox" in Women In Business (Vol. 61, August-September 2009, No. 4, pp. 7)
Pub: American Business Women's Association
Contact: Rene Street, Executive Director
Ed: Mimi Kopulos. Description: Business owners are increasingly turning to using social networking websites, such as Facebook, LinkedIn and Twitter, to promote their companies. The number of adult social media users has increased from 8 percent in 2005 to 35 percent in 2009. Availability: Online.

17778 ■ "What's Your Language Strategy? It Should Bind Your Company's Global Talent Management and Vision" in Harvard Business Review (Vol. 92, September 2014, No. 9, pp. 70)
Pub: Harvard Business Publishing
Contact: Diane Belcher, Managing Director
Price: $8.95. Description: Cultural awareness and language skills should be built into organizations to promote talent that is equally effective locally and globally. This will bridge gaps between non-native and native language speakers, fostering collaboration and increase competitiveness. Availability: Online; PDF.

17779 ■ "What's Your Social Media Strategy?" in Black Enterprise (Vol. 41, November 2010, No. 4, pp. 75)
Pub: Earl G. Graves Ltd.
Contact: Earl Graves, Jr., President
Ed: Denise A. Campbell. Description: Advice for using social media sites such as Twitter, Facebook and LinkedIn as a professional networking tool is given. Availability: Online.

17780 ■ When Family Businesses are Best: The Parallel Planning Process for Family Harmony and Business Success
Pub: Palgrave Macmillan
Ed: Randel S. Carlock, John L. Ward. Released: First edition. Description: An exploration into effective planning and communication to help small businesses grow into multi-generation family enterprises. Availability: E-book; Print.

17781 ■ "Who Hangs Out Where?" in Harvard Business Review (Vol. 90, July-August 2012, No. 7-8, pp. 34)
Pub: Harvard Business Review Press
Contact: Moderna V. Pfizer, Contact
Price: $6, PDF. Description: A chart breaks down participation in social media gathering places by gender, age group, educational level, and household income. Availability: PDF; Online.

17782 ■ "Why 'I'm Sorry' Doesn't Always Translate" in (Vol. 90, June 2012, No. 6, pp. 26)
Pub: Harvard Business Review Press
Contact: Moderna V. Pfizer, Contact
Ed: Jeanne Brett, Peter H. Kim, Tetsushi Okumura, William W. Maddux. Description: Studies indicate that Americans associate an apology with culpability and personal responsibility, while Japan and other countries with group-oriented cultures view an apology as an acknowledgment that a transgression has occurred and that it is unfortunate. Implications for the role of the apology in negotiations and establishing trust are presented.

17783 ■ "Why LinkedIn is the Social Network that Will Never Die" in Advertising Age (Vol. 81, December 6, 2010, No. 43, pp. 2)
Pub: Crain Communications, Inc.
Contact: Jessica Botos, Manager, Marketing
E-mail: jessica.botos@crainsnewyork.com
Ed: Irina Slutsky. Description: Despite the popularity of Facebook, LinkedIn in will always be a source for professionals who wish to network. Availability: Online.

17784 ■ "Wi-Fi Finds Its Way Despite Nixed Plan for Free System" in Crain's Cleveland Business (Vol. 28, November 12, 2007, No. 45, pp. 3)
Pub: Crain Communications Inc.
Contact: K. C. Crain, President
Ed: Jay Miller. Description: Discusses the issues facing Cleveland and Northeast Ohio concerning their proposal to offer citizens wireless Internet services for free or a small fee. Availability: Online.

17785 ■ "Words at Work" in Information Today (Vol. 26, February 2009, No. 2, pp. 25)
Description: Current new buzzwords include the following: digital amnesia, or overload by availability, speed and volume of digital information; maternal profiling, a form a discrimination against women; recipe malpractice, a reminder that just because you can turn on a stove it doesn't make you a chef; ringxiety, the act when everyone reaches for their cell phone when one rings; verbing, the practice of turning good nouns into verbs. Availability: Print; Online.

17786 ■ "Yammer Gets Serious" in Inc. (Volume 32, December 2010, No. 10, pp. 58)
Pub: Inc. Magazine
Ed: Eric Markowitz. Description: Yammer, an internal social network for companies, allows coworkers to share ideas and documents in real-time. Details of this service are included. Availability: Online.

17787 ■ "Your First 100 Days on Your New Job" in Women In Business (Vol. 63, Spring 2011, No. 1, pp. 28)
Pub: American Business Women's Association
Contact: Rene Street, Executive Director
Ed: Diane Stafford. Released: March 22, 2011. Description: The first 100 days on the job are crucial if the person's permanent hiring is conditional on surviving a probationary period. The new hire must do more than just master the job's technical details to maximize the chance of success. Details of some basic tips to fit into the corporate culture and get along with coworkers are also discussed. Availability: Print; Online.

TRADE PERIODICALS

17788 ■ The Facilitator
URL(s): www.thefacilitator.com
Released: Quarterly Price: $35, U.S.; $35, Institutions; $40, Out of country. Description: Provides articles written by facilitators that are designed to link facilitators from around the world in a forum of sharing, networking, and communicating. Includes updates on training, automated meeting tools, and resources. Recurring features include tips and techniques, a calendar of events, reports of meetings, news of educational opportunities, book reviews, and notices of publications available. Availability: Print.

VIDEO/AUDIO MEDIA

17789 ■ Elevated Entrepreneurship: David Wood: Navigating Tough Conversations
URL(s): mikemichalowicz.com//podcast/david-wood

Ed: Mike Michalowiicz. **Released:** May 11, 2020. **Description:** Podcast discusses the ability to have tough conversations with the office team, customers, and community.

17790 ■ *The How of Business: Caity Cronkhite - Better Writing Better Service*
URL(s): www.thehowofbusiness.com/421-caity-cronkhite-better-writing-better-service
Ed: Henry Lopez. **Released:** May 16, 2022. **Description:** Podcast explains how better writing (particularly of training content, customer support documents, and consumer product instructions) can improve productivity and even profitability. .

17791 ■ *The How of Business: Mickie Kennedy - Press Releases*
URL(s): www.thehowofbusiness.com/441-mickie-kennedy-press-releases
Ed: Henry Lopez. **Released:** December 19, 2022. **Description:** Podcast explains how to leverage press releases to launch and grow a small businesses.

17792 ■ *The Knowledge Project: The Storytelling Expert: The Architecture of Influence*
URL(s): fs.blog/knowleddge-project-podcast/matthew-dicks
Ed: Shane Parrish. **Released:** September 03, 2024. **Description:** Podcast discusses the framework behind storytelling mastery, a narrative architecture (and leadership tool) that can reshape boardrooms, pitch meetings, and executive communications.

17793 ■ *Nurture Small Business: Mastering the Unspoken: A Guide to Authentic Business Communication*
URL(s): nurturesmallbusiness.buzzsprout.com/900445/episodes/14093314-mastering-the-unspoken-a-guide-to-authentic-business-communication
Ed: Denise Cagan. **Released:** December 11, 2023. **Description:** Podcast discusses both verbal and nonverbal business communication.

17794 ■ *Nurture Small Business: TeamCatapult Talks: Unveiling the Secrets of Effective Communication*
URL(s): nurturesmallbusiness.buzzsprout.com/900445/episodes/13816972-teamcatapult-talks-unveiling-the-secrets-of-effective-communication
Ed: Denise Cagan. **Released:** October 30, 2023. **Description:** Podcast discusses structural dynamics and communication.

17795 ■ *Winning with Honest Feedback*
URL(s): www.startuphustlepodcast.com/winning-with-honest-feedback
Ed: Matthews DeCoursey. **Released:** October 26, 2023. **Description:** Podcast offers tips on discerning valid feedback on your product, handling negative input, and testing before investing. .

17796 ■ *Women Amplified: The Art & Science of Effective Communication*
URL(s): www.conferencesforwomen.org/the-art-science-of-effective-communication
Ed: Celeste Headlee. **Description:** Podcast discusses "power leaks" that undermine influence and strategies to overcome them.

TRADE SHOWS AND CONVENTIONS

17797 ■ IABC World Conference
International Association of Business Communicators (IABC)
330 N Wabash Ave., Ste. 2000
Chicago, IL 60611
Ph: (312)321-6868
Free: 800-218-8097
Fax: (312)673-6708
Co. E-mail: news@iabc.com
URL: http://www.iabc.com
Contact: Peter Finn, Executive Director
E-mail: pfinn@iabc.com
URL(s): wc.iabc.com/About/About-World-Conference
Frequency: Annual. **Description:** Exhibits relating to business communication. **Audience:** Business communication professionals. **Principal Exhibits:** Exhibits relating to business communication. Dates and Locations: 2025 Jun 08-11 Vancouver, BC. **Telecommunication Services:** registration@iabc.com.

17798 ■ Texas Press Association Annual Midwinter Conference and Trade Show
Texas Press Association (TPA)
8800 Business Pk. Dr., Ste. 100
Austin, TX 78759
Ph: (512)477-6755
Fax: (512)477-6759
URL: http://www.texaspress.com
Contact: Michael Hodges, Executive Director
E-mail: mhodges@texaspress.com
URL(s): www.texaspress.com/tags/midwinter-conference-trade-show
Frequency: Annual. **Description:** Equipment, supplies, and services for newspapers and corporate communication departments. **Audience:** Newspaper publishers, editors, and members of corporate communications departments. **Principal Exhibits:** Equipment, supplies, and services for newspapers and corporate communication departments.

CONSULTANTS

17799 ■ American English Academy (AEA) [American English College]
111 N Atlantic Blvd., Ste. 112
Monterey Park, CA 91754
Ph: (626)457-2800
Fax: (626)457-2808
Co. E-mail: info@aec.edu
URL: http://www.aec.edu
Facebook: www.facebook.com/americanenglishcollege
Linkedin: www.linkedin.com/company/american-english-college
Instagram: www.instagram.com/americanenglishcollege
YouTube: www.youtube.com/channel/UC6eS1MpXLDagYdZVZWWJO6A
Description: Specializes in providing on-site English language and communication development for corporations and individuals. Also develops and delivers training in speaking, writing, pronunciation, grammar, and idioms with an emphasis on business communication. Offers individual, small group, intensive, and long-distance learning. Programs tailor-made for each client. **Scope:** Specializes in providing on-site English language and communication development for corporations and individuals. Also develops and delivers training in speaking, writing, pronunciation, grammar, and idioms with an emphasis on business communication. Offers individual, small group, intensive, and long-distance learning. Programs tailor-made for each client. **Founded:** 1983.

17800 ■ Ann Welsh Communications Inc.
3080 Yonge St., Ste. 6060
Toronto, ON, Canada M4N 3N1
URL: http://annwelsh.com
Contact: Ann Welsh, Editor
Linkedin: www.linkedin.com/in/annwelshcommunications
X (Twitter): x.com/AnnWelsh
Instagram: www.instagram.com/theannwelsh
Description: Firm provides facilitation, communications, writing, editing human resources and organizational development services. **Scope:** Firm provides facilitation, communications, writing, editing human resources and organizational development services. **Founded:** 1990.

17801 ■ Beverly Hyman Ph.D. & Associates (BHA)
23 E 10th St., Ste. 212
New York, NY 10003
Ph: (917)370-1281
Co. E-mail: bev@beverlyhyman.com
URL: http://www.beverlyhyman.com
Contact: Beverly Hyman, President
E-mail: bev@beverlyhyman.com
Description: Firm provides training for organizational development, performance appraisal systems, leadership, executive coaching, communications, team building, and related services. **Scope:** Firm provides training for organizational development, performance appraisal systems, leadership, executive coaching, communications, team building, and related services. **Publications:** "Training for Productivity"; "How Successful Women Manage"; "The Trainers Handbook The AMA Guide to Effective Training"; "The Heart of the Sale Making the Customers Need to Buy the Key to Successful Selling"; "How to Market by Telephone, How to Interview Effectively, Total Time Management and How to Motivate for Superior Performance". **Training:** Training the Trainer; Advanced Training the Trainer; Coaching and Counseling; Constructive Feedback; Supervisory Skills; Writing Skills; Interpersonal Communications; Leadership Skills; Presentation Skills; Customer Service; Communication Skills; Public Speaking; Negotiating Skills Women in Management; Time Management; Sales Training Skills; Assertiveness Skills; Executive Coaching.

17802 ■ Blackmon Roberts Group Inc. (BRG)
902 S Florida Ave., Ste. 205
Lakeland, FL 33803-1116
Ph: (863)802-1280
Free: 877-450-3237
Fax: (863)802-1290
Co. E-mail: info@blackmonroberts.com
URL: http://www.blackmonroberts.com
Contact: Sylvia Blackmon Roberts, President
Description: Firm provides strategic and innovative solutions and industry expertise, public planning and management consulting services such as transportation and public planning, business management, and non-profit management. **Scope:** Firm provides strategic and innovative solutions and industry expertise, public planning and management consulting services such as transportation and public planning, business management, and non-profit management. **Founded:** 1992.

17803 ■ Business Communication Consultants Inc.
2822 3rd Ave., N Ste. 211
Billings, MT 59101
Contact: Charles Tooley, Contact
Description: Provider of speech training and speakers for meetings. **Scope:** Provider of speech training and speakers for meetings.

17804 ■ Business Communication Solutions L.L.C. (BCS)
4535 O'Hara Dr.
Evansville, IN 47711
Ph: (812)422-4955
Free: 866-305-7202
Fax: (812)422-9506
Co. E-mail: info@bcsservice.com
URL: http://bcsservice.com
Facebook: www.facebook.com/BusinessCommunicationsSolutions
Linkedin: www.linkedin.com/company/business-communications-solutions-llc
X (Twitter): x.com/bcsservice
Description: Provider of management consulting services. **Scope:** Provider of management consulting services. **Founded:** 2001. **Training:** Team Building; Teams in Conflict; Newcomer - Transferee Transitioning; Leadership Building; Presentational Skill Building.

17805 ■ Communispond Inc.
181 Montauk Hwy.
East Hampton, NY 11937
Ph: (631)907-8010
Free: 800-529-5925
Co. E-mail: info@communispond.com
URL: http://communispond.com
Contact: Bill Rosenthal, Chief Executive Officer
E-mail: brosenthal@communispond.com
Description: Offers training solutions in the areas of presentation, writing, sales, and leadership skills. **Scope:** Offers training solutions in the areas of presentation, writing, sales, and leadership skills. **Founded:** 1969. **Publications:** "Socratic Selling

GENERAL SMALL BUSINESS TOPICS

Skills: The Discipline of Customer-Centered Sales"; "It's Not What You Say, But How It Sounds"; "Butt Heads With the Boss Without Getting Fired"; "Five Critical Aspects to Getting More Return from Employee Training"; "Building Your Case: Five Forms of Evidence Reps Should Use to Persuade the Doctor"; "The Full Force of Your Ideas: Mastering the Science of Persuasion". **Training:** Executive Presentation Skills; Persuasive Dialogue, Aug, 2008; Sales Presentation Skills; Selling by Phone; Senior Executive Presentation Skills; Write up Front on the Web; Mastering Interpersonal Communication; Call Centers: Solving Customers Problems.

17806 ■ COMsciences Inc.
Los Angeles, CA
Co. E-mail: info@comsciences.com
URL: http://comsciences.com/comsciences.htm
Contact: Dr. Jack Torobin, Chief Executive Officer
Description: Firm provides strategic advices for products and services for consumer electronic brands. **Scope:** Firm provides strategic advices for products and services for consumer electronic brands. **Founded:** 1989. **Publications:** "Wanted: Radical Thinking," Pmg World Magazine, Mar, 2003. **Special Services:** iKIT®; imovio®.

17807 ■ Full Voice
9912B Holmes Rd., Ste. 237
Kansas City, MO 64131-4206
Description: Vocal performance training firm offering consulting services and personal training sessions in the implementation of effective vocal communication techniques for the development of business relationships and career enhancement. **Scope:** Vocal performance training firm offering consulting services and personal training sessions in the implementation of effective vocal communication techniques for the development of business relationships and career enhancement. **Publications:** "You Can Sound Like You Know What You're Saying". **Training:** You Can Sound Like You Know What You're Saying; The Psychology of Vocal Performance; Security. . .the Ability to Accept Change; Knowing. . .the Key to Relaxed Public Communication; The Effective Voice for Customer Service Enhancement; You Can Speak With Conviction; How To Make Yours a Championship Team; Functional English For Foreign Trade. **Special Services:** FULL VOICE™.

17808 ■ The Handler Group Inc.
425 W End Ave.
New York, NY 10024
Contact: Mark L. Handler, Chief Executive Officer
Description: Provider of marketing, communication planning and design services, specializing in development of internal and external business communications. Develops corporate identity, corporate literature, employee communications, sales promotion materials, consumer product packaging and information, brochures, annual reports and presentation materials. Industries served: Cable/television, technology software, business information, hospitality and banking. **Scope:** Provider of marketing, communication planning and design services, specializing in development of internal and external business communications. Develops corporate identity, corporate literature, employee communications, sales promotion materials, consumer product packaging and information, brochures, annual reports and presentation materials. Industries served: Cable/television, technology software, business information, hospitality and banking.

17809 ■ In Plain English
14501 Antigone Dr.
Gaithersburg, MD 20878-2484
Ph: (301)340-2821
Free: 800-274-9645
Fax: (301)279-0115
URL: http://www.inplainenglish.com
Description: Management consultants helping government and businesses research, design, write and produce user oriented management information for human resources, employee benefits, business process, corporate and marketing needs. Services include: GSA mob is schedule for consulting to the government; employee benefit communications, plain English business writing workshops for print and electronic media; communicating strategy and tactics; marketing research, business planning and communications; readability testing; usability testing and monitoring strategy. **Scope:** Management consultants helping government and businesses research, design, write and produce user oriented management information for human resources, employee benefits, business process, corporate and marketing needs. Services include: GSA mob is schedule for consulting to the government; employee benefit communications, plain English business writing workshops for print and electronic media; communicating strategy and tactics; marketing research, business planning and communications; readability testing; usability testing and monitoring strategy. **Founded:** 1977. **Publications:** "The Benefits Communication"; "The Employee Benefits Communication ToolKit," Commerce Clearinghouse; "Benefits Communication," Business and Legal Reports. **Training:** Plain English Writing Training; Summary Plan Description Compliance workshops; Re-Humanizing the Corporation, Human Resources and Employee Benefits Communication Workshop; 21 Writing Tips for the 21st Century; Make the Write Impression; Writing to Inform and Instruct; The Dreaded Nuts and Bolts; Writing to Persuade; Writing Policy and Procedure Manuals In Plain English; Writing for Accountants and Auditors In Plain English. **Special Services:** In Plain English®.

17810 ■ Miller, Leiby & Associates P.C.
32 Broadway, 13th Fl.
New York, NY 10004
Ph: (212)227-4200
Fax: (212)504-8369
URL: http://www.millerleiby.com
Contact: Doron Leiby, Partner
Facebook: www.facebook.com/MillerLeibyAssociatesPc
Linkedin: www.linkedin.com/company/1269719
Instagram: www.instagram.com/millerleiby
Description: Firm is engaged in legal counsel for individuals and businesses. **Scope:** Firm is engaged in legal counsel for individuals and businesses. **Training:** Objectives and standards/recruiting for boards of directors.

17811 ■ Reynolds Communication
184 Columbia Hts.
Brooklyn Heights, NY 11201
Ph: (718)625-6797
Co. E-mail: sreynold@stern.nyu.edu
URL: http://sanareynolds.com
Contact: Sana Reynolds, Consultant
Description: Consultant specializes in cross cultural and organizational communication. Areas of expertise include inter cultural communication, business and technical writing, presentation coaching, document design and plain language consulting. **Scope:** Consultant specializes in cross cultural and organizational communication. Areas of expertise include inter cultural communication, business and technical writing, presentation coaching, document design and plain language consulting. **Founded:** 2006. **Publications:** "Composing effective e-mail messages," Communication World, Jul, 1997; "Selling to another language," Communication World, Dec, 1996.

17812 ■ Roger S. Peterson Marketing & Communications
Rocklin, CA
Ph: (916)624-3069
URL: http://www.sacramentowriters.com
Contact: Roger S. Peterson, Contact
E-mail: peterson@sacramentowriters.com
Description: Firm specializes in business-to-business marketing communications, marketing diagnostics and marketing strategy for small to mid-sized firms. **Scope:** Firm specializes in business-to-business marketing communications, marketing diagnostics and marketing strategy for small to mid-sized firms. **Founded:** 1995. **Publications:** "The Secret to Incentive Program Success: Incentive ROI that makes bean counters smile!"; "The Magic Megaphone"; "Ama Handbook For: Managing Business-To-Business Marketing Communications," McGraw-Hill, Apr, 1997. **Training:** Essentials of Marketing; The Communications Audit; Survival Training for Product Managers; Marketing Positioning and Promotion; Marketing Tools and How to Use Them; Marketing for Small Business, various American Management Association Courses.

17813 ■ Syntaxis Inc.
2109 Broadway
New York, NY 10023
Ph: (212)799-3000
Co. E-mail: info@syntaxis.com
URL: http://www.syntaxis.com
Contact: Brandt Johnson, Co-Founder Principal
Linkedin: www.linkedin.com/company/syntaxis-inc-
Description: Provider of communication skills training for business professionals specializing in standard and customized on-site training and workshops that focuses on presentation skills, business writing, grammar, email etiquette, and English as a second language. **Founded:** 1999. **Publications:** "Presentation Skills for Business Professionals"; "A Writing Guide for Business Professionals"; "E-Mail Etiquette for Business Professionals".

17814 ■ Trendzitions Inc.
25691 Atlantic Ocean, Dr. No. B13
Lake Forest, CA 92630
Ph: (949)727-9100
URL: http://www.trendzitions.com
Contact: Chris Tooker, President
E-mail: ctooker@trendzitions.com
X (Twitter): x.com/trendzitions
Instagram: www.instagram.com/trendzitions
Description: Provider of services in the areas of communications consulting, project management, construction management, and furniture procurement. Offers information on spatial uses, building codes, ADA compliance and city ordinances. Also offers budget projections. **Scope:** Provider of services in the areas of communications consulting, project management, construction management, and furniture procurement. Offers information on spatial uses, building codes, ADA compliance and city ordinances. Also offers budget projections. **Founded:** 1986.

17815 ■ Write Wise Communications L.L.C.
488 W 19th St., Ste. 359
Houston, TX 77008
Ph: (713)557-6112
URL: http://www.writewisecommunications.com
Contact: Alise Isbell, President
Description: Firm provides instructional design services used in needs assessment, course and curriculum development, workbook, facilitator guide, power-point presentation, handout, revision and formatting, and job-aid publication applications, the company also delivers written, spoken, and interpersonal communication training courses. **Training:** Grammar Refresher for Adults; Business Writing for Business Professionals; Technical Writing; Writing Effective Proposals; Service Spotlight! Effective Written Presentations; Service Spotlight! Effective Verbal Presentations; Service Spotlight! Effective Distance Presentations; Effective Teamwork over Distance; Time Management; More Productive Meetings; Managing the Strategic Planning Process.

FRANCHISES AND BUSINESS OPPORTUNITIES

17816 ■ Alliance Franchise Brands LLC (AFB) [Allegra Marketing - Print - Mail]
47585 Galleon Dr.
Plymouth, MI 48170
URL: http://www.allegramarketingprint.com
Description: Full service printing centers. **No. of Franchise Units:** 300. **Founded:** 1976. **Franchised:** 1977. **Equity Capital Needed:** $162,464-$516,949 investment. **Franchise Fee:** $35,000 Start-up Model, $45,000 MatchMaker Model, $15,000 resale. **Training:** Yes.

PUBLICATIONS

17817 ■ *Business and Professional Communication Quarterly (BPCQ)*
2455 Teller Rd.
  Thousand Oaks, CA 91320
Contact: Tracey Ozmina, President
URL(s): journals.sagepub.com/home/bcq

Ed: Robyn Walker. **Released:** Quarterly **Price:** $979, Institutions for backfile lease, combined plus backfile (current volume print & all online content); $846, Institutions for backfile lease, e-access plus backfile (all online content); $3,918, Institutions for backfile purchase, e-access (content through 1998); $890, Institutions for combined (print & e-access); $12, Institutions for single print issue; $872, Institutions for print only; $757, Institutions for e-access. **Description:** Refereed journal focused on research that advances the teaching of communication in the workplace. Official publication of the Association for Business Communication. **Availability:** Print; PDF; Download; Online.

17818 ■ *International Journal of Business Communication (IJBC)*
2455 Teller Rd.
  Thousand Oaks, CA 91320
Contact: Tracey Ozmina, President
URL(s): journals.sagepub.com/home/JOB

Ed: Jacqueline Mayfield, Milton Mayfield, Robyn Walker. **Released:** Quarterly; January, April, July and October. **Price:** $120, Institutions for single print issue. **Description:** International, peer-reviewed journal focusing on professional business communication. Official publication of the Association for Business Communication. **Availability:** Print; PDF; Online.

17819 ■ *Journal of Business and Technical Communication (JBTC)*
2455 Teller Rd.
  Thousand Oaks, CA 91320
Contact: Tracey Ozmina, President
URL(s): journals.sagepub.com/home/JBT

Ed: Jo Mackiewicz. **Released:** Quarterly **Price:** $1,250, Institutions for institutional backfile purchase, e-access; $1,227, Institutions for subscription, e-access; $180, Individuals for subscription, e-access; $1,350, Institutions for online. **Description:** Peer-reviewed journal covering the latest communication practices, problems, and trends in both business and academic settings or sectors. Published in association between SAGE and Iowa State University. **Availability:** Print; PDF; Online.

Business Correspondence

ASSOCIATIONS AND OTHER ORGANIZATIONS

17820 ■ Association for Business Communication (ABC)
PO Box 304
  Natural Bridge Station, VA 24579-0304
Co. E-mail: abcoffice@businesscommunication.org
URL: http://www.businesscommunication.org
Contact: D. Joel Whalen, President
X (Twitter): x.com/A4_BC

Description: College teachers of business communication; management consultants in business communications; training directors and correspondence supervisors of business firms, direct mail copywriters, public relations writers, and others interested in communication for business. **Founded:** 1935. **Publications:** Video in the 90's: A Practical Guide to Professional Video; Association for Business Communication Bulletin--Membership Directory Issue; Making Communication Requirements More Explicit in the AACSB Standards for MBA Programs; International Journal of Business Communication (IJBC) (Quarterly). **Educational Activities:** ABC Annual International Conference (Annual). **Awards:** Kitty O. Locker Outstanding Researcher Award (Annual); Meada Gibbs Outstanding Teacher-Scholar Award (Annual); ABC Outstanding Dissertation Award (Annual); ABC Distinguished Publication on Business Communication (Annual); ABC Outstanding Article in Business and Professional Communication Quarterly (Annual); ABC Outstanding Article in the International Journal of Business Communication (Annual). **Geographic Preference:** National.

17821 ■ International Association of Business Communicators (IABC) - Library
330 N Wabash Ave., Ste. 2000
  Chicago, IL 60611
Ph: (312)321-6868
Free: 800-218-8097
Fax: (312)673-6708
Co. E-mail: news@iabc.com
URL: http://www.iabc.com
Contact: Peter Finn, Executive Director
E-mail: pfinn@iabc.com
Linkedin: www.linkedin.com/groups/international
  -association-business-communicators-iabc-58441/
  about
X (Twitter): x.com/iabc
Instagram: www.instagram.com/iabcsnaps
YouTube: www.youtube.com/user/IABClive

Description: Conducts research in the communication field and encourages establishment of college-level programs in organizational communication. Offers accreditation program; conducts surveys on employee communication effectiveness and media trends. **Scope:** Business communicators. **Founded:** 1970. **Holdings:** Figures not available. **Publications:** World Book of IABC Communicators; World Book of IABC Communicators; Communication World: The Magazine for Communication Professionals (Monthly). **Educational Activities:** IABC World Conference (Annual). **Awards:** IABC Gold Quill Awards (Annual); IABC Lifetime Foundation Friend Award (Annual); IABC Chapter Management Award (Annual); Excellence in Communication Leadership (EXCEL) Award (Annual); IABC Chair's Award (Annual); IABC Fellow (Annual). **Geographic Preference:** Multinational.

EDUCATIONAL PROGRAMS

17822 ■ Advanced Copyediting (Onsite)
URL(s): www.eeicom.com

Description: This course will help you develop and enhance both knowledge and skills in the editing and production process. **Audience:** Proofreader, copyeditor, or substantive editor, professionals. **Principal Exhibits:** This course will help you develop and enhance both knowledge and skills in the editing and production process.

17823 ■ Advanced Writing and Editing for Government Proposals
URL(s): www.eeicom.com

Description: Developed for anyone who regularly writes, edits, or manages government proposals to explore proposal-specific writing and editing challenges, including how to ensure consistent voice no matter how many writers are involved. **Audience:** Professionals, administrative. **Principal Exhibits:** Developed for anyone who regularly writes, edits, or manages government proposals to explore proposal-specific writing and editing challenges, including how to ensure consistent voice no matter how many writers are involved.

17824 ■ AGTS, Inc. Business English and Grammar Review (Onsite)
AGTS Inc.
  530 E McDowell Rd., Ste. 107-483
  Phoenix, AZ 85004
Ph: (480)967-7544
Free: 800-970-1270
Co. E-mail: help@agts.com
URL: http://www.agts.com
Contact: Dallas Porter-Stowe, President
E-mail: dallas@agts.com
URL(s): www.agts.com/class/business-english
  -grammar-review

Description: Covers grammatical errors, punctuation, sentence structure, spelling, and plurals and possessives. **Audience:** Anyone who uses written communication on the job. **Principal Exhibits:** Covers grammatical errors, punctuation, sentence structure, spelling, and plurals and possessives.

17825 ■ AMA How to Sharpen Your Business Writing Skills (Onsite)
URL(s): www.amanet.org

Description: Covers how to solve common writing problems, various writing concepts, and how to write effective letters, memos, reports, and business proposals. **Audience:** Line and staff supervisors, managers, executives and all businesspeople. **Principal Exhibits:** Covers how to solve common writing problems, various writing concepts, and how to write effective letters, memos, reports, and business proposals. **Telecommunication Services:** customerservice@amanet.org.

17826 ■ AMA's 2-Day Business Writing Workshop (Live Online)
American Management Association (AMA)
  1601 Broadway
  New York, NY 10019
Ph: (212)586-8100
Free: 800-262-9699
Fax: (212)903-8168
Co. E-mail: customerservice@amanet.org
URL: http://www.amanet.org
Contact: Manny Avramidis, President
URL(s): www.amanet.org/business-writing-workshop
Price: $2,095, Non-members; $1,895, Members AMA; $1,700, Members GSA. **Frequency:** Continuous. **Description:** Learn basic formats and formulas to compose documents and communicate what your readers need to know. **Audience:** Business professionals. **Principal Exhibits:** Learn basic formats and formulas to compose documents and communicate what your readers need to know. **Telecommunication Services:** customerservice@amanet.org.

17827 ■ Basics of Government Contract Administration (Onsite)
Seminar Information Service Inc. (SIS)
  250 El Camino Real., Ste. 112
  Tustin, CA 92780
Ph: (714)508-0340
Free: 877-736-4636
Fax: (714)734-8027
Co. E-mail: info@seminarinformation.com
URL: http://www.seminarinformation.com
Contact: Catherine Bellizzi, President
URL(s): www.seminarinformation.com

Description: Designed to show you how to fill out the most common standard forms, where the forms are found, and how proper forms preparation avoids administration pitfalls. **Audience:** General public. **Principal Exhibits:** Designed to show you how to fill out the most common standard forms, where the forms are found, and how proper forms preparation avoids administration pitfalls.

17828 ■ Business Grammar & Proofreading (Onsite)
Seminar Information Service Inc. (SIS)
  250 El Camino Real., Ste. 112
  Tustin, CA 92780
Ph: (714)508-0340
Free: 877-736-4636
Fax: (714)734-8027
Co. E-mail: info@seminarinformation.com
URL: http://www.seminarinformation.com
Contact: Catherine Bellizzi, President
URL(s): www.seminarinformation.com/details.cfm?qc
  =qqbsfh

Description: Designed for busy professionals who want to brush up on grammar, spelling, proofreading and business usage. **Audience:** Industry professionals. **Principal Exhibits:** Designed for busy professionals who want to brush up on grammar, spelling, proofreading and business usage.

17829 ■ Business Writing for Administrative Professionals
URL(s): www.amanet.org

Description: Learn the skills and techniques you need to write and edit various documents. **Audience:** Administrative professionals. **Principal Exhibits:** Learn the skills and techniques you need to write and edit various documents.

17830 ■ Business Writing and Grammar Skills Made Easy and Fun! (Onsite)
Seminar Information Service Inc. (SIS)
  250 El Camino Real., Ste. 112
  Tustin, CA 92780
Ph: (714)508-0340
Free: 877-736-4636
Fax: (714)734-8027
Co. E-mail: info@seminarinformation.com
URL: http://www.seminarinformation.com
Contact: Catherine Bellizzi, President
URL(s): www.seminarinformation.com/details.cfm?qc=qqayxc

Description: Learn how to project your ideas effectively and clearly through proven techniques. **Audience:** Professionals and public. **Principal Exhibits:** Learn how to project your ideas effectively and clearly through proven techniques.

17831 ■ Business Writing & Grammar Skills (Onsite)
Seminar Information Service Inc. (SIS)
  250 El Camino Real., Ste. 112
  Tustin, CA 92780
Ph: (714)508-0340
Free: 877-736-4636
Fax: (714)734-8027
Co. E-mail: info@seminarinformation.com
URL: http://www.seminarinformation.com
Contact: Catherine Bellizzi, President
URL(s): www.seminarinformation.com/details.cfm?qc=qqdqwc

Description: Two-day workshop where you'll learn techniques and shortcuts for getting your thoughts organized fast and your words flowing freely even if writing does not come naturally to you. **Audience:** Writers. **Principal Exhibits:** Two-day workshop where you'll learn techniques and shortcuts for getting your thoughts organized fast and your words flowing freely even if writing does not come naturally to you.

17832 ■ Business Writing and Grammar Skills (Onsite)
National Seminars Training L.L.C. (NST)
  14502 W 105th St.
  Lenexa, KS 66215
Free: 800-349-1935
Co. E-mail: info@findaseminar.com
URL: http://www.findaseminar.com/tpd/Padgett-Thompson-Seminars.asp
URL(s): skillpath.com/seminar/business-writing-and-grammar-skills-made-easy-and-fun#agenda

Description: Developed exclusively for business professionals, this two-day workshop delivers tools and techniques that will add clarity and power to business documents. **Audience:** Industry professionals. **Principal Exhibits:** Developed exclusively for business professionals, this two-day workshop delivers tools and techniques that will add clarity and power to business documents.

17833 ■ Business Writing for the Multilingual Professional
American Management Association (AMA)
  1601 Broadway
  New York, NY 10019
Ph: (212)586-8100
Free: 800-262-9699
Fax: (212)903-8168
Co. E-mail: customerservice@amanet.org
URL: http://www.amanet.org
Contact: Manny Avramidis, President
URL(s): www.amanet.org/training/seminars/onsite/business-writing-for-the-multilingual-professional.aspx

Price: $2,345, Non-members; $2,095, Members AMA; $1,889, Members GSA. **Description:** Learn practical techniques for creating effective business documents, with focus on correct English grammar and usage. **Audience:** Multilingual business professionals who would like to improve their fundamental business writing skills. **Principal Exhibits:** Learn practical techniques for creating effective business documents, with focus on correct English grammar and usage. **Telecommunication Services:** customerservice@amanet.org.

17834 ■ Clear Business, Technical, and E-mail Writing
Seminar Information Service Inc. (SIS)
  250 El Camino Real., Ste. 112
  Tustin, CA 92780
Ph: (714)508-0340
Free: 877-736-4636
Fax: (714)734-8027
Co. E-mail: info@seminarinformation.com
URL: http://www.seminarinformation.com
Contact: Catherine Bellizzi, President
URL(s): www.seminarinformation.com

Description: This workshop provides a step-by-step process for designing and writing a clear document, e-mail message, or report with the use of writing, revising, and editing exercises. **Audience:** Those who write emails and other business correspondence, professionals. **Principal Exhibits:** This workshop provides a step-by-step process for designing and writing a clear document, e-mail message, or report with the use of writing, revising, and editing exercises.

17835 ■ CMC Communicating Up, Down and Across the Organization
Canadian Management Centre (CMC)
  150 King St. W Ste. 271
  Toronto, ON, Canada M5H 1J9
Ph: (416)214-5678
Free: 877-262-2519
Fax: (416)214-6047
Co. E-mail: cmcinfo@cmcoutperform.com
URL: http://cmcoutperform.com
Contact: Chris Peacock, Director
URL(s): cmcoutperform.com/communicating-organization

Description: Seminar that encourages dialogue throughout the organization and between different departments, including gaining self-esteem, targeting your message by knowing your audience, building team commitment, develop interpersonal techniques for influencing, build persuasive business cases, and constructing an informative, attention getting project update. Held in Toronto, ON; Calgary, AB; and Ottawa, ON. **Audience:** Professionals and managers. **Principal Exhibits:** Seminar that encourages dialogue throughout the organization and between different departments, including gaining self-esteem, targeting your message by knowing your audience, building team commitment, develop interpersonal techniques for influencing, build persuasive business cases, and constructing an informative, attention getting project update. Held in Toronto, ON; Calgary, AB; and Ottawa, ON.

17836 ■ CMC How to Communicate with Diplomacy, Tact and Credibility
URL(s): cmcoutperform.com/communicate-diplomacy-tact-credibility-online

Description: Seminar covering how to mold your communication style to meet the needs of individual situations, develop active listening and questioning strategies, gain cooperation and respect by promoting and modeling tolerance with politically correct attitudes and communication, break through communication gridlock, expand the communication network, and turn communication conflicts into opportunities for cooperation and growth. Held in Edmonton, AB; Mississauga, ON; Vaughan, ON; Calgary, AB; Toronto, ON; and Ottawa, ON. **Audience:** Business professionals. **Principal Exhibits:** Seminar covering how to mold your communication style to meet the needs of individual situations, develop active listening and questioning strategies, gain cooperation and respect by promoting and modeling tolerance with politically correct attitudes and communication, break through communication gridlock, expand the communication network, and turn communication conflicts into opportunities for cooperation and growth. Held in Edmonton, AB; Mississauga, ON; Vaughan, ON; Calgary, AB; Toronto, ON; and Ottawa, ON. **Telecommunication Services:** cmcinfo@cmctraining.org.

17837 ■ Developing Procedures, Policies and Documentation (Onsite)
Seminar Information Service Inc. (SIS)
  250 El Camino Real., Ste. 112
  Tustin, CA 92780
Ph: (714)508-0340
Free: 877-736-4636
Fax: (714)734-8027
Co. E-mail: info@seminarinformation.com
URL: http://www.seminarinformation.com
Contact: Catherine Bellizzi, President
URL(s): www.seminarinformation.com/details.cfm?qc=qqbrhz

Description: Learn how to define audience information needs and requirements and how to design information that meets user needs, including how to develop information that is user-friendly and accessible and how to organized information in modular and flexible units for later re-use. **Audience:** General public. **Principal Exhibits:** Learn how to define audience information needs and requirements and how to design information that meets user needs, including how to develop information that is user-friendly and accessible and how to organized information in modular and flexible units for later re-use.

17838 ■ E-mail and Business Writing
Fred Pryor Seminars & CareerTrack
  5700 Broadmoor, Ste. 300
  Mission, KS 66202
Free: 800-780-8476
Fax: (913)967-8849
Co. E-mail: customerservice@pryor.com
URL: http://www.pryor.com
Contact: Janet Turner, Contact
E-mail: dmca@pryor.com
URL(s): www.pryor.com/training-seminars/email-business-writing

Description: Learn how to craft e-mail messages that are grammatically correct, concise, and to the point. **Audience:** Professionals. **Principal Exhibits:** Learn how to craft e-mail messages that are grammatically correct, concise, and to the point.

17839 ■ The E-Mail and Business Writing Workshop (Onsite)
National Seminars Training L.L.C. (NST)
  14502 W 105th St.
  Lenexa, KS 66215
Free: 800-349-1935
Co. E-mail: info@findaseminar.com
URL: http://www.findaseminar.com/tpd/Padgett-Thompson-Seminars.asp
URL(s): www.nationalseminarstraining.com/Onsite/OSP/BWE.cfm

Description: A one-day seminar that offers tips and techniques to guarantee that every message written will be polished and on target. **Audience:** Business industry professionals. **Principal Exhibits:** A one-day seminar that offers tips and techniques to guarantee that every message written will be polished and on target.

17840 ■ EEI Communications Substantive Editing III
URL(s): www.eeicom.com

Description: Evaluate your editing style, fine tune your ability to differentiate levels of edit, review documents at the appropriate level, learn to set clear expectations, find new ways to give constructive feedback to writers, and learn to coach, rather than edit, to encourage better writing. **Audience:** Proofreaders, and copyeditors. **Principal Exhibits:** Evaluate your editing style, fine tune your ability to differentiate levels of edit, review documents at the appropriate level, learn to set clear expectations, find new ways to give constructive feedback to writers, and learn to coach, rather than edit, to encourage better writing.

17841 ■ EEI Communications Writing the Perfect Business E-Mail (Onsite)
URL(s): www.eeicom.com
Description: Seminar that covers e-mails that get read and are understood, including keeping it short and simple, make it useful, spelling, grammar, and other problems, controlling emotion, writing attachments that get read, progress reports, instructions, and evaluations and recommendations. **Audience:** Writers and editors. **Principal Exhibits:** Seminar that covers e-mails that get read and are understood, including keeping it short and simple, make it useful, spelling, grammar, and other problems, controlling emotion, writing attachments that get read, progress reports, instructions, and evaluations and recommendations.

17842 ■ Effective Business Writing
Baker Communications Inc. (BCI)
10333 Richmond Ave.
Houston, TX 77042
Ph: (713)627-7700
Free: 877-253-8506
Fax: (713)784-2380
Co. E-mail: info@bakercommunications.com
URL: http://www.bakercommunications.com
Contact: Walter Rogers, President
URL(s): www.bakercommunications.com/effective_business_writing.htm
Description: Participants learn to convey ideas and information with clarity and precision in memos, letters, reports, and other business correspondence. Cloud-based training also available. **Audience:** Industry professionals. **Principal Exhibits:** Participants learn to convey ideas and information with clarity and precision in memos, letters, reports, and other business correspondence. Cloud-based training also available. **Telecommunication Services:** info@bakercommunications.com.

17843 ■ Effective Technical Writing (Onsite)
American Management Association (AMA)
1601 Broadway
New York, NY 10019
Ph: (212)586-8100
Free: 800-262-9699
Fax: (212)903-8168
Co. E-mail: customerservice@amanet.org
URL: http://www.amanet.org
Contact: Manny Avramidis, President
URL(s): www.amanet.org/effective-technical-writing
Frequency: Continuous. **Description:** Covers the basics of writing technical documents such as reports, manuals, specifications, proposals, and instructions. **Audience:** Engineers, scientists, IT/computer personnel and other professionals. **Principal Exhibits:** Covers the basics of writing technical documents such as reports, manuals, specifications, proposals, and instructions.

17844 ■ Exceptional Business Writing and Goof-Proof Grammar
Fred Pryor Seminars & CareerTrack
5700 Broadmoor, Ste. 300
Mission, KS 66202
Free: 800-780-8476
Fax: (913)967-8849
Co. E-mail: customerservice@pryor.com
URL: http://www.pryor.com
Contact: Janet Turner, Contact
E-mail: dmca@pryor.com
URL(s): www.pryor.com/training-seminars/exceptional-business-writing-goof-proof-grammar
Frequency: Irregular. **Description:** Learn how to communicate clearly and effectively so others view you as confident and capable. **Audience:** Business professionals. **Principal Exhibits:** Learn how to communicate clearly and effectively so others view you as confident and capable.

17845 ■ Fred Pryor Seminars & CareerTrack Business Writing for Results
Fred Pryor Seminars & CareerTrack
5700 Broadmoor, Ste. 300
Mission, KS 66202
Free: 800-780-8476
Fax: (913)967-8849
Co. E-mail: customerservice@pryor.com
URL: http://www.pryor.com
Contact: Janet Turner, Contact
E-mail: dmca@pryor.com
URL(s): www.pryor.com/training-seminars/business-writing-for-results
Frequency: Irregular. **Description:** Learn to write powerful letters, memos, reports, and proposals that get results. **Audience:** Administrative professionals. **Principal Exhibits:** Learn to write powerful letters, memos, reports, and proposals that get results.

17846 ■ Fred Pryor Seminars & CareerTrack Records Retention and Destruction (Onsite)
URL(s): www.pryor.com
Description: Gain valuable information for successfully organizing, storing, archiving and destroying your organization's critical business documents while eliminating risk and ensuring compliance with the latest legal requirements. **Audience:** Controllers, accountants, medical records professionals, legal professionals, administrators, information technolgy staff, financial professionals, human resource managers and staff. **Principal Exhibits:** Gain valuable information for successfully organizing, storing, archiving and destroying your organization's critical business documents while eliminating risk and ensuring compliance with the latest legal requirements.

17847 ■ Government Proposal Writing Basics
URL(s): www.eeicom.com
Description: Designed for proposal novices at any level of writing ability, this course explains the unique features of government proposals and the government procurement process. **Audience:** Administrative professionals. **Principal Exhibits:** Designed for proposal novices at any level of writing ability, this course explains the unique features of government proposals and the government procurement process.

17848 ■ Hands-On Business and Report Writing: The Art of Persuasion (Onsite)
Seminar Information Service Inc. (SIS)
250 El Camino Real., Ste. 112
Tustin, CA 92780
Ph: (714)508-0340
Free: 877-736-4636
Fax: (714)734-8027
Co. E-mail: info@seminarinformation.com
URL: http://www.seminarinformation.com
Contact: Catherine Bellizzi, President
URL(s): www.seminarinformation.com/qqbtnl/hands-on-business-and-report-writing-the-art-of
Description: Learn how to: Write compelling documents that focus your message; Compose targeted messages using a standard writing process; Improve document comprehension with polished grammar and punctuation; Produce winning proposals, recommendation reports and executive summaries; Create effective written communications that drive your business; Develop a clear, persuasive writing style. **Audience:** Industry professionals. **Principal Exhibits:** Learn how to: Write compelling documents that focus your message; Compose targeted messages using a standard writing process; Improve document comprehension with polished grammar and punctuation; Produce winning proposals, recommendation reports and executive summaries; Create effective written communications that drive your business; Develop a clear, persuasive writing style.

17849 ■ How to Write Effective Policies and Procedures (Onsite)
Seminar Information Service Inc. (SIS)
250 El Camino Real., Ste. 112
Tustin, CA 92780
Ph: (714)508-0340
Free: 877-736-4636
Fax: (714)734-8027
Co. E-mail: info@seminarinformation.com
URL: http://www.seminarinformation.com
Contact: Catherine Bellizzi, President
URL(s): www.seminarinformation.com/details.cfm?qc=qqbslv
Description: Covers rules, strategies, guidelines and shortcuts that will make your job easier and ensure you get the results of a well-written policies and procedures that are read and understood by all. **Audience:** Policymaker. **Principal Exhibits:** Covers rules, strategies, guidelines and shortcuts that will make your job easier and ensure you get the results of a well-written policies and procedures that are read and understood by all.

17850 ■ Mapping Business Communications (Onsite)
Seminar Information Service Inc. (SIS)
250 El Camino Real., Ste. 112
Tustin, CA 92780
Ph: (714)508-0340
Free: 877-736-4636
Fax: (714)734-8027
Co. E-mail: info@seminarinformation.com
URL: http://www.seminarinformation.com
Contact: Catherine Bellizzi, President
URL(s): www.seminarinformation.com/details.cfm?qc=qqbtfq
Description: Learn to identify the purpose of each communication define the specific action required from the reader customize the message for different audiences to achieve greater results organize communications to make information quick and easy to find, and present information in the way that best suits the target audience. **Audience:** Business professionals, managers, sales & marketing professionals, engineers and general public. **Principal Exhibits:** Learn to identify the purpose of each communication define the specific action required from the reader customize the message for different audiences to achieve greater results organize communications to make information quick and easy to find, and present information in the way that best suits the target audience.

17851 ■ Mistake-Free Grammar & Proofreading
Fred Pryor Seminars & CareerTrack
5700 Broadmoor, Ste. 300
Mission, KS 66202
Free: 800-780-8476
Fax: (913)967-8849
Co. E-mail: customerservice@pryor.com
URL: http://www.pryor.com
Contact: Janet Turner, Contact
E-mail: dmca@pryor.com
URL(s): www.pryor.com/training-seminars/mistake-free-grammar-proofreading
Frequency: Irregular. **Description:** Learn grammar rules and to proofread with perfection. **Audience:** Managers, secretaries, technical writers, editors, and proofreaders. **Principal Exhibits:** Learn grammar rules and to proofread with perfection.

17852 ■ Technical Writing: A Comprehensive Hands-On Introduction (Onsite)
Seminar Information Service Inc. (SIS)
250 El Camino Real., Ste. 112
Tustin, CA 92780
Ph: (714)508-0340
Free: 877-736-4636
Fax: (714)734-8027
Co. E-mail: info@seminarinformation.com
URL: http://www.seminarinformation.com
Contact: Catherine Bellizzi, President
URL(s): www.seminarinformation.com/qqbtkf/technical-writing-a-comprehensive-hands-on-introduction
Description: Learn how to: Write clear, effective technical = documents, including user manuals and technical reports; Assess your target audience and develop documents to meet their needs; Choose the appropriate writing style to communicate to specialized audiences; Build effective sentences, paragraphs and sections that explain information clearly; Employ

diagrams, tables, charts and other graphical tools effectively; Create informative and interesting content that your readers will comprehend and utilize. **Audience:** Technical writers. **Principal Exhibits:** Learn how to: Write clear, effective technical = documents, including user manuals and technical reports; Assess your target audience and develop documents to meet their needs; Choose the appropriate writing style to communicate to specialized audiences; Build effective sentences, paragraphs and sections that explain information clearly; Employ diagrams, tables, charts and other graphical tools effectively; Create informative and interesting content that your readers will comprehend and utilize. **Telecommunication Services:** info@seminarinformation.com.

17853 ■ Writing for the Web
American Management Association (AMA)
1601 Broadway
New York, NY 10019
Ph: (212)586-8100
Free: 800-262-9699
Fax: (212)903-8168
Co. E-mail: customerservice@amanet.org
URL: http://www.amanet.org
Contact: Manny Avramidis, President
URL(s): www.amanet.org/training/articles/writing-for-the-web.aspx

Description: Create online content that connects with readers to achieve better results in this two-day course. Held in Atlanta, GA; San Francisco, CA; and New York, NY. Also available live online. **Audience:** All business professionals who write online content, including content managers and editors, online help writers, business analysts and administrators, programmers, Web masters, copywriters, Web-content writers, designers and developers as well as marketing managers, brand managers and coordinators. **Principal Exhibits:** Create online content that connects with readers to achieve better results in this two-day course. Held in Atlanta, GA; San Francisco, CA; and New York, NY. Also available live online. **Telecommunication Services:** customerservice@amanet.org.

REFERENCE WORKS

17854 ■ *Be a Brilliant Business Writer: Write Well, Write Fast, and Whip the Competition*
Released: October 05, 2010. **Price:** $14.99, paperback; $5.99. **Description:** Tools for mastering the art of persuasive writing in every document created, from email and client letters to reports and presentations, this book will help any writer convey their message with clarity and power, increase productivity by reducing rewrites, and provide the correct tone for navigating office politics. **Availability:** E-book; Print.

17855 ■ *"Campaigner Survey: 46 Percent of Small Businesses Use Email Marketing" in Wireless News (November 21, 2009)*
Description: Almost half (46 percent) of small businesses surveyed by Campaigner's 2009 State of Small Business Online Marketing, say that they rely on email marketing to help them find new customers, keep existing ones and grow their businesses. The survey also found that 36 percent of small businesses plan to begin using email marketing over the next year. The trend to utilize Internet marketing tools is allowing small businesses to grow faster and generate higher revenues than those that are not using these mediums. **Availability:** Print; Online.

17856 ■ *"Conferencing Takes on High-Tech Futuristic Feel" in Crain's Cleveland Business (Vol. 28, October 29, 2007, No. 43, pp. 17)*
Pub: Crain Communications Inc.
Contact: K. C. Crain, President

Ed: Chuck Soder. **Description:** Overview of the newest technologies which are making local company's meetings more effective including: tele-presence, a videoconferencing technology, as well as virtual flip charts. **Availability:** Online.

17857 ■ *"Defend Your Research: I Can Make Your Brain Look Like Mine" in Harvard Business Review (Vol. 88, December 2010, No. 12, pp. 32)*
Pub: Harvard Business Publishing
Contact: Diane Belcher, Managing Director

Ed: Uri Hasson. **Price:** $6, PDF. **Description:** Psychology professor Uri Hasson discusses findings that the brain waves of a speaker and a listener become similar as the listener's comprehension increases. **Availability:** Online; PDF.

17858 ■ *"Defend Your Research: People Often Trust Eloquence More Than Honesty" in Harvard Business Review (Vol. 88, November 2010, No. 11, pp. 36)*
Pub: Harvard Business Publishing
Contact: Diane Belcher, Managing Director

Ed: Todd Rogers, Michael I. Norton. **Price:** $6, PDF. **Description:** The article shows how deftly sidestepping a question in an eloquent manner generates a more positive response in an audience than does a direct answer that is ineffectively delivered. Implications for both politics and business are discussed. **Availability:** Online; PDF.

17859 ■ *"Extreme Negotiations" in Harvard Business Review (Vol. 88, November 2010, No. 11, pp. 66)*
Pub: Harvard Business Publishing
Contact: Diane Belcher, Managing Director

Ed: Jeff Weiss, Aram Donigian, Jonathan Hughes. **Price:** $8.95, PDF. **Description:** Examination of military negotiation skills that are applicable in business situations. Skills include soliciting others' perspectives, developing and proposing multiple solutions, and inviting others to assess them. **Availability:** Online; PDF.

17860 ■ *"Facebook: A Promotional Budget's Best Friend" in Women Entrepreneur (February 1, 2009)*
Description: Facebook began as a social networking website but has become a valuable marketing tool for all types of businesses, organizations and causes. Tips are provided for creating a Facebook account and growing one's network on Facebook. **Availability:** Online.

17861 ■ *"Grooming Your Online Persona" in Women In Business (Vol. 62, June 2010, No. 2, pp. 36)*
Description: Employees' use of online social networks could become a basis on how their employers, clients, or business partners would judge them. Personal details, pictures and other online data should be filtered to avoid inappropriate or uncomfortable situations and distinguish personal from professional or work life. **Availability:** Online.

17862 ■ *Information Technology for the Small Business: How to Make IT Work For Your Company*
Description: Basics of information technology to help small companies maximize benefits are covered. Topics include pitfalls to avoid, email and Internet use, data backup, recovery and overall IT organization.

17863 ■ *"An Introvert's Guide to Schmoozing" in Canadian Business (Vol. 83, July 20, 2010, No. 11-12, pp. 73)*
Pub: Rogers Media Inc.
Contact: Neil Spivak, Chief Executive Officer

Ed: Jasmine Budak. **Description:** Writer Nancy Ankowitz says that introverts seem to get grouped with social misfits but introverts are people who recharge by spending time alone. Ankowitz advises introverts to use their strengths in quiet strengths such as writing and listening as well as learning to speak in public. **Availability:** Print; Online.

17864 ■ *"Is It Time to Ban Swearing in the Workplace?" in HR Specialist (Vol. 8, September 2010, No. 9, pp. 2)*
Pub: Capitol Information Group Inc.
Contact: Allie Ash, Chief Executive Officer

Description: Screening software has been developed to identify profanity used in business correspondence. **Availability:** PDF; Online.

17865 ■ *"Israeli Spam Law May Have Global Impact" in Information Today (Vol. 26, February 2009, No. 2, pp. 28)*
Pub: Information Today Inc.
Contact: Thomas H. Hogan, President

Ed: David Mirchin. **Description:** Israels new law, called Amendment 40 of the Communications Law, will regulate commercial solicitations including those sent without permission via email, fax, automatic phone dialing systems, or short messaging technologies. **Availability:** PDF; Online.

17866 ■ *"Key Tips to Keeping Corporate Minutes" in Legal Zoom (March 27, 2023)*
URL(s): www.legalzoom.com/articles/key-tips-to-keeping-corporate-minutes

Ed: Marcia Layton Turner. **Released:** March 27, 2023. **Description:** There are many steps towards being compliant with your registered business structure, and keeping corporate minutes is a big part of that. Advice on when to take these important notes, how to do so, and where to file them are included. **Availability:** Online.

17867 ■ *"LIBOR's Hidden Lesson: Instant Messages Are Deadly" in Canadian Business (Vol. 85, August 12, 2012, No. 14, pp. 75)*
Ed: Vanessa Farquharson. **Description:** The appropriate use of instant messaging in the workplace is discussed. Employees involved in a business that deals with other people's finances or intellectual property are advised to keep all of their work and private email accounts separate. **Availability:** Print; Online.

17868 ■ *"Life's Work: Oliver Sacks" in Harvard Business Review (Vol. 88, November 2010, No. 11, pp. 152)*
Pub: Harvard Business Publishing
Contact: Diane Belcher, Managing Director

Ed: Lisa Burrell. **Price:** $8.95, PDF. **Description:** Neurologist and author Oliver Sacks discusses whether different types of minds tend toward certain skills, physician-patient communication, and his own perspectives from being a patient himself. **Availability:** Online; PDF.

17869 ■ *"Mosaid Grants First Wireless Patent License To Matsushita" in Canadian Electronics (Vol. 23, June-July 2008, No. 5, pp. 1)*
Pub: Annex Buisness Media
Contact: Mike Fredericks, President

Description: Matsushita Electric Industrial Co. Ltd. has been granted a six-and-a-half-year license by Mosaid Technologies Inc. to manufacture the latter's products. The patent portfolio license agreement covers Mosaid's Wi-Fi, Wi-Max, CDMA-enabled notebook computers and other products.

17870 ■ *"Partnering for Success" in Art Business News (Vol. 36, October 2009, No. 10, pp. 4)*
Description: In such a volatile economy many savvy artists and gallery owners are turning to out-of-the-box partnerships for continued success; these partnerships are also pervading the Internet, especially with such social media networks as Facebook and Twitter where artists and businesses can develop a loyal following. **Availability:** PDF; Online.

17871 ■ *Persuasive Business Proposals*
Pub: HarperCollins Leadership
Contact: Donald Miller, Chief Executive Officer

Ed: Tom Sant. **Released:** 3rd edition. **Price:** $22.99, Paperback. **Description:** Writing to win more customers, clients, and contracts. **Availability:** E-book; Print.

17872 ■ *"Research and Markets Adds Report: The U.S. Mobile Web Market" in Entertainment Close-Up (December 10, 2009)*
Description: Highlights of the new Research and Markets report "The U.S. Mobile Web Market: Taking Advantage of the iPhone Phenomenon" include:

mobile Internet marketing strategies; the growth of mobile web usage; the growth of revenue in the mobile web market; and a look at Internet business communications, social media and networking. **Availability:** Print; Online.

17873 ■ *"Rogue Caller Infiltrates Cincinnati Firms' Analyst Calls: 'Mr. CEO, Please Do Elaborate On Your Firm's Metrics"* in *Business Courier (Vol. 24, February 28, 2008, No. 47, pp. 1)*
Pub: American City Business Journals, Inc.
Contact: Mike Olivieri, Executive Vice President
Ed: Jon Newberry. **Description:** Discusses a rogue caller who goes by the name of Joe Herrick, Steven Nissan and Joe Harris has joined in over a dozen conference calls, asking chief executive officers on their plans and commenting on the companies' operations. The mystery caller attempts to pass himself off as a financial analyst. Transcripts of some conference calls, in which the rogue caller is involved, are provided. **Availability:** Online.

17874 ■ *"Say Goodbye to Voicemail, Hello To Ribbit Mobile"* in *Agency Sales Magazine (Vol. 39, November 2009, No. 10, pp. 3)*
Description: Salespeople should think twice before leaving a voicemail. The emerging modern etiquette is to send a text message or to e-mail the customer or client. Communication suggestions for both salespeople and their principals are presented. **Availability:** Print; Online.

17875 ■ *Table Talk: The Savvy Girl's Alternative to Networking*
Pub: AuthorHouse Inc.
Contact: William Elliott, President
Ed: Diane Danielson. **Description:** Let's face it. Women and men are different. So why should we all have to network in the same way? And, why should women have to 'network' at all? Between family and work responsibilities, the idea of pressing flesh at some not-very-festive cocktail party is right up there in appeal with a root canal. But what if women could find a way to make career boosting connections that are actually fun? Enter 'table talk', a new way to network for time-pressed, professional women. **Availability:** Print.

17876 ■ *"The Ultimate Sales Letter: Attract New Customers. Boost Your Sales"*
Released: February 2011. **Description:** With email and instant communication, sales copy is indispensable to closing a deal. Most sales letters end up in the junk file or wastebasket. Updated text and examples, great headline formulas, and new exercises to be innovative with sales copy along with ways to use graphics successfully from an expert in direct-response copywriting.

17877 ■ *"Vision Statement: Why Mumbai at 1 PM is the Center of the Business World"* in *Harvard Business Review (Vol. 88, October 2010, No. 10, pp. 38)*
Pub: Harvard Business Publishing
Contact: Diane Belcher, Managing Director
Ed: Michael Segalla. **Price:** $6, PDF. **Description:** A time zone chart is presented for assisting in the planning of international conference calls. **Availability:** Online; PDF.

17878 ■ *"Vistaprint Survey Indicates that Online Marketing Taking Hold Among Small Businesses"* in *Marketwired (December 10, 2009)*
Pub: Comtex News Network Inc.
Contact: Kan Devnani, President
Description: According to a comprehensive survey from Vistaprint N.V., small businesses are very likely to increase their use of Internet marketing strategies such as paid and organic search, email marketing, social media networking and custom websites over the next year. Trends continue to show that more small businesses are indeed adapting to the changing marketplace and are more willing to diversify their marketing strategies than ever before. **Availability:** Print; Online.

17879 ■ *"Wi-Fi Finds Its Way Despite Nixed Plan for Free System"* in *Crain's Cleveland Business (Vol. 28, November 12, 2007, No. 45, pp. 3)*
Pub: Crain Communications Inc.
Contact: K. C. Crain, President
Ed: Jay Miller. **Description:** Discusses the issues facing Cleveland and Northeast Ohio concerning their proposal to offer citizens wireless Internet services for free or a small fee. **Availability:** Online.

17880 ■ *"Words at Work"* in *Information Today (Vol. 26, February 2009, No. 2, pp. 25)*
Description: Current new buzzwords include the following: digital amnesia, or overload by availability, speed and volume of digital information; maternal profiling, a form a discrimination against women; recipe malpractice, a reminder that just because you can turn on a stove it doesn't make you a chef; ringxiety, the act when everyone reaches for their cell phone when one rings; verbing, the practice of turning good nouns into verbs. **Availability:** Print; Online.

TRADE PERIODICALS

17881 ■ *Writing That Works*
Pub: Communications Concepts Inc.
Contact: John de Lellis, Editor Publisher Founder
URL(s): apexawards.com/about
Description: Advises corporate, nonprofit, agency and independent communicators on business writing and publishing. Also covers writing techniques, style matters, publication management, and online publishing. Publisher also sponsors annual APEX Awards for Publication Excellence. **Availability:** Print.

CONSULTANTS

17882 ■ **Alliance Management International Ltd.**
6200 Rockside Rd.
Cleveland, OH 44131
Contact: Carolyn K. Matheson, Contact
Description: A consulting company that helps to form national and international strategic alliances. Handles alliances between companies forming joint ventures. Staff specialized in small company-large company alliance, alliance assessment and analysis and alliance strategic planning. **Scope:** A consulting company that helps to form national and international strategic alliances. Handles alliances between companies forming joint ventures. Staff specialized in small company-large company alliance, alliance assessment and analysis and alliance strategic planning. **Training:** Joint Business Planning; Developing a Shared Vision; Current and New/Prospective Partner Assessment; Customer Service; Sales Training; Leader and Management Skills.

17883 ■ **American English Academy (AEA) [American English College]**
111 N Atlantic Blvd., Ste. 112
Monterey Park, CA 91754
Ph: (626)457-2800
Fax: (626)457-2808
Co. E-mail: info@aec.edu
URL: http://www.aec.edu
Facebook: www.facebook.com/americanenglishcollege
Linkedin: www.linkedin.com/company/american-english-college
Instagram: www.instagram.com/americanenglishcollege
YouTube: www.youtube.com/channel/UC6eS1MpXLDagYdZVZWWJO6A
Description: Specializes in providing on-site English language and communication development for corporations and individuals. Also develops and delivers training in speaking, writing, pronunciation, grammar, and idioms with an emphasis on business communication. Offers individual, small group, intensive, and long-distance learning. Programs tailor-made for each client. **Scope:** Specializes in providing on-site English language and communication development for corporations and individuals. Also develops and delivers training in speaking, writing, pronunciation, grammar, and idioms with an emphasis on business communication. Offers individual, small group, intensive, and long-distance learning. Programs tailor-made for each client. **Founded:** 1983.

17884 ■ **The Handler Group Inc.**
425 W End Ave.
New York, NY 10024
Contact: Mark L. Handler, Chief Executive Officer
Description: Provider of marketing, communication planning and design services, specializing in development of internal and external business communications. Develops corporate identity, corporate literature, employee communications, sales promotion materials, consumer product packaging and information, brochures, annual reports and presentation materials. Industries served: Cable/television, technology software, business information, hospitality and banking. **Scope:** Provider of marketing, communication planning and design services, specializing in development of internal and external business communications. Develops corporate identity, corporate literature, employee communications, sales promotion materials, consumer product packaging and information, brochures, annual reports and presentation materials. Industries served: Cable/television, technology software, business information, hospitality and banking.

17885 ■ **Write It Well (WIW)**
San Francisco, CA
Ph: (510)655-6477
URL: http://www.writeitwell.com
Contact: Natasha Terk, Founder
E-mail: natasha@adcomdesigns.com
Description: Firm develops training programs, instructional materials and procedures manuals, conducts customized in-house classes in communication skills and performance management and offers training for letter communications. **Scope:** Firm develops training programs, instructional materials and procedures manuals, conducts customized in-house classes in communication skills and performance management and offers training for letter communications. **Founded:** 1980. **Publications:** "Professional Writing Skills: A Self-Paced Training Program"; "Grammar for Grown ups A Self-Paced Training Program"; "Writing Performance Documentation A Self-Paced Training Program"; "Report and Proposal Writing for Environmental Professionals A Self-Paced Training Program"; "How to Write Reports and Proposals A Self-Paced Training Program"; "Just Commas 9 Basic Rules to Master Comma Usage"; "E-Mail - a Write it a Well Guide". **Training:** Business Writing; Effective E-Mail; Grammar Fundamentals; Technical Writing.

COMPUTER SYSTEMS/ SOFTWARE

17886 ■ *Better Business Writing*
Chris Learning Center Inc. (CLC)
9701 Dalmatia Dr.
Clinton, MD 20735
Ph: (301)203-0564
Fax: (301)248-1833
URL: http://chrislearningcenter.com
Contact: Christine Bland, Director
Released: January 29, 2013. **Price:** $19.95, paperback. **Description:** Based on the Better Business Writing video and book. Includes book and user's guide. **Availability:** E-book; Print.

RESEARCH CENTERS

17887 ■ **Colorado State University College of Liberal Arts - Center for Research on Writing and Communication Technologies**
Fort Collins, CO 80523-1773
URL: http://writing.colostate.edu/about/support.cfm
Description: Integral unit of College of Liberal Arts, Colorado State University. **Scope:** Health communication, risk communication, usability testing, diffusion of innovations, Web design, human factors,

human computer interactions, interface design, writing, writing processes, online writing centers, technology transfer, science communication, legibility, tobacco and alcohol warnings, digital television, communicating risk of sexually transmitted diseases, communication history. **Founded:** 1991.

17888 ■ University of Notre Dame - Mendoza College of Business - Eugene D. Fanning Center for Business Communication
Mendoza College of Business
 University of Notre Dame
 Notre Dame, IN 46556
Ph: (574)631-9153
URL: http://fanning.nd.edu
Contact: Mary J. O'Neil, Director

Description: Integral unit of Mendoza College of Business, University of Notre Dame. Offers instruction, counseling, and guidance in management and corporate communication. **Scope:** Business communication, including writing, speaking, listening, persuasion and other communication behaviors in the workplace; corporate communication, including the production of case studies designed to support instruction; intercultural communication, including the production of books and learning materials designed to support instruction. **Founded:** 1990. **Publications:** *Management and Corporate Communication Case Studies* (Semiannual). **Educational Activities:** Conference on Corporate Communication (Annual); Management Development Seminars; Fanning Center for Business Communication Workshops. **Awards:** Eugene D. Fanning Award (Annual); Lucy B. Pilkinton Memorial Award (Annual).

Business Growth and Statistics

START-UP INFORMATION

17889 ■ *Going Solo: Developing a Home-Based Consulting Business from the Ground Up*
Description: Ways to turn specialized knowledge into a home-based successful consulting firm, focusing on targeting client needs, business plans, and growth.

17890 ■ *"Kitchen Aid: D.C. Food Incubator Turns Growth Tactics Inward" in Washington Business Journal (Vol. 32, February 28, 2014, No. 46, pp. 6)*
Pub: American City Business Journals, Inc.
Contact: Mike Olivieri, Executive Vice President
Released: Weekly. **Price:** $4, introductory 4-week offer(Digital only). **Description:** The founders of the 14-month-old food business incubator, Union Kitchen, are considering their own growth strategies as they open up a second space for small business owners. The incubator has 55 members that pay monthly fees from $800 to $1,000, focusing on bar services and fine dining opportunities. **Availability:** Print; Online.

ASSOCIATIONS AND OTHER ORGANIZATIONS

17891 ■ **Association for Corporate Growth - Toronto Chapter (ACG) [Canadian Angus Association]**
411 Richmond St. E, Ste. 200
Toronto, ON, Canada M5A 3S5
Ph: (416)868-1881
Fax: (416)929-5256
Co. E-mail: toronto@acg.org
URL: http://www.acg.org/toronto
Contact: Mike Fenton, President
Linkedin: www.linkedin.com/company/association-for
-corporate-growth-toronto-chapter
X (Twitter): x.com/ACGGlobal
Description: Professionals with a leadership role in strategic corporate growth. Seeks to facilitate the professional advancement of members, and the practice of corporate growth management. Fosters communication and cooperation among members; conducts continuing professional education programs. **Founded:** 1954. **Educational Activities:** Annual Capital Connection Conference (Annual). **Geographic Preference:** National.

17892 ■ **Center for American Entrepreneurship (CAE)**
503 Arnon Lake Dr.
Great Falls, VA 22066
Co. E-mail: info@startupsusa.org
URL: http://startupsusa.org
Contact: John Dearie, President
Facebook: www.facebook.com/startupsusa
Linkedin: www.linkedin.com/company/center-for
-american-entrepreneurship
X (Twitter): x.com/startupsusaorg

YouTube: www.youtube.com/channel/UCGzBSPKA
1hn9dqHykNOMjEA
Description: Nonpartisan research, policy, and advocacy organization that works with policymakers in Washington DC and across the country to enact public policies that promote new business formation, survival, and growth. **Founded:** 2017.

SMALL BUSINESS ASSISTANCE PROGRAMS

17893 ■ *"CrowdFunding Platform, START.ac, Announces It Is Expanding Its International Scope From the US, Canada and the UK to 36 Countries Including Australia, India, Israel, Italy and Africa" in Benzinga.com (July 11, 2012)*
Benzinga.com
1 Campus Martius Ste. 200
Detroit, MI 48226
Free: 877-440-9464
Co. E-mail: info@benzinga.com
URL: http://www.benzinga.com
Contact: Jason Raznick, Founder
Ed: Aaron Wise. **Description:** START.ac is expanding its CrowdFunding site to include 36 countries and increasing its scope to include business startups, teen projects, as well as medical products. START.ac projects are in the fundraising stage at this point, with 23 percent located outside the United States. **Availability:** Online.

EDUCATIONAL PROGRAMS

17894 ■ **Total Productive Maintenance (TPM) & 5S (Onsite)**
TPC Trainco Inc.
225 E Robinson St., Ste. 570
Orlando, FL 32801
Free: 877-978-7246
Co. E-mail: sales@tpctraining.com
URL: http://live.tpctraining.com
URL(s): live.tpctraining.com/public-seminars/plan
t-management/total-productive-maintenance-tpm
-training
Description: Two-day seminar that focuses on getting managers, maintenance personnel and equipment users all working together to prevent equipment problems and reduce expenditures. **Audience:** Managers, maintenance personnel and equipment users. **Principal Exhibits:** Two-day seminar that focuses on getting managers, maintenance personnel and equipment users all working together to prevent equipment problems and reduce expenditures.

REFERENCE WORKS

17895 ■ *"3 Key Growth Elements for Small Security Integrators" in Security Distributing & Marketing (Vol. 42, July 2012, No. 7, pp. 108)*
Description: Local and regional integrators facing a choice between expansion and annihilation by global organizations face an uphill battle. Facing down giants requires critical use of key market principles including niche identity, co-branding, and planning for modest growth. **Availability:** Print; Online.

17896 ■ *"The 7 Wonders of Tourism" in Business Journal Portland (Vol. 31, May 9, 2014, No. 10, pp. 10)*
Pub: American City Business Journals, Inc.
Contact: Mike Olivieri, Executive Vice President
Description: Travel Oregon's new travel campaign called '7 Wonders of Oregon' is expected to generate the area's economy. Reports show that the travel industry contributed $9.6 billion to the state's economy in 2013. The sector also employed a total of 93,900 Oregonians during the same year. Statistical data included. **Availability:** Online.

17897 ■ *"10 Small Business Statistics" in Oberlo Blog (Jan. 1, 2022)*
URL(s): www.oberlo.com/blog/small-business-statis
tics
Ed: Maryam Mohsin. **Released:** January 01, 2022.
Description: Provides information on ten business statistics every future entrepreneur should know. **Availability:** Online.

17898 ■ *"39 Entrepreneur Statistics You Need to Know" in SmallBizGenius.net Blog (Feb. 4, 2022)*
URL(s): www.smallbizgenius.net/by-the-numbers/en
trepreneur-statistics/#gref
Ed: Dragomir Simovic. **Released:** February 04, 2022.
Description: Provides statistics on entrepreneurship, small business, minority-owned business, as well as benefits and challenges of entrepreneurship. **Availability:** Online.

17899 ■ *"73 Remarkable Small Business Statistics to Know" in Semrush Blog (Feb. 26, 2021)*
URL(s): www.semrush.com/blog/small-business-s
tats/
Ed: Georgi Todorov. **Released:** February 26, 2021.
Description: Discusses essential small business statistics for entrepreneurs to understand as they launch their business. **Availability:** Online.

17900 ■ *101 Secrets to Building a Winning Business*
Pub: Allen and Unwin Proprietary Ltd.
Ed: Andrew Griffiths. **Description:** Provides expert information for running and growing a small business. **Availability:** Print.

17901 ■ *"352 Media Group Opens New Tampa Web Design and Digital Marketing Office" in Entertainment Close-Up (May 2, 2011)*
Pub: Close-Up Media Inc.
Contact: Caroline S. Moore, President
E-mail: cms@closeupmedia.com

Description: 352 Media Group opened its newest office in Tampa, Florida in May 2011. The firm is noted for its achievements in Web design and digital marketing. **Availability:** Print; Online.

17902 ■ *"$560 Million Acquisition in Storage for CubeSmart"* in *Orlando Business Journal (Vol. 28, September 7, 2012, No. 30, pp. 1)*
Pub: Baltimore Business Journal
Contact: Rhonda Pringle, President
E-mail: rpringle@bizjournals.com
Description: CubeSmart has completed its $560 million acquisition of 22 storage facilities in late August 2012, making it one of the leading self-storage companies in the US. In light of this growth, an overview of CubeSmart is explored. **Availability:** Print; Online.

17903 ■ *"2011 a Record Year for New Wind Energy Installations in Canada"* in *CNW Group (September 26, 2011)*
Pub: CNW Group Ltd.
Description: Canada reports a record for new wind energy projects in 2011 with about 1,338 MW of newly installed wind energy capacity expected to come on line, compared to 690 MW installed in 2010. Statistical data included. **Availability:** Print; Online.

17904 ■ *"2011 Report on the $9 Billion US Trade Show & Event Planning Services Industry"* in *Investment Weekly (January 21, 2012, pp. 47)*
Description: The US trade show and event planning industry is made up of meeting planners and suppliers. These professionals organize, design, promote, and manage business and consumer trade shows, conferences, and meetings. The US trade show industry represents nearly 4,000 compaines and reports a $9 billion annual revenue. **Availability:** Online.

17905 ■ *"2012 Outlook: ROI Still Piles on the Pressure"* in *Conference & Incentive Travel (March 1, 2012, pp. 14)*
Description: According to a recnt poll, more than one-third of 500 event planners preict lower budgets for 2012 than last year. Event planners for EDF Energy, Deloitte, Allianz Insurance, Sanofi Pasteur MSD, and Fico discuss their predictions for the industry for 2012. **Availability:** Online.

17906 ■ *"ABC Supply Company Finally Finds Idaho"* in *Idaho Business Review (September 17, 2014)*
Pub: BridgeTower Media
Contact: Adam Reinebach, President
Description: The nation's largest wholesale distributor, ABC Supply Company, has entered a store in Idaho. The roofing supply firm has now has stores in 48 states. Franklin Lumber Supply, a home supply chain will be ABCs its major competitor in the area.

17907 ■ *"Accounting Firm Weaver is Still Pursuing Growth Via Mergers"* in *San Antonio Business Journal (Vol. 25, January 6, 2012, No. 50, pp. 1)*
Pub: Baltimore Business Journal
Contact: Rhonda Pringle, President
E-mail: rpringle@bizjournals.com
Description: Fort Worth, Texas-based Weaver LLP has worked out a merger to absorb the San Antonio-based John R. Hannah & Company LLP. The merger deal is Weaver's third in San Antonio area after it absorbed Polansky McNutt Perry & Company in 2008 and Edelman Arnold in 2009. Insights into the accounting firm's plan for Hannah are also provided. **Availability:** Print; Online.

17908 ■ *"Acquisition to Give Mylan Tax Benefits, Boost Sales"* in *Pittsburgh Business Times (Vol. 33, July 18, 2014, No. 53, pp. 3)*
Pub: American City Business Journals, Inc.
Contact: Mike Olivieri, Executive Vice President
Released: Weekly. **Price:** $4, introductory 4-week offer(Digital & Print). **Description:** Mylan Inc.'s acquisition of Abbot's foreign specialty and branded generic drug business is a win situation for the company. The acquisition will help Mylan expand and diversify in the largest markets outside the U.S. as well as prove beneficial in growth through enhanced financial flexibility and a more competitive global tax structure. **Availability:** Print; Online.

17909 ■ *"Actions to Implement Three Potent Post-Crisis Strategies"* in *Strategy & Leadership (Vol. 38, September-October 2010, No. 5)*
Pub: Emerald Inc.
Ed: Saul J. Berman, Richard Christner, Ragna Bell.
Description: The need for organizations to design and implement strategies to cope with the possible situations in the post-economic crisis environment is emphasized. The plans that organizations should implement to successfully manage uncertainty and complexity and to foster their eventual growth are discussed. **Availability:** PDF.

17910 ■ *"Add Aquatics to Boost Business"* in *Pet Product News (Vol. 64, December 2010, No. 12, pp. 20)*
Ed: David Lass. **Description:** Pet stores are encouraged to add aquatics departments to increase profitability through repeat sales. This goal can be realized by sourcing, displaying, and maintaining high quality live fish. Other tips regarding the challenges associated with setting up an aquatics department are presented. **Availability:** Online.

17911 ■ *"Adidas' Brand Ambitions"* in *Business Journal Portland (Vol. 27, December 10, 2010, No. 41, pp. 1)*
Pub: Portland Business Journal
Contact: Andy Giegerich, Managing Editor
E-mail: agiegerich@bizjournals.com
Ed: Erik Siemers. **Description:** Adidas AG, the second-largest sporting goods brand in the world, hopes to increase global revenue by 50 percent by 2015. The German company, which reported $14.5 billion sales, plans to improve its U.S. market. The U.S. is Adidas' largest, but also the most underperforming market for the firm. **Availability:** Print; Online.

17912 ■ *"Advancing the Ball"* in *Inside Healthcare (Vol. 6, December 2010, No. 7, pp. 31)*
Description: Profile of Medicalodges an elder-care specialty company that provides both patient care and technology development. President and CEO of the firm believes that hiring good employees is key to growth for any small business. **Availability:** Online.

17913 ■ *"Ag Firms Harvest Revenue Growth"* in *The Business Journal-Serving Metropolitan Kansas City (Vol. 26, July 18, 2008, No. 45, pp. 1)*
Description: Five of the biggest agricultural companies in the Kansas City area, except one, reported multibillion-dollar revenue increases in 2007. The companies, which include Lansing Trade Group, posted a combined $9.5 billion revenue growth. The factors that affected the revenue increase in the area's agricultural companies, such as prices and high demand, are also examined. **Availability:** Print; Online.

17914 ■ *"All In The Family: Weston Undergoes a Shakeup"* in *Canadian Business (Vol. 79, September 22, 2006, No. 19, pp. 75)*
Pub: Rogers Media Inc.
Contact: Neil Spivak, Chief Executive Officer
Ed: Zena Olijnyk. **Description:** Continuing ownership of Weston dynasty on Canada's largest chain Loblaw Co. is discussed. **Availability:** Online.

17915 ■ *"Allied Brokers of Texas Looking to Fill Private Lending Gap"* in *San Antonio Business Journal (Vol. 26, March 23, 2012, No. 8, pp. 1)*
Pub: Baltimore Business Journal
Contact: Rhonda Pringle, President
E-mail: rpringle@bizjournals.com
Description: San Antonio, Texas-based Allied Brokers of Texas has announced the expansion of its services to offer private lending. The move would provide direct private financing of $250,000 to $5 million to entrepreneurs looking to buy or sell a small business. Insights into the firm's new subsidiary, Allied Lending Services, are also offered. **Availability:** Print; Online.

17916 ■ *"Amcon Distributing Expands Into Northwest Arkansas"* in *Arkansas Business (Vol. 26, November 9, 2009, No. 45, pp. 13)*
Pub: Arkansas Business Publishing Group
Contact: Mitch Bettis, President
Description: Amcon Distributing Co., a consumer products company, has bought the convenience store distribution assets of Discount Distributors from its parent, Harps Food Stores Inc., significantly increasing its wholesale distribution presence in the northwest Arkansas market. The acquisition will be funded through Amcon's existing credit facilities. **Availability:** Online.

17917 ■ *"Analysis of the U.S. Residential Solar Power Market"* in *PR Newswire (September 19, 2012)*
Pub: PR Newswire Association LLC.
Description: Analysis of the residential solar power market in the United States is presented. Solar PV is the fastest growing technology in the energy sector for the nation during the last three years due to rising energy prices, volatile fuel costs, and government incentives for renewable energy.

17918 ■ *"Ann Arbor Google's Growth Dips: Few Worried about High-tech Firm's Future"* in *Crain's Detroit Business (Vol. 25, June 8, 2009, No. 23, pp. 3)*
Pub: Crain Communications Inc.
Contact: Barry Asin, President
Ed: Bill Shea. **Description:** Global recession has slowed the growth of Google Inc. Three years ago, when Google moved to Ann Arbor, Michigan it estimated it would provide 1,000 new jobs within five years, so far the firm employs 250. **Availability:** Online; PDF.

17919 ■ *"Annual Small Business Growth Reaches Record High, Data Shows"* in *The Ascent (Sept. 16, 2021)*
URL(s): www.fool.com/the-ascent/personal-finance/articles/annual-small-business-growth-reaches-record-high-data-shows/
Ed: Maurie Backman. **Released:** September 16, 2021. **Description:** Provides information and analysis on annual small business growth and statistics. **Availability:** Online.

17920 ■ *"Apartment Action: A Renewal in Rentals"* in *Barron's (Vol. 88, March 17, 2008, No. 11, pp. 17)*
Pub: Dow Jones & Company Inc.
Contact: Almar Latour, Chief Executive Officer
Ed: Robin Goldwyn Blumenthal. **Description:** Discusses the projected entry of the estimated 82 million echo-boomers into the rentals market and the influx of immigrants and displaced homeowners which could turn apartments into lucrative investments again. While apartment-building completions rose slowly since 2003, demand is expected to increase steeply until 2015. **Availability:** Online.

17921 ■ *"Are You Ignoring Trends That Could Shake Up Your Business?"* in *Harvard Business Review (Vol. 88, July-August 2010, No. 7-8, pp. 124)*
Pub: Harvard Business Publishing
Contact: Diane Belcher, Managing Director
Ed: Elie Ofek, Luc Wathieu. **Price:** $8.95, PDF.
Description: Ways for firms to capitalize on trends that might otherwise negatively affect their business are spotlighted. These include using certain aspects of the trend to augment traditional product/service offerings, and combining the trend with the offerings to transcend its traditional category. **Availability:** Online; PDF.

17922 ■ "Art Institute of Chicago Goes Green" in Contractor (Vol. 56, July 2009, No. 7, pp. 1)
Ed: Candace Roulo. Description: Art Institute of Chicago's Modern Wing museum addition will receive a certification that makes them one of the most environmentally sound museum expansions in the U.S. A modified variable-air-volume system is being used to meet temperature and humidity requirements in the building and it also has a double curtain wall to capture summer heat. Availability: Print; Online.

17923 ■ "Auction Company Grows with Much Smaller Sites" in Automotive News (Vol. 86, October 31, 2011, No. 6488, pp. 23)
Pub: Crain Communications Inc.
Contact: Barry Asin, President
Ed: Arlena Sawyers. Description: Auction Broadcasting Company has launched auction sites and is expanding into new areas. The family-owned business will provide auctions half the size traditionally used. The firm reports that 40 percent of the General Motors factory-owned vehicles sold on consignment were purchased by online buyers, up 30 percent over 2010. Availability: Online.

17924 ■ "Austin-Based Insuraprise Growing Fast" in Austin Business Journal (Vol. 31, April 22, 2011, No. 7, pp. 1)
Pub: Austin Business Journal
Contact: Rachel McGrath, Director
E-mail: rmcgrath@bizjournals.com
Ed: Sandra Zaragoza. Description: Austin, Texas-based Insuraprise Inc. is finalizing the purchase of a 24,000-square-foot office at 12116 Jekel Circle. The firm, with 23 salespeople and sales that are growing nearly 300 percent over the past 18 months, will now have room to grow. Insuraprise plans to hire 35 new salespersons for its call center. Availability: Print; Online.

17925 ■ "Auto Asphyxiation" in Canadian Business (Vol. 85, August 13, 2012, No. 13, pp. 38)
Ed: Michael McCullough. Description: The declining car ownership and utlization has profound business implications for oil companies and automakers and may bring substantial benefit to other sectors and the economy as a whole. The transition to the post-automotive age may happen in places where there is the will to change transportation practices but not in others. Availability: Print; Online.

17926 ■ "AutoZone Revs Up Sales With Focus on Commercial Market" in Memphis Business Journal (Vol. 35, January 24, 2014, No. 42, pp. 4)
Pub: American City Business Journals, Inc.
Contact: Mike Olivieri, Executive Vice President
Released: Weekly. Price: $4, introductory 4-week offer(Digital & Print). Description: Memphis, Tennessee-based automotive parts retailer AutoZone Inc. is focusing its growth on the commercial market after successfully dominating the retail division. The retailer is taking advantage of its strong supply chain to effectively deliver parts to its customers. Availability: Print; Online.

17927 ■ "Avalon Advisors Opens Alamo City Office" in San Antonio Business Journal (Vol. 28, April 18, 2014, No. 10, pp. 7)
Pub: American City Business Journals, Inc.
Contact: Mike Olivieri, Executive Vice President
Released: Weekly. Price: $4, Introductory 4-week offer(Digital only). Description: Avalon Advisors LLC opened an office in San Antonio, Texas. The wealth management firm has been serving prominent clients in the city over the past few years. Rob McCaline, director of the company's new office, reveals that the business enjoyed tremendous growth in the city through referrals by existing clients. Availability: Print; Online.

17928 ■ "Azaya Therapeutics Taking Big Steps" in San Antonio Business Journal (Vol. 28, March 28, 2014, No. 7, pp. 8)
Pub: American City Business Journals, Inc.
Contact: Mike Olivieri, Executive Vice President

Released: Weekly. Price: $4, Introductory 4-week offer(Digital only). Description: Azaya Therapeutics believes that its $5 million funding round will be completed in 2014. The convertible-note bridge funding was initiated in October 2013. The company, which plans to pursue regulatory approval for its cancer medications, is also focusing on expanding the business. Availability: Print; Online.

17929 ■ "Baldwin Connelly Partnership Splits" in Business Journal Serving Greater Tampa Bay (Vol. 30, November 19, 2010, No. 48, pp. 1)
Pub: Tampa Bay Business Journal
Contact: Ian Anderson, President
E-mail: ianderson@bizjournals.com
Description: The fast-growing insurance brokerage Baldwin Connelly is now breaking up after five years. Two different entrepreneurial visions have developed within the organization and founders Lowry Baldwin and John Connell will not take separate tracks. Staffing levels in the firm are expected to remain the same. Availability: Print; Online.

17930 ■ "Baltimore's Burger Market Sizzling with Newcomers" in Boston Business Journal (Vol. 29, June 10, 2011, No. 5, pp. 1)
Pub: Boston Business Journal
Contact: Carolyn M. Jones, President
E-mail: cmjones@bizjournals.com
Ed: Ryan Sharrow. Description: The burger trend in Maryland is on the rise with burger joints either opening up or expanding into several branches. Startup costs for this kind of business range between $250,000 to $400,000. With a growth rate of roughly 17 percent in 2009, this so-called better burger segment of the burger categories is expected to dominate the market for quite some time. Availability: Print; Online.

17931 ■ "Banking Sector To See Moderate Growth in 2014" in Houston Business Journal (Vol. 44, January 3, 2014, No. 35, pp. 5)
Pub: American City Business Journals, Inc.
Contact: Mike Olivieri, Executive Vice President
Released: January 03, 2014. Price: $4, introductory 4-week offer(Digital only). Description: The Greater Houston Partnership reported that Houston, Texas' finance industry recovered 50.9 percent of the 5,500 jobs it lost compared to the nation's recovery rate of 34.4 percent. However, Houston's banking sector remains strong and deposits have almost doubled since 2008. The banks that established or expanded operations in Houston are also presented. Availability: Print; Online.

17932 ■ "Banks Looking to Lend, Compete to Make Small-Business Loans" in Puget Sound Business Journal (Vol. 33, August 17, 2012, No. 17, pp. 1)
Pub: Baltimore Business Journal
Contact: Rhonda Pringle, President
E-mail: rpringle@bizjournals.com
Ed: Greg Lamm. Description: Mobile Tool Management has grown from four employees to 30 during the past five years, and its expansion was completed after owner Mike woogerd applied for a loan from Chase. Figures show that Chase lent $132 million in the second quarter of 2012 to businesses. A report by the Federal Reserve shows that large banks are owering their standatrds for lending to large and medium-sized companies. Availability: Print; Online.

17933 ■ "BankUnited, Banco do Brasil Lead Local Lenders" in South Florida Business Journal (Vol. 35, September 12, 2014, No. 7, pp. 5)
Pub: American City Business Journals, Inc.
Contact: Mike Olivieri, Executive Vice President
Description: South Florida banks have reported a $7.54 billion increase in loans in 2014. BankUnited registered the highest growth with a total of $3.75 billion in loans. National Bank of Florida came in second with $585 million.

17934 ■ "Baptist Health System Plans to Expand Stone Oak-Area Hospital: $32 Million Project Will Add Two Floors, 100 Beds" in San Antonio Business Journal (Vol. 26, May 25, 2012, No. 17, pp. 1)
Pub: Baltimore Business Journal
Contact: Rhonda Pringle, President
E-mail: rpringle@bizjournals.com
Price: $4, introductory 4-week offer(Digital & Print). Description: Baptist Health System is planning to start the $32 million expansion of the North Central Baptist Hospital in San Antonio, Texas that will include the addition of two floors and 100 beds. An estimate of hiring 200 new health care workers will be created by the expansion. Availability: Print; Online.

17935 ■ "Bargain Hunting In Vietnam" in Barron's (Vol. 88, July 14, 2008, No. 28, pp. M6)
Pub: Dow Jones & Company Inc.
Contact: Almar Latour, Chief Executive Officer
Ed: Elliot Wilson. Description: Vietnam's economy grew by just 6.5 percent for the first half of 2008 and its balance of payments ballooned to $14.4 billion. The falling stock prices in the country is a boon for bargain hunters and investing in the numerous domestic funds is one way of investing in the country. Some shares that investors are taking an interest in are also discussed. Availability: Online.

17936 ■ "Bark Up The Right Tree" in Small Business Opportunities (Winter 2009)
Released: February 09, 2016. Description: Profile of Central Bark, a daycare company catering to pets that offers franchise opportunities and is expanding rapidly despite the economic downturn; the company's growth strategy is also discussed.

17937 ■ "Bartering Trades on Talents" in Reading Eagle (June 20, 2010)
Description: Bartering is not just a way of trading goods and services, it can be an essential tool for small business to survive in a bad economy.

17938 ■ "Baskin-Robbins Expanding in China and U.S." in Ice Cream Reporter (Vol. 21, August 20, 2008, No. 9, pp. 1)
Description: Baskin-Robbins will open its first store in Shanghai, China along with plans for 100 more shops in that country. They will also be expanding their market in the Dallas/Fort Worth, Texas area as well as Greater Cincinnati/Northern Kentucky regions. Availability: Print; Online.

17939 ■ "Baskin-Robbins: New in U.S., Old in Japan" in Ice Cream Reporter (Vol. 23, August 20, 2010, No. 9, pp. 2)
Description: Baskin-Robbins is celebrating its first franchise in Japan. Availability: Print; Online.

17940 ■ "Baskin-Robbins Reopens in New Orleans" in Ice Cream Reporter (Vol. 23, September 20, 2010, No. 10, pp. 3)
Description: Baskin-Robbins will open its first shop in New Orleans, Louisiana after Hurricane Katrina in 2005. The shop stands in the exact location of a Baskin-Robbins shop destroyed by Katrina. Availability: Print; Online.

17941 ■ "Baskin-Robbins Tests New Upscale Concept" in Ice Cream Reporter (Vol. 21, September 20, 2008, No. 10, pp. 1)
Description: Baskin-Robbins is opening its new upscale store, Cafe 31 in an effort to invigorate its brand. The shop will serve fondues, cakes and other treats prepared by an in-store chef. Availability: Print; Online.

17942 ■ "BCE Mulls Radical Changes With Industry Under Pressure" in Globe & Mail (March 30, 2007, pp. B1)
Ed: Andrew Willis, Jacquie McNish, Catherine McLean. Description: An account on the expansion plans of BCE Inc., which plans to acquire TELUS Corp., is presented. Availability: Online.

17943 ■ "Bedandbreakfast.eu: Bed & Breakfast Emerging in Europe" in Travel & Leisure Close-Up (January 11, 2012)
Pub: Close-Up Media Inc.
Contact: Caroline S. Moore, President
E-mail: cms@closeupmedia.com
Description: According to experts, only 15 percent of all bed and breakfast operations in Europe were launched before the year 2000, with the majority opening after 2005. Reports show approximately 2,400 new operations opening on a monthly basis. Bedandbreakfast.eu offer current offerings for vacationers interested in staying at a bed and breakfast while visiting Europe. **Availability:** Online.

17944 ■ "Behind the Numbers: When It Comes to Earnings, Look for Quality, Not Just Quantity" in Black Enterprise (Vol. 38, July 2008, pp. 35)
Pub: Earl G. Graves Ltd.
Contact: Earl Graves, Jr., President
Description: It is important for investors to examine the quality of a company's earnings rather than fixate on the quantity of those earnings. Advice is given regarding issues investors can look at when trying to determine the potential growth of a firm.

17945 ■ "Benchmark Makes Granduca Entrance" in Houston Business Journal (Vol. 40, January 8, 2010, No. 35, pp. 2)
Pub: Houston Business Journal
Contact: Bob Charlet, President
E-mail: bcharlet@bizjournals.com
Ed: Jennifer Dawson. **Description:** Houston, Texas-based Interfin Company, owner of the Hotel Granduca, has tapped the services of Benchmark Hospitality International to manage the property. The hiring of Benchmark is part of Interfin's efforts to develop Granduca hotels in other markets. Statistical data included. **Availability:** Print; Online.

17946 ■ "Best Cash Flow Generators" in Canadian Business (Vol. 82, Summer 2009, No. 8, pp. 40)
Description: Agrium Inc. and FirstService Corporation are in the list of firms that are found to have the potential to be the best cash flow generators in Canada. The list also includes WestJet Airlines Ltd., which accounts for 385 flights each day. More than 80 percent of analysts rate the airline stocks a Buy. **Availability:** Print; Online.

17947 ■ "Best Turnaround Stocks" in Canadian Business (Vol. 81, Summer 2008, No. 9, pp. 65)
Description: Share prices of Sierra Wireless Inc. and EXFO Electro Optical Engineering Inc. have fallen over the past year but have good chance at a rebound considering that the companies have free cash flow and no long-term debt. One-year stock performance analysis of the two companies is presented. **Availability:** Print; Online.

17948 ■ "Best Value Stocks" in Canadian Business (Vol. 81, Summer 2008, No. 9, pp. 63)
Description: Table showing the one-year performance of bargain or best-value stocks is presented. These stocks are undervalued compared to their North American peers, but it is projected that their five-year average return on equity is greater. **Availability:** Online.

17949 ■ "Better Made's Better Idea: Diversify Despite Rising Costs" in Crain's Detroit Business (Vol. 24, September 22, 2008, No. 38, pp. 18)
Pub: Crain Communications Inc.
Contact: Barry Asin, President
Ed: Nathan Skid. **Description:** Better Made Snack Foods Inc. is planning to expand its product lines and market reach as well as boost manufacturing capability during a time in which the company is being buffeted by rising commodity and fuel costs. The company feels that diversification is the key to maintain sales and growth. **Availability:** Online.

17950 ■ "Between the Lines: Intangible Assets" in Canadian Business (Vol. 79, July 17, 2006, No. 14-15, pp. 17)
Pub: Rogers Media Inc.
Contact: Neil Spivak, Chief Executive Officer
Ed: Al Rosen. **Description:** Need for investors to check the actual worth of a company and not to get carried away by the inflated claims made by the company is emphasized.

17951 ■ Beyond Booked Solid: Your Business, Your Life, Your Way-It's All Inside
Pub: John Wiley & Sons, Inc.
Contact: Christina Van Tassell, Executive Vice President Chief Financial Officer
Ed: Michael Port. **Released:** December 2010. **Price:** $21.99, e-book; $32.50, hardcover. **Description:** Professional service providers and small business owners will discover tactics and strategies for growing and expanding their companies while allowing them to find time to relax and enjoy their lives. Owners will learn to attract new clients and grow profits. **Availability:** E-book; Print; Online; PDF.

17952 ■ "Biodiesel Poised to Regain Growth" in Farm Industry News (January 21, 2011)
Pub: Informa Business Media, Inc.
Contact: Charlie McCurdy, President
Ed: Lynn Grooms. **Description:** According to Gary Haer, vice president of sales and marketing for Renewable Energy Group, the biodiesel industry is positioned to regain growth in 2011 with the reinstatement of the biodiesel blendersa tax credit of $1 per gallon. **Availability:** Print; Online.

17953 ■ "Birmingham Tech Firms Eye Growth in 2014" in Birmingham Business Journal (Vol. 31, January 10, 2014, No. 2, pp. 4)
Pub: American City Business Journals, Inc.
Contact: Mike Olivieri, Executive Vice President
Released: Weekly. **Price:** $4, introductory 4-week offer(Digital & Print). **Description:** Birmingham, Alabama-based high-tech firms, ProctorU and Chronicle Studio are planning to expand their work forces in 2014. ProctorU will add more than 50 employees, while Chronicle will add three more positions to their staff. **Availability:** Print; Online.

17954 ■ "BK Menu Gives Casual Dining Reason to Worry" in Advertising Age (Vol. 79, November 17, 2008, No. 43, pp. 12)
Pub: Crain Communications, Inc.
Contact: Jessica Botos, Manager, Marketing
E-mail: jessica.botos@crainsnewyork.com
Ed: Emily Bryson York. **Description:** Burger King is beginning to compete with such casual dining restaurants as Applebees and the Cheesecake Factory with new premium menu items, including thicker burgers and ribs; statistical data regarding the casual dining segment which continues to fall and Burger King, whose sales continue to rise is included. **Availability:** Online.

17955 ■ "Blach Builds on Teamwork" in Silicon Valley/San Jose Business Journal (Vol. 30, August 24, 2012, No. 22, pp. 1)
Pub: Baltimore Business Journal
Contact: Rhonda Pringle, President
E-mail: rpringle@bizjournals.com
Description: Blach Construction chief executive, Mike Blach, has grown the firm into a top contractor in San Jose, California. The construction company's earnings have increased to $98 million in 2011. **Availability:** Print; Online.

17956 ■ "Blue Bell Breaks Ground in South Carolina" in Ice Cream Reporter (Vol. 23, August 20, 2010, No. 9, pp. 3)
Description: Texas-based Blue Bell Creameries will open a new 2,000 square foot transfer facility in North Charleston, South Carolina. The facility will expand Blue Bell's distribution efforts in the state. **Availability:** Print.

17957 ■ "Boeing Moving 1,000 Washington Engineering Jobs to California" in Business Journal Portland (Vol. 31, April 11, 2014, No. 6)
Pub: American City Business Journals, Inc.
Contact: Mike Olivieri, Executive Vice President
Released: Weekly. **Description:** Boeing plans to move 1,000 engineering jobs from Portland, Oregon to Southern California. The company says the move helps support planes in service at the company's Commercial Airplanes Engineering Center in Southern California and position the aerospace manufacturer for further growth. **Availability:** Print; Online.

17958 ■ "The Book On Indigo" in Canadian Business (Vol. 81, July 22, 2008, No. 12-13, pp. 29)
Description: Indigo Books & Music Inc. reported record sales of $922 million resulting in a record net profit of $52.8 million for the 2008 fiscal year ended March 29, 2008. Earnings per share were $2.13, greater than Standard & Poor's expected $1.70 per share. Additional information concerning Indigo Books is presented.

17959 ■ "Book Publishing is Growing" in Information Today (Vol. 28, October 2011, No. 9, pp. 10)
Pub: Information Today Inc.
Contact: Thomas H. Hogan, President
Ed: Paula J. Hane. **Description:** U.S. book publishing industry is reporting growth in its sector, despite the poor economy. BookStats, a comprehensive statistical survey conducted on the modern publishing industry in the U.S. reported Americans are reading in all print and digital formats. In 2011, 114 million ebooks were sold and now account for 13.6 percent of revenue from adult fiction. In contrast, 603 million trade hardcover books (fiction and nonfiction) were sold in 2011, a 5.8 percent increase over 2008.

17960 ■ "Boom has Tech Grads Mulling Their Options" in Globe & Mail (March 14, 2006, pp. B1)
Ed: Grant Robertson. **Description:** Internet giant Google Inc. has stepped up its efforts to hire the talented people, in Canada, at Waterloo University in southern Ontario, to expand its operations. The details of the job market and increasing salaries are analyzed. **Availability:** Online.

17961 ■ "Bose Seeking Expansion Options in Framingham" in Boston Business Journal (Vol. 34, June 13, 2014, No. 19, pp. 15)
Pub: American City Business Journals, Inc.
Contact: Mike Olivieri, Executive Vice President
Released: Weekly. **Description:** Bose Corporation, the Framingham-based high-end audio products manufacturer, is in talks to buy a 10-acre property near its headquarters. Bose is negotiating with the owner of three buildings on Pennsylvania Avenue near the Bose headquarters. Bose already owns five buildings in Framingham, but is looking at real estate for growth and expansion. **Availability:** Print; Online.

17962 ■ "Bottom-Fishing and Speed-Dating in India-How Investors Feel About the Indian Market" in Barron's (Vol. 88, March 24, 2008, No. 12, pp. M12)
Pub: Dow Jones & Company Inc.
Contact: Almar Latour, Chief Executive Officer
Ed: Elliot Wilson. **Description:** Indian stocks have fallen hard in 2008, with Mumbai's Sensex 30 down 30 percent from its January 2008 peak of 21,000 to 14,995 in March. The India Private Equity Fair 2008 attracted 140 of the world's largest private equity firms and about 24 of India's fastest-growing corporations. Statistical data included. **Availability:** Online.

17963 ■ "Bountiful Barrels: Where to Find $140 Trillion" in Barron's (Vol. 88, July 14, 2008, No. 28, pp. 40)
Pub: Dow Jones & Company Inc.
Contact: Almar Latour, Chief Executive Officer

Ed: Andrew Bary. **Description:** Surge in oil prices has caused a large transfer of wealth to oil-producing countries thereby reshaping the global economy. Oil reserves of oil exporting countries are now valued at $140 trillion. Economist Stephen Jen believes that this wealth will be transformed into paper assets as these countries invest in global stocks and bonds. **Availability:** Online.

17964 ■ *"Branching Out: Towards a Trait-based Understanding of Fungal Ecology"* in *Canadian Business (Vol. 79, July 17, 2006, No. 14-15, pp. 41)*
Availability: Print; Online.

17965 ■ *"Branding Spree"* in *Pet Product News (Vol. 66, September 2012, No. 9, pp. 40)*
Ed: Michael Ventre. **Description:** The extent to which pet security firm PetSafe has continued to diversify into new product categories to realize growth opportunities is explored. An arm of Radio Systems Corporation, PetSafe has been known for manufacturing products such as wireless fences and electronic pet collars. **Availability:** Print; Online.

17966 ■ *"Breaking Through"* in *Inc. (January 2008, pp. 90-93)*
Ed: Mike Hofman. **Description:** Entrepreneur Keith R. McFarland, shares insight into why most successful companies eventually plateau, while others keep on growing. **Availability:** Online.

17967 ■ *"Briarcliff Office Building Fills Up Fast"* in *The Business Journal-Serving Metropolitan Kansas City (Vol. 26, Sept. 5, 2008, pp. 1)*
Pub: American City Business Journals, Inc.
Contact: Mike Olivieri, Executive Vice President
Ed: Rob Roberts. **Description:** Prior to its opening the Hilltop Office Building in Kansas City Missouri has attained 80 percent occupancy. FCStone Group Inc.'s plan to move to the building has boosted the facility's occupancy. Description and dimensions of the office building are also provided. **Availability:** Online.

17968 ■ *"Bringing Healthcare Home"* in *Austin Business Journal (Vol. 34, June 6, 2014, No. 16, pp. B13)*
Pub: American City Business Journals, Inc.
Contact: Mike Olivieri, Executive Vice President
Description: Chris Hester, founder and president of Kinnser Software feels that the company's growth since its inception has been both a blessing and a challenge. He states that his company's policy not to hire people until there's a strong need has increased productiveness of the company and the singular focus on customer service success has driven the company forward. **Availability:** Online.

17969 ■ *"Building Fast-Growing Companies"* in *South Florida Business Journal (Vol. 35, September 19, 2014, No. 8, pp. 16)*
Pub: American City Business Journals, Inc.
Contact: Mike Olivieri, Executive Vice President
Description: Members of Florida's construction industry have registered continuous growth in 2014. Recovery from the economic crisis is driving the construction growth. Economic resilience and proper debt management have also contributed to the sector's growth. **Availability:** Online.

17970 ■ *"Built For Growth"* in *Canadian Business (Vol. 87, July 2014, No. 7, pp. 50)*
Description: The impressive 7,308 percent revenue growth of FourQuest Energy Inc. has earned it the top spot in the 2014 Profit 500 ranking of Canada's fastest growing firms. The Edmonton, Alberta-based company provides mechanical pre-commissioning, shutdown and maintenance for oil-and-gas facilities and diversifying its service offerings and looking to non oil-and-gas verticals as well. **Availability:** Online.

17971 ■ *"Bullish Alert: A Brave Market Call"* in *Barron's (Vol. 92, July 23, 2012, No. 30, pp. 12)*
Pub: Dow Jones & Company Inc.
Contact: Almar Latour, Chief Executive Officer

Ed: Jacqueline Doherty. **Description:** Seth Masters, chief investment officer of Bernstein Global Wealth Management, predicts that the Dow Jones will reach the 20,000 level within five years. He also predicts that the Standard & Poor's 500 index will rise to 2,000 points. **Availability:** Online.

17972 ■ *Business Analysis for Dummies*
Pub: John Wiley & Sons, Inc.
Contact: Christina Van Tassell, Executive Vice President Chief Financial Officer
URL(s): www.wiley.com/en-us/Business+Analysis +For+Dummies%2C+2nd+Edition-p-97811199 12507
Ed: Alison Cox. **Released:** 2nd edition. **Price:** $18, e-book; $29.99, paperback. **Description:** Get help with analyzing data to help your business grow. This guide will help your business become more profitable by teaching you identify where your company needs to improve and how to achieve higher performance. **Availability:** E-book; Print.

17973 ■ *"Business Briefs: Alcoholic Beverage Manufacturing Is Big Business In Idaho"* in *Idaho Business Review (August 19, 2014)*
Pub: BridgeTower Media
Contact: Adam Reinebach, President
Description: Idaho's alcoholic beverage manufacturing industry is growing at a steady pace, reporting an $8.7 million payroll in 2013. Breweries, as well as wineries and distilleries are also strong. Statistical data included.

17974 ■ *Business Development for Dummies*
Pub: John Wiley & Sons, Inc.
Contact: Christina Van Tassell, Executive Vice President Chief Financial Officer
URL(s): www.wiley.com/en-us/Business +Development+For+Dummies-p-9781118962718
Ed: Anna Kennedy. **Released:** February 2015. **Price:** $15, e-book; $24.99, paperback. **Description:** Focuses on B2B and B2C businesses. Discusses sales, strategy, marketing, and partnerships that will help your business grow. **Availability:** E-book; Print.

17975 ■ *"Business Diary"* in *Crain's Detroit Business (Vol. 24, October 6, 2008, No. 40, pp. 23)*
Pub: Crain Communications Inc.
Contact: Barry Asin, President
Description: Detailed listing of acquisitions, expansions, new products, new services, business contracts and startups from the Detroit area is provided. **Availability:** Print; Online.

17976 ■ *"Cadillac Tower Largest to Start in a Decade"* in *Globe & Mail (March 28, 2006, pp. B5)*
Ed: Elizabeth Church. **Description:** The plans of Cadillac Fairview Corporation Ltd. to build office towers, in downtown Canada, are presented. **Availability:** Print; Online.

17977 ■ *"California Wines Nab 64 Percent of U.S. Sales"* in *Sacramento Business Journal (Vol. 31, April 25, 2014, No. 9)*
Pub: American City Business Journals, Inc.
Contact: Mike Olivieri, Executive Vice President
Released: Weekly. **Description:** California wine sales represented 64 percent of all wine sales in the U.S. in 2013. This totaled $23.1 billion in sales at the retail level. California has held this level of market share in the U.S. wine market for some time. In 2003, the state shipped 65 percent of all wine in the country. **Availability:** Print; Online.

17978 ■ *"Calpine Gets Ready to Light It Up"* in *Barron's (Vol. 92, July 23, 2012, No. 30, pp. 15)*
Pub: Dow Jones & Company Inc.
Contact: Almar Latour, Chief Executive Officer
Ed: Jack Willoughby. **Description:** The stocks of electric power producer Calpine could gain value as natural gas-fired power plants increase their market share. The company's stock prices could rise by 50 percent from $17.50 but the company needs to complete its turnaround to fully realize these gains. **Availability:** Online.

17979 ■ *"Campaigner Survey: 46 Percent of Small Businesses Use Email Marketing"* in *Wireless News (November 21, 2009)*
Description: Almost half (46 percent) of small businesses surveyed by Campaigner's 2009 State of Small Business Online Marketing, say that they rely on email marketing to help them find new customers, keep existing ones and grow their businesses. The survey also found that 36 percent of small businesses plan to begin using email marketing over the next year. The trend to utilize Internet marketing tools is allowing small businesses to grow faster and generate higher revenues than those that are not using these mediums. **Availability:** Print; Online.

17980 ■ *"Campbell Clinic in Expansion Mode: Plans to Triple Size of Surgery Center, Add Employees"* in *Memphis Business Journal (Vol. 34, August 24, 2012, No. 19, pp. 1)*
Pub: Baltimore Business Journal
Contact: Rhonda Pringle, President
E-mail: rpringle@bizjournals.com
Description: The Campbell Clinic Inc. is pushing forward with its plan to expand and hire new employees. The clinic has filed a Certificate of Need with the Tennessee Health Services Development Agency worth $13 million. Expansion projects include the enlargement of the surgery center, which handles 700 cases a month, a figure which is expected to rise to 750 in August 2012. **Availability:** Print; Online.

17981 ■ *"Can You Hear Them Now?"* in *Hawaii Business (Vol. 54, August 2008, No. 2, pp. 48)*
Description: Coral Wireless LLC (dba Mobi PCS) is ranked 237 in Hawaii Business' list of the state's top 250 companies for 2008. The company is a local wireless phone provider, which has expanded its market to Oahu, Maui and the Big Island since opening in 2006, offering 13 phones and unlimited texts and calls. Details on the company's sales are provided. **Availability:** Print; Online.

17982 ■ *"Can You Make a Million Bucks in the House Cleaning Business?"* in *Cleaning Business Today (July 13, 2016)*
Ed: Terry Sambrowski. **Released:** July 13, 2016. **Description:** Discusses seven steps that control the costs that affect gross income potential of your cleaning business. **Availability:** Online.

17983 ■ *"Canada, Not China, Is Partner In Our Economic Prosperity"* in *Crain's Chicago Business (Vol. 31, April 14, 2008, No. 15, pp. 14)*
Pub: Crain Communications Inc.
Contact: Barry Asin, President
Ed: Paul O'Connor. **Description:** In 2005 more than $500 billion in two-way trade crossed the friendly border between the Great Lakes states and Canadian provinces and for decades Canada is every Great Lakes State's number one and growing export market. **Availability:** Online.

17984 ■ *"Canadian Patients Give Detroit Hospitals a Boost"* in *Crain's Detroit Business (Vol. 24, April 14, 2008, No. 15, pp. 10)*
Pub: Crain Communications Inc.
Contact: Barry Asin, President
Ed: Jay Greene. **Description:** Each year thousands of Canadians travel to Detroit area hospitals seeking quicker solutions to medical problems or access to services that are limited or unavailable in Canada. **Availability:** Online.

17985 ■ *"Canadian Solar Expands Into Puerto Rico With Planned 26MW Solar Power Plant Installation"* in *Benzinga.com (October 2, 2012)*
Pub: Benzinga.com
Contact: Jason Raznick, Founder

Description: Canadian Solar Inc. is expanding into Puerto Rico with the delivery of 26mg of CS6P-P solar power modules for the San Fermin solar power plant. Canadian Solar is one of the world's largest solar firms. The solar power system is expected to be completed and connected to the national grid by December 2012.

17986 ■ *"CanWEA Unveils WindVision for BC: 5,250 MW of Wind Energy by 2025"* in *CNW Group (October 4, 2011)*
Pub: CNW Group Ltd.
Description: Wind industry leaders are asking British Columbia, Canada policy makers to created conditions to further develop and integrate wind energy in accordance with greenhouse gas emission targets and projected economic growth. Statistical data included. **Availability:** PDF; Online.

17987 ■ *"Cash-Heavy Biovail on the Prowl for Deals"* in *Globe & Mail (March 24, 2006, pp. B1)*
Ed: Leonard Zehr. **Description:** Biovail Corp. posted 48 percent rise in profits for 2005. The business growth plans of the company through acquisitions are presented. **Availability:** Online.

17988 ■ *Cash In a Flash*
Released: December 28, 2010. **Price:** $13.68, hardcover; $22.50. **Description:** Proven, practical advice and techniques are given to help entrepreneurs make money quickly using skills and resources known to generate permanent and recurring income. **Availability:** E-book; Print; Audio; Online.

17989 ■ *"Casinos In Pitch Battle"* in *Philadelphia Business Journal (Vol. 28, July 20, 2012, No. 23, pp. 1)*
Pub: Baltimore Business Journal
Contact: Rhonda Pringle, President
E-mail: rpringle@bizjournals.com
Description: The extent to which casinos in Philadelphia, Pennsylvania have invested in marketing and rebranding effortsin the Philadelphia-Atlantic City markets is explored. These efforts are part of the goal of the casinos to compete for customers considering that casinos contribute about $6 billion in taxes to Pennsylvania. Statistics pertaining to casinos and their advertising expenditures are presented. **Availability:** Print; Online.

17990 ■ *"Caterpillar to Expand Research, Production in China"* in *Chicago Tribune (August 27, 2008)*
Description: Caterpillar Inc., the Peoria-based heavy-equipment manufacturer, plans to establish a new research-and-development center at the site of its rapidly growing campus in Wuxi. **Availability:** Print; Online.

17991 ■ *"Cemex Paves a Global Road to Solid Growth"* in *Barron's (Vol. 88, March 10, 2008, No. 10, pp. 24)*
Pub: Dow Jones & Company Inc.
Contact: Almar Latour, Chief Executive Officer
Ed: Sandra Ward. **Description:** Shares of Cemex are expected to perform well with the company's expected strong performance despite fears of a US recession. The company has a diverse geographical reach and benefits from a strong worldwide demand for cement. **Availability:** Online.

17992 ■ *"Certain Predicts 2012 as Breakthrough Year for Events"* in *Internet Wire (January 5, 2012)*
Pub: Comtex News Network Inc.
Contact: Kan Devnani, President
Description: Certain Inc. discusses its threetop predictions for 2012 on technology trends that will promote increased business value in the events industry. Certain Inc. is a leading provider of cloud-based event management software that is used for global meetings and events. **Availability:** Print; Online.

17993 ■ *"The Changing Face of the U.S. Consumer"* in *Advertising Age (Vol. 79, July 7, 2008, No. 26, pp. 1)*
Pub: Advertising Age
Contact: Dan Peres, President
Ed: Peter Francese. **Description:** It is essential for marketers to examine demographic shifts when looking at ways in which to market brands. The average head-of-households is aging and marketers must not continue to ignore them. Statistical data included. **Availability:** Print; Online.

17994 ■ *"Children's Hospital to Grow"* in *Austin Business Journal (Vol. 31, July 22, 2011, No. 20, pp. A1)*
Pub: Austin Business Journal
Contact: Rachel McGrath, Director
E-mail: rmcgrath@bizjournals.com
Ed: Sandra Zaragoza. **Description:** Austin, Texas-based Dell Children's Medical Center is set to embark on a tower expansion. The plan will accommodate more patients and make room for the hospital's growing specialty program. **Availability:** Print; Online.

17995 ■ *"The China Syndrome"* in *Canadian Business (Vol. 79, July 17, 2006, No. 14-15, pp. 25)*
Pub: Rogers Media Inc.
Contact: Neil Spivak, Chief Executive Officer
Ed: Peter Diekmeyer. **Description:** Contrasting pace of growth in China and India are presented. Reasons for the slow pace of growth of Canadian companies like CAE Inc. and Magna in India are also discussed. **Availability:** Online.

17996 ■ *"China's ZTE in Hunt for Partners"* in *Globe & Mail (February 27, 2006, pp. B1)*
Ed: Gordon Pitts. **Description:** The business growth plans of ZTE Corp. in Canada, through partnership, are presented. **Availability:** Online.

17997 ■ *"Chuy's Ready to Serve New Markets"* in *Austin Business Journal (Vol. 31, June 17, 2011, No. 15, pp. 1)*
Pub: Austin Business Journal
Contact: Rachel McGrath, Director
E-mail: rmcgrath@bizjournals.com
Ed: Cody Lyon. **Description:** Chuy's Holdings Inc. plans to expand into the Southeastern United States, particularly in Atlanta, Georgia. The restaurant, which secured $67.5 million in debt financing in May 2011, added 20 stores in five years and plans to open eight locations in 2011. **Availability:** Print; Online.

17998 ■ *"CIBC Spends $1.1 Billion on Caribbean Expansion"* in *Globe & Mail (March 14, 2006, pp. B1)*
Ed: Sinclair Stewart. **Description:** Canadian Imperial Bank of Commerce (CIBC), the fifth-largest bank of Canada, is planning to spend $1.1billion to buy major share of Barbados-based First Caribbean International Bank. The details of the acquisition plan are presented. **Availability:** Print; Online.

17999 ■ *"Clash of the Titans"* in *San Francisco Business Times (Vol. 28, February 7, 2014, No. 29, pp. 4)*
Pub: American City Business Journals, Inc.
Contact: Mike Olivieri, Executive Vice President
Released: September 01, 2017. **Description:** University of California, San Francisco (UCSF) Medical Center and Stanford Hospital and Clinics have been competing for dominance for San Francisco Bay Area's health care. Both medical centers are competing to affiliate with more doctors, gain more patients, and accomplish more fundraising. Ways the UCSF and Stanford plan to pursue their expansion and integration are also discussed. **Availability:** Print; Online.

18000 ■ *"Clean-Tech Focus Sparks Growth"* in *Philadelphia Business Journal (Vol. 28, January 15, 2010, No. 48, pp. 1)*
Pub: Philadelphia Business Journal
Contact: Sierra Quinn, Director
E-mail: squinn@bizjournals.com
Ed: Peter Key. **Description:** Keystone Redevelopment Group and economic development organization Ben Franklin Technology Partners of Southeastern Pennsylvania have partnered in supporting the growth of new alternative energy and clean technology companies. Keystone has also been developing the Bridge Business Center. **Availability:** Online.

18001 ■ *"ClickFuel Unveils Internet Marketing Tools for Small Businesses"* in *Marketwired (October 19, 2009)*
Pub: Comtex News Network Inc.
Contact: Kan Devnani, President
Description: ClickFuel, a firm that manages, designs and tracks marketing campaigns has unveiled a full software suite of affordable services and technology solutions designed to empower small business owners and help them promote and grow their businesses through targeted Internet marketing campaigns. **Availability:** Online.

18002 ■ *"Cloud Computing for a Crowd"* in *CIO (Vol. 24, October 2, 2010, No. 1, pp. 16)*
Pub: CIO
Ed: Stephanie Overby. **Description:** Information about a project which aimed to implement a cloud-based crowdsourcing platform and innovation-management process is provided. Chubb Group of Insurance Companies wanted to mine revenue-generating ideas from its 10,400 employees and hundreds of thousands of external agents. The company hosted its first innovation event using its new system in October 2008. **Availability:** Online.

18003 ■ *"Coca-Cola FEMSA, Family Dollar, Other Dividend Payers On a Roll"* in *Benzinga.com (June 21, 2012)*
Pub: Benzinga.com
Contact: Jason Raznick, Founder
Ed: Nelson Hem. **Description:** Dividend paying companies showing upward price trends are outlined. The firms highlighted include: Agnico-Eagle Mines, Coca-Cola FEMSA, Dean Foods, Expedia, Family Dollar Stores, Ferrellgas Partners, and InterContinental Hotels. **Availability:** Print; Online.

18004 ■ *"Commercial Water Efficiency Initiatives Announced"* in *Contractor (Vol. 56, November 2009, No. 11, pp. 5)*
Ed: Robert P. Mader. **Description:** Plumbing engineers John Koeller and Bill Gauley are developing a testing protocol for commercial toilets. The team said commercial toilets should have a higher level of flush performance than residential toilets for certification. The Environmental Protection Agency's WaterSense program wants to expand the program into the commercial/institutional sector. **Availability:** Print; Online.

18005 ■ *"Companies Must Innovate, Regardless of Economy"* in *Crain's Detroit Business (Vol. 25, June 1, 2009, No. 22, pp. M007)*
Pub: Crain Communications Inc.
Contact: Barry Asin, President
Ed: Sherri Begin Welch. **Description:** Despite the economy, leaders of Michigan's successful companies stress that small businesses must innovate in order to grow. **Availability:** Print; PDF; Online.

18006 ■ *"Company Hopes To Pack Profits With Self-Storage"* in *Crain's Detroit Business (Vol. 24, February 18, 2008, No. 7, pp. 15)*
Pub: Crain Communications Inc.
Contact: Barry Asin, President
Ed: Daniel Duggan. **Description:** Storage Opportunity Partners has purchased a vacant building to convert into a self-storage facility. **Availability:** Online.

18007 ■ *"Consignment Shops Use Web To Help Sell Used Clothing"* in *Chattanooga Times/Free Press (March 17, 2012)*
Ed: Carey O'Neil. **Description:** Chattanooga, Tennessee boasts a strong market for consignment shops. Children's clothing and toys are among best sellers. Tips are given to help increase sales for consignment/resale shops. **Availability:** Print; Online.

18008 ■ "Construction" in Inc. (Vol. 36, September 2014, No. 7, pp. 166)
Pub: Mansueto Ventures L.L.C.
Contact: Stephanie Mehta, Chief Executive Officer
Description: Listing of the fastest growing construction companies across the United States is presented.
Availability: Online.

18009 ■ "Consumer Contagion? A Bleak Earnings View" in Barron's (Vol. 88, March 10, 2008, No. 10, pp. 15)
Pub: Dow Jones & Company Inc.
Contact: Almar Latour, Chief Executive Officer
Ed: Robin Goldwyn Blumenthal. Description: Analysts expect consumer discretionary profits in the S&P 500 to drop 8.4 percent in the first quarter of 2008. A less confident consumer is expected to pull profits down, putting forecasts of earnings growth in the S&P 500 at risk. Statistical data included. Availability: Online.

18010 ■ "Consumers Turned Off? Not at Best Buy" in Barron's (Vol. 88, March 24, 2008, No. 12, pp. 29)
Pub: Dow Jones & Company Inc.
Contact: Almar Latour, Chief Executive Officer
Ed: Sandra Ward. Description: Shares of Best Buy, trading at $42.41 each, are expected to rise to an average of $52 a share due to the company's solid fundamentals. The company's shares have fallen 20 percent from their 52-week high and are attractive given the company's bright prospects in the video game sector and high-definition video. Availability: Online.

18011 ■ "Coping With a Shrinking Planet" in Agency Sales Magazine (Vol. 39, December 2009, No. 11, pp. 46)
Description: China and India are forcing big changes in the world and are posing a huge threat to U.S. manufacturers and their sales representatives. Reps may want to consider expanding into these territories. Helping sell American products out of the country presents an opportunity for economic expansion.
Availability: Online.

18012 ■ "Corner Bakery Readies Its Recipes for Growth" in Dallas Business Journal (Vol. 35, February 17, 2012, No. 23, pp. 1)
Pub: Baltimore Business Journal
Contact: Rhonda Pringle, President
E-mail: rpringle@bizjournals.com
Description: Corner Bakery Cafe is planning to add 10 corporate locations and 15-20 franchise locations in 2012. The company was acquired by Roark Capital. Availability: Print; Online.

18013 ■ "Corporate Travel Planners is Geared Up for More Growth" in San Antonio Business Journal (Vol. 26, September 7, 2012, No. 32, pp. 1)
Pub: Baltimore Business Journal
Contact: Rhonda Pringle, President
E-mail: rpringle@bizjournals.com
Description: San Antonio, Texas-based Corporate Travel Planners (CTP) registered an 11.6 percent increase in revenues through July compared to the same period in 2011 and it is expected to reach $135 million by the end of 2012. CTP is one of the companies that helped lead the travel industry out of the deep hole. Availability: Print; Online.

18014 ■ "Cost Cuts Lead Dealers to Record Profits" in Globe & Mail (March 24, 2006, pp. B3)
Ed: Omar El Akkad. Description: The reasons behind posting of $4.3 billion profit by Canadian securities sector, for 2005, are presented. Availability: Online.

18015 ■ "Counting on Engagement at Ernst & Young" in Workforce Management (Vol. 88, November 16, 2009, No. 12, pp. 25)
Pub: Crain Communications Inc.
Contact: Barry Asin, President
Ed: Ed Frauenheim. Description: Employee engagement has been difficult to maintain through the recession but firms such as Ernst & Young have found that the effort to keep their employees loyal has paid off.
Availability: Print; Online.

18016 ■ "Coupons.com Sees Growth In the Bargain" in Silicon Valley/San Jose Business Journal (Vol. 30, June 8, 2012, No. 11, pp. 1)
Pub: Baltimore Business Journal
Contact: Rhonda Pringle, President
E-mail: rpringle@bizjournals.com
Description: Coupons.com Inc. is expanding its headquarters in Mountain View, California by adding 17,000 square feet in additional space to handle a work force expected to grow to almost 700 by 2013. The digital coupon company also opened sales offices in New York, in Chicago, Illinois and Los Angeles. Availability: Print; Online.

18017 ■ "Courier 250 Companies Hope to Rebound From 2009" in Business Courier (Vol. 27, July 16, 2010, No. 11, pp. 1)
Pub: Business Courier
Ed: Dan Monk, Jon Newberry. Description: Private companies that are featured in the Courier 250 publication have lost almost $4 billion in revenue, while combined sales dropped by 11 percent to 32 billion in 2009. Courier 250 is a guide to public companies, large nonprofits, private firms, and other related entities in Ohio's Cincinnati region. Availability: Online.

18018 ■ "Battle-Tested Vestas Shrugs Off Ill Winds" in Business Journal Portland (Vol. 30, January 31, 2014, No. 48, pp. 4)
Pub: American City Business Journals, Inc.
Contact: Mike Olivieri, Executive Vice President
Released: Weekly. Price: $4, Introductory 4-week offer(Digital & Print). Description: The revenues of Vestas-American Wind Technology are expected to increase by 12 percent in 2014, despite the decline in US turbine sales. The company holds the second-highest market share in the US. However, Vestas is struggling with tax incentives and increased competition. Availability: Print; Online.

18019 ■ "CradlePoint Is Adding Workers, Seeking More Space" in Idaho Business Review (September 3, 2014)
Pub: BridgeTower Media
Contact: Adam Reinebach, President
Price: $11.99, Print, Digital & Mobile(1 Month); 149, Print, Digital & Mobile(1 Year); 99, Digital & Mobile Only(1 Year); $99, Digital & Mobile Only(For 1 Year); $9.95, Print, Digital & Mobile (For 1 Month Intro Rate); $149, Print, Digital & Mobile(For 1 Year). Description: CradlePoint makes networking routers and software, focusing on security for businesses. The firm is hiring new workers at a rate higher than predicted and is seeking new office space in downtown Boise, Idaho. CradlePoint is a major player in the growing wireless service and cloud platform market and is growing faster than its competitors. Availability: Print; Online.

18020 ■ "Craft-Spirits Maker Brings Art of Distilling to SoFlo Area" in San Antonio Business Journal (Vol. 28, March 7, 2014, No. 4, pp. 5)
Pub: American City Business Journals, Inc.
Contact: Mike Olivieri, Executive Vice President
Released: Weekly. Price: $4, Introductory 4-week offer(Digital only). Description: Chris Mobley and Boyan Kolusevic established Dorcol Distilling Company in the SoFlo area of San Antonio, Texas. Kolusevic reveals that the growth of San Antonio's craft spirits/brewery industry has been evident in recent years. Dorcol has been described as an urban, boutique craft distillery. Availability: Print; Online.

18021 ■ "Craning for Workers: Seattle Is Full of Cranes, but Not Enough Operators" in Puget Sound Business Journal (Vol. 35, August 15, 2014, No. 17, pp. 4)
Pub: American City Business Journals, Inc.
Contact: Mike Olivieri, Executive Vice President
Released: August 15, 2014. Description: The U.S. Department of Labor statistics show that Washington State has 15, 510 laborers in 2013. However, construction companies are having difficulty hiring skilled workers, particularly as apprentices. The Associated General Contractors of Washington's expansion of training slots for crane and other heave equipment operators is discussed. Availability: Print; Online.

18022 ■ Creativity and Innovation: Breaking New Ground..Without Breaking the Bank
Description: Advice is given to help small business owners be creative in order to compete in their sector. Availability: Print; Download.

18023 ■ "Crucible: Battling Back from Betrayal" in Harvard Business Review (Vol. 88, December 2010, No. 12, pp. 130)
Pub: Harvard Business Publishing
Contact: Diane Belcher, Managing Director
Ed: Daniel McGinn. Price: $8.95, PDF. Description: Stephen Greer's scrap metal firm, Hartwell Pacific, lost several million dollars due to a lack of efficient and appropriate inventory audits, accounting procedures, and new-hire reference checks for his foreign operations. Greer believes that balancing growth with control is a key component of success. Availability: Print; PDF.

18024 ■ "Cummins Is a Engine of Growth" in Barron's (Vol. 88, July 14, 2008, No. 28, pp. 43)
Pub: Dow Jones & Company Inc.
Contact: Almar Latour, Chief Executive Officer
Ed: Shirley A. Lazo. Description: Engine maker Cummins increased its quarterly common dividend by 40 percent to 17.5 cents per share from 12.5 cents. CVS Caremark's dividend saw a hike of 18.4 percent from 9.5 cents to 11.25 cents per share while its competitor Walgreen is continuing its 75th straight year of dividend distribution and its 33rd straight year of dividend hikes. Availability: Online.

18025 ■ "Customer Loyalty: Making Your Program Excel" in Franchising World (Vol. 42, August 2010, No. 8, pp. 47)
Pub: International Franchise Association
Contact: Matthew Haller, President
E-mail: mhaller@franchise.org
Ed: Steve Baxter. Description: Customer loyalty is key to any franchise operation's growth. Tips for identifying preferred customers are outlined. Availability: Online.

18026 ■ "Cutting Credit Card Processing Costs for Your Small Business" in Hawaii Business (Vol. 53, March 2008, No. 9, pp. 56)
Ed: Robert K.O. Lum. Description: Accepting credit card payments offers businesses with profits from the discount rate. The discount rate includes processing fee, VISA & MasterCard assessment and interchange. Details regarding merchant service cost and discount rate portions are discussed. Statistical data included. Availability: Online.

18027 ■ "Data: Nearly 80% of Black Entrepreneurs Believe They Run Thriving Businesses, Yet Gaining Access to Capital Still a Hurdle" in Black Enterprise(February 24, 2023)
URL(s): www.blackenterprise.com/data-nearly-80-of-black-entrepreneurs-believe-they-run-thriving-businesses-yet-gaining-access-to-capital-still-a-hurdle/
Ed: Jeffrey McKinney. Released: February 24, 2023. Description: After navigating a world-wide pandemic, many Black entrepreneurs are focused on building up their businesses and creating generational wealth while also supporting other Black-owned businesses. Even with these commitments, issues obtaining financing have been encountered. Tips for circumventing these hurdles are discussed. Availability: Online.

18028 ■ "Davis Family Expands Cable Empire" in St. Louis Business Journal (Vol. 32, June 15, 2012, No. 43, pp. 1)
Pub: Baltimore Business Journal
Contact: Rhonda Pringle, President

E-mail: rpringle@bizjournals.com
Description: Missouri-based Fidelity Communications has become a standout in the $98 billion cable industry through low-profile management of the Davis family, with the help of John Colbert. Fidelity has made five acquisitions since 1992 and has grown its subscriber base to more than 115,000 customers or revenue generating units. **Availability:** Print; Online.

18029 ■ *"Deal Braces Cramer for Growth Run" in The Business Journal-Serving Metropolitan Kansas City (Vol. 26, July 4, 2008, No. 43, pp. 1)*
Description: Gardner, Kansas-based Cramer Products Inc. bought 100 percent of the stocks of Louisville, Kentucky-based Active Ankle Inc. from 26 private investors increasing its revenue by 20 percent. The latter is the second largest vendor of Cramer. Other details of the merger are presented. **Availability:** Print; Online.

18030 ■ *"Dealer Gets a Lift with Acquisitions at Year's End" in Crain's Detroit Business (Vol. 26, January 11, 2010, No. 2, pp. 3)*
Pub: Crain Communications Inc.
Contact: Barry Asin, President
Ed: Ryan Beene. **Description:** Alta Equipment Co., a forklift dealer, closed 2009 with a string of acquisitions expecting to double the firm's employee headcount and triple its annual revenue. Alta Lift Truck Services, Inc., as the company was known before the acquisitions, was founded in 1984 as Michigan's dealer for forklift manufacturer Yale Materials Handling Corp. **Availability:** Print; Online.

18031 ■ *"A Decent Proposal" in Hawaii Business (Vol. 53, March 2008, No. 9, pp. 52)*
Pub: PacificBasin Communications
Contact: Chuck Tindle, Director
E-mail: chuckt@pacificbasin.net
Ed: Jacy L. Youn. **Description:** Bonnie Cooper and Brian Joy own Big Rock Manufacturing Inc., a stone manufacturing company, which sells carved rocks and bowls, lava benches, waterfalls, and Buddhas. Details about the company's growth are discussed. **Availability:** Print; Online.

18032 ■ *"Deere to Open Technology Center in Germany" in Chicago Tribune (September 3, 2008)*
Description: Deere & Co. plans to open a technology and innovation center in Germany; details of the company's expansion plans are discussed. **Availability:** Print; Online.

18033 ■ *"Delivering the Milk" in Barron's (Vol. 92, July 23, 2012, No. 30, pp. M7)*
Pub: Dow Jones & Company Inc.
Contact: Almar Latour, Chief Executive Officer
Ed: Kopin Tan. **Description:** The stocks of China Mengniu Dairy could continue losing value in the short term but could gain value in the long term. The company's revenue growth and profit margins face downward pressure due to aggressive pricing after food safety scandals. **Availability:** Online.

18034 ■ *"Design '07 (Fashion): Haute Flyers" in Canadian Business (Vol. 80, November 19, 2007, No. 23, pp. 68)*
Pub: Rogers Media Inc.
Contact: Neil Spivak, Chief Executive Officer
Ed: Rachel Pulfer. **Description:** Duckie Brown has been nominated by the Council of Fashion Designers of America as best menswear designer in the U.S. for 2007, along with leaders Calvin Klein and Ralph Lauren. The New York-based company was formed the day after September 11, 2001, but the timing did not hamper its growth. The works and plans of owners Steven Cox and Daniel Silver are described. **Availability:** Online.

18035 ■ *"Despite Higher Prices, Organic Food Gains" in MMR (Vol. 29, February 20, 2012, No. 4, pp. 39)*
Description: Despite higher prices, consumers are buying organic food products at a high rate. Total sales of organic products rose 15 to 20 percent due to shoppers increasing the number and variety of organic products they bought. Statistical data included. **Availability:** Print; Online.

18036 ■ *"Detroit Residential Market Slows; Bright Spots Emerge" in Crain's Detroit Business (Vol. 24, October 6, 2008, No. 40, pp. 11)*
Pub: Crain Communications Inc.
Contact: Barry Asin, President
Ed: Daniel Duggan. **Description:** Discusses the state of the residential real estate market in Detroit; although condominium projects receive the most attention, deals for single-family homes are taking place in greater numbers due to financing issues. Buyers can purchase a single family home with a 3.5 percent down payment compared to 20 percent for some condo deals because of the number of first-time homebuyer programs under the Federal Housing Administration.

18037 ■ *"Developers Poised to Pull Trigers" in Boston Business Journal (Vol. 30, November 12, 2010, No. 42, pp. 1)*
Description: Large residential projects are expected to break ground in Boston, Massachusetts in 2011, as real estate developers expect growth for the industry. Real estate experts expect more than 2,000 rental units to be available by 2011. Information on key real estate projects in Boston is presented. **Availability:** Print; Online.

18038 ■ *"Digital Duplication" in Crain's Cleveland Business (Vol. 28, October 1, 2007, No. 39, pp. 3)*
Pub: Crain Communications Inc.
Contact: K. C. Crain, President
Ed: David Bennett. **Description:** Profile of the business plan of eBlueprint Holdings LLC, a reprographics company that found success by converting customers' paper blueprints to an electronic format; the company plans to expand into other geographic markets by acquiring solid reprographics companies and converting their computer systems so that customers' blueprints can be managed electronically. **Availability:** Online.

18039 ■ *"Discovery Networks" in Brandweek (Vol. 49, April 21, 2008, No. 16, pp. SR9)*
Description: Provides contact information for sales and marketing personnel for the Discovery networks as well as a listing of the station's top programming and an analysis of the current season and the target audience for those programs running in the current season. The networks flagship station returned to the top 10 in 2007, averaging 1.28 million viewers.

18040 ■ *"Do Cool Sh*t: Quit Your Day Job, Start Your Own Business, and Live Happily Ever After"*
Pub: Harper Business
Contact: Hollis Heimbouch, Senior Vice President Publisher
Released: January 20, 2015. **Price:** $16.61, hardcover; $11.97, paperback; $11.49, e-book; $3.13, kindle; $0.05, hardcover(99 used from $0.05); $8, hardcover(44 new from $8.00); $2, paperback(76 used from $2.00); $5.47, paperback(64 new from $5.47). **Description:** Serial social entrepreneur, angel investor, and woman business leader, Miki Agrawal, teaches how to start and run a successful new business. She covers all issues from brainstorming, to raising money to getting press without any connections, and still have time to enjoy life. She created WILD, a farm-to-table pizzeria in New York City and Las Vegas. She also partnered in a children's multimedia company called Super Sprowtz--a story-driven nutrition program for children, and she launched a patented high-tech underware business called THINX. Agrawal also discusses the growth in her businesses. **Availability:** E-book; Print.

18041 ■ *"DocuSign Raises $85 Million for Electronic Signatures" in San Francisco Business Times (Vol. 28, March 7, 2014, No. 33, pp. 6)*
Pub: American City Business Journals, Inc.
Contact: Mike Olivieri, Executive Vice President
Released: Weekly. **Description:** DocuSign, the market leader in electronic signatures, reported that it was able to raise another $85 million in capital. The company is expected to file an initial public offering in 2014 or 2015. CFO, Mike Dinsdale, shares that the firm also wants to expand internationally. **Availability:** Print; Online.

18042 ■ *"Dodge Frets Over Flood of Fast Money" in Globe & Mail (May 2, 2007, pp. B1)*
Ed: Heather Scoffield. **Description:** The concern of governor of Bank of Canada, David Dodge, over the increase in global liquidity due to growth in the business of private equity, is discussed. **Availability:** Online.

18043 ■ *"The Dogs of TSX" in Canadian Business (Vol. 81, Summer 2008, No. 9, pp. 77)*
Description: Table showing the one-year stock performance of the ten highest dividend-yielding stocks on the S&P/TSX 60 Composite Index is presented. This technique is similar to the 'Dogs of the Dow' approach. The idea in this investment strategy is to buy equal amounts of stocks from these companies and selling them a year later, and then repeat the process. **Availability:** Online.

18044 ■ *"Dollar Thrifty Adds Franchises" in Journal Record (December 7, 2010)*
Pub: Dolan Media Newswires
Ed: D. Ray Tuttle. **Description:** Dollar Thrifty Automotive Group Inc. opened 31 franchise locations in 2010 as part of its expansion plan in the U.S. **Availability:** Print; Online.

18045 ■ *"Dollar Tree Store to Open Mid-July in Shelby Mall" in La Crosse Tribune (June 20, 2010)*
Pub: La Crosse Tribune
Contact: Josh Delarosa, Contact
E-mail: josh.delarosa@lee.net
Ed: Steve Cahalan. **Description:** Dollar Tree Inc. plans to open a new store in the location formerly occupied by Family Dollar.

18046 ■ *"Drilling Deep and Flying High" in Barron's (Vol. 88, June 30, 2008, No. 26, pp. 34)*
Pub: Dow Jones & Company Inc.
Contact: Almar Latour, Chief Executive Officer
Ed: Kenneth Rapoza. **Description:** Shares of Petrobras could rise another 25 percent if the three deepwater wells that the company has found proves as lucrative as some expect. Petrobras will become an oil giant if the reserves are proven. **Availability:** Online.

18047 ■ *"Drinking Buddies: S.F.'s New Round of Barkeeps" in San Francisco Business Times (Vol. 28, January 17, 2014, No. 26, pp. 4)*
Pub: American City Business Journals, Inc.
Contact: Mike Olivieri, Executive Vice President
Released: Weekly. **Price:** $4, Introductory 4-week offer(Digital & Print). **Description:** The influx of young workers in San Francisco, California contributed to the growth of the city's bar industry. Ben Bleiman of the tonic Nightlife Group reveals that his bars are doing well because of a rebound in the U.S. economy. Reports also show that smaller groups are now opening multiple drinking establishments across San Francisco. **Availability:** Print; Online.

18048 ■ *Duct Tape Marketing: The World's Most Practical Small Business Marketing Guide*
Pub: Thomas Nelson, Inc.
Contact: Thomas Nelson, Publisher
Ed: John Jantsch. **Released:** 2007. **Description:** Small business owners are provided the tools and tactics necessary to market and grow a business.

18049 ■ "Dunkin' Donuts Franchise Looking Possible for 2011" in Messenger-Inquirer (January 2, 2010)
Description: Dunkin' Donuts has approved expansion of their franchises in the Owensboro, Kentucky region.

18050 ■ "Duro Bag to Expand, Add 130 Jobs" in Business Courier (Vol. 27, August 6, 2010, No. 14, pp. 1)
Pub: Business Courier
Ed: Jon Newberry. Description: Duro Bag Manufacturing Company will expand capacity at its Florence, Kentucky plant and will add around 130 jobs over the next few years. The state of Kentucky has given preliminary approval for up to $1 million in tax incentives over 10 years, tied to the creation of new jobs. The company's investment will include new production and packaging equipment and building improvements. Availability: Print; Online.

18051 ■ "Dynamic Duo: Payouts Rise at General Dynamics, Steel Dynamics" in Barron's (Vol. 88, March 10, 2008, No. 10, pp. 45)
Pub: Dow Jones & Company Inc.
Contact: Almar Latour, Chief Executive Officer
Ed: Shirley A. Lazo. Description: General Dynamics, the world's sixth-largest military contractor, raised its dividend payout by 20.7 percent from 29 cents to 35 cents a share. Steel Dynamics, producer of structural steel and steel bar products, declared a 2-for-1 stock split and raised its quarterly dividend by 33 percent to a split-adjusted 10 cents a share. Availability: Online.

18052 ■ "Editorial: It's Not Perfect; But Illinois a Good Home for Business" in Crain's Chicago Business (Vol. 34, October 24, 2011, No. 42, pp. 18)
Pub: Crain Communications Inc.
Contact: Barry Asin, President
Description: Focusing on all factors that encompass Illinois' business environment, findings show that Illinois is a good place to start and grow a business. The study focused on corporate income tax rates and the fact that talent, access to capital and customers along with transportation connections are among the important factors the state has for small businesses. Availability: Print.

18053 ■ "An Educated Play on China" in Barron's (Vol. 88, June 30, 2008, No. 26, pp. M6)
Pub: Dow Jones & Company Inc.
Contact: Almar Latour, Chief Executive Officer
Ed: Mohammed Hadi. Description: New Oriental Education & Technology Group sells English-language courses to an increasingly competitive Chinese workforce that values education. The shares in this company have been weighed down by worries on the impact of the Beijing Olympics on enrollment and the Sichuan earthquake. These shares could be a great way to get exposure to the long-term growth in China. Availability: Online.

18054 ■ "The Emperor Strikes Back" in Canadian Business (Vol. 80, March 26, 2007, No. 7, pp. 48)
Description: The financial performance of Fairfax Financial Holdings Ltd. in 2006 is presented. The efforts of chief executive Prem Watsa to lead the company towards growth track are also presented. Availability: Online.

18055 ■ "Endeca Gears Up for Likely IPO Bid" in Boston Business Journal (Vol. 31, July 1, 2011, No. 23, pp. 1)
Pub: Boston Business Journal
Contact: Carolyn M. Jones, President
E-mail: cmjones@bizjournals.com
Ed: Kyle Alspach. Released: Weekly. Price: $4. Description: Endeca Inc. is readying itself for its plans to register as a public company. The search engine technology leader is enjoying continued growth with revenue up by 30 percent in 2010 while its expansion trend makes it an unlikely candidate for an acquisition. Availability: Print; Online.

18056 ■ "Energy Boom Spurring Manufacturing Growth" in Pittsburgh Business Times (Vol. 33, May 2, 2014, No. 42, pp. 7)
Pub: American City Business Journals, Inc.
Contact: Mike Olivieri, Executive Vice President
Released: May 02, 2014. Price: $4, introductory 4-week offer(Digital only). Description: The manufacturing and energy technology sectors both showed strong growth, according to the Pittsburgh Technology Council in Pennsylvania. Data shows that the sectors added about 7,000 jobs as a result of the growth in the Marcellus Shale from 2010 to 2012. Availability: Print; Online.

18057 ■ "Energy Consulting Company to Expand" in Austin Business JournalInc. (Vol. 28, November 7, 2008, No. 34, pp. A1)
Pub: Austin Business Journal
Contact: Rachel McGrath, Director
E-mail: rmcgrath@bizjournals.com
Ed: Kate Harrington. Description: CLEAresult Consulting Inc. is planning to increase its workforce and move its headquarters to a larger office. The company has posted 1,000 percent increase in revenues. The company's adoption of best practices and setting of benchmark goals are seen as the reason for its growth. Availability: Print; Online.

18058 ■ "Bartering Takes Businesses Back to Basics" in Buffalo News (July 9, 2010)
Pub: The Buffalo News, Inc.
Contact: Tom Wiley, President
E-mail: twiley@buffnews.com
Ed: Dino Grandoni. Description: Bartering clubs can help small businesses reach new customers and to expand their business. Availability: Print; Online.

18059 ■ Entrepreneurship: A Process Perspective
Ed: Robert A. Baron, Scott A. Shane. Released: 2nd Edition. Description: Entrepreneurial process covering team building, finances, business plan, legal issues, marketing, growth and exit strategies. Availability: Print.

18060 ■ "Equal Weighting's Heavy Allure" in Barron's (Vol. 92, July 23, 2012, No. 30, pp. 27)
Pub: Dow Jones & Company Inc.
Contact: Almar Latour, Chief Executive Officer
Ed: Brendan Conway. Description: Equal weight index exchange-traded funds are attracting investors due to their strong returns. This strategy gives investors a greater exposure to mid-capitalization companies and could provide strong returns over longer stretches. Availability: Online.

18061 ■ "Equity Crowdfunding Platform Initial Crowd Offering, Inc. Closes Equity Financing with Third-Party Investor" in GlobeNewswire (July 18, 2012)
Description: Initial Crowd Offering Inc. closed third-party equity financing round hat provided capital to finish development of its equity crowdfunding portal to the Website. A private angel investor provided development costs to promote the firm's marketing program. Discussion on equity crowdfunding is included. Availability: Print; PDF; Online.

18062 ■ "eResearch Issues Initiating Report on Aldershot Resources Ltd." in Marketwired (May 14, 2007)
Pub: Comtex News Network Inc.
Contact: Kan Devnani, President
Description: Overview of Bob Weir and Michael Wood's Initiating Report on Aldershot Resources Ltd., a junior Canadian-based uranium exploration company with prospective projects in Canada, Zambia, Australia, and a base metals project in Chile. Availability: Print; Online.

18063 ■ "Essential Releases Record First Quarter Results" in Marketwired (May 14, 2007)
Pub: Comtex News Network Inc.
Contact: Kan Devnani, President
Description: The first quarter of 2007 saw record financial performance despite numerous challenges for Essential Energy Services Trust. Statistical data included. Availability: Print; Online.

18064 ■ "Ex-Medical Student Stages Career In Event Planning: Barcelona Owner Makes Inroads with Luxury Car Dealerships" in Los Angeles Business Journal (Vol. 34, June 18, 2012, No. 25, pp. 10)
Pub: CBJ L.P.
Contact: Terri Cunningham, Contact
Description: Barcelona Enterprises started as a company designing menus for restaurants, organizing food shows, to planning receptions for luxury car dealers. The fim will be launching the first Las Vegas Chocolate Festival & Pastry Show in July 2012. Presently, the company runs 24 wine and food festivals, organizes events for an upscale dog shampoo maker, and sports car dealerships. Availability: Print; Online.

18065 ■ Exceptional Service, Exceptional Profit: The Secrets of Building a Five-Star Customer Service Organization
Pub: HarperCollins Leadership
Contact: Donald Miller, Chief Executive Officer
Ed: Leonardo Inghilleri, Micah Solomon. Released: April 14, 2010. Price: $19.99, paperback. Description: Team of insiders share exclusive knowledge of the loyalty-building techniques pioneered by the world's most successful service leaders, including brick-and-mortar stars such as The Ritz-Carlton and Lexus and online success stories such as Netflix and CD Baby. Availability: E-book; Print.

18066 ■ "Executive Decision: To Make Inroads Against RIM, Palm Steals Its Strategy" in Globe & Mail (March 25, 2006, pp. B3)
Ed: Simon Avery. Description: The Palm Inc., global leader in portable device manufacturing, is looking forward to improve its sales of Palm Treos, a wireless portable device that connects to internet and email. Palm is also planning to build partnerships, under the efficient management of Michael Moskowitz, general manager and vice-president of Palm Inc., with the other companies to increase the sales of its wireless devices.

18067 ■ "Expanding Middleby's Food Processing Biz" in Crain's Chicago Business (Vol. 31, April 21, 2008, No. 16, pp. 6)
Pub: Crain Communications Inc.
Contact: Barry Asin, President
Ed: David Sterrett. Description: Profile of the executive vice-president of the food processing company, Middleby Corp, whose business plan is to develop new products, begin looking for acquisitions and simplify operations in order to expand the firm. Availability: Online.

18068 ■ "Eyes to the Sky" in Canadian Business (Vol. 80, March 26, 2007, No. 7, pp. 33)
Description: The growth and prices of condominium market in the Canada are analyzed. Availability: Online.

18069 ■ The Facebook Effect: The Inside Story of the Company That Is Connecting the World
Ed: David Kirkpatrick. Released: 2011. Price: $18, paperback; $13.99, e-book. Description: There's never been a Website like Facebook: more than 350 million people have accounts, and if the growth rate continues, by 2013 every Internet user worldwide will have his or her own page. No one's had more access to the inner workings of the phenomenon than Kirkpatrick, a senior tech writer at Fortune magazine. Written with the full cooperation of founder Mark

Zuckerberg, the book follows the company from its genesis in a Harvard dorm room through its successes over Friendster and MySpace, the expansion of the user base, and Zuckerberg's refusal to sell. **Availability:** E-book; Print.

18070 ■ *"Faces: Q&A with Kevin Huyck, Chef/Owner of R.A. MacSammy's Food Truck Specializing in Mac and Cheese"* in *Saint Paul Pioneer Press (March 28, 2012)*
Ed: Kathie Jenkins. **Description:** Profile of 48 year old Kevin Huyck, chef and owner of his R.A. MacSammy food truck. Huyck specializes in serving a variety of macaroni and cheese dishes. He wanted to own his own restaurant but did not have the capital for such an investment at the time and hopes to expand with either another food truck or possibly a restaurant that features mac and cheese dishes. **Availability:** Online.

18071 ■ *"Fast-Growing Companies Stepped Up Pace in 2011"* in *Sacramento Business Journal (Vol. 29, July 6, 2012, No. 19, pp. 1)*
Pub: Baltimore Business Journal
Contact: Rhonda Pringle, President
E-mail: rpringle@bizjournals.com
Description: The growth of Sacramento, California-based businesses is seen as a sign of strong economic recovery, as reflected in this publication's annual list has revealed. Stuart James Construction Inc. got the top spot. Businesses registered two-year growth rates ranging from 29 to 632 percent. **Availability:** Print; Online.

18072 ■ *Faster Cheaper Better*
Released: December 28, 2010. **Price:** $27.50, hardcover. **Description:** Nine levels for transforming work in order to achieve business growth are outlined. The book helps small business compete against the low-wage countries. **Availability:** E-book; Print.

18073 ■ *"Fifth Third Spinoff Eyes More Space"* in *Business Courier (Vol. 27, July 16, 2010, No. 11, pp. 1)*
Pub: Business Courier
Ed: Dan Monk, Steve Watkins. **Description:** Electronic-funds transfer company Fifth Third Solutions (FTPS), a spinoff of Fifth Third Bancorp, is seeking as much as 200,000 square feet of new office space in Ohio. The bank's sale of 51 percent ownership stake to Boston-based Advent International Corporation has paved the way for the growth of FTPS. How real estate brokers' plans have responded to FTPS' growth mode is discussed. **Availability:** Print; Online.

18074 ■ *"The File On..Jenne Distributors"* in *Crain's Cleveland Business (Vol. 28, October 8, 2007, No. 40, pp. 26)*
Pub: Crain Communications Inc.
Contact: K. C. Crain, President
Ed: Kimberly Bonvissuto. **Description:** Overview of the telecommunications equipment company, Jenne Distributors, a firm that is projecting more than $125 million in revenue for 2007. **Availability:** Online.

18075 ■ *"Filling the Gap"* in *Canadian Business (Vol. 80, March 12, 2007, No. 6, pp. 62)*
Ed: Andrew Wahl. **Released:** October 09, 2016. **Description:** The chief executive officer of GAP, Bruce Poon Tip, shares his experience and efforts in the growth of the company to a leading position in Canada. **Availability:** Print; Online.

18076 ■ *"Finding the Right Resources to Get Started Overseas"* in *Pittsburgh Business Times (Vol. 33, January 3, 2014, No. 25, pp. 4)*
Pub: American City Business Journals, Inc.
Contact: Mike Olivieri, Executive Vice President
Description: Pittsburgh, Pennsylvania-based companies can develop relationships abroad and take advantage of the market opportunity to expand. Companies are unaware of the many helpful agencies, organizations and Websites that help them become international. Tips for developing relationships overseas are presented. **Availability:** Online.

18077 ■ *"Finding a Way to Continue Growing"* in *Green Industry Pro (Vol. 23, March 2011, No. 3, pp. 31)*
Ed: Gregg Wartgow. **Description:** Profile of Brett Lemcke, VP of R.M. Landscape located in Rochester, New York. Lemcke tells how his Landscape Industry Certified credentials helped him to grow his business and beat out his competition. **Availability:** Online.

18078 ■ *"Firms Start Increasing their Space"* in *Philadelphia Business Journal (Vol. 31, March 23, 2012, No. 6, pp. 1)*
Pub: Baltimore Business Journal
Contact: Rhonda Pringle, President
E-mail: rpringle@bizjournals.com
Description: Office occupancies in Philadelphia, Pennsylvania have grown in 2012. The economic recovery is seen to drive this trend. Comments from office/property management brokers are also included. **Availability:** Print; Online.

18079 ■ *"FirstMerit's Top Executive Turns Around Credit Quality"* in *Crain's Cleveland Business (Vol. 28, October 15, 2007, No. 41, pp. 3)*
Pub: Crain Communications Inc.
Contact: K. C. Crain, President
Ed: Shawn A. Turner. **Description:** Discusses the ways in which chairman and CEO Paul Greig has been able to improve FirstMerit Corp.'s credit quality and profit margin. Strategies included selling more than $70 million in bad loans, hiring a new chief credit officer and redirecting its focus on cross-selling its wealth and investment services to its commercial customers. Statistical data included. **Availability:** Online.

18080 ■ *"Flurry of Activity from Restaurant Groups as Industry Strengthens"* in *Wichita Business Journal (Vol. 27, February 17, 2012, No. 7, pp. 1)*
Pub: Baltimore Business Journal
Contact: Rhonda Pringle, President
E-mail: rpringle@bizjournals.com
Description: Atlanta, Georgia-based Chick-fil-A chain is set to open two restaurants in Wichita, Kansas and those additions were highly anticipated. However, there were other local management groups and franchisees that are investing on new buildings and refurbishing stores. Insights on the increasing restaurant constructions are also given. **Availability:** Print; Online.

18081 ■ *"Flying Colors for All American Label"* in *Memphis Business Journal (Vol. 34, June 1, 2012, No. 7, pp. 1)*
Pub: Baltimore Business Journal
Contact: Rhonda Pringle, President
E-mail: rpringle@bizjournals.com
Ed: Michael Sheffield. **Description:** All American Label has moved to a new location and reported a 20 percent increase in earnings. **Availability:** Print; Online.

18082 ■ *"Food Trucks Savor Rebirth in City"* in *Providence Business News (Vol. 27, April 16, 2012, No. 2, pp. 1)*
Description: Providence, Rhode Island has been experiencing the growth of the food truck business as the trucks and their devoted followers become regular fixtures in the city. Food trucks have a strong presence in the West Coast and have proliferated across the U.S. in recent years. Insights into Providence's food truck community are also given. **Availability:** Online.

18083 ■ *"For Gilead, Growth Beyond AIDS"* in *Barron's (Vol. 88, June 30, 2008, No. 26, pp. 18)*
Pub: Dow Jones & Company Inc.
Contact: Almar Latour, Chief Executive Officer
Ed: Jay Palmer. **Description:** First-quarter 2008 revenue for Gilead Sciences grew by 22 percent and an earnings gain of 19 percent thanks to their HIV-treatment drugs that comprised over two-thirds of the company's sales in 2007. An analyst has a 12-month target from June, 2008 of 65 per share. The factors behind the company's prospects are also discussed. **Availability:** Online.

18084 ■ *"Ford: Down, Not Out, and Still a Buy"* in *Barron's (Vol. 92, July 23, 2012, No. 30, pp. 14)*
Pub: Dow Jones & Company Inc.
Contact: Almar Latour, Chief Executive Officer
Ed: Vito J. Racanelli. **Description:** Stocks of Ford Motor Company could gain value as the company continues to improve its finances despite fears of slower global economic growth. The company's stock prices could double from $9.35 per share within three years. **Availability:** Online.

18085 ■ *"ForeSee Finds Satisfaction On Web Sites, Bottom Line"* in *Crain's Detroit Business (Vol. 24, February 25, 2008, No. 8, pp. 3)*
Pub: Crain Communications Inc.
Contact: Barry Asin, President
Ed: Tom Henderson. **Description:** Ann Arbor-based ForeSee Results Inc. evaluates user satisfaction on Web sites. The company expects to see an increase of 40 percent in revenue for 2008 with plans to expand to London, Germany, Italy and France by the end of 2009.

18086 ■ *"Forest Park Medical Center to Double Operations"* in *Dallas Business Journal (Vol. 35, April 13, 2012, No. 31, pp. 1)*
Pub: Baltimore Business Journal
Contact: Rhonda Pringle, President
E-mail: rpringle@bizjournals.com
Description: Dallas, Texas-based Neal Richards Group launched a growth plan for the Forest Park Medical Center System called '12 by 12' that will more than double its hospital count in the next two years. The group wants to have 12 Forest Park facilities open or in various levels of development by the end of 2012. Forest Park is a physician-owned system. **Availability:** Print; Online.

18087 ■ *"Forget the Pretzels and Soda, Shoppers Are Scooping Up Flowers and Salads at Convenience Stores"* in *CNBC.com (April 6, 2019)*
URL(s): www.cnbc.com/2019/04/05/convenience-s tores-see-record-sales-as-shoppers-buy-more-fresh -food.html
Ed: Maggie Fitzgerald. **Released:** April 06, 2019. **Description:** Convenience stores keep experiencing record sales and a lot of it has to do with the expanded selection of items they are selling. Instead of just chips and pop, these stores have started to sell fruits, vegetables, and healthier options for pre-made food. **Availability:** Online.

18088 ■ *"Formulating Policy With a Parallel Organization"* in *Strategy & Leadership (Vol. 38, September-October 2010, No. 5, pp. 33-38)*
Pub: Emerald Inc.
Ed: Dale E. Zand, Thomas F. Hawk. **Description:** A study analyzes a case to examine the parallel organization concept and its successful implementation by a CEO to integrate independent divisions of a firm. Findings reveal that the implementation of the parallel organization improved the policy formulation, strategic planning profitability of the firm while also better integrating its independent divisions.

18089 ■ *"Free Fall"* in *Canadian Business (Vol. 79, September 11, 2006, No. 18, pp. 28)*
Description: Second quarter results of Imax Corp are reviewed. The company's performance and its future prospects are also presented. **Availability:** Print; Online.

18090 ■ *"From Craft Biz To Wholesale Giant"* in *Women Entrepreneur (January 19, 2009)*
Description: Advice is given on how to turn a small craft business into a full-time venture; tips to help one transition from a part-time designer to a full-time wholesaler and brand are also included.

18091 ■ *"From Fat to Fit"* in *Canadian Business* (Vol. 79, September 22, 2006, No. 19, pp. 100)
Ed: Graham Scott. **Description:** The increase in physical fitness clubs across Canada is discussed. **Availability:** Online.

18092 ■ *"From Malls to Steel Plants"* in *Crain's Chicago Business* (Vol. 31, April 28, 2008, No. 17, pp. 30)
Pub: Crain Communications Inc.
Contact: Barry Asin, President
Ed: Samantha Stainburn. **Description:** Profile of the company Graycor Inc. which started out as a sandblasting and concrete-breaking firm but has grown into four businesses due to innovation and acquisitions. Graycor's businesses include: Graycor Industrial Constructors Inc., which builds and renovates power plants and steel mills; Graycor Construction Co., which erects stores, medical centers and office buildings; Graycor Blasting Co., which uses explosives and blasts tunnels for industrial cleaning, and Graycor International Inc., which provides construction services in Mexico. **Availability:** Online.

18093 ■ *"Frozen Dessert Year in Review.."* in *Ice Cream Reporter* (Vol. 22, January 20, 2009, No. 2, pp. 1)
Description: Falling economy caused the closing of several ice cream plants across the U.S. in 2008. Top stories of interest to the industry are presented. **Availability:** Print; Online.

18094 ■ *"Funeral Directors Get Creative As Boomers Near Great Beyond"* in *Advertising Age* (Vol. 79, October 13, 2008, No. 38, pp. 30)
Pub: Crain Communications, Inc.
Contact: Jessica Botos, Manager, Marketing
E-mail: jessica.botos@crainsnewyork.com
Ed: Lenore Skenazy. **Description:** Despite the downturn in the economy, the funeral business is thriving due to the number of baby boomers who realize the importance of making preparations for their death. Marketers are getting creative in their approach and many companies have taken into consideration the need for a more environmental friendly way to dispose of bodies and thus have created innovative businesses that reflect this need. **Availability:** Online.

18095 ■ *"Funky Footwear: Walk This Way"* in *Barron's* (Vol. 90, August 23, 2010, No. 34, pp. 13)
Pub: Barron's Editorial & Corporate Headquarters
Ed: Christopher C. Williams. **Description:** Crocs and Skechers are selling very popular shoes and sales show no signs of winding down. The shares of both companies are attractively prices. **Availability:** Online.

18096 ■ *"The Game of Operation"* in *Crain's Chicago Business* (Vol. 31, April 28, 2008, No. 17, pp. 26)
Pub: Crain Communications Inc.
Contact: Barry Asin, President
Ed: Samantha Stainburn. **Description:** Revenue at Medline Industries Inc., a manufacturer of medical products, has risen 12 percent a year since 1976, reaching $2.81 billion last year. Growth at the company is due to new and increasingly sophisticated operations by surgeons which brings about the need for more specialized tools. **Availability:** Online.

18097 ■ *"GE Milestone: 1,000th Wind Turbine Installed in Canada"* in *CNW Group* (October 4, 2011)
Pub: CNW Group Ltd.
Description: GE installed its 1,000th wind turbine in Canada at Cartier Wind Energy's Gros Morne project in the Gaspesie Region of Quebec, Canada. As Canada continues to expand its use of wind energy, GE plans to have over 1,100 wind turbines installed in the nation by the end of 2011. **Availability:** Online.

18098 ■ *"Georgia Looking to Expand Film Industry Tax Credits"* in *Atlanta Business Chronicle* (June 27, 2014, pp. 3A)
Pub: American City Business Journals, Inc.
Contact: Mike Olivieri, Executive Vice President
Released: Weekly. **Price:** $4, introductory 4-week offer(Digital only). **Description:** The lawmakers of the State of Georgia are looking to expand film tax incentives at a time when many states are eliminating or scaling back their film industry tax credits. A recently created legislative study committee will begin meeting to consider proposals to expand Georgia's film tax credit program to encourage an already rapidly growing industry. **Availability:** Print; Online.

18099 ■ *Get Your Business to Work!: 7 Steps to Earning More, Working Less and Living the Life You Want*
Pub: BenBella Books Inc.
Contact: Aida Herrera, Director
E-mail: aida@benbellabooks.com
Ed: George Hedley. **Released:** May 01, 2014. **Price:** $17.95, paperback; $9.99, E-Book (EPUB). **Description:** Complete step-by-step guide for the small business owner to realize profits, wealth and freedom. **Availability:** E-book; Print.

18100 ■ *"Global Economy: The World Tomorrow"* in *Canadian Business* (Vol. 81, December 19, 2007, No. 1, pp. 35)
Pub: Rogers Media Inc.
Contact: Neil Spivak, Chief Executive Officer
Ed: Zena Olijnyk. **Description:** Global economy is predicted to be in a difficult period as analysts expect a slowdown in economic growth. Germany's Deutsche Bank wrote in a report about 'growth recession' that the chances of the world growth falling below two percent being one in three. Forecasts on other global economic aspects are explored. **Availability:** Online.

18101 ■ *"Global Organic Food"* in *Investment Weekly News* (January 21, 2012, pp. 272)
Description: Research and Markets has added 'Global Organic Food' to its reporting of industry profiles. The report will offer top-line qualitative and quantitative summary information including, market size, description of leading players with key financial metrics and analysis of competitive pressures within the market covering the global organic food market. Market size and segmentation data, textual and graphical analysis of market growth trends, leading companies and macroeconomic information will be provided. **Availability:** Online.

18102 ■ *"The Globe: A Cautionary Tale for Emerging Market Giants"* in *Harvard Business Review* (Vol. 88, September 2010, No. 9, pp. 99)
Pub: Harvard Business Publishing
Contact: Diane Belcher, Managing Director
Ed: J. Stewart Black, Allen J. Morrison. **Price:** $8.95. **Description:** Key factors that negatively affected Japan corporate growth and organizational effectiveness include: devotion to established path, isolated domestic markets, homogenous executive teams, and a non-contentious labor force. Solutions include leadership development programs, multicultural input, and cross-cultural training. **Availability:** Online; PDF.

18103 ■ *"Golden Spoon Accelerates Expansion Here and Abroad"* in *Ice Cream Reporter* (Vol. 22, December 20, 2008, No. 1, pp. 2)
Description: Golden Spoon frozen yogurt franchise chain is developing 35 more locations in the Phoenix, Arizona area along with plans to open a store in Japan. **Availability:** Print; Online.

18104 ■ *"A Good Sign for Commercial Real Estate?"* in *Austin Business JournalInc.* (Vol. 29, December 18, 2009, No. 41, pp. 1)
Pub: Austin Business Journal
Contact: Rachel McGrath, Director
E-mail: rmcgrath@bizjournals.com
Ed: Kate Harrington. **Description:** Factors that could contribute to the reemergence of the commercial mortgage-backed securities market in Texas are discussed. These securities can potentially boost the commercial real estate market statewide as well as nationwide. Commercial mortgage-backed securities origination in 2009 is worth less that $1 billion, compared with $238 billion in 2008. **Availability:** Online.

18105 ■ *"Got Skills? Think Manufacturing"* in *Occupational Outlook Quarterly* (Vol. 58, Summer 2014, No. 2, pp. 28)
Pub: Government Publishing Office
Contact: Hugh Nathanial Halpern, Director
Released: June 22, 2014. **Description:** According to the U.S. Bureau of Labor Statistics, 264,000 job openings in manufacturing were reported in March 2014. Employers are finding it difficult to fill jobs for machinists and maintenance technicians, among other skilled trades. Manufacturers are also looking for welders, but also for workers outside of production, including biomedical engineers, dispatchers, and truck drivers. An overview of current manufacturing issues and statistics is included. **Availability:** Print; Online.

18106 ■ *"Graduates to the TSX in 2008"* in *Canadian Business* (Vol. 81, Summer 2008, No. 9, pp. 79)
Description: Table showing the market capitalization and stock performance of the companies that jumped to the TSX Venture Exchange is presented. The 17 companies that made the leap to the list will have an easier time raising capital, although leeway must be made in investing since they are still new businesses.

18107 ■ *"Grand Action Makes Grand Changes in Grand Rapids"* in *Crain's Detroit Business* (Vol. 25, June 1, 2009, No. 22, pp. M012)
Pub: Crain Communications Inc.
Contact: Barry Asin, President
Ed: Amy Lane. **Description:** Businessman Dick DeVos believes that governments are not always the best to lead certain initiatives. That's why, in 1991, he gathered 50 west Michigan community leaders and volunteers to look consider the construction of an arena and expanding or renovating local convention operations. Grand Action has undertaken four major projects in the city. **Availability:** Online.

18108 ■ *"Green Clean Machine"* in *Small Business Opportunities* (Winter 2010)
Pub: Harris Publishing, Inc.
Contact: Janet Chase, Contact
Description: Eco-friendly maid franchise plans to grow its $62 million sales base. Profile of Maid Brigade, a green-cleaning franchise is planning to expand across the country. **Availability:** Print; Online.

18109 ■ *"Green Collar: Green Buildings Support Job Creation, Workforce Transformation and Economic Recovery"* in *Environmental Design and Construction* (Vol. 15, July 2012, No. 7, pp. 31)
Pub: BNP Media
Contact: Harper Henderson, Owner Co-Chief Executive Officer
Ed: Maggie Comstock. **Description:** Despite construction being at an all-time low, green building construction has maintained its hold on nonresidential buildings. It has even shown growth in some sectors and accounts for over one-third of all nonresidential design and construction jobs and is expected to show further growth through 2014. Statistical details included.

18110 ■ *"Green Light"* in *The Business Journal-Portland* (Vol. 25, July 11, 2008, No. 18, pp. 1)
Description: Ecos Consulting, a sustainability consulting company based in Portland, Oregon, is seeing a boost in revenue as more businesses turn to sustainable practices. The company's revenue

rose by 50 percent in 2007 and employees increased from 57 to 150. Other details about Ecos' growth are discussed. **Availability:** Print; Online.

18111 ■ **Greening Your Small Business: How to Improve Your Bottom Line, Grow Your Brand, Satisfy Your Customers and Save the Planet**
Price: $19.95. **Description:** A definitive resource for anyone who wants their small business to be cutting-edge, competitive, profitable, and eco-conscious. Stories from small business owners address every aspect of going green, from basics such as recycling waste, energy efficiency, and reducing information technology footprint, to more in-depth concerns such as green marketing and communications, green business travel, and green employee benefits.

18112 ■ *"Greenlight's Mission: Poach California"* **in Business Journal Portland (Vol. 26, December 11, 2009, No. 40, pp. 1)**
Pub: Portland Business Journal
Contact: Andy Giegerich, Managing Editor
E-mail: agiegerich@bizjournals.com
Ed: Andy Giegerich. **Description:** Leaders of Greenlight Greater Portland, a privately funded economic development organization, will visit California five times in 2010 in an attempt to lure California businesses to expand or relocate in Oregon. **Availability:** Print; Online.

18113 ■ *"Groomers Eye Profit Growth Through Services"* **in Pet Product News (Vol. 64, December 2010, No. 12, pp. 26)**
Ed: Kathleen M. Mangan. **Description:** Pet groomers can successfully offer add-on services by taking into account insider customer knowledge, store image, and financial analysis in the decision-making process. Many pet groomers have decided to add services such as spa treatments and training due to a slump in the bathing and grooming business. How some pet groomers gained profitability through add-on services is explored. **Availability:** Online.

18114 ■ *"Grounds for Success"* **in Canadian Business (Vol. 87, July 2014, No. 7, pp. 73)**
Description: ECS Coffee Inc. has continued to evolve its business of selling single-serve brewing systems and market changes and growing competitors. The company has seen growth of 1,026 percent from 2008 to 2013, earning it the top 69 spot in the 2014 Profit ranking of fastest growing companies in Canada. **Availability:** Online.

18115 ■ **The Growing Business Handbook: Inspiration and Advice from Successful Entrepreneurs and Fast Growing UK Companies**
Pub: Kogan Page Ltd.
Contact: Christina Lindelholm, Manager, Sales
Ed: Adam Jolly. **Released:** 17th edition. **Price:** $90, hardback; $90, e-book. **Description:** Tips for growing and running a successful business are covered, focusing on senior managers in middle market and SME companies. **Availability:** E-book; Print.

18116 ■ *"A Growing Concern"* **in Canadian Business (Vol. 79, October 9, 2006, No. 20, pp. 90)**
Description: With rich dividends being harvested by companies producing ethanol, after ethanol became a petrol additive, is discussed. **Availability:** Online.

18117 ■ *"A Growing Dilemma"* **in Crain's Cleveland Business (Vol. 28, October 8, 2007, No. 40, pp. 19)**
Pub: Crain Communications Inc.
Contact: K. C. Crain, President
Ed: Kimberly Bonvissuto. **Description:** Discusses small business owners who often have to grapple with the decision on whether or not to expand their operations and the importance of a business plan which may help owners with that decision. **Availability:** Online.

18118 ■ *"Growing Field"* **in Crain's Detroit Business (Vol. 26, January 11, 2010, No. 2, pp. 3)**
Pub: Crain Communications Inc.
Contact: Barry Asin, President
Description: Detroit's TechTown was awarded a combination loan and grant of $4.1 million from the U.S. Department of Housing and Urban Development to build a 15,000-square-foot stem cell center, a collection of laboratories that will be available to both for-profit companies and university researchers. **Availability:** Online.

18119 ■ *"Growing Grocer"* **in Washington Business Journal (Vol. 32, March 21, 2014, No. 49, pp. 6)**
Pub: American City Business Journals, Inc.
Contact: Mike Olivieri, Executive Vice President
Description: Scott Allhouse, the regional president of Whole Foods Markets for the Mid-Atlantic region, discusses the grocer's expansion plans in the Washington DC area. The company wants to open a store at the Walter Reed redevelopment and plans to open two more stores in Washington DC. **Availability:** Online.

18120 ■ *"Growth Back on CIBC's Agenda"* **in Globe & Mail (March 3, 2006, pp. B1)**
Ed: Sinclair Stewart. **Description:** The details on business growth of Canadian Imperial Bank of Commerce, which posted $547 million profit for first quarter 2006, are presented. **Availability:** Online.

18121 ■ *"Growth at E Solutions Part of 'Opportunistic' Data Center Market"* **in Tampa Bay Business Journal (Vol. 30, January 29, 2010, No. 6, pp. 1)**
Pub: Tampa Bay Business Journal
Contact: Ian Anderson, President
E-mail: ianderson@bizjournals.com
Ed: Michael Hinman. **Description:** E Solutions Corporation is experiencing growth amid the economic downturn, with its Park Tower data center occupancy in Tampa Florida expanding from 14,000 square feet to 20,000 square feet. Details on the increased operations fueled by demand for information storage and management services offered by the company are discussed. **Availability:** Print; Online.

18122 ■ *"The Growth Opportunity That Lies Next Door: How Will the Logic of Globalization Change for Corporations from Countries such as India, China, Indonesia, Brazil, and Turkey if the Growth Opportunities..."* **in (Vol. 90, July-August 2012, No. 7-8, pp. 141)**
Pub: Harvard Business Review Press
Contact: Moderna V. Pfizer, Contact
Ed: Geoffrey G. Jones. **Description:** Brazilian company Natura Cosmeticos found that focusing on expanding into the emerging markets represented by neighboring countries, rather than on well-established markets in developed nations, offered more opportunities and greater rewards.

18123 ■ **Guerrilla Marketing Goes Green: Winning Strategies to Improve Your Profits and Your Planet**
Pub: John Wiley & Sons, Inc.
Contact: Christina Van Tassell, Executive Vice President Chief Financial Officer
Ed: Jay Conrad Levinson, Shel Horowitz, Jay Conrad Levinson. **Released:** 2010. **Description:** The latest tips on green marketing and sustainable business strategies are shared. **Availability:** E-book; Print; Electronic publishing; Online.

18124 ■ *"Habitat, Home Depot Expand Building Program"* **in Contractor (Vol. 56, September 2009, No. 9, pp. 16)**
Description: Habitat for Humanity International and The Home Depot Foundation are planning to expand their Partners in Sustainable Building program. The program will provide funds to help Habitat affiliates build 5,000 homes. Comments from executives are also included. **Availability:** Print; Online.

18125 ■ *"Halls Give Hospital Drive $11 Million Infusion"* **in The Business Journal-Serving Metropolitan Kansas City (Vol. 26, July 18, 2008)**
Description: Don Hall, chairman of Hallmark Cards Inc., and eight family members have announced that they will give $11 million to Children's Mercy Hospitals and Clinics for its $800 million expansion plan. Hall Family Foundation president Bill Hall that contributions such as that for Children's Mercy reflect the charitable interests of the foundation's board and founders. The possible impacts of the Hall's donation are analyzed.

18126 ■ *"Happy Trails: RV Franchiser Gives Road Traveling Enthusiasts a Lift"* **in Black Enterprise (Vol. 38, July 2008, No. 12, pp. 47)**
Pub: Earl G. Graves Ltd.
Contact: Earl Graves, Jr., President
Ed: Tamara E. Holmes. **Description:** Overview of Bates International Motor Home Rental Systems Inc., a growing franchise that gives RV owners the chance to rent out their big-ticket purchases to others when they are not using them; Sandra Williams Bate launched the company as a franchise in July 1997 and now has a fleet of 30 franchises across the country. She expects the company to reach 2.2 million for 2008 due to a marketing initiative that will expand the company's presence.

18127 ■ *"Hard Times Are 'In the Rearview Mirror' for Local Construction Industry"* **in San Antonio Business Journal (Vol. 28, March 14, 2014, No. 5, pp. 10)**
Pub: American City Business Journals, Inc.
Contact: Mike Olivieri, Executive Vice President
Released: March 14, 2014. **Price:** $4, Introductory 4-Week Offer(Digital & Print). **Description:** Analysts believe that San Antonio, Texas' construction industry is back on a growth track. Reports show that the sector had its second-best year in 2013, when it generated $1.14 billion worth of work. The public sector is widely seen as a prime market for the city's contractors. **Availability:** Print; Online.

18128 ■ *"Harleysville Eyes Growth After Nationwide Deal"* **in Philadelphia Business Journal (Vol. 30, October 7, 2011, No. 34, pp. 1)**
Pub: Philadelphia Business Journal
Contact: Sierra Quinn, Director
E-mail: squinn@bizjournals.com
Ed: Jeff Blumenthal. **Price:** $4, introductory 4-week offer(Digital & Print). **Description:** Harleysville Group announced growth plans after the company was sold to Columbus, Ohio-based Nationwide Mutual Insurance Company for about $1.63 billion. Nationwide gained an independent agency platform in 32 states with the Harleysville deal. **Availability:** Print; Online.

18129 ■ *"Hayes Lemmerz Reports Some Good News Despite Losses"* **in Crain's Detroit Business (Vol. 24, April 14, 2008, No. 15, pp. 4)**
Pub: Crain Communications Inc.
Contact: Barry Asin, President
Ed: Nancy Kaffer. **Description:** Hayes Lemmerz International Inc., a wheel manufacturer from Northville that has reported a positive free cash flow for the first time in years, a narrowed net loss in the fourth quarter and significant restructuring of the company's debt. **Availability:** Print; Online.

18130 ■ *"Healing Power from Medical Waste"* **in Memphis Business Journal (Vol. 33, March 30, 2012, No. 51, pp. 1)**
Pub: Baltimore Business Journal
Contact: Rhonda Pringle, President
E-mail: rpringle@bizjournals.com
Description: Tennessee-based BioD LLC has been using amniotic fluid in placenta from cesarian section births, which was considered as biomedical waste, to make various compounds that are used to develop stem cell-based healing products. BioD has sales of $3 million in 2011 and it expects sales of $6 million in 2012. **Availability:** Print; Online.

18131 ■ "Health Centers Plan Expansion: $3M from D.C. Expected; Uninsured a Target" in Crain's Detroit Business (Vol. 25, June 15, 2009, No. 24, pp. 3)
Pub: Crain Communications Inc.
Contact: Barry Asin, President

Ed: Jay Greene. **Description:** Detroit has five federally qualified health centers that plan to receive over $3 million in federal stimulus money that will be used to expand projects that will care for uninsured patients. **Availability:** Print; Online.

18132 ■ "Healthy Dose of New Vitality" in Business Courier (Vol. 24, February 28, 2008, No. 47, pp. 1)
Pub: American City Business Journals, Inc.
Contact: Mike Olivieri, Executive Vice President

Ed: Dan Monk. **Description:** Healthy Advice plans to become a leading consumer brand and expand to pharmacies and hospitals. The growth opportunities for healthy Advice are discussed. **Availability:** Online.

18133 ■ "Helping Customers Fight Pet Waste" in Pet Product News (Vol. 64, November 2010, No. 11, pp. 52)
Ed: Sandy Robins. **Description:** Pet cleaning products manufacturers have been enjoying high sales figures by paying attention to changing pet ownership trends and environmental awareness. Meanwhile, the inclusion of user-friendly features in these products has also been boosted by the social role of pets and the media attention to pet waste. How manufacturers have been responding to this demand is explored. **Availability:** Print; Online.

18134 ■ "High Energy: Gaurdie Banister Joins Aera As President and CEO" in Black Enterprise (Vol. 38, July 2008, No. 12, pp. 30)
Pub: Earl G. Graves Ltd.
Contact: Earl Graves, Jr., President

Ed: Brenda Porter. **Description:** Gaurdie Banister Jr. has been appointed president and CEO of Aera Energy L.L.C., becoming one of the first African Americans in the nation to run a major energy corporation. His plans for the firm include utilizing new, sophisticated technologies in order to unlock the 3-1/2 billion barrels of resources the company has on their books in a safe and environmentally friendly way. He also hopes to increase production and maintain cost leadership.

18135 ■ "The High-Intensity Entrepreneur" in Harvard Business Review (Vol. 88, September 2010, No. 9, pp. 74)
Pub: Harvard Business Publishing
Contact: Diane Belcher, Managing Director

Ed: Anne S. Habiby, Deirdre M. Coyle, Jr. **Price:** $8.95, PDF. **Description:** Examination of the role of small companies in promoting global economic growth is presented. Discussion includes identifying entrepreneurial capability. **Availability:** Online; PDF.

18136 ■ "High Touch Expands, Purchases Dallas Firms" in Wichita Business Journal (Vol. 27, February 3, 2012, No. 5, pp. 1)
Pub: Baltimore Business Journal
Contact: Rhonda Pringle, President
E-mail: rpringle@bizjournals.com

Description: Wichita, Kansas-based High Touch Inc. has finalized the acquisitions of the Dallas, Texas-based UniCom Data and Dallas Data Center, after a similar purchase of Newbase LLC at the start of the year. High Touch believes the acquisitions helped the company further expand its regional presence and services. **Availability:** Print; Online.

18137 ■ "Hollander 95 Business Park Project Getting Bigger" in Baltimore Business Journal (Vol. 29, September 23, 2011, No. 20, pp. 1)
Pub: Boston Business Journal
Contact: Carolyn M. Jones, President
E-mail: cmjones@bizjournals.com

Ed: Gary Haber. **Description:** Hollander 95 Business Park is in for a huge change as its new owners plan a $50 million expansion which calls for building as many as eight more buildings or a total of more than 500,000 square feed. FRP Development bought the site for $4.35 million at a foreclosure sale in July 2010 and is now seeking city approval for an Industrial Planned Unit Development designation. **Availability:** Online.

18138 ■ "Home Health Franchise Expands Across S. Fla." in South Florida Business Journal (Vol. 34, January 24, 2014, No. 27, pp. 5)
Pub: American City Business Journals, Inc.
Contact: Mike Olivieri, Executive Vice President

Released: Weekly. **Price:** $8, Introductory 4-week offer(Digital & Print). **Description:** Lucy Robellos' Synergy HomeCare franchise in South Florida is experiencing strong growth. The business has 90 active caregiver, and Robellow plans to hire 90 six to ten employees a month for her firm in 2014. She reveals that Synergy aims to keep its clients in the comfort of their own home. **Availability:** Print; Online.

18139 ■ "Home Improvement Service Chain Had to Fix Its Own House" in Crain's Detroit Business (Vol. 30, October 13, 2014, No. 41, pp. 15)
Pub: Crain Communications Inc.
Contact: Barry Asin, President

Description: Mr. Handyman International LLC is the franchising arm for the Mr. Handyman home improvement service chain. The franchises provide smaller home repair and improvement projects, mostly residential with only 15 percent of the jobs being commercial. Statistical data included. **Availability:** Online.

18140 ■ "Hospital Revenue Healthier in 2009" in Orlando Business Journal (Vol. 26, February 5, 2010, No. 36, pp. 1)
Pub: Orlando Business Journal
Contact: Julie Swyers, Director
E-mail: jswyers@bizjournals.com

Ed: Melanie Stawicki Azam. **Description:** Orlando Health, Health Central and Adventist Health System are Florida-based hospital systems that generated the most profits in 2009. Orlando Health had the highest profit in 2009 at $73.3 million, contrary to about $31 million in losses in 2008. The increased profits are attributed to stock market recovery, cost-cutting initiatives, and rising patient volumes. **Availability:** Print; Online.

18141 ■ "How Baltimore's Largest Private Companies Weathered the Recession's Punch; Top Private Companies" in Baltimore Business Journal (Vol. 28, August 27, 2010, No. 16, pp. 1)
Pub: Baltimore Business Journal
Contact: Rhonda Pringle, President
E-mail: rpringle@bizjournals.com

Ed: Gary Haber. **Description:** The combined revenue of the 100 largest private firms in Maryland's Baltimore region dropped from about $22.7 billion in 2008 to $21 billion in 2009, an annual decrease of more than 7 percent. To survive the recession's impact, these firms resorted to strategies such as government contracting and overseas expansion. How these strategies affected the revenue of some firms is described. **Availability:** Print; Online.

18142 ■ "How BBQ Can Be Birmingham's Secret Sauce" in Birmingham Business Journal (Vol. 31, May 9, 2014, No. 19, pp. 4)
Pub: American City Business Journals, Inc.
Contact: Mike Olivieri, Executive Vice President

Released: Weekly. **Price:** $4, introductory 4-week offer(Digital only). **Description:** Local barbecue joints in Birmingham, Alabama are branching out to new markets and extending distinct barbecue brand of the city through franchises and corporate expansions across the U.S. Experts say this trend is contributing to more brand awareness and tourists for Birmingham. **Availability:** Print; Online.

18143 ■ "How Busy Executives Manage to Live a Balanced Life" in Influencive(March 20, 2019)
URL(s): www.influencive.com/how-busy-executives-manage-to-live-a-balanced-life/

Ed: Kiara Williams. **Released:** March 20, 2019. **Description:** Discusses how those in the C-suite are able to run corporations while also maintaining some balance in their personal lives. **Availability:** Online.

18144 ■ "How Detroit Built Its Marquee Auto Show" in Crain's Detroit Business (Vol. 30, January 6, 2014, No. 1, pp. 17)
Pub: Crain Communications Inc.
Contact: Barry Asin, President

Description: Detroit-area automobile dealers and business leaders, along with staff from the Detroit Auto Dealers Association, promoted Detroit as the premier North American International Auto Show event, upstaging New York. Few would have considered cold and snowy Detroit as a January destination, but they succeeded in their marketing campaign and the show has continued to grow since. **Availability:** Online.

18145 ■ "How Exports Could Save America" in Barron's (Vol. 89, July 20, 2009, No. 29, pp. 15)
Pub: Dow Jones & Company Inc.
Contact: Almar Latour, Chief Executive Officer

Ed: Jonathan R. Laing. **Description:** Increase in US exports should help drive up the nation's economic growth, according to Wells Capital Management strategist Jim Paulsen. He believes US gross domestic product could grow by 3-3.5 percent annually starting in 2010 due to a more favorable trade balance. **Availability:** Online.

18146 ■ "How the Growth Outliers Do It: Few Companies Manage To Prosper Over the Long Term. Those That Do Are Both More Stable and More Innovative Than Their Competition" in Harvard Business Review (Vol. 90, January-February 2012, No.1-2, pp. 110)
Pub: Harvard Business Review Press
Contact: Moderna V. Pfizer, Contact

Ed: Rita McGrath. **Price:** $8.95, PDF and hardcover black and white. **Description:** Firms that reliably grow their bottom lines are both structured for innovation but are also extremely stable. They excel at entering new markets but also provide a historically consistent organizational environment. They adapt quickly, but maintain an established strategy. **Availability:** Print; PDF; Online.

18147 ■ "How Hard Could It Be? The Four Pillars of Organic Growth" in Inc. (January 2008, pp. 69-70)

Ed: Joel Spolsky. **Description:** Revenue, head count, public relations, and quality are the four most important aspects of any growing business. **Availability:** Online.

18148 ■ "How High Can Soybeans Fly?" in Barron's (Vol. 88, March 10, 2008, No. 10, pp. M14)
Pub: Dow Jones & Company Inc.
Contact: Almar Latour, Chief Executive Officer

Ed: Kenneth Rapoza. **Description:** Prices of soybeans have risen to $14.0875 a bushel, up 8.3 percent for the week. Increased demand, such as in China and in other developing economies, and the investment-driven commodities boom are boosting prices. **Availability:** Online.

18149 ■ How to Make Big Money in Your Own Small Business: Unexpected Rules Every Small Business Owner Needs to Know

Ed: Jeffrey J. Fox, Jeffrey J. Fox. **Released:** May 12, 2004. **Price:** $16.95; C$24.95; $16.95; C$24.95; $16.95; C$24.95. **Description:** Former sales and marketing pro offers advice on growing a small business. **Availability:** Print.

18150 ■ Business Growth and Statistics

18150 ■ *How to Make Money with Social Media: An Insider's Guide to Using New and Emerging Media to Grow Your Business*
Ed: Jamie Turner, Reshma Shah, PhD. **Released:** 2nd edition. **Description:** Marketers, executives, entrepreneurs are shown more effective ways to utilize Internet social media to make money. This guide brings together both practical strategies and proven execution techniques for driving maximum value from social media marketing. **Availability:** E-book; Print.

18151 ■ *"How Much Inequality Is Necessary for Growth?" in Harvard Business Review (Vol. 90, January-February 2012, No.1-2, pp. 28)*
Pub: Harvard Business Review Press
Contact: Moderna V. Pfizer, Contact
Ed: Fuad Hasanov, Oded Izraeli. **Price:** $6, hardcopy black and white. **Description:** Research on international economic inequality shows that when inequality rises to a specific level, growth declines; however if it is lower than a certain level, the same results occur. One standard deviation of growth in inequality would raise yearly growth by approximately 0.6 percent. **Availability:** Print; PDF; Online.

18152 ■ *"How to (Realistically) Start an Online Ecommerce Busines That Actually Grows in 2019" in Big Commerce*
URL(s): www.bigcommerce.com/blog/how-to-create-online-store/#learn-how-to-create-your-own-online-store
Ed: Tracey Wallace. **Description:** A 9-chapter guide on everything you need to know to start an online business. Topics include how to find niche products to sell; how to evaluate the market; online market research; conducting a competitive analysis; business laws; how to analyze your target market; how to source and manufacture products; and how to create, setup, and launch an online store. **Availability:** PDF; Online.

18153 ■ *"How to Scale Your Business and Stay Sane in the Process" in Legal Zoom (February 22, 2023)*
URL(s): www.legalzoom.com/articles/how-to-scale-your-business-and-stay-sane-in-the-process
Ed: Marcia Layton Turner. **Released:** February 22, 2023. **Description:** Read through this guide if your business is growing fast and you need to ramp up your operations to keep pace. **Availability:** Online.

18154 ■ *"How To Live To Be 100: John E. Green Co. Grows Through Diversification" in Crain's Detroit Business (February 18, 2008)*
Pub: Crain Communications Inc.
Contact: Barry Asin, President
Ed: Chad Halcom. **Description:** Continuity, name recognition, and inventiveness are keys to continuing growth for Highland Park, Michigan's John E. Green Company, designer of pipe systems and mechanical contractor. **Availability:** Online.

18155 ■ *"How To Make Finance Work: The U.S. Financial Sector Has Boomed, But That Hasn't Always Been Good News For the Rest of the Economy" in Harvard Business Review (Vol. 90, March 2012, No. 3, pp. 104)*
Pub: Harvard Business Review Press
Contact: Moderna V. Pfizer, Contact
Ed: David S. Scharfstein, Robin Greenwood. **Price:** $8.95, hardcover. **Description:** The growth of the financial sector has hindered overall US growth by shifting money from productive investments into residential real estate, and through high professional investment management costs. Private sector innovation and discipline will be needed to correct these flaws, as will regulatory changes. **Availability:** PDF; Online.

18156 ■ *"How To Win In Emerging Markets: Lessons From Japan" in Harvard Business Review (Vol. 90, May 2012, No. 5, pp. 126)*
Pub: Harvard Business Review Press
Contact: Moderna V. Pfizer, Contact
Ed: Shigeki Ichii, Susumu Hattori, David Michael. **Price:** $8.95. **Description:** Corporate Japan's four challenges in engaging emerging markets are an aversion to mergers and acquisitions, an aversion to low- and middle-end segments, lack of organizational or financial commitments to emerging markets, and a shortage of executive talent placed in emerging markets. By addressing these weaknesses, Japan can succeed in global expansion. **Availability:** Online; PDF.

18157 ■ *"Husky Proceeds on Heavy-Oil Expansion" in Globe & Mail (March 21, 2006, pp. B1)*
Ed: Patrick Brethour. **Description:** Canadian energy giant Husky Energy Inc. has started its $90 million engineering effort to determine the cost of the $2.3 billion heavy-oil up gradation expansion plan. Details of the project are elaborated upon. **Availability:** Online.

18158 ■ *"IBM's Best-Kept Secret: It's Huge in Software Too" in Canadian Business (Vol. 79, September 25, 2006, No. 19, pp. 19)*
Description: The contribution of IBM vice-president Steve Mills in company's development is discussed. **Availability:** Print; Online.

18159 ■ *"An Ice Boost in Revenue; Wings Score With Expanded Corporate Sales" in Crain's Detroit Business (Vol. 25, June 1, 2009, No. 22)*
Pub: Crain Communications Inc.
Contact: Barry Asin, President
Ed: Bill Shea. **Description:** Stanley Cup finals always boost business for the Detroit area, even during a recession. The Red Wings corporate office reported corporate sponsorship revenue luxury suite rentals, Legends Club seats and advertising were up 40 percent this year over 2008. **Availability:** Print; Online.

18160 ■ *"Ideas at Work: The Reality of Costs" in Business Strategy Review (Vol. 21, Summer 2010, No. 2, pp. 40)*
Ed: Jules Goddard. **Released:** June 24, 2010. **Description:** If you think that cost cutting is the surest way to business success, the author wants to challenge every assumption you hold. Costs are an outcome of sound strategy, never the goal of strategy. He offers a new perspective on what counts when it comes to costs. **Availability:** Print; PDF; Online.

18161 ■ *"Illinois Farmland Tops $11,000 Per Acre" in Farm Industry News (June 27, 2011)*
Pub: Informa Business Media, Inc.
Contact: Charlie McCurdy, President
Ed: Karen McMahon. **Description:** Farmland property in Illinois continues to grow in value, selling for $11,000 per acre. Statistical data included. **Availability:** Online.

18162 ■ *Import/Export Kit For Dummies*
Pub: John Wiley & Sons, Inc.
Contact: Christina Van Tassell, Executive Vice President Chief Financial Officer
Ed: John J. Capela. **Released:** 3rd Edition. **Price:** $26.99, paperback; $17.99, E-book. **Description:** Provides entrepreneurs and small- to medium-size businesses with information required to start exporting products globally and importing goods to the U.S. Topics covered include the ins and outs of developing or expanding operations to gain market share, with details on the top ten countries in which America trades, from Canada to Germany to China. **Availability:** E-book; Print.

18163 ■ *"In 2011, Wichita-Area Banks Cleaned Up Books, Grew Earnings" in Wichita Business Journal (Vol. 27, February 17, 2012, No. 7, pp. 1)*
Pub: Baltimore Business Journal
Contact: Rhonda Pringle, President
E-mail: rpringle@bizjournals.com
Description: Wichita, Kansas-based banks have reported smaller loan portfolios and higher loan-loss allowances at the end of 2011 compared to the previous year. The earnings of the 35 banks in the metro area also grew strongly both for the quarter and for the year, while their assets increased. How the banks managed to generate positive earnings results is also discussed. **Availability:** Print; Online.

18164 ■ *"Incapital Set to Add Jobs, Expand Space" in South Florida Business Journal (Vol. 33, August 3, 2012, No. 1, pp. 1)*
Pub: Baltimore Business Journal
Contact: Rhonda Pringle, President
E-mail: rpringle@bizjournals.com
Description: Chicago, Illinois-based Incapital has announced plans to hire 25 to 30 more financial professionals over the next 12 months. Incapital is also planning to expand its Boca Raton, Florida with construction totalling 5,000 additional square feet to accommodate future growth. **Availability:** Print; Online.

18165 ■ *"Indian Buyer Gives Life to Algoma Expansion" in Globe & Mail (April 17, 2007, pp. B1)*
Ed: Greg Keenan. **Description:** The proposed capacity expansion of Algoma Steel Inc. after its acquisition by Essar Global Ltd. is discussed. **Availability:** Online.

18166 ■ *"Indiana Collection Agency Announces Expansion Plans" in PaymentsSource (March 23, 2012)*
Description: DECA Financial Services plans to buy a vacant building in Fishers, Indiana and renovate the property. The agency specializes in collection consumer and tax debts for both companies and government agencies. The company plans to hire 140 new employees over the next 3 years. **Availability:** Print; Mailing list.

18167 ■ *"Innovating Globally" in Business Strategy Review (Vol. 21, Spring 2010, No. 1, pp. 24)*
Ed: Costas Markides, Stuart Crainer. **Description:** Costas Markides has spent over two decades studying business strategy and innovation. Recently, he has been focusing on the bigger picture of how people can address major social problems. Can the techniques used by managers to create innovation inside organizations work with global change?. **Availability:** Download; PDF; Online.

18168 ■ *"The Innovator's Solution: Creating and Sustaining Successful Growth"*
Pub: Harvard Business Review Press
Contact: Moderna V. Pfizer, Contact
Released: November 19, 2013. **Price:** $35, Hardcover/Hardcopy. **Description:** Even in today's hyperaccelerated business environment any small company can transform their business. Advice on business decisions crucial to achieving truly disruptive growth and purpose guidelines for developing their own disruptive growth engine is given. The forces that cause managers to make bad decisions as they plan new ideas for their company are identified and new frameworks to help develop the right conditions, at the right time, for a disruption to succeed. Managers and business leaders responsible for innovation and growth will benefit their business and their teams with this information. **Availability:** E-book; Print.

18169 ■ *"Inside Waterloo's Quiet Tech Titan" in Canadian Business (Vol. 87, July 2014, No. 7, pp. 39)*
Description: OpenText chief executive officer Mark Barrenechea feels confident about the financial health of the Waterloo, Ontario-based software company. He adds that the company is exploring opportunities by the big data phenomenon. **Availability:** Online.

18170 ■ *"Insurers No Longer Paying Premium for Advertising" in Brandweek (Vol. 49, April 21, 2008, No. 16, pp. SR3)*
Description: Insurance companies are cutting their advertising budgets after years of accelerated double-digit growth in spending due to the economic downturn, five years of record-breaking ad spend and a

need to cut expenditures as claims costs rise and a competitive market keeps premiums in place. Statistical data included. **Availability:** Print; Online.

18171 ■ *"Intermodal Makes Suppliers Look to Rack Up Big Sales to Distributors" in The Business Journal-Serving Metropolitan Kansas City (August 15, 2008)*
Pub: American City Business Journals, Inc.
Contact: Mike Olivieri, Executive Vice President
Ed: James Dornbrook. **Description:** Suppliers of shelving units, conveyor systems and other equipment used in distribution facilities are expecting new business opportunities along with the planned intermodal projects in the Kansas City area. Suppliers have already observed that small distributors have started to relocate to the city because of the intermodal projects. Demand for shelves and lifts have also increased. **Availability:** Online.

18172 ■ *International Growth of Small and Medium Enterprises*
Pub: Routledge, Taylor & Francis Group
Released: First edition. **Description:** This volume focuses on how companies expand their operations across borders through opportunity exploration and exploitation, and identification and development of innovations.

18173 ■ *"International Paper Weighs Expansion Options" in Memphis Business Journal (Vol. 34, September 14, 2012, No. 22, pp. 1)*
Pub: Baltimore Business Journal
Contact: Rhonda Pringle, President
E-mail: rpringle@bizjournals.com
Ed: Andy Ashby, Michael Sheffield. **Description:** Memphis, Tennessee-based International Paper Company (IP) has been evaluating options for additional space in order to manage the potential relocation of employees of recently acquired Temple-Inland Inc. in Austin, Texas. IP is occupying more than 450,000 square feet of Class A office space at its International Place headquarters. **Availability:** Print; Online.

18174 ■ *"Internet Sales of Pet Products Increasingly 'Big Box'" in Pet Product News (Vol. 66, September 2012, No. 9, pp. 4)*
Description: Internet sales account for nearly 4 percent of the $30 billion U.S. market for pet products in 2011, or about $1.2 billion retail. Meanwhile, overall pet product retail sales growth and overall Internet retail sales growth of 10 percent can be outpaced as Internet sales of pet products is seen to grow at a 12 percent compound annual rate through 2015. **Availability:** Online.

18175 ■ *"Invest in Energy-Efficient Equipment for Your Pet Store" in Pet Product News (Vol. 66, September 2012, No. 9, pp. 72)*
Ed: Leila Meyer. **Description:** Aquatic retailers can achieve business growth by offering lighting products, pumps, heaters, filters, and other aquarium supplies that would help customers realize energy efficiency. Aside from offering an education in energy efficiency as a customer service opportunity, retailers are encouraged to determine what supplies are crucial in helping customers achieve energy usage goals. **Availability:** Online.

18176 ■ *"Investment Market Heats Up on the Eastside" in Puget Sound Business Journal (Vol. 35, August 1, 2014, No. 15, pp. 4)*
Pub: American City Business Journals, Inc.
Contact: Mike Olivieri, Executive Vice President
Released: Weekly. **Price:** $4, Introductory 4-week offer(Digital & Print). **Description:** The real estate investment sales market in Puget Sound, Washington is experiencing growth along with construction activity. Office sales reached $787 million in the first half of the year, while the shortage of office space is driving up rents for office tenants and making the market attractive to investors. **Availability:** Print; Online.

18177 ■ *"Is Your Company Ready to Succeed?" in Business Strategy Review (Vol. 21, Spring 2010, No. 1, pp. 68)*
Ed: Srikumar Rao. **Released:** February 09, 2010. **Description:** The author asked thousands of students about the ideal company of the future, the kind of place where they would want to spend their lives. **Availability:** Print; PDF; Online.

18178 ■ *Islands of Profit in a Sea of Red Ink: Why 40 Percent of Your Business Is Unprofitable and How to Fix It*
Pub: Portfolio
Contact: Adrian Zackheim, President
Ed: Jonathan L. S. Byrnes. **Released:** October 14, 2010. **Price:** $27.95, hardcover; $14.99, e-book. **Description:** Top companies from around the world turn to Jonathan Byrnes to figure out where to find profit for their companies. He shows which parts of a business are worth expanding, and which are just a drain on resources. He has found that roughly 40 percent of any new client's business is unprofitable, and that profit increases of thirty percent or more are within reach. **Availability:** E-book; Print.

18179 ■ *It's Not Who You Know - It's Who Knows You!: The Small Business Guide to Raising Your Profits by Raising Your Profile*
Pub: John Wiley & Sons, Inc.
Contact: Christina Van Tassell, Executive Vice President Chief Financial Officer
Ed: David Arvin. **Released:** 2nd edition. **Price:** $8.69, hardcover. **Description:** When it comes to promoting a small business or a brand, it is essential to know how valuable high-profile attention can be. But for most small companies, the cost of hiring an outside firm to increase attention can be too expensive. **Availability:** Print; Online.

18180 ■ *"It's What You Know. It's Who You Know. It's China" in Inc. (Vol. 33, October 2011, No. 8, pp. 80)*
Description: Michael Lee will be the first American entrepreneur to build big in China. The company is piloting two large commercial real estate developments, one in New York City the other in Nanjing, China. **Availability:** Print; Online.

18181 ■ *"ITT Places Its Bet With Defense Buy: Selling Equipment to Army Pays Off" in Crain's New York Business (Vol. 24, January 6, 2008)*
Pub: Crain Communications, Inc.
Contact: Jessica Botos, Manager, Marketing
E-mail: jessica.botos@crainsnewyork.com
Description: ITT Corp.'s revenue has jumped by 20 percent in each of the past three years due to demand for the company's radio sets and night-vision goggles. The firm has acquired EDO Corp., which specializes in battlefield communications systems, in an attempt to expand its defense-industry division. **Availability:** Online.

18182 ■ *"Jacksonville-based Interline Expanding in Janitorial-Sanitation Market" in Florida Times-Union (May 10, 2011)*
Pub: Florida Times-Union
Ed: Mark Basch. **Description:** Interline Brands Inc., located in Jacksonville, Florida, aims to grow its business with two recent acquisitions of firms that distribute janitorial and sanitation products. Interline markets and distributes maintenance, repair and operations products. **Availability:** Online.

18183 ■ *"Janitorial Equipment and Supplies US Market" in PR Newswire (October 24, 2011)*
Description: United States demand for janitorial equipment and supplies (excluding chemical products) is predicted to rise 2.4 percent per year to $7.6 billion in 2013. New product development will lead to increased sales of higher-value goods in the industry. **Availability:** Print; Online.

18184 ■ *"Jet Sales Put Bombardier Back in Black" in Globe & Mail (March 30, 2006, pp. B1)*
Ed: Bertrand Morotte. **Description:** The details on Bombardier Inc., which posted 20 percent rise in shares following $86 million profit for fourth quarter 2005, are presented. **Availability:** Online.

18185 ■ *"Jobs Data Show A Slow Leak" in Barron's (Vol. 88, July 7, 2008, No. 27, pp. 34)*
Pub: Dow Jones & Company Inc.
Contact: Almar Latour, Chief Executive Officer
Ed: Gene Epstein. **Description:** In June 2008, the United States manufacturing sector showed an expansion, with the purchasing managers' index rising to 50.2 from 49.6; the unemployment rate in the US, which stayed steady at 5.5 percent in June 2008 is also discussed. Statistical data included. **Availability:** Online.

18186 ■ *"Jordan Still Soaring" in Business Journal Portland (Vol. 30, January 17, 2014, No. 46, pp. 7)*
Pub: American City Business Journals, Inc.
Contact: Mike Olivieri, Executive Vice President
Released: Weekly. **Price:** $4, introductory 4-week offer(Digital only). **Description:** Nike Inc. is planning to open retail stores that will exclusively sell Jordan Brand merchandise. The company is seeking to grow its direct-to-consumer sales to $8 billion by 2017. Nike's capital spending is also expected to increase by 3 to 4 percent. **Availability:** Print; Online.

18187 ■ *"Ketchup King Heinz Seeks to Boost Soy-Sauce Empire in China" in Advertising Age (Vol. 83, October 8, 2012, No. 36, pp. 3)*
Description: Heinz is buying up local soy sauce firms in China with a buy-and-build strategy to expand into other markets in the country. Soy sauce total sales are about $4 billion annually in China, while ketchup sales amount to $100 million to $200 million there. **Availability:** Print; Online.

18188 ■ *"Kinetico Exec Going Global to Increase Growth Flow" in Crain's Cleveland Business (Vol. 28, October 1, 2007, No. 39, pp. 5)*
Pub: Crain Communications Inc.
Contact: K. C. Crain, President
Ed: David Bennett. **Description:** Shamus Hurley, the new CEO and president of Kinetico Inc., a manufacturer of water filtering and softening equipment for residential, commercial and municipal use, plans to expand the company to target markets overseas. **Availability:** Online.

18189 ■ *"King of the Crib: How Good Samaritan Became Ohio's Baby HQ" in Business Courier (Vol. 27, June 18, 2010, No. 7, pp. 1)*
Pub: Business Courier
Ed: James Ritchie. **Description:** Cincinnati's Good Samaritan hospital had 6,875 live births in 2009, which is more than any other hospital in Ohio. They specialize in the highest-risk pregnancies and deliveries and other hospitals are trying to grab Good Samaritan's share in this niche. **Availability:** Print; Online.

18190 ■ *"Kinnser: Sales In Overdrive" in Austin Business Journal (Vol. 32, March 30, 2012, No. 4, pp. 1)*
Pub: American City Business Journals, Inc.
Contact: Mike Olivieri, Executive Vice President
Ed: Christopher Calnan. **Description:** Kinnser Software Inc.'s receipt of fresh capitalization is seen to enable the company to pursue its acquisition strategy. The company is planning to grow organically. It is also planning to double the number of its employees. **Availability:** Online.

18191 ■ *"Labor of Love" in Green Industry Pro (Vol. 23, March 2011, No. 3, pp. 14)*
Ed: Gregg Wartgow. **Description:** Profile of CLS Landscape Management in Chino, California and its owner who started the company when he was 21

years old. Kevin Davis built his landscape firm into a $20 million a year business without using any dedicated salesperson. **Availability:** Online.

18192 ■ *"LaSalle St. Firms Cherry-Pick Talent As Wall St. Tanks"* in *Crain's Chicago Business (Vol. 31, November 17, 2008, No. 46)*
Pub: Crain Communications Inc.
Contact: Barry Asin, President

Ed: H. Lee Murphy. **Description:** Many local businesses are taking advantage of the lay offs that many major Wall Street firms are undergoing in their workforces; these companies see the opportunity to woo talent and expand their staff with quality executives. **Availability:** Online.

18193 ■ *"Lavante, Inc. Joins Intersynthesis, Holistic Internet Marketing Company"* in *Marketwired (November 5, 2009)*
Pub: Comtex News Network Inc.
Contact: Kan Devnani, President

Description: Lavante, Inc., the leading provider of on-demand vendor information and profit recovery audit solutions for Fortune 1000 companies has chosen Intersynthesis, a new holistic Internet marketing firm, as a provider of pay for performance services. Lavante believes that Intersynthesis' expertise and knowledge combined with their ability to develop integrated strategies, will help them fuel more growth. **Availability:** Print; Online.

18194 ■ *"Leading Ohio Internet Marketing Firm Announces Growth in September"* in *Marketing Weekly News (September 26, 2009, pp. 24)*
Pub: Investment Weekly News

Description: Despite a poor economy, Webbed Marketing, a leading social media marketing and search engine optimization firm in the Midwest, has added five additional professionals to its fast-growing team. The company continues to win new business, provide more services and hire talented employees. **Availability:** Online.

18195 ■ *"Legoland Florida Plans $3M-$6M Expansion"* in *Orlando Business Journal (Vol. 29, August 24, 2012, No. 10, pp. 1)*
Pub: Baltimore Business Journal
Contact: Rhonda Pringle, President
E-mail: rpringle@bizjournals.com

Description: Legoland Florida is planning to add three new pirate attractions at the amusement park in 2013. The planned attractions will be named Pirate Shores. **Availability:** Print; Online.

18196 ■ *"Lending Grows as Banks Make Moves"* in *Pittsburgh Business Times (Vol. 33, May 9, 2014, No. 43, pp. 4)*
Pub: American City Business Journals, Inc.
Contact: Mike Olivieri, Executive Vice President

Released: May 2014. **Price:** $4, introductory 4-week offer(Digital only). **Description:** Pittsburgh, Pennsylvania-based biggest retail banks have bigger loan portfolios at the end of 2014s first quarter compared with the same period in 2013. Business lending has been driving activity and the surge also includes the impact of merger and acquisition strategies to capture customers in Ohio. The rising loan portfolio of the banks are examined. **Availability:** Print; Online.

18197 ■ *"Lessons Learned From Animals, Part II"* in *South Florida Business Journal (Vol. 35, September 19, 2014, No. 8, pp. 11)*
Pub: American City Business Journals, Inc.
Contact: Mike Olivieri, Executive Vice President

Description: Advice on how to achieve business growth is given. Striving to be in environments that offer mental, spiritual and physical growth to entrepreneurs is encouraged. Businesses should be consistent in practices that promote business growth. **Availability:** Online.

18198 ■ *"Let's Buy a Company: How to Accelerate Growth Through Acquisitions"*
Description: Advice for negotiating terms and pricing as well as other aspects of mergers and acquisitions in small companies. **Availability:** Print.

18199 ■ *"Life Sciences Become State's Growth Powerhouse"* in *Crain's Detroit Business (Vol. 25, June 1, 2009, No. 22, pp. M008)*
Pub: Crain Communications Inc.
Contact: Barry Asin, President

Ed: Amy Lane. **Description:** According to a study conducted by Anderson Economic Group, Michigan's University Research Corridor has helped grow the life sciences industry. Statistical details included. **Availability:** Online.

18200 ■ *"Life's Work: Ben Bradlee"* in *Harvard Business Review (Vol. 88, September 2010, No. 9, pp. 128)*
Pub: Harvard Business Publishing
Contact: Diane Belcher, Managing Director

Ed: Alison Beard. **Price:** $8.95, PDF. **Description:** Newspaper publisher Ben Bradlee discusses factors that lead to success, including visible supervisors, enthusiasm, appropriate expansion, and the importance in truth in reporting. **Availability:** Online; PDF.

18201 ■ *"Liquor Stores Sips on Growth Cocktail"* in *Globe & Mail (February 6, 2006, pp. B5)*
Description: The business growth plans of Liquor Stores Income Fund are presented. **Availability:** Online.

18202 ■ *"The Little Biotech that Could"* in *Barron's (Vol. 89, July 27, 2009, No. 30, pp. 19)*
Pub: Dow Jones & Company Inc.
Contact: Almar Latour, Chief Executive Officer

Ed: Christopher C. Williams. **Description:** OSI Pharmaceuticals' shares is a compelling investment bet among small biotech firms due to its Tarceva anticancer drug which has a 23 percent market share as well as their strong balance sheet. OSI is planning to expand the use of Tarceva which could re-ignite sales and one analyst expects the shares to trade in the 40s one year from July 2009. **Availability:** Online.

18203 ■ *"Little Gyms Are Getting Bigger"* in *Sacramento Business Journal (Vol. 31, April 25, 2014, No. 9)*
Pub: American City Business Journals, Inc.
Contact: Mike Olivieri, Executive Vice President

Released: Weekly. **Price:** $4, Introductory 4-week offer(Digital & Print). **Description:** The boutique gym is a growing segment of the consumer fitness market. One such smaller boutique gym is Orangetheory Fitness in Roseville, California. It focuses on small groups and commaraderie along with a promise of more personal attention for the fitness center members. The company is part of a national chain with plans to expand to 12 more locations in the Sacramento area in the next five years. **Availability:** Print; Online.

18204 ■ *"Loans Are Plentiful for Small Businesses"* in *South Florida Business Journal (Vol. 35, September 12, 2014, No. 7, pp. 16)*
Pub: American City Business Journals, Inc.
Contact: Mike Olivieri, Executive Vice President

Description: Banks have relaxed requirements for small business loans in South Florida. Total bank loans increased by 11.4 percent in 2014. It has also become easier for small businesses to secure credit for acquisitions and mergers and growth. **Availability:** Online.

18205 ■ *"Local Brewers Hop Onboard Craft-Beer Train"* in *Providence Business News (Vol. 29, April 14, 2014, No. 2, pp. 1)*
Pub: American City Business Journals, Inc.
Contact: Mike Olivieri, Executive Vice President

Released: April 12, 2014. **Description:** Rhode Island has become a home to more than a dozen breweries for craft beers. The state's craft brewers plan to create the infrastructure for a thriving, self-sustaining local brewing ecosystem and two groups in Providence announced separate plans for larger breweries capable of boosting more-established labels to larger markets. The growth of craft brewing is discussed. **Availability:** Print; Online.

18206 ■ *"Local Outlook: Stronger Growth Ahead"* in *Montana Business Quarterly (Vol. 49, Spring 2011, No. 1, pp. 10)*
Pub: University of Montana Bureau of Business and Economic Research
Contact: Patrick Barkey, Director
E-mail: patrick.barkey@business.umt.edu

Ed: Paul E. Polzin. **Released:** Quarterly. **Description:** Local economic growth is broken down into three areas: fastest growing in Richland, Gallatin and Flathead Counties; the second growth group consists of Yellowstone, Silver Bow, and Lewis and Clark Counties, which all grew at rates higher than the statewide average; slowest growth was seen in Missoula, Ravalli, Cascade, and Custer Counties. Statistical data included. **Availability:** Online.

18207 ■ *"Longmont's Comida Food Truck Now a Brick-and-Mortar Restaurant, Too"* in *Las Cruces Sun-News (February 17, 2012)*
Pub: Tribune News Service
Contact: Jack Barry, Vice President, Operations
E-mail: jbarry@tribpub.com

Ed: Tony Kindelspire. **Description:** Rayme Rosello discusses her plans to open her new Mexican-style restaurant, Comida Cantina, which grew from her pink food truck. Rosello started her food truck in 2010 and has frequented neighborhood parties as well as office parks to build her business. Details of the new restaurant are provided. **Availability:** Print; Online.

18208 ■ *"Loop Hotel Plan Locks Up Funding"* in *Crain's Chicago Business (Vol. 31, March 24, 2008, No. 12, pp. 2)*
Pub: Crain Communications Inc.
Contact: Barry Asin, President

Ed: Eddie Baeb. **Description:** Signaling further expansion in the downtown hotel market, the secured $395 million in financing will fund a 610-room luxury hotel operated by J.W. Marriott, a more upscale brand in the Marriott line. **Availability:** Online.

18209 ■ *"Lots More Mr. Nice Guy"* in *Canadian Business (Vol. 80, October 22, 2007, No. 21, pp. 58)*
Description: Galen Weston Jr., executive chairman of Loblaw and heir to the Weston family business, has his hands full running the company. Details of his turnaround strategies and ambitious plans to increase profitability of the business are discussed.

18210 ■ *Macrowikinomics: Rebooting Business and the World*
Pub: Portfolio Hardcover
Contact: Adrian Zackheim, President

Ed: Don Tapscott, Anthony D. Williams. **Released:** May 29, 2012. **Price:** $18, paperback; $6.99, e-book. **Description:** Wikinomics Don Tapscott and Anthony Williams showed how mass collaboration was changing the way businesses communicate, create value, and compete in the new global marketplace in 2007. Now, in the wake of the global financial crisis, the principles of wikinomics have become more powerful than ever. **Availability:** E-book; Print.

18211 ■ *"Made in San Francisco: Manufacturing a Comeback"* in *San Francisco Business Times (Vol. 28, February 14, 2014, No. 30, pp. 4)*
Pub: American City Business Journals, Inc.
Contact: Mike Olivieri, Executive Vice President

Released: February 14, 2014. **Price:** $4, print. **Description:** Reports show that San Francisco, California's manufacturing industry is making a comeback due to the rise in new entrepreneurs. However, some observers believe that the increasing costs of production could limit the sector's growth. San Francisco currently supports more than 4,000 manufacturing jobs. **Availability:** Print; Online.

18212 ■ *"The Main Ingredient of Change"* in *Harvard Business Review (Vol. 92, September 2014, No. 9, pp. 36)*
Pub: Harvard Business Publishing
Contact: Diane Belcher, Managing Director
Price: $6. **Description:** Courage and leadership were key factors in driving organizational change at Campbell Soup Company. Leadership improved decision making processes, while courage gave the 145-year-old firm the impetus to expand the business and enter new markets. **Availability:** Online; PDF.

18213 ■ *"The Making of a Building Boom"* in *Philadelphia Business Journal (Vol. 32, January 31, 2014, No. 51, pp. 4)*
Pub: American City Business Journals, Inc.
Contact: Mike Olivieri, Executive Vice President
Released: Weekly. Price: $4, introductory 4-week offer(Digital & Print). **Description:** Reports show that construction activity in Philadelphia, Pennsylvania is on the rise. However, the results of a recent study indicate that near-term shortages or skilled workers could be problematic. Projections on the cost of construction in 2014 are also discussed. **Availability:** Print; Online.

18214 ■ *"Management Matters with Mike Myatt: Are You Creating Growth in a Down Economy?"* in *Commercial Property News (March 17, 2008)*
Description: Senior executives are expected to create growth for their company regardless of recession, economic slowdown, inflation, or tight credit and capital markets. **Availability:** PDF; Online.

18215 ■ *Managing Economies, Trade and International Business*
Pub: Palgrave Macmillan
Released: 1st edition. Price: $89, e-book; $115, Hardcover; $110, softcover. **Description:** An in-depth look at the areas that affect and influence international business, exploring specific issues businesses face in terms of economic development, trade law, and international marketing and management. **Availability:** E-book; Print.

18216 ■ *"M&T On the March?"* in *Baltimore Business Journal (Vol. 28, November 12, 2010, No. 27, pp. 1)*
Pub: Baltimore Business Journal
Contact: Rhonda Pringle, President
E-mail: rpringle@bizjournals.com
Ed: Gary Haber. **Description:** Information on the growth of M&T Bank, as well as its expansion plans are presented. M&T recently acquired Wilmington Trust and took over $500 million in deposits from the failed K Bank. Analysts believe that M&T would continue its expansion through Washington DC and Richmond, Virginia, especially after a bank executive acknowledged that the markets in those areas are attractive. **Availability:** Print; Online.

18217 ■ *"Marine-Services Firm Eyes Expansion"* in *Providence Business News (Vol. 29, August 25, 2014, No. 21, pp. 8)*
Pub: American City Business Journals, Inc.
Contact: Mike Olivieri, Executive Vice President
Released: August 23, 2014. **Description:** Jamestown, Rhode Island-based Conanicut Marine Services Inc. is looking to expand the business with a bigger marina, the addition of a third boat to his ferry fleet, and a climate-controlled storage shed. Owner, Bill Munger, discusses his efforts to overcome the challenges of sustaining the business during the economic recession. **Availability:** Print; Online.

18218 ■ *"Market Resource Set for Expansion: Supply Chain Firm to Add Up to 700 Employees"* in *Memphis Business Journal (Vol. 34, May 11, 2012, No. 4, pp. 1)*
Pub: Baltimore Business Journal
Contact: Rhonda Pringle, President
E-mail: rpringle@bizjournals.com

Description: Market Resource Packaging LLC is planning to expand its operation in Memphis, Tennessee under the new ownership of IAM Acquisition. The supply chain services company plans to increase its distribution space from 260,000 square feet to 1 million square feet in three years and to grow its employees from 300 to 1,000 in 18 months. **Availability:** Print; Online.

18219 ■ *"Marketer Bets Big on U.S.'s Growing Canine Obsession"* in *Advertising Age (Vol. 79, April 14, 2008, No. 15, pp. 14)*
Pub: Crain Communications, Inc.
Contact: Jessica Botos, Manager, Marketing
E-mail: jessica.botos@crainsnewyork.com
Ed: Emily Bryson York. **Description:** Overview of FreshPet, a New Jersey company that began marketing two brands of refrigerated dog food-Deli Fresh and FreshPet Select-which are made from fresh ingredients such as beef, rice and carrots. The company projects continued success due to the amount of money consumers spend on their pets as well as fears derived from the 2007 recalls that inspired consumers to look for smaller, independent manufacturers that are less likely to source ingredients from China. **Availability:** Online.

18220 ■ *"Marketing is Everything, But Timing Helps"* in *Idaho Business Review (September 9, 2014)*
Pub: BridgeTower Media
Contact: Adam Reinebach, President
Description: Profile of Ladd Family Pharmacy, founded by husband and wife Kip and Elaine, who borrowed money from Idaho Banking Company to start their pharmacy. The firm has expanded from three workers in 2008 to 22 to date and reported $6.2 million in revenue for 2013.

18221 ■ *"Marriott Readies for Uptick in Leisure Travel"* in *Dallas Business Journal (Vol. 35, April 13, 2012, No. 31, pp. 1)*
Pub: Baltimore Business Journal
Contact: Rhonda Pringle, President
E-mail: rpringle@bizjournals.com
Description: Dallas Marriott City Center hotel has conducted a $16 million renovation that it hopes will attract leisure travelers visiting the upcoming improvements along Woodall Rodgers Freeway in Dallas. The Dallas Marriott's general manager, Nour Laasri, expects leisure travel and events to gro for the 416-room hotel. **Availability:** Print; Online.

18222 ■ *"Massage Heights Chasing Big Expansion Opportunities"* in *San Antonio Business Journal (Vol. 28, April 25, 2014, No. 11, pp. 6)*
Pub: American City Business Journals, Inc.
Contact: Mike Olivieri, Executive Vice President
Released: Weekly. Price: $4, Introductory 4-week offer(Digital only). **Description:** Massage Heights, offering deep tissue massage, hot stone massage and facials, has opened a second corporate-owned facility in Stone Oak, Texas. The company, founded in April 2004, is focusing on expansion plans due to investor interest in the firm's growth. Massage Heights currently has five facilities in Canada. **Availability:** Print; Online.

18223 ■ *Mastering the Business of Organizing: A Guide to Plan, Launch, Manage, Grow, and Leverage a Profitable, Professional Organizing Business*
Released: February 11, 2019. Price: $20.99, Paperback; $8.69, E-book. **Description:** A guide for people interested in starting their own professional organizing business. From start-up to growing your company, the author compiles all of the necessary tools needed to make your business a success. **Availability:** E-book; Print.

18224 ■ *"A Matter of Interest: Payday Loans"* in *Canadian Business (Vol. 79, July 17, 2006, No. 14-15, pp. 21)*
Pub: Rogers Media Inc.
Contact: Neil Spivak, Chief Executive Officer

Ed: Jeff Sanford. **Description:** With the steady decrease in savings, the need for growth in Canada's payloan industry is discussed. Also emphasized are the challenges faced by payloan operators. **Availability:** Online.

18225 ■ *"Meadowbrook To Acquire ProCentury in $272.6 Million Deal"* in *Crain's Detroit Business (Vol. 24, February 21, 2008, No. 8, pp. 4)*
Pub: Crain Communications Inc.
Contact: Barry Asin, President
Ed: Jay Greene. **Description:** Meadowbrook Insurance Group, based in Southfield, Michigan reports its proposed acquisition of ProCentury Corporation based in Columbus, Ohio. Meadowbrook provides risk-management to agencies, professional and trade associations and small-to-midsize businesses. **Availability:** Print; Online.

18226 ■ *"Medicaid Insurers See Growth in Small Biz Market"* in *Boston Business Journal (Vol. 31, July 15, 2011, No. 25, pp. 1)*
Pub: Boston Business Journal
Contact: Carolyn M. Jones, President
E-mail: cmjones@bizjournals.com
Ed: Julie M. Donnelly. **Description:** BMC HealthNet Plan announced plans to launch small business products to serve small businesses that are priced out of rising premium rates at large Massachusetts insurers. BMC joined competitors CeltiCare Health Plan and Neighborhood Health Plan in augmenting its core business. **Availability:** Print; Online.

18227 ■ *"Meet the New Convenience Store"* in *Supermarket News (August 3, 2018)*
URL(s): www.supermarketnews.com/retail-financial/meet-new-convenience-store
Ed: Gloria Dawson. Released: August 03, 2018. **Description:** Convenience stores have grown from a place to grab some candy, pop, and other snacks to offering more and better options for healthier pre-packed food. Consumers are craving more high-end products, and these new stores are delivering and growing the trend. **Availability:** Online.

18228 ■ *"Menchie's Tops Restaurant Business' Future 50 List"* in *Ice Cream Reporter (Vol. 23, August 20, 2010, No. 9, pp. 4)*
Description: Menchie's, frozen yogurt shop, announced it placed first in the Restaurant Business Magazine's Future 50, ranking the franchise the fastest-growing in the food industry. **Availability:** Print; Online.

18229 ■ *"Mercy Parent Nets Almost $1B in 2011"* in *Sacramento Business Journal (Vol. 28, September 30, 2011, No. 31, pp. 1)*
Pub: Sacramento Business Journal
Contact: Stephanie Fretwell, Director
E-mail: sfretwell@bizjournals.com
Ed: Kathy Robertson. Price: $4, Print & Digital introductory 4-week offer; $4, Digital introductory 4-week offer. **Description:** Catholic Healthcare West has reported almost $1 billion in profits for 2010. The company has reported a profit margin of 8.7 percent. It also absorbed more than $1 billion in costs from charity care and government programs. **Availability:** Print; Online.

18230 ■ *"Metamorphosis Makes Family Dollar a Destination"* in *MMR (Vol. 29, August 20, 2012, No. 13, pp. 8)*
Description: Family Dollar was launched as a store for low-incom customers, but is becoming a mainstream shopping destination for low- and middle-income consumers. Details of the firm are discussed with Howard Levine, chief executive officer. **Availability:** Print.

18231 ■ *"Michael Daszkal On Going Beyond the Role of CPA"* in *South Florida Business Journal (Vol. 34, April 25, 2014, No. 40)*
Pub: American City Business Journals, Inc.
Contact: Mike Olivieri, Executive Vice President

Released: Weekly. **Price:** $8, Introductory 4-week offer(Digital & Print). **Description:** Michael Daszkal launched his CPA firm, Daszkal Bolton CPAs in 1994. It has grown from two people to a staff of 115, with 2013 net revenue pegged at $16 million. **Availability:** Print; Online.

18232 ■ *"MicroTech Is Fastest Growing Private Company in Washington Area on Deloitte Technology Fast 500"* in *Hispanic Business (July-August 2009, pp. 20, 22)*
Ed: Suzanne Heibel. **Description:** Profile of Tony Jimenez, former lieutenant colonel in the Army and CEO and founder of Virginia-based information technology firm, Micro Tech LLC. Jimenez was named Latinos in Information Science and Technology Association's CEO of the Year for 2008.

18233 ■ *"Millennials: The Great White Hope for Wine Industry"* in *Advertising Age (Vol. 81, December 6, 2010, No. 43, pp. 2)*
Pub: Crain Communications, Inc.
Contact: Jessica Botos, Manager, Marketing
E-mail: jessica.botos@crainsnewyork.com
Ed: E.J. Schultz. **Description:** Generation offers category of most growth potential in 30 years and 7-Eleven and vintner are taking notice. **Availability:** Online.

18234 ■ *"MIR Growing With Help From Former Pfizer Workers"* in *Crain's Detroit Business (Vol. 24, January 28, 2008, No. 4, pp. 33)*
Pub: Crain Communications Inc.
Contact: Barry Asin, President
Ed: Tom Henderson. **Description:** Molecular Imaging Research Inc. helps fund research at its parent firm, Molecular Therapeutics Inc. The company provides imaging services and other in vivo and in vitro services to help pharmaceutical companies test new compounds. **Availability:** Print; Online.

18235 ■ *The Mirror Test: Is Your Business Really Breathing?*
Pub: Grand Central Publishing
Contact: Michael Pietsch, Chairman
Ed: Jeffrey W. Hayzlett. **Released:** May 05, 2010. **Price:** $9.99, e-book. **Description:** Consultant and author, Jeffrey Hayzlett, explains why a business is not doing well and asks the questions that most business managers are afraid to ask. **Availability:** E-book; Print.

18236 ■ *"A Mixed-Bag Quarter"* in *Barron's (Vol. 88, July 7, 2008, No. 27, pp. 19)*
Description: Seven component companies of the Dow Jones Industrial Average increased their dividend payouts in the second quarter of 2008 despite the weak performance of the index. Five companies in the Dow Jones Transportation index and three in the Dow Jones Utilities also increased their dividends. **Availability:** Online.

18237 ■ *"Mobile Marketing Grows With Size of Cell Phone Screens"* in *Crain's Detroit Business (Vol. 24, January 14, 2008, No. 2, pp. 13)*
Pub: Crain Communications Inc.
Contact: Barry Asin, President
Ed: Bill Shea. **Description:** Experts are predicting increased marketing for cell phones with the inception of larger screens and improved technology.

18238 ■ *"Montana Outlook: Stronger Growth Ahead"* in *Montana Business Quarterly (Vol. 49, Spring 2011, No. 1, pp. 7)*
Pub: University of Montana Bureau of Business and Economic Research
Contact: Patrick Barkey, Director
E-mail: patrick.barkey@business.umt.edu
Ed: Patrick M. Barkey. **Released:** Quarterly. **Description:** A look at Montana's economy and future growth is given. Experts are predicting that the state will experience new growth in 2011, with 2012 showing its best growth since 2006. Statistical data included. **Availability:** Online.

18239 ■ *"Montana's Manufacturing Industry"* in *Montana Business Quarterly (Vol. 49, Spring 2011, No. 1, pp. 29)*
Pub: University of Montana Bureau of Business and Economic Research
Contact: Patrick Barkey, Director
E-mail: patrick.barkey@business.umt.edu
Ed: Todd A. Morgan, Charles E. Keegan, III, Colin B. Sorenson. **Released:** Quarterly. **Description:** Manufacturing remains a vital part of Montana's economy despite the recession and decline in the production of wood products. Statistical data included. **Availability:** Online.

18240 ■ *"More SouthPark Shopping for Charlotte"* in *Charlotte Business Journal (Vol. 25, July 16, 2010, No. 17, pp. 1)*
Pub: Charlotte Business Journal
Contact: Robert Morris, Editor
E-mail: rmorris@bizjournals.com
Ed: Will Boye. **Description:** Charlotte, North Carolina-based Bissel Companies has announced plans to expand its retail presence at the Siskey and Sharon properties in SouthPark. Bissel Companies has requested a rezoning to a mixed-use development classification so that it can utilize the entire ground floor of the Siskey building for restaurant and retail uses. **Availability:** Print; Online.

18241 ■ *"Mortgage Servicer Wingspan Portfolio Advisors Makes Mark in Frisco"* in *Dallas Business Journal (Vol. 35, September 7, 2012, No. 52, pp. 1)*
Pub: Baltimore Business Journal
Contact: Rhonda Pringle, President
E-mail: rpringle@bizjournals.com
Ed: Candace Carlisle. **Description:** Carrollton, Texas-based Wingspan Portfolio Advisors LLC has seen rapid growth in its business and the company plans to hire another 500 employees. Wingspan has subleased a 125,000-square-foot building in Firsco, Texa to accommodate the expansion and making it the company's third site in North Texas.

18242 ■ *"MPI Expansion Goes Back to Family Roots"* in *Crain's Detroit Business (Vol. 25, June 1, 2009, No. 22, pp. M007)*
Pub: Crain Communications Inc.
Contact: Barry Asin, President
Ed: Sherri Begin Welch. **Description:** William Parfet, grandson of Upjohn Company founder, is expanding MPI Research's clinical and early clinical research operations into two buildings in Kalamazoo, land which was once part of his grandfather's farm. **Availability:** Print; PDF; Online.

18243 ■ *The Multinational Enterprise Revisited: The Essential Buckley and Casson*
Pub: Palgrave Macmillan
Ed: Peter J. Buckley, Mark Casson. **Released:** 2010. **Price:** $89, e-book; $120, hardcover; $120, hardcover. **Description:** A compilation of essays gathered from over thirty years discussing the future of the multinational enterprise, and includes a new introduction and conclusion to bond the pieces together in a comprehensive overview of the theory of the multinational enterprise. **Availability:** E-book; Print.

18244 ■ *"Myths of Deleveraging"* in *Barron's (Vol. 90, August 23, 2010, No. 34, pp. M14)*
Pub: Barron's Editorial & Corporate Headquarters
Ed: Gene Epstein. **Description:** The opposite is true against reports about deleveraging or the decrease in credit since inflation-adjusted-investment factories and equipment rose 7.8 percent in the first quarter of 2010. On consumer deleveraging, sales of homes through credit is weak but there is a trend towards more realistic homeownership and consumer spending on durable goods rose 8.8 percent. **Availability:** Online.

18245 ■ *"N.C. Data-Center Plan Bearing Fruit From Apple, Spec Center"* in *Charlotte Business Journal (Vol. 25, October 15, 2010, No. 30, pp. 1)*
Pub: Charlotte Business Journal
Contact: Robert Morris, Editor
E-mail: rmorris@bizjournals.com
Ed: Ken Elkins. **Description:** Apple Inc. is planning to expand its server farm at the North Carolina Data Center Corridor in Catawba County. T5 Partners, on the other hand, will build a shell building to house a server on the site. Infocrossing Inc. will also build an open data center in the area. **Availability:** Print; Online.

18246 ■ *"Neighboring Auto Body Shops Merge as Parks Royal Body Works"* in *Idaho Business Review (August 26, 2014)*
Pub: BridgeTower Media
Contact: Adam Reinebach, President
Description: Parks Royal Body Works and Auto Body Specialists operated next door to each other and were rivals for many years. Ted Vinson, owner of Auto Body, recently sold his business to Ted Thornton's son, Matt in order for Parks Royal to expand. Thornton discusses his company's 13 percent growth in 2013. Details of the purchase are discussed.

18247 ■ *"Nerd Alert on 3rd"* in *Philadelphia Business Journal (Vol. 28, August 17, 2012, No. 27, pp. 1)*
Pub: Baltimore Business Journal
Contact: Rhonda Pringle, President
E-mail: rpringle@bizjournals.com
Description: The transformation of North 3rd Street in the neighborhood of Old City in Philadelphia, Pennsylvania into a cluster of technology businesses and workers, dubbed at N3rd (pronounced 'nerd'), is described. Some of the firms located in the area include the Web engineering company Jarv.us Innovations and the collaborative workspace Devnuts. Prospects of the cluster's growth are also discussed. **Availability:** Print; Online.

18248 ■ *"New Food Concepts Flood Market"* in *Business Journal (Vol. 30, June 8, 2012, No. 2, pp. 1)*
Pub: American City Business Journals, Inc.
Contact: Mike Olivieri, Executive Vice President
Ed: John Vomhof, Jr. **Released:** Weekly. **Price:** $4, introductory 4-week offer(Digital only). **Description:** Twin Cities Metropolitan Area has seen the boom of the frozen yogurt segment over the past few years and the rise of fast casual sandwich shops, which are helping fuel activity in Minnesota's real estate market. However, there are skeptics who doubt whether all of the new concepts can survive. **Availability:** Print; Online.

18249 ■ *"New Holiday Inns Set for Airport Area, Graceland"* in *Memphis Business Journal (Vol. 34, August 17, 2012, No. 18, pp. 1)*
Pub: Baltimore Business Journal
Contact: Rhonda Pringle, President
E-mail: rpringle@bizjournals.com
Description: Two new Holiday Inn hotels are to be constructed in Memphis, Tennessee in the next two years. The plan is in line with the company's celebration of its 60th anniversary. **Availability:** Print; Online.

18250 ■ *"New Jersey Bio Grows Despite Turbulent Times"* in *Philadelphia Business Journal (Vol. 28, August 17, 2012, No. 27, pp. 1)*
Pub: Baltimore Business Journal
Contact: Rhonda Pringle, President
E-mail: rpringle@bizjournals.com
Description: The number of biotechnology firms with operations in New Jersey increased from about 300 to more than 340, while the number of employees working at those grew 9.3 percent from 15,000 in July 2012 to 16,400 in 2012. The growth has been realized despite issues that are said to affect the national and international economic situation. Calls to develop economic incentives are also examined. **Availability:** Print; Online.

18251 ■ *"New Jobs Coming From New Breed"* in *Memphis Business Journal (Vol. 34, September 21, 2012, No. 23, pp. 1)*
Pub: Baltimore Business Journal
Contact: Rhonda Pringle, President

E-mail: rpringle@bizjournals.com

Ed: Andy Ashby. **Description:** New Breed Logistics has opened a new distribution center in Southeast Memphis, Tennessee. It is believed that this new service will create hundreds of new jobs over the next two years. The company may become the largest-third party logistics company operating in Memphis. **Availability:** Print; Online.

18252 ■ *The New Role of Regional Management*

Pub: Palgrave Macmillan

Ed: Bjorn Ambos, Bodo B. Schlegelmilch. **Released:** 2010. **Description:** Regional management is becoming more important to companies as they expand globally. This book explores the challenges of European, United States and Asian companies and outlines how regional headquarters can develop into Dynamic Competence Relay centers to master these issues. **Availability:** E-book; Print.

18253 ■ *"New Year's Resolutions: How Three Companies Came Up With Their 2008 Growth Strategies"* in Inc. (January 2008, pp. 47-49)

Ed: Martha C. White. **Description:** Three companies share 2008 growth strategies; companies include a candle company, a voice mail and text messaging marketer, and hotel supplier of soap and shampoo. **Availability:** Online.

18254 ■ *"NKC Keeps Pace with Auto Industry"* in Memphis Business Journal (Vol. 34, September 14, 2012, No. 22, pp. 1)

Pub: Baltimore Business Journal

Contact: Rhonda Pringle, President

E-mail: rpringle@bizjournals.com

Ed: Michael Sheffield. **Description:** Memphis, Tennessee-based NKC of American Inc. has been expecting sales to increase to about $60 million for 2012 after its revenue dropped to about $20 million during the peak of the recession in 2008-2009. NKC's growth is being driven by new contracts with automotive manufacturers. **Availability:** Print; Online.

18255 ■ *"No Frills - And No Dodge"* in Crain's Detroit Business (Vol. 24, September 22, 2008, No. 38, pp. 3)

Pub: Crain Communications Inc.

Contact: Barry Asin, President

Ed: Bradford Wernle. **Description:** Chrysler LLC is in the middle of a business plan known as Project Genesis, a five-year strategy in which the company will reduce the dealer count by combining its Jeep, Chrysler and Dodge brands under one rooftop wherever possible. Not every dealer will be able to arrange this deal because of the investment required to expand stores in which have low-overhead; many of these stores feel that low-overhead structures are more likely to survive difficult times than the larger stores in which the Genesis consolidation plan intends to implement. **Availability:** Online.

18256 ■ *No Man's Land: What to Do When Your Company Is Too Big to Be Small but Too Small to Be Big*

Description: Insight to help fast-growing companies navigate the fatal trap of no-man's land, a perilous zone where they have outgrown the habits and practices that fueled their early growth but have not yet adopted new practices and resources in order to cope with new situations and challenges. **Availability:** E-book; Print.

18257 ■ *"The Numbers Speak For Themselves"* in Barron's (Vol. 88, July 14, 2008, No. 28, pp. 16)

Pub: Dow Jones & Company Inc.

Contact: Almar Latour, Chief Executive Officer

Ed: Bill Alpert. **Description:** Discusses quant fund managers versus traditional long-short equity funds after quants outperformed traditional funds in the year 2000. Causes for the underperformance are outlined and statistical data is included. **Availability:** Online.

18258 ■ *"Ohio Commerce Draws Closer to Profitability"* in Crain's Cleveland Business (Vol. 28, October 29, 2007, No. 43, pp. 14)

Pub: Crain Communications Inc.

Contact: K. C. Crain, President

Ed: Shawn A. Turner. **Description:** Overview of the business plan of Ohio Commerce Bank, a de novo, or startup bank that is close to turning the corner to profitability. The bank opened in November 2006 and focuses on dealing with small businesses totaling $5 million or less in annual revenues. **Availability:** Online.

18259 ■ *"Ohio Franchisee Buys 21 Jacksonville-Area Papa John's"* in Florida Times-Union (December 20, 2010)

Pub: Florida Times-Union

Ed: Mark Basch. **Description:** Ohio-based Papa John's pizza franchise acquired 21 of the restaurants in Duval, Clay and St. Johns counties in Jacksonville, Florida. **Availability:** Online.

18260 ■ *"OK, Bring in the Lawyers"* in Crain's Chicago Business (Vol. 31, November 17, 2008, No. 46, pp. 26)

Pub: Crain Communications Inc.

Contact: Barry Asin, President

Ed: Daniel Rome Levine. **Description:** Bankruptcy attorneys are finding the economic and credit crisis a benefit for their businesses due to the high number of business owners and mortgage holders that are need of their services. One Chicago firm is handling ten times the number of cases they did the previous year and of that about 80 percent of their new clients are related to the real estate sector. **Availability:** Online.

18261 ■ *"OmniSYS Plans Big Richardson Expansion"* in Dallas Business Journal (Vol. 35, June 8, 2012, No. 39, pp. 1)

Pub: Baltimore Business Journal

Contact: Rhonda Pringle, President

E-mail: rpringle@bizjournals.com

Ed: Bill Hethcock. **Description:** OmniSYS LLC will hire about 250 more people in the next two years and open a 50,000-square-foot office in Richardson, Texas in October 2012. The Medicare claims processing company posted revenue growth of more than 30 percent in 2011 primarily in the Medicare audit and compliance area. **Availability:** Print; Online.

18262 ■ *"Once Derided As Rabbit Food, Humble Salad Now Fuels Business Plans"* in Dallas Business Journal (Vol. 35, August 17, 2012, No. 49, pp. 1)

Pub: Baltimore Business Journal

Contact: Rhonda Pringle, President

E-mail: rpringle@bizjournals.com

Description: Establishments offering salad concepts are on the rise in Dallas, Texas. The Salad Stop, Greenz, Salata are only some of the restaurants that have ventured into meeting the demand for health food, particularly salads. The market is only getting bigger, urging the restaurants to expand in services and facilities. The beginnings, food choices, and business plans of these restaurants are discussed.

18263 ■ *"Once Is Not Enough for These Restaurateurs"* in Baltimore Business Journal (Vol. 31, April 25, 2014, No. 52, pp. 16)

Pub: American City Business Journals, Inc.

Contact: Mike Olivieri, Executive Vice President

Released: Weekly. **Description:** Five Baltimore restaurateurs explain why they are looking to expand their businesses by opening multiple eateries, despite the potential risks. Among these is Spike Gjerde, owner of Woodberry Kitchen who opened a new butcher shop and restaurant in Remington, called Parts and Labor; Jason Ambrose, who owns Salt and a second unnamed restaurant in Locust Point; and Sarah Simington of Blue Moon Café at Fells Point and Federal Hill. **Availability:** Print; Online.

18264 ■ *"Oracle: No Profit of Doom"* in Barron's (Vol. 88, March 31, 2008, No. 13, pp. 40)

Pub: Dow Jones & Company Inc.

Contact: Almar Latour, Chief Executive Officer

Ed: Mark Veverka. **Description:** Oracle's revenues grew by 21 percent but fell short of expectation and their profits came in at the low-end of expectations. The company's shares dropped 8 percent but investors are advised to pay more attention to the company's earnings expansion rather than revenue growth in a slow economy. Nokia's Rick Simonson points out that their markets in Asia and particularly India is growing so they are not as affected by the U.S. economic conditions. **Availability:** Online.

18265 ■ *"Organic Food Industry Goes to College"* in USA Today (April 9, 2012)

Ed: Chuck Raasch. **Description:** With the organic food industry growing the US Department of Agriculture is has pumped $117 million into organic research in the last three years. According to a recent report by the Organic Farming Research Foundation (OFRF), the number of states committing land for organic research has nearly doubled from 2003 to 2011. Universities offering academic programs in organic farming rose from none to nine. The OFRF supports organic farmers and producers. **Availability:** Online.

18266 ■ *Organizations Alive!: Six Things That Challenge - Seven That Bring Success*

Pub: Yuill & Associates

Ed: Jan Yuill. **Price:** C$18.95, paperback. **Description:** New insight into understanding how organizations function as individuals is presented by an international consultant. Customer service, resource management, outsourcing, and management are among the issues covered.

18267 ■ *"The Outcome of an Organization Overhaul"* in Black Enterprise (Vol. 41, December 2010, No. 5)

Pub: Earl G. Graves Ltd.

Contact: Earl Graves, Jr., President

Ed: Tamara E. Holmes. **Description:** Savvy business owners understand the need for change in order to stay competitive and be successful. This article examines how to manage change as well as what strategies can help employees to get with the program faster. **Availability:** Online.

18268 ■ *"Outlook 2008 (9 Sectors to Watch): Construction"* in Canadian Business (Vol. 81, December 19, 2007, No. 1, pp. 48)

Pub: Rogers Media Inc.

Contact: Neil Spivak, Chief Executive Officer

Ed: Jeff Sanford. **Description:** Infrastructure deficit of C$123 billion, and still growing, was recently reported by the Federation of Canadian Municipalities. Details on plans for infrastructure projects and forecasts on the construction sector for 2008 are discussed. **Availability:** Print; Online.

18269 ■ *"Outlook 2008 (9 Sectors to Watch): Gold"* in Canadian Business (Vol. 81, December 19, 2007, No. 1, pp. 53)

Pub: Rogers Media Inc.

Contact: Neil Spivak, Chief Executive Officer

Ed: John Gray. **Description:** Turmoil in the financial markets, triggered by the meltdown in subprime mortgages, has pushed the price of gold to more than $840 an ounce in November 2007. Details on investor interest in gold and prediction on price trends in trade are discussed. **Availability:** Online.

18270 ■ *"Outlook 2008 (9 Sectors to Watch): Metals"* in Canadian Business (Vol. 81, December 19, 2007, No. 1, pp. 46)

Pub: Rogers Media Inc.

Contact: Neil Spivak, Chief Executive Officer

Ed: John Gray. **Description:** Forecasts on the Canadian metal industries for 2008 are discussed. Details on mine production and the rise in prices are also presented. **Availability:** Print; Online.

18271 ■ "Outlook for Montana Agriculture" in *Montana Business Quarterly* (Vol. 49, Spring 2011, No. 1, pp. 26)
Pub: University of Montana Bureau of Business and Economic Research
Contact: Patrick Barkey, Director
E-mail: patrick.barkey@business.umt.edu

Ed: George Haynes. **Released:** Quarterly. **Description:** Montana farmers and ranchers are rebounding from lower prices and production to higher prices and record production in 2010. The state has limited dairy and hog production, but farm income is still likely rise between 15 to 25 percent in 2010 over previous year. **Availability:** Online.

18272 ■ *The Oz Principle*
Released: May 04, 2010. **Price:** $17, paperback. **Description:** The role of personal and organizational accountability in getting business results is profiled. **Availability:** E-book; Print.

18273 ■ "Parent Firm's Global Reach, Stricter Air Quality Rules Have Stock Smiling" in *Crain's Cleveland Business* (October 15, 2007)
Pub: Crain Communications Inc.
Contact: K. C. Crain, President

Ed: David Bennett. **Description:** Since Stock Equipment Co., a firm that makes industrial pollution control equipment, was acquired by Schenck Process Group, a diversified global manufacturer based in Germany, the company's orders from abroad have been on the rise. The purchase has opened the doors to regions such as Eastern and Central Europe, Latin America and Australia. **Availability:** Online.

18274 ■ "Patience Will Pay Off in Africa" in *Barron's* (Vol. 92, September 17, 2012, No. 38, pp. M8)
Description: The stocks of African companies present long-term capital appreciation opportunities for investors. This is due to a commodities boom, economic reform and relative political stability in many African countries. **Availability:** Online.

18275 ■ "Penney's Buys Wal-Mart Site" in *Crain's Chicago Business* (Vol. 31, March 31, 2008, No. 13, pp. 13)
Pub: Crain Communications Inc.
Contact: Barry Asin, President

Ed: Eddie Baeb. **Description:** J.C. Penny Co. bought the closed Wal-Mart location in Crystal Lake and plans to open a store next year in its push to become more prominent in non-mall locations; Penney plans to expand and renovate the store. **Availability:** Online.

18276 ■ "Penske Opens Its First Smart Car Dealership In Bloomfield Hills" in *Crain's Detroit Business* (Vol. 24, January 21, 2008, No. 3)
Pub: Crain Communications Inc.
Contact: Barry Asin, President

Ed: Sheena Harrison. **Description:** Information about Penske Automotive Group's Smart Car addition to its dealership lineup. Smart Car pricing starts at $11,590, with more than 30,000 individuals reserving vehicles. **Availability:** Print; Online.

18277 ■ "Pepperidge Farm Getting New Life" in *Orlando Business Journal* (Vol. 28, August 24, 2012, No. 28, pp. 1)
Pub: Baltimore Business Journal
Contact: Rhonda Pringle, President
E-mail: rpringle@bizjournals.com

Description: The Pepperidge Farm brand could see renewal with parent company Campbell Soup's hiring of Irene Chang Britt as president. Britt, reputed for growing brands and businesses through her attention on consumer needs and marketplace trends, will be the first woman to lead Pepperidge Farm after founder Margaret Rudkin. Other insights into Britt's career as a business leader are presented. **Availability:** Print; Online.

18278 ■ "Perfecting the Process: Creating a More Efficient Organization on Your Terms" in *Black Enterprise* (Vol. 41, October 2010, No. 3)
Pub: Earl G. Graves Ltd.
Contact: Earl Graves, Jr., President

Ed: Tamara E. Holmes. **Description:** More than ever, entrepreneurs need to identify new ways of doing business in a cost-effective manner in order to expand their companies, while remaining true to their customer demands. **Availability:** Online.

18279 ■ "The Perils of Partnering in Developing Markets: How a Health Care Provider Addresses the Risks That Come With Globalization" in *Harvard Business Review* (Vol. 90, June 2012, No. 6, pp23)
Pub: Harvard Business Review Press
Contact: Moderna V. Pfizer, Contact

Ed: Steven J. Thompson. **Price:** $6. **Description:** Effective evaluation of international risk includes assessing the opportunity; ramping up processes, operations, and metrics; and establishing long-term functionality. Warning signs for each stage are also presented. **Availability:** Online; PDF.

18280 ■ "Perry Ellis and G-III Apparel--Out of Fashion, but Still in Style" in *Barron's* (Vol. 88, March 17, 2008, No. 11, pp. 48)
Pub: Dow Jones & Company Inc.
Contact: Almar Latour, Chief Executive Officer

Ed: Robin Goldwyn Blumenthal. **Description:** Shares of Perry Ellis International and G-III Apparel Group have taken some beating in the market despite good growth earnings prospects. Perry Ellis sees earnings growth of 8 to 11 percent for fiscal 2009, while G-III Apparel expects earnings growth of 25 percent. **Availability:** Online.

18281 ■ "PetSmart: A Barking Buy" in *Barron's* (Vol. 89, July 6, 2009, No. 27, pp. 15)
Pub: Dow Jones & Company Inc.
Contact: Almar Latour, Chief Executive Officer

Ed: Jay Palmer. **Description:** Shares of PetSmart could climb from $21.70 to about $28 due to the company's improving profits, cash flow, and product portfolio. The company's shares are trading at 14 times projected 2010 earnings of $1.64 a share. **Availability:** Online.

18282 ■ "Philadelphia's Largest Employers Will Fill 6,000 Jobs Within 6 Months" in *Philadelphia Business Journal* (Vol. 28, February 5, 2010, No. 51, pp. 1)
Pub: Philadelphia Business Journal
Contact: Sierra Quinn, Director
E-mail: squinn@bizjournals.com

Ed: Peter Van Allen. **Description:** Philadelphia, Pennsylvania's largest employers have openings for at least 6,000 jobs. But businesses remain cautious and are selective in hiring or waiting to see what happens to federal policy changes. **Availability:** Online.

18283 ■ "A Pioneer of Paying With Plastic" in *Crain's Chicago Business* (Vol. 31, April 28, 2008, No. 17, pp. 39)
Pub: Crain Communications Inc.
Contact: Barry Asin, President

Ed: Phuong Ly. **Description:** Profile of Perfect Plastic Printing Corp., a family-owned company which manufactures credit cards, bank cards and gift cards and whose sales hit $50.1 million last year, a 16 percent jump from 2006. **Availability:** Online.

18284 ■ "Play It Safe At Home, Or Take a Risk Abroad? A US Lease-To-Own Chain Considers Whether To Test Its Business In Mexico" in *Harvard Business Review* (Vol. 90, January-February 2012, No.1-2, pp. 145)
Pub: Harvard Business Review Press
Contact: Moderna V. Pfizer, Contact

Ed: Michael Chu. **Price:** $8.95, hardcopy black and white. **Description:** A fictitious foreign-market entry scenario is presented, with contributors providing advice. Recommendations include ensuring that expansion will not compromise the firm's core business, and that expansion, while necessary to growth, must be done carefully. **Availability:** Print; Online; PDF.

18285 ■ "Port Canaveral Plans to Make Big Waves of Business in C. Fla." in *Orlando Business Journal* (Vol. 30, June 6, 2014, No. 50, pp. 4)
Pub: American City Business Journals, Inc.
Contact: Mike Olivieri, Executive Vice President

Released: Weekly. **Price:** $8, Introductory 4-week offer(Digital & Print). **Description:** Port Canaveral CEO, John Walsh, has big plans for the expansion of the Port, which include a $500 million cargo and cruise expansion that could net billions of dollars in new economic impact and create more than 15,000 new jobs. Walsh plans to expand cargo capacity, dig deeper harbors for large cruise ships and build a rail transport cargo and, eventually, passengers in and out of the 380-acre Port Canaveral. The Port is the fifth-largest cargo port in Central Florida. **Availability:** Print; Online.

18286 ■ "Portfolio Recovery Associates Expands Its Hampton Call Center" in *Marketwired* (January 20, 2010)
Pub: Comtex News Network Inc.
Contact: Kan Devnani, President

Description: Entering into a lease amendment in order to expand its Hampton, Virginia call center and extend its lease agreement, Portfolio Recovery Associates, Inc., a company that collects, purchases and manages defaulted consumer debt, plans to upgrade the existing space enabling them to draw on local talent. **Availability:** Print; Online.

18287 ■ "Portland Wooing Under Armour to West Coast Facility" in *Baltimore Business Journal* (Vol. 27, January 29, 2010, No. 39, pp. 1)
Pub: Baltimore Business Journal
Contact: Rhonda Pringle, President
E-mail: rpringle@bizjournals.com

Ed: Andy Giegerich. **Description:** Baltimore, Maryland sports apparel maker, Under Armour, is planning a west coast expansion with Portland, Oregon among the sites considered to house its apparel and footwear design center. Portland officials counting on the concentration of nearly 10,000 activewear workers in the city will help lure the company to the city. **Availability:** Print; Online.

18288 ■ "Potential for Water Pumping in Africa" in *Canadian Business* (Vol. 79, October 23, 2006, No. 21, pp. 162)
Description: EastCoast Energy Corp.'s business venture of opening a natural gas company based in Tanzania and marketing of natural gas to expanding markets in East Africa is discussed. **Availability:** Print; Online.

18289 ■ "The Power Brokers" in *Crain's Chicago Business* (Vol. 31, April 28, 2008, No. 17, pp. 41)
Pub: Crain Communications Inc.
Contact: Barry Asin, President

Ed: Samantha Stainburn. **Description:** Profile of BlueStar Energy Services Inc., one of the first suppliers to cash in on the deregulation f the electricity market by the Illinois Legislature; last year BlueStar's revenue was $171.1 million, up from $600,000 in 2002, the year the company was founded. **Availability:** Online.

18290 ■ "Power Partnerships" in *Business Courier* (Vol. 27, October 22, 2010, No. 25, pp. 1)
Description: The $400 million Harrah's casino and the $47 million redevelopment and expansion of Washington Park are project aimed at boosting the economy in downtown Cincinnati, Ohio. These projects will be done in cooperation with the National Association for the Advancement of Colored People. Insights into the role of minority-owned businesses in regional economic development are explored. **Availability:** Print; Online.

18291 ■ "Principles for Creating Growth in Challenging Times" in Agency Sales Magazine (Vol. 39, September-October 2009, No. 9, pp. 35)
Description: Creating a productive environment is one vital key for businesses to utilize during the challenging times that arise due to a weak economy; other important factors include maintaining a good relationship with the staff, responding appropriately to challenges and keeping a sense of humor.

18292 ■ "Private Label Manufacturers Association" in Ice Cream Reporter (Vol. 23, July 20, 2010, No. 8, pp. 7)
Description: Branded frozen dessert manufacturers sold more frozen desserts in terms of sales volume and revenue and market share in 2009. Statistical details included. **Availability:** Print; Online.

18293 ■ "Private-Sector Is Back, Roadblocks Be Damned" in Business Review Albany (Vol. 41, July 4, 2014, No. 15, pp. 4)
Pub: American City Business Journals, Inc.
Contact: Mike Olivieri, Executive Vice President
Released: Weekly. **Price:** $4, introductory 4-week offer(Digital only). **Description:** Private sector jobs in New York experienced significant growth, reaching an all-time high of almost 7.6 million jobs in May 2014, as government jobs suffered a decline. Large international corporations, including General Electric, are tapping into cash reserves, adding jobs and expanding operations after years of cutting staff. **Availability:** Print; Online.

18294 ■ "The Pumpkin Plan: A Simple Strategy to Grow a Remarkable Business in Any Field"
Pub: Portfolio Hardcover
Contact: Adrian Zackheim, President
Released: September 22, 2022. **Price:** $17.95, paperback. **Description:** One million new businesses are started every year in America and nearly 80 percent of them fail within the first five years. Entrepreneur, Mike Michalowicz discovered the inspiration he needed to successfully grow his business when reading an article about a pumpkin farmer who was committed to growing giant pumpkins. Michalowicz applied the same process to his small business and transformed his company into a multimillion dollar success. The pumpkin plan includes: planting the right seeds, wedding out the losers, and nurturing the winners. **Availability:** Print.

18295 ■ "Putting 'Extra' in Extra-Silky Shampoo" in Crain's Chicago Business (Vol. 31, April 28, 2008, No. 17, pp. 37)
Pub: Crain Communications Inc.
Contact: Barry Asin, President
Ed: Phuong Ly. **Description:** Profile of HallStar Co., a Chicago-based company which develops and manufactures specialty chemicals to upgrade existing products such as hair dye, lotion and deodorant. HallStar has seen its annual earnings rise more than 30 percent since 2002. **Availability:** Online.

18296 ■ "Putting 'Great' Back Into A&P" in Crain's New York Business (Vol. 24, January 6, 2008, No. 1, pp. 3)
Pub: Crain Communications, Inc.
Contact: Jessica Botos, Manager, Marketing
E-mail: jessica.botos@crainsnewyork.com
Description: After five straight years ending in 2005, A&P Grocery lost revenue; due to a sweeping plan to freshen up its supermarkets the company returned to growth mode and was able to acquire longtime competitor Pathmark Stores.

18297 ■ "Q&A: PSU's Tom Gillpatrick on How Quirkiness Gives Portland Its Edge" in Business Journal Portland (Vol. 30, January 17, 2014, No. 46, pp. 6)
Pub: American City Business Journals, Inc.
Contact: Mike Olivieri, Executive Vice President
Released: Weekly. **Price:** $4, introductory 4-week offer(Digital only). **Description:** Portland State University Food Industry Leadership Center executive director, Tom Gillpatrick, says consumers now prefer healthier food brands. He also stated the Portland, Oregon's food sector has grown owing to that trend. Gillpatrick added that the state's reputation for being different has also helped the sector. **Availability:** Print; Online.

18298 ■ "Quantivo Empowers Online Media Companies to Immediately Expand Audiences and Grow Online Profits" in Marketwired (November 18, 2009)
Pub: Comtex News Network Inc.
Contact: Kan Devnani, President
Description: Quantivo, the leader in on-demand Behavioral Analytics, has launched a new solution that includes 22 of the most critical Internet audience behavior insights as out-of-the-box reports; Internet marketers need to understand their audience, what they want and how often to offer it to them in order to gain successful branding and campaigns online. **Availability:** Online.

18299 ■ Raising Capital
Released: Third edition. **Price:** $34.95, Paperback/E-book. **Description:** Corporate attorney provides a comprehensive guide using in-depth, practical advice on raising money to start and grow a business. A 115-page appendix contains samples of financing agreements, forms and questionnaires. **Availability:** E-book; Print.

18300 ■ "R&R Launches Upscale Spoony's and Low Fat Dragon's Den" in Ice Cream Reporter (Vol. 23, August 20, 2010, No. 9, pp. 3)
Description: European ice cream manufacturer R&R has acquired French ice cream maker Rolland and will position itself as an upscale challenger to brands like Ben & Jerry's. **Availability:** Print; Online.

18301 ■ "The RBC Dynasty Continues" in Globe & Mail (January 30, 2006, pp. B1)
Description: The details on business growth of Royal Bank of Canada, under chief executive officer Gordon Nixon, are presented. **Availability:** Print; Online.

18302 ■ "Red Mango Set to Grow in Florida" in Ice Cream Reporter (Vol. 23, September 20, 2010, No. 10, pp. 2)
Description: Red Mango will add 12 new locations throughout Florida. The stores offer healthy, nutritious frozen yogurt, smoothies and parfaits. **Availability:** Print; Online.

18303 ■ "Region Wins as GE Puts Plants Close to R&D" in Business Review Albany (Vol. 41, July 4, 2014, No. 15, pp. 8)
Pub: American City Business Journals, Inc.
Contact: Mike Olivieri, Executive Vice President
Description: General Electric Company (GE) invested over $400 million into the expansion of its health care, battery and renewable energy businesses in the Albany, New York region. The company's local growth secured about 7,000 private-sector jobs in the area and strengthened the relationship between GE research and manufacturing. **Availability:** Print; Online.

18304 ■ "Retail in Austin Strong, Will Continue to Be" in Austin Business JournalInc. (Vol. 29, January 22, 2010, No. 46, pp. 1)
Pub: Austin Business Journal
Contact: Rachel McGrath, Director
E-mail: rmcgrath@bizjournals.com
Ed: Jacob Dirr. **Description:** Retail sector in Austin, Texas has outpaced the national average in value, mid-tier, high-end and drugs retail sectors, according to a report by Pitney Bowes. The national consulting firm's report has projected growth in every sector until the end of fiscal 2012. Data regarding other sectors is also included. **Availability:** Print; Online.

18305 ■ "Retail Slump Deflates Greater Cincinnati Development" in Business Courier (Vol. 24, February 28, 2008, No. 47, pp. 1)
Pub: American City Business Journals, Inc.
Contact: Mike Olivieri, Executive Vice President
Ed: Lisa Biank Fasig. **Description:** 2007 sales of the retail industry are the slowest since the year 2003, driving retail stores to reconsider their expansion plans for 2008. A number of retail projects have been delayed, cancelled or altered, including Newport Pavilion, Rivers Crossing, Wal-Mart Supercenters, Legacy Place and Millworks. The impacts of retail slowdown on development projects are analyzed further. **Availability:** Online.

18306 ■ "Revenge of the Scorned Protege" in Canadian Business (Vol. 85, September 17, 2012, No. 14, pp. 48)
Ed: Joanna Pachner. **Released:** September 17, 2012. **Description:** The prospect of a merger between Canadian distributor Alliance Films and international television and independent films distributor Entertainment One Group is expected to control the Canadian market and could rationalize competition in Great Britain. Entertainment One's offerings to broadcasters and other partners will be added with Alliance's 11,000 movie titles.

18307 ■ "Riding High" in Small Business Opportunities (November 2008)
Description: Profile of David Sanborn who found a way to turn his passion for biking into a moneymaking opportunity by opening his own bicycle shops; Sanborn's goal is to become the largest independent bike retailer in the United States.

18308 ■ "The Rise of the Supertemp: The Best Executive and Professional Jobs May No Longer Be Full-Time Gigs" in Harvard Business Review (Vol. 90, May 2012, No. 5, pp. 50)
Pub: Harvard Business Review Press
Contact: Moderna V. Pfizer, Contact
Ed: Jody Grenstone Miller, Matt Miller. **Price:** $8.95, hardcopy and PDF. **Description:** Supertemps are independent contractors who perform mission-critical work on a project basis. Supertemps enjoy a high degree of flexibility and freedom, and offer companies new opportunities for innovation and growth. **Availability:** Print; Online; PDF.

18309 ■ "Rising in the East; Research and Development" in The Economist (Vol. 390, January 3, 2009, No. 8612, pp. 47)
Description: Impressive growth of the technological research and development in Asian countries is discussed. Statistical data included. **Availability:** Online.

18310 ■ "The Road Map for Scotiabank's Asian Expansion" in Globe & Mail (April 7, 2007, pp. B3)
Ed: Tara Perkins. **Description:** Executive vice-president of Bank of Nova Scotia, Rob Pitfield shares his plan to expand the bank's Asian market. **Availability:** Online.

18311 ■ "Rock of Ages" in Barron's (Vol. 92, September 17, 2012, No. 38, pp. 23)
Description: Financial services firm Rockefeller & Company was hit hard by the global financial crisis of 2008, but managed to thrive despite it. The firm, which offers financial products from other firms aside from its own fund, grew its assets under management by 52 percent to $35 billion for the three-year period that ended June 2012. **Availability:** Online.

18312 ■ "Roger Rechler Played Major Role in Long Island's Evolution" in Commercial Property News (March 17, 2008)
Description: Profile of Roger Rechler, real estate developer on Long Island, New York, is presented. Rechler, who died in March 2008, was instrumental in the development, ownership and operations of the largest commercial real estate portfolio on Long Island. **Availability:** Online.

18313 ■ "Roundy's Pushing Chicago Expansion" in Milwaukee Business Journal (Vol. 27, February 12, 2010, No. 20, pp. A1)
Pub: The Business Journal
Contact: Heather Ladage, President

E-mail: hladage@bizjournals.com
Ed: Rich Kirchen. **Description:** Roundy Supermarkets Inc. is expanding in Chicago, Illinois as the Milwaukee-based company is set to open one store in downtown Chicago and another in the Arlington suburb. The store openings have been pushed back to spring and early summer in 2010 due to the economic downturn. **Availability:** Print; Online.

18314 ■ *"Rudy's Tortillas Wraps Up Expansion Plan in Carrollton"* in *Dallas Business Journal (Vol. 35, August 31, 2012, No. 51, pp. 1)*
Pub: Baltimore Business Journal
Contact: Rhonda Pringle, President
E-mail: rpringle@bizjournals.com
Ed: Candace Carlisle. **Released:** Weekly. **Description:** Rudy's Tortillas Corporation, a 67-year old family business based in Dallas, Texas, is moving into a new plant on Belt Line Road, Carrollton. The expansion will also involve the hiring of 150 new workers and enable the company to expand its operations. Rudy's will spend $14 million dollars on construction and equipment on the new tortilla plant. **Availability:** Print; Online.

18315 ■ *"Rule of the Masses: Reinventing Fashion Via Crowdsourcing"* in *WWD (Vol. 200, July 26, 2010, No. 17, pp. 1)*
Pub: Conde Nast Publications
Contact: Agnes Chu, President
Ed: Cate T. Corcoran. **Description:** Large apparel brands and retailers are crowdsourcing as a way to increase customer loyalty and to build their businesses. **Availability:** PDF; Download; Online.

18316 ■ *"Safety Products Firm Expanding"* in *Memphis Business Journal (Vol. 33, March 16, 2012, No. 49, pp. 1)*
Pub: Baltimore Business Journal
Contact: Rhonda Pringle, President
E-mail: rpringle@bizjournals.com
Description: Safety products importer and supplier International Sourcing Company Inc., the parent firm of Cordova Safety Products and Cordova Consumer Products, has purchased the 1 million-square-foot Cleo property in southeast Memphis, Tennessee. Aside from relocating its warehouse and office operations to the facility, the firm will add 20 new jobs as part of its growth initiative. **Availability:** Print; Online.

18317 ■ *"Salad Creations To Open 2nd Location"* in *Crain's Detroit Business (Vol. 24, March 3, 2008, No. 9, pp. 26)*
Description: Salad Creations, a franchise restaurant that allows customers to create their own salads and also offers soups and sandwiches; Salad Creations plans to open a total of five locations by the end of 2008. **Availability:** Online.

18318 ■ *"Samsung's Metamorphosis in Austin"* in *Austin Business Journal (Vol. 31, May 20, 2011, No. 11, pp. 1)*
Pub: Austin Business Journal
Contact: Rachel McGrath, Director
E-mail: rmcgrath@bizjournals.com
Ed: Christopher Calnan. **Description:** Samsung Austin Semiconductor LP, a developer of semiconductors for smartphones and tablet computers, plans to diversify its offerings to include niche products: flash memory devices and microprocessing devices. In light of this strategy, Samsung Austin will be hiring 300 engineers as part of a $3.6 billion expansion of its plant. **Availability:** Print; Online.

18319 ■ *"San Antonio's Craft-Brewing Industry is Gearing Up to Make More Suds"* in *San Antonio Business Journal (Vol. 26, August 3, 2012, No. 27, pp. 1)*
Pub: Baltimore Business Journal
Contact: Rhonda Pringle, President
E-mail: rpringle@bizjournals.com
Description: Craft brewery projects are underway in San Antonio, Texas as more companies look to take advantage of craft beer's growing market. Texas craft breweries registered over $75 million in sales and could have an economic impact of $6 billion by 2020. **Availability:** Print; Online.

18320 ■ *"San Jose Hopes to Build on Uptick in Manufacturing"* in *Silicon Valley/San Jose Business Journal (Vol. 30, July 13, 2012, No. 16, pp. 1)*
Pub: Baltimore Business Journal
Contact: Rhonda Pringle, President
E-mail: rpringle@bizjournals.com
Description: San Jose, California-based manufacturing companies that cater to high-technology companies and startups have been experiencing an uptick in business. The San Jose metropolitan area is the country's second-largest specialized manufacturing market and the city has rolled out its efforts to help support this growth. **Availability:** Print; Online.

18321 ■ *"Scary (But True) Small Business Statistics You Can't Afford to Ignore"* on *Digital.com (Jan. 27, 2022)*
URL(s): digital.com/small-business-statistics/
Ed: Katie Horne. **Released:** January 27, 2022. **Description:** Provides small business marketing statistics for entrepreneurs looking to start their own business. **Availability:** Online.

18322 ■ *"Scotiabank Targets More Baby Boomers"* in *Globe & Mail (March 4, 2006, pp. B5)*
Ed: Elizabeth Church. **Description:** Bank of Nova Scotia posted $844 million profit for first quarter 2006. The plans of the bank to achieve baby boomer client base are presented. **Availability:** Online.

18323 ■ *"Second to None"* in *Crain's Detroit Business (Vol. 26, January 18, 2010, No. 3, pp. 9)*
Pub: Crain Communications Inc.
Contact: Barry Asin, President
Ed: Nancy Kaffer. **Description:** Second-stage companies are beginning to attract more attention from government entities and the business community alike, due in part to their ability to create jobs more rapidly than their counterparts both smaller and larger. Second-stage companies have between 10-99 employees and consistently have supplied the most jobs, despite overall job declines in recent years. **Availability:** Online.

18324 ■ *"Secrets To Trade Show Success"* in *Women Entrepreneur (September 12, 2008)*
Description: Trade shows require an enormous amount of work, but they are an investment that can pay off handsomely because they allow a business to get their product or service in front of their target market. Advice regarding trade shows is given including selecting the correct venue, researching the affair and following up on leads obtained at the event. **Availability:** Online.

18325 ■ *"Sedentary Shoppers: Point, Click, Buy"* in *Barron's (Vol. 90, September 6, 2010, No. 36, pp. 11)*
Pub: Barron's Editorial & Corporate Headquarters
Ed: Vito J. Racanelli. **Description:** Non-travel online retail sales from January to July 2010 increased nine percent which indicates that online shopping for the coming holidays will be good. Online sales are outpacing traditional shopping, but pricing is still critical. **Availability:** Online.

18326 ■ *"Sedo Keeps Trucking in Good Times and Bad"* in *Crain's Chicago Business (Vol. 31, April 28, 2008, No. 17, pp. 35)*
Description: Discusses Seko Worldwide Inc., an Itasca-based freight forwarder, and its complicated road to growth and expansion on a global scale. **Availability:** Print; Online.

18327 ■ *"SEEing an Opportunity: Golden's Eyewear Chain Has a National Vision"* in *Crain's Detroit Business (Vol. 24, January 7, 2008, No. 1)*
Pub: Crain Communications Inc.
Contact: Barry Asin, President
Ed: Sheena Harrison. **Description:** Richard Golden, who recently sold D.O.C. Optics Corporation is planning to build a new national eyewear chain called SEE Inc., which stands for Selective Eyewear Elements. SEE will sell expensive-looking glasses at lower prices than designer styles. **Availability:** Online.

18328 ■ *"Sell a Movement Within a Smoothie"* in *Canadian Business (Vol. 87, July 2014, No. 7, pp. 58)*
Description: Vega is a nutritional and fitness supplement maker based in Vancouver, British Columbia that has increased its sales sevenfold from 2008 to 2013, earning the 9th spot in the 2014 Profit 500 ranking of fastest growing companies in Canada. The firm's strategy is to promote its flagship product Vega One using an in-store bicycle-powered blender. **Availability:** Online.

18329 ■ *"Sense of Discovery"* in *Business Journal Portland (Vol. 27, November 19, 2010, No. 38, pp. 1)*
Pub: Portland Business Journal
Contact: Andy Giegerich, Managing Editor
E-mail: agiegerich@bizjournals.com
Description: Tigard, Oregon-based Exterro Inc. CEO Bobby Balachandran announced plans to go public without the help of an institutional investor. Balachandran believes Exterro could grow to a $100 million legal compliance software company in the span of three years. Insights on Exterro's growth as market leader in the $1 billion legal governance software market are also given. **Availability:** Print; Online.

18330 ■ *"Seton Grows Heart Institute"* in *Austin Business Journal (Vol. 31, July 15, 2011, No. 19, pp. A1)*
Pub: Austin Business Journal
Contact: Rachel McGrath, Director
E-mail: rmcgrath@bizjournals.com
Ed: Sandra Zaragoza. **Description:** Seton Heart Institute experienced significant growth in the last six months. The organization added physicians, specialists and outreach offices across Central Texas. **Availability:** Print; Online.

18331 ■ *"Shear Profit"* in *Crain's Cleveland Business (Vol. 28, October 29, 2007, No. 43, pp. 3)*
Pub: Crain Communications Inc.
Contact: K. C. Crain, President
Ed: David Bennett. **Description:** Alpaca farms are becoming a very profitable business for a number of Northeast Ohio entrepreneurs due to the high return on initial investments, tax incentives and the rise in demand for the animals. Ohio leads the country in the number of alpaca farms with roughly one-third located in Northeast Ohio. **Availability:** Online.

18332 ■ *"Shell Profits Top $2 Billion as Oil Sands Output Surges"* in *Globe & Mail (January 26, 2006, pp. B6)*
Description: The reasons behind posting of $2 billion profits for 2005, by Shell Canada Ltd. are presented. **Availability:** Online.

18333 ■ *"The Silvery Moon Moves to Larger Location"* in *Bellingham Business Journal (Vol. March 2010, pp. 5)*
Pub: Sound Publishing Inc.
Contact: Josh O'Connor, President
Ed: Isaac Bonnell. **Description:** Jewelry store, the Silvery Moon, moved to a larger location in order to expand its business. The new location was chosen because it offers the firm more visibility. The store offers find silver and gold pieces and specializes in Pacific Northwest native jewelry.

18334 ■ *"The Skype's the Limit"* in *Canadian Business (Vol. 80, February 12, 2007, No. 4, pp. 70)*
Description: The increase in the market share of Skype Technologies S.A.'s Internet phone service to 171 million users is discussed. **Availability:** Print; Online.

GENERAL SMALL BUSINESS TOPICS

18335 ■ "Small Business Capital Outlays" in Small Business Economic Trends (April 2008, pp. 16)
Pub: National Federation of Independent Business
Contact: Brad Close, President
Ed: William C. Dunkelberg, Holly Wade. **Description:** Graphs and tables that present the capital outlays of small businesses in the U.S. are provided. The tables include figures on planned and actual capital expenditures, and type and amount of capital expenditures. **Availability:** PDF.

18336 ■ Small Business for Dummies
Pub: John Wiley & Sons, Inc.
Contact: Christina Van Tassell, Executive Vice President Chief Financial Officer
Ed: Eric Tyson, Jim Schell. **Released:** 5th Edition. **Price:** $24.99, paperback; $16.99, E-book. **Description:** Guidebook for anyone wanting to start or grow a small business; topics include information financing, budgeting, marketing, management and more. **Availability:** E-book; Print.

18337 ■ "Small Business Growth Statistics: 50 Facts of Successful Businesses" in SmartBooks (Nov. 20, 2019)
URL(s): smartbooks.com/resources/articles/small-business-growth-statistics-50-facts-of-successful-businesses/
Ed: Calvin Wilder. **Released:** November 20, 2019. **Description:** Provides important statistics related to small business growth for entrepreneurs to keep in mind for business growth. **Availability:** Online.

18338 ■ "Small Business Growth Statistics That May Surprise You" in SmartBiz Blog (Oct. 4, 2021)
URL(s): resources.smartbizloans.com/blog/business-finances/small-business-growth-statistics-that-may-surprise-you/
Ed: Suzanne Robertson. **Released:** October 04, 2021. **Description:** A culmination of small-business statistics providing an overview of the business landscape in the U.S as of 2021. **Availability:** Online.

18339 ■ "Small Business Outlook" in Small Business Economic Trends (September 2010, pp. 4)
Pub: National Federation of Independent Business
Contact: Brad Close, President
Ed: William C. Dunkelberg, Holly Wade. **Description:** A graph representing outlook among small businesses surveyed in the U.S. from January 1986 to August 2010 is presented. Tables showing small business outlook for expansion and outlook for general business conditions from January 2005 to August 2010, and most important reasons for expansion outlook are also given. **Availability:** Online.

18340 ■ "Small Business Sales: 6 Strategies for Prospecting" in Small Business Economic Trends (April 2008, pp. 7)
Pub: National Federation of Independent Business
Contact: Brad Close, President
Ed: William C. Dunkelberg, Holly Wade. **Description:** Two tables and a graph resenting sales figures of small businesses in the U.S. is presented. Statistics for sales changes and sales expectations are provided. The figures in the graph include data from 1986 to 2008. **Availability:** Print; Online.

18341 ■ Small Business Sourcebook
Released: 38th edition. **Price:** $1,001. **Description:** Two-volume guide to more than 27,300 listings of live and print sources for small business startups as well as small business growth and development. Over 30,500 topics are included. **Availability:** E-book; Print.

18342 ■ "Small Business Statistics" in Small Business Trends (July 9, 2021)
URL(s): smallbiztrends.com/tag/small-business-statistics
Released: July 09, 2021. **Description:** Compilation of essential small business statistics by subject to help entrepreneurs make informed decisions. **Availability:** Online.

18343 ■ "Small Business Statistics: 19 Essential Numbers to Know" in Fundera (Dec. 21, 2021)
URL(s): www.fundera.com/blog/small-business-statistics
Ed: Gretchen Schmid. **Released:** December 21, 2021. **Description:** Provides 19 small business statistics for entrepreneurs to understand to better run your business. **Availability:** Online.

18344 ■ "Small-Business Statistics: By the Numbers" in NerdWallet (May 14, 2021)
URL(s): www.nerdwallet.com/article/small-business/small-business-statistics
Ed: Kelsey Sheehy. **Released:** May 14, 2021. **Description:** Provides statistics that give a snapshot of the small business landscape as of 2021. **Availability:** Online.

18345 ■ Small Business Turnaround
Price: $17.95 paperback. **Availability:** Print.

18346 ■ "Small Wind Power Market to Double by 2015 at $634 Million" in Western Farm Press (September 30, 2011)
Description: Small wind power provides cost-effective electricity on a highly localized level, in both remote settings as well as in conjunction with power from the utility grid. Government incentives are spurring new growth in the industry. **Availability:** Online.

18347 ■ "Solar Gaining Power in Tennessee" in Memphis Business Journal (Vol. 34, June 15, 2012, No. 9, pp. 1)
Pub: Baltimore Business Journal
Contact: Rhonda Pringle, President
E-mail: rpringle@bizjournals.com
Ed: Michael Sheffield. **Description:** Tennessee's solar energy industry has grown, the Tennessee Solar Institute has reported. Solar energy use, manufacture and employment in the state have increase in the past four years. **Availability:** Print; Online.

18348 ■ "Some Credit Unions Are Big on Business Loans" in South Florida Business Journal (Vol. 35, September 5, 2014, No. 6, pp. 4)
Pub: American City Business Journals, Inc.
Contact: Mike Olivieri, Executive Vice President
Description: Business loans provided by credit unions in Florida have increased in 2014. Business loans in the state have risen to $1.36 billion. Jetstream Federal Credit Union increased its business loans by 456 percent. **Availability:** Online.

18349 ■ "The South Looks Yummy to Tastykakes" in Philadelphia Business Journal (Vol. 31, March 30, 2012, No. 7, pp. 1)
Pub: Baltimore Business Journal
Contact: Rhonda Pringle, President
E-mail: rpringle@bizjournals.com
Description: Tasty Baking Company owner, Flowers Foods, is planning to increase the number of stores selling Tastykake. Sales of Tastykake is expected to grow to as much as $225 million. **Availability:** Print; Online.

18350 ■ "Spam's Biggest Fan" in Barron's (Vol. 92, August 25, 2012, No. 35, pp. 42)
Pub: Dow Jones & Company Inc.
Contact: Almar Latour, Chief Executive Officer
Ed: Lawrence C. Strauss. **Description:** Jeffrey Ettinger, chief executive officer of meat packing and packaged food firm Hormel Foods, is credited with expanding the company's product offerings. Ettinger, who took over in 2006, involves himself in almost every aspect of the company's business. **Availability:** Online.

18351 ■ "Speed Traps: Every Fast-Growth Company Eventually Runs Into At Least One of These All-Too-Common Obstacles. How You Handle Them Can Make the Difference Between Success and a High-Speed Smashup" in Inc. (Vol. 34, September 2012, No. 7, pp. 53)
Pub: Mansueto Ventures L.L.C.
Contact: Stephanie Mehta, Chief Executive Officer

Business Growth and Statistics ■ 18359

Ed: Kimberly Weisul. **Released:** September 01, 2012. **Description:** Obstacles encountered by fast growing companies and suggestions to avoid falling into these traps are covered. According to a recent study conducted by Gary Kunkle, an economist and research fellowwith Edward Lowe Foundation's Institute for Exceptional Growth Companies, shows that fast growing companies share the same issues, which are different from those of industry peers or businesses of the same size. **Availability:** Print; Online.

18352 ■ Start, Run, & Grow a Successful Small Business
Pub: Toolkit Media Group
Ed: John L. Duoba, Joel Handelsman, Alice H. Magos, Catherine Gordon. **Released:** Sixth edition. **Availability:** Print.

18353 ■ "State of Play" in Canadian Business (Vol. 79, June 19, 2006, No. 13, pp. 25)
Description: Top 100 information technology companies in Canada are ranked by their market capitalization as of June 1. The statistics that show the revenues of these companies are also presented. **Availability:** Print; Online.

18354 ■ "Steady Spending In Retail, But Job Losses Are Rising" in Business Week (September 22, 2008, No. 4100, pp. 13)
Ed: Tara Kalwarski. **Description:** Retail jobs have begun to decline on the national level despite the two percent growth in the industry over the last year; much of the growth has been attributed to the sales of higher-priced oil products.

18355 ■ "Still Stretching" in Business Courier (Vol. 24, December 28, 2008, No. 37, pp. 1)
Description: Minority-owned businesses have experienced growth in 2007 as Cincinnati and Hamilton County used a workforce development and economic inclusion policy. Kroger Co., for example, has been inducted to the Billion Dollar Roundtable in 2007 for attaining $1 billion in annual spending with suppliers that are minority- owned. The need for more progress within the minority-owned enterprises is discussed. **Availability:** Online.

18356 ■ "Stop the Innovation Wars" in Harvard Business Review (Vol. 88, July-August 2010, No. 7-8, pp. 76)
Pub: Harvard Business Publishing
Contact: Diane Belcher, Managing Director
Ed: Vijay Govindarajan, Chris Trimble. **Price:** $8.95, PDF. **Description:** Methods for managing conflicts between partners during the innovation initiative process are highlighted. These include dividing the labor, assembling a dedicated team, and mitigating likelihood for any potential conflict. **Availability:** Online; PDF.

18357 ■ Streetwise Small Business Book of Lists: Hundreds of Lists to Help You Reduce Costs, Increase Revenues, and Boost Your Profits!
Price: Paperback. **Description:** Strategies to help small business owners locate services, increase sales, and lower expenses. **Availability:** Print.

18358 ■ Streetwise Small Business Turnaround: Revitalizing Your Struggling or Stagnant Enterprise
Description: Practical tips and advice are provided for rejuvenating an existing small business.

18359 ■ "Strengthen the Support for Women in Biz" in Crain's Detroit Business (Vol. 30, September 8, 2014, No. 36, pp. 1)
Pub: Crain Communications Inc.
Contact: Barry Asin, President
Description: According to the 2014 State of Women-Owned Businesses Report, the number of woman-owned businesses has almost doubled since 1997. The report was commissioned by American Express Open. Statistical data included. **Availability:** Online.

18360 ■ "StubHub Launches in the UK" in Entertainment Close-Up (March 25, 2012)
Description: StubHub, an eBay company, is expanding to the United Kingdom. The firm sells tickets, third party; to music, sport, and entertainment events by connecting buyers and sellers. Details of the service and expansion are explored. Availability: Online.

18361 ■ "Subaru of America Releases September Sales Figures" in Travel & Leisure Close-Up (October 8, 2012)
Description: Subaru of America Inc. reports a 32 percent increase in sales in September 2012 compared to September 2011. Sales were shown at 27,683 vehicles for the month. Statistical data included. Availability: Print; Online.

18362 ■ "Substantial Deal Expected to Create Jobs, Help Industrial Market" in Tampa Bay Business Journal (Vol. 30, January 8, 2010, No. 3)
Pub: Tampa Bay Business Journal
Contact: Ian Anderson, President
E-mail: ianderson@bizjournals.com
Ed: Janet Leiser. Description: Food distribution firm Gordon Food Service (GFS) is on the brink of purchasing Albertson's million-square-foot warehouse along with 158 acres of space. The deal between GFS and Albertson's could expand GFS' presence in west Central Florida. A history of GFS' growth is included. Availability: Print; Online.

18363 ■ "Sumitomo Invests in Desert Sunlight Solar Farm, the Largest PV Project Approved for Federal Land" in PR Newswire (October 2, 2012)
Pub: PR Newswire Association LLC.
Description: The Desert Sunlight Solar Farm, 550MW solar power project being constructed in the California desert area east of Palm Springs, is the largest solar photovoltaic (PV) facility approved for US public land. Sumitomo Corporation of America is investing in the project and plans to expand its renewable energy portfolio across the US.

18364 ■ "SunBank Plans Expansion Via Wal-Mart" in Business Journal-Serving Phoenix and the Valley of the Sun (Vol. 10, November 8, 2007)
Pub: Phoenix Business Journal
Contact: Alex McAlister, Director
E-mail: amcalister@bizjournals.com
Ed: Chris Casacchia. Description: SunBank plans to install 12 to 14 branches in Wal-Mart stores in Arizona and hire 100 bankers by the end of 2008. Wal-Mart also offers financial products at other stores through partnerships with other banks. Availability: Print; Online.

18365 ■ "Supermercado El Rancho Chain Grows Along with Hispanic Population" in Dallas Business Journal (Vol. 35, July 13, 2012, No. 44, pp. 1)
Pub: Baltimore Business Journal
Contact: Rhonda Pringle, President
E-mail: rpringle@bizjournals.com
Ed: Matt Joyce. Description: Garland, Texas-based Supermercado El Rancho has grown rapidly wit its take on the Hispanic grocery market and is planning to open 12 stores in six years. La Bodega Meat Inc., the chain's affiliate distribution company, is planning a $13.1 million renovation and double the size of its warehouse to accommodate the plans for more stores.

18366 ■ "Surge in the South" in Canadian Business (Vol. 85, June 11, 2012, No. 10, pp. 48)
Ed: Jeff Beer. Description: Canada should get involved as a trading partner in the emerging markets as South-South trade, which is between these markets, is projected to grow between 2012 and 2030 from 13 percent of global trade to 26 percent. Canadian firms can join the South-South trade by setting up operations in an emeging market and use it as a base for trade or by acting as facilitator between trade partners. Availability: Online.

18367 ■ "Survey: Confident Parts Makers Plan to Expand, Hire" in Crain's Detroit Business (Vol. 30, August 18, 2014, No. 33, pp. 5)
Pub: Crain Communications Inc.
Contact: Barry Asin, President
Description: North American automotive suppliers are increasing capital expenditure, hiring new workers, and raising funds for possible mergers and acquisitions. Automotive manufacturing suppliers are forecasting a rebound in new vehicle sales. Statistical data included. Availability: Online.

18368 ■ "Survey Reveals Shifting Preferences in Pool Chemicals and Sanitation Systems" in Pool and Spa News (November 20, 2017)
URL(s): www.poolspanews.com/how-to/maintenance/survey-reveals-shifting-preferences-in-pool-chemicals-and-sanitation-systems_o
Ed: Nate Traylor. Released: November 20, 2017. Description: Pool and Spa News conducted a survey to see which type of pool system consumers prefer to use and how loyal they are to their brands and local stores. Availability: Online.

18369 ■ "The Survey Says" in Collections and Credit Risk (Vol. 14, September 1, 2009, No. 8, pp. 16)
Description: Revenue for the top accounts receivable management firms rose nearly 20 percent in 2008 despite lower liquidation rates, a poor economy and riskier, albeit cheaper debt portfolios; the trend may continue this year as collection agencies expect revenue, on average, to increase 5.8 percent. Debt buyers, however, found that their revenue fell nearly 7 percent in 2008 and expect it to fall another 12 percent this year. Availability: Print; Online.

18370 ■ "Susan Leger Ferraro Built a $7.2 Million Day Care Business: Now She Wants To Expand-And Cash Out" in Inc. (January 2008, pp. 50-53)
Ed: Dalia Fahmy. Description: Profile of Susan Leger Ferraro who wants to expand her chain of day care centers into Florida and California and sell part of her 87 percent stake to reduce financial risk. Availability: Online.

18371 ■ "Sweet Tea From McDonald's: A Marketing 50 Case Study" in Advertising Age (Vol. 79, November 17, 2008, No. 43, pp. 4)
Pub: Crain Communications, Inc.
Contact: Jessica Botos, Manager, Marketing
E-mail: jessica.botos@crainsnewyork.com
Ed: Emily Bryson York. Description: McDonald's launch of iced coffee and sweat tea, which were promoted via price cuts over the summer, helped to boost sales at the fast-food chain. Availability: Online.

18372 ■ "SWOT Analysis Guide" in Small Business Trends (January 20, 2023)
Ed: Kevin Ocasio. Released: January 20, 2023. Description: A guide to conducting a SWOT analysis for your small business. Identifying the strengths, weaknesses, opportunities, and threats can help improve operations and plan for the future. Availability: Online.

18373 ■ "Table Games Get a Leg Up" in Philadelphia Business Journal (Vol. 28, January 15, 2010, No. 48, pp. 1)
Pub: Philadelphia Business Journal
Contact: Sierra Quinn, Director
E-mail: squinn@bizjournals.com
Ed: Athena D. Merritt, Peter Van Allen. Description: Casino operators expect the addition of live table games such as poker and blackjack at existing and planned casinos in Philadelphia will generate 1,000 new jobs. Most of the jobs will be dealers and floor supervisors. Availability: Online.

18374 ■ "Tabs Says Organic Food Sales Hit Record in 2011. Sales Jump 15-20 Percent" in Entertainment Close-Up (February 21, 2012)
Description: Tabs Group reported it found an increase in American consumers reporting they purchased organic products along with a rise in overall sales in its Annual Organic Product Survey. Statistical data included.

18375 ■ "Taking a Leap With Mobile Wi-Fi" in Austin Business Journal (Vol. 34, July 25, 2014, No. 23, pp. 10)
Pub: American City Business Journals, Inc.
Contact: Mike Olivieri, Executive Vice President
Released: July 25, 2014. Price: $4, introductory 4-week offer(Digital only). Description: Austin-based semi-conductor design company Nitero Inc.'s recent release of its Wi-Fi chip, Nietero's key rival Wilocity Ltd.'s acquisition by a tech giant, pushing demand for semiconductors; thus spurring growth for Nitero. It's Wi-Fi's system for mobile platforms will enable users to do more things on their Smartphones, thus converging more devices into one. Availability: Print; Online.

18376 ■ "Targeted Personal Trainer Business Strategies Build Clients, Income, Business and Success" in Marketing Weekly News (August 4, 2012)
Description: Various business strategies can help personal trainers build their business include getting certified, creating postcards or flyers, and partnering with other fitness professionals. Availability: Print; PDF; Online.

18377 ■ "Targeting New Growth" in San Antonio Business Journal (Vol. 28, May 23, 2014, No. 15, pp. 4)
Pub: American City Business Journals, Inc.
Contact: Mike Olivieri, Executive Vice President
Released: May 23, 2014. Description: Reports show that many retailers are discovering new opportunities along Austin Highway in Texas. Observers believe that the rise of multifamily housing contributed to the retail turnaround. However, the increase in property values can have a negative impact on the retail sector. Availability: Print; Online.

18378 ■ "Tax Services Firm Ryan Prepares for Growth" in Dallas Business Journal (Vol. 35, June 29, 2012, No. 42, pp. 1)
Pub: Baltimore Business Journal
Contact: Rhonda Pringle, President
E-mail: rpringle@bizjournals.com
Ed: Candace Carlisle. Description: Ryan LLC is seen to grow with three pending acquisitions. The tax services firm has opened offices in Australia and Singapore. Availability: Print; Online.

18379 ■ "The Tech 100" in Canadian Business (Vol. 81, July 21, 2008, No. 11, pp. 48)
Description: Absolute Software Corp. Day4 Energy Inc., Sandvine Corp., Norsat International Inc. and Call Genie Inc. are the five technology firms included in the annual ranking of top companies in Canada by market capitalization. The services and the one-year total return potential of the companies are presented. Availability: Online.

18380 ■ "Tech Jobs Rebound from Downturn" in Denver Business Journal (Vol. 65, March 7, 2014, No. 43, pp. A9)
Pub: American City Business Journals, Inc.
Contact: Mike Olivieri, Executive Vice President
Released: Weekly. Price: $4, Introductory 4-week offer(Digital & Print). Description: Denver, Colorado's employment in core technology industries has returned from pre-Great Recession figures. The computer software industry's surging job growth and the slight increase in the broadcasts and telecommunications industry offset the job losses in biotechnology and private aerospace industry from 2008 through 2013. The growth in specific industries is also discussed. Availability: Print; Online.

18381 ■ *"Thai Ice Cream Cremo Expanding to Middle East"* in *Ice Cream Reporter* (Vol. 23, September 20, 2010, No. 10, pp. 3)
Description: Thai-based frozen dessert manufacturer Chomthana, maker of Cremo brand ice cream, is expanding into the Middle East. **Availability:** Print; Online.

18382 ■ *"There's Risk, Reward for Business in Baltimore's Edgier Areas: Taking a Chance"* in *Baltimore Business Journal* (Vol. 28, July 16, 2010, No. 10, pp. 1)
Pub: Baltimore Business Journal
Contact: Rhonda Pringle, President
E-mail: rpringle@bizjournals.com
Ed: Scott Dance. **Description:** North Avenue in Baltimore, Maryland is considered a rough neighborhood due to the dangers of prostitution and drug dealing. However, some entrepreneurs have taken the risk of building their businesses on North Avenue as revitalization efforts grow. One of the challenges for businesses in rough neighborhoods is bringing customers to their stores or offices. **Availability:** Print.

18383 ■ *"These Are the Women Who Really Mean Business"* in *Canadian Business* (Vol. 87, October 2014, No. 10, pp. 67)
Description: A list of the top 100 women entrepreneurs in Canada are ranked, based on sales, three-year revenue growth rate, and profitability of their businesses is presented. Included in the list are Janet Stimpson of White House Design Company, Inc.; builder, Allison Grafton of Rockwood Custom Homes Inc.; and Janet Jing Di Zhang of Vancouver, BC of New Immigrants Information Services Inc. **Availability:** Online.

18384 ■ *The Thin Book of Naming Elephants: How to Surface Undiscussables for Greater Organizational Success*
Pub: Thin Book Publishing Co.
Contact: Sue Annis Hammond, Founder
E-mail: sue@thinbook.com
Ed: Sue Annis Hammond, Andrea B. Mayfield. **Description:** Organizational success is of upmost importance to today's entrepreneurs and organizations. The hierarchal system in which people are afraid to speak up in organizations is discussed. The points of view and inability to see things from an overall perspective can cause insecurity among employees. The three elephants present in every organization include: arrogance, hubris, and screamers and the damage caused by these elephants in any organization is examined. **Availability:** E-book.

18385 ■ *"Thirsty Lion Cooks Up Big Expansion Plan"* in *Business Journal Portland* (Vol. 27, November 5, 2010, No. 36, pp. 1)
Pub: Portland Business Journal
Contact: Andy Giegerich, Managing Editor
E-mail: agiegerich@bizjournals.com
Ed: Wendy Culverwell. **Description:** Concept Entertainment Inc.'s impending launch of the Thirsty Lion Pub and Grill at the Washington Square in downtown Portland, Oregon is part of its West Coast expansion plan. A discussion of the planning involved in realizing Thirsty Lion is discussed, along with pub offerings that are expected to be enjoyed by customers. **Availability:** Print; Online.

18386 ■ *"Thomson Eyes Asia for Expansion"* in *Globe & Mail* (February 10, 2006, pp. B4)
Description: The business growth plans of Thomson Corp., in Asia, are presented. **Availability:** Print; Online.

18387 ■ *"Thriving DFW Big Target for Franchisors"* in *Dallas Business Journal* (Vol. 35, March 30, 2012, No. 29, pp. 1)
Description: Dallas-Fort Worth Metropolitan Area has attracted outside franchisors looking to expand as Texas continues to fare better than other states during the recession. The Internation Franchising Association estimates that there will be 21,772 franchise establishments in DFW in 2012. **Availability:** Print; Online.

18388 ■ *"Time for a Little Pruning?"* in *Barron's* (Vol. 89, July 6, 2009, No. 27, pp. 13)
Pub: Dow Jones & Company Inc.
Contact: Almar Latour, Chief Executive Officer
Ed: Dimitra DeFotis. **Description:** Investors are advised to avoid the shares of Whole Foods, American Tower, T. Rowe Price, Iron Mountain, Intuitive Surgical, Salesforce.com, and Juniper Networks due to their high price to earnings ratios. The shares of Amazon.com, Broadcom, and Expeditors International of Washington remain attractive to investors despite their high price to earnings ratios due to their strong growth. **Availability:** Online.

18389 ■ *"Timken's Bearings Rolling in China, India"* in *Crain's Cleveland Business* (Vol. 28, October 29, 2007, No. 43, pp. 14)
Pub: Crain Communications Inc.
Contact: K. C. Crain, President
Ed: David Bennett. **Description:** Canton-based Timken Co., a manufacturer of bearings and specialty metals, is seeing growing demand for its line of tapered roller bearings, which allow rail users to carry heavy car loads. The company is finding significant growth in China and India due to their rapidly growing rail markets. **Availability:** PDF; Online.

18390 ■ *"Tips From a Turnaround Expert"* in *Business Owner* (Vol. 35, July-August 2011, No. 4, pp. 8)
Description: The book, 'The Six Month Fix: Adventures in Rescuing Failing Companies' by Gary Sutton is summarized. It provides lessons for finding and building profits in failing firms. **Availability:** Print; Online.

18391 ■ *"TiVo, Domino's Team to Offer Pizza Ordering by DVR"* in *Advertising Age* (Vol. 79, November 17, 2008, No. 43, pp. 48)
Pub: Crain Communications, Inc.
Contact: Jessica Botos, Manager, Marketing
E-mail: jessica.botos@crainsnewyork.com
Ed: Brian Steinberg. **Description:** Domino's Pizza and TiVo are teaming up to make it possible for customers to order from the restaurant straight from their DVR. The companies see that this kind of interactive television and consumer experience will only serve to generate more sales as the customer can be exposed to a fuller range of menu selections and will not have to interrupt their viewing, while workers can spend more time making the product. **Availability:** Online.

18392 ■ *"TMC Development Closes $1.1 Million Real Estate Purchase for Mansa, LLC Using SBA 504 Real Estate Financing"* in *Marketwired* (September 17, 2009)
Pub: Comtex News Network Inc.
Contact: Kan Devnani, President
Description: TMC Development announced the closing of a $1.1 million real estate purchase for Mansa, LLC dba Kwikee Mart, a Napa-based convenience store; TMC helped the company secure a Small Business Administration 504 loan in order to purchase the acquisition of a 3,464 square foot building. SBA created the 504 loan program to provide financing for growing small and medium-sized businesses. **Availability:** Online.

18393 ■ *"The Top 10: Prime Examples of Growth and Prosperity"* in *South Florida Business Journal* (Vol. 34, July 18, 2014, No. 52, pp. 13)
Pub: American City Business Journals, Inc.
Contact: Mike Olivieri, Executive Vice President
Released: June 18, 2014. **Price:** $4, Introductory 4-Week Offer(Digital & Print). **Description:** A list of the top ten private companies in South Florida in 2014 is presented. The companies represent the strength of the local economy and encompass a variety of industries, with combined revenue growth of $3.58 billion. **Availability:** Print; Online.

18394 ■ *"Top 49ers Alphabetical Listing with Five Years Rank and Revenue"* in *Alaska Business Monthly* (Vol. 27, October 2011, No. 10, pp. 100)
Pub: Alaska Business Publishing Company Inc.
Contact: Charles Bell, Vice President, Sales and Marketing
E-mail: cbell@akbizmag.com
Description: A listing of Alaska's top 49 performing companies ranked by revenue for years 2010 and 2011. **Availability:** Print; Online.

18395 ■ *"Top 50 In Total Revenue"* in *Canadian Business* (Vol. 81, Summer 2008, No. 9, pp. 119)
Description: Table showing the top 50 Canadian companies in terms of total revenue is presented. Manulife Financial Corp. topped the list with revenue of 34.5 billion. The financial services firm is the 6th largest provider of life insurance in the world and the second largest in North America. **Availability:** Print; Online.

18396 ■ *"Toyota Marks Record Profit Sales"* in *Globe & Mail* (February 7, 2007, pp. B10)
Description: The record quarterly sales and earnings reported by Japanese automaker Toyota Motor Corp. are discussed. The company sold 2.16 million vehicles during the quarter while registering 426.8 billion yen in profits. **Availability:** Print; Online.

18397 ■ *"Toyota Tops GM in Global Sales"* in *Globe & Mail* (April 24, 2007, pp. B1)
Ed: Greg Keenan. **Description:** The success of Toyota Motor Corp. in surpassing General Motors Corp. in its global sales is discussed. **Availability:** Online.

18398 ■ *"Training Essential For Growth; It Doesn't Have To Cost Much"* in *Crain's Detroit Business* (Vol. 24, January 21, 2008, No. 3, pp. 14)
Pub: Crain Communications Inc.
Contact: Barry Asin, President
Ed: Sheena Harrison. **Description:** Employee training is essential for small companies to achieve growth. **Availability:** Print; Online.

18399 ■ *"Transforming the Business Portfolio: How Multinationals Reinvent Themselves"* in *Journal of Business Strategy* (Vol. 35, May-June 2014, No. 3, pp. 4-17)
Pub: Emerald Group Publishing Limited
Contact: Erika Valenti, President
Description: Study on the process of business portfolio transformations to investigate its precursors, practices, and outcomes, including repositioning, refocusing, and diversifying of portfolio restructurings is presented. It is observed that poor performance and over-diversification induce portfolio restructuring. The results also revealed that diversifying or repositioning transformations feature a low success rate, whereas refocusing transformations generally happen to be more successful. **Availability:** Download; Online.

18400 ■ *"Tsingtao's Chairman On Jump-Starting a Sluggish Company"* in *Harvard Business Review* (Vol. 90, April 2012, No. 4, pp. 41)
Pub: Harvard Business Review Press
Contact: Moderna V. Pfizer, Contact
Ed: Jin Zhiguo. **Description:** The key challenge Tsingtao Brewery Company Ltd. faced was the focus on pleasing corporate superiors, rather than the firm's customers. By inventing a new model, the brewery was able to boost both employee productivity and product quality. First half profits and revenue for 2011 grew more than 20 percent over the previous year.

18401 ■ *"A Turn in the South"* in *The Economist* (Vol. 390, January 3, 2009, No. 8612, pp. 34)
Description: Overview of Charleston, South Carolina, a region that lost its navy base in 1996, which had provided work for more than 22,000 people; the city developed a plan called Noisette in order to

redevelop the area and today the economy is healthier and more diversified than it was a decade ago. Charleston was described as among the best cities for doing business by Inc. Magazine and seems to be handling the downturn of the economy fairly well. Statistical data regarding growth, business and population is included. **Availability:** Print; Online.

18402 ■ *"Two Local Firms Make Inc. List: Minority Business"* in Indianapolis Business Journal (Vol. 31, August 30, 2010, No. 26, pp. 13A)

Description: Smart IT staffing agency and Entap Inc., an IT outsourcing firm were among the top ten fastest growing black-owned businesses in the U.S. by Inc. magazine. **Availability:** Print; Online.

18403 ■ *"U-Swirl To Open in Salt Lake City Metro Market"* in Ice Cream Reporter (Vol. 23, November 20, 2010, No. 12, pp. 4)

Description: Healthy Fast Food Inc., parent company to U-SWIRL International Inc., the owner and franchisor of U-SWIRL Frozen Yogurt cafes signed a franchising area development agreement for the Salt Lake City metropolitan area with Regents Management and will open 5 cafes over a five year period. **Availability:** Print; Online.

18404 ■ *"UFC: Money and the Mayhem"* in Canadian Business (Vol. 83, September 14, 2010, No. 15, pp. 52)
Pub: Rogers Media Inc.
Contact: Neil Spivak, Chief Executive Officer

Ed: Greg Hudson. **Description:** Ultimate Fighting Championship (UFC) has hired Tom Wright as director of operations for Canada, who finally managed to get mixed martial arts sanctioned in Ontario. Canada is UFC's largest market after the US and accounting for about 15-20 percent in annual revenue. **Availability:** Print; Online.

18405 ■ *"Under Armour's Founder On Learning to Leverage Celebrity Endorsements"* in Harvard Business Review (Vol. 90, May 2012, No. 5, pp. 45)
Pub: Harvard Business Review Press
Contact: Moderna V. Pfizer, Contact

Ed: Kevin Plank. **Description:** Using his athletic apparel company Under Armour as an illustration, the author identifies two key points in effective utilization of endorsement advertising: balancing freebies with fair-price contracts, and offering stock opportunities so that celebrities can be personally engaged with growth.

18406 ■ *"An Unfair Knock on Nokia"* in Barron's (Vol. 88, March 10, 2008, No. 10, pp. 36)
Pub: Dow Jones & Company Inc.
Contact: Almar Latour, Chief Executive Officer

Ed: Mark Veverka. **Description:** Discusses the decision by the brokerage house Exane to recommend a Sell on Nokia shares, presumably due to higher inventories, which is unfounded. The news that the company's inventories are rising is not an indicator of falling demand for its products. The company is also benefiting from solid management and rising market share. **Availability:** Online.

18407 ■ *"U.S. Retailer Eyes 'Tween' Market"* in Globe & Mail (January 30, 2007, pp. B1)

Ed: Marina Strauss. **Description:** The decision of Tween Brands Inc. (Too Incorporated) to open 100 new stores in Canada as part of its expansion is discussed. The company's focus on targeting girls for its products is detailed. **Availability:** Online.

18408 ■ *"Unveiling the Secrets Behind Hispanic Business' 100 Fastest-Growing Companies"* in Hispanic Business (Vol. 30, July-August 2008, No. 7-8, pp. 22)

Ed: Michael Bowker. **Description:** CEO's of the five fastest growing Hispanic-owned companies discuss the success of their companies; most of them attribute their success to proper investment and diversification, effective innovations and seeing growth opportunities where others see roadblocks. **Availability:** Online.

18409 ■ *"Upsurge"* in Puget Sound Business Journal (Vol. 33, July 13, 2012, No. 12, pp. 1)

Description: Kent, Washington-based Flow International Corporation posted a record of $254 million in annual sales for fiscal 2012 and it is expected to reach about $300 million by 2014. Flow is being lifted by a global manufacturing revival and by its machines' ability to handle the carbon-fiber composites used in aerospace. Insights on Flow's water jet cutting tools are also given.

18410 ■ *"Uptick in Clicks: Nordstrom's Online Sales Surging"* in Puget Sound Business Journal (Vol. 29, August 22, 2008, No. 18, pp. 1)

Description: Nordstrom Inc.'s online division grew its sales by 15 percent in the second quarter of 2008, compared to 2007's 4.3 percent in overall decline. The company expects their online net sales to reach $700 million in 2008 capturing eight percent of overall sales. **Availability:** Print; Online.

18411 ■ *"The VC Shakeout"* in Harvard Business Review (Vol. 88, July-August 2010, No. 7-8, pp. 21)
Pub: Harvard Business Publishing
Contact: Diane Belcher, Managing Director

Ed: Joseph Ghalboun, iDominique Rouzies. **Price:** $6, PDF. **Description:** Authors argue that in order to be successful, venture capital needs to focus less on how to sell a newly acquired investment and more on ways to grow a good company. **Availability:** Online; PDF.

18412 ■ *"Veteran-Owned Business 3E Services Gains Recognition in 2011 and Welcomes 2012 With New Offerings"* in Marketwired (January 10, 2012)
Pub: Comtex News Network Inc.
Contact: Kan Devnani, President

Description: 3E Services Inc. specializes in the selling, repairing, and remanufacturing of electrical components. It is a veteran-owned busiens located in Tucker, Georgia near Atlanta.The Washington Post recognized 3E as an exemplary veteran-owned business. David Loftin, president and founder, learned his skills as a US Navy nuclear electrician and attributes that training to his firm's growth and success. **Availability:** Print; Online.

18413 ■ *"Victory Not Resting On Its Laurels"* in Philadelphia Business Journal (Vol. 33, April 11, 2014, No. 9, pp. 6)
Pub: American City Business Journals, Inc.
Contact: Mike Olivieri, Executive Vice President

Description: Downingtown, Pennsylvania-based Victory Brewing Company co-founder, Bill Covaleski, shares his views on the industry's rapid growth. Cavaleski says he got complacent with the brands while building their second brewery so they added three new brews in 2013. He says they are looking for better market penetration in the mid-Atlantic and Philadelphia markets. **Availability:** Online.

18414 ■ *"Virgin Mobile has Big Plans for Year Two"* in Globe & Mail (March 6, 2006, pp. B5)

Ed: Catherine McLean. **Description:** The business growth plans of Virgin Mobile Canada are presented. **Availability:** Online.

18415 ■ *"VISA: Canadians Spend $97 Million on Mom This Mother's Day"* in Canadian Corporate News (May 16, 2007)

Description: Visa Canada finds that Canadians are spending more on Mother's Day in recent years. Since 2002, sales of jewelry, flowers, and cards have climbed steadily in the week before Mother's Day weekend. **Availability:** Print; Online.

18416 ■ *"Vision for Camden in Better Focus"* in Philadelphia Business Journal (Vol. 30, September 30, 2011, No. 33, pp. 1)
Pub: Philadelphia Business Journal
Contact: Sierra Quinn, Director
E-mail: squinn@bizjournals.com

Ed: Natalie Kostelni. **Description:** More than $500 million worth of projects aimed at redeveloping the downtown and waterfront areas of Camden, New Jersey are being planned. These include the construction of residential, commercial, and education buildings. **Availability:** Online.

18417 ■ *"Wabtec Delivering Strategic Plan for Long-term Growth"* in Pittsburgh Business Times (Vol. 33, July 11, 2014, No. 52, pp. 10)
Pub: American City Business Journals, Inc.
Contact: Mike Olivieri, Executive Vice President

Released: July 2014. **Description:** Raymond Betler, new CEO of Wabtec Corporation, the only company with a 13-year streak of annual stock price increase on US exchanges is profiled. Betler attributes the company's growth to four corporate strategies, including to grow internationally, focus on new product development, expand after-market opportunities, and pursue acquisitions. **Availability:** Print; Online.

18418 ■ *"'Wal-Mart Effect' Feeds Grocer Price Wars"* in Globe & Mail (March 15, 2007, pp. B14)

Ed: Marina Strauss. **Description:** The decrease in profit reports by Canadian grocery giants amidst high expansion plans by Wal-Mart Stores Inc. are discussed. This industry is witnessing the most severe pricing competitions in recent times. **Availability:** Print; Online.

18419 ■ *"Wal-Mart Proposed for Timmerman Plaza"* in Business Journal-Milwaukee (Vol. 28, December 31, 2010, No. 14, pp. A1)
Pub: The Business Journal
Contact: Heather Ladage, President
E-mail: hladage@bizjournals.com

Ed: Sean Ryan. **Description:** Dickson, Tennessee-based Gatlin Development Company Inc. owner Franklin C. Gatlin III revealed plans for a new Wal-Mart store in Timmerman Plaza in Milwaukee, Wisconsin. Wal-Mart plans to open up approximately 18 new stores in southeast Wisconsin in 2012 and the Timmerman project is the first of four that Gatlin will submit for city approval. **Availability:** Print; Online.

18420 ■ *"Walmart's New-Store Roll-Out Proving to be Development Magnet"* in San Antonio Business Journal (Vol. 27, January 24, 2014, No. 51, pp. 4)
Pub: American City Business Journals, Inc.
Contact: Mike Olivieri, Executive Vice President

Released: Weekly. **Price:** $4, Introductory 4-week offer(Digital & Print). **Description:** Bentonville, Arkansas-based Walmart Stores have developed an aggressive plan to expand its base of business in greater San Antonio, Texas with new Supercenters that opened for business. The Walmart Supercenters are creating an impact on the city's retail market as it spurs the interests of other retailers. Walmart's concept is also examined. **Availability:** Print; Online.

18421 ■ *"Watchful Eye: Entrepreneur Protects Clients and His Bottom Line"* in Black Enterprise (Vol. 38, March 1, 2008, No. 8, pp. 46)
Pub: Earl G. Graves Ltd.
Contact: Earl Graves, Jr., President

Ed: Tennille M. Robinson. **Description:** Profile of Elijah Shaw, founder of Icon Services Corporation, a full service security and investigative service; Shaw shares his plans to protect clients while growing his business. **Availability:** Online.

18422 ■ *"Wegmans Adding 1,600-Plus Jobs Here Over the Next Year"* in Boston Business Journal (Vol. 34, February 14, 2014, No. 2, pp. 3)
Pub: American City Business Journals, Inc.
Contact: Mike Olivieri, Executive Vice President

Description: Wegmans, a family-owned grocery chain, is planning to add the most jobs of any firm in Massachusetts in 2014. The company will create more than 1,600 full- and part-time positions by opening three stores. Bill Congdon, Wegmans' New England division manager, reveals that the company is also planning to open a store in the city of Boston. **Availability:** Print; Online.

18423 ■ *What Works: Success in Stressful Times*
Ed: Hamish McRae. **Released:** August 04, 2011. **Price:** $14.95, paperback; $5.99, e-book. **Description:** Exploration of success stories from across the glove, and what Michelle Obama referred to as 'the flimsy difference between success and failure.' Why do some initiatives take off while others flounder? How have communities managed to achieve so much while others struggle? What distinguishes the good companies from the bad? What lessons can be learned from the well-ordered Mumbai community made famous by 'Slumdog Millionaire'? Why have Canadian manners helped Whistler become the most popular ski resort in North America?. **Availability:** E-book; Print.

18424 ■ *"What's Holding Down Small Business?" in Business Owner (Vol. 35, November-December 2011, No. 6, pp. 3)*
Description: According to a recent survey conducted by the National Federation of Independent Business, demand is the number one reason for slow growth to any small business in today's economy. **Availability:** PDF; Online.

18425 ■ *When Family Businesses are Best: The Parallel Planning Process for Family Harmony and Business Success*
Pub: Palgrave Macmillan
Ed: Randel S. Carlock, John L. Ward. **Released:** First edition. **Description:** An exploration into effective planning and communication to help small businesses grow into multi-generation family enterprises. **Availability:** E-book; Print.

18426 ■ *"Why the Gap is Stalking Lululemon" in Canadian Business (Vol. 85, August 22, 2012, No. 14, pp. 7)*
Ed: Jim Sutherland. **Description:** Lululemon Athletica is facing competition against Gap Inc.'s Athleta as the retail giant plans to have about 50 new shops across Canada by the end of 2012. Athleta is also carrying lines of yoga- and activewear similar to that of Lululemon's and are even located near their stores. **Availability:** Online.

18427 ■ *"Why the Rout in Financials Isn't Over" in Barron's (Vol. 88, June 30, 2008, No. 26, pp. 23)*
Pub: Dow Jones & Company Inc.
Contact: Almar Latour, Chief Executive Officer
Ed: Robin Goldwyn Blumenthal. **Description:** Top market technician Louise Yamada warns that the retreat in the shares of financial services is not yet over based on her analysis of stock charts. Yamada's analysis of the charts of Citigroup, Fifth Third Bancorp and Merrill Lynch are discussed together with the graphs for these shares. Statistical data included. **Availability:** Online.

18428 ■ *Why Small Businesses Still Need to Network in the Local Community*
URL(s): ducttapemarketing.com/local-network-community/
Ed: Deborah Sweeney. **Description:** Explores the continued importance of networking in your local community. **Availability:** Online.

18429 ■ *"Why We'll Never Escape Facebook" in Canadian Business (Vol. 83, June 15, 2010, No. 10, pp. 28)*
Pub: Rogers Media Inc.
Contact: Neil Spivak, Chief Executive Officer
Ed: James Cowan, Tamara Shopsin, Jason Fulford. **Description:** Facebook users are growing in numbers despite criticism of the site's privacy policies that have put the onus of keeping anonymous to the user. Facebook's business model and its growing influence on the Internet are discussed. **Availability:** Online.

18430 ■ *"Women Clicking to Earn Virtual Dollars" in Sales and Marketing Management (November 11, 2009)*
Ed: Stacy Straczynski. **Description:** According to a new report from Internet marketing firm Q Interactive, women are increasingly playing social media games where they are able to click on an ad or sign up for a promotion to earn virtual currency. Research is showing that this kind of marketing may be a potent tool, especially for e-commerce and online stores. **Availability:** Print; Online.

18431 ■ *"A World of Opportunity: Foreign Markets Offer Diversity to Keen Investors" in Canadian Business (Vol. 81, Summer 2008, No. 9)*
Description: International Monetary Fund projected in its 'World Economy Outlook' that there is a 25 percent chance that a global recession will occur in 2008 and 2009. Global growth rate is forecasted at 3.7 percent in 2008. Inflation in Asia emerging markets and forecasts on stock price indexes are presented. **Availability:** Online.

18432 ■ *"Wrigley's Newest Taste: Wolfberry" in Crain's Chicago Business (Vol. 31, March 31, 2008, No. 13, pp. 1)*
Pub: Crain Communications Inc.
Contact: Barry Asin, President
Ed: David Sterrett. **Description:** Wm. Wrigley Jr. Co. has introduced a gum line in China that touts the medicinal advantages of aloe vera to improve skin and wolfberry to boost energy in an attempt to keep the company positioned as the top candy firm in China. **Availability:** Online.

18433 ■ *"Yogun Fruz Adds First Location in Southern New York State" in Ice Cream Reporter (Vol. 23, September 20, 2010, No. 10, pp. 2)*
Description: Yogen Fruz signed a master franchise agreement to expand into the southern counties of New York State. The firm offers a healthy and beneficial option to fast food and typical dessert choices. **Availability:** Print; Online.

18434 ■ *"Yogurtini" in Ice Cream Reporter (Vol. 23, September 20, 2010, No. 10, pp. 7)*
Description: Self-serve frozen yogurt chain, Yogurtini has opened its second store in Kansas City, Missouri. **Availability:** Online.

18435 ■ *"You Won't Go Broke Filling Up On The Stock" in Barron's (Vol. 88, July 14, 2008, No. 28, pp. 38)*
Pub: Dow Jones & Company Inc.
Contact: Almar Latour, Chief Executive Officer
Ed: Assif Shameen. **Description:** Due to high economic growth, pro-business policies and a consumption boom, the Middle East is a good place to look for equities. The best ways in which to gain exposure to this market include investing in the real estate industry and telecommunications markets as well as large banks that serve corporations and consumers. **Availability:** Online.

18436 ■ *"Zara Eludes the Pain in Spain: Clothing Giant Inditex Sees Its First-Quarter Profits Rise By 30 Percent" in Canadian Business (Vol. 85, September 17, 2012, No. 14, pp. 67)*
Ed: Bryan Borzykowski. **Released:** September 17, 2012. **Description:** Clothing retailer Inditex reported a 30 percent increase in profit in the first quarter of 2012 and 15 percent increase in sales year over year. The company's unique business model was attributed to its growth, which also appeals to income investors.

18437 ■ *"Zoo Entertainment Inc. Aims for the Sky" in Business Courier (Vol. 27, September 24, 2010, No. 21, pp. 1)*
Pub: Business Courier
Ed: Dan Monk. **Description:** Video game company Zoo Entertainment Inc., which is based in Norwood near Cincinnati, Ohio aims to build a strong company and to position itself for future growth. The company reported $27.6 million in revenue for the first half of 2010 and analysts project $100 million in sales for 2011. **Availability:** Print; Online.

VIDEO/AUDIO MEDIA

18438 ■ *BS-Free Service Business Show: The Real Cost of Growing a Service Business*
URL(s): bsfreebusiness.com/growing-a-service-business-2024
Ed: Maggie Patterson. **Released:** February 05, 2024. **Description:** Podcast discusses why the cost of running a service business may be more than just the money you spend.

18439 ■ *Entrepreneurial Thought Leaders: Scaling Operations and People*
URL(s): ecorner.stanford.edu/podcasts/scaling-operations-and-people
Released: May 24, 2023. **Description:** Podcast describes a company that's ready to scale: strong foundation of values, well-built operating structures, and a complementary team.

18440 ■ *HBR Ideacast: Disruption Isn't the Only Path to Innovation*
URL(s): hbr.org/podcast/2023/05/disruption-isnt-the-only-path-to-innovation
Ed: Alison Beard. **Released:** May 02, 2023. **Description:** Podcast explains how some entrepreneurs have been able to grow in new markets rather than displacing existing ones.

18441 ■ *HBR Ideacast: Rethinking Growth at All Costs*
URL(s): hbr.org/podcast/2024/02/rethinking-growth-at-all-costs
Ed: Alison Beard. **Released:** February 27, 2024. **Description:** Podcast explains the importance of thinking strategically about growth--not just the rate but direction and method of growth.

18442 ■ *The How of Business: Is Your Small Business Scalable?*
URL(s): www.thehowofbusiness.com/episode-539-is-your-business-scalable
Ed: Henry Lopez. **Released:** September 23, 2024. **Description:** Podcast explains how to determine if a small business is ready to expand, reasons to expand, or the challenges of not scaling.

18443 ■ *How I Built This: Advice Line with Ariel Kaye of Parachute Home*
URL(s): wondery.com/shows/how-i-built-this/episode/10386-advice-line-with-ariel-kaye-of-parachute-home
Ed: Guy Raz. **Released:** August 29, 2024. **Description:** Podcast offers advice from founders on being both mindful and strategic in their expansion.

18444 ■ *How I Built This: Advice Line with Jeff Raider of Harry's*
URL(s): wondery.com/shows/how-i-built-this/episode/10386-advice-line-with-jeff-raider-of-harrys
Ed: Guy Raz. **Released:** August 01, 2024. **Description:** Podcast offers a conversation with three founders about strategic decisions.

18445 ■ *How I Built This: Advice Line with Scott and Ally Svenson of MOD Pizza*
Released: September 05, 2024. **Description:** Podcast offers advice from three founders about strategic expansion.

18446 ■ *Mastering Specialization for Growth*
URL(s): www.startuphustlepodcast.com/mastering-specialization-for-growth
Ed: Andrew Morgans. **Released:** December 05, 2023. **Description:** Podcast discusses focusing on core competencies to propel company growth.

18447 ■ *Nurture Small Business: Scaling Impact: Shortcuts for Entrepreneurial Growth*
URL(s): nurturesmallbusiness.buzzsprout.com/900445/episodes/14725064-scaling-impact-shortcuts-for-entrepreneurial-growth

Ed: Denise Cagan. **Released:** March 25, 2024. **Description:** Podcast offers shortcuts for building, scaling, and growing your business.

18448 ■ *Profit First Nation: The Owner's Trap*
URL(s): www.profitfirstnation.com/episodes/the-own ers-trap

Ed: Danielle Mulvey. **Released:** October 02, 2024. **Description:** Podcast discusses the owner's trap, in which business owners become too central to the operation and make it difficult to scale or sell the business, and offers strategies to avoid it.

18449 ■ *The Simple Checklist You Can Use to Grow Your Business with Donald Miller*
URL(s): www.eofire.com/podcast/donaldmiller2

Ed: Jon Lee Dumas. **Released:** February 25, 2024. **Description:** Podcast explains the importance of a mission statement, offers a step-by-step process to create a profitable product, and suggests ways to manage cashflow.

18450 ■ *Small Business, Big Mindset: Creating a Truly Scalable Offer*
URL(s): podcast.musclecreative.com/924061/episo des/12482775-creating-a-truly-scalable-offer

Ed: Erin Geiger. **Released:** March 28, 2023. **Description:** Podcast offers tactics for leveraging a scalable offer and grow a business.

18451 ■ *The Strategy Hour: What's Possible: From Solopreneur to Scalable Enterprise with Ryan Deiss*
URL(s): bossproject.com/podcast/from-solopreneur -to-scalable-enterprise-with-ryan-deiss

Ed: Abagail Pumphrey. **Released:** April 02, 2024. **Description:** Podcast offers insights on what it takes to scale a business.

18452 ■ *Team-Powered Scaling*
URL(s): www.startuphustlepodcast.com/team-powere d-scaling

Ed: Andrew Morgans. **Released:** December 19, 2023. **Description:** Podcast offers the essential elements for scaling a business successfully. Also discusses the strategic approach to building an elite mid-management team for sustainable growth.

18453 ■ *Think Business with Tyler: Analyzing Proft Margins and Core Metrics in Business - Brian Will*
URL(s): thinktyler.com/podcast_episode/profi t-margins-metrics-brian-will

Ed: Tyler Martin. **Released:** April 15, 2024. **Description:** Podcast discusses profits and management in the entrepreneurial journey.

18454 ■ *Think Business with Tyler: Building Business Value with Nick McLean*
URL(s): thinktyler.com/podcast_episode/building -business-value-nick-mclean

Ed: Tyler Martin. **Released:** May 13, 2024. **Description:** Podcast examines private equity and entrepreneurship through acquisition. Also asks if revenue growth trumps operational efficiency when improving the bottom line.

18455 ■ *This Is Small Business: Growth Secrets for Food Entrepreneurs: Expanding from Farmer's Markets to E-Commerce*
URL(s): www.smallbusiness.amazon/podcast-episo des/ep-65-growth-secrets-for-food-entrepreneurs -expanding-from-farmers-markets-to-e-commerce

Released: September 17, 2024. **Description:** Podcast discusses steps for scaling up by maintaining product quality, engaging with the community, and conducting market research.

18456 ■ *This Is Small Business: Steps to Accelerate Your Small Business Growth - With Amy Porterfield*
URL(s): www.smallbusiness.amazon/podcast-episo des/ep-57-7-steps-to-accelerate-your-small-busi ness-growth--with-amy-porterfield-2

Ed: Andrea Marquez. **Released:** May 15, 2024. **Description:** Podcast outlines how to manage your mindset, create a customer avatar, and grow your email list.

18457 ■ *Why Most Entrepreneurs Struggle to Get the Growth, Profit and Freedom They Want with Clate Mask*
URL(s): www.eofire.com/podcast/clatemask

Ed: Jon Lee Dumas. **Released:** February 20, 2024. **Description:** Podcast explains small business chaos and how to extricate yourself from it.

CONSULTANTS

18458 ■ **American Business Dynamics Corp.**
4501 Silhavy Rd.
  Valparaiso, IN 46383
Contact: Yvonne Schwedland, President

Description: Small business consulting firm specializing in helping businesses prepare and execute high impact growth strategies. **Scope:** Small business consulting firm specializing in helping businesses prepare and execute high impact growth strategies. **Publications:** "Small businesses don't work," "The entrepreneurial myth," "The balanced business owner," "How to find fulfillment from your business," "Strategic objectives - more than a financial plan Management," "Make business work - by system and staff," "How to manage with success," "How to make your business truly work," "A systematic approach to business," "Base your strategy on functions," "Build success by design," "Reliable employees are essential," "Create a system that works for you," "Save time with simple reminders," "Developing a systems strategy," "Marketing," "A new way to draw customers," "Attention to quality will pay rewards," "Choose a core market, then serve it well," "Build better customers with words," "Turn business into a game," "Image is everything, Finance," "Money, money, money".

18459 ■ **McMann & Ransford**
2950 N Loop. W Ste. 500
  Houston, TX 77092
Ph: (713)730-7519
URL: http://mcmannransford.com
Contact: Dean McMann, Chief Executive Officer
Linkedin: www.linkedin.com/company/mcmann -&-ransford_2

Description: Firm provides management consulting, training, executive recruiting, market research services, and specializes in the professional services industry. **Scope:** Firm provides management consulting, training, executive recruiting, market research services, and specializes in the professional services industry.

18460 ■ **The Sanderson Group Inc.**
515 E 85 St., Ste. 4E
  New York, NY 10028
Contact: Robin Sanderson, Chief Executive Officer
E-mail: robin@thesandersongroup.com

Description: Full-service marketing firm is engaged in providing traditional, digital and tailored marketing solutions, the company offers consulting, communications, lead generation, brand identity, events and promotions, and strategic planning services and serves both large corporations, small- and medium-sized businesses.

PUBLICATIONS

18461 ■ *Growing Business Handbook*
45 Gee St., 2nd Fl.
  London EC1V 3RS, United Kingdom
Ph: 44 20 7278-0433
Co. E-mail: kpinfo@koganpage.com
URL: http://www.koganpage.com
Contact: Christina Lindeholm, Manager, Sales
URL(s): www.koganpage.com/business-an d-management/growing-business-handbook-97807 49477905

Price: $89.99, for hard back US; $89.99, for e-book UK; $89.99, for paper book + eBook. **Description:** Focuses on key issues such as funding, innovation, customer service, business technology and international expansion. Includes case studies from top companies. **Availability:** E-book; Print; Download.

COMPUTERIZED DATABASES

18462 ■ *Report on Business Corporate Database*
Contact: Phillip Crawley, Chief Executive Officer
URL(s): www.theglobeandmail.com/report-on -business/rob-magazine

Ed: Elena Cherney. **Description:** Database covers current and historical information on over 3,000 Canadian companies, taken from their quarterly and annual reports. Includes company name, address, phone, description of business, financial data, officers, general corporate information. **Availability:** Diskette; CD-ROM; Print; Magnetic tape; Online.

INTERNET DATABASES

18463 ■ *Corporate Annual Reports at the Library of Congress*
URL(s): guides.loc.gov/corporate-annual-reports

Description: An online database of corporate filings from US businesses from 1974 through 1997. Also contains a link of financial reports from foreign companies. **Availability:** Online.

18464 ■ *Doing Company Research: A Resource Guide*
URL(s): guides.loc.gov/company-research/private

Description: Contains links that publish information on U.S. private and public companies. Also contains a section on foreign companies and where to locate information. **Availability:** Online.

LIBRARIES

18465 ■ **Buffalo & Erie County Public Library-Business, Science & Technology**
1 Lafayette Sq.
  Buffalo, NY 14203
URL: http://www.buffalolib.org

Scope: Investments, real estate, economics, marketing, engineering, computer science, technology, medical information for laymen, consumer information, automotive repair. **Services:** Interlibrary loan; copying; library open to the public. **Founded:** 1952. **Holdings:** 312,916 books; 60,516 bound periodical volumes; 600 periodical.

18466 ■ **U.S. Department of Commerce - Research Library**
1401 Constitution Ave. NW
  Washington, DC 20230
Co. E-mail: research@doc.gov
URL: http://library.doc.gov/home
Contact: Kelli Peterson, Librarian

Scope: Business; trade, industry; economics; legal; legislative; travel; technology and professional development. **Services:** Open to the public. **Founded:** 1913. **Holdings:** 150,000 books.

18467 ■ **University of South Carolina - Darla Moore School of Business - Elliott White Springs Business Library**
1014 Greene St.
  Columbia, SC 29208
URL: http://delphi.tcl.sc.edu/library/develop/develop .html
Contact: Kathy Snediker, Contact
E-mail: snediker@mailbox.sc.edu

Description: University Libraries connects people with resources, significant collections and expert research services. **Scope:** Corporations. **Services:** Interlibrary loan; copying; library open to the public with restrictions. **Founded:** 1973. **Subscriptions:** periodicals (includes journals) journals books; maps; rare books; music scores; archival collections; audiovisual materials.

GENERAL SMALL BUSINESS TOPICS

RESEARCH CENTERS

18468 ■ Minnesota Department of Labor and Industry - Research and Statistics Unit
443 Lafayette Rd. N
Saint Paul, MN 55155
URL: http://www.dli.mn.gov/our-areas-service/research-and-statistics/about-survey-occupational-injuries-and-illnesses
Description: Integral unit of Minnesota Department of Labor and Industry. **Scope:** Workers' compensation system and occupational safety and health programs in Minnesota. **Founded:** 1985. **Publications:** *Minnesota Minimum Wage Report* (Annual); *Minnesota Worker's Compensation System Report* (Annual); *Minnesota Workplace Safety Report* (Annual).

18469 ■ University of Illinois at Urbana-Champaign - College of Business - Bureau of Economic and Business Research
1206 S Sixth St. MC 706
Champaign, IL 61820
Ph: (217)333-2331
URL: http://directory.illinois.edu/detail?departmentld=illinois.eduKM446&search_type=&skinld=0
Description: Publishes scholarly articles for the academic community and the general business public and government sector. **Scope:** Economics and business, including studies in business expectations, health economics, forecasting and planning, innovation, entrepreneurship, consumer behavior, poverty problems, small business operations and problems, investment and growth, productivity, research methodology, organizational behavior, and international business and banking. **Founded:** 1921. **Publications:** *BEBR Bulletins*; *Project Reports*; *Quarterly Review of Economics and Finance* (Quarterly). **Educational Activities:** BEBR Provides assistance in faculty research and trains graduate students in research methods, Offer exemplary teaching and training programs.

Business Law

START-UP INFORMATION

18470 ■ *"How to Open and Operate a Financially Successful Florist and Floral Business Online and Off"*
Pub: Atlantic Publishing Co.
Contact: Dr. Heather L. Johnson, Contact
Released: Revised second edition. **Description:** A concise and easy to follow guide for opening a retail florist or floral business online or a traditional brick and mortar store. Knowledge shared includes: cost control systems, retail math and competitive pricing, legal concerns, tax reporting requirements and reporting, profit and loss statements, management skills, sales advertising, and marketing techniques, customer service, direct sales, internal marketing ideas, and more. **Availability:** CD-ROM; Print; Online.

18471 ■ *How to Start, Operate and Market a Freelance Notary Signing Agent Business*
Released: Revised second edition. **Description:** Due to the changes in the 2001 Uniform Commercial Code allowing notary public agents to serve as a witness to mortgage loan closings (eliminating the 2-witness requirement under the old code), notaries are working directly for mortgage, title and signing companies as mobile notaries.

18472 ■ *Legal Guide for Starting & Running a Small Business*
Pub: Nolo
Contact: Chris Braun, President
Ed: Fred S. Steingold. **Released:** 18th Edition. **Price:** $27.99, e-book. **Description:** Legal issues any small business owner needs to know for starting and running a successful business are outlined. **Availability:** Handheld; E-book; Print; Electronic publishing; PDF.

18473 ■ *"Legal Matters: 'Crowdfunding' a Boon for Entrepreneurs, If They Clear Regulatory Hurdles" in Finance and Commerce (July 17, 2012)*
Pub: BridgeTower Media
Contact: Adam Reinebach, President
Ed: Dan Heilman. **Description:** Part of the Jumpstart Our Business Startups Act (JOBS) is crowdfunding, which allows the funding of a company by selling small parts of equity to a group of investors. Kickstarter, a Website for raising funds for business entities, is primarily used for film and book projects. Most businesses cannot adopt Kickstarter's model because of the legality of receiving investor funds without offering security.

18474 ■ *"Office For One: The Sole Proprietor's Survival Guide"*
Pub: CreateSpace
Released: January 12, 2014. **Price:** $12.95, Paperback; $6.42, kindle; $3.95, Paperback. **Description:** Over thirty experts offer advice to any entrepreneur wishing to start a business by themselves. Tips and advice on tuning out negativity, maintaining balance and boundaries, handling legal issues and financial challenges, finding and keeping customers, marketing on a small budge, networking, cracking the media code, growing a sustainable vision, and addressing burnouts. **Availability:** Print.

18475 ■ *Partnership: Small Business Start-Up Kit*
Released: Second edition. **Description:** Guidebook detailing partnership law by state covering the formation and use of partnerships as a business form. Information on filing requirements, property laws, legal liability, standards, and the new Revised Uniform Partnership Act is covered.

18476 ■ *Raising Capital*
Released: Third edition. **Price:** $34.95, Paperback/E-book. **Description:** Corporate attorney provides a comprehensive guide using in-depth, practical advice on raising money to start and grow a business. A 115-page appendix contains samples of financing agreements, forms and questionnaires. **Availability:** E-book; Print.

ASSOCIATIONS AND OTHER ORGANIZATIONS

18477 ■ **Business Law Section of the Florida Bar**
651 E Jefferson St.
Tallahassee, FL 32399
Ph: (850)561-5630
Fax: (850)561-5825
Co. E-mail: flabizlaw@gmail.com
URL: http://flabizlaw.org
Contact: Kacy Donlon, Chairman
E-mail: kdonlon@jclaw.com
Facebook: www.facebook.com/flabizlaw/wall
X (Twitter): x.com/FlaBizLaw
Description: Furthers the development of business law, educating section members in business law and related professional responsibilities. Improves the practice of both in-house and outside business counsel through seminars, legislation, and committee activity in a wide variety of areas, such as high technology, small business, bankruptcy, banking, and commercial law. **Geographic Preference:** State.

18478 ■ **Mississippi Bar Business Law Section**
c/o Slates Veazey, Chair
Jackson, MS
Ph: (601)592-9925
Co. E-mail: sveazey@bradley.com
URL: http://www.msbar.org/inside-the-bar/sections/business-law
Contact: Slates Veazey, Chairman
E-mail: sveazey@bradley.com
Description: Furthers the development and improvement of business law, educating section members in business law and related professional responsibilities. Improves the practice of both in-house and outside business counsel through seminars, practical forums, legislation, and committee activity in a wide variety of areas, such as high technology, small business, bankruptcy, banking, and commercial law. **Geographic Preference:** State.

18479 ■ **State Bar of Georgia Business Law Section**
104 Marietta St. NW, Ste. 100
Atlanta, GA 30303
URL: http://www.gabar.org/committeesprogramssections/sections/business
Contact: Mike Carey, Chairman
Description: Furthers the development and improvement of business law, educating section members in business law and related professional responsibilities. Improves the practice of both in-house and outside business counsel through seminars, practical forums, legislation, and committee activity in a wide variety of areas, such as high technology, small business, bankruptcy, banking, and commercial law. **Geographic Preference:** State.

18480 ■ **State Bar of Michigan Business Law Section (SBM BLS)**
c/o John T. Schuring, Chairman
200 Ottawa Ave. NW, Ste. 900
Grand Rapids, MI 49503-2427
Ph: (616)336-1023
Co. E-mail: businesslaw@mi.rr.com
URL: http://connect.michbar.org/businesslaw/home
Contact: Kevin T. Block, Director, Communications Director, Development
E-mail: kblock@kerr-russell.com
Facebook: www.facebook.com/SBMBusinessLawSection
Description: Furthers the development and improvement of business law, educating section members in business law and related professional responsibilities. Improves the practice of both in-house and outside business counsel through seminars, practical forums, legislation, and committee activity in a wide variety of areas, such as high technology, small business, bankruptcy, banking, and commercial law. **Awards:** Stephen H. Schulman Outstanding Business Lawyer Award (Annual). **Geographic Preference:** State.

EDUCATIONAL PROGRAMS

18481 ■ **The Basics of Human Resource Law (Onsite)**
National Seminars Training L.L.C. (NST)
14502 W 105th St.
Lenexa, KS 66215
Free: 800-349-1935
Co. E-mail: info@findaseminar.com
URL: http://www.findaseminar.com/tpd/Padgett-Thompson-Seminars.asp
URL(s): www.findaseminar.com/event1.asp?eventID=910
Description: A one-day seminar covering the basics of human resources law. **Audience:** Business professionals. **Principal Exhibits:** A one-day seminar covering the basics of human resources law.

GENERAL SMALL BUSINESS TOPICS

18482 ■ Collections Laws
Fred Pryor Seminars & CareerTrack
5700 Broadmoor, Ste. 300
Mission, KS 66202
Free: 800-780-8476
Fax: (913)967-8849
Co. E-mail: customerservice@pryor.com
URL: http://www.pryor.com
Contact: Janet Turner, Contact
E-mail: dmca@pryor.com
URL(s): www.pryor.com/training-seminars/collections-law

Frequency: Irregular. **Description:** Learn to collect money effectively and legally with an understanding of the Fair Debt Collection Practices Act (FDCPA). **Audience:** Managers, supervisors, vice-presidents, and other professionals. **Principal Exhibits:** Learn to collect money effectively and legally with an understanding of the Fair Debt Collection Practices Act (FDCPA).

18483 ■ Concentrated Course in Construction Contracts (Onsite)
Seminar Information Service Inc. (SIS)
250 El Camino Real., Ste. 112
Tustin, CA 92780
Ph: (714)508-0340
Free: 877-736-4636
Fax: (714)734-8027
Co. E-mail: info@seminarinformation.com
URL: http://www.seminarinformation.com
Contact: Catherine Bellizzi, President
URL(s): www.seminarinformation.com/qqantv/concentrated-course-in-construction-contracts

Description: A solid week of practical education in construction operations and construction law, including job set-up, claims avoidance, bonds, liens and insurance, specifications and bidding, labor relations, subcontracting, and more. **Audience:** Construction professionals. **Principal Exhibits:** A solid week of practical education in construction operations and construction law, including job set-up, claims avoidance, bonds, liens and insurance, specifications and bidding, labor relations, subcontracting, and more.

18484 ■ Data Analysis for EEO Professionals (Onsite)
Seminar Information Service Inc. (SIS)
250 El Camino Real., Ste. 112
Tustin, CA 92780
Ph: (714)508-0340
Free: 877-736-4636
Fax: (714)734-8027
Co. E-mail: info@seminarinformation.com
URL: http://www.seminarinformation.com
Contact: Catherine Bellizzi, President
URL(s): www.seminarinformation.com

Description: Provides a solid understanding of the effective use of statistical analysis in EEO management and legal proceedings. Topics covered include: the legal basis for the use of statistics in EEO; which analytical tools are appropriate; how to interpret the results; when to conduct additional investigation; and strategies for presenting findings to management, agencies, and the courts. **Audience:** EEO Professionals. **Principal Exhibits:** Provides a solid understanding of the effective use of statistical analysis in EEO management and legal proceedings. Topics covered include: the legal basis for the use of statistics in EEO; which analytical tools are appropriate; how to interpret the results; when to conduct additional investigation; and strategies for presenting findings to management, agencies, and the courts.

18485 ■ Employment Discrimination Law Update (Onsite)
Seminar Information Service Inc. (SIS)
250 El Camino Real., Ste. 112
Tustin, CA 92780
Ph: (714)508-0340
Free: 877-736-4636
Fax: (714)734-8027
Co. E-mail: info@seminarinformation.com
URL: http://www.seminarinformation.com
Contact: Catherine Bellizzi, President
URL(s): www.seminarinformation.com/qqadfh/employment-discrimination-law-update

Description: Topics include the Civil Rights Act of 1991, changes in EEO law and enforcement, sexual harassment, resolving claims and implementing the ADA, and the FMLA. **Audience:** Employers, human resource professionals and counsel. **Principal Exhibits:** Topics include the Civil Rights Act of 1991, changes in EEO law and enforcement, sexual harassment, resolving claims and implementing the ADA, and the FMLA.

18486 ■ The Essentials of Collections Law (Onsite)
National Seminars Training L.L.C. (NST)
14502 W 105th St.
Lenexa, KS 66215
Free: 800-349-1935
Co. E-mail: info@findaseminar.com
URL: http://www.findaseminar.com/tpd/Padgett-Thompson-Seminars.asp
URL(s): www.findaseminar.com/in-house-seminar.asp?eventID=4008&Category=ACCOUNTING+-+Credit%2FCollection&x=12&y=6

Description: A one-day training session for accounts receivable professionals at all levels. **Audience:** Collection managers, financial managers, accountants, and sales professionals. **Principal Exhibits:** A one-day training session for accounts receivable professionals at all levels.

18487 ■ Harassment Prevention and Appropriate Behaviors in the Workplace (Onsite)
Seminar Information Service Inc. (SIS)
250 El Camino Real., Ste. 112
Tustin, CA 92780
Ph: (714)508-0340
Free: 877-736-4636
Fax: (714)734-8027
Co. E-mail: info@seminarinformation.com
URL: http://www.seminarinformation.com
Contact: Catherine Bellizzi, President
URL(s): www.seminarinformation.com/details.cfm?qc=qqaqur

Description: Explore the legal and policy concerns related to this complex workplace issue, including review and explore the guidelines for identifying inappropriate behavior; the laws, agency interpretations and court cases; and the key elements necessary for writing and implementing policies and procedures. **Audience:** Human resource professionals. **Principal Exhibits:** Explore the legal and policy concerns related to this complex workplace issue, including review and explore the guidelines for identifying inappropriate behavior; the laws, agency interpretations and court cases; and the key elements necessary for writing and implementing policies and procedures.

18488 ■ How to Legally Terminate Employees With Attitude Problems (Onsite)
National Seminars Training L.L.C. (NST)
14502 W 105th St.
Lenexa, KS 66215
Free: 800-349-1935
Co. E-mail: info@findaseminar.com
URL: http://www.findaseminar.com/tpd/Padgett-Thompson-Seminars.asp
URL(s): www.findaseminar.com/in-house-seminar.asp?eventID=14678&Category=GENERAL+MGMT&x=14&y=2

Description: Learn how to act with confidence as you terminate problem employees who are damaging productivity and the company's effectiveness. **Audience:** Human resource personnel, managers and supervisors. **Principal Exhibits:** Learn how to act with confidence as you terminate problem employees who are damaging productivity and the company's effectiveness.

18489 ■ How to Manage an Information Security Program (Onsite)
Seminar Information Service Inc. (SIS)
250 El Camino Real., Ste. 112
Tustin, CA 92780
Ph: (714)508-0340
Free: 877-736-4636
Fax: (714)734-8027
Co. E-mail: info@seminarinformation.com
URL: http://www.seminarinformation.com
Contact: Catherine Bellizzi, President
URL(s): www.seminarinformation.com

Description: Learn the components of a comprehensive plan, covering access control software applications; telecom/network security measures; physical protection of the computer facility; and the legal and regulatory aspects of information security. **Audience:** Industry professionals, persons who mange information security program. **Principal Exhibits:** Learn the components of a comprehensive plan, covering access control software applications; telecom/network security measures; physical protection of the computer facility; and the legal and regulatory aspects of information security.

18490 ■ Human Resources and the Law (Onsite)
Seminar Information Service Inc. (SIS)
250 El Camino Real., Ste. 112
Tustin, CA 92780
Ph: (714)508-0340
Free: 877-736-4636
Fax: (714)734-8027
Co. E-mail: info@seminarinformation.com
URL: http://www.seminarinformation.com
Contact: Catherine Bellizzi, President
URL(s): www.seminarinformation.com/details.cfm?qc=qqblnt

Description: Provides the human resources professional with an understanding of the laws that obligate employers, recent legislation and court cases defining employer/employee rights and obligations, legal and business considerations bearing on employer decisions, practical implications of the laws in day-to-day human resources operations, impact of the laws on the development of policies and procedures, and alternatives for minimizing the company's exposure to employee lawsuits and administrative charges. **Audience:** Human resources professionals. **Principal Exhibits:** Provides the human resources professional with an understanding of the laws that obligate employers, recent legislation and court cases defining employer/employee rights and obligations, legal and business considerations bearing on employer decisions, practical implications of the laws in day-to-day human resources operations, impact of the laws on the development of policies and procedures, and alternatives for minimizing the company's exposure to employee lawsuits and administrative charges.

18491 ■ Legal Issues in Real Estate Foreclosure (Onsite)
Seminar Information Service Inc. (SIS)
250 El Camino Real., Ste. 112
Tustin, CA 92780
Ph: (714)508-0340
Free: 877-736-4636
Fax: (714)734-8027
Co. E-mail: info@seminarinformation.com
URL: http://www.seminarinformation.com
Contact: Catherine Bellizzi, President
URL(s): www.seminarinformation.com

Description: Gain practical procedural pointers on how to assertively protect your clients' financial interests through an in-depth understanding of the foreclosure process. **Audience:** Creditor and debtor attorneys and paralegals. **Principal Exhibits:** Gain practical procedural pointers on how to assertively protect your clients' financial interests through an in-depth understanding of the foreclosure process.

18492 ■ Payroll Law
Fred Pryor Seminars & CareerTrack
5700 Broadmoor, Ste. 300
Mission, KS 66202
Free: 800-780-8476
Fax: (913)967-8849
Co. E-mail: customerservice@pryor.com
URL: http://www.pryor.com
Contact: Janet Turner, Contact
E-mail: dmca@pryor.com
URL(s): www.pryor.com/training-seminars/payroll-law

Frequency: Irregular. **Description:** Learn to handle payroll accurately, legally, and with confidence. **Audience:** Payroll professionals. **Principal Exhibits:** Learn to handle payroll accurately, legally, and with confidence.

18493 ■ Payroll Law (Onsite)
Seminar Information Service Inc. (SIS)
250 El Camino Real., Ste. 112
Tustin, CA 92780
Ph: (714)508-0340
Free: 877-736-4636
Fax: (714)734-8027
Co. E-mail: info@seminarinformation.com
URL: http://www.seminarinformation.com
Contact: Catherine Bellizzi, President
URL(s): www.seminarinformation.com/details.cfm?qc=qqbtaq

Description: Learn exactly where you're vulnerable in complying with complex FLSA mandates, identify common mistakes that get most companies hauled into court, and ensure 100 percent accuracy and compliance, as well as examine special payroll situations like garnishments and levies and involuntary deductions. **Audience:** Payroll management personnel. **Principal Exhibits:** Learn exactly where you're vulnerable in complying with complex FLSA mandates, identify common mistakes that get most companies hauled into court, and ensure 100 percent accuracy and compliance, as well as examine special payroll situations like garnishments and levies and involuntary deductions.

18494 ■ Payroll Law (Onsite)
National Seminars Training L.L.C. (NST)
14502 W 105th St.
Lenexa, KS 66215
Free: 800-349-1935
Co. E-mail: info@findaseminar.com
URL: http://www.findaseminar.com/tpd/Padgett-Thompson-Seminars.asp
URL(s): www.findaseminar.com/event1.asp?eventID=7347

Description: A one-day workshop that shows the vulnerabilities in your organization and how to fix the problems. **Audience:** Business professionals, and accountants. **Principal Exhibits:** A one-day workshop that shows the vulnerabilities in your organization and how to fix the problems.

18495 ■ Property Condition Assessments Featuring E2018 Standard Guide (Onsite)
Seminar Information Service Inc. (SIS)
250 El Camino Real., Ste. 112
Tustin, CA 92780
Ph: (714)508-0340
Free: 877-736-4636
Fax: (714)734-8027
Co. E-mail: info@seminarinformation.com
URL: http://www.seminarinformation.com
Contact: Catherine Bellizzi, President
URL(s): www.seminarinformation.com/qqbqvd/property-condition-assessments-featuring-e2018-standard

Description: Two-day course with focus of the ASTM Property Condition Assessment standard and explains why it was developed. **Audience:** Purchasers of commercial property, potential tenants, owners, lenders and property managers. **Principal Exhibits:** Two-day course with focus of the ASTM Property Condition Assessment standard and explains why it was developed.

18496 ■ Property Taking Through Eminent Domain: What You Need to Know (Onsite)
Seminar Information Service Inc. (SIS)
250 El Camino Real., Ste. 112
Tustin, CA 92780
Ph: (714)508-0340
Free: 877-736-4636
Fax: (714)734-8027
Co. E-mail: info@seminarinformation.com
URL: http://www.seminarinformation.com
Contact: Catherine Bellizzi, President
URL(s): www.seminarinformation.com

Description: Get the knowledge you need to exert the municipality's rights and achieve the best outcome possible, including how the Kelo ruling will affect your organization when considering a taking and get clear explanations of the parameters guiding the action. **Audience:** City, county and zoning board members, planners, engineers, architects, developers, real estate professionals, and attorneys. **Principal Exhibits:** Get the knowledge you need to exert the municipality's rights and achieve the best outcome possible, including how the Kelo ruling will affect your organization when considering a taking and get clear explanations of the parameters guiding the action.

18497 ■ Real Estate Law: Advanced Issues and Answers (Onsite)
Seminar Information Service Inc. (SIS)
250 El Camino Real., Ste. 112
Tustin, CA 92780
Ph: (714)508-0340
Free: 877-736-4636
Fax: (714)734-8027
Co. E-mail: info@seminarinformation.com
URL: http://www.seminarinformation.com
Contact: Catherine Bellizzi, President
URL(s): www.seminarinformation.com

Description: Go beyond the basics for an advanced look at complicated real estate concerns like resolving title defects, finding practical solutions to environmental conflicts, clearing difficult liens from titles, and dealing properly with property affected by a bankruptcy. **Audience:** Attorneys, lenders, commercial and industrial real estate agents, developers and real estate professionals, industry professionals. **Principal Exhibits:** Go beyond the basics for an advanced look at complicated real estate concerns like resolving title defects, finding practical solutions to environmental conflicts, clearing difficult liens from titles, and dealing properly with property affected by a bankruptcy.

18498 ■ Resolving Real Estate Title Defects (Onsite)
Seminar Information Service Inc. (SIS)
250 El Camino Real., Ste. 112
Tustin, CA 92780
Ph: (714)508-0340
Free: 877-736-4636
Fax: (714)734-8027
Co. E-mail: info@seminarinformation.com
URL: http://www.seminarinformation.com
Contact: Catherine Bellizzi, President
URL(s): www.seminarinformation.com/details.cfm?qc=qqbswz

Description: Learn to recognize and resolve title problems that may arise during real estate transactions; Apply the standards of title examination effectively to uncover problems and prevent them whenever possible; Confidently take the next step when you recognize a defect and ensure the transaction goes smoothly. **Audience:** Title and title insurance professionals, real estate professionals and bankers. **Principal Exhibits:** Learn to recognize and resolve title problems that may arise during real estate transactions; Apply the standards of title examination effectively to uncover problems and prevent them whenever possible; Confidently take the next step when you recognize a defect and ensure the transaction goes smoothly.

18499 ■ Writing Effective EEO Investigative Reports
Seminar Information Service Inc. (SIS)
250 El Camino Real., Ste. 112
Tustin, CA 92780
Ph: (714)508-0340
Free: 877-736-4636
Fax: (714)734-8027
Co. E-mail: info@seminarinformation.com
URL: http://www.seminarinformation.com
Contact: Catherine Bellizzi, President
URL(s): www.seminarinformation.com

Description: Focuses exclusively on the written product of an effective investigation. Topics include understanding the Faragher-Ellerth Affirmative Defense and addressing credibility. **Audience:** Industry professionals. **Principal Exhibits:** Focuses exclusively on the written product of an effective investigation. Topics include understanding the Faragher-Ellerth Affirmative Defense and addressing credibility.

REFERENCE WORKS

18500 ■ "The 6 Different Types of Lawyers for Small Businesses" in Fora Financial Blog (May 19, 2021)
URL(s): www.forafinancial.com/blog/small-business/types-of-lawyers/

Released: May 19, 2021. **Description:** Explores the importance of having a lawyer for your small business and provides details on six types of business lawyers. **Availability:** Online.

18501 ■ "11th Circuit: Don't Break the Law to Comply with It" in Miami Daily Business Review (October 21, 2009)
Pub: Incisive Media Inc.
Contact: Jonathon Whiteley, Chief Executive Officer
Ed: Janet L. Conley. **Description:** Niagara Credit Solutions argued with a three-judge panel that the company broke the rule saying debt collectors must identify themselves so that they could comply with a rule barring debt collectors from communicating about a debt with third parties. **Availability:** Print; Online.

18502 ■ "113D Filings: Investors Report to the SEC" in Barron's (Vol. 88, March 24, 2008, No. 12, pp. M13)
Pub: Dow Jones & Company Inc.
Contact: Almar Latour, Chief Executive Officer

Released: April 02, 2016. **Description:** HealthCor Management called as problematic the plan of Magellan Health Services to use its high cash balances for acquisitions. Carlson Capital discussed with Energy Partners possible changes in the latter's board. Investor Carl Icahn suggested that Enzon Pharmaceuticals consider selling itself or divest some of its assets. **Availability:** Print; Online.

18503 ■ "$100M Merger Stalled" in Philadelphia Business Journal (Vol. 31, February 17, 2012, No. 1, pp. 1)
Description: The $100 million merger between Originlio Beverage and All Star Beverage has been delayed by lawsuits. The merger will create an entity to distribute Yuengling Beer. But Yuengling and Son Inc. has sued All Star for breach of contract.

18504 ■ "2015 Corporate Counsel Legal Pricing Guide - Mergers & Acquisitions" in Economics & Business Week (August 16, 2014, pp. 3)
Pub: NewsRX LLC.
Contact: Kalani Rosell, Contact

Description: Research and Markets has added the 2015 Corporate Counsel Legal Pricing Guide - Mergers & Acquisitions to its report. The guide details how the mergers and acquisitions market for law firms has increased since the downturn in 2008-2009 due mostly to an improved economy, increased corporate liquidity and sometimes corporate tax policies of certain countries. **Availability:** Print; Online.

18505 ■ "Accountants Get the Hook" in Canadian Business (Vol. 80, October 22, 2007, No. 21, pp. 19)
Description: Chartered Accountants of Ontario handed down the decision on Douglas Barrington, Anthony Power and Claudio Russo's professional misconduct case. The three accountants of Deloitte & Touche LLP must pay C$100,000 in fines and C$417,000 in costs. Details of the disciplinary case are presented. **Availability:** Print; Online.

18506 ■ "AG Warns Slots MBE Plan Risky" in Boston Business Journal (Vol. 29, May 27, 2011, No. 3, pp. 1)
Description: Attorney General Doug Gansler states that the law extending the minority business program on slots parlors contracting through 2018 could be open to lawsuits. He recommended that the state should conduct a study proving that minority- and

women-owned businesses do not get a fair share in the gaming industry before it signs the bill to avoid lawsuits from majority-owned firms. **Availability:** Print; Online.

18507 ■ *"Agriculture Law 'Infoline' Available for Maryland Farmers"* in Ecology, Environment & Conservation Business (June 21, 2014, pp. 3)
Pub: NewsRX LLC.
Contact: Kalani Rosell, Contact
Description: The Agriculture Law Education Initiative created an Infoline phone number for the agricultural community to call for legal information resources related to their agricultural operation. The Infoline is answered by staff at the University of Maryland Francis King Carey School of Law and aims to assist in the preservation of family farms. The Infoline will connect family farmers with resources to further this goal. **Availability:** Online.

18508 ■ *"All About The Benjamins"* in Canadian Business (Vol. 81, September 29, 2008, No. 16, pp. 92)
Description: Discusses real estate developer Royal Indian Raj International Corp., a company that planned to build a $3 billion "smart city" near the Bangalore airport; to this day nothing has ever been built. The company was incorporated in 1999 by Manoj C. Benjamin one investor, Bill Zack, has been sued by the developer for libel due to his website that calls the company a scam. Benjamin has had a previous case of fraud issued against him as well as a string of liabilities and lawsuits. **Availability:** Online.

18509 ■ American Bar Association Legal Guide for Small Business: Everything You Need to Know About Small Business, from Start-up to Employment to Financing and Selling
Released: Second edition. **Description:** The American Bar Association provides insight into financial, health and family issues affecting small business, including start up issues, employment laws, financing a business, and selling a business.

18510 ■ *"Applications for Law School Drop"* in Philadelphia Business Journal (Vol. 28, June 8, 2012, No. 17, pp. 1)
Pub: Baltimore Business Journal
Contact: Rhonda Pringle, President
E-mail: rpringle@bizjournals.com
Description: Law School Admissions Council data for the past two years show the number of applicants have dropped by 25 percent ant the number of people who took the Law School Admissions Test fell by 26 percent. The numbers reflect the national trend that shows the struggling job market has affected decisions to go to law school. **Availability:** Print; Online.

18511 ■ *"Arkansas Attorney General Sues Collection Agency"* in PaymentsSource (July 18, 2012)
Description: National Credit Adjusters is being sued by Arkansas Attorney General Dustin McDaniel's office. The lawsuit alleges that the collection agency violated the Arkansas Deceptive Trade Practices Act while attempting to collect debts from payday and high-interest installment loan debts. **Availability:** Print; Online.

18512 ■ *"Assisted Living Facility Faces Bankruptcy and Care Issues"* in South Florida Business Journal (Vol. 33, August 17, 2012, No. 3, pp. 1)
Pub: Baltimore Business Journal
Contact: Rhonda Pringle, President
E-mail: rpringle@bizjournals.com
Description: FTMI Real Estate has filed for bankruptcy declaring a total debt of almost $29 million and assets of $19.6 million. The company owns The Lenox on the Lake, a 139-bed assisted living facility in Tamarac, which has at least one outstanding state complaint regarding patient care. **Availability:** Print; Online.

18513 ■ *Atiyah's Accidents, Compensation and the Law*
Pub: Cambridge University Press
Contact: Peter Phillips, Chief Executive Officer
Ed: Peter Cane. **Released:** 9th edition. **Description:** Leading authority on the law of personal injuries compensation and the social, political and economic issues surrounding it.

18514 ■ *"Attorney Panel Tackles Contract Questions"* in Agency Sales Magazine (Vol. 39, September-October 2009, No. 9, pp. 8)
Description: MANAfest conference tackled issues regarding a sales representative's contract. One attorney from the panel advised reps to go through proposed agreements with attorneys who are knowledgeable concerning rep laws. Another attorney advised reps to communicate with a company to ask about their responsibilities if that company is facing financial difficulty. **Availability:** Online.

18515 ■ *"Balancing Freedom of Speech with the Right to Privacy: How to Legally Cope with the Funeral Protest Problem"* in Pace Law Review (Fall 2007)
Description: Information is offered to help authorities and funeral directors cope with protests occurring during a funeral. **Availability:** PDF; Online.

18516 ■ *"Baltimore Businesses Put Cash Behind Bernstein"* in Baltimore Business Journal (Vol. 28, August 20, 2010, No. 15, pp. 1)
Pub: Baltimore Business Journal
Contact: Rhonda Pringle, President
E-mail: rpringle@bizjournals.com
Ed: Scott Dance. **Description:** Baltimore, Maryland-based businesses have invested $40,000 to support lawyer Gregg L. Bernstein in the 2010 State Attorney election. The election campaign is being fueled by fear of a crime surge. Many businesses have been dealing with crimes such as muggings, shootings, and car break-ins. **Availability:** Print.

18517 ■ *"Baltimore's Hispanic Businesses Try to Drum Up Cash to Battle Crime Spree"* in Baltimore Business Journal (Vol. 28, September 3, 2010, No. 17)
Pub: Baltimore Business Journal
Contact: Rhonda Pringle, President
E-mail: rpringle@bizjournals.com
Ed: Scott Dance. **Description:** Hispanic businesses in Baltimore, Maryland have been raising funds to pay off-duty police officers to patrol a few blocks of Broadway in Fells Point to help curb crime. Efforts to make the area a Latin Town have failed owing to muggings, prostitution and drug dealing. Comments from small business owners are also given. **Availability:** Print; Online.

18518 ■ *"Bankruptcies"* in Crain's Detroit Business (Vol. 24, March 24, 2008, No. 12, pp. 6)
Pub: Crain Communications Inc.
Contact: Barry Asin, President
Description: Current list of business that filed for Chapter 7 or 11 protection in U.S. Bankruptcy Court in Detroit include a construction company, a medical care company, a physical therapy firm and a communications firm. **Availability:** Online.

18519 ■ *"Bankruptcies"* in Crain's Detroit Business (Vol. 26, January 11, 2010, No. 2, pp. 7)
Pub: Crain Communications Inc.
Contact: Barry Asin, President
Ed: Dustin Walsh. **Description:** Listing of local businesses that filed for Chapter 7 or 11 protection in U.S. Bankruptcy Court in Detroit December 11-28. Under Chapter 11, a company files for reorganization. Chapter 7 involves total liquidation. **Availability:** Online.

18520 ■ *Bankruptcy for Small Business*
Description: Bankruptcy laws can be used to save a small business, homes or other property. The book provides general information for small business owners regarding the reasons for money problems, types of bankruptcy available and their alternatives, myths about bankruptcy, and the do's and don'ts for filing for bankruptcy. **Availability:** E-book; Print.

18521 ■ *"Be Wary of Legal Advice on Internet, Lawyers Warn"* in Crain's Detroit Business (Vol. 24, September 22, 2008, No. 38, pp. 16)
Pub: Crain Communications Inc.
Contact: Barry Asin, President
Ed: Harriet Tramer. **Description:** While some lawyers feel that the proliferation of legal information on the Internet can point people in the right direction, others maintain that it simply results in giving false hope, may bring about confusion or worse yet, it sometimes makes their jobs even harder. **Availability:** Online.

18522 ■ *"Bills Would Regulate Mortgage Loan Officers"* in Crain's Detroit Business (Vol. 24, February 25, 2008, No. 8, pp. 9)
Pub: Crain Communications Inc.
Contact: Barry Asin, President
Ed: Amy Lane. **Description:** New legislation in Michigan, if passed, would create a registration process for mortgage loan officers in the state in order to address the mortgage loan crisis. **Availability:** Print; Online.

18523 ■ *"BIM: What to Watch Out For"* in Contractor (Vol. 57, February 2010, No. 2, pp. 28)
Ed: Susan Linden McGreevy. **Description:** Legal and risk management issues surrounding Building Information Modeling (BIM) can be divided into three categories namely; intellectual property, liability for content, and the responsibility for the inputs into the model. The agreement should be done in a way that protects the intellectual rights of the authors when using BIM. **Availability:** Print; Online.

18524 ■ *"BIM and You: Know Its Benefits and Risks"* in Contractor (Vol. 57, January 2010, No. 1, pp. 46)
Ed: Susan Linden McGreevy. **Description:** Building Information Modeling is intended to be "collaborative" and this could raise legal issues if a contractor sends an electronic bid and it is filtered out. Other legal issues that mechanical contractors need to consider before using this technology are discussed. **Availability:** Print; Online.

18525 ■ *"Biovail Hits SAC With $4.6 Billion Suit"* in Globe & Mail (February 23, 2006, pp. B1)
Ed: Shawn McCarthy. **Description:** The details of Biovail Corp.'s securities fraud case against SAC Management LLC are presented. **Availability:** Online.

18526 ■ *"Blood Diamonds are Forever"* in Canadian Business (Vol. 83, August 17, 2010, No. 13-14, pp. 59)
Description: The failed case against Donald McKay who was found in possession of rough diamonds in a raid by Royal Canadian Mounted Police has raised doubts about Kimberley Process (KP) attempts to stop the illicit global trade in diamonds. KP has managed to reduce total global trade of blood diamonds by 1 percent in mid-2000. **Availability:** Print; Online.

18527 ■ *"Border Boletin: UA to Take Lie-Detector Kiosk to Poland"* in Arizona Daily Star (September 14, 2010)
Pub: Arizona Daily Star
Contact: John D'Orlando, President
E-mail: jdorlando@tucson.com
Ed: Brady McCombs. **Description:** University of Arizona's National Center for Border Security and Immigration Research will send a team to Warsaw, Poland to show border guards from 27 European Union countries the center's Avatar Kiosk. The Avatar technology is designed for use at border ports and airports to assist Customs officers detect individuals who are lying. **Availability:** Print; Online.

Business Law

18528 ■ *"Breaking Up: How Will It Affect Your Residence Permit?"* in *Canadian Business* (Vol. 80, March 12, 2007, No. 6, pp. 34)
Description: The need for business partners to draft a shareholder agreement in the beginning of their business to make it easier to break their relationship in case of disputes later is discussed. **Availability:** Online.

18529 ■ *"Bridging Diverging Perspectives and Repairing Damaged Relationships in the Aftermath of Workplace Transgressions"* in *Business Ethics Quarterly* (Vol. 24, July 2014, No. 3, pp. 443)
Pub: Business Ethics Quarterly
Contact: Dawn Elm, Executive Director
E-mail: drelm@stthomas.edu
Description: Workplace transgressions elicit a variety of opinions about their meaning and what is required to address them. This diversity in views makes it difficult for managers to identify a mutually satisfactory response and to enable repair of the relationships between the affected parties. A conceptual model is developed for understanding how to bridge these diverging perspectives and foster relationship repair. **Availability:** Online.

18530 ■ *"Brief: Janitorial Company Must Pay Back Wages"* in *Buffalo News* (September 24, 2011)
Description: Knights Facilities Management, located in Michigan, provides grounds maintenance and janitorial services at the Ralph Wilson Stadium in Buffalo, New York. The US Department of Labor ordered the firm to pay $22,000 in back wages and damages to 26 employees for overtime and minimum wage compensation. Details of the company's violation of the Fair Labor Standards Act are included. **Availability:** Online.

18531 ■ *"Business Diary"* in *Crain's Detroit Business* (Vol. 24, October 6, 2008, No. 40, pp. 23)
Pub: Crain Communications Inc.
Contact: Barry Asin, President
Description: Detailed listing of acquisitions, expansions, new products, new services, business contracts and startups from the Detroit area is provided. **Availability:** Print; Online.

18532 ■ *"Business Looks for Results in Congress"* in *Baltimore Business Journal* (Vol. 28, November 5, 2010, No. 26, pp. 1)
Pub: Baltimore Business Journal
Contact: Rhonda Pringle, President
E-mail: rpringle@bizjournals.com
Ed: Kent Hoover. **Description:** Republican candidates in the 2010 Congressional elections were overwhelmingly supported by the business community. Republican John Boehner, who will be the next Speaker of the House, says that the party's victory would end economic uncertainty and would assist small businesses to rehire workers. **Availability:** Print; Online.

18533 ■ *"California has a Plan B for Enacting Health Care Reform"* in *Sacramento Business Journal* (Vol. 29, May 18, 2012, No. 12, pp. 1)
Pub: Baltimore Business Journal
Contact: Rhonda Pringle, President
E-mail: rpringle@bizjournals.com
Description: California lawmakers are pushing for a bill that would implement health care reform in the state. The bill is in anticipation of the US Supreme Court's ruling on the Federal Affordable Healthcare Act. **Availability:** Print; Online.

18534 ■ *"Can He Win the Patent Game?"* in *Globe & Mail* (February 20, 2006, pp. B1)
Ed: Simon Avery, Paul Waldie. **Description:** A profile on managerial abilities of chief executive officer Jim Balsillie of Research In Motion Ltd., who will face the patent case with NTP Inc., is presented. **Availability:** Online.

18535 ■ *Canadian Small Business Kit for Dummies*
Ed: Margaret Kerr, JoAnn Kurtz, Andrew Dagys. **Released:** 4th edition. **Price:** $26.60, paperback; $39.99, paperback. **Description:** Resources include information on changes to laws and taxes for small businesses in Canada. **Availability:** Print; Online.

18536 ■ *"Canadian Wind Farm Sued Due to Negative Health Effects"* in *PC Magazine Online* (September 22, 2011)
Pub: PC Magazine
Contact: Dan Costa, Editor-in-Chief
E-mail: dan_costa@pcmag.com
Ed: Andrew Webster. **Description:** Suncor Energy is being sued by a family in Ontario, Canada. The family claims that Suncor's wind turbines have created health problems for them, ranging from vertigo and sleep disturbance to depression and suicidal thoughts. The family's home is over 1,000 meters from the eight wind turbines, and according to Ontario officials, wind turbines must be a minimum of 550 meters from existing homes. **Availability:** Online.

18537 ■ *"The Case for Treating the Sex Trade As an Industry"* in *Canadian Business* (Vol. 83, October 12, 2010, No. 17, pp. 9)
Pub: Rogers Media Inc.
Contact: Neil Spivak, Chief Executive Officer
Ed: Steve Maich. **Description:** It is believed that the worst aspects of prostitution in Canada are exacerbated by the fact that it must take place in secret. The laws that deal with the market for sex have led to an unsafe working environment. Prostitutes believe their industry needs to be sanctioned and regulated rather than ignored and reviled. **Availability:** Online.

18538 ■ *"Catch the Wind Announces Filing of Injunction Against Air Data Systems LLC and Philip Rogers"* in *CNW Group* (September 30, 2011)
Pub: CNW Group Ltd.
Description: Catch the Wind, providers of laser-based wind sensor products and technology, filed an injunction against Optical Air Data Systems (OADS) LLC and its former President and CEO Philip L. Rogers. The complaint seeks to have OADS and Rogers return tangible and intangible property owned by Catch the Wind, which the firm believes to be critical to the operations of their business. **Availability:** Online.

18539 ■ *"Cautions on Negotiating Business and Personal Contracts"* in *Business Owner* (Vol. 35, March-April 2011, No. 2, pp. 12)
Pub: DL Perkins L.L.C.
Contact: Brett Benton, Director
Description: Information is provided to help small business owners protect themselves during contract discussions, whether business or personal. A negotiating checklist is provided. **Availability:** Print; Online.

18540 ■ *"Changes Sought to Health Law"* in *Baltimore Business Journal* (Vol. 28, July 30, 2010, No. 12, pp. 1)
Pub: Baltimore Business Journal
Contact: Rhonda Pringle, President
E-mail: rpringle@bizjournals.com
Ed: Kent Hoover. **Description:** Business groups that opposed health care reform are working to undo parts of the new laws even before they go into effect. Business groups are gaining support for one legislative fix, which is repealing the law's provision that requires all businesses to file 1099 forms with the IRS any time they pay more than $600 a year to another business. **Availability:** Print; Online.

18541 ■ *"Child-Care Policy and the Labor Supply of Mothers with Young Children: A Natural Experiment from Canada"* in *University of Chicago Press* (Vol. 26, July 2008, No. 3)
Description: In 1997, the provincial government of Quebec, the second most populous province in Canada, initiated a new childcare policy. Licensed childcare service providers began offering day care spaces at the reduced fee of $5 per day per child for children aged four. By 2000, the policy applied to all children not in kindergarten. Using annual data (1993-2002) drawn from Statistics Canada's Survey of Labour and Income Dynamics, the results show that the policy had a large and statistically significant impact on the labor supply of mothers with preschool children. **Availability:** PDF.

18542 ■ *"China Vs the World: Whose Technology Is It?"* in *Harvard Business Review* (Vol. 88, December 2010, No. 12, pp. 94)
Pub: Harvard Business Publishing
Contact: Diane Belcher, Managing Director
Ed: Thomas M. Hout, Pankaj Ghemawat. **Price:** $8.95, PDF. **Description:** Examination of the regulation the Chinese government is implementing that require foreign corporations wishing to do business in the country to give up their new technologies. These regulations avoid World Trade Organization technology transfer provisions and complicate the convergence of socialism and capitalism. **Availability:** Online; PDF.

18543 ■ *Choosing the Right Legal Form of Business: The Complete Guide to Becoming a Sole Proprietor, Partnership, LLC, or Corporation*
Pub: Atlantic Publishing Co.
Contact: Dr. Heather L. Johnson, Contact
Ed: Pat Mitchell. **Released:** 2010. **Description:** According to the U.S. Small Business Administration, nearly 250,000 new businesses start up annually; currently there are over nine million small companies in the nation. The importance of choosing the proper legal form of business is stressed. **Availability:** Print; Online.

18544 ■ *"Citi Ruling Could Chill SEC, Street Legal Pacts"* in *Wall Street Journal Eastern Edition* (November 29, 2011, pp. C1)
Pub: Dow Jones & Company Inc.
Contact: Almar Latour, Chief Executive Officer
Ed: Jean Eaglesham, Chad Bray. **Description:** A $285 million settlement was reached between the Securities and Exchange Commission and Citigroup Inc. over allegations the bank misled investors over a mortgage-bond deal. Now, Judge Jed S. Rakoff has ruled against the settlement, a decision that will affect the future of such attempts to prosecute Wall Street fraud. Rakoff said that the settlement was "neither fair, nor reasonable, nor adequate, nor in the public interest." **Availability:** Online.

18545 ■ *Clicking Through: A Survival Guide for Bringing Your Company Online*
Released: First edition. **Description:** Summary of legal compliance issues faced by small companies doing business on the Internet, including copyright and patent laws.

18546 ■ *"Collateral Damage"* in *Business Courier* (Vol. 26, October 16, 2009, No. 25, pp. 1)
Pub: American City Business Journals, Inc.
Contact: Mike Olivieri, Executive Vice President
Ed: Jon Newberry. **Description:** Non-union construction firms representing Ohio Valley Associated Builders and Contractors Inc. have filed cases against unionized shops claiming violations of wage law in Ohio. Defendants say the violations are minor, however, they believe they are caught in the middle of the group's campaign to change the state's wage law. **Availability:** Print; Online.

18547 ■ *"Collection Agency Issues Whitepaper on Legal and Ethical Methods of Collecting on Overdue Accounts"* in *Marketwired* (July 20, 2009)
Pub: Comtex News Network Inc.
Contact: Kan Devnani, President
Description: American Profit Recovery, a collection agency based in Massachusetts and Michigan, has updated and reissued a whitepaper on what businesses can and cannot do regarding conversing with their customers in an attempt to collect on overdue

accounts and payments. A detailed summary on the federal laws associated with collecting on overdue accounts is outlined in such a way that any business owner, manager, or responsible party can easily understand. **Availability:** Print; Online.

18548 ■ *Complete Employee Handbook: A Step-by-Step Guide to Create a Custom Handbook That Protects Both the Employer and the Employee*

Description: Comprehensive guide for employers deal with personnel issues; CD-ROM contains sample employee handbooks, federal regulations and laws, forms for complying with government programs and worksheets for assessing personnel needs and goals. **Availability:** Online.

18549 ■ *The Complete Guide to Buying a Business*
Pub: Nolo
Contact: Chris Braun, President

Ed: Fred S. Steingold. **Released:** 2015. **Description:** Key steps in buying a business are highlighted, focusing on legal issues, tax considerations, approaches for valuing a business, financing, structuring the deal, along with forms and documents for taking ownership are included. **Availability:** Print.

18550 ■ *"Continuant's Big Win: A Lawsuit That Seemed Like a Lifetime" in Puget Sound Business Journal (Vol. 34, April 11, 2014, No. 52, pp. 4)*
Pub: American City Business Journals, Inc.
Contact: Mike Olivieri, Executive Vice President

Description: Fife, Washington-based Continuant has won a court ruling along with a $20 million verdict against Santa Clara, California-based Avaya Inc. after eight years in court. Avaya sued Continuant claiming the company did not have the right to service Avaya manufactured products. Insights into the lawsuit are given. **Availability:** Online.

18551 ■ *The Contract Mistakes Small Business Owners Make*
URL(s): www.pbl-law.com/news-articles-the-contract-mistakes-small-business-owners-make.html

Description: Discusses the importance of understanding small business contracts, legal things to look out for, and provides a list of the most common issues to look out for before signing any contracts. **Availability:** Online.

18552 ■ *"Councilman Addresses Union Harassment Accusations" in Philadelphia Business Journal (Vol. 33, March 28, 2014, No. 7, pp. 7)*
Pub: American City Business Journals, Inc.
Contact: Mike Olivieri, Executive Vice President

Released: Weekly. **Price:** $4, introductory 4-week offer(Digital & Print). **Description:** City Councilman Bobby Heron shares his perspective on the alleged violence and intimidation from building and trade unions in Philadelphia, Pennsylvania. Heron believes that the indictment of the leadership of the Ironworkers Local 401 for harassment was an isolated incident and should not reflect on the good and hardworking building and trades construction workers they represent. **Availability:** Print; Online.

18553 ■ *"Crime and Punishment" in Canadian Business (Vol. 81, December 24, 2007, No. 1, pp. 21)*

Description: Cmpass Inc.'s survey of 137 Canadian chief executive officers showed that they want tougher imposition of sentences on white-collar criminals, as they believe that the weak enforcement of securities laws gives an impression that Canada is a country where it is easy to get away with fraud. **Availability:** Online.

18554 ■ *"Critics Target Bribery Law" in Wall Street Journal Eastern Edition (November 28, 2011, pp. B1)*
Pub: Dow Jones & Company Inc.
Contact: Almar Latour, Chief Executive Officer

Ed: Joe Palazzolo. **Description:** Concern about how the Foreign Corrupt Practices Act, the United States' anti-bribery law, is enforced has drawn the focus of corporate lobbyists. Corporations have paid some $4 billion in penalties in cases involving the law, which prohibits companies from paying foreign officials bribes. The US Chamber of Commerce believes amending the act should be a priority. **Availability:** Online.

18555 ■ *"Crowdsourcing the Law" in LJN's Legal Tech Newsletter (October 1, 2010)*
Pub: Minnesota State Bar Association
Contact: Jennifer Thompson, President

Ed: Robert J. Ambrogi. **Released:** August 01, 2010. **Description:** Spindle Law strives to make legal research faster and smarter using crowdsourcing as one means to reach users. **Availability:** Print; Online.

18556 ■ *"Crucible: Battling Back from Betrayal" in Harvard Business Review (Vol. 88, December 2010, No. 12, pp. 130)*
Pub: Harvard Business Publishing
Contact: Diane Belcher, Managing Director

Ed: Daniel McGinn. **Price:** $8.95, PDF. **Description:** Stephen Greer's scrap metal firm, Hartwell Pacific, lost several million dollars due to a lack of efficient and appropriate inventory audits, accounting procedures, and new-hire reference checks for his foreign operations. Greer believes that balancing growth with control is a key component of success. **Availability:** Print; PDF.

18557 ■ *"Dairy Queen Aims to Blitz Blizzberry" in Ice Cream Reporter (Vol. 23, August 20, 2010, No. 9, pp. 1)*

Description: International Diary Queens has filed a lawsuit to stop Yogubliz Inc. from using Blizzberry and Blizz Frozen Yogurt as the name of its shops because the name is so close to Dairy Queen's Blizzard frozen dessert. **Availability:** Print; Online.

18558 ■ *"Dallas Law Firms Play Big Role in State's M&A Deals" in Dallas Business Journal (Vol. 37, July 18, 2014, No. 45, pp. 9)*
Pub: American City Business Journals, Inc.
Contact: Mike Olivieri, Executive Vice President

Released: June 18, 2014. **Price:** $4, Introductory 4-Week Offer(Digital & Print). **Description:** Law firms in Dallas, Texas have played a crucial role in several mergers and acquisitions in the state, which has been the highest in 2014. the pace of mergers and acquisitions is expected to stay the same or improve during the second half of 2014. **Availability:** Print; Online.

18559 ■ *"Day-Care Center Owner to Argue Against Liquor Store Opening Nearby" in Chicago Tribune (March 13, 2008)*
Pub: Tribune News Service
Contact: Jack Barry, Vice President, Operations
E-mail: jbarry@tribpub.com

Ed: Matthew Walberg. **Description:** NDLC's owner feels that Greenwood Liquors should not be granted its liquor license due to the claim that the NDLC is not only a day-care center but also a school that employs state-certified teachers. **Availability:** Print; Online.

18560 ■ *"Decorated Marine Sues Contractor" in Wall Street Journal Eastern Edition (November 29, 2011, pp. A4)*
Pub: Dow Jones & Company Inc.
Contact: Almar Latour, Chief Executive Officer

Ed: Julian E. Barnes. **Description:** Marine Devon Maylie, who was awarded the Congressional Medal of Honor for bravery, has filed a lawsuit against defense contractor BAE Systems PLC claiming that the company prevented his hiring by another firm by saying he has a mental condition and a drinking problem. Maylie says that this was in retaliation for his objections to the company's plan to sell the Pakistani military high-tech sniper scopes. **Availability:** Online.

18561 ■ *"Defendants in Ponzi Case Seek Relief from Court" in Denver Business Journal (Vol. 64, September 7, 2012, No. 16, pp. 1)*
Pub: Baltimore Business Journal
Contact: Rhonda Pringle, President
E-mail: rpringle@bizjournals.com

Price: $4, Introductory 4-Week Offer(Digital Only). **Description:** A US District Court judge has turned down the petition of Ponzi scheme suspects Michael Turnock and William P. Sullivan II to release their assets. The two have been accused of fraud and operating a Ponzi scheme worth $15.7 million. They argued that they are suffering from economic hardship and health issues. **Availability:** Print.

18562 ■ *"Denton to Consider Texas' First Fracking Ban" in Dallas Business Journal (Vol. 37, July 11, 2014, No. 44, pp. 12)*
Pub: American City Business Journals, Inc.
Contact: Mike Olivieri, Executive Vice President

Released: June 11, 2014. **Price:** $4, Introductory 4-Week Offer(Digital & Print). **Description:** The process of hydraulic fracturing or fracking and its disadvantages is discusses, focusing on Denton City Council's plan to declare the first fracking ban in Texas. The ban is expected to make oil and gas companies to file legal challenges. It is reported that Denton residents had to be relocated after oil well were re-drilled and transformed into deeper and horizontal Barnett Shale natural gas wells. **Availability:** Print; Online.

18563 ■ *Dictionary of Real Estate Terms*
Pub: Barron's Educational Series Inc.
Contact: Manuel H. Barron, Contact

Ed: Jack P. Friedman, Jack C. Harris, J. Bruce Lindeman. **Released:** 9th edition. **Price:** $16.99, paperback, plus shipping charges $5.99. **Description:** More than 2,500 real estate terms relating to mortgages and financing, brokerage law, architecture, rentals and leases, property insurance, and more. **Availability:** E-book; Print.

18564 ■ *"Direct Recovery Associates Debt Collection Agency Beats Industry Record" in Internet Wire (June 24, 2010)*

Description: Direct Recovery Associates Inc. was named as one of the highest collection records in the industry, which has consistently improved over 18 years. The firm is an international attorney-based debt collection agency. **Availability:** Print; Online.

18565 ■ *"Disunion in the House: the Steep Price We Pay" in Philadelphia Business Journal (Vol. 33, March 28, 2014, No. 7, pp. 4)*
Pub: American City Business Journals, Inc.
Contact: Mike Olivieri, Executive Vice President

Released: Weekly. **Price:** $4, introductory 4-week offer(Digital & Print). **Description:** Some members of the Ironworkers Local 401 Union in Philadelphia, Pennsylvania face federal indictment on charges of participating in an alleged conspiracy to commit extortion, arson, assault and destruction of property. The alleged motive of their actions was to force construction contractors to hire union ironworkers. **Availability:** Print; Online.

18566 ■ *The Diversity Code: Unlock the Secrets to Making Differences Work in the Real World*
Pub: HarperCollins Leadership
Contact: Donald Miller, Chief Executive Officer

Ed: Michelle T. Johnson. **Released:** January 24, 2019. **Description:** The most diligent compliance with laws and regulations can't foster true work place diversity. The best organizations have become genuine cross-cultural communities that believe equality in reconciling difference and valuing them. The book promotes understanding by answering many of the toughest questions that professionals and their employers are afraid to ask. **Availability:** Print.

18567 ■ "DOL Stiffens Child Labor Penalties" in HR Specialist (Vol. 8, September 2010, No. 9, pp. 2)
Pub: Capitol Information Group Inc.
Contact: Allie Ash, Chief Executive Officer
Description: U.S. Department of Labor (DOL) will impose new penalties for employers that violate U.S. child labor laws. Details of the new law are included.

18568 ■ "Economic Loss Rule and Franchise Attorneys" in Franchise Law Journal (Vol. 27, Winter 2008, No. 3, pp. 192)
Ed: Christian C. Burden, Scott Trende. **Released:** Volume 27. **Description:** Economic loss rule prohibits recovery of damages in tort when the subject injury is unaccompanied by either property damage or personal injury.

18569 ■ "Employees Change Clothes at Work? Heed New Pay Rules" in HR Specialist (Vol. 8, September 2010, No. 9, pp. 1)
Pub: Capitol Information Group Inc.
Contact: Allie Ash, Chief Executive Officer
Description: U.S. Department of Labor issued a new interpretation letter that states times spent changing in and out of 'protective clothing' (e.g., helmets, smocks, aprons, gloves, etc.) is considered paid time. It also says time spent changing 'ordinary clothes' (i.e., uniform) may not be compensable itself, but could start the clock on the workday, meaning all activities after - such as walking to the workstation - would be paid time. More details and a link to the DOL are included. **Availability:** PDF; Online.

18570 ■ Employer Legal Forms Simplified
Released: First edition. **Description:** Business reference containing the following forms needed to handle employees in any small business environment: application, notice, confidentiality, absence, federal employer forms and notices, and many payroll forms. All forms are included on a CD that comes in both PDF and text formats. Adobe Acrobat Reader software is also included on the CD. The forms are valid in all fifty states and Washington, DC. **Availability:** Print.

18571 ■ "Employers See Workers' Comp Rates Rising" in Sacramento Business Journal (Vol. 28, April 8, 2011, No. 6, pp. 1)
Pub: Sacramento Business Journal
Contact: Stephanie Fretwell, Director
E-mail: sfretwell@bizjournals.com
Ed: Kelly Johnson. **Released:** Weekly. **Price:** $4. **Description:** Employers in California are facing higher workers compensation costs. Increased medical costs and litigation are seen to drive the trend. **Availability:** Online.

18572 ■ Entrepreneurship: A Process Perspective
Ed: Robert A. Baron, Scott A. Shane. **Released:** 2nd Edition. **Description:** Entrepreneurial process covering team building, finances, business plan, legal issues, marketing, growth and exit strategies. **Availability:** Print.

18573 ■ "Estate Tax Problems may Soon Disappear" in Contractor (Vol. 56, September 2009, No. 9, pp. 60)
Ed: Irving L. Blackman. **Description:** Advice on how to effectively plan estate tax in the United States. Pending changes to US estate tax laws are seen to resolve inheritance problems. Captive insurance firms can lower property and casualty insurance costs to transfer businesses to children. **Availability:** Print; Online.

18574 ■ "The Evolution of the Laws of Software Evolution: a Discussion Based On a Systematic Literature Review" in ACM Computing Surveys (Vol. 46, Summer 2014, No. 2, pp. 28)
Pub: Association for Computing Machinery - Manor College Student Chapter
Contact: Mary Cecilia Jurasinski, President
Description: After more than 40 years of life, software evolution should be considered as a mature field. However, despite such a long history, many research questions still remain open, and controversial studies about the validity of the laws of software evolution are common. During the first part of these 40 years, the laws themselves evolved to adapt to the changes in both the research and the software industry environments. This process of adaption to new paradigms, standards, and practices stopped about 15 years ago, when the laws were revised for the last time. The current state of affairs about the validity of software laws, how they are perceived by the research community, and the developments and challenges likely to occur in the future are addressed. **Availability:** Print; PDF; Online.

18575 ■ "Experts Sound Off On Top Legal Trends" in Birmingham Business Journal (Vol. 31, January 17, 2014, No. 3, pp. 4)
Pub: American City Business Journals, Inc.
Contact: Mike Olivieri, Executive Vice President
Released: Weekly. **Price:** $4, introductory 4-week offer(Digital & Print). **Description:** Lawyers' views on potential legal trends in Birmingham, Alabama for 2014 are presented, with the Affordable Care Act leading the agenda. One attorney addressed the challenges associated with the use of social media. **Availability:** Print; Online.

18576 ■ "Extortion: How Politicians Extract Your Money, Buy Votes, and Line Their Own Pockets"
Pub: Mariner Books
Released: October 22, 2013. **Price:** $12.79, Paperback. **Description:** Politicians and lawmakers have developed a new set of legislative tactics designed to extort wealthy industries and donors into huge contributions. This money is then funneled into the pockets of their friends and family members. Schweizer reveals the secret 'fees' each political party charges politicians for top committee assignments; how fourteen members of Congress received hundreds of thousands of dollars using a self-loan loophole; how PAC money is used to bankroll their lavish lifestyles; and more. The first time these unethical issues have been reported to the public. **Availability:** E-book; Print.

18577 ■ "Facebook, Google, LinkedIn Line Up In Patent Case Before Supreme Court" in San Francisco Business Times (Vol. 28, March 28, 2014, No. 36)
Pub: American City Business Journals, Inc.
Contact: Mike Olivieri, Executive Vice President
Released: Weekly. **Description:** The U.S. Supreme Court is set to hear a case involving Alice Corporation Pty. Ltd. and CLS Bank International in a dispute over a patented computer-implemented escrow service. The case has larger implications to tech companies concerning whether a business method can be patented if it is made electronic. **Availability:** Print; Online.

18578 ■ "Family Dollar Reaches Preliminary Class Action Settlement" in Benzinga.com (September 12, 2012)
Pub: Benzinga.com
Contact: Jason Raznick, Founder
Description: Family Dollar Stores Inc. has reached a preliminary settlement with New York store managers. The settlement provides 1,700 managers a maximum payment of $14 million. A profile of the Family Dollar Stores company is also included. **Availability:** Print; Online.

18579 ■ "Family Takes Wind Turbine Companies to Court Over Gag Clauses on Health Effects of Turbines" in CNW Group (September 12, 2011)
Pub: CNW Group Ltd.
Description: Shawn and Trisha Drennan are concerned about the negative experiences other have had with wind turbines close to their homes, including adverse health effects. The couple's home will be approximately 650 meters from the Kingsbridge II wind farm project in Ontario, Canada. **Availability:** Online.

18580 ■ "Feds Battling to Put the Brakes on Ambulance Billing Fraud" in Philadelphia Business Journal (Vol. 33, April 25, 2014, No. 11, pp. 4)
Pub: American City Business Journals, Inc.
Contact: Mike Olivieri, Executive Vice President
Released: Weekly. **Price:** $4, introductory 4-week offer(Digital & Print). **Description:** The Department of Health and Human Services, Office of Inspector General, Federal Bureau of Investigation and the U.S. Attorney's Office are working together to crack down on ambulance companies involved in fraudulent Medicare claims. A ban on new ground ambulance companies in southeastern Philadelphia was issued due to ambulance fraud in the Philadelphia region. **Availability:** Print; Online.

18581 ■ "Feds Finalize I-9 Form Rules Allowing Electronic Storage" in HR Specialist (Vol. 8, September 2010, No. 9, pp. 5)
Pub: Capitol Information Group Inc.
Contact: Allie Ash, Chief Executive Officer
Description: U.S. Department of Homeland Security issued regulations that give employers more flexibility to electronically sing and store I-9 employee verification forms. **Availability:** Print; PDF; Online.

18582 ■ "Feds to Pay University Hospital $20M" in Business Courier (Vol. 27, July 23, 2010, No. 12, pp. 3)
Pub: Business Courier
Ed: James Ritchie. **Description:** The U.S. government is set to pay University Hospital and medical residents who trained there $20 million as part of a tax dispute settlement. Around 1,000 former residents are to receive tax refunds. But the hospital must provide the U.S. Internal Revenue Service with extensive documentation. **Availability:** Print; Mailing list; Online.

18583 ■ "Fight Ensues Over Irreplaceable Princess Diana Gowns" in Tampa Bay Business Journal (Vol. 30, January 15, 2010, No. 4, pp. 1)
Pub: Tampa Bay Business Journal
Contact: Ian Anderson, President
E-mail: ianderson@bizjournals.com
Ed: Janet Leiser. **Description:** People's Princess Charitable Foundation Inc. founder Maureen Rorech Dunkel has sought Chapter 11 bankruptcy protection before a state court decides on the fate of the five of 13 Princess Diana Gowns. Dunkel and the nonprofit were sued by Patricia Sullivan of HRH Venture LLC who claimed they defaulted on $1.5 million in loans. **Availability:** Print; Online.

18584 ■ "Fines Can't Snuff Out Hookah Sales" in Providence Business News (Vol. 28, March 3, 2014, No. 48, pp. 1)
Pub: American City Business Journals, Inc.
Contact: Mike Olivieri, Executive Vice President
Released: March 01, 2014. **Description:** The City of Providence, Rhode Island initiated a crackdown on bars and restaurants serving Middle Eastern-style water pipes, known as hookahs in violation of state anti-smoking laws. Gianfranco Marrocco, owner of several Federal Hill nightspots, believes that many bar owners will just pay the fine because hookah lounges are a good revenue source. **Availability:** Print; Online.

18585 ■ "Firms Sue Doracon to Recoup More Than $1M in Unpaid Bills" in Baltimore Business Journal (Vol. 28, July 9, 2010, No. 9, pp. 1)
Pub: Baltimore Business Journal
Contact: Rhonda Pringle, President
E-mail: rpringle@bizjournals.com
Ed: Scott Dance. **Description:** Concrete supplier Paul J. Rach Inc., Selective Insurance Company, and equipment leasing firm Colonial Pacific Leasing Corporation intend to sue Baltimore, Maryland-based

Doracon Contracting Inc. for $1 million in unpaid bills. Doracon owed Colonial Pacific $794,000 and the equipment is still in Doracon's possession. Selective Insurance and Paul J. Rach respectively seek $132,000 and $88,000. **Availability:** Print.

18586 ■ *"First-Time Landlord: Your Guide to Renting Out a Single-Family Home"*
Pub: Nolo
Contact: Chris Braun, President
Released: 6th Edition. **Price:** $17.49, e-book (downloadable); $19.99, book and e-book. **Description:** The basics for becoming an landlord for anyone wishing to start an entrepreneurial pursuit in home rentals are outlined. Concise information for renting out a single-family home includes, how to determine whether the property will turn a profit, landlord business basics, finding the right tenants, preparing and signing a lead, handling repairs, complying with state rental laws, dealing with problem tenants, and preparing for the sale of the property. **Availability:** E-book.

18587 ■ *"For Tech Companies, Holding Onto Prized Patents Can Be Expensive"* in *Puget Sound Business Journal (Vol. 33, May 18, 2012, No. 4, pp. 1)*
Pub: Baltimore Business Journal
Contact: Rhonda Pringle, President
E-mail: rpringle@bizjournals.com
Description: Patent lawsuits have been rising steadily over the past 20 years and the damage rewards are also growing. Microsoft is currently engaged in more than 60 patent infringement lawsuits worldwide and the largest is a 2 year fight over a series of patents that Motorola holds and Microsoft uses. **Availability:** Print; Online.

18588 ■ *"Former Collection Agency CFO Sentenced"* in *PaymentsSource (April 24, 2012)*
Description: Leslie Jean McIntosh, CFO of FITEC LLC, a collection agency located in Kalispell, Montana was sentenced to 21 months in federal prison for tax evasion. McIntosh was ordered to pay $159,000 in restitution. McIntosh deposited $131,000 in client money into her personal account. **Availability:** Print; Online.

18589 ■ *"Free Speech Vs. Privacy in Data Mining"* in *Information Today (Vol. 28, September 2011, No. 8, pp. 22)*
Pub: Information Today Inc.
Contact: Thomas H. Hogan, President
Ed: George H. Pike. **Description:** The U.S. Constitution does not explicitly guarantee the right of privacy. Organizations and businesses that require obtaining and disseminating information can be caught in the middle of privacy rights. The long-term impact on data mining, Internet marketing, and Internet privacy issues are examined.

18590 ■ *"From the Editors: Plagiarism Policies and Screening at AMJ"* in *Academy of Management Journal (Vol. 55, August 2012, No. 4, pp. 749)*
Pub: Academy of Management
Contact: Sharon Alvarez, President
Description: The plagiarism policies and practices of the Academy of Management Journal (AMJ) based on the Committee on Publications Ethics and AOM guidelines are described. The function of the Cross-Check software tool for screening manuscripts for plagiarism is explained. **Availability:** Download; Electronic publishing; PDF; Online.

18591 ■ *"Full-Court Press for Apple"* in *Barron's (Vol. 88, March 24, 2008, No. 12, pp. 47)*
Pub: Dow Jones & Company Inc.
Contact: Almar Latour, Chief Executive Officer
Ed: Mark Veverka. **Description:** Apple Inc. is facing more intellectual property lawsuits in 2008, with 30 patent lawsuits filed compared to 15 in 2007 and nine in 2006. The lawsuits, which involve products such as the iPod and the iPhone, present some concern for Apple's shareholders. **Availability:** Online.

18592 ■ *"Full Speed Ahead?"* in *San Antonio Business Journal (Vol. 28, May 9, 2014, No. 13, pp. 4)*
Pub: American City Business Journals, Inc.
Contact: Mike Olivieri, Executive Vice President
Released: May 09, 2014. **Price:** $4, Introductory 4-Week Offer(Digital & Print). **Description:** Lyft and Uber Technologies Inc. have launched ride-sharing services in San Antonio, Texas without the city's permission and the objections of taxi and limousine industries. The ride-sharing service issues were brought into court and to the City Council, while the San Antonio Police Department issued a cease-and-desist order to the ride-sharing companies. The complaints against Lyft and Uber are outlined. **Availability:** Print; Online.

18593 ■ *"Funeral Picketing Laws and Free Speech"* in *Kansas Law Review (Vol. 55, April 2007, No. 3, pp. 575-627)*
Description: In-depth information covering laws governing protests and freedom of speech during funerals is presented. **Availability:** Download; PDF; Online.

18594 ■ *"Get Prepared for New Employee Free Choice Act"* in *HRMagazine (Vol. 53, December 2008, No. 12, pp. 22)*
Description: According to the director of global labor and employee relations with Ingersoll Rand Company, unions may have started having employees signing authorization cards in anticipation of the Employee Free Choice Act. Once signed, the cards are good for one year and employers would have only ten days in which to prepare for bargaining with unions over the first labor contract. The Act also requires these negotiations be subject to mandatory arbitration if a contract is not reached within 120 days of negotiations with unions, resulting in employers' wage rates, health insurance, retirement benefits and key language about flexibility would be determined by an arbitrator with no vested interest in the success of the company. **Availability:** Print; Online.

18595 ■ *"Hearing Damage Leads to Settlement"* in *Register-Guard (August 13, 2011)*
Description: Cynergy Pest Control lost a court battle when a rural Cottage Grove man was granted a $37,000 settlement after his hearing was damaged by the pest control companies method to eradicate gophers, using blasts in his neighbor's yard. **Availability:** Print; Online.

18596 ■ *"Hike in Md.'s Alcohol Tax May Be Hard For Lawmakers to Swallow"* in *Baltimore Business Journal (Vol. 28, November 19, 2010, No. 28)*
Pub: Baltimore Business Journal
Contact: Rhonda Pringle, President
E-mail: rpringle@bizjournals.com
Ed: Emily Mullin. **Description:** Maryland's General Assembly has been reluctant to support a dime-per-drink increase in alcohol tax that was drafted in the 2009 bill if the tax revenue goes into a separate fund. The alcohol tax increase is considered unnecessary by some lawmakers and business leaders due to impending federal spending boosts. **Availability:** Print; Online.

18597 ■ *"Houston Law Firms Plan Rate Bumps"* in *Houston Business Journal (Vol. 40, December 25, 2009, No. 33, pp. 1)*
Pub: Houston Business Journal
Contact: Bob Charlet, President
E-mail: bcharlet@bizjournals.com
Ed: Ford Gunter. **Description:** Survey shows that Houston, Texas-based law firms were in line with a 3.2 percent average rate hike projected for 2010. The big firms were ready to offset some losses with a rate bump of 4 percent while smaller firms have been expecting an increase of about 3 percent. **Availability:** Print; Online.

18598 ■ *"How to Avoid Leave-Related Lawsuits"* in *Employee Benefit News (Vol. 25, December 1, 2011, No. 15, pp. 12)*
Pub: SourceMedia LLC
Contact: Gemma Postlethwaite, Chief Executive Officer
Ed: John F. Galvin. **Description:** Tips for employers when adding disability and maternity leave benefits to workers are outlined, with focus on ways to avoid leave-related lawsuits.

18599 ■ *"How to Find a Startup Lawyer: The Ultimate Guide"* in *NerdWallet (May 7, 2021)*
URL(s): www.nerdwallet.com/article/small-business/how-to-find-a-startup-lawyer
Ed: Priyanka Prakash. **Released:** May 07, 2021. **Description:** Discusses the essential nature of having a lawyer for your business startup and how to go about finding the right one. **Availability:** Online.

18600 ■ *How to Start a Bankruptcy Forms Processing Service*
Released: First edition. **Description:** Due to the increase in bankruptcy filings, attorneys are outsourcing related jobs in order to reduce overhead.

18601 ■ *How to Start and Run Your Own Corporation: S-Corporations For Small Business Owners*
Pub: HCM Publishing
Ed: Peter I. Hupalo. **Description:** Basics of corporate business structure are explained. Topics include discovering the best business structure for your company; how to decided between an S-Corporation and LLC; choosing the state in which to incorporate, how to form a corporation, angel investing, special issues for one-person corporations, the role of bylaws and corporate minutes, board of directors, taxes, workers' compensation issues, retirement plans, and more. **Availability:** Print.

18602 ■ *"Human Capital: When Change Means Terminating an Employee"* in *Black Enterprise (Vol. 41, November 2010, No. 4, pp. 40)*
Pub: Earl G. Graves Ltd.
Contact: Earl Graves, Jr., President
Ed: Tamara E. Holmes. **Description:** Covering successful business change strategies, this article focuses on how the law and nondiscrimination policies can affect this aspect of the workplace. **Availability:** Online.

18603 ■ *"IJ Challenges Atlanta's Vending Monopoly"* in *Benzinga.com (July 28, 2011)*
Pub: Benzinga.com
Contact: Jason Raznick, Founder
Description: A lawsuit was filed by The Institute for Justice to challenge Atlanta's unconstitutional vending monopoly on behalf of two Atlanta street vendors. **Availability:** Print; Online.

18604 ■ *"Illinois Regulators Revoke Collection Agency's License"* in *Collections & Credit Risk (Vol. 15, August 1, 2010, No. 7, pp. 13)*
Pub: SourceMedia LLC
Contact: Gemma Postlethwaite, Chief Executive Officer
Description: Creditors Service Bureau of Springfield, Illinois had its license revoked by a state regulatory agency and was fined $55,000 because the owner and president, Craig W. Lewis, did not turn over portions of collected funds to clients. **Availability:** Print; Online.

18605 ■ *Incorporate Your Business: A Legal Guide to Forming a Corporation in Your State*
Pub: Nolo
Contact: Chris Braun, President
Ed: Anthony Mancuso. **Released:** 11th edition. **Price:** $34.99, e-book; $39.99, book and e-book; $34.99, e-book. **Description:** Legal guide to incorporating a business in the U.S., covering all 50 states. **Availability:** E-book; Print.

18606 ■ *"Individual and Organizational Reintegration After Ethical or Legal Transgressions: Challenges and Opportunities"* in *Business Ethics Quarterly (Vol. 24, July 2014, No. 3, pp. 315)*
Pub: Business Ethics Quarterly
Contact: Dawn Elm, Executive Director
E-mail: drelm@stthomas.edu
Description: Individual and organizational reintegration in the aftermath of transgressions that violate ethical and legal boundaries are explored. **Availability:** Download; PDF; Online.

18607 ■ *"International Business Law: Interpreting the Term 'Like Products"* in *Business Recorder (June 7, 2012)*
Ed: Zafar Azeem. **Description:** The term 'like products' needs to be defined for international trade. The battle between the United States and Indonesia regarding this issue is discussed. A technical barrier clause being used by foreign countries is prohibiting imports and hurting competitiveness. **Availability:** Online.

18608 ■ *"Investing in an HR Team Can Ease the Burden of Mass Hiring"* in *Crain's Detroit Business (Vol. 36, September 8, 2014, No. 36, pp. 15)*
Pub: American City Business Journals, Inc.
Contact: Mike Olivieri, Executive Vice President
Description: Computing Source is a computer networking firm that helps small businesses recover computer files from backup tapes, particularly for law firms. Profile of the company and information about its CEO, Mark St. Peter is included. **Availability:** Print; Online.

18609 ■ *"Investment Firms Unite: Coalition Fights New Tax Law"* in *Black Enterprise (Vol. 38, December 2007, No. 5, pp. 52)*
Description: Minorities working in private equity, real estate and investment management firms have united to form the Access to Capital Coalition to oppose legislation that they feel would adversely affect their ability to attract investments and executives. Details of the group are included. **Availability:** Print; Online.

18610 ■ *"Israeli Spam Law May Have Global Impact"* in *Information Today (Vol. 26, February 2009, No. 2, pp. 28)*
Pub: Information Today Inc.
Contact: Thomas H. Hogan, President
Ed: David Mirchin. **Description:** Israels new law, called Amendment 40 of the Communications Law, will regulate commercial solicitations including those sent without permission via email, fax, automatic phone dialing systems, or short messaging technologies. **Availability:** PDF; Online.

18611 ■ *"Judge Gives RIM One Last Chance"* in *Globe & Mail (February 24, 2006, pp. B5)*
Ed: Barrie McKenna, Paul Waldie. **Description:** United States District Court Judge James Spencer offers more time for Research In Motion Ltd. (RIM) to settle the patent infringement dispute with NTP Inc. RIM's shares increase by 6.2 percent following the decision. **Availability:** Online.

18612 ■ *"Judgment Day"* in *Canadian Business (Vol. 79, September 11, 2006, No. 18, pp. 27)*
Description: The long, drawn out legal proceedings carried out by Bre-X Minerals Ltd. whose case against its former vice chairman and chief geolist, John Felderhof are presented. **Availability:** Online.

18613 ■ *"Just a Slight Rate Bump for Local Law Firms"* in *Philadelphia Business Journal (Vol. 30, January 20, 2012, No. 49, pp. 1)*
Pub: Baltimore Business Journal
Contact: Rhonda Pringle, President
E-mail: rpringle@bizjournals.com
Description: Philadelphia, Pennsylvania-based law firms have increased billing rates by only one percent in 2011. Law firms show moderate increased in revenue in 2012. **Availability:** Print; Online.

18614 ■ *"Law Firms Cash In On Alcohol"* in *Business Journal Portland (Vol. 27, November 19, 2010, No. 38, pp. 1)*
Pub: Portland Business Journal
Contact: Andy Giegerich, Managing Editor
E-mail: agiegerich@bizjournals.com
Ed: Andy Giegerich. **Description:** Oregon-based law firms have continued to corner big business on the state's growing alcohol industry as demand for their services increased. Lawyers, who represent wine, beer and liquor distillery interests, have seen their workload increased by 20 to 30 percent in 2009. **Availability:** Print; Online.

18615 ■ *"Law Firms See Improvement in Financing Climate"* in *Sacramento Business Journal (Vol. 28, October 14, 2011, No. 33, pp. 1)*
Pub: Sacramento Business Journal
Contact: Stephanie Fretwell, Director
E-mail: sfretwell@bizjournals.com
Ed: Kathy Robertson. **Description:** Sacramento, California-based Weintraub Genshlea Chediak Law Corporation has helped close 26 financing deals worth more than $1.6 billion in 2010, providing indication of improvement in Sacramento's economy. Lawyers have taken advantage of low interest rates to make refinancing agreements and help clients get new funds. **Availability:** Online.

18616 ■ *"Law School Not Such a Great Idea?"* in *Philadelphia Business Journal (Vol. 33, February 28, 2014, No. 3, pp. 8)*
Pub: American City Business Journals, Inc.
Contact: Mike Olivieri, Executive Vice President
Released: Weekly. **Price:** $4, introductory 4-week offer(Digital & Print). **Description:** Several law schools in Philadelphia, Pennsylvania saw a 31.5 percent decline in combined first-year enrollment from 2000-2014. The University of Pennsylvania gained less than one percent during the period, while Widener University's Hidener Campus had the biggest drop from 181 first-year students in 2009-2010 to just 74 in 2013-2014. **Availability:** Print; Online.

18617 ■ *"Lawsuit Seeks To Shut Down Illinois Collection Agency"* in *PaymentsSource (January 12, 2012)*
Pub: SourceMedia LLC
Contact: Gemma Postlethwaite, Chief Executive Officer
Description: PN Financial is facing charges by the Illinois State Attorney General's Office, alleging that the company used abusive and threatening actions against consumers. Details of the lawsuit are covered. **Availability:** Online.

18618 ■ *"Lawsuits Claim Coke Sent Illegal Ad Texts"* in *Atlanta Business Chronicle (June 13, 2014, pp. 4A)*
Pub: American City Business Journals, Inc.
Contact: Mike Olivieri, Executive Vice President
Description: Coca-Cola Company is facing lawsuits in San Diego and California from consumers who claim to have received unsolicited ads to their wireless phones, thus putting Coke in violation of the Federal law, called the Telephone Consumer Protection Act. The plaintiff of the California lawsuit is seeking damages amounting to $1,500 for each text message sent. **Availability:** Print; Online.

18619 ■ *"Lawyers Lock Up Cops as Clients"* in *Sacramento Business Journal (Vol. 28, April 8, 2011, No. 6, pp. 1)*
Pub: Sacramento Business Journal
Contact: Stephanie Fretwell, Director
E-mail: sfretwell@bizjournals.com
Ed: Kathy Robertson. **Released:** Weekly. **Price:** $4. **Description:** Sacramento-based law firm Mastagni, Holstedt and Chiurazzi has grown its client base by specializing in law enforcement labor issues. The firm represents 80,000 public sector correctional officers in the US. The firm has been experiencing an increase in new business as public sector employers face huge budget deficits. **Availability:** Online.

18620 ■ *"Lawyers Object to New Online Court Fees"* in *Sacramento Business Journal (Vol. 31, August 8, 2014, No. 24, pp. 3)*
Pub: American City Business Journals, Inc.
Contact: Mike Olivieri, Executive Vice President
Description: Lawyers and consumer advocates have complained that the Sacramento County Superior Court's new fee system for online access to online court records hinders access to justice. However, court administrators argue that the charging of fees will only help offset the online record system's maintenance costs. **Availability:** Print; Online.

18621 ■ *"Lawyers Sued Over Lapsed Lacrosse Patent"* in *Crain's Detroit Business (Vol. 25, June 8, 2009, No. 23, pp. 5)*
Pub: Crain Communications Inc.
Contact: Barry Asin, President
Ed: Chad Halcom. **Description:** Warrior Sports Inc., a manufacturer of lacrosse equipment located in Warren, Michigan is suing the law firm Dickinson Wright PLLC and two of its intellectual property lawyers over patent rights to lacrosse equipment. **Availability:** Print; Online.

18622 ■ *"Leaning Tower"* in *Business Courier (Vol. 27, June 4, 2010, No. 5, pp. 1)*
Pub: Business Courier
Ed: Jon Newberry. **Description:** New York-based developer Armand Lasky, owner of Tower Place Mall in downtown Cincinnati, Ohio has sued Birmingham, Alabama-based Regions Bank to prevent the bank's foreclosure on the property. Regions Bank claims Lasky was in default on an $18 million loan agreement. Details on the mall's leasing plan are also discussed. **Availability:** Online.

18623 ■ *"Legal Assistance for Startups: Everything You Need to Know"* in *UpCounsel (June 26, 2020)*
URL(s): www.upcounsel.com/legal-assistance-for-startups
Released: June 26, 2020. **Description:** Provides information on how small business owners can obtain legal assistance. Includes details about hiring a lawyer, why a start-up might need a lawyer, how much it costs to hire a lawyer, and where to get low-cost legal advice. **Availability:** Online.

18624 ■ *"Legal Barriers Keep 16-Story Horizon at Ground Level"* in *Memphis Business Journal (Vol. 34, August 24, 2012, No. 19, pp. 1)*
Pub: Baltimore Business Journal
Contact: Rhonda Pringle, President
E-mail: rpringle@bizjournals.com
Description: Construction on the Horizon building at 717 Riverside Drive remains unfinished as legal battles ensue among banks and construction firms involved in the project. The root of the legal proceedings is the Bryan Company's defaulting from a $58.6 million loan from four banks and the foreclosureof the property. **Availability:** Print; Online.

18625 ■ *A Legal Guide for Startups*
URL(s): www.rocketlawyer.com/business-and-contracts/starting-a-business/legal-guide/a-legal-guide-for-startups
Description: A legal guide for entrepreneurs who are starting a busienss. Includes information on safeguarding your interests, setting up a legal entity, finding legal advice, and additional steps to protect yourself. **Availability:** Online.

18626 ■ *"The Legal Side of Owning a Food Truck"* in *Entrepreneur (2020)*
Ed: Rich Mintzer. **Description:** Details the legal side of owning a food truck including licenses, permits, registrations, and laws. **Availability:** Online.

18627 ■ *"Legislating the Cloud"* in *Information Today (Vol. 28, October 2011, No. 9, pp. 1)*
Pub: Information Today Inc.
Contact: Thomas H. Hogan, President

Ed: Kurt Schiller. **Description:** Internet and telecommunications industry leaders are asking for legislation to address the emerging market in cloud computing. Existing communications laws do not adequately govern the modern Internet.

18628 ■ *"Local Law Firms Quietly Boost Poaching" in Boston Business Journal (Vol. 31, July 29, 2011, No. 27, pp. 3)*
Pub: Boston Business Journal
Contact: Carolyn M. Jones, President
E-mail: cmjones@bizjournals.com

Ed: Lisa Van der Pool. **Released:** Weekly. **Price:** $4, Introductory 4-Week Offer(Digital Only). **Description:** National law firms Jones Day and Latham & Watkins LLP set up offices in Boston, Massachusetts. Their move also created an upswing on confidential conversation as both firms are aggressively poaching lawyers from Boston's other top firms. **Availability:** Print; Online.

18629 ■ *"Locals Eager for $785M Medical Marijuana Business" in Orlando Business Journal (Vol. 30, March 21, 2014, No. 39, pp. 4)*
Pub: American City Business Journals, Inc.
Contact: Mike Olivieri, Executive Vice President

Released: Weekly. **Price:** $8, introductory 4-week offer(Digital & Print). **Description:** A number of local companies in Central Florida are preparing for a ballot initiative to legalize medical marijuana in November 2014. The National Cannabis Association estimates the medical marijuana market in Florida at $785 million, with about 260,000 patients, while Orlando's share is estimated at $89.1 million, with 29,518 potential patients. **Availability:** Print; Online.

18630 ■ *"Look Before You Lease" in Women Entrepreneur (February 3, 2009)*
Description: Top issues to consider before leasing an office space are discussed including: additional charges that may be expected on top of the basic rental price; determining both short- and long-term goals; the cost of improvements to the space; the cost of upkeep; and the conditions of the lease. **Availability:** Online.

18631 ■ *"Look Out, Barbie, Bratz are Back" in Canadian Business (Vol. 83, August 17, 2010, No. 13-14, pp. 18)*
Pub: Rogers Media Inc.
Contact: Neil Spivak, Chief Executive Officer

Ed: Joe Castaldo. **Description:** California-based MGA Entertainment has wrestled back control over Bratz from Mattel after a six-year legal battle. However, MGA owner Isaac Larian could still face legal hurdles if Mattel pursues a retrial. He now has to revive the brand which virtually disappeared from stores when Mattel won the rights for Bratz. **Availability:** Online.

18632 ■ *"Loss of Rutgers Name Causing a Stir for Law School" in Philadelphia Business Journal (Vol. 28, April 20, 2012, No. 10, pp. 1)*
Pub: Baltimore Business Journal
Contact: Rhonda Pringle, President
E-mail: rpringle@bizjournals.com

Description: The plan to merge Rutgers University-Camden with Rowan University is being opposed by those from Rutgers who feel they will have problems recruiting students if they lose the Rutgers brand. Rowan on the other hand, is more known in the South Jersey area only. **Availability:** Print; Online.

18633 ■ *Managing Economies, Trade and International Business*
Pub: Palgrave Macmillan

Released: 1st edition. **Price:** $89, e-book; $115, Hardcover; $110, softcover. **Description:** An in-depth look at the areas that affect and influence international business, exploring specific issues businesses face in terms of economic development, trade law, and international marketing and management. **Availability:** E-book; Print.

18634 ■ *"M&A Weakness Takes Toll on Phila. Law Firms" in Philadelphia Business Journal (Vol. 28, August 10, 2012, No. 26, pp. 1)*
Pub: Baltimore Business Journal
Contact: Rhonda Pringle, President
E-mail: rpringle@bizjournals.com

Released: Weekly. **Price:** $4, introductory 4-week offer(Digital & Print). **Description:** Slowdown in mergers and acquisitions impact law firms in Philadelphia, Pennsylvania. Data show that M&A activity involving the US has decreased by 35 percent int he first half of 2012. With the number of deals decreasing, local firms have become cautious about hiring transactional lawyers in terms of selecting those from high revenue areas such as intellectual property. **Availability:** Print; Online.

18635 ■ *"Maryland Ready to Defend Slots Minority Policy" in Boston Business Journal (Vol. 29, July 8, 2011, No. 9, pp. 3)*
Pub: Boston Business Journal
Contact: Carolyn M. Jones, President
E-mail: cmjones@bizjournals.com

Ed: Scott Dance. **Description:** The legality of Maryland's minority inclusion policy may be put under scrutiny once the lawsuit filed by rejected slots developer Baltimore City Entertainment Group on July 5, 2011 is heard in court. The lawsuit aims to stop the bidding process on a proposed casino in Baltimore because the minority policy amounts to reverse discrimination. **Availability:** Print; Online.

18636 ■ *"Md. Pension System Tries to Recoup $73M from Actuary" in Baltimore Business Journal (Vol. 28, June 11, 2010, No. 5, pp. 1)*
Pub: Baltimore Business Journal
Contact: Rhonda Pringle, President
E-mail: rpringle@bizjournals.com

Ed: Gary Haber. **Description:** Maryland State Retirement and Pension System has won nearly $73 million in administrative ruling against Milliman Inc. over pension loss miscalculations. However, Milliman filed two court cases seeking to reverse the decision and to recoup to the state any money a court orders. **Availability:** Print; Online.

18637 ■ *"Medical Collection Agency Refutes Allegations In AG's Report" in PaymentsSource (May 1, 2012)*
Description: Accretive Health Inc. denies allegations by the Minnesota State Attorney General's Office that the firm used heavy-handed tactics pressuring patients to pay for services before receiving treatment. The medical collection agency's report states 'inaccuracies, innuendo and unfounded speculation' in the charges. **Availability:** Print; Online.

18638 ■ *"Meet Houston's Top Legal Dealmakers" in Austin Business Journal (Vol. 34, June 27, 2014, No. 19, pp. A15)*
Pub: American City Business Journals, Inc.
Contact: Mike Olivieri, Executive Vice President

Description: Austin-based law firm, Vinson & Elkins LLP emerged at the biggest player in Texas in the 12-month period between second quarter 2013 through first quarter 2014 when it comes to mergers and acquisitions. The firm handled 68 deals worth a total of $61.8 billion. **Availability:** Print; Online.

18639 ■ *"Melnyk Loses Round in Battle for Hemosol" in Globe & Mail (January 24, 2007, pp. B3)*
Ed: Leonard Zehr. **Description:** Biovail Corp. chairman Eugene Melnyk's loosing of the case against Catalyst Capital Group Inc. over the acquisition of Hemosol Corp. is discussed. **Availability:** Online.

18640 ■ *Mergers and Acquisitions from A to Z*
Pub: HarperCollins Leadership
Contact: Donald Miller, Chief Executive Officer

Released: 2nd edition. **Price:** $19.99, Paperback. **Description:** Guide for the entire process of mergers and acquisitions, including taxes, accounting, laws, and projected financial gain. **Availability:** E-book; Print.

18641 ■ *"Millions of Senior Citizens Swindled by Financial Fraud" in Black Enterprise (Vol. 41, September 2010, No. 2, pp. 24)*
Pub: Earl G. Graves Ltd.
Contact: Earl Graves, Jr., President

Description: One of every five citizens over the age of 65 have been victims of financial fraud. Statistical data included.

18642 ■ *"Monsanto Wins Patent Case Against DuPont" in Farm Journal (Vol. 136, September 2012, No. 8, pp. 8)*
Pub: Farm Journal Media Inc.

Description: Monsanto Company was awarded a $1 billion settlement by a federal jury for a patent infringement lawsuit the company filed agaalnst DuPont regarding Roundup Ready seed technolgy. Details of the lawsuit are included. **Availability:** Online.

18643 ■ *"Mosaid Grants First Wireless Patent License To Matsushita" in Canadian Electronics (Vol. 23, June-July 2008, No. 5, pp. 1)*
Pub: Annex Buisness Media
Contact: Mike Fredericks, President

Description: Matsushita Electric Industrial Co. Ltd. has been granted a six-and-a-half-year license by Mosaid Technologies Inc. to manufacture the latter's products. The patent portfolio license agreement covers Mosaid's Wi-Fi, Wi-Max, CDMA-enabled notebook computers and other products.

18644 ■ *"New Rule Rankles In Jersey" in Philadelphia Business Journal (Vol. 30, September 16, 2011, No. 31, pp. 1)*
Pub: Philadelphia Business Journal
Contact: Sierra Quinn, Director
E-mail: squinn@bizjournals.com

Ed: Jeff Blumenthal. **Description:** A new rule in New Jersey which taxes out-of-state companies that conduct business in the state earned the ire of several banks, mortgage lenders and credit card companies and prompted opponents to threaten to file lawsuits. The new rule is an amendment to New Jersey Division of Taxation's corporate business tax regulation and is retroactive to 2002. Details are given. **Availability:** Online.

18645 ■ *"The Next Step in Patent Reform" in Information Today (Vol. 28, November 2011, No. 10, pp. 1)*
Pub: Information Today Inc.
Contact: Thomas H. Hogan, President

Ed: George H. Pike. **Description:** The Leahy-Smith America Invents Act was signed into law in September 2011. The new act reformed the previous US patent system. Information involving the new patent law process is discussed.

18646 ■ *"Nobel Prize Winners Provide Insight on Outsourcing, Contract Work" in Workforce Management (Vol. 88, November 16, 2009, No. 12, pp. 11)*
Pub: Crain Communications Inc.
Contact: Barry Asin, President

Ed: Jeremy Smerd. **Description:** Insights into such workforce management issues as bonuses, employee contracts and outsourcing has been recognized by the Nobel Prize winners in economics whose research sheds a light on the way economic decisions are made outside markets. **Availability:** Online.

18647 ■ *"Nortel Plays Big to Settle Lawsuits" in Globe & Mail (February 9, 2006, pp. B1)*
Description: The details on Nortel Networks Corp.'s settlement of cases with shareholders are presented. **Availability:** Online.

18648 ■ "Not In Our Backyard" in Canadian Business (Vol. 80, October 22, 2007, No. 21, pp. 76)
Description: Alberta Energy and Utilities Board's proposed construction of electric transmission line has let to protests by landowners. The electric utility was also accused of spying on ordinary citizens and violating impartiality rules. Details of the case between Lavesta Area Group and the Board are discussed. **Availability:** Online.

18649 ■ "Of Marks and Men" in Canadian Business (Vol. 80, March 12, 2007, No. 6, pp. 59)
Description: The importance on the part of business enterprises to register for trademarks to avoid any threat of litigation in future is discussed. **Availability:** Print; Online.

18650 ■ "Ohio Regulator Sues Collection Agency" in PaymentsSource (September 21, 2012)
Pub: SourceMedia LLC
Contact: Gemma Postlethwaite, Chief Executive Officer
Description: Mike DeWine, Ohio Attorney General, is suing Royal Oak Financial Services, a collection agency doing business as Collection and Recovery Bureau. The suit alleges that the firm used collection tactics banned by federal law and also attempting to collect unverified debts.

18651 ■ "Oil Markets: A Nasty Russian Tale" in Canadian Business (Vol. 81, March 3, 2008, No. 3, pp. 85)
Pub: Rogers Media Inc.
Contact: Neil Spivak, Chief Executive Officer
Ed: Andrew Nikiforuk. **Description:** Billionaires Alex Shnaider and Michael Shtaif entered a partnership for an oil venture which ended in a slew of litigations. Cases of breach of contract, injurious falsehood and other related lawsuits were filed against Shnaider. Details of the lawsuits and the other parties involved in the disputes are presented. **Availability:** Online.

18652 ■ "OK, Bring in the Lawyers" in Crain's Chicago Business (Vol. 31, November 17, 2008, No. 46, pp. 26)
Pub: Crain Communications Inc.
Contact: Barry Asin, President
Ed: Daniel Rome Levine. **Description:** Bankruptcy attorneys are finding the economic and credit crisis a benefit for their businesses due to the high number of business owners and mortgage holders that are need of their services. One Chicago firm is handling ten times the number of cases they did the previous year and of that about 80 percent of their new clients are related to the real estate sector. **Availability:** Online.

18653 ■ "On the U.S. Election: Shaky on Free Trade" in Canadian Business (Vol. 81, December 19, 2007, No. 1, pp. 29)
Pub: Rogers Media Inc.
Contact: Neil Spivak, Chief Executive Officer
Ed: Rachel Pulfer. **Description:** Rhetoric at the U.S. presidential elections seems to be pointing toward a weaker free trade consensus, with Democratic candidates being against the renewal of free trade deals, while Republican candidates seem to be for free trade. **Availability:** Online.

18654 ■ "Online Business Laws Your Small Business Needs to Know" in Business News Daily (Nov. 9, 2020)
URL(s): www.businessnewsdaily.com/15904-online-business-laws.html
Ed: Donna Fuscaldo. **Released:** November 09, 2020. **Description:** Explains what online business laws are and details five rules and regulations that govern e-commerce. **Availability:** Online.

18655 ■ "Open Price Agreements: Good Faith Pricing in the Franchise Relationship" in Franchise Law Journal (Vol. 27, Summer 2007, No. 1, pp. 45)
Pub: American Bar Association
Contact: Mary L. Smith, President
Ed: Douglas C. Berry, David M. Byers, Daniel Oates. **Description:** Open price term contracts are important to franchise businesses. Details of open price contracts are examined.

18656 ■ "OSC Eyes New Tack on Litigation" in Globe & Mail (April 9, 2007, pp. B1)
Ed: Janet McFarland. **Description:** The efforts of the Ontario Securities Commission to set up a tribunal for the investigation and control of securities fraud are described. The rate of the conviction of corporate officials in cases heard by the courts is discussed. **Availability:** Online.

18657 ■ "The Overlicensed Society" in Harvard Business Review (Vol. 90, April 2012, No. 4, pp. 38)
Pub: Harvard Business Review Press
Contact: Moderna V. Pfizer, Contact
Ed: Robert E. Litan. **Price:** $6, hardcover. **Description:** The author argues that certification and licensing requirements are hindering professionals who might otherwise be able to find positions and provide services inexpensively. To key areas are healthcare and law. Federal mutual recognition agreements may be one method of addressing both practice and consumer protection issues. **Availability:** PDF; Online.

18658 ■ "Owner of Skin Care Business Offers Westfield State Scholarships If Ex-President Drops Lawsuit" in Boston Business Journal (Vol. 34, April 25, 2014, No. 12, pp. 5)
Pub: American City Business Journals, Inc.
Contact: Mike Olivieri, Executive Vice President
Description: John Walsh, CEO of Elizabeth Grady Company, has offered $100,000 in scholarships if Westfield State University President, Evan Dobelle, drops his lawsuits against the university. Dobelle decided to sue the school after he was placed on paid leave by three trustees. **Availability:** Print; Online.

18659 ■ "Paging Dr. Phil" in Canadian Business (Vol. 79, September 25, 2006, No. 19, pp. 21)
Description: Increasing corporate crimes in software industry is discussed by focusing on recent case of Hewlett and Packard. **Availability:** Print; Mailing list; Online.

18660 ■ "Patently Absurd" in Globe & Mail (January 28, 2006, pp. B4)
Description: An overview of facts about patent dispute between Research In Motion Ltd. and NTP Inc. is presented. **Availability:** Online.

18661 ■ "PBSJ Launches Internal Probe" in Tampa Bay Business Journal (Vol. 30, January 8, 2010, No. 3, pp. 1)
Pub: Tampa Bay Business Journal
Contact: Ian Anderson, President
E-mail: ianderson@bizjournals.com
Ed: Margie Manning. **Description:** Florida-based engineering firm PBSJ Corporation has started an internal investigation into possible violations of any laws, including the Foreign Corrupt Practices Act. Projects handled by subsidiary PBS&J International in foreign countries are the focus of the investigation. **Availability:** Print; Online.

18662 ■ "Pearson Bitman Strives to be the 'Google' of Law Firms" in Orlando Business Journal (Vol. 30, June 6, 2014, No. 50, pp. 3)
Pub: American City Business Journals, Inc.
Contact: Mike Olivieri, Executive Vice President
Released: Weekly. **Price:** $8, Introductory 4-week offer(Digital & Print). **Description:** Ronnie Bitman, who launched law firm Pearson Bitman LLP, states that he wants to make his firm the Google of law firms, that is, he wants to create and foster an environment of fun and not just work. He feels that in today's times it is important to get away from the public image of a lawyer standing in front of law books and give people something that's fresher, hipper. **Availability:** Print; Online.

18663 ■ "Points of Law: Unbundling Corporate Legal Services to Unlock Value" in (Vol. 90, July-August 2012, No. 7-8, pp. 126)
Pub: Harvard Business Review Press
Contact: Moderna V. Pfizer, Contact
Ed: Danny Ertel, Mark Gordon. **Price:** $8.95. **Description:** Maintaining the relationship between law firms and corporate legal departments requires aligning incentives between in-house counsel and law firm, and allocating work to the providers who are best-positioned to address it. **Availability:** Online; PDF.

18664 ■ PPC's Small Business Tax Guide
Released: January 2005. **Price:** $189.00. **Description:** Business tax laws are covered in an easy to understand format.

18665 ■ PPC's Small Business Tax Guide, Vol. 2
Description: Second volume containing technical guide covering business tax laws. **Availability:** Online.

18666 ■ "Prichard the Third" in Canadian Business (Vol. 83, October 12, 2010, No. 17, pp. 34)
Pub: Rogers Media Inc.
Contact: Neil Spivak, Chief Executive Officer
Ed: Thomas Watson. **Description:** Robert Prichard, the new chair of international business law firm Torys, talks about his current role; his job involved advising clients, representing the firm, being part of the leadership team, and recruiting talent. He considers 'Seven Days in Tibet' as the first book to have an influence on his world view. **Availability:** Online.

18667 ■ "Privacy Concern: Are 'Group' Time Sheets Legal?" in HR Specialist (Vol. 8, September 2010, No. 9, pp. 4)
Pub: Capitol Information Group Inc.
Contact: Allie Ash, Chief Executive Officer
Description: Under the Fair Labor Standards Act (FLSA) employers are required to maintain and preserve payroll or other records, including the number of hours worked, but it does not prescribe a particular order or form in which these records must be kept. **Availability:** PDF; Online.

18668 ■ "Procter & Gamble vs. IRS: Split Decision" in Business Courier (Vol. 27, July 16, 2010, No. 11, pp. 1)
Pub: Business Courier
Ed: Jon Newberry. **Description:** Implications of a court ruling in a $435 million legal dispute between Procter & Gamble Company (P&G) and the Internal Revenue Service (IRS) are discussed. A $21 million win has been realized for P&G for its interpretation of research and development tax credits. However, the said case might involve more than $700 million in P&G tax deductions from 2001 through 2004 that the IRS had disallowed. **Availability:** Print; Online.

18669 ■ "Protect Your Domain Name From Cybersquatters" in Idaho Business Review (September 1, 2014)
Pub: BridgeTower Media
Contact: Adam Reinebach, President
Description: Cybersquatting is the practice of registering, trafficking in or using domain names with the intent to profit from the goodwill of recognizable trade names or trademarks of other companies. Companies can protect their Website domain by following these steps: register domain names, promptly renew registrations, maintain proper records, obtain additional top-level domains, and monitor your site for cybersquatters.

18670 ■ "The Rage Offstage at Marvel" in Barron's (Vol. 88, June 30, 2008, No. 26, pp. 19)
Pub: Dow Jones & Company Inc.
Contact: Almar Latour, Chief Executive Officer
Ed: Bill Alpert. **Description:** Lawsuits against Marvel Entertainment and Stan Lee are pushing the claims from Peter F. Paul that Stan Lee Media was undone by the actions of the accused. Paul's associates

argue that Stan Lee Media owns rights to Marvel characters and that they want half the profits that Marvel is making. **Availability:** Online.

18671 ■ *"Ralcorp Investigated for Rejecting ConAgra Bid" in Saint Louis Business Journal (Vol. 32, September 16, 2011, No. 3, pp. 1)*
Pub: Saint Louis Business Journal
Contact: Robert Bobroff, President
E-mail: rbobroff@bizjournals.com

Ed: Evan Binns. **Description:** New York-based Levi & Korsinsky started investigating Ralcorp Holidngs Inc. after it rejected ConAgra Foods Inc.'s third and latest takeover bid of $5.17 billion. The investigation would determine whether Ralcorp's directors had acted on behalf of shareholders' best interest. **Availability:** Print; Online.

18672 ■ *"Receiver's Report Uncovers Trouble in Fashion Mall Redevelopment" in South Florida Business Journal (Vol. 34, July 4, 2014, No. 50, pp. 4)*
Pub: American City Business Journals, Inc.
Contact: Mike Olivieri, Executive Vice President

Released: Weekly. **Price:** $8, introductory 4-week offer(Digital only). **Description:** A report by receiver, Charles Lichtman, reveals possible fraud of fiduciary duty by Wei Chen, who manages the redevelopment of Fashion Mall in Plantation Florida. Chen used funds from the account of Tangshan Ganglu Iron and Steel Company to make a deposit on a purchase contract for the Sheraton Suites Plantation hotel and resort for a company he personally owned. **Availability:** Print; Online.

18673 ■ *"Recovery on Tap for 2010?" in Orlando Business Journal (Vol. 26, January 1, 2010, No. 31, pp. 1)*
Pub: Orlando Business Journal
Contact: Julie Swyers, Editor
E-mail: jswyers@bizjournals.com

Ed: Melanie Stawicki Azam, Richard Bilbao, Christopher Boyd, Anjali Fluker. **Description:** Economic forecasts for Central Florida's leading business sectors in 2010 are presented. These sectors include housing, film and TV, sports business, law, restaurants, aviation, tourism and hospitality, banking and finance, commercial real estate, retail, health care, insurance, higher education, and manufacturing. According to some local executives, Central Florida's economy will slowly recover in 2010. **Availability:** Online.

18674 ■ *"A Responsive Approach to Organizational Misconduct: Rehabilitation, Reintegration, and the Reduction of Reoffense" in Business Ethics Quarterly (Vol. 24, July 2014, No. 3, pp. 343)*
Pub: Business Ethics Quarterly
Contact: Dawn Elm, Executive Director
E-mail: drelm@stthomas.edu

Description: Examination of ways regulators, prosecutors, and courts might support and encourage the efforts of organizations to not only reintegrate after misconduct, but to also improve their conduct in a way that reduces their likelihood of re-offense (rehabilitation). An experiment in creative sentencing in Alberta, Canada that aimed to try to change the behavior of an industry by publicly airing the root causes of a failure of one of the industry's leaders is examined. A model for a responsive and restorative approach to organizational misconduct that balances the punitive role of regulators and courts with new roles in supporting and overseeing rehabilitation are observed. **Availability:** Online.

18675 ■ *"Retailers, Your Will, and More" in Agency Sales Magazine (Vol. 39, July 2009, No. 7, pp. 46)*
Description: IRS audit guide for small retail businesses is presented. Tips on how to make a will with multiple beneficiaries are discussed together with medical expenses that cannot be deducted.

18676 ■ *"Reversal of Fortune" in Canadian Business (Vol. 85, June 11, 2012, No. 10, pp. 32)*
Ed: Matthew McClearn. **Description:** First Quantum Minerals of Vancouver, British Columbia contested the decisio of the Democratic Republic of Congo to revoke their mining license in the Kolwezi Tailings by means of political pressure and international law. Eurasian National Resources Corporation agreed to pay First Quantum $1.25 billion in return for uncontested title to Congo mines and a ceasefire in January 2012. **Availability:** Print; Online.

18677 ■ *"Richard Faulk Covers Climate in Copenhagen" in Houston Business Journal (Vol. 40, December 25, 2009, No. 33, pp. 1)*
Pub: Houston Business Journal
Contact: Bob Charlet, President
E-mail: bcharlet@bizjournals.com

Ed: Ford Gunter. **Description:** Houston environmental attorney Richard Faulk talks to the United Nations Climate Change Conference in Copenhagen, Denmark. Faulk believes the conference failed due to political differences between countries like US and China. Faulk believed the discussion of developed and developing countries on verification and limits on carbon emissions is something good that came from the conference. **Availability:** Print; Online.

18678 ■ *"Ride Apps Uber, Lyft, Sidecar Hit Speed Bumps" in San Francisco Business Times (Vol. 28, January 24, 2014, No. 27, pp. 4)*
Pub: American City Business Journals, Inc.
Contact: Mike Olivieri, Executive Vice President

Released: Weekly. **Price:** $4, Introductory 4-week offer(Digital & Print). **Description:** California's Public Utilities Commission (PUC) has reversed its earlier prohibition and allowed mobile app ride services, while imposing insurance and safety regulations on these alternatives to taxicabs and limousine services. However, the PUC did not take action when the issue of liability and insurance were raised due to the death of Sofia Liu, who was hit by an Uber driver. The lawsuits against Uber are discussed. **Availability:** Print; Online.

18679 ■ *"RIM's Options Story Under Fire" in Globe & Mail (March 16, 2007, pp. B1)*
Ed: Janet McFarland. **Description:** The investigation of the backdating of options by Research In Motion Ltd. is discussed. The analysis of the backdating of company's options issues by Professor Erik Lie from the University of Iowa is presented. **Availability:** Online.

18680 ■ *"RPA Preps for Building Radiant Conference, Show" in Contractor (Vol. 57, January 2010, No. 1, pp. 5)*
Description: Radiant Panel Association is accepting registrations for its Building Radiant 2010 Conference and Trade Show. The conference will discuss radiant heating as well as insurance and other legal matters for mechanical contractors. **Availability:** Print; Online.

18681 ■ *"Running Your Business: What Do You Need to Do to Retain Good Corporate Standing?" in Legal Zoom (March 28, 2023)*
URL(s): www.legalzoom.com/articles/running-your-business-what-do-you-need-to-do-to-retain-good-corporate-standing
Ed: Heleigh Bostwick. **Released:** March 28, 2023. **Description:** Discusses obtaining a certificate in good standing from your state in order to prove to customers that your business has complied with tax laws and is current in its filings. **Availability:** Online.

18682 ■ *"Sabia Signals a Bold, New Course for BCE" in Globe & Mail (February 2, 2006, pp. B1)*
Description: The reasons behind the decision of chief executive officer Michael Sabia to streamline operations of BCE Inc. are presented. **Availability:** Online.

18683 ■ *"Santander 'Redlining' Suit is a Crass and Opportunistic Shakedown" in Boston Business Journal (Vol. 34, June 6, 2014, No. 18, pp. 7)*
Pub: American City Business Journals, Inc.
Contact: Mike Olivieri, Executive Vice President

Released: Weekly. **Description:** Santander Bank's residential mortgage lending to minorities in Providence, Massachusetts has declined by 34 percent in recent years. The development is a violation of the US Fair Housing Act and the Equal Credit Opportunity Act. The city has sued Santander over the issue. **Availability:** Print; Online.

18684 ■ *"Scott Rothstein Ponzi Reveals Ethics Issues in Jewelry Biz" in South Florida Business Journal (Vol. 33, September 14, 2012, No. 7, pp. 1)*
Pub: Baltimore Business Journal
Contact: Rhonda Pringle, President
E-mail: rpringle@bizjournals.com

Description: JR Dunn Jewelers of Florida is suing New York jewelry company JB International for an 8.91 carat diamond it claims is tainted because it was allegedly sold offby Ponzi schemer Scott Rothstein or his wife Kimberly. Dunn is being sued for $748,000 in the bankruptcy of Rothstein Rosenfelt Adler, Rothstein's former law firm. **Availability:** Print; Online.

18685 ■ *"SEC FAQs About Crowdfunding Intermediaries" in Mondaq Business Briefing (June 11, 2012)*
Pub: Mondaq Ltd.
Contact: Tim Harty, Chief Executive Officer

Ed: Yelena Barychev, Christin R. Cerullo, Francis E. Dehel, Melissa Palat Murawsky, Michael E. Plunkett. **Description:** Guide for implementing crowdfunding intermediary provisions of Title III of the JOBS Act is provided. Operating restrictions and legal obligations are outlined. **Availability:** Print; Online.

18686 ■ *Selling the Invisible: A Field Guide to Modern Marketing*
Ed: Harry Beckwith. **Released:** March 20, 2012. **Price:** $16, paperback, ($21.00 in canada); $13.98, audiobook abridged library($16.99 in canada); $16.98, audiobook abridged($19.75 in canada); $9.98, audiobook abridged($12.98 in canada); $9.99, electronic book($9.99 in canada). **Description:** Tips for marketing and selling intangibles such as health care, entertainment, tourism, legal services, and more are provided. **Availability:** audiobook; E-book; Print.

18687 ■ *"Senator Grills Collection Agency, Health System Executives" in Collections & Credit Risk (May 31, 2012)*
Pub: SourceMedia LLC
Contact: Gemma Postlethwaite, Chief Executive Officer

Description: Accretive Health Inc. and Fairview Health Services executives were questioned by Senator Al Franken about its debt collection practices. The suit was initiated after unencrypted private information on 23,500 patients was stolen from an Acrretive employee's vehicle. Details of the lawsuit are outlined.

18688 ■ *"Sense of Discovery" in Business Journal Portland (Vol. 27, November 19, 2010, No. 38, pp. 1)*
Pub: Portland Business Journal
Contact: Andy Giegerich, Managing Editor
E-mail: agiegerich@bizjournals.com

Description: Tigard, Oregon-based Exterro Inc. CEO Bobby Balachandran announced plans to go public without the help of an institutional investor. Balachandran believes Exterro could grow to a $100 million legal compliance software company in the span of three years. Insights on Exterro's growth as market leader in the $1 billion legal governance software market are also given. **Availability:** Print; Online.

18689 ■ "Should State Invest in Startups?" in Providence Business News (Vol. 28, March 3, 2014, No. 48, pp. 1)
Pub: American City Business Journals, Inc.
Contact: Mike Olivieri, Executive Vice President
Released: March 01, 2014. **Description:** The U.S. Treasury Department is investigating whether Rhode Island violated Federal rules when it used funds from the State Small Business Credit Initiative (SSBCI) to invest in Betaspring, a startup accelerator program for technology and design entrepreneurs ready to launch their businesses. The Lyon Park audit claims that Rhode Island violated SSBCI rules because a large portion of the money went to the business accelerator's operating expenses and not to the startups themselves. **Availability:** Print; Online.

18690 ■ "Sign of the Times: Temp-To-Perm Attorneys" in HRMagazine (Vol. 54, January 2009, No. 1, pp. 24)
Description: A growing number of law firms are hiring professional staff on a temp-to-perm basis according to the president of Professional Placement Services in Florida. Firms can save money while testing potential employees on a temporary basis. **Availability:** Print; Online.

18691 ■ "A Simple Old Reg that Needs Dusting Off" in Barron's (Vol. 88, June 30, 2008, No. 26, pp. 35)
Pub: Dow Jones & Company Inc.
Contact: Almar Latour, Chief Executive Officer
Ed: Gene Epstein. **Description:** Senator Joe Lieberman has a point when he accused speculators of inflating the prices of food and fuel futures but introducing legislation to address speculation has an alternative. The senator's committee should instead demand that the Commodity Futures Trading Commission enforce position limits on the maximum number of contracts in a given market per speculative entity. **Availability:** Online.

18692 ■ Small Business Legal Advice: 10 Basics for Business Owners
URL(s): aofund.org/resource/small-business-legal-advice-10-basics-business-owners/
Description: Provides information related to the ten most important legal issues that small business owners may face. **Availability:** Online.

18693 ■ Small Business Legal Issues
URL(s): corporatefinanceinstitute.com/resources/knowledge/other/small-business-legal-issues/
Description: Small businesses face a wide range of legal issues. This article discusses some of the most common legal issues small businesses face and the best ways to avoid or handle them. **Availability:** Online.

18694 ■ Small Business Survival Guide
Released: First edition. **Description:** Small business expert provides strategies to start a company and survive in the 21st Century. He shows small business owners how to succeed despite challenges that can defeat any firm. His advice covers suppliers; customers and contractors; competitors and creditors; spouses, family and friends; as well as the ways lawyers, accountants and other can steal an entrepreneur's success. Ennico also describes how startups can comply with local regulations. **Availability:** E-book; Print.

18695 ■ Small Time Operator: How to Start Your Own Business, Keep Your Books, Pay Your Taxes, and Stay Out of Trouble
Ed: Bernard B. Kamoroff. **Released:** 14th edition. **Price:** $18.95, paperback. **Description:** Comprehensive guide for starting any kind of business. **Availability:** Print.

18696 ■ "Social Media Privacy Law Impacts Employers" in Providence Business News (Vol. 29, July 21, 2014, No. 16, pp. 14)
Pub: American City Business Journals, Inc.
Contact: Mike Olivieri, Executive Vice President
Released: July 19, 2014. **Description:** Rhode Island's new social media privacy law, which was enacted on June 30, 2014, will have an impact on all employers in the state. The implications of the new law and some best practices employers can implement with regard to the legislation are discussed. **Availability:** PDF; Online.

18697 ■ "Soldiers as Consumers: Predatory and Unfair Business Practices Harming the Military Community"
Pub: CreateSpace
Released: October 05, 2014. **Price:** $9.81, paperback. **Description:** Soldiers, airmen, sailors, and marines are young consumers and are appealing targets for unscrupulous businesses. There are lending organizations that prey upon our military offering products to help them bridge financial problems. Unethical elements of these loans includes higher interest rates and/or high fees or waivers of certain rights in fine print of contracts. A Federal Law called the Military Lending Act is supposed to protect service members from this kind of abuse, but the law only covers loans with terms of six months or less. **Availability:** Print.

18698 ■ "Stan Chesley Fighting Kentucky Disbarment" in Business Courier (Vol. 27, September 10, 2010, No. 19, pp. 1)
Pub: Business Courier
Ed: Jon Newberry. **Description:** Stan Chesley, a Cincinnati attorney, has been accused of making false statements to the courts and bar officials, self-dealing in violation of the bar's conflict of interest rules, and failing to adequately inform clients. Kentucky Bar Association officials will seek to have Chesley permanently disbarred. **Availability:** Print; Online.

18699 ■ "State Democrats Push for Changes to Plant Security Law" in Chemical Week (Vol. 172, July 19, 2010, No. 17, pp. 8)
Description: Legislation has been introduced to revise the existing U.S. Chemical Facility Anti-Terrorism Standards (CFATS) that would include a requirement for facilities to use inherently safer technology (IST). The bill would eliminate the current law's exemption of water treatment plants and certain port facilities and preserve the states' authority to establish stronger security standards. **Availability:** PDF; Online.

18700 ■ "State Reverses Food Truck Order" in Cape Cod Times (May 15, 2012)
Ed: Patrick Cassidy. **Description:** Massachusetts Department of Transportation is developing a plan that will allow food truck owners to operate under a new pilot program. Owners must obtain a license to operate through the Transportation Department's legal division. License requirements will be modeled on present license applications and some modifications may be necessary. Insurance issues must be addressed. **Availability:** Online.

18701 ■ "State Unemployment Fraud Rising Sharply" in Sacramento Business Journal (Vol. 28, October 21, 2011, No. 34, pp. 1)
Pub: Sacramento Business Journal
Contact: Stephanie Fretwell, Director
E-mail: sfretwell@bizjournals.com
Ed: Michael Shaw. **Description:** California's Employment Development Department has reported that overpayments, especially due to fraud or misrepresentation, have increased from $88 million in 2008 to more than $250 million in 2010. However, criminal prosecutions in 2010 were fewer than in 2008 as the agency struggles to recover the money. **Availability:** Online.

18702 ■ "Stikemans' Ascent, Its Legacy, and Its Future" in Globe & Mail (January 29, 2007, pp. B2)
Description: Pierre Raymond, chairman of legal firm Stikeman Elliott LLP, talks about his strategies to handle competition, his challenges, and about Canada's present mergers and acquisition scenario. Stikeman achieved the first place in 2006 M&A legal rankings. **Availability:** Online.

18703 ■ "Stock Car Racing" in Canadian Business (Vol. 81, September 15, 2008, No. 14-15, pp. 29)
Description: Some analysts predict a Chapter 11-style tune-up making GM and Ford a speculative turnaround stock. However, the price of oil could make or break the shares of the Big Three U.S. automobile manufacturers and if oil goes up too high then a speculative stock to watch is an electric car company called Zenn Motor Co. **Availability:** Online.

18704 ■ "Success Fees: A Word of Warning" in Canadian Business (Vol. 80, March 12, 2007, No. 6)
Description: Legal issues regarding payment of lawyer fees termed 'fair fee' in Canada are discussed with an instance of Inmet Mining Corp.'s dealing with lawyer Irwin Nathanson. **Availability:** Online.

18705 ■ "Suit: Bank Bypassing Minorities" in Providence Business News (Vol. 29, June 9, 2014, No. 10, pp. 1)
Pub: American City Business Journals, Inc.
Contact: Mike Olivieri, Executive Vice President
URL(s): pbn.com/suit-bank-bypassing-minorities97644
Description: The City of Providence, Rhode Island filed a lawsuit against the U.S. operations of Santander Bank for purposely bypassing minority neighborhoods in prime mortgage lending. The lawsuit alleges the Madrid, Spain-based bank of violating the Fair Housing Act by not lending into the minority communities of the city.

18706 ■ "Suits Keep Flying in Wireless Service Marketing Wars" in Globe & Mail (March 22, 2007, pp. B3)
Ed: Catherine McLean. **Description:** The suit filed by Telus Corp. against BCE Mobile Communications Inc. over the latter's alleged misleading advertisement in the press is discussed. **Availability:** Print; Online.

18707 ■ "Sutter Court Win is Part of Trend" in Sacramento Business Journal (Vol. 31, July 25, 2014, No. 22, pp. 3)
Pub: American City Business Journals, Inc.
Contact: Mike Olivieri, Executive Vice President
Released: July 25, 2014. **Description:** The Third District Court of Appeals dismissed 13 coordinated data-breach lawsuits filed against Sutter Health of Sacramento, California. The plaintiffs claim $4 billion in damages over theft of patient data from a local Sutter Health office in October 2011.

18708 ■ "Take on an Elephant Without Getting Trampled" in Globe & Mail (March 17, 2007, pp. B3)
Ed: Grant Robertson. **Description:** The plan of chief executive officer of Canpages Inc. Olivier Vincent to beat the profit margin and market share of Yellow Pages Group is discussed. **Availability:** Online.

18709 ■ Tax Savvy for Small Business
Pub: Nolo
Contact: Chris Braun, President
Ed: Frederick W. Daily, Jeffrey A. Quinn. **Released:** 22nd edition. **Price:** $31.99, book & e-book; $20.99, E-Book; $23.99; $22.99, E-book. **Description:** Tax strategies for small business. Includes the latest tax numbers and laws as well as current Internal Revenue Service forms and publications. **Availability:** E-book; Print; Electronic publishing; PDF.

18710 ■ "The Ten Commandments of Legal Risk Management" in Business Horizons (Vol. 51, January-February 2008, No. 1, pp. 13)
Pub: Elsevier Advanced Technology Publications
Ed: Michael B. Metzger. **Description:** Effective legal risk management is tightly linked with ethical and good management, and managers' behaviors have to be professional and based on ethically defensible principles of action. Basic human tendencies cannot

be used in justifying questionable decisions in court. Guidelines for legal risk management are presented. **Availability:** Print; Online.

18711 ■ *"Tesla Eyes Two Sites for New Battery-Pack Plant" in San Antonio Business Journal (Vol. 28, May 16, 2014, No. 14, pp. 8)*
Pub: American City Business Journals, Inc.
Contact: Mike Olivieri, Executive Vice President

Released: Weekly. **Price:** $4, introductory 4-week offer(Digital only). **Description:** The City of San Antonio, Texas is competing with other cities in five states to land the contract for the $5 million battery-pack plant of Texla Motors. Bill Avila of Bracewell & Giuliani LLPO law firm believes that San Antonio has an edge over some of the cities competing for the Tesla manufacturing plant because of its successful recruitment of Toyota in 2003. **Availability:** Print; Online.

18712 ■ *"'Those Days In New York Are Over'" in Philadelphia Business Journal (Vol. 33, March 28, 2014, No. 7, pp. 6)*
Pub: American City Business Journals, Inc.
Contact: Mike Olivieri, Executive Vice President

Released: Weekly. **Price:** $4, introductory 4-week offer(Digital & Print). **Description:** Building Trades Employers' Association of New York president and CEO, Louis J. Coletti, comments on the alleged intimidating union activity in Philadelphia, Pennsylvania to hire union members outlined in a federal indictment against Ironworkers Local 401. Coletti believes the limited open-shop market era will remain in the New York construction industry. **Availability:** Print; Online.

18713 ■ *"TIA Wrestles with Procurement Issues" in Business Journal Serving Greater Tampa Bay (Vol. 30, November 12, 2010, No. 47, pp. 1)*
Pub: Tampa Bay Business Journal
Contact: Ian Anderson, President
E-mail: ianderson@bizjournals.com

Ed: Mark Holan. **Description:** Tampa International Airport (TIA) has been caught in conflict of interest and procurement policy issues after the Hillsborough County Aviation Authority learned of the spousal relationship of an employee with his wife's firm, Gresham Smith and Partners. Gresham already won contracts with TIA and was ahead of other firms in a new contract. **Availability:** Print; Online.

18714 ■ *"'Tone-Deaf' Suitor or True Harasser: How to Tell" in HR Specialist (Vol. 8, September 2010, No. 9, pp. 1)*
Pub: Capitol Information Group Inc.
Contact: Allie Ash, Chief Executive Officer

Description: Details are critical to any harassment charge in the workplace. Courts now list factors employers should consider when trying to determine whether an employee has been sexually harassed at work. **Availability:** PDF; Online.

18715 ■ *"Top Law Firms Join Forces" in Business Journal Portland (Vol. 27, December 3, 2010, No. 40, pp. 1)*
Pub: Portland Business Journal
Contact: Andy Giegerich, Managing Editor
E-mail: agiegerich@bizjournals.com

Description: Law Firms Powell PC and Roberts Kaplan LLP will forge a collaboration, whereby 17 Roberts Kaplan attorneys will join the Portland, Oregon-based office of Lane Powell. The partnership is expected to strengthen the law firms' grip on Portland's banking clients. **Availability:** Print; Online.

18716 ■ *"Trial of Enron Ex-Bosses to Begin Today" in Globe & Mail (January 30, 2006, pp. B1)*

Description: The details of the case against former executives Kenneth L. Lay and Jeffrey Skilling of Enron Corp. are presented. **Availability:** Online.

18717 ■ *"Troy Patent Law Firm Launches Rent-Free Tech Incubator" in Crain's Detroit Business (Vol. 25, June 8, 2009, No. 23, pp. 4)*
Pub: Crain Communications Inc.
Contact: Barry Asin, President

Ed: Tom Henderson. **Description:** Young Basile Hanlon MacFarlane & Helmholdt PC, a patent law firm located in Troy, Michigan has created a small, rent-free technology incubator on site. The incubator will be called North Woodward Tech Incubator and has room for four or five startups. The incubator is for the earliest or pre-seed stage for entrepreneurs who have not yet gotten significant investment capital. **Availability:** Online.

18718 ■ *"Under Fire, Sabia Triggers Battle for BCE" in Globe & Mail (April 14, 2007, pp. B1)*
Ed: Boyd Erman. **Description:** The announcement of negotiations for the sale of BCE Inc. by its chief executive officer Michael Sabia is discussed. The efforts of Ontario Teachers Pension Plan to submit its proposal for the sale are described. **Availability:** Online.

18719 ■ *"Unfair Distraction of Employees" in Business Owner (Vol. 35, March-April 2011, No. 2, pp. 8)*
Description: Fair Credit Collection Practices Act makes it illegal for collectors to contact a debtor at his or her place of employment if the collector is made aware that it is against personnel policy of the employer for the worker to take such a call. **Availability:** Print; Online.

18720 ■ *"Union, Heal Thyself" in Canadian Business (Vol. 81, July 21, 2008, No. 11, pp. 9)*
Description: General Motors Corp. was offered by the federal government a $250 million fund after the company declared plans to close its facility in Ontario. The government move is geared towards supporting the workers who have refused to support the automotive company. Details of the labor contract between General Motors and the Canadian Auto Workers are presented. **Availability:** Print; Online.

18721 ■ *"Unlicensed Utah Collection Agency Settles with State Finance Department" in Idaho Business Review, Boise (July 15, 2010)*
Pub: Idaho Business Review
Contact: Autumn Kersey, Sales Executive
E-mail: akersey@idahobusinessreview.com

Description: Federal Recovery Acceptance Inc., doing business as Paramount Acceptance in Utah, agreed to pay penalties and expenses after the firm was investigated by the state for improprieties. The firm was charged with conducting unlicensed collection activity. **Availability:** Print; Online.

18722 ■ *"Unpleasant Surprise - When a Stock Distribution is Taxed as Dividend Income" in Barron's (Vol. 88, March 24, 2008, No. 12, pp. 60)*
Pub: Dow Jones & Company Inc.
Contact: Almar Latour, Chief Executive Officer

Ed: Shirley A. Lazo. **Description:** Discusses the $175 million that footwear company Genesco received in a settlement with Finish Line and UBS is considered as a stock distribution and is taxable as dividend income. Railroad company CSX raised its quarterly common payout from 15 cents to 18 cents. **Availability:** Online.

18723 ■ *"Up To Code? Website Eases Compliance Burden for Entrepreneurs" in Black Enterprise (Vol. 38, March 1, 2008, No. 8, pp. 48)*
Pub: Earl G. Graves Ltd.
Contact: Earl Graves, Jr., President

Ed: Robin White-Goode. **Description:** Business.gov is a presidential E-government project created to help small businesses easily find, understand, and comply with laws and regulations pertaining to a particular industry. **Availability:** Online.

18724 ■ *"Valuation of Intangible Assets in Franchise Companies and Multinational Groups: A Current Issue" in Franchise Law Journal (Vol. 27, No. 3, Winter 2008)*
Ed: Bruce D. Schaeffer, Susan J. Robins. **Released:** Volume 27. **Description:** Intangible assets, also known as intellectual properties are the most valuable assets for companies today. Legal intellectual property issues faced by franchises firms are discussed.

18725 ■ *"Voices: Breaking the Corruption Habit" in Business Strategy Review (Vol. 21, Autumn 2010, No. 3, pp. 67)*
Ed: David De Cremer. **Released:** September 22, 2010. **Description:** In times of crisis, it seems natural that people will work together for the common good. David De Cremer cautions that, on the contrary, both economic and social research prove otherwise. He proposes steps for organizations to take to prevent corrupt behaviors. **Availability:** Print; Electronic publishing; PDF; Online.

18726 ■ *"VPA to Pay $9.5 Million to Settle Whistle-Blower Lawsuits" in Crain's Detroit Business (Vol. 26, January 11, 2010, No. 2, pp. 13)*
Pub: Crain Communications Inc.
Contact: Barry Asin, President

Ed: Jay Greene. **Description:** According to Terrence Berg, first assistant with the U.S. Attorney's Office in Detroit, Voluntary Physicians Association, a local home health care company, has agreed to pay $9.5 million to settle four whistle-blower lawsuits; the agreement settles allegations that VPA submitted claims to TriCare, the Michigan Medicaid program and Medicare for unnecessary home visits, tests and procedures. **Availability:** Online.

18727 ■ *"Waukesha Firm Hit for $8.9M for Junk Faxes" in Business Journal Milwaukee (Vol. 29, August 3, 2012, No. 45, pp. 1)*
Pub: American City Business Journals, Inc.
Contact: Mike Olivieri, Executive Vice President

Ed: Stacy Vogel Davis. **Released:** Weekly. **Price:** $4, introductory 4-week offer(Digital & Print). **Description:** Waukesha County, Wisconsin-based Easy PC Solutions LLC has been facing an $8.9 million settlement for sending unsolicited faxes to 7,000 health care providers. However, the company won't have to pay since the plaintiffs are expected to go after its insurance company. **Availability:** Print; Online.

18728 ■ *"A Well-Crafted Employee Handbook Can Make Work Run More Smoothly" in Idaho Business Review (September 17, 2014)*
Pub: BridgeTower Media
Contact: Adam Reinebach, President

Description: An employee handbook will provide a complaint process, provide company management flexibility and clarity and keep a company out of legal problems. Training, compensation, benefits, security, health, performance appraisals, and safety issues must be covered. Human resource managers and other mangers should cover basics to help communicate with workers.

18729 ■ *"We're Drowning In Fine Print" in Canadian Business (Vol. 87, July 2014, No. 7, pp. 30)*
Description: The implications of mandatory disclosure rules for Canadian businesses and consumers are discussed. Businesses are advised to pay more attention to costs and benefits rather than force their customers to claim they have read and agree with the terms and conditions of lengthy and complex disclosures and privacy agreements. **Availability:** Print; Online.

18730 ■ *"What's Good Faith Got to Do With Contracts?" in Contractor (Vol. 56, November 2009, No. 11, pp. 41)*
Ed: Susan Linden McGreevy. **Description:** Uniform Commercial Code makes the obligation to act in good faith a term of every commercial transaction. The code generally applies to the sale of goods and not

to construction contracts but parties to a construction contract have the right to expect people to act in good faith and forego actions not related to the contract itself. **Availability:** Online.

18731 ■ *"When Are Sales Representatives Also Franchisees?" in Franchise Law Journal (Vol. 27, Winter 2008, No. 3, pp. 151)*
Ed: John R.F. Baer, David A. Beyer, Scott P. Weber. **Released:** Volume 27. **Description:** Review of the traditional definitions of sales representatives along with information on how these distribution models could fit into various legal tests for a franchise.

18732 ■ *"Where to Get Free Legal Advice for Your Business: 5 Options for Businesses on a Budget" in Fundera Blog (May 7, 2021)*
URL(s): www.fundera.com/blog/free-legal-advice
Ed: Priyanka Prakash. **Released:** May 07, 2021. **Description:** Provides information on five free legal service providers for small business owners as well as advice on when to enlist the help of a business lawyer. **Availability:** Online.

18733 ■ *"Will Focus on Maryland Businesses Continue?" in Baltimore Business Journal (Vol. 28, November 5, 2010, No. 26, pp. 1)*
Pub: Baltimore Business Journal
Contact: Rhonda Pringle, President
E-mail: rpringle@bizjournals.com
Ed: Scott Dance. **Description:** The 2010 election may call for new efforts to teach new lawmakers to assure that the viewpoints of businesses are considered and accurately delivered. The Greater Baltimore Committee and similar groups have gathered reports on the competitiveness of Maryland and are planning to use them to make a case of keeping business a top priority. **Availability:** Print; Online.

18734 ■ *Working for Yourself: Law & Taxes for Independent Contractors, Freelancers & Consultants*
Pub: Nolo
Contact: Chris Braun, President
Ed: Stephen Fishman. **Released:** 12th Edition. **Price:** $27.99, e-book(downloadable); $34.99, book and e-book; $27.99, E-book. **Description:** In-depth information is shared for contractors, freelancers and consultants involving business law and small business taxes. **Availability:** E-book; Print; Electronic publishing; PDF.

VIDEO/AUDIO MEDIA

18735 ■ *The How of Business: Christy Foley - Conflict Resolution*
URL(s): www.thehowofbusiness.com/427-christy-foley-conflict-resolution
Ed: Henry Lopez. **Released:** June 20, 2022. **Description:** Podcast explains how to resolve or avoid common conflicts faced in small businesses. Topics include mediation, arbitration, contracts, partnerships, and intellectual property.

18736 ■ *The How of Business: Danya Shakfeh - Legal Considerations of Buying a Business*
URL(s): www.thehowofbusiness.com/507-danya-shakfeh-legal-considerations-buying-small-business
Ed: Henry Lopez. **Released:** January 29, 2024. **Description:** Podcast offers legal considerations when buying a small business, including research, NDAs, and contracts.

18737 ■ *Nurture Small Business: A Small Business Guide to the Corporate Transparency Act*
URL(s): nurturesmallbusiness.buzzsprout.com/900445/episodes/14562915-a-small-business-guide-to-the-corporate-transparency-act
Ed: Denise Cagan. **Released:** February 26, 2024. **Description:** Podcast defines the Corporate Transparency Act and the importance of filing a Beneficial Ownership Information (BOI) report.

18738 ■ *Small Biz 101: Legal Considerations for Small Business Owners*
URL(s): podcasts.apple.com/us/podcast/legal-considerations-for-small-business-owners-sb014/id1179203265?i=1000609091943
Ed: Connie Whitesell. **Released:** April 15, 2023. **Description:** Podcast discusses the importance of having an attorney at all stages of a business.

18739 ■ *What Contracts Do You Need for Your Business?*
URL(s): podcasts.apple.com/us/podcast/what-contracts-do-you-need-for-your-business/id1377376636?i=1000604302892
Ed: Mike Jesowshek. **Released:** March 15, 2023. **Description:** Podcast discusses necessary legal protections for small businesses.

18740 ■ *Why Do You Need a Trademark or Copyright for Your Business?*
URL(s): podcasts.apple.com/us/podcast/why-do-you-need-a-trademark-or-copyright-for-your-business/id1377276636?i=1000605336276
Ed: Mike Jesowshek. **Released:** March 22, 2023. **Description:** Podcast discussed the importance of protecting your brand by filing applications and navigating copyright law.

TRADE SHOWS AND CONVENTIONS

18741 ■ **ALA Annual Conference & Expo**
Association of Legal Administrators (ALA)
8600 W Bryn Mawr Ave., Ste. 400N
Chicago, IL 60631-4600
Ph: (847)267-1252
Co. E-mail: membership@alanet.org
URL: http://www.alanet.org
Contact: Sarah L. Evenson, President
URL(s): www.alanet.org/events/2024-events/2024-annual-conference---expo
Frequency: Annual; usually held in Sunday to wednesday. **Description:** Computers, hardware, and software; office equipment and supplies; publications, printers, and engravers; insurance; travel consultants; litigation support; facilities management; hotels; and coffee suppliers. **Audience:** ALA members, business partners and law firms. **Principal Exhibits:** Computers, hardware, and software; office equipment and supplies; publications, printers, and engravers; insurance; travel consultants; litigation support; facilities management; hotels; and coffee suppliers. Dates and Locations: 2025 May 18-22 Music City Center, Nashville, TN; 2026 Apr 12-15 Gaylord National Harbor, National Harbor, MD. **Telecommunication Services:** info@alaconferences.org.

18742 ■ **Alsb Annual Conference**
Academy of Legal Studies in Business (ALSB)
c/o Daniel Herron, Exec. Secretary
434 Flat Gap Trl.
Cullowhee, NC 28723
Co. E-mail: info@alsb.org
URL: http://www.alsb.org
Contact: Daniel Herron, Executive Secretary
E-mail: herron3653@gmail.com
URL(s): centennial.alsb.org/centennial-conference
Frequency: Annual. **Description:** Promotes and encourages business law scholarship and teaching outside of the law school environment. **Audience:** Teachers and scholars in the fields of business law, legal environment, members, and law-related courses outside of professional law schools. **Principal Exhibits:** Promotes and encourages business law scholarship and teaching outside of the law school environment. **Telecommunication Services:** sjmoore@umich.edu.

CONSULTANTS

18743 ■ **The Business Law Center on WestlawNext**
1333 H St. NW
Washington, DC 20005
Ph: (202)898-6300
URL: http://ca.practicallaw.thomsonreuters.com/7-382-3628?transitionType=Default&contextData=(sc.Default)&firstPage=true
Description: Research organization specializing in the real time dissemination of vital business information released by the Securities and Exchange Commission and other government agencies that oversee the financial markets. Provides demand and subscription services to remain aware of the current securities markets. Also offers LIVEDGAR, a full text searching research tool that provides real time, desktop access to all EDGAR (electronic data gathering analysis and retrieval) files. Advanced search capabilities include full-text and progressive searching, Boolean logic and search by example for precedent research. **Scope:** Research organization specializing in the real time dissemination of vital corporate information released by the Securities and Exchange Commission and other government agencies that oversee the financial markets. Provides demand and subscription services to remain aware of the current securities markets. Also offers LIVEDGAR, a full text searching research tool that provides real time, desktop access to all EDGAR (electronic data gathering analysis and retrieval) files. Advanced search capabilities include full-text and progressive searching, Boolean logic and search by example for precedent research. **Founded:** 1988. **Special Services:** GSI®; LIVEDGAR®.

18744 ■ **Don Phin, Esq.**
114 C. Ave., No. 200
Coronado, CA 92118
Ph: (619)852-4580
URL: http://www.donphin.com
Contact: Don Phin, Contact
E-mail: don@donphin.com
Linkedin: www.linkedin.com/in/donphin
X (Twitter): x.com/donphin12
YouTube: www.youtube.com/donphin
Description: Firm is engaged in consulting services on training, coaching and mentoring for the individuals and small businesses. **Scope:** Firm is engaged in consulting services on training, coaching and mentoring for the individuals and small businesses. **Founded:** 1983. **Publications:** "Doing Business Right!"; "HR That Works!"; "Lawsuit Free! How to Prevent Employee Lawsuits"; "Building Powerful Employment Relationships!"; "Victims, Villains and Heroes: Managing Emotions in The Workplace". **Training:** Doing Business Right!; HR That Works!; Building Powerful Employment Relationships; Lawsuit Free!.

18745 ■ **Juroviesky & Ricci L.L.P.**
3080 Yonge St., Ste. 5072
Toronto, ON, Canada M4N 3N1
Ph: (416)481-0718
Free: 877-578-7529
Fax: (416)481-1792
URL: http://www.jruslaw.com
Contact: Henry Juroviesky, Managing Partner
E-mail: hjuroviesky@uslegaladvice.com
Description: A law firm providing legal services on both sides of the United States, Canadian border. Practice areas include international business and corporate law, corporate governance, U.S., Canadian litigation, U.S. and Canadian corporate tax planning, state, provincial and local tax planning and international tax planning. **Scope:** A law firm providing legal services on both sides of the United States, Canadian border. Practice areas include international business and corporate law, corporate governance, U.S., Canadian litigation, U.S. and Canadian corporate tax planning, state, provincial and local tax planning and international tax planning. **Publications:** "The New Energy Consumer Protection Act- New Protection For Consumers?," Jan, 2011; "Is the United States the Next Great Tax Haven," Feb, 2005; "Under What Circumstances may Canadian Citizens Enter the United States as a Business Visitor," Feb, 2005; "Massachusetts Unsuccessful in its Sales and Use Tax Revenue Grab Against Drop Shippers," Feb, 2005; "Tax and Legal Hiccups in the Course of a US

Acquisition," Feb, 2005; "Do I Need To Worry About Collecting and Remitting Sales/Use Tax When I Sell to US Customers," Jan, 2005.

18746 ■ Nixon Peabody L.L.P.
53 State St.
 Boston, MA 02109-2835
Ph: (617)345-1000
Fax: (617)345-1300
Co. E-mail: info@nixonpeabody.com
URL: http://www.nixonpeabody.com/en
Contact: Stephen D. Zubiago, Chief Executive Officer
E-mail: szubiago@nixonpeabody.com
Linkedin: www.linkedin.com/company/nixon-peabody
X (Twitter): x.com/NixonPeabodyLLP
Instagram: www.instagram.com/nixonpeabodyllp
YouTube: www.youtube.com/user/nixonpeabodyllp
Description: Law firm provides legal services. **Scope:** Multi-practice law firm serving business, industry and individuals. Practice areas include antitrust, class actions, corporate governance and regulatory, corporate transactions, corporate trust, environmental, equipment finance, FDA regulatory, financial restructuring and bankruptcy, franchise and distribution, global finance, government contracts, government investigations and white collar defense, immigration, intellectual property, international, international arbitration, labor and employment, litigation and dispute resolution, private clients, private equity, products liability, mass and complex tort, project finance, public finance, real estate, securities, syndication and tax. **Founded:** 1999. **Publications:** "QandA with Deborah VanAmerongen: Direct Purchase Bonds (One on One: Industry Insight)," Mar, 2012; "Patient-Centered medical homes may reduce health care costs and improve patient health," Feb, 2012; "FDA's Draft Guidance on Social Media and Off-Label Communications," Jan, 2012; "The Investor Guide: Are Chinese Companies Still Worth Investing In?," Jan, 2012; "Passage to India: Ensuring 'safe travels' in business," Dec, 2008; "The Deputization of State AGs Under CPSIA," Dec, 2008; "New Rules Mandating the Disclosure of Consumer Complaints," Dec, 2008.

18747 ■ Ruf & Associates, L.L.C.
510 E 770 N
 Orem, UT 84097
Ph: (801)764-9100
Fax: (866)589-8871
Co. E-mail: info@rufassociates.com
URL: http://www.rufassociates.com
Contact: Harold B. Ruf, Chief Executive Officer
Description: Firm provides consulting and expert witness services for construction claims, cost segregation studies, litigation support, insurance claims, and much more. **Scope:** Firm provides consulting and expert witness services for construction claims, cost segregation studies, litigation support, insurance claims, and much more. **Founded:** 1993. **Publications:** "The Cash Benefits of Cost Segregation," Jul, 2007.

FRANCHISES AND BUSINESS OPPORTUNITIES

18748 ■ AAA Franchise Legal Help advice hotline
San Francisco, CA
Ph: (415)225-3010
Free: 800-942-4402
URL: http://www.franchisefoundations.com
Contact: Kevin B. Murphy, Contact
Description: Firm providing strategic franchise planning services. **Founded:** 1980.

18749 ■ Angiuli Katkin and Gentile L.L.P. (A & G)
1493 Hylan Blvd.
 Staten Island, NY 10305
Ph: (718)816-0005
URL: http://www.aglawnyc.com
Contact: Stefanie L. DeMario-Germershausen, Managing Partner
Facebook: www.facebook.com/AGLawFirmNYC
Linkedin: www.linkedin.com/company/angiuli-&-gentile-llp
X (Twitter): x.com/AngiuliGentile
Description: Provider of legal services for franchise operation. **Founded:** 1985.

18750 ■ Dickinson and Wheelock P.C. (D&W)
1001 S Dairy Ashford Rd., Ste. 375
 Houston, TX 77077
Ph: (713)722-8118
Fax: (713)722-7003
URL: http://dwlegal.com
Contact: Jeffrey W. Wheelock, Contact
E-mail: jwheelock@dwlegal.com
Description: Law firm dedicated to business and franchise law. **Founded:** 1998.

18751 ■ Franchise Law Team
30021 Tomas, Ste. 260
 Rancho Santa Margarita, CA 92688
Ph: (949)459-7474
Free: 888-276-2976
Fax: (949)459-7772
URL: http://www.franchising.com/ads/franchiseattorneys/franchiselaw.shtml
Contact: Robin Day Glenn, Contact
E-mail: rdglenn@franchiselawteam.com
Description: Registration, advice, and dispute resolution. **Scope:** Firm provides resources for franchise buyers, multi-unit franchisees, and franchisors. **Founded:** 1987.

18752 ■ Friedman, Rosenwasser & Goldbaum P.A. (FRG)
Boca Financial Ctr, Ste. 500, 5550 Glades Rd.
 Boca Raton, FL 33431
Ph: (561)395-5511
Co. E-mail: info@frglaw.com
URL: http://frglaw.com
Contact: Ronald N. Rosenwasser, Contact
E-mail: rrosenwasser@frglaw.com
Description: Law firm offers legal services. **Founded:** 1996.

18753 ■ Harold L. Kestenbaum, Esq.
3401 Merrick Rd., Ste. 4
 Wantagh, NY 11793
Ph: (516)745-0099
Fax: (516)745-0293
URL: http://www.spadealaw.com
Description: Law firm provides legal services. **Founded:** 1977.

18754 ■ Huck Bouma Pc. Attorneys at Law
1755 S Naperville Rd., Ste. 200
 Wheaton, IL 60189
Ph: (630)221-1755
Co. E-mail: attorneys@huckbouma.com
URL: http://www.huckbouma.com
Contact: William J. Strons, Managing Partner
E-mail: wstrons@huckbouma.com
Facebook: www.facebook.com/HuckBoumaPC
Linkedin: www.linkedin.com/company/huck-bouma-pc
X (Twitter): x.com/huckboumapc
Description: Assist start-up franchisees and franchisors. **Scope:** Firm provides legal services for franchisors, sub franchisors, master franchisees, and area developers such as franchise agreements, state franchise registrations, and much more. **Founded:** 1991. **Training:** Franchise Law Compliance Attorneys.

18755 ■ The iFranchise Group Inc.
905 W 175th St., 2nd Fl.
 Homewood, IL 60430
URL: http://www.ifranchisegroup.com
Contact: David E. Hood, President
Linkedin: www.linkedin.com/company/ifranchise-group
X (Twitter): x.com/ifranchisegroup
Instagram: www.instagram.com/ifranchisegroup
Description: Firm provides franchise consulting, development and marketing services. **Scope:** Firm provides franchise consulting, development and marketing services. **Founded:** 1998. **Publications:** "Is Your Business Franchisable?"; "The Right Marketing Materials". **Training:** Franchise Sales and Marketing Techniques; Minimizing Franchise Litigation; How to Franchise a Business; Developing and Maintaining Good Franchisee Relations.

18756 ■ Joseph J. Walczak P.C.
12628 S Harlem Ave.
 Palos Heights, IL 60463
Ph: (708)361-3390
Co. E-mail: joseph@josephwalczak.com
URL: http://josephwalczak.com
Contact: Joseph J. Walczak, Contact
E-mail: joseph@josephwalczak.com
Description: Law Firm provides legal services such as divorce, custody and child support. **Founded:** 1988.

18757 ■ Kanouse and Walker P.A.
6879 Giralda Cir.
 Boca Raton, FL 33433
Ph: (561)451-8090
Fax: (561)451-8089
URL: http://www.kanouse.com
Contact: Susan Walker, Vice President
E-mail: swalker@kanouse.com
Description: Firm offers legal services in matters of real estate, leasing and security law. **Founded:** 1974.

18758 ■ Law Offices of Suzanne C. Cummings and Associates P.C.
2 Main St., Ste. 300
 Stoneham, MA 02180
Co. E-mail: scummings@cummingsfranchiselaw.com
URL: http://cummingsfranchiselaw.com/attorneys/suzanne-c-cummings
Contact: Suzanne C. Cummings, Founder
E-mail: scummings@cummingsfranchiselaw.com
Description: Services: Franchise law and business advisory solutions.

18759 ■ Marks and Klein L.L.P. (MK)
63 Riverside Ave.
 Red Bank, NJ 07701
Ph: (732)747-7100
Fax: (732)219-0625
URL: http://marksklein.com
Contact: Timothy J. Randall, Counsel
Description: Law firm provides legal services. **Founded:** 1971.

18760 ■ Mitchell J. Kassoff, Esq., Attorney
South Orange, NJ
Ph: (862)250-2266
Co. E-mail: franchiselaw@icloud.com
URL: http://legal-franchise.com
Contact: Mitchell J. Kassoff, Contact
Description: Law firm provides legal services. **Founded:** 1979.

18761 ■ Peter C. Lagarias, Esq.
1629 5th Ave.
 San Rafael, CA 94901
Ph: (415)460-0100
Fax: (415)460-1099
Co. E-mail: info@franchiselawadvocates.com
URL: http://www.franchiselawadvocates.com
Contact: Peter C. Lagarias, Senior Partner
E-mail: pcl@franchiselawadvocates.com
Linkedin: www.linkedin.com/in/peter-lagarias-953b519
Description: Franchise litigation and service. **Founded:** 1982.

18762 ■ Zarco Einhorn Salkowski and Brito P.A.
2 S Biscayne Blvd., 34th Fl.
 Miami, FL 33131
Ph: (305)374-5418
Free: 800-299-4929
Fax: (305)374-5428
Co. E-mail: info@zarcolaw.com
URL: http://www.zarcolaw.com
Contact: Kaari-Lynn S. Gagnon, Partner
E-mail: kgagnon@zarcolaw.com
Facebook: www.facebook.com/zarcolaw
Linkedin: www.linkedin.com/company/zarco-einhorn-salkowski-law
X (Twitter): x.com/zarcolaw

Instagram: www.instagram.com/zarcolaw
YouTube: www.youtube.com/channel/UCK71VW
3NnjXqXVG99sKGs0Q
Description: Law firm provides legal services. **Founded:** 1992.

PUBLICATIONS

18763 ■ *American Business Law Journal (ABLJ)*
c/o Daniel Herron, Exec. Secretary
434 Flat Gap Trl.
Cullowhee, NC 28723
Co. E-mail: info@alsb.org
URL: http://www.alsb.org
Contact: Daniel Herron, Executive Secretary
E-mail: herron3653@gmail.com
URL(s): onlinelibrary.wiley.com/journal/17441714
X (Twitter): x.com/the_ablj
Released: Quarterly **Price:** $1,136, Institutions for print+online Canada; $1,507, Institutions for print+online India; $1,136, Institutions for print+online USA; $1,011, Institutions for online Canada; $1,055, Institutions for print Canada; $1,342, Institutions for online India; $1,400, Institutions for print India; $1,011, Institutions for online USA; $1,055, Institutions for print USA. **Description:** Law review journal focused on business law. Published by Wiley on behalf of the Academy of Legal Studies in Business. **Availability:** Print; PDF; Download; Online.

18764 ■ *Business & Commercial Law Journal*
25 E Jackson Blvd.
Chicago, IL 60604
Ph: (312)362-8701
Co. E-mail: lawinfo@depaul.edu
URL: http://law.depaul.edu/Pages/default.aspx
Contact: Jennifer Rosato Perea, Dean
E-mail: jrosato@depaul.edu
URL(s): via.library.depaul.edu/bclj
Description: Journal covering legal issues about business and commercial law. **Availability:** Print; Download; PDF; Online.

18765 ■ *Business Law Journal (BLJ)*
400 Mrak Hall Dr.
Davis, CA 95616-5201
Ph: (530)752-6477
Fax: (530)752-7279
Co. E-mail: admissions@law.ucdavis.edu
URL: http://law.ucdavis.edu
Contact: Karen Charney, Executive Director
E-mail: klcharney@ucdavis.edu
URL(s): blj.ucdavis.edu
Released: Semiannual; fall and spring. **Price:** $44.50, for per year. **Description:** Journal containing articles on legal and business analysis. **Availability:** Print; Online.

18766 ■ *Business Law Monographs*
NY
URL: http://store.lexisnexis.com/categories/publishers/matthew-bender-850
Contact: Mike Walsh, Chief Executive Officer
URL(s): store.lexisnexis.com/products/business-law-monographs-skuusSku10238
Released: Quarterly **Price:** $12,882, Individuals for e-book: epub; $12,882, Individuals for print book. **Description:** Covers various areas of business law, with a special slant towards in-house counsel. **Availability:** CD-ROM; E-book; Print; Electronic publishing; Download.

18767 ■ *Business Law Today (BLT)*
321 N Clark St.
Chicago, IL 60654
Ph: (312)988-5000
Free: 800-285-2221
Co. E-mail: service@americanbar.org
URL: http://www.americanbar.org
Contact: Mary L. Smith, President
URL(s): businesslawtoday.orgwww.americanbar.org/groups/business_law/resources/business-law-today
Facebook: www.facebook.com/ABABusinessLaw
Linkedin: www.linkedin.com/showcase/aba-business-law-section

X (Twitter): x.com/ABABusLaw
Released: Continuous **Description:** Peer-reviewed, online only publication covering all aspects of business law. **Availability:** Print; PDF; Online. **Type:** Full-text.

18768 ■ *The Business Lawyer*
321 N Clark St.
Chicago, IL 60654-4746
Ph: (312)988-5588
Free: 800-285-2221
Fax: (312)988-5578
Co. E-mail: businesslaw@americanbar.org
URL: http://www.americanbar.org/groups/business_law
Contact: Nicole F. Munro, Chairman
URL(s): www.americanbar.org/groups/business_law/resources/business-lawyer
Released: Quarterly; Winter, Spring, Summer and Fall. **Price:** $100, U.S. for 1 year; $25, Single issue. **Description:** Law journal providing topics of professional interest to business lawyers, including scholarly articles analyzing emerging trends, commentaries on practical deliberations, checklists for specific transactions, and proceedings from the Section of Corporation, Banking, and Business Law's educational seminars. **Availability:** Print; Online.

18769 ■ *Duquesne Business Law Journal*
Hanley Hall
600 Forbes Ave.
Pittsburgh, PA 15282
Ph: (412)396-6300
Co. E-mail: lawschool@duq.edu
URL: http://www.duq.edu/academics/schools/law
Contact: Ken Gormley, President
E-mail: president@duq.edu
URL(s): sites.law.duq.edu/blj
Released: Semiannual **Price:** $15, for per volume; $8, for per copy. **Description:** Journal containing articles not only on topics that are currently affecting the world of business, but also on evolving Supreme Court case law, and influential persons in the business community. **Availability:** Print; Online.

18770 ■ *Global Business Law Review*
1801 Euclid Ave., LB 138
Cleveland, OH 44115
Ph: (216)687-2300
Free: 888-687-2304
Fax: (216)687-6881
Co. E-mail: law.admissions@csuohio.edu
URL: http://www.law.csuohio.edu
Contact: Lauren M. Collins, Director
E-mail: l.m.collins36@csuohio.edu
URL(s): www.law.csuohio.edu/academics/curriculum/coursedescriptions/law818www.law.csuohio.edu/currentstudents/studentorganizations
Released: Semiannual; Fall and the Spring. **Description:** Publishes two volumes annually. Fall volume is the Symposium Edition with articles from the speakers of our Annual Symposium held the previous spring. Spring volume is The Global Business Law Review with articles from scholars and students. **Availability:** Print.

18771 ■ *Hofstra Journal of International Business and Law (JIBL)*
121 Hofstra University
Hempstead, NY 11549
Ph: (516)463-5858
URL: http://law.hofstra.edu
Contact: Gail Prudenti, Dean
URL(s): www.hofstrajibl.org
Description: Journal containing studies regarding the interaction of business and law in the global marketplace. **Availability:** Online; PDF.

18772 ■ *Illinois Business Law Journal (IBLJ)*
504 E Pennsylvania Ave.
Champaign, IL 61820
Ph: (217)333-0931
Fax: (217)244-1478
Co. E-mail: law-cllpj@illinois.edu
URL: http://law.illinois.edu
Contact: Dan Safran, President
URL(s): publish.illinois.edu/illinoisblj

Ed: Jackie McManus, Derek Franklin. **Released:** 5/year **Description:** Journal containing information on recent developments affecting business law. **Availability:** Print; PDF.

18773 ■ *International Business Planning: Law and Taxation (United States)*
NY
URL: http://store.lexisnexis.com/categories/publishers/matthew-bender-850
Contact: Mike Walsh, Chief Executive Officer
URL(s): store.lexisnexis.com/products/international-business-planning-law-and-taxation-us-skuusSku 10255
Ed: William P. Streng. **Price:** $1,750, for eBook, mobi, epub, print. **Description:** Addresses the most common legal, tax, and financial planning issues associated with international business transactions, with pertinent legislation and sample forms throughout the set. **Availability:** CD-ROM; E-book; Print; Online; Electronic publishing; Download.

18774 ■ *Journal of Business Law (JBL)*
3501 Sansom St.
Philadelphia, PA 19104-6204
Ph: (215)898-7483
Co. E-mail: contactadmissions@law.upenn.edu
URL: http://law.upenn.edu
Contact: Arlene Finkelstein, Associate Dean
E-mail: arfinkel@law.upenn.edu
URL(s): www.law.upenn.edu/journals/jblwww.sweetandmaxwell.co.uk/Product/Commercial-Law/Journal-of-Business-Law/Journal/30791434
Ed: Prof. Robert Merkin, Clive M. Schmitthoff, Laura Harrison. **Released:** 8/year **Description:** Law periodical. **Availability:** Print; PDF; Online; Download.

18775 ■ *Journal of International Law and Business*
357 E Chicago Ave.
Chicago, IL 60611-3069
Ph: (312)503-3100
Co. E-mail: law-website@law.northwestern.edu
URL: http://www.law.northwestern.edu
Contact: Henry Booth, Founder
URL(s): jilb.law.northwestern.edu
Released: 3/year **Price:** $40, U.S. for rest of world Canada; $15, Single issue. **Description:** Journal covering analysis of transnational and international law and its effects on private entities. **Availability:** Print; PDF; Online; Download.

18776 ■ *Journal of Law and Business (JLB)*
40 Washington Sq. S
New York, NY 10012
Ph: (212)998-6100
Co. E-mail: law.moreinfo@nyu.edu
URL: http://www.law.nyu.edu
Contact: Franco Ferrari, Director
URL(s): www.nyujlb.org
Facebook: www.facebook.com/NYUJLB
Released: 3/year; summer, spring, fall, latest issue. **Price:** $22, for single issue year; $30, for domestic year; $35, for international year. **Description:** Journal containing studies and analysis of current issues, ideas, and problems at the intersection of two dynamic fields of law and business. **Availability:** Print.

18777 ■ *Journal of World Energy Law & Business*
2001 Evans Rd.
Cary, NC 27513
Free: 800-280-0280
Fax: (919)678-1435
Co. E-mail: highered.us@oup.com
URL: http://global.oup.com/?cc=jp
URL(s): academic.oup.com/jwelb
Ed: Peter Roberts, Sarah Harris, Orrick Partner, Prof. Thomas Walde. **Released:** 6/year **Price:** $842, Institutions for online subscription. **Description:** Peer-reviewed journal covering legal, business, and policy issues in the international energy industry. **Availability:** Print; PDF; Online.

GENERAL SMALL BUSINESS TOPICS

18778 ■ Legal Environments of Business
826 Riviera Dr.
  Mansfield, TX 76063
Free: 800-990-4273
URL: http://www.americancpe.com
Contact: Dennis Gatlin, President
URL(s): www.americancpe.com/CPE-Courses/
  24-Business-Law---The-Legal-Environments-of
  -Business.html
Price: $109, for download searchable text and exam for apple computers; $109, for download searchable text and exam; $124, for searchable CD-ROM; $134, for printed text; $55, for additional exams. **Description:** Contains detailed training information covering legal structures and environments in which businesses operate in the United States. **Availability:** CD-ROM; Print; Download. **Type:** Full-text.

18779 ■ Northwestern Journal of International Law & Business (JILB)
375 E Chicago Ave.
  Chicago, IL 60611
Co. E-mail: law-website@law.northwestern.edu
URL: http://www.law.northwestern.edu/about/marke ting-communications/web
URL(s): jilb.law.northwestern.eduscholarlycommons .law.northwestern.edu/njilb/vol44/iss2/1
Released: 3/year **Price:** $40, for Canada; $40, for rest of world; $40, for U.S. **Description:** Journal covering business law issues worldwide. **Availability:** Print; PDF; Online.

18780 ■ Richmond Journal of Global Law and Business
203 Richmond Way
  Richmond, VA 23173
Ph: (804)289-8740
URL: http://law.richmond.edu
Contact: Wendy Collins Perdue, Dean
E-mail: wperdue@richmond.edu
URL(s): rjglb.richmond.edu
Released: Quarterly **Price:** $12, Single issue; $30, for per year. **Description:** Journal featuring articles on the intersection of international law and global business. **Availability:** Download; PDF; Online.

18781 ■ Texas Journal of Business Law
1303 San Jacinto St.
  Houston, TX 77002-7006
Ph: (713)659-8040
Co. E-mail: alumni@stcl.edu
URL: http://www.stcl.edu
Contact: Michael F. Barry, President
URL(s): www.stcl.edu/academics/transactional-prac tice-center/texas-journal-of-business-law
Description: Professional journal covering business law. **Availability:** Print; Online.

18782 ■ UC Law Business Journal (HBLJ)
200 McAllister St.
  San Francisco, CA 94102
Co. E-mail: scholarp@uchastings.edu
URL: http://www.uchastings.edu/academics/journals
URL(s): repository.uclawsf.edu/hastings_business _law_journal
Released: Current Issue: Volume 20, Number 1 2024. **Description:** Journal containing issues regarding international and domestic events between law and business. **Availability:** Print; PDF.

18783 ■ Wake Forest Journal of Business & Intellectual Property Law
1834 Wake Forest Rd.
  Winston Salem, NC 27106
Ph: (336)758-5437
Fax: (336)758-3930
Co. E-mail: lawadmissions@wfu.edu
URL: http://law.wfu.edu
Contact: Elenora Haag, Assistant Director
E-mail: haage@wfu.edu
URL(s): jbipl.pubpub.org
X (Twitter): x.com/wfulawjbipl
Released: Quarterly; January, March, June, and October. **Price:** $75, for 2 year; $40, for 1 year. **Description:** Journal publishing topics pertaining to intellectual property law and business law as well as the intersection between the two. **Availability:** Print; PDF; Download; Online.

COMPUTERIZED DATABASES

18784 ■ The Bar Register of Preeminent Lawyers™
Martindale-Hubbell
  121 Chanlon Rd., Ste. 110
  New Providence, NJ 07974
Ph: (908)464-6800
Free: 800-526-4902
Fax: (908)771-8704
URL: http://www.martindale.com
URL(s): www.martindale.com/bar-register-of -preeminent-lawyers
Released: Annual **Availability:** Print. **Type:** Directory.

18785 ■ CCH ProSystem fx Tax™
Wolters Kluwer
  90 Sheppard Ave. E, Ste. 300
  Toronto, ON, Canada M2N 6X1
Ph: (416)224-2248
URL: http://www.wolterskluwer.com/en-in
Contact: Kevin Entricken, Chief Financial Officer
URL(s): www.wolterskluwer.com/en/solutions/cch -prosystem-fx/tax
Availability: PDF; Download; Online. **Type:** Bulletin board.

18786 ■ DART: British Columbia Statute Service on Internet
Carswell
  2075 Kennedy Rd.
  Toronto, ON, Canada M1T 3V4
URL: http://store.thomsonreuters.ca/en-ca/products/ carswells-pension-manual-formerly-mercer-pension -manual-30843906
Contact: Steve Hasker, President
URL(s): www.thomsonreuters.ca/fr/login.html
Availability: Online. **Type:** Full-text.

18787 ■ A Guide to Federal Sector Equal Employment Opportunity (EEO) Law and Practice
Dewey Publications Inc.
  1840 Wilson Blvd., Ste. 203
  Arlington, VA 22201
Ph: (703)524-1355
Fax: (703)524-1463
Co. E-mail: deweypublications@gmail.com
URL: http://deweypub.com/store
Contact: Peter Broida, President
URL(s): deweypub.com/store/23EEO.html
Released: Annual **Price:** $775, for pdf download; $875, for pdf download & CD-ROMs or usb stick; $975, for pdf download & softcover; $995, for pdf download & CD-ROMs, softcover book or usb stick; $825, for soft book; $775, for pdf e-book on CD-ROM or USB stick; $975, for pdf sofrbook on CD-ROM or USB stick. **Availability:** CD-ROM; Online; Download; PDF. **Type:** Full-text.

18788 ■ A Guide to Merit Systems Protection Board (MSPB) Law and Practice
Dewey Publications Inc.
  1840 Wilson Blvd., Ste. 203
  Arlington, VA 22201
Ph: (703)524-1355
Fax: (703)524-1463
Co. E-mail: deweypublications@gmail.com
URL: http://deweypub.com/store
Contact: Peter Broida, President
URL(s): deweypub.com/store/23MSPB.html
Released: Current edition 2023. **Price:** $775, for price; $825, for softcover book; $775, for PDF, e-book, CD-ROM USB; $975, for softcover book, PDF, CD-ROM , USB; $875, for PDF, Download, CD-ROM , USB, Softcover. **Availability:** PDF; Online. **Type:** Full-text.

18789 ■ Industrial Patent Activity in the United States Parts 1 and 2, 1974-1998
U.S. Department of Commerce United States Patent and Trademark Office
Ph: (571)272-1000
Free: 800-786-9199
URL: http://www.uspto.gov
Contact: Joseph Matal, Director
URL(s): www.ntis.govwww.uspto.gov
Type: Full-text.

18790 ■ The National Law Journal
ALM Media Properties LLC.
  150 E 42nd St.
  New York, NY 10017
Ph: (212)457-9400
Free: 877-256-2472
Co. E-mail: customercare@alm.com
URL: http://www.alm.com
Contact: Bill Carter, Chief Executive Officer
URL(s): www.law.com/nationallawjournal
Availability: Print. **Type:** Full-text.

LIBRARIES

18791 ■ Alberta Securities Commission (ASC)
250-5th St. SW, Ste. 600
  Calgary, AB, Canada T2P 0R4
Ph: (403)297-6454
Free: 877-355-0585
Fax: (403)297-6156
Co. E-mail: inquiries@asc.ca
URL: http://www.asc.ca
Contact: Stan Magidson, Chief Executive Officer
Facebook: www.facebook.com/ASCUpdates
Linkedin: www.linkedin.com/company/alberta-securi ties-commission_2
X (Twitter): x.com/ASCUpdates
Description: Aims to foster a fair and efficient capital market in Alberta. We've made it easy for you to find the information you need. **Founded:** 1955.

18792 ■ Arnold & Porter Kaye Scholer LLP - Library
250 W 55th St.
  New York, NY 10019-9710
Ph: (212)836-8000
Fax: (212)836-8689
URL: http://www.arnoldporter.com/en
Contact: Arthur E. Brown, Partner
E-mail: arthur.brown@arnoldporter.com
Description: Law firm provides legal services. **Scope:** Law. **Services:** Interlibrary loan; copying; SDI; library open to members of SLA and Law Library Association of Greater New York by appointment. **Founded:** 2017. **Holdings:** 45,546 books; 520 bound periodical volumes; 6220 microfiche; 2007 ultrafiche; 1866 reels of microfilm; 264 VF drawers.; 20,000 books; 400 bound periodical volumes. **Subscriptions:** ; 205 journals and other serials; 15 newspapers.

18793 ■ Bryan Cave L.L.P., Law Library
1155 F St. NW, Ste. 700
  Washington, DC 20004-1357
URL: http://www.bclplaw.com/en-US/people/pedro-j -martinez-fraga.html
Scope: Government and politics; law - commercial, corporate, environmental, intellectual property, taxation. **Services:** Interlibrary loan; copying; faxing; library open to the public with restrictions. **Founded:** 1978. **Holdings:** 11,000 volumes.

18794 ■ HP Inc.
HP Inc.
  1501 Page Mill Rd.
  Palo Alto, CA 94304
Ph: (650)857-1501
Free: 800-752-0900
Co. E-mail: myhpsales@hp.com
URL: http://www.hp.com
Contact: Enrique Lores, President
Facebook: www.facebook.com/HP
Linkedin: www.linkedin.com/company/hp
X (Twitter): twitter.com/HP

Instagram: www.instagram.com/hp/
YouTube: www.youtube.com/hp
Description: Provider of personal computing and other access devices, imaging and printing products, and related technologies, solutions, and services. **Founded:** 1947. **Publications:** *ServiceCenter*, *X.25*. **Educational Activities:** ACM Conference on Computer and Communications Security (CCS) (Annual).

18795 ■ Long & Levit Library
465 California St., Fifth Fl.
  San Francisco, CA 94104
Ph: (415)397-2222
URL: http://www.longlevit.com
Contact: Jennifer W. Suzuki, Partner
E-mail: jsuzuki@longlevit.com
Scope: Insurance; environment; professional liability; construction. **Services:** Interlibrary loan; copying; library open to the public at librarian's discretion. **Founded:** 1927. **Holdings:** 10,000 books.

18796 ■ McCarthy Tetrault Library
745 Thurlow St., Ste. 2400
  Vancouver, BC, Canada V6E 0C5
Ph: (604)643-7100
Free: 877-244-7711
Fax: (604)643-7900
Co. E-mail: info@mccarthy.ca
URL: http://www.mccarthy.ca/en/contact-us/vancouver
Contact: Sven O. Milelli, Managing Partner
E-mail: smilelli@mccarthy.ca
X (Twitter): x.com/McCarthy_ca
YouTube: www.youtube.com/user/McCarthyTetrault
Description: Client-focused law firm in British Columbia. **Scope:** Law; corporate law; securities. **Services:** Library not open to the public. **Founded:** 1960. **Holdings:** Figures not available.

18797 ■ Miller Thomson L.L.P.
Scotia Plz., 40 King St. W, Ste. 5800
  Toronto, ON, Canada M5H 3S1
Ph: (416)595-8500
Free: 888-762-5559
Fax: (416)595-8695
Co. E-mail: toronto@millerthomson.com
URL: http://www.millerthomson.com
Contact: Jessica Rubin, Director
E-mail: jrubin@millerthomson.com
Facebook: www.facebook.com/MillerThomsonLaw
Linkedin: www.linkedin.com/company/miller-thomson-llp
X (Twitter): x.com/millerthomson
Instagram: www.instagram.com/millerthomsonllp
Description: Services: Legal services in areas such as aboriginal, agribusiness and food, anti-corruption and international governance, anti-spam and automotive. **Scope:** Law. **Founded:** 1957. **Holdings:** 2000 books. **Subscriptions:** 20 journals and other serials; 6 newspapers.

18798 ■ University of Hawaii at West O'ahu - Center for Labor Education and Research - CLEAR Labor Law Library
91-1001 Farrington Hwy.
  Kapolei, HI 96707
URL: http://www.hawaii.edu/uhwo/clear/home/library.html
Contact: Dr. William Puette, Contact
E-mail: puette@hawaii.edu
Description: Contains reference materials, journals, books, online materials, and video and audio materials on legal studies. **Scope:** Labor law. **Services:** Library open to the public by appointment; copying. **Founded:** 1976. **Holdings:** Figures not available.

Business Networks (Social Groups)

ASSOCIATIONS AND OTHER ORGANIZATIONS

18799 ■ American Association of Business Networking (ABN)
822 A1A N, Ste. 310
Ponte Vedra Beach, FL 32082
Ph: (904)342-6630
URL: http://abnetworking.org
Description: Offers networking opportunities and educational information to business professionals, such as attorneys, accountants, physicians, architects, engineers, mortgage professionals, dentists, veterinarians, occupational therapists, pharmacists, nurses, and real estate agents. Offers such resources as templates for employee handbooks, nondiscrimination policies, and guides. **Founded:** 2001.

18800 ■ Business Network International Inc. (BNI)
11525 N Community House Rd., No. 475
Charlotte, NC 28277
Ph: (704)248-4800
Free: 800-825-8286
Co. E-mail: support@bni.com
URL: http://www.bni.com
Contact: Dan Haggerty, President
Linkedin: www.linkedin.com/company/bni
X (Twitter): x.com/bni_official_pg
YouTube: www.youtube.com/user/BNIOfficialChannel
Description: Firm provides consulting services on business, planning and management. **Founded:** 1985.

18801 ■ eWomenNetwork - Birmingham Chapter
Birmingham, AL
URL: http://www.ewomennetwork.com/chapters/birmingham-668
Description: Strives to connect and promote female entrepreneurs and their businesses worldwide. Provides members with such resources as networking opportunities, marketing, coaching, events, podcasts, speaking engagements, scholarships, grants, and video production to help grow their businesses.

18802 ■ eWomenNetwork - Boca Raton Chapter
Boca Raton, FL
URL: http://www.ewomennetwork.com/chapters/621
Description: Strives to connect and promote female entrepreneurs and their businesses worldwide. Provides members with such resources as networking opportunities, marketing, coaching, events, podcasts, speaking engagements, scholarships, grants, and video production to help grow their businesses.

18803 ■ eWomenNetwork - Calabasas Chapter
Calabasas, CA
URL: http://www.ewomennetwork.com/chapters/calabasas-665
Contact: Julie Kraschinsky, Managing Director
E-mail: juliekraschinsky@ewomennetwork.com
Facebook: www.facebook.com/ewncalabasas
Description: Strives to connect and promote female entrepreneurs and their businesses worldwide. Provides members with such resources as networking opportunities, marketing, coaching, events, podcasts, speaking engagements, scholarships, grants, and video production to help grow their businesses.

18804 ■ eWomenNetwork - Colorado Springs Chapter
c/o Brenda Layton
 Managing Director
 Colorado Springs, CO
Ph: (719)661-7483
Co. E-mail: brendalayton@ewomennetwork.com
URL: http://www.ewomennetwork.com/chapters/colorado-springs-513
Contact: Brenda Layton, Manager Director
E-mail: brendalayton@ewomennetwork.com
Facebook: www.facebook.com/ewncoloradosprings
Description: Strives to connect and promote female entrepreneurs and their businesses worldwide. Provides members with such resources as networking opportunities, marketing, coaching, events, podcasts, speaking engagements, scholarships, grants, and video production to help grow their businesses.

18805 ■ eWomenNetwork - Denver Chapter
c/o Renee Vejvoda, Managing Director
 Denver, CO
Ph: (720)840-4001
Co. E-mail: reneevejvoda@ewomennetwork.com
URL: http://www.ewomennetwork.com/chapters/denver-654
Contact: Abbey Harrison, Contact
E-mail: abbey@assistforthewin.com
Facebook: www.facebook.com/ewndenver

18806 ■ eWomenNetwork - Ft. Lauderdale Chapter
Fort Lauderdale, FL
URL: http://www.ewomennetwork.com/chapters/ft-lauderdale-515
Contact: Aigerim Kuanysh, Contact
Facebook: www.facebook.com/eWNFtLauderdaleMiami
Description: Strives to connect and promote female entrepreneurs and their businesses worldwide. Provides members with such resources as networking opportunities, marketing, coaching, events, podcasts, speaking engagements, scholarships, grants, and video production to help grow their businesses.

18807 ■ eWomenNetwork - Fresno Chapter
Fresno, CA
URL: http://www.ewomennetwork.com/chapters/fresno-608
Contact: Alison Haugan, Contact

Description: Strives to connect and promote female entrepreneurs and their businesses worldwide. Provides members with such resources as networking opportunities, marketing, coaching, events, podcasts, speaking engagements, scholarships, grants, and video production to help grow their businesses.

18808 ■ eWomenNetwork - Greater Hartford Chapter
Hartford, CT
Ph: (860)227-3054
URL: http://www.ewomennetwork.com/chapters/greater-hartford-673
Contact: Aina Hoskins, Executive Director
E-mail: ainahoskins@ewomennetwork.com
Description: Strives to connect and promote female entrepreneurs and their businesses worldwide. Provides members with such resources as networking opportunities, marketing, coaching, events, podcasts, speaking engagements, scholarships, grants, and video production to help grow their businesses.

18809 ■ eWomenNetwork - Jacksonville Chapter
Jacksonville, FL
URL: http://www.ewomennetwork.com/chapters/625
Contact: Rebecca Sullivan, Managing Director
E-mail: rebeccasullivan@ewomennetwork.com
Description: Strives to connect and promote female entrepreneurs and their businesses worldwide. Provides members with such resources as networking opportunities, marketing, coaching, events, podcasts, speaking engagements, scholarships, grants, and video production to help grow their businesses.

18810 ■ eWomenNetwork - Ladera Heights Chapter
Ladera Heights, CA
URL: http://www.ewomennetwork.com/chapters/ladera-heights-675
Contact: Melanie Mack, Member
Description: Strives to connect and promote female entrepreneurs and their businesses worldwide. Provides members with such resources as networking opportunities, marketing, coaching, events, podcasts, speaking engagements, scholarships, grants, and video production to help grow their businesses.

18811 ■ eWomenNetwork - Los Angeles Chapter
Los Angeles, CA 90022
Ph: (213)296-4448
URL: http://www.ewomennetwork.com/chapters/los-angeles-588
Contact: Johnell McCauley, Director
E-mail: johnellmccauley@ewomennetwork.com
Facebook: www.facebook.com/ewnlosangeles
Description: Strives to connect and promote female entrepreneurs and their businesses worldwide. Provides members with such resources as network-

18812 ■ Business Networks (Social Groups)

ing opportunities, marketing, coaching, events, podcasts, speaking engagements, scholarships, grants, and video production to help grow their businesses.

18812 ■ eWomenNetwork - Miami Chapter
Miami, FL
URL: http://www.ewomennetwork.com/chapters/miami-534
Description: Strives to connect and promote female entrepreneurs and their businesses worldwide. Provides members with such resources as networking opportunities, marketing, coaching, events, podcasts, speaking engagements, scholarships, grants, and video production to help grow their businesses.

18813 ■ eWomenNetwork - Palo Alto Chapter
Palo Alto, CA
URL: http://www.ewomennetwork.com/chapters/543
Description: Strives to connect and promote female entrepreneurs and their businesses worldwide. Provides members with such resources as networking opportunities, marketing, coaching, events, podcasts, speaking engagements, scholarships, grants, and video production to help grow their businesses.

18814 ■ eWomenNetwork - Phoenix/Scottsdale Chapter
Phoenix, AZ
URL: http://www.ewomennetwork.com/chapters/phoenix-scottsdale-511
Contact: Veronica Bahn, Managing Director
E-mail: veronicabahn@ewomennetwork.com
Description: Strives to connect and promote female entrepreneurs and their businesses worldwide. Provides members with such resources as networking opportunities, marketing, coaching, events, podcasts, speaking engagements, scholarships, grants, and video production to help grow their businesses.

18815 ■ eWomenNetwork - Sacramento Chapter
Sacramento, CA
URL: http://www.ewomennetwork.com/chapters/sacramento-661
Contact: Janet Fish, Managing Director
E-mail: janetfish@ewomennetwork.com
Description: Strives to connect and promote female entrepreneurs and their businesses worldwide. Provides members with such resources as networking opportunities, marketing, coaching, events, podcasts, speaking engagements, scholarships, grants, and video production to help grow their businesses.

18816 ■ eWomenNetwork - San Diego Chapter
San Diego, CA
URL: http://www.ewomennetwork.com/chapters/san-diego-512
Contact: Jenny Harkleroad, Managing Director
E-mail: jennyharkleroad@ewomennetwork.com
Description: Strives to connect and promote female entrepreneurs and their businesses worldwide. Provides members with such resources as networking opportunities, marketing, coaching, events, podcasts, speaking engagements, scholarships, grants, and video production to help grow their businesses.

18817 ■ eWomenNetwork - San Jose Chapter
San Jose, CA
URL: http://www.ewomennetwork.com/chapters/540
Description: Strives to connect and promote female entrepreneurs and their businesses worldwide. Provides members with such resources as networking opportunities, marketing, coaching, events, podcasts, speaking engagements, scholarships, grants, and video production to help grow their businesses.

18818 ■ eWomenNetwork - Tucson Chapter
Tucson, AZ
URL: http://www.ewomennetwork.com/chapters/tucson-581
Contact: Carol Johnson, Manager Director
E-mail: caroljohnson@ewomennetwork.com
Description: Strives to connect and promote female entrepreneurs and their businesses worldwide. Provides members with such resources as networking opportunities, marketing, coaching, events, podcasts, speaking engagements, scholarships, grants, and video production to help grow their businesses.

18819 ■ eWomenNetwork - Washington D.C. Metro Chapter
Washington, DC
URL: http://www.ewomennetwork.com/chapters/washington-dc-metro-728
Contact: Johnell McCauley, Director
E-mail: johnellmccauley@ewomennetwork.ca
Description: Strives to connect and promote female entrepreneurs and their businesses worldwide. Provides members with such resources as networking opportunities, marketing, coaching, events, podcasts, speaking engagements, scholarships, grants, and video production to help grow their businesses.

18820 ■ eWomenNetwork - Wilmington Chapter
Wilmington, DE
URL: http://www.ewomennetwork.com/chapters/wilmington-640
Contact: Susan Salter, Managing Director
E-mail: susansalter@ewomennetwork.com
Description: Strives to connect and promote female entrepreneurs and their businesses worldwide. Provides members with such resources as networking opportunities, marketing, coaching, events, podcasts, speaking engagements, scholarships, grants, and video production to help grow their businesses.

18821 ■ Silicon Slopes
2600 Executive Pky., Ste. 140
Salt Lake City, UT 84101
Co. E-mail: privacy@siliconslopes.com
URL: http://siliconslopes.com
Contact: Tim Cook, Chief Executive Officer
Facebook: www.facebook.com/SiliconSlopes
Linkedin: www.linkedin.com/company/silicon-slopes
X (Twitter): x.com/siliconslopes
Instagram: www.instagram.com/siliconslopes
Description: Connects Utah's tech and entrepreneurship community with networking events, podcasts, and conferences. Hosts an annual Tech Summit.
Founded: 2006.

18822 ■ Silicon Slopes - Brigham City
Brigham City, UT
URL: http://community.siliconslopes.com/brigham-city
Contact: Beau Lewis, Chairman
Description: Connects Utah's tech and entrepreneurship community with networking events, podcasts, and conferences.

18823 ■ Silicon Slopes - Cedar City
Cedar City, UT
URL: http://siliconslopes.com/cedar-city
Contact: Tenia Wallace, Chairman
Description: Connects Utah's tech and entrepreneurship community with networking events, podcasts, and conferences.

18824 ■ Silicon Slopes - Central Utah
2600 Executive Pky., Ste. 140
Salt Lake City, UT 84101
URL: http://newsroom.siliconslopes.com/magazine/ephraim-crossing-magnifies-central-utahs-commitment-to-the-tech-industry
Contact: Steve Starks, President
Description: Connects Utah's tech and entrepreneurship community with networking events, podcasts, and conferences. Focuses on connecting the rural and tech communities.

18825 ■ Silicon Slopes - Farmington
Farmington, UT

URL: http://community.siliconslopes.com/farmington/#:~:text=The%20Silicon%20Slopes%20Ogden%2DFarmington,%2C%20and%20high%2Dgrowth%20companies
Contact: Ben Rollins, Contact
Description: Connects Utah's tech and entrepreneurship community with networking events, podcasts, and conferences.

18826 ■ Silicon Slopes - Heber Valley
Heber Valley, UT
URL: http://community.siliconslopes.com/heber-city
Contact: Ryan Starks, Chairman
Description: Connects Utah's tech and entrepreneurship community with networking events, podcasts, and conferences.

18827 ■ Silicon Slopes - Logan
Logan, UT
URL: http://www.siliconslopes.com
Description: Connects Utah's tech and entrepreneurship community with networking events, podcasts, and conferences.

18828 ■ Silicon Slopes - Ogden
Ogden, UT
URL: http://community.siliconslopes.com/ogden
Contact: Alex Lawrence, Assistant Professor
Description: Connects Utah's tech and entrepreneurship community with networking events, podcasts, and conferences.

18829 ■ Silicon Slopes - Park City
Park City, UT
URL: http://community.siliconslopes.com/park-city
Contact: Adrian Stalder, Founder
Description: Connects Utah's tech and entrepreneurship community with networking events, podcasts, and conferences.

18830 ■ Silicon Slopes - Price
2600 W Executive Pky., Ste., 140
Lehi, UT 84043
Contact: Trisha Thomas, President
Description: Connects Utah's tech and entrepreneurship community with networking events, podcasts, and conferences.

18831 ■ Silicon Slopes - St. George
Saint George, UT
URL: http://community.siliconslopes.com/st-george
Contact: Shirlayne Quayle, Contact
X (Twitter): twitter.com/siliconslopesS
Description: Connects Utah's tech and entrepreneurship community with networking events, podcasts, and conferences.

18832 ■ Silicon Slopes - Salt Lake City
Salt Lake City, UT
URL: http://community.siliconslopes.com/salt-lake-city
Contact: Blake McClary, Chairman
Description: Connects Utah's tech and entrepreneurship community with networking events, podcasts, and conferences.

18833 ■ Silicon Slopes - Sandy
Sandy, UT
URL: http://www.siliconslopes.com
Description: Connects Utah's tech and entrepreneurship community with networking events, podcasts, and conferences.

18834 ■ Silicon Slopes - Vernal
Vernal, UT 84078
URL: http://jobs.siliconslopes.com/company/20250/lifepoint-health
Description: Connects Utah's tech and entrepreneurship community with networking events, podcasts, and conferences.

18835 ■ Small Giants Community (SGC)
482 Dunston Ct.
Bloomfield Hills, MI 48304
Ph: (313)444-0348
Co. E-mail: hello@smallgiants.org
URL: http://smallgiants.org
Contact: Hamsa Daher, Executive Director

GENERAL SMALL BUSINESS TOPICS

Linkedin: www.linkedin.com/company/small-giants-community
X (Twitter): x.com/smallgiantsbuzz
YouTube: www.youtube.com/channel/UCh6uYy8aUCx6cSKMQ0I-gug
Description: Supports entrepreneurs around the world by providing resources, events, mentorship, and networking to enhance and develop their businesses. **Founded:** 2009.

REFERENCE WORKS

18836 ▪ *"4 Small Business Groups You Can Join for Free"* in Nav (February 22, 2017)
Released: February 22, 2017. **Description:** Business networking groups are a great way to meet advisors and mentors who can help during the journey, as well as to find new professional connections, opportunities and ideas. This article lists for organizations with free services for small businesses that can help no matter where members are on the path to entrepreneurship. **Availability:** Online.

18837 ▪ *"5 Tips for Better Small Business Networking"* in The Balance Small Business (October 17, 2018)
Ed: Alyssa Gregory. **Released:** October 17, 2018. **Description:** Discusses the importance of business networking and how it can aid in growing your customer base and generate referrals in addition to providing numerous opportunities for learning, development, and growth. **Availability:** Online.

18838 ▪ *"The 5 Types of Business Networking Organizations"* in Entrepreneur (November 1, 2017)
Ed: Ivan Misner. **Released:** November 01, 2017. **Description:** Discusses the five main types of business networking groups and what can work best for you. **Availability:** Online.

18839 ▪ *"6 Top-Ranked Business Networking Groups on the Web"* in GoDaddy (January 30, 2018)
Ed: Ariana Crisafulli. **Released:** January 30, 2018. **Description:** The benefits of joining business networking groups include the chance to learn from experts, to be part of a support community of like-minded peers, to forge partnerships, and, especially if you're a B2B business, find leads. This article lists great online groups where you can start making connections. **Availability:** Online.

18840 ▪ *"The 7 Best Small Business Groups for Networking"* in insureon Small Business Blog (December 7, 2016)
Ed: Meredith Wood. **Released:** December 07, 2016. **Description:** Discusses the importance that relationships and partnerships with the right people have on business growth. This article provides seven of the top small business groups for networking. **Availability:** Online.

18841 ▪ *"7 Useful Ways to Successfully Network with Other Small Businesses"* in Fundera (July 30, 2020)
Ed: Emily Kate Pope. **Released:** July 30, 2020. **Description:** Discusses the importance of networking as a way to generate business leads in the way of a new partner, a future project, or a new customer. Networking is also a good way to stay up-to-date on the latest trends in your industry. **Availability:** Online.

18842 ▪ *"9 Best Business Networking Groups for New Businesses"* in Next Insurance website (Sept. 16, 2020)
URL(s): www.nextinsurance.com/blog/best-business-networking-groups/
Released: September 16, 2020. **Description:** Explores how to build a professional network by utilizing small business networking groups to bridge the gap. Provides a list of nine of the best networking organizations for small business owners. **Availability:** Online.

18843 ▪ *"10 Small-Business Networking Tools and Vendors to Watch in 2020"* in CRN Magazine (January 20, 2020)
Ed: Gina Narcisi. **Released:** January 20, 2020. **Description:** Discusses ten small business networking vendors and their portfolio SMB-focused hardware and software-based products and services that solutions providers should look at. **Availability:** Online.

18844 ▪ *"11 Tips for Successful Business Networking"* in ZenBusiness Blog (Aug. 11, 2021)
URL(s): www.zenbusiness.com/blog/networking/
Ed: April Maguire. **Released:** August 11, 2021. **Description:** Discusses the benefits of building a strong business network and provides 11 tips to help you build relationships that bring in business. **Availability:** Online.

18845 ▪ *"12 Business Networking Tips"* in Business 2 Community (Jan. 27, 2021)
URL(s): www.business2community.com/communications/12-business-networking-tips-02382669
Ed: Alaina Brandenburger. **Released:** January 27, 2021. **Description:** Explores reasons why small business owners should value networking as a marketing tool and provides tips on how to network effectively. **Availability:** Online.

18846 ▪ *"20 Important LinkedIn Groups for Business"* in Small Business Trends (May 19, 2014)
Ed: Mark O'Neill. **Released:** May 19, 2014. **Description:** Provides information on a variety of LinkedIn Groups that small businesses may join to connect with fellow small business professionals. **Availability:** Online.

18847 ▪ *"25 LinkedIn Groups Every Entrepreneur Should Belong To"* in Business News Daily (Nov. 18, 2021)
URL(s): www.businessnewsdaily.com/7185-entrepreneur-linkedin-groups.html
Ed: Julianna Lopez. **Released:** November 18, 2021. **Description:** Provides a list of 25 LinkedIn groups that can be invaluable resources for entrepreneurs. **Availability:** Online.

18848 ▪ *"Build Your Business Through Networking"* in U.S. Small Business Administration website (Nov. 16, 2018)
URL(s): www.sba.gov/blog/build-your-business-through-networking
Ed: Rieva Lesonsksy. **Released:** November 16, 2018. **Description:** Discusses the continued effectiveness and importance of social networking for your small business. Explores how to set networking goals and strategies. **Availability:** Online.

18849 ▪ *"Joining Business Organizing and Networking Groups"* in The Balance Small Business (July 28, 2019)
Ed: Susan Ward. **Released:** July 28, 2019. **Description:** The best way to increase name recognition and overall success for your business is to join business organizations and face-to-face business networking groups, allowing you to interact with like-minded people who can be invaluable sources of information and support. This article discusses types of networking groups and costs to join. **Availability:** Online.

18850 ▪ *"Networking Groups You Should Join to Grow Your Business"* in InvoiceBerry Blog (July 3, 2018)
Released: July 03, 2018. **Description:** Networking groups gather like-minded individuals who hope to propel their business forward by cultivating new relationships. This article provides a list of networking essentials for small businesses. **Availability:** Online.

18851 ▪ *Networking: The Cheapest Way to Grow Your Small Business*
URL(s): paysimple.com/blog/networking-the-cheapest-way-to-grow-your-small-business/

Description: Discusses why people like to support local business and provides ten tips to help you network your small business within your community. **Availability:** Online.

18852 ▪ *"There's a New Strategy for Networking in the Digital Age"* in Entrepreneur (Jan. 22, 2022)
URL(s): www.entrepreneur.com/article/404234
Ed: Tim Madden. **Released:** January 22, 2022. **Description:** While digital networking creates ample opportunity to connect with a wide pool, it also brings in a new set of networking etiquette and methods. This article brings forth basic principles to keep in mind when navigating networking your small business in the digital age. **Availability:** Online.

18853 ▪ *"What Is Business Networking?"* in The Balance Small Business (Jan. 17, 2021)
URL(s): www.thebalancesmb.com/what-is-business-networking-and-what-are-the-benefits-2947183
Ed: Susan Ward. **Released:** January 17, 2021. **Description:** Explores what business networking is, how it works, the benefits of it, and types of business networking. **Availability:** Online.

18854 ▪ *Why Networking Is Important for Small Business*
URL(s): www.olympiabenefits.com/blog/why-networking-is-important-for-small-business
Released: July 08, 2021. **Description:** Provides key reasons that clearly outline why networking is important for small business. **Availability:** Online.

VIDEO/AUDIO MEDIA

18855 ▪ *How I Built This: Advice Line with Brett Schulman of CAVA*
URL(s): wondery.com/shows/how-i-built-this/episode/10386-advice-line-with-brett-schulman-of-cava
Ed: Guy Raz. **Released:** July 04, 2024. **Description:** Podcast answers questions from early-stage founders experiencing growing pains as they scale their businesses.

PUBLICATIONS

18856 ▪ *Handbook of Research on Business Social Networking: Organizational, Managerial, and Technological Dimensions*
701 E Chocolate Ave.
  Hershey, PA 17033
Ph: (717)533-8845
Free: 866-342-6657
Fax: (717)533-8661
Co. E-mail: cust@igi-global.com
URL: http://www.igi-global.com
Contact: Jan Travers, Director
URL(s): www.igi-global.com/book/handbook-research-business-social-networking/52733
Released: Release Date: October, 2011. **Price:** $595, for hardcover + e-book; $37.50, for on demand (individual chapters); $495, for e-book and hardcover. **Description:** Published by IGI Global. Investigates the beginning of social networks and provides perspectives on how they can enhance business, covering discussions on the main issues, challenges, opportunities, and trends related to the range of new developments and applications in business social networking. **Availability:** E-book; Print; PDF.

18857 ▪ *Virginia Law and Business Review*
580 Massie Rd.
  Charlottesville, VA 22903
Ph: (785)864-4530
Free: 888-577-5268
Co. E-mail: comm@law.virginia.edu
URL: http://www.law.virginia.edu
URL(s): www.vlbr.org
Linkedin: www.linkedin.com/company/virginia-law-business-review
Released: 3/year **Price:** $90, Individuals; $90, Institutions. **Availability:** Print; Online.

Business Planning

INTERNATIONAL TRADE ADMINISTRATION

18858 ■ *Datasets at the Library of Congress: A Research Guide*
URL(s): guides.loc.gov/datasets/repositories
Description: Provides links to online resources on a variety of topics and subjects, which include business and management, computer science, technology, and more. **Availability:** Online.

START-UP INFORMATION

18859 ■ *Become Your Own Boss in 12 Months: A Month-by-Month Guide to a Business that Works*
Ed: Melinda F. Emerson. **Released:** Second edition. **Price:** $16.99, paperback; $19.99, audio download; $12.99, e-book. **Description:** Realistic planning guide to help would-be entrepreneurs transition from working for someone else to working for themselves is given. The key to successfully starting a new company lies in thoughtful preparation at least a year and a half before quitting a job. **Availability:** E-book; Print; Download.

18860 ■ *EBay Income: How ANYONE of Any Age, Location, and/or Background Can Build a Highly Profitable Online Business with eBay*
Pub: Atlantic Publishing Co.
Contact: Dr. Heather L. Johnson, Contact
Description: A complete overview of eBay is given and guides any small company through the entire process of creating the auction and auction strategies, photography, writing copy, text and formatting, multiple sales, programming tricks, PayPal, accounting, creating marketing, merchandising, managing email lists, advertising plans, taxes and sales tax, best time to list items and for how long, sniping programs, international customers, opening a storefront, electronic commerce, buy-it now pricing, keywords, Google marketing and eBay secrets.

18861 ■ *Entrepreneurship*
Pub: John Wiley & Sons, Inc.
Contact: Christina Van Tassell, Executive Vice President Chief Financial Officer
Ed: William D. Bygrave, Andrew Zacharakis. **Released:** Fourth edition. **Price:** $75.95, paperback. **Description:** Information for starting a new business is shared, focusing on marketing and financing a product or service. **Availability:** Print.

18862 ■ *"Faces: Q&A With Katie Johnson, Co-Owner of Bloomy's Roast Beef Food Truck" in Saint Paul Pioneer Press (June 13, 2012)*
Ed: Kathie Jenkins. **Description:** Profile of Katie Johnson, 29 year old co-owner of Bloomy's Roast Beef food truck. Johnson discusses how her and her friend Ryan planned and started their food truck business and why they chose roast beef for their menu. **Availability:** Print; Online.

18863 ■ *"Follow the Numbers: It's the Best Way To Spot Problems Before They Become Life-Threatening" in Inc. (January 2008, pp. 63-64)*
Ed: Norm Brodsky. **Description:** It is important for any small business to track monthly sales and gross margins by hand for the first year or two. When writing the numbers, be sure to break them out by product category or service type and by customer. **Availability:** Online.

18864 ■ *"The Food Truck Handbook: Start, Grow, and Succeed in the Mobile Food Business"*
Pub: John Wiley & Sons, Inc.
Contact: Christina Van Tassell, Executive Vice President Chief Financial Officer
Released: March 2012. **Price:** $19.95, paperback; $12.99, e-book. **Description:** Food truck businesses have grown so much in popularity, there are actually food truck competitions and was once a television show featuring them. A practical, step-by-step handbook is offered to help an entrepreneur start a mobile food delivery service. Information includes tips on choosing vending locations, opening and closing checklists; creation of a business plan with budget and finding vendor services, daily operation issues; common operating mistakes; and insight into delivery high quality food. **Availability:** E-book; Print.

18865 ■ *Going Solo: Developing a Home-Based Consulting Business from the Ground Up*
Description: Ways to turn specialized knowledge into a home-based successful consulting firm, focusing on targeting client needs, business plans, and growth.

18866 ■ *"Making 'Freemium' Work: Many Start-Ups Fail to Recognize the Challenges of This Popular Business Model" in Harvard Business Review (Vol. 92, May 2014, No. 5, pp. 27)*
Pub: Harvard Business Publishing
Contact: Diane Belcher, Managing Director
Price: $6. **Description:** The key to successful 'freemium' business model is identifying which features to offer free of charge, and how to price the remaining features. Target conversion rates conversion life cycle preparation, and commitment to innovation are also discussed. **Availability:** Online; PDF.

18867 ■ *"The Self Starting Entrepreneurs Handbook"*
Pub: CreateSpace
Released: September 24, 2014. **Price:** $17.99; $11.03, paperback. **Description:** Information for starting a business is provided. Advice is given for writing a business plan, naming your new business, obtaining a business license if required, and building a marketing strategy for entrepreneurs. **Availability:** Print.

18868 ■ *Start and Run a Delicatessen: Small Business Starters Series*
Description: Information for starting and running a successful delicatessen is provided. Insight is offered into selecting a location, researching the market, writing a business plan and more.

18869 ■ *The Toilet Paper Entrepreneur: The Tell-It-Like-It-Is Guide to Cleaning Up In Business, Even If You Are At the End of Your Roll*
Pub: Obsidian Launch L.L.C.
Contact: Kelsey Ayres, President
Ed: Mike Michalowicz. **Description:** The founder of three multimillion-dollar companies, including Obsidian Launch, a company that partners with first-time entrepreneurs to grow their concepts into industry leaders. **Availability:** Print; Online.

ASSOCIATIONS AND OTHER ORGANIZATIONS

18870 ■ **Auto Suppliers Benchmarking Association (ASBA)**
The Benchmarking Network
Houston, TX 77069-9949
Ph: (281)440-5044
URL: http://asbabenchmarking.com
Facebook: www.facebook.com/people/The-Benchmarking-Network/100075504566399
X (Twitter): twitter.com/benchmarkingnet
Description: Promotes the use of benchmarking, wherein businesses compare their processes with those of their competitors, as a means of improving corporate efficiency and profitability among automotive supplier firms; facilitates exchange of information among members; conducts target operations, procurement, development, and maintenance studies; and identifies model business practices. **Founded:** 1996. **Geographic Preference:** National.

18871 ■ **The International Association for Strategy Professionals (ASP)**
411 Richmond St., E, Ste. 200
Toronto, ON, Canada M5A 3S5
Free: 844-345-2828
Fax: (416)929-5256
URL: http://www.strategyassociation.org
Description: Advances thought and practice in strategy development and deployment for business, nonprofit and government organizations. Provides opportunities to explore strategy principles and practices that enhance organizational success and enhance members' and organizations' knowledge, capability and capacity for innovation and professionalism. **Founded:** 1999. **Publications:** *The Strategic Edge* (Monthly). **Awards:** ASP Member of the Year (Annual); Richard Goodman Strategic Planning Award (Annual); ASP Chapter of the Year (An-

GENERAL SMALL BUSINESS TOPICS

nual); Association for Strategic Planning Distinguished Service Award (Annual). **Geographic Preference:** National.

EDUCATIONAL PROGRAMS

18872 ■ Business Plan Basics
URL(s): cwewbc.ecenterdirect.com/events/977281
Description: This online class offered by the Center for Women and Enterprise discusses how to write a business plan, plus provides resources and support. **Audience:** Women small business owners. **Principal Exhibits:** This online class offered by the Center for Women and Enterprise discusses how to write a business plan, plus provides resources and support.

18873 ■ Design Reviews for Effective Product Development (Onsite)
Seminar Information Service Inc. (SIS)
250 El Camino Real., Ste. 112
Tustin, CA 92780
Ph: (714)508-0340
Free: 877-736-4636
Fax: (714)734-8027
Co. E-mail: info@seminarinformation.com
URL: http://www.seminarinformation.com
Contact: Catherine Bellizzi, President
URL(s): www.seminarinformation.com

Description: Seminar covering how formal design reviews can improve products by uncovering potential problems before they are discovered at a latter stage of development when the costs of correction are much higher, as well as the requirements for successful reviews. **Audience:** Engineers, and product development managers. **Principal Exhibits:** Seminar covering how formal design reviews can improve products by uncovering potential problems before they are discovered at a latter stage of development when the costs of correction are much higher, as well as the requirements for successful reviews.

18874 ■ Disaster Recovery Planning: Ensuring Business Continuity (Onsite)
Learning Tree International Inc.
13650 Dulles Technology Dr., Ste. 400
Herndon, VA 20171-6156
Free: 888-843-8733
Co. E-mail: info@learningtree.com
URL: http://www.learningtree.com
URL(s): http://www.learningtree.com/courses/289/disaster-recovery-planning-ensuring-business-continuity

Description: Create, document, and test continuity arrangements for the organization. This course is valuable for those managing and maintaining the continuity of an organization's critical processes. **Audience:** Project and business managers, help desk personnel and human resources professionals. **Principal Exhibits:** Create, document, and test continuity arrangements for the organization. This course is valuable for those managing and maintaining the continuity of an organization's critical processes.

18875 ■ Maintenance Planning & Scheduling (Onsite)
TPC Trainco Inc.
225 E Robinson St., Ste. 570
Orlando, FL 32801
Free: 877-978-7246
Co. E-mail: sales@tpctraining.com
URL: http://live.tpctraining.com
URL(s): live.tpctraining.com/public-seminars/plant-management/maintenance-planning-and-scheduling

Description: Learn to reduce maintenance costs by better planning with your existing workforce. **Audience:** Maintenance personnel, maintenance managers, purchasing agents, operations managers, plant managers, manufacturing managers, production managers. **Principal Exhibits:** Learn to reduce maintenance costs by better planning with your existing workforce.

18876 ■ Project Management: Skills for Success (Onsite)
Seminar Information Service Inc. (SIS)
250 El Camino Real., Ste. 112
Tustin, CA 92780
Ph: (714)508-0340
Free: 877-736-4636
Fax: (714)734-8027
Co. E-mail: info@seminarinformation.com
URL: http://www.seminarinformation.com
Contact: Catherine Bellizzi, President
URL(s): www.seminarinformation.com/qqaanv/project-management-skills-for-success

Description: Learn how to: Produce a project plan for successful delivery; Plan and run projects using best practices in a 6-step project management process; Implement risk management techniques and mitigation strategies; Estimate and schedule task work and duration with confidence; Implement monitoring tools and controls to keep you fully in command of the project; Recognize and practice the leadership skills needed to run a motivated team. **Audience:** Project managers. **Principal Exhibits:** Learn how to: Produce a project plan for successful delivery; Plan and run projects using best practices in a 6-step project management process; Implement risk management techniques and mitigation strategies; Estimate and schedule task work and duration with confidence; Implement monitoring tools and controls to keep you fully in command of the project; Recognize and practice the leadership skills needed to run a motivated team.

18877 ■ Project Quality Management for Project Managers - Delivering Consistent Quality (Onsite)
Seminar Information Service Inc. (SIS)
250 El Camino Real., Ste. 112
Tustin, CA 92780
Ph: (714)508-0340
Free: 877-736-4636
Fax: (714)734-8027
Co. E-mail: info@seminarinformation.com
URL: http://www.seminarinformation.com
Contact: Catherine Bellizzi, President
URL(s): www.seminarinformation.com

Description: Learn how to: Implement effective project quality management best practices; Apply a proven analysis method to identify stakeholder quality expectations and refine project scope; Leverage an industry standard template to create a project Quality Management Plan (QMP); Generate a quality assurance task list that incorporates project, product and process; Transform quality assurance recommendations into corrective and improvement actions; Design and implement quality control gates throughout the project and product life cycles. **Audience:** Project managers, and professionals. **Principal Exhibits:** Learn how to: Implement effective project quality management best practices; Apply a proven analysis method to identify stakeholder quality expectations and refine project scope; Leverage an industry standard template to create a project Quality Management Plan (QMP); Generate a quality assurance task list that incorporates project, product and process; Transform quality assurance recommendations into corrective and improvement actions; Design and implement quality control gates throughout the project and product life cycles.

REFERENCE WORKS

18878 ■ "The 4 Hottest Industries to Start a Businesses in for 2020" in Bplans
Ed: Nina Bamberger. **Description:** Discusses four industries that show the most promise for business startups in 2020: transportation, technology, health and medical, and green products and services. **Availability:** Online.

18879 ■ "5 Steps for Writing an Executive Summary" in Business News Daily (February 21, 2023)
URL(s): www.businessnewsdaily.com/15814-write-an-executive-summary.html

Ed: Skye Schooley. **Released:** February 21, 2023. **Description:** Formal business plans require an executive summary, but what exactly does that entail? This article defines and discusses these types of summaries. **Availability:** Online.

18880 ■ "113D Filings: Investors Report to the SEC" in Barron's (Vol. 88, March 24, 2008, No. 12, pp. M13)
Pub: Dow Jones & Company Inc.
Contact: Almar Latour, Chief Executive Officer

Released: April 02, 2016. **Description:** HealthCor Management called as problematic the plan of Magellan Health Services to use its high cash balances for acquisitions. Carlson Capital discussed with Energy Partners possible changes in the latter's board. Investor Carl Icahn suggested that Enzon Pharmaceuticals consider selling itself or divest some of its assets. **Availability:** Print; Online.

18881 ■ 16-Step Legal Checklist for Startups and Small Businesses
URL(s): lydagroup.com/blog/startups-checklist/

Released: July 19, 2021. **Description:** Provides a 16-step legal checklist for startups and small businesses. Covers pre-planning, goal setting, writing a mission statement, defining liabilities, and drafting legal contracts. **Availability:** Online.

18882 ■ "67 Creative and Effective Ways to Get Students to Register for Dance Class" in DanceStudioOwner
URL(s): www.dancestudioowner.com/public/67_Ways_Register_for_Class.cfm

Description: A list of ideas for small dance studio owners to use to get students to sign up for dance classes. **Availability:** Online.

18883 ■ 101 Internet Businesses You Can Start from Home: How to Choose and Build Your Own Successful E-Business
Pub: Maximum Press

Ed: Susan Sweeney. **Released:** Third edition. **Description:** Guide for starting and growing an Internet business; information for developing a business plan, risk levels, and promotional techniques are included.

18884 ■ "Aeronautics Seeking New HQ Site" in The Business Journal-Milwaukee (Vol. 25, September 5, 2008, No. 50, pp. 1)

Description: Milwaukee, Wisconsin-based Aeronautics Corp. of America is planning to move its headquarters to a new site. The company has started to search for a new site. It also plans to consolidate its operations under one roof.

18885 ■ "The Agency Model Is Bent But Not Broken" in Advertising Age (Vol. 79, July 7, 2008, No. 26, pp. 17)
Pub: Crain Communications, Inc.
Contact: Jessica Botos, Manager, Marketing
E-mail: jessica.botos@crainsnewyork.com

Ed: Stephen Fajen. **Description:** In the new-media environment, advertising agencies must change the way in which they do business and receive payment. **Availability:** Online.

18886 ■ "The Agency-Selection Process Needs Fixing Now" in Advertising Age (Vol. 79, July 7, 2008, No. 26, pp. 18)
Pub: Crain Communications, Inc.
Contact: Jessica Botos, Manager, Marketing
E-mail: jessica.botos@crainsnewyork.com

Ed: Avi Dan. **Description:** Marketers are facing increased challenges in this sagging economic climate and must realize the importance of choosing the correct advertising agency for their company in order to benefit from a more-stable relationship that yields better business results. Advice for marketers regarding the best way to choose an agency is included. **Availability:** Online.

18887 ■ *"Air Canada to Slash 600 Non-Union Jobs"* in *Globe & Mail (February 11, 2006, pp. B3)*
Ed: Brent Jang. **Description:** The reasons behind workforce reduction by ACE Aviation Holdings Inc. at Air Canada are presented. **Availability:** Online.

18888 ■ *"All Fired Up!"* in *Small Business Opportunities (November 2008)*
Description: Profile of Brixx Wood Fired Pizza, which has launched a franchising program due to the amount of interest the company's founders received over the years; franchisees do not need experience in the food industry or pizza restaurant service business in order to open a franchise of their own because all franchisees receive comprehensive training in which they are educated on all of the necessary tools to effectively run the business. **Availability:** Print; Online.

18889 ■ *"Are You Ready for a Transformation?"* in *Women Entrepreneur (November 28, 2008)*
Description: Marlene J. Waldock, an expert in women's empowerment and reinvention, discusses brand modification and what a business owner should consider before attempting to change or modify their brand. **Availability:** Online.

18890 ■ *"Are Your Goals Hitting the Right Target?"* in *Business Strategy Review (Vol. 21, Autumn 2010, No. 3, pp. 46)*
Ed: Alan Meekings, Steve Briault, Andy Neely. **Description:** Setting targets is normal in most organizations. The authors think such a practice can cause more harm than good. They offer a better plan. **Availability:** Download; PDF; Online.

18891 ■ *"Automaker Foundations Run Leaner"* in *Crain's Detroit Business (Vol. 26, January 11, 2010, No. 2, pp. 1)*
Pub: Crain Communications Inc.
Contact: Barry Asin, President
Ed: Sherri Welch. **Description:** Overview of the Detroit automobile industry includes restoring profitability, smarter marketing strategies and philanthropy. Each company comprising the Big 3 is examined, as is their vision for the future. **Availability:** Print; Online.

18892 ■ *"Avoid These 5 Common Business Plan Mistakes"* in *Legal Zoom (March 21, 2023)*
URL(s): www.legalzoom.com/articles/avoid-these-5-common-business-plan-mistakes
Ed: Jane Haskins, Esq. **Released:** March 21, 2023. **Description:** Discusses some pitfalls when small business owners face when writing up their official business plans. **Availability:** Online.

18893 ■ *"Avoid the Traps That Can Destroy Family Businesses: An Emerging Set of Best Practices Can Turn the Age-Old Problem of Generational Succession Into an Opportunity To Thrive"* in *Harvard Business Review (Vol. 90, January-February 2012, No.1, pp. 25)*
Pub: Harvard Business Review Press
Contact: Moderna V. Pfizer, Contact
Ed: George Stalk, Henry Foley. **Price:** $6, hardcopy black and white. **Description:** Tips to efffective succession planning in family-owned businesses include proper screening and training for family members, managing family-member entry with company growth, and appointing non-family mentors to provide cross training. **Availability:** Print; PDF; Online.

18894 ■ *"Back in the Race. New Fund Manager Has Whipped Sentinel International Equity Back into Shape"* in *Barron's (Vol. 88, March 17, 2008, No. 11, pp. 43)*
Pub: Dow Jones & Company Inc.
Contact: Almar Latour, Chief Executive Officer
Ed: Leslie P. Norton. **Description:** Katherine Schapiro was able to get Sentinel International Equity's Morningstar classification to blended fund from a value fund rating after joining Sentinel from her former jobs at Strong Overseas Fund. Schapiro aims to benefit from the global rebalancing as the U.S.'s share of the world economy shrinks. **Availability:** Online.

18895 ■ *"Baltimore-Area Businesses Still on the Mend 10 Years After 9/11"* in *Baltimore Business Journal (Vol. 29, September 9, 2011, No. 18, pp. 1)*
Pub: Boston Business Journal
Contact: Carolyn M. Jones, President
E-mail: cmjones@bizjournals.com
Ed: Scott Dance. **Description:** The 9/11 terrorist attacks have caused many companies in the US to dramatically shift course in response to changes in the economy. The concern that the cost of being unprepared for future disasters could be larger has remained among many companies. **Availability:** Online.

18896 ■ *"Bank On It: New Year, New Estate Plan"* in *Hawaii Business (Vol. 53, February 2008, No. 8, pp. 54)*
Pub: PacificBasin Communications
Contact: Chuck Tindle, Director
E-mail: chuckt@pacificbasin.net
Ed: Antony M. Orme. **Description:** Discusses the start of the new year which can be a time to revise wills and estate plans as failure to do so may create problems of unequal inheritance and increase in estate tax exemption, which could disinherit beneficiaries. Other circumstances that can prompt changes in wills and estate plans are presented. **Availability:** Print; Online.

18897 ■ *"Bark Up The Right Tree"* in *Small Business Opportunities (Winter 2009)*
Released: February 09, 2016. **Description:** Profile of Central Bark, a daycare company catering to pets that offers franchise opportunities and is expanding rapidly despite the economic downturn; the company's growth strategy is also discussed.

18898 ■ *"Barnes Shakes Up Sara Lee Exec Suite"* in *Crain's Chicago Business (Vol. 31, April 21, 2008, No. 16, pp. 1)*
Pub: Crain Communications Inc.
Contact: Barry Asin, President
Ed: David Sterrett. **Description:** In an attempt to cut costs and boost profits, Sara Lee Corp.'s CEO Brenda Barnes is restructuring the company's management team. **Availability:** Online.

18899 ■ *"BCE Mulls Radical Changes With Industry Under Pressure"* in *Globe & Mail (March 30, 2007, pp. B1)*
Ed: Andrew Willis, Jacquie McNish, Catherine McLean. **Description:** An account on the expansion plans of BCE Inc., which plans to acquire TELUS Corp., is presented. **Availability:** Online.

18900 ■ *"Best of Breed"* in *Barron's (Vol. 92, September 17, 2012, No. 38, pp. 24)*
Description: Private banks are offering financial services outside mutual funds to broadn their product portfolio. This move to open architecture has changed traditional corporate culture in Wall Street and has changed the companies' business models. **Availability:** Print.

18901 ■ *"The Best Option for All"* in *American Executive (Vol. 7, September 2009, No. 5, pp. 170)*
Ed: Ashley McGown. **Description:** Plaza Associates, a collections agency that conducts business primarily in the accounts receivable management sector, is the first in the industry to purchase 100 percent of the company from the founders through the formation of a leveraged Employee Stock Ownership Plan (ESOP).

18902 ■ *"Better Made's Better Idea: Diversify Despite Rising Costs"* in *Crain's Detroit Business (Vol. 24, September 22, 2008, No. 38, pp. 18)*
Pub: Crain Communications Inc.
Contact: Barry Asin, President
Ed: Nathan Skid. **Description:** Better Made Snack Foods Inc. is planning to expand its product lines and market reach as well as boost manufacturing capability during a time in which the company is being buffeted by rising commodity and fuel costs. The company feels that diversification is the key to maintain sales and growth. **Availability:** Online.

18903 ■ *"A Big Dream That 'Was Going Nowhere"* in *Globe & Mail (February 4, 2006, pp. B4)*
Description: The reasons behind the decision of Bombardier Inc. to terminate its plans to develop jet airplanes are presented. **Availability:** Online.

18904 ■ *"Blackstone Set to Sell Stake"* in *Globe & Mail (March 17, 2007, pp. B6)*
Description: The plan of Blackstone Group to sell 10 percent of its stake to raise $4 billion and its proposal to go for initial public offering is discussed.

18905 ■ *"Breaking Down Walls - 2 Kinds"* in *Puget Sound Business Journal (Vol. 35, August 22, 2014, No. 18, pp. 9)*
Pub: American City Business Journals, Inc.
Contact: Mike Olivieri, Executive Vice President
Released: Weekly. **Price:** $4, Introductory 4-week offer(Digital & Print). **Description:** Boeing Company's demolition of its office building in Everett, Washington along with its plan to build a new production facility may reduce jobs. Many workers at the manufacturing facility have been replaced by robots. The plant will be used to build the company's new version of the 777 twin engine. **Availability:** Print; Online.

18906 ■ *"Briarcliff Office Building Fills Up Fast"* in *The Business Journal-Serving Metropolitan Kansas City (Vol. 26, Sept. 5, 2008, pp. 1)*
Pub: American City Business Journals, Inc.
Contact: Mike Olivieri, Executive Vice President
Ed: Rob Roberts. **Description:** Prior to its opening the Hilltop Office Building in Kansas City Missouri has attained 80 percent occupancy. FCStone Group Inc.'s plan to move to the building has boosted the facility's occupancy. Description and dimensions of the office building are also provided. **Availability:** Online.

18907 ■ *"Building a Sustainable Business"* developed by the Minnesota Institute for Sustainable Agriculture; published by Sustainable Agriculture Research and Education.
URL(s): www.sare.org/wp-content/uploads/Building-a-Sustainable-Business.pdf
Ed: Gigi DiGiacomo, Robert King, Dale Nordquist. **Description:** A guide to developing a business plan for farms and rural businesses. **Availability:** Online.

18908 ■ *Business Plan Writing Help Center*
URL(s): www.growthink.com/businessplan/help-center
Description: An online resource with links on articles, guides, and templates for writing business plans. **Availability:** Online.

18909 ■ *Business Plans for Dummies*
Pub: John Wiley & Sons, Inc.
Contact: Christina Van Tassell, Executive Vice President Chief Financial Officer
URL(s): www.wiley.com/en-us/Business+Plans+For+Dummies%2C+3rd+Edition-p-9781119866398
Ed: Paul Tiffany, Steven D. Peterson. **Released:** 3rd edition. **Price:** $18, e-book; $29.99, paperback. **Description:** Details on how to create a business plan are in this guide, with updated practices in the business world included in this new edition. **Availability:** E-book; Print.

18910 ■ *Business Plans Handbook*
Pub: Gale, part of Cengage Group
Contact: Paul Gazzolo, General Manager Senior Vice President
URL(s): www.gale.com/intl/ebooks/9780028667638/business-plans-handbook

Price: $421, for print edition. **Description:** Publication includes 24 actual business plans, including executive summaries, market profiles and analyses, product and production information, and management, personnel, and financial data. Appendix includes a sample business plan template; two fictional plans; listings of small business associations, consultants, venture capital/finance companies; SBA and SBDC offices; SCORE offices; small business term glossary; and a cumulative index. **Indexes:** Alphabetical by company type. **Availability:** E-book; Print; PDF.

18911 ■ *Business Plans Kit for Dummies*
Pub: John Wiley & Sons, Inc.
Contact: Christina Van Tassell, Executive Vice President Chief Financial Officer
Ed: Steven D. Peterson, Peter E. Jaret, Barbara Findlay Schenck. **Released:** Fifth edition. **Price:** $34.99, paperback; $22.99, e-book. **Availability:** E-book; Print.

18912 ■ *Business Plans That Work: A Guide for Small Business*
Released: Second Edition. **Description:** Guide for preparing a small business plan along with an analysis of potential business opportunities. **Availability:** Print; Online.

18913 ■ *"Business Succession Planning From an Estate Planner's Perspective"* in *New Jersey Law Review (December 7, 2007)*
Pub: New Jersey Law Journal
Ed: Robert W. Cockren, Elga A. Goodman. **Description:** Ninety percent of American businesses are family-owned. The importance of estate planning for family-owned or controlled firms is covered. **Availability:** Online.

18914 ■ *"Business Tips on Spending Smart in Tough Times"* in *Legal Zoom (March 27, 2023)*
URL(s): www.legalzoom.com/articles/business-tips-on-spending-smart-in-tough-times
Ed: Sherry Ciurczak. **Released:** March 27, 2023. **Description:** The economy is never steady and experiences lows and highs. How do you weather the lean times with a small business? Tips on what to look out for and take advantage of are given. **Availability:** Online.

18915 ■ *"Cadillac Tower Largest to Start in a Decade"* in *Globe & Mail (March 28, 2006, pp. B5)*
Ed: Elizabeth Church. **Description:** The plans of Cadillac Fairview Corporation Ltd. to build office towers, in downtown Canada, are presented. **Availability:** Print; Online.

18916 ■ *"Can You Make a Million Bucks in the House Cleaning Business?"* in *Cleaning Business Today (July 13, 2016)*
Ed: Terry Sambrowski. **Released:** July 13, 2016. **Description:** Discusses seven steps that control the costs that affect gross income potential of your cleaning business. **Availability:** Online.

18917 ■ *"Captain Planet"* in *(Vol. 90, June 2012, No. 6, pp. 112)*
Pub: Harvard Business Review Press
Contact: Moderna V. Pfizer, Contact
Ed: Paul Polman, Adi Ignatius. **Price:** $8.95, hardcopy black and white. **Description:** Paul Polman, chief executive officer of Unilever N.V., discusses his company's sustainable living plan, which integrates social responsibility with corporate objectives. Topics include sustainable sourcing, abolishing quarterly reporting in favor of long-term perspectives, the impact of the 2008 global economic crisis, and turning a company into a learning organization. **Availability:** Print; Online; PDF.

18918 ■ *"Carbon Capture and Storage: Grave Concerns"* in *Canadian Business (Vol. 81, July 21 2008, No. 11, pp. 25)*
Ed: Andrew Nikiforuk. **Released:** January 01, 2017. **Description:** Air pollution control regulations to reduce greenhouse gasses have been implemented by the Canadian government. The federal government is planning to construct a carbon funeral industry that will store the global warming gases, however the expenditure for the project will be shifted to the taxpayers. Details of the Bruce Peachy's initiative on how to reduce GHGs are presented. **Availability:** Print; Online.

18919 ■ *"The Caterer Interview - Patrick Harbour and Nathan Jones"* in *Caterer & Hotelkeeper (October 28, 2011, No. 288)*
Description: Profiles of Patrick Harbour and Nathan Jones who quit their jobs to start their own catering business. The partners discuss their business strategy when launching their boutique catering firm and ways they are adapting to the slow economy in order to remain successful. **Availability:** Print; Mailing list; Online.

18920 ■ *"Centerra Caught in Kyrgyzstan Dispute"* in *Globe & Mail (April 19, 2007, pp. B5)*
Ed: Andy Hoffman. **Description:** The details of the demonstrations carried against government proposal to nationalize Centerra Gold Inc.'s assets are presented. **Availability:** Online.

18921 ■ *The Checklist Manifesto: How to Get Things Right*
Ed: Atul Gawande. **Released:** January 4, 2011. **Price:** $32, hardcover; $16, paperback; $9.99, e-book; $34.99, CD-ROM; $9.99, hardcover(4 Collectible from $9.99); $2.87, hardcover(180 Used from $2.87); $7.76, hardcover(84 New from $7.76); $13.60, Paperback; $3.61, Paperback(191 Used from $3.61); $9.64, Paperback(90 New from $9.64); $8.99, Paperback(3 Collectible from $8.99); $25.09, Audio CD; $15.94, Audio CD; $19.29, Audio CD. **Description:** How tragic errors can be sharply reduced with a piece of paper, hand-drawn boxes, and a pencil. **Availability:** CD-ROM; E-book; Print; Audio.

18922 ■ *"China's ZTE in Hunt for Partners"* in *Globe & Mail (February 27, 2006, pp. B1)*
Ed: Gordon Pitts. **Description:** The business growth plans of ZTE Corp. in Canada, through partnership, are presented. **Availability:** Online.

18923 ■ *"Chip Heath: Get Over Your Fear of Change"* in *Canadian Business (Vol. 83, June 15, 2010, No. 10, pp. 38)*
Pub: Rogers Media Inc.
Contact: Neil Spivak, Chief Executive Officer
Ed: Michelle Magnan. **Description:** Organizational behavior professor Chip Heath says that resistance to change is based on the conflict between our analytical, rational side and our emotional side that is in love with comfort. Heath states that businesses tend to focus on the negatives during an economic crisis while they should be focusing on what is working and ways to do more of that. **Availability:** Print; Online.

18924 ■ *"CIBC Spends $1.1 Billion on Caribbean Expansion"* in *Globe & Mail (March 14, 2006, pp. B1)*
Ed: Sinclair Stewart. **Description:** Canadian Imperial Bank of Commerce (CIBC), the fifth-largest bank of Canada, is planning to spend $1.1billion to buy major share of Barbados-based First Caribbean International Bank. The details of the acquisition plan are presented. **Availability:** Print; Online.

18925 ■ *"Cincinnati Museum Center to Exhibit New Look"* in *Business Courier (Vol. 24, February 21, 2008, No. 46, pp. 1)*
Pub: American City Business Journals, Inc.
Contact: Mike Olivieri, Executive Vice President
Ed: Dan Monk. **Description:** Discusses a $120 million renovation is being planned for the Cincinnati Museum Center complex at Union Terminal. The project aims to build a 14-acre park and office spaces in the area. Details of the Museum Center's renovation plans are given. **Availability:** Online.

18926 ■ *"Citadel Hires Three Lehman Execs"* in *Chicago Tribune (October 2, 2008)*
Description: Citadel Investment Group LLC, Chicago hedge-fund operator, has hired three former senior executives of bankrupt investment banker Lehman Brothers Holding Inc. Citadel believes that the company's hiring spree will help them to further expand the firm's capabilities in the global fixed income business. **Availability:** Online.

18927 ■ *"Cleanup to Polish Plating Company's Bottom Line"* in *Crain's Cleveland Business (Vol. 28, October 29, 2007, No. 43, pp. 4)*
Pub: Crain Communications Inc.
Contact: K. C. Crain, President
Ed: Jay Miller. **Description:** Barker Products Co, a manufacturer of nuts and bolts, is upgrading its aging facility which will allow them to operate at capacity and will save the company several hundred thousand dollars a year in operating costs. The new owners secured a construction loan from the county's new Commercial Redevelopment Fund which will allow them to upgrade the building which was hampered by years of neglect. **Availability:** Online.

18928 ■ *"Companies Must Set Goals for Diversity"* in *Crain's Detroit Business (Vol. 24, April 14, 2008, No. 15, pp. 16)*
Pub: Crain Communications Inc.
Contact: Barry Asin, President
Ed: Laura Weiner. **Description:** Diversity programs should start with a plan that takes into account exactly what the company wants to accomplish; this may include wanting to increase the bottom line with new contracts or wanting a staff that is more innovative in their ideas due to their varied backgrounds. **Availability:** Online.

18929 ■ *"Continuously Monitoring Workers' Comp Can Limit Costs"* in *Crain's Cleveland Business (Vol. 28, October 8, 2007, No. 40, pp. 21)*
Pub: Crain Communications Inc.
Contact: K. C. Crain, President
Ed: Michael Agnoni. **Description:** When operating without a plan for managing its workers' compensation program, a company risks losing money. For most companies workers' compensation insurance premiums are often reduced to an annual budget entry but employers who are actively involved in the management of their programs are more likely to experience reductions in premiums and limit indirect costs associated with claims. **Availability:** Online.

18930 ■ *"Corporate Event Management Best Practices: 2020 Guide"* in *The Bizzabo Blog (January 9, 2020)*
Released: January 09, 2020. **Description:** Details best practices that lead to a strong corporate event management strategy. **Availability:** Online.

18931 ■ *"Creative Cost-Cutting Ideas for Small Businesses"* in *Legal Zoom (March 9, 2023)*
URL(s): www.legalzoom.com/articles/creative-cost-cutting-ideas-for-small-businesses
Ed: Katherine Gustafson. **Released:** March 09, 2023. **Description:** Refer to this list if you are looking to save some of your small business budget. **Availability:** Online.

18932 ■ *"Crucible: A New Will to Win"* in *Harvard Business Review (Vol. 88, September 2010, No. 9, pp. 110)*
Pub: Harvard Business Publishing
Contact: Diane Belcher, Managing Director
Ed: Daniel McGinn. **Price:** $8.95, PDF. **Description:** Importance of succession and contingency planning are emphasized in this account of Rick Hendrick's response to business loss coupled with personal tragedy. Focus and determination in leadership are also discussed. **Availability:** Online; PDF.

18933 ■ *"DaimlerChrysler Bears Down on Smart"* in *Globe & Mail (March 27, 2006, pp. B11)*

Ed: Oliver Suess. **Description:** DaimlerChrysler AG, German automobile industry giant, is planning to cut down its workforce its Smart division. The Chrysler is also planning to stop the production of its four-seater models, to end losses at Smart division. **Availability:** Print; Online.

18934 ■ *"December is National Write a Business Plan Month"* in *Small Business Trends(December 2, 2022)*
URL(s): smallbiztrends.com/2022/12/national-write-a-business-plan-month.html

Ed: Annie Pilon. **Released:** December 02, 2022. **Description:** Tips for writing business plans are given. **Availability:** Online.

18935 ■ *"Deere to Open Technology Center in Germany"* in *Chicago Tribune (September 3, 2008)*

Description: Deere & Co. plans to open a technology and innovation center in Germany; details of the company's expansion plans are discussed. **Availability:** Print; Online.

18936 ■ *"Digital Duplication"* in *Crain's Cleveland Business (Vol. 28, October 1, 2007, No. 39, pp. 3)*
Pub: Crain Communications Inc.
Contact: K. C. Crain, President

Ed: David Bennett. **Description:** Profile of the business plan of eBlueprint Holdings LLC, a reprographics company that found success by converting customers' paper blueprints to an electronic format; the company plans to expand into other geographic markets by acquiring solid reprographics companies and converting their computer systems so that customers' blueprints can be managed electronically. **Availability:** Online.

18937 ■ *"Do You Have A Retirement Parachute?"* in *Barron's (Vol. 88, July 7, 2008, No. 27, pp. 32)*
Pub: Dow Jones & Company Inc.
Contact: Almar Latour, Chief Executive Officer

Ed: Jane White. **Description:** The idea that American companies should emulate the Australian retirement system which implements a forced contribution rate for all employers regarding an adequate retirement plan for their employees is discussed. **Availability:** Online.

18938 ■ *"The Dogs of TSX"* in *Canadian Business (Vol. 81, Summer 2008, No. 9, pp. 77)*

Description: Table showing the one-year stock performance of the ten highest dividend-yielding stocks on the S&P/TSX 60 Composite Index is presented. This technique is similar to the 'Dogs of the Dow' approach. The idea in this investment strategy is to buy equal amounts of stocks from these companies and selling them a year later, and then repeat the process. **Availability:** Online.

18939 ■ *"Don't Quit When The Road Gets Bumpy"* in *Women Entrepreneur (November 25, 2008)*

Description: Discusses techniques four women entrepreneurs are utilizing to keep their businesses successful despite the credit crunch and the economic downturn.

18940 ■ *"Doyle: Domino's New Pizza Seasoned with Straight Talk"* in *Crain's Detroit Business (Vol. 26, January 11, 2010, No. 2, pp. 8)*
Pub: Crain Communications Inc.
Contact: Barry Asin, President

Ed: Nathan Skid. **Description:** Interview with J. Patrick Doyle, the CEO of Domino's Pizza, Inc.; the company has launched a new marketing campaign that focuses on its bold new vision. **Availability:** Online.

18941 ■ *"Dry Cleaners, Seeking New Ways to Survive, Take Inspiration from Restaurants and Retail"* in *Chicago Tribune (March 24, 2017)*
URL(s): www.chicagotribune.com/business/ct-dry-cleaning-industry-washing-up-0326-biz-20170324-story.html

Ed: Becky Yerak. **Released:** March 24, 2017. **Description:** Traditional dry cleaners are closing up shop as more people buy easier to wear clothing and fast fashion that is disposed quickly. However, CD One Price Cleaners is taking an innovative approach by marketing other servies, such as cleaning rugs, making pickup and delivery more convenient, and adapting new environmental credentials. **Availability:** Online.

18942 ■ *"Economic Outlook 2009: In Search of New Tools and Initiatives"* in *Hispanic Business (January-February 2009, pp. 30, 32)*

Ed: Dr. Juan Solana. **Description:** Successful business policies of the past no longer work in this economic climate. New tools and initiatives regarding monetary policy, fiscal policy and a higher multiplier are required to survive the crisis. **Availability:** PDF; Online.

18943 ■ *"The Emperor Strikes Back"* in *Canadian Business (Vol. 80, March 26, 2007, No. 7, pp. 48)*

Description: The financial performance of Fairfax Financial Holdings Ltd. in 2006 is presented. The efforts of chief executive Prem Watsa to lead the company towards growth track are also presented. **Availability:** Online.

18944 ■ *"EnCana Axes Spending on Gas Wells"* in *Globe & Mail (February 16, 2006, pp. B1)*

Ed: Dave Ebner. **Description:** The reasons behind EnCana Corp.'s cost spending measures by $300 million on natural gas wells are presented. The company projects 2 percent cut in gas and oil sales for 2006. **Availability:** Print; Online.

18945 ■ *Entrepreneur Magazine's Ultimate Guide to Buying or Selling a Business*
Released: Fourth edition. **Description:** Proven strategies to evaluate, negotiate, and buy or sell a small business. Franchise and family business succession planning is included.

18946 ■ *"Entrepreneurial Orientation and Firm Performance: The Unique Impact of Innovativeness, Proactiveness, and Risk-taking"* in *Journal of Small Business and Entrepreneurship (Vol. 23, Winter 2010, No. 1)*
Pub: Canadian Council for Small Business and Entrepreneurship
Contact: John MacRitchie, President

Ed: Patrick M. Kreisera, Justin Davis. **Description:** The article develops a theoretical model of the relationship between firm-level entrepreneurship and firm performance. This model is intended to further clarify the consequences of an 'entrepreneurial orientation', paying particular attention to the differential relationship that exists between the three sub-dimensions of entrepreneurial orientation and firm performance. Included in the theoretical model are other important variables (such as organizational structure and environmental characteristics) that may impact the EO-performance relationship. Propositions are developed regarding the various configurations of the sub-dimensions of EO and organizational structure that would be most appropriate in a given environmental context. Future research may also benefit from considering the important role that organizational strategy and life cycle stage play in this model. The implications of this model for both researchers and managers are discussed.

18947 ■ *Entrepreneurship*
Pub: McGraw-Hill Higher Education
Contact: Michael Ryan, President

Ed: Robert D. Hisrich, Michael P. Peters, Dean A. Shepherd. **Released:** 10th edition. **Price:** $169.06, hardcopy. **Description:** Advice is offered to entrepreneurs in formulating, planning, and implementing a business plan. **Availability:** Print.

18948 ■ *Entrepreneurship: A Process Perspective*

Ed: Robert A. Baron, Scott A. Shane. **Released:** 2nd Edition. **Description:** Entrepreneurial process covering team building, finances, business plan, legal issues, marketing, growth and exit strategies. **Availability:** Print.

18949 ■ *"Event Planning Guide 2020"* in *Cvent Blog (August 27, 2019)*

Ed: Madison Layman. **Released:** August 27, 2019. **Description:** A guide that walks through a basic event planning template, what it means to be an event planner, and how event management software can simplify the event planning process. **Availability:** Online.

18950 ■ *"The Event Planning Recipe for Success"* in *Entrepreneur*

Ed: Cheryl Kimball. **Description:** Explains how to get started in the event planning industry. Discusses part-time vs. full-time planning as well as a variety of party types, fundraisers, and product launches. **Availability:** Online.

18951 ■ *"Every Business Needs a Succession Plan: Here's How to Get Started"* in *Legal Zoom (February 13, 2023)*
URL(s): www.legalzoom.com/articles/every-business-needs-a-succession-plan-heres-how-to-get-started

Ed: Michelle Kaminsky. **Released:** February 13, 2023. **Description:** Keep your business running even if you retire by having a succession plan and transitioning it to someone else when the time comes. **Availability:** Online.

18952 ■ *"Executive Decision: Damn the Profit Margins, Sleeman Declares War on Buck-a-Beer Foes"* in *Globe & Mail (January 28, 2006, pp. B3)*

Description: The cost savings plans of chief executive officer John Sleeman of Sleeman Breweries Ltd. are presented. **Availability:** Online.

18953 ■ *"Executive Decision: To Make Inroads Against RIM, Palm Steals Its Strategy"* in *Globe & Mail (March 25, 2006, pp. B3)*

Ed: Simon Avery. **Description:** The Palm Inc., global leader in portable device manufacturing, is looking forward to improve its sales of Palm Treos, a wireless portable device that connects to internet and email. Palm is also planning to build partnerships, under the efficient management of Michael Moskowitz, general manager and vice-president of Palm Inc., with the other companies to increase the sales of its wireless devices.

18954 ■ *"Executive Training"* in *Black Enterprise (Vol. 37, December 2006, No. 5, pp. 70)*

Description: Roy N. Gundy Jr. was preparing to introduce a new strategic plan within his division and understood that his plan may fail if not executed properly. He discusses his experience in the Wharton School's executive education workshop Implementing Strategy, at the University of Pennsylvania and gives tips on putting strategy into action. **Availability:** Print; Online.

18955 ■ *"Expanding Middleby's Food Processing Biz"* in *Crain's Chicago Business (Vol. 31, April 21, 2008, No. 16, pp. 6)*
Pub: Crain Communications Inc.
Contact: Barry Asin, President

Ed: David Sterrett. **Description:** Profile of the executive vice-president of the food processing company, Middleby Corp, whose business plan is to develop new products, begin looking for acquisitions and simplify operations in order to expand the firm. **Availability:** Online.

18956 ■ *"Family Feud: Pawn Shop Empire Stalls with Transition to Second Generation"* in *Billings Gazette (December 19, 2010)*
Pub: The Billings Gazette
Ed: Jan Falstad. **Description:** Profile of Ben L. Brown Sr. and his pawn shop located in Billings, Montana is presented. Brown discusses his plan to transition his business to his children. **Availability:** Print; Online.

18957 ■ *"A Flood of New Construction: Will You Tap into the $400B Seawall Pipeline?"* in *ConstructionDive (October 16, 2019)*
URL(s): www.constructiondive.com/news/a-flood-of-new-construction-will-you-tap-into-the-400b-seawall-pipeline/565083/
Ed: Jean Goodman. **Released:** October 16, 2019. **Description:** With rising sea levels, many U.S. communities are bidding out new seawall projects, which is projected to produce a construction boom. It's being advised for construction firms to start planning now to get into these projects and to start bidding on the work. **Availability:** Online.

18958 ■ *"Formulating Policy With a Parallel Organization"* in *Strategy & Leadership (Vol. 38, September-October 2010, No. 5, pp. 33-38)*
Pub: Emerald Inc.
Ed: Dale E. Zand, Thomas F. Hawk. **Description:** A study analyzes a case to examine the parallel organization concept and its successful implementation by a CEO to integrate independent divisions of a firm. Findings reveal that the implementation of the parallel organization improved the policy formulation, strategic planning profitability of the firm while also better integrating its independent divisions.

18959 ■ *"Founding Family Acquires Airport Marriott"* in *Crain's Cleveland Business (Vol. 28, November 5, 2007, No. 44, pp. 3)*
Pub: Crain Communications Inc.
Contact: K. C. Crain, President
Ed: Stan Bullard. **Description:** Big River Real Estate LLC, part of the Marriott family's investment fund, is the new owner of the Cleveland Airport Marriott; renovations estimated at about $11 million will ensure that the hotel meets Marriott's standards. **Availability:** Online.

18960 ■ *"From Craft Biz To Wholesale Giant"* in *Women Entrepreneur (January 19, 2009)*
Description: Advice is given on how to turn a small craft business into a full-time venture; tips to help one transition from a part-time designer to a full-time wholesaler and brand are also included.

18961 ■ *"Game On: When Work Becomes Play"* in *Canadian Business (Vol. 80, February 12, 2007, No. 4, pp. 15)*
Description: The plan of president of TransGaming Vikas Gupta to create innovative software programs for games that can be played in different operating systems is discussed. **Availability:** Online.

18962 ■ *"Game Plan: The Business of Bingo"* in *Canadian Business (Vol. 79, September 11, 2006, No. 18, pp. 50)*
Ed: Joe Castaldo. **Released:** September 08, 2016. **Description:** Strategies adopted by gaming companies to revitalize their business and give a stimulus to their falling resources are presented. **Availability:** Print; Online.

18963 ■ *"Get Off The Rollercoaster"* in *Michigan Vue (Vol. 13, July-August 2008, No. 4, pp. 19)*
Description: Benefits of creating and implementing a solid financial plan during these rocky economic times are examined. Things to keep in mind before meeting with a financial planner include risk assessments, investment goals, the length of time required to meet those goals and the amount of money one has available to invest. **Availability:** Print; Online.

18964 ■ *"Great Canadian's President Folds His Cards"* in *Globe & Mail (February 21, 2006, pp. B4)*
Ed: Peter Kennedy. **Description:** The reasons behind the resignation of Anthony Martin as president of Great Canadian Gaming Corp. are presented. **Availability:** Print; Online.

18965 ■ *"'Groundhog Day' B&B Likely Will Be Converted Into One In Real Life"* in *Chicago Tribune (October 21, 2008)*
Pub: Tribune News Service
Contact: Jack Barry, Vice President, Operations
E-mail: jbarry@tribpub.com
Ed: Carolyn Starks. **Description:** Everton Martin and Karla Stewart Martin have purchased the Victorian house that was featured as a bed-and-breakfast in the 1993 hit move "Groundhog Day"; the couple was initially unaware of the structure's celebrity status when they purchased it with the hope of fulfilling their dream of owning a bed-and-breakfast. **Availability:** Print; Online.

18966 ■ *"A Growing Dilemma"* in *Crain's Cleveland Business (Vol. 28, October 8, 2007, No. 40, pp. 19)*
Pub: Crain Communications Inc.
Contact: K. C. Crain, President
Ed: Kimberly Bonvissuto. **Description:** Discusses small business owners who often have to grapple with the decision on whether or not to expand their operations and the importance of a business plan which may help owners with that decision. **Availability:** Online.

18967 ■ *"Handleman Liquidation Leaves Questions For Shareholders"* in *Crain's Detroit Business (Vol. 24, October 6, 2008, No. 40, pp. 4)*
Pub: Crain Communications Inc.
Contact: Barry Asin, President
Ed: Nancy Kaffer. **Description:** Discusses Handleman Co., a Troy-based music distribution company, and their plan of liquidation and dissolution as well as how shareholders will be affected by the company's plan. Handleman filed its plan to liquidate and dissolve assets with the Securities and Exchange Commission in mid-August, following several quarters of dismal earnings. **Availability:** Online.

18968 ■ *"Has Microsoft Found a Way to Get at Yahoo?"* in *Advertising Age (Vol. 79, July 7, 2008, No. 26, pp. 4)*
Pub: Crain Communications, Inc.
Contact: Jessica Botos, Manager, Marketing
E-mail: jessica.botos@crainsnewyork.com
Ed: Abbey Klaassen. **Description:** Microsoft's attempt to acquire Yahoo's search business is discussed as is Yahoo's plans for the future at a time when the company's shares have fallen dangerously low. **Availability:** Print; Online.

18969 ■ *"High Energy: Gaurdie Banister Joins Aera As President and CEO"* in *Black Enterprise (Vol. 38, July 2008, No. 12, pp. 30)*
Pub: Earl G. Graves Ltd.
Contact: Earl Graves, Jr., President
Ed: Brenda Porter. **Description:** Gaurdie Banister Jr. has been appointed president and CEO of Aera Energy L.L.C., becoming one of the first African Americans in the nation to run a major energy corporation. His plans for the firm include utilizing new, sophisticated technologies in order to unlock the 3-1/2 billion barrels of resources the company has on their books in a safe and environmentally friendly way. He also hopes to increase production and maintain cost leadership.

18970 ■ *"Higher Freight Rates Keep CPR Rolling in Profit"* in *Globe & Mail (February 1, 2006, pp. B3)*
Description: Canadian Pacific Railway Ltd. posted $135.4 million in revenues for fourth quarter 2005. The company's earnings projections for 2006 and workforce reduction plans are presented. **Availability:** Print; Online.

18971 ■ *"Hit the Green: Golf Technology"* in *Canadian Business (Vol. 79, August 14, 2006, No. 16-17, pp. 73)*
Pub: Rogers Media Inc.
Contact: Neil Spivak, Chief Executive Officer
Ed: Andrew Wahl. **Description:** Reorganization of the bankrupt 4everSports golf company in the United States is discussed. **Availability:** Print; Online.

18972 ■ *How to Build a Business Others Want to Buy*
Pub: John Wiley & Sons, Inc.
Contact: Christina Van Tassell, Executive Vice President Chief Financial Officer
URL(s): www.wiley.com/en-us/How+to+Build+a+Business+Others+Want+to+Buy-p-9781394194605
Ed: Kobi Simmat. **Released:** September 2023. **Price:** $19.05, paperback. **Description:** Outlines how to build a profitable business that is attractive to external buyers. **Availability:** Print.

18973 ■ *"How to Choose Board Members for Your Company"* in *Legal Zoom (March 27, 2023)*
URL(s): www.legalzoom.com/articles/how-to-choose-board-members-for-your-company
Ed: Heleigh Bostwick. **Released:** March 27, 2023. **Description:** Depending on your corporate setup, you may need to choose board members in order to remain compliant. Gives advice on how to proceed with approaching people to be on your board and what it entails. **Availability:** Online.

18974 ■ *"How Contractors Can Survive a Downturn"* in *ConstructionDive (October 21, 2019)*
URL(s): www.constructiondive.com/news/how-contractors-can-survive-a-downturn/565058/
Ed: Kim Slowey. **Released:** October 21, 2019. **Description:** Even though there is a huge construction boom happening, recessions are bound to happen and the construction industry always slows down as a result. Managing cash flow is one of several tips to get contractors and small construction companies from folding. **Availability:** Online.

18975 ■ *"How to Create an Auto Repair Shop Business Plan"* in *The Bottom Line (January 9, 2020)*
Ed: Sonya Stinson. **Released:** January 09, 2020. **Description:** Discusses the importance of a business plan and how to structure it for your auto repair business. Shows the difference between lean and traditional business plans. Also includes information on auto repair business loans. **Availability:** Online.

18976 ■ *"How to Find the Perfect Business Name"* in *Business News Daily (March 17, 2023)*
URL(s): www.businessnewsdaily.com/8829-choosing-business-name.html
Ed: Skye Schooley. **Released:** March 17, 2023. **Description:** The name of your small business is a crucial element for future success and branding. If you are having trouble finding a suitable name, this article will assist you. **Availability:** Online.

18977 ■ *"How I Did It: Xerox's Former CEO On Why Succession Shouldn't Be a Horse Race"* in *Harvard Business Review (Vol. 88, October 2010, No. 10, pp. 47)*
Pub: Harvard Business Publishing
Contact: Diane Belcher, Managing Director
Ed: Anne Mulcahy. **Price:** $8.95, PDF. **Description:** The importance of beginning talks between chief executive officers and boards of directors as early as possible to ensure a smooth transition is stressed. This can also prevent turning successions into competitions, with the resultant loss of talent when other candidates 'lose'. **Availability:** Online; PDF.

18978 ■ *"How to Keep Your Sales from Running Out of Gas"* in *Agency Sales Magazine (Vol. 39, July 2009, No. 7, pp. 30)*
Description: Salespeople can let the good times deceive them into thinking that success will go on forever. Salespeople and businesses should see prospecting as a strategy for creating a continuing flow of business. **Availability:** Online.

18979 ■ *How to Make Big Money in Your Own Small Business: Unexpected Rules Every Small Business Owner Needs to Know*
Ed: Jeffrey J. Fox, Jeffrey J. Fox. **Released:** May 12, 2004. **Price:** $16.95; C$24.95; $16.95; C$24.95; $16.95; C$24.95. **Description:** Former sales and marketing pro offers advice on growing a small business. **Availability:** Print.

18980 ■ *"How to Make Business Plans during Unpredictable Times" in Legal Zoom (February 22, 2023)*
URL(s): www.legalzoom.com/articles/how-to-make-business-plans-during-unpredictable-times
Ed: Gwen Moran. **Released:** February 22, 2023. **Description:** Remaining flexible when times get tough is a key factor in business success. But, how can one make and follow through on business plans when there is a shaky economy and other negative factors?. **Availability:** Online.

18981 ■ *"How to Make my House Cleaning Service Business Unique" in A Janitor's Story*
Ed: Stacy Freeman. **Description:** Information on how to make your house cleaning business unique. **Availability:** Online.

18982 ■ *"How to Organize Business Expenses: 7 Important Tips" in Legal Zoom (February 17, 2023)*
URL(s): www.legalzoom.com/articles/how-to-organize-expenses-for-small-business-owners
Released: February 17, 2023. **Description:** Follow these tips to get your business expenses under control and organized with income statements, financial statements, and spreadsheets. **Availability:** Online.

18983 ■ *"How to Recover from a Bad Business Decision" in Legal Zoom (February 15, 2023)*
URL(s): www.legalzoom.com/articles/how-to-recover-from-a-bad-business-decision
Ed: Marcia Layton Turner. **Released:** February 15, 2023. **Description:** It is possible that one day you will make a bad business decision, which will impact the employees, you, or the company as a whole. How do you get past it and rectify your mistakes? This article gives pointers on what to do so your company can move on. **Availability:** Online.

18984 ■ *"How to Spot Secondary Revenue Streams for Your Business" in Legal Zoom (February 21, 2023)*
URL(s): www.legalzoom.com/articles/how-to-spot-secondary-revenue-streams-for-your-business
Ed: Jenn Morson. **Released:** February 21, 2023. **Description:** Defines revenue streams and gives advice on how to utilize that concept to improve cash flow for your business. **Availability:** Online.

18985 ■ *"How to Start a Cleaning Business" in Entrepreneur (June 14, 2003)*
Released: June 14, 2003. **Description:** Information on how to start a successful cleaning business. Topics include target market, location, pricing, marketing, and resources. **Availability:** Online.

18986 ■ *"How to Start a Cleaning Business in 7 Steps" in JustBusiness (September 15, 2020)*
Ed: Meredith Wood. **Released:** September 15, 2020. **Description:** Provides practical steps for starting a cleaning business including funding, marketing, business planning and budgeting, registering, and finding and maintaining clients. **Availability:** Online.

18987 ■ *How to Start a Home-based Craft Business*
Ed: Kenn Oberrecht, Patrice Lewis. **Released:** Sixth edition. **Price:** $18.99, e-book; Paperback. **Description:** Step-by-step guide for starting and growing a home-based craft business. **Availability:** Print.

18988 ■ *How to Start and Run Your Own Corporation: S-Corporations For Small Business Owners*
Pub: HCM Publishing
Ed: Peter I. Hupalo. **Description:** Basics of corporate business structure are explained. Topics include discovering the best business structure for your company; how to decided between an S-Corporation and LLC; choosing the state in which to incorporate, how to form a corporation, angel investing, special issues for one-person corporations, the role of bylaws and corporate minutes, board of directors, taxes, workers' compensation issues, retirement plans, and more. **Availability:** Print.

18989 ■ *"How To Disaster-Proof Your Business" in Inc. (Vol. 33, September 2011, No. 7, pp. 38)*
Pub: Inc. Magazine
Ed: J.J. McCorvey, Dave Smith. **Description:** Twelve products to and services designed to help small businesses run smoothly in the event of a disaster are outlined. **Availability:** Online.

18990 ■ *How to Write a Business Plan*
Pub: Nolo
Contact: Chris Braun, President
Ed: Mike McKeever. **Released:** November 2018. **Price:** E-Book. **Description:** Author, teacher and financial manager shows how to write an effective business plan. Examples and worksheets are included. **Availability:** E-book; Print.

18991 ■ *How to Write a Business Plan*
Pub: Kogan Page Ltd.
Contact: Christina Lindeholm, Manager, Sales
Ed: Brian Finch. **Released:** Seventh edition. **Description:** Starting with the premise that there's only one chance to make a good impression, this book covers all the issues involved in producing a successful business plan, from profiling competitors to forecasting marketing development. **Availability:** Print; Electronic publishing.

18992 ■ *How to Write a Business Plan*
Pub: Kogan Page Ltd.
Contact: Christina Lindeholm, Manager, Sales
URL(s): www.koganpage.com/general-business-interest/how-to-write-a-business-plan-9781399860 5640
Price: $61, for hardback. **Description:** Provides expert guidance to help make an impact with your plan, including advice on researching competitors, presenting your management skills and successfully communicating your strategic vision. **Availability:** E-book; Print; Online.

18993 ■ *"How to Write a Business Plan" in Small Business Trends (November 11, 2021)*
URL(s): smallbiztrends.com/2021/11/how-to-write-a-business-plan.html
Ed: Shubhomita Bose. **Released:** November 11, 2021. **Description:** One of the first things anyone starting a businesses needs to accomplish is writing a business plan. This article discusses what to include and what not to include. **Availability:** Online.

18994 ■ *"How to Write a Business Proposal" in Business News Daily (February 23, 2023)*
URL(s): www.businessnewsdaily.com/10417-writing-business-proposal.html
Ed: Sammi Caramela. **Released:** February 23, 2023. **Description:** If you are struggling with writing a business proposal, this article can help since it provides tips and links to further resources. **Availability:** Online.

18995 ■ *How to Write a Great Business Plan for Your Small Business in 60 Minutes or Less*
Pub: Atlantic Publishing Co.
Contact: Dr. Heather L. Johnson, Contact
Ed: Sharon L. Fullen. **Released:** 2013. **Description:** A good business plan outlines goals and works as a company's resume to obtain funding, credit from suppliers, management of the operations and finances, promotion and marketing, and more. **Availability:** CD-ROM; E-book; Print; Online.

18996 ■ *"Husky Proceeds on Heavy-Oil Expansion" in Globe & Mail (March 21, 2006, pp. B1)*
Ed: Patrick Brethour. **Description:** Canadian energy giant Husky Energy Inc. has started its $90 million engineering effort to determine the cost of the $2.3 billion heavy-oil up gradation expansion plan. Details of the project are elaborated upon. **Availability:** Online.

18997 ■ *"Ideas at Work: The Reality of Costs" in Business Strategy Review (Vol. 21, Summer 2010, No. 2, pp. 40)*
Ed: Jules Goddard. **Released:** June 24, 2010. **Description:** If you think that cost cutting is the surest way to business success, the author wants to challenge every assumption you hold. Costs are an outcome of sound strategy, never the goal of strategy. He offers a new perspective on what counts when it comes to costs. **Availability:** Print; PDF; Online.

18998 ■ *"Ill Winds; Cuba's Economy" in The Economist (Vol. 390, January 3, 2009, No. 8612, pp. 20)*
Description: Cuba's long-term economic prospects remain poor with the economy forecasted to grow only 4.3 percent for the year, about half of the original forecast, due in part to Hurricane Gustav which caused $10 billion in damage and disrupted the food-supply network and devastated farms across the region; President Raul Castro made raising agricultural production a national priority and the rise in global commodity prices hit the country hard. The only bright spot has been the rise in tourism which is up 9.3 percent over 2007. **Availability:** Online.

18999 ■ *"Independent Contractor, Sole Proprietor, and LLC Taxes Explained in 100 Pages or Less"*
Description: A small business tax primer which includes information of home office deduction, estimated tax payments, self-employment tax, business retirement plans, numerous business deductions, and audit protection. **Availability:** Print; Online.

19000 ■ *"Inland Snaps Up Rival REITs" in Crain's Chicago Business (Vol. 31, November 17, 2008, No. 46, pp. 3)*
Pub: Crain Communications Inc.
Contact: Barry Asin, President
Ed: Alby Gallun. **Description:** Discusses Inland American Real Estate Trust Inc., a real estate investment trust that is napping up depressed shares of publicly traded competitors, a possible first step toward taking over these companies; however, with hotel and retail properties accounting for approximately 70 percent of its portfolio, the company could soon face its own difficulties. **Availability:** Online.

19001 ■ *"Innovating Globally" in Business Strategy Review (Vol. 21, Spring 2010, No. 1, pp. 24)*
Ed: Costas Markides, Stuart Crainer. **Description:** Costas Markides has spent over two decades studying business strategy and innovation. Recently, he has been focusing on the bigger picture of how people can address major social problems. Can the techniques used by managers to create innovation inside organizations work with global change?. **Availability:** Download; PDF; Online.

19002 ■ *"The Innovator's Solution: Creating and Sustaining Successful Growth"*
Pub: Harvard Business Review Press
Contact: Moderna V. Pfizer, Contact
Released: November 19, 2013. **Price:** $35, Hardcover/Hardcopy. **Description:** Even in today's hyper-accelerated business environment any small company can transform their business. Advice on business decisions crucial to achieving truly disruptive growth and purpose guidelines for developing their own disruptive growth engine is given. The forces that cause managers to make bad decisions as they

GENERAL SMALL BUSINESS TOPICS   Business Planning ■ 19024

plan new ideas for their company are identified and new frameworks to help develop the right conditions, at the right time, for a disruption to succeed. Managers and business leaders responsible for innovation and growth will benefit their business and their teams with this information. **Availability:** E-book; Print.

19003 ■ "Install a Tasting System to Improve Food Truck Consistency" in Mobile-Cuisine.com
Ed: Richard Myrick. **Description:** Provides information on how to implement a tasting system for your food truck to ensure consistency. **Availability:** Online.

19004 ■ Instinct: Tapping Your Entrepreneurial DNA to Achieve Your Business Goals
Description: Research shows that entrepreneurs may attribute their success to genetics. **Availability:** Online.

19005 ■ "Insurers No Longer Paying Premium for Advertising" in Brandweek (Vol. 49, April 21, 2008, No. 16, pp. SR3)
Description: Insurance companies are cutting their advertising budgets after years of accelerated double-digit growth in spending due to the economic downturn, five years of record-breaking ad spend and a need to cut expenditures as claims costs rise and a competitive market keeps premiums in place. Statistical data included. **Availability:** Print; Online.

19006 ■ "Integrating Your Compliance Program" in Franchising World (Vol. 42, November 2010, No. 11, pp. 49)
Pub: International Franchise Association
Contact: Matthew Haller, President
E-mail: mhaller@franchise.org
Ed: Melanie Bergeron. **Description:** Compliance is integral to every part of any business operation and it is necessary for a company to make standards and compliance to those standards a priority. **Availability:** Online.

19007 ■ "Intermodal Makes Suppliers Look to Rack Up Big Sales to Distributors" in The Business Journal-Serving Metropolitan Kansas City (August 15, 2008)
Pub: American City Business Journals, Inc.
Contact: Mike Olivieri, Executive Vice President
Ed: James Dornbrook. **Description:** Suppliers of shelving units, conveyor systems and other equipment used in distribution facilities are expecting new business opportunities along with the planned intermodal projects in the Kansas City area. Suppliers have already observed that small distributors have started to relocate to the city because of the intermodal projects. Demand for shelves and lifts have also increased. **Availability:** Online.

19008 ■ "Intrawest Puts Itself on Market" in Globe & Mail (March 1, 2006, pp. B1)
Ed: Elizabeth Church. **Description:** The reasons behind the decision of Intrawest Corp. to go for sale or seek partnerships are presented. The company appointed Goldman Sachs & Co. to meet the purpose. **Availability:** Online.

19009 ■ "Jamieson Eyes $175 Million Trust IPO" in Globe & Mail (March 7, 2006, pp. B1)
Ed: Sinclair Stewart, Leonard Zehr. **Description:** The reasons behind $175 million initial public offering plans of Jamieson Laboratories Ltd. are presented. **Availability:** Print; Online.

19010 ■ "JK Lasser's New Rules for Estate, Retirement, and Tax Planning"
Pub: John Wiley & Sons, Inc.
Contact: Christina Van Tassell, Executive Vice President Chief Financial Officer
Released: 6th Edition. **Price:** $24.95, paperback; $16.99, E-book. **Description:** The authoritative guide to estate, retirement and tax planning is fully updated and reflects the new changes and legal updates. Estate planning section covers: planning, taxation, investing, wills, executors, trusts, life insurance, retirement planning, Social Security, business planning, succession, asset protection and family limited partnerships. **Availability:** E-book; Print.

19011 ■ "Just Hang Up" in Barron's (Vol. 88, March 10, 2008, No. 10, pp. 45)
Description: Sprint's shares are expected to continue falling while the company attempts to attract subscribers by cutting prices, cutting earnings in the process. The company faces tougher competition from better-financed AT&T and Verizon Communications.

19012 ■ "Keeping Railcars 'Busy At All Times' At TTX" in Crain's Chicago Business (Vol. 31, April 28, 2008, No. 17, pp. 6)
Pub: Crain Communications Inc.
Contact: Barry Asin, President
Ed: Bob Tita. **Description:** Profile of the president of Chicago railcar pool operator TTX Co. and his business plan for the company which includes improving fleet management and car purchasing through better use of data on railroad demand. **Availability:** Online.

19013 ■ "Kinetico Exec Going Global to Increase Growth Flow" in Crain's Cleveland Business (Vol. 28, October 1, 2007, No. 39, pp. 5)
Pub: Crain Communications Inc.
Contact: K. C. Crain, President
Ed: David Bennett. **Description:** Shamus Hurley, the new CEO and president of Kinetico Inc., a manufacturer of water filtering and softening equipment for residential, commercial and municipal use, plans to expand the company to target markets overseas. **Availability:** Online.

19014 ■ A Legal Guide for Startups
URL(s): www.rocketlawyer.com/business-and-contracts/starting-a-business/legal-guide/a-legal-guide-for-startups
Description: A legal guide for entrepreneurs who are starting a busienss. Includes information on safeguarding your interests, setting up a legal entity, finding legal advice, and additional steps to protect yourself. **Availability:** Online.

19015 ■ LLC Beginner's Guide: The Most Complete and Easy-to-Follow Handbook on How to Form, Manage and Maintain Your Limited Liability Company
Ed: Steven Carlson. **Released:** October 29, 2022. **Price:** $17.36, paperback; $8.97, e-book. **Description:** A guide that explains the process of setting up a limited liability company (LLC) in simple terms. **Availability:** E-book; Print.

19016 ■ "A Look at 2020 Food Trends" in FoodTruckOperator.com (February 20, 2020).
Ed: Christine Potts. **Released:** February 20, 2020.

19017 ■ "Loss of Tobacco Revenue Is Unlikely To Cost CVS" in Providence Business News (Vol. 28, February 17, 2014, No. 46, pp. 1)
Pub: American City Business Journals, Inc.
Contact: Mike Olivieri, Executive Vice President
URL(s): pbn.com/loss-of-tobacco-revenue-is-unlikely-to-cost-cvs95149
Description: CVS Caremark Corporation will stop selling tobacco products beginning October 1, 2014. CEO, Larry J. Merlo believes the sale of tobacco products is inconsistent with the drug retailer's purpose. The company's role in providing care through its nurse practitioners and pharmacists is also examined. **Availability:** Online. **Telecommunication Services:** Anderson@pbn.com.

19018 ■ "Lotus Starts Slowly, Dodges Subprime Woes" in Crain's Detroit Business (Vol. 24, April 14, 2008, No. 15, pp. 3)
Pub: Crain Communications Inc.
Contact: Barry Asin, President
Ed: Tom Henderson. **Description:** Discusses Lotus Bancorp Inc. and their business plan, which although is not right on target due to the subprime mortgage meltdown, is in a much better position than its competitors due to the quality of their loans. **Availability:** Online.

19019 ■ "Managers as Visionaries: a Skill That Can Be Learned" in Strategy and Leadership (Vol. 39, September-October 2011, No. 5, pp. 56-58)
Pub: Emerald Group Publishing Limited
Contact: Erika Valenti, President
Ed: Stephen M. Millett. **Description:** A study uses research findings to examine whether visionary management can be learned. Results conclude that managers can learn visionary management through intuitive pattern recognition of trends and by using scenarios for anticipating and planning for likely future occurrences.

19020 ■ "Managing the Facebookers; Business" in The Economist (Vol. 390, January 3, 2009, No. 8612, pp. 10)
Pub: Economist Newspaper Ltd.
Contact: Lara Boro, Chief Executive Officer
Description: According to a report from PricewaterhouseCoopers, a business consultancy, workers from Generation Y, also known as the Net Generation, are more difficult to recruit and integrate into companies that practice traditional business acumen. 61 percent of chief executive managers say that they have trouble with younger employees who tend to be more narcissistic and more interested in personal fulfillment with a need for frequent feedback and an overprecise set of objectives on the path to promotion which can be hard for managers who are used to a different relationship with their subordinates. Older bosses should prepare to make some concessions to their younger talent since some of the issues that make them happy include cheaper online ways to communicate and additional coaching, both of which are good for business. **Availability:** Online.

19021 ■ "Many Roads Lead to Value Says David J. Williams, Manager of Excelsior Value & Restructuring Fund" in Barron's (Vol. 88, March 10, 2008, No. 10, pp. 46)
Pub: Dow Jones & Company Inc.
Contact: Almar Latour, Chief Executive Officer
Ed: Lawrence C. Strauss. **Description:** David J. Williams, lead manager of Excelsior Value & Restructuring Fund, invests in struggling companies and those companies whose turnarounds show promise. Morgan Stanley, Lehman Brothers, and Petroleo Brasileiro are some of the companies he holds shares in, while he has unloaded shares of Citigroup, Freddie Mac, and Sallie Mae. **Availability:** Online.

19022 ■ "A Master Chef's Recipe for Business Success" in Business Strategy Review (Vol. 23, Spring 2012, No. 1, pp. 65)
Description: Often called the world's greatest chef, Ferran Adria, longtime owner of El Built, Spain's three-star Michelin rated revolutionary restaurant, is now embarking on a new venture: the El Built Foundation, a place where chefs can create, interact, and discuss their ideas with researchers from other disciplines. He recently spoke at London Business School as part of his tour of a number of select universities to invite students to enter a competition to design an innovative business model for the new Foundation. **Availability:** Print; Online.

19023 ■ "McCormick Focuses on Customer, Dealer Service" in Farm Industry News (September 17, 2010)
Pub: Informa Business Media, Inc.
Contact: Charlie McCurdy, President
Price: $4, Print and Online; Special Offers only for 4 weeks. **Description:** McCormick has developed a new plan that focuses on fast and complete service to both customers and dealers. **Availability:** Print; Online.

19024 ■ "Microsoft's Big Gamble" in Canadian Business (Vol. 81, March 3, 2008, No. 3, pp. 13)
Description: Microsoft Corp. is taking a big risk in buying Yahoo, as it is expected to pay more than $31 a share to finalize the acquisition. The deal would be

seven and a half times bigger than any other that Microsoft has entered before, an execution of such deal is also anticipated to become a challenge for Microsoft. Recommendations on how Microsoft should handle the integration of the two businesses are given. **Availability:** Print; Online.

19025 ■ *"Needed: A Strategy; Banking In China"* in *The Economist (Vol. 390, January 3, 2009, No. 8612, pp. 54)*
Description: International banks are competing for a role in China but are finding obstacles in their paths such as a reduction in the credit their operations may receive from Chinese banks and the role they can play in the public capital markets which remain limited. **Availability:** Print; Online.

19026 ■ *"New Sales. Simplified: The Essential Handbook for Prospecting and New Business Development"*
Pub: HarperCollins Leadership
Contact: Donald Miller, Chief Executive Officer
Released: September 04, 2012. **Price:** $19.99, Paperback. **Description:** The constant flow of new accounts is essential for any small business to grow and thrive. A proven formula for prospecting; customer-focused selling; proactive telephone calling that leads to face-to-face meetings; the use of email, voicemail, and social media; prevent the buyer's anti-salesperson response; build a rapport; winning sales; communicating with clients; plan time for business development activities; and more. **Availability:** E-book; Print; Audio; Download.

19027 ■ *"Nexen, OPTI Boost Oil Sands Spending"* in *Globe & Mail (February 18, 2006, pp. B5)*
Ed: Dave Ebner. **Description:** The reasons behind the decision of Nexen Inc. and OPTI Canada Inc., to allocate 10 percent more funding on oil sands, are presented. **Availability:** Print; Online.

19028 ■ *"No Frills - And No Dodge"* in *Crain's Detroit Business (Vol. 24, September 22, 2008, No. 38, pp. 3)*
Pub: Crain Communications Inc.
Contact: Barry Asin, President
Ed: Bradford Wernle. **Description:** Chrysler LLC is in the middle of a business plan known as Project Genesis, a five-year strategy in which the company will reduce the dealer count by combining its Jeep, Chrysler and Dodge brands under one rooftop wherever possible. Not every dealer will be able to arrange this deal because of the investment required to expand stores in which have low-overhead; many of these stores feel that low-overhead structures are more likely to survive difficult times than the larger stores in which the Genesis consolidation plan intends to implement. **Availability:** Online.

19029 ■ *"'Nobody Knows What To Do' To Make Money on the Web"* in *Barron's (Vol. 88, March 17, 2008, No. 11, pp. 40)*
Pub: Dow Jones & Company Inc.
Contact: Almar Latour, Chief Executive Officer
Ed: Mark Veverka. **Description:** Attendees of the South by Southwest Interactive conference failed to get an insight on how to make money on the Web from former Walt Disney CEO Michael Eisner when Eisner said there's no proven business model for financing projects. Eisner said he finances his projects with the help of his connections to get product-placement deals. **Availability:** Online.

19030 ■ *"Nortel Starting From Scratch, New CEO Says"* in *Globe & Mail (February 24, 2006, pp. B3)*
Ed: Catherine McLean. **Description:** The restructuring efforts of chief executive officer Mike Zafirovski of Nortel Networks Corp. are presented. **Availability:** Online.

19031 ■ *"Nursing Home Group Put on the Block"* in *Globe & Mail (February 23, 2006, pp. B1)*
Ed: Elizabeth Church. **Description:** The reasons behind the decision of Exetendicare Inc. to go for sale are presented. **Availability:** Online.

19032 ■ *"Office Depot Closing 400 Stores"* in *San Antonio Business Journal (Vol. 28, May 9, 2014, No. 13, pp. 3)*
Pub: American City Business Journals, Inc.
Contact: Mike Olivieri, Executive Vice President
Released: Weekly. **Description:** Boca Raton, Florida-based Office Depot announced a plan to close at least 400 stores in the U.S. by the end of 2016. Office Depot joins a growing list of national retailers decreasing store locations in order to increase their bottom line. The problems facing the big players in the office supplies/equipment industry are presented. **Availability:** Print; Online.

19033 ■ *"Ohio Commerce Draws Closer to Profitability"* in *Crain's Cleveland Business (Vol. 28, October 29, 2007, No. 43, pp. 14)*
Pub: Crain Communications Inc.
Contact: K. C. Crain, President
Ed: Shawn A. Turner. **Description:** Overview of the business plan of Ohio Commerce Bank, a de novo, or startup bank that is close to turning the corner to profitability. The bank opened in November 2006 and focuses on dealing with small businesses totaling $5 million or less in annual revenues. **Availability:** Online.

19034 ■ *"Olympus is Urged to Revise Board"* in *Wall Street Journal Eastern Edition (November 28, 2011, pp. B3)*
Pub: Dow Jones & Company Inc.
Contact: Almar Latour, Chief Executive Officer
Ed: Phred Dvorak. **Description:** Koji Miyata, once a director on the board of troubled Japanese photographic equipment company, is urging the company to reorganize its board, saying the present group should resign their board seats but keep their management positions. The company has come under scrutiny for its accounting practices and costly acquisitions. **Availability:** Online.

19035 ■ *"OMERS Joins Bid for U.K. Port Giant"* in *Globe & Mail (March 28, 2006, pp. B1)*
Ed: Paul Waldie. **Description:** The plans of Ontario Municipal Employees Retirement Board to partner with Goldman Sachs Group Inc., in order to acquire Associated British Ports PLC, are presented. **Availability:** Online.

19036 ■ *"Once Derided As Rabbit Food, Humble Salad Now Fuels Business Plans"* in *Dallas Business Journal (Vol. 35, August 17, 2012, No. 49, pp. 1)*
Pub: Baltimore Business Journal
Contact: Rhonda Pringle, President
E-mail: rpringle@bizjournals.com
Description: Establishments offering salad concepts are on the rise in Dallas, Texas. The Salad Stop, Greenz, Salata are only some of the restaurants that have ventured into meeting the demand for health food, particularly salads. The market is only getting bigger, urging the restaurants to expand in services and facilities. The beginnings, food choices, and business plans of these restaurants are discussed.

19037 ■ *"Organization Redesign and Innovative HRM"* in *Human Resource Management (Vol. 49, July-August 2010, No. 4, pp. 809-811)*
Pub: John Wiley & Sons, Inc.
Contact: Christina Van Tassell, Executive Vice President Chief Financial Officer
Ed: Pat Lynch. **Released:** July 01, 2010. **Description:** An overview of the book, 'Organization Redesign and Innovative HRM' is presented. **Availability:** PDF; Online.

19038 ■ *"Organizing the Family-Run Business"* in *Small Business Opportunities (Get Rich At Home 2010)*
Pub: Harris Publishing, Inc.
Contact: Janet Chase, Contact
Ed: Gene Siciliano. **Description:** The good, the bad and the ugly of succession planning for any small business is spotlighted. **Availability:** Online.

19039 ■ *"The Outcome of an Organization Overhaul"* in *Black Enterprise (Vol. 41, December 2010, No. 5)*
Pub: Earl G. Graves Ltd.
Contact: Earl Graves, Jr., President
Ed: Tamara E. Holmes. **Description:** Savvy business owners understand the need for change in order to stay competitive and be successful. This article examines how to manage change as well as what strategies can help employees to get with the program faster. **Availability:** Online.

19040 ■ *"Paramount Said to be Working on Sale of Oil Sands Assets"* in *Globe & Mail (April 24, 2007, pp. B1)*
Ed: Norval Scott. **Description:** The proposed sale of oil sands in Surmont and the shares of North American Oil Sands Corp. by Paramount Resources Ltd. is discussed. **Availability:** Online.

19041 ■ *"People; E-Commerce, Online Games, Mobile Apps"* in *Advertising Age (Vol. 80, October 19, 2009, No. 35, pp. 14)*
Pub: Crain Communications Inc.
Contact: Jessica Botos, Manager, Marketing
E-mail: jessica.botos@crainsnewyork.com
Ed: Nat Ives. **Description:** Profile of People Magazine and the ways in which the publisher is moving its magazine forward by exploring new concepts in a time of declining newsstand sales and advertising pages; among the strategies are e-commerce such as the brand People Style Watch in which consumers are able highlight clothing and jewelry and then connect to retailers' sites and a channel on Taxi TV, the network of video-touch screens in New Your City taxis. **Availability:** Online.

19042 ■ *"Perfecting the Process: Creating a More Efficient Organization on Your Terms"* in *Black Enterprise (Vol. 41, October 2010, No. 3)*
Pub: Earl G. Graves Ltd.
Contact: Earl Graves, Jr., President
Ed: Tamara E. Holmes. **Description:** More than ever, entrepreneurs need to identify new ways of doing business in a cost-effective manner in order to expand their companies, while remaining true to their customer demands. **Availability:** Online.

19043 ■ *"PhotoMedex Bouncing Back from Brink of Bankruptcy"* in *Philadelphia Business Journal (Vol. 30, January 6, 2012, No. 47, pp. 1)*
Pub: Baltimore Business Journal
Contact: Rhonda Pringle, President
E-mail: rpringle@bizjournals.com
Description: PhotoMedex Inc. has managed to avoid bankruptcy through reorganization. The company appointed Dennis McGrath as president and chief executive. Details of the business reorganization plans are covered. **Availability:** Print; Online.

19044 ■ *"The Play's the Thing"* in *Business Strategy Review (Vol. 21, Summer 2010, No. 2, pp. 58)*
Ed: Michael G. Jacobides. **Released:** March 07, 2018. **Description:** Those who study and plan strategies risk falling into the traps that maps, graphs, charts and matrices present. The author feels that strategy might best be cast as a dramatic playscript that can reveal the unfolding plots of business far better than traditional strategic tools, as the landscape shifts around us. **Availability:** Print; PDF; Online.

19045 ■ *"Portfolio Recovery Associates Expands Its Hampton Call Center"* in *Marketwired (January 20, 2010)*
Pub: Comtex News Network Inc.
Contact: Kan Devnani, President
Description: Entering into a lease amendment in order to expand its Hampton, Virginia call center and extend its lease agreement, Portfolio Recovery Associates, Inc., a company that collects, purchases and manages defaulted consumer debt, plans to upgrade the existing space enabling them to draw on local talent. **Availability:** Print; Online.

GENERAL SMALL BUSINESS TOPICS   Business Planning ■ 19070

19046 ■ *The Power of Pull: How Small Moves, Smartly Made, Can Set Big Things in Motion*
Ed: John Hagel, III, John Seely Brown, Lang Davison. **Released:** April 13, 2010. **Price:** $11.99; C$14.99. **Description:** Examination of how we can effectively address the most pressing challenges in a rapidly changing and increasingly interdependent world is addressed. New ways in which passionate thinking, creative solutions, and committed action can and will make it possible for small businesses owners to seize opportunities and remain in step with change. **Availability:** E-book; Print.

19047 ■ *"The Price Is Right: Turning a Profit in the Event Planning Business"* in *Entrepreneur*
Ed: Cheryl Kimball. **Description:** Details how to get started in the event planning industry as well as explains how to determine what to charge clients to turn a profit. **Availability:** Online.

19048 ■ *"Purdue Agronomist: Consider Costs Before Tilling"* in *Farm Industry News (November 8, 2011)*
Pub: Informa Business Media, Inc.
Contact: Charlie McCurdy, President
Ed: Lisa Schluttenhofer. **Description:** Farmers consider soil drainage, fertilizer and planting needs as well as economic thresholds before making tillage decisions, according to a Purdue extension agronomist. **Availability:** Online.

19049 ■ *"Raytheon Stock Up, Will Pay New Quarterly Dividend"* in *Barron's (Vol. 88, March 31, 2008, No. 13)*
Pub: Dow Jones & Company Inc.
Contact: Almar Latour, Chief Executive Officer
Ed: Shirley A. Lazo. **Description:** Raytheon hiked their quarterly dividend to 28 cents per share from 25.5 cents. Aircastle slashed their quarterly common dividend by 64 percent for them to retain additional capital that can be used to increase their liquidity position. **Availability:** Online.

19050 ■ *"Refreshing! A Clearly Canadian Comeback"* in *Canadian Business (Vol. 79, September 11, 2006, No. 18, pp. 22)*
Pub: Rogers Media Inc.
Contact: Neil Spivak, Chief Executive Officer
Ed: Joe Castaldo. **Description:** Turnaround strategies and initiatives adopted by Canadian Beverage Corp. to boost its declining sales are presented. **Availability:** Print; Online.

19051 ■ *"Retiring Baby Boomers and Dissatisfied Gen-Xers Cause..Brain Drain"* in *Agency Sales Magazine (Vol. 39, November 2009, No. 10)*
Description: Due to the impending retirement of the baby boomers a critical loss of knowledge and experience in businesses will result. Creating a plan to address this loss of talent centered on the development of the younger generation is discussed.

19052 ■ *"Return to Wealth; Bank Strategy"* in *The Economist (Vol. 390, January 3, 2009, No. 8612, pp. 56)*
Description: UBS' strategy to survive these trying economic times is presented. Statistical data included. UBS has a stronger balance-sheet than most of its investment-banking peers and has reduced its portfolio. **Availability:** Print; Online.

19053 ■ *Rework*
Ed: Jason Fried, David Heinemeier Hansson. **Released:** 2010. **Price:** $19.62, hardcover; $14.99, e-book; $9, audiobook. **Description:** Works to help entrepreneurs and business owners to rethink strategy, customers, and getting things accomplished. **Availability:** E-book; Print.

19054 ■ *"The Road Map for Scotiabank's Asian Expansion"* in *Globe & Mail (April 7, 2007, pp. B3)*
Ed: Tara Perkins. **Description:** Executive vice-president of Bank of Nova Scotia, Rob Pitfield shares his plan to expand the bank's Asian market. **Availability:** Online.

19055 ■ *"Rogue Caller Infiltrates Cincinnati Firms' Analyst Calls: 'Mr. CEO, Please Do Elaborate On Your Firm's Metrics"* in *Business Courier (Vol. 24, February 28, 2008, No. 47, pp. 1)*
Pub: American City Business Journals, Inc.
Contact: Mike Olivieri, Executive Vice President
Ed: Jon Newberry. **Description:** Discusses a rogue caller who goes by the name of Joe Herrick, Steven Nissan and Joe Harris has joined in over a dozen conference calls, asking chief executive officers on their plans and commenting on the companies' operations. The mystery caller attempts to pass himself off as a financial analyst. Transcripts of some conference calls, in which the rogue caller is involved, are provided. **Availability:** Online.

19056 ■ *Save Your Small Business: 10 Crucial Strategies to Survive Hard Times or Close Down & Move On*
Pub: Nolo
Contact: Chris Braun, President
Ed: Ralph Warner, Bethany Laurence. **Description:** According to a study among 500 businesses, 44 percent used credit cards in order to meet their firm's needs in the previous six months. Written by a business owner, this book provides twelve strategies to protect personal assets from creditors and survive the current recession. **Availability:** Print.

19057 ■ *"Scanning Dell's Shopping List"* in *Barron's (Vol. 89, July 13, 2009, No. 28, pp. 24)*
Pub: Dow Jones & Company Inc.
Contact: Almar Latour, Chief Executive Officer
Ed: Mark Veverka. **Description:** It is believed that Dell will be looking for companies to acquire since they poached an experienced mergers-and-acquisitions executive. In addition Dell's CEO is reportedly telling people he plans to go shopping. Dell executives have also stated an interest in data storage. **Availability:** Online.

19058 ■ *"Scotiabank Targets More Baby Boomers"* in *Globe & Mail (March 4, 2006, pp. B5)*
Ed: Elizabeth Church. **Description:** Bank of Nova Scotia posted $844 million profit for first quarter 2006. The plans of the bank to achieve baby boomer client base are presented. **Availability:** Online.

19059 ■ *"The Search for Big Oil"* in *Canadian Business (Vol. 80, April 9, 2007, No. 8, pp. 10)*
Description: The continuing effort of Canmex Minerals Corp. to explore for oil in Somalia despite the failure of several other companies is discussed. **Availability:** Print; Online.

19060 ■ *"Shell Venture Aims at 'Oil Rocks'"* in *Globe & Mail (March 22, 2006, pp. B1)*
Ed: Patrick Brethour. **Description:** Royal Dutch Shell PLC is all set to launch its Alberta's operations in bitumen deposits trapped in limestone. Details of the new venture are analyzed. **Availability:** Online.

19061 ■ *"Shermag Says Refinishing Not Complete"* in *Globe & Mail (February 14, 2006, pp. B3)*
Ed: Bertrand Marotte. **Description:** The details on restructuring efforts of Shermag Inc. are presented. **Availability:** Online.

19062 ■ *"Should You Go Into Business With Your Spouse?"* in *Women Entrepreneur (September 1, 2008)*
Description: Things to consider before starting a business with one's spouse are discussed. Compatible work ethics, clear expectations of one another, long-term goals for the company and the status of the relationship are among the things to consider before starting a business endeavor with a spouse. **Availability:** Online.

19063 ■ *"Sleeman Cuts Again as Cheap Suds Bite"* in *Globe & Mail (March 3, 2006, pp. B3)*
Ed: Andy Hoffman. **Description:** The details on 5 percent employee reduction at Sleeman Breweries Ltd., which posted 86 percent decline in profits for fourth quarter 2005, are presented. **Availability:** Online.

19064 ■ *"Slimmed-Down Supplier TI Automotive Relaunches"* in *Crain's Detroit Business (Vol. 26, January 11, 2010, No. 2, pp. 14)*
Pub: Crain Communications Inc.
Contact: Barry Asin, President
Ed: Robert Sherefkin. **Description:** TI Automotive Ltd., one of the world's largest suppliers of fuel storage and delivery systems, has reorganized the company by splitting it into five global divisions and is relaunching its brand which is now more focused on new technology. **Availability:** Print; Online.

19065 ■ *"Small is the New Big in Autos"* in *Globe & Mail (February 16, 2006, pp. B3)*
Ed: Greg Keenan. **Description:** The reasons behind the introduction of subcompact cars by companies such as Ford Motor Co. are presented. The automobiles were unveiled at Canadian International Auto Show in Toronto.

19066 ■ *"So You Think You Want to Own a Dance Studio?"* in *DanceTeacher (September 12, 2017)*
URL(s): www.dance-teacher.com/so-you-think-you-want-to-own-a-dance-studio-2392417191.html
Ed: Rachel Rizzuto. **Released:** September 12, 2017. **Description:** Tips on the best way to start your own dance studio businesses. Becoming an apprentice, making a name for yourself, and practicing good business techniques can help make a successful dance studio. **Availability:** Online.

19067 ■ *"So You Want to Start a Business? So You Want to Start a Business: What's Your First Move?"* in *Women Entrepreneur (August 5, 2008)*
Description: Advice for taking an idea and turning it into a legitimate business is given. **Availability:** Online.

19068 ■ *"Social Networking: Growing Pains"* in *Canadian Business (Vol. 81, July 22, 2008, No. 12-13, pp. 35)*
Pub: Rogers Media Inc.
Contact: Neil Spivak, Chief Executive Officer
Ed: Alex Mlynek. **Description:** Laughing Stock Vineyards' Cynthia Enns and David Enns plan to target young buyers by using social media. The Enns however, are concerned that targeting younger buyers may affect Laughing Stock's image as a premium brand. Additional information regarding the company's future plans is presented. **Availability:** Print; Online.

19069 ■ *"A Socko Payout Menu: Rural Phone Carrier Plots to Supercharge Its Shares"* in *Barron's (Vol. 88, June 30, 2008, No. 26, pp. M5)*
Description: CenturyTel boosted its quarterly common payout to 70 cents from 6.75 cents per share die to its strong cash flows and solid balance sheet. Eastman Kodak's plan for a buyback will be partially funded by its $581 million tax refund. CME Group will buyback stocks through 2009 worth $1.1 billion. **Availability:** Online.

19070 ■ *"Sorrell Digs Deep to Snag TNS"* in *Advertising Age (Vol. 79, July 14, 2008, No. 7, pp. 1)*
Pub: Crain Communications, Inc.
Contact: Jessica Botos, Manager, Marketing
E-mail: jessica.botos@crainsnewyork.com
Ed: Michael Bush. **Description:** Martin Sorrell's strategic vision for expansion in order to become the largest ad-agency holding company in the world is discussed. **Availability:** Online.

GENERAL SMALL BUSINESS TOPICS

19071 ■ *"Spring Cleaning: Refreshing Your Business Plans"* in *Legal Zoom* (February 17, 2023)
URL(s): www.legalzoom.com/articles/spring-cleaning-refreshing-your-business-plan
Ed: Sandra Beckwith. **Released:** February 17, 2023. **Description:** It's a good thing when you can take some time and look over your original business plan and see where your business has grown or even grown out of. Then, you can determine what needs to be adjusted to keep your business successful. **Availability:** Online.

19072 ■ *"Stadium Developers Seek a Win With the State"* in *The Business Journal-Serving Metropolitan Kansas City* (Vol. 26, August 22, 2008)
Description: Three Trails Redevelopment LLC is hoping to win $30 million in state tax credits from the Missouri Development Finance Board for the construction of an 18,500-seat Wizards stadium. The project is contingent on state tax incentives and the company remains optimistic about their goal.

19073 ■ *"Starbucks' Wheel Strategy"* in *Puget Sound Business Journal* (Vol. 29, October 3, 2008, No. 24, pp. 1)
Description: Starbuck Corporation has placed drive-through windows in nearly 50 percent of its locations. Dorothy Kim, executive vice president of global strategy, revealed that the firm's transformation strategy includes the addition of even more drive-through windows since people want the car-friendly conveniences. **Availability:** Print; Online.

19074 ■ *"Start Your Business Off Right with a Business Plan Outline"* in *Legal Zoom* (March 14, 2023)
URL(s): www.legalzoom.com/articles/what-you-should-know-about-zoning-laws
Ed: Sandra Beckwith. **Released:** March 14, 2023. **Description:** All small businesses start off with an idea. Be sure to start planning the right way by developing a business plan outline. **Availability:** Online.

19075 ■ *"Still Unprepared For Natural Disasters: Blacks More Likely to be Affected and Less Prepared"* in *Black Enterprise* (Vol. 38, January 2008, No. 6, pp. 28)
Pub: Earl G. Graves Ltd.
Contact: Earl Graves, Jr., President
Ed: Alexis McCombs. **Description:** According to a study conducted by the American Red Cross, 19 percent of African Americans are not prepared for a natural disaster, compared to 10 percent of white Americans. **Availability:** Online.

19076 ■ *"Stock Car Racing"* in *Canadian Business* (Vol. 81, September 15, 2008, No. 14-15, pp. 29)
Description: Some analysts predict a Chapter 11-style tune-up making GM and Ford a speculative turnaround stock. However, the price of oil could make or break the shares of the Big Three U.S. automobile manufacturers and if oil goes up too high then a speculative stock to watch is an electric car company called Zenn Motor Co. **Availability:** Online.

19077 ■ *"Strategic Issue Management as Change Catalyst"* in *Strategy and Leadership* (Vol. 39, September-October 2011, No. 5, pp. 20-29)
Pub: Emerald Group Publishing Limited
Contact: Erika Valenti, President
Ed: Bruce E. Perrott. **Description:** A study analyzes the case of a well-known Australian healthcare organization to examine how a company's periodic planning cycle is supplemented with a dynamic, real-time, strategic-issue-management system under high turbulence conditions. Findings highlight the eight steps that a company's management can use in its strategic issue management (SIM) process to track, monitor and manage strategic issues so as to ensure that the corporate, strategy, and capability are aligned with one another in turbulent times. **Availability:** Download; PDF; Online.

19078 ■ *"A Strong, Aligned Board of Directors Is Ideal"* in *South Florida Business Journal* (Vol. 35, August 1, 2014, No. 1, pp. 8)
Pub: American City Business Journals, Inc.
Contact: Mike Olivieri, Executive Vice President
Released: Weekly. **Price:** $8, introductory 4-week offer(Digital only). **Description:** The advantages of an informed and congruent board of directors to a company are described. The board of directors should provide the company with a strategic business perspective, access to prospective investors, and potential strategic business partners to help a firm achieve its vision and goals. **Availability:** Print; Online.

19079 ■ *"Stung by Recession, Hemmer Regroups with New Strategy"* in *Business Courier* (Vol. 27, June 4, 2010, No. 5, pp. 1)
Pub: Business Courier
Ed: Lucy May. **Description:** Paul Hemmer Companies reduced its work force and outsourced operations such as marketing and architecture, in order for the commercial and construction firm to survive the recession. Hammer's total core revenue in 2009 dropped to less than $30 million forcing the closure of its Chicago office. **Availability:** PDF; Online.

19080 ■ *"Talisman CEO Touts Benefits of Going It Alone"* in *Globe & Mail* (March 2, 2006, pp. B1)
Ed: Dave Ebner. **Description:** The opinions of chief executive officer Jim Buckee of Talisman Energy Inc. on the benefits for the company to remain autonomous are presented. **Availability:** Online.

19081 ■ *Technology Ventures: From Idea to Enterprise*
Pub: McGraw-Hill Higher Education
Contact: Michael Ryan, President
Ed: Richard C. Dorf, Thomas H. Byers, Andrew Nelson. **Released:** Fifth edition. **Price:** $130.66; $80. **Description:** Textbook examining technology entrepreneurship on a global basis; technology management theories are explored. **Availability:** E-book; Print.

19082 ■ *Testing Business Ideas: A Field Guide for Rapid Experimentation*
Pub: John Wiley & Sons, Inc.
Contact: Christina Van Tassell, Executive Vice President Chief Financial Officer
URL(s): www.wiley.com/en-us/Testing+Business+Ideas%3A+A+Field+Guide+for+Rapid+Experimentation-p-9781119551447
Ed: David J. Bland, Alexander Osterwalder. **Released:** November 2019. **Price:** $21, e-book; $35, paperback. **Description:** Describes how to test business ideas and plans to see if they work and how well, before committing time and resources to your endeavor. **Availability:** E-book; Print.

19083 ■ *"Thirsty Lion Cooks Up Big Expansion Plan"* in *Business Journal Portland* (Vol. 27, November 5, 2010, No. 36, pp. 1)
Pub: Portland Business Journal
Contact: Andy Giegerich, Managing Editor
E-mail: agiegerich@bizjournals.com
Ed: Wendy Culverwell. **Description:** Concept Entertainment Inc.'s impending launch of the Thirsty Lion Pub and Grill at the Washington Square in downtown Portland, Oregon is part of its West Coast expansion plan. A discussion of the planning involved in realizing Thirsty Lion is discussed, along with pub offerings that are expected to be enjoyed by customers. **Availability:** Print; Online.

19084 ■ *"Thomson Eyes Asia for Expansion"* in *Globe & Mail* (February 10, 2006, pp. B4)
Description: The business growth plans of Thomson Corp., in Asia, are presented. **Availability:** Print; Online.

19085 ■ *"Top Expenses Taking the Biggest Bite out of Your Business"* in *Legal Zoom* (March 27, 2023)
URL(s): www.legalzoom.com/articles/top-expenses-taking-the-biggest-bite-out-of-your-business
Ed: Stephanie Morrow. **Released:** March 27, 2023. **Description:** Lists and discusses five areas where your business may be draining money and gives advice on what to do to stop it. **Availability:** Online.

19086 ■ *"Transforming the Business Portfolio: How Multinationals Reinvent Themselves"* in *Journal of Business Strategy* (Vol. 35, May-June 2014, No. 3, pp. 4-17)
Pub: Emerald Group Publishing Limited
Contact: Erika Valenti, President
Description: Study on the process of business portfolio transformations to investigate its precursors, practices, and outcomes, including repositioning, refocusing, and diversifying of portfolio restructurings is presented. It is observed that poor performance and over-diversification induce portfolio restructuring. The results also revealed that diversifying or repositioning transformations feature a low success rate, whereas refocusing transformations generally happen to be more successful. **Availability:** Download; Online.

19087 ■ *"Unilever's CMO Finally Gets Down To Business"* in *Advertising Age* (Vol. 79, July 7, 2008, No. 26, pp. 11)
Description: Overview of Unilever's chief marketing officer Simon Clift's strategy for promoting its products; now that the company has restructured, Clift is able to focus all of his energy on the challenges of the new-media climate that marketers are having to face. **Availability:** Print; Online.

19088 ■ *"Union, Heal Thyself"* in *Canadian Business* (Vol. 81, July 21, 2008, No. 11, pp. 9)
Description: General Motors Corp. was offered by the federal government a $250 million fund after the company declared plans to close its facility in Ontario. The government move is geared towards supporting the workers who have refused to support the automotive company. Details of the labor contract between General Motors and the Canadian Auto Workers are presented. **Availability:** Print; Online.

19089 ■ *"U.S. Primaries: An Amazing Race"* in *Canadian Business* (Vol. 81, February 12, 2008, No. 3, pp. 25)
Pub: Rogers Media Inc.
Contact: Neil Spivak, Chief Executive Officer
Ed: Rachel Pulfer. **Description:** U.S. presidential candidates Barack Obama and Hilary Clinton lead the Democratic Part primaries while John McCain is a frontrunner at the Republican Party. These leading candidates have different plans for the U.S. economy which will affect Canada's own economy particularly concerning trade policies. The presidential candidates' proposals and the impacts of U.S. economic downturn on Canada are examined. **Availability:** Print; Online.

19090 ■ *"Virgin Mobile has Big Plans for Year Two"* in *Globe & Mail* (March 6, 2006, pp. B5)
Ed: Catherine McLean. **Description:** The business growth plans of Virgin Mobile Canada are presented. **Availability:** Online.

19091 ■ *"Walker Seeks More Business Participation"* in *Business Journal-Milwaukee* (Vol. 28, December 10, 2010, No. 10, pp. A1)
Pub: The Business Journal
Contact: Heather Ladage, President
E-mail: hladage@bizjournals.com
Ed: Rich Kirchen. **Description:** Wisconsin governor Scott Walker is seeking the aid of Milwaukee business leaders to participate in resolving the challenges posed by the economic crisis. Walker is aiming to create 250,000 jobs. He is also planning to call a special session of the legislature to enact strategies to jumpstart the economy. **Availability:** Print; Online.

GENERAL SMALL BUSINESS TOPICS

19092 ■ *"Weathering the Economic Storm"* in *Playthings* (Vol. 107, January 1, 2009, No. 1, pp. 10)
Ed: J. Tol Broome, Jr. **Description:** Six steps for toy companies to survive the economic turndown are outlined: Outline your business model; seek professional input; meet with your banker; cut your costs; manage your inventory; and use your trade credit. **Availability:** Print; Online.

19093 ■ *"Weyerhaeuser's REIT Decision Shouldn't Scare Investors Away"* in *Barron's* (Vol. 88, June 30, 2008, No. 26, pp. 18)
Pub: Dow Jones & Company Inc.
Contact: Almar Latour, Chief Executive Officer
Ed: Christopher Williams. **Description:** Weyerhaeuser Co.'s management said that a conversion to a real estate investment trust was not likely in 2009 since the move is not tax-efficient as of the moment and would overload its non-timber assets with debt. The company's shares have fallen by 19.5 percent. However, the company remains an asset-rich outfit and its activist shareholder is pushing for change. **Availability:** Online.

19094 ■ *"What Are You Doing Differently?"* in *Agency Sales Magazine* (Vol. 39, December 2009, No. 11, pp. 3)
Description: Strategies that sales representatives can do to plan for a good year include professional development, networking with other reps, and making more sales calls and seeing more people. The end of the year is the perfect time for reps to write or re-write their mission statement and to conduct line profitability. **Availability:** Print; Download; Online.

19095 ■ *"What Direction Is Your Company Moving In?"* in *South Florida Business Journal* (Vol. 35, August 29, 2014, No. 5, pp. 8)
Pub: American City Business Journals, Inc.
Contact: Mike Olivieri, Executive Vice President
Released: Weekly. **Price:** $8, introductory 4-week offer(Digital only). **Description:** Senior management should have a clear perspective about the direction of a company and work hard to effectively communicate such perspective to all stakeholders. Some ways on how corporate leaders can clarify the strategic plan of a company to its key stakeholders are suggested. **Availability:** Print; Online.

19096 ■ *"What to Do When Your Business Model No Longer Work"* in *Legal Zoom* (February 21, 2023)
URL(s): www.legalzoom.com/articles/what-to-do-when-your-business-model-no-longer-works
Ed: Marcia Layton Turner. **Released:** February 21, 2023. **Description:** Gives advice to business owners on what to do if their current business model is not yielding any results to do a change in the economy or a shift in the market. **Availability:** Online.

19097 ■ *"What Is A Profit And Loss Statement?"* in *Business News Daily* (March 6, 2023)
URL(s): www.businessnewsdaily.com/2359-profit-loss-statement-bndmp.html
Ed: Adam Uzialko. **Released:** March 06, 2023. **Description:** Explains what a profit and loss statement is and how businesses can use them to their advantage. **Availability:** Online.

19098 ■ *"What Is the Profit Potential with a New Cleaning Business?"* on *The Maid Coach* (November 8, 2019)
Ed: Debbie Sardone. **Released:** November 08, 2019. **Description:** Describes the profit potential of a cleaning business based on the work put into the business, business expenses, number of employees and quality of employees. **Availability:** Online.

19099 ■ *When Family Businesses are Best: The Parallel Planning Process for Family Harmony and Business Success*
Pub: Palgrave Macmillan

Ed: Randel S. Carlock, John L. Ward. **Released:** First edition. **Description:** An exploration into effective planning and communication to help small businesses grow into multi-generation family enterprises. **Availability:** E-book; Print.

19100 ■ *"Why CVS May Not Get Burned By Its Tobacco Decision (Part 2); Looking at CVS' Decision To Discontinue Selling Tobacco Products In Purely Dollar Terms Misses the Bigger Picture"* in *Gallup Business Journal* (March 20, 2014)
Pub: Gallup, Inc.
Contact: Jon Clifton, Chief Executive Officer
Description: Drug retailer, CVS, made a strategic play in organizational identity, mission, and purpose when it decided to quit selling cigarettes at its retail stores. The decision to discontinue sales of tobacco products could, long term, strengthen the company's identity in the U.S. marketplace, thus increasing sales. **Availability:** Print; Online.

19101 ■ *"Why Intel Should Dump Its Flash-Memory Business"* in *Barron's* (Vol. 88, March 10, 2008, No. 10, pp. 35)
Pub: Dow Jones & Company Inc.
Contact: Almar Latour, Chief Executive Officer
Ed: Eric J. Savitz. **Description:** Intel Corp. must sell its NAND flash-memory business as soon as it possibly can to the highest bidder to focus on its PC processor business and take advantage of other business opportunities. Apple should consider a buyback of 10 percent of the company's shares to lift its stock. **Availability:** Online.

19102 ■ *"Worth His Salt"* in *Hawaii Business* (Vol. 53, January 2008, No. 7, pp. 45)
Pub: PacificBasin Communications
Contact: Chuck Tindle, Director
E-mail: chuckt@pacificbasin.net
Ed: Jolyn Okimoto Rosa. **Description:** Bryan Zada owns three PretzelMaker franchises, whose total loss amounted to $40,000 in 2003. Zada believes that listening to employees was one of the key steps in turning the business around. The efforts made to improve the franchises' products are also given. **Availability:** Online.

19103 ■ *"Young Entrepreneur's Business Plan? An Ice Cream Boat? Really Floats: Maine at Work"* in *Portland Press Herald* (August 9, 2010)
Pub: Portland Press Herald
Contact: Lisa DeSisto, Chief Executive Officer
Ed: Ray Routhier. **Description:** Profile of Jake Viola, founder of and ice cream boat located near Portland, Maine. Viola is a sophomore at Yale University and sells ice cream from his pontoon boat on Little Sebago lake. **Availability:** Print; Online.

19104 ■ *"Young Millionaires"* in *Entrepreneur* (Vol. 35, October 2007, No. 10, pp. 76)
Pub: Entrepreneur Media Inc.
Contact: Dan Bova, Director
E-mail: dbova@entrepreneur.com
Ed: Jason Ankeny. **Description:** Young successful entrepreneurs of 2007 were chosen to talk about their success story and their business strategies in the past and those for the future. Among those featured are Kelly Flatley, Brendan Synnott, Herman Flores, Myles Kovacs, Haythem Haddad, Jim Wetzel, Lance Lawson, Jacob DeHart, Jake Nickell, Tim Vanderhook, Chris Vanderhook, Russell Vanderhook, Megan Duckett, Brad Sugars, John Vechey, Brian Fiete, Jason Kapalka, Nathan Jones, Devon Rifkin, Ryan Black, Ed Nichols, Jeremy Black, Amy Smilovic, Bob Shallenberger, and John Cavanagh.

19105 ■ *Your Guide to Preparing a Plan to Raise Money for Your Own Business*
Pub: Productive Publications
Contact: Iain Williamson, Author Publisher
Ed: Iain Williamson. **Released:** Revised edition. **Price:** C$68.95, softcover, Postage/handling $19.95 on first title, Add postage/handling of $3.50 per title thereafter. **Description:** A good business plan is essential for raising money for any small business. **Availability:** Print.

19106 ■ *"Zell Takes a Gamble on Tribune"* in *Globe & Mail* (April 3, 2007, pp. B1)
Ed: Sinclair Stewart. **Description:** The purchase of the majority share in Tribune Co. by Samuel Zell is described. Samuel Zell's plans to keep the company's assets intact are discussed. **Availability:** Online.

19107 ■ *"Zucker's HBC Shakeup Imminent"* in *Globe & Mail* (February 20, 2006, pp. B3)
Ed: Marina Strauss. **Description:** The plans of investor Jerry Zucker to revamp Hudson's Bay Co., upon its acquisition, are presented. **Availability:** Online.

VIDEO/AUDIO MEDIA

19108 ■ *The How of Business: Annual Strategic Plan*
URL(s): www.thehowofbusiness.com/504-annual-strategic-plan
Ed: Henry Lopez. **Released:** January 08, 2024. **Description:** Podcast explains why an annual strategic plan is essential for small business owners.

19109 ■ *The How of Business: Entrepreneurial Leap - Your Nightmare or Dream*
URL(s): www.thehowofbusiness.com/episode-350-entrepreneurial-nightmare-dream
Ed: Henry Lopez. **Released:** January 12, 2021. **Description:** Podcast explains how to avoid a nightmare business scenario.

19110 ■ *The How of Business: Is Your Business Model Broken?*
URL(s): www.thehowofbusiness.com/532-broken-business-model
Ed: Henry Lopez. **Released:** August 05, 2024. **Description:** Podcast examines profit, scaling, and competition to determine whether you have a solid business model.

19111 ■ *The How of Business: Peter Mehit - Business Planning*
URL(s): www.thehowofbusiness.com/episode-048-peter-mehit
Ed: Henry Lopez. **Released:** October 17, 2016. **Description:** Podcast offers tips on business plans for small businesses.

19112 ■ *The How of Business: Rebecca Ryan - Strategic Foresight*
URL(s): www.thehowofbusiness.com/422-rebecca-ryan-strategic-foresight
Ed: Henry Lopez. **Released:** May 16, 2022. **Description:** Podcast discusses the difference between strategic planning and strategic foresight; suggests how small business owners can anticipate future impacts on business.

19113 ■ *The How of Business: Small Business Plans*
URL(s): www.thehowofbusiness.com/382-small-business-plans
Ed: Henry Lopez. **Released:** July 26, 2021. **Description:** Podcast describes and explains how to create a small business plan.

19114 ■ *Market, Traction, and Milestones - Back of the Napkin to Business Plan in 11 Slides with Brandon White*
URL(s): podcasts.apple.com/us/podcast/market-traction-and-milestones-back-of-the/id1377376636?i=1000618609475
Ed: Mike Jesowshek. **Released:** June 28, 2023. **Description:** Podcast offers tip on identifying market opportunities and developing a go-to-market plan.

19115 ■ *This Is Small Business: Next Generation: Balancing Act*
URL(s): www.smallbusiness.amazon/podcast-episodes/next-generation-balancing-act

Ed: Andrea Marquez. **Released:** July 11, 2023. **Description:** Podcast follows teams in the Rice Business Plan Competition as they pefect their pitches.

19116 ■ *This Is Small Business: Next Generation: High $takes*
URL(s): www.smallbusiness.amazon/podcast-episodes/next-generation-high-stakes
Ed: Andrea Marquez. **Released:** June 20, 2023. **Description:** Podcast discusses making your pitch and polishing your business plan. Offered through the Amazon Small Business Academy.

19117 ■ *This Is Small Business: Next Generation: The First Eliminations*
URL(s): www.smallbusiness.amazon/podcast-episodes/next-generation-the-first-eliminations
Released: July 25, 2023. **Description:** Podcast highlights the first round of eliminations in the Rice Business Plan Competition.

19118 ■ *This Is Small Business: Next Generation: The Practice Pitch (Navigating Nerves and Feedback)*
URL(s): www.smallbusiness.amazon/podcast-episodes/next-generation-the-practice-pitch-navigating-nerves-and-feedback
Ed: Andrea Marquez. **Released:** July 18, 2023. **Description:** Podcast follows competitors in the Rice Business Plan Competition as the receive feedback on their pitches.

19119 ■ *This Is Small Business: Next Generation: Unveiling the Contenders (Part One)*
URL(s): www.smallbusiness.amazon/podcast-episodes/next-generation-unveiling-the-contenders-part-one
Ed: Andrea Marquez. **Released:** July 27, 2023. **Description:** Podcast introduces the Rice Business Plan Competition.

19120 ■ *This Is Small Business: Next Generation: Unveiling the Contenders (Part Two)*
URL(s): www.smallbusiness.amazon/podcast-episodes/next-generation-unveiling-the-contenders-part-two
Ed: Andrea Marquez. **Released:** July 04, 2023. **Description:** Podcast discusses the Rice Business Plan Competition.

19121 ■ *This Is Small Business: Next Generation: We Win Some, We Lose Some*
URL(s): www.smallbusiness.amazon/podcast-episodes/next-generation-we-win-some-we-lose-some
Ed: Andrea Marquez. **Released:** August 01, 2023. **Description:** Podcast reveals the winners of the Rice Business Plan Competition.

19122 ■ *This Is Small Business: Next Generation: What Comes Next?*
URL(s): www.smallbusiness.amazon/podcast-episodes/next-generation-what-comes-next
Ed: Andrea Marquez. **Released:** August 01, 2023. **Description:** Podcast follows up on the contestants from the Rice Business Plan Competition.

19123 ■ *Title, Problem, and Solution - Back of the Napkin to Business Plan in 11 Slides with Brandon White*
URL(s): podcasts.apple.com/us/podcast/title-problem-and-solution-back-of-the-napkin-id1377276636?i=1000617835520
Released: June 21, 2023. **Description:** Podcast offers advice on creating an elevator pitch and developing a business plan.

19124 ■ *What Is Strategic Planning?*
URL(s): podcasts.apple.com/us/podcast/what-is-strategic-planning/id1377376636?i=1000595201598
Ed: Mike Jesowshek. **Released:** January 18, 2023. **Description:** Podcast discusses the importance of bookkeeping, tax planning, and strategic planning.

TRADE SHOWS AND CONVENTIONS

19125 ■ **OPEX Business Transformation World Summit**
Frequency: Annual. **Description:** An operational excellence and business transformation conference. Provides talks on new business practices, innovation, change leadership, AI, process improvement, plus other topics. **Audience:** Decision makers and transformation leaders for businesses. **Principal Exhibits:** An operational excellence and business transformation conference. Provides talks on new business practices, innovation, change leadership, AI, process improvement, plus other topics.

CONSULTANTS

19126 ■ **Ameriwest Business Consultants Inc. (ABCI)**
PO Box 26266
Colorado Springs, CO 80936
Ph: (719)380-7096
Fax: (719)380-7096
Co. E-mail: email@abchelp.com
URL: http://www.abchelp.com
Description: Firm specializes in assisting startup businesses and those with sales of five million dollars or less and lesser than 50 employees. **Scope:** Firm specializes in assisting startup businesses and those with sales of five million dollars or less and lesser than 50 employees. **Founded:** 1984.

19127 ■ **Beacon Management-Management Consultants**
Pompano Beach, FL 33069
Co. E-mail: md@beaconmgmt.com
URL: http://www.beaconmgmt.com
Contact: Michael J. Donnelly, Consultant Managing Director Principal
Description: Provider of management consulting services such as strategic and business planning, market intelligence, decision support services, corporate finance, and much more. **Scope:** Provider of management consulting services such as strategic and business planning, market intelligence, decision support services, corporate finance, and much more. **Founded:** 1985. **Publications:** "Sun-Sentinel Article," Oct, 2012.

19128 ■ **Biomedical Management Resources (BMR)**
4131 Fortuna Way
Salt Lake City, UT 84124
Contact: Ping Fong, Jr., Contact
E-mail: pfongbmr@gmail.com
Description: Provides business development, interim management and executive search services. Assists companies in strategic alliances, corporate partnering, business acquisition. Demonstrated success in identifying recruiting and placing key managers in difficult to hire positions. **Scope:** Provides business development, interim management and executive search services. Assists companies in strategic alliances, corporate partnering, business acquisition. Demonstrated success in identifying recruiting and placing key managers in difficult to hire positions.

19129 ■ **Business Development Group Inc. (BDG)**
29255 Laurel Wood Dr., No. 202
Southfield, MI 48034
Ph: (248)358-0121
URL: http://www.busdevgroup.com
Contact: Shernon Harriyton, Director
Description: Consulting firm with expertise in leadership development, strategic thinking, organizational transformation, team-based work systems, organizational learning, rapid change, knowledge management, competitive intelligence, crisis management, merger and acquisition integration, product integration and new product development. **Scope:** Consulting firm with expertise in leadership development, strategic thinking, organizational transformation, team-based work systems, organizational learning, rapid change, knowledge management, competitive intelligence, crisis management, merger and acquisition integration, product integration and new product development. **Publications:** "Navigating in the Sea of Change," Competitive Intelligence Review Journal; "The Influence of Cultural Aspects of Strategic Information, Analysis and Delivery"; "What Leadership Needs From Competitive Intelligence Professionals," Journal of Association for Global and Strategic Information. **Training:** Process of Self-Design for the Evolving Organization; Large System Change Intervention; Self Assessment and the Transformational Process; The Knowledge Exchange - Shared Practices Workshop.

19130 ■ **Business Planning Consultants, Inc.**
9305 172nd St. E
South Hill, WA 98375
Contact: Michael Cady, Governor
Description: Firm is engaged in the preparation of business plans and feasibility studies for multi-use developments including shopping centers, manufacturing, and mining and also prepares financing proposals for seed and venture capital and bank loans and plans community economic development programs recruiting new business, business retention programs, financing programs and central business district revitalization. **Scope:** Firm is engaged in the preparation of business plans and feasibility studies for multi-use developments including shopping centers, manufacturing, and mining and also prepares financing proposals for seed and venture capital and bank loans and plans community economic development programs recruiting new business, business retention programs, financing programs and central business district revitalization.

19131 ■ **Business Visions L.L.C.**
5806 W Duffy Rd.
Georgetown, IN 47122
Contact: Sandra M. Ringer, Contact

19132 ■ **BusinessPlanWorld.com**
PO Box 1322, Sta. B
Mississauga, ON, Canada L4Y 4B6
Co. E-mail: theboss@businessplanworld.com
URL: http://www.businessplanworld.com
Description: Provider of tools for new entrepreneurs to evaluate business ideas and develop business plans. **Scope:** Provider of tools for new entrepreneurs to evaluate business ideas and develop business plans. **Founded:** 1989. **Publications:** "How to open a Bed and Breakfast"; "How to open a Bookstore"; "How to open a Restaurant"; "How to open a Youth Center"; "How to open a Rough Collie Kennel"; "How to open a Video Store"; "How to open a Confectionery Store"; "How to open a Night Club/Bar".

19133 ■ **CRO Engineering Ltd.**
1895 William Hodgins Ln.
Carp, ON, Canada K0A 1L0
Ph: (613)839-1108
Fax: (305)832-8232
Co. E-mail: grefford@ieee.org
URL: http://www.oocities.org
Description: Provider of system engineering and project management services. **Scope:** Provider of system engineering and project management services. **Founded:** 1997. **Publications:** "A setup-planning prototype implemented in tolerance graphs and related matrices," International Journal of Production Research, 2001. **Training:** The Importance of Early Child Care and Development, July, 2001.

19134 ■ **DRI Consulting Inc. (DRIC)**
Two Otter Ln.
Saint Paul, MN 55127
Ph: (651)415-1400
Co. E-mail: dric@dric.com
URL: http://www.dric.com
Contact: Dr. John Fennig, Director
Description: Provides high-quality, research-based services and training in leadership, team processes, supervision, and management, and organizational development, clients with direct and substantial impact on individual and team performance and on

GENERAL SMALL BUSINESS TOPICS

organizational success through proven processes for selecting, developing and deploying leaders. **Scope:** Provides high-quality, research-based services and training in leadership, team processes, supervision, and management, and organizational development, clients with direct and substantial impact on individual and team performance and on organizational success through proven processes for selecting, developing and deploying leaders. **Founded:** 1991.

19135 ■ Elizabeth Capen
415 Madison Ave., 17th Fl.
New York, NY 10017
Ph: (212)644-2222
Co. E-mail: ecapen@lansco.com
URL: http://www.lansco.com
Contact: Elizabeth Capen, Contact
E-mail: ecapen@lansco.com

Description: Focuses on strategic marketing planning and positioning. Identifies effective marketing tools, plans and reviews advertising and collateral materials, writes business plans and performs secondary research and competitive analysis. Industries served services, small businesses and entrepreneurial ventures in northeastern and middle Atlantic regions. **Scope:** Focuses on strategic marketing planning and positioning. Identifies effective marketing tools, plans and reviews advertising and collateral materials, writes business plans and performs secondary research and competitive analysis. Industries served services, small businesses and entrepreneurial ventures in northeastern and middle Atlantic regions. **Training:** Handling Issues of Growth; Using Published Information as a Marketing Tool.

19136 ■ Healthscope Inc.
129 Cedarbrook Rd.
Ardmore, PA 19003
Ph: (610)687-6199
Co. E-mail: healthscope@verizon.net
URL: http://healthscopeinc.net
Contact: Brain R. King, President

Description: An independent health care management and consulting firm. Provides business planning, decision making and implementation support. Specialties include strategic business consulting, business plan development focused on bottom line improvement, revenue enhancement expense reduction planning and implementation, practice expansion consolidation, feasibility studies and decision making and more. **Scope:** An independent health care management and consulting firm. Provides business planning, decision making and implementation support. Specialties include strategic business consulting, business plan development focused on bottom line improvement, revenue enhancement expense reduction planning and implementation, practice expansion consolidation, feasibility studies and decision making and more. **Founded:** 1986.

19137 ■ Hewitt Development Enterprises (HDE)
1717 N Bayshore Dr., Ste. 2154
Miami, FL 33132
Ph: (305)372-0941
Fax: (305)372-0941
Co. E-mail: info@hewittdevelopment.com
URL: http://www.hewittdevelopment.com
Contact: Robert G. Hewitt, Contact
E-mail: bob@hewittdevelopment.com

Description: Firm specializes in strategic planning, profit enhancement, startup businesses, interim and crisis management, turnarounds, production planning, just-in-time inventory and project management, serves senior management and acquirers of distressed businesses. **Scope:** Firm specializes in strategic planning, profit enhancement, startup businesses, interim and crisis management, turnarounds, production planning, just-in-time inventory and project management, serves senior management and acquirers of distressed businesses. **Founded:** 1985.

19138 ■ Horizon Consulting Services
12660 S Fig Ave.
Caruthers, CA 93609
Contact: Jon Robison, Contact

Description: Firm assists start-up to mid-sized businesses to grow and increase profits through effective business plans and operational programs and areas of expertise include business plans and strategies, market evaluations, competitive analysis, pricing, financial plans and budgets, financial management, marketing strategies, product positioning and introduction, forecasting and analysis and business policies and procedures. **Scope:** Firm assists start-up to mid-sized businesses to grow and increase profits through effective business plans and operational programs and areas of expertise include business plans and strategies, market evaluations, competitive analysis, pricing, financial plans and budgets, financial management, marketing strategies, product positioning and introduction, forecasting and analysis and business policies and procedures.

19139 ■ John Alan Cohan
16133 Ventura Blvd., NO.700
Encino, CA 91436
Ph: (310)278-0203
Co. E-mail: johnalancohan@aol.com
URL: http://cohanlawoffice.com
Contact: John Alan Cohan, Contact
E-mail: johnalancohan@aol.com

Description: Specializes in tax law, probate, and conservatorships. The company handles complex tax audits, prepares tax compliance and regulatory opinion letters for trade associations, tax-exempt organizations and individual clients. It also offers in-depth knowledge regarding livestock, horse, and agricultural matters. **Founded:** 1981.

19140 ■ Market Focus, Inc.
2307 Fenton Pkwy. No. 134
San Diego, CA 92108
Free: 800-708-9715
Co. E-mail: sales@emarketfocus.com
URL: http://www.emarketfocus.com
Contact: Chris Carter, Contact
Facebook: www.facebook.com/marketfocusinc

Description: Provider of custom qualitative and quantitative market research designed to answer key questions and then offers ideas that generate results. Provides counsel in marketing research and planning and marketing programs, particularly for financial service organizations, banking, insurance, electronics, publishing and industrial organizations. **Founded:** 1992. **Publications:** "Surviving in Hard Times," NJ Contractor. **Training:** Charting a Course for Future Company Growth; Marketing Planning; Construction Marketing in the 90's; Marketing and The CFO.

19141 ■ McShane Group L.L.C.
2119 E Franklin St.
Richmond, VA 23223
URL: http://www.mcshanegroup.com
Contact: Jim L. Huitt, Jr., Principal
E-mail: jhuitt@mcshanegroup.com

Description: Firm provides diligence services, interim management, strategic business realignments, marketing, and much more. **Scope:** Firm provides diligence services, interim management, strategic business realignments, marketing, and much more. **Founded:** 1987.

19142 ■ Mefford, Knutson & Associates Inc. (MKA)
6437 Lyndale Ave. S
Richfield, MN 55423
Co. E-mail: info@mkcconsulting.com
URL: http://mkaconsulting.com
Contact: Jeanette Mefford, Co-Founder

Description: Provider of consulting services to home health and related sectors. **Scope:** Provider of consulting services to home health and related sectors. **Founded:** 1990.

19143 ■ MoneySoft Inc.
2415 E Camelback Rd., Ste. 700
Phoenix, AZ 85016
Ph: (602)266-7710
Free: 800-966-7797
Co. E-mail: contact@moneysoft.com
URL: http://moneysoft.com

Linkedin: www.linkedin.com/company/moneysoft-inc-/about
X (Twitter): x.com/MoneySoftUSA

Description: Developer of finance applications software. **Scope:** Specializes in the publication of software for the corporate acquisition and development communities. **Founded:** 1991. **Publications:** "The Price is Right? Or is It?"; "Preparing Financial Projections and Valuations"; "Negotiating Business Acquisitions"; "Managing the Process of Buying a Business"; "The Overpayment Trap"; "Strategies to Avoid the Overpayment Trap"; "The Value, Price and Cost of an Acquisition"; "The Trouble with EBITDA". **Special Services:** Corporate Valuation Professional®; DealSense®; Buy-OutPlan®; Corporate Valuation Professional®; Lightning Deal Reviewer?; Fixed Asset Pro®; Benchmark Pro 2006®; DealSense Plus; Mergerstat?.

19144 ■ Nightingale Associates
7445 Setting Sun Way
Columbia, MD 21046
Ph: (410)381-4280
URL: http://www.nightingaleassociates.net
Contact: Frederick C. Nightingale, Managing Director
E-mail: fredericknightingale@nightingaleassociates.net
X (Twitter): x.com/FCNightingale

Description: Management training and consulting firm offering the following skills productivity and accomplishment, leadership skills for the experienced manager, management skills for the new manager, leadership and teambuilding, supervisory development, creative problem solving, real strategic planning. **Scope:** Management training and consulting firm offering the following skills productivity and accomplishment, leadership skills for the experienced manager, management skills for the new manager, leadership and teambuilding, supervisory development, creative problem solving, real strategic planning. **Founded:** 1984. **Training:** Productivity and Accomplishment Management Skills for the New Manager; Leadership and Team building; Advanced Management; Business Process Re engineering; Strategic Thinking; Creative Problem Solving; Customer Service; International Purchasing and Materials Management; Fundamentals of Purchasing; Negotiation Skills Development; Providing superior customer service; Leadership skills for the experienced manager.

19145 ■ The One Page Business Plan Co.
21001 San Ramon Valley Blvd., Ste. A4101
San Ramon, CA 94583
Ph: (510)705-8400
Co. E-mail: info@onepagebusinessplan.com
URL: http://onepagebusinessplan.com
Contact: Robert Sher, Chief Executive Officer
Linkedin: www.linkedin.com/company/the-one-page-business-plan-company

Description: Publishes a series of books on writing one-page business plans. Reaches market through publisher's website. **Scope:** Specializing in innovative planning and enterprise performance management tools. Specializes in planning and performance management systems. **Publications:** "The One Page Business Plan for the Creative Entrepreneur"; "The One Page Business Plan for the Busy Executive"; "The One Page Business Plan for Non-Profit Organizations"; "The One Page Business Plan for the Professional Consultant"; "The One Page Business Plan for Financial Services Professionals"; "The One Page Business Plan for the Creative Entrepreneur"; "The One Page Business Plan for Women in Business".

19146 ■ Performance Consultants Group, Inc. (PCG)
1 Innovation Way., Ste. 400
Newark, DE 19711
Ph: (302)738-7532
Free: 888-724-3578
URL: http://www.pcgius.com

Description: Firm provides consulting services in the areas of strategic planning, profit enhancement, product development, and production planning.

Scope: Firm provides consulting services in the areas of strategic planning, profit enhancement, product development, and production planning. **Founded:** 1988.

19147 ■ Performance Consulting Associates, Inc. (PCA)
3700 Crestwood Pky., Ste. 100
Duluth, GA 30096
Ph: (770)717-2737
Co. E-mail: info@pcaconsulting.com
URL: http://pcaconsulting.com
Contact: Richard deFazio, President
Linkedin: www.linkedin.com/company/pcaconsulting
Description: Firm provides asset management solutions, business process optimization, and much more. **Scope:** Firm provides asset management solutions, business process optimization, and much more. **Founded:** 1976. **Publications:** "Does Planning Pay," Plant Services, Nov, 2000; "Asset Reliability Coordinator," Maintenance Technology, Oct, 2000; "Know What it is You Have to Maintain," Maintenance Technology, May, 2000; "Does Maintenance Planning Pay," Maintenance Technology, Nov, 2000.; "What is Asset Management?"; "Implementing Best Business Practices".

19148 ■ S-FX.com Small Business Solutions
NJ
Ph: (609)318-3489
Co. E-mail: solutions@s-fx.com
Contact: Victoria Sous, Manager
E-mail: victoria@s-fx.com
X (Twitter): twitter.com/sfxdotcom
Instagram: www.instagram.com/sfxdotcom
YouTube: www.youtube.com/channel/
UCFKCGYUBUcS7MyY30jnlkuw
Description: A technology consulting agency specializing in web design, digital marketing, branding, and business development for small businesses, non-profit organizations, and startups. **Scope:** A technology consulting agency specializing in web design, digital marketing, branding, and business development for small businesses, non-profit organizations, and startups.

19149 ■ Tamayo Consulting Inc.
662 Encinitas Blvd., Ste. 236
Encinitas, CA 92024
Ph: (760)479-1352
URL: http://www.tamayoconsulting.com
Contact: Jennifer Dreyer, President
Description: It Provides training and consulting services. And also it specializes in leadership and team development. Industries served: private, non-profit, government, educational. **Scope:** It Provides training and consulting services. And also it specializes in leadership and team development. Industries served: private, non-profit, government, educational. **Training:** Presentation AdvantEdge Program; Lead point Development Program; Supervisor Development Programs.Identify Presentation Objectives; Implement 360-degree presentation assessment; conduct baseline-coaching session; Develop coaching plan; Staying connected.

COMPUTER SYSTEMS/ SOFTWARE

19150 ■ *Automate Your Business Plan*
Out of Your Mind..and Into the Marketplace
13381 White Sand Dr.
Tustin, CA 92780-4565
Ph: (714)544-0248
Fax: (714)730-1414
URL: http://www.business-plan.com
Contact: Linda Pinson, Contact
E-mail: lpinson@aol.com
URL(s): www.business-plan.com/automate.html
Price: $80, for software without eBook; $90, for software with eBook; $95, Individuals for shipment of software package. **Description:** A computer program designed to help prepare a business plan. **Availability:** Print; Online; Download; PDF.

INTERNET DATABASES

19151 ■ *Business and Labor History: Primary Sources at the Library of Congress*
URL(s): guides.loc.gov/business-and-labor-history
Description: An online resource providing links to key topics to business and labor history. Contains links to company records, presidential papers, government agencies, judicial papers, and primary sources. **Availability:** Online.

RESEARCH CENTERS

19152 ■ Chadron State College - Nebraska Business Development Center (NBDC)
200 Mammel Hall, 67th & Pine St.
Omaha, NE 68106
Ph: (402)554-2521
Co. E-mail: nbdc@unomaha.edu
URL: http://www.csc.edu/academics/business/nebraska-business-development-center
Contact: Veronica Doga, Director
E-mail: vdoga@unomaha.edu
Description: A cooperative program of the U.S. Small Business Administration and Chadron State College. Offers clinical services. **Scope:** Involves in management education, market research, marketing plans, strategic planning, financial planning, cash flow budgeting, capital budgeting, loan packaging, rural development, and business plans. **Founded:** 1977. **Publications:** *NBDC Business Calendar* (Annual). **Educational Activities:** Chadron State College Continuing education programs.

19153 ■ University of Nebraska, Omaha College of Business Administration - Nebraska Business Development Center (NBDC)
6001 Dodge St.
Omaha, NE 68182
Ph: (402)554-6232
Co. E-mail: nbdc@unomaha.edu
URL: http://www.unomaha.edu/nebraska-business-development-center/index.php
Contact: Tony Schultz, Director
E-mail: tonyschultz@unomaha.edu
Facebook: www.facebook.com/
NebraskaBusinessDevelopmentCenter
Linkedin: www.linkedin.com/company/nebraska-business-development-center
X (Twitter): x.com/NBDC_nebraska
YouTube: www.youtube.com/c/
NebraskaBusinessDevelopmentCenterNBDC
Description: Serves the Nebraska community. **Scope:** Sustainable development, technology commercialization, management education, market research, marketing plans, strategic planning, financial planning, cash flow budgeting, capital budgeting, loan packaging, and rural development. **Founded:** 1977. **Publications:** *Keys to Successful Business Start-Up in Nebraska*; *NBDC Business Calendar* (Annual). **Educational Activities:** Professional and Organizational Development Workshop, Offer exemplary teaching and training programs. **Geographic Preference:** Local.

Business Relocation

REFERENCE WORKS

19154 ■ *"1Q Office Vacancies Mainly Up; Class A Space Bucks Trend, Falls"* in *Crain's Detroit Business (Vol. 24, April 14, 2008, No. 15)*
Pub: Crain Communications Inc.
Contact: Barry Asin, President
Ed: Daniel Duggan. **Description:** Although more office space became vacant in the first quarter, Class A space went in the opposite direction with several local businesses are moving from less-desirable to more desirable areas. **Availability:** Online.

19155 ■ *"Aeronautics Seeking New HQ Site"* in *The Business Journal-Milwaukee (Vol. 25, September 5, 2008, No. 50, pp. 1)*
Description: Milwaukee, Wisconsin-based Aeronautics Corp. of America is planning to move its headquarters to a new site. The company has started to search for a new site. It also plans to consolidate its operations under one roof.

19156 ■ *"Aircraft Maker May Land in Austin"* in *Austin Business Journal (Vol. 31, April 15, 2011, No. 6, pp. 1)*
Pub: Austin Business Journal
Contact: Rachel McGrath, Director
E-mail: rmcgrath@bizjournals.com
Ed: Jacob Dirr. **Description:** Icon Aircraft Inc. is planning to build a manufacturing facility in Austin, Texas. The company needs 100,000 square feet of space in a new or renovated plant. Executive comments are included. **Availability:** Print; Online.

19157 ■ *"Airmall Mulls I-95 Travel Plazas Bid"* in *Baltimore Business Journal (Vol. 29, September 2, 2011, No. 17, pp. 3)*
Pub: Boston Business Journal
Contact: Carolyn M. Jones, President
E-mail: cmjones@bizjournals.com
Ed: Alexander Jackson. **Description:** Airmall USA is planning to move its food courts from the Baltimore/Washington International Thurgood Marshall Airport to the new travel plazas on Interstate 95. The plazas are up for bid. **Availability:** Online.

19158 ■ *"Another California Firm Moving to Austin"* in *Austin Business Journal (Vol. 31, May 6, 2011, No. 9, pp. 1)*
Pub: Austin Business Journal
Contact: Rachel McGrath, Director
E-mail: rmcgrath@bizjournals.com
Ed: Christopher Calnan. **Description:** Main Street Hub Inc. is planning to build a facility in Austin, Texas. The company helps businesses manage their online reputations. Main Street has selected Aquila Commercial LLC as its real estate broker. **Availability:** Print; Online.

19159 ■ *"Atlanta BeltLine Inc. Could Leave Underground Atlanta"* in *Atlanta Business Chronicle (July 11, 2014, pp. 14A)*
Pub: American City Business Journals, Inc.
Contact: Mike Olivieri, Executive Vice President

Released: July 11, 2014. **Price:** $4, introductory 4-week offer(Digital only). **Description:** Paul Morris, CEO of Atlanta BeltLine Inc. reports that the firm may leave its present location in Underground Atlanta. The company is looking to relocate to another location in the downtown Atlanta area. **Availability:** Print; Online; Mailing list.

19160 ■ *"Bellingham Boatbuilder Norstar Yachts Maintains Family Tradition"* in *Bellingham Business Journal (Vol. February 2010, pp. 12)*
Description: Profile of Norstar Yachts and brothers Gary and Steve Nordtvedt who started the company in 1994. The company recently moved its operations to a 12,000 square foot space in the Fairhaven Marine Industrial Park. **Availability:** Print; Online.

19161 ■ *"Boeing Moving 1,000 Washington Engineering Jobs to California"* in *Business Journal Portland (Vol. 31, April 11, 2014, No. 6)*
Pub: American City Business Journals, Inc.
Contact: Mike Olivieri, Executive Vice President
Released: Weekly. **Description:** Boeing plans to move 1,000 engineering jobs from Portland, Oregon to Southern California. The company says the move helps support planes in service at the company's Commercial Airplanes Engineering Center in Southern California and position the aerospace manufacturer for further growth. **Availability:** Print; Online.

19162 ■ *"Bond Hill Cinema Site To See New Life"* in *Business Courier (Vol. 27, October 29, 2010, No. 26, pp. 1)*
Pub: Business Courier
Ed: Dan Monk. **Description:** Avondale, Ohio's Corinthian Baptist Church will redevelop the 30-acre former Showcase Cinema property to a mixed-use site that could feature a college, senior home, and retail. Corinthian Baptist, which is one of the largest African-American churches in the region, is also planning to relocate the church. **Availability:** Print; Online.

19163 ■ *"Cengage Learning Makes Boston Its Headquarters"* in *Boston Business Journal (Vol. 34, April 25, 2014, No. 12, pp. 6)*
Pub: American City Business Journals, Inc.
Contact: Mike Olivieri, Executive Vice President
Released: April 14, 2014. **Description:** Cengage Learning's office in Boston, Massachusetts will become the company's new corporate headquarters. The educational publishing firm, which has more than 400 employees in Boston, is also expected to develop new digital products for higher education. **Availability:** Print; Mailing list; Online.

19164 ■ *"Central Freight Lines Relocates Irving Terminal"* in *Dallas Business Journal (Vol. 35, March 2, 2012, No. 25, pp. 1)*
Pub: Baltimore Business Journal
Contact: Rhonda Pringle, President
E-mail: rpringle@bizjournals.com

Description: Waco, Texas-based trucking firm Central Freight Lines Inc. is relocating its operational headquarters to Fort Worth from Irving. The relocation is the result of the changing vision for the old Texas stadium area, along with safety concerns related to highway and light rail construction. **Availability:** Print; Online.

19165 ■ *"Chuy's Ready to Serve New Markets"* in *Austin Business Journal (Vol. 31, June 17, 2011, No. 15, pp. 1)*
Pub: Austin Business Journal
Contact: Rachel McGrath, Director
E-mail: rmcgrath@bizjournals.com
Ed: Cody Lyon. **Description:** Chuy's Holdings Inc. plans to expand into the Southeastern United States, particularly in Atlanta, Georgia. The restaurant, which secured $67.5 million in debt financing in May 2011, added 20 stores in five years and plans to open eight locations in 2011. **Availability:** Print; Online.

19166 ■ *"Cities Work to Attract Small Biz: Officials Review 'Hoops' and Master Plans"* in *Crain's Detroit Business (Vol. 25, June 8, 2009, No. 23, pp. 20)*
Pub: Crain Communications Inc.
Contact: Barry Asin, President
Ed: Nancy Kaffer. **Description:** Royal Oak and other metropolitan cities are trying to attract small companies to their towns. **Availability:** Print; Online; PDF.

19167 ■ *"City, County May Kill VC Tax"* in *Business Journal-Portland (Vol. 24, October 12, 2007, No. 33, pp. 1)*
Pub: Portland Business Journal
Contact: Andy Giegerich, Managing Editor
E-mail: agiegerich@bizjournals.com
Ed: Aliza Earnshow. **Description:** City of Portland and Multnomah County in Oregon may soon kill taxes levied on venture capital (VC) firms, which is expected to take place in late October 2007. Capitalists have long been saying that taxation is driving them out of town, but this change is expected to generate more investments and persuade VC firms to relocate within city limits. **Availability:** Print; Online.

19168 ■ *"Cynergy Data May Pick Memphis for HQ Move"* in *Memphis Business Journal (Vol. 33, February 10, 2012, No. 44, pp. 1)*
Pub: Baltimore Business Journal
Contact: Rhonda Pringle, President
E-mail: rpringle@bizjournals.com
Ed: Christopher Sheffield. **Description:** Cynergy Data LLC is planning to relocate its corporate headquarters to Memphis, Tennessee. The company will move 200 jobs to the new facility. **Availability:** Print; Online.

19169 ■ *"Exxon Mobil Campus 'Clearly Happening"* in *Houston Business Journal (Vol. 40, January 15, 2010, No. 36, pp. 1)*
Pub: Houston Business Journal
Contact: Bob Charlet, President
E-mail: bcharlet@bizjournals.com

Small Business Sourcebook • 42nd Edition

Ed: Jennifer Dawson. **Description:** Oil and gas company Exxon Mobil intends to relocate its employees from Houston, Texas and Fairfax, Virginia into a 400-acre site near the town of Spring, Texas. Meanwhile, Exxon Mobil has refused to disclose further details of the relocation plan. Insights from real estate professionals on this relocation plan are examined. **Availability:** Print; Online.

19170 ■ *"FIS-Metavante Deal Paying Off for Many"* in *Business Journal-Milwaukee (Vol. 28, December 17, 2010, No. 11, pp. A1)*
Pub: The Business Journal
Contact: Heather Ladage, President
E-mail: hladage@bizjournals.com
Ed: Rich Kirchen. **Description:** Jacksonville, Florida-based Fidelity National Information Services Inc., also known as FIS, has remained committed to Milwaukee, Wisconsin more than a year after purchasing Metavante Technologies Inc. FIS has transferred several operations into Metropolitan Milwaukee and has continued its contribution to charitable organizations in the area. **Availability:** Print; Online.

19171 ■ *"Flying Colors for All American Label"* in *Memphis Business Journal (Vol. 34, June 1, 2012, No. 7, pp. 1)*
Pub: Baltimore Business Journal
Contact: Rhonda Pringle, President
E-mail: rpringle@bizjournals.com
Ed: Michael Sheffield. **Description:** All American Label has moved to a new location and reported a 20 percent increase in earnings. **Availability:** Print; Online.

19172 ■ *"Frontage Labs Moves, Plans to Hire 100"* in *Philadelphia Business Journal (Vol. 28, July 13, 2012, No. 22, pp. 1)*
Pub: Baltimore Business Journal
Contact: Rhonda Pringle, President
E-mail: rpringle@bizjournals.com
Ed: Natalie Kostelni, John George. **Description:** Frontage Pharmaceuticals will relocate its headquarters from the Valley Creek Corporate Center in Exton, Pennsylvania after signing a long-term lease on 80,000 square feet of space at the Eagleview Corporate Center. The relocation came as the company intended to consolidate its offices. Frontage Pharmaceuticals will also hire up to 100 new employees. **Availability:** Print; Online.

19173 ■ *"Fur Centre Stakes Former Byron Cade Spot in Clayton"* in *St. Louis Business Journal (Vol. 33, August 10, 2012, No. 51, pp. 1)*
Pub: Baltimore Business Journal
Contact: Rhonda Pringle, President
E-mail: rpringle@bizjournals.com
Description: The Fur & Leather Centre is relocating from 601 S. Lindbergh Blvd. to the Byron Cade Building at 7901 Clayton Road in Saint Louis, Missouri. The store purchased the building for an undisclosedprice, while its current lease is set to expire in March 2013. **Availability:** Print; Online.

19174 ■ *"German Firm Ifm Electronic to Open Second Local Unit"* in *Philadelphia Business Journal (Vol. 28, July 20, 2012, No. 23, pp. 1)*
Pub: Baltimore Business Journal
Contact: Rhonda Pringle, President
E-mail: rpringle@bizjournals.com
Description: German electronic control and sensor manufacturer, ifm electronic gmbh, has established ifm prover USA in January 2012, its second subsidiary in Exton, Pennsylvania after ifm efector Inc. Ifm prover will relocate in July 2012 to a new 36,000 square foot building that features a product development area and multiple laboraties for testing and quality control. **Availability:** Print; Online.

19175 ■ *"Good for Business: Houston is a Hot Spot for Economic Growth"* in *Black Enterprise (Vol. 37, October 2006, No. 3, pp. 216)*
Pub: Earl G. Graves Ltd.
Contact: Earl Graves, Jr., President
Ed: Jeanette Valentine. **Description:** Fast-growing sectors in the biotechnology and healthcare industries are among the driving forces of Houston's economic growth. More than 76,000 small businesses in the area employ about one in four area workers, according to the Small Business Administration. Housing and business costs are 26 and 11 percent below the national average, respectively, garnering the attention of corporate giants.

19176 ■ *"Greenlight's Mission: Poach California"* in *Business Journal Portland (Vol. 26, December 11, 2009, No. 40, pp. 1)*
Pub: Portland Business Journal
Contact: Andy Giegerich, Managing Editor
E-mail: agiegerich@bizjournals.com
Ed: Andy Giegerich. **Description:** Leaders of Greenlight Greater Portland, a privately funded economic development organization, will visit California five times in 2010 in an attempt to lure California businesses to expand or relocate in Oregon. **Availability:** Print; Online.

19177 ■ *"Growing Encryptics Trades Frisco for Austin"* in *Austin Business Journal (Vol. 34, April 25, 2014, No. 10, pp. A8)*
Pub: American City Business Journals, Inc.
Contact: Mike Olivieri, Executive Vice President
Released: Weekly. **Price:** $4, Introductory 4-week offer(Digital & Print). **Description:** Frisco, Texas-based Encryptics Inc. has announced plans to relocate its headquarters with its 21 employees and negotiating for office space in West Austin's Loop 360 area. Encryptics also plans to increase the number of its employees to about 80 next year. Insights into Encryptics' email security softwar area also given. **Availability:** Print; Online.

19178 ■ *"Houston Tech Company Eyes California for HQ Move"* in *Houston Business Journal (Vol. 45, July 18, 2014, No. 10, pp. 10A)*
Pub: American City Business Journals, Inc.
Contact: Mike Olivieri, Executive Vice President
Released: Weekly. **Price:** $4, Introductory 4-week offer(Digital & Print). **Description:** Ed Chipul, CEO of Tendenci, a longtime Houston technology company, has stated that they are looking for a headquarters move to California. The decision to move to Silicon Valley is mainly due to a lack of synergy within the venture capital community in Houston. **Availability:** Print; Online.

19179 ■ *"In Chesterfield: Paletta's Operations Raise Competitors' Blood Pressure"* in *St. Louis Business Journal (Vol. 33, August 17, 2012, No. 52, pp. 1)*
Pub: Baltimore Business Journal
Contact: Rhonda Pringle, President
E-mail: rpringle@bizjournals.com
Description: The proposed relocation of Doctor George Paletta Jr.'s Orthopedic Center of Saint Louis to a new 62,000-square-foot facility was met with opposition by local hospital officials and the Missouri Hospital Association. Officials state the facility must be licensed as a hospital in order to provide overnight post-operative care as planned by Paletta.

19180 ■ *"Insurance Firm Consolidates Offices: Integro Finds the Right Price Downtown"* in *Crain's New York Business (January 13, 2008)*
Pub: Crain Communications, Inc.
Contact: Jessica Botos, Manager, Marketing
E-mail: jessica.botos@crainsnewyork.com
Description: Integro insurance brokers is relocating its headquarters to 1 State Street Plaza, where it will consolidate its operations in March. The firm feels that the upscale design will provide an appropriate setting for entertaining clients and an engaging work environment for employees. **Availability:** Online.

19181 ■ *"Intermodal Makes Suppliers Look to Rack Up Big Sales to Distributors"* in *The Business Journal-Serving Metropolitan Kansas City (August 15, 2008)*
Pub: American City Business Journals, Inc.
Contact: Mike Olivieri, Executive Vice President
Ed: James Dornbrook. **Description:** Suppliers of shelving units, conveyor systems and other equipment used in distribution facilities are expecting new business opportunities along with the planned intermodal projects in the Kansas City area. Suppliers have already observed that small distributors have started to relocate to the city because of the intermodal projects. Demand for shelves and lifts have also increased. **Availability:** Online.

19182 ■ *"International Paper Weighs Expansion Options"* in *Memphis Business Journal (Vol. 34, September 14, 2012, No. 22, pp. 1)*
Pub: Baltimore Business Journal
Contact: Rhonda Pringle, President
E-mail: rpringle@bizjournals.com
Ed: Andy Ashby, Michael Sheffield. **Description:** Memphis, Tennessee-based International Paper Company (IP) has been evaluating options for additional space in order to manage the potential relocation of employees of recently acquired Temple-Inland Inc. in Austin, Texas. IP is occupying more than 450,000 square feet of Class A office space at its International Place headquarters. **Availability:** Print; Online.

19183 ■ *"Jacksonville Doing Well In Growing Economy"* in *Orlando Business Journal (Vol. 30, June 27, 2014, No. 53, pp. 8)*
Pub: American City Business Journals, Inc.
Contact: Mike Olivieri, Executive Vice President
Released: June 27, 2014. **Description:** Jerry Mallot is the president of JaxUSA Partnership, the economic development arm of the Jax Chambers. According to Mallot, Northeast Florida's strongest selling points for business site or relocation there include advanced manufacturing, financial services, aviation and aerospace technology, life sciences, logistics and information technology.

19184 ■ *"KXAN Seeks Larger Studio, Office Space in Austin"* in *Austin Business Journal (Vol. 31, May 27, 2011, No. 12, pp. A1)*
Pub: Austin Business Journal
Contact: Rachel McGrath, Director
E-mail: rmcgrath@bizjournals.com
Ed: Cody Lyon. **Description:** Austin NBC affiliate KXAN Television is opting to sell its property north of downtown and relocate to another site. The station is now inspecting possible sites to house its broadcasting facility and employees totaling as many as 200 people. Estimated cost of the construction of the studios and offices is $13 million plus another million in moving the equipment. **Availability:** Print; Online.

19185 ■ *"LatinWorks Cozies Up to Chevy in Detroit"* in *Austin Business Journal (Vol. 31, August 12, 2011, No. 23, pp. A1)*
Pub: Austin Business Journal
Contact: Rachel McGrath, Director
E-mail: rmcgrath@bizjournals.com
Ed: Sandra Zaragoza. **Description:** Hispanic marketing agency LatinWorks opened an office in Detroit to better serve its client Chevrolet and to potentially secure more contracts from its parent company General Motors, whose offices are located nearby. **Availability:** Print; Online.

19186 ■ *"Look Before You Lease"* in *Women Entrepreneur (February 3, 2009)*
Description: Top issues to consider before leasing an office space are discussed including: additional charges that may be expected on top of the basic rental price; determining both short- and long-term goals; the cost of improvements to the space; the cost of upkeep; and the conditions of the lease. **Availability:** Online.

19187 ■ *"MBT Add-On: Gone by 2012?"* in *Crain's Detroit Business (Vol. 24, October 6, 2008, No. 40, pp. 1)*
Pub: Crain Communications Inc.
Contact: Barry Asin, President
Ed: Amy Lane. **Description:** Discusses the Michigan Business Tax (MBT), which has angered many businesses in the state due to the addition of a 21.99

percent surcharge. Although the tax policy will cut taxes on 63 percent of businesses in the state and represent no tax liability change for another nine percent of firms, other businesses will see increases of 100 percent or more. This increase means that many business owners will be forced to relocate or close their establishment and others will have to eliminate jobs. Lawmakers are attempting to find a solution to this problem. **Availability:** Print; Online.

19188 ■ *"A New Mix of Tenants Settles In Downtown" in Crain's New York Business (Vol. 24, January 13, 2008, No. 2, pp. 26)*
Pub: Crain Communications, Inc.
Contact: Jessica Botos, Manager, Marketing
E-mail: jessica.botos@crainsnewyork.com

Ed: Andrew Marks. **Description:** More and more nonfinancial firms are relocating downtown due to the new retailers and restaurants that are reshaping the look and feel of lower Manhattan.

19189 ■ *"One-on-One with Enterprise Florida's Gray Swoope" in Orlando Business Journal (Vol. 31, August 15, 2014, No. 7, pp. 4)*
Pub: American City Business Journals, Inc.
Contact: Mike Olivieri, Executive Vice President
Released: Weekly. **Price:** $8, introductory 4-week offer(Digital only); $8, introductory 4-week offer(Digital & Print). **Description:** Gray Swoope is the president and CEO of Enterprise Florida, who is in charge of a $19.9 million operating budget for fiscal year 2014-15 used to attract new businesses, relocations, and expansions to the state. He believes in focusing on game-changing projects that create thousands of jobs, with wages close to $100,000 a year and a capital investment of half-billion dollars by a private sector company. **Availability:** Print; Online.

19190 ■ *"Opportunity Knocks" in Small Business Opportunities (September 2008)*
Description: Profile of YourOffice USA, a franchise that provides home-based and small businesses cost-effective and efficient support through "virtual" offices that are available as much or as little as the client needs it; they also supply necessary tools such as a professional business address, private mailbox service, personalized telephone answering and more that supports clients who want to look, act and operate with an advanced business image. **Availability:** Online.

19191 ■ *"Parts, Tooling Manufacturer Machinists Inc. Opts to Expand in South Park" in Puget Sound Business Journal (Vol. 34, February 21, 2014, No. 45, pp. 6)*
Pub: American City Business Journals, Inc.
Contact: Mike Olivieri, Executive Vice President
Description: Seattle, Washington-based Machinists Inc. announced an expansion with a seventh building in South Park. The new 20,000-square-foot building will increase the company's footprint to 115,000-square-feet when fully outfitted. The machine manufacturer shares insight into its decision to stay in Seattle rather than relocate is offered. **Availability:** Online.

19192 ■ *"Penney's Buys Wal-Mart Site" in Crain's Chicago Business (Vol. 31, March 31, 2008, No. 13, pp. 13)*
Pub: Crain Communications Inc.
Contact: Barry Asin, President

Ed: Eddie Baeb. **Description:** J.C. Penny Co. bought the closed Wal-Mart location in Crystal Lake and plans to open a store next year in its push to become more prominent in non-mall locations; Penney plans to expand and renovate the store. **Availability:** Online.

19193 ■ *"Portland Wooing Under Armour to West Coast Facility" in Baltimore Business Journal (Vol. 27, January 29, 2010, No. 39, pp. 1)*
Pub: Baltimore Business Journal
Contact: Rhonda Pringle, President
E-mail: rpringle@bizjournals.com

Ed: Andy Giegerich. **Description:** Baltimore, Maryland sports apparel maker, Under Armour, is planning a west coast expansion with Portland, Oregon among the sites considered to house its apparel and footwear design center. Portland officials counting on the concentration of nearly 10,000 activewear workers in the city will help lure the company to the city. **Availability:** Print; Online.

19194 ■ *"Race Benefits: Changes Afoot for Ironman" in Business Journal Serving Greater Tampa Bay (Vol. 30, October 29, 2010, No. 45, pp. 1)*
Pub: Tampa Bay Business Journal
Contact: Ian Anderson, President
E-mail: ianderson@bizjournals.com

Ed: Margaret Cashill. **Description:** World Triatholon Corporation, organizer of the Ironman World Championship 70.3, will move the sports event from Florida to Nevada in 2011. A replacement event, the 5150 Triathlon Series, will be held in 2011 and the series finale will be staged in Florida's Clearwater Beach. How hotels and motels in the area will benefit from the 5150 Triathlon Series is discussed. **Availability:** Online.

19195 ■ *"Real Deals for Vacant Big Boxes" in Memphis Business Journal (Vol. 33, January 6, 2012, No. 39, pp. 1)*
Pub: Baltimore Business Journal
Contact: Rhonda Pringle, President
E-mail: rpringle@bizjournals.com

Ed: Andy Ashby. **Description:** VH Foods Inc. is planning to relocate to a retail facility at Cross Creek Shopping Center in Memphis, Tennessee. The company will expand its grocery food offerings at the new location. **Availability:** Print; Online.

19196 ■ *"Renal Solutions Move Not a Sign of the Times" in Pittsburgh Business Times (Vol. 33, February 14, 2014, No. 31, pp. 5)*
Pub: American City Business Journals, Inc.
Contact: Mike Olivieri, Executive Vice President
Released: Weekly. **Price:** $4, Introductory 4-week offer(Digital only). **Description:** Renal Solutions, a Pittsburgh, Pennsylvania-based company, has decided to relocate to California. Company founder, Pete DeComo, believes that the firm's move should not be a cause for concern within the city's business community. Renal Solutions was acquired by Fresenius Medical Care North America in 2007. **Availability:** Print; Online.

19197 ■ *"RES Stakes Its Claim in Area" in Philadelphia Business Journal (Vol. 28, January 29, 2010, No. 50, pp. 1)*
Pub: Philadelphia Business Journal
Contact: Sierra Quinn, Director
E-mail: squinn@bizjournals.com

Ed: Peter Key. **Description:** RES Software Company Inc. of Amsterdam, Netherlands appointed Jim Kirby as president for the Americas and Klaus Besier as chairman in an effort to boost the firm's presence in the US. Brief career profiles of Kirby and Besier are included. RES develops software that allows management of information flow between an organization and its employees regardless of location. **Availability:** Online.

19198 ■ *"Rudy's Tortillas Wraps Up Expansion Plan in Carrollton" in Dallas Business Journal (Vol. 35, August 31, 2012, No. 51, pp. 1)*
Pub: Baltimore Business Journal
Contact: Rhonda Pringle, President
E-mail: rpringle@bizjournals.com

Ed: Candace Carlisle. **Released:** Weekly. **Description:** Rudy's Tortillas Corporation, a 67-year old family business based in Dallas, Texas, is moving into a new plant on Belt Line Road, Carrollton. The expansion will also involve the hiring of 150 new workers and enable the company to expand its operations. Rudy's will spend $14 million dollars on construction and equipment on the new tortilla plant. **Availability:** Print; Online.

19199 ■ *"S.A. Officials Hunting for Prospects in California" in San Antonio Business Journal (Vol. 26, August 17, 2012, No. 29, pp. 1)*
Released: August 17, 2012. **Description:** Officials of the San Antonio Economic Development Foundation in Texas will meet with 15 or more companies in Los Angeles, California in a bid to convince these businesses to relocated some of their operations to Alamo City. Officials are hoping the companies will recognize the advantages of San Antonio as they face pressures due to increased taxes and added government regulations in California.

19200 ■ *"Safety Products Firm Expanding" in Memphis Business Journal (Vol. 33, March 16, 2012, No. 49, pp. 1)*
Pub: Baltimore Business Journal
Contact: Rhonda Pringle, President
E-mail: rpringle@bizjournals.com

Description: Safety products importer and supplier International Sourcing Company Inc., the parent firm of Cordova Safety Products and Cordova Consumer Products, has purchased the 1 million-square-foot Cleo property in southeast Memphis, Tennessee. Aside from relocating its warehouse and office operations to the facility, the firm will add 20 new jobs as part of its growth initiative. **Availability:** Print; Online.

19201 ■ *"San Antonio Luring Biotech Firms With Venture Capital" in San Antonio Business Journal (Vol. 28, August 8, 2014, No. 26, pp. 6)*
Pub: American City Business Journals, Inc.
Contact: Mike Olivieri, Executive Vice President

Description: Bluegrass Vascular Technologies Inc. has secured $4.5 million in funding from Targeted Technology Fund II. Under the deal, the company will be required to relocate to San Antonio, Texas. A portion of the funding will be used on regulatory approval submissions for the company's Surfacer Inside-Out Catheter System. **Availability:** Print; Online.

19202 ■ *"Shire Seeking New Digs for Headquarters" in Philadelphia Business Journal (Vol. 30, September 2, 2011, No. 29, pp. 1)*
Pub: Philadelphia Business Journal
Contact: Sierra Quinn, Director
E-mail: squinn@bizjournals.com

Ed: Natalie Kostelni. **Description:** Dublin, Ireland-based Shire PLC announced plans to relocate its North American headquarters from Chesterbrook Corporate Center in Wayne, Pennsylvania and currently evaluating their options. The specialty biopharmaceutical firm is also considering a move to New Jersey or Delaware. **Availability:** Online.

19203 ■ *"The Silvery Moon Moves to Larger Location" in Bellingham Business Journal (Vol. March 2010, pp. 5)*
Pub: Sound Publishing Inc.
Contact: Josh O'Connor, President

Ed: Isaac Bonnell. **Description:** Jewelry store, the Silvery Moon, moved to a larger location in order to expand its business. The new location was chosen because it offers the firm more visibility. The store offers find silver and gold pieces and specializes in Pacific Northwest native jewelry.

19204 ■ *"Snappy Moves Headquarters to Marietta" in Atlanta Business Chronicle (June 27, 2014, pp. 13A)*
Pub: American City Business Journals, Inc.
Contact: Mike Olivieri, Executive Vice President

Description: Snappy, the leading supplier of metal pipes for the residential HVAC market is shifting its headquarters from Philadelphia to Marietta, Georgia. The company will move its employees to an existing building on Johnson Ferry Road in Marietta. Snappy will close its Philadelphia plant and will increase its manufacturing operations at other plants in Powder Springs, Georgia and Medina, New York. **Availability:** Print; Online.

19205 ■ Business Relocation　　　**GENERAL SMALL BUSINESS TOPICS**

19205 ■ "Suburban Retailers Go Urban" in Philadelphia Business Journal (Vol. 28, August 17, 2012, No. 27, pp. 1)
Pub: Baltimore Business Journal
Contact: Rhonda Pringle, President
E-mail: rpringle@bizjournals.com
Description: Traditional suburban retailers in the retail corridor of Philadelphia, Pennsylvania such as cosmetics retailer Ulta Beauty have been seeking population density and are relocating to urban settings, which represent untapped markets. How Vesper Property Group signed with Ulta Beauty a long-term lease on three levels totaling 13,600 square feet is also discussed. **Availability:** Print; Online.

19206 ■ "Surgical Center Relocating to St. Joseph Campus" in Business First of Buffalo (Vol. 30, January 24, 2014, No. 19, pp. 3)
Pub: American City Business Journals, Inc.
Contact: Mike Olivieri, Executive Vice President
Released: Weekly. **Price:** $140, One-Year Print & Digital; $115, One-Year Digital. **Description:** The Sisters of Charity Hospital is relocating its off-site ambulatory surgery center to its St. Joseph campus in Buffalo, New York. the moves makes better use of available space, reduces costs and allows for ongoing redevelopment of the Cheektowaga campus, according to vice president of operations, Marty Boryszak. **Availability:** Print; Online.

19207 ■ "Taking the Over-the-Counter Route to U.S." in Barron's (Vol. 88, July 7, 2008, No. 27, pp. 24)
Pub: Dow Jones & Company Inc.
Contact: Almar Latour, Chief Executive Officer
Ed: Eric Uhlfelder. **Description:** Many multinational companies have left the New York Stock Exchange and allowed their shares to trade over-the-counter. The companies have taken advantage of a 2007 SEC rule allowing publicly listed foreign companies to change trading venues if less than 5 percent of global trading volume in the past 12 months occurred in the US. **Availability:** Online.

19208 ■ "Theranos Growing Close to Home in Palo Alto" in Silicon Valley/San Jose Business Journal (Vol. 30, June 29, 2012, No. 14, pp. 1)
Pub: Baltimore Business Journal
Contact: Rhonda Pringle, President
E-mail: rpringle@bizjournals.com
Description: Theranos Inc. will move its headquarters near Facebook Inc.'s former building in Palo Alto, California. The company will then relocate into a building on Page Mill Road near Hillview Avenue. The medical-advice maker is currently growing, and it is also said to be taking space across the San Francisco Bay. **Availability:** Print; Online.

19209 ■ "Tri-State to Get New Headquarters" in Business Courier (Vol. 27, October 22, 2010, No. 25, pp. 1)
Description: Hong Kong-based corn processing firm Global Bio-Chem Technology is set to choose Greater Cincinnati, Ohio as a location of its North American headquarters. The interstate access, central location, and low labor and property costs might have enticed Global Bio-Chem to invest in the region. Statistics on Chinese direct investment in U.S. are also presented. **Availability:** Online; PDF.

19210 ■ "Waterloo Gardens Files for Bankruptcy" in Philadelphia Business Journal (Vol. 28, July 20, 2012, No. 23, pp. 1)
Pub: Baltimore Business Journal
Contact: Rhonda Pringle, President
E-mail: rpringle@bizjournals.com
Description: Nursery and garden center Waterloo Gardens Inc. has voluntarily filed Chapter 11 bankruptcy protection in the Eastern District of Pennsylvania as it attempts to reorganize. Watrloos' Devon location will be closing, while its inventory will be relocated to its Exton location. Factors that might have contributed to the bankruptcy filing are also discussed. **Availability:** Print; Online.

CONSULTANTS

19211 ■ The Boyd Company Inc.
103 Carnegie Ctr., Ste. 300
Princeton, NJ 08540
URL: http://www.theboydcompany.com
Contact: John H. Boyd, Jr., Contact
Description: Provider of site selection services to corporate clients expanding or relocating manufacturing, office, and distribution warehousing facilities. Provides corporate management with objective and authoritative analyzes of all geographically variable costs and other quantitative and qualitative location factors affecting optimum site selection. Firm works throughout the 50 states on behalf of leading United States corporations and overseas companies planning direct investment in the United States. **Scope:** Provider of site selection services to corporate clients expanding or relocating manufacturing, office, and distribution warehousing facilities. Provides corporate management with objective and authoritative analyzes of all geographically variable costs and other quantitative and qualitative location factors affecting optimum site selection. Firm works throughout the 50 states on behalf of leading United States corporations and overseas companies planning direct investment in the United States. **Special Services:** BizCosts®.

19212 ■ C.D.S. Building Movers
8 Sweetnam Dr.
Ottawa, ON, Canada K2S 1G2
Ph: (613)836-1215
Fax: (613)831-0240
Co. E-mail: info@cdsmovers.com
URL: http://www.cdsmovers.com
Contact: Max Maderson, Chief Executive Officer
Facebook: www.facebook.com/CDSBuildingMovers
X (Twitter): x.com/cdsmovers
Description: Provider of structural moving and consulting services for commercial and residential building related projects. **Scope:** Provider of structural moving and consulting services for commercial and residential building related projects.

19213 ■ Daniel Bloom and Associates Inc. (DBAI)
11517 128th Ave. N
Largo, FL 33778
Ph: (727)581-6216
URL: http://dbaiconsulting.com
Contact: Daniel T. Bloom, Chief Executive Officer
Description: Human resources management consultant with a specialization in corporate relocation. Offers clients a turn key service aimed at meeting the unique relocation needs of their employees. Develops and implements training programs within the relocation industry. **Scope:** Human resources management consultant with a specialization in corporate relocation. Offers clients a turn key service aimed at meeting the unique relocation needs of their employees. Develops and implements training programs within the relocation industry. **Founded:** 1980. **Publications:** "Where Have All the Elders Gone," Aug, 2002; "Recoup Your Hiring Investment," Brainbuzz.com, Aug, 2000; "Managing Your Lump Sum Program," Brainbuzz.com, Jun, 2000; "Buyer Value Options," Brainbuzz.com, Apr, 2000; "Just Get Me There". **Training:** Chaos in the Workplace: Multiple Generational Interactions; Training Effectiveness: Is the Cost Justified?; Human Capital Resource Management: A Six-Sigma Based Approach to Paving Your Way to the Table; Welcome to My World.

19214 ■ Hartford Despatch International
225 Prospect St.
East Hartford, CT 06108
Ph: (860)528-9551
URL: http://hartforddespatch.com
Contact: Ted Brown, Chief Executive Officer
Description: Domestic and international relocation services company. An independent provider of worldwide moving and storage services. **Scope:** Domestic and international relocation services company. An independent provider of worldwide moving and storage services.

19215 ■ NRI Relocation Inc.
1110 W Lake Cook Rd., Ste. 301
Buffalo Grove, IL 60089
Ph: (847)215-5000
Free: 800-598-8887
Co. E-mail: info@nrirelocation.com
URL: http://www.nrirelocation.com
Contact: John Zilka, President
Facebook: www.facebook.com/NRIRelocation
Linkedin: www.linkedin.com/company/nri-relocation-inc.
X (Twitter): x.com/nricorprelo
Description: Firm provides a complete suite of tailored relocation services such as proactive relocation policy consulting, home sale options, destination settling-in services, also assists corporate human resources departments with document process streamlining and management services. **Founded:** 1985.

19216 ■ Overland, Pacific & Cutler Inc. (OPC)
3750 Schaufele Ave., Ste. 150
Long Beach, CA 90808
Contact: Mark La Bonte, Director
Description: Firm offers a wide variety of turnkey right of way and real estate services and provides program management, right of way and real estate acquisition, relocation assistance, appraisal and appraisal review, utility coordination, cost studies, right of way certification, and right of way risk management services and serves the transportation, housing and development, energy and utility industries, as well as the public sector. **Training:** Right of Way Acquisition for Engineers, 2008; Commercial Relocations, 2008; Relax, It's Only Business Relocation, Dec, 2007; Relocation Nightmares, Aug, 2007; Relax. It's Only Residential Relocation, Mar, 2007.

19217 ■ Wadley-Donovan GrowthTech L.L.C. (WDGT)
235 Main Str., Ste. 286
Madison, NJ 07940
Ph: (973)593-9200
Fax: (973)593-9210
URL: http://wdgtech.com
Description: Provider of strategic issues for the geographic deployment of people and facilities, delineating alternatives to the current geographic configuration, relocation feasibility analyses, identification and evaluation of locations for new facilities. **Scope:** Provider of strategic issues for the geographic deployment of people and facilities, delineating alternatives to the current geographic configuration, relocation feasibility analyses, identification and evaluation of locations for new facilities. **Founded:** 1975. **Holdings:** The computer-readable Locational Profiles database is updated at least once per year. **Publications:** "Benefits from Economic and Workforce Development Collaboration"; "Finger lakes WiB transformation and integration of Workforce and Economic Development". **Training:** Corporate Location Trends in the Mid 1990s; Labor Challenges Facing Corporate America; Labor Quality Challenges and Employment Growth Opportunities for Center Cities.

Business Sale

REFERENCE WORKS

19218 ■ *"5 Mistakes to Avoid When Selling Your Small Business"* in The Balance Small Business (April 12, 2019)
Ed: Debbie Allen. **Released:** April 12, 2019. **Description:** Details common mistakes small business owners make when selling their business, resulting in thousands of dollars lost. Offers tips to help you avoid business sale pitfalls, disappointment, and lost money. **Availability:** Online.

19219 ■ *"The 6 Legal Steps to Closing Sale of Your Business"* in ExitAdviser (August 31, 2018)
Released: August 31, 2018. **Description:** Describes the legal process involved in selling your small business. Provides six legal steps that are necessary when you are ready to close the sale of your business. **Availability:** Online.

19220 ■ *"7 Steps to Selling Your Small Business"* in Investopedia (February 27, 2020)
Ed: Brigitte Yuille. **Released:** February 27, 2020. **Description:** Details seven considerations that can help you build a sold plan and make negotiation a success when you are selling your small business. **Availability:** Online.

19221 ■ *"7 Tax Strategies to Consider When Selling a Business"* in SBA Blog (February 21, 2020)
Ed: Barbara Weltman. **Released:** February 21, 2020. **Description:** Selling a business is a highly complex matter from a legal and tax perspective. This article offers seven tax considerations to keep in mind throughout the process. **Availability:** Online.

19222 ■ *The Essential Entrepreneur: What It Takes to Start, Scale, and Sell a Successful Business*
Pub: John Wiley & Sons, Inc.
Contact: Christina Van Tassell, Executive Vice President Chief Financial Officer
URL(s): www.wiley.com/en-us/The+Essential+Entrepreneur%3A+What+It+Takes+to+Start%2C+Scale%2C+and+Sell+a+Successful+Business-p-9781119984559
Released: November 2022. **Price:** $13, e-book; $21.99, paperback. **Description:** Take your business to the next level with the tips included in this guide. **Availability:** E-book; Print.

19223 ■ *How to Build a Business Others Want to Buy*
Pub: John Wiley & Sons, Inc.
Contact: Christina Van Tassell, Executive Vice President Chief Financial Officer
URL(s): www.wiley.com/en-us/How+to+Build+a+Business+Others+Want+to+Buy-p-9781394194605
Ed: Kobi Simmat. **Released:** September 2023. **Price:** $19.05, paperback. **Description:** Outlines how to build a profitable business that is attractive to external buyers. **Availability:** Print.

19224 ■ *"How to Buy a Business"* in Small Business Trends (May 11, 2021)
URL(s): smallbiztrends.com/2019/08/how-to-buy-a-business.html
Ed: Rob Starr. **Released:** May 11, 2021. **Description:** A guide on what to expect while purchasing an established business. **Availability:** Online.

19225 ■ *"How to Sell a Business"* in Small Business Trends (May 4, 2021)
URL(s): smallbiztrends.com/2021/05/how-to-sell-a-business.html
Ed: Lisa Price. **Released:** May 04, 2021. **Description:** A guide on what to expect while you sell your business. **Availability:** Online.

19226 ■ *"How to Sell Your Company for More"* in Small Business Trends (October 17, 2022)
URL(s): smallbiztrends.com/2022/10/selling-your-company-for-more.html
Released: October 17, 2022. **Description:** John Vitti, CEO of VersusGame, gives his tips on selling a company based on his experience. **Availability:** Online.

19227 ■ *Legal Documents Needed to Sell a Business*
Description: Details six documents needed to sell your small business. **Availability:** Online.

19228 ■ *Mergers & Acquisitions for Dummies*
Pub: John Wiley & Sons, Inc.
Contact: Christina Van Tassell, Executive Vice President Chief Financial Officer
URL(s): www.wiley.com/en-us/Mergers+%26+Acquisitions+For+Dummies%2C+2nd+Edition-p-9781394169504
Ed: Bill R. Snow. **Released:** 2nd edition. **Price:** $34.99, paperback. **Availability:** Print.

19229 ■ *"Owner's Guide to Selling a Business"* in ExitAdviser (November 16, 2018)
Description: Selling your small business requires thorough planning and creation of a sales strategy. This article provides detailed information on how, to whom, and where you are going to sell your business. **Availability:** Online.

19230 ■ *Selling Your Business: Eight Steps*
Ed: Fred S. Steingold. **Description:** Guides small business owners through the entire process of selling their business. **Availability:** Online.

19231 ■ *"What Can You Implement into Your Business to Make It More Attractive to Buyers?"* in Minority Business Entrepreneur (Vol. 39, Fall, 2022, No. 4, pp. 34-35)
URL(s): digital.mbemag.com/?m=53732&i=769780&p=34&ver=html5
Ed: Gareth Smyth. **Price:** $7.95. **Description:** Discusses some action items you can take when selling your business. **Availability:** Print; Online.

19232 ■ *"When, Why and How to Sell Your Small Business"* in SCORE.org (April 4, 2019)
Ed: Christine Soeun Choi. **Released:** April 04, 2019. **Description:** If you're considering selling your small businesses, this article offers things to keep in mind, including how to sell at the right time, being ready to answer tough questions, knowing what your business is worth, and being able to defend your price. **Availability:** Online.

19233 ■ *"Where to Find a Small Business for Sale"* in JustBusiness (October 22, 2020)
Ed: Georgia McIntyre. **Released:** October 22, 2020. **Description:** Provides details on how to find and buy an existing small business that is for sale. Also discusses next steps involved after you've found a small business for sale. **Availability:** Online.

VIDEO/AUDIO MEDIA

19234 ■ *Quitting with Purpose with Erica Courdae and Tasha L. Harrison*
URL(s): beingboss.club/podcast/quitting-with-purpose
Ed: Emily Thompson. **Released:** June 13, 2023. **Description:** Podcast discusses making tough choices and quitting with purpose.

INTERNET DATABASES

19235 ■ *Mergers, Acquisitions, and Joint Ventures: A Resource Guide*
URL(s): guides.loc.gov/mergers-acquisitions-joint-ventures
Description: Provides links to further resources regarding mergers, acquisitions, and joint ventures within companies. Links include: SEC laws and filings, general print resources, current transaction data, historical data, and internet resources. **Availability:** Online.

Business to Business Market

REFERENCE WORKS

19236 ■ *"10 B2B Marketing Strategies to Grow Your Presence" in The Blueprint (September 23, 2020)*

Ed: John Rampton. **Released:** September 23, 2020. **Description:** Discusses how business-to-business marketing has changed in the digital age, defines why B2B marketing strategies have to be different than business-to-consumer strategies, discusses what to consider before developing your B2B strategy and the best strategies to use for your business. **Availability:** Online.

19237 ■ *13 B2B E-commerce Brands Unveil the Secrets to Scalable Online Success*

Ed: Tracey Wallace. **Description:** Discusses business-to-business e-commerce and benefits of selling online, e-commerce misconceptions, and e-commerce marketing. **Availability:** Online.

19238 ■ *B2B Marketing: 10 Key Differences from Consumer Marketing*

Description: Details the importance of good quality market intelligence and close attention to target markets for business-to-business marketers. Provides ten key differences between B2B and consumer marketing. **Availability:** Online.

19239 ■ *"B2B Marketing: How to Grow Your Business" in Evinex (November 2, 2020)*

Ed: Carlos Trillo. **Released:** November 02, 2020. **Description:** Discusses business-to-business marketing strategies and fundamentals to help generate growth and increase your sales. **Availability:** Online.

19240 ■ *"B2B vs. B2C Marketing: What's the Difference in Marketing to the Business Market?" in Catalyst (January 3, 2019)*

Ed: Doug Fairbrother. **Released:** January 03, 2019. **Description:** Discusses how marketing to the business world is different than marketing to consumers. Provides information on the major differences and how to put the best strategies into action. **Availability:** Online.

19241 ■ *"Best of the Best: 20 Business-to-Business Examples to Check Out" in Disruptive Advertising (March 17, 2020)*

Ed: Cydney Hatch. **Released:** March 17, 2020. **Description:** Lists twenty examples of business-to-business companies who do a great job of targeting precise audiences, creating meaningful and engaging content, and optimizing efforts for business and social media. **Availability:** Online.

19242 ■ *"Selling to Other Businesses: 8 Sales Promotion Methods for a B2B Market" in business.com (April 28, 2020)*

Released: April 28, 2020. **Description:** Discusses the fact that selling to businesses is different than selling to individual customers and provides promotional tactics small businesses can use for B2B products. **Availability:** Online.

19243 ■ *"That Was a B2B Ad? How the Pandemic Forced Business Marketers to Pivot Forever" in The Drum (September 22, 2020)*

Ed: Kenneth Hein. **Released:** September 22, 2020. **Description:** Discusses how the business-to-business market is becoming increasingly indistinguishable from consumer marketing. **Availability:** Online.

19244 ■ *"The Ultimate Guide to B2B Marketing in 2020" in HubSpot (December 16, 2019)*

Ed: Allie Decker. **Released:** December 16, 2019. **Description:** Provides tips and strategies to understand your B2B audience, round out your buyer personas, and effectively use B2B marketing strategies that reach them. **Availability:** Online.

19245 ■ *"What Is B2B?" in Business News Daily (June 23, 2020)*

Ed: Adam Uzialko. **Released:** June 23, 2020. **Description:** A guide including all you need to know about businesses that primarily provide goods or services to other companies. Includes information on how to develop a marketing plan for a B2B company and information for digital B2B companies. **Availability:** Online.

TRADE PERIODICALS

19246 ■ *Inside Tucson Business*
Pub: Territorial Newspapers
Contact: Thomas P. Lee, Publisher
E-mail: tlee@azbiz.com
URL(s): www.insidetucsonbusiness.com
Facebook: www.facebook.com/insidetucsonbusiness
X (Twitter): x.com/azbiz
Ed: Jim Nintzel. **Released:** Weekly **Description:** Newspaper featuring business news. **Availability:** Print; Online.

PUBLICATIONS

19247 ■ *The Business to Business Marketer*
155 E 44th St.
New York, NY 10017
Ph: (212)697-5950
URL: http://www.marketing.org
Contact: Elizabeth Bamonte, President
URL(s): chicagobusinessmarketing.net/Event/Power-of-Mentorship-for-B2B-Marketers
Released: Quarterly **Description:** Provides information for business-to-business marketing strategies and tactics. **Availability:** Print.

19248 ■ *Journal of Business-to-Business Marketing: Innovations in Basic and Applied Research for Industrial Marketing*
711 3rd Ave.
New York, NY 10017
URL: http://www.taylorandfrancis.com
Contact: Annie Callanan, Chief Executive Officer
URL(s): www.tandfonline.com/journals/wbbm20
Ed: J. David Lichtenthal, Prof. David J. Lichtenthal, PhD, David T. Wilson. **Released:** Quarterly **Price:** $1,128, Institutions for print and online; $269, Individuals for print and online; $237, Individuals for online only; $925, Institutions for online only; $269, Individuals for print only. **Description:** Encourages diversity in approaches to business marketing theory development, research methods, and managerial problem solving. **Availability:** Print; Download; PDF; Online.

Business Scams (How to Avoid)

ASSOCIATIONS AND OTHER ORGANIZATIONS

19249 ■ **BBB Wise Giving Alliance [Better Business Bureau - Wise Giving Alliance]**
3033 Wilson Blvd., Ste. 710
Arlington, VA 22201
Ph: (703)247-9321
Co. E-mail: info@give.org
URL: http://give.org
Contact: Art H. Taylor, President
Facebook: www.facebook.com/BBB-Wise-Giving-Alliance-146493838709799
X (Twitter): x.com/wisegiving
Instagram: www.instagram.com/bbbwisegive
Description: Sets accountability standards and provides information for nonprofit organizations that solicit contributions from the public. Formerly National Charities Information Bureau. **Founded:** 2001. **Publications:** *Wise Giving Guide* (3/year). **Geographic Preference:** Multinational.

REFERENCE WORKS

19250 ■ *5 Ways to Spot Small Business Fraud*
URL(s): www.nationwide.com/lc/resources/small-business/articles/spot-small-business-fraud
Description: Discusses median losses experienced by small businesses that fall victim to fraud and provides five strategies that can help you spot and avoid small business fraud. **Availability:** Online.

19251 ■ *6 Common Scams That Target Small Businesses*
URL(s): businesshub.santanderbank.com/protecting-your-business/6-common-scams-that-target-small-business/
Released: 2022. **Description:** Describes the six most common cyber fraud schemes that target small businesses as well as tips on how to avoid getting compromised by these attacks. **Availability:** Online.

19252 ■ *"7 Statistics About Fraud Your Business Should Know in 2022"* in asmag.com (July 14, 2022)
URL(s): www.asmag.com/showpost/33017.aspx
Ed: Prasanth Aby Thomas. **Released:** July 14, 2022. **Description:** Presents seven statistics that businesses should know about fraud. **Availability:** Online.

19253 ■ *"10 Scams That Prey on Small Businesses"* in business.com (September 20, 2022)
URL(s): www.business.com/articles/scams-that-prey-on-small-businesses/
Ed: Jennifer Dublino. **Released:** September 20, 2022. **Description:** Presents information on how small businesses are at risk of attacks by scammers and hackers. Lists ten common scams that prey on small businesses and offers tips for steering clear of business scams. **Availability:** Online.

19254 ■ *"Report to the Nations - 2020 Global Study on Occupational Fraud and Abuse"* in Association of Certified Fraud Examiners (2020)
URL(s): legacy.acfe.com/report-to-the-nations/2020/
Released: 2020. **Description:** A report by the Association of Certified Fraud Examiners that examines the costs and effects of occupational fraud. **Availability:** PDF.

19255 ■ *"All About The Benjamins"* in Canadian Business (Vol. 81, September 29, 2008, No. 16, pp. 92)
Description: Discusses real estate developer Royal Indian Raj International Corp., a company that planned to build a $3 billion "smart city" near the Bangalore airport; to this day nothing has ever been built. The company was incorporated in 1999 by Manoj C. Benjamin one investor, Bill Zack, has been sued by the developer for libel due to his website that calls the company a scam. Benjamin has had a previous case of fraud issued against him as well as a string of liabilities and lawsuits. **Availability:** Online.

19256 ■ *"BBB Business Tip: Top 10 Scams Targeting Small Businesses"* in Better Business Bureau website (April 12, 2022)
URL(s): www.bbb.org/article/news-releases/19932-bbb-warning-businesses-dont-fall-for-that-scam
Released: April 12, 2022. **Description:** Discusses why scams are a particular problem for small businesses and provides details on common business scams so that your small business can gain awareness. **Availability:** Online.

19257 ■ *"Business Scams 101: Common Schemes and How to Avoid Them"* in business.com (Sept. 20, 2022)
URL(s): www.business.com/security/business-scam-guide/
Ed: Chad Brooks. **Released:** September 20, 2022. **Description:** A guide for avoiding scams in business, especially the kind that take the form of business-to-business (B2B) interactions. **Availability:** Online.

19258 ■ *Cybersecurity for Small Business*
URL(s): www.fcc.gov/general/cybersecurity-small-business
Description: Provides information on an online resource -- Small Biz Cyber Planner 2.0 -- that helps small businesses create customized cybersecurity plans. Also offers 10 cyber security tips for small business. **Availability:** Online.

19259 ■ *"Don't Let Your Small Business Fall Victim to These Four Scams"* in Forbes (August 16, 2022)
URL(s): www.forbes.com/sites/forbesbusinesscouncil/2022/08/16/dont-let-your-small-business-fall-victim-to-these-four-scams/?sh=25017904447a
Ed: Brandon Grable. **Released:** August 16, 2022. **Description:** Discusses the importance of awareness when it comes to common and current tactics used by criminal business scammers. Provides four practices that business owners should know in order to avoid business losses. **Availability:** Online.

19260 ■ *"'Friendly Fraud' Is on the Rise, and Small Business Owners May Bear the Brunt of the Impact"* in Select (Jan. 28, 2021)
URL(s): www.cnbc.com/select/friendly-fraud-impact-on-small-businesses/
Ed: Megan DeMatteo. **Released:** January 28, 2021. **Description:** Explains what "friendly fraud" is and offers tips for how small businesses can avoid chargeback fees to you can protect yourself. **Availability:** Online.

19261 ■ *"A History of Neglect: Health Care for Blacks and Mill Workers in the Twentieth-Century South"* in Canadian Business (Vol. 79, September 11, 2006, No. 18, pp. 21)
Description: Faulty practices being followed by auditors and regulators of Canada are discussed. The need for appropriate steps to protect investors against these frauds are emphasized. **Availability:** PDF.

19262 ■ *How to Detect and Deter Fraud in a Small Business*
URL(s): www.wolterskluwer.com/en/expert-insights/how-to-detect-and-deter-fraud-in-a-small-business
Ed: Mike Enright. **Released:** January 12, 2021. **Description:** Discusses the scope of small business fraud and offers steps that every small business needs to take against fraud. **Availability:** Online.

19263 ■ *"How to Protect Your Small Business Against Fraud"* in Entrepreneur (Jan. 14, 2021)
URL(s): www.entrepreneur.com/article/362383
Ed: Chris Porteous. **Released:** January 14, 2021. **Description:** Provides three steps small businesses can follow to boost security and keep scammers at bay. **Availability:** Online.

19264 ■ *How to Protect Your Small Business from Fraud*
URL(s): smallbusinessbc.ca/article/how-protect-your-small-business-fraud/
Description: Discusses the importance of fraud prevention for your small business. **Availability:** Online.

19265 ■ *How to Protect Yourself: Small Business Scams*
URL(s): myfloridalegal.com/pages.nsf/main/8be56222bbd1923b85256cc9005ecf4d!OpenDocument
Released: 2022. **Description:** Discusses how small businesses have increasingly become a target of scam artists who use their knowledge of small business practices to fraudulently induce these businesses to pay for services never performed or for products never delivered. Provides things to consider to avoid small business scams. **Availability:** Online.

19266 ■ "How Small Businesses Can Protect Themselves against Counterfeiters" in Legal Zoom (February 15, 2023)
URL(s): www.legalzoom.com/articles/how-small-businesses-can-protect-themselves-against-counterfeiters

Ed: Katherine Gustafson. **Released:** February 15, 2023. **Description:** Discusses protecting your brand and merchandise from counterfeiters who steal product ideas and can ruin your business by selling cheaper and fake products that look like yours. **Availability:** Online.

19267 ■ "How to Spot and Then Avoid Getting Caught Out by Scams Targeting Businesses" in Business Companion website (May 2022)
URL(s): www.businesscompanion.info/en/quick-guides/miscellaneous/business-scams

Released: May 2022. **Description:** A guide to how to spot and avoid getting caught in scams that target small businesses. **Availability:** Online.

19268 ■ "Invention Submission Companies: Scams or Valuable Services?" in Legal Zoom (March 27, 2023)
URL(s): www.legalzoom.com/articles/invention-submission-companies-scams-or-valuable-services

Ed: Stephanie Morrow. **Released:** March 27, 2023. **Description:** Outsourcing the legwork to patent or trademark your invention or idea may seem like a great idea, until you find out the company you used is a scam. Included are profiles on inventors who fell for scams. **Availability:** Online.

19269 ■ "Investment Bank Dinan & Company Launches ConfidentCrowd Exclusive Crowdfunding Portal for FINRA Broker-Dealers" in Investment Weekly (June 9, 2012, pp. 458)
Description: ConfidentCrowd is a newly developed portal created by Dinan & Company to provide exclusive use of FINRA-registered broker-dealers to participate as members in order to screen firms seeking funding. This process will eleviate risk in equity-based crowdfunding. **Availability:** Online.

19270 ■ Keep Your Small Business Safe from Scams: Here's How to Handle Fraud Prevention
URL(s): www.chase.ca/en/support/insights/keep-your-small-business-safe-from-scams

Ed: Chase Canada. **Description:** Details seven types of fraud that can affect small business owners. **Availability:** Online.

19271 ■ "The Most Common Frauds in Small Business" in GoCardless website (August 2021)
URL(s): gocardless.com/en-us/guides/posts/the-most-common-frauds-in-small-business/

Released: August 2021. **Description:** Provides information for small businesses about how to prevent fraud including the most common frauds and tips to prevent the occurrence of fraud in your small business. **Availability:** Online.

19272 ■ "Oil Markets: A Nasty Russian Tale" in Canadian Business (Vol. 81, March 3, 2008, No. 3, pp. 85)
Pub: Rogers Media Inc.
Contact: Neil Spivak, Chief Executive Officer

Ed: Andrew Nikiforuk. **Description:** Billionaires Alex Shnaider and Michael Shtaif entered a partnership for an oil venture which ended in a slew of litigations. Cases of breach of contract, injurious falsehood and other related lawsuits were filed against Shnaider. Details of the lawsuits and the other parties involved in the disputes are presented. **Availability:** Online.

19273 ■ "One-Time Area Trust Executive Finds Trouble in N.H." in The Business Journal-Serving Metropolitan Kansas City (September 12, 2008)
Description: About 200 investors, some from Missouri's Kansas City area, claim that they had conducted business with Noble Trust Co. The trust company was placed under New Hampshire Banking Department's conservatorship after $15 million was discovered to be missing from its account. It is alleged that the money was lost in a Colorado Ponzi scheme. **Availability:** Print; Online.

19274 ■ "Phone Scam Preys on Small Business Owners Looking for a Loan" in Small Business Trends (Jan. 19, 2022)
URL(s): smallbiztrends.com/2022/01/phone-scam-targets-small-business-loan-seekers.html

Ed: Gabrielle Pickard-Whitehead. **Released:** January 19, 2022. **Description:** Provides information on small business scams, particularly one related to taking advantage of small business owners who have applied for loans from the Small Business Administration. **Availability:** Online.

19275 ■ "Retailers Report 'Shrinkage' - Disappearance of Inventory - on the Rise" in Arkansas Business (Vol. 26, September 28, 2009, No. 39, pp. 17)
Pub: Arkansas Business Publishing Group
Contact: Mitch Bettis, President

Ed: Mark Friedman. **Description:** According to a National Retail Security Survey report released last June, retailers across the country have lost about $36.5 billion in shrinkage, most of it at the hands of employees and shoplifters alike. Statistical data included. **Availability:** Online.

19276 ■ "Ringgold Computer Repair Owner Accused of Swindling Customers" in Chattanooga Times/Free Press (February 15, 2012)
Availability: Online.

19277 ■ "Rogue Caller Infiltrates Cincinnati Firms' Analyst Calls: 'Mr. CEO, Please Do Elaborate On Your Firm's Metrics" in Business Courier (Vol. 24, February 28, 2008, No. 47, pp. 1)
Pub: American City Business Journals, Inc.
Contact: Mike Olivieri, Executive Vice President

Ed: Jon Newberry. **Description:** Discusses a rogue caller who goes by the name of Joe Herrick, Steven Nissan and Joe Harris has joined in over a dozen conference calls, asking chief executive officers on their plans and commenting on the companies' operations. The mystery caller attempts to pass himself off as a financial analyst. Transcripts of some conference calls, in which the rogue caller is involved, are provided. **Availability:** Online.

19278 ■ Scams & Fraud
URL(s): www.aarp.org/money/scams-fraud/info-2020/small-business.html

Description: Describes a variety of scams that target small businesses and provides a list of Do's and Don'ts for small businesses to follow to help avoid falling into a scam trap. **Availability:** Online.

19279 ■ "Scams Targeting Small Business" in Incorp website (2022)
URL(s): www.incorp.com/help-center/business-articles/top-scams-targeting-small-business

Description: As technology advances, methods of fraud and business scams continue to increase. This article provides information on ten common scams that small business owners face and how to avoid them. **Availability:** Online.

19280 ■ "Scams and Your Small Business: A Guide for Business" (May 2018)
URL(s): www.ftc.gov/business-guidance/resources/scams-your-small-business-guide-business

Released: May 2018. **Description:** A report by the Federal Trade Commission for small business owners that provides information on how to recognize the signs of scams that target businesses as well as information on how to relay this to your employees and colleagues. **Availability:** PDF.

19281 ■ Six Strategies for Fraud Prevention in Your Business
URL(s): www.cgteam.com/six-strategies-for-fraud-prevention-in-your-business/

Released: February 11, 2022. **Description:** Presents six strategies for fraud prevention in your small business. **Availability:** Online.

19282 ■ Small Business Fraud and the Trusted Employee
URL(s): www.fraud-magazine.com/article.aspx?id=4294976289

Ed: G. Stevenson Smith, Theresa Hrncir, Stephanie Metts. **Description:** Small businesses are often vulnerable to fraud because they lack the resources to implement complete protection systems. This article provides some viable options for small businesses to explore. **Availability:** Online.

19283 ■ Small Business Has a Big Fraud Problem
URL(s): www.bai.org/banking-strategies/article-detail/small-business-has-a-big-fraud-problem/

Ed: Andy Shank. **Released:** June 09, 2021. **Description:** Discusses the problem of fraud in small businesses. Presents low-cost strategies that can significantly reduce the risk and impact of fraud. **Availability:** Online.

19284 ■ Top 6 Fraud Risks for Small Businesses
URL(s): programs.online.utica.edu/resources/article/top-six-fraud-risks-for-small-businesses

Description: Small business owners should be aware of many different types of fraud so that they can protect their employees, their finances, and themselves. This article details six types of fraud that economic crime investigation professionals encourage small businesses to be aware of. **Availability:** Online.

19285 ■ "Trademark and Patent Scams: What to Watch out For" in Legal Zoom (February 17, 2023)
URL(s): www.legalzoom.com/articles/trademark-and-patent-scams-what-to-watch-out-for

Ed: Stephanie Morrow. **Released:** February 17, 2023. **Description:** Read thought this article to learn about how scammers could take advantage of your trademarks and patents. **Availability:** Online.

19286 ■ "What Online Brokers Are Doing To Keep Their Customers' Accounts Safe" in Barron's (Vol. 88, March 10, 2008, No. 10, pp. 37)
Pub: Dow Jones & Company Inc.
Contact: Almar Latour, Chief Executive Officer

Ed: Theresa W. Carey. **Description:** Online brokerage firms employ different methods to protect the accounts of their customers from theft. These methods include secure Internet connections, momentary passwords, and proprietary algorithms. **Availability:** Online.

Business Travel

ASSOCIATIONS AND OTHER ORGANIZATIONS

19287 ■ **Arizona Business Travel Association (AZBTA)**
2303 N 44th St., Ste. 14-1520
Phoenix, AZ 85008
URL: http://www.azbta.org
Contact: Mary Thompson, President
E-mail: mary@vitesseworldwide.com
Facebook: www.facebook.com/AZBTA
X (Twitter): x.com/azbta
Description: Represents travel managers and providers. Promotes the value of the travel manager in meeting corporate travel needs and financial goals. Cultivates a positive public image of the corporate travel industry. Protects the interests of members and their corporations in legislative and regulatory matters. Promotes safety, security, efficiency and quality travel. Provides a forum for the exchange of information and ideas among members. **Geographic Preference:** State.

19288 ■ **Austin Business Travel Association (ABTA)**
4301 W William Cannon Dr., Ste. B-150
Austin, TX 78749
Co. E-mail: info@gbta-austinbta.org
URL: http://gbta-austinbta.org
Contact: John Hampton, Chairman
E-mail: john.a.hampton@ehi.com
Facebook: www.facebook.com/gbtatx
X (Twitter): x.com/GBTA_AustinBTA
Description: Represents travel managers and providers. Promotes the value of the travel manager in meeting corporate travel needs and financial goals. Cultivates a positive public image of the corporate travel industry. Protects the interests of members and their corporations in legislative and regulatory matters. Promotes safety, security, efficiency and quality travel. Provides a forum for the exchange of information and ideas among members. **Founded:** 1990. **Geographic Preference:** Local.

19289 ■ **Bay Area Business Travel Association (BABTA)**
San Francisco, CA
URL: http://babta.org
Contact: Carey Ann Pascoe, President
E-mail: president@babta.org
Facebook: www.facebook.com/pages/BABTA-Bay-Area-Business-Travel-Association/250003017431
Linkedin: www.linkedin.com/groups
X (Twitter): x.com/WeAreBABTA
Description: Represents travel managers and providers. Promotes the value of the travel manager in meeting corporate travel needs and financial goals. Cultivates a positive public image of the corporate travel industry. Protects the interests of members and their corporations in legislative and regulatory matters. Promotes safety, security, efficiency and quality travel. Provides a forum for the exchange of information and ideas among members. **Founded:** 1975. **Geographic Preference:** Local.

19290 ■ **Caribbean - Central American Action (CCAA)**
1625 K St. NW, Ste. 200
Washington, DC 20006
URL: http://c-caa.org
Description: Promotes private-sector-led economic development in the Caribbean Basin and throughout the hemisphere; facilitates trade and investment in the region by stimulating a constructive dialogue between the private and public sectors to improve the policy and regulatory environments for business on both international and local levels. **Founded:** 1980. **Publications:** *CCAA Quarterly* (Quarterly). **Educational Activities:** Miami Conference on the Caribbean Basin (Annual). **Geographic Preference:** Multinational.

19291 ■ **Central & North Florida Business Travel Association (CNFBTA)**
9150 International Dr.
Orlando, FL 32803-5127
Co. E-mail: membership@cnfbta.org
URL: http://cnfbta.org
Contact: Darren LAppanna, Co-President
Description: Represents travel managers and providers. Promotes the value of the travel manager in meeting corporate travel needs and financial goals. Cultivates a positive public image of the corporate travel industry. Protects the interests of members and their corporations in legislative and regulatory matters. Promotes safety, security, efficiency and quality travel. Provides a forum for the exchange of information and ideas among members. **Founded:** 1989. **Geographic Preference:** Local.

19292 ■ **Chicago Business Travel Association (CBTA) [Global Business Travel Association - Chicago Chapter]**
PO Box 877
Chicago, IL 60690
Co. E-mail: info@chicagobta.org
URL: http://chicagobta.org
Contact: Wayne Urbanek, Chairperson
Facebook: www.facebook.com/ChicagoBTA
X (Twitter): x.com/chicagobta
Instagram: www.instagram.com/chicagobusinesstravel
Description: Promotes the value of business travel management by representing corporate travel managers and travel service providers. Monitors developments in the business travel field and provides current, critical industry information.

19293 ■ **Dallas Fort Worth Business Travel Association (DFWBTA)**
4400 N O'Connor Rd.
Irving, TX 75062
Co. E-mail: info@dfw-bta.org
URL: http://www.dfw-bta.org
Contact: Gloria Gonzalez, President
X (Twitter): x.com/GBTA_DFW
Instagram: www.instagram.com/gbta_dfw
Description: Represents travel managers and providers. Promotes the value of the travel manager in meeting corporate travel needs and financial goals. Cultivates a positive public image of the corporate travel industry. Protects the interests of members and their corporations in legislative and regulatory matters. Promotes safety, security, efficiency and quality travel. Provides a forum for the exchange of information and ideas among members. **Founded:** 1970. **Geographic Preference:** Local.

19294 ■ **European Travel Commission (ETC) [Commission Europeenne du Tourisme (CET)]**
Rue de Marche aux Herbes 61
1000 Brussels, Belgium
Ph: 32 2 5489000
Co. E-mail: info@visiteurope.com
URL: http://www.etc-corporate.org
Contact: Luís Araújo, President
Linkedin: www.linkedin.com/company/european-travel-commission
X (Twitter): x.com/etc_corporate
YouTube: www.youtube.com/channel/UCkPU8vpoOkC-9M0fw5lm0ow
Description: National tourist organizations from 33 countries working to promote Europe as a tourist destination overseas. Conducts research and New Media activities. **Founded:** 1948. **Publications:** *VisitEurope*. **Educational Activities:** Trans-Atlantic Travel Marketing Conference (Annual). **Geographic Preference:** Multinational.

19295 ■ **Florida Business Travel Association - South Florida Chapter (FBTA) [Global Business Travel Association - South Florida Chapter]**
PO Box 824405
Pembroke Pines, FL 33082
Co. E-mail: gbtasf@gmail.com
URL: http://gbtasouthflorida.org
Contact: Alyssa Young, Co-President
Facebook: www.facebook.com/FLBTA
Linkedin: www.linkedin.com/company/florida-business-travel-association
Description: Promotes the value of business travel management by representing corporate travel managers and travel service providers. Monitors developments in the business travel field and provides current, critical industry information. **Founded:** 1990.

19296 ■ **GBTA Tampa Bay Chapter, Inc.**
PO Box 20192
Tampa, FL 33622
Co. E-mail: contact@gbta-tampabay.org
URL: http://gbta-tampabay.org
Contact: Mindy Owen, President
Facebook: www.facebook.com/TampaBayBusinessTravelAssociation
Linkedin: www.linkedin.com/company/tampa-bay-business-travel-association

19297 ■ Business Travel

Instagram: www.instagram.com/gbta_tampa_bay
_chapter
Description: Represents travel managers and providers. Promotes the value of the travel manager in meeting corporate travel needs and financial goals. Cultivates a positive public image of the corporate travel industry. Protects the interests of members and their corporations in legislative and regulatory matters. Promotes safety, security, efficiency and quality travel. Provides a forum for the exchange of information and ideas among members. **Founded:** 1988. **Geographic Preference:** Local.

19297 ■ Georgia Business Travel Association, Inc. (GBTA)
2421 Whitemarsh Way
Savannah, GA 31410
Co. E-mail: info@georgiabta.org
URL: http://georgiabta.org
Contact: Will Begnaud, President
Description: Represents travel managers and providers. Promotes the value of the travel manager in meeting corporate travel needs and financial goals. Cultivates a positive public image of the corporate travel industry. Protects the interests of members and their corporations in legislative and regulatory matters. Promotes safety, security, efficiency and quality travel. Provides a forum for the exchange of information and ideas among members. **Founded:** 1979. **Geographic Preference:** State.

19298 ■ Global Business Travel Association (GBTA)
107 SW St., Ste. 762
Alexandria, VA 22314
Ph: (703)684-0836
Fax: (703)783-8686
Co. E-mail: info@gbta.org
URL: http://www.gbta.org
Contact: Denise Truso, President
E-mail: dtruso@gbta.org
Facebook: www.facebook.com/GBTAonFB
Linkedin: www.linkedin.com/company/global-busi-ness-travel-association
X (Twitter): x.com/GlobalBTA
Instagram: www.instagram.com/gbta_global
YouTube: www.youtube.com/user/GBTATV
Description: Provides its members access to education, networking, events, and research and information on matters concerning global business travel industry. **Founded:** 1968. **Publications:** *Global Business Travel Association--Membership Directory.* **Awards:** Mike Kabo Global Scholarships; Mike Kabo Scholarship. **Geographic Preference:** National.

19299 ■ Global Business Travel Association - Upstate New York Chapter
5325 Sheridan Dr.
Williamsville, NY 14231
Co. E-mail: info@gbta-upstatenewyork.org
URL: http://gbta-upstatenewyork.org
Contact: Terri J. B. Moreno, President
Facebook: www.facebook.com/GBTAUpsta teNewYorkChapter
X (Twitter): x.com/GBTA_UpstateNY
Instagram: www.instagram.com/bgtaupstatenewyork
Description: Represents travel managers and providers. Promotes the value of the travel manager in meeting corporate travel needs and financial goals. Cultivates a positive public image of the corporate travel industry. Protects the interests of members and their corporations in legislative and regulatory matters. Promotes safety, security, efficiency and quality travel. Provides a forum for the exchange of information and ideas among members. **Founded:** 1990. **Geographic Preference:** State.

19300 ■ Greater DC Metro Chapter of GBTA (NVBTA)
1101 King St., Ste. 500
Alexandria, VA 22314
URL: http://gbta-greaterdcmetro.org
Contact: Carmen Smith, Co-President
Description: Represents travel managers and providers. Promotes the value of the travel manager in meeting corporate travel needs and financial goals.

Cultivates a positive public image of the corporate travel industry. Protects the interests of members and their corporations in legislative and regulatory matters. Promotes safety, security, efficiency and quality travel. Provides a forum for the exchange of information and ideas among members. **Founded:** 1988. **Geographic Preference:** Local.

19301 ■ *IBAC Update*
999 Robert-Bourrassa Blvd., Ste. 16-33
Montreal, QC, Canada H3C 5J9
Ph: (514)954-8054
Co. E-mail: info@ibac.org
URL: http://ibac.org
Contact: Kurt Edwards, Member
URL(s): ibac.org/news/newsletters
Released: Irregular **Description:** Contains information on the activities of the aviation community and member organizations. **Availability:** Print.

19302 ■ International Business Aviation Council (IBAC)
999 Robert-Bourrassa Blvd., Ste. 16-33
Montreal, QC, Canada H3C 5J9
Ph: (514)954-8054
Co. E-mail: info@ibac.org
URL: http://ibac.org
Contact: Kurt Edwards, Member
Facebook: www.facebook.com/IBACBizAv1
Linkedin: www.linkedin.com/company/18677197
X (Twitter): x.com/IBACBizAv1
Description: Aims to provide information on all aspects of international business aircraft operations; ensure that the interests of international business aviation are brought to the attention of and understood by authorities; and improve the safety, efficiency, and economic use of business aircraft operating internationally. Stresses the importance of business aviation to the economy and to the well-being of all nations and maintains liaison with international aviation organizations to ensure growth of the field throughout the world. **Founded:** 1981. **Publications:** *IBAC Update* (Irregular). **Geographic Preference:** Multinational.

19303 ■ Kansas City Business Travel Association (KCBTA) [Global Business Travel Association - Kansas City Chapter]
Kansas City, MO
URL: http://kcbta.org
Contact: Kelsey Pulley, Contact
X (Twitter): x.com/gbtakansascity
Description: Promotes the value of business travel management by representing corporate travel managers and travel service providers. Monitors developments in the business travel field and provides current, critical industry information. **Founded:** 1990.

19304 ■ Los Angeles Business Travel Association (LABTA)
Los Angeles, CA
Co. E-mail: admin@labta.org
URL: http://labta.org
Contact: Lee Palmer Turner, President
Facebook: www.facebook.com/labtaofficial
Linkedin: www.linkedin.com/company/labta
X (Twitter): x.com/labtaofficial
Instagram: www.instagram.com/labtaofficial
Description: Represents travel managers and providers. Promotes the value of the travel manager in meeting corporate travel needs and financial goals. Cultivates a positive public image of the corporate travel industry. Protects the interests of members and their corporations in legislative and regulatory matters. Promotes safety, security, efficiency and quality travel. Provides a forum for the exchange of information and ideas among members. **Founded:** 1970. **Geographic Preference:** Local.

19305 ■ Mid South Area Business Travel Association (MSA-BTA)
PO Box 11441
Memphis, TN 38111-0441
Co. E-mail: info@msabta.org
URL: http://www.msabta.org
Contact: Scott Harmon, President
Facebook: www.facebook.com/MidsouthAreaBTA

X (Twitter): x.com/MidsouthAreaBTA
Description: Represents travel managers and providers. Promotes the value of the travel manager in meeting corporate travel needs and financial goals. Cultivates a positive public image of the corporate travel industry. Protects the interests of members and their corporations in legislative and regulatory matters. Promotes safety, security, efficiency and quality travel. Provides a forum for the exchange of information and ideas among members. **Founded:** 2003. **Geographic Preference:** Regional.

19306 ■ New England Business Travel Association (NEBTA)
PO Box 276
Boston, MA 02215
URL: http://nebta.org
Contact: Kristen Reeves, President
E-mail: kristen.reeves@mksinst.com
X (Twitter): x.com/NEWENGLANDBTA
Description: Promotes the value of business travel management by representing corporate travel managers and travel service providers. Monitors developments in the business travel field and provides current, critical industry information. **Founded:** 1969.

19307 ■ New Jersey Business Travel Association (NJBTA)
NJ
Co. E-mail: info@njbta.org
URL: http://njbta.org
Contact: Zorian Ricks, President
E-mail: zorian74@gmail.com
Facebook: www.facebook.com/NJBTA
Linkedin: www.linkedin.com/in/gbtanj
X (Twitter): x.com/newjerseyBTA
Description: Represents travel managers and providers. Promotes the value of the travel manager in meeting corporate travel needs and financial goals. Cultivates a positive public image of the corporate travel industry. Protects the interests of members and their corporations in legislative and regulatory matters. Promotes safety, security, efficiency and quality travel. Provides a forum for the exchange of information and ideas among members. **Founded:** 1967. **Geographic Preference:** State.

19308 ■ New York City Business Travel Association (NYCBTA)
PO Box 67
New York, NY 10163-0067
URL: http://nycbta.org
Contact: Rosemary Maloney, Chairman of the Board
E-mail: president@nycbta.org
Facebook: www.facebook.com/NYCBTA
Linkedin: www.linkedin.com/company/new-york-city-business-travel-association
X (Twitter): x.com/nycbta
Description: Represents travel managers and providers. Promotes the value of the travel manager in meeting corporate travel needs and financial goals. Cultivates a positive public image of the corporate travel industry. Protects the interests of members and their corporations in legislative and regulatory matters. Promotes safety, security, efficiency and quality travel. Provides a forum for the exchange of information and ideas among members. **Founded:** 1953. **Geographic Preference:** Local.

19309 ■ North Carolina Business Travel Association (NCBTA)
c/o Kathy Melton, Administrator
PO Box 896
Harrisburg, NC 28075
Ph: (704)907-8703
URL: http://www.ncbta.org
Contact: Lena Sanok, Contact
E-mail: lena.sanok@hilton.com
Facebook: www.facebook.com/GBTA.NC/timeline
X (Twitter): x.com/ncbta
Description: Represents travel managers and providers. Promotes the value of the travel manager in meeting corporate travel needs and financial goals. Cultivates a positive public image of the corporate travel industry. Protects the interests of members and their corporations in legislative and regulatory mat-

ters. Promotes safety, security, efficiency and quality travel. Provides a forum for the exchange of information and ideas among members. **Founded:** 1974. **Geographic Preference:** State.

19310 ■ **North Central Global Business Travel Association (NCBTA)**
5108 W 74th St. 390452
  Minneapolis, MN 55439
URL: http://gbta-northcentral.org
Contact: Kari Bigot, President
Facebook: www.facebook.com/gbtancc
Linkedin: www.linkedin.com/company/gbta-north-central-chapter
X (Twitter): x.com/gbtancc
Description: Represents travel managers and providers. Promotes the value of the travel manager in meeting corporate travel needs and financial goals. Cultivates a positive public image of the corporate travel industry. Protects the interests of members and their corporations in legislative and regulatory matters. Promotes safety, security, efficiency and quality travel. Provides a forum for the exchange of information and ideas among members. **Founded:** 1987. **Publications:** *Travel Times* (Bimonthly). **Geographic Preference:** Regional.

19311 ■ **Ohio Valley Business Travel Association (OVBTA)**
715 Shawan Falls
  Dublin, OH 43017
Ph: (614)638-4337
Co. E-mail: communications@ovbta.org
URL: http://ovbta.org
Contact: Renee V. Huff, President
E-mail: president@ovbta.org
Facebook: www.facebook.com/OVBTA
Linkedin: www.linkedin.com/company/gbta-ohio-valley-ovbta
X (Twitter): x.com/Ohio_Valley_BTA
Description: Represents travel managers and providers. Promotes the value of the travel manager in meeting corporate travel needs and financial goals. Cultivates a positive public image of the corporate travel industry. Protects the interests of members and their corporations in legislative and regulatory matters. Promotes safety, security, efficiency and quality travel. Provides a forum for the exchange of information and ideas among members. **Founded:** 1969. **Geographic Preference:** Local.

19312 ■ **Oregon Business Travel Association (OBTA)**
101 SW Madison St.
  Portland, OR 97207-8602
Ph: (503)200-5556
Co. E-mail: info@obta.org
URL: http://obta.org
Contact: Ronda Dean, President
E-mail: r.dean@f5.com
Facebook: www.facebook.com/gbtaoregon
Linkedin: www.linkedin.com/company/gbta-oregon
Description: Represents travel managers and providers. Promotes the value of the travel manager in meeting corporate travel needs and financial goals. Cultivates a positive public image of the corporate travel industry. Protects the interests of members and their corporations in legislative and regulatory matters. Promotes safety, security, efficiency and quality travel. Provides a forum for the exchange of information and ideas among members. **Founded:** 1987. **Geographic Preference:** State.

19313 ■ **Philadelphia Business Travel Association**
12 Anne Marie Ln.
  Titusville, NJ 08560
URL: http://www.phillybta.org
Contact: Tom Wilkinson, Treasurer
Facebook: www.facebook.com/PHLBTA
X (Twitter): x.com/phillybta
Description: Represents travel managers and providers. Promotes the value of the travel manager in meeting corporate travel needs and financial goals. Cultivates a positive public image of the corporate travel industry. Protects the interests of members and their corporations in legislative and regulatory mat-

ters. Promotes safety, security, efficiency and quality travel. Provides a forum for the exchange of information and ideas among members. **Founded:** 2001. **Geographic Preference:** Local.

19314 ■ **Puget Sound Business Travel Association (PSBTA)**
PO Box 55365
  Shoreline, WA 98155
Ph: (425)890-1516
Co. E-mail: administrator@psbta.org
URL: http://psbta.org
Contact: Michelle Amos, President
E-mail: chapterpresident@psbta.org
Facebook: www.facebook.com/PSBTA
Description: Represents travel managers and providers. Promotes the value of the travel manager in meeting corporate travel needs and financial goals. Cultivates a positive public image of the corporate travel industry. Protects the interests of members and their corporations in legislative and regulatory matters. Promotes safety, security, efficiency and quality travel. Provides a forum for the exchange of information and ideas among members. **Geographic Preference:** Local.

19315 ■ **Rocky Mountain Business Travel Association (RMBTA)**
PO Box 890
  Firestone, CO 80520
Co. E-mail: rmbtadenver@msn.com
URL: http://rockymountainbta.org
Contact: Laurie Etcheverry, President
E-mail: president@rockymountainbta.org
Facebook: www.facebook.com/GBTARockyMtn
X (Twitter): x.com/gbtarockymtn
Instagram: www.instagram.com/gbta_rm
Description: Represents travel managers and providers. Promotes the value of the travel manager in meeting corporate travel needs and financial goals. Cultivates a positive public image of the corporate travel industry. Protects the interests of members and their corporations in legislative and regulatory matters. Promotes safety, security, efficiency and quality travel. Provides a forum for the exchange of information and ideas among members. **Founded:** 1982. **Geographic Preference:** Regional.

19316 ■ **Saint Louis Business Travel Association (STLBTA)**
c/o Kelly Christner, President
  8534 Colonial Ln.
  Saint Louis, MO 63124
URL: http://www.stlbta.org
Contact: Becky Schlereth, President
Facebook: www.facebook.com/stlbta
Linkedin: www.linkedin.com/company/gbta-st-louis-chapter
Instagram: www.instagram.com/gbta.stl
Description: Represents travel managers and providers. Promotes the value of the travel manager in meeting corporate travel needs and financial goals. Cultivates a positive public image of the corporate travel industry. Protects the interests of members and their corporations in legislative and regulatory matters. Promotes safety, security, efficiency and quality travel. Provides a forum for the exchange of information and ideas among members. **Founded:** 1986. **Geographic Preference:** Local.

19317 ■ **San Diego Business Travel Association (SDBTA)**
PO Box 720596
  San Diego, CA 92172
Co. E-mail: enquiries@gbta.org
URL: http://www.sdbta.org
Contact: Christine Ehly, President
E-mail: cehlygbta@gmail.com
X (Twitter): x.com/SDBTA
Description: Represents travel managers and providers. Promotes the value of the travel manager in meeting corporate travel needs and financial goals. Cultivates a positive public image of the corporate travel industry. Protects the interests of members and their corporations in legislative and regulatory mat-

ters. Promotes safety, security, efficiency and quality travel. Provides a forum for the exchange of information and ideas among members. **Geographic Preference:** Local.

19318 ■ **Silicon Valley Business Travel Association (SVBTA) [GBTA, Silicon Valley Chapter]**
1101 King St., Ste. 500
  Alexandria, VA 22314
Co. E-mail: membership@svbta.org
URL: http://svbta.org
Contact: Michele Wilson, President
E-mail: president@svbta.org
Description: Represents travel managers and providers. Promotes the value of the travel manager in meeting corporate travel needs and financial goals. Cultivates a positive public image of the corporate travel industry. Protects the interests of members and their corporations in legislative and regulatory matters. Promotes safety, security, efficiency and quality travel. Provides a forum for the exchange of information and ideas among members. **Geographic Preference:** Local.

19319 ■ **Tennessee Business Travel Association (TBTA)**
PO Box 293037
  Nashville, TN 37229
Co. E-mail: info@tennesseebta.org
URL: http://tennesseebta.org
Contact: Sabrina Kronk, President
E-mail: sabrina.kronk@vanderbilt.edu
Facebook: www.facebook.com/TennesseeBusinessTravelAssociation
X (Twitter): x.com/tbta2021
Description: Represents travel managers and providers. Promotes the value of the travel manager in meeting corporate travel needs and financial goals. Cultivates a positive public image of the corporate travel industry. Protects the interests of members and their corporations in legislative and regulatory matters. Promotes safety, security, efficiency and quality travel. Provides a forum for the exchange of information and ideas among members. **Founded:** 1994. **Geographic Preference:** State.

19320 ■ **Texas Business Travel Association (TBTA)**
PO Box 1001
  Houston, TX 77251
Co. E-mail: info@texasbta.org
URL: http://texasbta.org
Contact: Trish Earles, President
Facebook: www.facebook.com/Texas.BTA
X (Twitter): x.com/tbtahouston
Instagram: www.instagram.com/texas.business.travel.assoc
Description: Represents travel managers and providers. Promotes the value of the travel manager in meeting corporate travel needs and financial goals. Cultivates a positive public image of the corporate travel industry. Protects the interests of members and their corporations in legislative and regulatory matters. Promotes safety, security, efficiency and quality travel. Provides a forum for the exchange of information and ideas among members. **Founded:** 1971. **Geographic Preference:** State.

19321 ■ **Utah Business Travel Association (UBTA)**
PO Box 1293
  Salt Lake City, UT 84123
Co. E-mail: info@ubta.org
URL: http://ubta.org
Contact: Peter Nardelli, President
Facebook: www.facebook.com/people/Utah-Business-Travel-Association/100064802438105
X (Twitter): x.com/UBTA
Description: Represents travel managers and providers. Promotes the value of the travel manager in meeting corporate travel needs and financial goals. Cultivates a positive public image of the corporate travel industry. Protects the interests of members and their corporations in legislative and regulatory matters. Promotes safety, security, efficiency and quality

travel. Provides a forum for the exchange of information and ideas among members. **Founded:** 2001. **Geographic Preference:** State.

19322 ■ Virginia Business Travel Association (VBTA)
PO Box 3540
  Glen Allen, VA 23058
Co. E-mail: info@vbta.org
URL: http://vbta.org
Contact: Samantha Bean, President
E-mail: sbean@ltdhospitality.com
Facebook: www.facebook.com/VABTA

Description: Represents travel managers and providers. Promotes the value of the travel manager in meeting corporate travel needs and financial goals. Cultivates a positive public image of the corporate travel industry. Protects the interests of members and their corporations in legislative and regulatory matters. Promotes safety, security, efficiency and quality travel. Provides a forum for the exchange of information and ideas among members. **Founded:** 1993. **Geographic Preference:** State.

19323 ■ Wisconsin Business Travel Association [Global Business Travel Association - Wisconsin Chapter]
PO Box 842
  Milwaukee, WI 53201
Contact: Margaret Anne Bahr, Contact

Description: Promotes the value of business travel management by representing corporate travel managers and travel service providers. Monitors developments in the business travel field and provides current, critical industry information. **Founded:** 1990.

REFERENCE WORKS

19324 ■ "100 Brilliant Companies" in Entrepreneur (May 2014)
Pub: Entrepreneur Media Inc.
Contact: Dan Bova, Director
E-mail: dbova@entrepreneur.com

Description: Entrepreneur magazine annually selects 100 companies, ideas, innovations and applications which the editors feel offer unique, simple and high-tech solutions to various everyday problems. These may include design developments, innovations in wearable gadgets, travel applications and other new ideas which represent 21st Century breakthroughs and thinking outside the box. The list is divided into ten categories, including Fashion, The Human Factor, and Travel and Transportation. **Availability:** Online.

19325 ■ "Advertising May Take a Big Hit in Southwest/AirTran Merger" in Baltimore Business Journal (Vol. 28, October 1, 2010, No. 21, pp. 1)
Pub: Baltimore Business Journal
Contact: Rhonda Pringle, President
E-mail: rpringle@bizjournals.com

Ed: Gary Haber. **Description:** Advertising on television stations and the publishing industry in Baltimore could drop as a result of the merger between rival discount airlines Southwest Airlines and AirTran Airways. Southwest is among the top advertisers in the U.S., spending $126 million in 2009. No local jobs are expected to be affected because neither airline uses a local advertising firm. **Availability:** Print.

19326 ■ "Airlines Show Reality 'Behind the Scenes" in Dallas Business Journal (Vol. 35, March 23, 2012, No. 28, pp. 1)
Description: American Airlines and Southwest Airlines are set to launch video programs that would give customers a realistic look at their operations. American Airliens started its video on YouTube. Southwest, on the other hand, is planning to luanch its customer-oriented version on TLC.

19327 ■ "Airmall Mulls I-95 Travel Plazas Bid" in Baltimore Business Journal (Vol. 29, September 2, 2011, No. 17, pp. 3)
Pub: Boston Business Journal
Contact: Carolyn M. Jones, President
E-mail: cmjones@bizjournals.com

Ed: Alexander Jackson. **Description:** Airmall USA is planning to move its food courts from the Baltimore/Washington International Thurgood Marshall Airport to the new travel plazas on Interstate 95. The plazas are up for bid. **Availability:** Online.

19328 ■ "Airport Adds More Detroit Flavor; Local Brands Bolster Metro Dining, Retail" in Crain's Detroit Business (Vol. 30, July 28, 2014, No. 30, pp. 3)
Pub: Crain Communications Inc.
Contact: Barry Asin, President

Description: Gayle's Chocolates, Hockeytown Café, and National Coney Island have operated at the Detroit Metropolitan Airport for years. Soon new Detroit favorites will be joining the lineup for the enjoyment of both business and leisure travelers with a food court offering local foods and beverages, including wine and 18 craft brewery beers. There will also be a self-serve kiosk where travelers can buy items to take with them. **Availability:** Print; Online.

19329 ■ "American Airlines Works to Keep Its Brand Aloft" in Dallas Business Journal (Vol. 35, May 18, 2012, No. 36, pp. 1)
Pub: Baltimore Business Journal
Contact: Rhonda Pringle, President
E-mail: rpringle@bizjournals.com

Ed: Matt Joyce. **Description:** As American Airlines is undergoing restructuring, the company is planning to redesign its international aircraft as part of its marketing strategy. But the airline's efforts to improve its brand image present a challenge made difficult by labor relations. Labor unions representing American Airlines employees are fighting the company over their collective bargaining agreements. **Availability:** Print; Online.

19330 ■ "Analysts Expect American Airlines Bankruptcy to Raise Ticket Prices" in Dallas Business Journal (Vol. 35, February 17, 2012, No. 23, pp. 1)
Pub: Baltimore Business Journal
Contact: Rhonda Pringle, President
E-mail: rpringle@bizjournals.com

Description: American Airlines' bankruptcy may cause ticking prices to rise. The average domesic fare has increased nearly 17 percent in the past two years. **Availability:** Print; Online.

19331 ■ "Are Your Goals Hitting the Right Target?" in Business Strategy Review (Vol. 21, Autumn 2010, No. 3, pp. 46)
Ed: Alan Meekings, Steve Briault, Andy Neely. **Description:** Setting targets is normal in most organizations. The authors think such a practice can cause more harm than good. They offer a better plan. **Availability:** Download; PDF; Online.

19332 ■ Average Small Business Travel
Ed: Mike Michalowicz. **Released:** December 16, 2019. **Description:** Knowing average expenses for business travel costs can help your small business define travel budgets, policies and best practices. This article includes resources that provide average costs of travel for different locations so that small business owners can fine-tune their costs. **Availability:** Online.

19333 ■ "The Best in Business Travel" in Entrepreneur (May 2014)
Pub: Entrepreneur Media Inc.
Contact: Dan Bova, Director
E-mail: dbova@entrepreneur.com

Description: A number of companies have been recognized for making business travel more efficient, comfortable and enjoyable. Kayak CEO Steve Hafner's goal to create the world's best travel Website with the fewest people has made the travel search engine profitable. The subscription model of Surf Air, starting at $1,599 per month for unlimited flights, provides more efficient travel experience for executives. The Club Lounge at the Langham Hotel in Chicago, Illinois combines the efficiency of a working office with a private ambiance.

19334 ■ "Best Cash Flow Generators" in Canadian Business (Vol. 82, Summer 2009, No. 8, pp. 40)
Description: Agrium Inc. and FirstService Corporation are in the list of firms that are found to have the potential to be the best cash flow generators in Canada. The list also includes WestJet Airlines Ltd., which accounts for 385 flights each day. More than 80 percent of analysts rate the airline stocks a Buy. **Availability:** Print; Online.

19335 ■ Best Small Business Credit Cards for Travel Rewards 2020
Ed: Geoff Whitmore. **Released:** November 05, 2020. **Description:** The best small business credit cards for travel in 2020 are the ones that provide value when people aren't traveling. This article compares some of the most popular credit cards for businesses on the market and looks at options for new businesses, sole-proprietorships, businesses working with average credit, businesses looking to finance upcoming purchases, and businesses wanting to earn rewards on their regular spending. **Availability:** Online.

19336 ■ "Bidding On Airport Terminal is Big Job In Itself" in Wichita Business Journal (Vol. 27, February 10, 2012, No. 6, pp. 1)
Pub: Baltimore Business Journal
Contact: Rhonda Pringle, President
E-mail: rpringle@bizjournals.com

Description: The city of Wichita, Kansas has started calling for construction bids to build the new terminal at Wichita Mid-Continent Airport, a project considered a big job in construction industry norms. Efforts that have been done by construction firms in making bids are discussed, along with the economic impact of this project. **Availability:** Print; Online.

19337 ■ "Border Boletin: UA to Take Lie-Detector Kiosk to Poland" in Arizona Daily Star (September 14, 2010)
Pub: Arizona Daily Star
Contact: John D'Orlando, President
E-mail: jdorlando@tucson.com

Ed: Brady McCombs. **Description:** University of Arizona's National Center for Border Security and Immigration Research will send a team to Warsaw, Poland to show border guards from 27 European Union countries the center's Avatar Kiosk. The Avatar technology is designed for use at border ports and airports to assist Customs officers detect individuals who are lying. **Availability:** Print; Online.

19338 ■ "Business Builders: Tradeshow Attendance Incentives Add Up" In Pet Product News (Vol. 64, December 2010, No. 12, pp. 14)
Ed: Mark E. Battersby. **Description:** Pointers on how pet specialty retailers can claim business travel tax and income tax deductions for expenses paid or incurred in participation at tradeshows, conventions, and meetings are presented. Incentives in form of these deductions could allow pet specialty retailers to gain business benefits, aside from the education and enjoyment involved with the travel. **Availability:** Online.

19339 ■ "Business Travel Can be a Trip if Structured Right" in Globe & Mail (February 3, 2007, pp. B11)
Description: The importance of arranging a proper business trip for executives by employers, in order to achieve good benefits for the company, is discussed. **Availability:** Online.

19340 ■ "Business Wisdom from the Mountaintops" in Canadian Business (Vol. 83, October 12, 2010, No. 17, pp. 91)
Ed: Matthew McClearn. **Released:** October 12, 2010. **Description:** Techniques used to save lives on the world's highest mountains could make companies more creative. Mountaineers have time to talk to one another, and the resulting flow of ideas help climbers

reach the summit. Organizations are expected to foster communication both internally and externally. **Availability:** Print; Online.

19341 ■ *"Coca-Cola FEMSA, Family Dollar, Other Dividend Payers On a Roll"* in *Benzinga.com (June 21, 2012)*
Pub: Benzinga.com
Contact: Jason Raznick, Founder
Ed: Nelson Hem. **Description:** Dividend paying companies showing upward price trends are outlined. The firms highlighted include: Agnico-Eagle Mines, Coca-Cola FEMSA, Dean Foods, Expedia, Family Dollar Stores, Ferrellgas Partners, and InterContinental Hotels. **Availability:** Print; Online.

19342 ■ *"Congestion Relief: The Land Use Alternative"* in *Canadian Business (Vol. 80, February 12, 2007, No. 4, pp. 31)*
Description: The development of a satellite-based system for traffic management including paying for parking fees by Skymeter Corp. is discussed. **Availability:** Download; PDF.

19343 ■ *Corporate Travel Management for Small Businesses*
Ed: Geoff Williams. **Released:** December 12, 2019. **Description:** This article discusses when your small business should find a corporate travel management solution to avoid wasted money, unorganized travel plans, and undue stress. **Availability:** Online.

19344 ■ *"Corporate Travel Planners is Geared Up for More Growth"* in *San Antonio Business Journal (Vol. 26, September 7, 2012, No. 32, pp. 1)*
Pub: Baltimore Business Journal
Contact: Rhonda Pringle, President
E-mail: rpringle@bizjournals.com
Description: San Antonio, Texas-based Corporate Travel Planners (CTP) registered an 11.6 percent increase in revenues through July compared to the same period in 2011 and it is expected to reach $135 million by the end of 2012. CTP is one of the companies that helped lead the travel industry out of the deep hole. **Availability:** Print; Online.

19345 ■ *"Empowered"* in *Harvard Business Review (Vol. 88, July-August 2010, No. 7-8, pp. 94)*
Pub: Harvard Business Publishing
Contact: Diane Belcher, Managing Director
Ed: Josh Bernoff, Ted Schadler. **Price:** $8.95, PDF. **Description:** HERO concept (highly empowered and resourceful operative) which builds a connection between employees, managers, and IT is outlined. The resultant additional experience and knowledge gained by employees improves customer relationship management. **Availability:** Online; PDF.

19346 ■ *"Entrepreneurs: Search Party"* in *Business Strategy Review (Vol. 21, Autumn 2010, No. 3, pp. 30)*
Ed: Georgina Peters. **Released:** September 22, 2010. **Description:** Entrepreneurs tend to be fixated on coming up with a foolproof idea for a new business and then raising money to start it. Raising startup funds is difficult, but it doesn't have to be that way. Search funds offer an innovative alternative, and the results are often impressive. **Availability:** Electronic publishing; Online.

19347 ■ *"First Airport Location for Paciugo Gelato"* in *Ice Cream Reporter (Vol. 23, October 20, 2010, No. 11, pp. 2)*
Description: Paciugo Gelato and Caffee has partnered with airport concessions developer Airmail to open a shop in the Cleveland Hopkins International Airport. The firm will create a wide variety of choices for travelers. **Availability:** Print; Online.

19348 ■ *"Flights of Fancy"* in *Crain's Chicago Business (Vol. 31, April 21, 2008, No. 16, pp. 27)*
Ed: Sarah A. Klein. **Released:** June 17, 2017. **Description:** Due to the competition for business travelers, who account for 30 percent of airline revenue, airlines are offering a number of luxury amenities, especially on long-haul routes. **Availability:** Print; Online.

19349 ■ *"Flying Discounted Skies"* in *Barron's (Vol. 92, September 17, 2012, No. 38, pp. 20)*
Description: Business aviation services provider Xojet offers highly competitive pricing due to its efficient fleet utilization. The firm adopts unconventional methods in running its airplane fleet and has a transparent pricing scheme. **Availability:** Online.

19350 ■ *"Flying the Unfriendly Skies"* in *Crain's Chicago Business (Vol. 31, April 21, 2008, No. 16, pp. 26)*
Pub: Crain Communications Inc.
Contact: Barry Asin, President
Ed: Sarah A. Klein. **Description:** Due to the number of Chicago companies and entrepreneurs who are traveling overseas more frequently in order to strengthen ties with customers, companies and oftentimes even business partners, the number of flights leaving O'Hare International Airport for destinations abroad has surged; In 2007, international passengers departing O'Hare totaled 5.7 million, up from 2.4 million in 1990. **Availability:** Online.

19351 ■ *"'Focusing On the Moment'"* in *Dallas Business Journal (Vol. 37, June 27, 2014, No. 42, pp. 4)*
Pub: American City Business Journals, Inc.
Contact: Mike Olivieri, Executive Vice President
Description: Southwest Airlines chairman, president, and CEO Gary Kelly, believes the key to the carrier's growth in 2014 will be to 'focus on the moment' and ensure that new projects are launched and strategies implemented successfully. Kelly discusses the potential impact of the repeal of the Wright Amendment on October 13, as well as Southwest's merger with AirTran and the launch of nonstop flights from New York and Washington DC. **Availability:** Print; Online.

19352 ■ *"Full Speed Ahead: How to Get the Most Out of Your Company Vehicles"* in *Entrepreneur (Vol. 37, October 2009, No. 10, pp. 78)*
Pub: Entrepreneur Media Inc.
Contact: Dan Bova, Director
E-mail: dbova@entrepreneur.com
Ed: Jill Amadio. **Description:** Methods of saving costs on purchasing and maintaining vehicles are described. Tips include shopping online, choosing hybrid vehicles, and choosing cars with incentives and lower insurance costs.

19353 ■ *"Geico and the USO of Metropolitan Washington Have Teamed Up to Provide Military Troops with a New 'Home Away From Home'"* in *Best's Review (Vol. 113, September 2012, No. 5, pp. 13)*
Description: Geico and the USO of Metropolitan Washington have partnered to provide military troops and their families an area in the USO airport lounge at Ronald Reagan Washington National Airport with wireless Internet access, seating area with large-screen TV, assistance with travel-related questions, and a snack bar. **Availability:** Online.

19354 ■ *"The Globe: Singapore Airlines' Balancing Act"* in *Harvard Business Review (Vol. 88, July-August 2010, No. 7-8, pp. 145)*
Pub: Harvard Business Publishing
Contact: Diane Belcher, Managing Director
Ed: Loizos Heracleous, Jochen Wirtz. **Price:** $8.95. **Description:** Singapore Airlines is used as an illustration of organizational effectiveness. The article includes the firm's 4-3-3 rule of spending, its promotion of centralized as well as decentralized innovation, use of technology, and strategic planning. **Availability:** Online; PDF.

19355 ■ *Greening Your Small Business: How to Improve Your Bottom Line, Grow Your Brand, Satisfy Your Customers and Save the Planet*
Price: $19.95. **Description:** A definitive resource for anyone who wants their small business to be cutting-edge, competitive, profitable, and eco-conscious. Stories from small business owners address every aspect of going green, from basics such as recycling waste, energy efficiency, and reducing information technology footprint, to more in-depth concerns such as green marketing and communications, green business travel, and green employee benefits.

19356 ■ *"'Groundhog Day' B&B Likely Will Be Converted Into One In Real Life"* in *Chicago Tribune (October 21, 2008)*
Pub: Tribune News Service
Contact: Jack Barry, Vice President, Operations
E-mail: jbarry@tribpub.com
Ed: Carolyn Starks. **Description:** Everton Martin and Karla Stewart Martin have purchased the Victorian house that was featured as a bed-and-breakfast in the 1993 hit move "Groundhog Day"; the couple was initially unaware of the structure's celebrity status when they purchased it with the hope of fulfilling their dream of owning a bed-and-breakfast. **Availability:** Print; Online.

19357 ■ *"The HBR Interview:"We Had to Own the Mistakes""* in *Harvard Business Review (Vol. 88, July-August 2010, No. 7-8, pp. 108)*
Pub: Harvard Business Publishing
Contact: Diane Belcher, Managing Director
Ed: Adi Ignatius. **Description:** Interview with Howard Schultz, CEO of Starbucks, covers topics that include investment in retraining, the impact of competition, premium quality, authenticity, customer services, strategy development, work-and-life issues, and international presence. **Availability:** Online.

19358 ■ *"Heavy Duty: The Case Against Packing Lightly"* in *Crain's Chicago Business (Vol. 31, April 21, 2008, No. 16, pp. 29)*
Pub: Crain Communications Inc.
Contact: Barry Asin, President
Ed: Sarah A. Klein. **Description:** Penelope Biggs, a Northern Trust executive who manages sales teams in North America, Europe and Asia gives advice on traveling abroad for business including time management skills, handling time-zone hops and avoiding jet-lag. **Availability:** Online.

19359 ■ *"Hotels Get a Fill-Up: Fee Helps Bring Back Hot Rod Tour, Replace Biz Travel"* in *Crain's Detroit Business (Vol. 25, June 1, 2009, No. 22, pp. 1)*
Pub: Crain Communications Inc.
Contact: Barry Asin, President
Ed: Daniel Duggan. **Description:** Hot Rod Power Tour will have a $1 million economic impact on the area when it arrives in June 2009; the tour will bring 3,500 out-of-state custom vehicles to the event, whose owners will be needing hotel rooms. **Availability:** Print; Online.

19360 ■ *"Hotels' Healthy Finish in '07"* in *Crain's Chicago Business (Vol. 31, March 24, 2008, No. 12, pp. 16)*
Pub: Crain Communications Inc.
Contact: Barry Asin, President
Ed: Alby Gallun. **Description:** Chicago's hotel market saw mostly rising occupancies and room rates in the fourth quarter of 2007, reflecting continued strong demand from leisure and business travelers; however, due to the current state of the economy hoteliers face an increasingly uncertain outlook. **Availability:** Online.

19361 ■ *"How Hierarchy Can Hurt Strategy Execution"* in *Harvard Business Review (Vol. 88, July-August 2010, No. 7-8, pp. 74)*
Pub: Harvard Business Publishing
Contact: Diane Belcher, Managing Director
Price: $8.95, PDF. **Description:** A series of charts illustrate Harvard Business Review's Advisory Council survey results regarding perceptions of strategy development and execution identifying obstacles and key factors affecting implementation. **Availability:** Online; PDF.

19362 ■ "How Profitable Are Add-On Airline Fees?" in Canadian Business (Vol. 85, September 17, 2012, No. 14, pp. 82)

Ed: David Fielding. **Description:** A chart of the top ten airlines by ancillary revenue is presented. **Availability:** Online.

19363 ■ "Huberman Failing to Keep CTA on Track" in Crain's Chicago Business (Vol. 31, April 21, 2008, No. 16, pp. 22)

Pub: Crain Communications Inc.
Contact: Barry Asin, President

Description: Discusses the deplorable service of CTA, the Chicago Transit Authority, as well as CTA President Ron Huberman who, up until last week had riders hoping he had the management skills necessary to fix the system's problems; Tuesday's event left hundreds of riders trapped for hours and thousands standing on train platforms along the Blue Line waiting for trains that never came. **Availability:** Online.

19364 ■ "Ideas at Work: The Reality of Costs" in Business Strategy Review (Vol. 21, Summer 2010, No. 2, pp. 40)

Ed: Jules Goddard. **Released:** June 24, 2010. **Description:** If you think that cost cutting is the surest way to business success, the author wants to challenge every assumption you hold. Costs are an outcome of sound strategy, never the goal of strategy. He offers a new perspective on what counts when it comes to costs. **Availability:** Print; PDF; Online.

19365 ■ "Ihilani's New Day" in Pacific Business News (Vol. 26, August 22, 2014, No. 26, pp. 14)

Pub: American City Business Journals, Inc.
Contact: Mike Olivieri, Executive Vice President

Description: JW Marriott Ihilani Resort and Spa is likely to be rebranded in 2014 as the Four Seasons Hotels and Resorts, making it the chain's fifth largest property in Hawaii. The implications of the hotel's renovation and rebranding for West Oahu's leisure and business travel sectors are discussed. **Availability:** Online.

19366 ■ "In China, Railways to Riches" in Barron's (Vol. 88, July 7, 2008, No. 27, pp. M9)

Pub: Dow Jones & Company Inc.
Contact: Almar Latour, Chief Executive Officer

Ed: Assif Shameen. **Description:** Shares of Chinese railway companies look to benefit from multimillion-dollar investments aimed at upgrading the Chinese railway network. Investment in the sector is expected to reach $210 billion for the 2006-2010 period. **Availability:** Online.

19367 ■ "Innovating Globally" in Business Strategy Review (Vol. 21, Spring 2010, No. 1, pp. 24)

Ed: Costas Markides, Stuart Crainer. **Description:** Costas Markides has spent over two decades studying business strategy and innovation. Recently, he has been focusing on the bigger picture of how people can address major social problems. Can the techniques used by managers to create innovation inside organizations work with global change?. **Availability:** Download; PDF; Online.

19368 ■ "Innovation's Holy Grail" in Harvard Business Review (Vol. 88, July-August 2010, No. 7-8, pp. 132)

Pub: Harvard Business Publishing
Contact: Diane Belcher, Managing Director

Ed: C.K. Prahalad, R.A. Mashelkar. **Price:** $8.95. **Description:** Three forms of business innovation are presented, inspired by the tenets of Mahatma Gandhi. They are: changing organizational capabilities, sourcing or creating new capabilities, and disrupting conventional business models. Illustrations for these methods are also included. **Availability:** Online; PDF.

19369 ■ "Is It OK To Expense a Parking Ticket? Straight Answers To Some Common Expense Report Conundrums" in Canadian Business (Vol. 85, June 11, 2012, No. 10, pp. 70)

Ed: Sarah Barmak. **Description:** Human resource experts Andrea Fraser of DAC Group and Fiorella Callocchia of Deloitte offer advice to employees on personal costs and when to charge the company for travel expenses. The experts say expense claims should be reasonable and should depend on the firm's culture. **Availability:** Online.

19370 ■ The Itty Bitty Guide to Business Travel

Description: Advice on all aspects of business travel, including low-price airfare, packing and coping with stress.

19371 ■ "Keeping Railcars 'Busy At All Times' At TTX" in Crain's Chicago Business (Vol. 31, April 28, 2008, No. 17, pp. 6)

Pub: Crain Communications Inc.
Contact: Barry Asin, President

Ed: Bob Tita. **Description:** Profile of the president of Chicago railcar pool operator TTX Co. and his business plan for the company which includes improving fleet management and car purchasing through better use of data on railroad demand. **Availability:** Online.

19372 ■ "Las Vegas Convention and Visitors Authority Kicks Off Halloween Promotion" in Travel & Leisure Close-Up (October 8, 2012)

Description: Las Vegas Convention and Visitors Authority (LVCVA) is promoting the city as the premier destination for Halloween celebrations. LVCVA sites the holiday as a favorite for events and experiences for visitors. **Availability:** Print; Online.

19373 ■ "Leave It Behind" in Crain's Chicago Business (Vol. 31, April 21, 2008, No. 16, pp. 32)

Pub: Crain Communications Inc.
Contact: Barry Asin, President

Ed: Sarah A. Klein. **Description:** Patrick Brady who investigates possible violations of the Foreign Corrupt Practices Act has a novel approach when traveling to frequent destinations which allows him to travel with only a carry-on piece of luggage: he leaves suits at dry cleaners in the places he visits most often and since he mainly stays at the same hotels, he also leaves sets of workout clothes and running shoes with hotel staff. **Availability:** Online.

19374 ■ "Lindbergh Receives Kiosks to Expedite Travel Through Customs: Vetting Process 'Pre-Screens' Low-Risk Travelers" in San Diego Business Journal (Vol. 33, August 20, 2012, No. 34, pp. 8)

Pub: CBJ L.P.
Contact: Terri Cunningham, Contact

Ed: Mike Allen. **Description:** Lindbergh Field airport in California installed two automated kiosks to help international travelers pass through customs in minutes. Global Entry verifies identification and allows declaration of items and is used for low risk passsengers. **Availability:** Online.

19375 ■ "Local Hotels Brace for Downturn" in Crain's Chicago Business (Vol. 31, March 31, 2008, No. 13, pp. 3)

Pub: Crain Communications Inc.
Contact: Barry Asin, President

Ed: Bob Tita. **Description:** Chicago hotels are seeing a noticeable drop in business-related guests so far this year due to a slumping national economy, tighter corporate expense budgets and higher airfares. **Availability:** Online.

19376 ■ "London's Gold-Medal Hotels" in Canadian Business (Vol. 85, August 13, 2012, No. 13, pp. 65)

Ed: Chris Johns. **Description:** Several new hotels in London, England, including Me by Melia, Apex Temple Court Hotel, and Bulgari Hotel London are presented. Prices and tips on how to best maximize the service are provided. **Availability:** Print; Online.

19377 ■ "The Long Game" in Business Strategy Review (Vol. 21, Summer 2010, No. 2, pp. 36)

Ed: Stuart Crainer. **Released:** June 24, 2010. **Description:** Profile of Alibaba.com and its CEO David Wei. **Availability:** Print; PDF; Online.

19378 ■ "The Lords of Ideas" in Business Strategy Review (Vol. 21, Autumn 2010, No. 3, pp. 57)

Ed: Stuart Crainer. **Released:** September 22, 2010. **Description:** True originators of modern strategy are profiled. **Availability:** Print; Electronic publishing; PDF; Online.

19379 ■ "Muirhead Farmhouse B&B Owners Get Hospitality Wright" in Chicago Tribune (July 31, 2008)

Pub: Tribune News Service
Contact: Jack Barry, Vice President, Operations
E-mail: jbarry@tribpub.com

Ed: Glenn Jeffers. **Description:** Profile of the Muirhead Farmhouse, a bed-and-breakfast owned by Mike Petersdorf and Sarah Muirhead Petersdorf; Frank Lloyd Wright designed the historic farmhouse which blends farm life and history into a unique experience that is enhanced by the couple's hospitality. **Availability:** Online.

19380 ■ "Nighttime Shuttle to Connect Detroit, Ferndale, Royal Oak" in Crain's Detroit Business (Vol. 24, October 6, 2008, No. 40, pp. 24)

Pub: Crain Communications Inc.
Contact: Barry Asin, President

Ed: Nancy Kaffer. **Description:** With hopes of bridging the social gap between the cities and suburbs, Chris Ramos has launched The Night Move, a new shuttle service that will ferry passengers between Royal Oak, Ferndale and downtown Detroit. The cost for a round trip ticket is $12. **Availability:** Online.

19381 ■ "On the Go: a Busy Executive Is Always Well-Equipped for Travel" in Black Enterprise (Vol. 40, July 2010, No. 12, pp. 106)

Pub: Earl G. Graves Ltd.
Contact: Earl Graves, Jr., President

Ed: Sonia Alleyne. **Description:** Successful sales executive, Henry Watkins, shares tips on business travel. **Availability:** Online.

19382 ■ "Pack Mentality: Why Black Can Be Slimming" in Crain's Chicago Business (Vol. 31, April 21, 2008, No. 16, pp. 31)

Pub: Crain Communications Inc.
Contact: Barry Asin, President

Ed: Sarah A. Klein. **Description:** Jill Smart, the head of human resources for a company with 170,000 employees worldwide, frequently travels to India, London and Singapore; Ms. Smart provides advice concerning efficiency, time management and avoiding jet-lag. **Availability:** Online.

19383 ■ "Packing Chic" in Black Enterprise (Vol. 38, February 2008, No. 7, pp. 154)

Pub: Earl G. Graves Ltd.
Contact: Earl Graves, Jr., President

Ed: Sonia Alleyne. **Description:** Profile of Angela Theodora's leather overnight bags that offer a variety of smart compartments for the business traveler.

19384 ■ "The Play's the Thing" in Business Strategy Review (Vol. 21, Summer 2010, No. 2, pp. 58)

Ed: Michael G. Jacobides. **Released:** March 07, 2018. **Description:** Those who study and plan strategies risk falling into the traps that maps, graphs, charts and matrices present. The author feels that strategy might best be cast as a dramatic playscript that can reveal the unfolding plots of business far better than traditional strategic tools, as the landscape shifts around us. **Availability:** Print; PDF; Online.

19385 ■ "Portion of Silver Line Will Run By Year's End" in Crain's Cleveland Business (Vol. 28, November 5, 2007, No. 44, pp. 6)
Pub: Crain Communications Inc.
Contact: K. C. Crain, President

Ed: Jay Miller. Description: Cleveland's new Silver Line rapid transit will board its first passengers before the end of the year. The project is expected to spur economic development in the area and will speed transportation along Euclid Avenue. Availability: Online.

19386 ■ "Power Play" in Harvard Business Review (Vol. 88, July-August 2010, No. 7-8, pp. 84)
Pub: Harvard Business Publishing
Contact: Diane Belcher, Managing Director

Ed: Jeffrey Pfeffer. Price: $8.95, PDF. Description: Guidelines include in-depth understanding of resources at one's disposal, relentlessness that still provides opponents with opportunities to save face, and a determination not to be put off by the processes of politics. Availability: Online; PDF.

19387 ■ "Pride Lands Janitorial Work at New Terminal" in Sacramento Business Journal (Vol. 28, June 10, 2011, No. 15, pp. 1)
Pub: Sacramento Business Journal
Contact: Stephanie Fretwell, Director
E-mail: sfretwell@bizjournals.com

Ed: Kelly Johnson. Description: Pride Industries Inc. won the five-year $9.4 million contract to clean the Sacramento International Airport's new Terminal B, which will open in fall 2011. The nonprofit organization posts a revenue of $191 million for 2011 and currently employs more than 2,400 people with disabilities. The contract is expected to provide savings of over $3 million a year to the airport. Availability: Online.

19388 ■ "Research and Markets Offers Report on US Business Traveler's Green, New Technology Views" in Airline Industry Information (July 30, 2012)

Description: The US Business Traveler Expectations of Green and Technology Initiatives in Hotels in 2012 contains comprehensive analysis on US business travelers views on green and technology initiative and socially responsible measures geared towards the business traveler. Availability: Print; Online.

19389 ■ "RIAC: Green Air Link to Ireland No Flight of Fancy" in Providence Business News (Vol. 29, May 26, 2014, No. 8, pp. 1)
Pub: American City Business Journals, Inc.
Contact: Mike Olivieri, Executive Vice President
URL(s): pbn.com/riac-green-air-link-to-ireland-no-flight-of-fancy97335

Ed: Kelly Anderson. Description: Rhode Island Airport Corporation president and CEO, Kelly Fredericks, joined the European trade mission led by the state government to pitch nonstop flights from T.F. Green Airport in Warwick, RI to Ireland. Fredericks is in discussions with Shannon Airport and Ireland West Airport Knock about cargo/freight forwarding and passenger services.

19390 ■ "Road Warriors: How To Survive Business Travel" in Crain's Detroit Business (Vol. 24, February 4, 2008, No. 5, pp. 11)
Pub: Crain Communications Inc.
Contact: Barry Asin, President

Ed: Maureen McDonald. Description: Entrepreneurs share tips that help save time and energy at airports when traveling for business. Availability: Print; Online.

19391 ■ "Route Optimization Impacts the Bottom Line" in Contractor (Vol. 56, November 2009, No. 11, pp. 48)

Ed: Dave Beaudry. Description: Plumbing and HVAC businesses can save a significant amount of money from route optimization. The process begins with gathering information on a fleet and a routing software tool can determine the effectiveness of current route configurations and identify preferable route plans. Availability: Print; Online.

19392 ■ "RT Seeking Ways to Finance Expansion" in Sacramento Business Journal (Vol. 28, July 29, 2011, No. 22, pp. 1)
Pub: Sacramento Business Journal
Contact: Stephanie Fretwell, Director
E-mail: sfretwell@bizjournals.com

Ed: Melanie Turner. Description: Sacramento Regional Transit District is considering ways to finance all its capital projects outlined in a 30-year transit master plan which would cost more than $7 billion to complete. Current funding sources include developer fees and state and federal assistance and fares. Part of the master plan is a light-rail line to Sacramento International Airport. Availability: Print.

19393 ■ "Salmon's Gem Air Wants Grant For Year-round Boise Flight" in Idaho Business Review (September 3, 2014)
Pub: BridgeTower Media
Contact: Adam Reinebach, President

Description: Gem Air offers four flights between Salmon and Boise, for both tourists and businesspeople including doctors and architects. The airline is requesting a $250,000 federal grant in order to compete with larger airlines and hopes to attract more business travelers with a direct flight between Boise and Atlanta.

19394 ■ "Sleep It Off In a Silo B&B" in Chicago Tribune (December 14, 2008)
Pub: Tribune News Service
Contact: Jack Barry, Vice President, Operations
E-mail: jbarry@tribpub.com

Ed: Bill Daley. Description: Profile of Oregon's Abbey Road Farm bed-and-breakfast which is located on an 82-acre working farm; guests stay in shiny metal farm silos which have been converted into luxury rooms with views of the farm.

19395 ■ "Small Dutch Islands Saba, Statia Content With Low-Key Niche" in Travel Weekly (Vol. 69, August 16, 2010, No. 33, pp. 22)
Pub: NorthStar Travel Media

Ed: Gay Nagle Myers. Description: Small Caribbean islands market and promote their region for tourism by never competing with the bigger destinations. Saba and Statia are the two smallest islands in the Caribbean and rely on repeat guests, word-of-mouth recommendations and travel agents willing to promote them. Availability: Print; Online.

19396 ■ "Sometimes You Have to Ignore the Rule Book" in Canadian Business (Vol. 83, September 14, 2010, No. 15, pp. 13)
Pub: Rogers Media Inc.
Contact: Neil Spivak, Chief Executive Officer

Ed: Richard Branson. Released: September 14, 2010. Description: The rule book has provided a clear framework for employees particularly when cash and accounting are at issue. However, sometimes rules were made to be broken and the rule book should not become an excuse for poor customer service or hinder great service. How Virgin Atlantic practices this type of corporate culture is discussed. Availability: Print; Online.

19397 ■ "South Lake Tahoe B&B Blocks Out Nevada's Neon" in Chicago Tribune (May 18, 2008)
Pub: Tribune News Service
Contact: Jack Barry, Vice President, Operations
E-mail: jbarry@tribpub.com

Ed: Randall Weissman. Description: Profile of the Black Bear Inn, a small bed-and-breakfast in South Lake Tahoe owned by Jerry Birdwell and Kevin Chandler; the welcoming ambience is a delightful departure from ski resort hotel rooms. Pricing and further details of the various rooms are described. Availability: Print; Online.

19398 ■ "Southwest Expected to Forego Subsidy Eventually" in Wichita Business Journal (Vol. 27, February 3, 2012, No. 5, pp. 1)

Description: Southwest Airlines has taken over AirTran Airways service from Wichita to Atlanta and it would be using the subsidies that AirTran received as part of the Kansas-backed Affordable Airfares program. However, Southwest will only use the subsidies for two years since these are not part of its usual business model. Insights on the Afordable Airfares program are also given. Availability: Print; Online.

19399 ■ "Southwest Expected to Up ICT Passenger Counts by Nearly 30 Percent: Taking Off" in Wichita Business Journal (Vol. 27, January 20, 2012, No. 3, pp. 1)
Pub: Baltimore Business Journal
Contact: Rhonda Pringle, President
E-mail: rpringle@bizjournals.com

Ed: Daniel McCoy. Description: Passenger numbers at Wichita Mid-Continent Airport are expected to rise with the entry of Southwest Airlines. The airline will start serving the area uponn completion of its merger with AirTran Airways. Availability: Print; Online.

19400 ■ "State Aviation Fuel Tax Proposal Runs Into Turbulence" in Crain's Detroit Business (Vol. 25, June 15, 2009, No. 24, pp. 5)
Pub: Crain Communications Inc.
Contact: Barry Asin, President

Ed: Amy Lane. Description: Delta Airlines Inc. is concerned about a proposal that would change the way Michigan taxes aviation fuel. The plan would go from the current cents-per-gallon tax to a percentage tax on the wholesale price of fuel, which would raise the taxes significantly. Availability: Online.

19401 ■ "Ten Ways to Save on Business Travel" in Women Entrepreneur (November 21, 2008)

Description: Advice regarding ways in which to save money when traveling for business is given. Availability: Online.

19402 ■ "TIA Wrestles with Procurement Issues" in Business Journal Serving Greater Tampa Bay (Vol. 30, November 12, 2010, No. 47, pp. 1)
Pub: Tampa Bay Business Journal
Contact: Ian Anderson, President
E-mail: ianderson@bizjournals.com

Ed: Mark Holan. Description: Tampa International Airport (TIA) has been caught in conflict of interest and procurement policy issues after the Hillsborough County Aviation Authority learned of the spousal relationship of an employee with his wife's firm, Gresham Smith and Partners. Gresham already won contracts with TIA and was ahead of other firms in a new contract. Availability: Print; Online.

19403 ■ "To Build for the Future, Reach Beyond the Skies" in Canadian Business (Vol. 83, June 15, 2010, No. 10, pp. 11)
Pub: Rogers Media Inc.
Contact: Neil Spivak, Chief Executive Officer

Ed: Richard Branson. Description: Richard Branson says that tackling an engineering challenge or a scientific venture is a real adventure for an entrepreneur. Branson discusses Virgin's foray into the aviation business and states that at Virgin, they build for the future. Availability: Print; Online.

19404 ■ "TomTom GO910: On the Road Again" in Black Enterprise (Vol. 37, January 2007, No. 6, pp. 52)
Pub: Earl G. Graves Ltd.
Contact: Earl Graves, Jr., President

Ed: Stephanie Young. Description: TomTom GO 910 is a GPS navigator that offers detailed maps of the U.S., Canada, and Europe. Consumers view their routes by a customizable LCD screen showing everything from the quickest to the shortest routes available or how to avoid toll roads. Business travelers may find this product invaluable as it also functions as a cell phone and connects to a variety of other multi-media devices. **Availability:** Online.

19405 ■ *"Travel Leery" in Crain's Chicago Business (Vol. 31, March 31, 2008, No. 13, pp. 3)*
Pub: Crain Communications Inc.
Contact: Barry Asin, President
Ed: John Pletz. **Description:** Due to the rise in airline prices and a possible recession, many companies are starting to change their travel policies and limit travel spending. **Availability:** Online.

19406 ■ *"Travel Rewards Take Off" in Inc. (Vol. 33, October 2011, No. 8, pp. 46)*
Description: Credit card companies are offering travel reward cards with special perks, including sign-up bonuses; three such cards are described. **Availability:** Online.

19407 ■ *"Travel Tears" in Crain's Chicago Business (Vol. 31, November 17, 2008, No. 46, pp. 3)*
Pub: Crain Communications Inc.
Contact: Barry Asin, President
Ed: Bob Tita. **Description:** Hotels, restaurants and conventions are seeing a decline in profits due to corporate travel cutbacks and the sagging economy. City and state revenues derived from taxes on tourism-related industries are also suffering. **Availability:** Online.

19408 ■ *"Travel Tech: 4 Gadgets for Running Your Business on the Fly" in Entrepreneur (May 2014)*
Pub: Entrepreneur Media Inc.
Contact: Dan Bova, Director
E-mail: dbova@entrepreneur.com
Description: The Goal Zero Sherpa 100 Power Pack includes two USB ports, a 12-volt plug and a proprietary laptop port that can fill a MacBook Air's battery faster on a single charge. The Nomad ChargeKey is lightweight, flexible and allows users to connect their spent smartphones to any full-size USB outlet. The Jawbone Era Bluetooth headset features a sleek carrying case that also functions as a battery-powered charger. The Belkin WeMo Insight Switch is a mobile wall plug that connects to a Wi-Fi and links to smartphones through an application. **Availability:** Online.

19409 ■ *"TSA PreCheck: What It Is, How to Apply, and Benefits" in Fit Small Business (November 1, 2019)*
Ed: Jordan Tarver. **Released:** November 01, 2019. **Description:** TSA PreCheck can help frequent travelers save a ton of time at the airport, which is important when travel is important for your small business. This article describes what TSA PreCheck is, how it works, who it's right for, how much it costs, and eligibility information. **Availability:** Online.

19410 ■ *"Turbulent Times and Golden Opportunities" in Business Strategy Review (Vol. 21, Spring 2010, No. 1, pp. 34)*
Ed: Don Sull. **Released:** February 09, 2010. **Description:** For those feeling storm-tossed by today's economy, the author believes there's much to learn from Carnival Cruise Lines, a company that discovered that turbulence often has an upside. **Availability:** Print; PDF; Online.

19411 ■ *"TW Trade Shows to Offer Seminars On Niche Selling, Social Media" in Travel Weekly (Vol. 69, October 4, 2010, No. 40, pp. 9)*
Pub: NorthStar Travel Media
Description: Travel Weekly's Leisure World 2010 and Fall Home Based Travel Agent Show focused on niche selling, with emphasis on all-inclusives, young consumers, groups, incentives, culinary vacations, and honeymoon or romance travel. **Availability:** Print; Online.

19412 ■ *"The Ultimate Guide to Business Travel" in Fora Financial (January 24, 2020)*
Released: January 24, 2020. **Description:** Discusses efficient travel practices to help alleviate the stress of traveling for business purposes. **Availability:** Online.

19413 ■ *"Up In the Air" in The Business Journal-Serving Greater Tampa Bay (Vol. 28, July 18, 2008, No. 30, pp. 1)*
Description: Views and information on Busch Gardens and on its future, are presented. The park's 3,769 employees worry for their future, after tourism industry experts have expressed concerns on possible tax cuts and other cost reductions. The future of the park, which ranks number 19 as the most visited park in the world, is expected to have a major impact on the tourism industry. **Availability:** Online.

19414 ■ *"Vacation, What Vacation?" in Black Enterprise (Vol. 41, August 2010, No. 1, pp. 36)*
Description: Nearly 50 percent of employers expect employees to check in with the office while they are away on vacation.

19415 ■ *"Vino Volo Debuts at the Airmall at Boston Logan" in Travel & Leisure Close-Up (October 8, 2012)*
Description: Concessions developer, Airmall USA, presents Vino Volo, the company offering travelers a place to unwind with a glass of wine in a comfortable setting. The restaurant will offer tapas and wine or will create a themed tasting flights of two or three glasses of wine. **Availability:** Print; Online.

19416 ■ *"When One Business Model Isn't Enough: LAN Airlines Flourishes By Running Three Distinctly Different Operations at the Same Time" in Harvard Business Review (Vol. 90, January-February 2012, No.1-2, pp. 132)*
Pub: Harvard Business Review Press
Contact: Moderna V. Pfizer, Contact
Ed: Ramon Casadesus-Masanell, Jorge Tarzijan. **Description:** Chilean carrier LAN Airlines successfully blends three distinct business models: a full-service international passenger airline, a no-frills domestic airline, and an air-cargo line. The cargo revenues complement the passenger business to ensure more fully loaded flights.

19417 ■ *"Why Loyalty Programs Alienate Great Customers" in Harvard Business Review (Vol. 90, July-August 2012, No. 7-8, pp. 38)*
Pub: Harvard Business Review Press
Contact: Moderna V. Pfizer, Contact
Ed: Hal Brierley. **Price:** $6. **Description:** Airline loyalty programs should replace the mileage metric with money spent, and should also extend rewards to second-tier customers. Rewars should also be accessible sooner, and retirees should be granted emeritus status. **Availability:** Online; PDF.

TRADE PERIODICALS

19418 ■ **Business Travel News**
Pub: NorthStar Travel Media
URL(s): www.businesstravelnews.com
Facebook: www.facebook.com/businesstravelnews
Released: Daily **Price:** $142, U.S. and Canada; $129, U.S.; $205, for foreign; $65, for digital. **Description:** Tabloid newspaper covering business travel. **Availability:** Print; PDF; Online.

CONSULTANTS

19419 ■ **Off the Beaten Path, L.L.C.**
7 E Beall St.
Bozeman, MT 59715
Ph: (406)586-1311
Free: 800-445-2995
Fax: (406)587-4147
Co. E-mail: travel@offthebeatenpath.com
URL: http://www.offthebeatenpath.com
Contact: Bill Bryan, Co-Founder

Facebook: www.facebook.com/TravelOfftheBeatenPath
Description: Provider of travel planning and consulting services. **Scope:** Provider of travel planning and consulting services. **Founded:** 1986. **Training:** Soil to Bottle.

PUBLICATIONS

19420 ■ **Business Jet Traveler**
214 Franklin Ave.
Midland Park, NJ 07432
Ph: (201)444-5075
Co. E-mail: info@ainonline.com
URL: http://www.ainonline.com
Contact: Nancy O'Brien, Director
E-mail: nobrien@ainonline.com
URL(s): bjtonline.com
Facebook: www.facebook.com/business.jet.traveler
Linkedin: www.linkedin.com/company/business-jet-traveler
X (Twitter): x.com/bjtonline
YouTube: www.youtube.com/channel/UC0-e8G6cFot717mpZPlbTNA
Ed: Jeff Burger. **Released:** Annual **Description:** Magazine that offers focuses on airlines and travel for business men and women. **Availability:** Print; Download; PDF; Online.

LIBRARIES

19421 ■ **Maritz Travel Company Resource Center**
1375 N Hwy., Dr.
Fenton, MO 63099
Free: 877-462-7489
Co. E-mail: corpcomm@maritz.com
URL: http://www.maritz.com
Facebook: www.facebook.com/corporatemaritz
Linkedin: www.linkedin.com/company/maritz
X (Twitter): x.com/Maritz_MHI
YouTube: www.youtube.com/user/MaritzCorpComm
Scope: Travel data - hotels, restaurants, sightseeing, steamships, countries and cities. **Services:** Interlibrary loan; library not open to the public. **Founded:** 1969. **Holdings:** 300 books; 177 bound periodical volumes; 95 VF drawers of travel-related brochures and reports; 2200 videotapes.

19422 ■ **Nádasdy Ferenc Múzeum Könyvtár**
Varkerulet 1
H-9600 Sarvar, Hungary
Ph: 36 95 320-158
Co. E-mail: muzeum.sarvar@mail.globonet.hu
URL: http://www.museum.hu/muzeum/669/Nadasdy_Ferenc_Muzeum
Description: Nádasdy Ferenc Museum. **Scope:** Regional history. **Founded:** 1951. **Holdings:** Figures not available.

19423 ■ **U.S. Travel Association - Library**
1100 New York Ave. NW Ste. 450
Washington, DC 20005
Ph: (202)408-8422
Co. E-mail: feedback@ustravel.org
URL: http://www.ustravel.org
Contact: Roger Dow, President
Facebook: www.facebook.com/U.S.TravelAssociation
Linkedin: www.linkedin.com/company/ustravelassociation
X (Twitter): twitter.com/USTravel
Instagram: www.instagram.com/ustravel_association
Description: Facilitates communication and cooperation among members. **Scope:** Travel. **Founded:** 1941. **Holdings:** Figures not available. **Publications:** *Survey of State Travel Offices* (Annual); *Travel Industry Association of America--Travel Media Directory* (Annual); *Survey of State Tourism Offices* (Annual); *Outlook for Travel and Tourism*; *Survey of Business Travelers*. **Educational Activities:** IPW (Annual); Sports Travel Forum. **Awards:** Travel Hall of Leaders (Annual); Ronald H. Brown Memorial Scholarship; Hall of Leaders (Annual); U.S. Travel Association Mercury Awards (Annual). **Geographic Preference:** National.

Business Vision/Goals

START-UP INFORMATION

19424 ■ "Leading Digital: Turning Technology into Business Transformation"
Pub: Harvard Business Review Press
Contact: Moderna V. Pfizer, Contact
Released: October 14, 2014. **Price:** $32, Hardcover/Hardcopy. **Description:** Mobile technology, analytics, social media, sensors, and cloud computing have changed the entire business environment in every industry. A guide to help any small startup business in any industry gain strategic advantage using digital, including where to invest in digital technologies and how to lead the transformation. The guide teaches how to engage better with customers, digitally enhance operations, create a digital vision, and govern digital activities. **Availability:** E-book; Print.

19425 ■ Lean In: Women, Work, and the Will to Lead
Pub: Knopf Doubleday Publishing Group
Contact: Nan A. Talese, Contact
E-mail: ddaypub@randomhouse.com
Ed: Sheryl Sandberg. **Released:** March 11, 2013. **Description:** The chief operating officer at Facebook examines women's progress in achieving leadership roles and provides solutions to help women fully achieve their goals. **Availability:** Print.

19426 ■ "Old Town Just the First Stop for Carluccio's" in Washington Business Journal (Vol. 33, May 30, 2014, No. 6, pp. 7)
Pub: American City Business Journals, Inc.
Contact: Mike Olivieri, Executive Vice President
Description: United Kingdom-based Carluccio's announced the opening of its first U.S. location in Old Town Alexandria, Virginia. The Italian restaurant chain reveals plans to open two more restaurants in the region to test out the various styles of their concept. Insights into the selection of the DC are as their first market is examined. **Availability:** Print; Online.

ASSOCIATIONS AND OTHER ORGANIZATIONS

19427 ■ National Business Development Association (NBDA)
6023 Maxie St., Ste. B
Houston, TX 77007
Co. E-mail: info@nbda.co
URL: http://nbda.co
Contact: Catherine Brown, President
Facebook: www.facebook.com/NBDAHouston
Linkedin: www.linkedin.com/company/nbda-national-business-development-association
Description: Offers professional training, coaching, and networking opportunities for entrepreneurs and business owners. **Founded:** 2012.

EDUCATIONAL PROGRAMS

19428 ■ Advanced Critical Thinking Applications Workshop (Onsite)
American Management Association (AMA)
1601 Broadway
New York, NY 10019
Ph: (212)586-8100
Free: 800-262-9699
Fax: (212)903-8168
Co. E-mail: customerservice@amanet.org
URL: http://www.amanet.org
Contact: Manny Avramidis, President
URL(s): www.amanet.org/training/seminars/Critical-Thinking-Workshop.aspx
Price: $1,245, Non-members; $1,095, Members AMA; $938, Members GSA. **Description:** Two-day seminar applying critical thinking skills and how they influence challenges in the work environment. **Audience:** Business professionals. **Principal Exhibits:** Two-day seminar applying critical thinking skills and how they influence challenges in the work environment.

19429 ■ Air Conditioning & Refrigeration (Onsite)
TPC Trainco Inc.
225 E Robinson St., Ste. 570
Orlando, FL 32801
Free: 877-978-7246
Co. E-mail: sales@tpctraining.com
URL: http://live.tpctraining.com
URL(s): live.tpctraining.com/public-seminars/hvac-training/air-conditioning-refrigeration
Description: Course designed for anyone who needs to understand basic operation, maintenance, and troubleshooting of air conditioning and refrigeration systems in order to improve efficiencies and uptime at their industrial plants and large building facilities. **Audience:** Industry professionals. **Principal Exhibits:** Course designed for anyone who needs to understand basic operation, maintenance, and troubleshooting of air conditioning and refrigeration systems in order to improve efficiencies and uptime at their industrial plants and large building facilities.

19430 ■ AMA's Advanced Financial Forecasting and Modeling Workshop (Onsite)
American Management Association (AMA)
1601 Broadway
New York, NY 10019
Ph: (212)586-8100
Free: 800-262-9699
Fax: (212)903-8168
Co. E-mail: customerservice@amanet.org
URL: http://www.amanet.org
Contact: Manny Avramidis, President
URL(s): www.amanet.org/advanced-financial-forecasting-and-modeling-workshop
Price: $2,645, Non-members; $2,395, Members AMA; $2,174, Members GSA. **Frequency:** Continuous. **Description:** Create more powerful and accurate forecasting models that steer you to fast-track, business-improving decision making. **Audience:** Financial executives, business professionals and operations managers. **Principal Exhibits:** Create more powerful and accurate forecasting models that steer you to fast-track, business-improving decision making.

19431 ■ Arc Flash Protection & Electrical Safety 70E
TPC Trainco Inc.
225 E Robinson St., Ste. 570
Orlando, FL 32801
Free: 877-978-7246
Co. E-mail: sales@tpctraining.com
URL: http://live.tpctraining.com
URL(s): live.tpctraining.com/public-seminars/electrical-training/fundamentals/arc-flash-electrical-safety-nfpa-70e
Description: Training course designed to save lives, prevent disabling injuries, and prevent damage to plants, buildings and equipment. Participants learn about personal safety for working on or around electrical systems and equipment, how to use proper materials and procedures for doing electrical work, and the potential consequences for themselves and others if they don't. **Audience:** Electricians, maintenance supervisors, and machine operators. **Principal Exhibits:** Training course designed to save lives, prevent disabling injuries, and prevent damage to plants, buildings and equipment. Participants learn about personal safety for working on or around electrical systems and equipment, how to use proper materials and procedures for doing electrical work, and the potential consequences for themselves and others if they don't.

19432 ■ Auditing the Manufacturing Process (Onsite)
Seminar Information Service Inc. (SIS)
250 El Camino Real., Ste. 112
Tustin, CA 92780
Ph: (714)508-0340
Free: 877-736-4636
Fax: (714)734-8027
Co. E-mail: info@seminarinformation.com
URL: http://www.seminarinformation.com
Contact: Catherine Bellizzi, President
URL(s): www.seminarinformation.com
Description: Learn how to identify key manufacturing data to help objectively perform risk assessment of the conversion cycle, while discovering how to analyze the impact of shop floor activities on the balance sheet and income statement, and review the audit concerns in implementing new technologies. **Audience:** Internal audit directors, managers, staff, IT auditors, external auditors. **Principal Exhibits:** Learn how to identify key manufacturing data to help objectively perform risk assessment of the conversion cycle, while discovering how to analyze the impact of shop floor activities on the balance sheet and income statement, and review the audit concerns in implementing new technologies.

19433 ■ Basic Electricity for the Non Electrician (Onsite)
TPC Trainco Inc.
225 E Robinson St., Ste. 570
Orlando, FL 32801
Free: 877-978-7246
Co. E-mail: sales@tpctraining.com
URL: http://live.tpctraining.com

URL(s): live.tpctraining.com/public-seminars/elec trical-training/fundamentals/basic-electrical-training
Description: Understanding and working with industrial electricity. **Audience:** Mechanics, HVAC technicians, and machine operators. **Principal Exhibits:** Understanding and working with industrial electricity.

19434 ■ Boiler Operation, Maintenance & Safety (Onsite)
TPC Trainco Inc.
225 E Robinson St., Ste. 570
Orlando, FL 32801
Free: 877-978-7246
Co. E-mail: sales@tpctraining.com
URL: http://live.tpctraining.com
URL(s): live.tpctraining.com/public-seminars/hvac -training/boiler-operation-maintenance-safety-train ing
Description: Seminar designed to teach building and facility maintenance personnel how to service their own boiler safely reducing the need for outside service contractors, while at the same time increases your confidence and comfort level in operating and maintaining your own broilers. **Audience:** Building maintenance personnel, technicians and engineers . **Principal Exhibits:** Seminar designed to teach building and facility maintenance personnel how to service their own boiler safely reducing the need for outside service contractors, while at the same time increases your confidence and comfort level in operating and maintaining your own broilers.

19435 ■ Building a Strategy Focused Organization (Onsite)
URL(s): www.eeicom.com
Description: Identifies strategies that can help your organization meet the challenges of the competitive environment and improve overall effectiveness across organizational boundaries. **Audience:** Industry professionals, general public. **Principal Exhibits:** Identifies strategies that can help your organization meet the challenges of the competitive environment and improve overall effectiveness across organizational boundaries.

19436 ■ Chilled Water Systems (Onsite)
TPC Trainco Inc.
225 E Robinson St., Ste. 570
Orlando, FL 32801
Free: 877-978-7246
Co. E-mail: sales@tpctraining.com
URL: http://live.tpctraining.com
URL(s): live.tpctraining.com/public-seminars/hvac -training/chilled-water-systems
Description: Learn to control your systems and properly maintain them, getting the most out of them. **Audience:** Students. **Principal Exhibits:** Learn to control your systems and properly maintain them, getting the most out of them.

19437 ■ The Conference on Social Media (Onsite)
Seminar Information Service Inc. (SIS)
250 El Camino Real., Ste. 112
Tustin, CA 92780
Ph: (714)508-0340
Free: 877-736-4636
Fax: (714)734-8027
Co. E-mail: info@seminarinformation.com
URL: http://www.seminarinformation.com
Contact: Catherine Bellizzi, President
URL(s): www.seminarinformation.com/details.cfm?qc =qqbvul
Description: Learn how to make social media link your organization, including new tools and ways to grow your business, and how to define your strategy and create your plan prior to taking the leap into social media. **Audience:** Marketing professionals. **Principal Exhibits:** Learn how to make social media link your organization, including new tools and ways to grow your business, and how to define your strategy and create your plan prior to taking the leap into social media.

19438 ■ Developing a Balanced Scorecard for Business & Government
URL(s): www.eeicom.com
Description: The Balanced ScoreCard evaluates performance from four basic perspectives, Customer, Financial, Internal Processes and Learning and Growth. By utilizing Key Performance Indicators (KPIs) to reflect the performance of the organization at a variety of levels, the Balanced ScoreCard allows organizations to better understand, communicate and improve on organizational performance. **Audience:** Industry professionals. **Principal Exhibits:** The Balanced ScoreCard evaluates performance from four basic perspectives, Customer, Financial, Internal Processes and Learning and Growth. By utilizing Key Performance Indicators (KPIs) to reflect the performance of the organization at a variety of levels, the Balanced ScoreCard allows organizations to better understand, communicate and improve on organizational performance.

19439 ■ Developing Your Analytical Skills: How to Research and Present Information (Onsite)
American Management Association (AMA)
1601 Broadway
New York, NY 10019
Ph: (212)586-8100
Free: 800-262-9699
Fax: (212)903-8168
Co. E-mail: customerservice@amanet.org
URL: http://www.amanet.org
Contact: Manny Avramidis, President
URL(s): www.amanet.org/training/seminars/onsite/ Improve-Your-Analytical-Skills-Making-Information -Work-for-You.aspx
Price: $2,095, Non-members; $1,895, Members AMA; $1,700, Members GSA. **Description:** Learn how to assimilate, assess, organize, and analyze information. **Audience:** Business professionals. **Principal Exhibits:** Learn how to assimilate, assess, organize, and analyze information.

19440 ■ Electrical Ladder Drawings, Schematics & Diagrams (Onsite)
TPC Trainco Inc.
225 E Robinson St., Ste. 570
Orlando, FL 32801
Free: 877-978-7246
Co. E-mail: sales@tpctraining.com
URL: http://live.tpctraining.com
URL(s): live.tpctraining.com/public-seminars/elec trical-training/electrical-controls/electrical-ladder -drawings-schematics-and-diagrams
Description: Training will include exercises where participants create schematic diagrams based on circuit descriptions, as well as interpreting schematic drawings so that they can provide verbal or written circuit descriptions and an understanding of several types of drawings and diagrams including Block, Pictorial, One-line, Wiring, Terminal, and Schematic. **Audience:** Engineers, electricians, plant and facility managers and mechanics. **Principal Exhibits:** Training will include exercises where participants create schematic diagrams based on circuit descriptions, as well as interpreting schematic drawings so that they can provide verbal or written circuit descriptions and an understanding of several types of drawings and diagrams including Block, Pictorial, One-line, Wiring, Terminal, and Schematic.

19441 ■ Generators & Emergency Power (Onsite)
TPC Trainco Inc.
225 E Robinson St., Ste. 570
Orlando, FL 32801
Free: 877-978-7246
Co. E-mail: sales@tpctraining.com
URL: http://live.tpctraining.com
URL(s): www.tpctrainco.com/public-seminars/elec trical-training/emergency-power/generators-emer gency-power-training
Description: Learn what you can do, and should do with generators, to make sure your facility will keep running even when the electricity to your facility doesn't. **Audience:** Facility managers, building owners, maintenance managers, building engineers and maintenance technicians. **Principal Exhibits:** Learn what you can do, and should do with generators, to make sure your facility will keep running even when the electricity to your facility doesn't.

19442 ■ How to Conduct Your Own Energy Audit (Onsite)
TPC Trainco Inc.
225 E Robinson St., Ste. 570
Orlando, FL 32801
Free: 877-978-7246
Co. E-mail: sales@tpctraining.com
URL: http://live.tpctraining.com
URL(s): www.tpctrainco.com
Description: Two-day hands-on seminar shows you how to find quick and inexpensive ways to immediately cut energy costs at your plant or facility. **Audience:** Industry professionals. **Principal Exhibits:** Two-day hands-on seminar shows you how to find quick and inexpensive ways to immediately cut energy costs at your plant or facility.

19443 ■ HVAC Electrical Controls & Air Distribution (Onsite)
TPC Trainco Inc.
225 E Robinson St., Ste. 570
Orlando, FL 32801
Free: 877-978-7246
Co. E-mail: sales@tpctraining.com
URL: http://live.tpctraining.com
URL(s): live.tpctraining.com/public-seminars/hvac -training/hvac-electrical-controls-air-distribution
Description: Learn how to "control" their controls, and how to use fundamental air distribution principles for achieving consistent HVAC comfort and efficiency in buildings, plants and facilities. **Audience:** Supervisors, building owners, managers, building maintenance technicians and engineers. **Principal Exhibits:** Learn how to "control" their controls, and how to use fundamental air distribution principles for achieving consistent HVAC comfort and efficiency in buildings, plants and facilities.

19444 ■ Instrumentation, Process Measurement & Control (Onsite)
TPC Trainco Inc.
225 E Robinson St., Ste. 570
Orlando, FL 32801
Free: 877-978-7246
Co. E-mail: sales@tpctraining.com
URL: http://live.tpctraining.com
URL(s): live.tpctraining.com/on-site-training/specialty -on-site-training-topics/instrumentation-process -measurement-and-control
Description: Learn why it is necessary to measure what is going on with your systems and equipment, how to measure it, and what those measurements may mean in terms of action that should be taken to eliminate future downtime and unnecessary expense. **Audience:** Electricians, mechanics, and engineers. **Principal Exhibits:** Learn why it is necessary to measure what is going on with your systems and equipment, how to measure it, and what those measurements may mean in terms of action that should be taken to eliminate future downtime and unnecessary expense.

19445 ■ Inventory Control for Maintenance (Onsite)
TPC Trainco Inc.
225 E Robinson St., Ste. 570
Orlando, FL 32801
Free: 877-978-7246
Co. E-mail: sales@tpctraining.com
URL: http://live.tpctraining.com
URL(s): live.tpctraining.com/on-site-training/specialty -on-site-training-topics/inventory-control-for-main tenance
Description: Focus on building an inventory management system that will lead to better control through optimization of inventory quantities, organization of inventory and access to inventory. **Audience:** Maintenance, operations and purchasing managers and personnel. **Principal Exhibits:** Focus on building an inventory management system that will lead to better control through optimization of inventory quantities, organization of inventory and access to inventory.

GENERAL SMALL BUSINESS TOPICS

19446 ■ Maintenance Planning & Scheduling (Onsite)
TPC Trainco Inc.
225 E Robinson St., Ste. 570
Orlando, FL 32801
Free: 877-978-7246
Co. E-mail: sales@tpctraining.com
URL: http://live.tpctraining.com
URL(s): live.tpctraining.com/public-seminars/plant-management/maintenance-planning-and-scheduling

Description: Learn to reduce maintenance costs by better planning with your existing workforce. **Audience:** Maintenance personnel, maintenance managers, purchasing agents, operations managers, plant managers, manufacturing managers, production managers. **Principal Exhibits:** Learn to reduce maintenance costs by better planning with your existing workforce.

19447 ■ Maintenance Welding (Onsite)
TPC Trainco Inc.
225 E Robinson St., Ste. 570
Orlando, FL 32801
Free: 877-978-7246
Co. E-mail: sales@tpctraining.com
URL: http://live.tpctraining.com
URL(s): live.tpctraining.com/on-site-training/specialty-on-site-training-topics/maintenance-welding

Description: Learn welding techniques, welding processes, metal and filler selection, cutting processes, new fabrications, troubleshooting defects, welding repair, personal safety, managing costs, record keeping and more. **Audience:** Welders, maintenance and repair personnel, multi-craft technicians, fabricators, maintenance supervisors and managers, and inspectors. **Principal Exhibits:** Learn welding techniques, welding processes, metal and filler selection, cutting processes, new fabrications, troubleshooting defects, welding repair, personal safety, managing costs, record keeping and more.

19448 ■ Motor Selection, Maintenance, Testing & Replacement
TPC Trainco Inc.
225 E Robinson St., Ste. 570
Orlando, FL 32801
Free: 877-978-7246
Co. E-mail: sales@tpctraining.com
URL: http://live.tpctraining.com
URL(s): www.tpctrainco.com

Description: Seminar designed for anyone whose work is affected by motors at their facility, whether they are mechanics doing the work, a supervisor in charge of fixing problems, or purchasing agents responsible for saving money. **Audience:** Mechanics, foremen, supervisors, purchasing agents, and HVAC technicians. **Principal Exhibits:** Seminar designed for anyone whose work is affected by motors at their facility, whether they are mechanics doing the work, a supervisor in charge of fixing problems, or purchasing agents responsible for saving money.

19449 ■ PLC Programming & Applications (Onsite)
TPC Trainco Inc.
225 E Robinson St., Ste. 570
Orlando, FL 32801
Free: 877-978-7246
Co. E-mail: sales@tpctraining.com
URL: http://live.tpctraining.com
URL(s): live.tpctraining.com/public-seminars/electrical-training/electrical-controls/plc-programming-applications

Description: Provides skills needed to organize, plan, write, enter, test, and document SLC500 programs using the basic programming instructions and RSLogix software. **Audience:** Apprentice and experienced electricians, instrumentation technicians, and building maintenance personnel. **Principal Exhibits:** Provides skills needed to organize, plan, write, enter, test, and document SLC500 programs using the basic programming instructions and RSLogix software.

19450 ■ PLCs for Non-Programmers (Onsite)
TPC Trainco Inc.
225 E Robinson St., Ste. 570
Orlando, FL 32801
Free: 877-978-7246
Co. E-mail: sales@tpctraining.com
URL: http://live.tpctraining.com
URL(s): live.tpctraining.com/public-seminars/electrical-training/electrical-controls/plcs-for-non-programmers

Description: Seminar designed for maintenance technicians, electricians, or other non-programmers who need a general understanding of automation and Programmable Logic Controllers. **Audience:** Apprentice and experienced electricians, instrumentation technicians, and all building maintenance personnel. **Principal Exhibits:** Seminar designed for maintenance technicians, electricians, or other non-programmers who need a general understanding of automation and Programmable Logic Controllers.

19451 ■ Plumbing & Pipefitting for Plants & Buildings (Onsite)
TPC Trainco Inc.
225 E Robinson St., Ste. 570
Orlando, FL 32801
Free: 877-978-7246
Co. E-mail: sales@tpctraining.com
URL: http://live.tpctraining.com
URL(s): live.tpctraining.com/on-site-training/specialty-on-site-training-topics/plumbing-pipefitting-for-plants-and-buildings

Description: Covers the necessary requirements to follow code and safety regulations while providing the student with a practical foundation to quickly identify problems and solve them on their own, whether it's a low-pressure water supply line problem, drippy valve or a clogged drain trap. **Audience:** Plumbing and pipefitting professionals. **Principal Exhibits:** Covers the necessary requirements to follow code and safety regulations while providing the student with a practical foundation to quickly identify problems and solve them on their own, whether it's a low-pressure water supply line problem, drippy valve or a clogged drain trap.

19452 ■ Predictive Maintenance and Condition Monitoring (Onsite)
TPC Trainco Inc.
225 E Robinson St., Ste. 570
Orlando, FL 32801
Free: 877-978-7246
Co. E-mail: sales@tpctraining.com
URL: http://live.tpctraining.com
URL(s): live.tpctraining.com/public-seminars/plant-management/predictive-maintenance-and-condition-monitoring

Description: Provides the fundamentals of PdM and condition monitoring applicable to plants, facilities, and manufacturing lines. **Audience:** Maintenance, operations, purchasing managers and personnel. **Principal Exhibits:** Provides the fundamentals of PdM and condition monitoring applicable to plants, facilities, and manufacturing lines.

19453 ■ The Proactive Leader I: Develop an Effective Agenda, Build Support, and Gain Traction
Seminar Information Service Inc. (SIS)
250 El Camino Real., Ste. 112
Tustin, CA 92780
Ph: (714)508-0340
Free: 877-736-4636
Fax: (714)734-8027
Co. E-mail: info@seminarinformation.com
URL: http://www.seminarinformation.com
Contact: Catherine Bellizzi, President
URL(s): www.seminarinformation.com

Description: Learn to identify and prioritize arenas where you can effect change in your organization, including the skills of political competence to take the next steps toward building support and gaining traction for your idea. **Audience:** Industry professionals. **Principal Exhibits:** Learn to identify and prioritize arenas where you can effect change in your organization, including the skills of political competence to take the next steps toward building support and gaining traction for your idea.

19454 ■ Project Initiation and Planning (Onsite)
URL(s): www.eeicom.com

Description: Learn how to incorporate project charter, work breakdown structure, a risk and change management plan, communications plan, schedule and budget to guarantee a successful project. **Audience:** Professionals, general public. **Principal Exhibits:** Learn how to incorporate project charter, work breakdown structure, a risk and change management plan, communications plan, schedule and budget to guarantee a successful project.

19455 ■ Project Quality Management for Project Managers - Delivering Consistent Quality (Onsite)
Seminar Information Service Inc. (SIS)
250 El Camino Real., Ste. 112
Tustin, CA 92780
Ph: (714)508-0340
Free: 877-736-4636
Fax: (714)734-8027
Co. E-mail: info@seminarinformation.com
URL: http://www.seminarinformation.com
Contact: Catherine Bellizzi, President
URL(s): www.seminarinformation.com

Description: Learn how to: Implement effective project quality management best practices; Apply a proven analysis method to identify stakeholder quality expectations and refine project scope; Leverage an industry standard template to create a project Quality Management Plan (QMP); Generate a quality assurance task list that incorporates project, product and process; Transform quality assurance recommendations into corrective and improvement actions; Design and implement quality control gates throughout the project and product life cycles. **Audience:** Project managers, and professionals. **Principal Exhibits:** Learn how to: Implement effective project quality management best practices; Apply a proven analysis method to identify stakeholder quality expectations and refine project scope; Leverage an industry standard template to create a project Quality Management Plan (QMP); Generate a quality assurance task list that incorporates project, product and process; Transform quality assurance recommendations into corrective and improvement actions; Design and implement quality control gates throughout the project and product life cycles.

19456 ■ Project Scheduling and Budgeting - Achieving Cost-Effective and Timely Delivery (Onsite)
Seminar Information Service Inc. (SIS)
250 El Camino Real., Ste. 112
Tustin, CA 92780
Ph: (714)508-0340
Free: 877-736-4636
Fax: (714)734-8027
Co. E-mail: info@seminarinformation.com
URL: http://www.seminarinformation.com
Contact: Catherine Bellizzi, President
URL(s): www.seminarinformation.com

Description: Learn how to: Build schedules and budgets that transform project constraints into project success; Construct Work Breakdown Structures (WBS) and network diagrams and estimate task durations; Calculate Critical Path and optimize your project plan; Allocate costs and chart expected cash flow; Assign resources effectively and respond to end-date changes; Perform Earned Value Analysis (EVA) to keep the project on track. **Audience:** Industry professionals. **Principal Exhibits:** Learn how to: Build schedules and budgets that transform project constraints into project success; Construct Work Breakdown Structures (WBS) and network diagrams and estimate task durations; Calculate Critical Path and optimize your project plan; Allocate costs and chart expected cash flow; Assign resources effectively and respond to end-date changes; Perform Earned Value Analysis (EVA) to keep the project on track.

19457 ■ Pump Repair & Maintenance (Onsite)
TPC Trainco Inc.
225 E Robinson St., Ste. 570
Orlando, FL 32801
Free: 877-978-7246
Co. E-mail: sales@tpctraining.com
URL: http://live.tpctraining.com
URL(s): live.tpctraining.com/public-seminars/mechanical-and-industrial-training/pump-repair-maintenance

Description: Learn common sense pump maintenance and repair techniques to keep facilities and equipment up and running. **Audience:** Multi-craft technicians, maintenance technicians, plumbers and pipefitters and pump system engineers. **Principal Exhibits:** Learn common sense pump maintenance and repair techniques to keep facilities and equipment up and running.

19458 ■ Pumps & Pump Systems: Specification, Installation & Operation (Onsite)
TPC Trainco Inc.
225 E Robinson St., Ste. 570
Orlando, FL 32801
Free: 877-978-7246
Co. E-mail: sales@tpctraining.com
URL: http://live.tpctraining.com
URL(s): live.tpctraining.com/public-seminars/mechanical-and-industrial-training/pumps-pump-systems-specification-installation-operation

Description: From the pump and pump system, to the people who operate, maintain and design the pump system, this seminar will teach students how to identify the real problems causing pump failure, and how to avoid repeating those problems in the future. **Audience:** Maintenance technicians. **Principal Exhibits:** From the pump and pump system, to the people who operate, maintain and design the pump system, this seminar will teach students how to identify the real problems causing pump failure, and how to avoid repeating those problems in the future.

19459 ■ Steam Systems Maintenance, Safety & Optimization (Onsite)
TPC Trainco Inc.
225 E Robinson St., Ste. 570
Orlando, FL 32801
Free: 877-978-7246
Co. E-mail: sales@tpctraining.com
URL: http://live.tpctraining.com
URL(s): live.tpctraining.com/on-site-training/specialty-on-site-training-topics/steam-systems-maintenance-safety-optimization

Description: This course will teach you how to keep your steam system working efficiently and how to fix common problems and work safely reducing energy loss. **Audience:** Boiler operators, technicians and mechanics, plant engineers, steam drive equipment operators and energy management personnel. **Principal Exhibits:** This course will teach you how to keep your steam system working efficiently and how to fix common problems and work safely reducing energy loss.

19460 ■ Strategic Planning for Organizational Success (Onsite)
Seminar Information Service Inc. (SIS)
250 El Camino Real., Ste. 112
Tustin, CA 92780
Ph: (714)508-0340
Free: 877-736-4636
Fax: (714)734-8027
Co. E-mail: info@seminarinformation.com
URL: http://www.seminarinformation.com
Contact: Catherine Bellizzi, President
URL(s): www.seminarinformation.com

Description: Learn how to: Formulate strategic plans to help your organization advance and grow; Detect the strengths, weaknesses, opportunities and threats (SWOT) that drive strategy; Identify strategies to better position your organization for long-term competitive advantage; Translate strategy into action; Execute strategy and deliver results through people and processes; Establish strategic planning, monitoring and controlling mechanisms that ensure positive results. **Audience:** Managers and leaders, supervisors. **Principal Exhibits:** Learn how to: Formulate strategic plans to help your organization advance and grow; Detect the strengths, weaknesses, opportunities and threats (SWOT) that drive strategy; Identify strategies to better position your organization for long-term competitive advantage; Translate strategy into action; Execute strategy and deliver results through people and processes; Establish strategic planning, monitoring and controlling mechanisms that ensure positive results. **Telecommunication Services:** info@seminarinformation.com.

19461 ■ Troubleshooting Mechanical Drive Systems & Rotating Equipment (Onsite)
TPC Trainco Inc.
225 E Robinson St., Ste. 570
Orlando, FL 32801
Free: 877-978-7246
Co. E-mail: sales@tpctraining.com
URL: http://live.tpctraining.com
URL(s): live.tpctraining.com/on-site-training/specialty-on-site-training-topics/troubleshooting-mechanical-drive-systems-rotating-equipment

Description: Provide a new perspective on troubleshooting mechanical and rotating equipment and learn about basic mechanical applications, failures, life expectancy and maintenance shafts, bearings, couplings, chains, sprockets, bushings, gears, belts, sheaves and other mechanical components. You'll learn what data to measure, track and trend so that when equipment fails you can get quick answers to what is wrong, as well as fix the real problems with your equipment and not just the symptoms. **Audience:** Maintenance technicians, mechanics, HVAC technicians, electricians and machine operators. **Principal Exhibits:** Provide a new perspective on troubleshooting mechanical and rotating equipment and learn about basic mechanical applications, failures, life expectancy and maintenance shafts, bearings, couplings, chains, sprockets, bushings, gears, belts, sheaves and other mechanical components. You'll learn what data to measure, track and trend so that when equipment fails you can get quick answers to what is wrong, as well as fix the real problems with your equipment and not just the symptoms.

19462 ■ Understanding & Troubleshooting Hydraulics (Onsite)
TPC Trainco Inc.
225 E Robinson St., Ste. 570
Orlando, FL 32801
Free: 877-978-7246
Co. E-mail: sales@tpctraining.com
URL: http://live.tpctraining.com
URL(s): live.tpctraining.com/public-seminars/mechanical-and-industrial-training/understanding-troubleshooting-hydraulics

Description: Provides the basic building blocks and information you need to become proficient in working with industrial hydraulics and fluid power, whether a small mobile unit or large industrial installation. **Audience:** Mechanics, fluid power technicians, machine operators, plant and facility managers and building engineers. **Principal Exhibits:** Provides the basic building blocks and information you need to become proficient in working with industrial hydraulics and fluid power, whether a small mobile unit or large industrial installation.

19463 ■ Uninterruptable Power Supply (UPS) Maintenance and Readiness (Onsite)
TPC Trainco Inc.
225 E Robinson St., Ste. 570
Orlando, FL 32801
Free: 877-978-7246
Co. E-mail: sales@tpctraining.com
URL: http://live.tpctraining.com
URL(s): live.tpctraining.com/on-site-training/specialty-on-site-training-topics/uninterruptible-power-supply-ups-maintenance

Description: Seminar designed for personnel responsible for the UPS systems in industrial plants, public facilities, and commercial buildings. **Audience:** Electricians, maintenance technicians, maintenance managers, supervisors, plant and building engineers. **Principal Exhibits:** Seminar designed for personnel responsible for the UPS systems in industrial plants, public facilities, and commercial buildings.

19464 ■ Variable Frequency Drives (Onsite)
TPC Trainco Inc.
225 E Robinson St., Ste. 570
Orlando, FL 32801
Free: 877-978-7246
Co. E-mail: sales@tpctraining.com
URL: http://live.tpctraining.com
URL(s): live.tpctraining.com/public-seminars/electrical-training/electrical-controls/variable-frequency-drives

Description: Learn how to troubleshoot common VFD problems, take care of your own equipment, and avoid costly repairs or service repairs, including how to identify hazards associated with working on VFDs, an understanding of the importance of safe work practices, recognition of the main components of a VFD system, and the different methods of controlling a VFD. **Audience:** Industry professionals. **Principal Exhibits:** Learn how to troubleshoot common VFD problems, take care of your own equipment, and avoid costly repairs or service repairs, including how to identify hazards associated with working on VFDs, an understanding of the importance of safe work practices, recognition of the main components of a VFD system, and the different methods of controlling a VFD.

19465 ■ Water Treatment for Boilers, Chillers & Cooling Towers (Onsite)
TPC Trainco Inc.
225 E Robinson St., Ste. 570
Orlando, FL 32801
Free: 877-978-7246
Co. E-mail: sales@tpctraining.com
URL: http://live.tpctraining.com
URL(s): live.tpctraining.com/on-site-training/specialty-on-site-training-topics/water-treatment-for-boilers-chillers-and-cooling-towers

Description: One-day seminar to take the mystery out of creating, and stabilizing high water quality for your HVAC systems. **Audience:** Building maintenance personnel, engineers and plant maintenance technicians. **Principal Exhibits:** One-day seminar to take the mystery out of creating, and stabilizing high water quality for your HVAC systems.

REFERENCE WORKS

19466 ■ "3 Questions with Andrew Tosh, CEO of GameSim Inc. - and Brother to a Star" in Orlando Business Journal (Vol. 30, April 18, 2014, No. 43, pp. 8)
Pub: American City Business Journals, Inc.
Contact: Mike Olivieri, Executive Vice President

Released: Weekly. **Price:** $8, introductory 4-week offer(Digital & Print). **Description:** GameSim Inc. CEO, Andrew Tosh, says Orlando, Florida's talent pool is the reason for the company's expansion into the city. He also said that the city government's incentive programs also influenced the video game producer's choice of this location. Tosh added that the firm is set to open satellite office in other states. **Availability:** Print; Online.

19467 ■ "6 Goals Every Small Business Needs to Set" in inBusiness
URL(s): inbusinessphx.com/leadership-management/6-goals-every-small-business-needs-to-set-for-2022?utm_source=rss&utm_medium=rss&utm_campaign=6-goals-every-small-business-needs-to-set-for-2022#.YgvhUt_MKUk

Ed: Edgar Olivo. **Description:** Explores the importance of updating your small business strategy on an annual basis and provides six goals every small business owner should consider. **Availability:** Online.

19468 ■ "10 Goals You Can Set to Grow Your Small Business" in Economic Development Collaborative (Apr 29, 2021)
URL(s): edcollaborative.com/blog/goals-that-you-can-set-to-grow-your-small-business/

GENERAL SMALL BUSINESS TOPICS   Business Vision/Goals ■ 19491

Released: April 29, 2021. **Description:** Discusses the importance of setting realistic business goals and provides ten examples of achievable goals you can set to grow your small business. **Availability:** Online.

19469 ■ *"113D Filings: Investors Report to the SEC"* in *Barron's* (Vol. 88, March 24, 2008, No. 12, pp. M13)
Pub: Dow Jones & Company Inc.
Contact: Almar Latour, Chief Executive Officer
Released: April 02, 2016. **Description:** HealthCor Management called as problematic the plan of Magellan Health Services to use its high cash balances for acquisitions. Carlson Capital discussed with Energy Partners possible changes in the latter's board. Investor Carl Icahn suggested that Enzon Pharmaceuticals consider selling itself or divest some of its assets. **Availability:** Print; Online.

19470 ■ *"22 Vision Statement Examples"* in *Small Business Trends* (Nov. 22, 2021)
URL(s): smallbiztrends.com/2021/11/vision-statement-examples.html
Ed: Samantha Lile. **Released:** November 22, 2021. **Description:** Explains what a vision statement is, why it is important for your small business and how to write a vision statement. Includes 22 vision statement examples. **Availability:** Online.

19471 ■ *"ACE Aims High With Spinoff of Repair Unit"* in *Globe & Mail* (January 31, 2007, pp. B15)
Description: The decision of ACE Aviation Holdings Inc. to sell its aircraft maintenance division and add workforce at its El Salvador plant is discussed. **Availability:** Online.

19472 ■ *"Adrian Ellis Wears No Cape, But His Firm Protects Execs From Bad Guys"* in *Orlando Business Journal* (Vol. 30, March 14, 2014, No. 38, pp. 3)
Pub: American City Business Journals, Inc.
Contact: Mike Olivieri, Executive Vice President
Released: Weekly. **Description:** Infinity Protection Service chief executive officer, Adrian Ellis, says his experience in providing security details led to the formation of the company. He added that some of the company's clients are high-profile individuals who may have received threats. Ellis also stated that the company is planning to expand in the U.S. through mergers and acquisitions. **Availability:** Print; Online.

19473 ■ *"The Agency Model Is Bent But Not Broken"* in *Advertising Age* (Vol. 79, July 7, 2008, No. 26, pp. 17)
Pub: Crain Communications, Inc.
Contact: Jessica Botos, Manager, Marketing
E-mail: jessica.botos@crainsnewyork.com
Ed: Stephen Fajen. **Description:** In the new-media environment, advertising agencies must change the way in which they do business and receive payment. **Availability:** Online.

19474 ■ *"The Agency-Selection Process Needs Fixing Now"* in *Advertising Age* (Vol. 79, July 7, 2008, No. 26, pp. 18)
Pub: Crain Communications, Inc.
Contact: Jessica Botos, Manager, Marketing
E-mail: jessica.botos@crainsnewyork.com
Ed: Avi Dan. **Description:** Marketers are facing increased challenges in this sagging economic climate and must realize the importance of choosing the correct advertising agency for their company in order to benefit from a more-stable relationship that yields better business results. Advice for marketers regarding the best way to choose an agency is included. **Availability:** Online.

19475 ■ *"Air Canada to Slash 600 Non-Union Jobs"* in *Globe & Mail* (February 11, 2006, pp. B3)
Ed: Brent Jang. **Description:** The reasons behind workforce reduction by ACE Aviation Holdings Inc. at Air Canada are presented. **Availability:** Online.

19476 ■ *"Air Canada's Flight Plan for 777s Excludes India"* in *Globe & Mail* (March 28, 2007, pp. B5)
Ed: Brent Jang. **Description:** The decision of Air Canada to exclude India and to fly its Boeing 777s due to poor economic returns is discussed. **Availability:** Online.

19477 ■ *"All Eyes On Iris"* in *Canadian Business* (Vol. 81, July 22, 2008, No. 12-13, pp. 20)
Description: Provincial governments in Canada are believed to be awaiting Alberta Finance Minister Iris Evans' financial and investment policies as well as Evans' development of a new saving strategy. Alberta is the only Canadian province that is in position to invest in sovereign wealth funds after it eliminated its debt in 2005. **Availability:** Print; Online.

19478 ■ *"All Fired Up!"* in *Small Business Opportunities* (November 2008)
Description: Profile of Brixx Wood Fired Pizza, which has launched a franchising program due to the amount of interest the company's founders received over the years; franchisees do not need experience in the food industry or pizza restaurant service business in order to open a franchise of their own because all franchisees receive comprehensive training in which they are educated on all of the necessary tools to effectively run the business. **Availability:** Print; Online.

19479 ■ *"Are You Ready for a Transformation?"* in *Women Entrepreneur* (November 28, 2008)
Description: Marlene J. Waldock, an expert in women's empowerment and reinvention, discusses brand modification and what a business owner should consider before attempting to change or modify their brand. **Availability:** Online.

19480 ■ *"Automaker Foundations Run Leaner"* in *Crain's Detroit Business* (Vol. 26, January 11, 2010, No. 2, pp. 1)
Pub: Crain Communications Inc.
Contact: Barry Asin, President
Ed: Sherri Welch. **Description:** Overview of the Detroit automobile industry includes restoring profitability, smarter marketing strategies and philanthropy. Each company comprising the Big 3 is examined, as is their vision for the future. **Availability:** Print; Online.

19481 ■ *"Avoid the Traps That Can Destroy Family Businesses: An Emerging Set of Best Practices Can Turn the Age-Old Problem of Generational Succession Into an Opportunity To Thrive"* in *Harvard Business Review* (Vol. 90, January-February 2012, No.1, pp. 25)
Pub: Harvard Business Review Press
Contact: Moderna V. Pfizer, Contact
Ed: George Stalk, Henry Foley. **Price:** $6, hardcopy black and white. **Description:** Tips to efffective succession planning in family-owned businesses include proper screening and training for family members, managing family-member entry with company growth, and appointing non-family mentors to provide cross training. **Availability:** Print; PDF; Online.

19482 ■ *"Baldwin Connelly Partnership Splits"* in *Business Journal Serving Greater Tampa Bay* (Vol. 30, November 19, 2010, No. 48, pp. 1)
Pub: Tampa Bay Business Journal
Contact: Ian Anderson, President
E-mail: ianderson@bizjournals.com
Description: The fast-growing insurance brokerage Baldwin Connelly is now breaking up after five years. Two different entrepreneurial visions have developed within the organization and founders Lowry Baldwin and John Connell will not take separate tracks. Staffing levels in the firm are expected to remain the same. **Availability:** Print; Online.

19483 ■ *"Bark Up The Right Tree"* in *Small Business Opportunities* (Winter 2009)
Released: February 09, 2016. **Description:** Profile of Central Bark, a daycare company catering to pets that offers franchise opportunities and is expanding rapidly despite the economic downturn; the company's growth strategy is also discussed.

19484 ■ *"Battered Loblaw Makes Deep Job Cuts"* in *Globe & Mail* (January 23, 2007)
Ed: Marina Strauss. **Description:** Loblaw Companies Ltd., supermarket giant, is eliminating up to 1,000 administrative jobs and shifting more buying responsibilities to its suppliers. The grocer will also introduce a national inventory strategy called "category management". **Availability:** Online.

19485 ■ *"BCE Mulls Radical Changes With Industry Under Pressure"* in *Globe & Mail* (March 30, 2007, pp. B1)
Ed: Andrew Willis, Jacquie McNish, Catherine McLean. **Description:** An account on the expansion plans of BCE Inc., which plans to acquire TELUS Corp., is presented. **Availability:** Online.

19486 ■ *"Better Made's Better Idea: Diversify Despite Rising Costs"* in *Crain's Detroit Business* (Vol. 24, September 22, 2008, No. 38, pp. 18)
Pub: Crain Communications Inc.
Contact: Barry Asin, President
Ed: Nathan Skid. **Description:** Better Made Snack Foods Inc. is planning to expand its product lines and market reach as well as boost manufacturing capability during a time in which the company is being buffeted by rising commodity and fuel costs. The company feels that diversification is the key to maintain sales and growth. **Availability:** Online.

19487 ■ *"Between the Lines: Intangible Assets"* in *Canadian Business* (Vol. 79, July 17, 2006, No. 14-15, pp. 17)
Pub: Rogers Media Inc.
Contact: Neil Spivak, Chief Executive Officer
Ed: Al Rosen. **Description:** Need for investors to check the actual worth of a company and not to get carried away by the inflated claims made by the company is emphasized.

19488 ■ *"A Big Dream That 'Was Going Nowhere"* in *Globe & Mail* (February 4, 2006, pp. B4)
Description: The reasons behind the decision of Bombardier Inc. to terminate its plans to develop jet airplanes are presented. **Availability:** Online.

19489 ■ *"BlackBerry 10 Unlikely to Save RIM. RIM Has Few Options. Staying the Course Isn't One of Them"* in *Canadian Business* (Vol. 85, July 16, 2012, No. 11-12, pp. 12)
Ed: Joe Castaldo. **Description:** Research in Motion (RIM) plans to launch a new line of Blackberry 10 Smartphones in 2012 as part of a strategy to stay in business despite expected operating loss in the first quarter and strong competition. Other options for RIM include a sale, opening its network to offer added security and data compression services, or reinventing itself as a niche handset provider. **Availability:** Print; Online.

19490 ■ *"Blackstone Set to Sell Stake"* in *Globe & Mail* (March 17, 2007, pp. B6)
Description: The plan of Blackstone Group to sell 10 percent of its stake to raise $4 billion and its proposal to go for initial public offering is discussed.

19491 ■ *"Blaze Pizza Adds Nine Franchise Groups"* in *FastCasual.com* (September 2, 2014)
Pub: Networld Media Group
Contact: Kathy Doyle, President
E-mail: publisher@networldmediagroup.com
Description: Blaze Fast Fire'd Pizza has signed nine new San Diego area development agreements that will add 67 franchise restaurants to its firm. The

Small Business Sourcebook • 42nd Edition   1423

company will also open 315 company-owned and franchised pizza restaurants in 33 states by the end of 2015. **Availability:** Online.

19492 ■ *"Boatyard Expansion 8-Year Odyssey" in Providence Business News (Vol. 28, March 31, 2014, No. 52, p. 1)*
Pub: American City Business Journals, Inc.
Contact: Mike Olivieri, Executive Vice President
Released: March 29, 2014. **Description:** Bristol Marine owner, Andy Tyska, has found it challenging to operate and improve the boatyard due to lack of available coastal land and restrictive environmental regulations. Tyska made a large investment in plans for expanding the property he purchased in 1998. Tyska discusses the challenges faced while trying to improve his boatyard. **Availability:** Print; Online.

19493 ■ *"CanWest Plotting Buyback of Newspaper Income Trust" in Globe & Mail (February 7, 2007, pp. B1)*
Description: The CanWest Global Communications Corp.'s decision to sell its media assets in Australia and New Zealand in order to finance its plans of repurchasing its newspaper income trust CanWest MediaWorks Income Fund is discussed. **Availability:** Online.

19494 ■ *"Captain Planet" in (Vol. 90, June 2012, No. 6, pp. 112)*
Pub: Harvard Business Review Press
Contact: Moderna V. Pfizer, Contact
Ed: Paul Polman, Adi Ignatius. **Price:** $8.95, hardcopy black and white. **Description:** Paul Polman, chief executive officer of Unilever N.V., discusses his company's sustainable living plan, which integrates social responsibility with corporate objectives. Topics include sustainable sourcing, abolishing quarterly reporting in favor of long-term perspectives, the impact of the 2008 global economic crisis, and turning a company into a learning organization. **Availability:** Print; Online; PDF.

19495 ■ *"The Carpenter: A Story About the Greatest Success Strategies of All"*
Pub: John Wiley & Sons, Inc.
Contact: Christina Van Tassell, Executive Vice President Chief Financial Officer
Released: May 23, 2014. **Price:** $23, hardcover; $14.99, e-book. **Description:** John Gordon draws upon his with work with business leaders, sales people, professional and college sports teams, nonprofit organizations and schools to share a story that will inspire people to build a better life, career and team with successful business strategies. **Availability:** E-book; Print.

19496 ■ *"Chuck E. Cheese's CEO to Retire" in Dallas Business Journal (Vol. 37, March 28, 2014, No. 29, pp. 6)*
Pub: American City Business Journals, Inc.
Contact: Mike Olivieri, Executive Vice President
Released: Weekly. **Price:** $4, introductory 4-week offer(Digital only). **Description:** CEC Entertainment Inc. president and CEO, Michael Magusiak, is retiring after spending almost 27 years with the parent company Chuck E. Cheese. Magusiak is confident that the future of Chuck E. Cheese's brand will continue to grow in the U.S. and globally. **Availability:** Print; Online.

19497 ■ *"Citadel Hires Three Lehman Execs" in Chicago Tribune (October 2, 2008)*
Description: Citadel Investment Group LLC, Chicago hedge-fund operator, has hired three former senior executives of bankrupt investment banker Lehman Brothers Holding Inc. Citadel believes that the company's hiring spree will help them to further expand the firm's capabilities in the global fixed income business. **Availability:** Online.

19498 ■ *"Conquering the Seven Summits of Sales: From Everest to Every Business, Achieving Peak Performance"*
Pub: Harper Business
Contact: Hollis Heimbouch, Senior Vice President Publisher
Released: October 07, 2014. **Price:** $4.99, e-book; $6.19, hardcover; $0.10, hardcover(39 used from $0.10); $3.75, hardcover(19 new from $3.75); $9.10, kindle. **Description:** Sales professionals are taught to overcome their perceived limitations and strive for success. The guide shows how to define goals, build the right team, commit to a vision, time management, and tracking of progress. **Availability:** E-book; Print.

19499 ■ *"Cooking With Celeb Chef Jet Tila" in Dallas Business Journal (Vol. 37, June 6, 2014, No. 39, pp. 6)*
Pub: American City Business Journals, Inc.
Contact: Mike Olivieri, Executive Vice President
Released: June 06, 2014. **Price:** $4, Introductory 4-Week Offer(Digital & Print). **Description:** Celebrity chef, Jet Tila, discloses his plans for the Pakpao restaurant which he co-owns at Dallas Design District in Texas. He hopes to leverage the authentic Thai cuisine offered by the restaurant and bring the concept to airports or hotels. **Availability:** Print; Online.

19500 ■ *"Couple Hopes to Lead Schlotzsky's Twin Cities Revival" in Business Journal (Vol. 31, January 17, 2014, No. 34, pp. 4)*
Pub: American City Business Journals, Inc.
Contact: Mike Olivieri, Executive Vice President
Description: Austin, Texas-based Schlotzsky's announced plans to open six Minnesota locations as it tries to regain its national prominence. The bankruptcy in 2004 and the reduction of its restaurant count had wiped out eight Minnesota restaurants and left only the Edina location. Schlotzsky's six-restaurant deal with the local franchisees is examined. **Availability:** Print; Online.

19501 ■ *"Craft Brewers Want 20 Percent of U.S. Market" in Denver Business Journal (Vol. 65, April 18, 2014, No. 49, pp. A8)*
Pub: American City Business Journals, Inc.
Contact: Mike Olivieri, Executive Vice President
Description: The United States Brewers Association aims to increase the national craft brewing industry's share of beer sales to 20 percent by 2020. However, the industry will need to take more of the market from large domestic beer manufacturers. Reports show that beer sales in smaller breweries have reached 14.3 percent in 2014. **Availability:** Print; Online.

19502 ■ *"Cultural Change That Sticks: Start With What's Already Working" in (Vol. 90, July-August 2012, No. 7-8, pp. 110)*
Pub: Harvard Business Review Press
Contact: Moderna V. Pfizer, Contact
Ed: Jon R. Katzenach, Ilona Steffen, Caroline Kronley. **Description:** Working with, rather than altering, corporate culture can enhance successful implementation of change initiatives. Identifying corporate culture strengths while aligning initiatives with business priorities can generate competitive advantage.

19503 ■ *"Deep Thoughts: Getting Employees to Think Better Requires a Bit of Creative Thinking Itself" in Canadian Business (March 17, 2008)*
Description: Discusses the reason a company needs to make their employees understand that ideas are the stuff of life. For employees to be more creative, they need to cultivate spark moments, play with possibilities, and venture into the unknown. **Availability:** Print; Online; PDF.

19504 ■ *"Desmarais Makes Move into U.S." in Globe & Mail (February 2, 2007, pp. B1)*
Ed: Andrew Willis. **Description:** The decision of Desmarais family, which runs Great-West Lifeco Inc., to acquire Putnam Investment Trust for $4.6 billion to enter the United States market, is discussed. **Availability:** Online.

19505 ■ *"Discipline In Your Business" in South Florida Business Journal (Vol. 34, June 6, 2014, No. 46, pp. 10)*
Pub: American City Business Journals, Inc.
Contact: Mike Olivieri, Executive Vice President
Released: Weekly. **Price:** $8, introductory 4-week offer(Digital only). **Description:** Ways a business can maintain a disciplined response to market conditions and achieve success are discussed. Organizations are advised to set clear goals, communicate these goals, and establish clear lines of accountability. The importance of compensation to motivate staff is also explained. **Availability:** Print; Online.

19506 ■ *"Don't Quit When The Road Gets Bumpy" in Women Entrepreneur (November 25, 2008)*
Description: Discusses techniques four women entrepreneurs are utilizing to keep their businesses successful despite the credit crunch and the economic downturn.

19507 ■ *"Doyle: Domino's New Pizza Seasoned with Straight Talk" in Crain's Detroit Business (Vol. 26, January 11, 2010, No. 2, pp. 8)*
Pub: Crain Communications Inc.
Contact: Barry Asin, President
Ed: Nathan Skid. **Description:** Interview with J. Patrick Doyle, the CEO of Domino's Pizza, Inc.; the company has launched a new marketing campaign that focuses on its bold new vision. **Availability:** Online.

19508 ■ *"EnCana Axes Spending on Gas Wells" in Globe & Mail (February 16, 2006, pp. B1)*
Ed: Dave Ebner. **Description:** The reasons behind EnCana Corp.'s cost spending measures by $300 million on natural gas wells are presented. The company projects 2 percent cut in gas and oil sales for 2006. **Availability:** Print; Online.

19509 ■ *"Entrepreneurial Orientation and Firm Performance: The Unique Impact of Innovativeness, Proactiveness, and Risk-taking" in Journal of Small Business and Entrepreneurship (Vol. 23, Winter 2010, No. 1)*
Pub: Canadian Council for Small Business and Entrepreneurship
Contact: John MacRitchie, President
Ed: Patrick M. Kreisera, Justin Davis. **Description:** The article develops a theoretical model of the relationship between firm-level entrepreneurship and firm performance. This model is intended to further clarify the consequences of an 'entrepreneurial orientation', paying particular attention to the differential relationship that exists between the three sub-dimensions of entrepreneurial orientation and firm performance. Included in the theoretical model are other important variables (such as organizational structure and environmental characteristics) that may impact the EO-performance relationship. Propositions are developed regarding the various configurations of the sub-dimensions of EO and organizational structure that would be most appropriate in a given environmental context. Future research may also benefit from considering the important role that organizational strategy and life cycle stage play in this model. The implications of this model for both researchers and managers are discussed.

19510 ■ *"Entrepreneurs Conference Recap: the Business Revolution: Start Focusing On a Growth Strategy For Your Company" in Black Enterprise (Vol. 45, July-August, 2014, No. 1, pp. 17)*
Pub: Earl G. Graves Ltd.
Contact: Earl Graves, Jr., President
Released: 2014. **Description:** Small business owners must concentrate on growth in order to survive using a vision and strategic focus. The 2014 Black Enterprise Entrepreneurs Conference and Expo, sponsored by Nationwide, drew about 1,000 entrepreneurs and professionals.

19511 ■ *"Executive Decision: Damn the Profit Margins, Sleeman Declares War on Buck-a-Beer Foes" in Globe & Mail (January 28, 2006, pp. B3)*
Description: The cost savings plans of chief executive officer John Sleeman of Sleeman Breweries Ltd. are presented. **Availability:** Online.

19512 ■ "Expanding Middleby's Food Processing Biz" in Crain's Chicago Business (Vol. 31, April 21, 2008, No. 16, pp. 6)
Pub: Crain Communications Inc.
Contact: Barry Asin, President

Ed: David Sterrett. Description: Profile of the executive vice-president of the food processing company, Middleby Corp, whose business plan is to develop new products, begin looking for acquisitions and simplify operations in order to expand the firm. Availability: Online.

19513 ■ "Fast-Growing Office Pride Franchise Targets Louisville For Expansion" in Internet Wire (September 9, 2014)
Pub: Comtex News Network Inc.
Contact: Kan Devnani, President

Description: Office Pride is a commercial cleaning service that is built on principles that include: honesty, trustworthy service, excellence, and treating everyone with dignity and respect. The commercial cleaning franchise is seeking a developer to help expand its business in Louisville, Kentucky. Availability: Online.

19514 ■ "FirstMerit's Top Executive Turns Around Credit Quality" in Crain's Cleveland Business (Vol. 28, October 15, 2007, No. 41, pp. 3)
Pub: Crain Communications Inc.
Contact: K. C. Crain, President

Ed: Shawn A. Turner. Description: Discusses the ways in which chairman and CEO Paul Greig has been able to improve FirstMerit Corp.'s credit quality and profit margin. Strategies included selling more than $70 million in bad loans, hiring a new chief credit officer and redirecting its focus on cross-selling its wealth and investment services to its commercial customers. Statistical data included. Availability: Online.

19515 ■ "Flat or Slight Decline Seen for Nortel 2007 Revenue" in Globe & Mail (March 17, 2007, pp. B3)

Ed: Catherine McLean. Description: The forecast about Nortel Network Corp's decrease in the 2007 revenue and its restructuring to reduce costs is discussed. Availability: Online.

19516 ■ "'Focusing On the Moment'" in Dallas Business Journal (Vol. 37, June 27, 2014, No. 42, pp. 4)
Pub: American City Business Journals, Inc.
Contact: Mike Olivieri, Executive Vice President

Description: Southwest Airlines chairman, president, and CEO Gary Kelly, believes the key to the carrier's growth in 2014 will be to 'focus on the moment' and ensure that new projects are launched and strategies implemented successfully. Kelly discusses the potential impact of the repeal of the Wright Amendment on October 13, as well as Southwest's merger with AirTran and the launch of nonstop flights from New York and Washington DC. Availability: Print; Online.

19517 ■ "Founding Family Acquires Airport Marriott" in Crain's Cleveland Business (Vol. 28, November 5, 2007, No. 44, pp. 3)
Pub: Crain Communications Inc.
Contact: K. C. Crain, President

Ed: Stan Bullard. Description: Big River Real Estate LLC, part of the Marriott family's investment fund, is the new owner of the Cleveland Airport Marriott; renovations estimated at about $11 million will ensure that the hotel meets Marriott's standards. Availability: Online.

19518 ■ "Free Fall" in Canadian Business (Vol. 79, September 11, 2006, No. 18, pp. 28)

Description: Second quarter results of Imax Corp are reviewed. The company's performance and its future prospects are also presented. Availability: Print; Online.

19519 ■ "From Craft Biz To Wholesale Giant" in Women Entrepreneur (January 19, 2009)

Description: Advice is given on how to turn a small craft business into a full-time venture; tips to help one transition from a part-time designer to a full-time wholesaler and brand are also included.

19520 ■ Get Your Business to Work!: 7 Steps to Earning More, Working Less and Living the Life You Want
Pub: BenBella Books Inc.
Contact: Aida Herrera, Director
E-mail: aida@benbellabooks.com

Ed: George Hedley. Released: May 01, 2014. Price: $17.95, paperback; $9.99, E-Book (EPUB). Description: Complete step-by-step guide for the small business owner to realize profits, wealth and freedom. Availability: E-book; Print.

19521 ■ "Global Business Speaks English: Why You Need a Language Strategy Now" in Harvard Business Review (Vol. 90, May 2012, No. 5, pp. 116)
Pub: Harvard Business Review Press
Contact: Moderna V. Pfizer, Contact

Ed: Tsedal Neeley. Price: $8.95. Description: English is rapidly becoming the language of businesses regardless of where they are located. To improve efficiency, the author advocates implementing an English-only policy. However, this must be conducted with sufficient training and support, and appropriate cultural sensitivity. Availability: PDF; Online.

19522 ■ "Goals for Small Business Owners" in Chron
URL(s): smallbusiness.chron.com/goals-small-business-owners-21468.html

Ed: Mary Jane. Description: Discusses the importance of setting both, short- and long-term goals for your small business startup.

19523 ■ "'Groundhog Day' B&B Likely Will Be Converted Into One In Real Life" in Chicago Tribune (October 21, 2008)
Pub: Tribune News Service
Contact: Jack Barry, Vice President, Operations
E-mail: jbarry@tribpub.com

Ed: Carolyn Starks. Description: Everton Martin and Karla Stewart Martin have purchased the Victorian house that was featured as a bed-and-breakfast in the 1993 hit move "Groundhog Day"; the couple was initially unaware of the structure's celebrity status when they purchased it with the hope of fulfilling their dream of owning a bed-and-breakfast. Availability: Print; Online.

19524 ■ "Handleman Liquidation Leaves Questions For Shareholders" in Crain's Detroit Business (Vol. 24, October 6, 2008, No. 40, pp. 4)
Pub: Crain Communications Inc.
Contact: Barry Asin, President

Ed: Nancy Kaffer. Description: Discusses Handleman Co., a Troy-based music distribution company, and their plan of liquidation and dissolution as well as how shareholders will be affected by the company's plan. Handleman filed its plan to liquidate and dissolve assets with the Securities and Exchange Commission in mid-August, following several quarters of dismal earnings. Availability: Online.

19525 ■ "High Energy: Gaurdie Banister Joins Aera As President and CEO" in Black Enterprise (Vol. 38, July 2008, No. 12, pp. 30)
Pub: Earl G. Graves Ltd.
Contact: Earl Graves, Jr., President

Ed: Brenda Porter. Description: Gaurdie Banister Jr. has been appointed president and CEO of Aera Energy L.L.C., becoming one of the first African Americans in the nation to run a major energy corporation. His plans for the firm include utilizing new, sophisticated technologies in order to unlock the 3-1/2 billion barrels of resources the company has on their books in a safe and environmentally friendly way. He also hopes to increase production and maintain cost leadership.

19526 ■ "Hit the Green: Golf Technology" in Canadian Business (Vol. 79, August 14, 2006, No. 16-17, pp. 73)
Pub: Rogers Media Inc.
Contact: Neil Spivak, Chief Executive Officer

Ed: Andrew Wahl. Description: Reorganization of the bankrupt 4everSports golf company in the United States is discussed. Availability: Print; Online.

19527 ■ Hoover's Vision

Released: 1st edition. Description: Founder of Bookstop Inc. and Hoover's Inc. provides a plan to turn an enterprise into a success by showing entrepreneurs how to address inputs with an open mind in order to see more than what other's envision. Hoover pushes business owners to create and feed a clear and consistent vision by recognizing the importance of history and trends, then helps them find the essential qualities of entrepreneurial leadership. Availability: Print.

19528 ■ Hoover's Vision: Original Thinking for Business Success

Ed: Gary Hoover. Released: First edition. Description: Three keys to business success are to observe and understand other people, serve others while making their lives better, and develop a business style that expresses your5 own passions while serving others. Availability: Print.

19529 ■ "How to Create a Manifesto That Will Help You Achieve Your Goals in 2022 and Beyond" in Entrepreneur (Dec. 22, 2021)
URL(s): www.entrepreneur.com/article/403354

Ed: Krista Mashore. Released: December 22, 2021. Description: Explores the importance of having a business manifesto. Provides details on understanding the "why" of your business and how to create and express your vision. Availability: Online.

19530 ■ "How the Growth Outliers Do It: Few Companies Manage To Prosper Over the Long Term. Those That Do Are Both More Stable and More Innovative Than Their Competition" in Harvard Business Review (Vol. 90, January-February 2012, No.1-2, pp. 110)
Pub: Harvard Business Review Press
Contact: Moderna V. Pfizer, Contact

Ed: Rita McGrath. Price: $8.95, PDF and hardcover black and white. Description: Firms that reliably grow their bottom lines are both structured for innovation but are also extremely stable. They excel at entering new markets but also provide a historically consistent organizational environment. They adapt quickly, but maintain an established strategy. Availability: Print; PDF; Online.

19531 ■ "How to Keep Your Sales from Running Out of Gas" in Agency Sales Magazine (Vol. 39, July 2009, No. 7, pp. 30)

Description: Salespeople can let the good times deceive them into thinking that success will go on forever. Salespeople and businesses should see prospecting as a strategy for creating a continuing flow of business. Availability: Online.

19532 ■ "How to Write a Good Vision Statement" in Cascade Blog (Jan. 24, 2022)
URL(s): www.cascade.app/blog/write-good-vision-statement

Ed: Tom Wright. Released: January 24, 2022. Description: Provides specific information on how to write a vision statement and discusses how a well-written vision statement can anchor your strategic plan. Availability: Online.

19533 ■ "Husky Proceeds on Heavy-Oil Expansion" in Globe & Mail (March 21, 2006, pp. B1)

Ed: Patrick Brethour. Description: Canadian energy giant Husky Energy Inc. has started its $90 million engineering effort to determine the cost of the $2.3 billion heavy-oil up gradation expansion plan. Details of the project are elaborated upon. Availability: Online.

19534 ■ **"Inland Snaps Up Rival REITs"** in *Crain's Chicago Business* (Vol. 31, November 17, 2008, No. 46, pp. 3)
Pub: Crain Communications Inc.
Contact: Barry Asin, President

Ed: Alby Gallun. **Description:** Discusses Inland American Real Estate Trust Inc., a real estate investment trust that is napping up depressed shares of publicly traded competitors, a possible first step toward taking over these companies; however, with hotel and retail properties accounting for approximately 70 percent of its portfolio, the company could soon face its own difficulties. **Availability:** Online.

19535 ■ **"Innovate or Stagnate: How Doing Things Differently Helps Business"** in *South Florida Business Journal* (Vol. 34, January 10, 2014, No. 25, pp. 10)
Pub: American City Business Journals, Inc.
Contact: Mike Olivieri, Executive Vice President

Released: Weekly. **Price:** $8, Introductory 4-week offer(Digital & Print). **Description:** Business enterprises can drive growth by focusing on innovations. Companies are advised to consider radical ideas, invent different ways of working and avoid bureaucracy. Peter Drucker, a management consultant, believes that business has two functions: marketing and innovation. **Availability:** Print; Online.

19536 ■ **"Innovation Despite Reorganization"** in *Journal of Business Strategy* (Vol. 35, May-June 2014, No. 3, pp. 18-25)
Pub: Emerald Group Publishing Limited
Contact: Erika Valenti, President

Description: Innovation can be sustained through a downsizing event. The articles shows how prevailing formal and informal networks can be used for reestablishing connections between employees after a company is downsized. **Availability:** Download; Online.

19537 ■ **"Intermodal Makes Suppliers Look to Rack Up Big Sales to Distributors"** in *The Business Journal-Serving Metropolitan Kansas City* (August 15, 2008)
Pub: American City Business Journals, Inc.
Contact: Mike Olivieri, Executive Vice President

Ed: James Dornbrook. **Description:** Suppliers of shelving units, conveyor systems and other equipment used in distribution facilities are expecting new business opportunities along with the planned intermodal projects in the Kansas City area. Suppliers have already observed that small distributors have started to relocate to the city because of the intermodal projects. Demand for shelves and lifts have also increased. **Availability:** Online.

19538 ■ **"Intrawest Puts Itself on Market"** in *Globe & Mail* (March 1, 2006, pp. B1)

Ed: Elizabeth Church. **Description:** The reasons behind the decision of Intrawest Corp. to go for sale or seek partnerships are presented. The company appointed Goldman Sachs & Co. to meet the purpose. **Availability:** Online.

19539 ■ **"Just Be Nice: Providing Good Customer Service"** in *Canadian Business* (Vol. 79, October 9, 2006, No. 20, pp. 141)
Pub: Rogers Media Inc.
Contact: Neil Spivak, Chief Executive Officer

Ed: Joe Castaldo. **Description:** The customer relationship management strategies on customer retention and satisfaction adopted by WestJet are discussed. **Availability:** Print; Online.

19540 ■ **"Kinnser: Sales In Overdrive"** in *Austin Business Journal* (Vol. 32, March 30, 2012, No. 4, pp. 1)
Pub: American City Business Journals, Inc.
Contact: Mike Olivieri, Executive Vice President

Ed: Christopher Calnan. **Description:** Kinnser Software Inc.'s receipt of fresh capitalization is seen to enable the company to pursue its acquisition strategy. The company is planning to grow organically. It is also planning to double the number of its employees. **Availability:** Online.

19541 ■ **"Labatt to Swallow Lakeport"** in *Globe & Mail* (February 2, 2007, pp. B1)

Ed: Keith McArthur. **Description:** The decision of Labatt Brewing Company Ltd. to acquire Lakeport Brewing Income Fund for $201.4 million is discussed. **Availability:** Print; Online.

19542 ■ **"Laurent Beaudoin Interview: Deja Vu"** in *Canadian Business* (Vol. 81, July 22, 2008, No. 12-13, pp. 38)
Pub: Rogers Media Inc.
Contact: Neil Spivak, Chief Executive Officer

Ed: Joe Castaldo. **Description:** Laurent Beaudoin has retired as chief executive officer for Bombardier Inc.'s, a manufacturer of regional and business aircraft, but kept a role in the firm as a non-executive chairman. Beaudoin first resigned from the company in 1999, but had to return in 2004 to address challenging situations faced by the company. Beaudoin's views on management and the company are presented. **Availability:** Online.

19543 ■ **"Lending Grows as Banks Make Moves"** in *Pittsburgh Business Times* (Vol. 33, May 9, 2014, No. 43, pp. 4)
Pub: American City Business Journals, Inc.
Contact: Mike Olivieri, Executive Vice President

Released: May 2014. **Price:** $4, introductory 4-week offer(Digital only). **Description:** Pittsburgh, Pennsylvania-based biggest retail banks have bigger loan portfolios at the end of 2014s first quarter compared with the same period in 2013. Business lending has been driving activity and the surge also includes the impact of merger and acquisition strategies to capture customers in Ohio. The rising loan portfolio of the banks are examined. **Availability:** Print; Online.

19544 ■ **Limited Liability Companies for Dummies**
Pub: John Wiley & Sons, Inc.
Contact: Christina Van Tassell, Executive Vice President Chief Financial Officer
URL(s): www.wiley.com/en-us/Limited+Liability+Companies+For+Dummies%2C+4th+Edition-p-9781394183333

Ed: Jennifer Reuting. **Released:** Fourth edition. **Price:** $29.99, paperback. **Description:** Guide on how to set up an LLC, or limited liability company. Discusses the pros and cons of this structure, how to manage it, and all of the new laws surrounding LLCs. **Availability:** Print.

19545 ■ **LLC Beginner's Guide: The Most Complete and Easy-to-Follow Handbook on How to Form, Manage and Maintain Your Limited Liability Company**

Ed: Steven Carlson. **Released:** October 29, 2022. **Price:** $17.36, paperback; $8.97, e-book. **Description:** A guide that explains the process of setting up a limited liability company (LLC) in simple terms. **Availability:** E-book; Print.

19546 ■ **"The Lords of Ideas"** in *Business Strategy Review* (Vol. 21, Autumn 2010, No. 3, pp. 57)

Ed: Stuart Crainer. **Released:** September 22, 2010. **Description:** True originators of modern strategy are profiled. **Availability:** Print; Electronic publishing; PDF; Online.

19547 ■ **"Managing Risks: A New Framework: Smart Companies Match Their Approach to the Nature of the Threats They Face"** in *Harvard Business Review* (Vol. 90, June 2012, No. 6, pp. 48)
Pub: Harvard Business Review Press
Contact: Moderna V. Pfizer, Contact

Ed: Anette Mikes, Robert S. Kaplan. **Description:** The importance of strategic planning in effect risk management practices is stressed. Discussion includes preventable risks, strategy risks, and external risks and provides objectives, control models, staff functions, and the business-unit interrelationships of each.

19548 ■ **"The Melting Pot Targets Calgary, Canada For Franchise Expansion"** in *CNW Group* (September 9, 2014)
Pub: Comtex News Network Inc.
Contact: Kan Devnani, President

Description: The Melting Pot, a premier fondue restaurant, is seeking franchisees in the Calgary, Canada region. The restaurants offer posh, casual interactive dining to their guests. The franchise is also offering franchise opportunities in the Vancouver and Greater Toronto areas. Details covering Melting Pot restaurants are included. **Availability:** Print; Online.

19549 ■ **"Microbrewery Aims Big with New Facility"** in *Business Journal* (Vol. 31, May 9, 2014, No. 50, pp. 6)
Pub: American City Business Journals, Inc.
Contact: Mike Olivieri, Executive Vice President

Released: Weekly. **Description:** Insight Brewing Company is opening an unusually large production brewery with a tap room in Northeast Minneapolis, Minnesota in fall 2014. The company purchased equipment with annual production capacity of up to 5,400 barrels of beer and should the business continue to grow, the large building will allow the firm to brew up to 40,000 barrels annually. **Availability:** Print; Online.

19550 ■ **"Microsoft's Big Gamble"** in *Canadian Business* (Vol. 81, March 3, 2008, No. 3, pp. 13)

Description: Microsoft Corp. is taking a big risk in buying Yahoo, as it is expected to pay more than $31 a share to finalize the acquisition. The deal would be seven and a half times bigger than any other that Microsoft has entered before, an execution of such deal is also anticipated to become a challenge for Microsoft. Recommendations on how Microsoft should handle the integration of the two businesses are given. **Availability:** Print; Online.

19551 ■ **"Microsoft's Diversity Program Clicks into High Speed"** in *Hispanic Business* (Vol. 30, July-August 2008, No. 7-8, pp. 54)

Ed: Derek Reveron. **Description:** Microsoft's diversity hiring and vendor diversity program to capture more Hispanic consumer and business-to-business market is described. One of the main goals of these programs is to hire more Hispanic executives and managers who will help the company develop and market products and services that will appeal and benefit Hispanic consumers.

19552 ■ **"Nailing the Next Five Years: Three Deceptively Simple Questions Will Change the Way You Think About Your Company's Future"** in *Inc.* (Vol. 36, September 2014, No. 7, pp. 145)
Pub: Mansueto Ventures L.L.C.
Contact: Stephanie Mehta, Chief Executive Officer

Description: Three simples questions to ask that will change the way you think of your small business and its future: What's important? What should be the same? and What needs to change? . **Availability:** Print; Online.

19553 ■ **"Navigating Your Way to Business Success: An Entrepreneur's Journey**

Ed: Kathryn B. Freeland. **Released:** January 01, 2010. **Price:** $24.95, hardcover. **Description:** Learn first-hand from a successful entrepreneur about assessing skills and talent, envisioning your company, planning a path to success, and then tapping into available government agencies to make your business become a reality. **Availability:** Print.

19554 ■ **"Needed: A Strategy; Banking In China"** in *The Economist* (Vol. 390, January 3, 2009, No. 8612, pp. 54)

Description: International banks are competing for a role in China but are finding obstacles in their paths such as a reduction in the credit their operations may receive from Chinese banks and the role they can play in the public capital markets which remain limited. **Availability:** Print; Online.

GENERAL SMALL BUSINESS TOPICS

19555 ■ *"The New and Improved Ski Shop"* in *Powder (January 11, 2017)*
URL(s): www.powder.com/stories/news/the-new-and-improved-ski-shop/
Ed: Devon O'Neil. **Released:** January 11, 2017. **Description:** Traditional ski shop have found they must compete with online sales, especially since consumers bought about $1 billion worth of snow sports equipment from the internet. Big chains have closed but some smaller shops are actually thriving due to innovations and an eye for great customer service. **Availability:** Online.

19556 ■ *"Nexen, OPTI Boost Oil Sands Spending"* in *Globe & Mail (February 18, 2006, pp. B5)*
Ed: Dave Ebner. **Description:** The reasons behind the decision of Nexen Inc. and OPTI Canada Inc., to allocate 10 percent more funding on oil sands, are presented. **Availability:** Print; Online.

19557 ■ *"No Frills - And No Dodge"* in *Crain's Detroit Business (Vol. 24, September 22, 2008, No. 38, pp. 3)*
Pub: Crain Communications Inc.
Contact: Barry Asin, President
Ed: Bradford Wernle. **Description:** Chrysler LLC is in the middle of a business plan known as Project Genesis, a five-year strategy in which the company will reduce the dealer count by combining its Jeep, Chrysler and Dodge brands under one rooftop wherever possible. Not every dealer will be able to arrange this deal because of the investment required to expand stores in which have low-overhead; many of these stores feel that low-overhead structures are more likely to survive difficult times than the larger stores in which the Genesis consolidation plan intends to implement. **Availability:** Online.

19558 ■ *Nonprofit Management All-in-One for Dummies*
URL(s): www.wiley.com/en-us/Nonprofit+Management+All+in+One+For+Dummies-p-9781394172436
Ed: Beverly A. Browining, Sharon Farris, Maire Loughran. **Released:** May 2023. **Price:** $49.99, paperback. **Description:** A thorough guide on how to handle the accounting for nonprofits and general business practices for these organizations. **Availability:** Print.

19559 ■ *"Nortel Starting From Scratch, New CEO Says"* in *Globe & Mail (February 24, 2006, pp. B3)*
Ed: Catherine McLean. **Description:** The restructuring efforts of chief executive officer Mike Zafirovski of Nortel Networks Corp. are presented. **Availability:** Online.

19560 ■ *"Numerous Changes Made to Crop Production and Consumption Forecasts"* in *Farm Industry News (November 9, 2011)*
Pub: Informa Business Media, Inc.
Contact: Charlie McCurdy, President
Ed: Darrel Good. **Description:** USDA November Crop Production and WASDE reports contained various changes in production and consumption forecasts for corn, soybeans, and what for the current marketing year. A brief summary for each crop is included. **Availability:** Online.

19561 ■ *"Oliver Russell Acquiring Social Good Network"* in *Idaho Business Review (August 29, 2014)*
Pub: BridgeTower Media
Contact: Adam Reinebach, President
Description: Oliver Russell, owner of a Boise advertising firm, is acquiring the assets of startup Social Good Network, an online fundraising firm that was turned down for additional funding beyond its seed funding. Details of the deal and future plans are discussed.

19562 ■ *"Once Is Not Enough for These Restaurateurs"* in *Baltimore Business Journal (Vol. 31, April 25, 2014, No. 52, pp. 16)*
Pub: American City Business Journals, Inc.
Contact: Mike Olivieri, Executive Vice President
Released: Weekly. **Description:** Five Baltimore restaurateurs explain why they are looking to expand their businesses by opening multiple eateries, despite the potential risks. Among these is Spike Gjerde, owner of Woodberry Kitchen who opened a new butcher shop and restaurant in Remington, called Parts and Labor; Jason Ambrose, who owns Salt and a second unnamed restaurant in Locust Point; and Sarah Simington of Blue Moon Café at Fells Point and Federal Hill. **Availability:** Print; Online.

19563 ■ *"Ontario Keeps Bleeding Jobs as Michelin Closes Tire Plant"* in *Globe & Mail (February 3, 2006, pp. B1)*
Description: The reasons behind facility shutdown and workforce reduction by Michelin SA, in Ontario, are presented. **Availability:** Online.

19564 ■ *"Paramount Said to be Working on Sale of Oil Sands Assets"* in *Globe & Mail (April 24, 2007, pp. B1)*
Ed: Norval Scott. **Description:** The proposed sale of oil sands in Surmont and the shares of North American Oil Sands Corp. by Paramount Resources Ltd. is discussed. **Availability:** Online.

19565 ■ *"Pearson Bitman Strives to be the 'Google' of Law Firms"* in *Orlando Business Journal (Vol. 30, June 6, 2014, No. 50, pp. 3)*
Pub: American City Business Journals, Inc.
Contact: Mike Olivieri, Executive Vice President
Released: Weekly. **Price:** $8, Introductory 4-week offer(Digital & Print). **Description:** Ronnie Bitman, who launched law firm Pearson Bitman LLP, states that he wants to make his firm the Google of law firms, that is, he wants to create and foster an environment of fun and not just work. He feels that in today's times it is important to get away from the public image of a lawyer standing in front of law books and give people something that's fresher, hipper. **Availability:** Print; Online.

19566 ■ *"People; E-Commerce, Online Games, Mobile Apps"* in *Advertising Age (Vol. 80, October 19, 2009, No. 35, pp. 14)*
Pub: Crain Communications, Inc.
Contact: Jessica Botos, Manager, Marketing
E-mail: jessica.botos@crainsnewyork.com
Ed: Nat Ives. **Description:** Profile of People Magazine and the ways in which the publisher is moving its magazine forward by exploring new concepts in a time of declining newsstand sales and advertising pages; among the strategies are e-commerce such as the brand People Style Watch in which consumers are able highlight clothing and jewelry and then connect to retailers' sites and a channel on Taxi TV, the network of video-touch screens in New Your City taxis. **Availability:** Online.

19567 ■ *"Perfecting the Process: Creating a More Efficient Organization on Your Terms"* in *Black Enterprise (Vol. 41, October 2010, No. 3)*
Pub: Earl G. Graves Ltd.
Contact: Earl Graves, Jr., President
Ed: Tamara E. Holmes. **Description:** More than ever, entrepreneurs need to identify new ways of doing business in a cost-effective manner in order to expand their companies, while remaining true to their customer demands. **Availability:** Online.

19568 ■ *"The Perils of Partnering in Developing Markets: How a Health Care Provider Addresses the Risks That Come With Globalization"* in *Harvard Business Review (Vol. 90, June 2012, No. 6, pp23)*
Pub: Harvard Business Review Press
Contact: Moderna V. Pfizer, Contact
Ed: Steven J. Thompson. **Price:** $6. **Description:** Effective evaluation of international risk includes assessing the opportunity; ramping up processes, operations, and metrics; and establishing long-term functionality. Warning signs for each stage are also presented. **Availability:** Online; PDF.

19569 ■ *"Port Canaveral Plans to Make Big Waves of Business in C. Fla."* in *Orlando Business Journal (Vol. 30, June 6, 2014, No. 50, pp. 4)*
Pub: American City Business Journals, Inc.
Contact: Mike Olivieri, Executive Vice President
Released: Weekly. **Price:** $8, Introductory 4-week offer(Digital & Print). **Description:** Port Canaveral CEO, John Walsh, has big plans for the expansion of the Port, which include a $500 million cargo and cruise expansion that could net billions of dollars in new economic impact and create more than 15,000 new jobs. Walsh plans to expand cargo capacity, dig deeper harbors for large cruise ships and build a rail transport cargo and, eventually, passengers in and out of the 380-acre Port Canaveral. The Port is the fifth-largest cargo port in Central Florida. **Availability:** Print; Online.

19570 ■ *"The Power of Purpose"* in *Journal of Business Strategy (Vol. 35, May-June 2014, No. 3, pp. 55-58)*
Pub: BNP Media
Contact: Harper Henderson, Owner Co-Chief Executive Officer
Description: Report states that the defining a corporation's highest purpose holds momentous importance in a business environment overwhelmed by short-termism. It is observed that the contemporary business environment greatly values the short-term financial results and ignores a corporation's true customer-centered purpose.

19571 ■ *"QuaDPharma Tripling Sales"* in *Business First of Buffalo (Vol. 30, January 31, 2014, No. 20, pp. 3)*
Pub: American City Business Journals, Inc.
Contact: Mike Olivieri, Executive Vice President
Released: Weekly. **Price:** $140, One-Year Print & Digital; $115, One-Year Digital. **Description:** New York-based QuaDPharma LLC is predicting growth in 2014. The firm expects sales to increase by 300 percent. QuaDPharma is focusing on the production of pre-commercial and commercial pharmaceutical products. **Availability:** Print; Online.

19572 ■ *"Quintessential Gentleman: Going Old-School on Calvert"* in *Baltimore Business Journal (Vol. 31, February 7, 2014, No. 41, pp. 6)*
Pub: American City Business Journals, Inc.
Contact: Mike Olivieri, Executive Vice President
Description: Quintessential Gentleman owner, Craig Martin shares his vintage idea in the expansion of his men's barbershop, spa, and tailor business in the Jewelers Building at South Calvert Street in downtown Baltimore, Maryland. Martin says his idea is to bring back tradition combined with modern amenities. He also shares his plan to model the business on a department store. **Availability:** Print; Online.

19573 ■ *"Refreshing! A Clearly Canadian Comeback"* in *Canadian Business (Vol. 79, September 11, 2006, No. 18, pp. 22)*
Pub: Rogers Media Inc.
Contact: Neil Spivak, Chief Executive Officer
Ed: Joe Castaldo. **Description:** Turnaround strategies and initiatives adopted by Canadian Beverage Corp. to boost its declining sales are presented. **Availability:** Print; Online.

19574 ■ *"The Reinvention of Management"* in *Strategy and Leadership (Vol. 39, March-April 2011, No. 2, pp. 9)*
Pub: Emerald Group Publishing Limited
Contact: Erika Valenti, President
Ed: Stephen Denning. **Description:** An examination found that critical changes in management practice involves five shifts. These shifts involve the firm's goals, model of coordination, the role of managers and values practiced. Other findings of the study are discussed. **Availability:** Download; Online.

19575 ■ "A Responsive Approach to Organizational Misconduct: Rehabilitation, Reintegration, and the Reduction of Reoffense" in *Business Ethics Quarterly* (Vol. 24, July 2014, No. 3, pp. 343)
Pub: Business Ethics Quarterly
Contact: Dawn Elm, Executive Director
E-mail: drelm@stthomas.edu
Description: Examination of ways regulators, prosecutors, and courts might support and encourage the efforts of organizations to not only reintegrate after misconduct, but to also improve their conduct in a way that reduces their likelihood of re-offense (rehabilitation). An experiment in creative sentencing in Alberta, Canada that aimed to try to change the behavior of an industry by publicly airing the root causes of a failure of one of the industry's leaders is examined. A model for a responsive and restorative approach to organizational misconduct that balances the punitive role of regulators and courts with new roles in supporting and overseeing rehabilitation are observed. **Availability:** Online.

19576 ■ "Return to Wealth; Bank Strategy" in *The Economist* (Vol. 390, January 3, 2009, No. 8612, pp. 56)
Description: UBS' strategy to survive these trying economic times is presented. Statistical data included. UBS has a stronger balance-sheet than most of its investment-banking peers and has reduced its portfolio. **Availability:** Print; Online.

19577 ■ Rework
Ed: Jason Fried, David Heinemeier Hansson. **Released:** 2010. **Price:** $19.62, hardcover; $14.99, e-book; $9, audiobook. **Description:** Works to help entrepreneurs and business owners to rethink strategy, customers, and getting things accomplished. **Availability:** E-book; Print.

19578 ■ "The Road Map for Scotiabank's Asian Expansion" in *Globe & Mail* (April 7, 2007, pp. B3)
Ed: Tara Perkins. **Description:** Executive vice-president of Bank of Nova Scotia, Rob Pitfield shares his plan to expand the bank's Asian market. **Availability:** Online.

19579 ■ "Sabia Signals a Bold, New Course for BCE" in *Globe & Mail* (February 2, 2006, pp. B1)
Description: The reasons behind the decision of chief executive officer Michael Sabia to streamline operations of BCE Inc. are presented. **Availability:** Online.

19580 ■ "Samsung's Metamorphosis in Austin" in *Austin Business Journal* (Vol. 31, May 20, 2011, No. 11, pp. 1)
Pub: Austin Business Journal
Contact: Rachel McGrath, Director
E-mail: rmcgrath@bizjournals.com
Ed: Christopher Calnan. **Description:** Samsung Austin Semiconductor LP, a developer of semiconductors for smartphones and tablet computers, plans to diversify its offerings to include niche products: flash memory devices and microprocessing devices. In light of this strategy, Samsung Austin will be hiring 300 engineers as part of a $3.6 billion expansion of its plant. **Availability:** Print; Online.

19581 ■ "Sawatdee Rethinks Express Eatery Model" in *Business Journal* (Vol. 31, January 10, 2014, No. 33, pp. 4)
Pub: American City Business Journals, Inc.
Contact: Mike Olivieri, Executive Vice President
Released: Weekly. **Price:** $4, Introductory 4-week offer(Digital & Print). **Description:** The two Sawatdee Express restaurants owned by Supenn Harrison closed their uptown and downtown locations in Minneapolis, Minnesota in December 2013. Harrison and her family own six other traditional, sit-down models of the Sawatdee restaurants. **Availability:** Print; Online.

19582 ■ "Serious Growth Ahead for Tokyo Joe's" in *Denver Business Journal* (Vol. 65, April 4, 2014, No. 47, pp. A9)
Pub: American City Business Journals, Inc.
Contact: Mike Olivieri, Executive Vice President
Released: Weekly. **Price:** $4, introductory 4-week offer(Digital only). **Description:** Tokyo Joe's founder and chief innovation officer, Larry Leith, shares his perspective on the franchising and expansion of the Colorado-based Asian fast food chain. Leith describes the fast-casual chain market in Denver and considers the possibility of going public in the future. **Availability:** Print; Online.

19583 ■ "Setting Business Goals: The First Step to a Successful Business" in Asana website (Sept. 14, 2021)
URL(s): asana.com/resources/business-goals-examples
Ed: Sarah Laoyan. **Released:** September 14, 2021. **Description:** Discusses the importance of business goals and reasons why you should set them for your small business. **Availability:** Online.

19584 ■ "Shermag Says Refinishing Not Complete" in *Globe & Mail* (February 14, 2006, pp. B3)
Ed: Bertrand Marotte. **Description:** The details on restructuring efforts of Shermag Inc. are presented. **Availability:** Online.

19585 ■ "Shoppers Targets an Upscale Move" in *Globe & Mail* (January 19, 2007, pp. B4)
Ed: Marina Strauss. **Description:** Shoppers Drug Mart Corp.'s plan to boost sales of cosmetics and take up global sourcing to offer new products is discussed. **Availability:** Online.

19586 ■ "Should You Go Into Business With Your Spouse?" in *Women Entrepreneur* (September 1, 2008)
Description: Things to consider before starting a business with one's spouse are discussed. Compatible work ethics, clear expectations of one another, long-term goals for the company and the status of the relationship are among the things to consider before starting a business endeavor with a spouse. **Availability:** Online.

19587 ■ "Sleeman Cuts Again as Cheap Suds Bite" in *Globe & Mail* (March 3, 2006, pp. B3)
Ed: Andy Hoffman. **Description:** The details on 5 percent employee reduction at Sleeman Breweries Ltd., which posted 86 percent decline in profits for fourth quarter 2005, are presented. **Availability:** Online.

19588 ■ "Slimmed-Down Supplier TI Automotive Relaunches" in *Crain's Detroit Business* (Vol. 26, January 11, 2010, No. 2, pp. 14)
Pub: Crain Communications Inc.
Contact: Barry Asin, President
Ed: Robert Sherefkin. **Description:** TI Automotive Ltd., one of the world's largest suppliers of fuel storage and delivery systems, has reorganized the company by splitting it into five global divisions and is relaunching its brand which is now more focused on new technology. **Availability:** Print; Online.

19589 ■ Small Business Goals 101: Your Guide to Setting Business Goals the SMART Way
URL(s): www.berxi.com/resources/articles/small-business-goals-101/
Released: October 14, 2021. **Description:** Explains how to use the SMART goal framework to set goals for your small business. Also provides examples of different types of goals to get you started and to provide inspiration. **Availability:** Online.

19590 ■ "Small is the New Big in Autos" in *Globe & Mail* (February 16, 2006, pp. B3)
Ed: Greg Keenan. **Description:** The reasons behind the introduction of subcompact cars by companies such as Ford Motor Co. are presented. The automobiles were unveiled at Canadian International Auto Show in Toronto.

19591 ■ "So You Want to Start a Business? So You Want to Start a Business: What's Your First Move?" in *Women Entrepreneur* (August 5, 2008)
Description: Advice for taking an idea and turning it into a legitimate business is given. **Availability:** Online.

19592 ■ "Social Networking: Growing Pains" in *Canadian Business* (Vol. 81, July 22, 2008, No. 12-13, pp. 35)
Pub: Rogers Media Inc.
Contact: Neil Spivak, Chief Executive Officer
Ed: Alex Mlynek. **Description:** Laughing Stock Vineyards' Cynthia Enns and David Enns plan to target young buyers by using social media. The Enns however, are concerned that targeting younger buyers may affect Laughing Stock's image as a premium brand. Additional information regarding the company's future plans is presented. **Availability:** Print; Online.

19593 ■ "Sorrell Digs Deep to Snag TNS" in *Advertising Age* (Vol. 79, July 14, 2008, No. 7, pp. 1)
Pub: Crain Communications, Inc.
Contact: Jessica Botos, Manager, Marketing
E-mail: jessica.botos@crainsnewyork.com
Ed: Michael Bush. **Description:** Martin Sorrell's strategic vision for expansion in order to become the largest ad-agency holding company in the world is discussed. **Availability:** Online.

19594 ■ "Stadium Developers Seek a Win With the State" in *The Business Journal-Serving Metropolitan Kansas City* (Vol. 26, August 22, 2008)
Description: Three Trails Redevelopment LLC is hoping to win $30 million in state tax credits from the Missouri Development Finance Board for the construction of an 18,500-seat Wizards stadium. The project is contingent on state tax incentives and the company remains optimistic about their goal.

19595 ■ "Stikemans' Ascent, Its Legacy, and Its Future" in *Globe & Mail* (January 29, 2007, pp. B2)
Description: Pierre Raymond, chairman of legal firm Stikeman Elliott LLP, talks about his strategies to handle competition, his challenges, and about Canada's present mergers and acquisition scenario. Stikeman achieved the first place in 2006 M&A legal rankings. **Availability:** Online.

19596 ■ "Stock Car Racing" in *Canadian Business* (Vol. 81, September 15, 2008, No. 14-15, pp. 29)
Description: Some analysts predict a Chapter 11-style tune-up making GM and Ford a speculative turnaround stock. However, the price of oil could make or break the shares of the Big Three U.S. automobile manufacturers and if oil goes up too high then a speculative stock to watch is an electric car company called Zenn Motor Co. **Availability:** Online.

19597 ■ "Stoneham Drilling Trust Announces Cash Distribution for May 2007" in *Canadian Corporate News* (May 16, 2007)
Description: Stoneham Drilling Trust, an income trust that provides contract drilling services to natural gas and oil exploration and production companies operating in western Canada, announced that its cash distribution for the period from May 1, 2007 to May 31, 2007 will be $0.15 per trust unit ($1.80 per annum). **Availability:** Print; Online.

19598 ■ Streetwise Small Business Turnaround: Revitalizing Your Struggling or Stagnant Enterprise
Description: Practical tips and advice are provided for rejuvenating an existing small business.

19599 ■ "A Strong, Aligned Board of Directors Is Ideal" in *South Florida Business Journal* (Vol. 35, August 1, 2014, No. 1, pp. 8)
Pub: American City Business Journals, Inc.
Contact: Mike Olivieri, Executive Vice President

GENERAL SMALL BUSINESS TOPICS

Released: Weekly. **Price:** $8, introductory 4-week offer(Digital only). **Description:** The advantages of an informed and congruent board of directors to a company are described. The board of directors should provide the company with a strategic business perspective, access to prospective investors, and potential strategic business partners to help a firm achieve its vision and goals. **Availability:** Print; Online.

19600 ■ *"Take on an Elephant Without Getting Trampled"* in Globe & Mail (March 17, 2007, pp. B3)
Ed: Grant Robertson. **Description:** The plan of chief executive officer of Canpages Inc. Olivier Vincent to beat the profit margin and market share of Yellow Pages Group is discussed. **Availability:** Online.

19601 ■ *"Talisman CEO Touts Benefits of Going It Alone"* in Globe & Mail (March 2, 2006, pp. B1)
Ed: Dave Ebner. **Description:** The opinions of chief executive officer Jim Buckee of Talisman Energy Inc. on the benefits for the company to remain autonomous are presented. **Availability:** Online.

19602 ■ *"Tell Me Why"* in Business Strategy Review (Vol. 25, Summer 2014, No. 2, pp. 50)
Released: June 02, 2014. **Description:** Successful entrepreneurs constantly ask why their ideas will or won't work to help with business visions and goals. **Availability:** Print; PDF; Online.

19603 ■ *"Thomson Eyes Asia for Expansion"* in Globe & Mail (February 10, 2006, pp. B4)
Description: The business growth plans of Thomson Corp., in Asia, are presented. **Availability:** Print; Online.

19604 ■ *"Top Expenses Taking the Biggest Bite out of Your Business"* in Legal Zoom (March 27, 2023)
URL(s): www.legalzoom.com/articles/top-expenses-taking-the-biggest-bite-out-of-your-business
Ed: Stephanie Morrow. **Released:** March 27, 2023. **Description:** Lists and discusses five areas where your business may be draining money and gives advice on what to do to stop it. **Availability:** Online.

19605 ■ *Training & Development for Dummies*
Pub: John Wiley & Sons, Inc.
Contact: Christina Van Tassell, Executive Vice President Chief Financial Officer
URL(s): www.wiley.com/en-us/Training+%26+Development+For+Dummies%2C+2nd+Edition-p-9781119896029
Ed: Elaine Biech. **Released:** 2nd edition. **Price:** $18, e-book; $29.99, paperback. **Description:** Retaining your most valuable talent in your workplace is crucial and this guide will help you develop the skills and programs to keep your top employees. Training and development is crucial for team growth and there are various ways to complete these programs, which are outlined in this book. **Availability:** E-book; Print.

19606 ■ *"Tri-State Lags Peer Cities in Jobs, Human Capital, Study Says"* in Business Courier (Vol. 27, September 24, 2010, No. 21, pp. 1)
Pub: Business Courier
Ed: Dan Monk, Lucy May. **Description:** Greater Cincinnati, Ohio has ranked tenth overall in the 'Agenda 360/Vision 2015 Regional Indicators Project' report. The study ranked 12-city-peer groups in categories such as job indicators standing and people indicators standing. The ranking of jobs and human capital study is topped by Minneapolis, followed by Denver, Raleigh, and Austin. **Availability:** Print; Online.

19607 ■ *"Tsingtao's Chairman On Jump-Starting a Sluggish Company"* in Harvard Business Review (Vol. 90, April 2012, No. 4, pp. 41)
Pub: Harvard Business Review Press
Contact: Moderna V. Pfizer, Contact

Ed: Jin Zhiguo. **Description:** The key challenge Tsingtao Brewery Company Ltd. faced was the focus on pleasing corporate superiors, rather than the firm's customers. By inventing a new model, the brewery was able to boost both employee productivity and product quality. First half profits and revenue for 2011 grew more than 20 percent over the previous year.

19608 ■ *"Under Armour Hopes to Stomp on Nike with Basketball Shoe"* in Baltimore Business Journal (Vol. 28, October 22, 2010, No. 24, pp. 1)
Pub: Baltimore Business Journal
Contact: Rhonda Pringle, President
E-mail: rpringle@bizjournals.com
Ed: Erik Siemers. **Description:** Uner Armour Inc. will release its Micro G line of four basketball sneakers on October 23, 2010. The company's executives mentioned that Under Armour's goal is to appeal to customers, and not to chip away at Nike Inc.'s supremacy in basketball shoes. The new sneakers will range from $80 to $110. **Availability:** Print; Online.

19609 ■ *"Under Fire, Sabia Triggers Battle for BCE"* in Globe & Mail (April 14, 2007, pp. B1)
Ed: Boyd Erman. **Description:** The announcement of negotiations for the sale of BCE Inc. by its chief executive officer Michael Sabia is discussed. The efforts of Ontario Teachers Pension Plan to submit its proposal for the sale are described. **Availability:** Online.

19610 ■ *"Unilever's CMO Finally Gets Down To Business"* in Advertising Age (Vol. 79, July 7, 2008, No. 26, pp. 11)
Description: Overview of Unilever's chief marketing officer Simon Clift's strategy for promoting its products; now that the company has restructured, Clift is able to focus all of his energy on the challenges of the new-media climate that marketers are having to face. **Availability:** Print; Online.

19611 ■ *"U.S. Retailer Eyes 'Tween' Market"* in Globe & Mail (January 30, 2007, pp. B1)
Ed: Marina Strauss. **Description:** The decision of Tween Brands Inc. (Too Incorporated) to open 100 new stores in Canada as part of its expansion is discussed. The company's focus on targeting girls for its products is detailed. **Availability:** Online.

19612 ■ *"Use Perceived Value to Determine Your Food Truck Menu Prices"* in Mobile-Cuisine.com (October 16, 2017)
Ed: Richard Myrick. **Released:** October 16, 2017. **Description:** Provides details on using the perceived value of your food truck dishes and setting appropriate menu prices. **Availability:** Online.

19613 ■ *"Virgin Mobile has Big Plans for Year Two"* in Globe & Mail (March 6, 2006, pp. B5)
Ed: Catherine McLean. **Description:** The business growth plans of Virgin Mobile Canada are presented. **Availability:** Online.

19614 ■ *"Vision vs. Mission Statement: What's the Difference?"* in MasterClass (Dec. 3, 2021)
URL(s): www.masterclass.com/articles/vision-vs-mission
Released: December 13, 2021. **Description:** Mission and vision statements are important to help guide current operations and future goals. Explains the differences between mission and vision statements along with examples of each. **Availability:** Online.

19615 ■ *"Wabtec Delivering Strategic Plan for Long-term Growth"* in Pittsburgh Business Times (Vol. 33, July 11, 2014, No. 52, pp. 10)
Pub: American City Business Journals, Inc.
Contact: Mike Olivieri, Executive Vice President
Released: July 2014. **Description:** Raymond Betler, new CEO of Wabtec Corporation, the only company with a 13-year streak of annual stock price increase on US exchanges is profiled. Betler attributes the company's growth to four corporate strategies, includ-

ing to grow internationally, focus on new product development, expand after-market opportunities, and pursue acquisitions. **Availability:** Print; Online.

19616 ■ *"Walker Seeks More Business Participation"* in Business Journal-Milwaukee (Vol. 28, December 10, 2010, No. 10, pp. A1)
Pub: The Business Journal
Contact: Heather Ladage, President
E-mail: hladage@bizjournals.com
Ed: Rich Kirchen. **Description:** Wisconsin governor Scott Walker is seeking the aid of Milwaukee business leaders to participate in resolving the challenges posed by the economic crisis. Walker is aiming to create 250,000 jobs. He is also planning to call a special session of the legislature to enact strategies to jumpstart the economy. **Availability:** Print; Online.

19617 ■ *"'We Have Surpassed Our Early Goals...Everything Else Is a Bonus"* in Business Journal (Vol. 32, June 6, 2014, No. 2, pp. 13)
Pub: American City Business Journals, Inc.
Contact: Mike Olivieri, Executive Vice President
Released: June 2014. **Description:** Lift Bridge Brewing Company co-founder and president, Dan Schwarz, shares his views about making the transition into a regional player. Schwarz discusses the quality of their beer as the main reason for their relevance to beer drinkers in Minnesota. The firm plans to become a regional brewery and distributor of beer across the nation. **Availability:** Print; Online.

19618 ■ *"Wegmans Adding 1,600-Plus Jobs Here Over the Next Year"* in Boston Business Journal (Vol. 34, February 14, 2014, No. 2, pp. 3)
Pub: American City Business Journals, Inc.
Contact: Mike Olivieri, Executive Vice President
Description: Wegmans, a family-owned grocery chain, is planning to add the most jobs of any firm in Massachusetts in 2014. The company will create more than 1,600 full- and part-time positions by opening three stores. Bill Congdon, Wegmans' New England division manager, reveals that the company is also planning to open a store in the city of Boston. **Availability:** Print; Online.

19619 ■ *"Weyerhaeuser's REIT Decision Shouldn't Scare Investors Away"* in Barron's (Vol. 88, June 30, 2008, No. 26, pp. 18)
Pub: Dow Jones & Company Inc.
Contact: Almar Latour, Chief Executive Officer
Ed: Christopher Williams. **Description:** Weyerhaeuser Co.'s management said that a conversion to a real estate investment trust was not likely in 2009 since the move is not tax-efficient as of the moment and would overload its non-timber assets with debt. The company's shares have fallen by 19.5 percent. However, the company remains an asset-rich outfit and its activist shareholder is pushing for change. **Availability:** Online.

19620 ■ *"What Are You Doing Differently?"* in Agency Sales Magazine (Vol. 39, December 2009, No. 11, pp. 3)
Description: Strategies that sales representatives can do to plan for a good year include professional development, networking with other reps, and making more sales calls and seeing more people. The end of the year is the perfect time for reps to write or re-write their mission statement and to conduct line profitability. **Availability:** Print; Download; Online.

19621 ■ *"What Direction Is Your Company Moving In?"* in South Florida Business Journal (Vol. 35, August 29, 2014, No. 5, pp. 8)
Pub: American City Business Journals, Inc.
Contact: Mike Olivieri, Executive Vice President
Released: Weekly. **Price:** $8, introductory 4-week offer(Digital only). **Description:** Senior management should have a clear perspective about the direction of a company and work hard to effectively communicate such perspective to all stakeholders. Some

ways on how corporate leaders can clarify the strategic plan of a company to its key stakeholders are suggested. **Availability:** Print; Online.

19622 ■ "What Is a Vision Statement?" in Business News Daily (Dec. 21, 2021)
URL(s): www.businessnewsdaily.com/3882-vision-statement.html
Ed: Sean Peek. **Released:** December 21, 2021. **Description:** A powerful vision statement brings customers in and brings them back. This article provides information on how to write a vision statement, includes vision statement templates and resources, and shares 20 examples of inspiring vision statements. **Availability:** Online.

19623 ■ "What Kind of Leader Are You?" in Inc. (Vol. 36, September 2014, No. 7, pp. 76)
Pub: Mansueto Ventures L.L.C.
Contact: Stephanie Mehta, Chief Executive Officer
Description: Ranking of leadership skills for entrepreneurs and managers is presented, with being a visionary leading each category. **Availability:** Print; Online.

19624 ■ "Why CVS May Not Get Burned By Its Tobacco Decision (Part 2); Looking at CVS' Decision To Discontinue Selling Tobacco Products In Purely Dollar Terms Misses the Bigger Picture" in Gallup Business Journal (March 20, 2014)
Pub: Gallup, Inc.
Contact: Jon Clifton, Chief Executive Officer
Description: Drug retailer, CVS, made a strategic play in organizational identity, mission, and purpose when it decided to quit selling cigarettes at its retail stores. The decision to discontinue sales of tobacco products could, long term, strengthen the company's identity in the U.S. marketplace, thus increasing sales. **Availability:** Print; Online.

19625 ■ "Why Intel Should Dump Its Flash-Memory Business" in Barron's (Vol. 88, March 10, 2008, No. 10, pp. 35)
Pub: Dow Jones & Company Inc.
Contact: Almar Latour, Chief Executive Officer
Ed: Eric J. Savitz. **Description:** Intel Corp. must sell its NAND flash-memory business as soon as it possibly can to the highest bidder to focus on its PC processor business and take advantage of other business opportunities. Apple should consider a buyback of 10 percent of the company's shares to lift its stock. **Availability:** Online.

19626 ■ "Why Successful Entrepreneurs Are Effective Delegators; Shifting from a Do-It-Yourself Executive Style to a More Hands-Off Approach is Essential When They're Growing a Business" in Gallup Business Journal (August 26, 2014)
Pub: Gallup, Inc.
Contact: Jon Clifton, Chief Executive Officer
Description: It is critical for entrepreneurs to step away from a do-it-yourself executive style to a more hands-off approach when a company begins to grow. **Availability:** Print; Online.

19627 ■ "Worth His Salt" in Hawaii Business (Vol. 53, January 2008, No. 7, pp. 45)
Pub: PacificBasin Communications
Contact: Chuck Tindle, Director
E-mail: chuckt@pacificbasin.net
Ed: Jolyn Okimoto Rosa. **Description:** Bryan Zada owns three PretzelMaker franchises, whose total loss amounted to $40,000 in 2003. Zada believes that listening to employees was one of the key steps in turning the business around. The efforts made to improve the franchises' products are also given. **Availability:** Online.

19628 ■ "Zara Eludes the Pain in Spain: Clothing Giant Inditex Sees Its First-Quarter Profits Rise By 30 Percent" in Canadian Business (Vol. 85, September 17, 2012, No. 14, pp. 67)
Ed: Bryan Borzykowski. **Released:** September 17, 2012. **Description:** Clothing retailer Inditex reported a 30 percent increase in profit in the first quarter of 2012 and 15 percent increase in sales year over year. The company's unique business model was attributed to its growth, which also appeals to income investors.

19629 ■ "Zell Takes a Gamble on Tribune" in Globe & Mail (April 3, 2007, pp. B1)
Ed: Sinclair Stewart. **Description:** The purchase of the majority share in Tribune Co. by Samuel Zell is described. Samuel Zell's plans to keep the company's assets intact are discussed. **Availability:** Online.

19630 ■ "Zucker's HBC Shakeup Imminent" in Globe & Mail (February 20, 2006, pp. B3)
Ed: Marina Strauss. **Description:** The plans of investor Jerry Zucker to revamp Hudson's Bay Co., upon its acquisition, are presented. **Availability:** Online.

VIDEO/AUDIO MEDIA

19631 ■ 4 Final Lessons of Being Boss
URL(s): beingboss.club/podcast/4-final-lessongs-of-being-boss
Ed: Emily Thompson. **Released:** June 20, 2023. **Description:** Podcast discusses the importance of living your values and cultivating a supportive community. .

19632 ■ Be a Profitable Badass Small Business Owner: Do You Need Goals to Have a Successful Small Business Owner?
URL(s): traffic.libsyn.com/secure/localsmallbusinessownercoach/610_do_you_need_goals_to_be_successful.mp3
Ed: Tammy Adams. **Released:** July 08, 2024. **Description:** Podcast explains how goals tie into growing a profitable small business.

19633 ■ The How of Business: Small Business Culture
URL(s): www.thehowofbusiness.com/436-small-business-culture
Ed: Henry Lopez. **Released:** August 22, 2022. **Description:** Podcast discusses how to develop and maintain a successful small business culture.

19634 ■ The Knowledge Project: Alan Mulally: The Power of Working Together
URL(s): fs.blog/knowldege-project-podcast/alan-mulally
Ed: Shane Parrish. **Released:** November 21, 2022. **Description:** Podcast discusses working together toward a larger goal, creating a culture, and the role of leadership.

19635 ■ The Knowledge Project: Bethany McLean: Crafting a Narrative
URL(s): fs.blog/knowldege-project-podcast/bethany-mclean
Ed: Shane Parrish. **Released:** June 09, 2020. **Description:** Podcast discusses the power of story (even in business) and the behaviors of CEOs, visionaries, and fraudsters.

19636 ■ Nurture Small Business: Purpose-Driven Entrepreneurship: A Path for Business Success
URL(s): nurturesmallbusiness.buzzsprout.com/900445/episodes/14655072-purpose-driven-entrepreneurship-a-path-for-business-success
Ed: Denise Cagan. **Released:** March 11, 2024. **Description:** Podcast discusses how personal purpose can inform your entrepreneurial experience.

CONSULTANTS

19637 ■ Ameriwest Business Consultants Inc. (ABCI)
PO Box 26266
Colorado Springs, CO 80936
Ph: (719)380-7096
Fax: (719)380-7096
Co. E-mail: email@abchelp.com
URL: http://www.abchelp.com
Description: Firm specializes in assisting startup businesses and those with sales of five million dollars or less and lesser than 50 employees. **Scope:** Firm specializes in assisting startup businesses and those with sales of five million dollars or less and lesser than 50 employees. **Founded:** 1984.

19638 ■ Blue Garnet Associates L.L.C.
8405 Pershing Dr., Ste. 205
Playa del Rey, CA 90293
Ph: (310)439-1930
Co. E-mail: hello@bluegarnet.net
URL: http://bluegarnet.net
Contact: Jen Oki, Business Manager
E-mail: jen.oki@bluegarnet.net
Linkedin: www.linkedin.com/company/blue-garnet-associates
X (Twitter): x.com/hellobluegarnet
Description: Provider of management consulting services including employee benefits, managed care and intranet applications. **Founded:** 2002.

19639 ■ BroadVision, Inc.
460 Seaport Ct., Ste. 102
Redwood City, CA 94063
Ph: (650)331-1000
URL: http://broadvision.com/broadvision
Contact: Dr. Pehong Chen, President
Description: Provides application solutions for large scale, personalized business on the internet, intranets, and extranets. Serves the retail and distribution, financial services, high-tech, travel, and telecom industries. Offer expertise in areas such as task management, content sharing, email consolidation, instant messaging and chat, workflow consolidation, process improvement, social networking, internal and external communication, templates and blogs, reports and analytics, e-commerce and transactional portals. **Founded:** 1993.

19640 ■ LHA
800 3rd Ave., 17th Fl.
New York, NY 10022
Ph: (212)838-3777
Co. E-mail: info@lhai.com
URL: http://www.lhai.com
Contact: Jeff Hart, Director
Linkedin: www.linkedin.com/company/lha-lippert-heilshorn
X (Twitter): x.com/LHA_IR_PR
Description: Provider of investor relations services. **Scope:** An independent investor relations firm creating and supporting practices investor and media relations programs.. **Founded:** 1984. **Training:** CME-accredited, UDMNJ Robert Wood Johnson School of Medicine, May, 2011.

19641 ■ ReCourses Inc.
4851 Vincion Rd.
Murfreesboro, TN 37130-7909
Ph: (615)831-2277
Fax: (615)831-2277
URL: http://www.davidcbaker.com
Contact: Bob Lalasz, Chief Executive Officer
X (Twitter): x.com/ReCourses
Description: A privately held advisory firm providing business management advice to entrepreneurial experts worldwide. It is committed to a research-based, educational contribution to principals of expert firms through free position papers, webinars, a podcast, books (print, ebook, audible), and speaking engagements, as well as affordable seminars and advisory services. **Scope:** A privately held advisory firm providing business management advice to entrepreneurial experts worldwide. It is committed to a research-based, educational contribution to principals of expert firms through free position papers, webinars, a podcast, books (print, ebook, audible), and speaking engagements, as well as affordable seminars and advisory services. **Founded:** 1996. **Publications:** -"Managing (Right) for the First Time"; "Financial Management of a Marketing Firm". - "Financial Management of a Marketing Firm"; "Guidebook used worldwide for independent agencies". - "The Business of Expertise"; "How Entrepreneurial Experts Convert Insight to Impact and Wealth". **Training:** 10th Annual New Business Summit, Jan, 2013; Event - TEDx Nashville: Success from the Inside Out--Alignment & Engagement, Apr, 20163; Event - AIGA Brand Academy (Emory Executive Education @ Goi-

zueta Business School), Apr, 2013; Measuring Economic Performance: Measuring and Enhancing Performance in a Marketing Firm, Dec, 2012; Managing Client Relationships: Being Indispensable, Growing the Account, Making Money, Nov, 2012; The Business of Design Oct, 2012; Getting a Good Start in Your Creative Career, Nov, 2011; Research and Insights, Nov, 2011; Managing Client Relationships; Research and Strategy; Financial Management: Measuring and Enhancing Performance in a Marketing Firm, Sep, 2009; Building and Leading a Staff: The When, How, and What of Growth and Culture, Sep, 2009; Doing Effective Work: Adding Significance to the Strategic Portion of Your Work for Clients, Sep, 2009; Resourcing the Creative Process: Managing Pricing, Deadlines, Budgets, Quality, and Capacity, Apr, 2009.

LIBRARIES

19642 ■ University of South Carolina - Darla Moore School of Business - Elliott White Springs Business Library
1014 Greene St.
Columbia, SC 29208

URL: http://delphi.tcl.sc.edu/library/develop/develop.html
Contact: Kathy Snediker, Contact
E-mail: snediker@mailbox.sc.edu

Description: University Libraries connects people with resources, significant collections and expert research services. **Scope:** Corporations. **Services:** Interlibrary loan; copying; library open to the public with restrictions. **Founded:** 1973. **Subscriptions:** periodicals (includes journals) journals books; maps; rare books; music scores; archival collections; audiovisual materials.

Buying a Business

START-UP INFORMATION

19643 ■ *"Allied Brokers of Texas Looking to Fill Private Lending Gap"* in *San Antonio Business Journal (Vol. 26, March 23, 2012, No. 8, pp. 1)*
Pub: Baltimore Business Journal
Contact: Rhonda Pringle, President
E-mail: rpringle@bizjournals.com
Description: San Antonio, Texas-based Allied Brokers of Texas has announced the expansion of its services to offer private lending. The move would provide direct private financing of $250,000 to $5 million to entrepreneurs looking to buy or sell a small business. Insights into the firm's new subsidiary, Allied Lending Services, are also offered. **Availability:** Print; Online.

REFERENCE WORKS

19644 ■ *"7 Steps to Acquiring a Small Business"* in *Entrepreneur (Dec. 3, 2019)*
URL(s): www.entrepreneur.com/article/343129
Released: December 03, 2019. **Description:** Explores the idea of not having to start a business in order to own one. Includes steps to buy profitable businesses without spending your own money. **Availability:** Online.

19645 ■ *10 Warning Signs to Look for When Buying a Business*
URL(s): www.myob.com/au/blog/10-warning-signs-to-look-for-when-buying-a-business/
Ed: Matthew Snelleksz. **Released:** January 01, 2021.
Description: Explores the importance of doing your due diligence when you are looking to buy an existing small business. Includes ten warning signs to look for as you research the business you are interested in. **Availability:** Online.

19646 ■ *12 Tough Lessons Learned from Buying a Business (Plus 15-Point Checklist)*
URL(s): www.levelingup.com/management/buying-a-business/
Description: Lists twelve lessons learned from an entrepreneur who has experienced the highs and lows of buying a small business. Also includes a list of fifteen important items to check off your list when taking over a company. **Availability:** Online.

19647 ■ *"Bank Buys May Heat Up In Birmingham"* in *Birmingham Business Journal (Vol. 31, May 9, 2014, No. 19, pp. 8)*
Pub: American City Business Journals, Inc.
Contact: Mike Olivieri, Executive Vice President
Released: Weekly. **Price:** $4, introductory 4-week offer(Digital & Print). **Description:** The banking industry in Birmingham, Alabama is poised for more mergers and acquisitions in the next two years as bank failures drop and potential sellers look for protection from increasing regulations. Experts suggest Birmingham is an attractive market for potential buyers because of its rich history as a top financial center and its stable economic environment. **Availability:** Print; Online.

19648 ■ *Buy an Existing Business or Franchise*
URL(s): www.sba.gov/business-guide/plan-your-business/buy-existing-business-or-franchise
Description: Explains the difference between franchising and buying a business and explores three things to consider before franchising or buying a business. **Availability:** Online.

19649 ■ *"Buyout Rumors Have Rackspace Back in the News"* in *San Antonio Business Journal (Vol. 28, September 12, 2014, No. 31, pp. 6)*
Pub: American City Business Journals, Inc.
Contact: Mike Olivieri, Executive Vice President
Description: Louisiana-based CenturyLink Inc. has offered to buyout San Antonio, Texas-based Rackspace Hosting in order to boost its Internet and cloud services. The latest stock market valuation of Rackspace was at $5.33 billion. The potential impact of the CenturyLink and Rackspace merger deal on the managed hosting services market is also analyzed. **Availability:** Online.

19650 ■ *"Calista Sells Rural Newspapers"* in *Alaska Business Monthly (Vol. 27, October 2011, No. 10, pp. 8)*
Pub: Alaska Business Publishing Company Inc.
Contact: Charles Bell, Vice President, Sales and Marketing
E-mail: cbell@akbizmag.com
Ed: Nancy Pounds. **Description:** Calista sold its six newspapers, a magazine, shoppers and its printing house. Details of the sales are given.

19651 ■ *"CanWest Plotting Buyback of Newspaper Income Trust"* in *Globe & Mail (February 7, 2007, pp. B1)*
Description: The CanWest Global Communications Corp.'s decision to sell its media assets in Australia and New Zealand in order to finance its plans of repurchasing its newspaper income trust CanWest MediaWorks Income Fund is discussed. **Availability:** Online.

19652 ■ *"Capital Position: M&I Acquisition Opens the Door for Rivals to Gain Market Share"* in *Business Journal-Milwaukee (Vol. 28, December 24, 2010, No. 12, pp. A1)*
Pub: The Business Journal
Contact: Heather Ladage, President
E-mail: hladage@bizjournals.com
Ed: Rich Kirchen. **Description:** Canada-based BMO Financial Group has purchased Marshall and Isley Corporation (M and I), which dominated lending among Wisconsin businesses for decades. The sale of M and I will enable other banks to recruit M and I's customers but BMO Financial remains a stronger competitor since it possesses a more potent capital position. **Availability:** Print; Online.

19653 ■ *"CGB Purchases Illinois Grain-Fertilizer Firm"* in *Farm Industry News (December 2, 2011)*
Pub: Informa Business Media, Inc.
Contact: Charlie McCurdy, President
Description: CGB Enterprises Inc. bought Twomey Company's grain and fertilizer assets. The purchase includes eight locations and a barge loading terminal near Gladstone, Illinois and storage capacity of 51 million bushels and 18,000 tons of liquid fertilizer. **Availability:** Online.

19654 ■ *"Cirrus Logic: Too Much Apple?"* in *Austin Business Journal (Vol. 32, April 6, 2012, No. 5, pp. A1)*
Pub: American City Business Journals, Inc.
Contact: Mike Olivieri, Executive Vice President
Ed: Christopher Calnan. **Description:** Austin, Texas-based Cirrus Logic has been moving to reduce its growing dependence on supplying components for Apple Inc. products. Cirrus Logic has disclosed that it deveoped a controller designed to enable light dimmer switches for incandescent lights to work with light emitting diodes. Insights on Cirrus Logic's sale to Apple are also given. **Availability:** Online.

19655 ■ *The Complete Guide to Buying a Business*
Pub: Nolo
Contact: Chris Braun, President
Ed: Fred S. Steingold. **Released:** 2015. **Description:** Key steps in buying a business are highlighted, focusing on legal issues, tax considerations, approaches for valuing a business, financing, structuring the deal, along with forms and documents for taking ownership are included. **Availability:** Print.

19656 ■ *The Complete Guide to Selling a Business*
Pub: Nolo
Contact: Chris Braun, President
Ed: Fred S. Steingold. **Released:** August 2017. **Description:** When selling a business it is critical that a sales agreement covers all key concerns from price and payment terms to liability protection and restrictions on future competition. **Availability:** Print.

19657 ■ *"Dow AgroSciences Buys Wheat-Breeding Firm in Pacific Northwest"* in *Farm Industry News (July 29, 2011)*
Pub: Informa Business Media, Inc.
Contact: Charlie McCurdy, President
Description: Dow AgroSciences purchased Northwest Plant Breeding Company, a cereals breeding station in Washington in 2011. The acquisition will help Dow expand its Hyland Seeds certified wheat seed program foundation in the Pacific Northwest. Financial terms of the deal were not disclosed. **Availability:** Online.

19658 ■ *"Downtown Bank Got High Marks for Irwin Purchase, Is Looking For More"* in *Business Courier (Vol. 27, September 3, 2010, No. 18, pp. 1)*
Pub: Business Courier

GENERAL SMALL BUSINESS TOPICS

Buying a Business ■ 19681

Ed: Steve Watkins. **Price:** $4, Introductory 4-Week Offer(Digital & Print). **Description:** First Financial Bancorp is looking to acquire more troubled banks following its purchase of Irwin Union Bank. The bank has reported a $383 million bargain purchase gain during the third quarter of 2009. **Availability:** Print; Online.

19659 ■ *Entrepreneur Magazine's Ultimate Guide to Buying or Selling a Business*
Released: Fourth edition. **Description:** Proven strategies to evaluate, negotiate, and buy or sell a small business. Franchise and family business succession planning is included.

19660 ■ *"Facebook Purchased Push Pop Press" in Information Today (Vol. 28, October 2011, No. 9, pp. 12)*
Description: Facebook purchased Push Pop Press, a digital publishing company that developed a multi-touch interface for ebook publishing on the iPad.

19661 ■ *"FIS-Metavante Deal Paying Off for Many" in Business Journal-Milwaukee (Vol. 28, December 17, 2010, No. 11, pp. A1)*
Pub: The Business Journal
Contact: Heather Ladage, President
E-mail: hladage@bizjournals.com
Ed: Rich Kirchen. **Description:** Jacksonville, Florida-based Fidelity National Information Services Inc., also known as FIS, has remained committed to Milwaukee, Wisconsin more than a year after purchasing Metavante Technologies Inc. FIS has transferred several operations into Metropolitan Milwaukee and has continued its contribution to charitable organizations in the area. **Availability:** Print; Online.

19662 ■ *"For Allegiance Capital, Oil and Gas are Hot" in Dallas Business Journal (Vol. 37, May 30, 2014, No. 38, pp. 8)*
Pub: American City Business Journals, Inc.
Contact: Mike Olivieri, Executive Vice President
Released: Weekly. **Price:** $4, introductory 4-week offer(Digital & Print). **Description:** Allegiance Capital Corporation has completed four merger and acquisition deals involving oil and gas companies totaling $350 million, as of May 30, 2014. Company founder and chairman, David Mahmood, says it is the right time to sell oil and gas companies because prices are at their peak. **Availability:** Print; Online.

19663 ■ *"Former Prov. Mayor Sees Potential in Newport Grand" in Providence Business News (Vol. 29, July 21, 2014, No. 16, pp. 4)*
Pub: American City Business Journals, Inc.
Contact: Mike Olivieri, Executive Vice President
URL(s): pbn.com/former-prov-mayor-sees-potential -in-newport-grand98638
Description: Joseph R. Paolino, Jr., managing partner at Paolino Properties and former Providence Mayor, believes introducing table games to Newport Grand can help the gambling casino generate needed revenues. Paolino notes that if voters approve a ballot referendum to authorize table games in November, he and his partners will acquire and renovate Newport Grand as an entertainment center. **Telecommunication Services:** Daddona@pbn.com.

19664 ■ *"Franchisee to Add 10 New Applebee's" in Memphis Business Journal (Vol. 34, June 8, 2012, No. 8, pp. 1)*
Pub: Baltimore Business Journal
Contact: Rhonda Pringle, President
E-mail: rpringle@bizjournals.com
Ed: Andy Ashby. **Description:** Apple Investor Group LLC seeks to open 10 more Applebee's restaurants in Memphis over the next two years. The franchisee purchased the 70-county market from DineEquity for $23 million in early 2012. The group is upgrading 17 Mid-South Applbee's units. **Availability:** Print; Online.

19665 ■ *"Getting Emotional Over Microsoft's Minecraft" in Puget Sound Business Journal (Vol. 35, September 19, 2014, No. 22, pp. 7)*
Pub: American City Business Journals, Inc.
Contact: Mike Olivieri, Executive Vice President

Description: Microsoft's acquisition of Minecraft maker Mojan AB is helps to promote STEM education. Microsoft will purchase the company for $2.5 billion. Minecraft game creator, Markus Persson, will not be joining the new Microsoft team. **Availability:** Online.

19666 ■ *"Graphic Tech Acquires First U.S. :M-Press Tiger with Inline Screen Printing" in American Printer (Vol. 128, June 1, 2011, No. 6)*
Description: Graphic Tech located in California bought M-Press Tiger, the first in North America with an inline screen printing unit. **Availability:** Online.

19667 ■ *"The Hard Thing About Hard Things: Building a Business When There Are No Easy Answers"*
Pub: HarperCollins Publishers L.L.C.
Contact: Brian Murray, President
Released: 2014. **Price:** $29.99, Hardcover; $14.99, E-book; $23.99, Digital Audiobook Unabridged. **Description:** Cofounder of Andreessen Horowitz and well-respected Silicon Valley entrepreneur, offers advice for building and running a startup small business. Horowitz analyzes issues confronting leaders daily and shares insights he gained from managing, selling, buying investing in, and supervising technology firms. **Availability:** E-book; Print; Download.

19668 ■ *"Harleysville Eyes Growth After Nationwide Deal" in Philadelphia Business Journal (Vol. 30, October 7, 2011, No. 34, pp. 1)*
Pub: Philadelphia Business Journal
Contact: Sierra Quinn, Director
E-mail: squinn@bizjournals.com
Ed: Jeff Blumenthal. **Price:** $4, introductory 4-week offer(Digital & Print). **Description:** Harleysville Group announced growth plans after the company was sold to Columbus, Ohio-based Nationwide Mutual Insurance Company for about $1.63 billion. Nationwide gained an independent agency platform in 32 states with the Harleysville deal. **Availability:** Print; Online.

19669 ■ *"Hospitals Vying to Buy Physician Associates LLC" in Orlando Business Journal (Vol. 29, August 31, 2012, No. 11, pp. 1)*
Pub: Baltimore Business Journal
Contact: Rhonda Pringle, President
E-mail: rpringle@bizjournals.com
Description: Hospitals are battling it out on who gets to buy Physician Associates LLC, the largest multi-specialty practice in Central Florida. The most likely candidates to purchase the practice are Orlando Health and Florida Hospital. The deal could be worth $20 million to $60 million and it could also hike health care costs since Physician Acoiates serves 19 percent of Central Florida's uninsured population. **Availability:** Print; Online.

19670 ■ *"How to Buy a Business: Everything You Need to Know" in NerdWallet (Oct. 22, 2020)*
URL(s): www.nerdwallet.com/article/small-business/ buying-an-existing-business
Ed: Priyanka Prakash. **Released:** October 22, 2020. **Description:** Covers the pros and cons of buying a business while you're still thinking about it and explores how to actually buy the business when you're ready to close the deal. **Availability:** Online.

19671 ■ *"How to Buy a Business or Franchise" in Guidant (Nov. 25, 2021)*
URL(s): www.guidantfinancial.com/blog/buying-a -business-good-idea/
Released: November 25, 2021. **Description:** A guide to buying a business versus starting a business from scratch. **Availability:** Online.

19672 ■ *"How to Buy a Company With Someone Else's Money" in Small Business Trends(January 23, 2023)*
URL(s): smallbiztrends.com/2023/01/buying-a-com-pany-with-someone-elses-money.html

Released: January 23, 2023. **Description:** Interview with Jonathan Jay about buying and selling businesses. **Availability:** Online.

19673 ■ *"How to Buy a Small Business" in Funding Circle (March 27, 2020)*
URL(s): www.fundingcircle.com/us/resources/how-to -buy-a-small-business/
Released: March 27, 2020. **Description:** A guide to how to buy a small business for aspiring new owners. **Availability:** Online.

19674 ■ *"How to Purchase an Existing Business" in LegalZoom (Nov. 2, 2021)*
URL(s): www.legalzoom.com/articles/how-to -purchase-an-existing-business
Ed: Mariah Wojdacz. **Released:** November 02, 2021. **Description:** Evaluates the advantages and disadvantages of buying an existing business. Also provides tips on how to proceed if you decide that buying a business is the right choice for you. **Availability:** Online.

19675 ■ *Is Buying an Existing Business Right for You?*
URL(s): www.paychex.com/articles/startup/pros-an d-cons-of-buying-a-business
Released: August 29, 2019. **Description:** Includes pros and cons of buying an existing business and examines the process to follow to determine if buying the business is right for you. **Availability:** Online.

19676 ■ *"Ketchup King Heinz Seeks to Boost Soy-Sauce Empire in China" in Advertising Age (Vol. 83, October 8, 2012, No. 36, pp. 3)*
Description: Heinz is buying up local soy sauce firms in China with a buy-and-build strategy to expand into other markets in the country. Soy sauce total sales are about $4 billion annually in China, while ketchup sales amount to $100 million to $200 million there. **Availability:** Print; Online.

19677 ■ *"Kratos Announces Buy of Critical Infrastructure Security Business" in M & A Navigator (January 3, 2012)*
Description: Kratos Defense & Security Solutions Inc., a US national security firm, purchased a competitor for USD $20 million. The acquisition will help expand its critical infrastructure security business. **Availability:** Print.

19678 ■ *Let's Buy a Company: How to Accelerate Growth Through Acquisitions*
Description: Advice for negotiating terms and pricing as well as other aspects of mergers and acquisitions in small companies. **Availability:** Print.

19679 ■ *"Local Firm Snaps up 91 Area Pizza Huts" in Orlando Business Journal (Vol. 26, January 8, 2010, No. 32, pp. 1)*
Pub: Orlando Business Journal
Contact: Julie Swyers, Director
E-mail: jswyers@bizjournals.com
Ed: Alexis Muellner, Anjali Fluker. **Description:** Orlando, Florida-based CFL Pizza LLC bought the 91 Orlando-area Pizza Hut restaurants for $35 million from parent company Yum! Brands Inc. CFL Pizza plans to distribute parts of the business to Central Florida vendors and the first business up for grabs is the advertising budget. **Availability:** Print; Online.

19680 ■ *Mergers and Acquisitions from A to Z*
Pub: HarperCollins Leadership
Contact: Donald Miller, Chief Executive Officer
Released: 2nd edition. **Price:** $19.99, Paperback. **Description:** Guide for the entire process of mergers and acquisitions, including taxes, accounting, laws, and projected financial gain. **Availability:** E-book; Print.

19681 ■ *"Monsanto Acquires Targeted-Pest Control Technology Start-Up; Terms Not Disclosed" in Benzinga.com (September 2011)*
Pub: Benzinga.com
Contact: Jason Raznick, Founder

Ed: Eddie Staley. **Description:** Monsanto Company acquired Beelogics, a firm that researches and develops biological tools that control pests and diseases. Research includes a product that will help protect bee health. **Availability:** Online.

19682 ■ "Neighboring Auto Body Shops Merge as Parks Royal Body Works" in Idaho Business Review (August 26, 2014)

Pub: BridgeTower Media
Contact: Adam Reinebach, President

Description: Parks Royal Body Works and Auto Body Specialists operated next door to each other and were rivals for many years. Ted Vinson, owner of Auto Body, recently sold his business to Ted Thornton's son, Matt in order for Parks Royal to expand. Thornton discusses his company's 13 percent growth in 2013. Details of the purchase are discussed.

19683 ■ "Phillip Frost: 'Technology Is the Future'" in South Florida Business Journal (Vol. 34, June 20, 2014, No. 48, pp. 16)

Pub: American City Business Journals, Inc.
Contact: Mike Olivieri, Executive Vice President

Released: Weekly. **Price:** $8, introductory 4-week offer(Digital only). **Description:** Entrepreneur, Phillip Frost, shares his strategies and perspectives on the business climate of Miami, Florida. He describes investment strategy for the diverse holdings of Opko Health and his criteria for buying companies and licensing technologies. **Availability:** Print; Online.

19684 ■ "Pizza or Beer? Why Kalil Made Right Call" in Business Journal (Vol. 31, January 31, 2014, No. 36, pp. 6)

Pub: American City Business Journals, Inc.
Contact: Mike Olivieri, Executive Vice President

Released: January 31, 2014. **Price:** $4, Introductory 4-week offer(Digital & Print). **Description:** Businessman, Matt Kalil, purchased the Pieology franchise rights for Minnesota. Kalil will open his first locations in Maple Grove and Saint Paul's Highland Park. The restaurant franchise is expected to have six locations by the end of 2014. **Availability:** Print; Online.

19685 ■ "Points of Light Sells MissionFish to eBay" in Non-Profit Times (Vol. 25, May 15, 2011, No. 7, pp. May 15, 2011)

Description: eBay purchased MissionFish, a subsidiary of Points of Light Institute for $4.5 million. MissionFish allows eBay sellers to give proceeds from sales to their favorite nonprofit organization and helps nonprofits raise funds by selling on eBay. **Availability:** Print; Online.

19686 ■ "Portland's Hilton For Sale" in Business Journal Portland (Vol. 27, October 22, 2010, No. 34, pp. 1)

Pub: Portland Business Journal
Contact: Andy Giegerich, Managing Editor
E-mail: agiegerich@bizjournals.com

Ed: Wendy Culverwell. **Description:** Hilton Portland & Executive Tower, Portland's biggest hotel, is being sold by Cornerstone Real Estate Advisers LLC. Cornerstone hopes to close the deal for the 782-room complex by the end of 2010. Cornerstone contracted Jones Lang LaSalle to manage the sale, but terms to the deal are not available. **Availability:** Print; Online.

19687 ■ "RipCode Founder Starts Private Equity Firm Vspeed Capital" in Dallas Business Journal (Vol. 35, September 9, 2012, No. 51, pp. 1)

Pub: Baltimore Business Journal
Contact: Rhonda Pringle, President
E-mail: rpringle@bizjournals.com

Ed: Jeff Bounds. **Description:** Brendon Mills, founder of Genband Inc., cofounds Vspeed Capital LLC, a new private equity firm. The company has joined forces with Galatyn Private Equity to make its first purchase, that of Fortress Solutions Ltd. Vspeed plans to acquire companies in the manufacturing and distribution sectors, and double its revenue in the next 24 months. **Availability:** Print; Online.

19688 ■ "Rosewood Site Faces Big Cleanup Before Stevenson Can Expand" in Baltimore Business Journal (Vol. 27, February 6, 2010, No. 40, pp. 1)

Pub: Baltimore Business Journal
Contact: Rhonda Pringle, President
E-mail: rpringle@bizjournals.com

Ed: Daniel J. Sernovitz. **Description:** Environmental assessment report states that Maryland's Rosewood Center for the Developmentally Disabled has significant amounts of toxic chemicals, which could impact Stevenson University's decision to purchase the property. Senator Robert A. Zirkin believes that the state should pay for the cleanup, which is expected to cost millions. **Availability:** Print; Online.

19689 ■ "Sale of Owings Mills Solo Cup Plant Pending" in Boston Business Journal (Vol. 29, June 17, 2011, No. 6, pp. 1)

Pub: Boston Business Journal
Contact: Carolyn M. Jones, President
E-mail: cmjones@bizjournals.com

Ed: Daniel J. Sernovitz. **Released:** Weekly; X. **Price:** $4, Print. **Description:** Baltimore developers Vanguard Equities Inc. and Greenberg Gibbons Commercial have contracted to buy the Solo Cup Company facility in Owing Mills and are now considering several plans for the property. Sale should be completed by September 2011 but no proposed sale terms are disclosed. **Availability:** Print; Online.

19690 ■ "San Antonio's Alamo Iron Works Is On the Prowl for Acquisitions" in San Antonio Business Journal (Vol. 26, August 3, 2012, No. 27, pp. 1)

Pub: Baltimore Business Journal
Contact: Rhonda Pringle, President
E-mail: rpringle@bizjournals.com

Description: Alamo Iron Works is preparing for acquisitions two years after emerging from Chapter 11 bankruptc reorganization. The company is in talks to purchase other firms to strengthen its share in the Texas steel market and serve the state's energy industry.

19691 ■ "Skype Ltd. Acquired GroupMe" in Information Today (Vol. 28, October 2011, No. 9, pp. 12)

Description: Skype Ltd. acquired GroupMe, a group messaging company that allows users to form impromptu groups where they can text message, share data, and make conference calls for free and is supported on Android, iPhone, BlackBerry, and Windows phones. **Availability:** Print; Online.

19692 ■ "Start or Buy? It's a Tough Question for Eager Entrepreneurs" in Crain's Cleveland Business (Vol. 28, October 8, 2007, No. 40, pp. 24)

Pub: Crain Communications Inc.
Contact: K. C. Crain, President

Ed: David Prizinsky. **Description:** Discusses different approaches to becoming a small business owner. **Availability:** Online.

19693 ■ "Symantic Completes Acquisition of VeriSign's Security Business" in Internet Wire (August 9, 2010)

Description: Symantec Corporation acquired VeriSign's identity and authentication business, which includes Secure Sockets Layer (SSL) and Code Signing Certificate Services, the Managed Public Key Infrastructure (MPKI) Services, the VeriSign Trust Seal, the VeriSign Identity Protection (VIP) Authentication Service and the VIP Fraud Protection Service (FDS). The agreement also included a majority stake in VeriSign Japan. **Availability:** Online.

19694 ■ "Syracuse Gear Manufacturer Buys Buffalo Company" in Business First of Buffalo (Vol. 30, January 24, 2014, No. 19, pp. 3)

Pub: American City Business Journals, Inc.
Contact: Mike Olivieri, Executive Vice President

Released: Weekly. **Price:** $140, One-Year Print & Digital; $115, One-Year Digital. **Description:** Niagara Gear Corporation of Buffalo, New York was acquired by Gear Motions Inc., in a deal that could make Gear Motions the largest precision gear manufacturer for the commercial and industrial compressor market. Niagara Gear will supply larger ground and cut spur and helical gears to existing customers as part of the sale. **Availability:** Print; Online.

19695 ■ "Teakwood Capital Raises $40M to Buy Tech Companies" in Dallas Business Journal (Vol. 35, March 2, 2012, No. 25, pp. 1)

Pub: Baltimore Business Journal
Contact: Rhonda Pringle, President
E-mail: rpringle@bizjournals.com

Description: Dallas, Texas-based private equity firm Teakwood Capital LP has raised $40 million following the raising of $25 million as its initial fund in 2006. Teakwood Capital LP targets the purchase of businesses that apply technology to enhance operational efficiencies of their clients, mainly through software deals. The fund raising process of Teakwood Capital LP is also described. **Availability:** Print; Online.

19696 ■ "Today's Business Sale Climate" in Business Owner (Vol. 35, September-October 2011, No. 5, pp. 10)

Description: Despite the weak economy, there is a surplus of individuals wanting to purchase a small business. The Small Business Administration loan guarantees program helps with its loans for purchase/sale of business assistance. **Availability:** Print; Online.

19697 ■ "Unexpected Guest: Caterpillar-Bucyrus Deal Came Out of Nowhere" in Business Journal-Milwaukee (Vol. 28, November 19, 2010, No. 7, pp. A1)

Pub: The Business Journal
Contact: Heather Ladage, President
E-mail: hladage@bizjournals.com

Ed: Rich Rovito. **Description:** Caterpillar has agreed to purchase Bucyrus for $92 per share. The deal, which is subjected to a $200 million termination fee, is expected to close in mid-2011. **Availability:** Print; Online.

19698 ■ "Wenmat Sells Last Fitness Clubs" in Sacramento Business Journal (Vol. 31, June 6, 2014, No. 15, pp. 6)

Pub: American City Business Journals, Inc.
Contact: Mike Olivieri, Executive Vice President

Released: Weekly. **Price:** $4, Introductory 4-week offer(Digital & Print). **Description:** Wenmat Fitness sold all of its health clubs while expanding its presence in Sacramento, California. Fitness Evolution purchased Wenmat's Signature Athletic Club as well as its Incentive Fitness. Meanwhile, California Family Fitness bought two Wenmat locations. **Availability:** Print; Online.

19699 ■ "Where to Find Businesses for Sale" in Small Business Trends (Apr 13, 2021)

URL(s): smallbiztrends.com/2021/03/where-to-buy-a-business.html

Ed: Annie Pilon. **Released:** April 13, 2021. **Description:** Provides information on how and where to find small businesses that are for sale. Includes details on how much money you may need as well as the steps involved in buying an existing business. **Availability:** Online.

TRADE PERIODICALS

19700 ■ *Venture Capital and Private Equity*

URL(s): thomsonreuters.com/en/products-services/financial/venture-capital-and-private-equity.html

Released: Monthly **Price:** $2,395, Individuals. **Description:** Hard news, analysis and data on the North American private equity market. **Availability:** Print; Online.

VIDEO/AUDIO MEDIA

19701 ■ *The How of Business: Danya Shakfeh - Legal Considerations of Buying a Business*
URL(s): www.thehowofbusiness.com/507-danya-shakfeh-legal-considerations-buying-small-business

Ed: Henry Lopez. **Released:** January 29, 2024.
Description: Podcast offers legal considerations when buying a small business, including research, NDAs, and contracts.

19702 ■ *This Is Small Business: How to Buy the Right Business for You*
URL(s): www.smallbusiness.amazon/podcast-episodes/ep-58-how-to-buy-the-right-business-for-you

Ed: Andrea Marquez. **Released:** May 21, 2024.
Description: Podcast explains why you should consider buying a business, breaks down the due diligence, and explores financing options. .

CONSULTANTS

19703 ■ **Business Team (BT)**
1475 S Bascom Ave., Ste. 113
Campbell, CA 95008
Ph: (408)246-1102
Fax: (408)246-2219
Co. E-mail: sanjose@business-team.com
URL: http://www.business-team.com
Contact: Armstrong Wong, Officer
E-mail: armstrong@business-team.com

Description: A business brokerage firm that specializes in merger, acquisition, and divestiture services for privately held, mid-sized companies. The company's value-added services include business valuation, pre-marketing consultation, and exit strategy planning. **Founded:** 1981. **Training:** Business Valuation Enhancing the Value of Your Company.

19704 ■ **Pundmann & Company Inc.**
119 No. 11 Green Dr.
Saint Charles, MO 63303-5073
Contact: William R. Pundmann, Contact
E-mail: will@pundmann.com

Description: Private investment banking firm provides advice to companies on matters concerning corporate financing, venture capital, mergers and acquisitions, the company matches its own risk capital and funds of other investors with companies seeking venture capital and private financing and also manages investment portfolios for clients.

Cash Flow

REFERENCE WORKS

19705 ■ *"4 Cash Flow Challenges Facing Small Business Owners Today"* in *Forbes* (April 21, 2019)
Released: April 21, 2019. **Description:** Discusses the top four factors affecting cash flow issues for small businesses and how to resolve them. **Availability:** Online.

19706 ■ *"5 Cash Management Tactics Small Businesses Use to Become Bigger Businesses"* in *Entrepreneur* (April 23, 2018)
Ed: Lisa Stevens. **Released:** April 23, 2018. **Description:** Discusses how to reach your highest potential as a business owner and how to serve your customers effectively as you maintain positive cash flow. Provides tips to help keep your business financially strong and position your company for success. **Availability:** Online.

19707 ■ *"5 Marketing Missteps That Make Cash Flow and Business Growth Stumble"* in *Entrepreneur* (January 25, 2018)
Ed: Shaun Buck. **Released:** January 25, 2018. **Description:** Discusses the fact that mistakes that many entrepreneurs make are often made with marketing, sales, and business growth and these mistakes are causing cash flow issues. Discusses the success and growth that comes from creating marketing assets and business systems and processes. **Availability:** Online.

19708 ■ *"5 Ways to Get More Cash Flowing Into Your Business"* in *Forbes* (February 24, 2019)
Ed: Elaine Pofeldt. **Released:** February 24, 2019. **Description:** With a majority of small businesses indicating that they have problems with cash flow, surveys indicate that the problem is caused by outstanding receivables. This article provides tips on how small businesses can improve their cash flow. **Availability:** Online.

19709 ■ *"The 5 Worst Cash-Flow Mistakes Small-Business Owners Make"* in *Entrepreneur* (September 25, 2015)
Ed: Jared Hecht. **Released:** September 25, 2015. **Description:** Discusses the fact that studies show as many as 82 percent of startups and small businesses fail due to poor cash-flow management and goes into five of the most common cash-flow problems. **Availability:** Online.

19710 ■ *"6 Ways to Manage Cash Flow for Your Business"* in *NerdWallet* (Jan. 12, 2021)
URL(s): www.nerdwallet.com/article/small-business/business-cash-flow
Ed: Teddy Nykiel. **Released:** January 12, 2021. **Description:** Outlines six strategies for managing small business cash flow. **Availability:** Online.

19711 ■ *"6 Ways to Manage Your Small-Business Cash Flow"* in *NerdWallet* (October 5, 2020)
Ed: Teddy Nykiel. **Released:** October 05, 2020. **Description:** Discusses how maintaining favorable cash flow gives you the capacity to meet your financial obligations and the flexibility to grow with new opportunities. This article details six strategies for managing business cash flow. **Availability:** Online.

19712 ■ *"10 Tips To Help Improve Your Company's Cash Flow"* in *Signature Analytics Blog*
URL(s): signatureanalytics.com/blog/10-tips-to-help-improve-your-companys-cash-flow/
Description: Provides statistics on small business failure as it relates to poor cash flow management and provides ten tips to ensure you are managing your company's cash flow in the most effective way. **Availability:** Online.

19713 ■ *"11 Ways to Better Manage Cash Flow in Business"* in *SCORE.org Blog* (Nov. 5, 2020)
URL(s): www.score.org/blog/11-ways-better-manage-cash-flow-business
Ed: Brett Farmiloe. **Released:** November 05, 2020. **Description:** Gathers tips from 11 small business owners on effective cash flow management. **Availability:** Online.

19714 ■ *Avoiding Business Failure by Improving Cash Flow*
URL(s): smallbusinessbc.ca/article/avoiding-business-failure-improving-cash-flow/
Ed: Nafees Chaudhry. **Description:** Discusses the complexities of small business cash flow and includes eight cash flow strategies that your business can employ to improve cash flow. **Availability:** Online.

19715 ■ *"Cash Flow: The Reason 82% of Small Businesses Fail"* in *Preferred CFO* (June 8, 2020)
URL(s): preferredcfo.com/cash-flow-reason-small-businesses-fail/
Ed: Michael Flint. **Released:** June 08, 2020. **Description:** Explores why the majority of small businesses fail within the first five years and delves into how to know if your small business has a cash flow problem and how to address it. **Availability:** Online.

19716 ■ *"Common Cash Flow Problems Facing Small Businesses and How to Solve Them"* *FreshBooks Blog* (June 2020)
Released: June 2020. **Description:** Discusses the importance of fixing cash flow problems when you start your business as starting off on the wrong foot can be difficult to recover from. This article looks at seven cash flow problems and how small businesses can work to solve them. **Availability:** Online.

19717 ■ *"Former Robinhood Employees Launch Parafin, a Finance Startup for Small Business"* in *The Wall Street Journal* (September 29, 2021)
URL(s): www.wsj.com/articles/former-robinhood-employees-launch-parafin-a-finance-startup-for-small-business-11632913201
Released: September 29, 2021. **Description:** Discusses the new startup, Parafin.

19718 ■ *Here Are the Top 7 Cash Flow Mistakes That Can Cripple Your Small Business*
URL(s): www.zoho.com/books/articles/here-are-the-top-7-cash-flow-mistakes-that-can-cripple-your-small-business.html
Ed: Vidhya Krishnan. **Description:** Discusses common cash flow problems small businesses face and what you can do to save yours from experiencing these problems. **Availability:** Online.

19719 ■ *"How Small Businesses Can Overcome Common Cash Flow Challenges"* in *Williston Herald* (Aug. 27, 2021)
URL(s): www.willistonherald.com/news/business/how-small-businesses-can-overcome-common-cash-flow-challenges/article_151a729a-0756-11ec-9d5e-7ff2b1341f68.html
Released: August 27, 2021. **Description:** Explores the challenges that small businesses face related to balancing money coming in and money going out. **Availability:** Online.

19720 ■ *"How To Manage Cash Flow"* in *Inc.*
URL(s): www.inc.com/encyclopedia/cashflow.html
Description: Gives a rundown on the basics of cash-flow, how you can improve it, and how to manage it. **Availability:** Online.

19721 ■ *"Never Worry About Cash Flow Again Using These 5 Strategies"* in *Entrepreneur* (August 15, 2018)
Ed: Amad Ebrahimi. **Released:** August 15, 2018. **Description:** Shares five tips that have been learned from working with partners and building an online publishing business to ensure that your cash flow stays positive. **Availability:** Online.

19722 ■ *"Struggling for Cash Flow? Strategies for Survival"* in *Business News Daily* (Jan. 21, 2022)
URL(s): www.businessnewsdaily.com/15017-cash-flow-strategies.html
Ed: Skye Schooley. **Released:** January 21, 2022. **Description:** Provides nine survival tips for businesses that are struggling for cash flow. **Availability:** Online.

19723 ■ *"Unique Ways Small Businesses Can Increase Cash Flow"* in *business.com* (Jan. 5, 2022)
URL(s): www.business.com/articles/increase-cash-flow/

Ed: Donna Fuscaldo. **Released:** January 05, 2022. **Description:** Discusses the importance of cash flow for your small business. Includes a list of strategies small business owners can employ to increase cash flow. **Availability:** Online.

19724 ■ *"What Is Cash Flow? Cash Flow Guide for Small Businesses" in Wave Blog (March 4, 2019)*
Released: March 04, 2019. **Description:** A guide to help small business owners curb common missteps and better understand how to keep money moving. Provides the ins and outs of cash flow to help you build a financial plan to keep capital circulating through your business. **Availability:** Online.

VIDEO/AUDIO MEDIA

19725 ■ *The How of Business: Cash Flow Management*
URL(s): www.thehowofbusiness.com/439-cash-flow-management
Ed: Henry Lopez. **Released:** September 12, 2022. **Description:** Podcast explains how to manage and forecast small business cash flow.

19726 ■ *Think Business: Revolutionize Your Cash Flow and Achieve Financial Freedom with Rocky Lalvani*
URL(s): thinktyler.com/podcast_episode/your-cash-flow-rocky-lalvani
Ed: Tyler Martin. **Released:** November 06, 2023. **Description:** Podcast discusses the "Proft First" formula, how to build wealth, and how to set clear business goals.

Compensation

ASSOCIATIONS AND OTHER ORGANIZATIONS

19727 ■ Council on Employee Benefits (CEB)
64 Walker St., Ste. 2
Lenox, MA 01240
Ph: (413)644-6034
Fax: (202)861-6027
Co. E-mail: info@ceb.org
URL: http://www.ceb.org
Contact: Lisa Woods, President
X (Twitter): x.com/FollowCEB

Description: Employers seeking informal exchange of experiences and information on the design, financing, and administration of employee benefit programs, both domestic and international. Provides a medium for the exchange of ideas, information, and statistics; sponsors or conducts research projects on benefits; makes known its views on legislative matters affecting employee benefits. **Founded:** 1946. **Geographic Preference:** National.

19728 ■ Employee Benefit Research Institute (EBRI) - Library
901 D St., SW Ste. 802
Washington, DC 20024
Ph: (202)659-0670
Fax: (202)775-6360
Co. E-mail: info@ebri.org
URL: http://www.ebri.org
Contact: Lori Lucas, Chief Executive Officer

Description: Corporations, consulting firms, banks, insurance companies, unions, and others with an interest in the future of employee benefit programs. Seeks to contribute to the development of effective and responsible public policy in the field of employee benefits through research, publications, educational programs, seminars, and direct communication. Sponsors studies on retirement income, health, disability, and other benefit programs; disseminates study results. **Scope:** A public policy research organization serving as an employee benefits information source on health, welfare and retirement issues. Services include: basic benefit program descriptions, legislation analysis, media coverage and interpretation and long-range planning. Specializes in research on pensions, social security, health care, Medicare, long-term care and flexible benefits. Serves government, academic consumers, consultants, banks, insurance companies, investment managers, law and accounting firms, corporations and individuals. **Founded:** 1978. **Holdings:** Figures not available. **Publications:** Dedicated to providing unbiased, fact-based research on employee benefits. **Training:** Policy Forums, Congressional Briefings. **Awards:** EBRI Lillywhite Award (Annual). **Geographic Preference:** National.

19729 ■ Employers Council on Flexible Compensation (ECFC)
1802 Vernon St. NW, No. 1035
Washington, DC 20009
Ph: (202)659-4300
Fax: (202)618-6060
URL: http://ecfc.org
Contact: Christa Day, Executive Director
E-mail: cday@ecfc.org
Linkedin: www.linkedin.com/company/go-ecfc
X (Twitter): x.com/GoECFC
YouTube: www.youtube.com/channel/UCKeDNB97ZKHywpHFNz7a1Bw

Description: Employers and service providers who have implemented or are interested in flexible compensation plans. Promotes flexible compensation plans including cafeteria plans, health reimbursement arrangements, cash-or-deferred plans and other defined contribution plans. Monitors legislation and represents member's interests before Congress. Lobbies to preserve and simplify the flexible compensation provisions of the Internal Revenue Code. **Founded:** 1979. **Educational Activities:** ECFC Annual Symposium (Annual). **Geographic Preference:** National.

19730 ■ International Foundation of Employee Benefit Plans (IFEBP) - Library
18700 W Bluemound Rd.
Brookfield, WI 53045
Ph: (262)786-6700
Free: 888-334-3327
Co. E-mail: infocenter@ifebp.org
URL: http://www.ifebp.org/home
Contact: Donald D. Crosatto, President
Facebook: www.facebook.com/IFEBP
Linkedin: www.linkedin.com/company/international-foundation-of-employee-benefit-plans
X (Twitter): x.com/ifebp
Instagram: www.instagram.com/international.foundation
YouTube: www.youtube.com/user/IFEBP

Description: Provides sources for employee benefits and compensation information and education, including seminars and conferences, books and an information center, CEBS and Certificate Series. Conducts more than 100 educational programs. Provides Internet job and resume posting service. **Scope:** Employee benefits and compensation. **Founded:** 1954. **Holdings:** Figures not available. **Publications:** Benefits Magazine (Monthly); InfoQuick; Employee Benefits Journal (Quarterly); Benefits & Compensation Digest; Legal-Legislative Reporter (Monthly); Employee Benefits Infosource. **Educational Activities:** Annual Employee Benefits Conference (Annual). **Geographic Preference:** National.

19731 ■ UWC: Strategic Services on Unemployment and Workers' Compensation (UWC)
PO Box 1110
Worthington, OH 43085
Ph: (614)805-2208
Co. E-mail: info@uwcstrategy.org
URL: http://www.uwcstrategy.org
Contact: Douglas J. Holmes, President
E-mail: holmesd@uwcstrategy.org

Description: Serves the business community by promoting Unemployment Insurance and Workers' Compensation programs that provide fair benefits to workers at affordable cost to employers and the community. **Founded:** 1933. **Educational Activities:** Fall Forum for Staff Association Executives; National UI Issues Conference (Annual). **Geographic Preference:** National.

19732 ■ WorldatWork, the Total Rewards Association - Library
14040 N Northsight Blvd.
Scottsdale, AZ 85260
Ph: (480)951-9191
Free: 877-951-9191
Co. E-mail: customerexperience@worldatwork.org
URL: http://worldatwork.org
Contact: Scott Cawood, President
Facebook: www.facebook.com/WorldatWorkAssociation
Linkedin: www.linkedin.com/company/worldatwork
X (Twitter): x.com/WorldatWork
Instagram: www.instagram.com/worldatwork
YouTube: www.youtube.com/user/WorldatWorkTV

Description: Dedicated to knowledge leadership in compensation, benefits and total rewards, focusing on disciplines associated with attracting, retaining and motivating employees. **Scope:** Specializes in the design, implementation and management of employee compensation, benefits and total rewards programs. **Services:** Library access to members only. **Holdings:** Books; publications; periodicals. **Publications:** "Telework A Critical Component of Your Total Rewards Strategy," World at Work Press. **Training:** Consumerism in Practice: It's More than Account-Based Plans, It's Changing Behaviors; Competitive Market Pay: Pricing Critical Skills and Unique Positions; How-to: Employee Benefits Basics; Sales Compensation Design: Five Action Steps to Success; Regulatory Environments for Compensation Programs; Job Analysis, Documentation and Evaluation. **Educational Activities:** WorldatWork Conferences (Annual). **Geographic Preference:** Multinational. **Special Services:** WorldatWork®; workspan®; WorldatWork Society of Certified Professionals®; Alliance for Work-Life Progress®.

REFERENCE WORKS

19733 ■ "CEOs Keep Bringing Home the Perks" in Baltimore Business Journal (Vol. 30, May 18, 2012, No. 2, pp. 1)
Pub: American City Business Journals, Inc.
Contact: Mike Olivieri, Executive Vice President

Ed: Gary Haber. **Description:** According to the annual proxy statement of Baltimore-based Stanley Black & Decker, executive chairman Nolan D. Archibald received a $12.3 million compensation package in 2011. According to the company, Archibald's perks are part of his employment agreement which was duly approved by the shareholders during the merger of Stanley Works and Black & Decker. **Availability:** Print; Online.

19734 ■ "CEOs With Headsets" in Harvard Business Review (Vol. 88, September 2010, No. 9, pp. 21)
Pub: Harvard Business Publishing
Contact: Diane Belcher, Managing Director

Ed: Andrew Zimbalist. Price: $6, PDF. Description: Placing a salary cap on college coaches' compensation would not significantly affect coaching quality or an institution's ability to obtain talent. A salary growth rate comparison between coaches, university presidents, and full professors for the period 1986 to 2007 is also presented. Availability: Online; PDF.

19735 ■ "Discipline In Your Business" in South Florida Business Journal (Vol. 34, June 6, 2014, No. 46, pp. 10)
Pub: American City Business Journals, Inc.
Contact: Mike Olivieri, Executive Vice President

Released: Weekly. Price: $8, introductory 4-week offer(Digital only). Description: Ways a business can maintain a disciplined response to market conditions and achieve success are discussed. Organizations are advised to set clear goals, communicate these goals, and establish clear lines of accountability. The importance of compensation to motivate staff is also explained. Availability: Print; Online.

19736 ■ "The Entrepreneur Salary: How Much Should You Pay Yourself?" in NerdWallet (Oct. 30, 2020)
URL(s): www.nerdwallet.com/article/small-business/entrepreneur-salary

Ed: Meredith Wood. Released: October 30, 2020. Description: Explores how paying yourself an entrepreneur salary can help you and your business grow. Includes 5 steps to deciphering how to pay yourself. Availability: Online.

19737 ■ "Executive Compensation: Both Eyes on the Prize" in Canadian Business (Vol. 83, September 14, 2010, No. 15, pp. 42)
Pub: Rogers Media Inc.
Contact: Neil Spivak, Chief Executive Officer

Ed: Jacqueline Nelson. Description: North American executive compensation has fundamentally shifted partly due to pressure from the US government and recent adjustments in the way CEO pay packages are structured. The changes have also become common practice in Canada and helped in scrutinizing the executive pay. Availability: Online.

19738 ■ "Fairness First" in Canadian Business (Vol. 80, April 23, 2007, No. 9, pp. 45)
Description: The need for the fair treatment of employees from the perspective of employee compensation is discussed. Availability: Online.

19739 ■ "Hello, and Goodbye" in Entrepreneur (June 2014)
Released: December 19, 2015. Description: Companies must implement strategies to ensure the creation of an ethical workplace. They must be able to deal with clients that experience problems and try to bully their counterparts as a result. Executive search firms must be responsible for compensating new executive hires by helping them find new jobs. Businesses must communicate to their employees about their importance as a way of making them feel appreciated and, thus, contribute to ethical behavior. Availability: Online.

19740 ■ "Highest-Paid Public Company CEO" in San Antonio Business Journal (Vol. 28, June 27, 2014, No. 20, pp. 6)
Pub: American City Business Journals, Inc.
Contact: Mike Olivieri, Executive Vice President

Description: Rankings of the highest paid public company CEOs in the San Antonio, Texas area are presented. Rankings are based on the total compensation for the 2013 fiscal year. Availability: Print; Online.

19741 ■ "Implementing a Small Business Compensation Structure" in Salary.com Blog (May 1, 2018)
URL(s): www.salary.com/blog/implementing-a-small-business-pay-structure/

Released: May 01, 2018. Description: Discusses different types of pay structures and how to create a compensation structure for your small business employees. Availability: Online.

19742 ■ "Importance of Compensation in the Workplace" in Chron (March 1, 2019)
URL(s): smallbusiness.chron.com/importance-compensation-workplace-38470.html

Ed: Kimberlee Leonard. Released: March 01, 2019. Description: Discusses the variety of factors to consider when formulating your compensation and benefits package for your small business employees. Availability: Online.

19743 ■ "Is It Ever OK to Break a Promise? A Student Must Decide Whether to Leave the Company that Sponsored His MBA for a Dream Job" in Harvard Business Review (Vol. 92, September 2014, No. 9, pp. 119)
Pub: Harvard Business Publishing
Contact: Diane Belcher, Managing Director

Price: $8.95. Description: A fictitious decision making scenario is presented, with contributors providing advice. One notes that change, requiring people to adapt and, in some cases, alter contracts. Another states that the original contract should be honored and that other opportunities are likely to present themselves to the student considering leaving the firm that sponsored his MBA. Availability: Online; PDF.

19744 ■ "Is Raising CPP Premiums a Good Idea?" in Canadian Business (Vol. 83, July 20, 2010, No. 11-12, pp. 37)
Description: Big labor is pushing for an increase in Canada Pension Plan premiums but pension consultants believe this system is not broken and that the government needs to focus on addressing the low rate of personal retirement savings. If the premiums go up, even those with high savings will be forced to pay more and it could block other plans that really address the real issue. Availability: Print; Online.

19745 ■ "It's Good To Be a CEO: Top Execs Pull Millions In Raises for 2013" in Atlanta Business Chronicle (June 20, 2014, pp. 22A)
Pub: American City Business Journals, Inc.
Contact: Mike Olivieri, Executive Vice President

Description: Discussion regarding the highest paid CEOs in Georgia in 2013, with an average of 8.8 percent increase from 2012. The largest increase went to Jeffrey C. Sprecher, chairman and CEO of Intercontinental Exchange Inc., followed by John F. Brock, chairman and CEO of Coca-Cola Enterprises Inc. Availability: Print; Online.

19746 ■ "Life's Work: Interview with Alain Ducasse" in Harvard Business Review (Vol. 92, May 2014, No. 5, pp. 136)
Pub: Harvard Business Press
Contact: Gabriela Allmi, Regional Manager
E-mail: gabriela.allmi@hbsp.harvard.edu

Price: $8.95. Description: Alain Ducasse believes supervision is secondary to shared experience, and emphasizes the importance of communicating with employees to engage them and enable them to perform well. Job satisfaction is dependent on individual growth, appropriate compensation, and harmony. Availability: PDF; Online.

19747 ■ "Mismanaging Pay and Performance" in Business Strategy Review (Vol. 21, Summer 2010, No. 2, pp. 54)
Ed: Rupert Merson. Released: June 24, 2010. Description: Understanding the relationship between performance measurement and desired behaviors is an important element of a company's talent management. Availability: Print; PDF; Online.

19748 ■ "Notes on Current Labor Statistics" in Montly Labor Review (Vol. 133, September 2010, No. 9, pp. 75)
Pub: U.S. Department of Labor Bureau of Labor Statistics
Contact: Amrit Kohli, Director
E-mail: kohli.amrit@bls.gov

Description: Principal statistics and calculated by the Bureau of Labor Statistics are presented. The series includes statistics on labor force; employment; unemployment; labor compensation; consumer, producer, and international prices; productivity; international comparisons; and injury and illness statistics. Availability: Online; PDF.

19749 ■ "On the Money" in San Antonio Business Journal (Vol. 28, June 27, 2014, No. 20, pp. 4)
Description: The total compensation for the top 18 highest paid public company CEOs in San Antonio, Texas has increased 11 percent in the 2013 fiscal year to $74.8 million compared to 2012 fiscal year. The average total CEO compensation in the city was $4.15 million, an 11 percent increase from the 2013 list. The trend in the 2014 highest paid CEOs list is discussed. Availability: Print; Online.

19750 ■ "Pay Fell for Many Baltimore Execs in '09" in Baltimore Business Journal (Vol. 28, July 2, 2010, No. 8, pp. 1)
Pub: Baltimore Business Journal
Contact: Rhonda Pringle, President
E-mail: rpringle@bizjournals.com

Ed: Gary Haber. Description: Compensation for the 100 highest-paid executives in the Baltimore, Maryland area decreased in 2009, compared with 2008. At least $1 million were received by 59 out of 100 executives in 2009, while 75 earned the said amount in 2008. Factors that contributed to the executives' decisions to take pay cuts are discussed. Availability: Print.

19751 ■ "Raise vs. Bonus for Your Small Business Employees" in Investopedia (July 27, 2020)
URL(s): www.investopedia.com/articles/personal-finance/092915/raise-vs-bonus-your-small-business-employees.asp

Ed: James McWhinney. Released: July 27, 2020. Description: Explores how to evaluate the pros and cons of giving raises versus bonuses to your small business employees. Availability: Online.

19752 ■ "Record Share of U.S. Small Businesses Raised Wages In December" in Bloomberg.com (Jan. 6, 2022)
URL(s): www.bloomberg.com/news/articles/2022-01-06/record-share-of-u-s-small-businesses-raised-wages-in-december

Ed: Reade Pickert. Released: January 06, 2022. Description: Discusses the state of small business economics and increased wages for small business employees. Availability: Online.

19753 ■ "Screening-Oriented Recruitment Messages: Antecedents and Relationships with Applicant Pool Quality" in Human Resource Management (Vol. 51,May- June 2012, No. 3, pp. 343-360)
Pub: John Wiley & Sons, Inc.
Contact: Christina Van Tassell, Executive Vice President Chief Financial Officer

Ed: Brian R. Dineen, Ian O. Williamson. Released: May 25, 2012. Description: Factors associated with the use of screening-oriented messages for recruitment are investigated. Results indicate that labor supply perceptions, the reputation of recruiting firms and quality-based compensation incentives are associated with the use of screening-oriented messages, which are associated with the quality of the applicant pool. Availability: Print; PDF; Online.

19754 ■ Small Business Employee Compensation Packages: Choosing What's Right for You
URL(s): pacesferrywealth.com/small-business-employee-compensation-packages-choosing-whats-right-for-you/

Ed: Zachary Morris. **Released:** September 13, 2021. **Description:** Discusses things to consider when developing employee compensation packages for your small business employees. **Availability:** Online.

19755 ■ *This Is How Much to Pay Yourself If You Run Your Own Business*
URL(s): www.cnbc.com/2020/02/28/this-is-how-much-to-pay-yourself-as-a-business-owner.html
Ed: Bryan Borzykowski. **Released:** February 29, 2020. **Description:** Explores the business of how to pay yourself when you are a small business owner, how to determine your salary, and when to give yourself a raise. **Availability:** Online.

19756 ■ *"Top 6 Questions about Compensation from Small Businesses and High Growth Companies" in PayScale (May 1, 2018)*
URL(s): www.payscale.com/compensation-trends/small-business-compensation/
Ed: Rita Patterson. **Released:** May 01, 2018. **Description:** Shares answers to six frequently asked questions about compensation specific to small businesses with growing workforces. **Availability:** Online.

19757 ■ *"A Well-Crafted Employee Handbook Can Make Work Run More Smoothly" in Idaho Business Review (September 17, 2014)*
Pub: BridgeTower Media
Contact: Adam Reinebach, President
Description: An employee handbook will provide a complaint process, provide company management flexibility and clarity and keep a company out of legal problems. Training, compensation, benefits, security, health, performance appraisals, and safety issues must be covered. Human resource managers and other mangers should cover basics to help communicate with workers.

19758 ■ *"What Are Employee Compensation Packages?" in business.com (Feb. 3, 2022)*
URL(s): www.business.com/articles/types-of-employee-compensation/
Ed: Skye Schooley. **Released:** February 03, 2022. **Description:** The types of compensation packages you offer to your employees can have a big impact on your business. This article presents the five primary types of compensation packages to consider. **Availability:** Online.

19759 ■ *"What's the Ticket to a Higher-Paying Corporate Position?" in Orlando Business Journal (Vol. 29, September 14, 2012, No. 13, pp. 1)*
Pub: Baltimore Business Journal
Contact: Rhonda Pringle, President
E-mail: rpringle@bizjournals.com
Description: Advice on how to land higher-paying executive jobs in the US is presented. Understanding organization politics as well as compensation is encouraged. Employment alternatives for executives are also given. **Availability:** Print; Online.

19760 ■ *"Why Does Firm Reputation In Human Resource Policies Influence College Students? The Mechanisms Underlying Job Pursuit Intentions" in Human Resource Management (Vol. 51, January-February 2012, No. 1, pp. 121-142)*
Pub: John Wiley & Sons, Inc.
Contact: Christina Van Tassell, Executive Vice President Chief Financial Officer
Ed: Julie Holliday Wayne, Wendy J. Casper. **Released:** January 26, 2012. **Description:** The effects of reputational information about human resource practices of companies on college students seeking employment are examined. The reputation of firms in compensation, work-family, and diversity efforts are found to increase intentions to pursue employment in these firms. **Availability:** Print; PDF; Online.

19761 ■ *"Winners Dream: A Journey from Corner Store to Corner Office"*
Pub: Simon & Schuster Adult Publishing Group
Contact: Jonathan Karp, President
Released: October 14, 2014. **Price:** $28.99, hardcover, plus $2.24 shipping charges. **Description:** Bill McDermott, CEO of the world's largest business software company, SAP, profiles his career. He discusses his career moves, sales strategies, employee incentives to create high performance teams, and the competitive advantages of optimism and hard work. The entrepreneur offers a blueprint for success and the knowledge that the real dream is the journey, not the preconceived destination. **Availability:** E-book; Print; Download; Audio.

VIDEO/AUDIO MEDIA

19762 ■ *The How of Business: Variable Compensation Plans*
URL(s): www.thehowofbusiness.com/445-variable-compensation-plans
Ed: Henry Lopez. **Released:** November 07, 2022. **Description:** Podcast discusses variable compensation plans for small businesses.

19763 ■ *Nurture Small Business: Fostering Pay Equity at Work*
URL(s): nurturesmallbusiness.buzzsprout.com/900445/13717143-fostering-pay-equity-at-work
Ed: Denise Cagan. **Released:** October 16, 2023. **Description:** Podcast discusses the importance of detaching performance management from compensation.

CONSULTANTS

19764 ■ Nyhart
FuturePlan
750 Castle Creek Pkwy., Ste. 245
Indianapolis, IN 46250
Ph: (817)563-3400
Free: 866-831-3526
Fax: (817)563-3445
URL: http://www.futureplan.com/transition/401k-plus
Contact: Carter Angell, Chief Executive Officer
E-mail: carter.angell@nyhart.com
Description: An employee-owned national actuarial and retirement firm. **Founded:** 1943.

Competition

START-UP INFORMATION

19765 ■ *Small Business Survival Guide*
Released: First edition. **Description:** Small business expert provides strategies to start a company and survive in the 21st Century. He shows small business owners how to succeed despite challenges that can defeat any firm. His advice covers suppliers; customers and contractors; competitors and creditors; spouses, family and friends; as well as the ways lawyers, accountants and other can steal an entrepreneur's success. Ennico also describes how startups can comply with local regulations. **Availability:** E-book; Print.

19766 ■ *"Zero to One: Notes on Startups, or How to Build the Future"*
Released: September 16, 2014. **Price:** $28, hardcover; $14.99, e-book; $30, CD; $15, audiobook download. **Description:** Entrepreneur and investor, Peter Thiel, covers new frontiers and new inventions yet to be discovered. Progress can be achieved in more industries than information technology, but thinking for one's self is critical to any entrepreneur in order to start and build a new venture. Tomorrow's leaders will avoid competition and create a unique business that will stand on its own. **Availability:** E-book; Print; Download; Audio.

REFERENCE WORKS

19767 ■ *"3Par: Storing Up Value" in Barron's (Vol. 90, August 30, 2010, No. 35, pp. 30)*
Pub: Barron's Editorial & Corporate Headquarters
Ed: Mark Veverka. **Description:** Dell and Hewlett Packard are both bidding for data storage company 3Par. The acquisition would help Dell and Hewlett Packard provide customers with a one-stop shop as customers move to a private cloud in the Internet. **Availability:** Online.

19768 ■ *"5 Effective Ways to Beat Your Competition" in business.com (Jan. 31, 2022)*
URL(s): www.business.com/articles/5-ways-to-beat-competition/
Ed: Max Freedman. **Released:** January 31, 2022. **Description:** Provides five simple, yet powerful ways to beat your competition. **Availability:** Online.

19769 ■ *"10 Competitive Advantages Small Businesses Have Over Big Companies" in ZenBusiness (Dec. 6, 2021)*
URL(s): www.zenbusiness.com/blog/10-competitive-advantages-small-businesses-have-over-big-companies/
Released: December 06, 2021. **Description:** Provides a list and details on 10 competitive advantages that small businesses can utilize over large companies. **Availability:** Online.

19770 ■ *"12 Simple (Yet Effective!) Ways Small Businesses Can Compete with the Big Brands" in LOCALiQ Blog (Oct. 7, 2020)*
URL(s): localiq.com/blog/ways-small-businesses-can-compete-with-big-businesses/
Ed: Stephanie Heitman. **Released:** October 07, 2020. **Description:** Provides 12 small business marketing tips to help you get noticed and win when you're competing with a household name brand. **Availability:** Online.

19771 ■ *"113D Filings: Investors Report to the SEC" in Barron's (Vol. 88, March 24, 2008, No. 12, pp. M13)*
Pub: Dow Jones & Company Inc.
Contact: Almar Latour, Chief Executive Officer
Released: April 02, 2016. **Description:** HealthCor Management called as problematic the plan of Magellan Health Services to use its high cash balances for acquisitions. Carlson Capital discussed with Energy Partners possible changes in the latter's board. Investor Carl Icahn suggested that Enzon Pharmaceuticals consider selling itself or divest some of its assets. **Availability:** Print; Online.

19772 ■ *"The 490 Made Chevy a Bargain Player" in Automotive News (Vol. 86, October 31, 2011, No. 6488, pp. S22)*
Pub: Crain Communications Inc.
Contact: Barry Asin, President
Ed: David Phillips. **Description:** The first Chevrolet with the 490 engine was sold in 1913, but it was too expensive for masses. In 1914 the carmaker launched a lower-priced H-series of cars competitively priced. Nameplates such as Corvette, Bel Air, Camaro and Silverado have defined Chevrolet through the years. **Availability:** Online.

19773 ■ *"ABC Supply Company Finally Finds Idaho" in Idaho Business Review (September 17, 2014)*
Pub: BridgeTower Media
Contact: Adam Reinebach, President
Description: The nation's largest wholesale distributor, ABC Supply Company, has entered a store in Idaho. The roofing supply firm has now has stores in 48 states. Franklin Lumber Supply, a home supply chain will be ABCs its major competitor in the area.

19774 ■ *"The Advantage: Why Organizational Health Trumps Everything Else in Business (J-B Lencioni Series)"*
Pub: Jossey-Bass
Released: February 01, 2012. **Price:** $28.95, hardcover. **Description:** A comprehensive examination of the unique advantage organizational health provides any small business and sets them apart from their competition. A healthy organization is whole, consistent and complete, is free of politics and confusion, and provides an environment where star performers want to stay. **Availability:** E-book; Print.

19775 ■ *"The AHA Moment" in Hispanic Business (December 2010)*
Description: An interview with Gisela Girard on how competitive market conditions push buttons. Girard stepped down from her 18-month position as chairwoman the Association of Hispanic Advertising Agencies. She has more than 20 years of experience in advertising and research marketing. **Availability:** Print; Online.

19776 ■ *"All-Star Execs: Top CEO: Gordon Nixon" in Canadian Business (Vol. 80, November 24, 2008, No. 22, pp. 9)*
Pub: Rogers Media Inc.
Contact: Neil Spivak, Chief Executive Officer
Ed: Jeff Sanford. **Description:** Royal Bank of Canada (RBC) CEO, Gordon Nixon, believes the Canadian financial services segment is heavily regulated. Nixon also feels that it has become difficult for local banks to enter the market since foreign banks can easily come in and compete with them. His views on RBC's success are provided. **Availability:** Print; Online.

19777 ■ *"American Chemistry Council Launches Flagship Blog" in Ecology, Environment & Conservation Business (October 29, 2011, pp. 5)*
Pub: PR Newswire Association LLC.
Description: American Chemistry Council (ACC) launched its blog, American Chemistry Matters, where interactive space allows bloggers to respond to news coverage and to discuss policy issues and their impact on innovation, competitiveness, job creation and safety. **Availability:** Online.

19778 ■ *"Amistee Air Duct Acquires Ducts R Us, Looks at 2nd Competitor" in Crain's Detroit Business (Vol. 35, September 1, 2014, No. 35, pp. 5)*
Pub: Crain Communications Inc.
Contact: Barry Asin, President
Description: Details of the Novi-based Amistee Air Duct Cleaning & Insulation firm's acquisition of their competitor Ducts R Us Air Duct Cleaning of Clinton Township, Michigan. Co-owners of Amistee revealed the plan to acquire another competitor in Southeast Michigan. Details of the deal are included. **Availability:** Online.

19779 ■ *"The Anatomy of a High Potential" in Business Strategy Review (Vol. 21, Autumn 2010, No. 3, pp. 52)*
Ed: Doug Ready, Jay Conger, Linda Hill, Emily Stecker. **Released:** September 22, 2010. **Description:** Companies have long been interested in identifying high potential employees, but few firms know how to convert top talent into game changers, or people who can shape the future of the business. The authors have found the 'x factors' that can make a high-potential list into a strong competitive advantage. **Availability:** Print; Electronic publishing; PDF; Online.

19780 ■ *"As Technology Changes, So Must African American Business" in Black Enterprise (Vol. 41, August 2010, No. 1, pp. 61)*
Pub: Earl G. Graves Ltd.
Contact: Earl Graves, Jr., President

Ed: Sonya A. Donaldson. **Description:** Social media is essential to compete in today's business environment, especially for African American firms. **Availability:** Online.

19781 ■ *"At the Drugstore, the Nurse Will See You Now"* in Globe & Mail (April 13, 2007, pp. B1)

Ed: Marina Strauss. **Description:** The appointment of several health professionals including nurse, podiatrists, etc. by Rexall Co. at its drugstores to face competition from rivals, is discussed. **Availability:** Online.

19782 ■ *"Bank of America Fights To Keep Top Spot in Mobile Banking"* in Charlotte Business Journal (Vol. 27, June 15, 2012, No. 13, pp. 1)

Pub: American City Business Journals, Inc.
Contact: Mike Olivieri, Executive Vice President
Released: Weekly. **Price:** $20, Introductory 12-week offer(Digital & Print). **Description:** Bank of America has been fighting to maintain its lead in mobile banking services. Financial institutions, payment processors and e-commerce firms have started offering mobile banking services. **Availability:** Print; Online.

19783 ■ *Be a Brilliant Business Writer: Write Well, Write Fast, and Whip the Competition*

Released: October 05, 2010. **Price:** $14.99, paperback; $5.99. **Description:** Tools for mastering the art of persuasive writing in every document created, from email and client letters to reports and presentations, this book will help any writer convey their message with clarity and power, increase productivity by reducing rewrites, and provide the correct tone for navigating office politics. **Availability:** E-book; Print.

19784 ■ *"Birmingham's Turf War"* in Birmingham Business Journal (Vol. 31, January 24, 2014, No. 4, pp. 4)

Pub: American City Business Journals, Inc.
Contact: Mike Olivieri, Executive Vice President
Description: Metropolitan Birmingham, Alabama area incentive battles have been a mainstay for years and smaller cities were forced to compete against cities with larger cash reserves. The fight often means paying up to protect their turf and tax revenue. The rising trend among local municipalities to use incentives to lure companies is discussed. **Availability:** Print; Online.

19785 ■ *"BK Menu Gives Casual Dining Reason to Worry"* in Advertising Age (Vol. 79, November 17, 2008, No. 43, pp. 12)

Pub: Crain Communications, Inc.
Contact: Jessica Botos, Manager, Marketing
E-mail: jessica.botos@crainsnewyork.com
Ed: Emily Bryson York. **Description:** Burger King is beginning to compete with such casual dining restaurants as Applebees and the Cheesecake Factory with new premium menu items, including thicker burgers and ribs; statistical data regarding the casual dining segment which continues to fall and Burger King, whose sales continue to rise is included. **Availability:** Online.

19786 ■ *"BlackBerry 10 Unlikely to Save RIM. RIM Has Few Options. Staying the Course Isn't One of Them"* in Canadian Business (Vol. 85, July 16, 2012, No. 11-12, pp. 12)

Ed: Joe Castaldo. **Description:** Research in Motion (RIM) plans to launch a new line of Blackberry 10 Smartphones in 2012 as part of a strategy to stay in business despite expected operating loss in the first quarter and strong competition. Other options for RIM include a sale, opening its network to offer added security and data compression services, or reinventing itself as a niche handset provider. **Availability:** Print; Online.

19787 ■ *"Bombardier Deja Vu"* in Canadian Business (Vol. 83, August 17, 2010, No. 13-14, pp. 28)

Pub: Rogers Media Inc.
Contact: Neil Spivak, Chief Executive Officer
Ed: Laura Cameron. **Description:** Foreign competitors have accused the Quebec government and the Societe de transport de Montreal of giving Bombardier preferential treatment when it bids for contract to replace Montreal metro's rail cars. Bombardier was in a similar situation in 1974 when it won the contract to build the metro's second generation rail cars. **Availability:** Online.

19788 ■ *"Breaking from Tradition Techstyle"* in Providence Business News (Vol. 28, March 17, 2014, No. 50, pp. 1)

Pub: American City Business Journals, Inc.
Contact: Mike Olivieri, Executive Vice President
Released: March 15, 2014. **Description:** Providence, Rhode Island's Techstyle Haus is being constructed by a group of students from Brown University. The textile house features a flexible exterior that uses high-performance materials and solar cells. Techstyle Haus is one of two entries from the U.S. competing in the Solar Decathlon Europe 2014. **Availability:** Print; Online.

19789 ■ *"Builders Aim to Cut Costs: Pushing Changes to Regain Share of Residential Market; Seek Council's Help"* in Crain's New York Business

Pub: Crain Communications, Inc.
Contact: Jessica Botos, Manager, Marketing
E-mail: jessica.botos@crainsnewyork.com
Ed: Erik Engquist. **Description:** Union contractors and workers are worried about a decline in their market share for housing so they intend to ask the City Council to impose new safety and benefit standards on all contractors to avoid being undercut by nonunion competitors. **Availability:** Print; Online.

19790 ■ *Business Warrior: Strategy for Entrepreneurs*

Price: $9.99. **Description:** Advice to help entrepreneurs understand competitive strategies in order to succeed, focusing on sales, marketing, and personnel management. **Availability:** Print; Download; PDF.

19791 ■ *"Business Without Borders: All For One, None for All?"* in Canadian Business (Vol. 83, October 12, 2010, No. 17, pp. 60)

Pub: Rogers Media Inc.
Contact: Neil Spivak, Chief Executive Officer
Ed: Michael McCullogh. **Description:** The effect of the growth of Canada's overseas provincial trade offices on Canadian trade is discussed. Economic development commissions in the country have devised a single 'Consider Canada' campaign to pitch foreign investors. It is hoped that large cities will gain from banding together rather than competing against one another. **Availability:** Print; Online.

19792 ■ *"Capital Position: M&I Acquisition Opens the Door for Rivals to Gain Market Share"* in Business Journal-Milwaukee (Vol. 28, December 24, 2010, No. 12, pp. A1)

Pub: The Business Journal
Contact: Heather Ladage, President
E-mail: hladage@bizjournals.com
Ed: Rich Kirchen. **Description:** Canada-based BMO Financial Group has purchased Marshall and Isley Corporation (M and I), which dominated lending among Wisconsin businesses for decades. The sale of M and I will enable other banks to recruit M and I's customers but BMO Financial remains a stronger competitor since it possesses a more potent capital position. **Availability:** Print; Online.

19793 ■ *"Casinos In Pitch Battle"* in Philadelphia Business Journal (Vol. 28, July 20, 2012, No. 23, pp. 1)

Pub: Baltimore Business Journal
Contact: Rhonda Pringle, President
E-mail: rpringle@bizjournals.com
Description: The extent to which casinos in Philadelphia, Pennsylvania have invested in marketing and rebranding effortsin the Philadelphia-Atlantic City markets is explored. These efforts are part of the goal of the casinos to compete for customers considering that casinos contribute about $6 billion in taxes to Pennsylvania. Statistics pertaining to casinos and their advertising expenditures are presented. **Availability:** Print; Online.

19794 ■ *"Challenges Await Quad in Going Public"* in Milwaukee Business Journal (Vol. 27, January 29, 2010, No. 18, pp. A1)

Pub: The Business Journal
Contact: Heather Ladage, President
E-mail: hladage@bizjournals.com
Ed: Rich Rovito. **Description:** Sussex, Wisconsin-based Quad/Graphics Inc.'s impending acquisition of rival Canadian World Color Press Inc. will transform it into a publicly held entity for the first time. Quad has operated as a private company for nearly 40 years and will need to adjust to changes, such as the way management shares information with Quad/Graphics' employees. Details of the merger are included. **Availability:** Print; Online.

19795 ■ *"Characteristics of Great Salespeople"* in Agency Sales Magazine (Vol. 39, November 2009, No. 10, pp. 40)

Description: Tips for managers in order to maximize the performance of their sales personnel are presented through several vignettes. Using performance based commission that rewards success, having business systems that support sales activity, and having an organizational culture that embraces sales as a competitive edge are some suggestions. **Availability:** Online.

19796 ■ *"Choosing the United States: In Contests to Attract High-Value Business Activities, the U.S. Is Losing out More than It Should"* in Harvard Business Review (Vol. 90, March 2012, No. 3, pp. 80)

Pub: Harvard Business Review Press
Contact: Moderna V. Pfizer, Contact
Ed: Jan W. Rivkin, Michael E. Porter. **Price:** $8.95. **Description:** Weaknesses in the US business environment have contributed to decisions to outsource work, or have influenced foreign-firm decisions not to locate bases in US. This in turn has compromised US competitiveness. However, signs are that managers are reevaluating outsourcing and are beginning to bring business back to the US. **Availability:** Online; PDF.

19797 ■ *"Cincinnati Business Committee's Tom Williams: Future is Now"* in Business Courier (Vol. 27, August 13, 2010, No. 15, pp. 1)

Pub: Business Courier
Ed: Lucy May. **Description:** Tom Williams, chairman of the Cincinnati Business Committee (CBC), maintains that politicians and business leaders must cooperate to ensure the competitiveness of the city for the 21st Century. Under Williams' leadership, the CBC has put emphasis on initiatives related to government efficiency, economic development, and public education. Williams' views on a proposed inland port are given. **Availability:** Print; Online.

19798 ■ *"Citadel Hires Three Lehman Execs"* in Chicago Tribune (October 2, 2008)

Description: Citadel Investment Group LLC, Chicago hedge-fund operator, has hired three former senior executives of bankrupt investment banker Lehman Brothers Holding Inc. Citadel believes that the company's hiring spree will help them to further expand the firm's capabilities in the global fixed income business. **Availability:** Online.

19799 ■ *"Clash of the Titans"* in Canadian Business (Vol. 80, March 12, 2007, No. 6, pp. 27)

Description: The frequent allegations of Google Inc. and Microsoft Corp. against each other over copyright and other legal issues, with a view to taking away other's market share, is discussed. **Availability:** Print; Online.

19800 ■ *"Clash of the Titans"* in San Francisco Business Times (Vol. 28, February 7, 2014, No. 29, pp. 4)

Pub: American City Business Journals, Inc.
Contact: Mike Olivieri, Executive Vice President

Released: September 01, 2017. **Description:** University of California, San Francisco (UCSF) Medical Center and Stanford Hospital and Clinics have been competing for dominance in San Francisco Bay Area's health care. Both medical centers are competing to affiliate with more doctors, gain more patients, and accomplish more fundraising. Ways the UCSF and Stanford plan to pursue their expansion and integration are also discussed. **Availability:** Print; Online.

19801 ■ *"Clearwire Struggling, Banks on Deals with Competitors"* in *Puget Sound Business Journal (Vol. 33, August 24, 2012, No. 18, pp. 1)*
Pub: Baltimore Business Journal
Contact: Rhonda Pringle, President
E-mail: rpringle@bizjournals.com
Ed: Emily Parkhurst, Alyson Raletz. **Description:** Clearwire Corporation's chief executive, Erik Prusch, is planning to lease the wireless spectrum of the company to major mobile providers that run out of their own supply. At issue is whether the Bellevue, Washington-based telecommunication company can manage its $4 billion debt and maximize the value of its technology while managing its partners all at the same time. **Availability:** Print; Online.

19802 ■ *"Clicks Vs. Bricks"* in *Birmingham Business Journal (Vol. 31, April 25, 2014, No. 17, pp. 4)*
Pub: American City Business Journals, Inc.
Contact: Mike Olivieri, Executive Vice President
Released: May 22, 2018. **Description:** Birmingham, Alabama's retail industry has been evolving as investment to brick-and-mortar stores by mall and shopping center owners double. The hope is that the social shopping experience, economic recovery, and Fair Marketplace legislation for an online sales tax will make co-existence with Internet stores more viable. The survival and expansion of retail are discussed. **Availability:** Print; Online.

19803 ■ *"Closures Pop Cork on Wine Bar Sector Consolidation"* in *Houston Business Journal (Vol. 40, January 22, 2010, No. 37, pp. A2)*
Pub: Houston Business Journal
Contact: Bob Charlet, President
E-mail: bcharlet@bizjournals.com
Ed: Allison Wollam. **Description:** Wine bar market in Houston, Texas is in the midst of a major shift and heads toward further consolidation due to the closure of pioneering wine bars that opened in the past decade. The Corkscrew owner, Andrew Adams, has blamed the creation of competitive establishments to the closure which helped wear out his concept. **Availability:** Print; Online.

19804 ■ *"Cloudy Future for VMware?"* in *Barron's (Vol. 90, September 13, 2010, No. 37, pp. 21)*
Pub: Barron's Editorial & Corporate Headquarters
Ed: Jonathan R. Laing. **Description:** VMWare dominated the virtualization market for years, but it may be ending as it faces more competition from rivals that offer cloud computing services. The company's stocks are also expensive and are vulnerable to the smallest mishap. **Availability:** Online.

19805 ■ *"Co-Working a Hit in Seattle Market"* in *Puget Sound Business Journal (Vol. 34, March 14, 2014, No. 48, pp. 8)*
Pub: American City Business Journals, Inc.
Contact: Mike Olivieri, Executive Vice President
Released: Weekly. **Price:** $4, introductory 4-week offer(Digital & Print). **Description:** Companies in Seattle, Washington are learning about the new trend in co-working. The city's co-working industry continues to grow, which is why competitors have established a trade group. Co-working is the process of sharing office space within business centers. Regus, which manages 21 business centers in the city, plans to introduce private booths called WorkBoxes. **Availability:** Print; Online.

19806 ■ *"Competing on Talent Analytics"* in *Harvard Business Review (Vol. 88, October 2010, No. 10, pp. 52)*
Pub: Harvard Business Publishing
Contact: Diane Belcher, Managing Director
Ed: Thomas H. Davenport, Jeanne Harris, Jeremy Shapiro. **Price:** $8.95, PDF. **Description:** Six ways to use talent analytics to obtain the highest level of value from employees are listed. These include human-capital investment analysis, talent value models, workforce forecasts, and talent supply chains. **Availability:** Online; PDF.

19807 ■ *"Competition Is Fierce For Hospital Rankings"* in *Dallas Business Journal (Vol. 35, July 20, 2012, No. 45, pp. 1)*
Pub: Baltimore Business Journal
Contact: Rhonda Pringle, President
E-mail: rpringle@bizjournals.com
Ed: Bill Hethcock. **Description:** U.S. News and World Report has released its ranking of Best Hospitals and triggering press releases in the highly competitive North Texas health care market. The press releases are being taken seriously by the hospitals since they learn from each other. **Availability:** Print; Online.

19808 ■ *"Competition Qualms Overblown: Inco"* in *Globe & Mail (February 15, 2006, pp. B1)*
Ed: Wendy Stueck. **Description:** Inco Ltd. plans the acquisition of Falconbridge Ltd., for $12.5 billion. The advantages of the acquisition for Inco Ltd. are presented. **Availability:** Online.

19809 ■ *"Competitors Eye Whole Foods"* in *Sacramento Business Journal (Vol. 31, August 8, 2014, No. 24, pp. 6)*
Pub: American City Business Journals, Inc.
Contact: Mike Olivieri, Executive Vice President
Released: Weekly. **Price:** $4, Introductory 4-week offer(Digital & Print). **Description:** Whole Foods Market has confirmed its plans to open a store in midtown Sacramento, California. However, Sacramento Natural Foods Co-op and Gluten Free Specialty says the announcement would not affect their own expansion plans into the same neighborhood. The proposed mixed-use building that will house the Whole Foods healthy grocery store is also discussed. **Availability:** Print; Online.

19810 ■ *The Complete Guide to Selling a Business*
Pub: Nolo
Contact: Chris Braun, President
Ed: Fred S. Steingold. **Released:** August 2017. **Description:** When selling a business it is critical that a sales agreement covers all key concerns from price and payment terms to liability protection and restrictions on future competition. **Availability:** Print.

19811 ■ *Corporate Entrepreneurship & Innovation*
Ed: Michael H. Morris, Donald F. Kuratko, Jeffrey G. Covin. **Released:** 3rd edition. **Price:** $22.49, e-book; $279.95, hardcover. **Description:** Innovation is the key to running a successful small business. The book helps entrepreneurs to develop the skills and business savvy to sustain a competitive edge. **Availability:** E-book; Print.

19812 ■ *"Cost of Creating Health Insurance Exchange in Md. 'Largely Unknown'"* in *Baltimore Business Journal (Vol. 28, September 3, 2010, No. 17, pp. 1)*
Pub: Baltimore Business Journal
Contact: Rhonda Pringle, President
E-mail: rpringle@bizjournals.com
Ed: Emily Mullin. **Description:** United States health reform is seen to result in increased health insurance prices in Maryland. However, health care reform advocates claim a new marketplace and increased competition will help keep costs down. **Availability:** Print.

19813 ■ *"Battle-Tested Vestas Shrugs Off Ill Winds"* in *Business Journal Portland (Vol. 30, January 31, 2014, No. 48, pp. 4)*
Pub: American City Business Journals, Inc.
Contact: Mike Olivieri, Executive Vice President
Released: Weekly. **Price:** $4, Introductory 4-week offer(Digital & Print). **Description:** The revenues of Vestas-American Wind Technology are expected to increase by 12 percent in 2014, despite the decline in US turbine sales. The company holds the second-highest market share in the US. However, Vestas is struggling with tax incentives and increased competition. **Availability:** Print; Online.

19814 ■ *"CradlePoint Is Adding Workers, Seeking More Space"* in *Idaho Business Review (September 3, 2014)*
Pub: BridgeTower Media
Contact: Adam Reinebach, President
Price: $11.99, Print, Digital & Mobile(1 Month); 149, Print, Digital & Mobile(1 Year); 99, Digital & Mobile Only(1 Year); $99, Digital & Mobile Only(For 1 Year); $9.95, Print, Digital & Mobile (For 1 Month Intro Rate); $149, Print, Digital & Mobile(For 1 Year). **Description:** CradlePoint makes networking routers and software, focusing on security for businesses. The firm is hiring new workers at a rate higher than predicted and is seeking new office space in downtown Boise, Idaho. CradlePoint is a major player in the growing wireless service and cloud platform market and is growing faster than its competitors. **Availability:** Print; Online.

19815 ■ *Creativity and Innovation: Breaking New Ground..Without Breaking the Bank*
Description: Advice is given to help small business owners be creative in order to compete in their sector. **Availability:** Print; Download.

19816 ■ *"Cultural Change That Sticks: Start With What's Already Working"* in *(Vol. 90, July-August 2012, No. 7-8, pp. 110)*
Pub: Harvard Business Review Press
Contact: Moderna V. Pfizer, Contact
Ed: Jon R. Katzenach, Ilona Steffen, Caroline Kronley. **Description:** Working with, rather than altering, corporate culture can enhance successful implementation of change initiatives. Identifying corporate culture strengths while aligning initiatives with business priorities can generate competitive advantage.

19817 ■ *"Cummins Is a Engine of Growth"* in *Barron's (Vol. 88, July 14, 2008, No. 28, pp. 43)*
Pub: Dow Jones & Company Inc.
Contact: Almar Latour, Chief Executive Officer
Ed: Shirley A. Lazo. **Description:** Engine maker Cummins increased its quarterly common dividend by 40 percent to 17.5 cents per share from 12.5 cents. CVS Caremark's dividend saw a hike of 18.4 percent from 9.5 cents to 11.25 cents per share while its competitor Walgreen is continuing its 75th straight year of dividend distribution and its 33rd straight year of dividend hikes. **Availability:** Online.

19818 ■ *"Dairy Queen Ends Effort Against Yogubliz"* in *Ice Cream Reporter (Vol. 23, November 20, 2010, No. 12, pp. 1)*
Description: Dairy Queen has stopped demands that Yogubliz Inc. change its Blizzberry and Blizz Frozen Yogurt shops because they sound too much like Dairy Queen's Blizzard frozen dessert treat. Dairy Queen feared consumers would confuse the two brands. **Availability:** Print; Online.

19819 ■ *"The Danger of Doing Nothing"* in *Harvard Business Review (Vol. 90, April 2012, No. 4, pp. 38)*
Pub: Harvard Business Review Press
Contact: Moderna V. Pfizer, Contact
Ed: Erskine Bowles. **Price:** $6. **Description:** Solving the US economic crisis will require a blend of revenue increases, spending cuts, and bipartisan cooperation in Congress. The National Commission on Fiscal

Responsibility and Reform, also known as Simpson-Bowles, has proposed a plan intended to make America competitive again. **Availability:** PDF; Online.

19820 ■ *"The Darwinian Workplace: New Technology Is Helping Employers Systematically Shift More Work To Their Best Employees"* **in Harvard Business Review (Vol. 90, May 2012, No. 5, pp. 25)**
Pub: Harvard Business Review Press
Contact: Moderna V. Pfizer, Contact
Ed: Serguei Netessine, Valery Yakubovich. **Price:** $6. **Description:** The winners-take-all model is a productivity-based system that shifts work and incentives to a firm's most productive employees. Challenges such as unpredictable pay swings, excessive competition, and unfair comparisons are addressed. **Availability:** Online; PDF.

19821 ■ *"Death of the PC"* **in Canadian Business (Vol. 83, October 12, 2010, No. 17, pp. 44)**
Description: The future of the personal computer (PC) is looking bleak as consumers are relying more on new mobile devices instead of their PC. A 'Wall Street Journal' article published in September 2010 reported that the iPad had cannibalized sales of laptops by as much as 50 percent. The emergence of tablet computers running alternative operating systems is also explained. **Availability:** Print; Online.

19822 ■ *"Denver Airport Picks New Contractors As It Struggles to Conclude Previous Relationship"* **in ConstructionDive (October 14, 2019)**
URL(s): www.constructiondive.com/news/denver-airport-picks-new-contractors-as-it-struggles-to-conclude-previous-r/564859/
Ed: Kim Slowey. **Released:** October 14, 2019. **Description:** Denver International Airport has chosen construction manager and general contractor Hensel Phelps for Phase 1, replacing Great Hall Partners. Stantec is the preferred lead designer for the entire project. Plans are in place to settle the terms to end the old construction relationship. **Availability:** Online.

19823 ■ *"Design Challenge Seeks to Expand Access"* **in Philadelphia Business Journal (Vol. 33, April 25, 2014, No. 11, pp. 7)**
Pub: American City Business Journals, Inc.
Contact: Mike Olivieri, Executive Vice President
Description: The Thomas Scattergood Behavioral Health Foundation sponsored the 2014 design challenge on making mental healthcare education, access and services available at retail clinics. The winner was the mental health screening tool, 'Wellness at Your Fingertips', submitted by the Philadelphia Department of Behavioral Health and Intellectual Disability Services in Pennsylvania. **Availability:** Online.

19824 ■ *"The Devolution of Home-Electronics Stores"* **in Philadelphia Business Journal (Vol. 28, June 8, 2012, No. 17, pp. 1)**
Pub: Baltimore Business Journal
Contact: Rhonda Pringle, President
E-mail: rpringle@bizjournals.com
Description: Philadelphia, Pennsylvania-area consumer electronics stores have mirrored the national trend in which big-box retailers are taking a bigger share of the home-electronics market. However, smaller, locally-based chains are competing in terms of pricing transparency and custom electronics. **Availability:** Print; Online.

19825 ■ *"Disney's High Hopes for Duffy"* **in Canadian Business (Vol. 83, October 12, 2010, No. 17, pp. 14)**
Pub: Rogers Media Inc.
Contact: Neil Spivak, Chief Executive Officer
Ed: James Cowan. **Description:** The reintroduction of Duffy is expected to create a new, exclusive product line that distinguishes Disney's parks and stores from competitors. Duffy, a teddy bear, was first introduced at a Disney World store in Florida in 2002. The character was incorporated into the Disney mythology when its popularity grew in Japan. **Availability:** Online.

19826 ■ *"Diving Into Internet Marketing"* **in American Agent and Broker (Vol. 81, December 2009, No. 12, pp. 24)**
Ed: Steve Anderson. **Description:** Internet marketing is becoming an essential tool for most businesses; advice is provided regarding the social networking opportunities available for marketing one's product or service on the Internet. **Availability:** Online.

19827 ■ *"Dollar Store Growth Presents New Challenge to Larger Mass Retailers"* **in Pet Product News (Vol. 66, August 2012, No. 8, pp. 4)**
Description: Dollar stores have been rising as a direct competitor to bigger mass-market retailers in the pet market. Aside from focusing on low prices, dollar stores' competitive strategy has been marked by smaller store size and convenience of edited assortments. Other factors that have lured a growing consumer base to dollar stores are described. **Availability:** Online.

19828 ■ *"Elanco Challenges Bayer's Advantage, K9 Advantix Ad Claims"* **in Pet Product News (Vol. 64, November 2010, No. 11, pp. 11)**
Description: Elanco Animal Health has disputed Bayer Animal Health's print and Web advertising claims involving its flea, tick, and mosquito control products Advantage and K9 Advantix. The National Advertising Division of the Council of Better Business Bureaus recommended the discontinuation of ads, while Bayer Animal Health reiterated its commitment to self-regulation. **Availability:** Online.

19829 ■ *"ENERGY: Georgia Power to Buy More Solar: Customer Bills Will Not Be Affected By Renewable Energy Plan, Utility Says"* **in Atlanta Journal-Constitution (September 27, 2012, pp. A13)**
Pub: The Atlanta Journal-Constitution
Contact: Kevin Riley, Editor
E-mail: kriley@ajc.com
Description: Georgia Power announces plans to increase the amount of solar power it distributes to consumers due to the falling prices of solar energy, making it more competitive. However, customers will not see a reduction in their rates. **Availability:** Online.

19830 ■ *"Evaluate Your Process and Do It Better"* **in Modern Machine Shop (Vol. 84, October 2011, No. 5, pp. 34)**
Pub: Gardner Business Media Inc.
Contact: Rick Kline, Jr., President
E-mail: rkline2@gardnerweb.com
Ed: Wayne Chaneski. **Released:** September 15, 2011. **Description:** In order to be more competitive, many machine shops owners are continually looking at their processes and procedures in order to be more competitive. **Availability:** Print; Online.

19831 ■ *"Evolutionary Psychology in the Business Sciences"*
Pub: Springer Publishing Co.
Contact: Bernhard Springer, Founder
Released: First edition. **Description:** All individuals operating in the business sphere share a common biological heritage, including consumers, employers, employees, entrepreneurs, or financial traders, to name a few. The evolutionary behavioral sciences and specific business contexts including marketing, consumer behavior, advertising, innovation and creativity and invention, intertemporal choice, negotiations, competition and cooperation in organizational settings, sex differences in workplace patterns, executive leadership, business ethics, store and office design, behavioral decision making, and electronic communications and commerce are all addressed. **Availability:** E-book; Print.

19832 ■ *"Executive Decision: XM Mulls Betting the Bank in Competitive Game of Subscriber Growth"* **in Globe & Mail (March 18, 2006, pp. B3)**
Ed: Grant Robertson. **Description:** Canadian Satellite Radio Inc., XM Canada, president and Chief Operating Officer Stephen Tapp feel that establishing a profile in satellite radio to attract subscribers is a very big challenge. His views on the Canadian radio market are detailed. **Availability:** Print; Online.

19833 ■ *"Face Time: Fastenal founder Bob Kierlin and CEO Will Oberton"* **in Business Journal (Vol. 31, January 31, 2014, No. 36, pp. 9)**
Pub: American City Business Journals, Inc.
Contact: Mike Olivieri, Executive Vice President
Released: Weekly. **Price:** $4, Introductory 4-week offer(Digital & Print). **Description:** Fastenal founder, Bob Kierline, keeps hiring standards high in order to promote his firm's growth. He also said Fastenal's School of Business employs 40 licensed teachers. Their CEO, Will Oberton, said the company has done a better job in customer relations than its competitors. **Availability:** Print; Online.

19834 ■ *Faster Cheaper Better*
Released: December 28, 2010. **Price:** $27.50, hardcover. **Description:** Nine levels for transforming work in order to achieve business growth are outlined. The book helps small business compete against the low-wage countries. **Availability:** E-book; Print.

19835 ■ *"The Favorite In the Casino, Racino Race"* **in Business Review Albany (Vol. 41, July 25, 2014, No. 18, pp. 7)**
Released: 2014. **Description:** The New York Government's plan to license four casinos could adversely impact the earnings of racinos. Racinos combine harness racing with video slot machines. The planned casinos are expected to attract racino customers creating competition. **Availability:** Print; Online.

19836 ■ *"Fighting for Civil Rights Tourism"* **in Memphis Business Journal (Vol. 33, March 2, 2012, No. 47, pp. 1)**
Pub: Baltimore Business Journal
Contact: Rhonda Pringle, President
E-mail: rpringle@bizjournals.com
Ed: Michael Sheffield. **Description:** Memphis, Tennessee-based National Civil Rights Museum will complete its $27 million renovation in late 2013. It faces competition from Smithosonian Institution's National Museum of African-American History and Culture in Washington DC and the National Center for Civil and Human Rights in Atlanta, Georgia. **Availability:** Print; Online.

19837 ■ *"Finding Competitive Advantage in Adversity"* **in Harvard Business Review (Vol. 88, November 2010, No. 11, pp. 102)**
Pub: Harvard Business Publishing
Contact: Diane Belcher, Managing Director
Ed: Bhaskar Chakravorti. **Price:** $8.95, PDF. **Description:** Four opportunities in adversity are identified and applied to business scenarios. These are matching unmet needs with unneeded resources, seeking collaboration from unlikely partners, developing small/appropriate solutions to large/complex issues, and focusing on the platform as well as the product. **Availability:** Online; PDF.

19838 ■ *"Finding a Way to Continue Growing"* **in Green Industry Pro (Vol. 23, March 2011, No. 3, pp. 31)**
Ed: Gregg Wartgow. **Description:** Profile of Brett Lemcke, VP of R.M. Landscape located in Rochester, New York. Lemcke tells how his Landscape Industry Certified credentials helped him to grow his business and beat out his competition. **Availability:** Online.

19839 ■ *"Firms Bet On Games To Hike Wellness"* **in Business Journal (Vol. 30, June 1, 2012, No. 1, pp. 1)**
Pub: American City Business Journals, Inc.
Contact: Mike Olivieri, Executive Vice President

Ed: Katharine Grayson. **Released:** Weekly. **Price:** $4, introductory 4-week offer(Digital only). **Description:** Twin Cities-based firms providing corporate wellness services are integrating games into these programs. These games include friendly competitions between work teams or high-tech smartphone applications. **Availability:** Print; Online.

19840 ■ *"Five Reasons Why the Gap Fell Out of Fashion"* in Globe & Mail (January 27, 2007, pp. B4)
Description: The five major market trends that have caused the decline of fashion clothing retailer Gap Inc.'s sales are discussed. The shift in brand, workplace fashion culture, competition, demographics, and consumer preferences have lead to the Gap's brand identity. **Availability:** Online.

19841 ■ *"Flights of Fancy"* in Crain's Chicago Business (Vol. 31, April 21, 2008, No. 16, pp. 27)
Ed: Sarah A. Klein. **Released:** June 17, 2017. **Description:** Due to the competition for business travelers, who account for 30 percent of airline revenue, airlines are offering a number of luxury amenities, especially on long-haul routes. **Availability:** Print; Online.

19842 ■ *"Florida Hospital, UCF Affiliation in Danger?"* in Orlando Business Journal (Vol. 29, September 21, 2012, No. 29, pp. 1)
Pub: Baltimore Business Journal
Contact: Rhonda Pringle, President
E-mail: rpringle@bizjournals.com
Description: Florida Hospital is said to be considering the possibility of terminating its affiliation agreement with the University of Central Florida's (UCF) College of Medicine that ends June 30, 2018. Two of the reasons for the move include UCF's plans for a teaching hospital and a new graduate medical education program that could place Florida Hospital into competition with UCF. **Availability:** Print; Online.

19843 ■ *"The Food Truck Handbook: Start, Grow, and Succeed in the Mobile Food Business"*
Pub: John Wiley & Sons, Inc.
Contact: Christina Van Tassell, Executive Vice President Chief Financial Officer
Released: March 2012. **Price:** $19.95, paperback; $12.99, e-book. **Description:** Food truck businesses have grown so much in popularity, there are actually food truck competitions and was once a television show featuring them. A practical, step-by-step handbook is offered to help an entrepreneur start a mobile food delivery service. Information includes tips on choosing vending locations, opening and closing checklists; creation of a business plan with budget and finding vendor services, daily operation issues; common operating mistakes; and insight into delivery high quality food. **Availability:** E-book; Print.

19844 ■ *"Forward Motion"* in Green Industry Pro (July 2011)
Ed: Gregg Wartgow. **Description:** Several landscape contractors have joined this publication's Working Smarter Training Challenge over the last year. This process is helping them develop ways to improve work processes, boost morale, drive out waste, reduce costs, improve customer service, and be more competitive. **Availability:** Print; Online.

19845 ■ *"From Common To Uncommon Knowledge: Foundations of Firm-Specific Use of Knowledge as a Resource"* in Academy of Management Journal (Vol. 55, April 1, 2012, No. 2, pp. 421)
Pub: Academy of Management
Contact: Sharon Alvarez, President
Ed: Rajiv Nag. **Description:** A model of how top managers seek, use, and transform common knowledge into distinctive, uncommon knowledge as an approach to competitive advantage is developed. In this context, knowledge is not just regarded as a basis for strategy but also a strategic resource. Characteristics of knowledge adaptation and augmentation are also described as distinct forms of knowledge-use-in-practice. **Availability:** Electronic publishing; Download; PDF; Online.

19846 ■ *From Concept To Consumer: How to Turn Ideas Into Money*
Ed: Phil Baker. **Released:** 1st edition. **Price:** $27.99, paperback. **Description:** Renowned product developer Phil Baker explains how a great idea accounts for only 5 percent of all the factors of success and why the majority of success is dependent upon a myriad of other factors, including the time it takes to get to market, price, marketing and distribution. By being their own best competition, a small company can stay one step ahead of competitors. **Availability:** Print.

19847 ■ *"The Future of Private Equity"* in Canadian Business (Vol. 80, March 26, 2007, No. 7, pp. 19)
Description: The impact growing Canadian economy and competition in global business on the performance of private equity funds is analyzed. **Availability:** Online; PDF.

19848 ■ *"Galveston Invests In Future as Major Cruise Destination"* in Houston Business Journal (Vol. 44, February 28, 2014, No. 43, pp. 4)
Pub: American City Business Journals, Inc.
Contact: Mike Olivieri, Executive Vice President
Released: Weekly. **Price:** $4, introductory 4-week offer(Digital only). **Description:** The Port of Galveston in Texas is planning to build a third cruise terminal to capitalize on the growing cruise industry as it faces new competition with the Bayport Cruise terminal of the Port of Houston Authority. Architecture firm McTigue of Los Angeles, California was commissioned to design the new terminal. **Availability:** Print; Online.

19849 ■ *"GeoEye CEO Sees Investors In His Future: Matt O'Connell Eyeing Intel Startup Post-Sale"* in Washington Business Journal (Vol. 31, September 14, 2012, No. 21, pp. 1)
Pub: Baltimore Business Journal
Contact: Rhonda Pringle, President
E-mail: rpringle@bizjournals.com
Description: GeoEye Inc. chief executive officer, Matt O'Connell, plans to start a new technology venture in Northern Virginia like the one that supports intelligence gathering once DigitalGlobe Inc. has completed the acquisition of his company in 2013. He will work in an advisory role for DigitalGlobal following the acquisition and will not be involved in satellite imagery security for competitive reasons. **Availability:** Print; Online.

19850 ■ *"Global Organic Food"* in Investment Weekly News (January 21, 2012, pp. 272)
Description: Research and Markets has added 'Global Organic Food' to its reporting of industry profiles. The report will offer top-line qualitative and quantitative summary information including, market size, description of leading players with key financial metrics and analysis of competitive pressures within the market covering the global organic food market. Market size and segmentation data, textual and graphical analysis of market growth trends, leading companies and macroeconomic information will be provided. **Availability:** Online.

19851 ■ *"Good and Bad Effects of Competition for Large and Small Businesses"* in ToughNickel (June 16, 2020)
URL(s): toughnickel.com/business/Business-Competition-The-Good-and-Bad-Effects-for-Businesses-Large-and-Small
Released: June 16, 2020. **Description:** Discusses how small business competition can be seen as both, positive and negative and how to use it to your company's advantage. **Availability:** Online.

19852 ■ *"Google 'Drive' May Run Over Some Local Cloud Competitors"* in Silicon Valley/San Jose Business Journal (Vol. 29, February 17, 2012, No. 47, pp. 1)
Pub: Baltimore Business Journal
Contact: Rhonda Pringle, President
E-mail: rpringle@bizjournals.com
Description: Google Inc. has been preparing to roll out a cloud storage service called "Drive" that will allow people to store large files online. However, the move would put Google in competition with companies offering similar services and it could affect other companies looking to enter the space. Insights on reactions of the other companies are also provided. **Availability:** Print; Online.

19853 ■ *Greening Your Small Business: How to Improve Your Bottom Line, Grow Your Brand, Satisfy Your Customers and Save the Planet*
Price: $19.95. **Description:** A definitive resource for anyone who wants their small business to be cutting-edge, competitive, profitable, and eco-conscious. Stories from small business owners address every aspect of going green, from basics such as recycling waste, energy efficiency, and reducing information technology footprint, to more in-depth concerns such as green marketing and communications, green business travel, and green employee benefits.

19854 ■ *"Grounds for Success"* in Canadian Business (Vol. 87, July 2014, No. 7, pp. 73)
Description: ECS Coffee Inc. has continued to evolve its business of selling single-serve brewing systems and market changes and growing competitors. The company has seen growth of 1,026 percent from 2008 to 2013, earning it the top 69 spot in the 2014 Profit ranking of fastest growing companies in Canada. **Availability:** Online.

19855 ■ *"Health care: Medicare Inc."* in Canadian Business (Vol. 80, October 8, 2007, No. 20, pp. 160)
Pub: Rogers Media Inc.
Contact: Neil Spivak, Chief Executive Officer
Ed: Erin Pooley. **Description:** State of Canada's health care system is discussed. A report by the Fraser Institute in Vancouver predicts that public health spending in six of ten provinces in the country will use more than half the revenues from all sources by 2020. Experts believe competition in the health care industry will help solve the current problems in the sector. **Availability:** Print; Online.

19856 ■ *"Health Clinic Expansion Fuels Debate Over Care In Massachusetts"* in Boston Business Journal (Vol. 34, June 27, 2014, No. 21, pp. 9)
Pub: American City Business Journals, Inc.
Contact: Mike Olivieri, Executive Vice President
Released: Weekly. **Description:** The announcement of expansion by several retail health clinics has fueled debate over their quality and competiveness. AFC Doctors Express, a fast-growing chain of retail health clinics, announced its plan to open two new locations in Massachusetts in 2014 and CVS's MinuteClinic announced its intention to open nine additional locations. Concerns are being raised about the cost and quality of this type of healthcare, with a medical society expressing concern that this is fragmented care, not comprehensive care. **Availability:** Print; Online.

19857 ■ *"Hopkins, University of Maryland, Baltimore Worry Reduced NIH Budget Will Impact Research"* in Baltimore Business Journal (Vol. 29, August 19, 2011, No. 15, pp. 1)
Pub: Boston Business Journal
Contact: Carolyn M. Jones, President
E-mail: cmjones@bizjournals.com
Ed: Scott Dance. **Description:** The budget for the National Institutes of Health (NIH) is slated to be cut by at least 7.9 percent to $2.5 billion in 2013. This will have a big negative effect on medical and biotech research in Maryland, especially Johns Hopkins University and University of Maryland, Baltimore which could face stiffer completion for grants from the NIH. **Availability:** Online.

19858 ■ "Hostess Names $10,000 Grand Prize Winner of its 'CupCake Jackpot' Promotion" in Entertainment Close-Up (August 19, 2011)
Pub: Close-Up Media Inc.
Contact: Caroline S. Moore, President
E-mail: cms@closeupmedia.com
Description: Tricia Botbyl was the grand prize winner of the Hostess 'CupCake Jackpot' promotion that asked consumers to 'spin' online to win $10,000. Consumers were asked to vote for their favorite Hostess Brand cupcake flavor. **Availability:** Online.

19859 ■ Housecleaning Business: Organize Your Business - Get Clients and Referrals - Set Rates and Services
Ed: Laura Jorstad, Melinda Morse. **Price:** Paperback,softback. **Description:** This book shares insight into starting a housecleaning business. It shows how to develop a service manual, screen clients, serve customers, select cleaning products, competition, how to up a home office, using the Internet to grow the business and offering green cleaning options to clients. **Availability:** E-book; Print.

19860 ■ How to Get Rich
Ed: Felix Dennis. **Released:** 2013. **Price:** $8.16, paperback. **Description:** The author, publisher of Maxim, The Week, and Stuff magazines, discusses the mistakes he made running his companies. He didn't understand that people who buy computer gaming magazines wanted a free game with each copy, as one of his rivals was offering. And he laments not diversifying into television and exploiting the Internet. **Availability:** E-book; Print.

19861 ■ How to Handle Competition in Business: 10 Tips to Beat Competition
URL(s): barometrics.com/academy/handle-competition-in-business
Description: Every small business deals with competition. This article discusses how to develop a plan that helps you better serve your customers, understand your competition, and support your team. **Availability:** Online.

19862 ■ "How I Did It: Xerox's Former CEO On Why Succession Shouldn't Be a Horse Race" in Harvard Business Review (Vol. 88, October 2010, No. 10, pp. 47)
Pub: Harvard Business Publishing
Contact: Diane Belcher, Managing Director
Ed: Anne Mulcahy. **Price:** $8.95, PDF. **Description:** The importance of beginning talks between chief executive officers and boards of directors as early as possible to ensure a smooth transition is stressed. This can also prevent turning successions into competitions, with the resultant loss of talent when other candidates 'lose'. **Availability:** Online; PDF.

19863 ■ How to Make Big Money in Your Own Small Business: Unexpected Rules Every Small Business Owner Needs to Know
Ed: Jeffrey J. Fox, Jeffrey J. Fox. **Released:** May 12, 2004. **Price:** $16.95; C$24.95; $16.95; C$24.95; $16.95; C$24.95. **Description:** Former sales and marketing pro offers advice on growing a small business. **Availability:** Print.

19864 ■ "How Small Businesses Can Stand Out From Their Competition" in Linchpin SEO (Jan. 13, 2022)
URL(s): linchpinseo.com/competitive-strategies-small-businesses-can-use-to-stand-out/
Released: January 13, 2022. **Description:** Details twenty ways to stand out from the crowd, gain a following, and succeed in today's competitive small business environment. **Availability:** Online.

19865 ■ How to Write a Business Plan
Pub: Kogan Page Ltd.
Contact: Christina Lindeholm, Manager, Sales
Ed: Brian Finch. **Released:** Seventh edition. **Description:** Starting with the premise that there's only one chance to make a good impression, this book covers all the issues involved in producing a successful business plan, from profiling competitors to forecasting marketing development. **Availability:** Print; Electronic publishing.

19866 ■ "Iconic Boise Skateboard Shop to Close" in Idaho Business Review (August 19, 2014)
Pub: BridgeTower Media
Contact: Adam Reinebach, President
Description: Lori Wright and Lori Ambur have owned Newt & Harold's for over 30 years. The partners are closing the firm that sold skateboards and snowboards. Wright focused on the marketing and inventory aspects of the retail shop, while Ambur ran the organizational and financial end. Wright and Ambur say they are leaving retail because the industry has faced so many changes since they first opened, particularly competing with online stores.

19867 ■ If You Have to Cry, Go Outside: And Other Things Your Mother Never Told You
Pub: HarperCollins Publishers L.L.C.
Contact: Brian Murray, President
Ed: Kelly Cutrone, Meredith Bryan. **Released:** February 02, 2010. **Price:** $10.99, e-book; $7.24, e-book. **Description:** Women's mentor advices on how to make it in one of the most competitive industries in the world, fashion. She has kicked people out of fashion shows, forced some of reality television's shiny start to fire their friends, and built her own company which is one of the most powerful public relations firms in the fashion business. **Availability:** E-book; Print.

19868 ■ "Inco's Takeover Offer Extended Four Months" in Globe & Mail (February 22, 2006, pp. B1)
Description: United States and Europe competition authorities wanted more time to investigate Inco Ltd.'s takeover of Falconbridge Ltd. and compelling Inco to extend its $12.5 billion offer for the third time. **Availability:** Online.

19869 ■ "Inland Snaps Up Rival REITs" in Crain's Chicago Business (Vol. 31, November 17, 2008, No. 46, pp. 3)
Pub: Crain Communications Inc.
Contact: Barry Asin, President
Ed: Alby Gallun. **Description:** Discusses Inland American Real Estate Trust Inc., a real estate investment trust that is napping up depressed shares of publicly traded competitors, a possible first step toward taking over these companies; however, with hotel and retail properties accounting for approximately 70 percent of its portfolio, the company could soon face its own difficulties. **Availability:** Online.

19870 ■ "Insurers No Longer Paying Premium for Advertising" in Brandweek (Vol. 49, April 21, 2008, No. 16, pp. SR3)
Description: Insurance companies are cutting their advertising budgets after years of accelerated double-digit growth in spending due to the economic downturn, five years of record-breaking ad spend and a need to cut expenditures as claims costs rise and a competitive market keeps premiums in place. Statistical data included. **Availability:** Print; Online.

19871 ■ "International Business Law: Interpreting the Term 'Like Products'" in Business Recorder (June 7, 2012)
Ed: Zafar Azeem. **Description:** The term 'like products' needs to be defined for international trade. The battle between the United States and Indonesia regarding this issue is discussed. A technical barrier clause being used by foreign countries is prohibiting imports and hurting competitiveness. **Availability:** Online.

19872 ■ "Into the Light: Making Our Way Through the Economic Tunnel" in Agency Sales Magazine (Vol. 39, August 2009, No. 8, pp. 26)
Description: Ways in which to avoid business stagnation brought about by the economic downturn is presented. Being different, being a puzzle solver, and knowing the competition are among the things marketing personnel should do in order to wade through the economic downturn. Marketing via direct mail and the Internet also recommended. **Availability:** Online.

19873 ■ "IU Health Bloomington's Contract with Local Cleaning Service Set to Expire" in Herald-Times (March 16, 2012)
Pub: McClatchy Tribune Information Services
Contact: Patrick J. Talamantes, President
Ed: Dann Denny. **Description:** Groff Enterprises, a building maintenace firm in Monroe and other surrounding counties of Indiana. The firm will have to let go some 20 or so employees due to the loss of its contract to provide services to IU Health in Bloomington. IU Health Bloomington Hospital sent out a request for proposals from cleaning companies that could provide services to off-site locations that were comparable to those of the in-house staff working at the hospital. **Availability:** Print; Online.

19874 ■ "Jeffrey Watanabe: 'Promise Less and Deliver More" in Canadian Business (Vol. 85, August 13, 2012, No. 13, pp. 16)
Ed: Richard Branson. **Description:** Setting realistic customer expectations and then exceeding them in unexpected and helpful ways provides businesses an advantage over their competitors. Pricing and excellent customer service are some ways to exceed customer expectations. **Availability:** Print; Online.

19875 ■ "Job Seeker's Readiness Guide: Unemployment's High and Competition is Tough" in Black Enterprise (Vol. 40, July 2010, No. 12, pp. 83)
Description: Five key areas to help someone seeking employment gain the competitive edge are listed. **Availability:** Print; Online.

19876 ■ "Joe Wikert, General Manager, O'Reilly Technology Exchange" in Information Today (Vol. 26, February 2009, No. 2, pp. 21)
Description: Joe Wikert, general manager of O'Reilly Technology Exchange discusses his plans to develop a free content model that will evolve with future needs. O'Reilly's major competitor is Google. Wikert plans to expand the firm's publishing program to include print, online, and in-person products and services. **Availability:** Online.

19877 ■ "Just Hang Up" in Barron's (Vol. 88, March 10, 2008, No. 10, pp. 45)
Description: Sprint's shares are expected to continue falling while the company attempts to attract subscribers by cutting prices, cutting earnings in the process. The company faces tougher competition from better-financed AT&T and Verizon Communications.

19878 ■ "Keep Customers Out of the Yellow Pages" in Contractor (Vol. 56, November 2009, No. 11, pp. 47)
Ed: Matt Michel. **Description:** Mechanical contractors should keep customers away from the Yellow Pages where they could find their competition by putting stickers on the water heater or the front of the directory. Giving out magnets to customers and putting the company name on sink rings and invoices are other suggestions. **Availability:** Print; Online.

19879 ■ "Keeping the Faith in Fuel-Tech" in Barron's (Vol. 88, March 24, 2008, No. 12, pp. 20)
Pub: Dow Jones & Company Inc.
Contact: Almar Latour, Chief Executive Officer
Ed: Christopher C. Williams. **Description:** Shares of air pollution control company Fuel-Tech remain on track to reach $40 each from their $19 level due to a continued influx of contracts. The stock has suffered from lower-than-expected quarterly earnings and tougher competition but stand to benefit from increased orders. **Availability:** Online.

19880 ■ "Kerkorian Shakes Up Chrysler Race" in Globe & Mail (April 6, 2007, pp. B1)
Ed: Greg Keenan. **Description:** The bid of Kirk Kerkorian's Tracinda Corp. to acquire Daimler-Chrysler AG for $4.5 billion is discussed. **Availability:** Online.

GENERAL SMALL BUSINESS TOPICS

Competition ■ 19898

19881 ■ *"King of the Crib: How Good Samaritan Became Ohio's Baby HQ"* in *Business Courier* (Vol. 27, June 18, 2010, No. 7, pp. 1)
Pub: Business Courier
Ed: James Ritchie. Description: Cincinnati's Good Samaritan hospital had 6,875 live births in 2009, which is more than any other hospital in Ohio. They specialize in the highest-risk pregnancies and deliveries and other hospitals are trying to grab Good Samaritan's share in this niche. Availability: Print; Online.

19882 ■ *"Kraft Taps Cheese Head; Jordan Charged With Fixing Foodmaker's Signature Product"* in *Crain's Chicago Business* (April 14, 2008)
Pub: Crain Communications Inc.
Contact: Barry Asin, President
Ed: David Sterrett. Description: Kraft Foods Inc. has assigned Rhonda Jordan, a company veteran, to take charge of the cheese and dairy division which has been losing market shares to cheaper store-brand cheese among cost-sensitive shoppers as Kraft and its competitors raise prices to offset soaring dairy costs. Availability: Online.

19883 ■ *"Labor Shortage Creates Growing Pains"* in *Orlando Business Journal* (Vol. 30, January 31, 2014, NO. 32, pp. 5)
Pub: American City Business Journals, Inc.
Contact: Mike Olivieri, Executive Vice President
Released: January 31, 2014. Description: The reactions of residential real estate industry executives on the labor shortage created by the growing demand for new homes is presented. There were plenty of tradesmen and laborers on hand when the housing market recovery began, however, construction management faces labor competition from other builders and this trend slows the industry. Availability: Print; Online.

19884 ■ *"Lessons from Turnaround Leaders"* in *Strategy and Leadership* (Vol. 39, May-June 2011, No. 3, pp. 36-43)
Pub: Emerald Group Publishing Limited
Contact: Erika Valenti, President
Ed: David P. Boyd. Description: A study analyzes the cases of some successful turnaround leaders to present a strategic model to help firms tackle challenges such as employee inertia, competition and slow organizational renewal. It describes a change model consisting of five major steps to be followed by firms with environmental uncertainty for the purpose. Availability: Download; Online.

19885 ■ *"Life After Cod"* in *Globe & Mail* (March 18, 2006, pp. B1)
Pub: The Globe & Mail Inc.
Ed: Gordon Pitts. Description: Canadian fishing industry is under threat because of Chinese processing competition, high energy costs, rise of powerful retailers and the rise of Canadian dollar value. Fishing industry of Canada is analyzed. Availability: Print; PDF; Online.

19886 ■ *"Lights, Camera, Action: Tools for Creating Video Blogs"* in *Inc.* (Volume 32, December 2010, No. 10, pp. 57)
Pub: Mansueto Ventures L.L.C.
Contact: Stephanie Mehta, Chief Executive Officer
Ed: John Brandon. Description: A video blog is a good way to spread company news, talk about products, and stand out among traditional company blogs. New editing software can create two- to four-minute blogs using a webcam and either Windows Live Essentials, Apple iLife 2011, Powerdirector 9 Ultra, or Adobe Visual Communicator 3. Availability: Online.

19887 ■ *"Linking Human Capital to Competitive Advantages: Flexibility in a Manufacturing Firm's Supply Chain"* in *Human Resource Management* (Vol. 49, September-October 2010, No. 5)
Pub: John Wiley & Sons, Inc.

Contact: Christina Van Tassell, Executive Vice President Chief Financial Officer
Ed: Yan Jin, Margaret M. Hopkins, Jenell L.S. Wittmer. Released: September 01, 2010. Description: A study was conducted to confirm the links among human capital, firm flexibility, and firm performance. The study also examines the emerging role of flexibility for a company's performance. A total of 201 senior supply chain management professionals from several manufacturing companies were included in the study.

19888 ■ *"Little Guy is Taking On Potent Competition"* in *Philadelphia Business Journal* (Vol 32, January 10, 2014, No. 48, pp. 4)
Pub: American City Business Journals, Inc.
Contact: Mike Olivieri, Executive Vice President
Released: Weekly. Price: $4, introductory 4-week offer(Digital & Print). Description: Auxilium Pharmaceuticals has introduced the erectile dysfunction drug Stendra, which it licensed from Vivus Inc. in a $300 million deal. Auxilium CEO, Adrian Adams, says Stendra has some advantages over competing products. Availability: Print; Online.

19889 ■ *"Local Law Firms Quietly Boost Poaching"* in *Boston Business Journal* (Vol. 31, July 29, 2011, No. 27, pp. 3)
Pub: Boston Business Journal
Contact: Carolyn M. Jones, President
E-mail: cmjones@bizjournals.com
Ed: Lisa Van der Pool. Released: Weekly. Price: $4, Introductory 4-Week Offer(Digital Only). Description: National law firms Jones Day and Latham & Watkins LLP set up offices in Boston, Massachusetts. Their move also created an upswing on confidential conversation as both firms are aggressively poaching lawyers from Boston's other top firms. Availability: Print; Online.

19890 ■ *"Lotus Starts Slowly, Dodges Subprime Woes"* in *Crain's Detroit Business* (Vol. 24, April 14, 2008, No. 15, pp. 3)
Pub: Crain Communications Inc.
Contact: Barry Asin, President
Ed: Tom Henderson. Description: Discusses Lotus Bancorp Inc. and their business plan, which although is not right on target due to the subprime mortgage meltdown, is in a much better position than its competitors due to the quality of their loans. Availability: Online.

19891 ■ *Macrowikinomics: Rebooting Business and the World*
Pub: Portfolio Hardcover
Contact: Adrian Zackheim, President
Ed: Don Tapscott, Anthony D. Williams. Released: May 29, 2012. Price: $18, paperback; $6.99, e-book. Description: Wikinomics Don Tapscott and Anthony Williams showed how mass collaboration was changing the way businesses communicate, create value, and compete in the new global marketplace in 2007. Now, in the wake of the global financial crisis, the principles of wikinomics have become more powerful than ever. Availability: E-book; Print.

19892 ■ *"Market and Technology Orientations for Service Delivery Innovation: the Link of Innovative Competence"* in *Journal of Business & Industrial Marketing* (Vol. 29, July 2014, No. 6)
Pub: Emerald Group Publishing Limited
Contact: Erika Valenti, President
Description: A study to formulate an alternative method of predicting service delivery innovation based on market and technology orientations and innovative competence is examined. Five hypotheses were proposed and tested using the Partial Least Square (PLS) analysis. It was observed that proactive market orientation and technology orientation regulate exploratory and exploitative innovative competences, while exploitative competence influences service delivery innovation. Availability: Download; Online.

19893 ■ *"A Master Chef's Recipe for Business Success"* in *Business Strategy Review* (Vol. 23, Spring 2012, No. 1, pp. 65)
Description: Often called the world's greatest chef, Ferran Adria, longtime owner of El Built, Spain's three-star Michelin rated revolutionary restaurant, is now embarking on a new venture: the El Built Foundation, a place where chefs can create, interact, and discuss their ideas with researchers from other disciplines. He recently spoke at London Business School as part of his tour of a number of select universities to invite students to enter a competition to design an innovative business model for the new Foundation. Availability: Print; Online.

19894 ■ *Mastering the Complex Sale: How to Compete and Win When the Stakes Are High!*
Pub: John Wiley & Sons, Inc.
Contact: Christina Van Tassell, Executive Vice President Chief Financial Officer
Ed: Jeff Thull. Released: Second edition. Price: $24.95, hardcover; $16.99, e-book. Description: Guide to compete for and win in complex selling, the business-to-business transactions involving multiple decisions by multiple people from multiple perspectives. Availability: E-book; Print; Online; PDF.

19895 ■ *"Miller's Crossroad"* in *Canadian Business* (Vol. 83, September 14, 2010, No. 15, pp. 58)
Ed: Joe Castaldo. Released: September 14, 2010. Description: Future Electronics founder and billionaire Robert Miller shares the secret of Future's unique operating model, which is based on inventory and market research. Miller attributes much of the company's success to its privately held status that enables quick movement against competitors. Availability: Print; Online.

19896 ■ *"Minnesota State Fair Vendors Accept Big Risks for Big Rewards"* in *Business Journal* (Vol. 32, August 22, 2014, No. 13, pp. 10)
Pub: American City Business Journals, Inc.
Contact: Mike Olivieri, Executive Vice President
Released: Weekly. Price: $4, introductory 4-week offer(Digital & Print). Description: Food and beverage concessionaires compete for booths at the Minnesota State Fair and there are many vendors that wait for years to get one, especially a large booth with room for tables and a beer garden. The State Fair has been a good business opportunity and a family bonding experience for most of the vendors. Availability: Video; Print; Online.

19897 ■ *"The Moment You Can't Ignore: When Big Trouble Leads to a Great Future"*
Pub: PublicAffairs
Contact: Jaime Leifer, Director
Released: October 07, 2014. Price: $14.99, E-book; $25.99, hardcover. Description: New forms of work, communication, and technology are exposing the ways in which an organization's culture conflicts with new competitive demands. Questions for small companies to ask about identity, leadership, and capacity for innovation are addressed. Availability: E-book; Print.

19898 ■ *"MoneyGram Hopes Digital Push Will Click With Customers"* in *Dallas Business Journal* (Vol. 37, July 4, 2014, No. 43, pp. 17)
Pub: American City Business Journals, Inc.
Contact: Mike Olivieri, Executive Vice President
Released: Weekly. Price: $4, introductory 4-week offer(Digital only). Description: Reports on MoneyGram's recent release of a digital monitoring system, which will allow it to work more closely with customers, is profiled. This digital monitoring system will aggregate data from social media platforms and enable the company to identify customer needs and trends across the money transfer industry. It will help MoneyGram outshine its rivals in the money transfer business. Availability: Print; Online.

19899 ■ "Needed: A Strategy; Banking In China" in The Economist (Vol. 390, January 3, 2009, No. 8612, pp. 54)

Description: International banks are competing for a role in China but are finding obstacles in their paths such as a reduction in the credit their operations may receive from Chinese banks and the role they can play in the public capital markets which remain limited. **Availability:** Print; Online.

19900 ■ "Neighboring Auto Body Shops Merge as Parks Royal Body Works" in Idaho Business Review (August 26, 2014)

Pub: BridgeTower Media

Contact: Adam Reinebach, President

Description: Parks Royal Body Works and Auto Body Specialists operated next door to each other and were rivals for many years. Ted Vinson, owner of Auto Body, recently sold his business to Ted Thornton's son, Matt in order for Parks Royal to expand. Thornton discusses his company's 13 percent growth in 2013. Details of the purchase are discussed.

19901 ■ "New Tailor Shop in Uptown Dallas Is a Great Fit for the Neighborhood's Renewed Energy" in Dallas News (July 26, 2019)

URL(s): www.dallasnews.com/arts-entertainment/2019/07/26/new-tailor-shop-in-uptown-dallas-is-a-great-fit-for-the-neighborhood-s-renewed-energy/

Ed: Kimber Westphall. **Released:** July 26, 2019. **Description:** Edit Alternations has joined the crowd in Uptown Dallas and hopes to fill a quality void in the tailoring industry. The business caters to both men and women and will even make house calls, which is something the competition doesn't offer. **Availability:** Online.

19902 ■ "The Next Great Canadian Idea: Peripiteia Generator" in Canadian Business (Vol. 81, July 21, 2008, No. 11, pp. 45)

Pub: Rogers Media Inc.

Contact: Neil Spivak, Chief Executive Officer

Ed: Sharda Prashad. **Description:** Thane Heins has invented a generator that produces energy in an isolated system which contradicts the law of conservation of energy. Perepiteia generator is referred to as a 'perpetual motion machine.' Other inventions slated for the Canadian invention competition include Rob Matthies' batteries and Frank Naumann's Smart Trap. **Availability:** Online.

19903 ■ Niche and Grow Rich

Description: Consultants share insight to entrepreneurs wishing to find a profitable niche market. Authors write that good niche businesses are easy to start and easy to defend from competitors. They also report that finding a successful niche can attract and maintain good customers who are willing to pay more for unique goods and services.

19904 ■ "Outside In: The Power of Putting Customers at the Center of Your Business"

Description: Customer experience is the most powerful and least understood element of corporate strategy in today's business world. Customer experience is the way your customers perceive their interactions with a company. It drives sales and provides a competitive advantage. **Availability:** Audio.

19905 ■ "The Perils of Popularity" in Business Strategy Review (Vol. 23, Spring 2012, No. 1, pp. 51)

Description: The iPhone's worldwide success would seem to be an unqualified win-win for Apple and the mobile operators that sell it. Not so, explains Marco Bertini and Ricardo Cabornero, as mobile operators they must maintain a delicate balance between winning new customers and retaining existing ones. This task is made more difficult when their own brands can actually be diminished by selling the competitor's iPhone. **Availability:** Print; Online.

19906 ■ "Pharmacies Vie for Sites, Customers" in Philadelphia Business Journal (Vol. 30, January 6, 2012, No. 47, pp. 1)

Pub: Baltimore Business Journal

Contact: Rhonda Pringle, President

E-mail: rpringle@bizjournals.com

Description: CVS, Rite Aid and Walgreens are set to open new store formats in Philadelphia, Pennsylvania. The stores will offer services such as in-store nurse practitioners. Of the competitors, CVS has the largest market share in the area. **Availability:** Print; Online.

19907 ■ "Play By Play: These Video Products Can Add New Life to a Stagnant Website" in Black Enterprise (Vol. 41, December 2010, No. 5)

Pub: Earl G. Graves Ltd.

Contact: Earl Graves, Jr., President

Ed: Marcia Wade Talbert. **Description:** Web Visible, provider of online marketing products and services, cites video capability as the fastest-growing Website feature for small business advertisers. Profiles of various devices for adding video to a Website are included. **Availability:** Online.

19908 ■ "Please Pass the Mayo" in Crain's Chicago Business (Vol. 31, April 28, 2008, No. 17, pp. 32)

Pub: Crain Communications Inc.

Contact: Barry Asin, President

Ed: Samantha Stainburn. **Description:** Fort Dearborn Co. has come a long way since it started as on one-press print shop; the family-owned company was struggling to keep up with the technology of making consumer product labels for curvy bottles of products like V8 V-Fusion juice and in 2006 sold off to Genstar Capital LLC which has pushed for acquisitions; last year, Fort Derborn bought its biggest competitor, Renaissance Mark Inc., doubling its size and adding spirit and wine makers to its client roster. **Availability:** Online.

19909 ■ "Port in the Storm" in Canadian Business (Vol. 81, October 13, 2008, No. 17, pp. 101)

Description: Interport Inc.'s state-of-the-art studio complex in Toronto is discussed. The strong Canadian dollar, along with disputes within the movie industry, are creating challenges for the studio to secure Hollywood projects. Interport plans to compete for Hollywood projects based on quality. **Availability:** Print; Online.

19910 ■ "Prepaid Phones Surge in Bad Economy" in Advertising Age (Vol. 79, November 17, 2008, No. 43, pp. 6)

Pub: Crain Communications, Inc.

Contact: Jessica Botos, Manager, Marketing

E-mail: jessica.botos@crainsnewyork.com

Ed: Rita Chang. **Description:** Prepay cell phone offerings are becoming increasingly competitive amid a greater choice of plans and handsets. In an economic environment in which many consumers are unable to pass the credit checks required for traditional cell phone plans, the prepay market is surging.

19911 ■ "Putting 'Great' Back Into A&P" in Crain's New York Business (Vol. 24, January 6, 2008, No. 1, pp. 3)

Pub: Crain Communications, Inc.

Contact: Jessica Botos, Manager, Marketing

E-mail: jessica.botos@crainsnewyork.com

Description: After five straight years ending in 2005, A&P Grocery lost revenue; due to a sweeping plan to freshen up its supermarkets the company returned to growth mode and was able to acquire longtime competitor Pathmark Stores.

19912 ■ "Q&A: RBC's Gordon Nixon" in Canadian Business (Vol. 80, May 31, 2011, No. 22, pp. 9)

Pub: Rogers Media Inc.

Contact: Neil Spivak, Chief Executive Officer

Ed: Rachel Pulfer. **Description:** Royal Bank of Canada (RBC) chief executive officer Gordon Nixon believes that the Canadian financial services segment is heavily regulated. Nixon also feels that it has become difficult for local banks to enter the market since foreign banks can easily come in and compete with Canadian banks. His views on RBC's success are provided. **Availability:** Online.

19913 ■ "Q&A: The CAPP's Greg Stringham" in Canadian Business (Vol. 81, February 12, 2008, No. 3, pp. 8)

Pub: Rogers Media Inc.

Contact: Neil Spivak, Chief Executive Officer

Ed: Michelle Magnan. **Description:** Canadian Association of Petroleum Producers' Greg Stringham thinks that the new royalty plan will result in companies pulling out their investments for Alberta's conventional oil and gas sector. Stringham adds that Alberta is losing its competitive advantage and companies must study their cost profiles to retrieve that advantage. The effects of the royalty system on Alberta's economy are examined further. **Availability:** Print; Online.

19914 ■ "R&R Launches Upscale Spoony's and Low Fat Dragon's Den" in Ice Cream Reporter (Vol. 23, August 20, 2010, No. 9, pp. 3)

Description: European ice cream manufacturer R&R has acquired French ice cream maker Rolland and will position itself as an upscale challenger to brands like Ben & Jerry's. **Availability:** Print; Online.

19915 ■ "Ready for Our Ships to Come In" in Philadelphia Business Journal (Vol. 33, April 11, 2014, No. 9, pp. 4)

Pub: American City Business Journals, Inc.

Contact: Mike Olivieri, Executive Vice President

Description: Philadelphia Regional Port Authority planned the construction of the Southport Marine Terminal in South Philadelphia at a cost of $300 million to capitalize on changes in the shipping industry. The Tioga Marine Terminal in Port Richmond is also being improved using a mix of public and private money. The growing competition among the East Coast ports is also discussed. **Availability:** Online.

19916 ■ Reality Check: The Irreverent Guide to Outsmarting, Outmanaging, and Outmarketing Your Competition

Pub: Penguin Publishing Group

Ed: Guy Kawasaki. **Released:** February 22, 2011. **Price:** $13.34, paperback; $4.99, e-book; $19.89, hardcover; $20.43, audio. **Description:** Marketing guru and entrepreneur, Guy Kawasaki, provides a compilation of his blog posts on all aspects of starting and operating a business. **Availability:** E-book; Print.

19917 ■ "Rethinking School: For the U.S. To Remain Competitive, Its Students Need To Learn Vastly More, Much More Quickly" in Harvard Business Review (Vol. 90, March 2012, No. 3, pp. 76)

Pub: Harvard Business Review Press

Contact: Moderna V. Pfizer, Contact

Ed: Stacey Childress. **Price:** $8.95, hardcover. **Description:** Improving primary education is a key component to future US economic growth. The article emphasizes the importance of personalized learning and educational technology to enhance academic achievement. **Availability:** PDF; Online.

19918 ■ "Revenge of the Scorned Protege" in Canadian Business (Vol. 85, September 17, 2012, No. 14, pp. 48)

Ed: Joanna Pachner. **Released:** September 17, 2012. **Description:** The prospect of a merger between Canadian distributor Alliance Films and international television and independent films distributor Entertainment One Group is expected to control the Canadian market and could rationalize competition in Great Britain. Entertainment One's offerings to broadcasters and other partners will be added with Alliance's 11,000 movie titles.

GENERAL SMALL BUSINESS TOPICS   Competition ■ 19938

19919 ■ *"A Reverse-Innovation Playbook: Insights From a Company That Developed Products For Emerging Markets and Then Brought Them Back Home"* in Harvard Business Review (Vol. 90, April 2012, No. 4, pp. 120)
Pub: Harvard Business Review Press
Contact: Moderna V. Pfizer, Contact
Ed: Vijay Govindarajan. **Price:** $8.95, hardcover. **Description:** An overview is presented on the organizational change implemented by Harman International Industries Inc. to create products for emerging markets and ensure that they would be accepted in already established middle markets. Components include setting radical goals, selecting team leaders with no competing interests, and leveraging global resources. **Availability:** PDF; Online.

19920 ■ *"Rich or Poor, Hospitals Must Work Together"* in Crain's Chicago Business (Vol. 31, April 28, 2008, No. 17, pp. 22)
Pub: Crain Communications Inc.
Contact: Barry Asin, President
Description: Chicago-area safety-net hospitals that serve the poor, uninsured and underinsured are struggling to stay open while wealthier areas compete to build advanced facilities for the expensive surgical procedures their privately insured patients can afford. If these safety-net hospitals close, their patients, many of them in ambulances, will show up at the remaining hospitals resulting in a strain that will test the ability of hospitals across the region to care for all of their patients. Hospitals need to address the threats to the local health care system before it slips into crisis since the current every-hospital-for-itself approach that pays off big for some will eventually will make losers of everyone. **Availability:** Online.

19921 ■ *"Sales and the Absolute Power of Information"* in Agency Sales Magazine (Vol. 39, July 2009, No. 7, pp. 16)
Description: Having good information can help a sales representative deliver effective sales performance. A process for collecting information about customers, prospects, and competitors is discussed.

19922 ■ *"Salmon's Gem Air Wants Grant For Year-round Boise Flight"* in Idaho Business Review (September 3, 2014)
Pub: BridgeTower Media
Contact: Adam Reinebach, President
Description: Gem Air offers four flights between Salmon and Boise, for both tourists and businesspeople including doctors and architects. The airline is requesting a $250,000 federal grant in order to compete with larger airlines and hopes to attract more business travelers with a direct flight between Boise and Atlanta.

19923 ■ *"The Secret to Keeping a School Supplies Store Open in the Amazon Era"* in The New York Times (September 13, 2018)
URL(s): www.nytimes.com/2018/09/13/nyregion/the-secret-to-keeping-a-school-supplies-store-open-in-the-amazon-era.html
Ed: Fabrice Robinet. **Released:** September 13, 2018. **Description:** Amazon has once again helped cause the demise of a once-booming business — the teacher supply store. Thousands used to be open around the country, but nowadays there are only a few hundred. Still, those that are still around do well because of the customer service they provide, plus it's once stop shopping for teachers and they can see all of the merchandise in one setting. **Availability:** Online.

19924 ■ *The Secret Language of Competitive Intelligence: How to See Through and Stay Ahead of Business Disruptions, Distortions, Rumors, and Smoke*

19925 ■ *"Shattering the Myths About U.S. Trade Policy: Stop Blaming China and India. A More Active Trade Policy Can Lead to a Stronger U.S. Economy"* in Harvard Business Review (Vol. 90, March 2012, No. 3, pp. 149)
Pub: Harvard Business Review Press
Contact: Moderna V. Pfizer, Contact

Ed: Robert Z. Lawrence, Lawrence Edwards. **Price:** $8.95, hardcopy black and white. **Description:** Myths debunked include the belief that the US open trade policy has caused job losses, and that living standards are falling due to export market competition. American must leverage China's need for global economic engagement and secure an open domestic market in China. It must also persuade the World Trade Organization to improve market access. **Availability:** Print; PDF; Online.

19926 ■ *"Sheet Metal Union Locals Join Forces: Could Help Local Contractors Compete for Bay Area Jobs"* in Sacramento Business Journal (Vol. 29, June 29, 2012, No. 18, pp. 1)
Pub: Baltimore Business Journal
Contact: Rhonda Pringle, President
E-mail: rpringle@bizjournals.com
Description: The Sacramento Local 162 and Local 104 of Sheet Metal Workers International Association in California's Bay Area have merged, leading to an action that is expected to help local contractors compete for jobs in the area. Aside from improving efficiency in operations, the merger could also prevent duplication of services. Other potential benefits of the merger are discussed. **Availability:** Print; Online.

19927 ■ *"Sinai Doctor's Research May Lead to Rival Plavix Drug"* in Baltimore Business Journal (Vol. 28, July 16, 2010, No. 10, pp. 1)
Pub: Baltimore Business Journal
Contact: Rhonda Pringle, President
E-mail: rpringle@bizjournals.com
Ed: Emily Mullin. **Description:** Paul Gurbel, Sinai Hospital Center for Thrombosis Research director, is seeking an FDA approval of Brilinta, a drug which he helped create and test. Gurbel says that the approval could bring the drug to market as early as December 2010. The drug is expected to rival Bristol-Myers' Plavix, which generated almost $6.2 billion in 2009. **Availability:** Print; Online.

19928 ■ *"Size Does Matter"* in International Journal of Globalisation and Small Business (Vol. 4, September 21, 2010, No. 1, pp. 61)
Ed: Julia Connell, Ranjit Voola. **Description:** Examination of how members of an Australian-based manufacturing and engineering cluster share knowledge through networking as a means to improve competitive advantage. **Availability:** Online.

19929 ■ *"Sizing Up Bentley"* in Barron's (Vol. 92, September 17, 2012, No. 38, pp. 16)
Description: The energy efficiencies of cars produced by Bentley Motors have shown little improvement over time. The company needs to invest in improving the fuel efficiencies of its vehicles to attract new customers and remain competitive. **Availability:** Online.

19930 ■ *"Slow but Steady into the Future"* in Barron's (Vol. 88, July 7, 2008, No. 27, pp. M)
Pub: Dow Jones & Company Inc.
Contact: Almar Latour, Chief Executive Officer
Ed: Mark Veverka. **Description:** Investors are advised to maintain their watch on the shares of business software company NetSuite. The company's chief executive officer, Zach Nelson, claims that the company has a 10-year lead on its competitors with the development of software-as-a service. **Availability:** Online.

19931 ■ *"Small Dutch Islands Saba, Statia Content With Low-Key Niche"* in Travel Weekly (Vol. 69, August 16, 2010, No. 33, pp. 22)
Pub: NorthStar Travel Media
Ed: Gay Nagle Myers. **Description:** Small Caribbean islands market and promote their region for tourism by never competing with the bigger destinations. Saba and Statia are the two smallest islands in the Caribbean and rely on repeat guests, word-of-mouth recommendations and travel agents willing to promote them. **Availability:** Print; Online.

19932 ■ *The Social Media Bible: Tactics, Tools, and Strategies for Business Success*
Pub: John Wiley & Sons, Inc.
Contact: Christina Van Tassell, Executive Vice President Chief Financial Officer
Ed: Lon Safko. **Released:** Third edition. **Price:** $29.95, paperback; $19.99, E-Book. **Description:** Information is given to build or transform a business into social media, where customers, employees, and prospects connect, collaborate, and champion products and services in order to increase sales and to beat the competition. **Availability:** E-book; Print.

19933 ■ *"Some Relief Possible Following Painful Week"* in Barron's (Vol. 88, July 14, 2008, No. 28, pp. M3)
Pub: Dow Jones & Company Inc.
Contact: Almar Latour, Chief Executive Officer
Ed: Kopin Tan. **Description:** Dow Chemical is offering a 74 percent premium to acquire Rohm & Haas' coatings and electronics materials operations. Frontline amassed a 5.6 percent stake in rival Overseas Shipholding Group and a merger between the two would create a giant global fleet with pricing power. Highlights of the U.S. stock market during the week that ended in July 11, 2008 are discussed. Statistical data included. **Availability:** Online.

19934 ■ *"Staging a Martini-and-GQ Lifestyle"* in Crain's Chicago Business (April 21, 2008)
Pub: Crain Communications Inc.
Contact: Barry Asin, President
Ed: Kevin Davis. **Description:** Due to the competition of the slumping housing market, home stagers are becoming more prominent and are using creative ways to make an impression beyond de-cluttering, painting and cleaning by using accents such as casually placed magazines, candles and table settings. **Availability:** Online.

19935 ■ *"State Wants to Add Escape Clause to Leases"* in Sacramento Business Journal (Vol. 28, October 14, 2011, No. 33, pp. 1)
Pub: Sacramento Business Journal
Contact: Stephanie Fretwell, Director
E-mail: sfretwell@bizjournals.com
Ed: Michael Shaw. **Description:** California Governor Jerry Brown's administration has decided to add escape clauses to new lease agreements, which created new worry for building owners and brokers in Sacramento, California. Real estate brokers believe the appropriation of funds clauses have been making the lenders nervous and would result in less competition. **Availability:** Online.

19936 ■ *"Stikemans' Ascent, Its Legacy, and Its Future"* in Globe & Mail (January 29, 2007, pp. B2)
Description: Pierre Raymond, chairman of legal firm Stikeman Elliott LLP, talks about his strategies to handle competition, his challenges, and about Canada's present mergers and acquisition scenario. Stikeman achieved the first place in 2006 M&A legal rankings. **Availability:** Online.

19937 ■ *"Stuck With Two Mortgages"* in Crain's Chicago Business (Vol. 31, April 21, 2008, No. 16)
Pub: Crain Communications Inc.
Contact: Barry Asin, President
Ed: Darci Smith. **Description:** Discusses the problem a number of people are facing due to the slump in the housing market: being stuck with two mortgages when they move because their former homes have not sold. Many thought they could afford to move to a larger home, anticipating significant equity appreciation that did not occur; now they are left with lowering their price and competing with the host of new developments. **Availability:** Online.

19938 ■ *"Suited for Success"* in Retail Merchandiser (Vol. 51, July-August 2011, No. 4, pp. 6)
Description: MyBestFit is a size-matching body scanner that helps consumers find the perfect size clothing for themselves, giving brick and mortar retailers an edge on ecommerce competitors. **Availability:** Online.

Small Business Sourcebook • 42nd Edition   1449

19939 ■ *"The Superpower Dilemma"* in *Canadian Business* (Vol. 83, August 17, 2010, No. 13-14, pp. 42)
Description: Canada has been an energy superpower partly because it controls the energy source and the production means, particularly of fossil fuels. However, Canada's status as superpower could diminish if it replaces petroleum exports with renewable technology for using sources of energy available globally. **Availability:** Online.

19940 ■ *"Survey Reveals Shifting Preferences in Pool Chemicals and Sanitation Systems"* in *Pool and Spa News* (November 20, 2017)
URL(s): www.poolspanews.com/how-to/maintenance/survey-reveals-shifting-preferences-in-pool-chemicals-and-sanitation-systems_o
Ed: Nate Traylor. **Released:** November 20, 2017. **Description:** Pool and Spa News conducted a survey to see which type of pool system consumers prefer to use and how loyal they are to their brands and local stores. **Availability:** Online.

19941 ■ *"T-Mobile's Risky Strategy Aims to Get iPhone Owners to Switch"* in *Puget Sound Business Journal* (Vol. 33, September 7, 2012, No. 20, pp. 1)
Pub: Baltimore Business Journal
Contact: Rhonda Pringle, President
E-mail: rpringle@bizjournals.com
Description: Bellevue, Washington-based T-Mobile has offered unlimited data to customers in a risky strategy to attract competitor iPhone customers withoutoffering an iPhone on its own. T-Mobile is also encouraging existing iPhone user to unlock their phones and then switch to T-Mobile service. **Availability:** Print; Online.

19942 ■ *"Take Command: Lessons in Leadership: How to Be a First Responder in Business"*
Released: 2018. **Price:** $25. **Description:** What do elite members of the military, first responders in a disaster zone, and successful business leaders have in common? Clarity of mind and purpose in the midst of chaos. Cofounder and CEO of Team Rubicon and former Marine Sniper Jake Wood, teaches the lessons in leadership and teamwork to help managers and entrepreneurs succeed in this hyper-competitive business environment today.

19943 ■ *"Tale of the Tape: IPhone Vs. G1"* in *Advertising Age* (Vol. 79, October 27, 2008, No. 40, pp. 6)
Pub: Crain Communications, Inc.
Contact: Jessica Botos, Manager, Marketing
E-mail: jessica.botos@crainsnewyork.com
Ed: Rita Chang. **Description:** T-Mobile's G1 has been positioned as the first serious competitor to Apple's iPhone. G1 is the first mobile phone to run on the Google-backed, open-source platform Android.

19944 ■ *"ThredUP Launches Online Concierge Service to Compete With Children's Consignment"* in *Benzinga.com* (January 25, 2012)
Description: Concierge is a new service offered by thredUP, the top online site for used children's clothing. Concierge simplifies the process of recycling children's clothing. Users sign up at the Website and request a prepaid, ready to ship recycling bag. After filling the bag, it is placed on the doorstep, and thredUp takes it from there. After consignors inspect the items, senders are given rewards up to $5 per piece, based on quality and quantity of items shipped. The received items are then sold on thredUP's online shop.

19945 ■ *"Three Megatrends to Help Your Business Compete in 2014"* in *South Florida Business Journal* (Vol. 34, January 3, 2014, No. 24, pp. 10)
Pub: American City Business Journals, Inc.
Contact: Mike Olivieri, Executive Vice President
Released: Weekly. **Price:** $8, Introductory 4-week offer(Digital & Print). **Description:** Businesses can improve their competitive edge in 2014 by adapting several mega small business trends in marketing and communications. Brands can use brand bridging to get customers attention, use wearable technology to increase their value, and adapt environmental sustainability and corporate social responsibility to keep their customers. **Availability:** Print; Online.

19946 ■ *"Tiny Telecom Big Prize in Bell Aliant Bid Battle"* in *Globe & Mail* (April 4, 2007, pp. B1)
Ed: Catherine McLean. **Description:** The competition between Bell Aliant Regional Communications Income Fund of BCE Inc. and Bragg Communications Inc. to bid for acquiring Amtelecom Income Fund is discussed. **Availability:** Online.

19947 ■ *"To Keep Freight Rolling, Ill. Has to Grease the Hub"* in *Crain's Chicago Business* (Vol. 31, April 21, 2008, No. 16, pp. 22)
Pub: Crain Communications Inc.
Contact: Barry Asin, President
Ed: Paul O'Connor. **Description:** Discusses the importance of upgrading Chicago's continental-hub freight rail system which is integral to moving international products as well as domestic ones. Global tonnage is expected to double by 2020 and unless more money is designated to upgrade the infrastructure the local and national economy will suffer. **Availability:** Online.

19948 ■ *"Top Design Award for Massey Ferguson 7624 Dyna-VT"* in *Farm Industry News* (November 14, 2011)
Pub: Informa Business Media, Inc.
Contact: Charlie McCurdy, President
Description: Massey Ferguson won top honors for its MF 7624 Dyna-VT as the Golden Tractor for Design award in the 2012 Tractor of the Year competition. The award is presented annually by journalists from 22 leading farming magazines in Europe and manufacturers have to be nominated to enter. **Availability:** Online.

19949 ■ *"Train Now to Get the Competitive Edge"* in *Contractor* (Vol. 56, October 2009, No. 10, pp. 58)
Ed: Merry Beth Hall. **Description:** Due to the harsh economic climate, mechanical contractors would be well-served to train their employees while they have time to take them out of the field. This will help ensure that they are not behind when the economic recovery happens. Suggestions on how to choose the best type of training are presented. **Availability:** Print; Online.

19950 ■ *"Travel Rewards Take Off"* in *Inc.* (Vol. 33, October 2011, No. 8, pp. 46)
Description: Credit card companies are offering travel reward cards with special perks, including sign-up bonuses; three such cards are described. **Availability:** Online.

19951 ■ *"Tropeano Takes Charge"* in *Philadelphia Business Journal* (Vol. 33, August 22, 2014, No. 28, pp. 11)
Pub: American City Business Journals, Inc.
Contact: Mike Olivieri, Executive Vice President
Released: Weekly. **Price:** $4, introductory 4-week offer(Digital only). **Description:** Dan Tropeano will serve as the new head of United Healthcare of Pennsylvania, while continuing in his position as executive director of United Healthcare's Pennsylvania and Delaware health plans. Tropeano discusses his new role and notes that the medical insurance market has become increasingly competitive as consumers seek cheaper and more flexible products. **Availability:** Print; Online.

19952 ■ *"Under Armour Hopes to Stomp on Nike with Basketball Shoe"* in *Baltimore Business Journal* (Vol. 28, October 22, 2010, No. 24, pp. 1)
Pub: Baltimore Business Journal
Contact: Rhonda Pringle, President
E-mail: rpringle@bizjournals.com
Ed: Erik Siemers. **Description:** Uner Armour Inc. will release its Micro G line of four basketball sneakers on October 23, 2010. The company's executives mentioned that Under Armour's goal is to appeal to customers, and not to chip away at Nike Inc.'s supremacy in basketball shoes. The new sneakers will range from $80 to $110. **Availability:** Print; Online.

19953 ■ *Understand Your Competitors*
URL(s): www.infoentrepreneurs.org/en/guides/understand-your-competitors/
Description: A guide for small business owners that presents information on how to analyze who your competitors are, how to research what they're doing, and how to act on the information you gain. **Availability:** Online.

19954 ■ *"Unfilled Hotels Go All Out for Business Meetings"* in *Crain's Detroit Business* (Vol. 25, June 8, 2009, No. 23, pp. 9)
Pub: Crain Communications Inc.
Contact: Barry Asin, President
Ed: Daniel Duggan. **Description:** Hotels in Michigan are offering discounts to companies holding business meetings at their properties. Details of competition and plans are included. **Availability:** Print; Online.

19955 ■ *"U.S. Competitiveness and the Chinese Challenge"* in *Harvard Business Review* (Vol. 90, March 2012, No. 3, pp. 40)
Pub: Harvard Business Review Press
Contact: Moderna V. Pfizer, Contact
Ed: Xu Xiaonian. **Price:** $6, hardcover. **Description:** Although China's shift from cntral planningto market-oriented policies has boosted innovation, intellectual property rights and original research are still insufficiently valued. The U.S. has the edge on China in this respect; it remains for the U.S. to restore confidence in its innovation and creativity. **Availability:** PDF; Online.

19956 ■ *"Vancouver, B.C. Shines - at Seattle's Expense?"* in *Puget Sound Business Journal* (Vol. 35, May 9, 2014, No. 3, pp. 6)
Pub: American City Business Journals, Inc.
Contact: Mike Olivieri, Executive Vice President
Description: Reports show that Vancouver, British Columbia, Canada is becoming Seattle, Washington's biggest competitor because of the British Columbia's business-friendly policies. Microsoft is increasing their number of workers in in Vancouver, while Amazon will open an office in the city. The similarities between Seattle and Vancouver are explored. **Availability:** Online.

19957 ■ *"Warning Lights Flashing for Air Canada: Carty's Back"* in *Globe & Mail* (February 22, 2006, pp. B1)
Ed: Brent Jang. **Description:** Air Canada's rival, Donald Carty, former chief executive officer at American Airlines and new chairman of Toronto based Regco Holdings Inc., launches Porter Airlines Inc. out of Toronto City Center Airport this fall.

19958 ■ *"Way More Than Mowing"* in *Green Industry Pro* (Vol. 23, September 2011)
Ed: Rod Dickens. **Description:** Shipp Shape Lawn Services located in Sylvester, Georgia now offers aeration, fertilizing and weed control, mulching, yard renovation, flowerbed maintenance, landscaping, as well as irrigation repairs and installation in order to diversify the business and stay competitive. **Availability:** Online.

19959 ■ *"WestJet Gears Up for Domestic Dogfight"* in *Globe & Mail* (May 1, 2007, pp. B6)
Ed: Brent Jang. **Description:** The effort of WestJet Airlines Ltd. to compete with Air Canada for greater market share of passengers is discussed. **Availability:** Online.

19960 ■ *"What's Your Language Strategy? It Should Bind Your Company's Global Talent Management and Vision"* in *Harvard Business Review* (Vol. 92, September 2014, No. 9, pp. 70)
Pub: Harvard Business Publishing
Contact: Diane Belcher, Managing Director
Price: $8.95. **Description:** Cultural awareness and language skills should be built into organizations to promote talent that is equally effective locally and globally. This will bridge gaps between non-native and native language speakers, fostering collaboration and increase competitiveness. **Availability:** Online; PDF.

19961 ■ *"Where Pet Nutrition Meets Love"* in *Pet Product News* (Vol. 66, September 2012, No. 9, pp. S14)
Description: Michael Landa, coowner of Nulo Pet Products, discusses the role of his company in reducing pet obesity through the manufacture of high-protein foods. Aside from explaining his interest in pet obesity, Landa also describes how the company differentiates itself from competitors. **Availability:** Online.

19962 ■ *"Why "Competition" Is Great for Small Businesses"* in *Business 2 Community* (Aug. 19, 2019)
URL(s): www.business2community.com/small-business/why-competition-is-great-for-small-businesses-02233045
Ed: Ravindra Savaram. **Released:** August 19, 2019. **Description:** Discusses the significance of small business competition for small businesses. **Availability:** Online.

19963 ■ *Why Competition Is Good for Business*
URL(s): smallbusinessify.com/why-competition-is-good-for-business/
Description: Discusses why competition is good for your small business and provides ways in which having competitors can be advantageous to everyone in the market. **Availability:** Online.

19964 ■ *"Why Competition Is a Good Thing"* in *Bplans*
URL(s): articles.bplans.com/why-competition-is-a-good-thing/
Ed: Noah Parsons. **Description:** Explores why having business competition is a good thing, but brings forth reasons why focusing too much on your competition can be a detriment. **Availability:** Online.

19965 ■ *"Why the Gap is Stalking Lululemon"* in *Canadian Business* (Vol. 85, August 22, 2012, No. 14, pp. 7)
Ed: Jim Sutherland. **Description:** Lululemon Athletica is facing competition against Gap Inc.'s Athleta as the retail giant plans to have about 50 new shops across Canada by the end of 2012. Athleta is also carrying lines of yoga- and activewear similar to that of Lululemon's and are even located near their stores. **Availability:** Online.

19966 ■ *"Why LinkedIn is the Social Network that Will Never Die"* in *Advertising Age* (Vol. 81, December 6, 2010, No. 43, pp. 2)
Pub: Crain Communications, Inc.
Contact: Jessica Botos, Manager, Marketing
E-mail: jessica.botos@crainsnewyork.com
Ed: Irina Slutsky. **Description:** Despite the popularity of Facebook, LinkedIn will always be a source for professionals who wish to network. **Availability:** Online.

19967 ■ *"Why Nestle Should Sell Alcon"* in *Barron's* (Vol. 88, March 17, 2008, No. 11, pp. M12)
Pub: Dow Jones & Company Inc.
Contact: Almar Latour, Chief Executive Officer
Ed: Sean Walters. **Description:** Nestle should sell Alcon because Nestle can't afford to be complacent as its peers have made changes to their portfolios to boost competitiveness. Nestle's stake in Alcon and L'Oreal have been ignored by investors and Nestle could realize better value by strengthening its nutrition division through acquisitions. **Availability:** Online.

19968 ■ *"Why U.S. Competitiveness Matters to All of Us: The World Wants America to Regain Its Vibrancy. Let's Stop Assigning Blame and Instead Focus on Solutions"* in *Harvard Business Review* (Vol. 90, March 2012, No. 3, pp. 49)
Pub: Harvard Business Review Press
Contact: Moderna V. Pfizer, Contact
Ed: Nitin Nohria. **Description:** The introduction to this special issue presents perspectives on the US economy from citizens of other nations. While they realize globalization means countries are interdependent and that a strong America provides an international boost, they feel US leaders are concerned more with politics than economic growth. Action is needed instead.

19969 ■ *"Will Focus on Maryland Businesses Continue?"* in *Baltimore Business Journal* (Vol. 28, November 5, 2010, No. 26, pp. 1)
Pub: Baltimore Business Journal
Contact: Rhonda Pringle, President
E-mail: rpringle@bizjournals.com
Ed: Scott Dance. **Description:** The 2010 election may call for new efforts to teach new lawmakers to assure that the viewpoints of businesses are considered and accurately delivered. The Greater Baltimore Committee and similar groups have gathered reports on the competitiveness of Maryland and are planning to use them to make a case of keeping business a top priority. **Availability:** Print; Online.

19970 ■ *"Winners Dream: A Journey from Corner Store to Corner Office"*
Pub: Simon & Schuster Adult Publishing Group
Contact: Jonathan Karp, President
Released: October 14, 2014. **Price:** $28.99, hardcover, plus $2.24 shipping charges. **Description:** Bill McDermott, CEO of the world's largest business software company, SAP, profiles his career. He discusses his career moves, sales strategies, employee incentives to create high performance teams, and the competitive advantages of optimism and hard work. The entrepreneur offers a blueprint for success and the knowledge that the real dream is the journey, not the preconceived destination. **Availability:** E-book; Print; Download; Audio.

19971 ■ *"Who's On Top in the Telecom Turf Fight"* in *Dallas Business Journal* (Vol. 37, April 25, 2014, No. 33, pp. 4)
Pub: American City Business Journals, Inc.
Contact: Mike Olivieri, Executive Vice President
Released: Weekly. **Price:** $4, introductory 4-week offer(Digital & Print). **Description:** The four major wireless providers in the U.S. are competing for customers in North Texas and around the country. Experts say AT&T, Verizon, Sprint and T-Mobile have to offer better quality services, faster service and lower pricing to win customers from each other. **Availability:** Print; Online.

19972 ■ *"A Woman's Advantage"* in *Black Enterprise* (Vol. 38, December 2007, No. 5, pp. 86)
Pub: Earl G. Graves Ltd.
Contact: Earl Graves, Jr., President
Ed: Marcia A. Reed-Woodard. **Description:** Leadership development is essential for any small business. Simmons College's Strategic Leadership for Women educational course offers a five-day program for professional women teaching powerful strategies to perform, compete, and win in the workplace. **Availability:** Online.

19973 ■ *Your First Year in Real Estate: Making the Transition from Total Novice to Successful Professional*
Released: Second edition. **Price:** $22, paperback; $9.99, e-book. **Description:** Zeller helps new realtors to select the right company, develop mentor and client relationships, using the Internet and social networking to stay ahead of competition, to set and reach career goals, to stay current in the market, and more. **Availability:** E-book; Print.

VIDEO/AUDIO MEDIA

19974 ■ *The Best Small Business Podcast: Co-Opetition - Growing Your Small Business with Unexpected Competitive Alliances*
URL(s): richgee.libsyn.com/296-co-opetition-growing-your-small-business-with-unexpected-competitive-alliances
Ed: Rich Gee. **Released:** May 22, 2023.

19975 ■ *The Best Small Business Show: How to Gain a Competitive Advantage Over Your Competition*
URL(s): richgee.libsyn.com/299-how-to-gain-a-competitive-advantage-over-your-competition
Ed: Rich Gee. **Released:** June 12, 2023. **Description:** Podcast discusses how to earn competitive advantages.

19976 ■ *The How of Business: Is Your Small Business Competitive?*
URL(s): www.thehowofbusiness.com/episode-540-is-your-business-competitive
Ed: Henry Lopez. **Released:** October 07, 2024. **Description:** Podcast explains how to remain competitive in your market or expand/shift into new markets.

19977 ■ *How I Built This: Advice Line with Sarah Kauss of S'well*
URL(s): wondery.com/shows/how-i-built-this/episode/10386-advice-line-with-sarah-kauss-of-swell
Ed: Guy Raz. **Released:** June 20, 2024. **Description:** Podcast offers questions from early-stage founders about positioning their products in competitive markets.

19978 ■ *How I Built This: Less Competition, More Creation with Renée Mauborgne*
URL(s): wondery.com/shows/how-i-built-this/episode/10386-less-competition-more-creation-with-renee-mauborgne
Ed: Guy Raz. **Released:** April 25, 2024. **Description:** Podcast asserts that too many entrepreneurs focus on competition instead of creating new markets.

CONSULTANTS

19979 ■ **ARDITO Information and Research Inc.**
910 Foulk Rd., Ste. 200
Wilmington, DE 19803
Description: A full-service information and research firm. Provides information in areas of financial data, published research, demographic data, industry-specific publications, competitor data, marketing and sales trends, new product developments, government relations, bibliographies. Industries served are pharmaceutical, health, publishing and environment and business. **Scope:** A full-service information and research firm. Provides information in areas of financial data, published research, demographic data, industry-specific publications, competitor data, marketing and sales trends, new product developments, government relations, bibliographies. Industries served are pharmaceutical, health, publishing and environment and business. **Publications:** "The Swine flu pandemic: Authoritative information versus community gossip," Searcher, Oct, 2009; "The Medical blogosphere: How social networking platforms are changing medical searching," Searcher, May, 2009; "Social Networking and Video Web Sites: MySpace and YouTube Meet the Copyright Cops," Searcher, May, 2007; "Copyright Clearance Center raises transactional fees," Information Today, Jul, 2004.

19980 ■ **Queen's Business Consulting (QBC)**
Queen's University
Stephen J. R. Smith School of Business
Goodes Hall, Rm. LL201
Kingston, ON, Canada K7L 3N6

Ph: (613)893-2327
Co. E-mail: sbc@queensu.ca
URL: http://smith.queensu.ca/index.php
Contact: Charlie Mignault, Director
E-mail: cem10@queensu.ca
Description: Provider of management consulting services such as strategy, sales, marketing, data analysis, and operational planning. **Scope:** Provider of management consulting services such as strategy, sales, marketing, data analysis, and operational planning. **Founded:** 1973. **Publications:** "Information technology, network structure and competitive action. Information Systems Research," 2010; "The role of dominance in the appeal of violent media depictions. Journal of Advertising," 2010; "Great expectations and broken promises: Misleading claims, product failure, expectancy disconfirmation and consumer distrust. Journal of the Academy of Marketing Science," 2010; "Development and psychometric properties of the Transformational Teaching Questionnaire. Journal of Health Psychology," 2010; ". Predicting workplace aggression: myths, realities, and remaining questions," 2009; "The Inconvenient Truth about Improving Vehicle Fuel Efficiency: An MultiAttribute Analysis of the Efficient Frontier of the U.S. Automobile Industry, Transportation Research-Part," 2009; "Fraud in Canadian Nonprofit Organizations as Seen through the Eyes of Canadian Newspapers," 2009; "Disentangling the Indirect Links between SES and Health: The Dynamic Roles of Work Stressors and Personal Contro," 2009; "The strong situation hypothesis. Personality and Social Psychology Review," 2009; " Planning Your Next Crisis Decisively and Effectively. Ivey Business Journal," 2009. **Training:** Enabling Innovation Discussion Highlights, 2011; Intellectual Capital, 2010; On the diffusion of knowledge inside the organization, 2010; A model of the tacit knowledge lifecycle for decision-making: From creation to utilization, 2010; Individual, group, and organizational learning; A knowledge management perspective, 2009; Political economies of knowledge, with an example, 2009; The alignment of business and knowledge strategies and structures, 2009; Using IT To Support the Discovery of Novel Knowledge in Organizations, 2008; Leadership: Knowledge Management by a New Name?, 2007; Every User Tells a Story, 2007.

Competitive Pricing

START-UP INFORMATION

19981 ■ *"Making 'Freemium' Work: Many Start-Ups Fail to Recognize the Challenges of This Popular Business Model"* in *Harvard Business Review* (Vol. 92, May 2014, No. 5, pp. 27)
Pub: Harvard Business Publishing
Contact: Diane Belcher, Managing Director
Price: $6. **Description:** The key to successful 'freemium' business model is identifying which features to offer free of charge, and how to price the remaining features. Target conversion rates conversion life cycle preparation, and commitment to innovation are also discussed. **Availability:** Online; PDF.

EDUCATIONAL PROGRAMS

19982 ■ **How to Bargain & Negotiate with Vendors and Suppliers**
Fred Pryor Seminars & CareerTrack
5700 Broadmoor, Ste. 300
Mission, KS 66202
Free: 800-780-8476
Fax: (913)967-8849
Co. E-mail: customerservice@pryor.com
URL: http://www.pryor.com
Contact: Janet Turner, Contact
E-mail: dmca@pryor.com
URL(s): www.pryor.com/training-seminars/bargain-negotiate-vendors-suppliers/?zip=90012
Frequency: Irregular. **Description:** Learn how to get lower prices, quicker delivery, higher quality and better service through negotiation. **Audience:** Business professionals. **Principal Exhibits:** Learn how to get lower prices, quicker delivery, higher quality and better service through negotiation.

REFERENCE WORKS

19983 ■ *7 Smart Pricing Strategies to Attract Customers*
URL(s): www.uschamber.com/co/run/finance/pricing-strategies-for-your-business
Ed: Emily Heaslip. **Description:** A guide to helping your small business determine the best pricing strategies for continued sales success. **Availability:** Online.

19984 ■ *"The 490 Made Chevy a Bargain Player"* in *Automotive News* (Vol. 86, October 31, 2011, No. 6488, pp. S22)
Pub: Crain Communications, Inc.
Contact: Barry Asin, President
Ed: David Phillips. **Description:** The first Chevrolet with the 490 engine was sold in 1913, but it was too expensive for masses. In 1914 the carmaker launched a lower-priced H-series of cars competitively priced. Nameplates such as Corvette, Bel Air, Camaro and Silverado have defined Chevrolet through the years. **Availability:** Online.

19985 ■ *"2015 Corporate Counsel Legal Pricing Guide - Mergers & Acquisitions"* in *Economics & Business Week* (August 16, 2014, pp. 3)
Pub: NewsRX LLC.
Contact: Kalani Rosell, Contact
Description: Research and Markets has added the 2015 Corporate Counsel Legal Pricing Guide - Mergers & Acquisitions to its report. The guide details how the mergers and acquisitions market for law firms has increased since the downturn in 2008-2009 due mostly to an improved economy, increased corporate liquidity and sometimes corporate tax policies of certain countries. **Availability:** Print; Online.

19986 ■ *"Analysts Expect American Airlines Bankruptcy to Raise Ticket Prices"* in *Dallas Business Journal* (Vol. 35, February 17, 2012, No. 23, pp. 1)
Pub: Baltimore Business Journal
Contact: Rhonda Pringle, President
E-mail: rpringle@bizjournals.com
Description: American Airlines' bankruptcy may cause ticking prices to rise. The average domesic fare has increased nearly 17 percent in the past two years. **Availability:** Print; Online.

19987 ■ *"Auctions and Bidding: A Guide for Computer Scientists"* in *ACM Computing Surveys* (Vol. 43, Summer 2011, No. 2, pp. 10)
Pub: Association for Computing Machinery
Contact: Yannis Ioannidis, President
Ed: Simon Parsons, Juan A. Rodriguez-Aguilar, Mark Klein. **Released:** Volume 43 Issue 2. **Price:** $10, Members; $15, Nonmembers; $5, Students. **Description:** There are various actions: single dimensional, multi-dimensional, single-sided, double-sided, first-price, second-price, English, Dutch, Japanese, sealed-bid, and these have been extensively discussed and analyzed in economics literature. This literature is surveyed from a computer science perspective, primarily from the viewpoint of computer scientists who are interested in learning about auction theory, and to provide pointers into the economics literature for those who want a deeper technical understanding. In addition, since auctions are an increasingly important topic in computer science, the article also looks at work on auctions from the computer science literature. The aim is to identify what both bodies of work tell us about creating electronic auctions. **Availability:** Download; PDF.

19988 ■ *"Baltimore's Steamed Crab Prices Reach New Highs: Paying the Price"* in *Baltimore Business Journal* (Vol. 28, July 9, 2010, No. 9, pp. 1)
Pub: Baltimore Business Journal
Contact: Rhonda Pringle, President
E-mail: rpringle@bizjournals.com
Ed: Emily Mullin. **Description:** Crab prices have never been higher in Baltimore, Maryland and businesses have been led to count on strengthening demand for seafood. For instance, the average price for a dozen large crabs has increased by 5 percent to $58.90. How restaurants have responded to the increase in prices is discussed, along with factors that might have caused the harvest of smaller crabs. **Availability:** Print.

19989 ■ *"BK Menu Gives Casual Dining Reason to Worry"* in *Advertising Age* (Vol. 79, November 17, 2008, No. 43, pp. 12)
Pub: Crain Communications, Inc.
Contact: Jessica Botos, Manager, Marketing
E-mail: jessica.botos@crainsnewyork.com
Ed: Emily Bryson York. **Description:** Burger King is beginning to compete with such casual dining restaurants as Applebees and the Cheesecake Factory with new premium menu items, including thicker burgers and ribs; statistical data regarding the casual dining segment which continues to fall and Burger King, whose sales continue to rise is included. **Availability:** Online.

19990 ■ *"Bubble Trouble? Many Experts Say Seattle Housing Market Is Headed for a Fall"* in *Puget Sound Business Journal* (Vol. 34, April 18, 2014, No. 53, pp. 4)
Pub: American City Business Journals, Inc.
Contact: Mike Olivieri, Executive Vice President
Description: Redfin disclosed that nearly one third of homes listed in the real estate market in King County, Washington were sold above the listing price in February 2014 and it is forecast that the housing market is headed into a new bubble. Statistics indicate that the trend in rising prices is slowing even in the face of a declining supply of available homes. The impact of international buyers is also discussed.

19991 ■ *"Buick Prices Verano Below Rival Luxury Compacts"* in *Automotive News* (Vol. 86, October 31, 2011, No. 6488, pp. 10)
Pub: Crain Communications Inc.
Contact: Barry Asin, President
Ed: Mike Colias. **Description:** General Motors's Verano will compete with other luxury compacts such as the Lexus IS 250 and the Acura TSX, but will be prices significantly lower coming in with a starting price of $23,470, about $6,000 to $10,000 less than those competitors. **Availability:** Online.

19992 ■ *"Builders Aim to Cut Costs: Pushing Changes to Regain Share of Residential Market; Seek Council's Help"* in *Crain's New York Business*
Pub: Crain Communications, Inc.
Contact: Jessica Botos, Manager, Marketing
E-mail: jessica.botos@crainsnewyork.com
Ed: Erik Engquist. **Description:** Union contractors and workers are worried about a decline in their market share for housing so they intend to ask the City Council to impose new safety and benefit standards on all contractors to avoid being undercut by nonunion competitors. **Availability:** Print; Online.

19993 ■ *"Cash Rents Reach Sky-High Levels"* in *Farm Industry News* (November 23, 2011)
Pub: Informa Business Media, Inc.
Contact: Charlie McCurdy, President

Ed: Karen McMahon. **Description:** Strong commodity prices are driving land values creating a hot rental market for farm land. Highest rents occur when farmers compete head-to-head for land. **Availability:** Online.

19994 ■ *"Colorado Companies Adjust as Drought Boosts Food Prices" in Denver Business Journal (Vol. 64, August 17, 2012, No. 13, pp. 1)*
Pub: Baltimore Business Journal
Contact: Rhonda Pringle, President
E-mail: rpringle@bizjournals.com

Description: The drought engulfing most of the US has led some Colorado companies to modify product offerings and declare that food prices will be raised by four percent next year. The federal government has already declared all of Colorado and half of the nation's counties as disaster areas, making them accessible for federal aid. **Availability:** Print; Online.

19995 ■ *"Competitive Pricing Strategy" in Chron (Jan. 25, 2019)*
URL(s): smallbusiness.chron.com/competitive-pricing-strategy-59220.html

Ed: Catherine Lovering. **Released:** January 25, 2019. **Description:** Effective pricing can make or break a business. This article discusses pricing strategy options and things to consider about competitive pricing for your small business. **Availability:** Online.

19996 ■ *Competitive Pricing Strategy – See How Products Are Priced*
URL(s): www.intelligencenode.com/blog/competitive-pricing-strategy-see-products-priced/

Description: Effective pricing strategy is essential to ensure your business is in line with the competition, and will maximize revenue and deliver a good profit. This blog post provides information on 4 major e-commerce pricing strategies and discusses competitive pricing strategies. **Availability:** Online.

19997 ■ *The Competitive Pricing Strategy Guide (Covers B2B and B2C Businesses)*
URL(s): www.singlegrain.com/marketing-strategy/competitive-pricing-strategies-b2c-b2b/

Ed: Joydeep Bhattacharya. **Description:** A guide that details competitive pricing, its advantages, and how your small business can implement a competitive pricing strategy. **Availability:** Online.

19998 ■ *"Competitive Pricing: What It Is and How to Use It for Your Business" in QuickBooks Blog (May 31, 2020)*
URL(s): quickbooks.intuit.com/r/midsize-business/pricing-strategies-models-competitive/

Ed: Thomas Tracy. **Released:** May 31, 2020. **Description:** Details what competitive pricing is, provides examples, and shares three competitive pricing strategies. **Availability:** Online.

19999 ■ *"Competitor Based Pricing Strategy: Competition Based Pricing for SAAS" in ProfitWell Blog (Sept. 6, 2021)*
URL(s): www.priceintelligently.com/blog/bid/161610/competitor-based-pricing-101-the-necessities-and-your-pricing-strategy

Ed: Vivian Guo. **Released:** September 06, 2021. **Description:** Discusses one of the most important aspects of your small business - pricing. Includes information on competition-based pricing, including pros and cons. **Availability:** Online.

20000 ■ *The Complete Idiot's Guide to Starting an eBay® Business*
Pub: Penguin Publishing Group

Released: April 03, 2012. **Price:** $19.95, paperback; $12.99, e-book. **Description:** Guide for starting an eBay business includes information on products to sell, how to price merchandise, and details for working with services like PayPal, and how to organize fulfillment services. **Availability:** E-book; Print.

20001 ■ *"Consumers Seek to Redo Rate Structure: Smaller Biz Paid Big Rates" in Crain's Detroit Business (Vol. 25, June 22, 2009)*
Pub: Crain Communications Inc.
Contact: Barry Asin, President

Ed: Amy Lane. **Description:** Consumers Energy Company charged small business customers disproportionately higher rates on June 2009 electric bills than other consumers. **Availability:** Print; Online.

20002 ■ *"Corn Belt Farmland Prices Hit Record Levels" in Farm Industry News (December 1, 2011)*
Pub: Informa Business Media, Inc.
Contact: Charlie McCurdy, President

Ed: David Hest. **Description:** Farmland prices have set records over the last six months in Iowa. Farmland broker and auction company owner, Murray Wise, believes this is not a bubble, that the economics of this market are solid. **Availability:** Print; Online.

20003 ■ *"Cost of Creating Health Insurance Exchange in Md. 'Largely Unknown'" in Baltimore Business Journal (Vol. 28, September 3, 2010, No. 17, pp. 1)*
Pub: Baltimore Business Journal
Contact: Rhonda Pringle, President
E-mail: rpringle@bizjournals.com

Ed: Emily Mullin. **Description:** United States health reform is seen to result in increased health insurance prices in Maryland. However, health care reform advocates claim a new marketplace and increased competition will help keep costs down. **Availability:** Print.

20004 ■ *"Craft Businesses That Make (the MOST) Money" in Made Urban (April 12, 2018)*
URL(s): www.madeurban.com/blog/craft-businesses-that-make-money/

Released: April 12, 2018. **Description:** If you are a crafter and engage in selling your crafts, are you considering all of your costs? It may surprise you how little profit, if any, you are making. Some crafts have a larger demand than others, so there is a bigger chance of making more money by selling those crafts. Included is a list of these types of crafts and a discussion about each one. **Availability:** Online.

20005 ■ *"Crouser Releases Offline UV Coating Price Report" in American Printer (Vol. 128, June 1, 2011, No. 6)*

Description: Crouser and Associates will offer the 'Pricing Off-Line UV Coating' report that provides background information on all three types of protective printing coatings and price guidance. The report will also offer comparisons of four popular types of offline equipment.

20006 ■ *"Customers Will Pay More For Less" in (Vol. 90, June 2012, No. 6, pp. 30)*
Pub: Harvard Business Review Press
Contact: Moderna V. Pfizer, Contact

Ed: Alexander Chernev. **Price:** $6. **Description:** Research indicates that bundling an expensive product and an inexpensive product together makes customers less willing to pay for them than for a single expensive item. Categorical reasoning makes people perceive the inexpensive item to have a negative impact on the expensive item when presented as a single offering. **Availability:** PDF; Online.

20007 ■ *The Designer's Guide to Marketing and Pricing: How to Win Clients and What to Charge Them*

Released: First edition. **Description:** Guide to running a creative services business teaches designers how to be more effective, attract new clients, wages, and how to accurately estimate a project.

20008 ■ *"The Devolution of Home-Electronics Stores" in Philadelphia Business Journal (Vol. 28, June 8, 2012, No. 17, pp. 1)*
Pub: Baltimore Business Journal
Contact: Rhonda Pringle, President
E-mail: rpringle@bizjournals.com

Description: Philadelphia, Pennsylvania-area consumer electronics stores have mirrored the national trend in which big-box retailers are taking a bigger share of the home-electronics market. However, smaller, locally-based chains are competing in terms of pricing transparency and custom electronics. **Availability:** Print; Online.

20009 ■ *"Digital-Physical Mashups: To Consumers, the Real and Virtual Worlds Are One. The Same Should Go For Your Company" in Harvard Business Review (Vol. 92, September 2014, No. 9, pp. 84)*
Pub: Harvard Business Publishing
Contact: Diane Belcher, Managing Director

Price: $8.95. **Description:** By merging their physical and virtual operations, companies can provide a seamless experience for customers, boosting competitive advantage. These include strengthening customer/engagement links, approaching innovation through complementary expertise, and ensure that chief executive officers possess adequate technological knowledge. **Availability:** Online; PDF.

20010 ■ *"Dollar Store Growth Presents New Challenge to Larger Mass Retailers" in Pet Product News (Vol. 66, August 2012, No. 8, pp. 4)*

Description: Dollar stores have been rising as a direct competitor to bigger mass-market retailers in the pet market. Aside from focusing on low prices, dollar stores' competitive strategy has been marked by smaller store size and convenience of edited assortments. Other factors that have lured a growing consumer base to dollar stores are described. **Availability:** Online.

20011 ■ *"Drop in the Bucket Makes a lot of Waves" in Globe & Mail (March 22, 2007, pp. B1)*

Ed: Greg Keenan. **Description:** The concern of several auto makers in Canada over the impact of providing heavy rebates to customers buying energy-efficient cars is discussed. **Availability:** Online.

20012 ■ *EBay Income: How ANYONE of Any Age, Location, and/or Background Can Build a Highly Profitable Online Business with eBay*
Pub: Atlantic Publishing Co.
Contact: Dr. Heather L. Johnson, Contact

Description: A complete overview of eBay is given and guides any small company through the entire process of creating the auction and auction strategies, photography, writing copy, text and formatting, multiple sales, programming tricks, PayPal, accounting, creating marketing, merchandising, managing email lists, advertising plans, taxes and sales tax, best time to list items and for how long, sniping programs, international customers, opening a storefront, electronic commerce, buy-it now pricing, keywords, Google marketing and eBay secrets.

20013 ■ *"The Ethics of Price Discrimination" in Business Ethics Quarterly (Vol. 21, October 2011, No. 4, pp. 633)*

Ed: Juan M. Elegido. **Released:** Volume 21, Issue 4. **Description:** Price discrimination is the practice of charging different customers different prices for the same product. Many people consider price discrimination unfair, but economists argue that in many cases price discrimination is more likely to lead to greater welfare than is the uniform pricing alternative, sometimes even for every party in the transaction. **Availability:** Online.

20014 ■ *The Everything Store: Jeff Bezos and the Age of Amazon*
Pub: Little, Brown and Company
Contact: Judy Clain, Editor-in-Chief

Released: October 15, 2013. **Price:** $28, hardcover; $30, audiobook CD; $24.98, audiobook downloadable; $12.99, e-book; $18, paperback; $30, hardcover(large print); $28. **Description:** Amazon.com started as a bookseller, a company delivering books through the mail. Today, the online store, offers a limitless selection of goods at competitively low prices. Profile of entrepreneur Jeff Bezos that outlines his endless pursuit of new markets and risky new ventures to transform retail. **Availability:** audiobook; CD-ROM; E-book; Print.

20015 ■ *"Fast-Growing Envision Joins Billion-Dollar Club"* in *Sacramento Business Journal (Vol. 29, March 9, 2012, No. 2, pp. 1)*
Pub: Baltimore Business Journal
Contact: Rhonda Pringle, President
E-mail: rpringle@bizjournals.com
Price: $4, Introductory 4-Week Offer(Digital & Print).
Description: Envision Pharmaceutical Services has generated an annual revenue of $1 billion in 2011. The company helps employers, unions, insurers and governments to control pharmacy costs. It has also increased its market share. **Availability:** Print; Online.

20016 ■ *Faster Cheaper Better*
Released: December 28, 2010. **Price:** $27.50, hardcover. **Description:** Nine levels for transforming work in order to achieve business growth are outlined. The book helps small business compete against the low-wage countries. **Availability:** E-book; Print.

20017 ■ *"Flint Group Raises Prices of Offset Inks in EMEA"* in *American Printer (Vol. 128, August 1, 2011, No. 8)*
Description: Due to the rising cost for raw materials, Flint Group is raising their prices for inks and coatings in North American. **Availability:** Online.

20018 ■ *"Flying Discounted Skies"* in *Barron's (Vol. 92, September 17, 2012, No. 38, pp. 20)*
Description: Business aviation services provider Xojet offers highly competitive pricing due to its efficient fleet utilization. The firm adopts unconventional methods in running its airplane fleet and has a transparent pricing scheme. **Availability:** Online.

20019 ■ *"For His Bigness of Heart: Larry O'Toole: Gentle Giant Moving, Somerville, Massachusetts"* in *Inc. (Volume 32, December 2010)*
Pub: Mansueto Ventures L.L.C.
Contact: Stephanie Mehta, Chief Executive Officer
Ed: Leigh Buchanan. **Released:** December 01, 2010. **Description:** Profile of Larry O'Toole, owners of Gentle Giant Moving Company, where his company charges more, but in return consumers receive a higher quality service. **Availability:** Online.

20020 ■ *"Fossil Fuel, Renewable Fuel Shares Expected to Flip Flop"* in *Farm Industry News (April 29, 2011)*
Pub: Informa Business Media, Inc.
Contact: Charlie McCurdy, President
Ed: Lynn Grooms. **Description:** Total energy use of fossil fuels is predicted to fall 5 percent by the year 2035, with renewable fuel picking it up. **Availability:** Online.

20021 ■ *Free: The Future of a Radical Price*
Description: A new trend shows companies using giveaways as a means to attract business and increase profits.

20022 ■ *From Concept To Consumer: How to Turn Ideas Into Money*
Ed: Phil Baker. **Released:** 1st edition. **Price:** $27.99, paperback. **Description:** Renowned product developer Phil Baker explains how a great idea accounts for only 5 percent of all the factors of success and why the majority of success is dependent upon a myriad of other factors, including the time it takes to get to market, price, marketing and distribution. By being their own best competition, a small company can stay one step ahead of competitors. **Availability:** Print.

20023 ■ *"Fuel Costs Curb Food Truck Trend"* in *Tampa Tribune (March 26, 2012)*
Ed: Jeff Houck. **Description:** Owner of Maggie on the Move food truck, Margaret Loflin, has had to raise the cost of drinks served in order to cover the increased cost of gasoline to run her business. She also added smaller, less costly items to her menu. Her husband has gone back to a part-time job in he hopes of keeping their food truck running. **Availability:** Print; Online.

20024 ■ *"H&M Offers a Dress for Less"* in *Canadian Business (Vol. 83, September 14, 2010, No. 15, pp. 20)*
Pub: Rogers Media Inc.
Contact: Neil Spivak, Chief Executive Officer
Ed: Laura Cameron. **Description:** Swedish clothing company H&M has implemented loss leader strategy by pricing some dresses at extremely low prices. The economy has forced retailers to keep prices down despite the increasing cost of manufacturing, partly due to Chinese labor becoming more expensive. How the trend will affect apparel companies is discussed. **Availability:** Print; Online.

20025 ■ *"High Anxiety"* in *Canadian Business (Vol. 80, November 19, 2007, No. 23, pp. 11)*
Description: Value of Canadian dollar continues to rise, and consumers are asking for lower prices of goods. Retailers, on the other hand, are facing concerns over losing sales. The impacts of the rising Canadian dollar on the business sector and consumer behavior are examined. **Availability:** Online.

20026 ■ *"Houston Law Firms Plan Rate Bumps"* in *Houston Business Journal (Vol. 40, December 25, 2009, No. 33, pp. 1)*
Pub: Houston Business Journal
Contact: Bob Charlet, President
E-mail: bcharlet@bizjournals.com
Ed: Ford Gunter. **Description:** Survey shows that Houston, Texas-based law firms were in line with a 3.2 percent average rate hike projected for 2010. The big firms were ready to offset some losses with a rate bump of 4 percent while smaller firms have been expecting an increase of about 3 percent. **Availability:** Print; Online.

20027 ■ *How to Get Rich*
Ed: Felix Dennis. **Released:** 2013. **Price:** $8.16, paperback. **Description:** The author, publisher of Maxim, The Week, and Stuff magazines, discusses the mistakes he made running his companies. He didn't understand that people who buy computer gaming magazines wanted a free game with each copy, as one of his rivals was offering. And he laments not diversifying into television and exploiting the Internet. **Availability:** E-book; Print.

20028 ■ *"How Has Cincinnati's City Golf Privatization Played?"* in *Business Courier (Vol. 27, September 10, 2010, No. 19, pp. 1)*
Pub: Business Courier
Ed: Dan Monk. **Description:** It was reported that private contractors are getting more revenue from fewer golfers on city-owned courses in Cincinnati, Ohio. In 1998, the city handed over seven municipal courses to private management. However, some believe that the city has escalated a price war among the region's golf courses. **Availability:** Print; Online.

20029 ■ *How to Make Big Money in Your Own Small Business: Unexpected Rules Every Small Business Owner Needs to Know*
Ed: Jeffrey J. Fox, Jeffrey J. Fox. **Released:** May 12, 2004. **Price:** $16.95; C$24.95; $16.95; C$24.95; $16.95; C$24.95. **Description:** Former sales and marketing pro offers advice on growing a small business. **Availability:** Print.

20030 ■ *"How Much For a Magic Bullet?"* in *San Francisco Business Times (Vol. 28, April 25, 2014, No. 40, pp. 4)*
Pub: American City Business Journals, Inc.
Contact: Mike Olivieri, Executive Vice President
Released: April 25, 2014. **Price:** $4, Introductory 4-Week Offer(Digital & Print). **Description:** Novel gene therapies being developed by San Francisco, California--based research companies entail high prices. Gilead Sciences Inc. developed the hepatitis drug called Sovaldt that is being sold for $1,000 per pill. Health insurers may not be able to finance long-term treatments at these high prices. **Availability:** Print; Online.

20031 ■ *"How Much Profit is Enough?"* in *Automotive News (Vol. 86, October 31, 2011, No. 6488, pp. 12)*
Pub: Crain Communications Inc.
Contact: Barry Asin, President
Description: Workers at the big three automobile companies are unhappy about the issues of class wealth, like the high compensations offered to CEOs. **Availability:** Print; Online.

20032 ■ *How to Price Products - 7 Competitive Pricing Strategies to Make a Profit*
URL(s): www.godaddy.com/garage/how-to-price-products/
Released: April 28, 2021. **Description:** Lists 7 steps to establish a competitive pricing strategy for your e-commerce business. **Availability:** Online.

20033 ■ *"How Profitable Are Add-On Airline Fees?"* in *Canadian Business (Vol. 85, September 17, 2012, No. 14, pp. 82)*
Ed: David Fielding. **Description:** A chart of the top ten airlines by ancillary revenue is presented. **Availability:** Online.

20034 ■ *How to Start a Home-Based Senior Care Business: Develop a Winning Business Plan*
Ed: James L. Ferry. **Released:** Second edition. **Price:** paperback; softback; Electronic Book. **Description:** Everything needed to know in order to start and run a profitable, ethical, and satisfying senior care business from your home. Information covers writing a good business plan, marketing services to families, creating a fee structure, and developing a network of trusted caregivers and service providers. **Availability:** E-book; Print.

20035 ■ *"Importance of Pricing in Business"* in *Chron (Jan. 28, 2019)*
URL(s): smallbusiness.chron.com/importance-pricing-business-57904.html
Ed: Steve Milano. **Released:** January 28, 2019. **Description:** Discusses the importance of understanding how pricing affects your business model in addition to your bottom line and how it will help you best choose pricing levels. **Availability:** Online.

20036 ■ *The Importance of Pricing for the Profitability of Your Business*
URL(s): www.growthforce.com/blog/the-importance-of-pricing-for-the-profitability-of-your-business
Ed: Stephen King. **Description:** Provides information on three pricing strategies small business owners should understand to increase profitability. **Availability:** Online.

20037 ■ *"Innovating Low-Cost Business Models"* in *Strategy and Leadership (Vol. 39, March-April 2011, No. 2, pp. 43)*
Pub: Emerald Group Publishing Limited
Contact: Erika Valenti, President
Ed: Nicolas Kachaner, Zhenya Lindgardt, David Michael. **Description:** A process that can be used to implement low-cost innovation is presented. The process can be used to address the competitive challenges presented by multinationals' practice of presenting applications and price points that are intended for developing markets into developed markets. The process involves targeting large, and low-income segments of the market.

20038 ■ *"Insurers No Longer Paying Premium for Advertising"* in *Brandweek (Vol. 49, April 21, 2008, No. 16, pp. SR3)*
Description: Insurance companies are cutting their advertising budgets after years of accelerated double-digit growth in spending due to the economic downturn, five years of record-breaking ad spend and a

need to cut expenditures as claims costs rise and a competitive market keeps premiums in place. Statistical data included. **Availability:** Print; Online.

20039 ■ *"International Business Law: Interpreting the Term 'Like Products" in Business Recorder (June 7, 2012)*
Ed: Zafar Azeem. **Description:** The term 'like products' needs to be defined for international trade. The battle between the United States and Indonesia regarding this issue is discussed. A technical barrier clause being used by foreign countries is prohibiting imports and hurting competitiveness. **Availability:** Online.

20040 ■ *"Is That the Best You Can Do?" in Entrepreneur (Vol. 37, October 2009, No. 10, pp. 85)*
Description: Small business owners can deal with hagglers better by setting parameters in advance. They should convince hagglers by offering the best value and separating this from price. **Availability:** Print; Online.

20041 ■ *"Jeffrey Watanabe: 'Promise Less and Deliver More" in Canadian Business (Vol. 85, August 13, 2012, No. 13, pp. 16)*
Ed: Richard Branson. **Description:** Setting realistic customer expectations and then exceeding them in unexpected and helpful ways provides businesses an advantage over their competitors. Pricing and excellent customer service are some ways to exceed customer expectations. **Availability:** Print; Online.

20042 ■ *"Just Hang Up" in Barron's (Vol. 88, March 10, 2008, No. 10, pp. 45)*
Description: Sprint's shares are expected to continue falling while the company attempts to attract subscribers by cutting prices, cutting earnings in the process. The company faces tougher competition from better-financed AT&T and Verizon Communications.

20043 ■ *"Just a Slight Rate Bump for Local Law Firms" in Philadelphia Business Journal (Vol. 30, January 20, 2012, No. 49, pp. 1)*
Pub: Baltimore Business Journal
Contact: Rhonda Pringle, President
E-mail: rpringle@bizjournals.com
Description: Philadelphia, Pennsylvania-based law firms have increased billing rates by only one percent in 2011. Law firms show moderate increased in revenue in 2012. **Availability:** Print; Online.

20044 ■ *"Local Startup Hits Big Leagues" in Austin Business JournalInc. (Vol. 28, December 19, 2008, No. 40, pp. 1)*
Description: Qcue LLC, an Austin, Texas-based company founded in 2007 is developing a software system that can be used by Major League Baseball teams to change the prices of their single-game tickets based on variables affecting demand. The company recently completed a trial with the San Francisco Giants in 2008. **Availability:** Print; Online.

20045 ■ *"Major Advances in Heat Pump Technology - Part Two" in Contractor (Vol. 57, February 2010, No. 2, pp. 22)*
Ed: Mark Eatherton. **Description:** Chinese and Japanese companies have come up with refrigerant based heat pump products that are air based which will significantly lower the installed cost of heat pump based systems. Some of these newer models have variable speed, soft start compressors and have the ability to perform high-efficiency heat pump operation on a modulating basis. **Availability:** Print; Online.

20046 ■ *"Medicaid Insurers See Growth in Small Biz Market" in Boston Business Journal (Vol. 31, July 15, 2011, No. 25, pp. 1)*
Pub: Boston Business Journal
Contact: Carolyn M. Jones, President
E-mail: cmjones@bizjournals.com
Ed: Julie M. Donnelly. **Description:** BMC HealthNet Plan announced plans to launch small business products to serve small businesses that are priced out of rising premium rates at large Massachusetts insurers. BMC joined competitors CeltiCare Health Plan and Neighborhood Health Plan in augmenting its core business. **Availability:** Print; Online.

20047 ■ *"Mobile Discounts: A Matter of Distance and Time" in Harvard Business Review (Vol. 92, May 2014, No. 5, pp. 30)*
Pub: Harvard Business Publishing
Contact: Diane Belcher, Managing Director
Price: $6. **Description:** Geolocation via smartphone enables companies to offer consumers real-time incentives and discounts. Research shows that time and distance are key factors in a customers' receptiveness for these promotions: same day and close proximity increase the odds of a sales purchase. **Availability:** Online; PDF.

20048 ■ *"Notes on Current Labor Statistics" in Montly Labor Review (Vol. 133, September 2010, No. 9, pp. 75)*
Pub: U.S. Department of Labor Bureau of Labor Statistics
Contact: Amrit Kohli, Director
E-mail: kohli.amrit@bls.gov
Description: Principal statistics and calculated by the Bureau of Labor Statistics are presented. The series includes statistics on labor force; employment; unemployment; labor compensation; consumer, producer, and international prices; productivity; international comparisons; and injury and illness statistics. **Availability:** Online; PDF.

20049 ■ *"Prepaid Phones Surge in Bad Economy" in Advertising Age (Vol. 79, November 17, 2008, No. 43, pp. 6)*
Pub: Crain Communications, Inc.
Contact: Jessica Botos, Manager, Marketing
E-mail: jessica.botos@crainsnewyork.com
Ed: Rita Chang. **Description:** Prepay cell phone offerings are becoming increasingly competitive amid a greater choice of plans and handsets. In an economic environment in which many consumers are unable to pass the credit checks required for traditional cell phone plans, the prepay market is surging.

20050 ■ *"Pricing To Create Shared Value: Rethinking the Way Prices Are Set Can Expand the Pie for Everyone" in Harvard Business Review (Vol. 90, June 2012, No. 6, pp. 96)*
Pub: Harvard Business Review Press
Contact: Moderna V. Pfizer, Contact
Ed: John T. Gourville, Marco Bertini. **Description:** Five pricing strategies to create shared value are: focusing on relationships rather than transactions; being proactive; placing a premium on flexibility; promoting transparency; and managing market standards for fairness. Pricing practices for the 2012 Olympic Games in London, England are used as an illustration.

20051 ■ *"The Proven 3 Step Formula For Growing Retail Profits: Without Having to Resort to Coupons or Discount Sales"*
Pub: CreateSpace
Released: September 24, 2014. **Price:** $4.89, paperback. **Description:** Previously published under the name, "How Some Retailers Make More Money Than Others". Retailers, whether a franchise or independent brand face challenges for increasing sales. An explanation for growing customer base without mass advertising, how to increase each customers spending, and improve gross margins are reported. A proven three-step process for increasing retail profits without the use of coupons or discounts is provided. **Availability:** Print.

20052 ■ *"Reality Check at the Bottom of the Pyramid: To Succeed in the World's Poorest Markets, Aim For Much Higher Margins and Prices Than You Thought Were Necessary-Or Possible" in Harvard Business Review (Vol. 90, June 2012, No. 6, pp. 120)*
Pub: Harvard Business Review Press
Contact: Moderna V. Pfizer, Contact
Ed: Erik Simanis. **Price:** $8.95, hardcopy black and white. **Description:** Margin-enhancing platforms are identified. Bundling products increases customer access and enables firms to sell more in each transaction. Including services with products creates value for customers and raises each transaction's gross margin. Customer peer groups boost aggregate sales and as a result reduce costs. **Availability:** Print; Online; PDF.

20053 ■ *"St. Louis Blues Asking Price Out of Their League" in Saint Louis Business Journal (Vol. 32, September 23, 2011, No. 4, pp. 1)*
Pub: Saint Louis Business Journal
Contact: Robert Bobroff, President
E-mail: rbobroff@bizjournals.com
Ed: Armir Kurtovic. **Description:** St. Louis Blues owner Dave Checketts wanted the hockey team sold before the start of the season and he believed the team could fetch $200 million or more. However, Hockey insiders believe the price was too high when considering the team's high debt ratio and several other National Hockey League teams on the market. **Availability:** Online.

20054 ■ *"Sedentary Shoppers: Point, Click, Buy" in Barron's (Vol. 90, September 6, 2010, No. 36, pp. 11)*
Pub: Barron's Editorial & Corporate Headquarters
Ed: Vito J. Racanelli. **Description:** Non-travel online retail sales from January to July 2010 increased nine percent which indicates that online shopping for the coming holidays will be good. Online sales are outpacing traditional shopping, but pricing is still critical. **Availability:** Online.

20055 ■ *"The Superpower Dilemma" in Canadian Business (Vol. 83, August 17, 2010, No. 13-14, pp. 42)*
Description: Canada has been an energy superpower partly because it controls the energy source and the production means, particularly of fossil fuels. However, Canada's status as superpower could diminish if it replaces petroleum exports with renewable technology for using sources of energy available globally. **Availability:** Online.

20056 ■ *"A Survey of Smart Data Pricing: Past Proposals, Current Plans, and Future Trends" in ACM Computing Surveys (Vol. 46, Summer 2014, No. 2, pp. 15)*
Pub: Association for Computing Machinery - University of Wyoming
Contact: Ed Seidel, President
E-mail: uwpres@uwyo.edu
Price: $15, Nonmembers; $42, Students. **Description:** Traditionally, network operators have used simple flat-rate broadband data plans for both wired and wireless network access. But today, with the popularity of mobile devices and exponential growth of apps, videos, and clouds, service providers are gradually moving toward more sophisticated pricing schemes. The benefits and challenges or pricing data are examined. **Availability:** PDF; Online.

20057 ■ *"The Swedish Solution" in San Francisco Business Times (Vol. 28, May 2, 2014, No. 41, pp. 4)*
Pub: American City Business Journals, Inc.
Contact: Mike Olivieri, Executive Vice President
Description: Seattle, Washington's Swedish Health Services decided to cut prices for outpatient procedures by about 35 percent. Some patients are hoping that the San Francisco Bay Area in California will see Swedish Health do the same, but observers think the region will have a hard time implementing price reductions. **Availability:** Print; Online.

20058 ■ *Top 15 Pricing Strategies for Your Small Business*
URL(s): www.saasant.com/blog/pricing-strategies-small-business/
Description: Looks at one of the most important aspects that small businesses should consider to increase their revenue--pricing strategy. **Availability:** Online.

20059 ■ *"Tropeano Takes Charge"* in *Philadelphia Business Journal (Vol. 33, August 22, 2014, No. 28, pp. 11)*
Pub: American City Business Journals, Inc.
Contact: Mike Olivieri, Executive Vice President
Released: Weekly. **Price:** $4, introductory 4-week offer(Digital only). **Description:** Dan Tropeano will serve as the new head of United Healthcare of Pennsylvania, while continuing in his position as executive director of United Healthcare's Pennsylvania and Delaware health plans. Tropeano discusses his new role and notes that the medical insurance market has become increasingly competitive as consumers seek cheaper and more flexible products. **Availability:** Print; Online.

20060 ■ *"Under Armour Hopes to Stomp on Nike with Basketball Shoe"* in *Baltimore Business Journal (Vol. 28, October 22, 2010, No. 24, pp. 1)*
Pub: Baltimore Business Journal
Contact: Rhonda Pringle, President
E-mail: rpringle@bizjournals.com
Ed: Erik Siemers. **Description:** Uner Armour Inc. will release its Micro G line of four basketball sneakers on October 23, 2010. The company's executives mentioned that Under Armour's goal is to appeal to customers, and not to chip away at Nike Inc.'s supremacy in basketball shoes. The new sneakers will range from $80 to $110. **Availability:** Print; Online.

20061 ■ *"Under Armour's Founder On Learning to Leverage Celebrity Endorsements"* in *Harvard Business Review (Vol. 90, May 2012, No. 5, pp. 45)*
Pub: Harvard Business Review Press
Contact: Moderna V. Pfizer, Contact
Ed: Kevin Plank. **Description:** Using his athletic apparel company Under Armour as an illustration, the author identifies two key points in effective utilization of endorsement advertising: balancing freebies with fair-price contracts, and offering stock opportunities so that celebrities can be personally engaged with growth.

20062 ■ *"Unfilled Hotels Go All Out for Business Meetings"* in *Crain's Detroit Business (Vol. 25, June 8, 2009, No. 23, pp. 9)*
Pub: Crain Communications Inc.
Contact: Barry Asin, President
Ed: Daniel Duggan. **Description:** Hotels in Michigan are offering discounts to companies holding business meetings at their properties. Details of competition and plans are included. **Availability:** Print; Online.

20063 ■ *"Unused Coupons Still Pay Off"* in *Harvard Business Review (Vol. 90, May 2012, No. 5, pp. 32)*
Pub: Harvard Business Review Press
Contact: Moderna V. Pfizer, Contact
Ed: Rajkumar Venkatesan, Paul Farris. **Price:** $6, hardcopy and PDF. **Description:** Unredeemed coupons have been found to create a sales lift for retailers as they increase awareness of a retailer or a brand even when consumers do not use them. Redemption rates should still be monitored however to assess campaign effectiveness. **Availability:** Print; Online.

20064 ■ *"Velvet Ice Cream"* in *Ice Cream Reporter (Vol. 21, July 20, 2008, No. 8, pp. 7)*
Description: Velvet Ice Cream is adding a $7 surcharge on deliveries of its products in order to offset rising fuel costs. **Availability:** Online.

20065 ■ *"'Wal-Mart Effect' Feeds Grocer Price Wars"* in *Globe & Mail (March 15, 2007, pp. B14)*
Ed: Marina Strauss. **Description:** The decrease in profit reports by Canadian grocery giants amidst high expansion plans by Wal-Mart Stores Inc. are discussed. This industry is witnessing the most severe pricing competitions in recent times. **Availability:** Print; Online.

20066 ■ *"When To Drop an Unprofitable Customer: A Supplier Contemplates Cutting Off One Of Its Biggest Accounts"* in *Harvard Business Review (Vol. 90, April 2012, No. 4, pp. 137)*
Pub: Harvard Business Review Press
Contact: Moderna V. Pfizer, Contact
Ed: Robert S. Kaplan. **Description:** A fictitious vendor relations challenge is presented, with contributors providing advice. The problem involves whether to break ties with a solidly loyal client but one that has become expensive to maintain. Suggestions include dropping the client's special low price privilege and introduce the client to products and services used by other clients, or help the client shift to a new supplier.

20067 ■ *"Why Good Jobs Are Good for Retailers: Some Companies Are Investing In Their Workers and Reaping Healthy Profits"* in *Harvard Business Review (Vol. 90, January-February 2012, No.1-2, pp. 124)*
Pub: Harvard Business Review Press
Contact: Moderna V. Pfizer, Contact
Ed: Zeynep Ton. **Price:** $8.95. **Description:** Four key operational practices can help retailers sever the trade-off between investing in employees and maintaining low prices. These are: offering fewer promotions and SKUs, cross-training workers rather than varifying their number to match customer traffic, eliminating waste while preserving staff, and empowering workers to make prompt decisions. **Availability:** Online; PDF.

20068 ■ *"Who's On Top in the Telecom Turf Fight"* in *Dallas Business Journal (Vol. 37, April 25, 2014, No. 33, pp. 4)*
Pub: American City Business Journals, Inc.
Contact: Mike Olivieri, Executive Vice President
Released: Weekly. **Price:** $4, introductory 4-week offer(Digital & Print). **Description:** The four major wireless providers in the U.S. are competing for customers in North Texas and around the country. Experts say AT&T, Verizon, Sprint and T-Mobile have to offer better quality services, faster service and lower pricing to win customers from each other. **Availability:** Print; Online.

20069 ■ *"The Zero Marginal Cost Society: The Internet of Things, the Collaborative Commons, and the Eclipse of Capitalism"*
Pub: Palgrave Macmillan
Released: April 04, 2014. **Price:** $18.99, paperback; $9.99, e-book; $29.99, hardcover. **Description:** The emerging Internet of things is speeding society to an ear of nearly free goods and services, causing the rise of a global Collaborative Commons and the eclipse of capitalism. Entrepreneurial dynamism of competitive markets that drives productivity up and marginal costs down, enabling businesses to reduce the price of their goods and services to win consumers and market share is slowly dying. **Availability:** E-book; Print.

Consultants

START-UP INFORMATION

20070 ■ *Going Solo: Developing a Home-Based Consulting Business from the Ground Up*
Description: Ways to turn specialized knowledge into a home-based successful consulting firm, focusing on targeting client needs, business plans, and growth.

20071 ■ *How to Start a Home-Based Consulting Business: Define Your Specialty Build a Client Base Make Yourself Indispensable*
Ed: Bert Holtje. **Released:** January 06, 2010. **Price:** Paperback. **Description:** Everything needed for starting and running a successful consulting business from home. **Availability:** Print.

20072 ■ *"No. 300: My Job Is To Solve Every Kind of Crisis" in Inc. (Vol. 36, September 2014, No. 7, pp. 72)*
Pub: Mansueto Ventures L.L.C.
Contact: Stephanie Mehta, Chief Executive Officer
Released: September 2014. **Description:** Saima Chowdhury started her integrated sourcing company in New York City after receiving an MBA from Wharton School. Noi Solutions helps retailers manufacture goods in Bangladesh while helping Bangladeshi factories market their capabilities to retailers. Chowdhury discusses the challenges and has learned to remain calm during any crisis. **Availability:** Print; Online.

20073 ■ *"SBA Program Helped New Company Survive As It Built Company Base" in Philadelphia Business Journal (Vol. 33, May 9, 2014, No. 13, pp. 4)*
Pub: American City Business Journals, Inc.
Contact: Mike Olivieri, Executive Vice President
Released: Weekly. **Description:** The Small Business Administration (SBA) Indiana District Business Office helped Netwise Resources set up its information technology (IT) consulting business with a six-month SBA-backed loan and the 8(a) Business Development Program for small disadvantaged businesses. Owner, Mark Gibson, attributes Netwise Resources' success to its focus on branding, recruiting skilled staff, and establishing relationships with clients within the target market. **Availability:** Print; Online.

20074 ■ *Starting Up On Your Own: How to Succeed as an Independent Consultant or Freelance*
Ed: Mike Johnson. **Released:** 2012. **Price:** $27.99, e-book; $55.98, book plus e-book bundle. **Description:** Concise guide for anyone wanting to start their own consulting firm is provided. **Availability:** E-book.

ASSOCIATIONS AND OTHER ORGANIZATIONS

20075 ■ **Association of Professional Canadian Consultants (APCC)**
157 Adelaide St W, Ste., 703
Toronto, ON, Canada M5H 4E7
Co. E-mail: information@apcconline.com
URL: http://www.apcconline.com
Contact: Frank McCrea, President
Facebook: www.facebook.com/APCCOnline
Linkedin: www.linkedin.com/company/apcc---association-of-professional-computer-consultants
X (Twitter): x.com/APCC_Canada
Description: Promotes the interests of independent contractors in Canada. Serves as industry advocate before government bodies. **Founded:** 1985. **Publications:** *Gateway* (Monthly). **Geographic Preference:** National.

20076 ■ **Association of Proposal Management Professionals (APMP)**
20130 Lakeview Ctr. Plz., Ste. 400
Ashburn, VA 20147
Free: 866-466-2767
Co. E-mail: membership@apmp.org
URL: http://www.apmp.org
Contact: Rick Harris, Chief Executive Officer
E-mail: rick.harris@apmp.org
Facebook: www.facebook.com/APMP.org
Linkedin: www.linkedin.com/company/apmp
X (Twitter): x.com/apmp_connect
YouTube: www.youtube.com/channel/UCAX6bGyVUHu89aBBq92rxQQ
Description: Proposal managers, proposal planners, proposal writers, consultants, desktop publishers and marketing managers. Encourages unity and cooperation among industry professionals. Seeks to broaden member knowledge and skills through developmental, educational and social activities. **Founded:** 1989. **Publications:** *Journal of the Association of Proposal Management Professionals* (Semiannual). **Awards:** APMP Fellows Award (Annual). **Geographic Preference:** National.

20077 ■ **Canadian Association of International Development Professionals (CAIDP) [Regroupement des consultants canadiens en developpement internationale]**
Ottawa, ON, Canada 516 555
Co. E-mail: caidprpcdi@gmail.com
URL: http://www.caidp-rpcdi.ca
Contact: Abbas Sumar, Member
Facebook: www.facebook.com/caidprpcdi
X (Twitter): x.com/CAIDP_RPCDI
YouTube: www.youtube.com/channel/UC-PGLvYZy9rTh944EatSrbg
Description: Aims to provide services for, and to represent the interests of, Canadian international development consultants. **Founded:** 1993. **Geographic Preference:** Multinational.

20078 ■ **International Association of Registered Financial Consultants (IARFC)**
146 N Breiel Blvd.
Middletown, OH 45042
Free: 800-532-9060
Fax: (513)345-9479
Co. E-mail: info@iarfc.org
URL: http://www.iarfc.org
Contact: Bradley K. Maples, President
Facebook: www.facebook.com/IARFCAssoc
Linkedin: www.linkedin.com/groups/166514/profile
X (Twitter): x.com/IARFCAssoc
YouTube: www.youtube.com/channel/UCsoztUiU3_OfEkFWHiOmCKA
Description: Financial professionals gathered to foster public confidence in the financial planning profession. Helps financial consultants exchange planning techniques. Offers educational programs and professional certifications. **Founded:** 1984. **Awards:** Loren Dunton Memorial Award (Annual). **Geographic Preference:** Multinational.

20079 ■ **Thrive-on-Line**
145 Thornway Ave.
Thornhill, ON, Canada L4J 7Z3
Ph: (416)410-8163
URL: http://www.aiconsult.ca/en
Price: free for members. **Availability:** Print; Online.

REFERENCE WORKS

20080 ■ *"5 Steps to Starting a Consulting Business" in Legal Zoom (March 24, 2023)*
URL(s): www.legalzoom.com/articles/5-steps-to-starting-a-consulting-business
Ed: Kylie Ora Lobell. **Released:** March 24, 2023. **Description:** Discusses setting up a consulting business and the steps you should follow to get it going and to find long-term success. **Availability:** Online.

20081 ■ *10 Make-or-Break Career Moments: Navigate, Negotiate, and Communicate for Success*
Price: $13.99, paperback. **Description:** Communication consultant, Casey Hawley, provides a guide to smart communication for any business setting. **Availability:** Print.

20082 ■ *"20 Advantages and Disadvantages of Outsourcing from Your Small Business" in Small Business Trends (March 11, 2021)*
Pub: Small Business Trends, LLC
Contact: Anita Campbell, Chief Executive Officer
URL(s): smallbiztrends.com/2017/02/advantages-and-disadvantages-of-outsourcing.html
Ed: Nash Riggins. **Released:** March 11, 2021. **Description:** The pros and cons of outsourcing staff is discussed. This includes using freelancers instead of using in-office employees. **Availability:** Online.

20083 ■ *"Altegrity Acquires John D. Cohen, Inc." in (November 19, 2009, pp. 14)*
Pub: Investment Weekly News
Description: John D. Cohen, Inc., a contract provider of national security policy guidance and counsel to the federal government, was acquired by Altegrity, Inc., a global screening and security solutions provider; the company will become part of US Investigations Services, LLC and operate under the auspices of Altegrity's new business, Altegrity Security Consulting. **Availability:** Print; Online.

20084 ■ *"The Americans Are Coming"* in *The Economist (Vol. 390, January 3, 2009, No. 8612, pp. 44)*
Description: Student recruitment consultancies, which help place international students at universities in other countries and offer services such as interpreting or translating guidelines, are discussed; American universities who have shunned these agencies in the past; the result has been that America underperforms in relation to its size with a mere 3.5 percent of students on its campuses that are from abroad. **Availability:** Print; Online.

20085 ■ *"Applying to Colleges? Consultants Can Demystify the Process"* in *Palm Beach Post (September 3, 2011)*
Pub: McClatchy Tribune Information Services
Contact: Patrick J. Talamantes, President
Ed: Susan Salisbury. **Released:** September 03, 2011. **Description:** More parents are turning to college consultants to help guide them through the process of applying to and choosing the right college or university. These specialized consultants assist with every detail for several years and students can reach them 24/7; costs can vary from several hundred dollars to $10,000 depending on services. **Availability:** Online.

20086 ■ *"Backtalk with Terrie M. Williams"* in *Black Enterprise (Vol. 38, December 2007, No. 5, pp. 204)*
Pub: Earl G. Graves Ltd.
Contact: Earl Graves, Jr., President
Ed: Tennille M. Robinson. **Description:** Profile of Terrie M. Williams, president of a public relations agency as well as founder of a youth empowerment organization called Stay Strong Foundation. Williams reflects on her bouts with depression and how the disease impacts sufferers and talks about her book that will inspire others dealing with depression. **Availability:** Online.

20087 ■ *"BDC Launches New Online Business Advice Centre"* in *Marketwired (July 13, 2010)*
Pub: Comtex News Network Inc.
Contact: Kan Devnani, President
Description: The Business Development Bank of Canada (BDC) offers entrepreneurs the chance to use their new online BDC Advice Centre in order to seek advice regarding the challenges of entrepreneurship. Free online business tools and information to help both startups and established firms are also provided. **Availability:** Print; Online.

20088 ■ *"Best Foot Forward"* in *Canadian Business (Vol. 80, October 22, 2007, No. 21, pp. 115)*
Description: Jeremy Shinewald's mbaMission admissions consulting business helps prospective MBA students with essay writing, mock interview preparation and school selection. The consulting fee for application to one school is $2,250. Details of the business schools' MBA programs and tuition fees are explored. **Availability:** Online.

20089 ■ *Business Black Belt: Develop the Strength, Flexibility and Agility to Run Your Company*
Price: $15.99. **Description:** Manual offering insights that will enable anyone to become successful in small business. Seventy short chapters included topics such as attitude, management, marketing, selling, employees, money, MBAs, lawyers, consultants, and investors. **Availability:** Print.

20090 ■ *Business as Usual*
Description: Founder of The Body Shop shares her story and gives her opinion on everything from cynical cosmetic companies to destructive consultants.

20091 ■ *"Capital Is a Good Bet as HQ Site, Report Says"* in *Sacramento Business Journal (Vol. 29, August 17, 2012, No. 25, pp. 1)*
Pub: Baltimore Business Journal
Contact: Rhonda Pringle, President
E-mail: rpringle@bizjournals.com
Ed: Sanford Nax. **Description:** Site-selection consultant, John Boyd, has identified the city of Sacramento, California as well positioned to land corporate headquarters but is one of the most expensive cities in North America. He suggests to create incentives specifically to attract headquarters offices from more costl locations in the Bay Area and Southern California.

20092 ■ *"CarBiz Inc. Speaking At NABD"* in *Marketwired (May 14, 2007)*
Pub: Comtex News Network Inc.
Contact: Kan Devnani, President
Description: CarBiz Inc., a leading provider of software, consulting, and training solutions to the United States' automotive industry, had two of its executive officers speak at the National Alliance of Buy Here - Pay Here Dealers (NABD), a conference that draws over 2,000 dealers, service providers, and experts from across the United States. **Availability:** Print; Online.

20093 ■ *"Carbon Capture and Storage: Grave Concerns"* in *Canadian Business (Vol. 81, July 21 2008, No. 11, pp. 25)*
Ed: Andrew Nikiforuk. **Released:** January 01, 2017. **Description:** Air pollution control regulations to reduce greenhouse gasses have been implemented by the Canadian government. The federal government is planning to construct a carbon funeral industry that will store the global warming gases, however the expenditure for the project will be shifted to the taxpayers. Details of the Bruce Peachy's initiative on how to reduce GHGs are presented. **Availability:** Print; Online.

20094 ■ *Case Master: Thoughtful Cases for Competitive Future Consultants*
Ed: Valentin Nugmanov, Ron Clouse. **Released:** November 12, 2018. **Price:** $22.75, Paperback; $9.99, E-book. **Description:** A collection of practice cases for consultants to study in order to gain a competitive edge when interviewing for a potential project. **Availability:** Print; Online.

20095 ■ *"Certification Experts Germanischer Lloyd Wind Energy Assist NaiKun's Offshore Wind Project"* in *Marketwired (May 14, 2007)*
Pub: Comtex News Network Inc.
Contact: Kan Devnani, President
Description: Germanischer Lloyd Wind Energy (GL Wind) will examine, inspect, and provide quality management services for the engineering, design, and construction of the offshore wind project planned by NaiKun Wind Development Inc. in northwest British Columbia. **Availability:** Online.

20096 ■ *"CFOs Walk a Tightrope When Picking Consultants"* in *The Wall Street Journal (July 26, 2016)*
URL(s): blogs.wsj.com/cfo/2016/07/26/cfos-walk-a-tightrope-when-picking-consultants/
Ed: Tatyana Shumsky. **Released:** July 26, 2016. **Description:** Choosing a business consultant is often tricky and picking someone who isn't a good fit for the company can waste funds and time. CFOs often bring in outside help and they need to do their due diligence to make sure this person will get the job done. That includes contacting references and making sure the consultant has actually done this type of work in the past. Giving them a small project to start is often advised, and then moving them onto bigger projects once the scope of their knowledge and skill set are known. **Availability:** Online.

20097 ■ *Consultants & Consulting Organizations Directory (CCOD)*
Pub: Gale, part of Cengage Group
Contact: Paul Gazzolo, General Manager Senior Vice President
URL(s): www.gale.com/ebooks/9780028668062/consultants--consulting-organizations-directory
Released: Latest 46th Edition. **Description:** Covers over 26,000 firms, individuals, and organizations active in consulting. **Entries include:** Individual or organization name, address, phone, fax, e-mail, URL, specialties, founding date, branch offices, names and titles of key personnel, number of employees, financial data, publications, seminars and workshops. **Arrangement:** By broad subject categories. **Indexes:** Subject, geographical, organization name. **Availability:** E-book; Download. **Type:** Directory.

20098 ■ *"The Consulting Business Booms Just as Consultants Disappear"* in *Bloomberg (July 29, 2021)*
URL(s): www.bloomberg.com/news/articles/2021-07-29/the-consulting-business-booms-just-as-consultants-disappear
Ed: Matthew Boyle. **Released:** July 29, 2021. **Description:** During these pandemic times, a lot of employees in consulting are making decisions to leave their current industries and look for work in other sectors. Often times poached by other companies or tired of the constant travel, these employees are often settling down for new work from home positions or joining high-interest fields. **Availability:** Online.

20099 ■ *"Consulting Firm Goes Shopping"* in *Crain's Chicago Business (Vol. 31, April 28, 2008, No. 17, pp. 45)*
Pub: Crain Communications Inc.
Contact: Barry Asin, President
Ed: Phuong Ly. **Description:** Clark & Wamberg LLC was created last year after the merger of Clark Inc. to a Dutch insurance conglomerate. Clark Inc. was a life insurance and benefits consultancy which had been on a downslide, returning just 5.6 percent a year to shareholders. In contrast Clark & Wamberg posted first-year revenue of $106.8 million, fueled by business from its executive compensation and health care clients. **Availability:** Online.

20100 ■ *Consulting Success: The Proven Guide to Start, Run and Grow a Successful Consulting Business*
Ed: Michael Zipursky. **Released:** October 18, 2018. **Price:** $14.99, Paperback; $9.99, E-book. **Description:** A guide to the time-tested principles, strategies, tactics, and best-practices successful consultants engage in. **Availability:** Online.

20101 ■ *"A Conversation With: Ron Gantner, Jones Lang LaSalle"* in *Crain's Detroit Business (Vol. 24, October 6, 2008, No. 40, pp. 9)*
Pub: Crain Communications Inc.
Contact: Barry Asin, President
Description: Interview with Ron Gantner who is a corporate real estate adviser with the real estate company Jones Lang LaSalle as well as the company's executive vice president and part of the tenant advisory team; Gantner speaks about the impact that the Wall Street crisis is having on the commercial real estate market in Detroit. **Availability:** Print; Online.

20102 ■ *"Cost Remains Top Factor In Considering Green Technology"* in *Canadian Sailings (June 30, 2008)*
Description: Improving its environmental performance remains a priority in the shipping industry; however, testing new technologies can prove difficult due to the harsh conditions that ships endure as well as installation which usually requires a dry dock. **Availability:** Online.

20103 ■ *"Counting on Engagement at Ernst & Young"* in *Workforce Management (Vol. 88, November 16, 2009, No. 12, pp. 25)*
Pub: Crain Communications Inc.
Contact: Barry Asin, President
Ed: Ed Frauenheim. **Description:** Employee engagement has been difficult to maintain through the recession but firms such as Ernst & Young have found that the effort to keep their employees loyal has paid off. **Availability:** Print; Online.

20104 ■ *"DMW Gets MBE Certification"* in *Wireless News (July 29, 2012)*
Description: Towson, Maryland's Daft McCune Walker (DMW) received the Minority Business Enterprise (MBE) Certification from the State of

20105 ■ **Consultants**

Maryland for Engineering, Surveying, Environmental and CAD services. The firm is a multidisciplinary consulting organization and is woman-owned. **Availability:** Print; Online.

20105 ■ *"Fail Forward's Ashley Good on How to Screw Up in the Best Possible Way"* in *Canadian Business (Vol. 87, October 2014, No. 10, pp. 47)*
Pub: American City Business Journals, Inc.
Contact: Mike Olivieri, Executive Vice President
Description: Ashley Good, founder and CEO of Toronto, Ontario-based consultancy firm, Fail Forward, offers advice on ways to recover from a business failure. The best way to separate from the failure is to share the story and get other people's perspectives. **Availability:** Online.

20106 ■ *Get Clients Now!: A 28-Day Marketing Program for Professionals, Consultants, and Coaches*
Pub: American Management Association
Contact: Manny Avramidis, President
Ed: C.J. Hayden. **Availability:** Print.

20107 ■ *"Greg Lueck: Glass Blowing"* in *Inc. (Volume 32, December 2010, No. 10, pp. 36)*
Pub: Mansueto Ventures L.L.C.
Contact: Stephanie Mehta, Chief Executive Officer
Ed: April Joyner. **Description:** Profile of Greg Lueck, partner and COO of Centerstance, a tech consulting firm in Portland, Oregon. Lueck opened Firehouse Glass, a studio that provides workspace and equipment for glass blowers. He says glass blowing serves as a welcome counterbalance to the cerebral work he does at the office. **Availability:** Online.

20108 ■ *"Housing Slide Picks Up Speed"* in *Crain's Chicago Business (Vol. 31, April 19, 2008, No. 16, pp. 2)*
Pub: Crain Communications Inc.
Contact: Barry Asin, President
Ed: Eddie Baeb. **Description:** According to Tracy Cross & Associates Inc., a real estate consultancy, sales of new homes in the Chicago area dropped 61 percent from the year-earlier period which is more bad news for homebuilders, contractors and real estate agents who are eager for an indication that market conditions are improving. **Availability:** Online.

20109 ■ *How to Make Big Money in Your Own Small Business: Unexpected Rules Every Small Business Owner Needs to Know*
Ed: Jeffrey J. Fox, Jeffrey J. Fox. **Released:** May 12, 2004. **Price:** $16.95; C$24.95; $16.95; C$24.95; $16.95; C$24.95. **Description:** Former sales and marketing pro offers advice on growing a small business. **Availability:** Print.

20110 ■ *"How to Start a Consulting Business: Determining Your Rates"* in *Entrepreneur (March 10, 2020)*
Ed: Terry Rice. **Released:** March 10, 2020. **Description:** Discusses factors involved in setting rates as a consultant. **Availability:** Online.

20111 ■ *"Innovate or Stagnate: How Doing Things Differently Helps Business"* in *South Florida Business Journal (Vol. 34, January 10, 2014, No. 25, pp. 10)*
Pub: American City Business Journals, Inc.
Contact: Mike Olivieri, Executive Vice President
Released: Weekly. **Price:** $8, Introductory 4-week offer(Digital & Print). **Description:** Business enterprises can drive growth by focusing on innovations. Companies are advised to consider radical ideas, invent different ways of working and avoid bureaucracy. Peter Drucker, a management consultant, believes that business has two functions: marketing and innovation. **Availability:** Print; Online.

20112 ■ *"Into the Groove: Fine-Tune Your Biz By Getting Into the Good Habit Groove"* in *Small Business Opportunities (Spring 2008)*
Description: Profile of Ty Freyvogel and his consulting firm Freyvogel Communications. Freyvogel serves the telecommunications need of Fortune 500 and mid-sized businesses.

20113 ■ *"Managing the Facebookers; Business"* in *The Economist (Vol. 390, January 3, 2009, No. 8612, pp. 10)*
Pub: Economist Newspaper Ltd.
Contact: Lara Boro, Chief Executive Officer
Description: According to a report from PricewaterhouseCoopers, a business consultancy, workers from Generation Y, also known as the Net Generation, are more difficult to recruit and integrate into companies that practice traditional business acumen. 61 percent of chief executive managers say that they have trouble with younger employees who tend to be more narcissistic and more interested in personal fulfillment with a need for frequent feedback and an over-precise set of objectives on the path to promotion which can be hard for managers who are used to a different relationship with their subordinates. Older bosses should prepare to make some concessions to their younger talent since some of the issues that make them happy include cheaper online ways to communicate and additional coaching, both of which are good for business. **Availability:** Online.

20114 ■ *The Mirror Test: Is Your Business Really Breathing?*
Pub: Grand Central Publishing
Contact: Michael Pietsch, Chairman
Ed: Jeffrey W. Hayzlett. **Released:** May 05, 2010. **Price:** $9.99, e-book. **Description:** Consultant and author, Jeffrey Hayzlett, explains why a business is not doing well and asks the questions that most business managers are afraid to ask. **Availability:** E-book; Print.

20115 ■ *The New Business of Consulting: The Basics and Beyond*
Ed: Elaine Biech. **Released:** April 30, 2019. **Description:** A guide for entrepreneurs who are venturing out into the consulting industry. **Availability:** E-book.

20116 ■ *Niche and Grow Rich*
Description: Consultants share insight to entrepreneurs wishing to find a profitable niche market. Authors write that good niche businesses are easy to start and easy to defend from competitors. They also report that finding a successful niche can attract and maintain good customers who are willing to pay more for unique goods and services.

20117 ■ *"Pay Heed to 'Smack Stack'"* in *Puget Sound Business Journal (Vol. 35, May 16, 2014, No. 4, pp. 6)*
Pub: American City Business Journals, Inc.
Contact: Mike Olivieri, Executive Vice President
Description: Technology consultant, Geoffrey Moore, discloses the topics he plans to discuss at the annual State of Technology Luncheon held in Washington on May 19, 2014. He will explore the impact of technology and business trends on public-policy making and regulations. **Availability:** Online.

20118 ■ *PPC's Guide to Small Business Consulting Engagements*
Released: Annual. **Price:** $365, book; $280, online. **Description:** Technical guide for conducting consulting engagements for small business. **Availability:** Print; Online.

20119 ■ *Professional Services Marketing: How the Best Firms Build Premier Brands, Thriving Lead Generation Engines, and Cultures of Business Development Success*
Pub: John Wiley & Sons, Inc.
Contact: Christina Van Tassell, Executive Vice President Chief Financial Officer
Ed: Mike Schultz, John E. Doerr, Lee Frederiksen. **Released:** Second edition. **Price:** $29.95, hardcover; $19.99, E-Book. **Description:** Research based on best practices and processes for the professional services industry is presented. The book covers five key areas: creating a custom marketing and growth strategy, establishing a brand, implementing a marketing communications program, developing a lead strategy, and winning new clients. **Availability:** E-book; Print.

20120 ■ *"Provinces Tackle E-Waste Problem"* in *Canadian Electronics (Vol. 23, June-July 2008, No. 4, pp. 1)*
Pub: Action Communication Inc.
Ed: Ken Manchen. **Description:** Canadian provinces are implementing measures concerning the safe and environmentally friendly disposal of electronic waste. Alberta, British Columbia, Nova Scotia, and Saskatchewan impose an e-waste recycling fee on electronic equipment purchases. **Availability:** Online.

20121 ■ *"Putting Vets to Work"* in *Business Week (September 22, 2008, No. 4100, pp. 18)*
Pub: Bloomberg L.P.
Contact: Michael Bloomberg, Chief Executive Officer
Ed: Deborah Stead. **Description:** Advice is provided by former Marine Sal Cepeda, a consultant who advises employers on hiring veterans, for former military personnel coming back into the workforce. **Availability:** Print; Online.

20122 ■ *"PwC to Add 400 Workers in North Texas"* in *Dallas Business Journal (Vol. 35, April 6, 2012, No. 30, pp. 1)*
Pub: Baltimore Business Journal
Contact: Rhonda Pringle, President
E-mail: rpringle@bizjournals.com
Description: London, England-headquartered PwC, formerly known as PricewaterhouseCoopers LLP, announced plans to hire 400 employees for its North Texas operations during the next 12 months. The firm provides auditing, consulting, and tax services to public, private and government clients. **Availability:** Print; Online.

20123 ■ *"Raptor Opens Austin Office"* in *Austin Business Journal (Vol. 31, July 8, 2011, No. 18, pp. 1)*
Pub: Austin Business Journal
Contact: Rachel McGrath, Director
E-mail: rmcgrath@bizjournals.com
Ed: Christopher Calnan. **Description:** Boston hedge fund operator Raptor Group launched Raptor Accelerator, a consulting business providing sales and advisory services to early-stage companies in Central Texas. Aside from getting involved with the startups in which the Raptor Group invests, Raptor Accelerator will target firms operating in the sports, media, entertainment, and content technology sectors. **Availability:** Print; Online.

20124 ■ *"Retail in Austin Strong, Will Continue to Be"* in *Austin Business JournalInc. (Vol. 29, January 22, 2010, No. 46, pp. 1)*
Pub: Austin Business Journal
Contact: Rachel McGrath, Director
E-mail: rmcgrath@bizjournals.com
Ed: Jacob Dirr. **Description:** Retail sector in Austin, Texas has outpaced the national average in value, mid-tier, high-end and drugs retail sectors, according to a report by Pitney Bowes. The national consulting firm's report has projected growth in every sector until the end of fiscal 2012. Data regarding other sectors is also included. **Availability:** Print; Online.

20125 ■ *"The Right Remedy: Entrepreneur's Success Is a Matter of Life and Death"* in *Black Enterprise (Vol. 38, February 2008, No. 7, pp. 46)*
Pub: Earl G. Graves Ltd.
Contact: Earl Graves, Jr., President
Ed: Tamara E. Holmes. **Description:** Profile of Leah Brown, whose company conducts clinical trials to determine if specific drugs will relieve particular symptoms. Her company will also visit physician's offices to make certain doctors are following proper protocol for a clinical trial or will collect data from patients. **Availability:** Online.

20126 ■ *"The Rise of Pompei"* in *Retail Merchandiser (Vol. 51, September-October 2011, No. 5, pp. 13)*
Description: Soho creative consulting group follows its C3 philosophy to create an invigorated brand experience that transforms customers from consum-

GENERAL SMALL BUSINESS TOPICS

ers to empowered buyers. Pompei AD is a leading creative consultancy that specializes in design and branding for retail, museum, hospitality, and other sectors. **Availability:** Print; Online.

20127 ■ *"Six Ways to Make Customer Programs Work; Most Customer Satisfaction Programs Aren't Effective. Two Consultants Explain Why and How Companies Can Fix Them"* in Gallup Business Journal (June 17, 2014)
Pub: Gallup, Inc.
Contact: Jon Clifton, Chief Executive Officer
Description: Consultants explain ways to help companies develop customer satisfaction programs that work. **Availability:** Print.

20128 ■ *"Sleeping with Your Smartphone: How to Break the 24/7 Habit and Change the Way You Work"*
Pub: Harvard Business Review Press
Contact: Moderna V. Pfizer, Contact
Released: May 29, 2012. **Price:** $30, Hardcover/ Hardcopy. **Description:** Harvard Business School professor, Leslie Perlow, reveals ways to become more productive after disconnecting from your smartphone. A six-person team was used in an experiment at The Boston Consulting Group, an elite management consulting firm, where teams changed the way they worked and became more efficient and effective by disconnecting. The team was better able to perform and recruit new talent. A step-by-step guide is offered to change your team. **Availability:** E-book; Print.

20129 ■ *"Small, But Mighty"* in Employee Benefit News (Vol. 25, November 1, 2011, No. 14, pp. 32)
Pub: SourceMedia LLC
Contact: Gemma Postlethwaite, Chief Executive Officer
Ed: Andrea Davis. **Description:** Three consulting firms are facing the challenge of helping clients understand the new health care reform in a tight economy. **Availability:** Print; PDF; Online.

20130 ■ *"South Florida Lodging Industry Poised for Strong Growth in 2014"* in South Florida Business Journal (Vol. 34, January 3, 2014, No. 24, pp. 3)
Pub: American City Business Journals, Inc.
Contact: Mike Olivieri, Executive Vice President
Released: Weekly. **Price:** $8, Introductory 4-week offer(Digital & Print). **Description:** Demand for the lodging industry in South Florida is expected to grow in 2014. According to hotel consulting and research firm, PKF Hospitality Research LLC, lodging demand in the U.S. would increase by 2.1 percent by the end of 2013 while airport, resort and suburban areas will achieve the biggest gains in revenue per available room in 2014. **Availability:** Print; Online.

20131 ■ *"Teksapiens, A Leading SEO Company, Offers Free SEO Consulting Services to Dallas Businesses"* in Wireless News (March 29, 2012)
Description: Dallas-based Web design firm, Teksapiens, offers free search engine optimization to Dallas businesss signing up at DallasBestSEO.com. The free service provides tips to outperform competition when marketing on the Internet. **Availability:** Print; Online.

20132 ■ *"Think Disruptive! How to Manage In a New Era of Innovation"* in Strategy & Leadership (Vol. 38, July-August 2010, No. 4, pp. 5-10)
Pub: Emerald Inc.
Ed: Brian Leavy, John Sterling. **Price:** $32, online only 30 days. **Description:** The views expressed by Scott Anthony, president of an innovation consultancy Innosight, on the need for corporate leaders to apply disruptive innovation in a recessionary environment are presented. His suggestion that disruptive innovation is the only way to survive during the economic crisis is discussed. **Availability:** Online; PDF.

20133 ■ *The Toilet Paper Entrepreneur: The Tell-It-Like-It-Is Guide to Cleaning Up In Business, Even If You Are At the End of Your Roll*
Pub: Obsidian Launch L.L.C.
Contact: Kelsey Ayres, President
Ed: Mike Michalowicz. **Description:** The founder of three multimillion-dollar companies, including Obsidian Launch, a company that partners with first-time entrepreneurs to grow their concepts into industry leaders. **Availability:** Print; Online.

20134 ■ *"TrendHR Changes Rockwall Landscape with $25M Office Tower"* in Dallas Business Journal (Vol. 35, May 25, 2012, No. 37, pp. 1)
Pub: Baltimore Business Journal
Contact: Rhonda Pringle, President
E-mail: rpringle@bizjournals.com
Ed: Candace Carlisle. **Description:** TrendHR Services is planning to build an executive tower in Rockwall, Texas. The company provides human resource outsourcing, employee benefits, and consulting services. **Availability:** Print; Online.

20135 ■ *A Whack on the Side of the Head: How You Can Be More Creative*
Ed: Roger von Oech. **Released:** 25th anniversary edition. **Price:** $17, paperback. **Description:** The author, a consultant, shares insight into increasing entrepreneurial creativity. **Availability:** Print.

20136 ■ *"What Is a Business Consultant?"* in Business News Daily (February 21, 2023)
URL(s): www.businessnewsdaily.com/4610-business-consultant.html
Ed: Sean Peek. **Released:** February 21, 2023. **Description:** Defines and discusses the advantages of a business consultant. **Availability:** Online.

20137 ■ *Working for Yourself: Law & Taxes for Independent Contractors, Freelancers & Consultants*
Pub: Nolo
Contact: Chris Braun, President
Ed: Stephen Fishman. **Released:** 12th Edition. **Price:** $27.99, e-book(downloadable); $34.99, book and e-book; $27.99, E-book. **Description:** In-depth information is shared for contractors, freelancers and consultants involving business law and small business taxes. **Availability:** E-book; Print; Electronic publishing; PDF.

VIDEO/AUDIO MEDIA

20138 ■ *Breaking into Business Consulting: Upleveling in the Impact Space with Paul Zelizer*
URL(s): www.awraepreneurs.com/podcast/292-business-consulting
Released: May 09, 2023. **Description:** Podcast discusses business consulting for impact organization.

20139 ■ *Ed Doherty Founder of One Degree Coaching*
URL(s): restaurantunstoppable.libsyn.com/1008-ed-doherty-founder-of-one-degree-coaching
Ed: Eric Cacciatore. **Released:** July 13, 2023. **Description:** Podcast offers a conversation with restauranteur-turned-business-coach.

20140 ■ *The How of Business: Amy Rasdal - Consulting Business*
URL(s): www.thehowofbusiness.com/479-amy-rasdal-consulting-business
Ed: Henry Lopez. **Released:** July 03, 2023. **Description:** Podcast discusses starting (and misconceptions about) a consulting business.

20141 ■ *How to Scale Your Consulting Business*
URL(s): omny.fm/shows/startup-hustle/how-to-scale-your-consulting-business

Consultants ■ 20148

Ed: Matt DeCoursey. **Released:** September 01, 2023. **Description:** Podcast discusses where to start and what questions to ask when the business starts to scale. Explores defining your product, the value of feedback, utilizing technology, and understanding customer behavior. Features Ihor Bauman, the CEO and co-founder of Workee.

20142 ■ *Launching and Growing a Consulting Business with Paul Beers*
URL(s): www.thehowofbusiness.com/episode-005-paul-beers
Description: Podcast discusses launching and growing a consulting business.

20143 ■ *Mindset, Curiosity, and Coaching Yourself with Antonia Bowring*
URL(s): www.makinggoodpodcast.com/episodes/250
Ed: Lauren Tilden. **Released:** July 30, 2024. **Description:** Podcast explains what business coaches do, how to coach yourself, how to shift your mindset from spectator to actor, and the importance of maintaining curiosity.

20144 ■ *Side Hustle to Small Business: How Justus Hillebrand Accidentally Became an Entrepreneur*
URL(s): www.hiscox.com/side-hustle-to-small-business/justus-hillebrand-digital-history-consulting-inc-podcast-season-4
Ed: Sanjay Parekh. **Released:** June 19, 2024. **Description:** Podcast features a historian-turned-consultant with large-scale clients like the United States Holocaust Memorial Museum.

20145 ■ *Side Hustle to Small Business: Using Telecommunications to Help Solve Crimes*
URL(s): www.hiscox.com/side-hustle-to-small-business/david-walker-icell-consulting-llc-podcast-season-4
Ed: Sanjay Parekh. **Released:** February 07, 2024. **Description:** Podcast features an entrepreneur who has helped solve criminal cases using telephone record analysis.

20146 ■ *The Small Business School Podcast: When to Hire Consultants in Your Business*
URL(s): podcasts.apple.com/us/podcast/when-to-hire-consultants-in-your-business/id1695210366?i=1000661885547
Ed: Staci Millard. **Released:** July 11, 2024. **Description:** Podcast offers tips on selecting a consultant and discusses how owner may find financing through consultancy. .

CONSULTANTS

20147 ■ **ADG Group (ADG)**
5952 Peachtree Industrial Blvd. – Ste. 2
Norcross, GA 30071
Ph: (770)447-9308
Fax: (770)447-9368
Co. E-mail: info@atldesigngroup.com
URL: http://atldesigngroup.com
Facebook: www.facebook.com/atldesigngroup
Linkedin: www.linkedin.com/company/atlanta-design-group
Instagram: www.instagram.com/atlantadesigngroup
Description: Corporate finance advisory firm specializing in arranging venture capital financing for emerging companies. Assists with mergers, acquisitions and divestitures. Offers balance sheet restructuring services for bankrupt and financially troubled companies. Also offers independent due diligence investigations. **Scope:** Corporate finance advisory firm specializing in arranging venture capital financing for emerging companies. Assists with mergers, acquisitions and divestitures. Offers balance sheet restructuring services for bankrupt and financially troubled companies. Also offers independent due diligence investigations.

20148 ■ **Advantage Group International**
20 Toronto St. 6th Fl.
Toronto, ON, Canada M5C 2B8

Small Business Sourcebook • 42nd Edition

Ph: (416)863-0685
URL: http://www.advantagegroup.com
Contact: John McLoughlin, Chief Executive Officer
E-mail: jmcloughlin@advantagegroup.com
Linkedin: www.linkedin.com/company/441758
YouTube: www.youtube.com/channel/UC 6hnG0aIVILvPbhkXKGmlog

Description: Specializes in two key areas performance benchmarking and pricing strategy. Each stream has developed a wide variety of customizable proprietary research tools to meet the needs of the clients. **Scope:** Specializes in two key areas performance benchmarking and pricing strategy. Each stream has developed a wide variety of customizable proprietary research tools to meet the needs of the clients. **Founded:** 1988. **Publications:** "7 Steps to building better customer relationships"; "How to Add Value to Customer Relationships"; "Top 10 Key Benefits of Building Business Relationships"; "Tips for Creating Better Relationships"; "Building Trust in Personal and Business Relationships"; "The Advantage Report Canadian Grocer"; "Customer Relationships"; "Customer Relationship Management: What it is and What it's not"; "The Advantage Report - Measuring the supplier-retailer relationship".

20149 ■ Advisory Management Services Inc.
9600 E 129th St.
Kansas City, MO 64149
Contact: William H. Wood, President

Description: A management consulting and training firm specializing in employee relations, management and staff training, organizational development, strategic planning and continuous quality improvement. **Scope:** A management consulting and training firm specializing in employee relations, management and staff training, organizational development, strategic planning and continuous quality improvement. **Founded:** 1979.

20150 ■ The Alliance Management Group Inc.
38 Old Chester Rd., Ste. 300
Gladstone, NJ 07934
Ph: (908)234-2344
Fax: (908)234-0638
URL: http://www.strategicalliance.com
Contact: Dr. Gene Slowinski, Director

Description: Firm is engaged in business management consultant such as integration, technology management and related services. **Scope:** Firm is engaged in business management consultant such as integration, technology management and related services. **Publications:** "Effective Practices For Sourcing Innovation," Jan-Feb, 2009; "Intellectual Property Issues in Collaborative Research Agreements," Nov-Dec, 2008; "Building University Relationships in China," Sep-Oct, 2008; "Reinventing Corporate Growth: Implementing the Transformational Growth Model"; "The Strongest Link"; "Allocating Patent Rights in Collaborative Research Agreements"; "Protecting Know-how and Trade Secrets in Collaborative Research Agreements," Aug, 2006; "Sourcing External Technology for Innovation," Jun, 2006. **Special Services:** "Want, Find, Get, Manage" Model®; "Want, Find, Get, Manage" Framework®; WFGM Framework®; The Alliance Implementation Program®; WFGM Paradigm®; WFGM Model®; "Want, Find, Get, Manage" Paradigm®, Transformational Growth®; T-growth®.

20151 ■ Alliance Management International Ltd.
6200 Rockside Rd.
Cleveland, OH 44131
Contact: Carolyn K. Matheson, Contact

Description: A consulting company that helps to form national and international strategic alliances. Handles alliances between companies forming joint ventures. Staff specialized in small company-large company alliance, alliance assessment and analysis and alliance strategic planning. **Scope:** A consulting company that helps to form national and international strategic alliances. Handles alliances between companies forming joint ventures. Staff specialized in small company-large company alliance, alliance assessment and analysis and alliance strategic planning. **Training:** Joint Business Planning; Developing a Shared Vision; Current and New/Prospective Partner Assessment; Customer Service; Sales Training; Leader and Management Skills.

20152 ■ Alternative Services Inc. (ASI)
32625 W 7 Mile Rd., Ste. 11
Livonia, MI 48152
Ph: (248)471-4880
URL: http://www.asi-mi.org
Contact: Jenny Bhaskaran, Executive Director
E-mail: jbhaskaran@asi-mi.org

Description: Services: Developmental disabilities training. **Scope:** Services: Developmental disabilities training. **Founded:** 1978.

20153 ■ Ambler Growth Strategy Consultants Inc.
3432 Reading Ave.
Hammonton, NJ 08037-8008
Fax: (609)567-3810

Description: Growth strategies, strategic assessments, CEO coaching. **Scope:** Growth strategies, strategic assessments, CEO coaching. **Founded:** 1979. **Publications:** "A joint venture can deliver more than growth"; "Achieving competitive advantage"; "Achieving resilience for your business during difficult times"; "Achieving resilient growth during challenging times"; "Acquisitions: A growth strategy to consider"; "Attracting and retaining longterm corporate sponsors"; "Celebrate Selling: The Consultative Relationship Way"; "A Joint Venture Can Deliver More Than Growth"; "Achieving Competitive Advantage"; "Achieving Resilience for Your Business During Difficult Times"; "Balancing Revenue Growth with Growth of a Business"; "Capture Your Competitive Advantage"; "Ease Succession Planning"; "Games Employees Play"; "How to Spark Innovation in an Existing Company"; "Managers demands must change with growth"; "Motivating Generation employees"; "Knowing when to hire ratios provide answers"; "Better customer service can bring black ink". **Training:** Strategic Leadership; Managing Innovation; Breaking Through Classic Barriers to Growth; Energize Your Enterprise; Capture Your Competitive Advantage; Four Entrepreneurial Styles; Perservance and Resilience; Real-Time Strategic Planning/RO1. **Special Services:** The Growth Strategist™.

20154 ■ American English Academy (AEA) [American English College]
111 N Atlantic Blvd., Ste. 112
Monterey Park, CA 91754
Ph: (626)457-2800
Fax: (626)457-2808
Co. E-mail: info@aec.edu
URL: http://www.aec.edu
Facebook: www.facebook.com/ americanenglishcollege
Linkedin: www.linkedin.com/company/american -english-college
Instagram: www.instagram.com/ americanenglishcollege
YouTube: www.youtube.com/channel/UC6eS 1MpXLDagYdZVZWWJO6A

Description: Specializes in providing on-site English language and communication development for corporations and individuals. Also develops and delivers training in speaking, writing, pronunciation, grammar, and idioms with an emphasis on business communication. Offers individual, small group, intensive, and long-distance learning. Programs tailor-made for each client. **Scope:** Specializes in providing on-site English language and communication development for corporations and individuals. Also develops and delivers training in speaking, writing, pronunciation, grammar, and idioms with an emphasis on business communication. Offers individual, small group, intensive, and long-distance learning. Programs tailor-made for each client. **Founded:** 1983.

20155 ■ Apex Innovations Inc.
19951 W 162nd St.
Olathe, KS 66062
Ph: (913)254-0250
Fax: (913)254-0320
URL: http://www.apex-innovations.com

Description: Developer of software for dynamically sharing information and processes between organizations. **Scope:** Developer of software for dynamically sharing information and processes between organizations. **Founded:** 2002. **Special Services:** i-INFO. EPR™; i-INFO.WORKS™; i-INFO Classes™.

20156 ■ Arnold S. Goldin & Associates Inc.
PO Box 276158
Boca Raton, FL 33427
Ph: (561)994-5810
Fax: (561)431-3102
URL: http://www.arnoldgoldin.com

Description: An accounting and management consulting firm. Serves clients worldwide. Provides management services. Handles monthly write-ups and tax returns. **Scope:** An accounting and management consulting firm. Serves clients worldwide. Provides management services. Handles monthly write-ups and tax returns.

20157 ■ Aurora Management Partners Inc.
1201 Peachtree St., Ste. 1570
Atlanta, GA 30361
Ph: (704)377-6010
Co. E-mail: info@auroramp.com
URL: http://www.auroramp.com
Contact: David Baker, CTP, Managing Partner
Linkedin: www.linkedin.com/company/aurora -management-partners/about

Description: Specializes in turnaround management and reorganization consulting, the company develops strategic initiatives, organize and analyze solutions, deal with creditor issues, review organizational structures and develop time frames for decision making. **Founded:** 2000. **Publications:** "TMA Turnaround of the Year Award, Small Company, Honorable Mention," Nov, 2005; "Back From The Brink - Bland Farms," Progressive Farmer, Oct, 2004; "New Breed of Turnaround Managers," Catalyst Magazine, Aug, 2004; "Key Performance Drivers - Bland Farms," The Produce News, Apr, 2004; "Corporate Governance: Averting Crisis's Before They Happen," ABJ journal, Feb, 2004.

20158 ■ Bahr International Inc.
12221 Merit Dr., Ste. 1305
Dallas, TX 75251
Contact: C. Charles Bahr, III, President

Description: Firm provides full-service turnaround management services and its operating solutions. **Scope:** Firm provides full-service turnaround management services and its operating solutions.

20159 ■ Beacon Management-Management Consultants
Pompano Beach, FL 33069
Co. E-mail: md@beaconmgmt.com
URL: http://www.beaconmgmt.com
Contact: Michael J. Donnelly, Consultant Managing Director Principal

Description: Provider of management consulting services such as strategic and business planning, market intelligence, decision support services, corporate finance, and much more. **Scope:** Provider of management consulting services such as strategic and business planning, market intelligence, decision support services, corporate finance, and much more. **Founded:** 1985. **Publications:** "Sun-Sentinel Article," Oct, 2012.

20160 ■ Bio-Technical Resources L.P. (BTR)
1035 S 7th St.
Manitowoc, WI 54220-5301
Ph: (920)684-5518
Fax: (920)684-5519
Co. E-mail: info@biotechresources.com
URL: http://www.biotechresources.com
Contact: Reinhardt A. Rosson, President

Description: Firm provides research and development of industrial fermentation processes service. **Scope:** Services include strain improvement, process development and metabolic engineering. **Founded:** 1962. **Publications:** "A Novel Fungus for the Production of Efficient Cellulases and Hemi-Cellulases," Jun, 2009; "Linoleic Acid Isomerase from Propionibacterium acnes: Purification, Characterization, Molecular

Cloning, and Heterologous Expression," 2007; "Purification and Characterization of a Membrane-Bound Linoleic Acid Isomerase from Clostridium sporogenes," 2007; "Metabolic Engineering of Sesquiterpene Metabolism in Yeast," 2007; "Purification and Characterization of a Membrane-Bound Linoleic AcidIsomerase from Clostridium sporogenes," 2007. **Training:** Metabolic Engineering for Industrial Production of Glucosamine and N-Acetylglucosamine, Aug, 2003; Metabolic Engineering of E. coli for the Industrial Production of Glucosamine, Apr, 2003.

20161 ■ BioChem Technology Inc.
1004 9th Ave., Ste. 230
  King of Prussia, PA 19406
Ph: (610)768-9360
Co. E-mail: sales@biochemtech.com
URL: http://www.biochemtech.com/about
Description: Firm engages in construction of monitoring, optimization, control of waste water treatment processes, technological optimization services and much more. **Scope:** Firm engages in construction of monitoring, optimization, control of waste water treatment processes, technological optimization services and much more. **Founded:** 1979. **Publications:** "Process Evaluation Provides Optimization and Energy Reduction"; "Effect of Ionic Strength on Ion Selective Electrodes in the Activated Sludge Process". **Training:** A Five Year Case Study of a Feed Forward Nitrogen Reduction Process Control System, Jun, 2009; Alternate DO Control Based on On-line Ammonia Measurement, Jun, 2009.

20162 ■ BioSciCon, Inc. [Biomedical Science Consulting Company, Inc.]
14905 Forest Landing Cir.
  Rockville, MD 20850
Ph: (301)610-9130
Fax: (301)610-7662
Co. E-mail: info@bioscicon.com
URL: http://www.bioscicon.com
Contact: Dr. Nenad Markovic, President
Description: Provider of biomedical science consulting and also a developer of biotechnology products. **Scope:** Provider of biomedical science consulting and also a developer of biotechnology products. **Founded:** 1996. **Publications:** "Cervical Acid Phosphates: A Biomarker of Cervical Dysplasia and Potential Surrogate Endpoint for Colposcopy," 2004; "Enhancing Pap test with a new biological marker of cervical dysplasia," 2004; "A cytoplasmic biomarker for liquid-based Pap," The FACEB Journal Experimental Biology, 2004; "Pap test and new biomarker-based technology for enhancing visibility of abnormal cells," 2004. **Special Services:** MarkPap®; PreservCyt®.

20163 ■ Birchfield Jacobs Foodsystems Inc.
519 N Charles St.
  Baltimore, MD 21201
Contact: John C. Birchfield, Jr., Contact
E-mail: jbirchfield@birchfieldjacobs.com
Description: Firm provides foodservice consulting services.

20164 ■ Blankinship & Associates Inc.
1615 5th St., Ste. A
  Davis, CA 95616
Ph: (530)757-0941
URL: http://www.h2osci.com
Contact: Michael Blankinship, President
Description: Provider of consulting services to support water resources, agriculture and risk evaluation and communication, water resources management and regulatory. **Scope:** Provider of consulting services to support water resources, agriculture and risk evaluation and communication, water resources management and regulatory. **Founded:** 2000. **Publications:** "Air Blast Sprayer Calibration and Chlorpyrifos Irrigation Study," Oct, 2007; "How Green is your golf course," Prosper Magazine, 2007. **Training:** CDFG Wildlands IPM Seminar, Oct, 2009.

20165 ■ Business Consulting Services
720 Highpoint Dr.
  Wexford, PA 15090
Contact: Reed Powell, Owner
Description: Management consulting organization dedicated to providing professional services to the business, government and non-profit communities and specializes in the two key areas of business performance improvement and information technology consulting and specifically for small business owners. **Scope:** Management consulting organization dedicated to providing professional services to the business, government and non-profit communities and specializes in the two key areas of business performance improvement and information technology consulting and specifically for small business owners. **Publications:** "If You Fail To Plan"; "The True Cost Of Technology"; "Why Projects Fail"; "Planning For A Business Disruption". **Training:** How To Select, Manage and Contract Consultants, and Other Resources; How To Market Professional Services; Introduction To Management Consulting.

20166 ■ Business Improvement Architects (BIA)
633 Lakelands Ave.
  Innisfil, ON, Canada L9S 4E5
Co. E-mail: info@bia.ca
URL: http://bia.ca
Contact: Rowena Lamy, Consultant
E-mail: rlamy@bia.ca
Facebook: www.facebook.com/BusinessImprovementArchitects
Linkedin: www.linkedin.com/company/business-improvement-architects
Description: Provider of the following services, strategic planning, leadership development, innovation and project and quality management. Specialize in strategic planning, change management, leadership assessment and development of skills. **Scope:** Provider of the following services, strategic planning, leadership development, innovation and project and quality management. Specialize in strategic planning, change management, leadership assessment and development of skills. **Founded:** 1989. **Publications:** "Avoiding Pit falls to Innovation"; "Create a New Dimension of Performance with Innovation"; "The Power of Appreciation in Leadership"; "Why It Makes Sense To Have a Strategic Enterprise Office"; "Burning Rubber at the Start of Your Project"; "Accounting for Quality"; "How Pareto Charts Can Help You Improve the Quality of Business Processes"; "Managing Resistance to Change". **Training:** The Innovation Process From Vision to Reality, San Diego, Oct, 2007; Critical Thinking, Kuala Lump or, Sep, 2007; Critical Thinking, Brunei, Sep, 2007; Delivering Project Assurance, Auckland, Jun, 2007; From Crisis to Control: A New Era in Strategic Project Management, Prague, May, 2007; What Project Leaders Need to Know to Help Them Sleep Better At Night, London, May, 2007; Innovation Process. From Vision To Reality, Orlando, Apr, 2007. **Special Services:** Project Planning Tool™.

20167 ■ ByrneMRG Corp.
5459 Rinker Cir.
  Doylestown, PA 18902
Ph: (215)630-7411
Co. E-mail: info@byrnemrg.com
URL: http://www.byrnemrg.com
Contact: Patrick Boyle, Founder Consultant
E-mail: pjboyle@byrnemrg.com
Description: Services: Management consulting. **Scope:** Services: Management consulting. **Founded:** 1972. **Publications:** "Implementing Solutions to Everyday Issues".

20168 ■ CBIZ, Inc.
CBIZ, Inc.
  5959 Rockside Woods Blvd. N, Ste. 600
  Independence, OH 44131
Ph: (216)447-9000
Fax: (216)447-9007
Co. E-mail: cbizwomensadvantage@cbiz.com
URL: http://www.cbiz.com
Contact: Jerome P. Grisko, Jr., President
Facebook: facebook.com/cbizmhmcareers
Linkedin: www.linkedin.com/company/cbiz
X (Twitter): twitter.com/cbz
YouTube: www.youtube.com/user/CBIZSolutions
Description: Diversified services company is engaged in providing an array of professional business services which include accounting and tax, healthcare and health benefits consulting, financial advisory, valuation, risk and advisory services, payroll, property and casualty insurance, retirement planning, managed networking and hardware services primarily to small and medium-sized businesses, as well as individuals, government agencies, and not-for-profit enterprises. **Founded:** 1996. **Training:** Health Care - What the Future Holds; Consumer Driven Health Plans; Executive Plans; Health Savings Accounts; Healthy Wealthy and Wise; Legislative Update; Medicare Part D; Retirement Plans.

20169 ■ Center for Lifestyle Enhancement-Columbia Medical Center of Plano
3901 West 15th St
  Plano, TX 75075
Ph: (972)596-6800
Fax: (972)519-1299
URL: http://medicalcityplano.com
Contact: Erol R. Akdamar, President
Facebook: www.facebook.com/medicalcityplano
X (Twitter): twitter.com/MedCityPlano
Description: Firm provides professional health counseling in the areas of general nutrition for weight management, eating disorders, diabetic education, cholesterol reduction and adolescent weight management. Offers work site health promotion and preventive services. Also coordinates speaker's bureau, cooking classes and physician referrals. **Scope:** Firm provides professional health counseling in the areas of general nutrition for weight management, eating disorders, diabetic education, cholesterol reduction and adolescent weight management. Offers work site health promotion and preventive services. Also coordinates speaker's bureau, cooking classes and physician referrals. **Founded:** 1975. **Training:** Rx Diet and Exercise; Smoking Cessation; Stress Management; Health Fairs; Fitness Screenings; Body Composition; Nutrition Analysis; Exercise Classes; Prenatal Nutrition; SHAPEDOWN; Successfully Managing Diabetes; Gourmet Foods for Your Heart; The Aging Heart; Heart Smart Saturday featuring Day of Dance; Weight-Loss Management Seminars; The Right Stroke for Men; Peripheral Artery Disease Screening; Menstruation: The Cycle Begins; Boot Camp for New Dads; Grand parenting 101: Caring for Kids Today; Teddy Bear C New Baby Day C Safe Sitter Babysitting Class.

20170 ■ The Center for Organizational Excellence, Inc. (COE)
15204 Omega Dr., Ste. 300
  Rockville, MD 20850
Contact: Stephen P. Goodrich, Contact
E-mail: sgoodrich@center4oe.com
Description: Firm provides consulting services such as designing and delivering consulting solutions in the areas of organizational effectiveness, human capital, information technology, and data management. **Scope:** Firm provides consulting services such as designing and delivering consulting solutions in the areas of organizational effectiveness, human capital, information technology, and data management. **Founded:** 1984.

20171 ■ CEO Advisors
848 Brickell Ave., Ste. 603
  Miami, FL 33131
Ph: (305)371-8560
URL: http://www.ceoadvisors.us
Contact: Roberto Arguello, Jr., President
Facebook: www.facebook.com/CEOAdvisors9
Linkedin: www.linkedin.com/company/wix-com
Description: Provider of clients services in strategy, mergers and acquisitions, corporate finance and advisory, supply chain management, government relations and public affairs. **Scope:** Provider of clients services in strategy, mergers and acquisitions, corporate finance and advisory, supply chain management, government relations and public affairs. **Founded:** 1989. **Preferred Investment Size:** $300,000 to $500,000. **Industry Preferences:** Com-

munications and media, computer hardware and software, semiconductors and other electronics, biotechnology, medical and health, consumer related.

20172 ■ CFI Group USA L.L.C.
3916 Ranchero Dr.
Ann Arbor, MI 48108
Ph: (734)930-9090
Fax: (734)930-0911
Co. E-mail: info@cfigroup.se
URL: http://cfigroup.com
Contact: Sheri Petras, Chief Executive Officer
Facebook: www.facebook.com/CFIGroup
Linkedin: www.linkedin.com/company/cfi-group
X (Twitter): x.com/cfigroup

Description: Management consulting firm helps its clients worldwide to maximize shareholder value by optimizing customer and employee satisfaction, their clients span from a variety of industries including manufacturing, telecommunication, retail and government. **Scope:** Management consulting firm helps its clients worldwide to maximize shareholder value by optimizing customer and employee satisfaction, their clients span from a variety of industries including manufacturing, telecommunication, retail and government. **Founded:** 1988. **Publications:** "Customer Satisfaction and Stock Prices: High Returns, Low Risk," American Marketing Association, Jan, 2006; "Customer Satisfaction Index Climbs," The Wall Street Journal, Feb, 2004; "What's Next? Customer Service is Key to Post-Boom Success," The Bottom Line, Mar, 2003; "Boost Stock Performance, Nation's Economy," Quality Progress, Feb, 2003.

20173 ■ Chartered Management Co.
100 Saunders Rd., Ste. 150
Lake Forest, IL 60045
Contact: William B. Avellone, President

Description: Operations improvement consultants. Specializes in strategic planning, feasibility studies, management audits and reports, profit enhancement, start-up businesses, mergers and acquisitions, joint ventures, divestitures, interim management, crisis management, turnarounds, business process re-engineering, venture capital and due diligence. **Scope:** Operations improvement consultants. Specializes in strategic planning, feasibility studies, management audits and reports, profit enhancement, start-up businesses, mergers and acquisitions, joint ventures, divestitures, interim management, crisis management, turnarounds, business process re-engineering, venture capital and due diligence. **Founded:** 1985.

20174 ■ Children's Psychological Health Center, Inc. (CPHC)
2105 Divisadero St.
San Francisco, CA 94115
Ph: (415)292-7119
Fax: (415)749-2802
URL: http://www.childrenspsychologicalhealthcenter.org
Contact: Jessie Rios, Executive Director
E-mail: jessie.rios@expertchildpsychiatry.org
Linkedin: www.linkedin.com/in/childrenspsychological

Description: Treats those with psychological trauma claimed from stressors including institutional negligence, vehicular and aviation accidents, wrongful death in the family, rape, molestation, fire, explosion, flood, earthquake, loss of parents, terrorism, kidnapping, disfiguring events, emotional damage from social work, medical malpractice or defective products. **Scope:** Treats those with psychological trauma claimed from stressors including institutional negligence, vehicular and aviation accidents, wrongful death in the family, rape, molestation, fire, explosion, flood, earthquake, loss of parents, terrorism, kidnapping, disfiguring events, emotional damage from social work, medical malpractice or defective products. **Founded:** 1992. **Publications:** "My Personal Story About Tropical Storm Stan," Feb, 2006; "My Personal Story About Hurricanes Katrina and Rita: A guided activity workbook to help coping, learning and Healthy expression," Sep, 2005; "Helping Patients and their Families Cope in a National Disaster," Jan, 2002; "The practice of behavioral treatment in the acute rehabilitation setting".

20175 ■ Comer & Associates L.L.C. (CA)
5255 Holmes Pl.
Boulder, CO 80303
Ph: (303)786-7986
URL: http://www.comerassociates.com
Contact: Gerald Comer, Contact

Description: Specialize in developing markets and businesses. Marketing support includes developing and writing strategic and tactical business plans, developing and writing focused, effective market plans, researching market potential and competition, implementing targeted marketing tactics to achieve company objectives, conducting customer surveys to determine satisfaction and attitudes toward client. **Scope:** Specialize in developing markets and businesses. Marketing support includes developing and writing strategic and tactical business plans, developing and writing focused, effective market plans, researching market potential and competition, implementing targeted marketing tactics to achieve company objectives, conducting customer surveys to determine satisfaction and attitudes toward client. **Training:** Developing a Strategic Market Plan; Market Research: Defining Your Opportunity; Management and Leadership Effectiveness; Team Building; Developing a Business Plan; How to Close; Using Questions to Sell; Sales System Elements and Checklist; Working With Independent Reps; Features vs. Benefits; Overcoming Objections; Sales Force Automation.

20176 ■ Consulting & Conciliation Service (CCS)
Sacramento, CA
Ph: (916)396-0480
URL: http://conciliation.org
Contact: Jane McCluskey, Contact
E-mail: jane@conciliation.org

Description: Firm offers consulting and conciliation services, they provide pre-mediation counseling, training and research on preparing for a peaceful society, mediation and facilitation, preparation for shifts in structure, policy, and personnel, it offers sliding scale business rates and free individual consultation. **Scope:** Firm offers consulting and conciliation services, they provide pre-mediation counseling, training and research on preparing for a peaceful society, mediation and facilitation, preparation for shifts in structure, policy, and personnel, it offers sliding scale business rates and free individual consultation. **Publications:** "Native America and Tracking Shifts in US Policy"; "Biogenesis: A Discussion of Basic Social Needs and the Significance of Hope". **Training:** Positive Approaches to Violence Prevention: Peace building in Schools and Communities.

20177 ■ The Consulting Source, Inc.
1403 S Addison Ct.
Aurora, CO 80018-6003
Ph: (303)366-4800
Fax: (303)366-4801
Co. E-mail: info@consultingsource.com
URL: http://www.consultingsource.com
Contact: Margaret A. Sobey, President

Description: Provider of web design, hosting, and IT consulting services. **Scope:** Provider of web design, hosting, and IT consulting services. **Founded:** 1990.

20178 ■ Corporate Consulting, Inc.
100 Fillmore St.
Denver, CO 80206
Contact: Devereux C. Josephs, Contact

Description: Engaged in feasibility studies, organizational development, small business management, mergers and acquisitions, joint ventures, divestitures, interim management, crisis management, turnarounds, financing, appraisals valuations and due diligence studies. **Scope:** Engaged in feasibility studies, organizational development, small business management, mergers and acquisitions, joint ventures, divestitures, interim management, crisis management, turnarounds, financing, appraisals valuations and due diligence studies.

20179 ■ COTC Technologies Inc.
PO Box 17413
Denver, CO 80217
Contact: Thomas I. Renz, Contact

Description: Firm provides software consulting services to organizations that require assistance with their HP3000 computer system. Firm provides systems analysis, programming, operations support and system management. Also provides PC software and hardware support and consulting. Additionally provides various training for the HP3000 computer system. **Scope:** Firm provides software consulting services to organizations that require assistance with their HP3000 computer system. Firm provides systems analysis, programming, operations support and system management. Also provides PC software and hardware support and consulting. Additionally provides various training for the HP3000 computer system.

20180 ■ David G. Schantz
29 Wood Run Cir.
Rochester, NY 14612-2271
Ph: (716)723-0760
Fax: (716)723-8724
Co. E-mail: daveschantz@yahoo.com
URL: http://www.daveschantz.freeservers.com

Description: Provider of industrial engineering services for photo finishing labs, including amateur-wholesale, professional, commercial, school and package. **Scope:** Provider of industrial engineering services for photo finishing labs, including amateur-wholesale, professional, commercial, school and package.

20181 ■ Diversified Health Resources Inc.
1209 N Astor St., No. 2N
Chicago, IL 60610-2655
Contact: Andrea Rice Rozran, President

Description: Offers health care consulting for hospitals, nursing homes including homes for the aged and other health related facilities and companies. Specializes in planning and marketing. Also conducts executive searches for top level health care administrative positions. Serves private industries as well as government agencies. **Scope:** Offers health care consulting for hospitals, nursing homes including homes for the aged and other health related facilities and companies. Specializes in planning and marketing. Also conducts executive searches for top level health care administrative positions. Serves private industries as well as government agencies. **Publications:** "City Finance".

20182 ■ DRI Consulting Inc. (DRIC)
Two Otter Ln.
Saint Paul, MN 55127
Ph: (651)415-1400
Co. E-mail: dric@dric.com
URL: http://www.dric.com
Contact: Dr. John Fennig, Director

Description: Provides high-quality, research-based services and training in leadership, team processes, supervision, and management, and organizational development, clients with direct and substantial impact on individual and team performance and on organizational success through proven processes for selecting, developing and deploying leaders. **Scope:** Provides high-quality, research-based services and training in leadership, team processes, supervision, and management, and organizational development, clients with direct and substantial impact on individual and team performance and on organizational success through proven processes for selecting, developing and deploying leaders. **Founded:** 1991.

20183 ■ Eastern Point Consulting Group Inc.
75 Oak St.
Newton, MA 02465
Ph: (617)965-4141
URL: http://www.eastpt.com
Contact: Katherine Herzog, President

Description: Firm specializes in bringing practical solutions to complex challenges and provides consulting and training in managing diversity, comprehensive sexual-harassment policies and programs, organizational development, benchmarks 360-degree skills assessment, executive coaching, strategic human resource planning, team building, leadership development for women, mentoring programs, and gender issues in the workplace. **Scope:** Firm specializes in bringing practical solutions to complex challenges and provides consulting and training in managing diversity, comprehensive sexual-harassment policies and programs, organizational development, benchmarks 360-degree skills assessment, executive coaching, strategic human resource planning, team building, leadership development for women, mentoring programs, and gender issues in the workplace. **Training:** Leadership Development for Women.

20184 ■ Education Development Center Inc. (EDC)
300 Fifth Ave., Ste. 2010
Waltham, MA 02451
Ph: (617)969-7100
Fax: (617)969-5979
Co. E-mail: contact@edc.org
URL: http://www.edc.org
Contact: Siobhan Murphy, Chief Executive Officer
Facebook: www.facebook.com/edc.worldwide
Linkedin: www.linkedin.com/company/education-development-center
X (Twitter): x.com/EDCtweets
YouTube: www.youtube.com/edcworldwide

Description: Delivers programs to address early childhood development, youth workforce development, and suicide prevention. Creates curricula and online courses and conducts surveys. **Scope:** Serves to design, deliver and evaluate innovative programs to address some of the world's most urgent challenges in education, health, and economic opportunity. Renders services to US. and foreign government agencies, private foundations, healthcare sectors, educational institutions, nonprofit organizations, universities, and corporations. **Founded:** 1958. **Publications:** "A Call to Action: HIV/AIDS, Health, Safety, and the Youth Employment Summit"; "A Case Against "Binge" as the Term of Choice: How to Get College Students to Personalize Messages about Dangerous Drinking"; "A Description of Foundation Skills Interventions for Struggling Middle-Grade Readers in Four Urban Northeast and Islands Region School Districts"; "A Guide to Facilitating Cases in Education"; "A Look at Social, Emotional, and Behavioral Screening Tools for Head Start and Early Head Start"; "A Multifaceted Social Norms Approach to Reduce High-Risk Drinking: Lessons from Hobart and William Smith Colleges"; "The New Media Literacy Handbook"; "Helping Children Outgrow War"; "Worms, Shadows, and Whirlpools: Science in the Early Childhood Classroom"; "Teacher Leadership in Mathematics and Science Casebook and Facilitator's Guide"; "Teachers' Professional Development and the Elementary Mathematics Classroom: Bringing Understandings to Light". **Training:** Designed to Introduce the Materials; To Guide Schools Through the Issues. **Geographic Preference:** Multinational.

20185 ■ Effective Compensation Inc. (ECI)
5856 S Lowell Blvd., Ste. 32 No 322
Littleton, CO 80123
Ph: (303)854-1000
Co. E-mail: eci@effectivecompensation.com
URL: http://www.effectivecompensation.com
Contact: Terry Isselhardt, President

Description: Independent compensation consulting firm specializing in working with clients on a collaborative basis to improve their organization's efficiency through competitive, focused total compensation processes. Helps organizations determine how to competitively pay their employees. Provides quality, culture sensitive, compensation consulting assistance to all types of employers. **Scope:** Independent compensation consulting firm specializing in working with clients on a collaborative basis to improve their organization's efficiency through competitive, focused total compensation processes. Helps organizations determine how to competitively pay their employees. Provides quality, culture sensitive, compensation consulting assistance to all types of employers. **Founded:** 1991. **Publications:** "Alternative Job Evaluation Approaches"; "Broad Banding: A Management Overview"; "Job Evaluation: Understanding the Issues"; "Industry Compensation Surveys"; "Skill Based Pay"; "Four Levels of Team Membership"; "Factors in Designing an Incentive Plan"; "Key Stock Allocation Issues"; "Stock Plans Primer". **Training:** Alternative Job Evaluation Approaches; Broad Banding: A Management Overview; Skill Based Pay; Job Evaluation: Understanding the Issues; Designing Compensation Programs that Motivate Employees; Master the Compensation Maze; Base Salary Administration Manual.

20186 ■ Effectiveness Resource Group Inc.
2215 2nd Ave. N
Seattle, WA 98109-2318
Contact: Donald Swartz, Governor

Description: Provider of problem solving help to client organizations in public and private sectors so they can release and mobilize the full potential of their personnel to achieve productive and satisfying results. **Scope:** Provider of problem solving help to client organizations in public and private sectors so they can release and mobilize the full potential of their personnel to achieve productive and satisfying results. **Training:** Life/Work Goals Exploration; Influencing Change Thru Consultation; Designing and Leading Participative Meetings; Designing, Leading and Managing Change; Project Management and Leadership; Performance Management; Productive Management of Differences; Performance Correction.

20187 ■ Family Resource Center on Disabilities (FRCD)
11 E Adams St., Ste. 1002
Chicago, IL 60603
Ph: (312)939-3513
Fax: (312)854-8980
Co. E-mail: info@frcd.org
URL: http://frcd.org
Contact: Michelle Phillips, Contact
X (Twitter): x.com/FRCDPTI
YouTube: www.youtube.com/user/frcd1231
Pinterest: www.pinterest.com/frcdpti

Description: Parents, professionals, and volunteers seeking to improve services for all children with disabilities. Organized as a result of the 1969 Illinois law mandating the education of all children with disabilities and operates as a coalition to inform and activate parents. Provides information and referral services, individualized support services for low-income Chicago families, transition services, and special education rights training. **Scope:** Provider of consulting services to advocacy groups and individuals seeking support for children with disabilities. **Founded:** 1969. **Publications:** "How to Get Services By Being Assertive"; "How to Organize an Effective Parent/Advocacy Group and Move Bureaucracies"; "Main roads Travel to Tomorrow - a Road Map for the Future"; "Does Your Child Have Special Education Needs"; "How to Prepare for a Successful Due Process Hearing"; "How to Participate Effectively in Your Child's IEP Meeting"; "Tax Guide for Parents". **Training:** How to Support Parents as Effective Advocates; How to Get Services by Being Assertive; How to Develop an Awareness Program for Nondisabled Children; How to Organize a Parent Support Group; How to Move Bureaucratic Mountains; How to Raise Money Painlessly through Publishing; How to Use Humor in Public Presentations. **Geographic Preference:** National.

20188 ■ First Strike Management Consulting Inc. (FSMC)
PO Box 1188
Little River, SC 29566-1188
Ph: (843)385-6338
Co. E-mail: info@fsmc.com
URL: http://www.fsmc.com

Description: Offers proposal management and program management services. Specializes in enterprise systems, management systems, and staff augmentation. Serves the following industries: Nuclear/Fossil Power, Petro-Chemical, Aerospace and Defense, Telecommunications, Engineering and Construction, Information Technology, Golf Course Construction/Management, Utility Engineering/Construction, Civil Works, and Housing Development. **Scope:** Offers proposal management and program management services. Specializes in enterprise systems, management systems, and staff augmentation. Serves the following industries: Nuclear/Fossil Power, Petro-Chemical, Aerospace and Defense, Telecommunications, Engineering and Construction, Information Technology, Golf Course Construction/Management, Utility Engineering/Construction, Civil Works, and Housing Development. **Founded:** 1991. **Publications:** "Project Management for Executives"; "Project Risk Management"; "Project Communications Management"; "Winning Proposals, Four Computer Based Training (CBT) courses"; "Principles of Program Management". **Training:** Preparing Winning Proposals in Response to Government RFPs.

20189 ■ Flett Research Ltd.
440 DeSalaberry Ave.
Winnipeg, MB, Canada R2L 0Y7
Ph: (204)667-2505
Fax: (204)667-2505
Co. E-mail: flett@flettresearch.ca
URL: http://www.flettresearch.ca
Contact: Dawn Gilbert, Coordinator

Description: Provider of environmental audits and assessments. Offers contract research and consultation on environmental topics, specializes in limnology, with emphasis in microbiology, bio-geo chemistry and radio-chemistry. **Scope:** Provider of environmental audits and assessments. Offers contract research and consultation on environmental topics, specializes in limnology, with emphasis in microbiology, bio-geo chemistry and radio-chemistry. **Founded:** 1978. **Training:** Comparison of Two Methods for the Measurement of Methyl Mercury Concentrations in Penobscot River Sediments.

20190 ■ Freese & Associates Inc. (F&A)
16105 Lucky Bell Ln.
Newbury, OH 44065
Ph: (440)487-4509
URL: http://www.freeseinc.com
Contact: Thomas L. Freese, Principal
E-mail: tfreese@freeseinc.com

Description: Provider of supply chain management and logistics consulting services such as customer service, material management, transportation, and much more. **Scope:** Provider of supply chain management and logistics consulting services such as customer service, material management, transportation, and much more. **Founded:** 1987. **Publications:** "Building Relationships is Key to Motivation," Distribution Center Management, Apr, 2006; "Getting Maximum Results from Performance Reviews," WERC Sheet, Oct, 2003; "SCM: Making the Vision a Reality," Supply Chain Management Review, Oct, 2003; "Contents Under Pressure," DC Velocity, Aug, 2003; "When Considering Outsourcing, It's Really a Financial Decision," Inventory Management Report, Mar, 2003. **Training:** WERC/CAWS Warehousing in China Conference, Sep, 2008; CSCMP Annual Conference, Denver, Oct, 2008; Keys to Retaining and Motivating Your Associates, Dallas, Mar, 2006; The Value and Challenges of Supply Chain Management, Dubai, Feb, 2006; Best Practices in Logistics in China, Jun, 2005; Keys to Motivating Associates, Dallas, May, 2005; The Goal and the Way of International Cooperation in Logistics, Jenobuk, Apr, 2005.

20191 ■ Full Voice
9912B Holmes Rd., Ste. 237
Kansas City, MO 64131-4206

Description: Vocal performance training firm offering consulting services and personal training sessions in the implementation of effective vocal communication techniques for the development of business relationships and career enhancement. **Scope:** Vocal performance training firm offering consulting services and personal training sessions in the implementation of effective vocal communication techniques for the development of business relationships and career enhancement. **Publications:** "You Can Sound Like You Know What You're Saying". **Training:** You Can Sound Like You Know What You're Saying; The

Psychology of Vocal Performance; Security...the Ability to Accept Change; Knowing...the Key to Relaxed Public Communication; The Effective Voice for Customer Service Enhancement; You Can Speak With Conviction; How To Make Yours a Championship Team; Functional English For Foreign Trade. **Special Services:** FULL VOICE™.

20192 ■ Global Technology Transfer L.L.C.
1500 Dixie Hwy.
Park Hills, KY 41011
Contact: Anthony R. Zembrodt, Sr., Member
Description: Firm specializes in product development, quality assurance, new product development, and total quality management focusing on household chemical specialties, especially air fresheners. Utilizes latest technology from global resources. Specializes in enhancement products for home and automobile. **Scope:** Firm specializes in product development, quality assurance, new product development, and total quality management focusing on household chemical specialties, especially air fresheners. Utilizes latest technology from global resources. Specializes in enhancement products for home and automobile.

20193 ■ Greenlight Business Solutions L.L.C.
95 Puritan Way
New Bedford, MA 02745
Ph: (774)701-0141
Co. E-mail: info@greenlightbizsolutions.com
URL: http://greenlightbizsolutions.com/
Facebook: www.facebook.com/greenlight.bs
Linkedin: www.linkedin.com/company/greenlight-biz-solutions
Instagram: https://www.instagram.com/greenlight.bs
Description: Cannabis consulting company specializing in the licensing process. **Founded:** 2018.

20194 ■ Harvey A. Meier Co. (HAM)
410 W Nevada St.
Ashland, OR 97520-1043
Ph: (509)458-3210
Fax: (541)488-7905
Co. E-mail: harvey@harveymeier.com
URL: http://www.harveymeier.com
Contact: Dr. Harvey A. Meier, President
E-mail: harvey@harveymeier.com
Description: Services: Management consulting. **Scope:** Services: Management consulting. **Publications:** "The D'Artagnan Way".

20195 ■ Hewitt Development Enterprises (HDE)
1717 N Bayshore Dr., Ste. 2154
Miami, FL 33132
Ph: (305)372-0941
Fax: (305)372-0941
Co. E-mail: info@hewittdevelopment.com
URL: http://www.hewittdevelopment.com
Contact: Robert G. Hewitt, Contact
E-mail: bob@hewittdevelopment.com
Description: Firm specializes in strategic planning, profit enhancement, startup businesses, interim and crisis management, turnarounds, production planning, just-in-time inventory and project management, serves senior management and acquirers of distressed businesses. **Scope:** Firm specializes in strategic planning, profit enhancement, startup businesses, interim and crisis management, turnarounds, production planning, just-in-time inventory and project management, serves senior management and acquirers of distressed businesses. **Founded:** 1985.

20196 ■ Human Resource Specialties, Inc. (HRS)
DCI Consulting Group Inc.
PO Box 1995
Missoula, MT 59806
Ph: (202)828-6900
URL: http://www.dciconsult.com
Contact: Sandy L. Henderson, President
Description: Provider of human resources assistance to organizations. Offers preparation of affirmative action plans, support documents, and adverse impact studies of personnel activities. Also offers customized consultations in small business services, diversity and discrimination, and investigations, complaints and grievances. Provides investigations, including allegations of unfair treatment, equal employment opportunity (EEO) and racial or sexual harassment. Offers customized web-based training (webinars) on a variety of HR, EEO and AAP-related topics. **Scope:** Provider of human resources assistance to organizations. Offers preparation of affirmative action plans, support documents, and adverse impact studies of personnel activities. Also offers customized consultations in small business services, diversity and discrimination, and investigations, complaints and grievances. Provides investigations, including allegations of unfair treatment, equal employment opportunity (EEO) and racial or sexual harassment. Offers customized web-based training (webinars) on a variety of HR, EEO and AAP-related topics. **Founded:** 1984.

20197 ■ In Plain English
14501 Antigone Dr.
Gaithersburg, MD 20878-2484
Ph: (301)340-2821
Free: 800-274-9645
Fax: (301)279-0115
URL: http://www.inplainenglish.com
Description: Management consultants helping government and businesses research, design, write and produce user oriented management information for human resources, employee benefits, business process, corporate and marketing needs. Services include: GSA mob is schedule for consulting to the government; employee benefit communications, plain English business writing workshops for print and electronic media; communicating strategy and tactics; marketing research, business planning and communications; readability testing; usability testing and monitoring strategy. **Scope:** Management consultants helping government and businesses research, design, write and produce user oriented management information for human resources, employee benefits, business process, corporate and marketing needs. Services include: GSA mob is schedule for consulting to the government; employee benefit communications, plain English business writing workshops for print and electronic media; communicating strategy and tactics; marketing research, business planning and communications; readability testing; usability testing and monitoring strategy. **Founded:** 1977. **Publications:** "The Benefits Communication"; "The Employee Benefits Communication ToolKit," Commerce Clearinghouse; "Benefits Communication," Business and Legal Reports. **Training:** Plain English Writing Training; Summary Plan Description Compliance workshops; Re-Humanizing the Corporation, Human Resources and Employee Benefits Communication Workshop; 21 Writing Tips for the 21st Century; Make the Write Impression; Writing to Inform and Instruct; The Dreaded Nuts and Bolts; Writing to Persuade; Writing Policy and Procedure Manuals In Plain English; Writing for Accountants and Auditors In Plain English. **Special Services:** In Plain English®.

20198 ■ Institute for Management Excellence
Trabuco Canyon, CA 92679
Ph: (949)667-1012
URL: http://www.itstime.com
Contact: Barbara Taylor, Executive Director
Description: Consulting firm and training focuses on improving productivity, using practices and creative techniques. **Scope:** Consulting firm and training focuses on improving productivity, using practices and creative techniques. **Founded:** 1995. **Publications:** "Income Without a Job," 2008; "The Other Side of Midnight, 2000: An Executive Guide to the Year 2000 Problem"; "Concordance to the Michael Teachings"; "Handbook of Small Business Advertising"; "The Personality Game"; "How to Market Yourself for Success". **Training:** The Personality Game; Power Path Seminars; Productivity Plus; Sexual Harassment and Discrimination Prevention; Worker's Comp Cost Reduction; Americans with Disabilities Act; In Search of Identify: Clarifying Corporate Culture.

20199 ■ Interminds & Federer Resources Inc.
PO Box 438
Pasadena, CA 91102
Ph: (512)261-0761
Co. E-mail: yesyoucan@interminds.com
URL: http://www.interminds.com
Description: Firm specializes in feasibility studies, startup businesses, small business management, mergers and acquisitions, joint ventures, divestitures, interim and crisis management, turnarounds, production planning, team building, appraisals, and valuations. **Scope:** Firm specializes in feasibility studies, startup businesses, small business management, mergers and acquisitions, joint ventures, divestitures, interim and crisis management, turnarounds, production planning, team building, appraisals, and valuations. **Founded:** 1985. **Publications:** "Yes You Can: How To Be A Success No Matter Who You Are Or Where You're From".

20200 ■ Johnston Co.
78 Bedford St.
Lexington, MA 02420
Ph: (781)862-7595
Fax: (781)862-9066
Co. E-mail: info@johnstoncompany.com
URL: http://johnstoncompany.com
Contact: Jim Johnston, Chief Executive Officer
E-mail: jimj@johnstoncompany.com
Description: Firm provides consulting on environmental and workplace services such as LSRP service, property acquisition and redevelopment, engineering and site remediation. **Scope:** Firm provides consulting on environmental and workplace services such as LSRP service, property acquisition and redevelopment, engineering and site remediation. **Publications:** "Why are board meetings such a waste of time," Boston Business Journal, Apr, 2004.

20201 ■ Liberty Business Strategies Ltd.
329 S 16th
Philadelphia, PA 19102
Ph: (267)858-4021
Co. E-mail: info@libertystrategies.com
URL: http://libertystrategies.com
Contact: Emmy Miller, President
Linkedin: www.linkedin.com/company/525207
X (Twitter): x.com/LibertyBusiness
Description: Management consulting firm provides executive coaching, strategic alignment, succession planning such as healthcare, consumer products, technology, and much more. **Scope:** Management consulting firm provides executive coaching, strategic alignment, succession planning such as healthcare, consumer products, technology, and much more. **Founded:** 1980. **Training:** Winning with Talent, Morison Annual Conference, Jul, 2009.

20202 ■ Linda Lipsky Restaurant Consultants Inc.
216 Foxcroft Rd.
Broomall, PA 19008
Ph: (610)325-3663
Co. E-mail: lipsky@restaurantconsult.com
URL: http://restaurantconsult.com
Contact: Linda Lipsky, Founder
E-mail: lipsky@restaurantconsult.com
Description: Provider of marketing and survey solutions such as management training, evaluation programs, recipe documentation, cost analysis and bridge management services for restaurants. **Scope:** Provider of marketing and survey solutions such as management training, evaluation programs, recipe documentation, cost analysis and bridge management services for restaurants. **Founded:** 1988. **Training:** Designing Menus for Maximum Sales and Profits; How to Maximize Your Check Average.

20203 ■ Mankind Research Unlimited (MRU) [Mankind Research Foundation]
1315 Apple Ave.
Silver Spring, MD 20910
URL: http://mankindresearchunlimited.weebly.com
Description: Publishes monographs, books, bibliographies and technical reports on health, education and energy resources. **Scope:** Firm provide an organization for scientific development and application of technology that could have positive impact on the health, education, and welfare of mankind.

Provide solution to seek and apply futuristic solutions to current problems. Provides services in the areas of advanced sciences, biotechnical, bionic, biocybernetic, biomedical, holistic health, bio immunology, solar energy, accelerated learning, and sensory aids for handicapped. Current specific activities involve research in AIDS, drug abuse, affordable housing, food for the hungry, and literacy and remedial education. **Founded:** 1966.

20204 ■ McShane Group L.L.C.
2119 E Franklin St.
 Richmond, VA 23223
URL: http://www.mcshanegroup.com
Contact: Jim L. Huitt, Jr., Principal
E-mail: jhuitt@mcshanegroup.com

Description: Firm provides diligence services, interim management, strategic business realignments, marketing, and much more. **Scope:** Firm provides diligence services, interim management, strategic business realignments, marketing, and much more. **Founded:** 1987.

20205 ■ Medical Imaging Consultants Inc. (MIC)
1037 US Hwy. 46, Ste. G-2
 Clifton, NJ 07013-2445
Ph: (973)574-8000
Free: 800-589-5685
Fax: (973)574-8001
Co. E-mail: info@micinfo.com
URL: http://www.micinfo.com
Contact: Philip A. Femano, President

Description: Provider of professional support services in radiology management and comprehensive continuing education programs for radiologic technologists such as professional educators, life scientists, biomedical engineers, and much more. **Scope:** Provider of professional support services in radiology management and comprehensive continuing education programs for radiologic technologists such as professional educators, life scientists, biomedical engineers, and much more. **Founded:** 1991. **Training:** Sectional Anatomy and Imaging Strategies; CT Cross-Trainer; CT Registry Review Program; MR Cross Trainer; MRI Registry Review Program; Digital Mammography Essentials for Technologists; Radiology Trends for Technologists.

20206 ■ Medical Outcomes Management Inc. (MOM)
15 S Main St., Ste. 208
 Sharon, MA 02067
Ph: (781)806-0275
URL: http://www.mom-inc.us
Contact: Dr. Alan Kaul, Chief Executive Officer
E-mail: alan@mom-inc.us
Facebook: www.facebook.com/akaul2019
Linkedin: www.linkedin.com/company/medical-outcomes-management

Description: Management and technology consulting firm providing a specially focused group of services such as disease management programs and pharmacoeconomic studies. Services include clinical and educational projects, medical writing and editing, marketing and sales projects, disease registries, educational seminars, strategic planning projects, managed care organizations and pharmaceutical and biotechnology companies. **Scope:** Management and technology consulting firm providing a specially focused group of services such as disease management programs and pharmacoeconomic studies. Services include clinical and educational projects, medical writing and editing, marketing and sales projects, disease registries, educational seminars, strategic planning projects, managed care organizations and pharmaceutical and biotechnology companies. **Founded:** 1991. **Publications:** "Treatment of acute exacerbation's of chronic bronchitis in patients with chronic obstructive pulmonary disease: A retrospective cohort analysis logarithmically extended release vs. Azithromycin," 2003; "A retrospective analysis of cyclooxygenase-II inhibitor response patterns," 2002; "DUE criteria for use of regional urokinase infusion for deep vein thrombosis,"2002; "The formulary management system and decision-making process at Horizon Blue Cross Blue Shield of New Jersey," Pharmaco therapy, 2001. **Training:** Economic Modeling as a Disease Management Tool, Academy of Managed Care Pharmacy, Apr, 2005; Integrating Disease State Management and Economics, Academy of Managed Care Pharmacy, Oct, 2004; Clinical and economic outcomes in the treatment of peripheral occlusive diseases, Mar, 2003.

20207 ■ Mefford, Knutson & Associates Inc. (MKA)
6437 Lyndale Ave. S
 Richfield, MN 55423
Co. E-mail: info@mkcconsulting.com
URL: http://mkaconsulting.com
Contact: Jeanette Mefford, Co-Founder

Description: Provider of consulting services to home health and related sectors. **Scope:** Provider of consulting services to home health and related sectors. **Founded:** 1990.

20208 ■ Midwest Computer Group L.L.C. (MCG)
6060 Franks Rd.
 House Springs, MO 63051
Contact: Leon Sanford, Jr., Contact

Description: Specializes in helping businesses create accounting, marketing and business information systems, software development and database design and management. **Scope:** Specializes in helping businesses create accounting, marketing and business information systems, software development and database design and management.

20209 ■ Midwest Research Institute (MRI) - Patterson Library
425 Dr. Martin Luther King, Jr Blvd.
 Kansas City, MO 64110
Co. E-mail: info@mriglobal.org
URL: http://www.mriglobal.org
Contact: Martin Nevshemal, Chief Financial Officer
Facebook: www.facebook.com/MRIGlobalResearch
Linkedin: www.linkedin.com/company/mriglobal
X (Twitter): x.com/mriglobal_news

Description: Nonprofit research institute offers scientific services in the areas of national defense, health sciences, agriculture and food safety, engineering, energy, and infrastructure. **Scope:** Nonprofit research institute offers scientific services in the areas of national defense, health sciences, agriculture and food safety, engineering, energy, and infrastructure. **Services:** Interlibrary loan; copying; center open to the public for reference use only and by appointment. **Founded:** 1944. **Holdings:** 22,000 volumes. **Subscriptions:** 100 journals and other serials. **Publications:** *Innovations*; *Midwest Research Institute Annual Report* (Annual).

20210 ■ Miller, Leiby & Associates P.C.
32 Broadway, 13th Fl.
 New York, NY 10004
Ph: (212)227-4200
Fax: (212)504-8369
URL: http://www.millerleiby.com
Contact: Doron Leiby, Partner
Facebook: www.facebook.com/MillerLeibyAssociatesPc
Linkedin: www.linkedin.com/company/1269719
Instagram: www.instagram.com/millerleiby

Description: Firm is engaged in legal counsel for individuals and businesses. **Scope:** Firm is engaged in legal counsel for individuals and businesses. **Training:** Objectives and standards/recruiting for boards of directors.

20211 ■ Murray Dropkin & Associates
390 George St.
 New Brunswick, NJ 08901
URL: http://dropkin.com
Contact: Murray Dropkin, Contact

Description: Firm specializes in feasibility studies, business management, business process reengineering, team building, healthcare, and housing. **Scope:** Firm specializes in feasibility studies, business management, business process reengineering, team building, healthcare, and housing. **Publications:** "Bookkeeping for Nonprofits," Jossey Bass, 2005; "Guide to Audits of Nonprofit Organizations," PPC; "The Nonprofit Report," Warren, Gorham & Lamont; "The Budget Building Book for Nonprofits," Jossey-Bass; "The Cash Flow Management Book for Nonprofits," Jossey-Bass.

20212 ■ National Center for Public Policy Research (NCPPR)
2005 Massachusetts Ave. NW
 Washington, DC 20036
Ph: (202)507-6398
Co. E-mail: info@nationalcenter.org
URL: http://nationalcenter.org
Contact: David A. Ridenour, President
E-mail: dridenour@nationalcenter.org
Facebook: www.facebook.com/NCPPR
X (Twitter): x.com/NationalCenter
YouTube: www.youtube.com/channel/UCFrgtYxKOBuDqXavBuK0FFA

Description: Educates the public about public policy issues. Conducts research; distributes national policy analysis papers, memorandums, brochures, newsletters, article reprints, and other materials to the public, libraries, and the media. **Scope:** A communications and research nonprofit organization offering advice and information on international affairs and United States domestic affairs. Sponsors Project 21. Gives special emphasis an environmental and regulatory issues and civil rights issues. **Founded:** 1982. **Publications:** "National Policy Analysis"; "Legal Briefs"; "White Paper: National Policy Analysis 523"; "Shattered Dreams: One Hundred Stories of Government Abuse"; "Shattered Lives: 100 Victims of Government Health Care". **Awards:** National Center for Public Policy Research Paid Internships. **Geographic Preference:** National.

20213 ■ Nightingale Associates
7445 Setting Sun Way
 Columbia, MD 21046
Ph: (410)381-4280
URL: http://www.nightingaleassociates.net
Contact: Frederick C. Nightingale, Managing Director
E-mail: fredericknightingale@nightingaleassociates.net
X (Twitter): x.com/FCNightingale

Description: Management training and consulting firm offering the following skills productivity and accomplishment, leadership skills for the experienced manager, management skills for the new manager, leadership and teambuilding, supervisory development, creative problem solving, real strategic planning. **Scope:** Management training and consulting firm offering the following skills productivity and accomplishment, leadership skills for the experienced manager, management skills for the new manager, leadership and teambuilding, supervisory development, creative problem solving, real strategic planning. **Founded:** 1984. **Training:** Productivity and Accomplishment Management Skills for the New Manager; Leadership and Team building; Advanced Management; Business Process Re engineering; Strategic Thinking; Creative Problem Solving; Customer Service; International Purchasing and Materials Management; Fundamentals of Purchasing; Negotiation Skills Development; Providing superior customer service; Leadership skills for the experienced manager.

20214 ■ North Carolina Fair Share CDC
3509 Haworth Dr., Ste. 303
 Raleigh, NC 27609
Contact: Akiba H. Byrd, Sr., Contact

Description: Social services firm consults on community organizing and lobbying for health issues. **Scope:** Social services firm consults on community organizing and lobbying for health issues.

20215 ■ Occupational & Environmental Health Consulting Services Inc. (OEHCS)
6877 Bonillo Dr.
 Las Vegas, NV 89103
Ph: (630)325-2083
URL: http://www.oehcs.com

Description: Provider of consulting services such as regulatory, safety, industrial hygiene and environmental engineering, and much more. **Scope:** Provider of consulting services such as regulatory, safety, industrial hygiene and environmental engineering, and much more. **Founded:** 1984. **Publications:** "Worldwide Exposure Standards for Mold and Bacteria"; "Global Occupational Exposure Limits for Over 5000 Specific Chemicals"; "Post-Remediation Verification and Clearance Testing for Mold and Bacteria Risk Based Levels of Cleanliness". **Training:** Right-To-Know Compliance; Setting Internal Exposure Standards; Hospital Right-to-Know and Contingency Response; Ethylene Oxide Control; Industrial Hygiene Training; Asbestos Worker Training; Biosafety; Asbestos Operations and Maintenance. **Special Services:** Safety Software Program, Audiogram Analysis, First Report of Injury Form, Human Resources Database; Material Safety Data Sheet (MSDS); NPDES Monthly Reports; Lockout/Tagout (LOTO) Procedure Software; VOC Usage Tracking and Reporting Software, Medical Department Patient Records Database, Pictorial Labels for Chemical Containers, TIER II Hazardous Material Inventory Form & Database.

20216 ■ Optimus | SBR
33 Yonge St., Ste. 900
Toronto, ON, Canada M5E 1G4
Ph: (416)649-6000
Co. E-mail: info@optimussbr.com
URL: http://www.optimussbr.com
Contact: Kevin Gauci, Chief Executive Officer
YouTube: www.youtube.com/channel/UCO1Dh 1VZyNDpm2dQ_CTcyUA

Description: Firm provides strategy, process and project management advisory services. **Scope:** Firm provides strategy, process and project management advisory services. **Founded:** 1979. **Training:** Electronic counter measures; Strategic planning; Project management.

20217 ■ Performance Consultants Group, Inc. (PCG)
1 Innovation Way., Ste. 400
Newark, DE 19711
Ph: (302)738-7532
Free: 888-724-3578
URL: http://www.pcgius.com

Description: Firm provides consulting services in the areas of strategic planning, profit enhancement, product development, and production planning. **Scope:** Firm provides consulting services in the areas of strategic planning, profit enhancement, product development, and production planning. **Founded:** 1988.

20218 ■ Performance Consulting Associates, Inc. (PCA)
3700 Crestwood Pky., Ste. 100
Duluth, GA 30096
Ph: (770)717-2737
Co. E-mail: info@pcaconsulting.com
URL: http://pcaconsulting.com
Contact: Richard deFazio, President
Linkedin: www.linkedin.com/company/pcaconsulting

Description: Firm provides asset management solutions, business process optimization, and much more. **Scope:** Firm provides asset management solutions, business process optimization, and much more. **Founded:** 1976. **Publications:** "Does Planning Pay," Plant Services, Nov, 2000; "Asset Reliability Coordinator," Maintenance Technology, Oct, 2000; "Know What it is You Have to Maintain," Maintenance Technology, May, 2000; "Does Maintenance Planning Pay," Maintenance Technology, Nov, 2000.; "What is Asset Management?"; "Implementing Best Business Practices".

20219 ■ Performance Dynamics Group L.L.C.
50 Virginia Key Dr.
Union Hall, VA 24176
Ph: (732)537-0381
URL: http://mark-green.com
Contact: Mark Green, Contact

Description: Provider of strategic advisors for top level people in businesses and coaches for executive team development and related services such as technology, professional, strategic and business planning, sales force hiring education and development, and much more. **Scope:** Provider of strategic advisors for top level people in businesses and coaches for executive team development and related services such as technology, professional, strategic and business planning, sales force hiring education and development, and much more. **Founded:** 2003. **Training:** Accelerated Approach to Change; Commitment to Quality; Managing Cultural Diversity; The Corporate Energizer; The Power Pole Experience; Team Assessment; Self-Directed Work Teams.

20220 ■ Practice Development Counsel
New York, NY
Ph: (212)593-1549
URL: http://www.pdcounsel.com
Contact: Phyllis Weiss Haserot, President
E-mail: pwhaserot@pdcounsel.com

Description: Firm is engaged in business development, organizational consulting and coaching. **Founded:** 1983. **Publications:** "The Rainmaking Machine: Marketing Planning, Strategy and Management For Law Firms"; "The Marketer's Handbook of Tips and Checklists"; "Venturesome Questions: The Law Firms Guide to Developing a New Business Venture"; "Navigating the Whitewater of Internal Politics"; "Changing Attitudes on Firm Flexibility"; "Transition Planning: A Looming Challenge"; "Don't You Think the Solution Is to Bring In a Good Rainmaker?"; "Aligning Firm Culture with the Needs of the Times"; "What New Partners Need to Know"; "Dangers of Lack of Diversity"; "Learn to Respect Emotion in Business"; "What New Partners Need to Know"; "Taking Responsibility: Implementing Personal Marketing Plans"; "How to Change Unwritten Rules"; "Mentoring and Networking Converge"; "Integrating a New Practice into the Firm"; "Using Conflict Resolution Skills for Marketing Success"; "Sports Team Models for Law Firm Management". **Training:** Managing Work Expectations; Effective Coaching Skills; Service Quality; End-Running the Resistance Professionals Have to Getting Client Input; Ancillary Business Activities; Marketing for Professional Firms; Marketing Ethics; Business Development Training; Trends in Professional Services Marketing; Client Relationship Management; Collaborative Culture; Reaching Consensus; Conflict Resolution; Work life Balance; Generational Issues; Preparing New Partners; Becoming the Employer of Choice; A Marketing Approach to Recruiting; Implementing Workplace Flexibility; The Business Case for Flexible Work Arrangements.

20221 ■ Public Sector Consultants Inc. (PSC)
230 N Washington Sq., Ste. 300
Lansing, MI 48933
Ph: (517)484-4954
Fax: (517)484-6549
Co. E-mail: psc@publicsectorconsultants.com
URL: http://publicsectorconsultants.com
Contact: Jonathon Beard, Director
E-mail: jbeard@publicsectorconsultants.com
Facebook: www.facebook.com/PublicSectorConsultants
X (Twitter): x.com/pscmichigan
YouTube: www.youtube.com/channel/ UCjoEsgFvA7ks_46qrf-pYqQ

Description: Offers policy research expertise, specializing in opinion polling, public relations, conference planning, and legislative and economic analysis. Industries served: Associations, education, environment, health-care, and public finance. **Scope:** Offers policy research expertise, specializing in opinion polling, public relations, conference planning, and legislative and economic analysis. Industries served: Associations, education, environment, health-care, and public finance. **Founded:** 1980. **Publications:** "The New Landscape of Civic Business: How Business Leadership Is Influencing Civic Progress in Our Metropolitan Regions Today," Feb, 2012; "Saginaw Bay Watershed and Area of Concern," Mar, 2012; "Michigan Public School Employees Retirement System: Major Changes in Recent Years and More Changes to Come," May, 2012; "Saginaw River/Bay Area of Concern: Restoration Plan for the Habitat and Populations BUIs," Sep, 2012; "Proposal 3: Key Questions and Answers," Sep, 2012; "Final Report of the Michigan State Park and Recreation Blue Ribbon Panel," Oct, 2012; "The Impact of Reducing PIP Coverage in Michigan," Sep, 2011; "Michigan Sales Tax Collection and the Internet: A Need for Fairness," Sep, 2011; "Ingham Community Voices Final Evaluation Report," Nov, 2008; "First Class Schools Analysis," Aug, 2008; "Opportunities for Achieving Efficiency in the Aging, Community Mental Health, Local Public Health, and Substance Abuse Coordinating Agency Networks," Aug, 2008; "Saginaw River Bay Area of Concern," Jun, 2008; "Portage Lake Water shed Forever Plan," May, 2008; "Smoke Free Workplaces," Apr, 2008; "Protecting and Restoring the Upper Looking Glass River," Feb, 2008; "Market Structures and the 21st Century Energy Plan," Sep, 2007; "The Growing Crisis of Aging Dams," Apr, 2007; "Financing Community Health Workers Why and How," Jan, 2007; "Hastings Area: Inter local Approaches to Growth Management," Jan, 2007; "Michigan's Part 201 Environmental Remediation Program Review," Jan, 2007.

20222 ■ Rental Relocation Inc. (RRI)
535 Colonial Pk. Dr., Bldg. A
Roswell, GA 30075
Free: 844-737-0611
Co. E-mail: info@rentalrelocation.com
URL: http://www.rentalrelocation.com
Contact: James Bilderback, President
Facebook: www.facebook.com/RentalRelocationInc
Linkedin: www.linkedin.com/company/rental-relocation-inc
YouTube: www.youtube.com/channel/UC3B3HJ4K3u _pZvNIT6omFXw

Description: Firm provides consulting services in corporate housing, rentals, locating free metro Atlanta apartment, property management, house and condo rental relocation tours. **Scope:** Firm provides consulting services in corporate housing, rentals, locating free metro Atlanta apartment, property management, house and condo rental relocation tours. **Founded:** 1989.

20223 ■ Rose & Crangle Ltd.
102 E Lincoln Ave.
Lincoln, KS 67455
Contact: S. Jeanne Crangle, Contact

Description: Provider of evaluation, planning and policy analyzes for universities, associations, foundations, governmental agencies and private companies engaged in scientific, technological or educational activities. Special expertise in the development of new institutions. Special skills in providing planning and related group facilitation workshops. **Scope:** Provider of evaluation, planning and policy analyzes for universities, associations, foundations, governmental agencies and private companies engaged in scientific, technological or educational activities. Special expertise in the development of new institutions. Special skills in providing planning and related group facilitation workshops. **Publications:** "Preface to Bulgarian Integration Into Europe and NATO: Issues of Science Policy And research Evaluation Practice," Ios Press, 2006; "Allocating Limited National Resources for Fundamental Research," 2005.

20224 ■ Schneider Consulting Group Inc.
2801 E 4th Ave.
Denver, CO 80206
Contact: Frank S. Schneider, Contact

Description: Firm assists family-owned and privately-held business transition to the next generation and or to a more professionally managed company, turn around consulting for small and medium-sized companies. **Scope:** Firm assists family-owned and privately-held business transition to the next generation and or to a more professionally managed company, turn around consulting for small and medium-sized companies. **Founded:** 1987. **Training:** Family Business Council; Impact of the Energy Renaissance.

20225 ■ Trendzitions Inc.
25691 Atlantic Ocean, Dr. No. B13
Lake Forest, CA 92630
Ph: (949)727-9100

URL: http://www.trendzitions.com
Contact: Chris Tooker, President
E-mail: ctooker@trendzitions.com
X (Twitter): x.com/trendzitions
Instagram: www.instagram.com/trendzitions
Description: Provider of services in the areas of communications consulting, project management, construction management, and furniture procurement. Offers information on spatial uses, building codes, ADA compliance and city ordinances. Also offers budget projections. **Scope:** Provider of services in the areas of communications consulting, project management, construction management, and furniture procurement. Offers information on spatial uses, building codes, ADA compliance and city ordinances. Also offers budget projections. **Founded:** 1986.

20226 ■ The Walk The Talk Co.
PO Box 480
  Youngsville, LA 70592
Free: 800-888-2811
Fax: (972)899-9291
Co. E-mail: info@walkthetalk.com
URL: http://www.walkthetalk.com
Contact: Eric Harvey, Founder
Facebook: www.facebook.com/WalkTheTalk.LPDC
X (Twitter): x.com/WalkTheTalk_com
YouTube: www.youtube.com/user/
  WalkTheTalkCompany
Description: Firm engages in performance management system developed by individual responsibility and decision-making instead of disciplinary penalties. **Scope:** Firm engages in performance management system developed by individual responsibility and decision-making instead of disciplinary penalties. **Founded:** 1978. **Publications:** "Positive Discipline"; "Leadership Secrets of Santa Claus"; "Start Right-Stay Right"; "Walk Awhile in My Shoes"; "Listen Up, Leader!"; "Five Star Teamwork"; "Ethics4Everyone"; "Leadership Courage"; "The Manager's Communication Handbook"; "180 Ways to Walk the Recognition Talk"; "The Manager's Coaching Handbook"; "The Best Leadership Advice I Ever Got"; "Power Exchange". **Training:** Walk the Talk; Coaching for Continuous Improvement; Managing Employee Performance; Customized Management Development Forums; Keynote presentations; Leadership Development Workshops; Consulting Services and Publications; Customer service training; Ethics and Values training.

20227 ■ ZS Engineering P.C. (ZSE)
99 Tulip Ave., Ste. 102
  Floral Park, NY 11001
Ph: (516)328-3200
Fax: (516)328-6195
Co. E-mail: office@zsengineering.com
URL: http://zsengineering.com/index.html
Contact: Zygmunt Staszewski, President
E-mail: staszewski@zsengineering.com
Description: Offers engineering consulting services to building owners, building managers and contractors. Specializes in design and inspections of fire alarm systems, sprinkler systems, smoke control systems, building evaluations for fire code compliance, violations removal. **Scope:** Offers engineering consulting services to building owners, building managers and contractors. Specializes in design and inspections of fire alarm systems, sprinkler systems, smoke control systems, building evaluations for fire code compliance, violations removal. **Founded:** 1989. **Training:** Fire protection courses for contractors and building management.

FRANCHISES AND BUSINESS OPPORTUNITIES

20228 ■ Biga & Associates Inc.
200 E Evergreen, Ste. 116
  Mount Prospect, IL 60056
Contact: Frank J. Biga, II, President
Description: Provider of business training, education and consulting solutions.

20229 ■ Franchise Development International
6278 N Federal Hwy., Ste. 382
  Fort Lauderdale, FL 33308
Contact: Linda D. Biciocchi, President
Description: Franchise development and marketing. **Founded:** 1991.

20230 ■ Franchise Developments Inc.
5840 Aylesboro Ave.
  Pittsburgh, PA 15217
Description: Franchise consultants that offer clients full development services for the purpose of designing and implementing a total franchise program. **Publications:** "Franchising Your Business," May/Jun, 2003; "Female Entrepreneur," May/Jun, 2003; "Franchising World," May/Jun, 2003; "Canadian Business Franchise," Jul/Aug, 2000. **Training:** Has presented franchising seminars under auspices of American Management Association, Management Center Europe and International Franchise Association. Recent programs include Expanding Your Business by Franchising; Writing Effective Franchise Operations Manuals. Also has franchise seminar on Prodigy.

20231 ■ Franchise Foundations (FF)
San Francisco, CA
Ph: (415)225-3010
Co. E-mail: franchise888@gmail.com
URL: http://www.franchisefoundations.com
Contact: Kevin B. Murphy, Contact
Facebook: www.facebook.com/franchisefoundations
Linkedin: www.linkedin.com/company/franchise-foun
  dations
X (Twitter): x.com/KevinB_Murphy
Pinterest: www.pinterest.com/franchisefoundations
Description: Firm provides franchise consulting services. **Founded:** 1980.

20232 ■ Franchise Specialists Inc.
801 E 2120 Greentree Rd.
  Pittsburgh, PA 15220
Contact: William F. Repack, President
Description: Firm is engaged in professional franchise development and sales. **Founded:** 1978.

20233 ■ Jones & Co.
67 Yonge St., Ste. 602
  Toronto, ON, Canada M5E 1J8
Ph: (416)703-5716
Fax: (416)703-6180
URL: http://www.jonesco-law.ca
Contact: Paul D. Jones, Principal
E-mail: pjones@jonesco-law.ca
Description: Law firm provides legal advice to businesses regarding the protection and distribution of their goods and services.

20234 ■ Kaufman & Canoles, P.C.
150 W Main St.
  Norfolk, VA 23514
Ph: (757)624-3000
Free: 888-360-9092
URL: http://www.kaufcan.com
Contact: Karen H. Burris, Manager
E-mail: khburris@kaufcan.com
Facebook: www.facebook.com/Kaufman-Canoles-PC
  -311214283886
Linkedin: www.linkedin.com/company/kaufman
  -&-canoles
X (Twitter): x.com/KaufCan
YouTube: www.youtube.com/user/KaufCan
Description: Firm provides litigation services. **Founded:** 1982.

20235 ■ L. Michael Schwartz, P.A. (LMSPA)
7631 Widmer
  Lenexa, KS 66215
Contact: L. Michael Schwartz, Contact
Description: Franchise consulting and full legal services.

20236 ■ Lite For Life
San Francisco Bay Area, CA
Ph: (650)535-0212
Co. E-mail: info@liteforlife.com
URL: http://liteforlife.com
Description: Weight loss and nutritional consulting. **Founded:** 1978. **Training:** Yes.

20237 ■ "Why Franchise Consulting Franchises Are Taking Off In 2022" in International Franchise Association blog
URL(s): www.franchise.org/blog/why-franchise-consul
  ting-franchises-are-taking-off-in-2022
Description: An article by the International Franchise Association detailing how the pandemic changed spending habits and supply and demand thus having an impact on opportunities in franchising. Recommends franchise consulting opportunities. **Availability:** Online.

VENTURE CAPITAL FIRM

20238 ■ Venture Coaches (VC)
Ottawa, ON, Canada
Ph: (613)301-0474
Co. E-mail: contact@venturecoaches.com
URL: http://www.venturecoaches.com
Contact: Claude Haw, President
Description: Management consulting and seed investment firm for early- and growth-stage companies. **Founded:** 2001.

Credit and Collection

START-UP INFORMATION

20239 ■ *How to Start a Bankruptcy Forms Processing Service*
Released: First edition. **Description:** Due to the increase in bankruptcy filings, attorneys are outsourcing related jobs in order to reduce overhead.

20240 ■ *The Ultimate Guide to Starting a Credit Repair Business*
Ed: Daniel Rosen. **Released:** April 15, 2016. **Description:** Launching a credit repair business out of the home is a great career choice for those who are looking for their own business opportunities. There are several methods of setting up this business and the author relates the steps to get the best possible results. Tips on credit repair basics, how to work with clients, how to remove difficult items from credit report, and many more. **Availability:** Print.

ASSOCIATIONS AND OTHER ORGANIZATIONS

20241 ■ **National Association of Credit Management (NACM)**
8840 Columbia 100 Pky.
 Columbia, MD 21045
Ph: (410)740-5560
Fax: (410)740-5574
Co. E-mail: nacm_national@nacm.org
URL: http://nacm.org
Contact: Robin Schauseil, President
Linkedin: www.linkedin.com/company/national
 -association-of-credit-management
X (Twitter): x.com/nacm_national
Pinterest: www.pinterest.com/nacmnational
Description: Credit and financial executives representing manufacturers, wholesalers, financial institutions, insurance companies, utilities, and other businesses interested in business credit. Promotes sound credit practices and legislation. Conducts Graduate School of Credit and Financial Management at Dartmouth College, Hanover, NH. **Founded:** 1896. **Publications:** *Credit Executives Handbook*; *Manual of Credit and Commercial Laws*; *Business Credit: The Publication for Credit and Finance Professionals* (9/year). **Educational Activities:** NACM Credit Congress and Exposition (Annual); Credit Congress & Exposition (Annual). **Awards:** O.D. Glaus Credit Executive of Distinction Award (Annual); Alice M.H. McGregor Award of Exceptional Achievement (Periodic); CCE Designation of Excellence Award (Annual); NACM Mentor of the Year (Annual). **Geographic Preference:** National.

REFERENCE WORKS

20242 ■ *"All-Star Advice 2010"* in *Black Enterprise* (Vol. 41, October 2010, No. 3, pp. 97)
Pub: Earl G. Graves Ltd.
Contact: Earl Graves, Jr., President
Ed: Renita Burns, Sheiresa Ngo, Marcia Wade Talbert. **Description:** Financial experts share tips on real estate, investing, taxes, insurance and debt management. **Availability:** Online.

20243 ■ *"American Apparel: When Dov Cries"* in *Canadian Business* (Vol. 83, June 15, 2010, No. 10, pp. 71)
Pub: Rogers Media Inc.
Contact: Neil Spivak, Chief Executive Officer
Ed: Joe Castaldo. **Description:** American Apparel disclosed that they will have problems meeting one of its debt covenants which could trigger a chain reaction that could lead to bankruptcy. The prospects look bleak, but eccentric company founder Dov Charney, has always defied expectations. **Availability:** Online.

20244 ■ *"Anxiety Saps Vigor of Small Businesses"* in *Barron's* (Vol. 92, September 15, 2012, No. 38, pp. 36)
Pub: Dow Jones & Company Inc.
Contact: Almar Latour, Chief Executive Officer
Ed: Gene Epstein. **Description:** The Index of Small Business Optimism reveals that optimism among small businesses in the US remains low three years after the 2008-2009 recession. Uncertainty over economic conditionsand government actions could be behind the low optimism as well as no access to credit. **Availability:** Online.

20245 ■ *"App Helps Consumers Spot Suspicious Charges"* in *Black Enterprise* (Vol. 44, June 2014, No. 10, pp. 34)
Pub: Earl G. Graves Ltd.
Contact: Earl Graves, Jr., President
Description: BiliGuard is a mobile app used to track activity on credit and debit card accounts. The app allows users to notify a merchant as soon as they see an unfamiliar charge. BiliGuard can also alert users to fees. **Availability:** Online.

20246 ■ *"Arkansas Attorney General Sues Collection Agency"* in *PaymentsSource* (July 18, 2012)
Description: National Credit Adjusters is being sued by Arkansas Attorney General Dustin McDaniel's office. The lawsuit alleges that the collection agency violated the Arkansas Deceptive Trade Practices Act while attempting to collect debts from payday and high-interest installment loan debts. **Availability:** Print; Online.

20247 ■ *"Asia Breathes a Sigh of Relief"* in *Business Week* (September 22, 2008, No. 4100, pp. 32)
Description: Foreign bankers, such as those in Asia, that had been investing heavily in the United States began to worry as the housing crisis deepened and the impact on Freddie Mac and Fannie Mae became increasingly clear. Due to the government bailout, however, central banks will most likely continue to buy American debt. **Availability:** Print; Online.

20248 ■ *"Au Revoir Or Goodbye?"* in *Barron's* (Vol. 88, July 14, 2008, No. 28, pp. 5)
Pub: Dow Jones & Company Inc.
Contact: Almar Latour, Chief Executive Officer
Ed: Alan Abelson. **Description:** Former Senator Phil Gramm's opinion that the U.S. is a "nation of whiners" as they moan about recession is another example of the disconnection between Washington and Wall Street on one hand and the real world on the other. It would be a catastrophe for most of the world if Fannie Mae and Freddie Mac were to go under and take their trillions of mortgage debt with them. **Availability:** Online.

20249 ■ *"Bad Loans Start Piling Up"* in *Crain's New York Business* (Vol. 24, January 6, 2008, No. 1, pp. 2)
Pub: Crain Communications, Inc.
Contact: Jessica Botos, Manager, Marketing
E-mail: jessica.botos@crainsnewyork.com
Ed: Tom Fredrickson. **Description:** Problems in the subprime mortgage industry have extended to other lending activities as evidenced by bank charge-offs on bad commercial and industrial loans which have more than doubled in the third quarter.

20250 ■ *"Banks, Retailers Squabble Over Fees"* in *Baltimore Business Journal* (Vol. 28, June 18, 2010, No. 6, pp. 1)
Pub: Baltimore Business Journal
Contact: Rhonda Pringle, President
E-mail: rpringle@bizjournals.com
Ed: Gary Haber. **Description:** How an amendment to the financial regulatory reform bill would affect the bankers' and retailers' conflict over interchange fees is discussed. Interchange fees are paid for by retailers every time consumers make purchases through debit cards. Industry estimates indicate that approximately $50 million in such fees are paid by retailers. **Availability:** Print; Online.

20251 ■ *"Best Business Loans for 2023"* in *Business News Daily* (February 24, 2023)
URL(s): www.businessnewsdaily.com/8448-bes
 t-business-loans.html
Ed: Max Freedman. **Released:** February 24, 2023. **Description:** A list of business loans is given and discussed, along with a comparison guide. **Availability:** Online.

20252 ■ *Best Credit and Collections Software for Small Businesses*
URL(s): www.g2.com/categories/credit-and-collec
 tions/small-business
Description: Lists the best credit and collections software for small businesses. **Availability:** Online.

20253 ■ *"The Best Option for All"* in *American Executive* (Vol. 7, September 2009, No. 5, pp. 170)
Ed: Ashley McGown. **Description:** Plaza Associates, a collections agency that conducts business primarily in the accounts receivable management sector, is the

first in the industry to purchase 100 percent of the company from the founders through the formation of a leveraged Employee Stock Ownership Plan (ESOP).

20254 ■ *"Best Turnaround Stocks"* in *Canadian Business (Vol. 81, Summer 2008, No. 9, pp. 65)*
Description: Share prices of Sierra Wireless Inc. and EXFO Electro Optical Engineering Inc. have fallen over the past year but have good chance at a rebound considering that the companies have free cash flow and no long-term debt. One-year stock performance analysis of the two companies is presented. **Availability:** Print; Online.

20255 ■ *"Bracing for a Bear of a Week"* in *Barron's (Vol. 88, March 17, 2008, No. 11, pp. 24)*
Pub: Dow Jones & Company Inc.
Contact: Almar Latour, Chief Executive Officer
Ed: Jacqueline Doherty. **Description:** JPMorgan Chase and the Federal Reserve Bank of New York's opening of a line of credit to Bear Stearns cut the stock price of Bear Stearns by 47 percent to 30 followed by speculation of an imminent sale. JP Morgan may be the only potential buyer for the firm and some investors say Bears could be sold at $20 to $30. Bears prime assets include its enormous asset base worth $395 billion. **Availability:** Online.

20256 ■ *"Branching Out: Towards a Trait-based Understanding of Fungal Ecology"* in *Canadian Business (Vol. 79, July 17, 2006, No. 14-15, pp. 41)*
Availability: Print; Online.

20257 ■ *"A Bull Market in Finger-Pointing"* in *Barron's (Vol. 88, March 10, 2008, No. 10, pp. 9)*
Pub: Dow Jones & Company Inc.
Contact: Almar Latour, Chief Executive Officer
Ed: Michael Santoli. **Description:** Discusses who is to blame for the financial crisis brought about by the credit crunch in the United States; the country's financial markets will eventually digest this crisis but will bottom out first before the situation improves. **Availability:** Online.

20258 ■ *"Canada Seeks Collection Agency To Pursue $129M In Fines"* in *PaymentsSource (August 21, 2012)*
Description: Canada's federal government has posted a letter of interest seeking a collection agency to recover about $129 million in unpaid fines. Details of the program are covered. **Availability:** Print; Online.

20259 ■ *"Chasing Credit"* in *Canadian Business (Vol. 81, November 10, 2008, No. 19, pp. 59)*
Pub: Rogers Media Inc.
Contact: Neil Spivak, Chief Executive Officer
Ed: Joe Castaldo. **Description:** Small and medium sized companies are dealing with tightening credit because they appear riskier than usual. Some of these businesses are turning to private investors, but this is not easy since many have invested everything in the stock market. The sector is expected to weaken with the broader Canadian market in the next six months from October 2008. **Availability:** Online.

20260 ■ *"Cincinnati Hospitals Feel Pain from Slow Economy"* in *Business Courier (Vol. 27, September 3, 2010, No. 18, pp. 1)*
Pub: Business Courier
Ed: James Ritchie. **Description:** Hospitals in Cincinnati, Ohio have suffered from decreased revenues owing to the economic crises. Declining patient volumes and bad debt have also adversely impacted hospitals. **Availability:** Print; Online.

20261 ■ *"Clock Ticks On Columbia Sussex Debt"* in *Business Courier (Vol. 27, July 30, 2010, No. 13, pp. 1)*
Pub: Business Courier

Ed: Dan Monk. **Description:** Cincinnati, Ohio-based Columbia Sussex Corporation has made plans to restructure a $1 billion loan bundle that was scheduled to mature in October 2010. The privately held hotel has strived in a weak hotel market to keep pace with its $3 billion debt load. **Availability:** Print; Online.

20262 ■ *"Collection Agency Issues Whitepaper on Legal and Ethical Methods of Collecting on Overdue Accounts"* in *Marketwired (July 20, 2009)*
Pub: Comtex News Network Inc.
Contact: Kan Devnani, President
Description: American Profit Recovery, a collection agency based in Massachusetts and Michigan, has updated and reissued a whitepaper on what businesses can and cannot do regarding conversing with their customers in an attempt to collect on overdue accounts and payments. A detailed summary on the federal laws associated with collecting on overdue accounts is outlined in such a way that any business owner, manager, or responsible party can easily understand. **Availability:** Print; Online.

20263 ■ *"Coming Soon: Bailouts of Fannie and Freddie"* in *Barron's (Vol. 88, July 14, 2008, No. 28, pp. 14)*
Pub: Dow Jones & Company Inc.
Contact: Almar Latour, Chief Executive Officer
Ed: Jonathan R. Laing. **Description:** Assurances from the government that Fannie Mae and Freddie Mac are adequately capitalized and able to carry on their duties as guarantors or owners of over $5 trillion of U.S. home mortgages are designed to keep both entities afloat until they attempt to raise $10 billion in new equity. The government would assume any losses in a bailout and owners of the banks' papers would profit as yields drop. **Availability:** Online.

20264 ■ *The Complete Idiot's Guide to Starting an eBay® Business*
Pub: Penguin Publishing Group
Released: April 03, 2012. **Price:** $19.95, paperback; $12.99, e-book. **Description:** Guide for starting an eBay business includes information on products to sell, how to price merchandise, and details for working with services like PayPal, and how to organize fulfillment services. **Availability:** E-book; Print.

20265 ■ *"A Conversation With: Ron Gantner, Jones Lang LaSalle"* in *Crain's Detroit Business (Vol. 24, October 6, 2008, No. 40, pp. 9)*
Pub: Crain Communications Inc.
Contact: Barry Asin, President
Description: Interview with Ron Gantner who is a corporate real estate adviser with the real estate company Jones Lang LaSalle as well as the company's executive vice president and part of the tenant advisory team; Gantner speaks about the impact that the Wall Street crisis is having on the commercial real estate market in Detroit. **Availability:** Print; Online.

20266 ■ *"Cost of Md.'s Business Banking May Soon Go Up"* in *Baltimore Business Journal (Vol. 28, October 29, 2010, No. 25, pp. 1)*
Pub: Baltimore Business Journal
Contact: Rhonda Pringle, President
E-mail: rpringle@bizjournals.com
Ed: Gary Haber. **Released:** Weekly. **Description:** Experts in the financial industry expect banks to charge credit card transactions, especially to small business owners and consumers to recover about $11 million in lost revenue annually. Banks are expected to charge old fees and new ones, including $5 to $10 a month for a checking account. **Availability:** Print; Online.

20267 ■ *"Credit Conditions Improve for Small Businesses"* in *Small Business Economic Trends (February 2008, pp. 12)*
Pub: National Federation of Independent Business
Contact: Brad Close, President

Ed: William C. Dunkelberg, Holly Wade. **Description:** Graphs and tables that present the credit conditions of small businesses in the U.S. are provided. The tables include figures on availability of loans, interest rates, and expected credit conditions. **Availability:** Print; PDF; Online.

20268 ■ *"The Credit Crisis Continues to Take Victims"* in *Barron's (Vol. 88, March 10, 2008, No. 10, pp. M12)*
Pub: Dow Jones & Company Inc.
Contact: Almar Latour, Chief Executive Officer
Ed: Randall W. Forsyth. **Description:** Short-term Treasury yields dropped to new cyclical lows in early March 2008, with the yield for the two-year Treasury note falling to 1.532 percent. Spreads of the mortgage-backed securities of Fannie Mae and Freddie Mac rose on suspicion of collapses in financing. **Availability:** Online.

20269 ■ *Credit Repair Business: 2 Manuscripts How to Fix Your Credit from Poor to Excellent and Raising Your Credit Score to 720+*
Ed: Ruben Hanson. **Released:** February 02, 2020. **Description:** A guide to boosting your credit score on your own. Discusses eradicating low credit scores in order to improve interest rates on loans and securing mortgages. **Availability:** Print.

20270 ■ *"Credit Unions Seek to Raise Lending for Small Business"* in *Denver Business Journal (Vol. 64, September 28, 2012, No. 64, pp. 1)*
Pub: Baltimore Business Journal
Contact: Rhonda Pringle, President
E-mail: rpringle@bizjournals.com
Description: United States Senator Mark Udall has introduced the Small Business Lending Enhancement Act, which aims to increase the commercial lending authority of credit unions. The bill's supporters claim that small business owners are still experiencing problems getting credit, and that the legislation will increase small business lending by $13 milliion within its first year of enactment. **Availability:** Print; Online.

20271 ■ *"Curbing the Debt Collector"* in *Business Journal-Portland (Vol. 24, October 5, 2007, No. 32, pp. 1)*
Pub: Portland Business Journal
Contact: Andy Giegerich, Managing Editor
E-mail: agiegerich@bizjournals.com
Ed: Andy Giergerich. **Description:** Republican representative Sal Esquivel, who had a bad personal experience with a Houston collector, is developing legislation that would give the state attorney general's office enforcement powers over debt collecting agencies. The existing Oregon legislation concerning the debt collection industry is also discussed. **Availability:** Print; Online.

20272 ■ *"Cutting Credit Card Processing Costs for Your Small Business"* in *Hawaii Business (Vol. 53, March 2008, No. 9, pp. 56)*
Ed: Robert K.O. Lum. **Description:** Accepting credit card payments offers businesses with profits from the discount rate. The discount rate includes processing fee, VISA & MasterCard assessment and interchange. Details regarding merchant service cost and discount rate portions are discussed. Statistical data included. **Availability:** Online.

20273 ■ *"Death Spiral"* in *Business Journal Serving Greater Tampa Bay (Vol. 30, October 29, 2010, No. 45, pp. 1)*
Pub: Tampa Bay Business Journal
Contact: Ian Anderson, President
E-mail: ianderson@bizjournals.com
Description: Bay Cities Bank has started working on the loan portfolio of its acquisition, Progress Bank of Florida. Regulators closed Progress Bank in October 2010 after capital collapsed due to charge-offs and increases in the provision for future loan losses. **Availability:** Print; Online.

20274 ■ Credit and Collection

GENERAL SMALL BUSINESS TOPICS

20274 ■ *"Debt-Collection Agency to Lay Off 368 in Hampton Center"* **in Virginian-Pilot (December 4, 2010)**
Pub: The Virginian-Pilot
Contact: Kevin Goyette, Director
E-mail: kgoyette@dailypress.com
Ed: Tom Shean. **Description:** NCO Financial Systems Inc., provider of debt-collection and outsourcing services will permanently lay off 368 workers at its Hampton call center in 2011. **Availability:** Print; Online.

20275 ■ *"Direct Recovery Associates Debt Collection Agency Beats Industry Record"* **in Internet Wire (June 24, 2010)**
Description: Direct Recovery Associates Inc. was named as one of the highest collection records in the industry, which has consistently improved over 18 years. The firm is an international attorney-based debt collection agency. **Availability:** Print; Online.

20276 ■ *"Directors May Revise HCA Collection Agency Regulations"* **in Standard-Speaker (May 20, 2012)**
Pub: McClatchy Tribune Information Services
Contact: Patrick J. Talamantes, President
Ed: Sam Galski. **Description:** Hazelton, Pennsylvania authorities are thinking about changing ts 42-year-old regulations, thus having a collection agency pursue payment of outstanding water and trash fees. Details of the plan are included. **Availability:** Online.

20277 ■ *"Dog Days and Stimulus Fatigue"* **in Barron's (Vol. 92, August 25, 2012, No. 38, pp. M10)**
Pub: Dow Jones & Company Inc.
Contact: Almar Latour, Chief Executive Officer
Ed: Michael Aneiro. **Description:** Credit market movements in August 2012 have been influenced by small news and speculation. US Federal Reserve Chairman Ben Bernanke has been more transparent, yet this transparency can also confound investors. **Availability:** Online.

20278 ■ *"Don't Quit When The Road Gets Bumpy"* **in Women Entrepreneur (November 25, 2008)**
Description: Discusses techniques four women entrepreneurs are utilizing to keep their businesses successful despite the credit crunch and the economic downturn.

20279 ■ *EBay Income: How ANYONE of Any Age, Location, and/or Background Can Build a Highly Profitable Online Business with eBay*
Pub: Atlantic Publishing Co.
Contact: Dr. Heather L. Johnson, Contact
Description: A complete overview of eBay is given and guides any small company through the entire process of creating the auction and auction strategies, photography, writing copy, text and formatting, multiple sales, programming tricks, PayPal, accounting, creating marketing, merchandising, managing email lists, advertising plans, taxes and sales tax, best time to list items and for how long, sniping programs, international customers, opening a storefront, electronic commerce, buy-it now pricing, keywords, Google marketing and eBay secrets.

20280 ■ *"Economic Trends for Small Business"* **in Small Business Economic Trends (April 2008, pp. 1)**
Description: Summary of economic trends for small businesses in the U.S. is presented. Economic indicators such as capital spending, inventories and sales, inflation, and profits are given. Analysis of credit markets is also provided. **Availability:** Online.

20281 ■ *"The Effect of Corporate Governance on Firm's Credit Ratings: Further Evidence Using Governance Score in the United States"* **in Accounting and Finance (Vol. 52, June 2012, No. 2, pp. 291)**
Ed: Fatima Alali, Asokan Anandarajan, Wei Jiang. **Released:** January 06, 2012. **Description:** An investigation into whether corporate governance affects a firm's credit ratings and whether improvement in corporate governance standards is associated with improvement in investing grade rating is presented. **Availability:** Print; PDF; Online.

20282 ■ *"End of the Beginning"* **in Canadian Business (Vol. 81, November 10, 2008, No. 19, pp. 17)**
Ed: David Wolf. **Released:** September 30, 2016. **Description:** The freeze in the money markets and historic decline in equity markets around the world finally forced governments into aggressive coordinated action. The asset price inflation brought on by cheap credit will now work in reverse and the tightening of credit will be difficult economically. Canada is exposed to the fallout everywhere, given that the U.S, the U.K. and Japan buy 30 percent of Canada's output. **Availability:** Print; Online.

20283 ■ *"Feds Battling to Put the Brakes on Ambulance Billing Fraud"* **in Philadelphia Business Journal (Vol. 33, April 25, 2014, No. 11, pp. 4)**
Pub: American City Business Journals, Inc.
Contact: Mike Olivieri, Executive Vice President
Released: Weekly. **Price:** $4, introductory 4-week offer(Digital & Print). **Description:** The Department of Health and Human Services, Office of Inspector General, Federal Bureau of Investigation and the U.S. Attorney's Office are working together to crack down on ambulance companies involved in fraudulent Medicare claims. A ban on new ground ambulance companies in southeastern Philadelphia was issued due to ambulance fraud in the Philadelphia region. **Availability:** Print; Online.

20284 ■ *"Fight Ensues Over Irreplaceable Princess Diana Gowns"* **in Tampa Bay Business Journal (Vol. 30, January 15, 2010, No. 4, pp. 1)**
Pub: Tampa Bay Business Journal
Contact: Ian Anderson, President
E-mail: ianderson@bizjournals.com
Ed: Janet Leiser. **Description:** People's Princess Charitable Foundation Inc. founder Maureen Rorech Dunkel has sought Chapter 11 bankruptcy protection before a state court decides on the fate of the five of 13 Princess Diana Gowns. Dunkel and the nonprofit were sued by Patricia Sullivan of HRH Venture LLC who claimed they defaulted on $1.5 million in loans. **Availability:** Print; Online.

20285 ■ *"Firms Sue Doracon to Recoup More Than $1M in Unpaid Bills"* **in Baltimore Business Journal (Vol. 28, July 9, 2010, No. 9, pp. 1)**
Pub: Baltimore Business Journal
Contact: Rhonda Pringle, President
E-mail: rpringle@bizjournals.com
Ed: Scott Dance. **Description:** Concrete supplier Paul J. Rach Inc., Selective Insurance Company, and equipment leasing firm Colonial Pacific Leasing Corporation intend to sue Baltimore, Maryland-based Doracon Contracting Inc. for $1 million in unpaid bills. Doracon owed Colonial Pacific $794,000 and the equipment is still in Doracon's possession. Selective Insurance and Paul J. Rach respectively seek $132,000 and $88,000. **Availability:** Print.

20286 ■ *"FirstMerit's Top Executive Turns Around Credit Quality"* **in Crain's Cleveland Business (Vol. 28, October 15, 2007, No. 41, pp. 3)**
Pub: Crain Communications Inc.
Contact: K. C. Crain, President
Ed: Shawn A. Turner. **Description:** Discusses the ways in which chairman and CEO Paul Greig has been able to improve FirstMerit Corp.'s credit quality and profit margin. Strategies included selling more than $70 million in bad loans, hiring a new chief credit officer and redirecting its focus on cross-selling its wealth and investment services to its commercial customers. Statistical data included. **Availability:** Online.

20287 ■ *"A Flawed Yardstick for Banks"* **in Barron's (Vol. 88, July 14, 2008, No. 28, pp. M6)**
Pub: Dow Jones & Company Inc.
Contact: Almar Latour, Chief Executive Officer
Ed: Arindam Nag. **Description:** Return on equity is no longer the best measure for investors to judge banks by in a post-subprime-crises world. Investors should consider the proportion of a bank's total assets that are considered risky and look out for any write-downs of goodwill when judging a bank's financial health. **Availability:** Online.

20288 ■ *"Florida's Housing Gloom May Add To Woes of National City"* **in Crain's Cleveland Business (Vol. 28, October 29, 2007, No. 43, pp. 1)**
Pub: Crain Communications Inc.
Contact: K. C. Crain, President
Ed: Shawn A. Turner. **Description:** Already suffering by bad loans in the troubled mortgage market, National City Corp. is attempting to diversify its geographic presence beyond the slow-growth industrial Midwest by acquiring two Florida firms. Analysts worry that the acquisitions may end up making National City vulnerable to a takeover if the housing slump continues and credit quality becomes more of an issue for the bank. **Availability:** Online.

20289 ■ *"Former Collection Agency CFO Sentenced"* **in PaymentsSource (April 24, 2012)**
Description: Leslie Jean McIntosh, CFO of FITEC LLC, a collection agency located in Kalispell, Montana was sentenced to 21 months in federal prison for tax evasion. McIntosh was ordered to pay $159,000 in restitution. McIntosh deposited $131,000 in client money into her personal account. **Availability:** Print; Online.

20290 ■ *"A Good Step, But There's a Long Way to Go"* **in Business Week (September 22, 2008, No. 4100, pp. 10)**
Ed: James C. Cooper. **Description:** Despite the historic action by the U.S. government to nationalize the mortgage giants Freddie Mac and Fannie Mae, rising unemployment rates may prove to be an even bigger roadblock to bringing back the economy from its downward spiral. The takeover is meant to restore confidence in the credit markets and help with the mortgage crisis but the rising rate in unemployment may make many households unable to take advantage of any benefits which arise from the bailout. Statistical data included. **Availability:** Online.

20291 ■ *"Goodwill Haunts Local Companies"* **in Crain's Chicago Business (Apr. 28, 2008)**
Pub: Crain Communications Inc.
Contact: Barry Asin, President
Ed: Ann Saphir. **Description:** Many companies are having to face the reality that they overpaid for acquisitions made in better economic times; investors often dismiss such one-time charges as mere accounting adjustments but writeoffs related to past acquisitions can signal future problems because they mean the expected profits that justified the purchase have not materialized. Writeoffs are particularly worrisome for firms with a lot of debt and whose banks require them to have enough assets to back up their borrowings. **Availability:** Online.

20292 ■ *"The Great Fall: Here Comes The Humpty Dumpty Economy"* **in Barron's (Vol. 88, March 10, 2008, No. 10, pp. 5)**
Pub: Dow Jones & Company Inc.
Contact: Almar Latour, Chief Executive Officer
Ed: Alan Abelson. **Description:** Discusses the US economy is considered to be in a recession, with the effects of the credit crisis expected to intensify as a result. Inflation is estimated at 4.3 percent in January 2008, while 63,000 jobs were lost in February 2008. **Availability:** Online.

20293 ■ *"Gregory Cunningham on Taking on Farm Credit of Florida"* **in South Florida Business Journal (Vol. 34, July 18, 2014, No. 52, pp. 11)**
Pub: American City Business Journals, Inc.
Contact: Mike Olivieri, Executive Vice President

Released: Weekly. Price: $8, introductory 4-week offer(Digital only). Description: Gregory Cunningham, president and CEO of Farm Credit of Florida, shares the lessons he learned from his military background that he applies to managing a company. He explains why he decided to take on the challenge of helping the agricultural credit group deal with its regulatory order. Availability: Print; Online.

20294 ■ "HBC Sells Credit Card Division" in Globe & Mail (February 8, 2006, pp. B1)
Description: The details on General Electric Co.'s acquisition of Hudson's Bay Co.'s credit card division, for $370 million, are presented. Availability: Print; Online.

20295 ■ "Headwinds From the New Sod Slow Aer Lingus" in Barron's (Vol. 88, March 10, 2008, No. 10, pp. M6)
Pub: Dow Jones & Company Inc.
Contact: Almar Latour, Chief Executive Officer
Ed: Sean Walters, Arindam Nag. Description: Aer Lingus faces a drop in its share prices with a falling US market, higher jet fuel prices, and lower long-haul passenger load factors. British media companies Johnston Press and Yell Group are suffering from weaker ad revenue and heavier debt payments due to the credit crunch. Availability: Online.

20296 ■ "Hit the Green: Golf Technology" in Canadian Business (Vol. 79, August 14, 2006, No. 16-17, pp. 73)
Pub: Rogers Media Inc.
Contact: Neil Spivak, Chief Executive Officer
Ed: Andrew Wahl. Description: Reorganization of the bankrupt 4everSports golf company in the United States is discussed. Availability: Print; Online.

20297 ■ "How to Accept Mobile Credit Card Payment" in Business News Daily (March 6, 2023)
URL(s): www.businessnewsdaily.com/5377-how-to-accept-mobile-credit-card-payments.html
Ed: Bennett Conlin. Released: March 06, 2023. Description: Processing credit cards is easy with all of the new technology available. This article discusses the options available so you can choose which one is best for your small business. Availability: Online.

20298 ■ "How to Build Business Credit in 7 Steps" in NerdWallet (Dec. 14, 2021)
Ed: Teddy Nykiel. Released: December 14, 2021. Description: Having a strong business credit profile shows financial stability. This article provides seven steps to guide you as you build your business credit. Availability: Online.

20299 ■ "How to Deal With Small Business Debt" in The Balance Small Business (Jan. 26, 2022)
URL(s): www.thebalance.com/how-to-deal-with-small-business-debt-5201573
Ed: Lisa Jo Rudy. Released: January 26, 2022. Description: Explores the legal protections impacting small businesses when it comes to debt and how business owners can manage debt collection. Availability: Online.

20300 ■ How to Write a Great Business Plan for Your Small Business in 60 Minutes or Less
Pub: Atlantic Publishing Co.
Contact: Dr. Heather L. Johnson, Contact
Ed: Sharon L. Fullen. Released: 2013. Description: A good business plan outlines goals and works as a company's resume to obtain funding, credit from suppliers, management of the operations and finances, promotion and marketing, and more. Availability: CD-ROM; E-book; Print; Online.

20301 ■ "Identity Theft Can Have Long-Lasting Impact" in Providence Business News (Vol. 28, February 10, 2014, No. 45, pp. 7)
Pub: American City Business Journals, Inc.
Contact: Mike Olivieri, Executive Vice President

URL(s): pbn.com/identity-theft-can-have-long-lasting-impact94959
Description: According to mortgage credit experts, recently reported massive data breaches at Nieman Marcus, Target, and other merchants could have negative impacts on several real estate deals scheduled for the upcoming months. Although victims are not liable for the unlawful debts, their credit reports and scores can be damaged for months, thus endangering loan applications for mortgages on home sale transactions. Availability: Online.

20302 ■ "Illinois Regulators Revoke Collection Agency's License" in Collections & Credit Risk (Vol. 15, August 1, 2010, No. 7, pp. 13)
Pub: SourceMedia LLC
Contact: Gemma Postlethwaite, Chief Executive Officer
Description: Creditors Service Bureau of Springfield, Illinois had its license revoked by a state regulatory agency and was fined $55,000 because the owner and president, Craig W. Lewis, did not turn over portions of collected funds to clients. Availability: Print; Online.

20303 ■ "Indiana Collection Agency Announces Expansion Plans" in PaymentsSource (March 23, 2012)
Description: DECA Financial Services plans to buy a vacant building in Fishers, Indiana and renovate the property. The agency specializes in collection consumer and tax debts for both companies and government agencies. The company plans to hire 140 new employees over the next 3 years. Availability: Print; Mailing list.

20304 ■ "Indiana Town Reports Success With Collection Agency" in PaymentsSource (August 20, 2012)
Description: Capital Recovery Systems has collected nearly $80,000 in unpaid parking fines in Bloomington, Indiana. The city's agreement with the collection agency allows them to pursue an unlimited amount of unpaid parking tickets at least 30 days late. Availability: Print; Online.

20305 ■ "Industry Associations Seek Clarity of CFPB's Large Collection Agency Definition" in PaymentsSource (May 24, 2012)
Description: ACA International and DBA International are questioning the Consumer Financial Protection Bureau's definition of a large collection agency. The ACA has filed comments arguing that the threshold needs to be raised to $250 million, rather than the $10 million or more in annual receipts or money recovered as its definition. Details are provided. Availability: Print; Online.

20306 ■ "Is Fannie Mae the Next Government Bailout?" in Barron's (Vol. 88, March 10, 2008, No. 10, pp. 21)
Pub: Dow Jones & Company Inc.
Contact: Almar Latour, Chief Executive Officer
Ed: Jonathan R. Laing. Description: Fannie Mae may need a government bailout as it faces huge hits brought about by the effects of the housing crisis. The shares of the government-sponsored enterprise have dropped 65 percent since the housing crisis began. Availability: Online.

20307 ■ "Lawsuit Seeks To Shut Down Illinois Collection Agency" in PaymentsSource (January 12, 2012)
Pub: SourceMedia LLC
Contact: Gemma Postlethwaite, Chief Executive Officer
Description: PN Financial is facing charges by the Illinois State Attorney General's Office, alleging that the company used abusive and threatening actions against consumers. Details of the lawsuit are covered. Availability: Online.

20308 ■ "Lawyers Object to New Online Court Fees" in Sacramento Business Journal (Vol. 31, August 8, 2014, No. 24, pp. 3)
Pub: American City Business Journals, Inc.
Contact: Mike Olivieri, Executive Vice President

Description: Lawyers and consumer advocates have complained that the Sacramento County Superior Court's new fee system for online access to online court records hinders access to justice. However, court administrators argue that the charging of fees will only help offset the online record system's maintenance costs. Availability: Print; Online.

20309 ■ "Lending Door Slams" in Puget Sound Business Journal (Vol. 29, October 24, 2008, No. 27, pp. 1)
Description: KeyBank's closure of its Puget Sound unit that services single-family homebuilders is part of a nationwide shutdown that includes similar closures in other cities. Bank of America is adopting more conservative terms for homebuilding loans while Union Bank of California is still offering credit for market rate housing. Availability: Print; Online.

20310 ■ "Littleton Firm Chips In On Security Solution" in Denver Business Journal (Vol. 65, May 9, 2014, No. 52, pp. A6)
Pub: American City Business Journals, Inc.
Contact: Mike Olivieri, Executive Vice President
Released: Weekly. Price: $4, introductory 4-week offer(Digital & Print). Description: CPI Card Group of Littleton, Colorado has been preparing for the nationwide transition to computer chip cards to secure credit and debit cards in the U.S. Banks and merchants in the country need to make the switch by October 2015 or risk being financially liable for fraud if not using the chipped cards in their retail establishments. Availability: Print; Online.

20311 ■ "Markets: The Great Deleveraging" in Canadian Business (Vol. 81, October 13, 2008, No. 17, pp. 45)
Pub: Rogers Media Inc.
Contact: Neil Spivak, Chief Executive Officer
Ed: Jeff Sanford. Description: 'Hell Week' of financial crisis on Wall Street is believed to have started with the downgrade of AIG Inc.'s credit rating. AIG is a major player in the credit derivatives market, and its bankruptcy would have affected firms on Wall Street. Availability: Online.

20312 ■ Mastering the Art of Debt Collection for Small Businesses
URL(s): www.whitemanborden.com/blog/2020/09/mastering-the-art-of-debt-collection-for-small-businesses/
Description: Discusses when your small business may require legal help when it comes to debt collection. Availability: Online.

20313 ■ "Md.'s Boring Bonds Gain Pizzazz as Investors Flock to Debt Issues" in Baltimore Business Journal (Vol. 28, June 11, 2010, No. 5, pp. 1)
Pub: Baltimore Business Journal
Contact: Rhonda Pringle, President
E-mail: rpringle@bizjournals.com
Ed: Gary Haber. Description: Companies and nonprofit organizations have increased the pace of bond offerings in order to take advantage of the bonds' appeal among willing investors. Companies mostly issued corporate bonds to replace existing debt at lower interest rates and save them money from interest payments.

20314 ■ "Medical Collection Agency Refutes Allegations In AG's Report" in PaymentsSource (May 1, 2012)
Description: Accretive Health Inc. denies allegations by the Minnesota State Attorney General's Office that the firm used heavy-handed tactics pressuring patients to pay for services before receiving treatment. The medical collection agency's report states 'inaccuracies, innuendo and unfounded speculation' in the charges. Availability: Print; Online.

20315 ■ "The Mortgage Red Flags that Bankers See" in Providence Business News (Vol. 29, August 4, 2014, No. 18, pp. 9)
Pub: American City Business Journals, Inc.
Contact: Mike Olivieri, Executive Vice President

20316 ■ Credit and Collection

URL(s): pbn.com/the-mortgage-red-flags-tha
t-bankers-see98980
Description: A survey of credit-score company FICO reveals that an excessive debt-to-income (DTI) ratio is the biggest reason why credit-risk managers reject potential new home buyers when applying for mortgages. Other factors that affect mortgage applications include new buyers credit scores and numerous recent credit applications.

20316 ■ "Needed: A Strategy; Banking In China" in The Economist (Vol. 390, January 3, 2009, No. 8612, pp. 54)
Description: International banks are competing for a role in China but are finding obstacles in their paths such as a reduction in the credit their operations may receive from Chinese banks and the role they can play in the public capital markets which remain limited. **Availability:** Print; Online.

20317 ■ "NetSpend and Family Dollar Announce New Prepaid Card Agreement" in GlobeNewswire (May 10, 2012)
Pub: Comtex News Network Inc.
Contact: Kan Devnani, President
Description: Partnership between Family Dollar and NetSpend will offer customers a NetSpend Visa(R) Prepaid Debit Card to be used at Family Dollar's 7,200 locations. NetSpend is a leading provider of general-purpose reloadable (GPR) prepaid debit cards and other related financial services. **Availability:** Print; Online.

20318 ■ "A New Kid on the Block" in Barron's (Vol. 88, March 17, 2008, No. 11, pp. 58)
Pub: Dow Jones & Company Inc.
Contact: Almar Latour, Chief Executive Officer
Ed: Thomas G. Donlan. **Description:** Discusses the Federal Reserve which has offered to lend $100 billion in cash to banks and $200 billion in Treasuries to Wall Street investment banks that have problems with liquidity. The reluctance of the banks to lend money to meet a margin call on securities that could still depreciate is the reason why the agency is going into the direct loan business. **Availability:** Online.

20319 ■ Nine Collection Tips for Small Business
URL(s): www.abc-amega.com/articles/nine-collection
-tips-for-small-business/
Description: Provides tips for small businesses that have delinquent accounts to manage and how to increase the chances of recovering them before they need to be handed off to collections. **Availability:** Online.

20320 ■ "North Carolina Town Hires Collection Agency" in PaymentsSource (April 24, 2012)
Description: Selma, North Carolina hired TekCollect to collect about $500,000 in unpaid utility bills. The collection agency will be paid $13,000 up frnt for guaranteed collections on 500 of the 1,200 acccounts. **Availability:** Online.

20321 ■ "Ohio Regulator Sues Collection Agency" in PaymentsSource (September 21, 2012)
Pub: SourceMedia LLC
Contact: Gemma Postlethwaite, Chief Executive Officer
Description: Mike DeWine, Ohio Attorney General, is suing Royal Oak Financial Services, a collection agency doing business as Collection and Recovery Bureau. The suit alleges that the firm used collection tactics banned by federal law and also attempting to collect unverified debts.

20322 ■ "OK, Bring in the Lawyers" in Crain's Chicago Business (Vol. 31, November 17, 2008, No. 46, pp. 26)
Pub: Crain Communications Inc.
Contact: Barry Asin, President
Ed: Daniel Rome Levine. **Description:** Bankruptcy attorneys are finding the economic and credit crisis a benefit for their businesses due to the high number of business owners and mortgage holders that are in need of their services. One Chicago firm is handling ten times the number of cases they did the previous year and of that about 80 percent of their new clients are related to the real estate sector. **Availability:** Online.

20323 ■ "Older, But Not Wiser" in Canadian Business (Vol. 85, July 16, 2012, No. 11-12, pp. 54)
Ed: Matthew McClearn, Michael McCullough. **Description:** Data from Statistics Canada revealed that two-thirds of workers aged 55 and above have some form of debt from mortgage to credit card balance while its one-third among the retired. Some factors contributing to the trend are the decline in borrowing costs, real estate, and older Canadians' car purchasing behavior. **Availability:** Print; Online.

20324 ■ "Opportunity Now Lies at Short End of the Market" in Barron's (Vol. 88, June 30, 2008, No. 26, pp. M9)
Pub: Dow Jones & Company Inc.
Contact: Almar Latour, Chief Executive Officer
Ed: Michael S. Derby. **Description:** Renewed credit concerns and the lesser chance of a Federal Reserve interest rate hike boosted the bond market. Some portfolio managers are more bullish on short-dated securities as they expect the market to adjust to a more appropriate outlook. **Availability:** Online.

20325 ■ "PayDragon Brings Mobile Payment App to Food-Truck Vendors" in PaymentsSource (April 16, 2012)
Pub: SourceMedia LLC
Contact: Gemma Postlethwaite, Chief Executive Officer
Ed: David Heun. **Description:** PayDragon is a new App for food truck vendors to collect payments. It is also used by other small merchants. Paperlinks, developed this unit to provide a fast technology that enables consumers to securely order and pay for food with credit and debit cards using email, which elimiantes these steps for the vendors. **Availability:** Print; Online.

20326 ■ "A Pioneer of Paying With Plastic" in Crain's Chicago Business (Vol. 31, April 28, 2008, No. 17, pp. 39)
Pub: Crain Communications Inc.
Contact: Barry Asin, President
Ed: Phuong Ly. **Description:** Profile of Perfect Plastic Printing Corp., a family-owned company which manufactures credit cards, bank cards and gift cards and whose sales hit $50.1 million last year, a 16 percent jump from 2006. **Availability:** Online.

20327 ■ "Portfolio Recovery Associates Expands Its Hampton Call Center" in Marketwired (January 20, 2010)
Pub: Comtex News Network Inc.
Contact: Kan Devnani, President
Description: Entering into a lease amendment in order to expand its Hampton, Virginia call center and extend its lease agreement, Portfolio Recovery Associates, Inc., a company that collects, purchases and manages defaulted consumer debt, plans to upgrade the existing space enabling them to draw on local talent. **Availability:** Print; Online.

20328 ■ Practical Debt Collecting for Small Companies and Traders
Description: Credit and collection guide for small companies. **Availability:** Online.

20329 ■ "Prepaid Phones Surge in Bad Economy" in Advertising Age (Vol. 79, November 17, 2008, No. 43, pp. 6)
Pub: Crain Communications, Inc.
Contact: Jessica Botos, Manager, Marketing
E-mail: jessica.botos@crainsnewyork.com
Ed: Rita Chang. **Description:** Prepay cell phone offerings are becoming increasingly competitive amid a greater choice of plans and handsets. In an economic environment in which many consumers are unable to pass the credit checks required for traditional cell phone plans, the prepay market is surging.

GENERAL SMALL BUSINESS TOPICS

20330 ■ "Ready for a Rally?" in The Economist (Vol. 390, January 3, 2009, No. 8612, pp. 54)
Description: Analysts predict that the recession could end by 2010. The current economic crisis is presented in detail. **Availability:** Print; Online.

20331 ■ "Research Reports" in Barron's (Vol. 88, March 24, 2008, No. 12, pp. M10)
Pub: Dow Jones & Company Inc.
Contact: Almar Latour, Chief Executive Officer
Ed: Anita Peltonen. **Description:** Investors are recommending purchasing shares of Ampco Pittsburgh due to an expected surge in earnings. Deteriorating credit quality presents problems for the shares of BankAtlantic Bancorp, whose price targets have been lowered from $7 to $5 each. Shares of Helicos Biosciences are expected to move sideways from their $6 level. Statistical data included.

20332 ■ "Retailers at the Ready to Adopt Mobile Pay Options" in Dallas Business Journal (Vol. 35, August 24, 2012, No. 50, pp. 1)
Pub: Baltimore Business Journal
Contact: Rhonda Pringle, President
E-mail: rpringle@bizjournals.com
Ed: Steven R. Thompson. **Description:** Dallas-Fort Worth-based major retailers have been looking for ways to integrate the apps and mobile technology into their customer experience. The retailers formed the Irving, Texas-based Merchant Customer Exchange to develop mobile payment technology. **Availability:** Print; Online.

20333 ■ "Return to Wealth; Bank Strategy" in The Economist (Vol. 390, January 3, 2009, No. 8612, pp. 56)
Description: UBS' strategy to survive these trying economic times is presented. Statistical data included. UBS has a stronger balance-sheet than most of its investment-banking peers and has reduced its portfolio. **Availability:** Print; Online.

20334 ■ "The Rise of Digital Currencies and Atlanta's Key Role" in Atlanta Business Chronicle (July 4, 2014, pp. 25A)
Pub: American City Business Journals, Inc.
Contact: Mike Olivieri, Executive Vice President
Released: Weekly. **Price:** $4, introductory 4-week offer(Digital only). **Description:** Virtual currency bitcoin, which is an Internet protocol that defines a decentralized online payment system is discussed. A description of how bitcoin and other virtual currencies are used and concerns over its future use are examined. A short profile of Atlanta-based startup BitPay, which provides software solutions to help businesses accept bitcoin payments without risking operating cash flow is included. BitPay also enables rapid currency conversion through bitcoin ATMs or kiosks. **Availability:** Print; Online.

20335 ■ "Santander 'Redlining' Suit is a Crass and Opportunistic Shakedown" in Boston Business Journal (Vol. 34, June 6, 2014, No. 18, pp. 7)
Pub: American City Business Journals, Inc.
Contact: Mike Olivieri, Executive Vice President
Released: Weekly. **Description:** Santander Bank's residential mortgage lending to minorities in Providence, Massachusetts has declined by 34 percent in recent years. The development is a violation of the US Fair Housing Act and the Equal Credit Opportunity Act. The city has sued Santander over the issue. **Availability:** Print; Online.

20336 ■ Save Your Small Business: 10 Crucial Strategies to Survive Hard Times or Close Down & Move On
Pub: Nolo
Contact: Chris Braun, President
Ed: Ralph Warner, Bethany Laurence. **Description:** According to a study among 500 businesses, 44 percent used credit cards in order to meet their firm's needs in the previous six months. Written by a busi-

ness owner, this book provides twelve strategies to protect personal assets from creditors and survive the current recession. **Availability:** Print.

20337 ■ *"SEC Report On Rating Agencies Falls Short" in Barron's (Vol. 88, July 14, 2008, No. 28, pp. 35)*
Pub: Dow Jones & Company Inc.
Contact: Almar Latour, Chief Executive Officer
Ed: Jack Willoughby. **Description:** The Securities and Exchange Commissions report on credit-rating firms should have drawn attention to the slipshod practices in the offerings of collateralized debt obligations. The report fell short of prescribing correctives for the flawed system of these agencies' relationship with their clients. **Availability:** Online.

20338 ■ *"Senator Grills Collection Agency, Health System Executives" in Collections & Credit Risk (May 31, 2012)*
Pub: SourceMedia LLC
Contact: Gemma Postlethwaite, Chief Executive Officer
Description: Accretive Health Inc. and Fairview Health Services executives were questioned by Senator Al Franken about its debt collection practices. The suit was initiated after unencrypted private information on 23,500 patients was stolen from an Acrretive employee's vehicle. Details of the lawsuit are outlined.

20339 ■ *"Sentiment Split on Financials: Is the Worse Over or Still to Come?" in Barron's (Vol. 88, March 24, 2008, No. 12, pp. M14)*
Pub: Dow Jones & Company Inc.
Contact: Almar Latour, Chief Executive Officer
Ed: Steven M. Sears. **Description:** Experts in the financial sector are split as to whether or not the worst of the financial crisis brought on by the credit crunch is over. Some options traders are trading on are defensive puts, expecting the worst, while investors buying calls are considered as bullish. **Availability:** Online.

20340 ■ *"A Slice of Danish; Fixing Finance" in The Economist (Vol. 390, January 3, 2009, No. 8612, pp. 55)*
Description: Denmark's mortgage-holders and the county's lending system is presented. **Availability:** Print; Online.

20341 ■ *Small-Business Collections Help*
URL(s): smallbusiness.chron.com/smallbusiness-collections-61351.html
Ed: Heidi Cardenas. **Description:** Discusses the importance of small business owners understanding debt collection laws and where they can turn for help with collections. **Availability:** Online.

20342 ■ *The Small Business Debt Collection Process*
URL(s): www.debt.com/collection/small-business-debt-collection/
Description: Provides detailed information on the small business debt collection process, including legalities as well as do's and don'ts. **Availability:** Online.

20343 ■ *Small Business Survival Guide*
Released: First edition. **Description:** Small business expert provides strategies to start a company and survive in the 21st Century. He shows small business owners how to succeed despite challenges that can defeat any firm. His advice covers suppliers; customers and contractors; competitors and creditors; spouses, family and friends; as well as the ways lawyers, accountants and other can steal an entrepreneur's success. Ennico also describes how startups can comply with local regulations. **Availability:** E-book; Print.

20344 ■ *"Small Businesses Finding It Easier To Get Capital" in Birmingham Business Journal (Vol. 31, July 11, 2014, No. 28, pp. 10)*
Pub: American City Business Journals, Inc.
Contact: Mike Olivieri, Executive Vice President
Description: According to the Federal Reserve Bank of Atlanta, small businesses that applied for credit received the financing requested, showing increased confidence among Birmingham businesses. With a robust lending environment, Birmingham is expecting the trend to continue in 2014 with more business plans for expansion and new capital spends. **Availability:** Print; Online.

20345 ■ *Strategies for a More Effective Collections Policy*
URL(s): www.dnb.com/resources/collections-policy.html
Description: Describes what a good collections policy entails, what your goals should be for your collections policy, and strategies for creating your collections strategy.

20346 ■ *"Stuck With Two Mortgages" in Crain's Chicago Business (Vol. 31, April 21, 2008, No. 16)*
Pub: Crain Communications Inc.
Contact: Barry Asin, President
Ed: Darci Smith. **Description:** Discusses the problem a number of people are facing due to the slump in the housing market: being stuck with two mortgages when they move because their former homes have not sold. Many thought they could afford to move to a larger home, anticipating significant equity appreciation that did not occur; now they are left with lowering their price and competing with the host of new developments. **Availability:** Online.

20347 ■ *"Summary. Economic Trends for Small Business" in Small Business Economic Trends (February 2008, pp. 1)*
Pub: National Federation of Independent Business
Contact: Brad Close, President
Ed: William C. Dunkelberg, Holly Wade. **Description:** Summary of economic trends for small businesses in the U.S. is provided. Economic indicators such as capital spending, inventories and sales, inflation, and profits are given. Analysis of credit markets is also provided.

20348 ■ *"The Survey Says" in Collections and Credit Risk (Vol. 14, September 1, 2009, No. 8, pp. 16)*
Description: Revenue for the top accounts receivable management firms rose nearly 20 percent in 2008 despite lower liquidation rates, a poor economy and riskier, albeit cheaper debt portfolios; the trend may continue this year as collection agencies expect revenue, on average, to increase 5.8 percent. Debt buyers, however, found that their revenue fell nearly 7 percent in 2008 and expect it to fall another 12 percent this year. **Availability:** Print; Online.

20349 ■ *"Too Much Information?" in Black Enterprise (Vol. 37, December 2006, No. 5, pp. 59)*
Pub: Earl G. Graves Ltd.
Contact: Earl Graves, Jr., President
Ed: James C. Johnson. **Description:** African American business owners often face the dilemma of whether or not to divulge their minority status when soliciting new customers and financial institutions. The quality of the products or services is always the key factor and race should never define one's business; however, it is appropriate to market oneself as a minority- or women-owned business, especially if the company is in an industry where those clients are offered top-tier contracts. **Availability:** Online.

20350 ■ *"Unfair Distraction of Employees" in Business Owner (Vol. 35, March-April 2011, No. 2, pp. 8)*
Description: Fair Credit Collection Practices Act makes it illegal for collectors to contact a debtor at his or her place of employment if the collector is made aware that it is against personnel policy of the employer for the worker to take such a call. **Availability:** Print; Online.

20351 ■ *"Unlicensed Utah Collection Agency Settles with State Finance Department" in Idaho Business Review, Boise (July 15, 2010)*
Pub: Idaho Business Review
Contact: Autumn Kersey, Sales Executive
E-mail: akersey@idahobusinessreview.com
Description: Federal Recovery Acceptance Inc., doing business as Paramount Acceptance in Utah, agreed to pay penalties and expenses after the firm was investigated by the state for improprieties. The firm was charged with conducting unlicensed collection activity. **Availability:** Print; Online.

20352 ■ *"Utah Collection Agency Settles File-Sharing Charges" inPaymentsSource (June 11, 2012)*
Pub: SourceMedia LLC
Contact: Gemma Postlethwaite, Chief Executive Officer
Ed: Darren Waggoner. **Description:** EPN Inc., doing business as Checknet Inc., settled charges filed by the Federal Trade Commission that it exposed sensitive information on its computers and networks creating a potential security risk to the consumer information it stored. Details of the suit are provided.

20353 ■ *"Valenti: Roots of Financial Crisis Go Back to 1998" in Crain's Detroit Business (Vol. 24, October 6, 2008, No. 40, pp. 25)*
Pub: Crain Communications Inc.
Contact: Barry Asin, President
Ed: Tom Henderson, Nathan Skid. **Description:** Interview with Sam Valenti III who is the chairman and CEO of Valenti Capital L.L.C., a wealth-management firm; Valenti discusses in detail the history that led up to the current economic crisis as well as his prediction for the future of the country. **Availability:** Print; Online.

20354 ■ *"Waukesha Firm Hit for $8.9M for Junk Faxes" in Business Journal Milwaukee (Vol. 29, August 3, 2012, No. 45, pp. 1)*
Pub: American City Business Journals, Inc.
Contact: Mike Olivieri, Executive Vice President
Ed: Stacy Vogel Davis. **Released:** Weekly. **Price:** $4, introductory 4-week offer(Digital & Print). **Description:** Waukesha County, Wisconsin-based Easy PC Solutions LLC has been facing an $8.9 million settlement for sending unsolicited faxes to 7,000 health care providers. However, the company won't have to pay since the plaintiffs are expected to go after its insurance company. **Availability:** Print; Online.

20355 ■ *"What the Future Holds for Consumers" in Black Enterprise (Vol. 41, August 2010, No. 1, pp. 47)*
Pub: Earl G. Graves Ltd.
Contact: Earl Graves, Jr., President
Ed: Sheiresa Ngo. **Description:** The way people purchase goods and service has changed with technology. With an increased focus on security (as well as privacy and fairness) the U.S. Congress began regulating the credit card industry with the Fair Credit Reporting Act of 1970 and the Credit CARD Accountability, Responsibility, and Disclosure (CARD) Act of 2009. **Availability:** Online.

20356 ■ *"Where to Stash Your Cash" in Barron's (Vol. 88, March 17, 2008, No. 11, pp. 41)*
Pub: Dow Jones & Company Inc.
Contact: Almar Latour, Chief Executive Officer
Ed: Mike Hogan. **Description:** Investors are putting their money in money-market mutual funds seeking fractionally better yields and a safe haven from the uncertainties that was brought about by subprime lending. These funds, however, are hovering near 3.20 percent which is less than the 4 percent inflation rate. **Availability:** Online.

20357 ■ *"Why Optimism Over Europe Won't Last" in Barron's (Vol. 92, August 25, 2012, No. 38, pp. M6)*
Pub: Dow Jones & Company Inc.
Contact: Almar Latour, Chief Executive Officer

20358 ■ Credit and Collection

Ed: Jonathan Buck. **Description:** European markets could experience losses in the second half of 2012 as uncertainty over political events could wipe out market gains. Greece has to abide by the terms of ts agreements with creditors to receive bailout funds. The stock prices of BG Group could gain as much as 20 percent in 2013 due to its strong lifquified natural gas business. **Availability:** Online.

20358 ■ *"Why Your Business Credit Score Matters" in Legal Zoom (March 9, 2023)*
URL(s): www.legalzoom.com/articles/why-your-business-credit-score-matters

Ed: Kylie Ora Lobell. **Released:** March 09, 2023. **Description:** Much like your personal credit score, your business credit score is used to help the business obtain financing, so be sure to set and maintain a good score. **Availability:** Online.

20359 ■ *"A Word With Connie Runia of Collection Bureau" in Idaho Business Review (September 8, 2014)*
Pub: BridgeTower Media
Contact: Adam Reinebach, President

Description: Connie Runia, attorney and general counsel for Collection Bureau, located in Nampa, Idaho, joined the firm four years ago. These collection bureaus are licensed by the Department of Finance and regulated by the Federal Trade Commission. The Consumer Financial Protection Bureau is developing new rules for collection agencies. Statistical data included. **Availability:** Online.

20360 ■ *"The Worst Lies Ahead for Wall Street: More Losses Certain; More Expensive Capital to Be Needed" in Crain's New York Business (Vol. 24, January 20, 2008, No. 3, pp. 1)*
Pub: Crain Communications, Inc.
Contact: Jessica Botos, Manager, Marketing
E-mail: jessica.botos@crainsnewyork.com

Ed: Aaron Elstein. **Description:** Due to the weakening economy, many financial institutions will face further massive losses forcing them to borrow more at higher interest rates and dragging down their earnings for years to come. The effects on commercial real estate and credit card loans are also discussed as well as the trend to investing in Asia and the Middle East. **Availability:** Online.

20361 ■ *"Your Exposure to Bear Stearns" in Barron's (Vol. 88, March 17, 2008, No. 11, pp. 45)*
Pub: Dow Jones & Company Inc.
Contact: Almar Latour, Chief Executive Officer

Ed: Tom Sullivan, Jack Willoughby. **Description:** Bear Stearns makes up 5.5 percent of Pioneer Independence's portfolio, 1.4 percent of Vanguard Windsor II's portfolio, 1.2 percent of Legg Mason Value Trust, about 1 percent of Van Kampen Equity & Income, and 0.79 percent of Putnam Fund for Growth & Income. Ginnie Mae securities are now trading at 1.78 percentage points over treasuries due to the mortgage crises. **Availability:** Online.

20362 ■ *"Your Guide to Credit Counseling Services" in Forbes Advisor (August 3, 2021)*
Ed: Rebecca Lake, Daphne Foreman. **Released:** August 03, 2021. **Description:** Discusses the role consumer credit counseling plays in helping people get their personal debt under control.

TRADE SHOWS AND CONVENTIONS

20363 ■ California Collectors Association Annual Conference and Expo
California Association of Collectors (CAC)
3200 Courthouse Ln.
Eagan, MN 55121-1585
Ph: (916)929-2125
Fax: (952)926-1624
Co. E-mail: info@calcollectors.net
URL: http://www.calcollectors.net
Contact: Maryrose Diaz, President
URL(s): www.acainternational.org/events/cac-conference-2024

Frequency: Annual. **Description:** Credit collection products and services, including computer maintenance, hardware and software, business machines, legal services, skip tracing devices, telephone services and forms. **Audience:** Members and collection professionals. **Principal Exhibits:** Credit collection products and services, including computer maintenance, hardware and software, business machines, legal services, skip tracing devices, telephone services and forms. **Telecommunication Services:** info@calcollectors.net.

20364 ■ NACM Credit Congress and Exposition
National Association of Credit Management (NACM)
8840 Columbia 100 Pky.
Columbia, MD 21045
Ph: (410)740-5560
Fax: (410)740-5574
Co. E-mail: nacm_national@nacm.org
URL: http://nacm.org
Contact: Robin Schauseil, President
URL(s): creditcongress.nacm.org

Frequency: Annual. **Description:** Exhibits of relevance to credit and financial executives. **Audience:** Business credit and financial management professionals. **Principal Exhibits:** Exhibits of relevance to credit and financial executives. Dates and Locations: 2025 May 18-21 Cleveland, OH; 2026 Jun 07-10 St. Louis, MO; 2027 Jun 13-16 Las Vegas, NV. **Telecommunication Services:** conventions_info@nacm.org.

20365 ■ RMA's Annual Annual Risk Management Conference
Risk Management Association (RMA)
1801 Market St., Ste. 300
Philadelphia, PA 19103-1613
Free: 800-677-7621
Fax: (215)446-4100
Co. E-mail: rmaar@rmahq.org
URL: http://www.rmahq.org/Default.aspx
Contact: Nancy Foster, President
URL(s): www.rmahq.org/conferences?gmssopc=1
Frequency: Annual. **Audience:** Credit and lending professionals. **Telecommunication Services:** registrar@rmahq.org.

PUBLICATIONS

20366 ■ *Business Credit: The Publication for Credit and Finance Professionals*
8840 Columbia 100 Pky.
Columbia, MD 21045
Ph: (410)740-5560
Fax: (410)740-5574
Co. E-mail: nacm_national@nacm.org
URL: http://nacm.org
Contact: Robin Schauseil, President
URL(s): bcm.nacm.org

Released: 9/year; except for combined issues in July/August, September/October, and November/December. **Price:** $66, Canada for 1 year; $99, Canada for 2 years; $134, Canada for 3 years; $9, Single issue; $59, U.S. for business 1 year; $60, Canada for 1 year agency; $79, for 1 year Foreign; $80, Canada for 2 years agency; $89, U.S. for business 2 year; $117, Canada for 3 years agency; $119, U.S. for business 3 year; $100, U.S. for library and student 3 year agency; $75, U.S. for library and student 2 year agency; $50, U.S. for library and student 1 year agency; $100, U.S. for library and student 3 year; $80, U.S. for library and student 2 year; $53, U.S. for library and student 1 year; $135, for 3 years foreign agency; $105, for 2 years foreign agency; $75, for 1 year foreign agency; $149, for 3 years foreign; $115, for 2 years foreign. **Description:** Magazine covering finance, business risk management, providing information for the extension of credit, maintenance of accounts receivable, and cash asset management. **Availability:** Print; Online.

Customer Service

START-UP INFORMATION

20367 ■ *"How to Open and Operate a Financially Successful Florist and Floral Business Online and Off"*
Pub: Atlantic Publishing Co.
Contact: Dr. Heather L. Johnson, Contact
Released: Revised second edition. **Description:** A concise and easy to follow guide for opening a retail florist or floral business online or a traditional brick and mortar store. Knowledge shared includes: cost control systems, retail math and competitive pricing, legal concerns, tax reporting requirements and reporting, profit and loss statements, management skills, sales advertising, and marketing techniques, customer service, direct sales, internal marketing ideas, and more. **Availability:** CD-ROM; Print; Online.

ASSOCIATIONS AND OTHER ORGANIZATIONS

20368 ■ **Help Desk Institute (HDI)**
121 S Tejon St., Ste. 1100
Colorado Springs, CO 80903
Free: 800-248-5667
Fax: (719)268-0184
Co. E-mail: hdisupport@informa.com
URL: http://www.thinkhdi.com
Contact: Tara Gibb, Senior Director
E-mail: tara.gibb@informa.com
Facebook: www.facebook.com/ThinkHDI
Linkedin: www.linkedin.com/company/hdi
X (Twitter): x.com/thinkhdi
Description: Provider of support, services, and guidance to the support and service management industry. **Founded:** 1989. **Publications:** *HDI Industry Insider* (Biweekly); *Support and Service Suppliers Directory* (Periodic); *SupportWorld*. **Awards:** HDI All Star Award (Monthly); All Star Award (Monthly); Help Desk Hero Award (Quarterly); Best Service and Support Analyst (Annual); Best Service and Support Analyst (Annual); HDI Best Service and Support Organization (Annual). **Geographic Preference:** Multinational.

EDUCATIONAL PROGRAMS

20369 ■ **Achieving Excellence in Customer Service (Onsite)**
Learning Tree International Inc.
13650 Dulles Technology Dr., Ste. 400
Herndon, VA 20171-6156
Free: 888-843-8733
Co. E-mail: info@learningtree.com
URL: http://www.learningtree.com
URL(s): www.learningtree.com/investor/releases/pr090129.htm
Description: This course provides the tools and techniques to ensure you build and maintain mutually beneficial relationships with customers. **Audience:** Professionals, and managers. **Principal Exhibits:** This course provides the tools and techniques to ensure you build and maintain mutually beneficial relationships with customers.

20370 ■ **AMA Customer Service Excellence: How to Win and Keep Customers**
American Management Association (AMA)
1601 Broadway
New York, NY 10019
Ph: (212)586-8100
Free: 800-262-9699
Fax: (212)903-8168
Co. E-mail: customerservice@amanet.org
URL: http://www.amanet.org
Contact: Manny Avramidis, President
URL(s): www.amaseminars.org/training/seminars/Customer-Service-Excellence-How-to-Win-and-Keep-Customers.aspx
Frequency: Continuous. **Description:** Covers the skills needed to communicate professionalism, gain respect, improve customer relationships, and secure competitive advantage. **Audience:** Customer service representatives, technical and support personnel, field service representatives, account managers, credit and billing specialists, small business owners. **Principal Exhibits:** Covers the skills needed to communicate professionalism, gain respect, improve customer relationships, and secure competitive advantage. **Telecommunication Services:** customerservice@amanet.org.

20371 ■ **The Conference on Customer Service (Onsite)**
Seminar Information Service Inc. (SIS)
250 El Camino Real., Ste. 112
Tustin, CA 92780
Ph: (714)508-0340
Free: 877-736-4636
Fax: (714)734-8027
Co. E-mail: info@seminarinformation.com
URL: http://www.seminarinformation.com
Contact: Catherine Bellizzi, President
URL(s): www.seminarinformation.com/details.cfm?qc=qqbhvr
Description: Learn techniques and tips for effectively and successfully dealing with customers, including what customer service representatives need to stay motivated and productive. **Audience:** Customer service representative, customer service managers and supervisors. **Principal Exhibits:** Learn techniques and tips for effectively and successfully dealing with customers, including what customer service representatives need to stay motivated and productive.

20372 ■ **Customer Satisfaction and Loyalty Research (Onsite)**
Seminar Information Service Inc. (SIS)
250 El Camino Real., Ste. 112
Tustin, CA 92780
Ph: (714)508-0340
Free: 877-736-4636
Fax: (714)734-8027
Co. E-mail: info@seminarinformation.com
URL: http://www.seminarinformation.com
Contact: Catherine Bellizzi, President
URL(s): www.seminarinformation.com
Description: Learn why it is important to assess customer satisfaction and the consequences of ignoring this vital area; how to design a study to measure customer satisfaction, how to structure and administer the survey questionnaire and how to select the sample; and how to implement results from the study to establish performance standards and goals for the future. **Audience:** Researchers, and customer service personnel. **Principal Exhibits:** Learn why it is important to assess customer satisfaction and the consequences of ignoring this vital area; how to design a study to measure customer satisfaction, how to structure and administer the survey questionnaire and how to select the sample; and how to implement results from the study to establish performance standards and goals for the future.

20373 ■ **Customer Service That Wows! (Onsite)**
Seminar Information Service Inc. (SIS)
250 El Camino Real., Ste. 112
Tustin, CA 92780
Ph: (714)508-0340
Free: 877-736-4636
Fax: (714)734-8027
Co. E-mail: info@seminarinformation.com
URL: http://www.seminarinformation.com
Contact: Catherine Bellizzi, President
URL(s): www.seminarinformation.com
Description: Learn how to determine what the customer needs before they ask and giving them more than they expect. **Audience:** Customer service professionals. **Principal Exhibits:** Learn how to determine what the customer needs before they ask and giving them more than they expect.

20374 ■ **How to Collect Accounts Receivable**
Fred Pryor Seminars & CareerTrack
5700 Broadmoor, Ste. 300
Mission, KS 66202
Free: 800-780-8476
Fax: (913)967-8849
Co. E-mail: customerservice@pryor.com
URL: http://www.pryor.com
Contact: Janet Turner, Contact
E-mail: dmca@pryor.com
URL(s): www.pryor.com/training-seminars/how-to-collect-account-receivable
Frequency: Irregular. **Description:** Learn to collect past due accounts without losing your customer. **Audience:** Business professionals. **Principal Exhibits:** Learn to collect past due accounts without losing your customer.

REFERENCE WORKS

20375 ■ *"3 Ways to Make Your Business More Customer-Centric" in Legal Zoom (February 21, 2023)*
URL(s): www.legalzoom.com/articles/3-ways-to-make-your-business-more-customer-centric

Ed: Katherine Gustafson. **Released:** February 21, 2023. **Availability:** Online.

20376 ■ *5 Ways to Build Customer Relationships for Your Small Business*
URL(s): www.paychex.com/articles/management/microbusinesses-build-customer-relationships
Released: December 31, 2020. **Description:** Provides 5 simple techniques to help your small business stand out to your customers and set you apart in a crowded marketplace. **Availability:** Online.

20377 ■ *9 Tips to Help Your Small Business Stand Out in Customer Service*
URL(s): www.benchmarkone.com/blog/small-business-customer-service/
Ed: Erin Posey. **Description:** Discusses the importance of excellent customer service in your small business and includes information on the qualities a strong customer service team employs. Provides 9 tips for improved customer service. **Availability:** Online.

20378 ■ *"16 Great Customer Service Tips and Examples" in Small Business Trends (Aug. 12, 2021)*
URL(s): smallbiztrends.com/2021/08/great-customer-service.html
Ed: Tom Coombe. **Released:** August 12, 2021. **Description:** Provides 16 tips for providing superior customer service and includes examples of real-life companies that have put them in place. **Availability:** Online.

20379 ■ *"20 Tips and Tricks for Zoom - before, during and after Meetings" in krisp(October 1, 2022)*
URL(s): krisp.ai/blog/zoom-tips/
Ed: Alexandra Cote. **Released:** October 01, 2022. **Description:** Tips on how to have successful Zoom meetings. Now that more corporations have embraced work-from-home, Zoom is one of the most needed tools to keep communication flowing between employees and to customers. **Availability:** Online.

20380 ■ *101 Ways to Sell More of Anything to Anyone: Sales Tips for Individuals, Business Owners and Sales Professionals*
Pub: Allen and Unwin Proprietary Ltd.
Ed: Andrew Griffiths. **Description:** Tips are shared to help anyone improve sales skills while providing strong customer service. **Availability:** Print.

20381 ■ *"Ahead of the Trend: What Will the World Map Look Like in Five Years?" in Pet Product News (Vol. 66, September 2012, No. 9, pp. S1)*
Description: How Whiskers Holistic Pet Care has transformed itself into the go-to place for naturally inclined pet owners in New York City's East Village is discussed. Since 1988, Whiskers Holistic Pet Care has emphasized careful product selection and customer education to serve a wide array of customers. **Availability:** Print; Online.

20382 ■ *"Airlines Show Reality 'Behind the Scenes" in Dallas Business Journal (Vol. 35, March 23, 2012, No. 28, pp. 1)*
Description: American Airlines and Southwest Airlines are set to launch video programs that would give customers a realistic look at their operations. American Airliens started its video on YouTube. Southwest, on the other hand, is planning to luanch its customer-oriented version on TLC.

20383 ■ *"The Alfond Inn: a Small Hotel that Packs a Punch" in Orlando Business Journal (Vol. 30, January 24, 2014, No. 31, pp. 6)*
Pub: American City Business Journals, Inc.
Contact: Mike Olivieri, Executive Vice President
Released: Weekly. **Price:** $8, introductory 4-week offer(Digital & Print). **Description:** The Alfond Inn general manager, Deanne Gabel, says the hotel was named after an alumni of the Alfond Foundation. She also said the hotel's architecture has a Spanish Mediterranean look. Gabel added that familiarity with guests gives the hotel an advantage over larger brands. **Availability:** Print; Online.

20384 ■ *"Almost Like Home" in Pet Product News (Vol. 66, September 2012, No. 9, pp. S18)*
Description: Treats Unleashed, a natural and functional pet foods and supplies store chain in Medwestern U.S., has been known for creating an aura that kept customers returning to each of its seven stores. It has also been reputed for a laidback atmosphere hat prioritizes customer education over sales. The chain's promotional and growth-related plans are also discussed. **Availability:** Online.

20385 ■ *"American Apparel: When Dov Cries" in Canadian Business (Vol. 83, June 15, 2010, No. 10, pp. 71)*
Pub: Rogers Media Inc.
Contact: Neil Spivak, Chief Executive Officer
Ed: Joe Castaldo. **Description:** American Apparel disclosed that they will have problems meeting one of its debt covenants which could trigger a chain reaction that could lead to bankruptcy. The prospects look bleak, but eccentric company founder Dov Charney, has always defied expectations. **Availability:** Online.

20386 ■ *"Attention, Shoppers Take a Deep Breath: Why It Pays to Help Customers Relax" in Inc. (Vol. 33, November 2011, No. 9, pp. 26)*
Pub: Mansueto Ventures L.L.C.
Contact: Stephanie Mehta, Chief Executive Officer
Ed: J.J. McCorvey. **Released:** November 01, 2011. **Description:** According to a current study, along with festive music and decorations for holiday shoppers, some merchants are considering back messages and pedicures to keep customers happy. **Availability:** Online.

20387 ■ *"Baseline Metrics CEOs Need for Online Brand Oversight" in South Florida Business Journal (Vol. 34, May 23, 2014, No. 44, pp. 16)*
Pub: American City Business Journals, Inc.
Contact: Mike Olivieri, Executive Vice President
Released: Weekly. **Price:** $8, Introductory 4-week offer(Digital & Print). **Description:** Chief executive officers have the option to use metrics that will allow them to monitor their online brands. Social media engagement is an effective customer service metric because it presents a clear assessment of a business social media prowess. Reputation management software, on the other hand, ranks a firm's weekly, hourly, and daily sentiments online. **Availability:** Print; Online.

20388 ■ *"Baylor Turns Around Carrollton Hospital" in Dallas Business Journal (Vol. 35, June 15, 2012, No. 40, pp. 1)*
Pub: Baltimore Business Journal
Contact: Rhonda Pringle, President
E-mail: rpringle@bizjournals.com
Ed: Bill Hethcock. **Description:** Baylor Health Care System has boosted the service performance of Trinity Medical Center in Carrollton, Texas. Trinity was the worst performing hospital in the area in terms of mortality rates and patient satisfaction. **Availability:** Print; Online.

20389 ■ *"Beep Fruit Drink Makes Comeback: Prodded by Fans, a Maritime Dairy Brings Back Retro Drink Beep" in Canadian Business (Vol. 85, August 13, 2012, No. 13, pp. 9)*
Ed: Matthew McClearn. **Description:** Farmers Co-Operative Dairy temporarily resumed production of the Beep fruit drink in response to customers' call to bring back the product that the company has been selling since 1962. As part of the relaunch, the company replicated the original 1960s packaging and used social media to connect with customers. **Availability:** Print; Online.

20390 ■ *"Best CRM Software of 2023" in Business News Daily (February 28, 2023)*
URL(s): www.businessnewsdaily.com/7839-best-crm-software.html
Ed: Jeff Hale. **Released:** February 28, 2023. **Description:** A list of the best CRM software and a comparison guide. **Availability:** Online.

20391 ■ *"Best In Show" in Pet Product News (Vol. 64, November 2010, No. 11, pp. 20)*
Ed: Lizett Bond. **Description:** Cherrybrook Premium Pet Supplies offers an expanded array of quality holistic products and is staffed by people who possess wide knowledge of these products. Aside from receiving the Outstanding Holistic Approach award, Cherrybook has opened three stores in New Jersey. How a holistic approach to service kept customers coming back is discussed. **Availability:** Print; Online.

20392 ■ *"Bethesda Firm Aims to Revitalize Hat Chain Lids" in Washington Business Journal (March 15, 2019)*
URL(s): www.bizjournals.com/washington/news/2019/03/15/bethesda-firm-aims-to-revitalize-hat-chain-lids.html
Ed: Katishi Maake. **Released:** March 15, 2019. **Description:** Ames Watson LLC acquired Lids Sports Group and is looking to have the chain sell more than just hats. This is due in part to consolidating Lids with Fanzz, a sports apparel retailer, which will offer customers a larger selection of items to choose from. **Availability:** Online.

20393 ■ *Beyond Booked Solid: Your Business, Your Life, Your Way-It's All Inside*
Pub: John Wiley & Sons, Inc.
Contact: Christina Van Tassell, Executive Vice President Chief Financial Officer
Ed: Michael Port. **Released:** December 2010. **Price:** $21.99, e-book; $32.50, hardcover. **Description:** Professional service providers and small business owners will discover tactics and strategies for growing and expanding their companies while allowing them to find time to relax and enjoy their lives. Owners will learn to attract new clients and grow profits. **Availability:** E-book; Print; Online; PDF.

20394 ■ *"Biblical Secrets to Business Success"*
Pub: CreateSpace
Released: October 02, 2014. **Price:** paperback. **Description:** Bob Diener share insight into his journey as an entrepreneur. He focuses on tough issues like: how to treat employees, how to please customers, whether or not to cut corners, whether to follow temptation of an unethical deal, and provides solutions to these dilemmas. He recommends abiding by the Bible's rules of business in order to prosper long term. **Availability:** Print.

20395 ■ *"Big Data at Work: Dispelling the Myths, Uncovering the Opportunities"*
Pub: Harvard Business Review Press
Contact: Moderna V. Pfizer, Contact
Released: February 25, 2014. **Price:** $35, Hardcover/Hardcopy. **Description:** What big data means from a technical, consumer, and management perspective; what big data opportunities cost; where it can have business impact; and what aspect of big data have been oversold. Insight is provided to help small businesses us big data to work to strengthen customer relationships. **Availability:** E-book; Print.

20396 ■ *"Boundaries for Leaders (Enhanced Edition): Results, Relationships, and Being Ridiculously In Charge"*
Pub: Harper Business
Contact: Hollis Heimbouch, Senior Vice President Publisher
Released: April 16, 2013. **Price:** $15.97, Default Title; $16.99. **Description:** Clinical psychologist and author explains how the best business leaders set boundaries within their organizations, with their teams and themselves, to improve performance and increase customer and employee satisfaction. Practical

advice is given to manage teams, coach direct reports, and create an organization with strong ethics and culture. **Availability:** E-book; Print.

20397 ■ *"Bringing Healthcare Home" in Austin Business Journal (Vol. 34, June 6, 2014, No. 16, pp. B13)*
Pub: American City Business Journals, Inc.
Contact: Mike Olivieri, Executive Vice President
Description: Chris Hester, founder and president of Kinnser Software feels that the company's growth since its inception has been both a blessing and a challenge. He states that his company's policy not to hire people until there's a strong need has increased productiveness of the company and the singular focus on customer service success has driven the company forward. **Availability:** Online.

20398 ■ *"Cashing In: Gleaning an Education from Our Economic State" in Agency Sales Magazine (Vol. 39, August 2009, No. 8, pp. 22)*
Description: Businesses have learned that cutting price can kill business and being tough is normal. The recession has also taught that getting the right vision and gaining the confidence and trust of consumers are important. **Availability:** Online.

20399 ■ *"The CEO of Williams-Sonoma on Blending Instinct with Analysis" in Harvard Business Review (Vol. 92, September 2014, No. 9, pp. 41)*
Pub: Harvard Business Publishing
Contact: Diane Belcher, Managing Director
Price: $8.95. **Description:** At Williams-Sonoma Inc., analytics are used to provide customers with experiences that best match their preferences, based on browsing history and/or previous purchases. This data is also used to inform designers, vendors, and distributors of supply and demand patterns. **Availability:** Online; PDF.

20400 ■ *"Certified Technicians can Increase Bottom Line" in Contractor (Vol. 56, September 2009, No. 9, pp. 37)*
Ed: Ray Isaac. **Description:** Certified technicians increase the value of HVAC firms, a survey by Service Round Table has reported. The increased value has been attributed to fewer callbacks, less warranty work and greater ability to educate consumers. Meanwhile, consumers are willing to pay more for the services of certified technicians. **Availability:** Print; Online.

20401 ■ *"Changing Prescriptions" in Business North Carolina (Vol. 28, March 2008, No. 3, pp. 52)*
Description: Profile of Moose Drug Company, founded by Archibald Walter Moose in 1882. Family owners share how they focus on pharmacoeconomics (cost-benefit analyses of drugs or drug therapy) and customer service. **Availability:** Print; Online.

20402 ■ *"Choosing the Right CRM Software for Your Business" in Small Business Trends (August 23, 2022)*
URL(s): smallbiztrends.com/2022/08/crm-for-small-businesses.html
Ed: Holly Chavez. **Released:** August 23, 2022. **Description:** Interview with Felena Hanson, founder of Hera Hub Co-working Space and Accelerator for Women, discusses CRM (Customer Relationship Management) systems and how to choose the best one for your small business. **Availability:** Online.

20403 ■ *"Come Together: A Thematic Collection of Times Articles, Essays, Maps and More About Creating Community" in Pet Product News (Vol. 64, December 2010, No. 12, pp. 28)*
Ed: Lizett Bond. **Description:** Pet supply retailers have posted improved sales and improved customer service by bundling their offerings. Bundling pertains to grouping related items such as collars and leashes into a single unit for marketing purposes. Aside from providing convenience and enhanced product information to customers, bundling has facilitated more efficient purchases. **Availability:** Online.

20404 ■ *Compare the Best Customer Service Software*
URL(s): www.quicksprout.com/best-customer-service-software/
Ed: Lars Lofgren. **Released:** February 13, 2022. **Description:** Good customer service software puts your support teams in the best position to deliver excellent service to your customers. This article lists the 8 best customer service software options for your small business. **Availability:** Online.

20405 ■ *"Conscious Capitalism: Liberating the Heroic Spirit of Business"*
Released: January 07, 2014. **Price:** $12.47, e-book; $16.79, paperback. **Description:** Conscious Capitalism companies include Whole Foods Market, Southwest Airlines, Costco, Google, Patagonia, The Container Store, UPS and others. These firms under the four specific tenants to success: higher purpose, stakeholder integration, conscious leadership, and conscious culture and management. These companies are able to create value for all stakeholders, including customers, employees, suppliers, investors, society, and the environment. A new preface by the authors is included. **Availability:** E-book; Print.

20406 ■ *Consumer Behavior*
Ed: Leon G. Schiffman, Joseph Wisenblit. **Released:** Fifth Edition. **Price:** $276.20, cloth; $112.99, adobe reader. **Description:** Consumer behavior is central to the planning, development and implementation of marketing strategies. **Availability:** Print; Online; PDF.

20407 ■ *"Conversations with Customers" in Business Journal Serving Greater Tampa Bay (Vol. 31, December 31, 2010, No. 1, pp. 1)*
Pub: Tampa Bay Business Journal
Contact: Ian Anderson, President
E-mail: ianderson@bizjournals.com
Description: Tampa Bay, Florida-based businesses have been using social media to interact with customers. Forty percent of businesses have been found to have at least one social media platform to reach customers and prospects. **Availability:** Print; Online.

20408 ■ *"Convert New Customers to Long Term Accounts" in Indoor Comfort Marketing (Vol. 70, February 2011, No. 2, pp. 22)*
Description: Marketing to new customers and suggestions for retaining them is covered. **Availability:** Online.

20409 ■ *"Customer Data Represents Huge Opportunities and Challenges: My, What Big Data You Have" in Canadian Business (Vol. 85, August 13, 2012, No. 13, pp. 14)*
Ed: Dominic Barton. **Description:** Mining gigabytes of data provides an opportunity for companies to better understand customer behavior at a lesser cost and with unimaginable precision. Human intuition and experience remain significant factors in maximizing the potential of understanding huge amounts of customer data. **Availability:** Print; Online.

20410 ■ *"The Customer Is Always Right Even When He's Wrong" in Contractor (Vol. 57, February 2010, No. 2, pp. 12)*
Ed: Al Schwartz. **Description:** Mechanical contractors should note that customers will make a judgment based upon the impression that they form on their first meeting. Contractors can maintain a professional image by washing their trucks and having the personnel dress uniformly. Contractors have every right to demand that employees clean up and make a better impression on customers. **Availability:** Print; Online.

20411 ■ *"Customer Loyalty: Making Your Program Excel" in Franchising World (Vol. 42, August 2010, No. 8, pp. 47)*
Pub: International Franchise Association
Contact: Matthew Haller, President
E-mail: mhaller@franchise.org
Ed: Steve Baxter. **Description:** Customer loyalty is key to any franchise operation's growth. Tips for identifying preferred customers are outlined. **Availability:** Online.

20412 ■ *"Customer Preferences Control Skid Steer Choices" in Rental Product News (Vol. 33, June 2011)*
Released: January 06, 2011. **Description:** Understanding the types of controls available on skid steer equipment is essential. The article provides a comprehensive guide to using and maintaining skid steers for rental agencies. **Availability:** Print; Online.

20413 ■ *"Customer Retention is Proportionate to Employee Retention" in Green Industry Pro (Vol. 23, September 2011)*
Description: Presented in a question-answer format, information is provided to help retain customers as well as keeping workers happy. **Availability:** Online.

20414 ■ *"The Customer Rules: The 39 Essential Rules for Delivering Sensational Service"*
Released: 2018. **Description:** Former executive vice president of Walt Disney World provides rules for serving customers with consistency, efficiency, creativity, sincerity, and excellence in order to win and retain them. He offers 39 chapters covering every aspect of customer service for any size business. **Availability:** E-book; Print; Download.

20415 ■ *"Customer Service Guide for Small Business" in The Balance Small Business (June 25, 2019)*
URL(s): www.thebalancesmb.com/customer-service-guide-for-small-business-2948068
Ed: Susan Ward. **Released:** June 25, 2019. **Description:** A guide designed to help your small business take a systematic approach to improving customer service. **Availability:** Online.

20416 ■ *Customer Service for Small Business Owners: Everything You Need to Know*
URL(s): sba.thehartford.com/business-management/marketing/customer-service/
Ed: Allie Johnson. **Released:** January 26, 2021. **Description:** A guide that walks small business owners through the basics of providing great customer service and arms you with the ideas and tools to ensure that you have happy customers. **Availability:** Online.

20417 ■ *"Customer Service Solutions for Small Businesses" in Business News Daily (Dec. 3, 2021)*
URL(s): www.businessnewsdaily.com/7575-customer-service-solutions.html
Ed: Sara Angeles. **Released:** December 03, 2021. **Description:** Excellent customer service is critical to running a successful business. This article provides 8 customer service solutions that can help your small business better connect with consumers. **Availability:** Online.

20418 ■ *"Designing Solutions Around Customer Network Identity Goals" in Journal of Marketing (Vol. 75, March 2011, No. 2, pp. 36)*
Pub: American Marketing Association
Contact: Bennie F. Johnson, Chief Executive Officer
Ed: Amber M. Epp, Linda L. Price. **Price:** $36. **Description:** The role relational and collective goals in creating customer solutions is investigated using in-depth interviews with 21 families. Findings revealed four integration processes in customer networks, namely, offerings formed around individual coalitions, concurrent participation, alternate participation, and offerings formed around priority goals.

20419 ■ *"Designing Women? Apparel Apparatchic at Kmart" in Barron's (Vol. 88, March 17, 2008, No. 11, pp. 16)*
Pub: Dow Jones & Company Inc.
Contact: Almar Latour, Chief Executive Officer
Ed: Robin Goldwyn Blumenthal. **Description:** Kmart began a nationwide search for women to represent the company in a national advertising campaign. Contestants need to upload their photos to Kmart's website and winners will be chosen by a panel of

celebrity judges. The contest aims to reverse preconceived negative notions about the store's quality and service. **Availability:** Online.

20420 ■ *"Digital-Physical Mashups: To Consumers, the Real and Virtual Worlds Are One. The Same Should Go For Your Company"* in *Harvard Business Review (Vol. 92, September 2014, No. 9, pp. 84)*
Pub: Harvard Business Publishing
Contact: Diane Belcher, Managing Director
Price: $8.95. **Description:** By merging their physical and virtual operations, companies can provide a seamless experience for customers, boosting competitive advantage. These include strengthening customer/engagement links, approaching innovation through complementary expertise, and ensure that chief executive officers possess adequate technological knowledge. **Availability:** Online; PDF.

20421 ■ *"Diversity in Business Awards: Minority Businessperson of the Year and Diversity Corporation of the Year Finalists"* in *ColoradoBiz (Vol. 30, July 2012, No. 7, pp. 32)*
Description: Finalists for the ColoradoBiz 18th annual award presentation are profiled. The journal acknowledges minority businesses and businesspeople as well as firms that have been committed to hiring, contracting, and customer/community service to minorities.

20422 ■ *"Do Social Deal Sites Really Work? A Theme Park Chain Considers Whether the Boost In Ticket Sales Is Worth the Trouble"* in *Harvard Business Review (Vol. 90, May 2012, No. 5, pp. 139)*
Pub: Harvard Business Review Press
Contact: Moderna V. Pfizer, Contact
Ed: Marco Bertini, Luc Wathieu, Betsy Page Sigman, Michael I. Norton. **Price:** $8.95. **Description:** A fictitious group-purchasing promotion scenario is presented, with contributors providing advice. At issue is whether deal-type promotions compromise the customer experience to the point where it offsets any marketing benefit from the deal. While one approach is to more effectively manage the traffic generated from deals, the other is to more closely target promotions to optimize outcomes. **Availability:** Online; PDF.

20423 ■ *"Does the Hierarchical Position of the Buyer Make a Difference? The Influence of Perceived Adaptive Selling on Customer Satisfaction and Loyalty in a Business-To-Business Context"* in *Journal of Business & Industrial Marketing (Vol. 29, June 2014, No. 5)*
Pub: Emerald Group Publishing Limited
Contact: Erika Valenti, President
Description: A study to evaluate the influence of adaptive selling on customer satisfaction with the salesperson and the company is examined. The effects of buyer's organizational position on customer satisfaction and loyalty were also analyzed. The results highlighted the positive effects of the perceived adaptive selling and indicated that these effects were stronger when the contact person at the buying company was higher in the hierarchy. **Availability:** Download; Online.

20424 ■ *"Don't' Hate the Cable Guy"* in *Saint Louis Business Journal (Vol. 31, August 5, 2011, No. 50, pp. 1)*
Pub: Saint Louis Business Journal
Contact: Robert Bobroff, President
E-mail: rbobroff@bizjournals.com
Ed: Angela Mueller. **Description:** Charter Communications named John Birrer as senior vice president of customer experience. The company experienced problems with its customer services. **Availability:** Print; Online.

20425 ■ *"Emack & Bolio's Founder Blames Brookline Store Closure on Rising Rents"* in *Ice Cream Reporter (Vol. 23, October 20, 2010, No. 11, pp. 8)*
Released: Weekly. **Description:** Emack & Bolio's is engaging in scent marketing using various odors to help boost sales by attracting consumers with scents appropriate to their products. **Availability:** Print; Online.

20426 ■ *"Empowered"* in *Harvard Business Review (Vol. 88, July-August 2010, No. 7-8, pp. 94)*
Pub: Harvard Business Publishing
Contact: Diane Belcher, Managing Director
Ed: Josh Bernoff, Ted Schadler. **Price:** $8.95, PDF. **Description:** HERO concept (highly empowered and resourceful operative) which builds a connection between employees, managers, and IT is outlined. The resultant additional experience and knowledge gained by employees improves customer relationship management. **Availability:** Online; PDF.

20427 ■ *Exceptional Service, Exceptional Profit: The Secrets of Building a Five-Star Customer Service Organization*
Pub: HarperCollins Leadership
Contact: Donald Miller, Chief Executive Officer
Ed: Leonardo Inghilleri, Micah Solomon. **Released:** April 14, 2010. **Price:** $19.99, paperback. **Description:** Team of insiders share exclusive knowledge of the loyalty-building techniques pioneered by the world's most successful service leaders, including brick-and-mortar stars such as The Ritz-Carlton and Lexus and online success stories such as Netflix and CD Baby. **Availability:** E-book; Print.

20428 ■ *"Experts Strive to Educate on Proper Pet Diets"* in *Pet Product News (Vol. 64, November 2010, No. 11, pp. 40)*
Ed: Joan Hustace Walker. **Description:** Pet supply manufacturers have been bundling small mammal food and treats with educational sources to help retailers avoid customer misinformation. This action has been motivated by the customer's quest to seek proper nutritional advice for their small mammal pets. **Availability:** Online.

20429 ■ *"Feet on the Street: Reps Are Ready to Hit the Ground Running"* in *Agency Sales Magazine (Vol. 39, July 2009, No. 7, pp. 12)*
Description: One of the major benefits to manufacturers in working with sales representatives is the concept of synergistic selling where the rep shows his mettle. The rep of today is a solution provider that anticipates and meets the customer's needs.

20430 ■ *"Forward Motion"* in *Green Industry Pro (July 2011)*
Ed: Gregg Wartgow. **Description:** Several landscape contractors have joined this publication's Working Smarter Training Challenge over the last year. This process is helping them develop ways to improve work processes, boost morale, drive out waste, reduce costs, improve customer service, and be more competitive. **Availability:** Print; Online.

20431 ■ *"From Economy to Luxury, What Matters Most to Hotel Guests; To Win More Repeat Customers, Hotels Must Create a Tailored Guest Experience"* in *Gallup Business Journal (September 5, 2014)*
Pub: Gallup, Inc.
Contact: Jon Clifton, Chief Executive Officer
Description: The most successful hotels know their customers and offer products and services that meet their needs. **Availability:** Print; Online.

20432 ■ *"The Globe: Let Emerging Market Customers Be Your Teachers"* in *Harvard Business Review (Vol. 88, December 2010, No. 12, pp. 115)*
Pub: Harvard Business Publishing
Contact: Diane Belcher, Managing Director
Ed: Guillermo D'Andrea, David Marcotte, Gwen Dixon Morrison. **Price:** $8.95, PDF. **Description:** Examination of effective strategies for emerging markets is presented. These include helping educate customers as well as selling to them, adapting to customers' habits, and focusing brands appropriately. Magazine Luiza, a chain store in Brazil, is used to illustrate these points. **Availability:** Online; PDF.

20433 ■ *"Good Questions and the Basics of Selling"* in *Agency Sales Magazine (Vol. 39, September-October 2009, No. 9, pp. 14)*
Description: Six basic elements to enhance the job of a sales person in regards to his relationship to a customer are presented. **Availability:** Online.

20434 ■ *Greening Your Small Business: How to Improve Your Bottom Line, Grow Your Brand, Satisfy Your Customers and Save the Planet*
Price: $19.95. **Description:** A definitive resource for anyone who wants their small business to be cutting-edge, competitive, profitable, and eco-conscious. Stories from small business owners address every aspect of going green, from basics such as recycling waste, energy efficiency, and reducing information technology footprint, to more in-depth concerns such as green marketing and communications, green business travel, and green employee benefits.

20435 ■ *Guerrilla Marketing Goes Green: Winning Strategies to Improve Your Profits and Your Planet*
Pub: John Wiley & Sons, Inc.
Contact: Christina Van Tassell, Executive Vice President Chief Financial Officer
Ed: Jay Conrad Levinson, Shel Horowitz, Jay Conrad Levinson. **Released:** 2010. **Description:** The latest tips on green marketing and sustainable business strategies are shared. **Availability:** E-book; Print; Electronic publishing; Online.

20436 ■ *"Hasslochers Welcome Home a San Antonio Tradition"* in *San Antonio Business Journal (Vol. 28, July 25, 2014, No. 24, pp. 8)*
Pub: American City Business Journals, Inc.
Contact: Mike Olivieri, Executive Vice President
Released: Weekly. **Price:** $4, introductory 4-week offer(Digital & Print). **Description:** Hasslocher Enterprises Inc. acquired the rights to the shuttered Texan-Mexican restaurant La Fonda Alamo Heights and brought it back to life with a grand reopening in North Central San Antonio, Texas. Restaurant general manager, Bill Sheridan, says the customers and the employees are like family to each other. **Availability:** Print; Online.

20437 ■ *"The HBR Interview:"We Had to Own the Mistakes""* in *Harvard Business Review (Vol. 88, July-August 2010, No. 7-8, pp. 108)*
Pub: Harvard Business Publishing
Contact: Diane Belcher, Managing Director
Ed: Adi Ignatius. **Description:** Interview with Howard Schultz, CEO of Starbucks, covers topics that include investment in retraining, the impact of competition, premium quality, authenticity, customer services, strategy development, work-and-life issues, and international presence. **Availability:** Online.

20438 ■ *"Help Wanted: Only the Best Need Apply"* in *Pet Product News (Vol. 66, April 2012, No. 4, pp. 24)*
Description: Simi Valley, California-based pet supplies store, Theresa's Country Feed and Pet is said to have achieved success by hiring quality customer-oriented employees. In view of its receipt of the Pet Product News International's 2011-2012 Retailer of the Year Award for Outstanding General Pet Store, Theresa's approach to recruitment and customer relations are discussed. **Availability:** Print; Online.

20439 ■ *"Hey, Bike Shops: Stop Treating Cusotmers Like Garbage"* in *Bicycling (June 12, 2019)*
URL(s): www.bicycling.com/culture/a27496999/bike-shops-need-change/
Ed: Gloria Liu. **Released:** June 12, 2019. **Description:** Poor customer service within bike shops has been well-documented with the advent of social media reviews. Females, overweight people, and older people are more likely to feel these negative effects and shop anecdotes are discussed in this article. Some solutions are also presented. **Availability:** Online.

20440 ■ *Housecleaning Business: Organize Your Business - Get Clients and Referrals - Set Rates and Services*
Ed: Laura Jorstad, Melinda Morse. **Price:** Paperback,softback. **Description:** This book shares insight into starting a housecleaning business. It shows how to develop a service manual, screen clients, serve customers, select cleaning products, competition, how to up a home office, using the Internet to grow the business and offering green cleaning options to clients. **Availability:** E-book; Print.

20441 ■ *"How to Address a Negative Review on Social Media"* in *Archery Business* (December 11, 2018)
URL(s): www.archerybusiness.com/address-negative-review-social-media
Ed: Michaelean Pike. **Released:** December 11, 2018. **Description:** With the emergence of websites and social media that encourages leaving business reviews, how a business owner responds can either help or hurt the situation. Tips for writing a follow-up response are given, so that high customer service is maintained while keeping the integrity of the business intact. **Availability:** Online.

20442 ■ *"How to Boost Your Business with These Customer Service Tips"* in *Simply Business* (Dec. 23, 2020)
URL(s): www.simplybusiness.com/simply-u/articles/2020/12/customer-service-tips-for-small-businesses/
Ed: Emily Thompson. **Released:** December 23, 2020. **Description:** Provides customer service tips that can transform your small business. **Availability:** Online.

20443 ■ *"How COVID-19 Has Changed Customer Behavior, and How Businesses Can Respond"* in *Legal Zoom* (February 22, 2023)
URL(s): www.legalzoom.com/articles/how-covid-19-has-changed-customer-behavior-and-how-businesses-can-respond
Ed: Kylie Ora Lobell. **Released:** February 22, 2023. **Description:** The worldwide pandemic altered a lot of human behaviors as we adjusted to a new normal, and that is especially true when it comes to behaviors about shopping. Find out what changed, what's new, and how businesses can adapt. **Availability:** Online.

20444 ■ *"How Good Advice 'Online' Can Attract Customers"* in *Indoor Comfort Marketing* (Vol. 70, August 2011, No. 8, pp. 20)
Pub: Spray Technology & Marketing
Contact: Ava Caridad, Director, Editorial
E-mail: acaridad@spraytm.com
Ed: Richard Rutigiliano. **Description:** Online marketing tips for heating and cooling small businesses are explained.

20445 ■ *"How Growers Buy"* in *Farm Industry News* (Vol. 42, January 1, 2009, No. 1)
Pub: Informa USA, Inc.
Contact: Stephen A. Carter, Chief Executive Officer
Ed: Karen McMahon. **Description:** According to a survey regarding the buying habits among large commercial growers, most prefer to purchase from local retailers, customer service is important concerning their decision on who to buy products from, and price and convenience seem to be more important then brand.

20446 ■ *"How I Did It: Zappos's CEO on Going to Extremes for Customers"* in *Harvard Business Review* (Vol. 88, July-August 2010, No. 7-8, pp. 41)
Pub: Harvard Business Publishing
Contact: Diane Belcher, Managing Director
Ed: Tony Hsieh. **Price:** $8.95, PDF. **Description:** Footwear firm Zappos.com Inc. improved corporate performance through enhanced customer service. Enhancements include highly visible phone numbers, avoidance of scripts, and viewing call centers as marketing departments. **Availability:** Online; PDF.

20447 ■ *"How to Manage Successful Crowdsourcing Projects"* in *eWeek* (September 29, 2010)
Ed: Lukas Biewald. **Released:** September 29, 2010. **Description:** The advantages, challenges and pitfalls faced when using crowdsourcing to improve a business are outlined. Crowdsourcing helps to eliminate the need to rely on an internal workforce and the need to forecast task volume. **Availability:** Online.

20448 ■ *"How a Mobile CRM Benefits Your Business"* in *Business News Daily* (February 21, 2023)
URL(s): www.businessnewsdaily.com/16065-mobile-crm-benefits.html
Ed: Max Freedman. **Released:** February 21, 2023. **Description:** Customer Relationship Management software (CRM) can be a useful tool for small businesses. Nowadays, this software is available on mobile devices instead of desktop computers, making it easier to access the data you need. **Availability:** Online.

20449 ■ *How to Set Up a Small Business Customer Service Call Center*
URL(s): hire.trakstar.com/blog/how-to-set-up-a-small-business-customer-service-call-center
Ed: Gere Jordan. **Description:** A guide to setting up a customer service call center for your small business. **Availability:** Online.

20450 ■ *I Love You More Than My Dog*
Pub: Portfolio
Contact: Adrian Zackheim, President
Ed: Jeanne Bliss. **Released:** October 15, 2009. **Price:** $14.99, E-book. **Description:** Ways to win passionate, loyal and vocal customers in order to build a small business is outlined. **Availability:** E-book; Print.

20451 ■ *"Increasing Business-to-Business Buyer Word-of-Mouth and Share-of-Purchase"* in *Journal of Business & Industrial Marketing* (Vol. 29, June 2014, No. 5)
Pub: Emerald Group Publishing Limited
Contact: Erika Valenti, President
Description: The satisfaction-loyalty framework pertaining to word-of-mouth communications and share-of-purchases was examined for situations in which business-to-business buyers are associated with the salesperson as well as the selling firm. The results indicated that satisfaction, loyalty, and WOMC relating to the salesperson directly affect satisfaction, loyalty, and WOMC with the selling firm, and that buyer satisfaction and loyalty also influence their post purchase conduct. **Availability:** Download; Online.

20452 ■ *"Industrial Buyers' Use of References, Word-of-Mouth and Reputation in Complex Buying Situation"* in *Journal of Business & Industrial Marketing* (Vol. 29, May 2014, No. 4, pp. 344-352)
Pub: Emerald Group Publishing Limited
Contact: Erika Valenti, President
Description: Exploration of how a buyer can assemble experience-based information dispersed across the business network using customer references, reputation, collegial advice networks, and word-of-mouth, and how this assists in the buying process. Different roles played by these factors are identified and it is suggested that experience-based information sheds light on offerings, suppliers, and problem solving situations in complex buying. **Availability:** Download; PDF; Online.

20453 ■ *"Interchangeable or Irreplaceable?"* in *American Printer* (Vol. 128, August 1, 2011, No. 8)
Description: Creating and maintaining customers is important for all graphic design and printing companies. Tips are shared to help maintain good customer satisfaction and repeat business. **Availability:** Online.

20454 ■ *"Invest in Energy-Efficient Equipment for Your Pet Store"* in *Pet Product News* (Vol. 66, September 2012, No. 9, pp. 72)
Ed: Leila Meyer. **Description:** Aquatic retailers can achieve business growth by offering lighting products, pumps, heaters, filters, and other aquarium supplies that would help customers realize energy efficiency. Aside from offering an education in energy efficiency as a customer service opportunity, retailers are encouraged to determine what supplies are crucial in helping customers achieve energy usage goals. **Availability:** Online.

20455 ■ *"Is That the Best You Can Do?"* in *Entrepreneur* (Vol. 37, October 2009, No. 10, pp. 85)
Description: Small business owners can deal with hagglers better by setting parameters in advance. They should convince hagglers by offering the best value and separating this from price. **Availability:** Print; Online.

20456 ■ *"Jab, Jab, Jab, Right Hook: How to Tell Your Story in a Noisy Social World"*
Pub: Harper Business
Contact: Hollis Heimbouch, Senior Vice President Publisher
Released: November 26, 2013. **Price:** $23.99, hardcover. **Description:** Author and social media expert shares advice on ways to connect with customers and beat the competition. Social media strategies for marketers and managers need to convert Internet traffic to sales. Communication is the key to online sales that are adapted to high quality social media platforms and mobile devices. **Availability:** E-book; Print.

20457 ■ *"James Donnelly on Keeping His Company's Edge: 'We Have Documented Best Practice for Everything"* in *South Florida Business Journal* (Vol. 34, May 23, 2014, No. 44, pp. 15)
Pub: American City Business Journals, Inc.
Contact: Mike Olivieri, Executive Vice President
Description: James Donnelly, CEO of Castle Group, a community management firm specializing in homeowners and condominium associations, believes that organizational culture is an important driver of business success. He reveals that the company keeps its edge by maintaining the best office technology and the best employees. His views about the importance of customer satisfaction are stressed. **Availability:** Print; Online.

20458 ■ *"Jeffrey Watanabe: 'Promise Less and Deliver More"* in *Canadian Business* (Vol. 85, August 13, 2012, No. 13, pp. 16)
Ed: Richard Branson. **Description:** Setting realistic customer expectations and then exceeding them in unexpected and helpful ways provides businesses an advantage over their competitors. Pricing and excellent customer service are some ways to exceed customer expectations. **Availability:** Print; Online.

20459 ■ *"Just Be Nice: Providing Good Customer Service"* in *Canadian Business* (Vol. 79, October 9, 2006, No. 20, pp. 141)
Pub: Rogers Media Inc.
Contact: Neil Spivak, Chief Executive Officer
Ed: Joe Castaldo. **Description:** The customer relationship management strategies on customer retention and satisfaction adopted by WestJet are discussed. **Availability:** Print; Online.

20460 ■ *"Keep The (Cage) Customer Satisfied"* in *Pet Product News* (Vol. 64, December 2010, No. 12, pp. 10)
Ed: Devon McPhee. **Description:** Windsor, California-based Debbie's Pet Boutique, recipient of Pet Product News International's Outstanding Customer Service Award, has been dedicated to combining topnotch grooming services with a robust retail selection. These features might gain return customers for Debbie's Pet Boutique. **Availability:** Online.

20461 ■ Customer Service   **GENERAL SMALL BUSINESS TOPICS**

20461 ■ "LivingSocial's New 'Glue'" in Washington Business Journal (Vol. 33, May 2, 2014, No. 2, pp. 10)
Pub: American City Business Journals, Inc.
Contact: Mike Olivieri, Executive Vice President
Description: LivingSocial Inc. CFO, John Bax, shares his views on the confluence of forces that shaped the company's first quarter results. Bax reports the company is pouring resources into the creation of a new retail merchant solution platform to help market products and services. Bax named the project Glue because it is geared to encouraging customer loyalty to merchants along with repeat business. **Availability:** Print; Online.

20462 ■ "Making Automated Royalty Payments Work for Your Franchise" in Franchising World (Vol. 42, October 2010, No. 10, pp. 30)
Pub: International Franchise Association
Contact: Matthew Haller, President
E-mail: mhaller@franchise.org
Ed: J.P. O'Brien. **Released:** October 10, 2010. **Description:** In the past, royalty payments were sent by franchisees through regular postal mail and accompanied by a single slip of paper with handwritten notes indicating the month's revenue numbers and royalty amounts. **Availability:** PDF; Online.

20463 ■ "Making It Click: Annual Ranking Of the Best Online Brokers" in Barron's (Vol. 88, March 17, 2008, No. 11, pp. 31)
Pub: Dow Jones & Company Inc.
Contact: Almar Latour, Chief Executive Officer
Ed: Theresa W. Carey. **Description:** Listing of 23 online brokers that are evaluated based on their trade experience, usability, range of offerings, research amenities, customer service and access, and costs. TradeStation Securities takes the top spot followed by thinkorswim by just a fraction. **Availability:** Online.

20464 ■ "Making It Work" in Pet Product News (Vol. 64, December 2010, No. 12, pp. S8)
Ed: Kerri Chladnicek. **Description:** How focusing on service and flexibility allowed New Jersey-based pet supply store B.C. Woof to achieve success is discussed. B.C. Woof began as a pet-sitting business which eventually concentrated on natural foods. Aside from conducting a do-it-yourself approach in food formulation for customers, B.C. Woof has also been guiding customers on nutrients they need for their pets. **Availability:** Print; Online.

20465 ■ "Making It Work" in Retail Merchandiser (Vol. 51, July-August 2011, No. 4, pp. 43)
Description: Profile of Anthony DiPaolo and his purchase of the Work 'N Gear retail store in 2002. The brick and mortar shop sells work wear and healthcare apparel and DiPaolo believes customer respect is essential to his success. **Availability:** Online.

20466 ■ "Managing Yourself: What Brain Science Tells Us About How to Excel" in Harvard Business Review (Vol. 88, December 2010, No. 12, pp. 123)
Pub: Harvard Business Publishing
Contact: Diane Belcher, Managing Director
Ed: Edward M. Hallowell. **Price:** $8.95, PDF. **Description:** Relevant discoveries in brain research as they apply to boosting employee motivation and organizational effectiveness are explained. Included is a checklist of 15 items for use in assessing the fitness of a person for a particular job, focusing on the intersection of what one likes to do, what one does best, and what increases organizational value. **Availability:** Print; PDF.

20467 ■ "McCormick Focuses on Customer, Dealer Service" in Farm Industry News (September 17, 2010)
Pub: Informa Business Media, Inc.
Contact: Charlie McCurdy, President
Price: $4, Print and Online; Special Offers only for 4 weeks. **Description:** McCormick has developed a new plan that focuses on fast and complete service to both customers and dealers. **Availability:** Print; Online.

20468 ■ "Mistakes to Avoid While Deploying CRM" in Small Business Trends (September 7, 2022)
URL(s): smallbiztrends.com/2022/09/mistakes-to-avoid-while-deploying-crm.html
Ed: Michael Guta. **Released:** September 07, 2022. **Description:** Interview with Gopal Sripada, Zoho's Head of Marketing, as challenges small businesses face while deploying CRM (Customer Relationship Management) software. **Availability:** Online.

20469 ■ The Mom & Pop Store: How the Unsung Heroes of the American Economy Are Surviving and Thriving
Ed: Robert Spector. **Description:** The history of small independent retail enterprises and how mom and pop stores in the U.S. continue to thrive through customer service and renewed community support for local businesses. **Availability:** Audio.

20470 ■ "MoneyGram Hopes Digital Push Will Click With Customers" in Dallas Business Journal (Vol. 37, July 4, 2014, No. 43, pp. 17)
Pub: American City Business Journals, Inc.
Contact: Mike Olivieri, Executive Vice President
Released: Weekly. **Price:** $4, introductory 4-week offer(Digital only). **Description:** Reports on MoneyGram's recent release of a digital monitoring system, which will allow it to work more closely with customers, is profiled. This digital monitoring system will aggregate data from social media platforms and enable the company to identify customer needs and trends across the money transfer industry. It will help MoneyGram outshine its rivals in the money transfer business. **Availability:** Print; Online.

20471 ■ "Muirhead Farmhouse B&B Owners Get Hospitality Wright" in Chicago Tribune (July 31, 2008)
Pub: Tribune News Service
Contact: Jack Barry, Vice President, Operations
E-mail: jbarry@tribpub.com
Ed: Glenn Jeffers. **Description:** Profile of the Muirhead Farmhouse, a bed-and-breakfast owned by Mike Petersdorf and Sarah Muirhead Petersdorf; Frank Lloyd Wright designed the historic farmhouse which blends farm life and history into a unique experience that is enhanced by the couple's hospitality. **Availability:** Online.

20472 ■ "Naresh Kumar on Using Heat Maps to Grow Your Business" in Small Business Trends (August 25, 2022)
URL(s): smallbiztrends.com/2022/08/heat-maps.html
Ed: Holly Chavez. **Released:** August 25, 2022. **Description:** Interview with Naresh Kumar, Zoho Corporation Product Manager, who discusses how small businesses can grow by utilizing heat maps, which is software that shows where website visitors spent their time at the website by recording where they clicked. **Availability:** Online.

20473 ■ "The Nation's #1 Children's Shoe Retailer, Payless ShoeSource(R), Launches Hassle-Free Back-to-School Shoe Shopping" in Benzinga.com (July 25, 2012)
Pub: PR Newswire Association LLC.
Description: Nation's largest shoe retailer, Payless ShoeSource(R), is offering a Happiness Guarantee for back-to-school shoe shopping. The firm's goal is to make shoppers happy and keep them returning to purchase shoes during the rest of the year.

20474 ■ "Next-Level E-Commerce" in Entrepreneur (June 2014)
Pub: Entrepreneur Media Inc.
Contact: Dan Bova, Director
E-mail: dbova@entrepreneur.com
Description: BloomReach's SNAP software enables consumers to see the products they want upon arriving at an e-commerce Website. The software does this by evaluating the users' intent and preferences based on previous site usage. The enterprise-level software, which costs retailers at least $7,500/month, aims to use big data to help consumers choose products based on their intent. The cloud-based service indexes every page on a client's site and automatically generates appropriate content for visitors. The use of machine learning reduces lag time between application and positive results. **Availability:** Print; Online.

20475 ■ Niche and Grow Rich
Description: Consultants share insight to entrepreneurs wishing to find a profitable niche market. Authors write that good niche businesses are easy to start and easy to defend from competitors. They also report that finding a successful niche can attract and maintain good customers who are willing to pay more for unique goods and services.

20476 ■ "The One Thing You Must Get Right When Building a Brand" in Harvard Business Review (Vol. 88, December 2010, No. 12, pp. 80)
Pub: Harvard Business Publishing
Contact: Diane Belcher, Managing Director
Ed: Patrick Barwise, Sean Meehan. **Price:** $8.95, PDF. **Description:** Four uses for new media include: communicating a clearly defined customer promise, creating trust via delivering on the promise, regularly improving on the promise, and innovating past what is familiar. **Availability:** Online; PDF.

20477 ■ Organizations Alive!: Six Things That Challenge - Seven That Bring Success
Pub: Yuill & Associates
Ed: Jan Yuill. **Price:** C$18.95, paperback. **Description:** New insight into understanding how organizations function as individuals is presented by an international consultant. Customer service, resource management, outsourcing, and management are among the issues covered.

20478 ■ "Outside In: The Power of Putting Customers at the Center of Your Business"
Description: Customer experience is the most powerful and least understood element of corporate strategy in today's business world. Customer experience is the way your customers perceive their interactions with a company. It drives sales and provides a competitive advantage. **Availability:** Audio.

20479 ■ "Pay or Play: Do Nice (Sales) Guys Finish Last?" in Agency Sales Magazine (Vol. 39, August 2009, No. 8, pp. 8)
Description: How positive interpersonal relationships among salespersons, program coordinators, and other business-related professions will pay in terms of business success is presented. Business people should know the ideal customers, promise only what they can do, refer out when needed, and follow through with any stated promise. Further insight into these ideas is presented. **Availability:** Online.

20480 ■ "Perfecting Customer Services" in Pet Product News (Vol. 64, November 2010, No. 11, pp. 18)
Ed: Alison Bour. **Description:** Pet supply retailers are encouraged to emphasize customer experience and sales representatives' knowledge of the store's product offerings to foster repeat business. Employee protocols could be implemented to improve customer interaction. Other guidelines on developing a pet supply retail environment that advances repeat business are presented. **Availability:** Online.

20481 ■ "Perfecting the Process: Creating a More Efficient Organization on Your Terms" in Black Enterprise (Vol. 41, October 2010, No. 3)
Pub: Earl G. Graves Ltd.
Contact: Earl Graves, Jr., President
Ed: Tamara E. Holmes. **Description:** More than ever, entrepreneurs need to identify new ways of doing business in a cost-effective manner in order to expand their companies, while remaining true to their customer demands. **Availability:** Online.

20482 ■ *"The Phone-Service Test: Call Centres"* in *Canadian Business* (Vol. 79, October 9, 2006, No. 20, pp. 137)

Pub: Rogers Media Inc.

Contact: Neil Spivak, Chief Executive Officer

Ed: Rachel Pulfer. **Description:** Suggestions to improve the customer services provided by airlines through call centers are discussed. **Availability:** Online.

20483 ■ *"The Power of Online"* in *Advertising Age* (Vol. 85, October 13, 2014, No. 21, pp. 4)

Pub: Crain Communications Inc.

Contact: Barry Asin, President

Description: According to Shop.org, online sales could increase by as much as 11 percent this holiday season. Retailers are not only focusing on when customers will start holiday shopping, but whether they will use online stores or shop at brick-and-mortar stores. Many retailers are expanding their online services using digital showrooms on their Websites. **Availability:** Online.

20484 ■ *"The Power of Purpose"* in *Journal of Business Strategy* (Vol. 35, May-June 2014, No. 3, pp. 55-58)

Pub: BNP Media

Contact: Harper Henderson, Owner Co-Chief Executive Officer

Description: Report states that the defining a corporation's highest purpose holds momentous importance in a business environment overwhelmed by short-termism. It is observed that the contemporary business environment greatly values the short-term financial results and ignores a corporation's true customer-centered purpose.

20485 ■ *"The Proven 3 Step Formula For Growing Retail Profits: Without Having to Resort to Coupons or Discount Sales"*

Pub: CreateSpace

Released: September 24, 2014. **Price:** $4.89, paperback. **Description:** Previously published under the name, "How Some Retailers Make More Money Than Others". Retailers, whether a franchise or independent brand face challenges for increasing sales. An explanation for growing customer base without mass advertising, how to increase each customers spending, and improve gross margins are reported. A proven three-step process for increasing retail profits without the use of coupons or discounts is provided. **Availability:** Print.

20486 ■ *"Providence Exec Explains Why the Deal with Boeing is the Way of the Future"* in *Puget Sound Business Journal* (Vol. 35, June 27, 2014, No. 10, pp. 6)

Pub: American City Business Journals, Inc.

Contact: Mike Olivieri, Executive Vice President

Description: Providence-Swedish Accountable Care Organization CEO, Joe Gifford, shares his views on the deal to provide health care to Boeing employees. Gifford says there is opportunity to grow the business if public image spreads showing they offer great quality and service in providing unique healthcare and benefits at a lower cost. Gifford believes meeting directly with the employer customer they create a direct loop of process improvement. **Availability:** Online.

20487 ■ *"Putting Customers' Wants First — Without Serving Bad Coffee"* in *Perfect Daily Grind* (August 2, 2017)

URL(s): www.perfectdailygrind.com/2017/08/putting-customers-wants-first-without-serving-bad-coffee/

Ed: Sam Koh. **Released:** August 02, 2017. **Description:** Baristas are often highly trained in the art of serving really good coffee, but what happens when a customer places an order that may not be that great, flavor-wise? Baristas need to provide great customer service as well, so they often have to delicately balance creating a great-tasting drink and not offending a paying customer. **Availability:** Online.

20488 ■ *"Reality Check at the Bottom of the Pyramid: To Succeed in the World's Poorest Markets, Aim For Much Higher Margins and Prices Than You Thought Were Necessary-Or Possible"* in *Harvard Business Review* (Vol. 90, June 2012, No. 6, pp. 120)

Pub: Harvard Business Review Press

Contact: Moderna V. Pfizer, Contact

Ed: Erik Simanis. **Price:** $8.95, hardcopy black and white. **Description:** Margin-enhancing platforms are identified. Bundling products increases customer access and enables firms to sell more in each transaction. Including services with products creates value for customers and raises each transaction's gross margin. Customer peer groups boost aggregate sales and as a result reduce costs. **Availability:** Print; Online; PDF.

20489 ■ *"Renters' Review ? Secret Shoppers Strike Again"* in *Rental Product News* (Vol. 33, June 2011)

Description: Staff of Rental Product News set out to rent various items from three different rental sources in order to evaluate the rental experience from the eyes of the average customer. **Availability:** Online.

20490 ■ *"Reps Have Needs Too!"* in *Agency Sales Magazine* (Vol. 39, December 2009, No. 11, pp. 16)

Description: There is common information that a sales representatives needs to know prior to choosing a manufacturer to represent. Both parties must keep promises made to customers and prospects. Reps also need the support from the manufacturers and to clear matters regarding their commission. Interviewing tips for representatives to get this vital information are presented. **Availability:** Online.

20491 ■ *"Rethinking the Organization"* in *Strategy & Leadership* (Vol. 38, September-October 2010, No. 5, pp. 13-19)

Pub: Emerald Inc.

Ed: Stephen Denning. **Description:** A study identifies the changes needed to be adopted by top managers to achieve game-changing innovation at an organization-wide level. Findings indicate that CEOs should practice pull management in order to nurture fruitful communication between employees and customers and achieve organizational involvement of customers. **Availability:** Print; PDF.

20492 ■ *Rework*

Ed: Jason Fried, David Heinemeier Hansson. **Released:** 2010. **Price:** $19.62, hardcover; $14.99, e-book; $9, audiobook. **Description:** Works to help entrepreneurs and business owners to rethink strategy, customers, and getting things accomplished. **Availability:** E-book; Print.

20493 ■ *"RIM Opts to Be Less Open"* in *Canadian Business* (Vol. 83, October 12, 2010, No. 17, pp. 13)

Pub: Rogers Media Inc.

Contact: Neil Spivak, Chief Executive Officer

Ed: Joe Castaldo. **Description:** RIM is planning to stop releasing quarterly subscriber updates. However, some analysts are skeptical about the change due to the previous drop in company subscribers. The company also decided to stop reporting the average selling price of the BlackBerry, which analysts have also scrutinized. **Availability:** Online.

20494 ■ *"RIM's Demise Stems from Arrogance: It Didn't Have To Come To This"* in *Canadian Business* (Vol. 85, August 13, 2012, No. 13, pp. 4)

Ed: James Cowan. **Description:** The business collapse of Research in Motion (RIM) was blamed on the management's arrogance in terms of recognizing that Apple's iPhone is dominating the consumer market and that corporate customers would remain loyal despite the emergence of better smartphones. It is speculated that the failure of RIM could lead to at least 5,000 job losses. **Availability:** Online.

20495 ■ *"Roger Hickel Contracting: Smoothing the Road for Owners"* in *Alaska Business Monthly* (Vol. 27, October 2011, No. 10, pp. 114)

Pub: Alaska Business Publishing Company Inc.

Contact: Charles Bell, Vice President, Sales and Marketing

E-mail: cbell@akbizmag.com

Ed: Gail West. **Description:** Profile of Roger Hickel and his contracting company that reports nearly $60 million annually in gross revenue. The firm focuses on customer service. **Availability:** Print; Online.

20496 ■ *"Rule of the Masses: Reinventing Fashion Via Crowdsourcing"* in *WWD* (Vol. 200, July 26, 2010, No. 17, pp. 1)

Pub: Conde Nast Publications

Contact: Agnes Chu, President

Ed: Cate T. Corcoran. **Description:** Large apparel brands and retailers are crowdsourcing as a way to increase customer loyalty and to build their businesses. **Availability:** PDF; Download; Online.

20497 ■ *"SEC Report On Rating Agencies Falls Short"* in *Barron's* (Vol. 88, July 14, 2008, No. 28, pp. 35)

Pub: Dow Jones & Company Inc.

Contact: Almar Latour, Chief Executive Officer

Ed: Jack Willoughby. **Description:** The Securities and Exchange Commissions report on credit-rating firms should have drawn attention to the slipshod practices in the offerings of collateralized debt obligations. The report fell short of prescribing correctives for the flawed system of these agencies' relationship with their clients. **Availability:** Online.

20498 ■ *"Seen & Noted: A Home's Identity in Black and White"* in *Crain's Chicago Business* (Vol. 31, April 21, 2008, No. 16, pp. 35)

Pub: Crain Communications Inc.

Contact: Barry Asin, President

Ed: Lisa Bertagnoli. **Description:** Real estate agents are finding that showing customers a written floor plan is a trend that is growing since many buyers feel that Online virtual tours distort a room. Although floor plans cost up to $500 to have drawn up, they clearly show potential buyers the exact dimensions of rooms and how they connect. **Availability:** Online.

20499 ■ *"Segmenting When It Matters"* in *Business Strategy Review* (Vol. 21, Spring 2010, No. 1, pp. 46)

Ed: Andreas Birnik, Richard Moat. **Released:** February 09, 2010. **Description:** Authors argue that business complexity is directly linked to the degree of segmentation implemented by a company. They propose an approach to map business activities at the segment level to make sure that complexity is only introduced when it really matters. **Availability:** Print; PDF; Online.

20500 ■ *"Serving Unfair Customers"* in *Business Horizons* (Vol. 51, January-February 2008, No. 1, pp. 29)

Pub: Elsevier Advanced Technology Publications

Ed: Leonard L. Berry, Kathleen Seiders. **Description:** Quality service is based on the maxim "the customer is always right", but customer behavior studies have revealed that customers can be glaringly unjust. These unfair customers exploit the customer service maxim, affecting both the company and other customers. Methods to effectively deal with unfair customers are explored. **Availability:** Print; Online.

20501 ■ *"Six Ways to Make Customer Programs Work; Most Customer Satisfaction Programs Aren't Effective. Two Consultants Explain Why and How Companies Can Fix Them"* in *Gallup Business Journal* (June 17, 2014)

Pub: Gallup, Inc.

Contact: Jon Clifton, Chief Executive Officer

Description: Consultants explain ways to help companies develop customer satisfaction programs that work. **Availability:** Print.

20502 ■ *Small Business Survival Guide*
Released: First edition. **Description:** Small business expert provides strategies to start a company and survive in the 21st Century. He shows small business owners how to succeed despite challenges that can defeat any firm. His advice covers suppliers; customers and contractors; competitors and creditors; spouses, family and friends; as well as the ways lawyers, accountants and other can steal an entrepreneur's success. Ennico also describes how startups can comply with local regulations. **Availability:** E-book; Print.

20503 ■ *"Smarts Drive Sales" in Pet Product News (Vol. 64, December 2010, No. 12, pp. 1)*
Ed: Karen Shugart. **Description:** Retailers could make smart decisions by deciding how to best attract customers into their stores or resolving whether to nurture in-store or buy herps (reptiles) from suppliers. Paying attention to these smart decisions could help boost customer interest in herps and address customer demands. **Availability:** Online.

20504 ■ *The Social Media Bible: Tactics, Tools, and Strategies for Business Success*
Pub: John Wiley & Sons, Inc.
Contact: Christina Van Tassell, Executive Vice President Chief Financial Officer
Ed: Lon Safko. **Released:** Third edition. **Price:** $29.95, paperback; $19.99, E-Book. **Description:** Information is given to build or transform a business into social media, where customers, employees, and prospects connect, collaborate, and champion products and services in order to increase sales and to beat the competition. **Availability:** E-book; Print.

20505 ■ *"Solutions for the Frustrating Feline" in Pet Product News (Vol. 64, November 2010, No. 11, pp. 46)*
Ed: Lori Luechtefeld. **Description:** Products that can help customers deal with problematic cat behaviors, such as out-of-the-box urination and scratching are described. Information on such products including litter box deodorants and disposable scratchers is provided. Feline territorial behaviors can also be addressed by pheromone products that can calm hyperactive cats. **Availability:** Online.

20506 ■ *"Sometimes You Have to Ignore the Rule Book" in Canadian Business (Vol. 83, September 14, 2010, No. 15, pp. 13)*
Pub: Rogers Media Inc.
Contact: Neil Spivak, Chief Executive Officer
Ed: Richard Branson. **Released:** September 14, 2010. **Description:** The rule book has provided a clear framework for employees particularly when cash and accounting are at issue. However, sometimes rules were made to be broken and the rule book should not become an excuse for poor customer service or hinder great service. How Virgin Atlantic practices this type of corporate culture is discussed. **Availability:** Print; Online.

20507 ■ *"Sound Check" in Agency Sales Magazine (Vol. 39, August 2009, No. 8, pp. 14)*
Description: Most customers believe salespersons are unable to do well in terms of listening, which is one of the four fundamental competencies of a sales person. Listening is the primary tool to uncover deeper and more powerful needs and motivations of the customer. A guide on how to listen better and improve listening effectiveness is presented. **Availability:** Online.

20508 ■ *"Sponsorships, Booths Available for Business Showcase" in Bellingham Business Journal (February 2010, pp. 3)*
Pub: Sound Publishing Inc.
Contact: Josh O'Connor, President
Ed: Lance Henderson. **Description:** Third Annual Spring Business Showcase still have space available for vendors and sponsors. The event gives local businesses the opportunity to increase their visibility and provides a means to increase sales and build relationships.

20509 ■ *"Stop Trying to Delight Your Customers" in Harvard Business Review (Vol. 88, July-August 2010, No. 7-8, pp. 116)*
Pub: Harvard Business Publishing
Contact: Diane Belcher, Managing Director
Ed: Matthew Dixon, Karen Freeman, Nicholas Toman. **Price:** $8.95, PDF. **Description:** Importance of resolving issues for customers is key to increasing their loyalty, rather than by exceeding customer expectations. Areas to address include decreasing customer need for follow-up calls, switching service channels, and the potential for negative emotional response. **Availability:** Online; PDF.

20510 ■ *"Stress-Test Your Strategy: the 7 Questions to Ask" in Harvard Business Review (Vol. 88, November 2010, No. 11, pp. 92)*
Pub: Harvard Business Publishing
Contact: Diane Belcher, Managing Director
Ed: Robert Simons. **Price:** $8.95, PDF. **Description:** Seven questions organizations should use to assess crisis management capabilities are: who is the primary customer, how do core values prioritize all parties, what performance variables are being tracked, what strategic boundaries have been set, how is creative tension being produced, how committed are workers to assisting each other, and what uncertainties are causing worry?. **Availability:** Online; PDF.

20511 ■ *"The Surprising Things You Can Do With CRM" in Small Business Trends (September 13, 2022)*
URL(s): smallbiztrends.com/2022/09/surprising-things-you-can-do-with-crm.html
Ed: Michael Guta. **Released:** September 13, 2022. **Description:** Interview with Vibhav Vankayala and Dilip Nagrajaran as they discuss how small businesses and utilize CRM (Customer Relationship Management) software. **Availability:** Online.

20512 ■ *"Tailoring Is the Secret of Well-Dressed Women" in The Wall Street Journal (December 11, 2013)*
URL(s): www.wsj.com/articles/tailoring-is-the-secret-of-welldressed-women-1386810054
Ed: Christina Binkley. **Released:** December 11, 2013. **Description:** With cheap clothing being bought, many people do not care if their clothes fit them well. Tailoring is slowly fading away across the nation as more men bypass the industry, but women have been requiring more tailoring to achieve a professional work look. Once a piece has been fixed, consumers often go back because the clothes fit better and it can often save money in the long run. **Availability:** Online.

20513 ■ *"Take This Job and Love It" in Green Industry Pro (Vol. 23, October 2011)*
Ed: Gregg Wartgow. **Description:** Details of the lawsuit filed by the Professional Landcare Network (PLANET) against the U.S. Department of Labor are explained. Challenges faced by landscape firms because of employment costs are outlined. Statistical data included. **Availability:** PDF; Online.

20514 ■ *"Tapping the 'Well' in Wellness" in Pet Product News (Vol. 64, November 2010, No. 11, pp. 1)*
Ed: Wendy Bedwell-Wilson. **Description:** Healthy food and treats are among the leading wellness products being sought by customers from specialty retailers to keep their pets healthy. With this demand for pet wellness products, retailers suggest making sure that staff know key ingredients to emphasize to customers. Other insights into this trend and ways to engage customers are discussed. **Availability:** Online.

20515 ■ *"Teachable Moments: Worth Every Penny" in Pet Product News (Vol. 64, December 2010, No. 12, pp. 34)*
Ed: Cheryl Reeves. **Description:** Pet bird retailers can attain both outreach to customers and enhanced profitability by staging educational events such as the annual Parrot Palooza event of Burlington, New Jersey-based Bird Paradise. Aside from attracting a global audience, Parrot Palooza features seminars, workshops, classes, and bird-related contests. **Availability:** Print; Online.

20516 ■ *"There's Risk, Reward for Business in Baltimore's Edgier Areas: Taking a Chance" in Baltimore Business Journal (Vol. 28, July 16, 2010, No. 10, pp. 1)*
Pub: Baltimore Business Journal
Contact: Rhonda Pringle, President
E-mail: rpringle@bizjournals.com
Ed: Scott Dance. **Description:** North Avenue in Baltimore, Maryland is considered a rough neighborhood due to the dangers of prostitution and drug dealing. However, some entrepreneurs have taken the risk of building their businesses on North Avenue as revitalization efforts grow. One of the challenges for businesses in rough neighborhoods is bringing customers to their stores or offices. **Availability:** Print.

20517 ■ *"Three Megatrends to Help Your Business Compete in 2014" in South Florida Business Journal (Vol. 34, January 3, 2014, No. 24, pp. 10)*
Pub: American City Business Journals, Inc.
Contact: Mike Olivieri, Executive Vice President
Released: Weekly. **Price:** $8, Introductory 4-week offer(Digital & Print). **Description:** Businesses can improve their competitive edge in 2014 by adapting several mega small business trends in marketing and communications. Brands can use brand bridging to get customers attention, use wearable technology to increase their value, and adapt environmental sustainability and corporate social responsibility to keep their customers. **Availability:** Print; Online.

20518 ■ *"Time to Tweet: Banks and Fun, Benefits in Social Media" in Philadelphia Business Journal (Vol. 31, February 24, 2012, No. 2, pp. 1)*
Pub: Baltimore Business Journal
Contact: Rhonda Pringle, President
E-mail: rpringle@bizjournals.com
Description: Pennsylvania-based banks have benefited from the use of social media to market their services. TD Bank used Twitter to respond to customer complaints. Citizens Bank uses Twitter to provide customers with financial tips. **Availability:** Print.

20519 ■ *"To Keep Your Customers, Keep It Simple: They Don't Want a 'Relationship' With You. Just Help Them Make Good Choices" in Harvard Business Review (Vol. 90, May 2012, No. 5, pp. 108)*
Pub: Harvard Business Review Press
Contact: Moderna V. Pfizer, Contact
Ed: Patrick Spenner, Karen Freeman. **Price:** $8.95. **Description:** Rather than attempt to engage consumers via social media, firms instead should simplify the customer's decision making and assist them through the purchase process. Tips include minimizing the number of purchase-process steps providing reliable product information, and enabling them to easily weigh their options. **Availability:** Online; PDF.

20520 ■ *"The Top 10 Customer Service Blogs for Businesses" in FORA Financial Blog (Oct. 22, 2020)*
URL(s): www.forafinancial.com/blog/small-business/customer-service-blogs/
Released: October 22, 2020. **Description:** Discusses the importance of keeping up with customer service best practices and includes 10 customer service blogs that all small business owners should read. **Availability:** Online.

20521 ■ *Trade-Off: The Ever-Present Tension Between Quality and Conscience*
Released: August 17, 2010. **Price:** $15. **Description:** The tension between fidelity (the quality of a consumer's experience) and convenience (the ease

of getting and paying for a product) are shown to be the forces that determine the success or failure of new products and services in the marketplace.

20522 ■ *"The Transparent Supply Chain"* in *Harvard Business Review (Vol. 88, October 2010, No. 10, pp. 76)*
Pub: Harvard Business Publishing
Contact: Diane Belcher, Managing Director
Ed: Steve New. **Price:** $8.95, PDF. **Description:** Examination of the use of new technologies to create a transparent supply chain, such as next-generation 2D bar codes in clothing labels that can provide data on a garment's provenance. **Availability:** Online; PDF.

20523 ■ *"Trouble Getting Customers to Pay?"* in *Legal Zoom (March 22, 2023)*
URL(s): www.legalzoom.com/articles/trouble-getting-customers-to-pay
Ed: Heleigh Botswick. **Released:** March 22, 2023. **Description:** There may come a time when your small business gets taken advantage of by a customer who refuses to pay for your goods or services. What are your options in a situation like this? Advice is given to deal with these customers. **Availability:** Online.

20524 ■ *"True Value Ranks No. 1 in National Customer Service Poll"* in *Hardware Retailing (November 1, 2019)*
URL(s): www.hardwareretailing.com/true-value-ranks-no-1-in-national-customer-service-poll/
Ed: Todd Taber. **Released:** November 01, 2019. **Description:** Topping Newsweek's 2020 list of America's Best Customer Service Brands in the "Home Improvement Stores" category is True Value. Their commitment to customer care has led to a trustworthy brand that customers come back to over and over again. **Availability:** Online.

20525 ■ *"Tsingtao's Chairman On Jump-Starting a Sluggish Company"* in *Harvard Business Review (Vol. 90, April 2012, No. 4, pp. 41)*
Pub: Harvard Business Review Press
Contact: Moderna V. Pfizer, Contact
Ed: Jin Zhiguo. **Description:** The key challenge Tsingtao Brewery Company Ltd. faced was the focus on pleasing corporate superiors, rather than the firm's customers. By inventing a new model, the brewery was able to boost both employee productivity and product quality. First half profits and revenue for 2011 grew more than 20 percent over the previous year.

20526 ■ *The Ultimate Guide to Small Business Customer Service*
URL(s): www.helpscout.com/blog/small-business-customer-service/
Ed: Jesse Short. **Description:** Discusses the importance of customer service for small businesses, provides 5 strategies and 13 tips to increase your customer service experience, and includes 3 approaches to scaling support for small businesses. **Availability:** Online.

20527 ■ *"The View from the Field: Six Leaders Offer Their Perspectives On Sales Success"* in *(Vol. 90, July-August 2012, No. 7-8, pp. 101)*
Pub: Harvard Business Review Press
Contact: Moderna V. Pfizer, Contact
Ed: Jim Koch, James Farley, Susan Silbermann, Duncan Mac Naughton, Phil Guido, Suresh Goklaney. **Price:** $8.95. **Description:** Six business leaders provide their perspectives on successful selling. Common themes include engaging customers and seeking their input, personalizing their services, ensuring accountability, implementing community outreach, being mindful of cultural and regulatory issues, providing unique offerings, incorporating experiential learning, and properly identifying a customer's needs. **Availability:** Online; PDF.

20528 ■ *"Vote Count Chocula in 2014"* in *Canadian Business (Vol. 87, July 2014, No. 7, pp. 28)*
Released: July 2014. **Description:** The current state of political marketing is criticized for exploiting the weaknesses of both the press and the electorate and is compared to brand marketing. The soul of brand marketing is perpetual accountability and marketers are expected to make sure that consumers are not disappointed.

20529 ■ *"What is a CRM System and What Can It Do for Small Businesses?"* in *Small Business Trends (August 30, 2022)*
URL(s): smallbiztrends.com/2022/08/what-does-a-crm-do.html
Ed: Holly Chavez. **Released:** August 30, 2022. **Description:** Interview with Dilip Nagarajan, product manager of Zoho CRM, as he discusses what is CRM (Customer Relationship Management) software and how it can be used by your small business. **Availability:** Online.

20530 ■ *"What Marketers Misunderstand about Online Reviews: Managers Must Analyze What's Really Driving Buying Decisions - and Adjust Their Strategies Accordingly"* in *Harvard Business Review (Vol. 92, January-February 2014, No. 1-2, pp. 23)*
Pub: Harvard Business Press
Contact: Gabriela Allmi, Regional Manager
E-mail: gabriela.allmi@hbsp.harvard.edu
Price: $6, hardcopy black and white. **Description:** Companies may overestimate the influence of online reviews, as consumers do not turn to reviews for certain products and services (for example, habitual low-involvement purchases such as groceries). Others' opinions matter more for purchases such as independent restaurants and electronics. **Availability:** Print; PDF; Online.

20531 ■ *"Why Business Focus Is a Crucial Entrepreneurial Talent; Successful Entrepreneurs are Profit-Oriented and Judge the Value of Decisions and Relationships By Their Effect On Business"* in *Gallup Business Journal (June 10, 2014)*
Pub: Gallup, Inc.
Contact: Jon Clifton, Chief Executive Officer
Description: Entrepreneurial traits and skills are highlighted. Successful business owners focus on profit and understand the value of an opportunity, relationship, or a decision can impact their business. It is critical, while focusing on profit, to never underestimate the value of a customer. **Availability:** Print; Online.

20532 ■ *"Why Customer Engagement Matters So Much Now; Wary Consumers Will Give More Money to the Businesses they Feel Emotionally Connected To -- While Ignoring Others"* in *Gallup Business Journal (July 22, 2014)*
Pub: Gallup, Inc.
Contact: Jon Clifton, Chief Executive Officer
Description: Gallup's daily tracking of the U.S. economy shows signs of recovery since the crash of 2008. When Americans purchase goods or services, they tend to choose businesses they feel emotionally connected to and might even ignore those that provide no value to them. They expect a company to earn their money. **Availability:** Print; Online.

20533 ■ *"Why Loyalty Programs Alienate Great Customers"* in *Harvard Business Review (Vol. 90, July-August 2012, No. 7-8, pp. 38)*
Pub: Harvard Business Review Press
Contact: Moderna V. Pfizer, Contact
Ed: Hal Brierley. **Price:** $6. **Description:** Airline loyalty programs should replace the mileage metric with money spent, and should also extend rewards to second-tier customers. Rewars should also be accessible sooner, and retirees should be granted emeritus status. **Availability:** Online; PDF.

20534 ■ *"Why Your Company Must Be Mission-Driven; A Clear Mission Inspires Employee Engagement, Fosters Customer Engagement, and Helps Boost Company Performance -- Among Other Benefits"* in *Gallup Business Journal (March 6, 2014)*
Pub: Gallup, Inc.
Contact: Jon Clifton, Chief Executive Officer
Description: It is stressed that executives need a clear mission in order to engage their workers, foster customer engagement, and to help boost their firm's performance. **Availability:** Print; Online.

20535 ■ *"Who's On Top in the Telecom Turf Fight"* in *Dallas Business Journal (Vol. 37, April 25, 2014, No. 33, pp. 4)*
Pub: American City Business Journals, Inc.
Contact: Mike Olivieri, Executive Vice President
Released: Weekly. **Price:** $4, introductory 4-week offer(Digital & Print). **Description:** The four major wireless providers in the U.S. are competing for customers in North Texas and around the country. Experts say AT&T, Verizon, Sprint and T-Mobile have to offer better quality services, faster service and lower pricing to win customers from each other. **Availability:** Print; Online.

TRADE PERIODICALS

20536 ■ *Journal of Relationship Marketing*
Pub: Taylor And Francis Group
Contact: Annie Callanan, Chief Executive Officer
URL(s): www.tandfonline.com/journals/wjrm20
Ed: David Bejou, PhD. **Released:** Quarterly **Price:** $1,165, Institutions for print & online; $255, Individuals for print & online; $223, Individuals for online only; $955, Institutions for online only. **Description:** Journal on marketing. **Availability:** Print; Download; PDF; Online.

VIDEO/AUDIO MEDIA

20537 ■ *The Best Small Business Show: Delighting Your Customers - Taking the Customer Experience to the Next Level*
URL(s): richgee.libsyn.com/315-delighting-your-customers-taking-the-customer-experience-to-the-next-level
Ed: rich Gee. **Released:** October 02, 2023. **Description:** Podcast focuses on the customer experience.

20538 ■ *The Best Small Business Show: Friction - The Expectation of Seamless Customer Experiences*
URL(s): richgee.libsyn.com/294-friction-the-expectation-of-seamless-customer-experiences
Ed: Rich Gee. **Released:** May 08, 2023. **Description:** Podcast discusses the customer experience expectations.

20539 ■ *This Is Small Business: How to Provide Great Customer Service*
URL(s): www.smallbusiness.amazon/podcast-episodes/ep-37-how-to-provide-great-customer-service
Released: October 17, 2023. **Description:** Podcast offers tips on providing excellent customer service no matter where you are in your small business journey.

TRADE SHOWS AND CONVENTIONS

20540 ■ Call and Contact Center Expo USA
URL(s): www.callandcontactcenterexpo.us
Facebook: www.facebook.com/Call-Contact-Center-Expo-US-105546980792676
X (Twitter): twitter.com/CallContactUS
Frequency: Annual. **Description:** Education and talks for the customer service industry. **Principal Exhibits:** Education and talks for the customer service industry.

CONSULTANTS

20541 ■ Advantage Group International
20 Toronto St. 6th Fl.
Toronto, ON, Canada M5C 2B8
Ph: (416)863-0685
URL: http://www.advantagegroup.com
Contact: John McLoughlin, Chief Executive Officer
E-mail: jmcloughlin@advantagegroup.com
Linkedin: www.linkedin.com/company/441758
YouTube: www.youtube.com/channel/UC6hnG0alVILvPbhkXKGmlog
Description: Specializes in two key areas performance benchmarking and pricing strategy. Each stream has developed a wide variety of customizable proprietary research tools to meet the needs of the clients. **Scope:** Specializes in two key areas performance benchmarking and pricing strategy. Each stream has developed a wide variety of customizable proprietary research tools to meet the needs of the clients. **Founded:** 1988. **Publications:** "7 Steps to building better customer relationships"; "How to Add Value to Customer Relationships"; "Top 10 Key Benefits of Building Business Relationships"; "Tips for Creating Better Relationships"; "Building Trust in Personal and Business Relationships"; "The Advantage Report Canadian Grocer"; "Customer Relationships"; "Customer Relationship Management: What it is and What it's not"; "The Advantage Report - Measuring the supplier-retailer relationship".

20542 ■ The Benchmarking Network, Inc. (TBN)
Houston, TX 77069-9949
Ph: (281)440-5044
Free: 888-323-6246
Fax: (281)440-6677
URL: http://benchmarkingnetwork.com
Facebook: www.facebook.com/profile.php
X (Twitter): twitter.com/benchmarkingnet
Description: Works to promote benchmarking among members. Provides networking services and information. **Scope:** Provider of measures and metrics expertise, training, research, and implementation in support of process improvement, reengineering efforts and six sigma programs. Industries served: service, manufacturing, financial, retail, telecommunications, utilities, insurance, information systems, and healthcare. **Founded:** 1992. **Training:** Benchmarking - Introduction; Benchmarking - Advanced Topics; Customer Satisfaction Measurement; Total Quality Management; New Product Development as well as others; Over a dozen annual networking meetings targeting various industries or business processes. **Geographic Preference:** National; Multinational.

20543 ■ Business Ventures Corp.
3883 Rogers Bridge Rd., Ste. 205-B
Duluth, GA 30097
Contact: King Ruth Anne, Chief Executive Officer
Description: Private equity firm provides investment services. **Scope:** Private equity firm provides investment services. **Publications:** "The Ugly Truth about Managing People," 2007; "The Ugly Truth about Small Business," 2006; "How to Write a Business Plan," Atlanta Business Chronicle; "Ask 10 Questions Before You Begin Your Business," Income Opportunities "HVAC Bookkeeping and Financial Statements"; "Service Manager's Guide to Running a Profitable Service Department"; "HVAC Career Training Manual"; "Technician's Procedures Manual"; "HVAC Residential Pricing Manual"; "21 Ways to Keep the Honest People Honest Manual"; "Keeping Score: Financial Management for Entrepreneurs"; "Keeping Score: Improving Contractor Productivity and Profitability"; "Keeping Score: Financial Management for Contractors". **Training:** The Seven Rules for Business Success; The Seven Greatest Lies of Small Business; Understanding the Financial Side of Business; Small Business Marketing; Strategic Business Planning.

20544 ■ Creative Concepts International, Inc. (CCI)
108 Eagle Glen Dr.
Woodstock, GA 30189
Ph: (404)630-1712
URL: http://www.geneswindell.com
Contact: Gene Swindell, Contact
E-mail: gene@geneswindell.com
Description: Services: Leadership and motivational training. **Scope:** Services: Leadership and motivational training. **Founded:** 1979. **Training:** Leadership for Mastering Change; Quality Customer Service; Team building That Works; Coach Management; Customer Service is Your Only Business; Consultative Sales; Team Dynamics.

20545 ■ Don Phin, Esq.
114 C. Ave., No. 200
Coronado, CA 92118
Ph: (619)852-4580
URL: http://www.donphin.com
Contact: Don Phin, Contact
E-mail: don@donphin.com
Linkedin: www.linkedin.com/in/donphin
X (Twitter): x.com/donphin12
YouTube: www.youtube.com/donphin
Description: Firm is engaged in consulting services on training, coaching and mentoring for the individuals and small businesses. **Scope:** Firm is engaged in consulting services on training, coaching and mentoring for the individuals and small businesses. **Founded:** 1983. **Publications:** "Doing Business Right!"; "HR That Works!"; "Lawsuit Free! How to Prevent Employee Lawsuits"; "Building Powerful Employment Relationships!"; "Victims, Villains and Heroes: Managing Emotions in The Workplace". **Training:** Doing Business Right!; HR That Works!; Building Powerful Employment Relationships; Lawsuit Free!.

20546 ■ Howick Associates
4906 Wakanda Dr.
Waunakee, WI 53597
Ph: (608)284-8416
Co. E-mail: info@howickassociates.com
URL: http://howickassociates.com
Contact: Drew Howick, Chief Executive Officer
Description: Firm is engaged in organizational development and serves businesses such as advertising, broadcasting, entertainment and their services include performance assessment, executive retreats, team building, growing talent, executive team coaching, conflict resolution, and values integration. **Scope:** Firm is engaged in organizational development and serves businesses such as advertising, broadcasting, entertainment and their services include performance assessment, executive retreats, team building, growing talent, executive team coaching, conflict resolution, and values integration. **Founded:** 1984. **Publications:** "The New Compleat Facilitator: A Handbook for Facilitators". **Training:** The Complete Virtual; Enhancing Your Presentation Style; Perceptive Communications; Listening; Effective Meeting Skills; Strategic Thinking and Planning; Performance Measurement; Facilitation Skills.

20547 ■ Joe Turner
3135 Adams St.
Denver, CO 80205
Contact: Joel Turner, Contact
Description: Provider of customer service consulting, materials, software and training for the new home industry. Specializes in construction defect litigation. Specific problem solving, including recruiting, validating employment information, meeting with homeowners and strategic assessment are available. Produces homeowner manuals for builders and developers. **Scope:** Provider of customer service consulting, materials, software and training for the new home industry. Specializes in construction defect litigation. Specific problem solving, including recruiting, validating employment information, meeting with homeowners and strategic assessment are available. Produces homeowner manuals for builders and developers. **Founded:** 1982. **Training:** TeamTraks.

20548 ■ Kutler Consultants
1420 Locust St., Ste. 35Q
Philadelphia, PA 19102
Contact: Edwin Kutler, Owner
Description: Merchandise operations management consultants whose focus is on maximizing customer service and profitability through effective inventory management-assuring that quality merchandise, properly packaged, is in the right place at the right time and to fill customer orders immediately. **Scope:** Merchandise operations management consultants whose focus is on maximizing customer service and profitability through effective inventory management-assuring that quality merchandise, properly packaged, is in the right place at the right time and to fill customer orders immediately.

20549 ■ Lieber & Associates
3740 N Lake Shore Dr., Ste. 15B-2
Chicago, IL 60613-4202
Ph: (773)325-9400
Fax: (773)325-0621
Co. E-mail: info@lieberandassociates.com
URL: http://www.lieberandassociates.com/Lieber-and-Associates-Call-Center-Consultants-Home.html
Contact: Mitchell Lieber, President
Facebook: www.facebook.com/LieberAndAssociates
Linkedin: www.linkedin.com/company/lieber-&-associates-contact-and-call-center-consultants
Description: Provider of telephone and database marketing, telecommunication technology, and call center services. **Scope:** Provider of telephone and database marketing, telecommunication technology, and call center services. **Founded:** 1984. **Publications:** "BTB, Inbound Regulation on Horizon," DM News, May, 2006; "ATA Summit: Be Proactive on Regulation," DM News, Apr, 2006; "Contact and Call Centers Today," 2005; "Six Ways to Conduct Successful Telemarketing in a Do-Not-Call World," Oct, 2004; "How to Integrate Telephone and Direct Marketing," 1993. **Training:** How to Integrate Telephone and Direct Marketing; Outsourcing Nuts and Bolts; How to Measure and Manage Telemarketing; How to Integrate Telephone, Direct and Internet Marketing-30 Ideas; Repackaging Tele services-A Public Image Make-Over; Transforming your Call Center into a Contact Center; Three Paradigm Shifts that are Changing Tele services Today.

20550 ■ McDargh Communications
33465 Dosinia Dr.
Dana Point, CA 92629
Ph: (949)496-8640
Co. E-mail: eileen@eileenmcdargh.com
URL: http://www.eileenmcdargh.com
Contact: Eileen McDargh, Contact
E-mail: eileen@eileenmcdargh.com
Description: Provides management communications consulting for team building, management communication and training in a variety of communication-related skills facilitates management retreats. **Scope:** Provides management communications consulting for team building, management communication and training in a variety of communication-related skills facilitates management retreats. **Founded:** 1980. **Publications:** "The Spirit of Nurse Leadership"; "Burn out, Balance & Bounty"; "Books: Work for a Living and Still Be Free to Live"; "The Resilient Spirit"; "Off the Chart Results"; "A Woman's Way to Incredible Success"; "Meditations for the Road Warrior"; "Talk Ain't Cheap...It's Priceless"; "Gifts from the Mountain". **Training:** Work for a Living and Still Be Free to Live; The Energy Connection.

20551 ■ The Plotkin Group
5650 El Camino Real, Ste. 223
Carlsbad, CA 92008
Ph: (760)603-8791
Free: 800-877-5685
URL: http://www.plotkingroup.com
Contact: Hank Plotkin, Founder
Description: Provider of employee assessment solutions and services. **Scope:** Provider of employee assessment solutions and services. **Founded:** 1968. **Publications:** "Building a Winning Team"; "Achieving Above and Beyond Service"; "American Businesses Face Mountain of Problems". **Training:** Building a Winning Team; Above and Beyond Customer Service Training; Taking the Guess Work Out of Hiring and Promoting.

20552 ■ Retail Management Consultants
Carlsbad, CA

Description: Engaged in helping retail organizations become more efficient, productive and profitable. Consulting services include advertising and marketing, employee training programs, customer service improvement and customer research. Industries served: All segments of the retail industry. **Scope:** Engaged in helping retail organizations become more efficient, productive and profitable. Consulting services include advertising and marketing, employee training programs, customer service improvement and customer research. Industries served: All segments of the retail industry. **Founded:** 1987. **Training:** Retail Success!; Great Store Managers Make Great Stores!; Competition: Powerful trends that are changing what people buy, how they buy, and where they buy!; Stop, Look, Touch, and Buy: The Dynamics of Merchandising; Double Your Sales and Triple Your Profits with High-Impact Marketing and Promotions!; Every Customer Every Day; Customer Focused Selling; Competition? What Competition! Standing Out in Today's Competitive Retail Marketplace; How to Find an Eagle in a Flock of Turkeys! Finding, Hiring, and Keeping the BEST Retail Employees; Double Your Sales and Triple Your Profits with High-Impact Marketing and Promotions!; Customer-Direct Marketing: Increase Retail Sales with High-Impact Direct Mail and E-Mail; Power, Punch and Pizzazz! Create Advertising that Grabs Customer Attention and Sells More Merchandise; 12 Powerful Advertising Secrets Every Retailer Should Know; Great Store Managers Make Great Stores!; Into the Future! Powerful Trends Shaping the Future of Retailing.

20553 ■ Service Quality Institute (SQI)
9201 E Bloomington Fwy.
Minneapolis, MN 55420
Ph: (952)884-3311
Free: 800-548-0538
Co. E-mail: quality@servicequality.com
URL: http://customer-service.com
Contact: John Tschohl, President
Facebook: www.facebook.com/servicequalityinstitute.US

Description: Offers customer service training. It provides 30 customers service training programs that businesses can pick and choose from to improve the quality of customer care. **Scope:** Offers customer service training. It provides 30 customers service training programs that businesses can pick and choose from to improve the quality of customer care. **Founded:** 1972. **Publications:** "Achieving Excellence Through Customer Service," Bestsellers Publishers; "Ca$hing In: Get Promoted, Make More Money, Love Your Job," Bestsellers Publishing; "The Spirit of Excellence"; "Servicio Al Cliente". **Training:** E-Service; Achieving Excellence Through Customer Service; Cashing In Feelings; Leading Empowered Teams for Service Quality; Exceptional Service; Attaining Excellence by Keeping More Customers; Customer Service Excellence; Five Star Service; Creating a Service Culture Strategy; Leading Empowered Teams.

20554 ■ Vanguard Communications Corp.
45 S Park Pl., Ste. 210
Morristown, NJ 07960
URL: http://www.vanguard.it

Description: Independent consulting company concentrating on call centers and other customer interaction capabilities including web, IVR and other self-service and assisted service opportunities. **Scope:** Independent consulting company concentrating on call centers and other customer interaction capabilities including web, IVR and other self-service and assisted service opportunities. **Founded:** 1980. **Publications:** "Needed: Better Communications for Unified Communications," VON Magazine, Sep, 2007; "Features, Advantages and Benefits of Unified Communications," ON Magazine, Aug, 2007. **Training:** Leading Practices in IVR Design: Turn Your IVR from a Liability to an Asset, Nov, 2009; Speech in The Customer Intimate Contact Center, Aug, 2009; Meeting Business Goals with Speech Technology: Cross Channel User Experience, Aug, 2008; Improve Your Customer Experience Through a Seamless Multi-Channel Approach, Feb, 2008; Technological Change: What Every Senior Financial Leader Should Know, Oct, 2007.

20555 ■ Your Writing Partner
1415 W Lunt No. 502
Chicago, IL 60626
URL: http://yourwritingpartner.net
Contact: Andy Nathan, Officer
Facebook: www.facebook.com/people/Your-Writing-Partner/100066455439716
X (Twitter): x.com/PartnerWriting

Description: Professional editorial service that also specializes in book layout, cover design and print recommendations, the company serves as a one-stop shop for authors and specializes in website, annual report, article, training material, and marketing material editing and design consultation services. **Publications:** "Writing for Big Results," Jan, 2008; "Writing Skills for the College-Bound Student "; "Don't Let Your Participles Dangle in Public," 2005; "Business Etiquette and Professionalism"; "Handling Diversity in the Workplace: Communication is the Key"; "How to Provide Excellent Service in Any Organization"; "Loving Mr. Lincoln". **Training:** Business Etiquette and Professionalism; Understanding and Communicating With Others; Politically Correct and Profitable Writing Skills; Setting the Stage for Excellent Service; The Art of Successful Presentations; Friendly Fire: How Being Your Own Sweet Self Can Burn Others; Ideas Into Action: How to Keep All Those Good Conference Ideas From Going to Waste; Management and Supervisory Skills; How to Proofread Like a Pro; How to Excel at Editing; Grammar for Grownups; Writing for Today's Busy Readers (and Writers); Grammar For Youth; Writing Skills For College-Bound Students.

20556 ■ Ziglar Inc.
5055 W Pk. Blvd., Ste. 700
Plano, TX 75093
Free: 800-527-0306
Fax: (469)326-7556
Co. E-mail: csell@ziglar.com
URL: http://www.ziglar.com
Facebook: www.facebook.com/ZigZiglar
Linkedin: www.linkedin.com/company/ziglar-inc
X (Twitter): x.com/TheZigZiglar
Instagram: www.instagram.com/thezigziglar
YouTube: www.youtube.com/channel/UCWd_FBG3nwrVVCP13AW1sNw

Description: Offers management planning, strategic planning, team building, skills assessment, and custom training to provide clients with the tools to build their business. **Scope:** Offers management planning, strategic planning, team building, skills assessment, and custom training to provide clients with the tools to build their business. **Founded:** 1970. **Publications:** "Better Than Good"; "Embrace the Struggle"; "God's Way Is Still the Best Way"; "Life Lifters"; "Secrets Of Closing The Sale"; "Raising Positive Kids In a Negative World"; "Ziglar on Selling"; "Over the Top"; "Qualities of Success"; "Changing the Picture"; "One Step at a Time". **Training:** Get Motivated, Salt Lake City, Jun, 2010; Born to win; Get Motivated; Ziglar Sales System; Essential Presentation Skills: Custom Curricula.

COMPUTER SYSTEMS/ SOFTWARE

20557 ■ *Measuring Customer Satisfaction*
Crisp Learning
10650 Toebben Dr.
Independence, KY 41051
Free: 800-354-9706
Fax: (800)487-8488
URL: http://www.cengage.com
Price: Paperback. **Description:** Based on the Measuring Customer Satisfaction video and book. Includes book and user's guide. **Availability:** E-book; Print; Download; Online.

Discrimination/Sexual Harassment

EDUCATIONAL PROGRAMS

20558 ■ Employment Discrimination Law Update (Onsite)
Seminar Information Service Inc. (SIS)
 250 El Camino Real., Ste. 112
 Tustin, CA 92780
Ph: (714)508-0340
Free: 877-736-4636
Fax: (714)734-8027
Co. E-mail: info@seminarinformation.com
URL: http://www.seminarinformation.com
Contact: Catherine Bellizzi, President
URL(s): www.seminarinformation.com/qqadfh/employment-discrimination-law-update
Description: Topics include the Civil Rights Act of 1991, changes in EEO law and enforcement, sexual harassment, resolving claims and implementing the ADA, and the FMLA. **Audience:** Employers, human resource professionals and counsel. **Principal Exhibits:** Topics include the Civil Rights Act of 1991, changes in EEO law and enforcement, sexual harassment, resolving claims and implementing the ADA, and the FMLA.

20559 ■ Harassment Prevention and Appropriate Behaviors in the Workplace (Onsite)
Seminar Information Service Inc. (SIS)
 250 El Camino Real., Ste. 112
 Tustin, CA 92780
Ph: (714)508-0340
Free: 877-736-4636
Fax: (714)734-8027
Co. E-mail: info@seminarinformation.com
URL: http://www.seminarinformation.com
Contact: Catherine Bellizzi, President
URL(s): www.seminarinformation.com/details.cfm?qc=qqaqur
Description: Explore the legal and policy concerns related to this complex workplace issue, including review and explore the guidelines for identifying inappropriate behavior; the laws, agency interpretations and court cases; and the key elements necessary for writing and implementing policies and procedures. **Audience:** Human resource professionals. **Principal Exhibits:** Explore the legal and policy concerns related to this complex workplace issue, including review and explore the guidelines for identifying inappropriate behavior; the laws, agency interpretations and court cases; and the key elements necessary for writing and implementing policies and procedures.

REFERENCE WORKS

20560 ■ "Blindspot: Hidden Biases of Good People"
Pub: Ballantine/ Del Rey/Fawcett/Ivy Books
Contact: Matt Shatz, Contact
E-mail: mshatz@randomhouse.com
Released: February 12, 2013. **Price:** $14, paperback; $14.50, Hardcover. **Description:** Perceptions of social groups that shape our likes and dislikes and our judgments about people's character, abilities and potential include exposure to and attitudes about age, gender, race, ethnicity, religion, social class, sexuality, disability status, and nationality are examined. Hidden biases impact everyone, including business leaders, entrepreneurs and managers in decision making. **Availability:** E-book; Print.

20561 ■ "Bullied Into Legislation" in Philadelphia Business Journal (Vol. 33, February 21, 2014, No. 2, pp. 4)
Pub: American City Business Journals, Inc.
Contact: Mike Olivieri, Executive Vice President
Released: Weekly. **Price:** $4, introductory 4-week offer(Digital & Print). **Description:** The results of a study indicate that 35 percent of workers in the U.S. experience bullying firsthand. Because of this, Pennsylvania and other states have considered enacting anti-workplace bullying legislation. Many of these states use some version of the Healthy Workplace Act for their bills. **Availability:** Print; Online.

20562 ■ "A Comparison of Adverse Impact Levels Based on Top-Down, Multisource, and Assessment Center Data: Promoting Diversity and Reducing Legal Challenges" in Human Resource Management (Vol. 51,May-June 2012, No. 3, pp. 313-341)
Pub: John Wiley & Sons, Inc.
Contact: Christina Van Tassell, Executive Vice President Chief Financial Officer
Ed: H. John Bernardin, Robert Konopaske, Christine M. Hagan. **Released:** May 25, 2012. **Description:** Levels of adverse impact against minorities and women were compared based on promotional decision methods. Results indicate significant effects for race and minority status in favor of white people but not for gender. **Availability:** Print; PDF; Online.

20563 ■ "Cracking the Code on Anti-Discrimination Policies for Your Small Business" in Small Business Trends (Nov. 5, 2017)
URL(s): smallbiztrends.com/2017/11/eeoc-best-practices-small-business.html
Ed: Rob Starr. **Released:** November 05, 2017. **Description:** Explains what your small business needs to know about dealing with the U.S. Equal Employment Opportunity Commission (EEOC) and how to ensure that you have good anti-discrimination and anti-harassment policies in place. **Availability:** Online.

20564 ■ Discrimination and Sexual Harassment Policies
URL(s): www.entrepreneur.com/article/80140
Description: Discusses discrimination and sexual harassment policies and how to ensure that you are providing a safe and comfortable working environment for your employees. **Availability:** Online.

20565 ■ "Disguised Age Bias at the Revel Casino?" in Philadelphia Business Journal (Vol. 31, February 17, 2012, No. 1, pp. 1)
Pub: Baltimore Business Journal
Contact: Rhonda Pringle, President
E-mail: rpringle@bizjournals.com
Description: Revel Atlantic City casino hotel's new employment policy is seen to entail age discrimination. The policy places term limits on employees of four, five or six years. The company cited employee burnout as reason for the policy. **Availability:** Print; Online.

20566 ■ "EEOC Issues Enforcement Guidance Addressing Pregnancy-Related Disabilities" in Idaho Business Review (August 18, 2014)
Pub: BridgeTower Media
Contact: Adam Reinebach, President
Description: An overview of the Pregnancy Discrimination Act (PDA) is presented. The EEOC is finally addressing this prohibited form of discrimination again pregnant women in the workplace. Requirements that link pregnancy-related disabilities with duties imposed by the Americans With Disabilities Act are covered.

20567 ■ "Emerging Equals" in Business Strategy Review (Vol. 25, Summer 2014, No. 2, pp. 38)
Released: June 02, 2014. **Description:** What role can and should businesses play in challenging gender inequality in emerging economies? . **Availability:** Print; PDF; Online.

20568 ■ "The Ethics of Price Discrimination" in Business Ethics Quarterly (Vol. 21, October 2011, No. 4, pp. 633)
Ed: Juan M. Elegido. **Released:** Volume 21, Issue 4. **Description:** Price discrimination is the practice of charging different customers different prices for the same product. Many people consider price discrimination unfair, but economists argue that in many cases price discrimination is more likely to lead to greater welfare than is the uniform pricing alternative, sometimes even for every party in the transaction. **Availability:** Online.

20569 ■ "How To Reduce the Risk of Discrimination" in Idaho Business Review (September 11, 2014)
Pub: BridgeTower Media
Contact: Adam Reinebach, President
Description: Human resource departments in small businesses in Boise are aware of the city's discrimination ordinance making it unlawful to use sexual orientation and gender identity/expression in any consideration of hiring or terminating an employee, or for any other issue. The impact of the ordinance is yet to be determined.

20570 ■ "Human Capital: When Change Means Terminating an Employee" in Black Enterprise (Vol. 41, November 2010, No. 4, pp. 40)
Pub: Earl G. Graves Ltd.
Contact: Earl Graves, Jr., President

Ed: Tamara E. Holmes. **Description:** Covering successful business change strategies, this article focuses on how the law and nondiscrimination policies can affect this aspect of the workplace. **Availability:** Online.

20571 ■ *"Looking To Hire Young? Be Careful" in Boston Business Journal (Vol. 30, November 19, 2010, No. 43, pp. 1)*
Pub: Boston Business Journal
Contact: Carolyn M. Jones, President
E-mail: cmjones@bizjournals.com
Ed: Lisa van der Pool. **Released:** Weekly. **Description:** The Massachusetts Commission Against Discrimination (MCAD) has been using undercover job applicants to expose discrimination. Cabot's Ice Cream and Restaurant has been accused of denying older workers equal employment opportunities. MCAD has discovered unfair hiring practices such as hiring high school and college students. **Availability:** Print; Online.

20572 ■ *"Mapping the Gender Gap" in Business Journal Portland (Vol. 31, April 25, 2014, No. 8, pp. 4)*
Pub: American City Business Journals, Inc.
Contact: Mike Olivieri, Executive Vice President
Released: April 25, 2014. **Price:** $4, introductory 4-week offer(Digital & Print). **Description:** The level of gender equality in the health care, banking, technology and commercial real estate industries of Oregon is examined. Gender bias in the workplace is one significant reason behind the wage gap and the lack of women in leadership positions. **Availability:** Print; Mailing list; Online.

20573 ■ *"Maryland Ready to Defend Slots Minority Policy" in Boston Business Journal (Vol. 29, July 8, 2011, No. 9, pp. 3)*
Pub: Boston Business Journal
Contact: Carolyn M. Jones, President
E-mail: cmjones@bizjournals.com
Ed: Scott Dance. **Description:** The legality of Maryland's minority inclusion policy may be put under scrutiny once the lawsuit filed by rejected slots developer Baltimore City Entertainment Group on July 5, 2011 is heard in court. The lawsuit aims to stop the bidding process on a proposed casino in Baltimore because the minority policy amounts to reverse discrimination. **Availability:** Print; Online.

20574 ■ *"Obama Orders Contractors To Raise Minimum Wage" in Atlanta Business Chronicle (June 20, 2014, pp. 9A)*
Pub: American City Business Journals, Inc.
Contact: Mike Olivieri, Executive Vice President
Description: Discussion of the new rules set out by President Obama, which includes the minimum wage of employees and discrimination against employees doing business with the Federal government is presented. The minimum wage law will increase to $10 per hour from $7.25 per hour; and discrimination against employees on the basis of sexual orientation or gender identity will not be tolerated. **Availability:** Print; Online.

20575 ■ *"Research: Mind the Gap" in Business Strategy Review (Vol. 21, Summer 2010, No. 2, pp. 84)*
Ed: Georgina Peters. **Released:** September 01, 2017. **Description:** Isabel Fernandez-Mateo's cumulative gender disadvantage in contract employment is presented. **Availability:** Print; PDF; Online.

20576 ■ *"Santander 'Redlining' Suit is a Crass and Opportunistic Shakedown" in Boston Business Journal (Vol. 34, June 6, 2014, No. 18, pp. 7)*
Pub: American City Business Journals, Inc.
Contact: Mike Olivieri, Executive Vice President
Released: Weekly. **Description:** Santander Bank's residential mortgage lending to minorities in Providence, Massachusetts has declined by 34 percent in recent years. The development is a violation of the US Fair Housing Act and the Equal Credit Opportunity Act. The city has sued Santander over the issue. **Availability:** Print; Online.

20577 ■ *Sexual Harassment and Assault at Work: Understanding the Costs*
URL(s): iwpr.org/iwpr-publications/briefing-paper/sexual-harassment-and-assault-at-work-understanding-the-costs/
Description: Highlights how workplace sexual harassment and assault affect women's advancement and security, as well as the costs of these harms to employers. Provides recommendations for preventing sexual harassment and reducing the negative effects of harassment for individuals and workplaces. **Availability:** Online.

20578 ■ *Sexual Harassment Policy for Small Businesses*
URL(s): smallbusiness.chron.com/sexual-harassment-policy-small-businesses-57063.html
Ed: Ruth Mayhew. **Description:** Discusses the importance of having a solid sexual harassment policy based on your company's commitment to ensuring fair treatment in the workplace. **Availability:** Online.

20579 ■ *"Small Business Contract Discrimination" in Investopedia (Sept. 25, 2021)*
URL(s): www.investopedia.com/discrimination-in-small-business-contracts-5113819
Ed: Daniel Thomas Mollenkamp. **Released:** September 25, 2021. **Description:** Explores the barriers that minority small business owners face as they look to procure and access financing. **Availability:** Online.

20580 ■ *The Small Business Guide to Avoiding Workplace Discrimination and Harassment*
URL(s): www.insureon.com/blog/avoid-workplace-discrimination
Description: Explains where in the workplace discrimination and harassment can occur and how to avoid them. **Availability:** Online.

20581 ■ *"Suit: Bank Bypassing Minorities" in Providence Business News (Vol. 29, June 9, 2014, No. 10, pp. 1)*
Pub: American City Business Journals, Inc.
Contact: Mike Olivieri, Executive Vice President
URL(s): pbn.com/suit-bank-bypassing-minorities97644
Description: The City of Providence, Rhode Island filed a lawsuit against the U.S. operations of Santander Bank for purposely bypassing minority neighborhoods in prime mortgage lending. The lawsuit alleges the Madrid, Spain-based bank of violating the Fair Housing Act by not lending into the minority communities of the city.

20582 ■ *"'Tone-Deaf' Suitor or True Harasser: How to Tell" in HR Specialist (Vol. 8, September 2010, No. 9, pp. 1)*
Pub: Capitol Information Group Inc.
Contact: Allie Ash, Chief Executive Officer
Description: Details are critical to any harassment charge in the workplace. Courts now list factors employers should consider when trying to determine whether an employee has been sexually harassed at work. **Availability:** PDF; Online.

20583 ■ *"Virtue and Vice" in Entrepreneur (September 2014)*
Pub: Entrepreneur Media Inc.
Contact: Dan Bova, Director
E-mail: dbova@entrepreneur.com
Description: Socially responsible investments (SRI) are rising in the U.S., but many claim that vice funds offer better returns. Vice fund proponents argue that any profitable company deserves a place in a good investment portfolio. SRI proponents emphasize investments that benefit the society. Analysts note that investors who restrict their investment landscape by selecting only vice funds or only SRI funds may lead to lower returns. Other specialized funds attract activist investors supporting advocacies like gender equality or a positive work environment. **Availability:** PDF; Online.

20584 ■ *The Ways Discrimination Negatively Affects Businesses*
URL(s): smallbusiness.chron.com/ways-discrimination-negatively-affects-businesses-36925.html
Ed: Tia Benjamin. **Description:** Discrimination in the small business workplace can have a significant impact on the bottom line....and financial effects can go far beyond cash liabilities to include things like internal workplace productivity, your ability to retain and recruit staff, and customer perception. **Availability:** Online.

20585 ■ *"We Must Put an End to 'Male, Pale, and Stale' Corporate Boards" in Black Enterprise (Vol. 45, July-August 2014, No. 1, pp. 10)*
Pub: Earl G. Graves Ltd.
Contact: Earl Graves, Jr., President
Description: Corporate governance behavior is addressed. With a surplus of black executive talent with impeccable professional credentials and reputations, publicly traded companies continue to ignore African Americans in the boardroom. **Availability:** Online.

20586 ■ *"What Small Business Owners Should Know About Wrongful Termination Lawsuits" in Entrepreneur (Feb. 4, 2020)*
URL(s): www.entrepreneur.com/article/344232
Ed: Brian Hughes. **Released:** February 04, 2020. **Description:** Employment discrimination and wrongful terminations are one of the most common types of lawsuits filed against small businesses. This article discusses things small business owners should know about wrongful termination lawsuits. **Availability:** Online.

20587 ■ *"Why His Merit Raise Is Bigger Than Hers" in Harvard Business Review (Vol. 90, April 2012, No. 4, pp. 26)*
Pub: Harvard Business Review Press
Contact: Moderna V. Pfizer, Contact
Ed: Stephen Benard. **Price:** $6, hardcover. **Description:** Research indicates that companies that utilize meritocracy as their pay-for-performance system are paradoxically more likely to award pay on biases, and specifically, to give smaller increases to women. Tranparency and accountability are therefore key in the implementation of merit pay. **Availability:** PDF; Online.

20588 ■ *"Words at Work" in Information Today (Vol. 26, February 2009, No. 2, pp. 25)*
Description: Current new buzzwords include the following: digital amnesia, or overload by availability, speed and volume of digital information; maternal profiling, a form a discrimination against women; recipe malpractice, a reminder that just because you can turn on a stove it doesn't make you a chef; ringxiety, the act when everyone reaches for their cell phone when one rings; verbing, the practice of turning good nouns into verbs. **Availability:** Print; Online.

20589 ■ *"Workplace Harassment: How to Recognize and Report It" in Business News Daily (Dec. 21. 2021)*
URL(s): www.businessnewsdaily.com/9426-workplace-harassment.html
Ed: Skye Schooley. **Released:** December 21, 2021. **Description:** Explains how to identify some of the most common forms of workplace harassment as well as what to do when you see it happening. **Availability:** Online.

TRADE PERIODICALS

20590 ■ *The Columbus Times*
Pub: Columbus Times
Contact: Petra Ophelia Gertjegerdes, Publisher Managing Editor
E-mail: petra@columbustimes.com
URL(s): www.columbustimes.com/main-news.html
Released: Weekly **Price:** $2.50, Individuals for single copy; $182, for Yearly (52 weeks)-local; $234, for Non local. **Description:** Black community newspaper. **Availability:** Print.

20591 ■ *Mealey's Emerging Insurance Disputes*
Pub: Mealey's Legal News & Litigation Reports
Contact: Mike Walsh, Chief Executive Officer
URL(s): store.lexisnexis.com/products/mealeys-emerging-insurance-disputes-skuusSku41076
Released: Semimonthly **Price:** $5,880, for email delivery, journal, eBook-Pdf and eBook-epub and eBook-Mobi. **Description:** Finds and tracks new areas of insurance litigation as they arise. Follows coverage actions involving underlying claims of sexual harassment and discrimination; sexual molestation and assualt; attorney liability; patent and trademark infringement; construction defects, directors and officers claims; emotional distress; and intentional acts. **Availability:** E-book; Print; PDF. **Type:** Full-text.

CONSULTANTS

20592 ■ Applied Personnel Research (APR)
62 Candlewood Rd.
Scarsdale, NY 10583
Ph: (617)244-8859
Fax: (617)244-8904
URL: http://www.appliedpersonnelresearch.com/index.php
Contact: Dr. Joel P. Wiesen, Director
E-mail: jwiesen@appliedpersonnelresearch.com
Description: Provider of industrial psychology consulting services in personnel assessment, selection and solution-oriented data collection and data analysis, and customized consulting solutions can be provided on the basis of needs. **Scope:** Provider of industrial psychology consulting services in personnel assessment, selection and solution-oriented data collection and data analysis, and customized consulting solutions can be provided on the basis of needs. **Training:** The Recent Judicial Decision Concerning Two NYC Firefighter Exams, 2009; Possible New Approaches to Reduce Adverse Impact, 2007; Thinking Outside the Box in Merit Selection, Princeton, Nov, 2006; Limitations and Flaws in the Research Supporting Field Sobriety Tests, Las Vegas, Oct, 2006.

20593 ■ DJT Consulting Group L.L.C.
3154 Granada Dr.
Cameron Park, CA 95682
Ph: (530)387-7089
Co. E-mail: sherry@djtconsulting.com
URL: http://www.djtconsulting.com
Contact: Dan Armenta, Principal
E-mail: dan@djtconsulting.com
Description: Provider of consulting services such as grant writing and fund development, grant monitoring and reporting, project management, program development, implementation, evaluation, and much more. **Founded:** 2000. **Training:** Finding and Winning Government Grants.

20594 ■ Eastern Point Consulting Group Inc.
75 Oak St.
Newton, MA 02465
Ph: (617)965-4141
URL: http://www.eastpt.com
Contact: Katherine Herzog, President
Description: Firm specializes in bringing practical solutions to complex challenges and provides consulting and training in managing diversity, comprehensive sexual-harassment policies and programs, organizational development, benchmarks 360-degree skills assessment, executive coaching, strategic human resource planning, team building, leadership development for women, mentoring programs, and gender issues in the workplace. **Scope:** Firm specializes in bringing practical solutions to complex challenges and provides consulting and training in managing diversity, comprehensive sexual-harassment policies and programs, organizational development, benchmarks 360-degree skills assessment, executive coaching, strategic human resource planning, team building, leadership development for women, mentoring programs, and gender issues in the workplace. **Training:** Leadership Development for Women.

20595 ■ The Kaleel Jamison Consulting Group Inc. (KJCG)
500 Federal St.
Troy, NY 12180
Ph: (518)271-7000
Free: 800-999-1809
Co. E-mail: kjcg411@kjcg.com
URL: http://www.kjcg.com
Contact: Frederick A. Miller, Chief Executive Officer
E-mail: fred411@kjcg.com
Facebook: www.facebook.com/kaleeljamison
Linkedin: www.linkedin.com/company/the-kaleel-jamison-consulting-group-inc
X (Twitter): x.com/kjcginc
Description: Management consulting firm provides long-term strategic culture alignment and assisting organizations in creating inclusive and collaborative workplaces that unleash the talent and creativity of their people. **Scope:** Management consulting firm provides long-term strategic culture alignment and assisting organizations in creating inclusive and collaborative workplaces that unleash the talent and creativity of their people. **Founded:** 1970. **Publications:** "The Next Leap Forward Diversity and Inclusion An OD Opportunity"; "Inclusion 3.5: Our Vision of the Future," Profiles in Diversity Journal, 2007; "The Next Leap Forward," 2007; "Tapping the Wisdom of the Ages: Ageism and the Need for Multi generational Organizations"; "Developing a Comprehensive Pipeline Strategy"; "White Awareness: Handbook for Anti-Racism Training," University of Oklahoma Press, 2003; "The Inclusion Breakthrough: Unleashing the Real Power of Diversity," Berrett-Koehler, 2002; "Eight Essential Axioms for Rapid Culture Change"; "The Need for Silence, Spontaneity and Thinking Time in 21st Century Organization"; "Road Map for the Path to Strategic Culture Change"; "Thee Path From Exclusive Club to Inclusive Organization". **Training:** Multicultural Forum on Workplace Diversity, Mar, 2012; Be BIG: Four Behaviors That Change Everything to Enable You to Step Up, Step Out, Be Bold, May, 2012, Singapore; Be Big: 4 Keys That Change Everything, Singapore, Jul, 2012; Be Big: 4 Keys That Change Everything, Chennai, India, Oct, 2012; OD Network Conference, Nov, 2011; Bring Your Whole Self To Life: Developing The Organizational And Personal Self (D/OPS), Potomac, Aug, 2008; D/Ops: Developing The Organizational And Personal Self; Dealing with Covert Processes.

20596 ■ Litigation Management and Training Services Inc.
301 E Ocean Blvd., Ste. 520
Long Beach, CA 90802-4862
Ph: (562)495-0098
Fax: (562)495-1786
Co. E-mail: info@preventlitigation.com
URL: http://www.preventlitigation.com
Description: Consultant with private industry employers and government agencies on proactive legal management of the workplace, including sexual harassment prevention, legal aspects of human resources management, how to hire, fire and manage employees legally. Special programs for adopting and enforcing e-mail and internet abuse policies. **Scope:** Consultant with private industry employers and government agencies on proactive legal management of the workplace, including sexual harassment prevention, legal aspects of human resources management, how to hire, fire and manage employees legally. Special programs for adopting and enforcing e-mail and internet abuse policies. **Founded:** 1987. **Publications:** "Heading off harassment. Effective training is critical to limiting legal exposure for workplace harassment".

20597 ■ UNIFIED
3968 Mt Elliott St.
Detroit, MI 48207
Ph: (313)446-9800
Fax: (313)446-9839
Co. E-mail: info@miunified.org
URL: http://miunified.org/Home
Contact: Leanne F. Savola, President
X (Twitter): x.com/miunified
YouTube: www.youtube.com/channel/UCpMdNw4Saav084WYrxRPhbg
Description: Services include case management, behavioral health services, AIDS Interfaith Network, Linda's Home Delivered Meals, Project Med-Line, transportation, Michigan AIDS Hotline, Teen link HIV/STD Hotline, speaker's bureau, and HIV counseling and testing. **Scope:** Offers advice to corporations on the effects of HIV and AIDS in the workplace. Focus is on infected employee rights, co-worker rights and employer responsibilities. Serves all industries. **Founded:** 1996. **Geographic Preference:** State.

LIBRARIES

20598 ■ U.S. Equal Employment Opportunity Commission (EEOC) - Collection
131 M St. NE
Washington, DC 20507
Ph: (202)921-3191
Free: 800-669-4000
Co. E-mail: info@eeoc.gov
URL: http://www.eeoc.gov
Contact: David Lopez, General Counsel
Facebook: www.facebook.com/USEEOC
Linkedin: www.linkedin.com/company/eeoc
X (Twitter): x.com/useeoc
Instagram: www.instagram.com/useeoc
YouTube: www.youtube.com/user/TheEEOC
Description: Strives to promote equal opportunity in employment through administrative and judicial enforcement of the federal civil rights laws and through education and technical assistance. Federal agency charged with enforcing laws prohibiting job discrimination. **Scope:** Employment law. **Founded:** 1965. **Holdings:** Figures not available. **Publications:** *EEOC Compliance Manual*; *United States Equal Employment Opportunity Commission Annual Report: Job Patterns for Minorities and Women in Private Industry* (Annual). **Geographic Preference:** National.

Distributing

ASSOCIATIONS AND OTHER ORGANIZATIONS

20599 ■ **Association nationale des distributeurs aux petites surfaces alimentaires [National Convenience Store Distributors Association (NACDA)]**
205-2140 Winston Park
 Oakville, ON, Canada L6H 5V5
Free: 888-686-2823
Co. E-mail: nacda@nacda.ca
URL: http://www.nacda.ca
Contact: Jackie Bellerose, Chairman of the Board
Description: Assists members in providing dependable distribution of convenience products between suppliers and retailers. Represents member's interests with the government and other industry key players. Conducts educational seminars and programs relevant to member's business needs, thus contributing to the improvement of the convenience supply chain. **Founded:** 1955. **Geographic Preference:** National.

20600 ■ *The Chemunicator*
1160 Blair Rd., Unit No. 1
 Burlington, ON, Canada L7M 1K9
Ph: (905)332-8777
Free: 844-237-4039
URL: http://www.cacd.ca
Contact: Cathy Campbell, Co-President
E-mail: ccampbell@cacd.ca
URL(s): rdcanada.ca/the-chemunicator
Released: 3/year; spring, summer & winter. **Price:** $4.95, for CDN. **Availability:** Print; Online; PDF.

20601 ■ **Distribution Business Management Association (DBMA)**
2938 Columbia Ave., Ste. 1102
 Lancaster, PA 17603
Ph: (717)295-0033
Co. E-mail: athorn@dbm-assoc.com
URL: http://www.dcenter.com
Description: Promotes education and continuing professional development in the materials handling, distribution, and supply chain industries; maintains standards of excellence, commitment, and integrity when seeking solutions to industry issues; conducts educational forums and programs. **Founded:** 1992. **Publications:** *Distribution Business Management Journal (DBMJ)* (Annual). **Awards:** DBMA Circle of Excellence Award (Annual); DBMA Distinguished Service Award (Annual). **Geographic Preference:** National.

20602 ■ **Global Market Development Center (GMDC)**
1653 Cypress Grove Ln.
 Diamond Bar, CA 91765
Ph: (909)861-6326
URL: http://gmdc.org
Contact: Ashleigh Villalobos, Contact

Description: Works to improve management operations, marketing programs, sales techniques, merchandising, and distribution functions of members; furthers management education and employee training; and promotes understanding and cooperation among members, the public, and government. Conducts research and compiles statistics. **Founded:** 1970. **Educational Activities:** GM Marketing Conference (Annual); HBW Marketing Conference (Annual). **Geographic Preference:** National.

20603 ■ **Institute for Distribution Excellence**
1325 G St. NW Ste. 1000
 Washington, DC 20005-3100
Co. E-mail: membership@naw.org
URL: http://www.naw.org/naw-institute-for-distribution-excellence
Contact: Patricia A. Lilly, Executive Director
E-mail: plilly@naw.org
Description: Firms that are members of the National Association of Wholesaler-Distributors, wholesalers, and trade associations. Seeks to advance knowledge in the field of wholesale distribution by means of long-range research projects. **Scope:** Wholesale distribution, focusing on long-range projects to advance knowledge in the field. **Publications:** *Facing the Forces of Change: The Road to Opportunity* (Triennial). **Geographic Preference:** National.

20604 ■ **National Association of Chemical Distributors (NACD)**
1560 Wilson Blvd., Ste. 1100
 Arlington, VA 22209
Ph: (703)527-6223
Fax: (703)527-7747
URL: http://www.nacd.com
Contact: Kurt Hettinga, Chairman
Linkedin: www.linkedin.com/company/national-association-of-chemical-distributors-nacd-
X (Twitter): x.com/NACD_RD
YouTube: www.youtube.com/user/nacdrdp
Description: Represents chemical distributor companies that purchase and take title of chemical products from manufacturers. Promotes professionalism in the chemical distribution industry. **Founded:** 1971. **Publications:** *Chemical Distributor* (Quarterly). **Educational Activities:** University of Innovative Distribution (Annual); NACD Western Region Meeting (Annual). **Geographic Preference:** National.

20605 ■ **National Association of Wholesaler-Distributors (NAW)**
1325 G St. NW, Ste. 1000
 Washington, DC 20005-3100
Ph: (202)872-0885
Fax: (202)785-0586
Co. E-mail: naw@naw.org
URL: http://www.naw.org
Contact: Eric Hoplin, Chief Executive Officer
Linkedin: www.linkedin.com/company/national-association-of-wholesaler-distributors
X (Twitter): x.com/NAWorg
YouTube: www.youtube.com/user/NAWInstitute

Description: Federation of national, state, and regional associations, and individual wholesaler-distributor firms. Represents industry's views to the federal government. Analyzes current and proposed legislation and government regulations affecting the industry. Maintains public relations and media programs and a research foundation. Conducts wholesale executive management courses. **Founded:** 1946. **Publications:** *NAW Annual Report* (Annual); *NAW Report*; *SmartBrief*. **Geographic Preference:** National.

20606 ■ **Responsible Distribution® Canada (CACD) [L'Association Canadienne des Distributeurs de Produits Chimiques]**
1160 Blair Rd., Unit No. 1
 Burlington, ON, Canada L7M 1K9
Ph: (905)332-8777
Free: 844-237-4039
URL: http://www.cacd.ca
Contact: Cathy Campbell, Co-President
E-mail: ccampbell@cacd.ca
Linkedin: www.linkedin.com/company/canadian-association-of-chemical-distributors
Description: Represents chemical distributors in Canada to governments, allied associations, and the public. **Founded:** 1986. **Publications:** *The Chemunicator* (3/year). **Geographic Preference:** National.

REFERENCE WORKS

20607 ■ *"3PL Logistics Team Enters Distribution Market" in Memphis Business Journal (Vol. 33, March 16, 2012, No. 49, pp. 1)*
Pub: Baltimore Business Journal
Contact: Rhonda Pringle, President
E-mail: rpringle@bizjournals.com
Ed: Andy Ashby. **Description:** Third-party logistics and transportation services firm Logistics Team has gained presence in the industrial submarket of southeast Memphis, Tennessee. Its distribution operation will be relocated in the submarket with the purchase of a 94,500-square-foot warehouse. The presence in the submarket is in line with Logistics Team's goal of setting up a rail-served network across the US. **Availability:** Print; Online.

20608 ■ *"ABC Supply Company Finally Finds Idaho" in Idaho Business Review (September 17, 2014)*
Pub: BridgeTower Media
Contact: Adam Reinebach, President
Description: The nation's largest wholesale distributor, ABC Supply Company, has entered a store in Idaho. The roofing supply firm has now has stores in 48 states. Franklin Lumber Supply, a home supply chain will be ABCs its major competitor in the area.

20609 ■ *"Amcon Distributing Expands Into Northwest Arkansas" in Arkansas Business (Vol. 26, November 9, 2009, No. 45, pp. 13)*
Pub: Arkansas Business Publishing Group
Contact: Mitch Bettis, President

Description: Amcon Distributing Co., a consumer products company, has bought the convenience store distribution assets of Discount Distributors from its parent, Harps Food Stores Inc., significantly increasing its wholesale distribution presence in the northwest Arkansas market. The acquisition will be funded through Amcon's existing credit facilities. **Availability:** Online.

20610 ■ *Associated Equipment Distributors--Membership Directory*
Pub: Associated Equipment Distributors
Contact: Brian P. McGuire, President
E-mail: bmcguire@aednet.org
URL(s): aednet.org/membership
Released: Latest Edition: May 2024. **Description:** Covers fifteen hundred U.S. and Canadian distributors. Available as a special issue of Construction Equipment Distribution magazine. **Entries include:** Information on each company's branches, manufacturer members, banks, finance companies, specialized service firms and trade press, and AED contact person. **Availability:** Print.

20611 ■ *"AV Concept Expands Into Green Energy Storage" in Wireless News (January 25, 2010)*
Description: Electronics distributor and manufacturer AV Concept Holdings Limited announced a marketing partnership with Boston-Power, a provider of lithium-ion batteries, with a focus in the Chinese and Korean markets. **Availability:** Online.

20612 ■ *"avVaa World Health Care Products Rolls Out Internet Marketing Program" in Health and Beauty Close-Up (September 18, 2009)*
Description: avVaa World Health Care Products, Inc., a biotechnology company, manufacturer and distributor of nationally branded therapeutic, natural health care and skin products, has signed an agreement with Online Performance Marketing to launch of an Internet marketing campaign in order to broaden its presence online. The impact of advertising on the Internet to generate an increase in sales is explored. **Availability:** Online.

20613 ■ *Best Distribution Channels for Small Businesses*
URL(s): seodesignchicago.com/marketing/what-types-of-distribution-channels-work-best-for-a-small-business/
Description: Discusses distribution channels in business, the key differences between direct and indirect distribution channels, and the various distribution methods within marketing. **Availability:** Online.

20614 ■ *"Blue Bell Breaks Ground in South Carolina" in Ice Cream Reporter (Vol. 23, August 20, 2010, No. 9, pp. 3)*
Description: Texas-based Blue Bell Creameries will open a new 2,000 square foot transfer facility in North Charleston, South Carolina. The facility will expand Blue Bell's distribution efforts in the state. **Availability:** Print.

20615 ■ *"Bob's Discount Furniture Moving into Harford County, Region" in Baltimore Business Journal (Vol. 27, January 22, 2010, No. 38, pp. 1)*
Pub: Baltimore Business Journal
Contact: Rhonda Pringle, President
E-mail: rpringle@bizjournals.com
Ed: Daniel J. Sernovitz. **Description:** Manchester, Connecticut-based Bob's Discount Furniture signed a lease for 672,000 square feet of space in Harford County, Maryland. The site will become the discount furniture retailer's distribution center in mid-Atlantic US. As many as 200 jobs could be generated when the center opens. **Availability:** Print; Online.

20616 ■ *"Brent Leary on Partnering with Amazon for the Last Mile" in Small Business Trends (September 20, 2022)*
URL(s): smallbiztrends.com/2022/09/amazon-last-mile.html
Ed: Holly Chavez. **Released:** September 20, 2022. **Description:** Brent Leary, managing director at CRM Essentials, discusses the Atlanta Amazon delivery station and how small businesses can partner with Amazon. **Availability:** Online.

20617 ■ *"CBC Eyes Partners for TV Downloads" in Globe & Mail (February 9, 2006, pp. B1)*
Description: The details on Canadian Broadcasting Corp.'s distribution agreement with Google Inc. and Apple Computer Inc. are presented. **Availability:** Online.

20618 ■ *"Cogs in R.I. Manufacturing Machine" in Providence Business News (Vol. 28, January 27, 2014, No. 43, pp. 1)*
Pub: American City Business Journals, Inc.
Contact: Mike Olivieri, Executive Vice President
URL(s): pbn.com/cogs-in-ri-manufacturing-machine94640
Description: Machine shops are capable of fixing or designing unique parts for manufacturing equipment and serve as a critical link in a company's production and distribution. Rhode Island has at least 50 machine shops capable of fabricating parts for companies. The Rhode Island Manufacturers Association's efforts to close the skills gap in machining are examined. **Availability:** Online.

20619 ■ *"Deal Braces Cramer for Growth Run" in The Business Journal-Serving Metropolitan Kansas City (Vol. 26, July 4, 2008, No. 43, pp. 1)*
Description: Gardner, Kansas-based Cramer Products Inc. bought 100 percent of the stocks of Louisville, Kentucky-based Active Ankle Inc. from 26 private investors increasing its revenue by 20 percent. The latter is the second largest vendor of Cramer. Other details of the merger are presented. **Availability:** Print; Online.

20620 ■ *"Distribution 101 for Entrepreneurs" on Score.org (June 21, 2019)*
URL(s): www.score.org/resource/distribution-101-entrepreneurs
Ed: Bridget Weston. **Released:** June 21, 2019. **Availability:** Online.

20621 ■ *"The Doomsday Scenario" in Conde Nast Portfolio (Vol. 2, June 2008, No. 6, pp. 91)*
Ed: Jeffrey Rothfeder. **Description:** Detroit and the U.S. auto industry are discussed as well as the ramifications of the demise of this manufacturing base. Similarities and differences between the downfall of the U.S. steel business and the impact it had on Pittsburg, Pennsylvania is also discussed.

20622 ■ *"Egg Fight: The Yolk's on the Shorts" in Barron's (Vol. 88, July 7, 2008, No. 27, pp. 20)*
Pub: Dow Jones & Company Inc.
Contact: Almar Latour, Chief Executive Officer
Ed: Christopher C. Williams. **Description:** Shares of Cal-Maine Foods, the largest egg producer and distributor in the US, are due for a huge rise because of the increase in egg prices. Short sellers, however, continue betting that the stock, priced at $31.84 each, will eventually go down. **Availability:** Online.

20623 ■ *"Expanding Distribution Channels" in business.com (Feb. 2, 2022)*
URL(s): www.business.com/articles/expanding-distribution-channels/
Ed: Sean Peek. **Released:** February 02, 2022. **Description:** Discusses the importance of getting your products or services to more customers as well as the benefit of having a mix of distribution channels. **Availability:** Online.

20624 ■ *"Fraser and Neave Acquires King's Creameries" in Ice Cream Reporter (Vol. 23, November 20, 2010, No. 12, pp. 1)*
Description: Fraser and Neave Ltd., a Singapore-based consumer products marketer, has entered a conditional agreement to acquire all outstanding shares of King's Creameries, the leading manufacturer and distributor of frozen desserts. **Availability:** Print; Online.

20625 ■ *From Concept To Consumer: How to Turn Ideas Into Money*
Ed: Phil Baker. **Released:** 1st edition. **Price:** $27.99, paperback. **Description:** Renowned product developer Phil Baker explains how a great idea accounts for only 5 percent of all the factors of success and why the majority of success is dependent upon a myriad of other factors, including the time it takes to get to market, price, marketing and distribution. By being their own best competition, a small company can stay one step ahead of competitors. **Availability:** Print.

20626 ■ *"Handleman Liquidation Leaves Questions For Shareholders" in Crain's Detroit Business (Vol. 24, October 6, 2008, No. 40, pp. 4)*
Pub: Crain Communications Inc.
Contact: Barry Asin, President
Ed: Nancy Kaffer. **Description:** Discusses Handleman Co., a Troy-based music distribution company, and their plan of liquidation and dissolution as well as how shareholders will be affected by the company's plan. Handleman filed its plan to liquidate and dissolve assets with the Securities and Exchange Commission in mid-August, following several quarters of dismal earnings. **Availability:** Online.

20627 ■ *How to Start a Distribution Business in 9 Steps*
URL(s): www.indeed.com/career-advice/finding-a-job/how-to-start-a-distribution-business
Released: September 03, 2021. **Description:** Include steps involved in creating a distribution business, including financial planning, organization and professional networking. **Availability:** Online.

20628 ■ *"How to Start a Wholesale Distribution Business" in Entrepreneur*
URL(s): www.entrepreneur.com/article/190460
Description: Discusses the role of a distributor, the state of the industry, and how to break into the business of distribution. **Availability:** Online.

20629 ■ *"Industry Escalates Lobbying Efforts For Loan Program" in Crain's Detroit Business (Vol. 24, September 22, 2008, No. 38, pp. 22)*
Pub: Crain Communications Inc.
Contact: Barry Asin, President
Ed: Jay Greene, Ryan Beene, Harry Stoffer. **Description:** Auto suppliers such as Lear Corp., which is best known for vehicle seating, also supplies high-voltage wiring for Ford hybrids and is developing other hybrid components. These suppliers are joining automakers in lobbying for the loan program which would promote the accelerated development of fuel-efficient vehicles. **Availability:** Print; PDF; Online.

20630 ■ *"Ingrian and Channel Management International Sign Distribution Agreement" in Canadian Corporate News (May 16, 2007)*
Description: Channel Management International (CMI), a Canadian channel management and distribution company, and Ingrian Networks, Inc., the leading provider of data privacy solutions, announced a Canadian distribution agreement to resell Ingrian encryption solutions to the Canadian market. **Availability:** Online.

20631 ■ *"Intermodal Makes Suppliers Look to Rack Up Big Sales to Distributors" in The Business Journal-Serving Metropolitan Kansas City (August 15, 2008)*
Pub: American City Business Journals, Inc.
Contact: Mike Olivieri, Executive Vice President
Ed: James Dornbrook. **Description:** Suppliers of shelving units, conveyor systems and other equipment used in distribution facilities are expecting new business opportunities along with the planned intermodal projects in the Kansas City area. Suppliers have already observed that small distributors have started to relocate to the city because of the intermodal projects. Demand for shelves and lifts have also increased. **Availability:** Online.

GENERAL SMALL BUSINESS TOPICS　　　Distributing ■ 20651

20632 ■ *"Jacksonville-based Interline Expanding in Janitorial-Sanitation Market"* in *Florida Times-Union (May 10, 2011)*
Pub: Florida Times-Union
Ed: Mark Basch. **Description:** Interline Brands Inc., located in Jacksonville, Florida, aims to grow its business with two recent acquisitions of firms that distribute janitorial and sanitation products. Interline markets and distributes maintenance, repair and operations products. **Availability:** Online.

20633 ■ *Logistics and Distribution Planning for Small Businesses*
URL(s): www.allbusiness.com/logistics-distribution-planning-small-businesses-17740-1.html
Ed: Ken Yancey. **Description:** Discusses the importance of having a well-researched and thoughtful logistics and distribution plan for your small business. **Availability:** Online.

20634 ■ *"Lynn Johnson, President: Dowland-Bach"* in *Alaska Business Monthly (Vol. 27, October 2011, No. 10, pp. 11)*
Pub: Alaska Business Publishing Company Inc.
Contact: Charles Bell, Vice President, Sales and Marketing
E-mail: cbell@akbizmag.com
Ed: Peg Stomierowski. **Description:** Profile of Lynn C. Johnson cofounder of Dowland-Bach Corporation, a manufacturing and distribution company is presented. The firms primary products are wellhead control and chemical injection systems for corrosion control, UL industrial control panels, and specialty stainless steel sheet metal fabrication. **Availability:** Print; Online.

20635 ■ *"Market Resource Set for Expansion: Supply Chain Firm to Add Up to 700 Employees"* in *Memphis Business Journal (Vol. 34, May 11, 2012, No. 4, pp. 1)*
Pub: Baltimore Business Journal
Contact: Rhonda Pringle, President
E-mail: rpringle@bizjournals.com
Description: Market Resource Packaging LLC is planning to expand its operation in Memphis, Tennessee under the new ownership of IAM Acquisition. The supply chain services company plans to increase its distribution space from 260,000 square feet to 1 million square feet in three years and to grow its employees from 300 to 1,000 in 18 months. **Availability:** Print; Online.

20636 ■ *Marketing and Distribution Channels for Small Businesses*
URL(s): www.bmt.com/marketing-and-distribution-channels-for-small-businesses/
Released: August 13, 2018. **Description:** Discusses how distribution channels differ from one company to another and explores different types of distribution channels, including retail, distributor/wholesaler, dealer, sales team, and online.

20637 ■ *Marketing for Entrepreneurs*
Pub: FT Press
Ed: Jurgen Wolff. **Released:** 1st edition. **Description:** This text identifies marketing as the entire process of researching, creating, distributing and selling a product or service. It isn't about theory and metrics, rather it is a practical guide that starts with the basics of all marketing aspects. **Availability:** Print.

20638 ■ *"Mazel Tov: L'Chaim Gets a Deal to Expand with Southern Wine"* in *South Florida Business Journal (Vol. 33, September 7, 2012, No. 6, pp. 1)*
Pub: Baltimore Business Journal
Contact: Rhonda Pringle, President
E-mail: rpringle@bizjournals.com
Description: L'Chaim Kosher Vodka could triple its sales in 2012. The company won a deal to expand with Southern Wine and Spirits, which is the largest distributor of wine and spirits in the United States. The Distilled Spirits Council of the United States reported that vodka drives 31 percent of all spirit sales.

20639 ■ *"Methods of Distributing a Product"* in *Chron (Jan. 28, 2019)*
URL(s): smallbusiness.chron.com/methods-distributing-product-45501.html
Ed: Devra Gartenstein. **Released:** January 28, 2019. **Description:** Provides information on how to choose the best distribution methods for your small business as you weigh the logistical ease against the cost. **Availability:** Online.

20640 ■ *"Minority Auto Suppliers Get Help Diversifying"* in *Crain's Detroit Business (Vol. 26, January 11, 2010, No. 2, pp. 3)*
Pub: Crain Communications Inc.
Contact: Barry Asin, President
Ed: Sherri Welch. **Description:** Displaced minority auto suppliers are being given assistance by the Kauffman's Foundation Urban Entrepreneur Partnership Detroit program, a three-year effort to assist 150 of the region's suppliers into more diversified businesses. **Availability:** Online.

20641 ■ *"Mobis to Set Up Lancaster Distribution Center"* in *Dallas Business Journal (Vol. 35, April 6, 2012, No. 30, pp. 1)*
Pub: Baltimore Business Journal
Contact: Rhonda Pringle, President
E-mail: rpringle@bizjournals.com
Description: Irvine, California-based Mobis Parts America bought a 442,000-square-foot Saint Pointe Building in Lancaster, Texas from KTR Capital Partners for an undisclosed price. Mobisplans to make the building a distribution center for regional Hyundai and Kia dealerships, creating more than 30 jobs to start. **Availability:** Print; Online.

20642 ■ *"New Jobs Coming From New Breed"* in *Memphis Business Journal (Vol. 34, September 21, 2012, No. 23, pp. 1)*
Pub: Baltimore Business Journal
Contact: Rhonda Pringle, President
E-mail: rpringle@bizjournals.com
Ed: Andy Ashby. **Description:** New Breed Logistics has opened a new distribution center in Southeast Memphis, Tennessee. It is believed that this new service will create hundreds of new jobs over the next two years. The company may become the largest-third party logistics company operating in Memphis. **Availability:** Print; Online.

20643 ■ *"Old Ford Plant to Sign New Tenants"* in *Business Courier (Vol. 27, August 13, 2010, No. 15, pp. 1)*
Pub: Business Courier
Ed: Dan Monk. **Description:** Ohio Realty Advisors LLC, a company handling the marketing of the 1.9 million-square-foot former Ford Batavia plant is on the brink of landing one distribution and three manufacturing firms as tenants. These tenants are slated to occupy about 20 percent of the facility and generate as many as 250 jobs in Ohio. **Availability:** Print; Online.

20644 ■ *"Online Marketing and Promotion of Canadian Films via Social Media Tools: Telefilm Launches New Initiative to Foster Innovative Distribution Strategies"* in *CNW Group (January 27, 2010)*
Pub: Comtex News Network Inc.
Contact: Kan Devnani, President
Description: Telefilm Canada announced the launch of a pilot initiative aimed at encouraging the integration of online marketing and the use of social media tools into means of distribution ahead of a films' theatrical release. During this pilot phase Web-Cine 360 will target French-language feature films. **Availability:** Online.

20645 ■ *"Pegasus Logistics Expanding in Coppell"* in *Dallas Business Journal (Vol. 35, July 6, 2012, No. 43, pp. 1)*
Pub: Baltimore Business Journal
Contact: Rhonda Pringle, President
E-mail: rpringle@bizjournals.com

Ed: Candace Carlisle. **Description:** Coppell, Texas-based Pegasus Logistic Group has signed a lease with Teachers Insurance and Annuity Association - College Retirement Equities Fund for 255,000-square-foot office and industrial space at 301 Airport Drive. Pegasus plans to consolidate its corporate headquarters with its distribution to keep up with its growth. Details are included. **Availability:** Print; Online.

20646 ■ *"Planned Rice MLP Latest In Series of Spinoffs"* in *Pittsburgh Business Times (Vol. 34, August 15, 2014, No. 4, pp. 6)*
Pub: American City Business Journals, Inc.
Contact: Mike Olivieri, Executive Vice President
Released: Weekly. **Price:** $4, introductory 4-week offer(Digital & Print). **Description:** Companies such as Rice Energy Inc., EQT Corporation and Consol Energy, are separating their midstream businesses from exploration and production by forming master limited partnerships (MLPs) to gain tax benefits and a higher valuation on midstream assets. However, Kinder Morgan Inc. plans to reorganize and reacquire its three separate MLPs in an effort to streamline the company and remove its distribution incentive rights. **Availability:** Print; Online.

20647 ■ *"Poisoning Relationships: Perceived Unfairness in Channels of Distribution"* in *Journal of Marketing (Vol. 75, May 2011, No. 3, pp. 99)*
Pub: American Marketing Association
Contact: Bennie F. Johnson, Chief Executive Officer
Ed: Stephen A. Samaha, Robert W. Palmatier, Rajiv P. Dant. **Released:** Volume: 75 issue: 3. **Description:** The effects of perceived unfairness on the relationships among members of distribution channels are examined. Perceived unfairness is found to directly damage relationships, aggravate the negative effects of conflict and opportunism, and undermine the benefits of the contract. **Availability:** PDF.

20648 ■ *Product Distribution 101: Get Your Product in Stores*
URL(s): aofund.org/resource/product-distribution-101-get-your-product-in-stores/
Description: Provides information on product distribution, best practices, examples, and easy-to-access resources that relate to initiating, building, and maintaining distributor relationshps. **Availability:** Online.

20649 ■ *"Quonset Steering To Import Records"* in *Providence Business News (Vol. 29, May 19, 2014, No. 7, pp. 1)*
Pub: American City Business Journals, Inc.
Contact: Mike Olivieri, Executive Vice President
Released: May 17, 2014. **Description:** The growing automobile import business at Port of Davisville in North Kingstown, Rhode Island is marked by four consecutive record-breaking years of imports, with 250,000 vehicles expected to arrive by the end of 2014. Quonset Development Corporation managing director, Steven J. King, attributes the success of the auto import business to North Atlantic Distribution Inc. **Availability:** Print; Online.

20650 ■ *"RipCode Founder Starts Private Equity Firm Vspeed Capital"* in *Dallas Business Journal (Vol. 35, September 9, 2012, No. 51, pp. 1)*
Pub: Baltimore Business Journal
Contact: Rhonda Pringle, President
E-mail: rpringle@bizjournals.com
Ed: Jeff Bounds. **Description:** Brendon Mills, founder of Genband Inc., cofounds Vspeed Capital LLC, a new private equity firm. The company has joined forces with Galatyn Private Equity to make its first purchase, that of Fortress Solutions Ltd. Vspeed plans to acquire companies in the manufacturing and distribution sectors, and double its revenue in the next 24 months. **Availability:** Print; Online.

20651 ■ *"Slimmed-Down Supplier TI Automotive Relaunches"* in *Crain's Detroit Business (Vol. 26, January 11, 2010, No. 2, pp. 14)*
Pub: Crain Communications Inc.
Contact: Barry Asin, President

Small Business Sourcebook • 42nd Edition

Ed: Robert Sherefkin. **Description:** TI Automotive Ltd., one of the world's largest suppliers of fuel storage and delivery systems, has reorganized the company by splitting it into five global divisions and is relaunching its brand which is now more focused on new technology. **Availability:** Print; Online.

20652 ■ Small Business Distribution Strategy
URL(s): www.mymarketingdept.com/small-business-distribution-strategy/
Description: Discusses how to create and implement a well thought out small business distribution strategy and how to decide on the right distribution channels for your business. **Availability:** Online.

20653 ■ "Sources" in Canadian Electronics (Vol. 23, August 2008, No. 5, pp. 12)
Description: Directory of electronic manufacturers, distributors and representatives in Canada is provided. The list presents distributors and representatives under each manufacturer.

20654 ■ "StyleCraft Consolidates HQ, Distribution Facility" in Memphis Business Journal (Vol. 34, June 1, 2012, No. 7, pp. 1)
Pub: Baltimore Business Journal
Contact: Rhonda Pringle, President
E-mail: rpringle@bizjournals.com
Ed: Andy Ashby. **Description:** StyleCraft Home Collection Inc. has combined its headquarters and distribution operations into one building in Memphis, Tennessee. The company has leased space at IDI's Airways Distribution Building E. **Availability:** Print; Online.

20655 ■ "Substantial Deal Expected to Create Jobs, Help Industrial Market" in Tampa Bay Business Journal (Vol. 30, January 8, 2010, No. 3)
Pub: Tampa Bay Business Journal
Contact: Ian Anderson, President
E-mail: ianderson@bizjournals.com
Ed: Janet Leiser. **Description:** Food distribution firm Gordon Food Service (GFS) is on the brink of purchasing Albertson's million-square-foot warehouse along with 158 acres of space. The deal between GFS and Albertson's could expand GFS' presence in west Central Florida. A history of GFS' growth is included. **Availability:** Print; Online.

20656 ■ "Supermercado El Rancho Chain Grows Along with Hispanic Population" in Dallas Business Journal (Vol. 35, July 13, 2012, No. 44, pp. 1)
Pub: Baltimore Business Journal
Contact: Rhonda Pringle, President
E-mail: rpringle@bizjournals.com
Ed: Matt Joyce. **Description:** Garland, Texas-based Supermercado El Rancho has grown rapidly wit its take on the Hispanic grocery market and is planning to open 12 stores in six years. La Bodega Meat Inc., the chain's affiliate distribution company, is planning a $13.1 million renovation and double the size of its warehouse to accommodate the plans for more stores.

20657 ■ "The Trouble With $150,000 Wine" in Barron's (Vol. 88, July 7, 2008, No. 27, pp. 33)
Pub: Dow Jones & Company Inc.
Contact: Almar Latour, Chief Executive Officer
Ed: Jay Palmer. **Description:** Review of the book, "The Billionaire's Vinegar: The Mystery of the World's Most Expensive Bottle of Wine," which discusses vintners along with the marketing and distribution of wine as well as the winemaking industry as a whole. **Availability:** Online.

20658 ■ "Unilever Acquiring EVGA's Ice Cream Brands in Greece" in Ice Cream Reporter (Vol. 23, October 20, 2010, No. 11, pp. 1)
Description: Unilever will acquire the ice cream brands and distribution network of the Greek frozen dessert manufacturer EVGA. **Availability:** Print; Online.

20659 ■ "United Natural Foods Establishes Charitable Foundation to Support Healthy, Sustainable and Organic Food Systems" in United Natural Foods, Inc. (May 14, 2012)
Pub: The Financial Times Ltd.
Contact: John Ridding, Chief Executive Officer
E-mail: john.ridding@ft.com
Description: United Natural Foods Inc. (UNFI) has established a foundation committed to supporting healthy, sustainable and organic food systems. UNFI distributes natural, organic and specialty foods and related products. **Availability:** PDF; Online.

20660 ■ "Vitabath: Sweet Smell of Success" in Retail Merchandiser (Vol. 51, September-October 2011, No. 5, pp. 82)
Pub: Phoenix Media Corp.
Description: After taking over at Vitabath, Rich Brands developed new scents and products and while discovering new channels to distribute these items. **Availability:** PDF; Online.

20661 ■ "'We Have Surpassed Our Early Goals...Everything Else Is a Bonus" in Business Journal (Vol. 32, June 6, 2014, No. 2, pp. 13)
Pub: American City Business Journals, Inc.
Contact: Mike Olivieri, Executive Vice President
Released: June 2014. **Description:** Lift Bridge Brewing Company co-founder and president, Dan Schwarz, shares his views about making the transition into a regional player. Schwarz discusses the quality of their beer as the main reason for their relevance to beer drinkers in Minnesota. The firm plans to become a regional brewery and distributor of beer across the nation. **Availability:** Print; Online.

20662 ■ "Web-Based Marketing Excites, Challenges Small Business Use" in Colorado Springs Business Journal (January 20, 2010)
Pub: BridgeTower Media
Contact: Adam Reinebach, President
Ed: Becky Hurley. **Description:** Business-to-business and consumer-direct firms alike are using the fast-changing Web technologies to increase sales, leads and track consumer behavior but once a company commits to an Online marketing plan, experts believe, they must be prepared to consistently tweak and overhaul content and distribution vehicles in order to keep up. **Availability:** Online.

20663 ■ "West Sacramento Food Shipper Changes Hands" in Sacramento Business Journal (Vol. 31, May 30, 2014, No. 3)
Pub: American City Business Journals, Inc.
Contact: Mike Olivieri, Executive Vice President
Released: Weekly. **Price:** $4, Introductory 4-week offer(Digital & Print). **Description:** United Natural Foods Inc. (UNFI) is acquiring Tony's Fine Foods in a $195 million deal that brings together two companies native to Sacramento, California. Tony's is the leading distributor of perishable food products since 1934 and will operate as a wholly-owned subsidiary of UNFI as part of the deal. **Availability:** Print; Online.

20664 ■ "When To Drop an Unprofitable Customer: A Supplier Contemplates Cutting Off One Of Its Biggest Accounts" in Harvard Business Review (Vol. 90, April 2012, No. 4, pp. 137)
Pub: Harvard Business Review Press
Contact: Moderna V. Pfizer, Contact
Ed: Robert S. Kaplan. **Description:** A fictitious vendor relations challenge is presented, with contributors providing advice. The problem involves whether to break ties with a solidly loyal client but one that has become expensive to maintain. Suggestions include dropping the client's special low price privilege and introduce the client to products and services used by other clients, or help the client shift to a new supplier.

20665 ■ "Worldwide Food Services (EREI) Tests Mini Dollar Store Program" in Marketwired (August 6, 2009)
Pub: Comtex News Network Inc.
Contact: Kan Devnani, President
Description: Mini Dollar Stores and Eagle View LLC, wholly-owned subsidiaries of Worldwide Food Services, Inc., recently met with government officials and purchasing agents to lay out a test program which would distribute Mini Dollar Store items into VA hospital gift shops.

TRADE PERIODICALS

20666 ■ Distribution Center Management
Pub: Alexander Research & Communications Inc.
URL(s): www.distributiongroup.com/45_proven_ways_to_cut_warehouse_costs.php
Ed: Jeff Ostrowski. **Released:** Monthly **Description:** The monthly newsletter for distribution centers and warehouse managers with ideas and information on how to run their facilities more productively. **Availability:** Print; Online.

TRADE SHOWS AND CONVENTIONS

20667 ■ Final Mile Forum and Expo
URL(s): clda.org/event/fmf-2022-staying-relevant-in-the-final-mile-b2b-b2c-be-prepared
Frequency: Annual. **Description:** Tradeshow organized by the Customized Logistics and Delivery Association to showcase new products and services from the logistics and delivery industry. **Principal Exhibits:** Tradeshow organized by the Customized Logistics and Delivery Association to showcase new products and services from the logistics and delivery industry.

20668 ■ The FMI Show
International Foodservice Distributors Association (IFDA)
1660 International Dr., Ste. 550
McLean, VA 22102
Ph: (703)532-9400
Fax: (703)880-7117
URL: http://www.ifdaonline.org
Contact: Mark S. Allen, President
E-mail: mallen@ifdaonline.org
URL(s): www.fmi.org/events-education/calendar
Frequency: Biennial. **Description:** Material handling equipment, trucks, fork lifts, trailers, trucks, racks and pallets, computers and software, warehouse and fleet consultants and other services and equipment related to warehousing, distribution, human resources, information technology, logistics and transportation. **Audience:** Food retailers. **Principal Exhibits:** Material handling equipment, trucks, fork lifts, trailers, trucks, racks and pallets, computers and software, warehouse and fleet consultants and other services and equipment related to warehousing, distribution, human resources, information technology, logistics and transportation.

CONSULTANTS

20669 ■ Clear Light Books [Clear Light Publishing]
823 Don Diego Ave.
Santa Fe, NM 87505
Free: 800-253-2747
Co. E-mail: info@clearlightbooks.com
URL: http://www.clearlightbooks.com
Facebook: www.facebook.com/clearlightbooks
X (Twitter): x.com/ClearLightBooks
Description: Business management consulting specifically in the area of profit planning, as well as warehouse and distribution assistance and additional expertise in computer system design and serves small, medium-sized businesses and warehouse and distribution. **Scope:** Publisher and distributor of books related to art, culture, children, cookbooks, environment, folklore, native American, politics, sovereignty, and spirituality. **Special Services:** Warestudy™; Profit Planning™.

GENERAL SMALL BUSINESS TOPICS

Distributing ■ 20676

20670 ■ Colonial Compliance Systems, Inc.
Colonial Group, Inc.
101 N LATHROP AVE.
Savannah, GA 31415-0576
Ph: (912)236-1331
Free: 800-944-3835
URL: http://www.colonialgroupinc.com
Contact: Deborah Nash, Manager, Accounting
E-mail: dnash@compliancesystemsinc.com
Linkedin: www.linkedin.com/company/ez-compliance-systems-inc.
X (Twitter): x.com/ColonialCompl1
Description: Provider of marine consultancy services such as maritime safety, security and environmental compliance, and offers assistance to ship owners, managers, and agents. **Scope:** Provider of marine consultancy services such as maritime safety, security and environmental compliance, and offers assistance to ship owners, managers, and agents. **Founded:** 1988. **Training:** Safety Training.

20671 ■ General Business Consultants Inc. (GBC)
2421 Brian Dr.
Northbrook, IL 60062
Ph: (224)723-5143
URL: http://www.genbuscon.com
Contact: Dick Friedman, Contact
E-mail: rcfriedman@att.net
Description: Consultancy is engaged in strategic planning, business process improvement, enterprise resource management, and materials requirements planning services to provide improved operations and inventory management systems for distributors, wholesalers, and manufacturers and also writes articles for trade magazines, conducts workshops and webinars for associations, trade groups, and individuals. **Founded:** 1976. **Publications:** "The Butler Did It: Errors That Get Customers Angry"; "Do You Really Need a New System"; "New Warehouse Management Technologies Beat the Old Ones"; "How to Avoid a Warehouse Management System Horror Story"; "Don't Sign That System Contract-Until Its Changed to Include Protections"; "Why Some Systems are Decreasing Customer Service, Margins and Inventory Profitability"; "How to Modify a System to Maximize Inventory-Based Customer Service and Roi"; "What Lists of Software Don't Show Can Kill a Distributor"; "Great Software Does Not Manage Inventory Effectively"; "System Contracts: Add Specific Performance Guarantees to Avoid Problems"; "RF, RFID, WMS, VDP, PTL: A Review of warehouse Technologies". **Training:** Tech Trends That Can Hurt Distributors And Wholesalers; Do you really need a new system?; Warehouse Management Systems (WMS): New Technologies, And Tips For A Successful WMS; Avoiding Excess Inventory And Shortages While Keeping Customer Service High; Why Some Systems Are Decreasing Customer Service, Margins And Return On Inventory Investment-And What To Do About It; Don't Sign That System Contract-Until You Change It To Protect Yourself; Talking Chips Replace Printed Bar Codes; Wireless Digital Networks Result in Go-Anywhere Data Communications; Warehouse Management Systems Become Affordable and Practical; Supply Chain Management Dramatically Alters Business Relationships; The Plot to Take Away Distributors Computers; Software Support Moves Overseas-the Pros and Cons.

20672 ■ Myron I. Blumenfeld & Associates (MIBA)
500 E 77th St., Ste. 2324
New York, NY 10162
Ph: (212)706-2112
Fax: (212)706-2118
URL: http://www.myroniblumenfeld.com
Contact: Mike Blumenfeld, Founder
E-mail: mike@myroniblumenfeld.com
Description: Firm provides consulting services to small and mid-sized businesses engaged in goods and services. **Founded:** 1981. **Training:** Starting Your Own Business. Business Planning. Inventory Management. New Innovations in Retail Distribution Technology. Bar Coding and Quick Response. Merchandise Planning for Quick Response. Global Marketing.

20673 ■ Shaw & Associates
950 Tharp Rd., Bldg. 100 Ste. 101
Yuba City, CA 95993
Ph: (530)674-1150
Fax: (530)674-7241
Co. E-mail: info@shawassociatesinc.com
URL: http://www.shawassociatesinc.com
Contact: David A. Shaw, President
Facebook: www.facebook.com/ShawAssociatesInc
Description: Management consultants specializing in facilities design for factories and distribution centers. Consulting includes, but is not limited to, factory layout, distribution center planning, materials handling improvement, organization, planning, scheduling and controls. Active with a variety of manufacturers and distribution companies. **Scope:** Management consultants specializing in facilities design for factories and distribution centers. Consulting includes, but is not limited to, factory layout, distribution center planning, materials handling improvement, organization, planning, scheduling and controls. Active with a variety of manufacturers and distribution companies. **Founded:** 1954.

20674 ■ Wesley-Kind Associates Inc.
6 E 43 St.
New York, NY 10017
Contact: Daniel A. Kind, Officer

Description: Material handling and distribution consultants offering advice on plant and warehouse layouts and operating systems for the movement, storage and control of materials and products. **Scope:** Material handling and distribution consultants offering advice on plant and warehouse layouts and operating systems for the movement, storage and control of materials and products. **Publications:** "How to Reengineer the Storage Function," Penton Publishing, 1995.

RESEARCH CENTERS

20675 ■ Institute for Distribution Excellence
1325 G St. NW Ste. 1000
Washington, DC 20005-3100
Co. E-mail: membership@naw.org
URL: http://www.naw.org/naw-institute-for-distribution-excellence
Contact: Patricia A. Lilly, Executive Director
E-mail: plilly@naw.org
Description: Firms that are members of the National Association of Wholesaler-Distributors, wholesalers, and trade associations. Seeks to advance knowledge in the field of wholesale distribution by means of long-range research projects. **Scope:** Wholesale distribution, focusing on long-range projects to advance knowledge in the field. **Publications:** *Facing the Forces of Change: The Road to Opportunity* (Triennial). **Geographic Preference:** National.

20676 ■ Texas A&M University - Dwight Look College of Engineering - Thomas and Joan Read Center
3127 TAMU
College Station, TX 77843-3127
URL: http://engineering.tamu.edu/etid/id/thomas-joan-read-center.html
Description: Integral unit of College of Engineering at Texas A&M University. **Scope:** Industrial distribution, sales force issues, quality assessment, logistics process design, e-commerce, distribution information systems interface, inventory management, supply chain management, financial analysis, organizational change, organizational culture, implementation of strategic plans, team building, benchmarking and gap analysis, developing core competencies, manufacturer-distributor relations, distributor profitability, purchasing, negotiations, distributor's asset management, financial transactions of the wholesaler-distributor, improving distributor return on investment, distribution operations management, product line profitability, trends, high-tech marketing, strategic alliances, strategic planning, market. **Founded:** 1988. **Publications:** *Thomas and Joan Read Center for Distribution Research and Education E-newsletter* (3/year). **Educational Activities:** Certificate in Distribution Management program; Continuing education programs for distributors and manufacturers; Distributor Management Development Seminars.

Economic Development

START-UP INFORMATION

20677 ■ *How to Start a Home-Based Mail Order Business*
Ed: Georganne Fiumara. **Released:** June 01, 2011. **Price:** Paperback. **Description:** Step-by-step guide for starting and growing a home-based mail order business. Information about equipment, pricing, online marketing, are included along with worksheets and checklists for planning. **Availability:** Print; Online.

20678 ■ *"'Passion Is the Key to Accomplishment" in South Florida Business Journal (Vol. 35, August 15, 2014, No. 3, pp. 11)*
Pub: American City Business Journals, Inc.
Contact: Mike Olivieri, Executive Vice President
Released: Weekly. **Price:** $8, introductory 4-week offer(Digital only). **Description:** Metro 1 president and CEO, Tony Cho, made his name by shaping neighborho9ods and large-scale urban projects in Miami, Florida. Cho says he got his first job when he was 11 years old working with a maintenance crew. Cho started his real estate firm during the economic downturn and believes surviving during the recession is his greatest entrepreneurial accomplishment to date. **Availability:** Print; Online.

ASSOCIATIONS AND OTHER ORGANIZATIONS

20679 ■ **Action for Enterprise (AFE)**
4600 N Fairfax Dr., Ste. 304
Arlington, VA 22203
Ph: (703)243-9172
Fax: (703)243-9123
URL: http://www.actionforenterprise.org
Contact: Frank Lusby, Executive Director
Description: Implements small enterprise development programs, based on a comprehensive analysis of business sectors and the interrelationships of enterprises that function with them. Initiates efforts to develop sustainable business development service providers at the local level. **Founded:** 1991. **Geographic Preference:** Multinational.

20680 ■ **Brazil-Canada Chamber of Commerce (BCCC) [Chambre de Commerce Brésil-Canada]**
401 Bay St., Ste. 1600
Toronto, ON, Canada M5H 0A6
Ph: (416)646-6770
Co. E-mail: info@brazcanchamber.org
URL: http://brazcanchamber.org
Contact: Carolina Mangabeira Albernaz, Chief Executive Officer
Facebook: www.facebook.com/brazcanchamber
Linkedin: www.linkedin.com/groups/2098563
X (Twitter): x.com/brazcanchamber
Instagram: www.instagram.com/brazcanchamber
Description: Promotes increased trade between Canada and Brazil. Provides assistance to companies wishing to trade with Brazil. Represents members before international trade organizations and government agencies and lobbies for removal of statutory barriers to commerce. **Founded:** 1973. **Geographic Preference:** Multinational.

20681 ■ **British Canadian Chamber of Trade and Commerce (BCCTC)**
c/o Idalia Obregon, Executive Director
Toronto, ON, Canada M5V 4A2
Co. E-mail: info@bcctc.ca
URL: http://www.britishcanadianchamber.com
Contact: Thomas J. O'Carroll, President
E-mail: tocarroll@bcctc.ca
Facebook: www.facebook.com/BCCTC1951
Linkedin: www.linkedin.com/company/the-british-canadian-chamber-of-trade-and-commerce
X (Twitter): x.com/bcctc
Instagram: www.instagram.com/bcctctoronto
Description: Canadian corporations doing business in the UK. Promotes increased trade between Britain and Canada. Lobbies for removal of statutory impediments to trade. **Founded:** 1951. **Geographic Preference:** Multinational.

20682 ■ *Business Barometer*
401-4141 Yonge St.
Toronto, ON, Canada M2P 2A6
Co. E-mail: cfib@cfib.ca
URL: http://www.cfib-fcei.ca/en
Contact: Dan Kelly, President
URL(s): www.cfib-fcei.ca/en/research-economic-analysis/business-barometer
Released: Monthly **Availability:** Print; PDF.

20683 ■ **Canada-Finland Chamber of Commerce (CFCC)**
191 Eglinton Ave. E
Toronto, ON, Canada M4P 1K1
Co. E-mail: info@canadafinlandcc.com
URL: http://canadafinlandcc.com
Contact: Marika Arovuo, President
Facebook: www.facebook.com/CanadaFinlandChamber
Linkedin: www.linkedin.com/company/canada-finland-chamber-of-commerce
YouTube: www.youtube.com/channel/UCDhvdB6vmQz07Rj-tdRaoDw
Description: Promotes trade between Canada and Finland. Provides information, assistance, and services to Finnish and Canadian corporations wishing to participate in international trade. **Founded:** 1971. **Geographic Preference:** National.

20684 ■ **Canada-India Business Council (C-IBC) [Conseil de Commerce Canada-Inde]**
80 Richmond St. W, Ste. 604
Toronto, ON, Canada M5H 2A4
Ph: (416)214-5947
Co. E-mail: info@canada-indiabusiness.com
URL: http://www.canada-indiabusiness.com
Contact: Victor T. Thomas, President
X (Twitter): twitter.com/CanadaIndiaBiz
YouTube: www.youtube.com/channel/UCScJED1GGJaMWkIMUEJLgEA
Description: Canadian businesses trading with India. Promotes increased trade between Canada and India. Advocates for legislation conducive to trade; represents members before trade and industrial organizations and the public. **Founded:** 1982. **Geographic Preference:** National.

20685 ■ **Canada-Pakistan Business Council (CPBC)**
15 All State Pky., Ste. 600
Markham, ON, Canada L3R 5B4
Ph: (905)752-4480
Co. E-mail: info@cpbconline.org
URL: http://cpbconline.org
Contact: Samir Dossal, President
Facebook: www.facebook.com/cpbconline
Description: Promotes increased trade between Canada and Pakistan. Facilitates mutual economic development through transfer of technology; encourages and assists in the formation of joint ventures involving Canadian and Pakistani companies. **Founded:** 1983. **Publications:** *Canada Pakistan Bulletin* (Quarterly). **Geographic Preference:** Multinational.

20686 ■ **Canadian Association for Business Economics (CABE) [Association Canadienne de Science Economique des Affaires]**
31 Adelaide St. E
Toronto, ON, Canada M5C 2J1
Free: 855-222-3321
Co. E-mail: info@cabe.ca
URL: http://www.cabe.ca
Contact: Bryan Yu, President
Facebook: www.facebook.com/CABEconomics
Linkedin: www.linkedin.com/company/canadian-association-for-business-economics
X (Twitter): x.com/CABE_Economics
Description: Individuals and organizations with an interest in business economics. Seeks to advance the study, teaching, and practice of business economics. Facilitates exchange of information among members; conducts research and educational programs. **Founded:** 1975. **Awards:** Doug Purvis Prize (Annual). **Geographic Preference:** National.

20687 ■ **Canadian Chamber of Commerce [La Chambre de Commerce du Canada]**
1700-275 Slater St.
Ottawa, ON, Canada K1P 5H9
Ph: (613)238-4000
Fax: (613)238-7643
Co. E-mail: info@chamber.ca
URL: http://www.chamber.ca
Contact: Perrin Beatty, President
E-mail: pbeatty@chamber.ca
Facebook: www.facebook.com/CdnChamberofCom
Linkedin: www.linkedin.com/company/cdnchamberofcom
X (Twitter): x.com/CdnChamberofCom
Instagram: www.instagram.com/cdnchamberofcom

Description: Primary connection between business and the federal government. Demonstrates impact on public policy and decision-making to the benefit of businesses, communities and families across Canada. **Founded:** 1925. **Geographic Preference:** National.

20688 ■ Canadian Council of Chief Executives
99 Bank St., Ste. 1001
Ottawa, ON, Canada K1P 6B9
URL: http://thebusinesscouncil.ca
X (Twitter): x.com/BizCouncilofCan
YouTube: www.youtube.com/user/CdnCEOCouncil
Description: Businesses and trade organizations. Promotes a healthy national economy. Conducts research; lobbies for legislation favorable to business; represents members' interests. **Founded:** 1976. **Geographic Preference:** National.

20689 ■ Canadian Federation of Independent Business (CFIB) - Research Library
401-4141 Yonge St.
Toronto, ON, Canada M2P 2A6
Co. E-mail: cfib@cfib.ca
URL: http://www.cfib-fcei.ca/en
Contact: Dan Kelly, President
Facebook: www.facebook.com/CFIB
Linkedin: www.linkedin.com/company/canadian-federation-of-independent-business
X (Twitter): x.com/CFIBNews
Instagram: www.instagram.com/cfib_fcei
YouTube: www.youtube.com/user/cfibdotca
Description: Promotes economic well-being of members and seeks to maintain a healthy domestic business climate. **Scope:** Business. **Founded:** 1971. **Holdings:** Figures not available. **Publications:** Mandate (Quarterly); Business Barometer (Monthly). **Geographic Preference:** National.

20690 ■ Canadian Labour Congress (CLC) - Library
2841 Riverside Dr.
Ottawa, ON, Canada K1V 8X7
Ph: (613)521-3400
Free: 800-387-3500
Fax: (613)521-4655
Co. E-mail: media@clcctc.ca
URL: http://canadianlabour.ca
Contact: Bea Bruske, President
E-mail: president-office@clcctc.ca
Facebook: www.facebook.com/clc.ctc
YouTube: www.youtube.com/user/canadianlabour
Description: Seeks to create a just and equitable society. **Scope:** Labor. **Founded:** 1956. **Holdings:** Figures not available. **Publications:** Canadian Labour (Quarterly); C.L.C. Fax-Press (Weekly); Sweatshop Alert; UI Bulletin (Periodic). **Geographic Preference:** National.

20691 ■ Centre de Commerce Mondial Montréal [World Trade Centre Montreal (WTCM)]
600-360 rue Saint-Antoine O
Montreal, QC, Canada H2Y3X4
Contact: Thomas P. Murray, President
Description: Businesses, professionals, and interested individuals. Seeks to foster the export of products and services by supporting, training and advising companies, associations and economic development institutions and organizations on certain activities on international markets through an integrated programme of export solutions. **Founded:** 1984. **Geographic Preference:** Local.

20692 ■ Conseil Canadien pour le Commerce Autochtone (CCAB) [Canadian Council for Aboriginal Business]
2 Berkeley St., Ste. 202
Toronto, ON, Canada M5A 4J5
Ph: (416)961-8663
Fax: (416)961-3995
Co. E-mail: memberrelations@ccab.com
URL: http://www.ccab.com
Contact: Tabatha Bull, President
E-mail: tbull@ccab.com
Facebook: www.facebook.com/CanadianCouncilforAboriginalBusiness
Linkedin: www.linkedin.com/company/canadian-council-for-aboriginal-business
X (Twitter): x.com/ccab_national
Instagram: www.instagram.com/ccab_national
Description: Promotes the full participation of aboriginal people in the Canadian economy. Seeks to connect aboriginal and non-aboriginal people and companies with the opportunities required to achieve personal and business success. Develops and operates the progressive aboriginal relations benchmarking and hallmarking program. **Founded:** 1982. **Awards:** Foundation for the Advancement of Aboriginal Youth Bursary Program; Foundation for the Advancement of Aboriginal Youth Scholarships. **Geographic Preference:** National.

20693 ■ Council of Development Finance Agencies (CDFA)
100 E Broad St., Ste. 1200
Columbus, OH 43215
Ph: (614)705-1300
Co. E-mail: info@cdfa.net
URL: http://www.cdfa.net
Contact: Toby Rittner, President
E-mail: trittner@cdfa.net
Linkedin: www.linkedin.com/company/council-of-development-finance-agencies
X (Twitter): x.com/CDFA_Update
Description: Works for the advancement of development finance concerns and interests. Represents members of the development finance community from the public, private and non-profit sectors. **Founded:** 1982. **Publications:** Development Finance Review Weekly (Weekly). **Educational Activities:** CDFA National Development Finance Summit (Annual). **Awards:** CDFA Practitioner's Showcase. **Geographic Preference:** National.

20694 ■ Dialogue on Diversity
1629 K St. NW, Ste. 300
Washington, DC 20006
Ph: (703)631-0650
Fax: (703)631-0617
Co. E-mail: dialog.div@prodigy.net
URL: http://www.dialogueondiversity.org
Contact: Maria Cristina C. Caballero, President
Facebook: www.facebook.com/dialogueondiversityorg
X (Twitter): x.com/dialogondiv
Instagram: www.instagram.com/dialogdiv
Description: Promotes social and political advancement of women and men from diverse ethnic and national traditions; fosters increased economic empowerment; aims to promote and develop entrepreneurial excellence, technology, networking, and education. **Founded:** 1990. **Geographic Preference:** National.

20695 ■ Edmonton Chamber of Commerce (ECC)
600 - 9990 Jasper Ave.
Edmonton, AB, Canada T5J 1P7
Ph: (780)426-4620
Fax: (780)424-7946
Co. E-mail: info@edmontonchamber.com
URL: http://www.edmontonchamber.com
Contact: Amir Shami, Co-Chief Executive Officer Co-President
Facebook: www.facebook.com/EdmontonChamber
Linkedin: www.linkedin.com/company/edmonton-chamber-of-commerce
X (Twitter): x.com/edmontonchamber
Instagram: www.instagram.com/edmontonchamber
YouTube: www.youtube.com/user/edmontonchamber
Description: Provides networking opportunities via special events held during the year. Provides discount and affinity programs, business referrals and business resources. Owns and operates the World Trade Center Edmonton (WTCE). Assists businesses, professionals, and interested individuals in developing national and international trade by providing information and advice on new markets and products. Organizes trade missions to World Trade Centers and facilitates contact with government agencies. Offers research and information gathering on trade opportunities, educational programs, and consumer and business assistance. **Founded:** 1889. **Publications:** Commerce News; Edmonton Commerce Directory (Annual); Commerce News (Monthly); Edmonton and Homersham Commerce & Industry: Report on Business (Monthly). **Geographic Preference:** Local.

20696 ■ Foundation Asie Pacifique du Canada [Asia Pacific Foundation of Canada (APFC)]
680-1066 W Hastings St.
Vancouver, BC, Canada V6E 3X2
Ph: (604)684-5986
Fax: (604)681-1370
Co. E-mail: info@asiapacific.ca
URL: http://www.asiapacific.ca
Contact: Pierre Pettigrew, Co-President Co-Chief Executive Officer
Facebook: www.facebook.com/asiapacificfoundationofcanada
Linkedin: www.linkedin.com/company/apfcanada
X (Twitter): x.com/AsiaPacificFdn
YouTube: www.youtube.com/channel/UCkieSwux1pmkNv2hvUsXjKg
Description: Seeks to remove barriers to international trade between Canada and Asia. **Scope:** Transpacific relations of Canada, focusing on its economic, political and social relations with Asia. **Founded:** 1984. **Publications:** Asia Pacific Foundation of Canada Annual report (Annual); Asia Pacific Foundation of Canada Research reports. **Awards:** Asia Pacific Foundation of Canada Post-Graduate Research Fellowships (Annual); Asia Pacific Foundation of Canada Media Fellowships (Annual). **Geographic Preference:** National.

20697 ■ Holland House Canada (CNBPA)
Toronto, ON, Canada
Co. E-mail: events@hollandhouse.ca
URL: http://www.cnbpa.ca
Contact: Sebastiaan Postma, President
E-mail: president@cnbpa.ca
Linkedin: www.linkedin.com/company/hollandhousecanada
Description: Business people and professionals in Canada and the Netherlands. Promotes increased trade and communication between Canada and the Netherlands. Serves as a forum for the exchange of information among members. **Founded:** 1979. **Geographic Preference:** Multinational.

20698 ■ I.E. Canada [Association canadienne des importateurs et exportateurs]
15 Allstate Pkwy., 6th Fl.
Markham, ON, Canada L3R 5B4
Free: 866-616-2243
Co. E-mail: info@iecanada.com
URL: http://iecanada.com
Contact: Keith Mussar, Contact
E-mail: kmussar@iecanada.com
Facebook: www.facebook.com/IECanada-1638214366455924
Instagram: www.instagram.com/ie_canada
Description: Individuals and firms with an interest in Canada's international trade. Promotes increased participation by Canada in the global economy; seeks to maintain a business climate conducive to increased international trade. Represents members' interests before government agencies; prepares model trade programs, regulations, and policies. Provides advice and assistance to members; serves as a clearinghouse on international trade. **Founded:** 1932. **Publications:** I.E. Global (Semiannual); Tradeweek (Semimonthly); Canadian Importers Association, Inc.--Membership Directory (Annual). **Educational Activities:** I.E. Canada Conference. **Geographic Preference:** National.

20699 ■ Insight Center for Community Economic Development
360 14th St., Ste. 500a
Oakland, CA 94612-3200
Ph: (510)466-1692
Co. E-mail: info@insightcced.org
URL: http://insightcced.org

Contact: Anne Price, President
Description: Aims to build economic health in vulnerable communities. Develops and promotes innovative solutions that help people and communities become, and remain, economically secure. Collaborates with foundations, nonprofits, educational institutions, government and businesses to develop, strengthen and promote programs and public policy that: lead to good jobs, strengthen early care and education systems, and enable people and communities to build financial and educational assets. **Scope:** Legal resources, business and employment development, and planning and implementation of community economic development strategies in low income neighborhoods. **Founded:** 1969. **Geographic Preference:** National.

20700 ■ International Economic Development Council (IEDC)
1275 K St., Ste. 300
Washington, DC 20005-4083
Ph: (202)223-7800
Fax: (202)223-4745
Co. E-mail: marketing@iedconline.org
URL: http://www.iedconline.org
Contact: Nathan Ohle, President
Facebook: www.facebook.com/iedcONLINE
Linkedin: www.linkedin.com/company/international-economic-development-council
X (Twitter): x.com/iedctweets
Description: Works to help economic development professionals improve the quality of life in their communities. **Founded:** 1967. **Publications:** *International Economic Development Council--Membership Directory*; *Annual Federal Review and Budget Overview* (Annual); *Economic Development Journal* (Quarterly); *Economic Development Now*; *Federal Review* (Annual); *Economic Development Review*. **Awards:** IEDC Internet and New Media Awards (Annual); IEDC Leadership Awards (Annual); Edward deLuca Lifetime Achievement Award for Excellence in Economic Development (Annual); IEDC Partnership Awards (Annual); IEDC Program Awards (Annual); IEDC Promotional Awards (Annual). **Geographic Preference:** National.

20701 ■ International Finance Corp. (IFC) - Library
2121 Pennsylvania Ave. NW
Washington, DC 20433
Co. E-mail: comms@ifc.org
URL: http://www.ifc.org/wps/wcm/connect/corp_ext_content/ifc_external_corporate_site/home
Contact: Makhtar Diop, Managing Director
Facebook: www.facebook.com/IFCwbg
Linkedin: www.linkedin.com/company/ifclinkedin
X (Twitter): x.com/IFC_org
Instagram: www.instagram.com/ifc_org
YouTube: www.youtube.com/user/IFCvideocasts
Description: Promotes sustainable private sector investments in developing countries as a way to reduce poverty and improve people's lives. **Scope:** Finance. **Founded:** 1956. **Holdings:** Figures not available. **Publications:** *Emerging Markets Data Base*; *ESTOCK*. **Geographic Preference:** National.

20702 ■ La Chambre Canadienne Allemande de l'Industrie et du Commerce Inc. (CGCIC) [Canadian German Chamber of Industry and Commerce. Inc (CGCIC)]
480 University Ave., Ste. 1500
Toronto, ON, Canada M5G 1V2
Ph: (416)598-3355
Fax: (416)598-1840
Co. E-mail: info.toronto@germanchamber.ca
URL: http://kanada.ahk.de/en
Contact: Yvonne Denz, Chief Executive Officer
Description: Promotes increased trade between Canada and Germany. Lobbies for removal of barriers to trade. **Founded:** 1968. **Publications:** *Canadian German Headlines* (Monthly); *Canadian German Chamber of Industry and Commerce--Membership Directory*. **Geographic Preference:** Multinational.

20703 ■ Main Street America
53 W Jackson Blvd., Ste. 350
Chicago, IL 60604
Ph: (312)610-5613
Co. E-mail: info@mainstreet.org
URL: http://mainstreet.org
Facebook: www.facebook.com/NatlMainStreet
Linkedin: www.lnkedin.com/company/main-street-america
X (Twitter): twitter.com/NatlMainStreet
Instagram: www.instagram.com/natlmainstreet
Description: Offers economic development and community revitalization in older commercial districts.

20704 ■ National Alliance of Community Economic Development Associations (NACEDA)
1660 L St. NW, Ste. 306
Washington, DC 20036
Ph: (202)518-2660
Co. E-mail: info@naceda.org
URL: http://www.naceda.org
Contact: Frank Woodruff, Executive Director
E-mail: fwoodruff@naceda.org
Facebook: www.facebook.com/NACEDAnetwork
X (Twitter): x.com/nacedatweets
Description: Serves as a vehicle and a national voice for developing and pursuing a national community development agenda. Supports the work of Community Economic Development associations, local Community Development Corporations and practitioners nationwide. Works to strengthen the role of state CED associations in promoting the efforts of local CDCs and building the capacity and reach of the CDC field. Convenes a national policy committee to gather input from the field, craft positions on public policy issues and develop strategies for their implementation. Coordinates with other like-minded national and regional organizations working on community development issues to leverage resources and maximize impact. **Founded:** 2006. **Geographic Preference:** National.

20705 ■ National Association of Development Organizations Research Foundation (NADO)
122 C St. NW, Ste. 830
Washington, DC 20001
Ph: (202)921-4440
Co. E-mail: info@nado.org
URL: http://www.nado.org
Contact: Misty Crosby, President
Facebook: www.facebook.com/NADO.org
X (Twitter): x.com/NADOWeb
Description: Identifies, studies and promotes regional solutions and approaches to improving local prosperity and services through the nationwide network of regional development organizations. Shares best practices and offers professional development training, analyzes the impact of federal policies and programs on regional development organizations, and examines the latest developments and trends in small metro and rural America. Provides federal advocacy, informative research, special reports and training to the nation's rural regional development organizations. **Founded:** 1988. **Educational Activities:** NADO Annual Training Conference (ATC) (Annual). **Awards:** NADO Congressional Partnership Award (Biennial); NADO Aliceann Wohlbruck Impact Awards (Annual). **Geographic Preference:** National.

20706 ■ National Development Council (NDC)
633 3rd Ave. 19th Fl., Ste. J
New York, NY 10017
Ph: (212)682-1106
Co. E-mail: info@ndconline.org
URL: http://ndconline.org
Contact: Tom Jackson, Director
Facebook: www.facebook.com/NationalDevelopmentCouncil
Linkedin: www.linkedin.com/company/national-development-council
X (Twitter): x.com/NatlDevCouncil
Description: Finances professionals' work with cities, counties, and states to: build permanent systems for developing financing; train local staff; structure and negotiate financing for development projects, local business development, and industrial expansion. **Founded:** 1969. **Publications:** *Developments* (Quarterly). **Geographic Preference:** National.

20707 ■ National Economic Association (NEA)
URL: http://neaecon.org
Contact: Valerie Wilson, President
Linkedin: www.linkedin.com/company/national-economic-association/
X (Twitter): twitter.com/neaecon
Description: Concerned with encouraging blacks to enter the economics profession. Conducts research on the economic problems of the black community. **Founded:** 1969.

20708 ■ Pacific Community Ventures Inc.
1700 Broadway, Ste. 300
Oakland, CA 94612
Ph: (415)442-4300
Fax: (415)442-4313
Co. E-mail: info@pcvmail.org
URL: http://www.pacificcommunityventures.org
Contact: Bulbul Gupta, President
Facebook: www.facebook.com/pacificcommunityventures
Linkedin: www.linkedin.com/company/pacificcv
X (Twitter): x.com/PCVtweets
Instagram: www.instagram.com/pacificcommunityventures
YouTube: www.youtube.com/channel/UCsCK261CCLrp8qvx2rKSBXg
Description: Supports small business owners and their communities in the fight for economic, racial, and gender justice. **Founded:** 1998.

20709 ■ Prosperity Now
1200 G St. NW Ste. 400
Washington, DC 20005
Ph: (202)408-9788
Co. E-mail: hello@prosperitynow.org
URL: http://www.prosperitynow.org
Contact: Gary Cunningham, Co-President Co-Chief Executive Officer
Facebook: www.facebook.com/ProsperityNow.org
Linkedin: www.linkedin.com/company/prosperity-now
X (Twitter): x.com/prosperitynow
Instagram: www.instagram.com/prosperitynow
YouTube: www.youtube.com/user/CFEDorg
Description: Provides assistance to public and private organizations concerned with increasing economic opportunity of individuals through the encouragement and support of enterprise development; serves as a forum for the exchange of ideas. Strives to research, develop, and disseminate entrepreneurial policy initiatives at the local, state, and federal levels. Conducts consulting services and compiles statistics. **Scope:** Offers expertise in economic research. Offers services as identify promising ideas, test and refine them in communities to find out what works, craft policies and products to help good ideas reach scale, and foster new markets to achieve greater economic impact. **Founded:** 1979. **Publications:** "Children's Savings Accounts and Financial Aid"; "Linking Youth Savings and Entrepreneurship". **Training:** Fighting Poverty: The Role of Asset Building in Public Policy; IDAS and Microenterprise; Self-Sustaining IDA Initiatives; Serving Multi-Cultural Markets; Asset Purchase Effective Practices; Policy Proposals, Opportunities, and Barriers for Youth Savings. **Educational Activities:** Prosperity Summit (Biennial). **Geographic Preference:** National.

20710 ■ Swedish-Canadian Chamber of Commerce (SCCC)
2 Bloor St. W, Ste. 2109
Toronto, ON, Canada M4W 3E2
Ph: (416)925-8661
Co. E-mail: info@sccc.ca
URL: http://sccc.ca
Contact: Marie Larsson, Executive Director
Facebook: www.facebook.com/SwedishCanadianChamber
Linkedin: www.linkedin.com/company/swedish-canadian-chamber-of-commerce
X (Twitter): x.com/SwedishCanadian

Description: Facilitates business and cultural development between Sweden and Canada. Serves as a forum allowing Swedes and Canadians with mutual interests to connect through business, cultural and social opportunities. **Founded:** 1965. **Geographic Preference:** Multinational.

20711 ■ **Technologies du Développement Durable Canada (TDDC) [Sustainable Development Technology Canada (SDTC)]**
45 O'Connor St., Ste. 1850
Ottawa, ON, Canada K1P 1A4
Ph: (613)234-6313
Co. E-mail: info@sdtc.ca
URL: http://www.sdtc.ca/fr
Contact: Leah Lawrence, President
Facebook: www.facebook.com/SustainableDevelopmentTechnologyCanada
Linkedin: www.linkedin.com/company/sustainable-development-technology-canada
X (Twitter): twitter.com/SDTC_TDDC

Description: Seeks to promote a sustainable development technology infrastructure in Canada. **Founded:** 2001. **Geographic Preference:** National.

20712 ■ **USA Engage**
1225 New York Ave. NW, Ste. 650B
Washington, DC 20005
Ph: (202)887-0278
Fax: (202)452-8160
Co. E-mail: sales@contentactive.com
URL: http://www.nftc.org/?id=1
Contact: Richard Sawaya, Vice President
E-mail: rsawaya@nftc.org

Description: Promotes economic strength in America as integral to the nation's security and worldwide leadership. **Founded:** 1997. **Geographic Preference:** National.

20713 ■ **World Trade Centre Vancouver (WTC-V) [WTC Vancouver]**
999 Canada Pl., Ste. 400
Vancouver, BC, Canada V6C 3E1
Ph: (604)640-5481
Co. E-mail: info@wtcvancouver.ca
URL: http://www.wtca.org/world-trade-center-vancouver
Contact: Austin Nairn, Executive Director
E-mail: anairn@boardoftrade.com
URL(s): www.boardoftrade.com/wtc/vancouver
Facebook: www.facebook.com/worldtradecentrevancouver
X (Twitter): x.com/BoardofTrade

Description: Businesses, professionals, and interested individuals. Facilitates the development of national and international trade by providing traders and investors with information and advice on new markets and products. Organizes trade missions to World Trade Centers and facilitates contact with government agencies. Offers research and information gathering on trade opportunities, educational programs, and consumer and business assistance. **Founded:** 1983. **Publications:** Sounding Board (Monthly). **Geographic Preference:** National.

SMALL BUSINESS ASSISTANCE PROGRAMS

20714 ■ **TruFund Financial Services, Inc.**
1927 1st Ave. N, Ste. 602
Birmingham, AL 35203
Ph: (205)715-2710
Co. E-mail: info@trufund.org
URL: http://www.trufund.org
Contact: James H. Bason, President
Facebook: www.facebook.com/TruFundFinancialServicesInc
X (Twitter): x.com/TruFundFinServ
YouTube: www.youtube.com/channel/UCc16yW-3HqQ-7bzwWE8xwDQ

Description: Looks to stimulate economic development in communities underserved by traditional banking institutions. Offers affordable capital, hands-on business assistance, and innovative solutions to small businesses, non-profits, and real estate developers.

20715 ■ **TruFund Financial Services, Inc.**
39 W 37 St., 7th Fl.
New York, NY 10018
Ph: (212)204-1303
Co. E-mail: info@trufund.org
URL: http://www.trufund.org
Contact: James H. Bason, President
Facebook: www.facebook.com/TruFundFinancialServicesInc
X (Twitter): x.com/TruFundFinServ
YouTube: www.youtube.com/channel/UCc16yW-3HqQ-7bzwWE8xwDQ

Description: Looks to stimulate economic development in communities underserved by traditional banking institutions. Offers affordable capital, hands-on business assistance, and innovative solutions to small businesses, non-profits, and real estate developers.

20716 ■ **TruFund Financial Services, Inc.**
935 Gravier St., Ste. 1120
New Orleans, LA 70112
Ph: (504)293-5550
Co. E-mail: info@trufund.org
URL: http://www.trufund.org
Contact: James H. Bason, President
X (Twitter): x.com/TruFundFinServ
YouTube: www.youtube.com/channel/UCc16yW-3HqQ-7bzwWE8xwDQ

Description: Looks to stimulate economic development in communities underserved by traditional banking institutions. Offers affordable capital, hands-on business assistance, and innovative solutions to small businesses, non-profits, and real estate developers.

REFERENCE WORKS

20717 ■ **"$3 Million in Repairs Prep Cobo for Auto Show"** in *Crain's Detroit Business (Vol. 26, January 4, 2010, No. 1, pp. 1)*
Pub: Crain Communications Inc.
Contact: Barry Asin, President
Ed: Nancy Kaffer. **Description:** Overview of the six projects priced roughly at $3 million which were needed in order to host the North American International Auto Show; show organizers stated that the work was absolutely necessary to keep the show in the city of Detroit. **Availability:** Print; Online.

20718 ■ **"The 7 Wonders of Tourism"** in *Business Journal Portland (Vol. 31, May 9, 2014, No. 10, pp. 10)*
Pub: American City Business Journals, Inc.
Contact: Mike Olivieri, Executive Vice President
Description: Travel Oregon's new travel campaign called '7 Wonders of Oregon' is expected to generate the area's economy. Reports show that the travel industry contributed $9.6 billion to the state's economy in 2013. The sector also employed a total of 93,900 Oregonians during the same year. Statistical data included. **Availability:** Online.

20719 ■ **"26 Things Holding Canadians Back"** in *Canadian Business (Vol. 85, August 13, 2012, No. 13, pp. 27)*
Description: A list of the problems that Canada needs to address in order to succeed as an economic superpower is presented. Some of these barriers include declining fertility rate, rising percentage of overweight and obese, and obsolete copyright laws. **Availability:** Print; Online.

20720 ■ **"2010: Important Year Ahead for Waterfront"** in *Bellingham Business Journal (Vol. March 2010, pp. 2)*
Description: A tentative timeline has been established for the environmental impact statement (EIS) slated for completion in May 2010. The plan for the Waterfront District includes detailed economic and architectural analysis of the feasibility of reusing remaining structures and retaining some industrial icons. **Availability:** Print; Online.

20721 ■ **"2015 Corporate Counsel Legal Pricing Guide - Mergers & Acquisitions"** in *Economics & Business Week (August 16, 2014, pp. 3)*
Pub: NewsRX LLC.
Contact: Kalani Rosell, Contact
Description: Research and Markets has added the 2015 Corporate Counsel Legal Pricing Guide - Mergers & Acquisitions to its report. The guide details how the mergers and acquisitions market for law firms has increased since the downturn in 2008-2009 due mostly to an improved economy, increased corporate liquidity and sometimes corporate tax policies of certain countries. **Availability:** Print; Online.

20722 ■ **"Actions to Implement Three Potent Post-Crisis Strategies"** in *Strategy & Leadership (Vol. 38, September-October 2010, No. 5)*
Pub: Emerald Inc.
Ed: Saul J. Berman, Richard Christner, Ragna Bell.
Description: The need for organizations to design and implement strategies to cope with the possible situations in the post-economic crisis environment is emphasized. The plans that organizations should implement to successfully manage uncertainty and complexity and to foster their eventual growth are discussed. **Availability:** PDF.

20723 ■ **Advantages of Small Business and the Economy**
URL(s): www.verizon.com/business/small-business-essentials/resources/advantages-of-small-business-and-the-economy/
Description: Examines the many areas of the economy and community where small businesses can make a real difference. **Availability:** Online.

20724 ■ **"After 4 Decades, Claypool's Moving On"** in *Philadelphia Business Journal (Vol. 33, June 27, 2014, No. 20, pp. 8)*
Pub: American City Business Journals, Inc.
Contact: Mike Olivieri, Executive Vice President
Released: Weekly. **Price:** $4, Introductory 4-week offer(Digital only). **Description:** John Claypool, former executive director of the Philadelphia chapter of the American Institute of Architects (AIA) and its affiliated Center for Architecture, discusses the changes he has seen over the forty years of his association with the city's business community and government. Claypool reflects on his achievements during his tenure at AIA and the impact of the recession on the architectural industry. **Availability:** Print; Online.

20725 ■ **"After Recession, Texas Cities Lead National Recovery"** in *Dallas Business Journal (Vol. 37, June 27, 2014, No. 42, pp. 28)*
Pub: American City Business Journals, Inc.
Contact: Mike Olivieri, Executive Vice President
Released: Weekly. **Price:** $4, introductory 4-week offer(Digital only). **Description:** A study of 510 U.S. cities by NeredWallet finds that 11 Texas cities are among those showing the fastest recovery since the recession began. NerdWallet analyst Sreekar Jasthi attributes this to growing business investment, rising employment, and an increase in median home values in cities such as Richardson and Gran Prairie. **Availability:** Print; Online.

20726 ■ **"Ailing Economy Nibbling at Tech-Sector Jobs"** in *Puget Sound Business Journal (Vol. 29, November 7, 2008, No. 29, pp. 1)*
Description: Seattle-area tech start-up companies including Redfin, Zillow, WildTangent, Daptiv, Avelle, and Intrepid Learning Solutions have cut staff as the nation's economy staggers. The layoffs are reminis-

cent of the tech bubble era, but most startups these days have been more prudent about spending and hiring as compared to that period. **Availability:** Print; Online.

20727 ■ *"Alberta: Help Wanted, Badly" in Globe & Mail (March 11, 2006, pp. B5)*
Ed: Patrick Brethour, Dawn Walton. **Description:** The issue of unemployment rate, which fell by 3.1 percent in Alberta, is discussed. **Availability:** Print; Online.

20728 ■ *"Anxiety Saps Vigor of Small Businesses" in Barron's (Vol. 92, September 15, 2012, No. 38, pp. 36)*
Pub: Dow Jones & Company Inc.
Contact: Almar Latour, Chief Executive Officer
Ed: Gene Epstein. **Description:** The Index of Small Business Optimism reveals that optimism among small businesses in the US remains low three years after the 2008-2009 recession. Uncertainty over economic conditionsand government actions could be behind the low optimism as well as no access to credit. **Availability:** Online.

20729 ■ *"Are You Ready for Dow 20,000?" in Barron's (Vol. 88, March 24, 2008, No. 12, pp. 26)*
Pub: Dow Jones & Company Inc.
Contact: Almar Latour, Chief Executive Officer
Ed: Jonathan R. Laing. **Description:** Stock strategist James Finucane forecasts that the Dow Jones Industrial Average will rise from its 12,361 level to as high as 20,000 from 2008 to 2009. He believes that stock liquidation and a buildup of cash provide the perfect conditions for a huge rally. **Availability:** Online.

20730 ■ *"Are You Rich? How Much of a Nest Egg Do You Need to Join the True Elite" in Barron's (Vol. 88, March 10, 2008, No. 10, pp. 27)*
Pub: Dow Jones & Company Inc.
Contact: Almar Latour, Chief Executive Officer
Ed: Tom Sullivan. **Description:** Discusses the minimum net worth of people considered as rich in America is now at $25 million. There are about 125,000 households in America that meet this threshold, while 49,000 households have a net worth between $25 million and $500 million, and about 1,400 US households have a net worth over $500 million. **Availability:** Online.

20731 ■ *"As Capital Gains Tax Hike Looms, Baltimore's Merger Activity Percolates" in Baltimore Business Journal (Vol. 28, August 27, 2010, No. 16, pp. 1)*
Pub: Baltimore Business Journal
Contact: Rhonda Pringle, President
E-mail: rpringle@bizjournals.com
Ed: Scott Dance. **Description:** Concerns for higher capital gains taxes in 2011 have been provoking buyers and sellers to engage in mergers and acquisitions activity, which is expected to gain momentum before the end of 2010. Companies that had saved cash during the recession have been taking advantage of the buyer's market. Other trends in local and national mergers and acquisitions activity are presented. **Availability:** Print.

20732 ■ *"Asia Breathes a Sigh of Relief" in Business Week (September 22, 2008, No. 4100, pp. 32)*
Description: Foreign bankers, such as those in Asia, that had been investing heavily in the United States began to worry as the housing crisis deepened and the impact on Freddie Mac and Fannie Mae became increasingly clear. Due to the government bailout, however, central banks will most likely continue to buy American debt. **Availability:** Print; Online.

20733 ■ *"At Last - Local Job Growth Picks Up" in Sacramento Business Journal (Vol. 30, February 21, 2014, No. 52, pp. 3)*
Pub: American City Business Journals, Inc.
Contact: Mike Olivieri, Executive Vice President

Released: Weekly. **Price:** $4, introductory 4-week offer(Digital & Print). **Description:** Local job growth rate in the Sacramento region of California rose by 2.3 percent in 2013, according to the Center for Strategic Economic Research. The number of non-farm jobs in the region increased 19,500 over the year, with leisure and hospitality adding 5,400 new job and government adding 2,900 jobs. **Availability:** Print; Online.

20734 ■ *"Athletes Face Wins and Losses After Pro Sports" in The Business Journal - Serving Phoenix and the Valley of the Sun (Vol. 29, September 21, 2008, No. 3, pp. 1)*
Pub: American City Business Journals, Inc.
Contact: Mike Olivieri, Executive Vice President
Ed: Chris Casacchia. **Description:** Professional athletes like hockey star Jeremy Roenick start businesses, while others like Joel Adamson work to boost local communities. Former athletes were found to be particularly interested with real estate businesses. Other views and information on former athletes and their life after sports are presented. **Availability:** Online.

20735 ■ *Atiyah's Accidents, Compensation and the Law*
Pub: Cambridge University Press
Contact: Peter Phillips, Chief Executive Officer
Ed: Peter Cane. **Released:** 9th edition. **Description:** Leading authority on the law of personal injuries compensation and the social, political and economic issues surrounding it.

20736 ■ *"Au Revoir Or Goodbye?" in Barron's (Vol. 88, July 14, 2008, No. 28, pp. 5)*
Pub: Dow Jones & Company Inc.
Contact: Almar Latour, Chief Executive Officer
Ed: Alan Abelson. **Description:** Former Senator Phil Gramm's opinion that the U.S. is a "nation of whiners" as they moan about recession is another example of the disconnection between Washington and Wall Street on one hand and the real world on the other. It would be a catastrophe for most of the world if Fannie Mae and Freddie Mac were to go under and take their trillions of mortgage debt with them. **Availability:** Online.

20737 ■ *"Auctions and Bidding: A Guide for Computer Scientists" in ACM Computing Surveys (Vol. 43, Summer 2011, No. 2, pp. 10)*
Pub: Association for Computing Machinery
Contact: Yannis Ioannidis, President
Ed: Simon Parsons, Juan A. Rodriguez-Aguilar, Mark Klein. **Released:** Volume 43 Issue 2. **Price:** $10, Members; $15, Nonmembers; $5, Students. **Description:** There are various actions: single dimensional, multi-dimensional, single-sided, double-sided, first-price, second-price, English, Dutch, Japanese, sealed-bid, and these have been extensively discussed and analyzed in economics literature. This literature is surveyed from a computer science perspective, primarily from the viewpoint of computer scientists who are interested in learning about auction theory, and to provide pointers into the economics literature for those who want a deeper technical understanding. In addition, since auctions are an increasingly important topic in computer science, the article also looks at work on auctions from the computer science literature. The aim is to identify what both bodies of work tell us about creating electronic auctions. **Availability:** Download; PDF.

20738 ■ *"Austin on Verge of Losing 7,500 Jobs" in Austin Business Journal (Vol. 31, May 6, 2011, No. 9, pp. 1)*
Pub: Austin Business Journal
Contact: Rachel McGrath, Director
E-mail: rmcgrath@bizjournals.com
Ed: Jacob Dirr. **Description:** Proposed state budget cuts are seen to result in the loss of as many as 7,500 public and private sector jobs in Austin, Texas, with the private sector losing the majority of workers. Comments from analysts are included. **Availability:** Print; Online.

20739 ■ *"Auto Asphyxiation" in Canadian Business (Vol. 85, August 13, 2012, No. 13, pp. 38)*
Ed: Michael McCullough. **Description:** The declining car ownership and utilization has profound business implications for oil companies and automakers and may bring substantial benefit to other sectors and the economy as a whole. The transition to the post-automotive age may happen in places where there is the will to change transportation practices but not in others. **Availability:** Print; Online.

20740 ■ *"Auto Show Aims to Electrify" in Crain's Detroit Business (Vol. 26, January 11, 2010, No. 2, pp. 1)*
Pub: Crain Communications Inc.
Contact: Barry Asin, President
Ed: Ryan Beene. **Description:** Overview of the North American International Auto show include sixteen production and concept vehicles including eight from the Detroit 3. High-tech battery suppliers as well as hybrid and electric vehicles will highlight the show. **Availability:** Print; Online.

20741 ■ *"BABs in Bond Land" in Barron's (Vol. 89, July 6, 2009, No. 27, pp. 14)*
Pub: Dow Jones & Company Inc.
Contact: Almar Latour, Chief Executive Officer
Ed: Jim McTague. **Description:** American Recovery and Reinvestment Act has created taxable Build America Bonds (BAB) to finance new construction projects. The issuance of the two varieties of taxable BABs is expected to benefit the municipal bond market. **Availability:** Online.

20742 ■ *"Back in the Race. New Fund Manager Has Whipped Sentinel International Equity Back into Shape" in Barron's (Vol. 88, March 17, 2008, No. 11, pp. 43)*
Pub: Dow Jones & Company Inc.
Contact: Almar Latour, Chief Executive Officer
Ed: Leslie P. Norton. **Description:** Katherine Schapiro was able to get Sentinel International Equity's Morningstar classification to blended fund from a value fund rating after joining Sentinel from her former jobs at Strong Overseas Fund. Schapiro aims to benefit from the global rebalancing as the U.S.'s share of the world economy shrinks. **Availability:** Online.

20743 ■ *"Baltimore-Area Businesses Still on the Mend 10 Years After 9/11" in Baltimore Business Journal (Vol. 29, September 9, 2011, No. 18, pp. 1)*
Pub: Boston Business Journal
Contact: Carolyn M. Jones, President
E-mail: cmjones@bizjournals.com
Ed: Scott Dance. **Description:** The 9/11 terrorist attacks have caused many companies in the US to dramatically shift course in response to changes in the economy. The concern that the cost of being unprepared for future disasters could be larger has remained among many companies. **Availability:** Online.

20744 ■ *"Baltimore's Businesses: Equipment Tax Breaks Help, But Money Still Tight: Weighing the Write-Off" in Baltimore Business Journal (Vol. 28, September 10, 2010, No. 18, pp. 1)*
Pub: Baltimore Business Journal
Contact: Rhonda Pringle, President
E-mail: rpringle@bizjournals.com
Ed: Daniel J. Sernovitz. **Description:** President Barrack Obama has proposed to let business write off their investments in plant and equipment upgrades under a plan aimed at getting the economy going. The plan would allow a company to write off 100 percent of the depreciation for their new investments at one time instead of over several years. **Availability:** Print.

20745 ■ *"Baltimore's Businesses, Latest Stats Show Growth may be an Aberration: Recovery a Ruse?" in Baltimore Business Journal (Vol. 28, August 6, 2010, No. 13, pp. 1)*
Pub: Baltimore Business Journal
Contact: Rhonda Pringle, President

E-mail: rpringle@bizjournals.com
Ed: Scott Dance. **Description:** Baltimore, Maryland-area businesses have remained cautious as their optimism faded along with the latest indicators on economic recovery. Economists believe they might be justified with their concern since sales were better, but there is no security that they will stay that way. **Availability:** Print.

20746 ■ *"Bank Buys May Heat Up In Birmingham"* in *Birmingham Business Journal (Vol. 31, May 9, 2014, No. 19, pp. 8)*
Pub: American City Business Journals, Inc.
Contact: Mike Olivieri, Executive Vice President
Released: Weekly. **Price:** $4, introductory 4-week offer(Digital & Print). **Description:** The banking industry in Birmingham, Alabama is poised for more mergers and acquisitions in the next two years as bank failures drop and potential sellers look for protection from increasing regulations. Experts suggest Birmingham is an attractive market for potential buyers because of its rich history as a top financial center and its stable economic environment. **Availability:** Print; Online.

20747 ■ *"Banking Sector To See Moderate Growth in 2014"* in *Houston Business Journal (Vol. 44, January 3, 2014, No. 35, pp. 5)*
Pub: American City Business Journals, Inc.
Contact: Mike Olivieri, Executive Vice President
Released: January 03, 2014. **Price:** $4, introductory 4-week offer(Digital only). **Description:** The Greater Houston Partnership reported that Houston, Texas' finance industry recovered 50.9 percent of the 5,500 jobs it lost compared to the nation's recovery rate of 34.4 percent. However, Houston's banking sector remains strong and deposits have almost doubled since 2008. The banks that established or expanded operations in Houston are also presented. **Availability:** Print; Online.

20748 ■ *"Bankruptcies"* in *Crain's Detroit Business (Vol. 26, January 11, 2010, No. 2, pp. 7)*
Pub: Crain Communications Inc.
Contact: Barry Asin, President
Ed: Dustin Walsh. **Description:** Listing of local businesses that filed for Chapter 7 or 11 protection in U.S. Bankruptcy Court in Detroit December 11-28. Under Chapter 11, a company files for reorganization. Chapter 7 involves total liquidation. **Availability:** Online.

20749 ■ *"Bargain Hunting In Vietnam"* in *Barron's (Vol. 88, July 14, 2008, No. 28, pp. M6)*
Pub: Dow Jones & Company Inc.
Contact: Almar Latour, Chief Executive Officer
Ed: Elliot Wilson. **Description:** Vietnam's economy grew by just 6.5 percent for the first half of 2008 and its balance of payments ballooned to $14.4 billion. The falling stock prices in the country is a boon for bargain hunters and investing in the numerous domestic funds is one way of investing in the country. Some shares that investors are taking an interest in are also discussed. **Availability:** Online.

20750 ■ *"Bark Up The Right Tree"* in *Small Business Opportunities (Winter 2009)*
Released: February 09, 2016. **Description:** Profile of Central Bark, a daycare company catering to pets that offers franchise opportunities and is expanding rapidly despite the economic downturn; the company's growth strategy is also discussed.

20751 ■ *"Bartering is Local Club's Stock in Trade"* in *Pueblo Chieftain (September 6, 2010)*
Description: As the economy waivers, a barter club in Pueblo, Colorado thrives. An examination of the club and the way it operates is included. **Availability:** Print; Online.

20752 ■ *"Bartering Trades on Talents"* in *Reading Eagle (June 20, 2010)*
Description: Bartering is not just a way of trading goods and services, it can be an essential tool for small business to survive in a bad economy.

20753 ■ *"The Bear's Back"* in *Barron's (Vol. 88, July 7, 2008, No. 27, pp. 17)*
Pub: Dow Jones & Company Inc.
Contact: Almar Latour, Chief Executive Officer
Ed: Randall W. Forsyth, Vito Racanelli. **Description:** US stock markets have formally entered the bear market after the Dow Jones Industrial Average dropped 20 percent from its high as of June 2008. Investors remain uncertain as to how long the bear market will persist, especially with the US economy on the edge of recession. **Availability:** Online.

20754 ■ *"The Beauty of Banking's Big Ugly"* in *Barron's (Vol. 89, July 27, 2009, No. 30, pp. 31)*
Pub: Dow Jones & Company Inc.
Contact: Almar Latour, Chief Executive Officer
Ed: Andrew Bary. **Description:** Appeal of the shares of Citigroup comes from its sharp discount to its tangible book value and the company's positive attributes include a strong capital position, high loan-loss reserves, and their appealing global-consumer. The shares have the potential to generate nice profits and decent stock gains as the economy turns. **Availability:** Online.

20755 ■ *"Bertha's Birth Stirs Juice"* in *Barron's (Vol. 88, July 14, 2008, No. 28, pp. M11)*
Pub: Dow Jones & Company Inc.
Contact: Almar Latour, Chief Executive Officer
Ed: Tom Sellen. **Description:** Price of frozen concentrated orange juice, which has risen to four-month highs of $1.3620 in July 2008 is due, in part, to the hurricane season that has come earlier than normal in the far eastern Atlantic thereby possibly harming the 2008-2009 Florida orange crop. Future tropical-storm development will affect the prices of this commodity. **Availability:** Online.

20756 ■ *"Best Turnaround Stocks"* in *Canadian Business (Vol. 81, Summer 2008, No. 9, pp. 65)*
Description: Share prices of Sierra Wireless Inc. and EXFO Electro Optical Engineering Inc. have fallen over the past year but have good chance at a rebound considering that the companies have free cash flow and no long-term debt. One-year stock performance analysis of the two companies is presented. **Availability:** Print; Online.

20757 ■ *"Best Value Stocks"* in *Canadian Business (Vol. 81, Summer 2008, No. 9, pp. 63)*
Description: Table showing the one-year performance of bargain or best-value stocks is presented. These stocks are undervalued compared to their North American peers, but it is projected that their five-year average return on equity is greater. **Availability:** Online.

20758 ■ *"Better than Advertised: Chip Plant Beats Expectations"* in *Business Review Albany (Vol. 41, June 27, 2014, No. 14, pp. 4)*
Pub: American City Business Journals, Inc.
Contact: Mike Olivieri, Executive Vice President
Released: Weekly. **Price:** $4, introductory 4-week offer(Digital only). **Description:** The $8.5 billion computer chip manufacturing plant and research center of GlobalFoundries in Malta, New York has strengthened the local economy in Saratoga County and helped the local manufacturing and construction industries recover from the recession. The Malta Plant construction project created more than 2,000 direct new construction jobs and over 10,000 indirect positions. **Availability:** Print; Online.

20759 ■ *"Better Made's Better Idea: Diversify Despite Rising Costs"* in *Crain's Detroit Business (Vol. 24, September 22, 2008, No. 38, pp. 18)*
Pub: Crain Communications Inc.
Contact: Barry Asin, President
Ed: Nathan Skid. **Description:** Better Made Snack Foods Inc. is planning to expand its product lines and market reach as well as boost manufacturing capability during a time in which the company is being buffeted by rising commodity and fuel costs. The company feels that diversification is the key to maintain sales and growth. **Availability:** Online.

20760 ■ *"Betting On Volatile Materials"* in *Barron's (Vol. 88, July 14, 2008, No. 28, pp. M11)*
Pub: Dow Jones & Company Inc.
Contact: Almar Latour, Chief Executive Officer
Ed: John Marshall. **Description:** Economic slowdowns in the U.S., Europe and China could cause sharp short-term declines in the materials sector. The S&P Materials sector is vulnerable to shifts in the flow of funds. Statistical data included. **Availability:** Online.

20761 ■ *"Beware of Rotting Money"* in *Barron's (Vol. 89, July 13, 2009, No. 28, pp. 31)*
Pub: Dow Jones & Company Inc.
Contact: Almar Latour, Chief Executive Officer
Ed: Thomas G. Donlan. **Description:** Inflation can take hold of a country and do it great harm; it is caused by people, most particularly central bankers in charge of the world's reserve currency. Arrogant economists pushed the belief that the government can engineer the economy and it is argued that there is trouble ahead when the government tries to control the economy. **Availability:** Online.

20762 ■ *"The Big Idea: The Judgment Deficit"* in *Harvard Business Review (Vol. 88, September 2010, No. 9, pp. 44)*
Pub: Harvard Business Publishing
Contact: Diane Belcher, Managing Director
Ed: Amar Bhide. **Price:** $8.95. **Description:** The importance of individual, decentralized initiative and judgment in the capitalist system is outlined. While financial models have their use, they cannot always account appropriately for the inherent uncertainty in economic decision making. **Availability:** Online; PDF.

20763 ■ *"Big Oil: Picks and Pans"* in *Canadian Business (Vol. 79, August 14, 2006, No. 16-17, pp. 67)*
Description: A survey on investments in Canadian energy companies and the inflation caused by oil price hike, are discussed. **Availability:** Print; Online.

20764 ■ *"'Biggest Loser' Adds Bit of Muscle to Local Economy"* in *Crain's Detroit Business (Vol. 26, January 4, 2010, No. 1, pp. 1)*
Pub: Crain Communications Inc.
Contact: Barry Asin, President
Ed: Chad Halcom. **Description:** NBC's weight-loss reality show, "The Biggest Loser" has helped the local economy and generated a new crop of local startup businesses due to past contestants that were from the Detroit area. **Availability:** Print; Online.

20765 ■ *"Boat Sales Sputter as Cash-Strapped Buyers Drift Away"* in *Puget Sound Business Journal (Vol. 29, August 15, 2008, No. 17, pp. 1)*
Description: Boat sales in Washington fell by 44 percent in the second quarter of 2008. The decline is attributed to the soft economy, which has given customers second thoughts on purchasing recreational water vehicles. **Availability:** Print; Online.

20766 ■ *"Bonds v. Stocks: Who's Right About Recession?"* in *Barron's (Vol. 90, August 23, 2010, No. 34, pp. M3)*
Pub: Barron's Editorial & Corporate Headquarters
Ed: Kopin Tan. **Description:** The future of treasury securities and stocks should the U.S. enter or avoid a recession are discussed. The back to school business climate and BHP Billiton's bid for Potash Corporation of Saskatchewan are also discussed. **Availability:** Online.

20767 ■ "Bottom-Fishing and Speed-Dating in India-How Investors Feel About the Indian Market" in *Barron's* (Vol. 88, March 24, 2008, No. 12, pp. M12)
Pub: Dow Jones & Company Inc.
Contact: Almar Latour, Chief Executive Officer

Ed: Elliot Wilson. **Description:** Indian stocks have fallen hard in 2008, with Mumbai's Sensex 30 down 30 percent from its January 2008 peak of 21,000 to 14,995 in March. The India Private Equity Fair 2008 attracted 140 of the world's largest private equity firms and about 24 of India's fastest-growing corporations. Statistical data included. **Availability:** Online.

20768 ■ "Bottom's Up: This Real-Estate Rout May Be Short-Lived" in *Barron's* (Vol. 88, July 14, 2008, No. 28, pp. 25)
Pub: Dow Jones & Company Inc.
Contact: Almar Latour, Chief Executive Officer

Ed: Jonathan R. Laing. **Description:** Economist Chip Case believes that home prices are nearing a bottom based on his analysis of the history of the housing market; surprisingly, in the past the housing market has rebounded after a quarter from a massive housing start drop. The drop in early stage delinquencies is another sign of the housing market's recovery. **Availability:** Online.

20769 ■ "Bracing for a Bear of a Week" in *Barron's* (Vol. 88, March 17, 2008, No. 11, pp. 24)
Pub: Dow Jones & Company Inc.
Contact: Almar Latour, Chief Executive Officer

Ed: Jacqueline Doherty. **Description:** JPMorgan Chase and the Federal Reserve Bank of New York's opening of a line of credit to Bear Stearns cut the stock price of Bear Stearns by 47 percent to 30 followed by speculation of an imminent sale. JP Morgan may be the only potential buyer for the firm and some investors say Bears could be sold at $20 to $30. Bears prime assets include its enormous asset base worth $395 billion. **Availability:** Online.

20770 ■ "Bracing for More Layoffs: This Week's Oil and Gas Jobs News" in *Sacramento Business Journal* (Vol. 28, September 30, 2011, No. 31, pp. 1)
Released: April 11, 2016. **Description:** Sacramento, California workers are preparing for a fresh wave of layoffs. The weak economy is seen to drive the development. **Availability:** Online.

20771 ■ "Brazil's New King of Food" in *Barron's* (Vol. 89, July 13, 2009, No. 28, pp. 28)
Pub: Dow Jones & Company Inc.
Contact: Almar Latour, Chief Executive Officer

Ed: Kenneth Rapoza. **Description:** Perdigao and Sadia's merger has resulted in the creation of Brasil Foods and the shares of Brasil Foods provides a play on both Brazil's newly energized consumer economy and its role as a major commodities exporter. Brasil Foods shares could climb as much as 36 percent. **Availability:** Online.

20772 ■ "Briarcliff Office Building Fills Up Fast" in *The Business Journal-Serving Metropolitan Kansas City* (Vol. 26, Sept. 5, 2008, pp. 1)
Pub: American City Business Journals, Inc.
Contact: Mike Olivieri, Executive Vice President

Ed: Rob Roberts. **Description:** Prior to its opening the Hilltop Office Building in Kansas City Missouri has attained 80 percent occupancy. FCStone Group Inc.'s plan to move to the building has boosted the facility's occupancy. Description and dimensions of the office building are also provided. **Availability:** Online.

20773 ■ "BRIEF: Montana Street Pawn Shop Closing Doors" in *Montana Standard* (November 6, 2010)
Pub: Montana Standard

Ed: John Grant Emeigh. **Description:** First National Pawn located in Butte, Montana will close its doors after losing its lease. Co-owner Pat Evenson reported the lease situation coupled with the economy prompted the decision to close. **Availability:** Online.

20774 ■ "Brisk Activity in North Fulton Office Market" in *Atlanta Business Chronicle* (July 11, 2014, pp. 2B)
Description: Activity appears to have pickup up briskly in the North Fulton office market during the first six months of 2014, mainly due to the high profile deals involving major players in the technology and health care sectors. **Availability:** Print; Online.

20775 ■ "Brown's Goal: 1,300 New Apartments and Condos" in *Business First of Buffalo* (Vol. 30, February 28, 2014, No. 24, pp. 6)
Pub: American City Business Journals, Inc.
Contact: Mike Olivieri, Executive Vice President

Released: February 28, 2014. **Price:** $140, Digital & Print; $115, Digital only. **Description:** Buffalo, New York Mayor Bryan Brown is planning for at least 1,300 new, market-rate residential units in the city's central business district over the next four years. The additional residential units are incorporated in Brown's larger strategy for creating a 24/7 downtown Buffalo. The impact of the residential development plan on the area's periphery is examined. **Availability:** Print; Online.

20776 ■ "Bryan Berg, Target Corp., Senior Vice President, Region 1" in *Hawaii Business* (Vol. 53, March 2008, No. 9, pp. 28)
Pub: PacificBasin Communications
Contact: Chuck Tindle, Director
E-mail: chuckt@pacificbasin.net

Ed: David K. Choo. **Description:** Bryan Berg, senior vice president at Target Corp.'s Region 1, shares his thoughts about entering the Hawaiian market and Target representatives bringing malasadas when visiting a business in the state. Berg finds the state's aloha spirit interesting and feels that it is important to be respectful of the Hawaiian culture and traditions in doing their business there. **Availability:** Online.

20777 ■ "Builder's Bankruptcy Fans Fears" in *Crain's Cleveland Business* (Vol. 28, October 22, 2007, No. 42, pp. 1)
Pub: Crain Communications Inc.
Contact: K. C. Crain, President

Ed: Stan Bullard. **Description:** Whitlatch & Co., Northeast Ohio's largest builder by unit volume in the early 1990s, has filed for Chapter 11 bankruptcy. This is causing builders and others in the real estate industry to wonder how long and severe the housing slump will be and which companies will survive. **Availability:** Online.

20778 ■ "Building a Portfolio, BRIC by BRIC" in *Barron's* (Vol. 92, August 25, 2012, No. 38, pp. M8)
Pub: Dow Jones & Company Inc.
Contact: Almar Latour, Chief Executive Officer

Ed: Reshma Kapadia. **Availability:** Online.

20779 ■ "A Bull Market in Finger-Pointing" in *Barron's* (Vol. 88, March 10, 2008, No. 10, pp. 9)
Pub: Dow Jones & Company Inc.
Contact: Almar Latour, Chief Executive Officer

Ed: Michael Santoli. **Description:** Discusses who is to blame for the financial crisis brought about by the credit crunch in the United States; the country's financial markets will eventually digest this crisis but will bottom out first before the situation improves. **Availability:** Online.

20780 ■ "Business Diary" in *Crain's Detroit Business* (Vol. 24, October 6, 2008, No. 40, pp. 23)
Pub: Crain Communications Inc.
Contact: Barry Asin, President

Description: Detailed listing of acquisitions, expansions, new products, new services, business contracts and startups from the Detroit area is provided. **Availability:** Print; Online.

20781 ■ "Business Guide and Employment Role"
Pub: AuthorHouse Inc.
Contact: William Elliott, President

Released: July 10, 2014. **Price:** $4.99, e-book; $15.18, softcover. **Description:** Financial expert discusses the importance of economic and business and their role in employment. The business and finance manager is crucial to any small business. The guide is an essential tool for any entrepreneur, the investor in business enterprise, the individual businessman, the human resources manager, and the business and finance professional to learn the merits to do business and play a role in employment. **Availability:** E-book; Print.

20782 ■ "Business Stands Firm for Reform: Battle Over 2011 Budget Expected" in *Crain's Detroit Business* (Vol. 26, January 4, 2010, No. 1, pp. 3)
Pub: Crain Communications Inc.
Contact: Barry Asin, President

Ed: Amy Lane. **Description:** As Michigan faces a new year of budgetary problems, many business groups are preparing to hold firm against tax increases and instead push for enacting spending reforms. **Availability:** Print; Online.

20783 ■ "C-Class Could Boost Auto Suppliers" in *Birmingham Business Journal* (Vol. 31, June 27, 2014, No. 26, pp. 10)
Pub: American City Business Journals, Inc.
Contact: Mike Olivieri, Executive Vice President

Released: June 27, 2014. **Description:** The 2014 model of the Mercedes-Benz C-Class will be the first to be built at the Vance, Alabama manufacturing plant, increasing business opportunities for auto suppliers in the region. Jason Hoff, president and CEO of Mercedes-Benz US International Inc. notes that the move will impact the local economy as several companies in the area expand their operations to meet the growing demand from Mercedes.

20784 ■ "C. Fla. Notches $5B in Real Estate Property Sales in Last 12 Months" in *Orlando Business Journal* (Vol. 31, July 4, 2014, No. 1, pp. 4)
Pub: American City Business Journals, Inc.
Contact: Mike Olivieri, Executive Vice President

Released: Weekly. **Price:** $8, Introductory 4-week offer(Digital & Print). **Description:** Real estate company Real Capital Analytics reports sales volumes totaling $5 billion in Central Florida's commercial real estate market between June 2013 and May 2014. Real estate deals in the region reflect investor interest in the Orlando market, as private equity and development firms renovate existing properties or build new construction projects, thus increasing property values, creating jobs and boosting the local economy. **Availability:** Print; Online.

20785 ■ "Calendar" in *Crain's Detroit Business* (Vol. 24, March 10, 2008, No. 10, pp. 21)
Pub: Crain Communications Inc.
Contact: Barry Asin, President

Description: Listing of events in the Detroit area include conferences addressing entrepreneurialism, economic development, and women business ownership. **Availability:** Print; Online.

20786 ■ "Calling All Creatives, Innovators, 'Expats': Detroit Is Hopping In September" in *Crain's Detroit Business* (Vol. 30, September 1, 2014, No. 35, pp. 6)
Pub: Crain Communications Inc.
Contact: Barry Asin, President

Description: Wayne State University is hosting a seminar September 16, 2014 which will focus on Detroit, Michigan as a center for innovation. Six other such seminars seeking investment in the city will be held in September. **Availability:** Online.

GENERAL SMALL BUSINESS TOPICS

20787 ■ *"Can Slow and Steady Win the Eco-Devo Race?"* in *Birmingham Business Journal* (Vol. 31, June 6, 2014, No. 23, pp. 8)
Pub: American City Business Journals, Inc.
Contact: Mike Olivieri, Executive Vice President
Released: Weekly. **Price:** $4, introductory 4-week offer(Digital & Print). **Description:** Evonik Corporation's expansion in Birmingham, Alabama reflects the city's economic development strategy. The company's creation of 25 jobs may be replicated by other companies. Birmingham is serious about becoming a biotechnology hub. **Availability:** Print; Online.

20788 ■ *"Can Tech Industry Share Wealth?"* in *Puget Sound Business Journal* (Vol. 35, May 23, 2014, No. 5, pp. 10)
Pub: American City Business Journals, Inc.
Contact: Mike Olivieri, Executive Vice President
Description: Nearly 700 local technology leaders gathered at the annual State of Technology event organized by Tech Alliance in Washington in May 2014. Trade show speaker, Geoffrey Moore, emphasized the role of the technology industry as a driver of local economies. **Availability:** Online.

20789 ■ *"Canada Nears European Trade Treaty"* in *Globe & Mail* (February 5, 2007, pp. B1)
Ed: Steven Chase. **Description:** The probable establishment of a treaty by Canada with Norway, Switzerland and Iceland for free-trade is discussed. The treaty will allow an annual business of $11 billion to take place in Canada. **Availability:** Print; Online.

20790 ■ *"Canada, Not China, Is Partner In Our Economic Prosperity"* in *Crain's Chicago Business* (Vol. 31, April 14, 2008, No. 15, pp. 14)
Pub: Crain Communications Inc.
Contact: Barry Asin, President
Ed: Paul O'Connor. **Description:** In 2005 more than $500 billion in two-way trade crossed the friendly border between the Great Lakes states and Canadian provinces and for decades Canada is every Great Lakes State's number one and growing export market. **Availability:** Online.

20791 ■ *"Canada Tops Again in G7: Study"* in *Globe & Mail* (March 22, 2006, pp. B8)
Description: Canada is still the cheapest place to do business among G7 countries, even though the rising dollar has eroded some of its advantages over the United States. The survey is detailed. **Availability:** Online.

20792 ■ *"Candidates Won't Bash Fed; Rate Cuts Bash Savers"* in *Barron's* (Vol. 88, March 24, 2008, No. 12, pp. 31)
Pub: Dow Jones & Company Inc.
Contact: Almar Latour, Chief Executive Officer
Ed: Jim McTague. **Description:** Candidates in the 2008 US presidential election, like the current administration, do not and will not bash the Federal Reserve. The Federal Reserve's aggressive interest rate cuts hurt the incomes of people depending on their savings accounts. **Availability:** Online.

20793 ■ *"Capitol Ideas: Regions to Lansing: Focus on Taxes, Reform, Keeping Talent"* in *Crain's Detroit Business* (Vol. 24, October 6, 2008)
Pub: Crain Communications Inc.
Contact: Barry Asin, President
Ed: Amy Lane. **Description:** Michigan must make bold and dramatic changes in public policy regarding business legislation. The tax structure, unemployment issues and attracting and retaining talent are among the issues the state must confront, especially in this tough economic climate. **Availability:** Online.

20794 ■ *"Captain Planet"* in (Vol. 90, June 2012, No. 6, pp. 112)
Pub: Harvard Business Review Press
Contact: Moderna V. Pfizer, Contact
Ed: Paul Polman, Adi Ignatius. **Price:** $8.95, hardcopy black and white. **Description:** Paul Polman, chief executive officer of Unilever N.V., discusses his company's sustainable living plan, which integrates social responsibility with corporate objectives. Topics include sustainable sourcing, abolishing quarterly reporting in favor of long-term perspectives, the impact of the 2008 global economic crisis, and turning a company into a learning organization. **Availability:** Print; Online; PDF.

20795 ■ *"The Case of the Deflated IPO"* in *Boston Business Journal* (Vol. 29, June 24, 2011, No. 7, pp. 1)
Pub: Boston Business Journal
Contact: Carolyn M. Jones, President
E-mail: cmjones@bizjournals.com
Ed: Scott Dance. **Description:** IPO market is on the rebound from the recession but for some companies in Maryland, the time is not yet ripe to go public. One of the companies that chooses to wait for better timing is SafeNet Inc. and it is eyeing some possible acquisitions while doing so. **Availability:** Print; Online.

20796 ■ *"Cash for Appliances Targets HVAC Products, Water Heaters"* in *Contractor* (Vol. 56, October 2009, No. 10, pp. 1)
Ed: Candace Roulo. **Description:** States and territories would need to submit a full application that specifies their implementation plans if they are interested in joining the Cash for Appliances program funded by the American Recovery and Reinvestment Act. The Department of Energy urges states to focus on heating and cooling equipment, appliances and water heaters since these offer the greatest energy savings potential. **Availability:** Print; Online.

20797 ■ *"Cashing In: Gleaning an Education from Our Economic State"* in *Agency Sales Magazine* (Vol. 39, August 2009, No. 8, pp. 22)
Description: Businesses have learned that cutting price can kill business and being tough is normal. The recession has also taught that getting the right vision and gaining the confidence and trust of consumers are important. **Availability:** Online.

20798 ■ *"Celebrate Success. Embrace Innovation"* in *Black Enterprise* (Vol. 37, February 2007, No. 7, pp. 145)
Description: 2007 Women of Power Summit provides networking opportunities, empowerment sessions, and nightly entertainment. More than 500 executive women of color are expected to attend this inspiring summit in Phoenix, February 7-10. **Availability:** Print; Online.

20799 ■ *"CEO Forecast: With Cloudy Economy, Executives Turn to Government Contracting"* in *Hispanic Business* (January-February 2009, pp. 34, 36)
Ed: Jessica Haro, Richard Kaplan. **Description:** As economic uncertainty fogs the future, executives turn to government contracts in order to boost business. Revenue sources, health care challenges, environmental consulting and remediation services, as well as technological strides are discussed. **Availability:** Print; Online.

20800 ■ *"The CEO Poll: Fuel for Thought II Canadian Business Leaders on Energy Policy"* in *Canadian Business* (Vol. 81, September 15, 2008, No. 14-15, pp. 12)
Pub: Rogers Media Inc.
Contact: Neil Spivak, Chief Executive Officer
Ed: Joe Castaldo. **Description:** Most Canadian business leaders worry about the unreliability of the oil supply but feel that Canada is in a better position to benefit from the energy supply crisis than other countries. Many respondents also highlighted the need to invest in renewable energy sources. **Availability:** Online.

20801 ■ *CFR: Title 13. Business Credit and Assistance*
Pub: U.S. Government Publishing Office
Ed: Department of Commerce Staff. **Released:** Annual; volume 14. **Description:** Title 13 covers regulations governing the activities of the Small Business Administration and the Department of Commerce. Book covers information on business credit, finance, and economic development. **Availability:** Print; PDF.

20802 ■ *"Challenges, Responses and Available Resources: Success in Rural Small Businesses"* in *Journal of Small Business and Entrepreneurship* (Vol. 23, Winter 2010, No. 1)
Pub: Canadian Council for Small Business and Entrepreneurship
Contact: John MacRitchie, President
Ed: Lynne Siemens. **Description:** Rural communities and their residents are exploring the potential of small business and entrepreneurship to address the economic changes they are facing. While these rural areas present many opportunities, business people in these areas face challenges which they must navigate to operate successfully. **Availability:** Download; PDF; Online.

20803 ■ *"Change Is in the Air"* in *Agency Sales Magazine* (Vol. 39, August 2009, No. 8, pp. 30)
Description: Highlights of the Power-Motion Technology Representatives Association (PTRA) 37th Annual Conference, which projected an economic upturn, are presented. Allan Bealulieu of the Institute for Trend Research gave the positive news while Manufacturer's Agents National Association (MANA) president Brain Shirley emphasized the need to take advantage of a turnaround. **Availability:** Print; Online.

20804 ■ *"Chasing Credit"* in *Canadian Business* (Vol. 81, November 10, 2008, No. 19, pp. 59)
Pub: Rogers Media Inc.
Contact: Neil Spivak, Chief Executive Officer
Ed: Joe Castaldo. **Description:** Small and medium sized companies are dealing with tightening credit because they appear riskier than usual. Some of these businesses are turning to private investors, but this is not easy since many have invested everything in the stock market. The sector is expected to weaken with the broader Canadian market in the next six months from October 2008. **Availability:** Online.

20805 ■ *"Cheap Deposits Fuel Bank Profits"* in *Boston Business Journal* (Vol. 31, July 29, 2011, No. 27, pp. 1)
Pub: Boston Business Journal
Contact: Carolyn M. Jones, President
E-mail: cmjones@bizjournals.com
Ed: Tim McLaughlin. **Price:** $4, Introductory 4-Week Offer(Digital Only). **Description:** Massachusetts-are banks increased profits primarily due to inexpensive deposits. The cheaper deposits have provided profit stability and fuel loan growth in an environment of historically low interest rates and uncertain economic recovery. Details of the banks' move to shed the more expensive certificates of deposit in favor of money market accounts are discussed. **Availability:** Print; Online.

20806 ■ *"The China Connection"* in *Crain's Chicago Business* (Vol. 31, March 24, 2008, No. 12, pp. 26)
Ed: Samantha Stainburn. **Description:** Interview with Ben Munoz who studied abroad in Beijing, China for three months to study international economics, e-commerce and global leadership. **Availability:** Print; Online.

20807 ■ *"China's Slowing Growth Could Benefit the Global Economy; An Expert On China's Economy Says the Country Is Seeing an Upside to Slowing Down"* in *Gallup Business Journal* (April 8, 2014)
Pub: Gallup, Inc.
Contact: Jon Clifton, Chief Executive Officer
Description: An expert on China's economy reports that the country is acknowledging an upside to slowing down, and is creating opportunities for a market economy never seen before. Ways that China is looking to expand its economy, thus expand the global economy, is investigated. **Availability:** Online.

20808 ■ *"Chip Heath: Get Over Your Fear of Change"* in *Canadian Business* (Vol. 83, June 15, 2010, No. 10, pp. 38)
Pub: Rogers Media Inc.
Contact: Neil Spivak, Chief Executive Officer
Ed: Michelle Magnan. **Description:** Organizational behavior professor Chip Heath says that resistance to change is based on the conflict between our analytical, rational side and our emotional side that is in love with comfort. Heath states that businesses tend to focus on the negatives during an economic crisis while they should be focusing on what is working and ways to do more of that. **Availability:** Print; Online.

20809 ■ *"Cincinnati Business Committee's Tom Williams: Future is Now"* in *Business Courier* (Vol. 27, August 13, 2010, No. 15, pp. 1)
Pub: Business Courier
Ed: Lucy May. **Description:** Tom Williams, chairman of the Cincinnati Business Committee (CBC), maintains that politicians and business leaders must cooperate to ensure the competitiveness of the city for the 21st Century. Under Williams' leadership, the CBC has put emphasis on initiatives related to government efficiency, economic development, and public education. Williams' views on a proposed inland port are given. **Availability:** Print; Online.

20810 ■ *"Cincinnati Hospitals Feel Pain from Slow Economy"* in *Business Courier* (Vol. 27, September 3, 2010, No. 18, pp. 1)
Pub: Business Courier
Ed: James Ritchie. **Description:** Hospitals in Cincinnati, Ohio have suffered from decreased revenues owing to the economic crises. Declining patient volumes and bad debt have also adversely impacted hospitals. **Availability:** Print; Online.

20811 ■ *"Clean-Tech Focus Sparks Growth"* in *Philadelphia Business Journal* (Vol. 28, January 15, 2010, No. 48, pp. 1)
Pub: Philadelphia Business Journal
Contact: Sierra Quinn, Director
E-mail: squinn@bizjournals.com
Ed: Peter Key. **Description:** Keystone Redevelopment Group and economic development organization Ben Franklin Technology Partners of Southeastern Pennsylvania have partnered in supporting the growth of new alternative energy and clean technology companies. Keystone has also been developing the Bridge Business Center. **Availability:** Online.

20812 ■ *"Closed Minds and Open Skies"* in *Barron's* (Vol. 88, March 10, 2008, No. 10, pp. 50)
Pub: Dow Jones & Company Inc.
Contact: Almar Latour, Chief Executive Officer
Ed: Thomas G. Donlan. **Description:** American politicians have closed minds when it comes to fair trade. The American government must not interfere with the country's manufacturing industries or worry about outsourcing defense contracts to European aerospace company Airbus. **Availability:** Online.

20813 ■ *"Colorado Statehouse Races Key for Business"* in *Denver Business Journal* (Vol. 64, August 31, 2012, No. 15, pp. 1)
Pub: Baltimore Business Journal
Contact: Rhonda Pringle, President
E-mail: rpringle@bizjournals.com
Description: The elections for Colorado's Senate and House of Representatives can have a great impact on the state's economy. Republicans are focusing on regulatory-reform measures, while Democrats are pushing for bidding priorities given to companies that buy and hire locally. Experts state that Republican and Democratic candidates seem to agree on job-creation proposals. **Availability:** Print; Online.

20814 ■ *A Colossal Failure of Common Sense: The Inside Story of the Collapse of Lehman Brothers*
Pub: Currency
Contact: Penny Simon, Contact
E-mail: psimon@randomhouse.com
Ed: Lawrence G. McDonald, Patrick Robinson. **Released:** October 12, 2010. **Price:** $17, Paperback; $5.99; $20. **Description:** Former employee of Lehman Brothers details the failure of leadership that led to the demise of the company. **Availability:** E-book; Print; Audio.

20815 ■ *"The Colt Effect"* in *Hawaii Business* (Vol. 53, January 2008, No. 7, pp. 30)
Pub: PacificBasin Communications
Contact: Chuck Tindle, Director
E-mail: chuckt@pacificbasin.net
Ed: David K. Choo. **Description:** Participation at the Bowl Championship Games can help the University of Hawaii financially. Playing at a prominent sports event could provoke donations from alumni and increase enrollment at the university. Examples of universities that earned generous income by becoming a part of prestigious sporting events are presented. **Availability:** Online.

20816 ■ *"Coming: Cheaper Oil and a Stronger Buck"* in *Barron's* (Vol. 88, March 24, 2008, No. 12, pp. 53)
Pub: Dow Jones & Company Inc.
Contact: Almar Latour, Chief Executive Officer
Ed: Lawrence C. Strauss. **Description:** Carl C. Weinberg, the chief economist of High Frequency Economics, forecasts that Chinese economic growth will slow down and that oil prices will drop to $80 a barrel in 2008. He also believes that the US dollar will start rising the moment the Federal Reserve stops cutting interest rates. **Availability:** Online.

20817 ■ *"Coming Soon: Bailouts of Fannie and Freddie"* in *Barron's* (Vol. 88, July 14, 2008, No. 28, pp. 14)
Pub: Dow Jones & Company Inc.
Contact: Almar Latour, Chief Executive Officer
Ed: Jonathan R. Laing. **Description:** Assurances from the government that Fannie Mae and Freddie Mac are adequately capitalized and able to carry on their duties as guarantors or owners of over $5 trillion of U.S. home mortgages are designed to keep both entities afloat until they attempt to raise $10 billion in new equity. The government would assume any losses in a bailout and owners of the banks' papers would profit as yields drop. **Availability:** Online.

20818 ■ *"Coming: The End of Fiat Money"* in *Barron's* (Vol. 92, July 23, 2012, No. 30, pp. 32)
Pub: Dow Jones & Company Inc.
Contact: Almar Latour, Chief Executive Officer
Ed: Leslie P. Norton. **Description:** Stephanie Pomboy, founder of MicroMavens, discusses her views on the global financial system. She believes that the global fiat currency system may collapse within five years and be replaced by a gold-backed currency system. **Availability:** Online.

20819 ■ *"Commentary. Economic Trends for Small Business"* in *Small Business Economic Trends* (April 2008, pp. 3)
Description: Commentary on the economic trends for small businesses in the U.S. is presented. Analysis of recession possibilities is given. Reports indicate that the number of business owners citing inflation as their number one problem is at its highest point since 1982.

20820 ■ *"Commercial Real Estate Brokers See Steady Growth In 2014"* in *Sacramento Business Journal* (Vol. 30, January 10, 2014, No. 46, pp. 3)
Pub: American City Business Journals, Inc.
Contact: Mike Olivieri, Executive Vice President
Released: Weekly. **Price:** $4, introductory 4-week offer(Digital & Print). **Description:** Analysts believe that the outlook for commercial real estate in Sacramento, California is positive. However, Elliot Williams of Jones Lang LaSalle thinks that the office market's recovery will depend on leases by smaller companies. Sacramento reported 10,000-square-feet of positive absorption in the fourth quarter of 2013. **Availability:** Print; Online.

20821 ■ *"Commercial Real Estate May Be Cooling, While Residential Clamors to Meet Demand"* in *Houston Business Journal* (Vol. 44, January 3, 2014, No. 35, pp. 6)
Pub: American City Business Journals, Inc.
Contact: Mike Olivieri, Executive Vice President
Released: January 03, 2014. **Description:** Greater Houston Partnership has predicted that the real estate industry will remain active for the years ahead in Houston, Texas. However, commercial real estate might cool down while residential sales are expected to remain hot with demand outpacing supply. Houston's construction boom in each sector is also discussed. **Availability:** Print; Online.

20822 ■ *"Companies Must Innovate, Regardless of Economy"* in *Crain's Detroit Business* (Vol. 25, June 1, 2009, No. 22, pp. M007)
Pub: Crain Communications Inc.
Contact: Barry Asin, President
Ed: Sherri Begin Welch. **Description:** Despite the economy, leaders of Michigan's successful companies stress that small businesses must innovate in order to grow. **Availability:** Print; PDF; Online.

20823 ■ *"Consumer Contagion? A Bleak Earnings View"* in *Barron's* (Vol. 88, March 10, 2008, No. 10, pp. 15)
Pub: Dow Jones & Company Inc.
Contact: Almar Latour, Chief Executive Officer
Ed: Robin Goldwyn Blumenthal. **Description:** Analysts expect consumer discretionary profits in the S&P 500 to drop 8.4 percent in the first quarter of 2008. A less confident consumer is expected to pull profits down, putting forecasts of earnings growth in the S&P 500 at risk. Statistical data included. **Availability:** Online.

20824 ■ *"Consumers Are Still Wary; Here's How To Win Them. The Great Recession Has Left Consumers Worried About Their Financial Future. But the Right Strategies Can Engage Leery Spenders"* in *Gallup Business Journal* (June 24, 2014)
Pub: Gallup, Inc.
Contact: Jon Clifton, Chief Executive Officer
Description: Because consumers are concerned about their financial futures, they are less likely to spend money. Strategies to increase sales while increasing consumer confidence are outlined. **Availability:** Online.

20825 ■ *"Conversation Starters for the Holiday"* in *Barron's* (Vol. 89, July 6, 2009, No. 27, pp. 7)
Pub: Dow Jones & Company Inc.
Contact: Almar Latour, Chief Executive Officer
Ed: Michael Santoli. **Description:** Investors are concerned that the US will experience high inflation due to low interest rates and improved money supply. US consumer spending has increased to 70 percent of gross domestic product, brought by health-care spending increases, while savings rates have risen to 6.9 percent. **Availability:** Online.

20826 ■ *"A Conversation with: Renea Butler"* in *Crain's Detroit Business* (Vol. 25, June 8, 2009, No. 23, pp. 12)
Pub: Crain Communications Inc.
Contact: Barry Asin, President
Ed: Ryan Beene. **Description:** Renea Butler, vice president of administration and human resources for Real Estate One Inc. in Southfield as well as vice president for public relations for the Human Resource Association of Greater Detroit, talks about how the economy has affected human resource services. **Availability:** Print; Online.

20827 ■ *"A Conversation With: Ron Gantner, Jones Lang LaSalle"* in *Crain's Detroit Business* (Vol. 24, October 6, 2008, No. 40, pp. 9)
Pub: Crain Communications Inc.
Contact: Barry Asin, President

Description: Interview with Ron Gantner who is a corporate real estate adviser with the real estate company Jones Lang LaSalle as well as the company's executive vice president and part of the tenant advisory team; Gantner speaks about the impact that the Wall Street crisis is having on the commercial real estate market in Detroit. **Availability:** Print; Online.

20828 ∎ *"Coping With a Shrinking Planet"* in *Agency Sales Magazine (Vol. 39, December 2009, No. 11, pp. 46)*
Description: China and India are forcing big changes in the world and are posing a huge threat to U.S. manufacturers and their sales representatives. Reps may want to consider expanding into these territories. Helping sell American products out of the country presents an opportunity for economic expansion. **Availability:** Online.

20829 ∎ *"Corporation, Be Good! The Story of Corporate Social Responsibility"* in *Business and Society (December 2007, pp. 479-485)*
Pub: SAGE Publications
Contact: Tracey Ozmina, President
Ed: David M. Wasieleski. **Description:** Review of the book, "Corporation, Be Good! The Story of Corporate Social Responsibility" is presented. The book examines the importance of corporate responsibility and its economic impact. **Availability:** Download; PDF; Online.

20830 ∎ *"Counting on Engagement at Ernst & Young"* in *Workforce Management (Vol. 88, November 16, 2009, No. 12, pp. 25)*
Pub: Crain Communications Inc.
Contact: Barry Asin, President
Ed: Ed Frauenheim. **Description:** Employee engagement has been difficult to maintain through the recession but firms such as Ernst & Young have found that the effort to keep their employees loyal has paid off. **Availability:** Print; Online.

20831 ∎ *"Courier 250 Companies Hope to Rebound From 2009"* in *Business Courier (Vol. 27, July 16, 2010, No. 11, pp. 1)*
Pub: Business Courier
Ed: Dan Monk, Jon Newberry. **Description:** Private companies that are featured in the Courier 250 publication have lost almost $4 billion in revenue, while combined sales dropped by 11 percent to 32 billion in 2009. Courier 250 is a guide to public companies, large nonprofits, private firms, and other related entities in Ohio's Cincinnati region. **Availability:** Online.

20832 ∎ *"CPI, Coal Lead Local Stock Decline"* in *Saint Louis Business Journal (Vol. 32, October 14, 2011, No. 7, pp. 1)*
Pub: Saint Louis Business Journal
Contact: Robert Bobroff, President
E-mail: rbobroff@bizjournals.com
Ed: Greg Edwards. **Description:** Coal companies and CPI Corporation were among those whose stocks have declined in St. Louis, Missouri. The stocks of local firms have plunged by 28 percent during the first nine months of 2011. **Availability:** Print; Online.

20833 ∎ *"Crash Landing? Serious Signal Flashing"* in *Barron's (Vol. 88, July 7, 2008, No. 27, pp. 11)*
Pub: Dow Jones & Company Inc.
Contact: Almar Latour, Chief Executive Officer
Description: Discusses the Hindenburg Omen, named after the airship disaster of May 1937, which is considered a predictor of market crashes and has appeared twice in June 2008. There is a 25 percent probability that the US stock market will suffer a crash in the July-October 2008 period. **Availability:** Online.

20834 ∎ *Crash Proof 2.0: How to Profit From the Economic Collapse*
Pub: John Wiley & Sons, Inc.
Contact: Christina Van Tassell, Executive Vice President Chief Financial Officer

Ed: Peter D. Schiff, John Downes. **Released:** Second edition. **Price:** $16.95, paperback; $27.95, hardcover; $18.99, e-book; $18.99, E-book. **Description:** Factors that will affect financial stability in the coming years are explained. A three step plan to battle the current economic downturn is also included. **Availability:** E-book; Print.

20835 ∎ *"'Crazy' Or Not, Baltimore-Area Restaurateurs Are Finding Ways to Open New Eateries"* in *Baltimore Business Journal (Vol. 28, October 8, 2010)*
Pub: Baltimore Business Journal
Contact: Rhonda Pringle, President
E-mail: rpringle@bizjournals.com
Ed: Joanna Sullivan. **Description:** New restaurants have been opening in Maryland. However, 515 restaurants have closed down due to the economic crisis. Comments from restaurateurs are also provided.

20836 ∎ *"The Credit Crisis Continues to Take Victims"* in *Barron's (Vol. 88, March 10, 2008, No. 10, pp. M12)*
Pub: Dow Jones & Company Inc.
Contact: Almar Latour, Chief Executive Officer
Ed: Randall W. Forsyth. **Description:** Short-term Treasury yields dropped to new cyclical lows in early March 2008, with the yield for the two-year Treasury note falling to 1.532 percent. Spreads of the mortgage-backed securities of Fannie Mae and Freddie Mac rose on suspicion of collapses in financing. **Availability:** Online.

20837 ∎ *"Crouching Tigers Spring to Life"* in *Globe & Mail (April 14, 2007, pp. B1)*
Ed: Grant Robertson. **Description:** The prospects of the acquisition of BCE Inc, by Canadian pension funds are discussed. The effect of the growth of these pension funds on the Canadian economy is described. **Availability:** Online.

20838 ∎ *"Crude Awakening"* in *Canadian Business (Vol. 81, October 27, 2008, No. 18, pp. 14)*
Description: Jim Grays believes that a global liquid fuels crisis is coming and hopes the expected transition from oil dependence will be smooth. Charles Maxwell, on the other hand, predicts that a new world economy will arrive in three waves. Views of both experts are examined. **Availability:** Print; Online.

20839 ∎ *"The Cudgel of Samson: How the Government Once Used 'Jawboning' to Fight Inflation"* in *Barron's (Vol. 88, March 24, 2008, No. 12, pp. 62)*
Pub: Dow Jones & Company Inc.
Contact: Almar Latour, Chief Executive Officer
Ed: Thomas G. Donlan. **Description:** Discusses the Federal Reserve is jawboning businesses against inflation while inflation is starting to rise because of the abundance of cheap money. The practice of jawboning has been used by the administrations of past US presidents with limited effect. **Availability:** Online.

20840 ∎ *"Dallas Top-Performing City for Small Business Growth"* in *Dallas Business Journal (Vol. 37, July 11, 2014, No. 44, pp. 13)*
Pub: American City Business Journals, Inc.
Contact: Mike Olivieri, Executive Vice President
Released: Weekly. **Price:** $4, introductory 4-week offer(Digital only). **Description:** Dallas has been ranked as Texas' top-performing metropolitan area for small business job growth in 2014. The 1.07 percent growth rate spike placed Dallas at 104.02 on the index, and it was observed that the market conditions and economy of Dallas made it easier to start a new business. It is reported that though the index indicated a drop, small business job growth in Dallas remained at a record high. **Availability:** Print; Online.

20841 ∎ *"The Danger of Doing Nothing"* in *Harvard Business Review (Vol. 90, April 2012, No. 4, pp. 38)*
Pub: Harvard Business Review Press
Contact: Moderna V. Pfizer, Contact

Ed: Erskine Bowles. **Price:** $6. **Description:** Solving the US economic crisis will require a blend of revenue increases, spending cuts, and bipartisan cooperation in Congress. The National Commission on Fiscal Responsibility and Reform, also known as Simpson-Bowles, has proposed a plan intended to make America competitive again. **Availability:** PDF; Online.

20842 ∎ *"Dedge Rejects Inflation Concerns"* in *Globe & Mail (January 26, 2007, pp. B3)*
Ed: Heather Scoffield. **Description:** The rejection of concern over inflation by Governor of the Bank of Canada David Dodge and his views on checking inflation in Alberta are discussed. **Availability:** Print; Online.

20843 ∎ *"Despite Economic Upheaval Generation Y is Still Feeling Green: RSA Canada Survey"* in *CNW Group (October 28, 2010)*
Pub: CNW Group Ltd.
Description: Canadian Generation Y individuals believe it is important for their company to be environmentally-friendly and one-third of those surveyed would quit their job if they found their employer was environmentally irresponsible, despite the economy. **Availability:** Online.

20844 ∎ *"Detroit Residential Market Slows; Bright Spots Emerge"* in *Crain's Detroit Business (Vol. 24, October 6, 2008, No. 40, pp. 11)*
Pub: Crain Communications Inc.
Contact: Barry Asin, President
Ed: Daniel Duggan. **Description:** Discusses the state of the residential real estate market in Detroit; although condominium projects receive the most attention, deals for single-family homes are taking place in greater numbers due to financing issues. Buyers can purchase a single family home with a 3.5 percent down payment compared to 20 percent for some condo deals because of the number of first-time homebuyer programs under the Federal Housing Administration.

20845 ∎ *"Do You Have A Retirement Parachute?"* in *Barron's (Vol. 88, July 7, 2008, No. 27, pp. 32)*
Pub: Dow Jones & Company Inc.
Contact: Almar Latour, Chief Executive Officer
Ed: Jane White. **Description:** The idea that American companies should emulate the Australian retirement system which implements a forced contribution rate for all employers regarding an adequate retirement plan for their employees is discussed. **Availability:** Online.

20846 ∎ *"The Dogs of TSX"* in *Canadian Business (Vol. 81, Summer 2008, No. 9, pp. 77)*
Description: Table showing the one-year stock performance of the ten highest dividend-yielding stocks on the S&P/TSX 60 Composite Index is presented. This technique is similar to the 'Dogs of the Dow' approach. The idea in this investment strategy is to buy equal amounts of stocks from these companies and selling them a year later, and then repeat the process. **Availability:** Online.

20847 ∎ *"Don't Bet Against The House"* in *Barron's (Vol. 88, July 14, 2008, No. 28, pp. 20)*
Pub: Dow Jones & Company Inc.
Contact: Almar Latour, Chief Executive Officer
Ed: Sandra Ward. **Description:** Shares of Nasdaq OMX have lost more than 50 percent of their value from November 2007 to July 2008 but the value of these shares could climb 50 percent on the strength of world security exchanges. Only 15 percent of the company's revenues come from the U.S. and the shares are trading at 12.5 times the amount expected for 2008. **Availability:** Online.

20848 ■ *"Don't Quit When The Road Gets Bumpy"* in *Women Entrepreneur (November 25, 2008)*
Description: Discusses techniques four women entrepreneurs are utilizing to keep their businesses successful despite the credit crunch and the economic downturn.

20849 ■ *"The Doomsday Scenario"* in *Conde Nast Portfolio (Vol. 2, June 2008, No. 6, pp. 91)*
Ed: Jeffrey Rothfeder. **Description:** Detroit and the U.S. auto industry are discussed as well as the ramifications of the demise of this manufacturing base. Similarities and differences between the downfall of the U.S. steel business and the impact it had on Pittsburg, Pennsylvania is also discussed.

20850 ■ *"Doubtful Donors"* in *Canadian Business (Vol. 81, December 8, 2008, No. 21, pp. 8)*
Ed: Denis Seguin. **Description:** Key information on fundraising consultancy Inspire, as well as views and information on charitable organizations in Canada is presented. Inspire designs the financial architecture of charitable foundations in Canada, which was affected by the current financial crisis. Inspire advises foundations to keep existing donors. **Availability:** Online.

20851 ■ *"Down a 'Peg'"* in *Canadian Business (Vol. 79, September 25, 2006, No. 19, pp. 41)*
Description: Economic development in Canada's Winnipeg city is evaluated. **Availability:** Online.

20852 ■ *"Down the Tracks, a Whistle Is a-Blowin"* in *Barron's (Vol. 89, July 27, 2009, No. 30, pp. 36)*
Pub: Dow Jones & Company Inc.
Contact: Almar Latour, Chief Executive Officer
Ed: Jim McTague. **Description:** Higher numbers of freight-rail carloads are a sign that the economy is improving and it is no stretch to imagine that this is aided by the American Recovery and Reinvestment Act. It is also predicted that 2009 municipal bond issuance will be above $373 billion with at least $55 billion of it made up of Buy America Bonds that are subsidized by the federal government. **Availability:** Online.

20853 ■ *"Downturn Tests HCL's Pledge to Employees"* in *Workforce Management (Vol. 88, November 16, 2009, No. 12, pp. 23)*
Pub: Crain Communications Inc.
Contact: Barry Asin, President
Ed: Ed Frauenheim. **Description:** HCL Technologies has kept its promise to keep from laying any employees off during the recession which served as a test for the tech firm's Employee First program, which seeks to give workers greater income security as well as a stronger voice in the firm. **Availability:** Online.

20854 ■ *"Dream On"* in *Barron's (Vol. 89, July 27, 2009, No. 30, pp. 21)*
Pub: Dow Jones & Company Inc.
Contact: Almar Latour, Chief Executive Officer
Ed: Jonathan R. Laing. **Description:** California's budget agreement which purports to eliminate a $26 billion deficit is discussed. The frequent budgetary dustups in the state calls for several reforms including a rainy day fund of 15 percent of any budget and a constitutional convention. Other reform suggestions are discussed.

20855 ■ *"Drinking Buddies: S.F.'s New Round of Barkeeps"* in *San Francisco Business Times (Vol. 28, January 17, 2014, No. 26, pp. 4)*
Pub: American City Business Journals, Inc.
Contact: Mike Olivieri, Executive Vice President
Released: Weekly. **Price:** $4, Introductory 4-week offer(Digital & Print). **Description:** The influx of young workers in San Francisco, California contributed to the growth of the city's bar industry. Ben Bleiman of the tonic Nightlife Group reveals that his bars are doing well because of a rebound in the U.S. economy. Reports also show that smaller groups are now opening multiple drinking establishments across San Francisco. **Availability:** Print; Online.

20856 ■ *"Drug, Seed Firms Offer Antidote For Inflation"* in *Crain's Chicago Business (Vol. 31, April 21, 2008, No. 16, pp. 4)*
Pub: Crain Communications Inc.
Contact: Barry Asin, President
Ed: Daniel Rome Levine. **Description:** Interview with Jerrold Senser, the CEO of Institutional Capital LLC in Chicago, in which he discusses the ways that the company is adjusting to the economic slowdown and rising inflation, his favorite firms for investment and his prediction of an economic turnaround; he also recommends five companies he feels are worth investing in. **Availability:** Online.

20857 ■ *"Early Spring Halts Drilling Season"* in *Globe & Mail (March 14, 2007, pp. B14)*
Ed: Norval Scott. **Description:** Decreased petroleum productivity in Canadian oil drilling rigs due to early spring season in western regions is discussed. **Availability:** Online.

20858 ■ *"Economic Crisis and Accounting Evolution"* in *Accounting and Business Research (Vol. 41, Summer 2011, No. 3, pp. 2159)*
Pub: Routledge, Taylor & Francis Group
Ed: Gregory Waymire, Sudipta Basu. **Description:** Financial reporting changes at the face of economic crises are studied using a punctuated equilibrium evolution. Findings show that financial reporting has a minor impact but may amplify economic crises. Attempts to enhance accounting and economic crises may not be as beneficial as planned. **Availability:** PDF; Online; Download.

20859 ■ *Economic Development Administration--Annual Report*
Pub: U.S. Economic Development Administration
Contact: Jeannette P. Tamayo, Regional Director
URL(s): www.eda.gov/annual-reports
Released: Annual; latest edition 2014. **Description:** Covers recipients of grants, grant supplements, and loan guarantees from the Economic Development Administration under the Public Works and Economic Development Act of 1965. Projects funded include public works, business development, research, planning, and disaster recovery. **Entries include:** Recipient name, location, date of obligation, funds received by type of assistance, type of project, identification number. **Arrangement:** Geographical. **Availability:** Print; Online.

20860 ■ *"Economic Distance and the Survival of Foreign Direct Investments"* in *Academy of Management Journal (Vol. 50, No. 5, October 1, 2007, pp. 1156)*
Pub: Academy of Management
Contact: Sharon Alvarez, President
Ed: Eric W.K. Tsang, Paul S.L. Yip. **Description:** Study was undertaken to assess the relationship between economic disparities of various countries and foreign direct investments, focusing on Singapore. Results revealed that economic distance has a definite impact on foreign direct investment hazard rates. **Availability:** Electronic publishing; Download; PDF; Online.

20861 ■ *Economic Freedom and the American Dream*
Pub: Palgrave Macmillan
Ed: Joseph Shaanan. **Released:** 2010. **Price:** $80, Hardcover; $75, softcover; $59.99, e-book. **Description:** An exploration into the effects of economic freedom on American in several areas such as markets, politics, and opportunities for would-be entrepreneurs. **Availability:** E-book; Print.

20862 ■ *"Economic Outlook 2009: In Search of New Tools and Initiatives"* in *Hispanic Business (January-February 2009, pp. 30, 32)*
Ed: Dr. Juan Solana. **Description:** Successful business policies of the past no longer work in this economic climate. New tools and initiatives regarding monetary policy, fiscal policy and a higher multiplier are required to survive the crisis. **Availability:** PDF; Online.

20863 ■ *"Economic Recovery Prognosis: Four More Years"* in *Barron's (Vol. 89, July 13, 2009, No. 28, pp. 11)*
Pub: Dow Jones & Company Inc.
Contact: Almar Latour, Chief Executive Officer
Ed: Karen Hube. **Description:** Loomis Sayles Bond Fund manager Dan Fuss believes that the economy is bottoming and that recovery will be long and drawn out. Fuss guesses that the next peak in 10-year Treasury yields will be about 6.25% in around 4 and a half or five years ahead of 2009. **Availability:** Online.

20864 ■ *"Economic Trends for Small Business"* in *Small Business Economic Trends (April 2008, pp. 1)*
Description: Summary of economic trends for small businesses in the U.S. is presented. Economic indicators such as capital spending, inventories and sales, inflation, and profits are given. Analysis of credit markets is also provided. **Availability:** Online.

20865 ■ *"Economics: The User's Guide"*
Released: 1st edition. **Price:** $27, hardback ; $18, paperback ; $16, ebook. **Description:** Cambridge economist explains how the global economy is working. He provides a concise knowledge of history with a disregard for conventional economic traditions and offers insights into economic behavior. **Availability:** E-book.

20866 ■ *"The Economics of Well-Being: Have We Found a Better Gauge of Success Than GDP?"* in *Harvard Business Review (Vol. 90, January-February 2012, No.1-2, pp. 78)*
Pub: Harvard Business Review Press
Contact: Moderna V. Pfizer, Contact
Ed: Justin Fox. **Price:** $8.95. **Description:** Gross domestic product is no longer a valid means of determining national success. GDP does not take into account factors such as unpaid housework and sustainability. Other metrics may be more accurate and encompassing, including life expectancy, individual freedom, and educational achievement. **Availability:** Online; PDF.

20867 ■ *"Economists Warn Against Smart Cap"* in *Orlando Business Journal (Vol. 29, September 21, 2012, No. 14, pp. 1)*
Pub: Baltimore Business Journal
Contact: Rhonda Pringle, President
E-mail: rpringle@bizjournals.com
Ed: Abraham Aboraya, Richard Bilbao. **Description:** Opponents to the proposed amendment to the Florida State Revenue Limitations warn about the economic impact of the plan to cap state government spending. Under the proposal, the amount of taxes that the state should spend each year will be capped and a rainy day fund will be created where excess revenue collected will be placed. **Availability:** Print; Online.

20868 ■ *"Egg Fight: The Yolk's on the Shorts"* in *Barron's (Vol. 88, July 7, 2008, No. 27, pp. 20)*
Pub: Dow Jones & Company Inc.
Contact: Almar Latour, Chief Executive Officer
Ed: Christopher C. Williams. **Description:** Shares of Cal-Maine Foods, the largest egg producer and distributor in the US, are due for a huge rise because of the increase in egg prices. Short sellers, however, continue betting that the stock, priced at $31.84 each, will eventually go down. **Availability:** Online.

20869 ■ *Electronic Commerce*
Ed: Gary P. Schneider, Bryant Chrzan, Charles McCormick. **Released:** 12th edition. **Price:** $29.49, e-book. **Description:** E-commerce can open the door to more opportunities than ever before for small business. Packed with real-world examples and cases, the book delivers comprehensive coverage of emerging online technologies and trends and their influence on the electronic marketplace. It details how the landscape of online commerce is evolving, reflecting changes in the economy and how business and society are responding to those changes. Balancing technological issues with the strategic business aspects of successful e-commerce, the new edition

GENERAL SMALL BUSINESS TOPICS   Economic Development ■ 20890

includes expanded coverage of international issues, social networking, mobile commerce, Web 2.0 technologies, and updates on spam, phishing, and identity theft. **Availability:** Print.

20870 ■ *"Empathy: An Entrepreneur's Killer App"* in Women Entrepreneur (February 3, 2009)
Description: It is just as important to treat employees with courtesy and respect during bad economic times as it is in a good economy. Employers sometimes take advantage of such bad economic times since they realize that employees are grateful to have a job and cannot just quit and easily find work elsewhere. The importance of empathy in a company's leadership personnel is discussed. **Availability:** Online.

20871 ■ *"End of the Beginning"* in Canadian Business (Vol. 81, November 10, 2008, No. 19, pp. 17)
Ed: David Wolf. **Released:** September 30, 2016. **Description:** The freeze in the money markets and historic decline in equity markets around the world finally forced governments into aggressive coordinated action. The asset price inflation brought on by cheap credit will now work in reverse and the tightening of credit will be difficult economically. Canada is exposed to the fallout everywhere, given that the U.S., the U.K. and Japan buy 30 percent of Canada's output. **Availability:** Print; Online.

20872 ■ *"End of an Era"* in Barron's (Vol. 88, July 7, 2008, No. 27, pp. 3)
Ed: Alan Abelson. **Released:** January 01, 2016. **Description:** June 2008 was a very bad month for US stocks, with investors losing as much as 41.9 percent in the first half of 2008 signaling an end to the financial environment that prevailed around the world since the 1980's. The US job market lost 62,000 jobs in June 2008. **Availability:** Print; Online.

20873 ■ *"Endowments for Colleges Hit Hard in '09"* in Milwaukee Business Journal (Vol. 27, February 12, 2010, No. 20, pp. A1)
Pub: The Business Journal
Contact: Heather Ladage, President
E-mail: hladage@bizjournals.com
Ed: Corrinne Hess. **Description:** Southeast Wisconsin college endowments declined by as much as 35 percent in 2009 due to the economic downturn. A list of 2009 endowments to colleges in southeast Wisconsin and their percent change from 2008 is presented. **Availability:** Print; Online.

20874 ■ *"Evaluating the 1996-2006 Employment Projections"* in Montly Labor Review (Vol. 133, September 2010, No. 9, pp. 33)
Pub: U.S. Department of Labor Bureau of Labor Statistics
Contact: Amrit Kohli, Director
E-mail: kohli.amrit@bls.gov
Description: Bureau of Labor Statistics employment projections outperformed alternative naive models, but not projecting the housing bubble or the rise in oil prices caused some inaccuracies in the projects. These projections are used by policymakers, economists, and students. **Availability:** PDF; Online.

20875 ■ *"Even Money on Recession"* in Barron's (Vol. 88, March 10, 2008, No. 10, pp. M9)
Pub: Dow Jones & Company Inc.
Contact: Almar Latour, Chief Executive Officer
Ed: Gene Epstein. **Description:** Discusses the US unemployment rate which was steady in February 2008 at 4.8 percent, while nonfarm payroll employment decreased by 63,000 in the same month, with the private sector losing 101,000 jobs. The economic indicators showed mixed signals on whether or not the US economy is in a recession. **Availability:** Online.

20876 ■ *"Events, Improved Economy Mean Full Hotels in Silicon Valley"* in Silicon Valley/San Jose Business Journal (Vol. 30, September 28, 2012, No. 27, pp. 1)
Pub: Baltimore Business Journal
Contact: Rhonda Pringle, President

E-mail: rpringle@bizjournals.com
Description: The increase in hotel occupancy rates in Silicon Valley was attributed to the improving economy and a wide range of local trade shows and events. The city of Santa Clara, California reached an 82 percent occupancy rate in August 2012, while in downtown San Jose, hotels said they started experiencing increased demand since late 2011. **Availability:** Print; Online.

20877 ■ *"Export Opportunity"* in Business Journal-Portland (Vol. 24, October 12, 2007, No. 33, pp. 1)
Description: U.S. dollar is weak, hitting an all-time low against the Euro, while the Canadian dollar is also performing well it hit parity for the first time after more than thirty years. The weak U.S. dollar is making companies that sell overseas benefit as it makes their goods cheaper to buy.

20878 ■ *"Facebook: A Promotional Budget's Best Friend"* in Women Entrepreneur (February 1, 2009)
Description: Facebook began as a social networking website but has become a valuable marketing tool for all types of businesses, organizations and causes. Tips are provided for creating a Facebook account and growing one's network on Facebook. **Availability:** Online.

20879 ■ *Falling Behind: How Rising Inequality Harms the Middle Class*
Ed: Robert H. Frank. **Released:** First edition. **Description:** Economist argues that though middle-class American families aren't earning much more than they were a few decades ago, they are spending considerably more, a pattern attributed primarily to the context of seeing and emulating the spending habits of the rich.

20880 ■ *"Falling Markets' Nastiest Habit"* in Barron's (Vol. 88, July 7, 2008, No. 27, pp. 7)
Pub: Dow Jones & Company Inc.
Contact: Almar Latour, Chief Executive Officer
Ed: Michael Santoli. **Description:** US market conditions reflect a bear market, with the S&P 500 index falling 20 percent below its recent high as of June 2008. The bear market is expected to persist in the immediate future, although bear market rallies are likely to occur. **Availability:** Online.

20881 ■ *Family Business*
Pub: Cengage Learning, Inc.
Contact: Michael E. Hansen, Chief Executive Officer
Ed: Ernesto J. Poza. **Released:** 2014. **Price:** $69.99, ETextbook. **Description:** Family-owned businesses face unique challenges in today's economy. This book provides the next generation of knowledge and skills required for profitable management and leadership in a family enterprise. **Availability:** E-book; Print.

20882 ■ *"Fast-Growing Companies Stepped Up Pace in 2011"* in Sacramento Business Journal (Vol. 29, July 6, 2012, No. 19, pp. 1)
Pub: Baltimore Business Journal
Contact: Rhonda Pringle, President
E-mail: rpringle@bizjournals.com
Description: The growth of Sacramento, California-based businesses is seen as a sign of strong economic recovery, as reflected in this publication's annual list has revealed. Stuart James Construction Inc. got the top spot. Businesses registered two-year growth rates ranging from 29 to 632 percent. **Availability:** Print; Online.

20883 ■ *"The Fed Still Has Ammunition"* in Barron's (Vol. 90, August 30, 2010, No. 35, pp. M9)
Pub: Barron's Editorial & Corporate Headquarters
Ed: Randall W. Forsyth. **Description:** Federal Reserve chairman Ben Bernanke said the agency still has tools to combat deflation and a second downturn but these strategies are not needed at this time. The prospects of the Federal Open Market Committee's purchasing of treasuries are also discussed. **Availability:** Online.

20884 ■ *"Fed Tackles Bear of a Crisis"* in Barron's (Vol. 88, March 17, 2008, No. 11, pp. M10)
Pub: Dow Jones & Company Inc.
Contact: Almar Latour, Chief Executive Officer
Ed: Randall W. Forsyth. **Description:** Emergency funding package for Bear Stearns from the Federal Reserve Bank of New York through JPMorgan Chase is one of the steps taken by the central bank shore up bank liquidity. Prior to the emergency funding, the central bank announced the Term Securities Lending Facility to allow dealers to borrow easily saleable Treasuries in exchange for less-liquid issues. **Availability:** Online.

20885 ■ *"Federal Bailout, Three Years Later"* in Business Owner (Vol. 35, September-October 2011, No. 5, pp. 6)
Description: State of the economy and small business sector three years after the government stimulus and bailout programs were instituted. **Availability:** Print; Online.

20886 ■ *"Feeding the Elephants While Searching for Greener Pastures"* in Inc. (Volume 32, December 2010, No. 10, pp. 34)
Pub: Mansueto Ventures L.L.C.
Contact: Stephanie Mehta, Chief Executive Officer
Ed: April Joyner. **Released:** December 2010. **Description:** Innovation is the future for small business. A new book, Inside Real Innovation: How the Right Approach Can Move Ideas from R&D to Market - And Get the Economy Moving helps to break down the process by which innovation occurs. **Availability:** Print.

20887 ■ *"A Few Points of Contention"* in Barron's (Vol. 88, July 14, 2008, No. 28, pp. 3)
Pub: Dow Jones & Company Inc.
Contact: Almar Latour, Chief Executive Officer
Ed: Michael Santoli. **Description:** Headline inflation tends to revert to the lower core inflation, which excludes food and energy in its calculation over long periods. Prominent private equity figures believe that regulators should allow more than the de facto 10 percent to 25 percent limit of commercial banks to hasten the refunding of the financial sector. **Availability:** Online.

20888 ■ *"Fight Over Casino Funds Limits Kitty for MEDC"* in Crain's Detroit Business (Vol. 24, January 21, 2008, No. 3, pp. 3)
Pub: Crain Communications Inc.
Contact: Barry Asin, President
Ed: Amy Lane. **Description:** Michigan Economic Development Corporation is facing uncertainty due to a Michigan American Indian tribe from the southwestern portion of the state withholding its 8 percent casino revenue share. **Availability:** Online.

20889 ■ *"Filling the Business Gap"* in Hispanic Business (December 2010)
Description: New York group seeks to increase state diversity supplier spending to help create jobs and boost the economy. According to a recent study, six out of 10 small business owners will increase capital spending but delay hiring in 2011. However, potential job creation is good among businesses owned by women and minorities. **Availability:** Print; Online.

20890 ■ *"Financial Stability: Fraud, Confidence, and the Wealth of Nations"*
Pub: John Wiley & Sons, Inc.
Contact: Christina Van Tassell, Executive Vice President Chief Financial Officer
Released: September 2014. **Price:** $48.99, e-book; $75, hardcover. **Description:** Instruction is provided to help modern investors and finance professionals to learn from past successes and failures and to gauge future market threats. Insight into today's financial markets and the political economy will help craft a strategy that leads to financial stability. Topics covered include: capital; forecasting; political reaction; and past, present, and future applications within all areas of business. A companion Website offers additional data and research, providing a comprehen-

sive resource for those wishing a better understanding of risk factors in investing. **Availability:** E-book; Print; Online; PDF.

20891 ■ *"Finding Competitive Advantage in Adversity"* in *Harvard Business Review (Vol. 88, November 2010, No. 11, pp. 102)*
Pub: Harvard Business Publishing
Contact: Diane Belcher, Managing Director
Ed: Bhaskar Chakravorti. **Price:** $8.95, PDF. **Description:** Four opportunities in adversity are identified and applied to business scenarios. These are matching unmet needs with unneeded resources, seeking collaboration from unlikely partners, developing small/appropriate solutions to large/complex issues, and focusing on the platform as well as the product. **Availability:** Online; PDF.

20892 ■ *"A Fine Time for Timber"* in *Barron's (Vol. 92, August 25, 2012, No. 38, pp. 18)*
Pub: Dow Jones & Company Inc.
Contact: Almar Latour, Chief Executive Officer
Ed: Christopher C. Williams. **Description:** The stocks of timber firm and real estate investment trust Weyerhaeuser could have their dividend raised by as much as 50 percent. The company is poised to benefit from a housing sector recovery, which could raise the value of its real estate and timberland holdings. **Availability:** Online.

20893 ■ *"Firms Start Increasing their Space"* in *Philadelphia Business Journal (Vol. 31, March 23, 2012, No. 6, pp. 1)*
Pub: Baltimore Business Journal
Contact: Rhonda Pringle, President
E-mail: rpringle@bizjournals.com
Description: Office occupancies in Philadelphia, Pennsylvania have grown in 2012. The economic recovery is seen to drive this trend. Comments from office/property management brokers are also included. **Availability:** Print; Online.

20894 ■ *"Fiscal Cliff Notes"* in *Barron's (Vol. 92, September 15, 2012, No. 38, pp. 27)*
Pub: Dow Jones & Company Inc.
Contact: Almar Latour, Chief Executive Officer
Ed: Mike Hogan. **Description:** Websites and blogs dedicated to providing information on the economic effects of the 'fiscal cliff' are described. These sites discuss possible effects on the US economy, budget, and personal finances. **Availability:** Online.

20895 ■ *"A Flawed Yardstick for Banks"* in *Barron's (Vol. 88, July 14, 2008, No. 28, pp. M6)*
Pub: Dow Jones & Company Inc.
Contact: Almar Latour, Chief Executive Officer
Ed: Arindam Nag. **Description:** Return on equity is no longer the best measure for investors to judge banks by in a post-subprime-crises world. Investors should consider the proportion of a bank's total assets that are considered risky and look out for any write-downs of goodwill when judging a bank's financial health. **Availability:** Online.

20896 ■ *"Florida Fast 100: D&D Construction Services"* in *South Florida Business Journal (Vol. 35, September 19, 2014, No. 8, pp. 16)*
Pub: American City Business Journals, Inc.
Contact: Mike Olivieri, Executive Vice President
Description: Profile of D and D Construction, who reports increased earnings in 2013 totaling $26.5 million. The increase has been attributed to the commercial real estate market's recovery from the economic recession. The company is focusing on offering hospitality (restaurant, hotel) projects. **Availability:** Online.

20897 ■ *"Ford Canada's Edsel of a Year: Revenue Plummets 24 Percent in '05"* in *Globe & Mail (February 2, 2006, pp. B1)*
Description: Ford Motor Company of Canada Ltd. posted 24% decline in revenues for 2005. The drop in earnings is attributed to plant shutdown in Oaksville, Canada. **Availability:** Online.

20898 ■ *"Ford: Down, Not Out, and Still a Buy"* in *Barron's (Vol. 92, July 23, 2012, No. 30, pp. 14)*
Pub: Dow Jones & Company Inc.
Contact: Almar Latour, Chief Executive Officer
Ed: Vito J. Racanelli. **Description:** Stocks of Ford Motor Company could gain value as the company continues to improve its finances despite fears of slower global economic growth. The company's stock prices could double from $9.35 per share within three years. **Availability:** Online.

20899 ■ *Freakonomics: A Rogue Economist Explores the Hidden Side of Everything*
Pub: William Morrow
Ed: Steven D. Levitt, Stephen J. Dubner. **Released:** Revised and Expanded Edition. **Price:** $29.99, hardcover; $16.99, paperback; $27.99, large print; $19.99, audiobook CD; $23.99, digital audiobook; $16.99, paperback; $15.19, Trade Paperback. **Availability:** Large print; CD-ROM; E-book; Print; Online; Audio.

20900 ■ *"Fuel Costs Curb Food Truck Trend"* in *Tampa Tribune (March 26, 2012)*
Ed: Jeff Houck. **Description:** Owner of Maggie on the Move food truck, Margaret Loflin, has had to raise the cost of drinks served in order to cover the increased cost of gasoline to run her business. She also added smaller, less costly items to her menu. Her husband has gone back to a part-time job in he hopes of keeping their food truck running. **Availability:** Print; Online.

20901 ■ *"Funeral Directors Get Creative As Boomers Near Great Beyond"* in *Advertising Age (Vol. 79, October 13, 2008, No. 38, pp. 30)*
Pub: Crain Communications, Inc.
Contact: Jessica Botos, Manager, Marketing
E-mail: jessica.botos@crainsnewyork.com
Ed: Lenore Skenazy. **Description:** Despite the downturn in the economy, the funeral business is thriving due to the number of baby boomers who realize the importance of making preparations for their death. Marketers are getting creative in their approach and many companies have taken into consideration the need for a more environmental friendly way to dispose of bodies and thus have created innovative businesses that reflect this need. **Availability:** Online.

20902 ■ *"The Future Is Another Country; Higher Education"* in *The Economist (Vol. 390, January 3, 2009, No. 8612, pp. 43)*
Description: Due to the growth of the global corporation, more ambitious students are studying at universities abroad; the impact of this trend is discussed. **Availability:** Print; Online.

20903 ■ *"The Future of Private Equity"* in *Canadian Business (Vol. 80, March 26, 2007, No. 7, pp. 19)*
Description: The impact growing Canadian economy and competition in global business on the performance of private equity funds is analyzed. **Availability:** Online; PDF.

20904 ■ *"Futures Shock for the CME"* in *Crain's Chicago Business (Vol. 31, November 10, 2008, No. 45, pp. 8)*
Pub: Crain Communications Inc.
Contact: Barry Asin, President
Ed: Ann Saphir. **Description:** Chicago-based CME Group Inc., the largest futures exchange operator in the U.S., is facing a potentially radically altered regulatory landscape as Congress weighs sweeping reform of financial oversight. The possible merger of the CFTC and the Securities and Exchange Commission are among CME's concerns. Other details of possible regulatory measures are provided. **Availability:** Online.

20905 ■ *"Gaming Infrastructure Paves Ready Path for Manufacturing"* in *Memphis Business Journal (No. 35, February 14, 2014, No. 45, pp. 4)*
Pub: American City Business Journals, Inc.
Contact: Mike Olivieri, Executive Vice President
Description: The city of Tunica, Mississippi is trying to expand its reputation as a gaming destination into manufacturing in an effort seek new opportunities for economic development and revenue. German crankshaft manufacturer, Feurer Powertrain, is building a $140 million manufacturing facility that will open in late 2014. **Availability:** Online.

20906 ■ *"Gas Supplies Low Heading Into Summer Season"* in *Globe & Mail (April 13, 2007, pp. B6)*
Ed: Shawn McCarthy. **Description:** The decrease in the supply of gas due to maintenance problems at refineries in the United States and Canada is discussed. **Availability:** Online.

20907 ■ *"German Win Through Sharing"* in *Canadian Business (Vol. 83, September 14, 2010, No. 15, pp. 16)*
Pub: Rogers Media Inc.
Contact: Neil Spivak, Chief Executive Officer
Ed: Jordan Timm. **Released:** September 14, 2010. **Description:** German economic historian Eckhard Hoffner has a two-volume work showing how German's relaxed attitude toward copyright and intellectual property helped it catch up to industrialized United Kingdom. Hoffner's research was in response to his interest in the usefulness of software patents. Information on the debate regarding Canada's copyright laws is given. **Availability:** Print; Online.

20908 ■ *"Get Off The Rollercoaster"* in *Michigan Vue (Vol. 13, July-August 2008, No. 4, pp. 19)*
Description: Benefits of creating and implementing a solid financial plan during these rocky economic times are examined. Things to keep in mind before meeting with a financial planner include risk assessment, investment goals, the length of time required to meet those goals and the amount of money one has available to invest. **Availability:** Print; Online.

20909 ■ *"Getting In on the Ground Floor With World-Class Companies"* in *Barron's (Vol. 89, July 27, 2009, No. 30, pp. 32)*
Ed: Jacqueline Doherty. **Description:** Shares of AvalonBay Communities have fallen 61 percent in the past two and a half years to July 2009 but at $56, the stock is trading near the asset value. The shares could rise as the economy improves and if the recovery takes longer, investors will be rewarded with a yield of 3.5 percent. **Availability:** Online.

20910 ■ *"Global Economy: The World Tomorrow"* in *Canadian Business (Vol. 81, December 19, 2007, No. 1, pp. 35)*
Pub: Rogers Media Inc.
Contact: Neil Spivak, Chief Executive Officer
Ed: Zena Olijnyk. **Description:** Global economy is predicted to be in a difficult period as analysts expect a slowdown in economic growth. Germany's Deutsche Bank wrote in a report about 'growth recession' that the chances of the world growth falling below two percent being one in three. Forecasts on other global economic aspects are explored. **Availability:** Online.

20911 ■ *"The Global Talent Hunt"* in *Business Strategy Review (Vol. 21, Spring 2010, No. 1, pp. 78)*
Ed: Richard Emerton. **Released:** February 09, 2010. **Description:** Richard Emerton explains how the new 'triple context' of economy, environment and society will have profound implications for human resource practices. He suggests that viewing talent as abundant is the right perspective for a manager. **Availability:** Print; PDF; Online.

20912 ■ *"Globalization: Canada Tomorrow"* in *Canadian Business (Vol. 80, October 8, 2007, No. 20, pp. 14)*
Description: An assessment of Canada's future in terms of its educational, social, and economic environment is presented. Concerns regarding the country's educational system such as the declining interest in science and technology and the possible lack of teachers in the future are discussed. In terms

of its social and economic aspects, the need to support entrepreneurs and other qualified people is explained. **Availability:** Online.

20913 ■ *"Go Green Or Go Home"* in *Black Enterprise* (Vol. 41, August 2010, No. 1, pp. 53)
Pub: Earl G. Graves Ltd.
Contact: Earl Graves, Jr., President
Ed: Robinson M. Tennille. **Description:** The green economy has become an essential part of every business, however, small business owners need to learn how to participate, including minority owned entrepreneurs. **Availability:** Online.

20914 ■ *"A Good Book Is Worth a Thousand Blogs"* in *Barron's* (Vol. 88, July 14, 2008, No. 28, pp. 42)
Pub: Dow Jones & Company Inc.
Contact: Almar Latour, Chief Executive Officer
Ed: Gene Epstein. **Description:** Nine summer book suggestions on economics are presented. The list includes 'The Revolution' by Ron Paul, 'The Forgotten Man' by Amity Shales, 'The Commitments of Traders Bible' by Stephen Briese, and 'Economic Facts and Fallacies' by Thomas Sowell. **Availability:** Online.

20915 ■ *"Good for Business: Houston is a Hot Spot for Economic Growth"* in *Black Enterprise* (Vol. 37, October 2006, No. 3, pp. 216)
Pub: Earl G. Graves Ltd.
Contact: Earl Graves, Jr., President
Ed: Jeanette Valentine. **Description:** Fast-growing sectors in the biotechnology and healthcare industries are among the driving forces of Houston's economic growth. More than 76,000 small businesses in the area employ about one in four area workers, according to the Small Business Administration. Housing and business costs are 26 and 11 percent below the national average, respectively, garnering the attention of corporate giants.

20916 ■ *"A Good Sign for Commercial Real Estate?"* in *Austin Business JournalInc.* (Vol. 29, December 18, 2009, No. 41, pp. 1)
Pub: Austin Business Journal
Contact: Rachel McGrath, Director
E-mail: rmcgrath@bizjournals.com
Ed: Kate Harrington. **Description:** Factors that could contribute to the reemergence of the commercial mortgage-backed securities market in Texas are discussed. These securities can potentially boost the commercial real estate market statewide as well as nationwide. Commercial mortgage-backed securities origination in 2009 is worth less that $1 billion, compared with $238 billion in 2008. **Availability:** Online.

20917 ■ *"A Good Step, But There's a Long Way to Go"* in *Business Week* (September 22, 2008, No. 4100, pp. 10)
Ed: James C. Cooper. **Description:** Despite the historic action by the U.S. government to nationalize the mortgage giants Freddie Mac and Fannie Mae, rising unemployment rates may prove to be an even bigger roadblock to bringing back the economy from its downward spiral. The takeover is meant to restore confidence in the credit markets and help with the mortgage crisis but the rising rate in unemployment may make many households unable to take advantage of any benefits which arise from the bailout. Statistical data included. **Availability:** Online.

20918 ■ *"Goodwill Haunts Local Companies"* in *Crain's Chicago Business* (Apr. 28, 2008)
Pub: Crain Communications Inc.
Contact: Barry Asin, President
Ed: Ann Saphir. **Description:** Many companies are having to face the reality that they overpaid for acquisitions made in better economic times; investors often dismiss such one-time charges as mere accounting adjustments but writeoffs related to past acquisitions can signal future problems because they mean the expected profits that justified the purchase have not materialized. Writeoffs are particularly worrisome for firms with a lot of debt and whose banks require them to have enough assets to back up their borrowings. **Availability:** Online.

20919 ■ *"Governor Candidates Differ on Oregon's Green Streak"* in *Business Journal Portland* (Vol. 27, October 22, 2010, No. 34, pp. 1)
Pub: Portland Business Journal
Contact: Andy Giegerich, Managing Editor
E-mail: agiegerich@bizjournals.com
Ed: Andy Giegerich. **Description:** The views of Oregon gubernatorial candidates Chris Dudley and John Kitzhaber on the state's economy and on environmental policies are presented. Both Dudley, who is a Republican, and his Democratic challenger believe that biomass could help drive the state's economy. Both candidates also pledged changes in Oregon's business energy tax credit (BETC) program.

20920 ■ *"Grainger Show Highlights Building Green, Economic Recovery"* in *Contractor* (Vol. 57, February 2010, No. 2, pp. 3)
Ed: Candace Roulo. **Description:** Chief U.S. economist told attendees of the Grainger's 2010 Total MRO Solutions National Customer Show that the economic recovery would be subdued. Mechanical contractors who attended the event also learned about building sustainable, green products, and technologies, and economic and business challenges. **Availability:** Print; Online.

20921 ■ *"The Great Deformation: The Corruption of Capitalism in America"*
Pub: PublicAffairs
Contact: Jaime Leifer, Director
Released: April 02, 2013. **Price:** $24.99, paperback; $14.99, E-book. **Description:** Washington's response to the recent financial crises and fiscal mismanagement is covered. The author provides a catalogue of economic corrupters and defenders of sound money, fiscal rectitude, and free markets. The book covers the history of political statesmen who championed balanced budgets and financial market discipline. The threat to free market prosperity and American political democracy are examined. **Availability:** E-book; Print.

20922 ■ *"The Great Fall of China"* in *Canadian Business* (Vol. 85, June 11, 2012, No. 10, pp. 26)
Ed: Michael McCullough. **Description:** China has a growing influence over the future of Canada's economy as emerging economies and commodity prices recover from the recession. Among the problems unique to China which could impact the Canadian economy are the housing market, its demographic risk and the lack of transparency in the corporate and financial sector. **Availability:** Online.

20923 ■ *"The Great Fall: Here Comes The Humpty Dumpty Economy"* in *Barron's* (Vol. 88, March 10, 2008, No. 10, pp. 5)
Pub: Dow Jones & Company Inc.
Contact: Almar Latour, Chief Executive Officer
Ed: Alan Abelson. **Description:** Discusses the US economy is considered to be in a recession, with the effects of the credit crisis expected to intensify as a result. Inflation is estimated at 4.3 percent in January 2008, while 63,000 jobs were lost in February 2008. **Availability:** Online.

20924 ■ *"The Great Moderation"* in *Canadian Business* (Vol. 80, February 12, 2007, No. 4, pp. 25)
Description: Caution over the changes to stock inventory levels and their adverse impact on the Canadian economy is discussed. **Availability:** Online.

20925 ■ *The Gridlock Economy: How Too Much Ownership Wrecks Markets, Stops Innovation, and Costs Lives*
Ed: Michael Heller. **Released:** February 23, 2010. **Price:** $11.99, paperback; C$14.99. **Description:** While private ownership generally creates wealth, the author believes that economic gridlock results when too many people own pieces of one thing, which results in too many people being able to block each other from creating or using a scarce source. **Availability:** E-book; Print.

20926 ■ *"Ground Forces: Insurance Companies Should Help Agents to Build the Skills and Relationships that Translate Into More Business"* in *Best's Review* (Vol. 113, September 2012, No. 5, pp. 25)
Description: The economic challenges of the past few years required insurance agents and financial professionals to better trained. Insurance companies should help their agents build skills and relationships in order to grow. **Availability:** Print; Online.

20927 ■ *"Grounded Condo Development Poised for Construction Takeoff"* in *Memphis Business Journal* (Vol. 35, February 7, 2014, No. 44, pp. 4)
Pub: American City Business Journals, Inc.
Contact: Mike Olivieri, Executive Vice President
Released: Weekly. **Price:** $4, introductory 4-week offer(Digital only). **Description:** Developers in Memphis, Tennessee are hoping that the economic recovery will help revive the condominium market. However, industry experts believe that inventory will have to all and prices will have to rise before the market recovers. The impact of loose lending practices on condominium developers is also discussed. **Availability:** Print; Online.

20928 ■ *"Growing Field"* in *Crain's Detroit Business* (Vol. 26, January 11, 2010, No. 2, pp. 3)
Pub: Crain Communications Inc.
Contact: Barry Asin, President
Description: Detroit's TechTown was awarded a combination loan and grant of $4.1 million from the U.S. Department of Housing and Urban Development to build a 15,000-square-foot stem cell center, a collection of laboratories that will be available to both for-profit companies and university researchers. **Availability:** Online.

20929 ■ *"Growth in Fits and Starts"* in *Canadian Business* (Vol. 83, July 20, 2010, No. 11-12, pp. 18)
Description: US home sales and manufacturing indicators have dropped and fears of a double-dip recession are widespread. However, a chief economist says that this is endemic to what can be seen after a recession caused by a financial crisis. In Canada, consumer optimism is rising and anxiety over losing one's job is waning. **Availability:** Print; Online.

20930 ■ *"H&M Offers a Dress for Less"* in *Canadian Business* (Vol. 83, September 14, 2010, No. 15, pp. 20)
Pub: Rogers Media Inc.
Contact: Neil Spivak, Chief Executive Officer
Ed: Laura Cameron. **Description:** Swedish clothing company H&M has implemented loss leader strategy by pricing some dresses at extremely low prices. The economy has forced retailers to keep prices down despite the increasing cost of manufacturing, partly due to Chinese labor becoming more expensive. How the trend will affect apparel companies is discussed. **Availability:** Print; Online.

20931 ■ *"Has Daylight Savings Time Fuelled Gasoline Consumption?"* in *Globe & Mail* (April 18, 2007, pp. B1)
Ed: Shawn McCarthy. **Description:** The prospects of the acquisition of BCE Inc, by Canadian pension funds are discussed. The effect of the growth of these pension funds on the Canadian economy is described. **Availability:** Online.

20932 ■ *"Headwinds From the New Sod Slow Aer Lingus"* in *Barron's* (Vol. 88, March 10, 2008, No. 10, pp. M6)
Pub: Dow Jones & Company Inc.
Contact: Almar Latour, Chief Executive Officer

Ed: Sean Walters, Arindam Nag. **Description:** Aer Lingus faces a drop in its share prices with a falling US market, higher jet fuel prices, and lower long-haul passenger load factors. British media companies Johnston Press and Yell Group are suffering from weaker ad revenue and heavier debt payments due to the credit crunch. **Availability:** Online.

20933 ■ *"Health care: Medicare Inc." in Canadian Business (Vol. 80, October 8, 2007, No. 20, pp. 160)*
Pub: Rogers Media Inc.
Contact: Neil Spivak, Chief Executive Officer
Ed: Erin Pooley. **Description:** State of Canada's health care system is discussed. A report by the Fraser Institute in Vancouver predicts that public health spending in six of ten provinces in the country will use more than half the revenues from all sources by 2020. Experts believe competition in the health care industry will help solve the current problems in the sector. **Availability:** Print; Online.

20934 ■ *"High Anxiety" in Canadian Business (Vol. 80, November 19, 2007, No. 23, pp. 11)*
Description: Value of Canadian dollar continues to rise, and consumers are asking for lower prices of goods. Retailers, on the other hand, are facing concerns over losing sales. The impacts of the rising Canadian dollar on the business sector and consumer behavior are examined. **Availability:** Online.

20935 ■ *"High-End Blunders" in Crain's Chicago Business (Vol. 31, April 21, 2008, No. 16, pp. 54)*
Pub: Crain Communications Inc.
Contact: Barry Asin, President
Ed: Laura Bianchi. **Description:** Discusses some of the biggest errors sellers make that keep their homes from selling including: pricing too high; expecting to recoup the cost of very high-end amenities and decor; avant-garde decorating; owners that hover when the house is being shown; stripping the home of top-quality light fixtures and hardware and replacing them with inferior versions with the assumption that the new buyer will come in with their own decorator and redo it; and poorly maintained properties. **Availability:** Online.

20936 ■ *"The High-Intensity Entrepreneur" in Harvard Business Review (Vol. 88, September 2010, No. 9, pp. 74)*
Pub: Harvard Business Publishing
Contact: Diane Belcher, Managing Director
Ed: Anne S. Habiby, Deirdre M. Coyle, Jr. **Price:** $8.95, PDF. **Description:** Examination of the role of small companies in promoting global economic growth is presented. Discussion includes identifying entrepreneurial capability. **Availability:** Online; PDF.

20937 ■ *"High-Yield Turns Into Road Kill" in Barron's (Vol. 88, July 7, 2008, No. 27, pp. M7)*
Pub: Dow Jones & Company Inc.
Contact: Almar Latour, Chief Executive Officer
Ed: Emily Barrett. **Description:** High-yield bonds have returned to the brink of collapse after profits have recovered from the shock brought about by the collapse of Bear Stearns. The high-yield bond market could decline again due to weakness in the automotive sector, particularly in Ford and General Motors. **Availability:** Online.

20938 ■ *"Hitting Bottom? Several Banks and Brokerages Are Ready to Pop Up for Air" in Barron's (Vol. 88, March 24, 2008, No. 12, pp. 21)*
Pub: Dow Jones & Company Inc.
Contact: Almar Latour, Chief Executive Officer
Ed: Jacqueline Doherty. **Description:** Brokerage houses and banks may stabilize in 2008 as a result of regulatory responses brought about by the near-collapse of Bear Stearns. Some of their shares may rise by as much as 20 percent from 2008 to 2009. **Availability:** Online.

20939 ■ *"Hold the McJobs: Canada's High-End Employment Boom" in Globe & Mail (February 17, 2006, pp. B1)*
Ed: Heather Scoffield. **Description:** A focus the increasing rate of high-end or professional jobs Canada and its negative influence on low-end and middle level jobs is presented. **Availability:** Print; Online.

20940 ■ *"Holiday Sales Look Uncertain for Microsoft and PC Sellers" in Puget Sound Business Journal (Vol. 29, November 28, 2008, No. 32)*
Ed: Todd Bishop. **Description:** Personal computer makers face uncertain holiday sales for 2008 as a result of the weak U.S. economy and a shift toward low-cost computers. Personal computer shipments for the fourth quarter 2008 are forecast to drop 1 percent compared to the same quarter 2007. **Availability:** Online.

20941 ■ *"Home Prices Sag" in Crain's Chicago Business (Vol. 31, April 28, 2008, No. 17, pp. 3)*
Pub: Crain Communications Inc.
Contact: Barry Asin, President
Ed: Alby Gallun. **Description:** Since the slump in the housing market is continuing with no sign of recovery, Chicago-area home prices are poised for an even steeper drop this year. In 2007, the region's home prices fell nearly 5 percent and according to a forecast by Fiserv Inc., they will decline 8.1 percent this year and another 2.2 percent in 2009. Statistical data included. **Availability:** Online.

20942 ■ *"Home Sweet (Second) Home" in Baltimore Business Journal (Vol. 30, May 25, 2012, No. 3, pp. 1)*
Ed: Leigh Somerville. **Description:** Home prices in Maryland have declined in 2012. A number of affluent homebuyers have been purchasing vacation homes in the state. **Availability:** Print; Online.

20943 ■ *"Homebuilding Thrives on Lot Prices" in Memphis Business Journal (Vol. 33, February 24, 2012, No. 46, pp. 1)*
Pub: Baltimore Business Journal
Contact: Rhonda Pringle, President
E-mail: rpringle@bizjournals.com
Ed: Christopher Sheffield. **Description:** Homebuilders in Memphis, Tennessee have survived the economic crises owing to the decrease in prices of lots. However, the increase in the purchase of lots is seen to adversely impact the sector in the long run. **Availability:** Print; Online.

20944 ■ *"Homes, Not Bars, Stay Well Tended" in Advertising Age (Vol. 79, January 28, 2008, No. 4, pp. 8)*
Pub: Crain Communications, Inc.
Contact: Jessica Botos, Manager, Marketing
E-mail: jessica.botos@crainsnewyork.com
Ed: Jeremy Mullman. **Description:** Due to the downturn in the economy, consumers are drinking less at bars and restaurants; however, according to the Distilled Spirits Council of the United States, they are still purchasing expensive liquor to keep in their homes. **Availability:** Online.

20945 ■ *"Hotel Woes Reflect Area Struggle" in Business Journal Serving Greater Tampa Bay (Vol. 30, December 3, 2010, No. 50, pp. 1)*
Pub: Tampa Bay Business Journal
Contact: Ian Anderson, President
E-mail: ianderson@bizjournals.com
Ed: Mark Holan. **Description:** Quality Inn and Suites in East Tampa, Florida has struggled against the sluggish economy but remained open to guests despite facing a foreclosure. The hotel project is the center of East Tampa's redevelopment plans and public officials defend the $650,000 investment in public amenities near the building. **Availability:** Print; Online.

20946 ■ *"Hotels' Healthy Finish in '07" in Crain's Chicago Business (Vol. 31, March 24, 2008, No. 12, pp. 16)*
Pub: Crain Communications Inc.
Contact: Barry Asin, President
Ed: Alby Gallun. **Description:** Chicago's hotel market saw mostly rising occupancies and room rates in the fourth quarter of 2007, reflecting continued strong demand from leisure and business travelers; however, due to the current state of the economy hoteliers face an increasingly uncertain outlook. **Availability:** Online.

20947 ■ *"Housing Markets Still Struggling" in Montana Business Quarterly (Vol. 49, Spring 2011, No. 1, pp. 17)*
Pub: University of Montana Bureau of Business and Economic Research
Contact: Patrick Barkey, Director
E-mail: patrick.barkey@business.umt.edu
Ed: Scott Rickard. **Released:** Quarterly. **Description:** Montana's economic conditions are a bit better than national averages. Data ranked by state, year-over-year price change, and total price peak is presented, along with statistical data for the entire nation. **Availability:** Online.

20948 ■ *"How Bad Is It?" in Hawaii Business (Vol. 54, July 2008, No. 1, pp. 35)*
Pub: PacificBasin Communications
Contact: Chuck Tindle, Director
E-mail: chuckt@pacificbasin.net
Ed: Jolyn Okimoto Rosa. **Description:** Donald G. Horner, chief executive officer of First Hawaiian Bank, says that the current Hawaiian economic situation is a cyclical slowdown. Maurice Kaya, an energy consultant, says the slowdown is due to overdependence on imported fuels. Other local leaders, such as Constance H. Lau, also discuss their view on the current economic situation in Hawaii.

20949 ■ *"How Baltimore's Largest Private Companies Weathered the Recession's Punch; Top Private Companies" in Baltimore Business Journal (Vol. 28, August 27, 2010, No. 16, pp. 1)*
Pub: Baltimore Business Journal
Contact: Rhonda Pringle, President
E-mail: rpringle@bizjournals.com
Ed: Gary Haber. **Description:** The combined revenue of the 100 largest private firms in Maryland's Baltimore region dropped from about $22.7 billion in 2008 to $21 billion in 2009, an annual decrease of more than 7 percent. To survive the recession's impact, these firms resorted to strategies such as government contracting and overseas expansion. How these strategies affected the revenue of some firms is described. **Availability:** Print; Online.

20950 ■ *"How to Beat the Pros" in Canadian Business (Vol. 81, Summer 2008, No. 9, pp. 59)*
Description: Table showing the results of the Investor 500 beat the S&P/TSX composite index is presented. The average total return, best performing stocks and total return of the 2007 stock screen are provided. **Availability:** Online.

20951 ■ *"How to Develop an Active Sales Program" in Green Industry Pro (Vol. 23, September 2011)*
Ed: Gregg Wartgow. **Description:** Craig den Hartog, owner of Emerald Magic Lawn Care located in Holtsville, New York, describes the various marketing tactics he has developed to increase sales in the current economic environment. Statistical data included. **Availability:** Online.

20952 ■ *"How Exports Could Save America" in Barron's (Vol. 89, July 20, 2009, No. 29, pp. 15)*
Pub: Dow Jones & Company Inc.
Contact: Almar Latour, Chief Executive Officer
Ed: Jonathan R. Laing. **Description:** Increase in US exports should help drive up the nation's economic growth, according to Wells Capital Management

strategist Jim Paulsen. He believes US gross domestic product could grow by 3-3.5 percent annually starting in 2010 due to a more favorable trade balance. **Availability:** Online.

20953 ■ *"How Important Are Small Businesses to Local Economies?"* in Chron (Oct. 15, 2018)
URL(s): smallbusiness.chron.com/important-small-businesses-local-economies-5251.html
Ed: J. Mariah Brown. **Released:** October 15, 2018. **Description:** Discusses the importance of small business to local communities. **Availability:** Online.

20954 ■ *"How Much Inequality Is Necessary for Growth?"* in Harvard Business Review (Vol. 90, January-February 2012, No.1-2, pp. 28)
Pub: Harvard Business Review Press
Contact: Moderna V. Pfizer, Contact
Ed: Fuad Hasanov, Oded Izraeli. **Price:** $6, hardcopy black and white. **Description:** Research on international economic inequality shows that when inequality rises to a specific level, growth declines; however if it is lower than a certain level, the same results occur. One standard deviation of growth in inequality would raise yearly growth by approximately 0.6 percent. **Availability:** Print; PDF; Online.

20955 ■ *"How Our Picks Beat The Bear"* in Barron's (Vol. 88, July 14, 2008, No. 28, pp. 18)
Pub: Dow Jones & Company Inc.
Contact: Almar Latour, Chief Executive Officer
Ed: Andrew Bary. **Description:** Performance of the stocks that Barron's covered in the first half of 2008 is discussed; some of the worst picks and most rewarding pans have been in the financial sector while the best plays were in the energy, materials, and the transportation sectors. **Availability:** Online.

20956 ■ *"How South Florida Can Revive a Flagging Sector"* in South Florida Business Journal (Vol. 34, April 4, 2014, No. 37, pp. 10)
Pub: American City Business Journals, Inc.
Contact: Mike Olivieri, Executive Vice President
Released: Weekly. **Price:** $8, Introductory 4-week offer(Digital & Print). **Description:** South Florida convention centers are trying to address the sluggish demand for conventions to the area by upgrading its facilities and adding hotels. The ancillary revenue generate by the attendees at hotels, restaurants, and other establishments makes a convention as key economic drivers. The efforts to boost the region's position as convention destinations are also addressed. **Availability:** Print; Online.

20957 ■ *"How To Make Finance Work: The U.S. Financial Sector Has Boomed, But That Hasn't Always Been Good News For the Rest of the Economy"* in Harvard Business Review (Vol. 90, March 2012, No. 3, pp. 104)
Pub: Harvard Business Review Press
Contact: Moderna V. Pfizer, Contact
Ed: David S. Scharfstein, Robin Greenwood. **Price:** $8.95, hardcover. **Description:** The growth of the financial sector has hindered overall US growth by shifting money from productive investments into residential real estate, and through high professional investment management costs. Private sector innovation and discipline will be needed to correct these flaws, as will regulatory changes. **Availability:** PDF; Online.

20958 ■ *"The Human Factor"* in Canadian Business (Vol. 80, October 8, 2007, No. 20, pp. 22)
Description: David Foot, a demographer and an economics professor at the University of Toronto, talks about Canada's future, including economic and demographic trends. He discusses activities that should be done by businessmen in order to prepare for the future. He also addresses the role of the Canadian government in economic development. **Availability:** Print; Online.

20959 ■ *"Ill Winds; Cuba's Economy"* in The Economist (Vol. 390, January 3, 2009, No. 8612, pp. 20)
Description: Cuba's long-term economic prospects remain poor with the economy forecasted to grow only 4.3 percent for the year, about half of the original forecast, due in part to Hurricane Gustav which caused $10 billion in damage and disrupted the food-supply network and devastated farms across the region; President Raul Castro made raising agricultural production a national priority and the rise in global commodity prices hit the country hard. The only bright spot has been the rise in tourism which is up 9.3 percent over 2007. **Availability:** Online.

20960 ■ *The Importance of Small Business to the U.S. Economy*
URL(s): courses.lumenlearning.com/baycollege-in trobusiness/chapter/reading-the-importance-of-small-business-to-the-u-s-economy/
Description: Explores the importance of small business to the U.S. economy. **Availability:** Online.

20961 ■ *"In the Options Market, Financial-Sector Trading Is Moody and Paranoid"* in Barron's (Vol. 88, March 10, 2008, No. 10, pp. M14)
Pub: Dow Jones & Company Inc.
Contact: Almar Latour, Chief Executive Officer
Ed: Steven M. Sears. **Description:** Discusses the options market which remains liquid but is cautious of possible failures, especially for financial companies. Investors are in absolute fear when trading with options involving the financial sector. **Availability:** Online.

20962 ■ *"In Surging Oil Industry, Good Fortune Comes In Stages"* in Barron's (Vol. 88, July 7, 2008, No. 27, pp. 12)
Pub: Dow Jones & Company Inc.
Contact: Almar Latour, Chief Executive Officer
Ed: Sandra Ward. **Description:** Shares of US land oil and gas driller Helmerich and Payne, priced at $69 each, are estimated to be at peak levels. The shares are trading at 17 times 2008 earnings and could be in for some profit taking. **Availability:** Online.

20963 ■ *"Indigenous Tourism Operators: The Vanguard of Economic Recovery in the Chatham Islands"* in International Journal of Entrepreneurship and Small Business (Vol. 10, July 6, 2010, No. 4)
Ed: Andrew Cardow, Peter Wiltshier. **Description:** Emergent enthusiasm for tourism as a savior for economic development in the Chatham Islands of New Zealand is highlighted. **Availability:** Online.

20964 ■ *"Indulgent Parsimony: an Enduring Marketing Approach"* in Strategy and Leadership (Vol. 39, March-April 2011, No. 2, pp. 36)
Pub: Emerald Group Publishing Limited
Contact: Erika Valenti, President
Ed: Kenneth Alan Grossberg. **Description:** Indulgent parsimony (IP), a marketing strategy employed on consumers that are affected by recession, is found to be a relevant and appropriate approach that can help encourage buying. IP involves the selling of cheaper goods and services that allow consumers experience comfort and relief from stress. **Availability:** Download; Online.

20965 ■ *"Industrial Vacancies Hit High"* in Crain's Chicago Business (Apr. 21, 2008)
Pub: Crain Communications Inc.
Contact: Barry Asin, President
Ed: Alby Gallun. **Description:** Hitting its highest level in four years in the first quarter is the Chicago-area industrial vacancy rate, a sign that the slumping economy is depressing demand for warehouse and manufacturing space. **Availability:** Online.

20966 ■ *"Infrastructure: Things Fall Apart"* in Canadian Business (Vol. 80, October 8, 2007, No. 20, pp. 187)
Pub: Rogers Media Inc.
Contact: Neil Spivak, Chief Executive Officer
Ed: Jeff Sanford. **Description:** Infrastructure crisis in Canada and in other countries in North America is examined. Incidents that demonstrate this crisis, such as the collapse of a bridge in Minneapolis and the collapse of an overpass in Quebec, Canada are presented. It is estimated that the reconstruction in the country will cost between C$44 billion and C$200 billion. **Availability:** Print; Online.

20967 ■ *"Inland Snaps Up Rival REITs"* in Crain's Chicago Business (Vol. 31, November 17, 2008, No. 46, pp. 3)
Pub: Crain Communications Inc.
Contact: Barry Asin, President
Ed: Alby Gallun. **Description:** Discusses Inland American Real Estate Trust Inc., a real estate investment trust that is napping up depressed shares of publicly traded competitors, a possible first step toward taking over these companies; however, with hotel and retail properties accounting for approximately 70 percent of its portfolio, the company could soon face its own difficulties. **Availability:** Online.

20968 ■ *Innovate to Great: Re-Igniting Sustainable Innovation to Win in the Global Economy*
Description: The author explores innovation and creativity as a means for small companies to survive and expand in the global economy. **Availability:** Print; PDF.

20969 ■ *"Innovation Despite Reorganization"* in Journal of Business Strategy (Vol. 35, May-June 2014, No. 3, pp. 18-25)
Pub: Emerald Group Publishing Limited
Contact: Erika Valenti, President
Description: Innovation can be sustained through a downsizing event. The articles shows how prevailing formal and informal networks can be used for reestablishing connections between employees after a company is downsized. **Availability:** Download; Online.

20970 ■ *"Innovation Station"* in Canadian Business (Vol. 80, October 8, 2007, No. 20, pp. 42)
Description: Study and teaching of entrepreneurship at the University of Waterloo is discussed. Research projects in the university are expected to be influential in Canada's economic development. In spite of the success of these studies, financing is still a problem for the university, especially in technological innovations. **Availability:** Online.

20971 ■ *"Innovators Critical in Technical Economy"* in Crain's Cleveland Business (Vol. 28, November 5, 2007, No. 44, pp. 10)
Pub: Crain Communications Inc.
Contact: K. C. Crain, President
Ed: Peter Rea. **Description:** Discusses the importance to attract, develop and retain talented innovators on Ohio's economy. Also breaks down the four fronts on which the international battle for talent is being waged. **Availability:** Online.

20972 ■ *"Insitu May Move to Oregon"* in Business Journal Portland (Vol. 27, October 29, 2010, No. 35, pp. 1)
Pub: Portland Business Journal
Contact: Andy Giegerich, Managing Editor
E-mail: agiegerich@bizjournals.com
Ed: Erik Siemers. **Description:** Bingen, Washington-based Insitu Inc. announced that it has narrowed the search for a new corporate campus into five locations within the Columbia Gorge region. However, state economic development officials are curious whether the company will land in Oregon or Washington. Insights on economic impact of Insitu's decision are also given.

20973 ■ **"Insurers No Longer Paying Premium for Advertising"** in Brandweek (Vol. 49, April 21, 2008, No. 16, pp. SR3)
Description: Insurance companies are cutting their advertising budgets after years of accelerated double-digit growth in spending due to the economic downturn, five years of record-breaking ad spend and a need to cut expenditures as claims costs rise and a competitive market keeps premiums in place. Statistical data included. **Availability:** Print; Online.

20974 ■ **International Economic Development Council--Membership Directory**
Pub: International Economic Development Council
Contact: Nathan Ohle, President
URL(s): www.iedconline.org/pages/member-benefits
Description: Covers approximately 2,700 economic development professionals working in local and state governments; private sector professionals and corporations; local and community development corporations; neighborhood and manpower groups. **Entries include:** For individual members--Name, address, phone. For corporations and community groups--Organization name, address, phone, fax, name and title of contact. **Arrangement:** Personal. **Indexes:** Geographical, Organizational. **Availability:** Print.

20975 ■ **"International ETFs: Your Passport to the World"** in Barron's (Vol. 89, July 13, 2009, No. 28, pp. L10)
Pub: Dow Jones & Company Inc.
Contact: Almar Latour, Chief Executive Officer
Ed: John Hintze. **Description:** International exchange traded funds give investors more choices in terms of investment plays and there are 174 U.S. ETF listings worth $141 billion as of July 2009. Suggestions on how to invest in these funds based on one's conviction on how the global economy will unfold are presented. **Availability:** Online.

20976 ■ **"Into the Light: Making Our Way Through the Economic Tunnel"** in Agency Sales Magazine (Vol. 39, August 2009, No. 8, pp. 26)
Description: Ways in which to avoid business stagnation brought about by the economic downturn is presented. Being different, being a puzzle solver, and knowing the competition are among the things marketing personnel should do in order to wade through the economic downturn. Marketing via direct mail and the Internet also recommended. **Availability:** Online.

20977 ■ **"Intrepid Souls: Meet a Few Who've Made the Big Leap"** in Crain's Chicago Business (Vol. 31, November 10, 2008, No. 45, pp. 26)
Description: Advice is given from entrepreneurs who have launched businesses in the last year despite the economic crisis. Among the types of businesses featured are a cooking school, a child day-care center, a children's clothing store and an Internet-based company. **Availability:** Online.

20978 ■ **"Is Fannie Mae the Next Government Bailout?"** in Barron's (Vol. 88, March 10, 2008, No. 10, pp. 21)
Pub: Dow Jones & Company Inc.
Contact: Almar Latour, Chief Executive Officer
Ed: Jonathan R. Laing. **Description:** Fannie Mae may need a government bailout as it faces huge hits brought about by the effects of the housing crisis. The shares of the government-sponsored enterprise have dropped 65 percent since the housing crisis began. **Availability:** Online.

20979 ■ **"Is the VIX in Denial?"** in Barron's (Vol. 88, July 7, 2008, No. 27, pp. M12)
Pub: Dow Jones & Company Inc.
Contact: Almar Latour, Chief Executive Officer
Ed: Lawrence McMillan. **Description:** Volatility Index (VIX) of the Chicago Board Options Exchange did not rise significantly despite the drop in the US stock markets, rising to near 25. This market decline, however, will eventually result in investor panic and the rise of the VIX. **Availability:** Online.

20980 ■ **"It Could Be Worse"** in Barron's (Vol. 89, July 27, 2009, No. 30, pp. 5)
Pub: Dow Jones & Company Inc.
Contact: Almar Latour, Chief Executive Officer
Ed: Alan Abelson. **Description:** Media sources are being fooled by corporate America who is peddling an economic recovery rather than reality as shown by the report of a rise in existing home sales which boosted the stock market even if it was a seasonal phenomenon. The phrase "things could be worse" sums up the reigning investment philosophy in the U.S. and this has been stirring up the market. **Availability:** Online.

20981 ■ **"It's Good To Be a CEO: Top Execs Pull Millions In Raises for 2013"** in Atlanta Business Chronicle (June 20, 2014, pp. 22A)
Pub: American City Business Journals, Inc.
Contact: Mike Olivieri, Executive Vice President
Description: Discussion regarding the highest paid CEOs in Georgia in 2013, with an average of 8.8 percent increase from 2012. The largest increase went to Jeffrey C. Sprecher, chairman and CEO of Intercontinental Exchange Inc., followed by John F. Brock, chairman and CEO of Coca-Cola Enterprises Inc. **Availability:** Print; Online.

20982 ■ **"It's Time To Swim"** in Canadian Business (Vol. 81, March 3, 2008, No. 3, pp. 37)
Description: Canadian manufacturers should consider Asian markets such as India and the United Arab Emirates as the U.S. economic downturn continues. Canada's shortage in skilled labor is also expected to negatively affect manufacturing industries. Ontario's plans to assist manufacturers are also presented. **Availability:** Print; PDF; Download; Online.

20983 ■ **"J.C. Evans Files for Ch. 11 Protection"** in Austin Business Journal (Vol. 31, August 12, 2011, No. 23, pp. A1)
Pub: Austin Business Journal
Contact: Rachel McGrath, Director
E-mail: rmcgrath@bizjournals.com
Ed: Vicky Garza. **Description:** J.C. Evans Construction Holdings Inc., as well as its affiliated companies, has filed for Chapter 11 bankruptcy following its continued financial breakdown which it blames on the tough economy. Details are included. **Availability:** Print; Online.

20984 ■ **"Jim Cramer's Get Rich Carefully"**
Pub: Penguin Publishing Group
Released: December 31, 2013 . **Price:** $17, paperback; $11.99, e-book; $20, audiobook download; $14.99. **Description:** Wall Street veteran and host of CNBC's Mad Money, Jim Cramer, provides a guide to high-yield, low-risk investing in a recovering economic market. **Availability:** audiobook; E-book; Print.

20985 ■ **"Jobs Gain Cast Shadow On Recovery"** in Providence Business News (Vol. 29, April 7, 2014, No. 1, pp. 1)
Pub: American City Business Journals, Inc.
Contact: Mike Olivieri, Executive Vice President
URL(s): pbn.com/job-gains-cast-shadow-on-recovery96249
Description: Rhode Island Department of Labor and Training data has indicated the creation of nearly 21,000 jobs in the state since summer of 2009. However, the 503,300 state's residents working in February 2014, was 45,586 fewer than pre-recession peak in December 2006, despite the job gains. The factors separating job growth from resident employment and the economic impact is discussed.

20986 ■ **"Jobs Data Show A Slow Leak"** in Barron's (Vol. 88, July 7, 2008, No. 27, pp. 34)
Pub: Dow Jones & Company Inc.
Contact: Almar Latour, Chief Executive Officer
Ed: Gene Epstein. **Description:** In June 2008, the United States manufacturing sector showed an expansion, with the purchasing managers' index rising to 50.2 from 49.6; the unemployment rate in the US, which stayed steady at 5.5 percent in June 2008 is also discussed. Statistical data included. **Availability:** Online.

20987 ■ **"KC Incentives Debate Rages on Unabated"** in The Business Journal-Serving Metropolitan Kansas City (Vol. 26, September 5, 2008, No. 52)
Pub: American City Business Journals, Inc.
Contact: Mike Olivieri, Executive Vice President
Ed: Rob Roberts. **Description:** Debate on the new economic development and incentives policy adopted by the Kansas City Council is still on. The city's Planned Industrial Expansion Authority has rejected a standard property tax abatement proposal. The real estate development community has opposed the rejection of proposed the tax incentives policy. **Availability:** Online.

20988 ■ **"Keene: Nominations are Being Sought by the Keene Cities for Climate Protection Committee for the Monadnock Green Business of the Year Award"** in New Hampshire Business Review (Vol. 34, February 24, 2012, No. 4, pp. 7)
Released: February 24, 2012. **Description:** Nominations are being sought by the Keene Cities for Climate Protection Committee for the Monadnock Green Business of the Year Award. The award recognizes socially and environmentally responsible companies in the region that have developed innovative practices or programs while contributing to the economic growth of the area.

20989 ■ **"Keith Crain: Business Must Stand Up And Be Counted"** in Crain's Detroit Business (Vol. 24, October 6, 2008, No. 40, pp. 6)
Pub: Crain Communications Inc.
Contact: Barry Asin, President
Description: Discusses the challenges that the new mayor of Detroit faces concerning business, the state of the economy and the exceptionally tight budget the city is running on, which includes a lot of red ink. It is very likely that the city is going to see tax revenues fall substantially in the next few months and business leaders may find it in their favor to lend their support to the new mayor as well as provide him with the executive talent necessary to overcome some of these crucial issues. **Availability:** Online.

20990 ■ **"Knocking On the World's Door"** in Business Journal Portland (Vol. 31, March 28, 2014, No. 4, pp. 4)
Pub: American City Business Journals, Inc.
Contact: Mike Olivieri, Executive Vice President
Released: Weekly. **Price:** $4, introductory 4-week offer(Digital & Print). **Description:** A list of things that the City of Portland, Oregon should do to achieve world-class status is provided. Portland must welcome companies as a site selection, build infrastructure, consider the economic and recreational potential of the Willamette River, allocate more education budget and provide greater access to capital. **Availability:** Print; Online.

20991 ■ **"Labor Pains"** in Canadian Business (Vol. 79, August 14, 2006, No. 16-17, pp. 80)
Description: Canada's employment insurance is analyzed in view of the growing shortage of labor. **Availability:** Print; Online.

20992 ■ **"Laced Up and Ready to Run"** in Barron's (Vol. 89, July 6, 2009, No. 27, pp. 12)
Pub: Dow Jones & Company Inc.
Contact: Almar Latour, Chief Executive Officer
Ed: Christopher C. Williams. **Description:** Shares of Foot Locker could raise from $10 to about $15 a share with the improvement of the economy. The company has benefited from prudent management and merchandising as well as better cost cutting, allowing it to better survive in a recession. **Availability:** Online.

GENERAL SMALL BUSINESS TOPICS   Economic Development ■ 21012

20993 ■ *"Land Squeeze Stalls Portland Homebuilders"* in *Business Journal Portland* (Vol. 31, March 21, 2014, No. 3, pp. 4)
Pub: American City Business Journals, Inc.
Contact: Mike Olivieri, Executive Vice President
Released: March 21, 2014. **Price:** $4, Introductory 4-Week Offer(Digital & Print). **Description:** Homebuilders in Portland, Oregon are building fewer homes that before the recession due to the impact of the 2008 economic collapse and the lack of available land on which to build. Prices in the residential real estate market are expected to increase as new single family home construction fails to keep pace with growing demand. **Availability:** Print; Online.

20994 ■ *"LaSalle St. Firms Cherry-Pick Talent As Wall St. Tanks"* in *Crain's Chicago Business* (Vol. 31, November 17, 2008, No. 46)
Pub: Crain Communications Inc.
Contact: Barry Asin, President
Ed: H. Lee Murphy. **Description:** Many local businesses are taking advantage of the lay offs that many major Wall Street firms are undergoing in their workforces; these companies see the opportunity to woo talent and expand their staff with quality executives. **Availability:** Online.

20995 ■ *"Last Call?"* in *Puget Sound Business Journal* (Vol. .35, August 8, 2014, No. 16, pp. 12)
Pub: American City Business Journals, Inc.
Contact: Mike Olivieri, Executive Vice President
Description: T-Mobile US cellular phone service is targeted for acquisition by large firms, but so far no deals have materialized. Analysts believe a deal will emerge soon as T-Mobile's parent company is seeking suitable bidders. The impact of a merger on Puget Sound's economy is viewed. **Availability:** Online.

20996 ■ *"The Last Word Dirty Work Required"* in *Workforce Management* (Vol. 88, November 16, 2009, No. 12, pp. 34)
Pub: Crain Communications Inc.
Contact: Barry Asin, President
Ed: John Hollon. **Description:** Due to salary freezes, pay cuts, layoffs, buyouts and a number of other stress factors brought about by the recession, employee engagement has been difficult to maintain by managers. **Availability:** Online.

20997 ■ *"The Latin Beat Goes On"* in *Barron's* (Vol. 88, July 7, 2008, No. 27, pp. L5)
Pub: Dow Jones & Company Inc.
Contact: Almar Latour, Chief Executive Officer
Ed: Tom Sullivan. **Description:** Latin American stocks have outperformed other regional markets due to rising commodities prices and favorable economic climate. Countries such as Brazil, Mexico, Chile, and Peru provide investment opportunities, while Argentina and Venezuela are tougher places to invest. **Availability:** Online.

20998 ■ *"Law Firms See Improvement in Financing Climate"* in *Sacramento Business Journal* (Vol. 28, October 14, 2011, No. 33, pp. 1)
Pub: Sacramento Business Journal
Contact: Stephanie Fretwell, Director
E-mail: sfretwell@bizjournals.com
Ed: Kathy Robertson. **Description:** Sacramento, California-based Weintraub Genshlea Chediak Law Corporation has helped close 26 financing deals worth more than $1.6 billion in 2010, providing indication of improvement in Sacramento's economy. Lawyers have taken advantage of low interest rates to make refinancing agreements and help clients get new funds. **Availability:** Online.

20999 ■ *"Lawmakers, Execs Launch Effort to Save Rural Hospitals"* in *Atlanta Business Chronicle* (June 13, 2014, pp. 7A)
Pub: American City Business Journals, Inc.
Contact: Mike Olivieri, Executive Vice President

Description: Governor Nathan Deal has appointed a committee of Georgia lawmakers and healthcare executives to launch an effort to save the state's financially burdened rural hospitals. In addition, he plans to allow rural hospitals that have closed or are on the verge of closing, to scale back their operations, under a new rule approved by the Georgia Board of Community Health. **Availability:** Print; Online.

21000 ■ *"Layoffs Continue to Be a Drag on Region's Recovery"* in *Philadelphia Business Journal* (Vol. 28, January 22, 2010, No. 49, pp. 1)
Pub: Philadelphia Business Journal
Contact: Sierra Quinn, Director
E-mail: squinn@bizjournals.com
Ed: Athena D. Merritt. **Description:** Mass layoffs continue to hamper Pennsylvania's economic recovery. Job losses are predicted to decline in 2010. **Availability:** Online.

21001 ■ *"Leaders and Lagards"* in *Barron's* (Vol. 89, July 13, 2009, No. 28, pp. 14)
Description: Statistical table that shows the returns of different mutual funds in different categories that include U.S. stock funds, sector funds, world equity funds, and mixed equity funds is presented. The data presented is for the second quarter of 2009. **Availability:** Print; Online.

21002 ■ *"Leading Ohio Internet Marketing Firm Announces Growth in September"* in *Marketing Weekly News* (September 26, 2009, pp. 24)
Pub: Investment Weekly News
Description: Despite a poor economy, Webbed Marketing, a leading social media marketing and search engine optimization firm in the Midwest, has added five additional professionals to its fast-growing team. The company continues to win new business, provide more services and hire talented employees. **Availability:** Online.

21003 ■ *"Legislators Must Cut Cost of Government"* in *Crain's Detroit Business* (Vol. 24, October 6, 2008, No. 40, pp. 6)
Pub: Crain Communications Inc.
Contact: Barry Asin, President
Description: Southeast and West Michigan business leaders are setting aside their differences and have proposed clear agendas, ranging from eliminating the Michigan Business Tax to overhauling public employee and retiree benefits and pensions. Lawmakers must also come together to find solutions for the state's economy and discover an entirely new vision for the future of Michigan business. **Availability:** Print; Online.

21004 ■ *"Lessons From My Father"* in *Crain's Chicago Business* (Vol. 31, November 10, 2008, No. 45, pp. 28)
Pub: Crain Communications Inc.
Contact: Barry Asin, President
Ed: Rance Crain. **Description:** Rance Crain discusses his father, G.D. Crain Jr., who founded Crain Communications Inc. during the Great Depression. Advice is given for sustaining a business, even one that seems to be failing, during tough economic times. **Availability:** Online.

21005 ■ *"Let Markets Decide?"* in *Canadian Business* (Vol. 80, October 8, 2007, No. 20, pp. 67)
Description: Need to protect Canadian companies that could help boost the country's economy is discussed. It is expected that free markets alone will solve economic problems. Suggested policies that will discourage the takeover of major companies in the country, such as the organization of capitalization with multiple voting shares, are also presented. **Availability:** Print; Online.

21006 ■ *"Let's Make a Deal"* in *Pittsburgh Business Times* (Vol. 33, July 18, 2014, No. 53, pp. 10)
Pub: American City Business Journals, Inc.
Contact: Mike Olivieri, Executive Vice President

Released: February 26, 2015. **Description:** The low interest rate, combined with regulation have reduced fixed income trading for banks, thus reducing their profits and increasing the volatility of quarterly earnings. Banks are being forced to consider new ways to make money as the low rates are a function of a Federally-structured government yield curve, reflecting lower economic growth and inflation expectations. **Availability:** Print; Online.

21007 ■ *"Life Science Companies in I-35 Corridor Get New Booster"* in *Dallas Business Journal* (Vol. 35, March 16, 2012, No. 2, pp. 1)
Pub: Baltimore Business Journal
Contact: Rhonda Pringle, President
E-mail: rpringle@bizjournals.com
Description: The Texas Bio Corridor Alliance intends to promote the development of life science firms along the Interstate 35 corridor. It comprises business incubators, cities, economic development organizations and companies in Texas. **Availability:** Print; Online.

21008 ■ *"Little Cheer in Holiday Forecast for Champagne"* in *Advertising Age* (Vol. 88, November 17, 2008, No. 43, pp. 6)
Pub: Crain Communications, Inc.
Contact: Jessica Botos, Manager, Marketing
E-mail: jessica.botos@crainsnewyork.com
Ed: Jeremy Mullman. **Description:** Due to a weak economy that has forced consumers to trade down from the most expensive alcoholic beverages as well as a weak U.S. dollar that has driven already lofty Champagne prices higher, makers of the French sparkling wine are anticipating a brutally slow holiday season. **Availability:** Online.

21009 ■ *"Live & Learn: Thomas D'Aquino"* in *Canadian Business* (Vol. 80, November 19, 2007, No. 23, pp. 92)
Pub: Rogers Media Inc.
Contact: Neil Spivak, Chief Executive Officer
Ed: Calvin Leung. **Description:** Thomas D'Aquino is the CEO and president of the Canadian Council of Chief Executives since 1981. D'Aquino thinks he has the best job in Canada because he can change the way policies are made and the way people think. Details of his career as a lawyer and CEO and his views on Canada's economy are provided. **Availability:** Print; Online.

21010 ■ *"Local Hotels Brace for Downturn"* in *Crain's Chicago Business* (Vol. 31, March 31, 2008, No. 13, pp. 3)
Pub: Crain Communications Inc.
Contact: Barry Asin, President
Ed: Bob Tita. **Description:** Chicago hotels are seeing a noticeable drop in business-related guests so far this year due to a slumping national economy, tighter corporate expense budgets and higher airfares. **Availability:** Online.

21011 ■ *"Local Industrial Vacancies Climb"* in *Crain's Chicago Business* (Vol. 31, November 17, 2008, No. 46, pp. 18)
Pub: Crain Communications Inc.
Contact: Barry Asin, President
Ed: Eddie Baeb. **Description:** Demand for local industrial real estate has declined dramatically as companies that use warehouse and factory space struggle to survive in an ailing economy. According to a report by Colliers Bennett & Kahnweiler Inc., a commercial real estate brokerage, the regional vacancy rate has risen to 9.86 percent in the third quarter, the fourth straight increase and the highest in the past 14 years. **Availability:** Online.

21012 ■ *"Local Outlook: Stronger Growth Ahead"* in *Montana Business Quarterly* (Vol. 49, Spring 2011, No. 1, pp. 10)
Pub: University of Montana Bureau of Business and Economic Research
Contact: Patrick Barkey, Director
E-mail: patrick.barkey@business.umt.edu

Ed: Paul E. Polzin. **Released:** Quarterly. **Description:** Local economic growth is broken down into three areas: fastest growing in Richland, Gallatin and Flathead Counties; the second growth group consists of Yellowstone, Silver Bow, and Lewis and Clark Counties, which all grew at rates higher than the statewide average; slowest growth was seen in Missoula, Ravalli, Cascade, and Custer Counties. Statistical data included. **Availability:** Online.

21013 ■ *"A Long Road to Recovery" in Barron's (Vol. 89, July 27, 2009, No. 30, pp. 37)*
Ed: Henry Kaufman. **Released:** November 01, 2016. **Description:** United States' economy remains hobbled by some underlying constraint and real recovery remains ephemeral. Much of the financial problems could have been avoided if t he Federal Reserve was effectively guarding the financial system. **Availability:** Print; Online.

21014 ■ *"Long-Term Bull, Short-Term Bear" in Barron's (Vol. 92, September 17, 2012, No. 38, pp. 24)*
Description: Jason DeSena Trennert, managing partner at Strategas Research Partners, discusses his views on the financial markets and the US economy. He is bullish on the stocks of Merck, McDonalds, IBM and Oracle. **Availability:** Online.

21015 ■ *"Loonie Tunes: When Will the Dollar Rise Again?" in Canadian Business (Vol. 81, November 10, 2008, No. 19, pp. 62)*
Pub: Rogers Media Inc.
Contact: Neil Spivak, Chief Executive Officer
Ed: Joe Castaldo. **Description:** The Canadian dollar has weakened against the U.S. Dollar as the U.S. financial crisis rocked global markets. A currency strategist says that the strength of the U.S. dollar is not based on people's optimism on the U.S. economy but on a structural demand where U.S. non-financial corporations have been repatriating greenbacks from foreign subsidiaries. **Availability:** Print; Online.

21016 ■ *"Lower Unemployment Hasn't Offset Total Losses" in Sacramento Business Journal (Vol. 31, May 23, 2014, No. 13, pp. 6)*
Pub: American City Business Journals, Inc.
Contact: Mike Olivieri, Executive Vice President
Released: Weekly. **Price:** $4, Introductory 4-week offer(Digital & Print). **Description:** The decline in Sacramento, California's unemployment rate has not reduced the city's economic losses. Unemployment in the area has decreased by 7.5 percent in April 2014. Meanwhile, educational and health services are expected to be the job growth sectors in the next 12 months. **Availability:** Print; Online.

21017 ■ *"Macroeconomic Policy and U.S. Competitiveness: A Reformed Fiscal Policy Is Vital To Renewing America's Productivity" in Harvard Business Review (Vol. 90, March 2012, No. 3, pp. 112)*
Pub: Harvard Business Review Press
Contact: Moderna V. Pfizer, Contact
Ed: Matthew Weinzierl, Richard H.K. Vietor. **Description:** Improving productivity requires increasing physical capital (such as equipment or technology), raising human capital, or using both of these types of capital more efficiently. The authors promote a plan that blends cuts in defense and health care spending, adjustments to Social Security, and carbon and gas taxes.

21018 ■ *Macrowikinomics: Rebooting Business and the World*
Pub: Portfolio Hardcover
Contact: Adrian Zackheim, President
Ed: Don Tapscott, Anthony D. Williams. **Released:** May 29, 2012. **Price:** $18, paperback; $6.99, e-book. **Description:** Wikinomics Don Tapscott and Anthony Williams showed how mass collaboration was changing the way businesses communicate, create value, and compete in the new global marketplace in 2007. Now, in the wake of the global financial crisis, the principles of wikinomics have become more powerful than ever. **Availability:** E-book; Print.

21019 ■ *"A Man of Courage: Leon Sullivan, First Black Corporate Director Who Fought against Inequality and Apartheid" in Black Enterprise(February 25, 2023)*
URL(s): www.blackenterprise.com/a-man-of-courage-leon-sullivan-first-black-corporate-director-who-fought-against-inequality-and-apartheid/
Ed: Atiya Jordan. **Released:** February 25, 2023. **Description:** Profile of Rev. Leon Sullivan, the first Black corporate director appointed to General Motors' board in 1971. **Availability:** Online.

21020 ■ *"Management Matters with Mike Myatt: Are You Creating Growth in a Down Economy?" in Commercial Property News (March 17, 2008)*
Description: Senior executives are expected to create growth for their company regardless of recession, economic slowdown, inflation, or tight credit and capital markets. **Availability:** PDF; Online.

21021 ■ *Managing Economies, Trade and International Business*
Pub: Palgrave Macmillan
Released: 1st edition. **Price:** $89, e-book; $115, Hardcover; $110, softcover. **Description:** An in-depth look at the areas that affect and influence international business, exploring specific issues businesses face in terms of economic development, trade law, and international marketing and management. **Availability:** E-book; Print.

21022 ■ *"Many Sectors Lost Jobs In Detroit Area, State" in Crain's Detroit Business (Vol. 24, February 11, 2008, No. 6, pp. 3)*
Pub: Crain Communications Inc.
Contact: Barry Asin, President
Ed: Amy Lane. **Description:** Southeast Michigan reported its highest jobless rate since 1992 in fourth quarter 2007. Statistical data included. **Availability:** Print; Online.

21023 ■ *"Market Watch" in Barron's (Vol. 88, March 24, 2008, No. 12, pp. M18)*
Ed: Ashraf Laidi, Marc Pado, David Kotok. **Released:** 2018. **Description:** Latest measures implemented by the Federal Reserve to address the credit crisis did not benefit the US dollar, with the Japanese yen and the euro recouping earlier losses against the dollar. Goldman Sachs reported earnings of $3.23 per share, claiming a stronger liquidity position. The US markets bottomed early on 22 January 2007, according to evidence. **Availability:** Print; Online.

21024 ■ *"Market Watch: A Sampling of Advisory Opinion" in Barron's (Vol. 88, March 17, 2008, No. 11, pp. M10)*
Pub: Dow Jones & Company Inc.
Contact: Almar Latour, Chief Executive Officer
Ed: Paul Schatz, William Gibson, Michael Darda, Peter Greene, Ian Wyatt, Stephanie Pomboy. **Released:** January 25, 2014. **Description:** S&P 500 bank stocks were down 46 percent from their 2007 peak while the peak to through fall in 1989-1990 was just over 50 percent. This suggests that the bottom on the bank stocks could be near. The Federal Reserve Board announced they will lend up to $200 billion to primary lenders in exchange other securities. **Availability:** Print; Online.

21025 ■ *"Market Watch: A Sampling of Advisory Opinion US Stock Price Trends, Economic Effects of Global Trade, Chinese Economic Trends" in Barron's (Vol. 92, July 23, 2012, No. 30, pp. M14)*
Ed: Richard M. Salsman, Jack Ablin, Francois Sicart. **Description:** US stocks are considered inexpensive due to their low price-earnings ratios compared to levels before the global financial crisis. The US economy is becoming more dependent on the rest of the worldas a result of global trade. The Chinese economy continues to have strong economic growth despite a slowdown. **Availability:** Online.

21026 ■ *"Markets: The Great Deleveraging" in Canadian Business (Vol. 81, October 13, 2008, No. 17, pp. 45)*
Pub: Rogers Media Inc.
Contact: Neil Spivak, Chief Executive Officer
Ed: Jeff Sanford. **Description:** 'Hell Week' of financial crisis on Wall Street is believed to have started with the downgrade of AIG Inc.'s credit rating. AIG is a major player in the credit derivatives market, and its bankruptcy would have affected firms on Wall Street. **Availability:** Online.

21027 ■ *"Mary Kramer: Good Things Happen When We Buy Local" in Crain's Detroit Business (Vol. 24, October 6, 2008, No. 40, pp. 7)*
Pub: Crain Communications Inc.
Contact: Barry Asin, President
Description: Michigan is facing incredibly difficult economic times. One way in which each one of us can help the state and the businesses located here is by purchasing our goods and services from local vendors. The state Agriculture Department projected that if Michigan households earmarked $10 per week in their grocery purchases to made-in-Michigan products, this would generate $30 million a week in economic impact. **Availability:** Online.

21028 ■ *"The Massachusetts Mess" in Barron's (Vol. 89, July 27, 2009, No. 30, pp. 39)*
Pub: Dow Jones & Company Inc.
Contact: Almar Latour, Chief Executive Officer
Ed: Thomas G. Donlan. **Description:** Massachusetts' mandatory health insurance has produced the highest rate of insurance coverage among the states but the state is now unable to afford its dream of universal coverage just three years after they enacted it. This supposed model for federal health-care reform is turning out to be a joke. **Availability:** Online.

21029 ■ *"Maximize Your Marketing Results In a Down Economy" in Franchising World (Vol. 42, November 2010, No. 11, pp. 45)*
Pub: International Franchise Association
Contact: Matthew Haller, President
E-mail: mhaller@franchise.org
Ed: Loren Rakich. **Description:** Strategies to help any franchisee to maximize their marketing efforts in a slow economy are outlined. **Availability:** Online.

21030 ■ *"MBT Add-On: Gone by 2012?" in Crain's Detroit Business (Vol. 24, October 6, 2008, No. 40, pp. 1)*
Pub: Crain Communications Inc.
Contact: Barry Asin, President
Ed: Amy Lane. **Description:** Discusses the Michigan Business Tax (MBT), which has angered many businesses in the state due to the addition of a 21.99 percent surcharge. Although the tax policy will cut taxes on 63 percent of businesses in the state and represent no tax liability change for another nine percent of firms, other businesses will see increases of 100 percent or more. This increase means that many business owners will be forced to relocate or close their establishment and others will have to eliminate jobs. Lawmakers are attempting to find a solution to this problem. **Availability:** Print; Online.

21031 ■ *"McDonald's Loses Its Sizzle" in Barron's (Vol. 88, March 17, 2008, No. 11, pp. 47)*
Description: McDonald's has promised to return $15 billion to $17 billion to shareholders in 2007-2009 but headwinds are rising for the company. December, 2007 same-store sales were flat and the company's traffic growth in the U.S. is slowing. Its shares are likely to trade in tandem with the market until recession fears recede. **Availability:** Online.

21032 ■ *"Memphis Pays Healthy Price To Compete for Jobs, Investment" in Memphis Business Journal (Vol. 35, January 3, 2014, No. 39, pp. 4)*
Pub: American City Business Journals, Inc.
Contact: Mike Olivieri, Executive Vice President

Released: Weekly. **Price:** $4, introductory 4-week offer(Digital & Print). **Description:** Memphis, Tennessee Mayor A.C. Wharton announced that Economic Development Growth Engine (EDGE) had a solid year and he thinks 2014 will be even better. EDGE has committed $103,718 in pilot-lieu-of-tax property tax reductions for every job created in 2013. The economic development projects in Memphis and in peer cities are also presented. **Availability:** Print; Online.

21033 ■ *"Michigan Means Growth: Sustaining Growth Through Thick and Thin: Michigan Companies Sustain Growth with Well-Timed Access to Capital"* **in Inc. (Vol. 36, September 2014, No. 7, pp. 164)**
Pub: Mansueto Ventures L.L.C.
Contact: Stephanie Mehta, Chief Executive Officer
Description: Successful companies possess flexibility, foresight and resources to turn adversity into opportunity. The small businesses in Michigan who have sustained experienced sales growth despite the recession of 2007. The Michigan Economic Development Corporation has introduced three initiatives to help Michigan businesses grow, including venture capital, collateral support and loan participation through the State Small Business Credit Initiative, and cash incentives for businesses looking to invest in urban communities or grow jobs. **Availability:** Print; Online.

21034 ■ *"Micro-Finance Agencies and SMEs: Model of Explication of Tacit Knowledge"* **in International Journal of Entrepreneurship and Small Business (Vol. 11, August 3, 2010)**
Ed: Patricia A. Rowe, Michael J. Christie, Frank Hoy.
Description: Institutional preparedness of economic development agencies for developing small and medium-sized enterprises (SMEs) is discussed. The cases presented illustrate variations in the microfinance lender agency-enterprise development of processes for sharing vision and interdependence. **Availability:** Online.

21035 ■ *"Microeconomic Methods: A Simple Introduction"*
Pub: CreateSpace
Released: October 21, 2014. **Price:** $5.49, paperback. **Description:** A guide to the mathematical methods of microeconomics is presented. **Availability:** Print.

21036 ■ *"Millennial Spending Influences County Budget"* **in Puget Sound Business Journal (Vol. 35, September 26, 2014, No. 23, pp. 6)**
Pub: American City Business Journals, Inc.
Contact: Mike Olivieri, Executive Vice President
Description: Washington State's tax system has been blamed by King County executive Dow Constantine for its proposed 2015-16 budget that cuts 500 positions. The millennial generation's spending was also partially blamed for the drop in sales tax revenue because they don't buy houses and cars as frequently compared to previous generations. How the millennial generation spends their money is also discussed. **Availability:** Online.

21037 ■ *"Mine Woes Could Rouse Zinc"* **in Barron's (Vol. 88, July 7, 2008, No. 27, pp. M12)**
Pub: Dow Jones & Company Inc.
Contact: Almar Latour, Chief Executive Officer
Ed: Andrea Hotter. **Description:** Prices of zinc could increase due to supply problems in producing countries such as Australia and China. London Metal Exchange prices for the metal have dropped about 36 percent in 2008. **Availability:** Online.

21038 ■ *"A Mixed-Bag Quarter"* **in Barron's (Vol. 88, July 7, 2008, No. 27, pp. 19)**
Description: Seven component companies of the Dow Jones Industrial Average increased their dividend payouts in the second quarter of 2008 despite the weak performance of the index. Five companies in the Dow Jones Transportation index and three in the Dow Jones Utilities also increased their dividends. **Availability:** Online.

21039 ■ *The Mom & Pop Store: How the Unsung Heroes of the American Economy Are Surviving and Thriving*
Ed: Robert Spector. **Description:** The history of small independent retail enterprises and how mom and pop stores in the U.S. continue to thrive through customer service and renewed community support for local businesses. **Availability:** Audio.

21040 ■ *"Montana Outlook: Stronger Growth Ahead"* **in Montana Business Quarterly (Vol. 49, Spring 2011, No. 1, pp. 7)**
Pub: University of Montana Bureau of Business and Economic Research
Contact: Patrick Barkey, Director
E-mail: patrick.barkey@business.umt.edu
Ed: Patrick M. Barkey. **Released:** Quarterly. **Description:** A look at Montana's economy and future growth is given. Experts are predicting that the state will experience new growth in 2011, with 2012 showing its best growth since 2006. Statistical data included. **Availability:** Online.

21041 ■ *"Most Americans Expect to Keep Working in Retirement"* **in Business News Daily (March 20, 2023)**
URL(s): www.businessnewsdaily.com/15330-retired-americans-to-keep-working.html
Ed: Andrew Martins. **Released:** March 20, 2023. **Description:** Americans are redefining retirement and adjusting its parameters after decades. Many are planning on working even after they can officially retire, due to economic necessity, but others plan to keep working to stay mentally sharp. **Availability:** Online.

21042 ■ *"Most See Gloomy Year For Michigan Business"* **in Crain's Detroit Business (Vol. 24, October 6, 2008, No. 40, pp. 4)**
Pub: Crain Communications Inc.
Contact: Barry Asin, President
Ed: Amy Lane. **Description:** Michigan residents are extremely concerned about the economic climate and business conditions in the state. According to the latest quarterly State of the State Survey, conducted by Michigan State University's Institute for Public Policy and Social Research, 63.9 percent of those surveyed anticipate bad times for Michigan businesses over the next year. Additional findings from the survey are also included. **Availability:** Online.

21043 ■ *"Mover and Sheika"* **in Conde Nast Portfolio (Vol. 2, June 2008, No. 6, pp. 104)**
Ed: John Arlidge. **Description:** Profile of Princess Sheika Lubna who is the first female foreign trade minister in the Middle East, the United Arab Emirates biggest business envoy, paving the way for billions in new investment, and also a manufacturer of her own perfume line. **Availability:** Online.

21044 ■ *"Myths of Deleveraging"* **in Barron's (Vol. 90, August 23, 2010, No. 34, pp. M14)**
Pub: Barron's Editorial & Corporate Headquarters
Ed: Gene Epstein. **Description:** The opposite is true against reports about deleveraging or the decrease in credit since inflation-adjusted-investment factories and equipment rose 7.8 percent in the first quarter of 2010. On consumer deleveraging, sales of homes through credit is weak but there is a trend towards more realistic homeownership and consumer spending on durable goods rose 8.8 percent. **Availability:** Online.

21045 ■ *"New Economy Initiative Gains Partners"* **in Crain's Detroit Business (Vol. 25, June 1, 2009, No. 22, pp. M014)**
Pub: Crain Communications Inc.
Contact: Barry Asin, President
Ed: Sherri Begin Welch. **Description:** New Economy Initiative is a $100 million philanthropic initiative that focuses on regional economic development. Recent grants awarded to Michigan companies are outlined. **Availability:** Print; Online.

21046 ■ *"New Texas South-International Alliance Seeking to Net Foreign Firms for South Texas"* **in San Antonio Business Journal (Vol. 26, June 22, 2012, No. 21, pp. 1)**
Pub: Baltimore Business Journal
Contact: Rhonda Pringle, President
E-mail: rpringle@bizjournals.com
Description: The city of San Antonio, Texas is partnering with Brownsville, Corpus Christi, Edinburg, Laredo, and San Marcos, to form the Texas South-International Alliance. The alliance is aimed at attracting more international economic development opportunities and investment to South Texas. **Availability:** Print; Online.

21047 ■ *"A New World"* **in Canadian Business (Vol. 80, October 8, 2007, No. 20, pp. 136)**
Description: Effects of climate change in Canada's economy are presented. A report published by Natural Resources Canada's Climate Change Impacts and Adaptation Program shows severe weather events such as droughts and storms will cause severe economic problems. Canada's infrastructure could also be affected by the rise in sea level over the next century. **Availability:** Print; Online.

21048 ■ *"Nexstar Super Meeting Breaks Business Barriers"* **in Contractor (Vol. 56, November 2009, No. 11, pp. 3)**
Ed: Candace Roulo. **Description:** Around 400 Nexstar members met to discuss the trends in the HVAC industry and the economic outlook for 2010. Former lead solo pilot John Foley for the Blue Angels made a presentation on how a business can increase overall productivity based on the culture of the Blue Angels. Some breakout sessions tackled how to optimize workflow and marketing. **Availability:** Print; Online.

21049 ■ *"The Next Economic Disaster: Why It's Coming and How to Avoid It"*
Released: 2014. **Description:** Findings from a team of economists show that the financial crisis of 2008 was from the rapid growth of private rather than public debt. Credit expert, Richard Vague, also argues that economic collapse over history and other economic downturns around the world were all preceded by a rise in privately held debt. He predicts China may soon be facing economic disaster. If banks in the U.S. do not embrace a policy of debt restructuring, economic growth will suffer.

21050 ■ *"The Next Wave"* **in Hawaii Business (Vol. 53, January 2008, No. 7, pp. 27)**
Pub: PacificBasin Communications
Contact: Chuck Tindle, Director
E-mail: chuckt@pacificbasin.net
Ed: Cathy S. Cruz-George. **Description:** Only 40,000 Koreans took a visit to Hawaii in 2007, a decline from the pre-September averages of 123,000 visits. The number of Korean visitors in Hawaii could increase if the visa waiver proposal is passed. Efforts to improve Hawaiian tourism are presented. **Availability:** Print; Online.

21051 ■ *"Nightmare on Wall Street"* **in Canadian Business (Vol. 81, October 13, 2008, No. 17, pp. 9)**
Description: Information on events that happened on Wall Street on the week that started September 15, 2008, as well on its effect on financial markets around the world, are presented. Lehman Brothers filed for bankruptcy on September 15, 2008 after negotiations with Barclays Group and Bank of America failed. Details on AIG and Morgan Stanley are also presented. **Availability:** Online.

21052 ■ *"N.J. Venture Investing Hits $39M"* **in Philadelphia Business Journal (Vol. 28, April 13, 2012, No. 9, pp. 1)**
Pub: Baltimore Business Journal
Contact: Rhonda Pringle, President

E-mail: rpringle@bizjournals.com

Description: The New Jersey Economic Development Authority will invest $3 million in Osage Venture Partner III and $2 million in NextStage Capital II. The two are Pennsylvania-based venture capital funds and both now have to establish offices in New Jersey and invest millions in New Jersey companies in return for the investment. **Availability:** Print; Online.

21053 ■ *"No End to the Nightmare; America's Car Industry"* in *The Economist (Vol. 390, January 3, 2009, No. 8612, pp. 46)*

Description: Detroit's struggling auto industry and the government loan package is discussed as well as the United Auto Worker union, which is loathed by Senate Republicans. **Availability:** Print; Online.

21054 ■ *"No Shortage of Challenges for Cross-Border Trade"* in *Canadian Sailings (June 30, 2008)*

Description: Pros and cons of the North American Free Trade Agreement are examined. The agreement between the U.S. and Canada concerning trade was an essential step toward securing economic growth for Canadian citizens. Two-way trade between the counties has tripled since the agreement and accounts for 7.1 million American and 3 million Canadian jobs. **Availability:** Print; Online; PDF.

21055 ■ *"Nonprofits Pressured to Rein in Fundraising Events"* in *Crain's Detroit Business (Vol. 25, June 15, 2009, No. 24, pp. 1)*

Pub: Crain Communications Inc.
Contact: Barry Asin, President

Ed: Sherri Begin Welch. **Description:** Local corporations have asked nonprofits to limit fundraising events in order to cut costs during the recession. **Availability:** Online.

21056 ■ *"Nvidia's Picture Brighter Than Stock Price Indicates"* in *Barron's (Vol. 88, March 24, 2008, No. 12, pp. 46)*

Pub: Dow Jones & Company Inc.
Contact: Almar Latour, Chief Executive Officer

Ed: Eric J. Savitz. **Description:** Shares of graphics chip maker Nvidia, priced at $18.52 each, do not indicate the company's strong position in the graphics chip market. The company's shares have dropped due to fears of slower demand for PCs, but the company is not as exposed to broader economic forces. **Availability:** Online.

21057 ■ *"October 2009: Recovery Plods Along"* in *Hispanic Business (October 2009, pp. 10-11)*

Description: Economist reports on a possible economic recovery which will not be allowed to rely on a strong domestic demand in order to sustain it. Consumers, looking to counterbalance years of leverage financing based on unrealistic, ever-increasing home and portfolio valuations, are saving rather than spending money.

21058 ■ *"OK, Bring in the Lawyers"* in *Crain's Chicago Business (Vol. 31, November 17, 2008, No. 46, pp. 26)*

Pub: Crain Communications Inc.
Contact: Barry Asin, President

Ed: Daniel Rome Levine. **Description:** Bankruptcy attorneys are finding the economic and credit crisis a benefit for their businesses due to the high number of business owners and mortgage holders that are in need of their services. One Chicago firm is handling ten times the number of cases they did the previous year and of that about 80 percent of their new clients are related to the real estate sector. **Availability:** Online.

21059 ■ *"Ottawa to Push for Gas Deal Between Petrocan, Gazprom"* in *Globe & Mail (February 13, 2006, pp. B1)*

Ed: Greame Smith. **Description:** Jim Flaherty, finance minister of Canada is negotiating a 1.3 billion dollar deal between state owned Petro-Canada and Russia's OAO Gazprom. This once again highlighted the country's increasing dependence on Russia for its energy requirements. **Availability:** Online.

21060 ■ *"Outlook 2008 (9 Sectors to Watch): Metals"* in *Canadian Business (Vol. 81, December 19, 2007, No. 1, pp. 46)*

Pub: Rogers Media Inc.
Contact: Neil Spivak, Chief Executive Officer

Ed: John Gray. **Description:** Forecasts on the Canadian metal industries for 2008 are discussed. Details on mine production and the rise in prices are also presented. **Availability:** Print; Online.

21061 ■ *"Outlook for Montana Agriculture"* in *Montana Business Quarterly (Vol. 49, Spring 2011, No. 1, pp. 26)*

Pub: University of Montana Bureau of Business and Economic Research
Contact: Patrick Barkey, Director
E-mail: patrick.barkey@business.umt.edu

Ed: George Haynes. **Released:** Quarterly. **Description:** Montana farmers and ranchers are rebounding from lower prices and production to higher prices and record production in 2010. The state has limited dairy and hog production, but farm income is still likely rise between 15 to 25 percent in 2010 over previous year. **Availability:** Online.

21062 ■ *"Over A Barrel"* in *Canadian Business (Vol. 81, July 21, 2008, No. 11, pp. 13)*

Description: Analysts predict that the skyrocketing price of fuel will cause a crackdown in the market as purported in the peak oil theory. It is forecasted that the price of oil will reach $200 per barrel. Details of the effect of the increasing oil prices on the market are presented.

21063 ■ *"Overqualified. Underemployed"* in *Philadelphia Business Journal (Vol. 33, August 1, 2104, No. 25, pp. 14)*

Pub: American City Business Journals, Inc.
Contact: Mike Olivieri, Executive Vice President

Description: Overqualified workers often find themselves in employment situations where their education, experience and skills are beyond the requirements of the job. The implications of underemployment for the worker, the organization and the overall U.S. economy are discussed. **Availability:** Print; Online.

21064 ■ *"An Overview of Energy Consumption of the Globalized World Economy"* in *Energy Policy (Vol. 39, October 2011, No. 10, pp. 5920-2928)*

Ed: Z. M. Chen, G. Q. Chen. **Released:** October 01, 2011. **Description:** Energy consumption and its impact on the global world economy is examined. **Availability:** Print; Online.

21065 ■ *"Panera Breadwinner Tries on Tattu Designer Jeans"* in *Houston Business Journal (Vol. 40, December 18, 2009, No. 32, pp. 1)*

Pub: Houston Business Journal
Contact: Bob Charlet, President
E-mail: bcharlet@bizjournals.com

Ed: Allison Wollam. **Description:** Chuck Cain, the franchisee who introduced Panera Bread to Houston, Texas has partnered with tax accountant Jim Jacobsen to introduce custom-make Tattu Jeans. As more Tattu Jeans outlets are being planned, Cain is using entrepreneurial lessons learned from Panera Bread in the new venture. Both Panera Bread and Tattu Jeans were opened by Cain during economic downturns. **Availability:** Print; Online.

21066 ■ *Paper Fortunes: Modern Wall Street: Where It's Been and Where It's Going*

Ed: Roy C. Smith. **Released:** 2010. **Description:** Comprehensive history of Wall Street and lessons learned with insight into ways Wall Street will reinvent itself in this new economy. **Availability:** E-book.

21067 ■ *"Paper Tigers"* in *Conde Nast Portfolio (Vol. 2, June 2008, No. 6, pp. 84)*

Ed: Roger Lowenstein. **Description:** Newspapers are losing their advertisers and readers and circulation today is equal to that of 1950, a time when the U.S. population was half its present size. **Availability:** Print; Online.

21068 ■ *"Patience Will Pay Off in Africa"* in *Barron's (Vol. 92, September 17, 2012, No. 38, pp. M8)*

Description: The stocks of African companies present long-term capital appreciation opportunities for investors. This is due to a commodities boom, economic reform and relative political stability in many African countries. **Availability:** Online.

21069 ■ *"Patients to Elect to Cut Care"* in *The Business Journal-Serving Metropolitan Kansas City (Vol. 27, November 21, 2008, No. 11, pp. 1)*

Pub: American City Business Journals, Inc.
Contact: Mike Olivieri, Executive Vice President

Ed: Rob Roberts. **Description:** Patients in Kansas City, Missouri are cutting down on health care services due to the economic crisis. A decline in diagnostic procedures has been observed at Northland Cardiology. Elective reconstructive procedures have also been reduced by 25 percent. Additional information and statistics regarding the healthcare sector is included. **Availability:** Online.

21070 ■ *"Paying for the Recession: Rebalancing Economic Growth"* in *Montana Business Quarterly (Vol. 49, Spring 2011, No. 1, pp. 2)*

Pub: University of Montana Bureau of Business and Economic Research
Contact: Patrick Barkey, Director
E-mail: patrick.barkey@business.umt.edu

Ed: Patrick M. Barkey. **Released:** Quarterly. **Description:** Four key issues required to address in order to rebalance economic growth in America are examined. They include: savings rates, global trade imbalances, government budgets and most importantly, housing price correction. **Availability:** Online.

21071 ■ *"The People Puzzle; Re-Training America's Workers"* in *The Economist (Vol. 390, January 3, 2009, No. 8612, pp. 32)*

Description: With thousands of workers losing their jobs, America is now facing the task of getting them back to work. With an overall unemployment rate of 6.7 percent, the federal government has three main ways for leading workers back to employment: training them for new jobs, providing unemployment insurance in order to replace lost wages during the period of job-hunting; and matching employers who desire a skill with workers who have that skill. Specialized staffing agencies provide employers and potential employees with the help necessary to find a job in some of the more niche markets. **Availability:** Online.

21072 ■ *"Phila.-Area Foreclosures Rising"* in *Philadelphia Business Journal (Vol. 28, May 18, 2012, No. 14, pp. 1)*

Pub: Baltimore Business Journal
Contact: Rhonda Pringle, President
E-mail: rpringle@bizjournals.com

Description: California-based RealtyTrac has reported residential mortgage foreclosures increased in Pennsylvania's Philadelphia region by 36 percent in first quarter from 2011's fourth quarter. Experts believe the numbers will continue to rise up to the end of the year and will negatively affect home values and the broader regional economy. Insights on bank robo-signing practices are also explained. **Availability:** Print; Online.

21073 ■ *"PNC Study Highlights Small Business Gloom"* in *Pittsburgh Business Times (Vol. 33, April 11, 2014, No. 39, pp. 5)*

Pub: American City Business Journals, Inc.
Contact: Mike Olivieri, Executive Vice President

Released: April 11, 2014. Price: $4, Introductory 4-week offer(Digital & Print). **Description:** PNC Financial Services Group Inc. economist, Kurth Rankin, offers insights into the perspective of local small business owners in Pennsylvania. Rankin explains that the mixed results of their semi-annual survey in the local area showed that small business owners are dealing with a difficult economy. **Availability:** Print; Online.

21074 ■ *"Poor Economy Inspires Rich Alternatives In a Modern, and Tax-Free, Twist on Bartering"* in Houston Chronicle (June 7, 2010)

Pub: Houston Chronicle

Ed: Michael Rubinkam. **Description:** Time banking helps individuals and firms receive goods or services by depositing time dollars into a bank reserved for receipt of goods and services.

21075 ■ *"Port Canaveral Plans to Make Big Waves of Business in C. Fla."* in Orlando Business Journal (Vol. 30, June 6, 2014, No. 50, pp. 4)

Pub: American City Business Journals, Inc.

Contact: Mike Olivieri, Executive Vice President

Released: Weekly. **Price:** $8, Introductory 4-week offer(Digital & Print). **Description:** Port Canaveral CEO, John Walsh, has big plans for the expansion of the Port, which include a $500 million cargo and cruise expansion that could net billions of dollars in new economic impact and create more than 15,000 new jobs. Walsh plans to expand cargo capacity, dig deeper harbors for large cruise ships and build a rail transport cargo and, eventually, passengers in and out of the 380-acre Port Canaveral. The Port is the fifth-largest cargo port in Central Florida. **Availability:** Print; Online.

21076 ■ *"Portion of Silver Line Will Run By Year's End"* in Crain's Cleveland Business (Vol. 28, November 5, 2007, No. 44, pp. 6)

Pub: Crain Communications Inc.

Contact: K. C. Crain, President

Ed: Jay Miller. **Description:** Cleveland's new Silver Line rapid transit will board its first passengers before the end of the year. The project is expected to spur economic development in the area and will speed transportation along Euclid Avenue. **Availability:** Online.

21077 ■ *The Post-American World*

Pub: W.W. Norton & Company Ltd.

Contact: Stanley Kubrick, Director

Ed: Fareed Zakaria. **Released:** Version 2.0. **Price:** $16.95, paperback; $26.95, hardcover. **Description:** Analyses of the changes taking place as new countries are rising as status players challenging American dominance. **Availability:** Print.

21078 ■ *"Power Partnerships"* in Business Courier (Vol. 27, October 22, 2010, No. 25, pp. 1)

Description: The $400 million Harrah's casino and the $47 million redevelopment and expansion of Washington Park are project aimed at boosting the economy in downtown Cincinnati, Ohio. These projects will be done in cooperation with the National Association for the Advancement of Colored People. Insights into the role of minority-owned businesses in regional economic development are explored. **Availability:** Print; Online.

21079 ■ *Predictably Irrational: The Hidden Forces That Shape Our Decisions*

Pub: HarperCollins Publishers L.L.C.

Contact: Brian Murray, President

Ed: Dan Ariely. **Released:** April 27, 2014. **Price:** $16.99, trade pb. **Description:** Behaviorists are bringing the economics profession around to realizing that human beings are impulsive, shortsighted and procrastinating in behavior. Economists are using this information to market products to consumers. **Availability:** E-book; Print.

21080 ■ *"Pricey Oil, High Dollar Wipe Out Jobs"* in Globe & Mail (February 11, 2006, pp. B6)

Ed: Heather Scoffield. **Description:** The impact of higher oil prices and dollar value, on manufacturing jobs in Canada, is discussed. **Availability:** Online.

21081 ■ *"Principles for Creating Growth in Challenging Times"* in Agency Sales Magazine (Vol. 39, September-October 2009, No. 9, pp. 35)

Description: Creating a productive environment is one vital key for businesses to utilize during the challenging times that arise due to a weak economy; other important factors include maintaining a good relationship with the staff, responding appropriately to challenges and keeping a sense of humor.

21082 ■ *"Private-Sector Is Back, Roadblocks Be Damned"* in Business Review Albany (Vol. 41, July 4, 2014, No. 15, pp. 4)

Pub: American City Business Journals, Inc.

Contact: Mike Olivieri, Executive Vice President

Released: Weekly. **Price:** $4, introductory 4-week offer(Digital only). **Description:** Private sector jobs in New York experienced significant growth, reaching an all-time high of almost 7.6 million jobs in May 2014, as government jobs suffered a decline. Large international corporations, including General Electric, are tapping into cash reserves, adding jobs and expanding operations after years of cutting staff. **Availability:** Print; Online.

21083 ■ *"Program for Women Entrepreneurs: Tips for Surviving this Economy"* in Crain's Detroit Business (Vol. 25, June 22, 2009, No. 25)

Pub: Crain Communications Inc.

Contact: Barry Asin, President

Description: Michigan Leadership Institute for Women Entrepreneurs will hold its third and final program, "Tough Times are Temporary, but Tough People are Permanent" at the Davenport University in Livonia, Michigan. **Availability:** Online.

21084 ■ *"Putting the World at Your Fingertips"* in Barron's (Vol. 88, July 7, 2008, No. 27, pp. L13)

Pub: Dow Jones & Company Inc.

Contact: Almar Latour, Chief Executive Officer

Ed: Neil A. Martin. **Description:** Currency-traded exchange funds allow investors to diversify their assets and take advantage of investment opportunities such as speculation and hedging. Investors can use these funds to build positions in favor of or against the US dollar. **Availability:** Online.

21085 ■ *"Q&A Interview With Perrin Beatty"* in Canadian Business (Vol. 80, October 8, 2007, No. 20, pp. 13)

Description: Perrin Beatty, president and chief executive officer of the Canadian Chamber of Commerce, talks about his move from the Canadian Manufacturers and Exporters to his current organization. He also discusses the state of Canada's economy, as well as the need for leadership.

21086 ■ *"Q&A: The CAPP's Greg Stringham"* in Canadian Business (Vol. 81, February 12, 2008, No. 3, pp. 8)

Pub: Rogers Media Inc.

Contact: Neil Spivak, Chief Executive Officer

Ed: Michelle Magnan. **Description:** Canadian Association of Petroleum Producers' Greg Stringham thinks that the new royalty plan will result in companies pulling out their investments for Alberta's conventional oil and gas sector. Stringham adds that Alberta is losing its competitive advantage and companies must study their cost profiles to retrieve that advantage. The effects of the royalty system on Alberta's economy are examined further. **Availability:** Print; Online.

21087 ■ *"Quality Performance of SMEs in a Developing Economy: Direct and Indirect Effects of Service Innovation and Entrepreneurial Orientation"* in Journal of Business & Industrial Marketing (Vol. 29, July 2014, No. 6)

Pub: Emerald Group Publishing Limited

Contact: Erika Valenti, President

Description: A study was conducted to investigate the effects of innovation and EO (entrepreneurial orientation) on organizational performance in Asian small enterprise context. Strategic management literature and the relationship between EO, innovation, and quality performance was tested. The results indicated that a noteworthy direct and indirect positive relationship exists between EO dimensions, innovation, and quality performance. **Availability:** Download; Online.

21088 ■ *"A Questionable Chemical Romance"* in Barron's (Vol. 88, July 14, 2008, No. 28, pp. 28)

Pub: Dow Jones & Company Inc.

Contact: Almar Latour, Chief Executive Officer

Ed: Andrew Bary. **Description:** Dow Chemical paid $78-a-share for the surprise takeover of Rohm & Haas. The acquisition is reducing Dow Chemical's financial flexibility at a time when chemical companies are being affected by high costs and a weak U.S. economy. **Availability:** Online.

21089 ■ *"Quick Earnings Revival Unlikely"* in Barron's (Vol. 88, June 30, 2008, No. 26, pp. 31)

Description: Analysts are pushing back their prediction of a U.S. economy turnaround to 2009. A recession in the first half of 2008 may not have happened but unemployment is rising and house prices continue to fall.

21090 ■ *"The Racial Divide and the Class Struggle in the United States"* in WorkingUSA (Vol. 11, September 2008, No. 3, pp. 311)

Description: An examination of such questions of race that continue to play such a prominent role in contemporary society is presented, focusing on the undermining of potential solidarity and strength of the working class movement, what sustains racists attitudes, practices and institutions, especially in the face of trends in world economic development. **Availability:** PDF; Online.

21091 ■ *"Rawlings-Blake Unveils Business Plan for Next Four Years"* in Baltimore Business Journal (Vol. 29, September 16, 2011, No. 19, pp. 1)

Pub: Boston Business Journal

Contact: Carolyn M. Jones, President

E-mail: cmjones@bizjournals.com

Ed: Gary Haber. **Description:** Mayor Stephanie Rawlings-Blake of Baltimore, Maryland unveiled her plan to push the economy forward. Her key objectives include giving more support for the city's technology companies and refocusing the Baltimore Development Corporation on job creation and retention. **Availability:** Online.

21092 ■ *"Ready for a Rally?"* in The Economist (Vol. 390, January 3, 2009, No. 8612, pp. 54)

Description: Analysts predict that the recession could end by 2010. The current economic crisis is presented in detail. **Availability:** Print; Online.

21093 ■ *"Real Estate Market Still in a Slump"* in Montana Business Quarterly (Vol. 49, Summer 2011, No. 2, pp. 15)

Pub: University of Montana Bureau of Business and Economic Research

Contact: Patrick Barkey, Director

E-mail: patrick.barkey@business.umt.edu

Ed: Patrick M. Barkey. **Released:** Quarterly. **Description:** Montana's housing market is still in decline with no sign of improving in the near future. Statistical data included. **Availability:** Online.

21094 ■ "Reasons Why Small Businesses Are Important" in Chron (Jan. 28, 2019)
URL(s): smallbusiness.chron.com/reasons-small-businesses-important-54131.html
Ed: Devra Gartenstein. **Released:** January 28, 2019. **Description:** Explains why small businesses are important as they foster local economies and provide opportunities for entrepreneurs. **Availability:** Online.

21095 ■ "Recession Creating Surge in Business for Auto Recyclers" in Business Journal-Serving Phoenix & the Valley of the Sun (Vol. 31, November 12, 2010, No. 10, pp. 1)
Pub: Phoenix Business Journal
Contact: Alex McAlister, Director
E-mail: amcalister@bizjournals.com
Ed: Patrick O'Grady. **Description:** Automotive parts recyclers in Arizona are benefiting from the challenging national economic conditions as well as from the green movement. Recyclers revealed that customers prefer recycled parts more because they are cheaper and are more environmentally friendly. Other information about the automotive parts recycling industry is presented. **Availability:** Print; Online.

21096 ■ "Recession and Recovery: Employment Change by Industry" in Occupational Outlook Quarterly (Vol. 58, Summer 2014, No. 2, pp. 45)
Pub: Government Publishing Office
Contact: Hugh Nathanial Halpern, Director
Description: Data from the U.S. Bureau of Labor Statistics (BLS) is presented showing that most industries added jobs between June 2009 and March 2014, a period spanning the end of the recession into the ongoing economic recovery. The small business trends sow percent change in industry employment classified by service providing industries, good producing industries, and employment March 2014. **Availability:** Print; Online.

21097 ■ "Recipe for Disaster?" in Sacramento Business Journal (Vol. 25, July 4, 2008, No. 18, pp. 1)
Pub: American City Business Journals, Inc.
Contact: Mike Olivieri, Executive Vice President
Ed: Mark Anderson. **Description:** Restaurateurs are challenged with balancing rising operating costs and what customers are willing to pay for their services. Flour prices in 2008 have increased by 46 percent from April 2007. Other views on the situation, as well as trends, forecasts and statistics on sales, outlook on economic conditions, consumer price index, and the typical split of restaurant revenue, are presented. **Availability:** Online.

21098 ■ "A Recipe for Food-Industry Growth?" in Providence Business News (Vol. 29, April 21, 2014, No. 3, pp. 1)
Pub: American City Business Journals, Inc.
Contact: Mike Olivieri, Executive Vice President
Released: April 19, 2014. **Description:** Industry experts believe that Rhode Island could become the 'Silicon Valley of Food'. The state is already known for its restaurants, chefs and ethnic cuisine, will host a Foods Innovation Summit in 2014. Ways that Rhode Island can take advantage of the economic benefits generated by the food industry are also examined. **Availability:** Print; Online.

21099 ■ "Recovering Economy Puts Real Estate on Solid Ground" in San Antonio Business Journal (Vol. 28, February 7, 2014, No. 53, pp. 13)
Pub: American City Business Journals, Inc.
Contact: Mike Olivieri, Executive Vice President
Released: Weekly. **Price:** $4, Introductory 4-week offer(Digital only). **Description:** With the economic recovery in San Antonio, the real estate market has shifted back to normal and a significant increase has been noted in new real estate deals and purchases. Pete Broderick, a shareholder at Cox Smith Mathews Inc. said that there have been more money-making deals of late, while another shareholder, Jimmy McDonough reports that banks are now willing to get into more long-term real estate deals. **Availability:** Print; Online.

21100 ■ "Recovery Starts to Set Roots in R.I." in Providence Business News (Vol. 28, January 20, 2014, No. 42, pp. 1)
Pub: American City Business Journals, Inc.
Contact: Mike Olivieri, Executive Vice President
URL(s): pbn.com/recovery-starts-to-set-roots-in-ri9 4397
Ed: Patrick Anderson. **Released:** January 18, 2014. **Description:** The results of a survey indicate that 84 percent of businesses in Rhode Island are expecting the state's economy to improve in 2014. Businesspeople had doubted the state's ability to recover because of fiscal crises. The impact of local firms' strong financial results on the economic recovery are discussed. **Availability:** Print; Online. **Telecommunication Services:** Anderson@pbn.com.

21101 ■ "Recovery on Tap for 2010?" in Orlando Business Journal (Vol. 26, January 1, 2010, No. 31, pp. 1)
Pub: Orlando Business Journal
Contact: Julie Swyers, Director
E-mail: jswyers@bizjournals.com
Ed: Melanie Stawicki Azam, Richard Bilbao, Christopher Boyd, Anjali Fluker. **Description:** Economic forecasts for Central Florida's leading business sectors in 2010 are presented. These sectors include housing, film and TV, sports business, law, restaurants, aviation, tourism and hospitality, banking and finance, commercial real estate, retail, health care, insurance, higher education, and manufacturing. According to some local executives, Central Florida's economy will slowly recover in 2010. **Availability:** Online.

21102 ■ "Reflecting State Economy, Banks Less Profitable in 1Q" in Providence Business News (Vol. 29, July 14, 2014, No. 15, pp. 8)
Pub: American City Business Journals, Inc.
Contact: Mike Olivieri, Executive Vice President
URL(s): pbn.com/reflecting-state-economy-banks-less-profitable-in-1q98467
Description: Rhode Island banks posted an aggregate return on assets (ROA) of 0.60 percent for the first quarter (1Q) of 2014, slightly lower than the 0.66 percent in the same quarter 2013, reflecting the downturn in the state's economy and its high unemployment rate. However, two Rhode Island banks, Union Federal Savings Bank and The Washington Trust Company, reported higher ROA for 1Q than the national average at 3.98 percent and 1.19 percent respectively.

21103 ■ "Region and City Need Influx of Youth" in Crain's Detroit Business (Vol. 24, April 14, 2008, No. 15, pp. 8)
Pub: Crain Communications Inc.
Contact: Barry Asin, President
Description: Discusses an upcoming report from Michigan Future Inc. which finds that young professionals, including those with children, are interested in living in an active urban environment. It also states that because many of those young professionals are entrepreneurial in nature, oftentimes businesses follow. **Availability:** Print; Online.

21104 ■ "Region's Small Business Lending Rises by $440M" in South Florida Business Journal (Vol. 33, September 7, 2012, No. 6, pp. 1)
Pub: Baltimore Business Journal
Contact: Rhonda Pringle, President
E-mail: rpringle@bizjournals.com
Description: Reports show that small business lending in South Florida increased by $440 million in 2011. Figures also indicate that banks originated $3.24 billion in small business loans during the same period, up from $2.8 billion in the previous year. It is believed that the region's economy is slowly improving. **Availability:** Print; Online.

21105 ■ "Rep Contracts: Simple, Clear, Fair" in Agency Sales Magazine (Vol. 39, September-October 2009, No. 9, pp. 3)
Description: Things that a manufacturer and a sales representative needs to strive for when creating an Agreement for Representation includes an agreement that is simple and complete, one that covers all the needs of both parties and is fair, equitable, and balanced. Sales representatives need to make more sales calls and find new opportunities during this recession.

21106 ■ "Research Highlights Disengaged Workforce" in Workforce Management (Vol. 88, November 16, 2009, No. 12, pp. 22)
Pub: Crain Communications Inc.
Contact: Barry Asin, President
Ed: Ed Frauenheim. **Description:** Most researchers have documented a drop in employee engagement during the recession due to such factors as layoffs, restructuring and less job security. **Availability:** Online.

21107 ■ "Research and Markets Adds Report: Cyprus: Convergence, Broadband and Internet Market" in Wireless News (September 4, 2009)
Description: Overview of a new report by Research and Markets entitled, "Cyprus Convergence, Broadband and Internet Market - Overview, Statistics and Forecasts." Highlights include information regarding broadband accounts which now account for the majority of household Internet connections. **Availability:** Print; Online.

21108 ■ "Restaurants Dish Up Meal Deals To Attract Customers" in Crain's Detroit Business (Vol. 24, October 6, 2008, No. 40, pp. 1)
Pub: Crain Communications Inc.
Contact: Barry Asin, President
Ed: Nathan Skid. **Description:** Restaurateurs are devising many creative and rewarding incentives to get customers to frequent their establishments during this economic crisis. Innovative ways in which even higher-end establishments are drawing in business are discussed. **Availability:** Online.

21109 ■ The Retail Revolution: How Wal-Mart Created a Brave New World of Business
Ed: Nelson Lichtenstein. **Released:** June 08, 2010. **Price:** $20, paperback; $7.99, e-book; $2.84, kindle; $15.89, hardcover; $1.93, hardcover(51 Used from $1.93); $15.86, hardcover(8 New from $15.86); $9.80, hardcover(1 Collectible from $9.80); $1.36, Paperback(50 Used from $1.36); $9.95, Paperback(31 New from $9.95). **Description:** Comprehensive discussion on how Wal-Mart changed retailing, and its place in the changing global economy. **Availability:** E-book; Print.

21110 ■ "Retail Slump Deflates Greater Cincinnati Development" in Business Courier (Vol. 24, February 28, 2008, No. 47, pp. 1)
Pub: American City Business Journals, Inc.
Contact: Mike Olivieri, Executive Vice President
Ed: Lisa Biank Fasig. **Description:** 2007 sales of the retail industry are the slowest since the year 2003, driving retail stores to reconsider their expansion plans for 2008. A number of retail projects have been delayed, cancelled or altered, including Newport Pavilion, Rivers Crossing, Wal-Mart Supercenters, Legacy Place and Millworks. The impacts of retail slowdown on development projects are analyzed further. **Availability:** Online.

21111 ■ "Rethinking School: For the U.S. To Remain Competitive, Its Students Need To Learn Vastly More, Much More Quickly" in Harvard Business Review (Vol. 90, March 2012, No. 3, pp. 76)
Pub: Harvard Business Review Press
Contact: Moderna V. Pfizer, Contact
Ed: Stacey Childress. **Price:** $8.95, hardcover. **Description:** Improving primary education is a key component to future US economic growth. The article

emphasizes the importance of personalized learning and educational technology to enhance academic achievement. **Availability:** PDF; Online.

21112 ■ *"Return to Wealth; Bank Strategy"* in *The Economist (Vol. 390, January 3, 2009, No. 8612, pp. 56)*
Description: UBS' strategy to survive these trying economic times is presented. Statistical data included. UBS has a stronger balance-sheet than most of its investment-banking peers and has reduced its portfolio. **Availability:** Print; Online.

21113 ■ *"RhodeMap for State Won't Focus on Finding a 'Big Fix'"* in *Providence Business News (Vol. 29, June 23, 2014, No. 12, pp. 4)*
Pub: American City Business Journals, Inc.
Contact: Mike Olivieri, Executive Vice President
Released: June 22, 2014. **Description:** Rhode Island Department of Administration Associate Director, Kevin Flynn, asserts that the new comprehensive plan for land use and economic development, RhodeMap RI, is not focused on one single big fix to solve the state's economic problems. Flynn notes that RhodeMap RI will address various social disparities, including education and income. **Availability:** Print; Online.

21114 ■ *"The Right Time for REITs"* in *Barron's (Vol. 88, July 14, 2008, No. 28, pp. 32)*
Pub: Dow Jones & Company Inc.
Contact: Almar Latour, Chief Executive Officer
Ed: Mike Hogan. **Description:** Discusses the downturn in U.S. real estate investment trusts so these are worth considering for investment. Several Websites that are useful for learning about real estate investment trusts for investment purposes are presented. **Availability:** Online.

21115 ■ *"Rising in the East; Research and Development"* in *The Economist (Vol. 390, January 3, 2009, No. 8612, pp. 47)*
Description: Impressive growth of the technological research and development in Asian countries is discussed. Statistical data included. **Availability:** Online.

21116 ■ *"Risk and Reward"* in *Canadian Business (Vol. 81, October 13, 2008, No. 17, pp. 21)*
Description: Macro-economist and currency analyst Mark Venezia believes that stable financial institutions, free-market reforms, and the role of central banks in keeping inflation and exchange rates stable could make emerging-market bonds strong performers for better future returns. Venezia's other views on emerging-market bonds are discussed. **Availability:** Print; Online.

21117 ■ *"Ritzy Retail"* in *Time (September 17, 2012)*
Ed: Christopher Matthews. **Description:** The continuing impact of the 2008 global economic crisis is evident in shopping mall vacancy rates, currently at 8.9 percent compared to the normal five to six percent prior to 2007. However, malls anchored by high-end, luxury retailers continues to do well because upscale malls target the wealthier demographic. Malls serving low- to middle-income shoppers are lagging because their target consumers cannot afford to shop. These consumers are trading down to discount and dollar stores creating a hollow in the middle of the retail spectrum. **Availability:** Online.

21118 ■ *"Riverfront Revival in Pawtucket?"* in *Providence Business News (Vol. 28, March 17, 2014, No. 50, pp. 1)*
Pub: American City Business Journals, Inc.
Contact: Mike Olivieri, Executive Vice President
URL(s): pbn.com/Riverfront-revival-in-Pawtucket,95766
Description: Pawtucket, Rhode Island is focusing on riverfront redevelopment projects due to an improving economy. City planning director, Barney Heath, reveals that Tai-O Group, Peregrine Group and Apex Development Company have already responded to a request for qualifications to begin construction projects. **Availability:** Online. **Telecommunication Services:** Anderson@pbn.com.

21119 ■ *The Road from Ruin: How to Revive Capitalism and Put America Back on Top*
Ed: Matthew Bishop, Michael Green. **Released:** 2011. **Description:** Authors show why American companies must respond to the economic crisis with long term vision and a renewed emphasis on values. **Availability:** E-book; Print.

21120 ■ *"Rock of Ages"* in *Barron's (Vol. 92, September 17, 2012, No. 38, pp. 23)*
Description: Financial services firm Rockefeller & Company was hit hard by the global financial crisis of 2008, but managed to thrive despite it. The firm, which offers financial products from other firms aside from its own fund, grew its assets under management by 52 percent to $35 billion for the three-year period that ended June 2012. **Availability:** Online.

21121 ■ *"Rough Trade: the Canada-Chile Free Trade Agreement"* in *Canadian Business (Vol. 79, September 11, 2006, No. 18, pp. 31)*
Pub: Rogers Media Inc.
Contact: Neil Spivak, Chief Executive Officer
Ed: Christina Campbell. **Description:** The divergence between trade policy agreements entered into by Chile and the Canadian government are highlighted. Canada-Chile Free Trade Agreement and the myth around the big benefits to be reaped by bilateral trade policy agreements are discussed. **Availability:** Print; Mailing list; Online.

21122 ■ *"Roundy's Pushing Chicago Expansion"* in *Milwaukee Business Journal (Vol. 27, February 12, 2010, No. 20, pp. A1)*
Pub: The Business Journal
Contact: Heather Ladage, President
E-mail: hladage@bizjournals.com
Ed: Rich Kirchen. **Description:** Roundy Supermarkets Inc. is expanding in Chicago, Illinois as the Milwaukee-based company is set to open one store in downtown Chicago and another in the Arlington suburb. The store openings have been pushed back to spring and early summer in 2010 due to the economic downturn. **Availability:** Print; Online.

21123 ■ *"Rural Employment Trends in Recession and Recovery"*
Pub: CreateSpace
Released: September 24, 2014. **Price:** $10.40, paperback. **Description:** Six years of economic growth in the United States ended with the most severe recession since the Great Depression. The nature and causes of geographic variation, which include differences in the mix of industries supporting a local economy, population growth trends, and demographics of local workforces are examined to trace economic trends in recession and recovery. **Availability:** Print.

21124 ■ *"Russia: Uncle Volodya's Flagging Christmas Spirit"* in *The Economist (Vol. 390, January 3, 2009, No. 8612, pp. 22)*
Description: Overview of Russia's struggling economy as well as unpopular government decisions such as raising import duties on used foreign vehicles so as to protect Russian carmakers. **Availability:** Print; Online.

21125 ■ *"Rust Belt No More: The Demise of Manufacturing"* in *Crain's Chicago Business (Vol. 31, March 31, 2008, No. 13, pp. 52)*
Pub: Crain Communications Inc.
Contact: Barry Asin, President
Ed: Sarah A. Klein. **Description:** Discusses the history of manufacturing in the Chicago area as well as the history of manufacturer International Harvester Co. **Availability:** Online.

21126 ■ *"S.A. Officials Hunting for Prospects in California"* in *San Antonio Business Journal (Vol. 26, August 17, 2012, No. 29, pp. 1)*
Released: August 17, 2012. **Description:** Officials of the San Antonio Economic Development Foundation in Texas will meet with 15 or more companies in Los Angeles, California in a bid to convince these businesses to relocated some of their operations to Alamo City. Officials are hoping the companies will recognize the advantages of San Antonio as they face pressures due to increased taxes and added government regulations in California.

21127 ■ *"A Safety Net in Need of Repair"* in *The Economist (Vol. 390, January 3, 2009, No. 8612, pp. 33)*
Description: America's unemployment-insurance scheme is outdated and skimpy compared to other industrialized countries despite the fact that Americans tend to work harder at returning to the job market; the benefits are lower and available for a smaller amount of time and less unemployed workers are even able to collect these benefits. Statistical data included.

21128 ■ *"St. Louis Lending Tumbles $10 Billion Since '08'"* in *Saint Louis Business Journal (Vol. 31, August 26, 2011, No. 53, pp. 1)*
Pub: Saint Louis Business Journal
Contact: Robert Bobroff, President
E-mail: rbobroff@bizjournals.com
Ed: Greg Edwards. **Description:** St. Louis, Missouri-based banks lending fell by more than 30 percent in less than three years, from about $30 billion in third and fourth quarters 2008 to about $20 billion in the most recent quarter. However, community banks revealed that they want to lend but there is no loan demand. **Availability:** Print; Online.

21129 ■ *"San Antonio Museum of Art in the Center of New Urban Revival"* in *San Antonio Business Journal (Vol. 28, July 11, 2014, No. 22, pp. 8)*
Pub: American City Business Journals, Inc.
Contact: Mike Olivieri, Executive Vice President
Description: San Antonio Museum of Art (SAMA) director, Katie Luber, acknowledges the significant economic improvement around the SAMA with the new Museum Reach projects in various stages of development. Luber hopes to spark greater interest at SAMA with a major exhibition of Henri Matisse and private development. **Availability:** Print; Online.

21130 ■ *"San Antonio Office Market: What a Difference a Year Makes"* in *San Antonio Business Journal (Vol. 28, August 8, 2014, No. 26, pp. 8)*
Pub: American City Business Journals, Inc.
Contact: Mike Olivieri, Executive Vice President
Released: August 08, 2014. **Price:** $4, Introductory 4-Week Offer(Digital & Print). **Description:** The San Antonio, Texas office market has grown in 2014. The market has absorbed over 610,000-square-feet of space during the first six months of the year. Meanwhile, a number of new office building construction projects are underway. **Availability:** Print; Online.

21131 ■ *Save Your Small Business: 10 Crucial Strategies to Survive Hard Times or Close Down & Move On*
Pub: Nolo
Contact: Chris Braun, President
Ed: Ralph Warner, Bethany Laurence. **Description:** According to a study among 500 businesses, 44 percent used credit cards in order to meet their firm's needs in the previous six months. Written by a business owner, this book provides twelve strategies to protect personal assets from creditors and survive the current recession. **Availability:** Print.

21132 ■ *"Seahawks' Win? A Seattle Windfall"* in *Puget Sound Business Journal (Vol. 34, January 10, 2014, No. 39, pp. 3)*
Pub: American City Business Journals, Inc.
Contact: Mike Olivieri, Executive Vice President
Released: Weekly. **Price:** $4, introductory 4-week offer(Digital & Print). **Description:** Seattle, Washington is anticipating a windfall from the Seattle Seahawks' ninth game of the season. The sold-out CenturyLink Field can hold 67,000 spectators, who are potential customers outside the stadium at restau-

21133 ■ Economic Development

rants, bars, hotels and attractions. The economic benefits of hosting a high-profile sports event are explored. **Availability:** Print; Online.

21133 ■ *"SEC Report On Rating Agencies Falls Short"* in Barron's (Vol. 88, July 14, 2008, No. 28, pp. 35)
Pub: Dow Jones & Company Inc.
Contact: Almar Latour, Chief Executive Officer
Ed: Jack Willoughby. **Description:** The Securities and Exchange Commissions report on credit-rating firms should have drawn attention to the slipshod practices in the offerings of collateralized debt obligations. The report fell short of prescribing correctives for the flawed system of these agencies' relationship with their clients. **Availability:** Online.

21134 ■ *"The Second Machine Age: Work, Progress, and Prosperity in a Time of Brilliant Technologies"*
Released: January 01, 2016. **Price:** $16.95, paperback; $26.95, hardcover. **Description:** Insights into ways digital technologies are transforming our economy in order to develop new business models, new technologies, and new policies to enhance human capabilities are provided. **Availability:** Print.

21135 ■ *"Sentiment Split on Financials: Is the Worse Over or Still to Come?"* in Barron's (Vol. 88, March 24, 2008, No. 12, pp. M14)
Pub: Dow Jones & Company Inc.
Contact: Almar Latour, Chief Executive Officer
Ed: Steven M. Sears. **Description:** Experts in the financial sector are split as to whether or not the worst of the financial crisis brought on by the credit crunch is over. Some options traders are trading on are defensive puts, expecting the worst, while investors buying calls are considered as bullish. **Availability:** Online.

21136 ■ *"Sharing's Not Just for Start-ups: What Marriott, GE, and Other Traditiional Companies are Learning About the Collaborative Economy"* in Harvard Business Review (Vol. 92, September 2014, No. 9, pp. 23)
Pub: Harvard Business Publishing
Contact: Diane Belcher, Managing Director
Ed: Rachel Botsman. **Price:** $6. **Description:** The collaborative economy answers five basic problems companies face: redundancy, broken trust, limited access, waste, and complexity. Online matches eliminate redundancy; peer-to-peer networks boost trust; online training answers access issues; online services can market what other entities are not utilizing (i.e., excess space); and other services can streamline or provide alternative solutions for complex processes. **Availability:** Online; PDF.

21137 ■ *"Sharp Restarts Toner Manufacturing: Production Moved from Japan to Serve China Market"* in Memphis Business Journal (Vol. 34, May 11, 2012, No. 4, pp. 1)
Pub: Baltimore Business Journal
Contact: Rhonda Pringle, President
E-mail: rpringle@bizjournals.com
Ed: Michael Sheffield. **Description:** Sharp Manufacturing Company of America has decided to reopen its ink toner production plant in Memphis, Tennessee because of cheaper material, labor and freight costs. The company's move was also attributed to local economic growth and the government support they received after a 2008 tornado hit the area surrounding the area. **Availability:** Print; Online.

21138 ■ *"Shattering the Myths About U.S. Trade Policy: Stop Blaming China and India. A More Active Trade Policy Can Lead to a Stronger U.S. Economy"* in Harvard Business Review (Vol. 90, March 2012, No. 3, pp. 149)
Pub: Harvard Business Review Press
Contact: Moderna V. Pfizer, Contact
Ed: Robert Z. Lawrence, Lawrence Edwards. **Price:** $8.95, hardcopy black and white. **Description:** Myths debunked include the belief that the US open trade policy has caused job losses, and that living standards are falling due to export market competition. American must leverage China's need for global economic engagement and secure an open domestic market in China. It must also persuade the World Trade Organization to improve market access. **Availability:** Print; PDF; Online.

21139 ■ *"Should the Fed Regulate Wall Street?"* in Barron's (Vol. 88, March 24, 2008, No. 12, pp. M15)
Pub: Dow Jones & Company Inc.
Contact: Almar Latour, Chief Executive Officer
Ed: Randall W. Forsyth. **Description:** Greater regulation of the financial sector by the Federal Reserve is essential for it to survive the crisis it is experiencing. The resulting regulation could be in complete contrast with the deregulation the sector previously experienced. **Availability:** Online.

21140 ■ *"The Signal and the Noise: Why So Many Predictions Fail - but Some Don't"*
Released: February 03, 2015. **Price:** $18, paperback; $27.95, hardcover; $14.99, e-book; $17.50, audiobook. **Description:** Statistician, writer, and founder of The New York Times political blog, FiveThirtyEight.com, describes the science of forecasting and shows what happens when Big Data meets baseball, weather forecasting, earthquake prediction, economics and polling and shows that predictions can go wrong because they are based on biases, vested interests, and overconfidence. **Availability:** E-book; Print.

21141 ■ *"Single Most Important Problem"* in Small Business Economic Trends (February 2008, pp. 18)
Pub: National Federation of Independent Business
Contact: Brad Close, President
Ed: William C. Dunkelberg, Holly Wade. **Description:** Two graphs and a table representing the economic problems encountered by small businesses in the U.S. are presented. The figures presented in the graphs include data from 1974 to 2008. **Availability:** Print; Online; PDF.

21142 ■ *"Sky Harvest Windpower Corp. - Operational Update"* in Investment Weekly News (March 10, 2012, pp. 744)
Pub: PR Newswire Association LLC.
Description: Sky Harvest Windpower Corporation is rebranding its focus on gas and power activities both nationally and internationally. The firm's Canadian projects are outlined as well as its commitment to purse the Green Options Partners Program in 2012. **Availability:** Online.

21143 ■ *"A Slice of Danish; Fixing Finance"* in The Economist (Vol. 390, January 3, 2009, No. 8612, pp. 55)
Description: Denmark's mortgage-holders and the county's lending system is presented. **Availability:** Print; Online.

21144 ■ *"Small Business Economic Trends: Moderate Improvement but No Clear Direction"* in Small Business Economic Trends (March 2008, pp. 3)
Pub: National Federation of Independent Business
Contact: Brad Close, President
Ed: William C. Dunkelberg, Holly Wade. **Description:** Commentary on the economic trends for small businesses in the U.S. is presented. Analysis of the labor market and low interest rates is given. The effect of the Federal Reserve's policy announcement on small business owner optimism is also discussed. **Availability:** Print; Online.

21145 ■ *"Small Business Outlook"* in Small Business Economic Trends (September 2010, pp. 4)
Pub: National Federation of Independent Business
Contact: Brad Close, President
Ed: William C. Dunkelberg, Holly Wade. **Description:** A graph representing outlook among small businesses surveyed in the U.S. from January 1986 to August 2010 is presented. Tables showing small business outlook for expansion and outlook for general business conditions from January 2005 to August 2010, and most important reasons for expansion outlook are also given. **Availability:** Online.

21146 ■ *"Small Businesses Finding It Easier To Get Capital"* in Birmingham Business Journal (Vol. 31, July 11, 2014, No. 28, pp. 10)
Pub: American City Business Journals, Inc.
Contact: Mike Olivieri, Executive Vice President
Description: According to the Federal Reserve Bank of Atlanta, small businesses that applied for credit received the financing requested, showing increased confidence among Birmingham businesses. With a robust lending environment, Birmingham is expecting the trend to continue in 2014 with more business plans for expansion and new capital spends. **Availability:** Print; Online.

21147 ■ *"Small, But Mighty"* in Employee Benefit News (Vol. 25, November 1, 2011, No. 14, pp. 32)
Pub: SourceMedia LLC
Contact: Gemma Postlethwaite, Chief Executive Officer
Ed: Andrea Davis. **Description:** Three consulting firms are facing the challenge of helping clients understand the new health care reform in a tight economy. **Availability:** Print; PDF; Online.

21148 ■ *"Smart Year-End Tax Moves"* in Business Owner (Vol. 35, November-December 2011, No. 6, pp. 8)
Description: Managing small business and individual taxes is more important in a bad economy. It is imperative to seek all tax incentives that apply to your business.

21149 ■ *Social Enterprise: Developing Sustainable Businesses*
Pub: Palgrave Macmillan
Ed: Frank Martin, Marcus Thompson. **Released:** 2010. **Description:** Social enterprises bring people and communities together for economic development and social gain and represent a growing sector of the business community.

21150 ■ *"Some Relief Possible Following Painful Week"* in Barron's (Vol. 88, July 14, 2008, No. 28, pp. M3)
Pub: Dow Jones & Company Inc.
Contact: Almar Latour, Chief Executive Officer
Ed: Kopin Tan. **Description:** Dow Chemical is offering a 74 percent premium to acquire Rohm & Haas' coatings and electronics materials operations. Frontline amassed a 5.6 percent stake in rival Overseas Shipholding Group and a merger between the two would create a giant global fleet with pricing power. Highlights of the U.S. stock market during the week that ended in July 11, 2008 are discussed. Statistical data included. **Availability:** Online.

21151 ■ *"Souled Out"* in Canadian Business (Vol. 81, March 3, 2008, No. 3, pp. 35)
Description: According to a survey of over 100 entrepreneurs, 78 percent responded that selling their business was emotionally draining for them. Greig Clark, for example, says that one of the toughest times of his life was selling College Pro Painters, after putting 18 years into that business. The economic impacts of selling out are also examined. **Availability:** Online.

21152 ■ *"Spectre of Iran War Spooks Oil Markets"* in Globe & Mail (March 28, 2007, pp. B1)
Ed: Shawn McCarthy. **Description:** The increase in the price of crude oil by $5 a barrel to reach $68 in the United States following speculation over war against Iran, is discussed. **Availability:** Online.

21153 ■ *"Spin Zone: Where Hawaii's Leaders Face Off, Have High-Tech Tax Credits Helped or Hurt Hawaii?"* in Hawaii Business (Vol. 53, December 2007, No. 6, pp. 28)
Pub: PacificBasin Communications
Contact: Chuck Tindle, Director

E-mail: chuckt@pacificbasin.net
Description: Presents the opinons of Channel Capital LLC's Walter R. Roth and Hawaii Venture Capital Association's Bill Spencer concerning the impacts of tax credits. Roth thinks that Act 221 appeals to investors who can earn despite business failure while Spencer thinks that the legislation promotes investments in innovative technology firms. The need to support tax credits is also discussed. **Availability:** Print; Online.

21154 ■ *"Spotlight On...Jim Alves, SMUD"* in *Sacramento Business Journal* (Vol. 31, March 28, 2014, No. 5)
Pub: American City Business Journals, Inc.
Contact: Mike Olivieri, Executive Vice President
Released: Weekly. **Price:** $4, Introductory 4-week offer(Digital & Print). **Description:** Jim Alves heads up Sacramento, California's Municipal Utility District's economic development program. He tries to attract and retain businesses in the Sacramento area. **Availability:** Print; Online.

21155 ■ *"Stadium Developers Seek a Win With the State"* in *The Business Journal-Serving Metropolitan Kansas City* (Vol. 26, August 22, 2008)
Description: Three Trails Redevelopment LLC is hoping to win $30 million in state tax credits from the Missouri Development Finance Board for the construction of an 18,500-seat Wizards stadium. The project is contingent on state tax incentives and the company remains optimistic about their goal.

21156 ■ *"Staffing Firms are Picking Up the Pieces, Seeing Signs of Life"* in *Milwaukee Business Journal* (Vol. 27, February 5, 2010, No. 19)
Pub: The Business Journal
Contact: Heather Ladage, President
E-mail: hladage@bizjournals.com
Ed: Rich Rovito. **Description:** Milwaukee, Wisconsin-based staffing firms are seeing signs of economic rebound as many businesses turned to temporary employees to fill the demands for goods and services. Economic observers believe the growth in temporary staffing is one of the early indicators of economic recovery. **Availability:** Print; Online.

21157 ■ *Start-Up Nation*
Released: September 07, 2011. **Price:** Paperback. **Description:** Amid the turmoil in the Middle East, Israel's economy continues to thrive. **Availability:** Print; Download.

21158 ■ *"Steady Spending In Retail, But Job Losses Are Rising"* in *Business Week* (September 22, 2008, No. 4100, pp. 13)
Ed: Tara Kalwarski. **Description:** Retail jobs have begun to decline on the national level despite the two percent growth in the industry over the last year; much of the growth has been attributed to the sales of higher-priced oil products.

21159 ■ *"Step Up to Help Regionalism Step Forward"* in *Crain's Cleveland Business* (Vol. 28, November 12, 2007, No. 45, pp. 10)
Pub: Crain Communications Inc.
Contact: K. C. Crain, President
Ed: Rob Briggs, William Currin. **Description:** Discusses the importance of regionalism for Northeast Ohio as being a broad, collaborative approach to spur economic development. **Availability:** Online.

21160 ■ *"Stuck With Two Mortgages"* in *Crain's Chicago Business* (Vol. 31, April 21, 2008, No. 16)
Pub: Crain Communications Inc.
Contact: Barry Asin, President
Ed: Darci Smith. **Description:** Discusses the problem a number of people are facing due to the slump in the housing market: being stuck with two mortgages when they move because their former homes have not sold. Many thought they could afford to move to a larger home, anticipating significant equity apprecia-
tion that did not occur; now they are left with lowering their price and competing with the host of new developments. **Availability:** Online.

21161 ■ *"Stung by Recession, Hemmer Regroups with New Strategy"* in *Business Courier* (Vol. 27, June 4, 2010, No. 5, pp. 1)
Pub: Business Courier
Ed: Lucy May. **Description:** Paul Hemmer Companies reduced its work force and outsourced operations such as marketing and architecture, in order for the commercial and construction firm to survive the recession. Hammer's total core revenue in 2009 dropped to less than $30 million forcing the closure of its Chicago office. **Availability:** PDF; Online.

21162 ■ *"Summary. Economic Trends for Small Business"* in *Small Business Economic Trends* (February 2008, pp. 1)
Pub: National Federation of Independent Business
Contact: Brad Close, President
Ed: William C. Dunkelberg, Holly Wade. **Description:** Summary of economic trends for small businesses in the U.S. is provided. Economic indicators such as capital spending, inventories and sales, inflation, and profits are given. Analysis of credit markets is also provided.

21163 ■ *Superfreakonomics*
Pub: William Morrow
Ed: Steven D. Levitt, Stephen J. Dubner. **Released:** May 24, 2011. **Price:** $13.59, Paperback. **Description:** A scholar and a journalist apply economic thinking to everything. **Availability:** Print; Online.

21164 ■ *"The Surplus Shell Game"* in *Canadian Business* (Vol. 80, March 12, 2007, No. 6, pp. 72)
Description: The effort of successive federal governments in Canada to ensure budget surpluses and its impact on the economy are discussed. **Availability:** Online.

21165 ■ *"Survey: Don't Expect Big Results From Stimulus"* in *Crain's Detroit Business* (Vol. 25, June 1, 2009, No. 22)
Pub: Crain Communications Inc.
Contact: Barry Asin, President
Ed: Nancy Kaffer, Chad Halcom. **Description:** In a recent survey, Michigan business owners, operators or managers showed that 48 percent of respondents oppose the President's stimulus package and believe it will have little or no effect on the economy. **Availability:** Print.

21166 ■ *"The Survey Says"* in *Collections and Credit Risk* (Vol. 14, September 1, 2009, No. 8, pp. 16)
Description: Revenue for the top accounts receivable management firms rose nearly 20 percent in 2008 despite lower liquidation rates, a poor economy and riskier, albeit cheaper debt portfolios; the trend may continue this year as collection agencies expect revenue, on average, to increase 5.8 percent. Debt buyers, however, found that their revenue fell nearly 7 percent in 2008 and expect it to fall another 12 percent this year. **Availability:** Print; Online.

21167 ■ *"Survey Says Commercial Real Estate Headed for Turbulence"* in *Commercial Property News* (March 17, 2008)
Description: Commercial real estate sector is declining due to the sluggish U.S. economy. According to a recent survey, national office, retail and hospitality markets are also on the decline. **Availability:** Online.

21168 ■ *"Surviving the Storm"* in *Canadian Business* (Vol. 81, July 22, 2008, No. 12-13, pp. 50)
Description: Investment adviser Harry Dent and finance professor Paul Marsh discuss their views and forecasts on the United States' economic condition. Dent believes advisors should concentrate on wealth preservation rather than on returns. Other views regarding U.S. economic conditions are also presented. **Availability:** Print; Online.

21169 ■ *"Sweeten Your Bottom Line: How To Bring In Dollars When Times Are Tough"* in *Small Business Opportunities* (November 2007)
Description: Adding a new product or promoting a product in a new way can help any small business during hard economic times. **Availability:** Online.

21170 ■ *"Taking the Jump Off the Fiscal Cliff"* in *Barron's* (Vol. 92, August 25, 2012, No. 35, pp. 47)
Pub: Dow Jones & Company Inc.
Contact: Almar Latour, Chief Executive Officer
Ed: Thomas G. Donlan. **Description:** The arrival of tax increases and spending cuts by the end of 2012 should help the United States reduce its budget deficit. Policy prescriptions advocating looser monetary and fiscal policies are not going to help the country solve its budget problems. **Availability:** Online.

21171 ■ *"Taking the Over-the-Counter Route to U.S."* in *Barron's* (Vol. 88, July 7, 2008, No. 27, pp. 24)
Pub: Dow Jones & Company Inc.
Contact: Almar Latour, Chief Executive Officer
Ed: Eric Uhlfelder. **Description:** Many multinational companies have left the New York Stock Exchange and allowed their shares to trade over-the-counter. The companies have taken advantage of a 2007 SEC rule allowing publicly listed foreign companies to change trading venues if less than 5 percent of global trading volume in the past 12 months occurred in the US. **Availability:** Online.

21172 ■ *"Tao of Downfall: the Failures of High-profile Entrepreneurs in the Chinese Economic Reform"* in *International Journal of Entrepreneurship and Small Business* (Vol. 11, August 31, 2010, No. 2, pp. 121)
Ed: Wenxian Zhang, Ilan Alon. **Description:** Through historical reviews and case studies, this research seeks to understand why some initially successful entrepreneurs failed in the economic boom of past decades. Among various factors contributing to their downfall are a unique political and business environment, fragile financial systems, traditional cultural influences and personal characteristics. **Availability:** Online.

21173 ■ *"Tattooed Bellwethers of Economic Development"* in *Austin Business Journal* (Vol. 34, May 2, 2014, No. 11, pp. A4)
Pub: American City Business Journals, Inc.
Contact: Mike Olivieri, Executive Vice President
Released: Weekly. **Price:** $4, Introductory 4-week offer(Digital & Print). **Description:** The creative community's art-centered business have helped Austin, Texas' growth by moving into transitional areas with low rents. Their kind of pioneering spirit primes the area for later commercial and residential development. The city's assistance programs for creative enterprises are also presented. **Availability:** Print; Online.

21174 ■ *"Tax Credits Drive MO Budget Crisis"* in *St. Louis Business Journal* (Vol. 33, September 14, 2012, No. 3, pp. 1)
Pub: Baltimore Business Journal
Contact: Rhonda Pringle, President
E-mail: rpringle@bizjournals.com
Description: Tax credits have adversely affected Missouri's annual operating budget. Tax credits were created as an economic incentive tool. **Availability:** Print; Online.

21175 ■ *"Tech Jobs Rebound from Downturn"* in *Denver Business Journal* (Vol. 65, March 7, 2014, No. 43, pp. A9)
Pub: American City Business Journals, Inc.
Contact: Mike Olivieri, Executive Vice President
Released: Weekly. **Price:** $4, Introductory 4-week offer(Digital & Print). **Description:** Denver, Colorado's employment in core technology industries has returned from pre-Great Recession figures. The computer software industry's surging job growth and

the slight increase in the broadcasts and telecommunications industry offset the job losses in biotechnology and private aerospace industry from 2008 through 2013. The growth in specific industries is also discussed. **Availability:** Print; Online.

21176 ■ *"That Empty Feeling" in Crain's Cleveland Business (Vol. 28, October 15, 2007, No. 41, pp. 1)*
Pub: Crain Communications Inc.
Contact: K. C. Crain, President
Ed: Stan Bullard. **Description:** Townhouses, cluster homes and condominiums lured both buyers and builders for most of this decade but now that market is suffering to an even greater degree than the single-family home market. Statistical data included. **Availability:** Online.

21177 ■ *"That's About It for Quantitative Easing" in Barron's (Vol. 89, July 20, 2009, No. 29, pp. M11)*
Pub: Dow Jones & Company Inc.
Contact: Almar Latour, Chief Executive Officer
Ed: Brian Blackstone. **Description:** US Federal Reserve appears to have decided to halt quantitative easing, causing bond prices to drop and yields to rise. The yield for the 1-year Treasury bond rose more than 0.3 percentage point to about 3.65 percent. **Availability:** Online.

21178 ■ *"Think Disruptive! How to Manage In a New Era of Innovation" in Strategy & Leadership (Vol. 38, July-August 2010, No. 4, pp. 5-10)*
Pub: Emerald Inc.
Ed: Brian Leavy, John Sterling. **Price:** $32, online only 30 days. **Description:** The views expressed by Scott Anthony, president of an innovation consultancy Innosight, on the need for corporate leaders to apply disruptive innovation in a recessionary environment are presented. His suggestion that disruptive innovation is the only way to survive during the economic crisis is discussed. **Availability:** Online; PDF.

21179 ■ *"Think of Start-Ups as Shots On Goal" in (Vol. 90, June 2012, No. 6, pp. 38)*
Pub: Harvard Business Review Press
Contact: Moderna V. Pfizer, Contact
Ed: Robert E. Litan. **Price:** $6. **Description:** The importance of start-up businesses to the nation's economic recovery is emphasized. Comprehensive legislation is necessary to improve start-up access to opportunity and talent. **Availability:** PDF; Online.

21180 ■ *"The Three Amigos" in Canadian Business (Vol. 81, March 17, 2008, No. 4, pp. 19)*
Description: Mexican president Felipe Calderon said that Mexico exported 30 percent more to Europe and 25 percent more to other countries in Latin America in 2006 in light of the downturn in the U.S. economy. Calderon made this announcement in a speech at Harvard University while protestors marched outside protesting against NAFTA. **Availability:** Online.

21181 ■ *"Three Trails Blazes Tax Credit Deal" in The Business Journal-Serving Metropolitan Kansas City (Vol. 27, November 7, 2008, No. 9)*
Description: Three Trails Redevelopment LLC plans to redevelop the Bannister Mall area. The Missouri Development Finance Board is expected to approve $30 million in tax credits for the project. A verbal agreement on the terms and conditions has already been reached according to the agency's executive director.

21182 ■ *"Thriving DFW Big Target for Franchisors" in Dallas Business Journal (Vol. 35, March 30, 2012, No. 29, pp. 1)*
Description: Dallas-Fort Worth Metropolitan Area has attracted outside franchisors looking to expand as Texas continues to fare better than other states during the recession. The Internation Franchising Association estimates that there will be 21,772 franchise establishments in DFW in 2012. **Availability:** Print; Online.

21183 ■ *"Time to Leave the Party? Re-Evaluating Commodities" in Barron's (Vol. 88, March 24, 2008, No. 12, pp. M16)*
Pub: Dow Jones & Company Inc.
Contact: Almar Latour, Chief Executive Officer
Ed: Andrea Hotter. **Description:** Prices of commodities such as gold, copper, crude oil, sugar, cocoa, and wheat have fallen from their all-time highs set in the middle of March 2008. Analysts, however, caution that this decline in prices may be temporary, and that a banking crisis may trigger new price rises in commodities. **Availability:** Online.

21184 ■ *"To Keep Freight Rolling, III. Has to Grease the Hub" in Crain's Chicago Business (Vol. 31, April 21, 2008, No. 16, pp. 22)*
Pub: Crain Communications Inc.
Contact: Barry Asin, President
Ed: Paul O'Connor. **Description:** Discusses the importance of upgrading Chicago's continental-hub freight rail system which is integral to moving international products as well as domestic ones. Global tonnage is expected to double by 2020 and unless more money is designated to upgrade the infrastructure the local and national economy will suffer. **Availability:** Online.

21185 ■ *"Today's Business Sale Climate" in Business Owner (Vol. 35, September-October 2011, No. 5, pp. 10)*
Description: Despite the weak economy, there is a surplus of individuals wanting to purchase a small business. The Small Business Administration loan guarantees program helps with its loans for purchase/sale of business assistance. **Availability:** Print; Online.

21186 ■ *"Toll Talker: CEO Takes Stock of His Company, the Housing Market" in Philadelphia Business Journal (Vol. 33, May 9, 2014, No. 13, pp. 4)*
Pub: American City Business Journals, Inc.
Contact: Mike Olivieri, Executive Vice President
Released: Weekly. **Price:** $4, introductory 4-week offer(Digital only). **Description:** Douglas C. Yearley, Jr., CEO of Toll Brothers Inc. discusses how his company capitalized on the economic recession in the housing market by acquiring large tracts of land between 2008 and 2010, including Shapell Homes in California for $1.2 billion. Yearley believes that while the housing downturn trend led to a rise in apartment living, the concept of home ownership remains relatively strong in the U.S., thus spurring construction. **Availability:** Print; Online.

21187 ■ *"Tooling Firm Thinks Being In U.P. Gives It Upper Hand" in Crain's Detroit Business (Vol. 30, October 13, 2014, No. 41, pp. 21)*
Pub: Crain Communications Inc.
Contact: Barry Asin, President
Description: Extreme Tool & Engineering is located in a remote region of Michigan's Upper Peninsula. The firm's employees average age is 28 and owner, Mike Zacharias, believes that combination contributes to the mold maker's success. He believes in the power of youth and reinvesting in training. Despite the economic challenges of the area, he employs nearly 80 workers. **Availability:** Online.

21188 ■ *"The Top 10: Prime Examples of Growth and Prosperity" in South Florida Business Journal (Vol. 34, July 18, 2014, No. 52, pp. 13)*
Pub: American City Business Journals, Inc.
Contact: Mike Olivieri, Executive Vice President
Released: June 18, 2014. **Price:** $4, Introductory 4-Week Offer(Digital & Print). **Description:** A list of the top ten private companies in South Florida in 2014 is presented. The companies represent the strength of the local economy and encompass a variety of industries, with combined revenue growth of $3.58 billion. **Availability:** Print; Online.

21189 ■ *"Trade Winds" in Canadian Sailings (June 30, 2008)*
Description: Trade between Canada and the United States is discussed as well as legislation concerning foreign trade and the future of this trade relationship. **Availability:** Online.

21190 ■ *"Trader Joe's Warehouse May Bring More Business to Daytona" in Orlando Business Journal (Vol. 30, March 14, 2014, No. 38, pp. 8)*
Pub: American City Business Journals, Inc.
Contact: Mike Olivieri, Executive Vice President
Released: March 14, 2014. **Price:** $8, introductory 4-week offer(Digital only). **Description:** Trader Joe's plan to open a retail warehouse grocery store in Daytona, Florida would benefit the city's economy. The firm is set to receive an incentive package from the Volusia County government. The new facility is expected to generate hundreds of jobs. **Availability:** Print; Online.

21191 ■ *"Train Now to Get the Competitive Edge" in Contractor (Vol. 56, October 2009, No. 10, pp. 58)*
Ed: Merry Beth Hall. **Description:** Due to the harsh economic climate, mechanical contractors would be well-served to train their employees while they have time to take them out of the field. This will help ensure that they are not behind when the economic recovery happens. Suggestions on how to choose the best type of training are presented. **Availability:** Print; Online.

21192 ■ *"Travel Leery" in Crain's Chicago Business (Vol. 31, March 31, 2008, No. 13, pp. 3)*
Pub: Crain Communications Inc.
Contact: Barry Asin, President
Ed: John Pletz. **Description:** Due to the rise in airline prices and a possible recession, many companies are starting to change their travel policies and limit travel spending. **Availability:** Online.

21193 ■ *"Trimming Costs, But Not Looking It" in Crain's Chicago Business (Vol. 31, November 17, 2008, No. 46, pp. 35)*
Pub: Crain Communications Inc.
Contact: Barry Asin, President
Ed: Shia Kapos. **Description:** Advice is given concerning ways in which to keep up appearances of success during these troubled financial times. **Availability:** Online.

21194 ■ *"Trust Tax Under Fire as Drain on Revenue" in Globe & Mail (April 9, 2007, pp. B1)*
Ed: Steven Chase. **Description:** The economic aspects of the implementation of the trust levy by the Canadian government are discussed. The acquisition of Canadian income trusts by Canadian and international financial institutions is described. **Availability:** Online.

21195 ■ *"Turbulent Times and Golden Opportunities" in Business Strategy Review (Vol. 21, Spring 2010, No. 1, pp. 34)*
Ed: Don Sull. **Released:** February 09, 2010. **Description:** For those feeling storm-tossed by today's economy, the author believes there's much to learn from Carnival Cruise Lines, a company that discovered that turbulence often has an upside. **Availability:** Print; PDF; Online.

21196 ■ *"A Turn in the South" in The Economist (Vol. 390, January 3, 2009, No. 8612, pp. 34)*
Description: Overview of Charleston, South Carolina, a region that lost its navy base in 1996, which had provided work for more than 22,000 people; the city developed a plan called Noisette in order to redevelop the area and today the economy is healthier and more diversified than it was a decade ago. Charleston was described as among the best cities for doing business by Inc. Magazine and seems

to be handling the downturn of the economy fairly well. Statistical data regarding growth, business and population is included. **Availability:** Print; Online.

21197 ■ *"Unemployment Rates"* **in The Economist (Vol. 390, January 3, 2009, No. 8612, pp. 75)**

Description: Countries that are being impacted the worst by rising unemployment rates are those that have also been suffering from the housing market crisis. Spain has been the hardest hit followed by Ireland. America and Britain are also seeing levels of unemployment that indicate too much slack in the economy. **Availability:** Print; Online.

21198 ■ *"U.S. Primaries: An Amazing Race"* **in Canadian Business (Vol. 81, February 12, 2008, No. 3, pp. 25)**
Pub: Rogers Media Inc.
Contact: Neil Spivak, Chief Executive Officer

Ed: Rachel Pulfer. **Description:** U.S. presidential candidates Barack Obama and Hilary Clinton lead the Democratic Part primaries while John McCain is a frontrunner at the Republican Party. These leading candidates have different plans for the U.S. economy which will affect Canada's own economy particularly concerning trade policies. The presidential candidates' proposals and the impacts of U.S. economic downturn on Canada are examined. **Availability:** Print; Online.

21199 ■ *"U.S. Recession Officially Over: Is Recovery Ever Going to Arrive?"* **in Montana Business Quarterly (Vol. 49, Spring 2011, No. 1, pp. 6)**
Pub: University of Montana Bureau of Business and Economic Research
Contact: Patrick Barkey, Director
E-mail: patrick.barkey@business.umt.edu

Ed: Patrick M. Barkey. **Released:** Quarterly. **Description:** Ten predictions regarding American's economy for 2012 are listed. **Availability:** Online.

21200 ■ *"Univest Charter Switch Signals Banking Trend"* **in Philadelphia Business Journal (Vol. 30, September 2, 2011, No. 29, pp. 1)**
Pub: Philadelphia Business Journal
Contact: Sierra Quinn, Director
E-mail: squinn@bizjournals.com

Ed: Jeff Blumenthal. **Description:** Univest Corporation of Pennsylvania changed from a federal to state charter because of cost savings and state agency has greater understanding of the intricacies of the local economy. The Pennsylvania Department of Banking has also received inquiries from seven other banks about doing the same this year. **Availability:** Online.

21201 ■ *"Unretirement: How Baby Boomers are Changing the Way We Think About Work, Community, and the Good Life"*

Released: 1st edition. **Price:** $16.20, paperback; $23.40, hardback; $14.40, ebook. **Description:** Baby boomers are transforming American economics and society in a positive way. Because boomers are living longer in better health and are extending their work lives, may times with new careers, entrepreneurial ventures, and socially responsible volunteering service. This trend will enrich the American workplace, economy, and the society as a whole for future generations. **Availability:** E-book; Print; Online.

21202 ■ *"Up In the Air"* **in The Business Journal-Serving Greater Tampa Bay (Vol. 28, July 18, 2008, No. 30, pp. 1)**

Description: Views and information on Busch Gardens and on its future, are presented. The park's 3,769 employees worry for their future, after tourism industry experts have expressed concerns on possible tax cuts and other cost reductions. The future of the park, which ranks number 19 as the most visited park in the world, is expected to have a major impact on the tourism industry. **Availability:** Online.

21203 ■ *"Up On The Farm"* **in Canadian Business (Vol. 81, March 31, 2008, No. 5, pp. 23)**

Description: Agricultural products have outperformed both energy and metal and even the prospect of a global economic slowdown does not seem to hinder its prospects. The Organization for Economic Cooperation and Development sees prices above historic equilibrium levels during the next ten years given that fuel and fertilizers remain high and greater demand from India and China remain steady. **Availability:** Print; Online.

21204 ■ *"The Upside of Fear and Loathing"* **in Barron's (Vol. 88, March 24, 2008, No. 12, pp. 11)**
Pub: Dow Jones & Company Inc.
Contact: Almar Latour, Chief Executive Officer

Ed: Michael Santoli. **Description:** Fear and risk aversion prevalent among investors may actually serve to cushion the decline and spark a rally in US stock prices. Surveys of investors indicate rising levels of anxiety and bearishness, indicating a possible positive turnaround. **Availability:** Online.

21205 ■ *"Valenti: Roots of Financial Crisis Go Back to 1998"* **in Crain's Detroit Business (Vol. 24, October 6, 2008, No. 40, pp. 25)**
Pub: Crain Communications Inc.
Contact: Barry Asin, President

Ed: Tom Henderson, Nathan Skid. **Description:** Interview with Sam Valenti III who is the chairman and CEO of Valenti Capital L.L.C., a wealth-management firm; Valenti discusses in detail the history that led up to the current economic crisis as well as his prediction for the future of the country. **Availability:** Print; Online.

21206 ■ *"Venture Gap"* **in Canadian Business (Vol. 81, February 26, 2008, No. 4, pp. 82)**
Pub: Rogers Media Inc.
Contact: Neil Spivak, Chief Executive Officer

Ed: Joe Castaldo. **Description:** Money raised by Canadian venture capitalist firms has been declining since 2001. A strong venture capital market is important if Canada is to build innovative companies. Fixing Canada's tax policy on foreign investments is a start in reviving the industry. **Availability:** Print; Online.

21207 ■ *"Viva Brazil"* **in Business Strategy Review (Vol. 21, Autumn 2010, No. 3, pp. 24)**

Ed: Georgina Peters. **Released:** September 29, 2010. **Description:** Brazil's current status as a major emerging market with a boundless economic horizon is a radical shift from its place in the world in the late 1960s to the mid 1990s. Lessons Brazil can teach other countries are outlined. **Availability:** Print; PDF; Online.

21208 ■ *"Voices: Breaking the Corruption Habit"* **in Business Strategy Review (Vol. 21, Autumn 2010, No. 3, pp. 67)**

Ed: David De Cremer. **Released:** September 22, 2010. **Description:** In times of crisis, it seems natural that people will work together for the common good. David De Cremer cautions that, on the contrary, both economic and social research prove otherwise. He proposes steps for organizations to take to prevent corrupt behaviors. **Availability:** Print; Electronic publishing; PDF; Online.

21209 ■ *"Walker Seeks More Business Participation"* **in Business Journal-Milwaukee (Vol. 28, December 10, 2010, No. 10, pp. A1)**
Pub: The Business Journal
Contact: Heather Ladage, President
E-mail: hladage@bizjournals.com

Ed: Rich Kirchen. **Description:** Wisconsin governor Scott Walker is seeking the aid of Milwaukee business leaders to participate in resolving the challenges posed by the economic crisis. Walker is aiming to create 250,000 jobs. He is also planning to call a special session of the legislature to enact strategies to jumpstart the economy. **Availability:** Print; Online.

21210 ■ *"Wannabe Buyers Take Their Own Sweet Time"* **in Crain's Chicago Business (Vol. 31, April 21, 2008, No. 16, pp. 50)**
Pub: Crain Communications Inc.
Contact: Barry Asin, President

Ed: Lisa Bertagnoli. **Description:** Although all factors are in place for a robust real-estate market in the Chicago area: low interest rates, plenty of inventory and the region's relatively strong employment, buyers are taking their time and doing more research in order to see how bad the economy will get. **Availability:** Online.

21211 ■ *"A Warning Sign From Global Companies"* **in Harvard Business Review (Vol. 90, March 2012, No. 3, pp. 74)**
Pub: Harvard Business Review Press
Contact: Moderna V. Pfizer, Contact

Ed: Laura D'Andrea Tyson, Matthew J. Slaughter. **Price:** $8.95, hardcover. **Description:** Multiple charts demonstrate the importance of the multinational corporation to the American economy, and that the US needs to become more attractive to these types of firms. **Availability:** PDF; Online.

21212 ■ *"A Way Forward for Small Businesses"* **in Harvard Business Review (April 13, 2020)**

Released: April 13, 2020. **Description:** Details the economic impact of the Coronavirus on small businesses and offers five recommendations for navigating the crisis. **Availability:** Online.

21213 ■ *"Weathering the Economic Storm"* **in Playthings (Vol. 107, January 1, 2009, No. 1, pp. 10)**

Ed: J. Tol Broome, Jr. **Description:** Six steps for toy companies to survive the economic turndown are outlined: Outline your business model; seek professional input; meet with your banker; cut your costs; manage your inventory; and use your trade credit. **Availability:** Print; Online.

21214 ■ *"The Weeks Ahead"* **in Crain's New York Business (Vol. 24, January 7, 2008, No. 1, pp. 26)**

Description: Listing of events in the Detroit area include conferences addressing entrepreneurialism, economic development, and women business ownership. **Availability:** Print; Online.

21215 ■ *"Well-Timed Entrance"* **in Barron's (Vol. 92, July 23, 2012, No. 30, pp. 24)**
Pub: Dow Jones & Company Inc.
Contact: Almar Latour, Chief Executive Officer

Ed: Michael Aneiro. **Description:** Dan Ivascyn, portfolio manager of Pimco Income Fund, discusses the fund's investment bonds. The fund is heavily invested in mortgage-backed securities and is positioned for a low-interest-rate environment well into 2014 or 2015. **Availability:** Online.

21216 ■ *"'We're Full," Car Dealers Say as Auto Sales Slow after a Long Boom"* **in The New York Times (July 23, 2019)**
URL(s): www.nytimes.com/2019/07/23/business/were-full-car-dealers-say-as-auto-sales-slow-after-a-long-boom.html

Ed: Neal E. Boudette. **Released:** July 23, 2019. **Description:** Car sales to individual buyers are slowing down, even with discounts and other incentives. The past decade saw a big boom in car and truck sales, but now these vehicles aren't moving off the lots fast enough and dealers are ordering less from manufacturers. **Availability:** Online.

21217 ■ *"What Can Michael Brown Do For Biz?"* **in Washington Business Journal (Vol. 31, June 15, 2012, No. 8, pp. 1)**
Pub: Baltimore Business Journal
Contact: Rhonda Pringle, President
E-mail: rpringle@bizjournals.com

Description: Michael Brown, Washington DC's new economic development point man, aims to ease business regulation, speed up retail development, and create opportunities for local contractors. He is also

21218 ■ Economic Development

expected to deal with oversight of all housing and economic development issues and agencies within the state. **Availability:** Print; Online.

21218 ■ *"What to Do in an Economic Upswing Before It's too Late"* in *Agency Sales Magazine* (Vol. 39, November 2009, No. 10, pp. 36)
Description: Some marketing suggestions for businesses as the economy recovers are presented. These include not waiting for the economy to change and telling your brand's story. Showing people what you can do for them and changing doubters into believers is also advised. **Availability:** Online.

21219 ■ *"What Has Sergey Wrought?"* in *Barron's* (Vol. 89, July 13, 2009, No. 28, pp. 8)
Pub: Dow Jones & Company Inc.
Contact: Almar Latour, Chief Executive Officer
Ed: Alan Abelson. **Description:** Sergey Aleynikov is a computer expert that once worked for Goldman Sachs but he was arrested after he left the company and charged with theft for bringing with him the code for the company's proprietary software for high-frequency trading. The stock market has been down for four straight weeks as of July 13, 2009 which reflects the reality of how the economy is still struggling. **Availability:** Online.

21220 ■ *"What Keeps Global Leaders Up at Night"* in *Harvard Business Review* (Vol. 90, April 2012, No. 4, pp. 32)
Pub: Harvard Business Review Press
Contact: Moderna V. Pfizer, Contact
Price: $6. **Description:** A chart uses colored squares to portray economic, environmental, geopolitical, societal, and technological concerns of industry leaders, and ranks them according to likelihood and impact. **Availability:** PDF; Online.

21221 ■ *"Whatever Happened to TGIF? How Much Of the Recession Is Priced into Stocks?"* in *Barron's* (Vol. 88, March 10, 2008, No. 10, pp. M3)
Pub: Dow Jones & Company Inc.
Contact: Almar Latour, Chief Executive Officer
Ed: Kopin Tan. **Description:** US stock markets fell in early March 2008 to their lowest level in 18 months, venturing close to entering a bear market phase. The S&P 500 has dropped an average of 0.78 percent on Fridays for 2008. **Availability:** Online.

21222 ■ *"What's Holding Down Small Business?"* in *Business Owner* (Vol. 35, November-December 2011, No. 6, pp. 3)
Description: According to a recent survey conducted by the National Federation of Independent Business, demand is the number one reason for slow growth to any small business in today's economy. **Availability:** PDF; Online.

21223 ■ *"What's More Important: Stag or Flation?"* in *Barron's* (Vol. 88, July 14, 2008, No. 28, pp. M8)
Pub: Dow Jones & Company Inc.
Contact: Almar Latour, Chief Executive Officer
Ed: Randall W. Forsyth. **Description:** Economists are divided on which part of stagflation, an economic situation in which inflation and economic stagnation occur simultaneously and remain unchecked for a period of time, is more important. Some economists say that the Federal government is focusing on controlling inflation while others see the central bank as extending its liquidity facilities to the financial sector. **Availability:** Online.

21224 ■ *"When Profit Is Not the Incentive"* in *Business North Carolina* (Vol. 28, February 2008, No. 2, pp. 42)
Pub: Business North Carolina
Contact: Peggy Knaack, Manager
E-mail: pknaack@businessnc.com
Ed: Amamda Parry. **Description:** Novant Health is North Carolina's fifth-largest private-sector employer and one of the largest nonprofit companies. Nonprofits grew 35 percent in North Carolina from 1995 to 2003. **Availability:** Online.

21225 ■ *"Where Are All the Builders?"* in *U.S. News & World Report* (June 15, 2018)
URL(s): www.usnews.com/news/the-report/articles/2018-06-15/the-us-construction-industry-is-booming-but-where-are-the-builders
Ed: Andrew Soergel. **Released:** June 15, 2018. **Description:** With the booming economy in the US, lots of construction projects are popping up. However, projects have been delayed and even redesigned due to a major shortage of construction workers. In the first quarter of 2018, employers were looking to fill 225,000 construction jobs per month, making it difficult to find skilled workers among the whole industry. **Availability:** Online.

21226 ■ *Why Are Small Businesses So Important for the Economy?*
URL(s): www.huffpost.com/entry/why-are-small-businesses-so-important-for-the-economy_b_58f61f9ae4b048372700db75
Ed: Jose Vasquez. **Released:** April 18, 2017. **Description:** Explores why small businesses and startups are some of the most important influencers for economic growth. **Availability:** Online.

21227 ■ *"Why Change?"* in *Canadian Business* (Vol. 80, October 8, 2007, No. 20, pp. 9)
Description: The need for economic change in Canada is discussed. Despite the country's economic growth and low unemployment rate, economic reform is needed in order to maximize its economic potential in the future. Other reasons for the need to further develop its economy, such as the rise of manufacturing and service industries in Asia and the emergence of regional trade pacts in South America are also tackled.

21228 ■ *"Why Customer Engagement Matters So Much Now; Wary Consumers Will Give More Money to the Businesses they Feel Emotionally Connected To -- While Ignoring Others"* in *Gallup Business Journal* (July 22, 2014)
Pub: Gallup, Inc.
Contact: Jon Clifton, Chief Executive Officer
Description: Gallup's daily tracking of the U.S. economy shows signs of recovery since the crash of 2008. When Americans purchase goods or services, they tend to choose businesses they feel emotionally connected to and might even ignore those that provide no value to them. They expect a company to earn their money. **Availability:** Print; Online.

21229 ■ *"Why Entrepreneurs Will Save the World"* in *Women In Business* (Vol. 61, December 2009, No. 6, pp. 12)
Pub: American Business Women's Association
Contact: Rene Street, Executive Director
Ed: Leigh Elmore. **Released:** May 27, 2012. **Description:** American economic growth is attributed to small businesses but more than one-third of these businesses have had to cut jobs in 2009, while only five percent have increased workforces. This trend motivated organizations, such as the Ewing Marion Kauffman Foundation, to bring together entrepreneurs and assist them in having greater participation in public dialogues about America's economy. **Availability:** Print; Online.

21230 ■ *"Why Optimism Over Europe Won't Last"* in *Barron's* (Vol. 92, August 25, 2012, No. 38, pp. M6)
Pub: Dow Jones & Company Inc.
Contact: Almar Latour, Chief Executive Officer
Ed: Jonathan Buck. **Description:** European markets could experience losses in the second half of 2012 as uncertainty over political events could wipe out market gains. Greece has to abide by the terms of its agreements with creditors to receive bailout funds. The stock prices of BG Group could gain as much as 20 percent in 2013 due to its strong lifquified natural gas business. **Availability:** Online.

GENERAL SMALL BUSINESS TOPICS

21231 ■ *"Why Taking a Vacation Is Your Patriotic Duty"* in *South Florida Business Journal* (Vol. 34, June 27, 2014, No. 49, pp. 14)
Pub: American City Business Journals, Inc.
Contact: Mike Olivieri, Executive Vice President
Released: Weekly. **Description:** The negative impact on the U.S. economy of unused vacation days is explained. Tips that employees should follow before taking a paid vacation leave benefit are presented. **Availability:** Print; Online.

21232 ■ *"Why U.S. Competitiveness Matters to All of Us: The World Wants America to Regain Its Vibrancy. Let's Stop Assigning Blame and Instead Focus on Solutions"* in *Harvard Business Review* (Vol. 90, March 2012, No. 3, pp. 49)
Pub: Harvard Business Review Press
Contact: Moderna V. Pfizer, Contact
Ed: Nitin Nohria. **Description:** The introduction to this special issue presents perspectives on the US economy from citizens of other nations. While they realize globalization means countries are interdependent and that a strong America provides an international boost, they feel US leaders are concerned more with politics than economic growth. Action is needed instead.

21233 ■ *"Wind Farm Is Planned for Yolo Farmland"* in *Sacramento Business Journal* (Vol. 29, September 21, 2012, No. 30, pp. 1)
Pub: Baltimore Business Journal
Contact: Rhonda Pringle, President
E-mail: rpringle@bizjournals.com
Ed: Melanie Turner. **Description:** Austin, Texas-based Pioneer Green Energy LLC has been planning to build as many as 400 wind turbines in Yolo County, California that could potentially generate up to 600 megawatts. The company has already raised $20 and it is expected to formally propose the project in early 2013. The economic impact on the farmers and landowners in the region is explored. **Availability:** Online.

21234 ■ *"Wing and a Prayer"* in *Canadian Business* (Vol. 81, November 10, 2008, No. 19, pp. 70)
Ed: Sean Silcoff. **Released:** January 09, 2016. **Description:** The 61st Annual National Business Aviation Association convention in Orlando, Florida saw unabashed display of wealth and privilege, but the U.S. market meltdown and possible economic crash has raised questions on the industry's future. Statistical details included. **Availability:** Print; Online.

21235 ■ *"Winners and Losers"* in *Crain's Detroit Business* (Vol. 25, June 22, 2009, No. 25, pp. 18)
Pub: Crain Communications Inc.
Contact: Barry Asin, President
Description: Rankings for Detroit's 50 top-compensated CEOs has changed due to the economic recession. The biggest changes are discussed. **Availability:** Online.

21236 ■ *"Winter of Discontent"* in *Philadelphia Business Journal* (Vol. 33, March 14, 2014, No. 5, pp. 4)
Pub: American City Business Journals, Inc.
Contact: Mike Olivieri, Executive Vice President
Description: The winter storm has adversely impacted businesses in Philadelphia, Pennsylvania. The snow storm has resulted in $50 billion in economic loss. Many companies suffered delays, early dismissals and cancellations, resulting in revenue decline. **Availability:** Online.

21237 ■ *"With the Indian Market, You Take Good With the Bad"* in *Globe & Mail* (March 23, 2007, pp. B11)
Ed: David Parkinson. **Description:** The performance of Bombay Stock Exchange in the month of February 2007 is analyzed. The impact of growing economy on the stock market performance is also analyzed. **Availability:** Print; Online.

GENERAL SMALL BUSINESS TOPICS
Economic Development ■ 21253

21238 ■ *"Woof Gang Bakery & Grooming Claws Through Recession"* in *Orlando Business Journal (Vol. 29, July 6, 2012, No. 3, pp. 1)*
Pub: Baltimore Business Journal
Contact: Rhonda Pringle, President
E-mail: rpringle@bizjournals.com
Ed: Anjali Fluker. **Description:** Woof Gang Bakery and Grooming has reported increased sales des;pite the economic crisis. The company is set to open its 30th store by the end of 2012. **Availability:** Print; Online.

21239 ■ *"A World of Opportunity: Foreign Markets Offer Diversity to Keen Investors"* in *Canadian Business (Vol. 81, Summer 2008, No. 9)*
Description: International Monetary Fund projected in its 'World Economy Outlook' that there is a 25 percent chance that a global recession will occur in 2008 and 2009. Global growth rate is forecasted at 3.7 percent in 2008. Inflation in Asia emerging markets and forecasts on stock price indexes are presented. **Availability:** Online.

21240 ■ *"Worry No. 1 at Auto Show: Recession"* in *Crain's Detroit Business (Vol. 24, January 21, 2008, No. 3, pp. 1)*
Pub: Crain Communications Inc.
Contact: Barry Asin, President
Ed: Brent Snavely. **Description:** Recession fears clouded activity at the 2008 Annual North American International Auto Show. Automakers are expecting to see a drop in sales due to slow holiday retail spending as well as fallout from the subprime lending crisis. **Availability:** Online.

21241 ■ *"The Worst Lies Ahead for Wall Street: More Losses Certain; More Expensive Capital to Be Needed"* in *Crain's New York Business (Vol. 24, January 20, 2008, No. 3, pp. 1)*
Pub: Crain Communications, Inc.
Contact: Jessica Botos, Manager, Marketing
E-mail: jessica.botos@crainsnewyork.com
Ed: Aaron Elstein. **Description:** Due to the weakening economy, many financial institutions will face further massive losses forcing them to borrow more at higher interest rates and dragging down their earnings for years to come. The effects on commercial real estate and credit card loans are also discussed as well as the trend to investing in Asia and the Middle East. **Availability:** Online.

21242 ■ *"Yield Vanishes, Inflation Lurks"* in *Barron's (Vol. 92, September 17, 2012, No. 38, pp. M12)*
Description: The US Federal Reserve's announcement of a third round of quantitative easing resulted in lower yields for bonds. Investors are becoming concerned with the probability of a rise in inflation after th quantitative easing program expires. **Availability:** Online.

21243 ■ *"Young Adults, Childless May Help Fuel Post-Recession Rebound"* in *Pet Product News (Vol. 64, November 2010, No. 11, pp. 4)*
Ed: David Lummis. **Description:** Pet industry retailers and marketers are encouraged to tap into the young adult and childless couple sectors to boost consumer traffic and sales to pre-recession levels. Among young adult owners, pet ownership increased from 40 percent in 2003 to 49 percent in 2009. Meanwhile, the childless couple sector represented 63 percent of all dog/cat owners in 2009. **Availability:** Online.

21244 ■ *"Your Exposure to Bear Stearns"* in *Barron's (Vol. 88, March 17, 2008, No. 11, pp. 45)*
Pub: Dow Jones & Company Inc.
Contact: Almar Latour, Chief Executive Officer
Ed: Tom Sullivan, Jack Willoughby. **Description:** Bear Stearns makes up 5.5 percent of Pioneer Independence's portfolio, 1.4 percent of Vanguard Windsor II's portfolio, 1.2 percent of Legg Mason Value Trust, about 1 percent of Van Kampen Equity & Income, and 0.79 percent of Putnam Fund for Growth & Income. Ginnie Mae securities are now trading at 1.78 percentage points over treasuries due to the mortgage crises. **Availability:** Online.

21245 ■ *"The Zero Marginal Cost Society: The Internet of Things, the Collaborative Commons, and the Eclipse of Capitalism"*
Pub: Palgrave Macmillan
Released: April 04, 2014. **Price:** $18.99, paperback; $9.99, e-book; $29.99, hardcover. **Description:** The emerging Internet of things is speeding society to an ear of nearly free goods and services, causing the rise of a global Collaborative Commons and the eclipse of capitalism. Entrepreneurial dynamism of competitive markets that drives productivity up and marginal costs down, enabling businesses to reduce the price of their goods and services to win consumers and market share is slowly dying. **Availability:** E-book; Print.

STATISTICAL SOURCES

21246 ■ US Retail and eCommerce & the Impact of COVID-19 - One Year Later 2021
URL(s): store.mintel.com/report/us-state-of-retail-ecommerce-impact-of-covid-19-one-year-later-market-report
Price: $4,366.35. **Description:** Downloadable report featuring analysis of the impact COVID-19 has had on the retail and eCommerce industries. Report includes an executive summary, interactive databook, PowerPoint presentation, infographic overview, report PDF, and previous years data. **Availability:** PDF.

TRADE PERIODICALS

21247 ■ Business Facilities: The Source for Corporate Site Selectors
Pub: Group C Media Inc.
Contact: Bill Corsini, Director
E-mail: bcorsini@groupc.com
URL(s): businessfacilities.comgroupcmedia.com/print-publications
Facebook: www.facebook.com/BusinessFacilities
Linkedin: www.linkedin.com/company/business-facilities-magazine
X (Twitter): x.com/bizfacilities
Instagram: www.instagram.com/businessfacilitiesmag
YouTube: www.youtube.com/user/businessfacilities
Pinterest: www.pinterest.com/commercial_industry_news/business-facilities-magazine-news
Ed: Mary Ellen McCandless. **Released:** Bimonthly **Price:** $52, Single issue for per year. **Description:** Professional magazine focusing on corporate expansion, commercial/industrial real estate, and economic development. **Availability:** Print; PDF; Download; Online.

21248 ■ Journal of Economics and Management Strategy (JEMS)
Pub: Wiley Periodicals Inc.
Contact: Brian Napack, Chief Executive Officer
URL(s): onlinelibrary.wiley.com/journal/15309134
Facebook: www.facebook.com/jemsjournal
Ed: Daniel F. Spulber, Ramon Casadesus-Masanell. **Released:** Quarterly **Price:** $756, Institutions for print and online US, Canada; $86, Individuals for online US, Canada, India; $1,161, Institutions for print and online India; $672, Institutions for online US, Canada; $701, Institutions for print US, Canada; $1,033, Institutions for online India; $1,078, Institutions for print India. **Description:** Journal covering theoretical and empirical industrial organization, applied game theory, and management strategy. **Availability:** Print; PDF; Download; Online.

VIDEO/AUDIO MEDIA

21249 ■ Main Street Business Insights: Amber Lambke, Maine Grains
URL(s): mainstreet.org/resources/knowledge-hub/podcast/amber-lambke-maine-grains
Ed: Matt Wagner. **Released:** August 01, 2023. **Description:** Podcast features a grist mill processing locally grown and heritage grains for bakers, brewers, and chefs in the Northeast. Also discusses its entrepreneurial ecosystem that creates jobs, improves land use, and provides healthy food.

21250 ■ Main Street Business Insights: Mileyka Burgos-Flores, Allapattah Collaborative CDC
URL(s): mainstreet.org/resources/knowledge-hub/podcast/mileyka-burgos-flores-allapattah-collaborative-cdc
Ed: Matt Wagner. **Released:** September 11, 2024. **Description:** Podcast discusses the importance of supporting small businesses with the CEO of a community development organization in Miami.

TRADE SHOWS AND CONVENTIONS

21251 ■ National Association Business Economics Annual Meeting
Wells Fargo & Company
420 Montgomery St.
San Francisco, CA 94104
Ph: (415)396-7392
Free: 866-249-3302
Co. E-mail: corpcsf@wellsfargo.com
URL: http://www.wellsfargo.com
Contact: Charles W. Scharf, President
URL(s): www.nabe.com/am2024
Frequency: Annual. **Description:** Includes sessions, speakers, and networking opportunities. **Audience:** Economists, analysts, business leaders and policymakers. **Principal Exhibits:** Includes sessions, speakers, and networking opportunities. **Telecommunication Services:** tbeers@nabe.com.

CONSULTANTS

21252 ■ Business and Government Strategies International (BGSI)
425 Princess St.
  Alexandria, VA 22314-2330
Ph: (703)683-3793
Fax: (703)683-3863
Co. E-mail: bgsi@bgsi.net
URL: http://www.bgsi.net
Description: Firm provides economic development consulting services for government reforms and private sector development. **Scope:** Firm provides economic development consulting services for government reforms and private sector development. **Founded:** 1990.

21253 ■ HyettPalma Inc.
Alexandria, VA
Ph: (917)226-9888
Co. E-mail: info@hyettpalma.com
URL: http://www.hyettpalma.com
Contact: Dolores Palma, Co-Founder Consultant
Description: Firm provides economic development in downtown and commercial districts and their services include comprehensive economic enhancement strategies, market analysis, business retention, creation, attraction and business clustering strategies and business district audits. **Scope:** Firm provides economic development in downtown and commercial districts and their services include comprehensive economic enhancement strategies, market analysis, business retention, creation, attraction and business clustering strategies and business district audits. **Founded:** 1985. **Publications:** "Creating the Future Downtown," 2002; "Lure Businesses to Your Downtown--By Making Life Easier for Them," NYCOM, Apr, 2001; "Recruiting Developers: Using Rfps To Package Projects"; "Focus Groups For Downtown"; "Business Clustering: How To Leverage Sales"; "The Arts "Hook" Downtown," 2001; "The Arts Help Revitalize Downtowns," 2001; "Making Downtown Renaissance a Reality," 2000; "Assistance Program Helps Revitalize Conroe, Texas," 2000. **Training:** Trends in the Revitalization of Pennsylvania's Downtowns Through the Blueprints for Pennsylvania's Down-

towns Program, York, 2005; America Downtown-New Thinking, New Life, Dec, 2005; Americas Downtown Renaissance: Retail Revitalization and More, NYS Tug Hill Commission, 2003; Indiana Downtown; Creating the Future Downtown; How to Revitalize Your Downtown; Trends in the Revitalization of America's Downtowns, Pennsylvania League of Cities and Municipalities, 2003; Indiana Downtown, Indiana Association of Cities and Towns, 2003; Creating the Future Downtown, Indiana Association of Cities and Towns, 2003; How to Revitalize Your Downtown, 2002. **Special Services:** America Downtown®; Indiana Downtown®.

21254 ■ Maingate Business Development Corp.
2695 E 55th St.
  Cleveland, OH 44104
Ph: (216)881-7111
Co. E-mail: maingatecleveland@gmail.com
URL: http://www.maingatecleveland.org
Contact: Joseph A. Carey, President
E-mail: jcarey@en.com

Description: Seeks to promote business through economic and community development. Assists businesses in their expansion and financing needs. Enhances the quality of life and fosters the growth of good jobs within the community. **Founded:** 1990. **Publications:** *The Main Dealer* (Periodic). **Geographic Preference:** Local.

PUBLICATIONS

21255 ■ *Auburn Journal*
268 E Main St.
  Auburn, WA 98002
Ph: (253)833-0700
Co. E-mail: auburncc@auburnareawa.org
URL: http://www.auburnareawa.org
Contact: Kacie Bray, President
URL(s): goldcountrymedia.com/live-content/auburn
  -journal

Description: Contains local news and advertisements. **Availability:** Print.

21256 ■ *Business Economics: Designed to Serve the Needs of People Who Use Economics in Their Work*
1020 19th St. NW Ste. 550
  Washington, DC 20036
Ph: (202)463-6223
Fax: (202)463-6239
Co. E-mail: nabe@nabe.com
URL: http://www.nabe.com
Contact: Paul Volcker, President
URL(s): www.nabe.com/NABE/Publications/NABE/
  Publications/Publications.aspx

Ed: Hossein Askari. **Released:** Quarterly **Description:** Features articles on applied economics. **Availability:** Print; PDF; Download; Online.

21257 ■ *BusinessLink*
230 E E Butler Pky.
  Gainesville, GA 30501
Ph: (770)532-6206
Fax: (770)535-8419
Co. E-mail: info@ghcc.com
URL: http://www.ghcc.com
Contact: Kit Dunlap, President
E-mail: kit@ghcc.com
URL(s): www.ghcc.com/membership/chamber-mem
  bership-benefits

Ed: McKemie West. **Released:** Monthly; latest issue May 2024. **Description:** Contains news about members and chamber activities. **Availability:** PDF; Online.

COMPUTERIZED DATABASES

21258 ■ *ABI/INFORM*
ProQuest LLC
  789 E Eisenhower Pky.
  Ann Arbor, MI 48108
Ph: (734)761-4700
Free: 800-521-0600
URL: http://www.proquest.com
Contact: Matti Shem Tov, Chief Executive Officer
URL(s): about.proquest.com/en/products-services/abi
  _inform_complete

Availability: Online. **Type:** Full-text; Bibliographic; Image.

INTERNET DATABASES

21259 ■ *LGBTQ+ Resources in Business and the Workplace*
URL(s): guides.loc.gov/lgbtq-business

Description: Provides links to resources about the LGBTQ+ community and the economic issues they face as employees, consumers, and within the business community. Links will take users to print materials; reports and articles; data and statistics; subscription databases; and external websites. **Availability:** Online.

LIBRARIES

21260 ■ U.S.D.A. National Agricultural Library - Rural Information Center (RIC)
10301 Baltimore Ave.
  Beltsville, MD 20705
URL: http://www.nal.usda.gov/programs/ric

Scope: Economic development; small business development; city and county government services; government and private grants and funding sources; rural communities; community leadership; natural resources. **Services:** Copying; center open to the public. **Founded:** 1987. **Holdings:** Figures not available.

21261 ■ University of Kentucky - Business & Economics Information Center
105 Main Bldg.
  Lexington, KY 40506-0132
URL: http://gatton.uky.edu

Description: Center that provides various programs involving business strategies and ideas about the economy. **Scope:** Business, economics, business management, marketing, finance, accounting. **Services:** Library open to the public for reference use only. **Founded:** 1993.

21262 ■ West Virginia University College of Business and Economics - Bureau of Business and Economic Research (BBER) - Research
2161 University Ave., Ste. 450
  Morgantown, WV 26505
Ph: (304)293-7831
Co. E-mail: bebureau@mail.wvu.edu
URL: http://business.wvu.edu/research-outreach/
  bureau-of-business-and-economic-research
Contact: John Deskins, Director
E-mail: john.deskins@mail.wvu.edu

Description: Publishes books on studies, forecasts, county data profiles and newsletters. Does not accept unsolicited manuscripts. **Scope:** Business and economic problems, policies, and institutions, especially those related to state and local economies of West Virginia, including economic forecasts, studies on public finance, labor force and employment, demographic projections, specific industries, plant location, business management, and marketing. Conducts consumer analyses, community trade surveys, travel and tourism, and studies of national or regional scope that are significant to residents and business communities of West Virginia. **Founded:** 1940. **Holdings:** Figures not available. **Publications:** *Morgantown MSA Monitor* (Quarterly); *West Virginia Business and Economic Review* (Quarterly); *Journal of Small Business Management (JSBM)* (6/year). **Educational Activities:** Economic Outlook Conference (Annual), Obtain a detailed and reliable forecast for the national and state economies.; West Virginia Economic Outlook Conference (Annual), Obtain a detailed and reliable forecast for the national and state economies.

RESEARCH CENTERS

21263 ■ Arizona State University - W.P. Carey School of Business - JPMorgan Chase Economic Outlook Center
660 S Mill Ave., Ste., 300
  Tempe, AZ 85281
URL: http://seidmaninstitute.com/economic-outlook
  -center
Contact: Dr. Lee McPheters, Director
E-mail: lee.mcpheters@asu.edu

Description: Integral unit of the W.P. Carey School of Business, Arizona State University. Provides forecasting newsletters and economic analysis. **Scope:** Economic and business climate forecasts for Arizona and the western United States, including California, Utah, Nevada, Oregon, New Mexico, Colorado, Idaho, Washington, and Texas. **Founded:** 1986. **Publications:** *Mexico Consensus Economic Forecast* (Quarterly); *Western Blue Chip Economic Forecast* (10/year).

21264 ■ Atlantic Institute for Market Studies (AIMS)
Ste. 1207, Duke Twr., 5251 Duke St.
  Halifax, NS, Canada B3J 1P3
Co. E-mail: info@aims.ca
URL: http://www.aims.ca
Contact: Marco Navarro Genie, President
E-mail: mng@aims.ca

Description: Independent, nonprofit public policy research organization. **Scope:** Current and emerging economic and public policy issues facing Atlantic Canadians and Canadians more generally, including the economic and social characteristics and potentials of Atlantic Canada and its four constituent provinces. **Founded:** 1994. **Publications:** *AIMS On-Line Newsletter*; *AIMS Books*; *AIMS Papers*. **Educational Activities:** AIMS Lectures.

21265 ■ Atlantic Provinces Economic Council (APEC) - Library [Conseil Économique des Provinces de l'Atlantique]
5121 Sackville St., Ste. 500
  Halifax, NS, Canada B3J 1K1
Ph: (902)422-6516
Co. E-mail: info@atlanticeconomiccouncil.ca
URL: http://atlanticeconomiccouncil.ca
Contact: David Chaundy, Co-President Co-Chief Executive Officer
Linkedin: www.linkedin.com/company/atlantic
  -economic-council
X (Twitter): x.com/atl_econcouncil

Description: An independent economic research and public policy organization focused on the promotion of economic development in Atlantic Canada. **Scope:** Economic development of the Atlantic Region of Canada by monitoring and analyzing current and emerging economic trends and policies. **Founded:** 1954. **Holdings:** Figures not available. **Educational Activities:** APEC Annual Business Outlook Conference (Annual).

21266 ■ Ball State University - Center for Business and Economic Research (CBER)
2000 W University Ave.
  Muncie, IN 47306
Ph: (765)285-5926
Co. E-mail: cber@bsu.edu
URL: http://www.bsu.edu/academics/centersandinsti
  tutes/cber
Contact: Michael Joseph Hicks, Director
E-mail: mhicks@bsu.edu

Description: Integral unit of College of Business at Ball State University. Offers publication services: develops, designs, produces hard copy and electronic publications for college and community clients. **Scope:** Business and economics, including special studies designed to contribute to policy research, economic development and growth of eastern/central Indiana. Compiles and disseminates current economic and business data. **Founded:** 1970. **Publications:** *Indiana Business Bulletin* (Weekly).

21267 ■ Baylor University - Hankamer School of Business - Center for Business and Economic Research
PO Box 98003
Waco, TX 76798
Ph: (254)710-4146
Fax: (254)710-6142
URL: http://business.baylor.edu//tom_kelly/VITA.htm
Contact: Dr. Thomas M. Kelly, Professor
E-mail: tom_kelly@baylor.edu
Description: Integral unit of Hankamer School of Business at Baylor University. **Scope:** Local business and economic conditions. Conducts community economic base studies and supplies social and economic data to local agencies. Compiles and releases monthly indexes of business activity, indexes of consumer prices, and estimates of retail sales to newspapers. Tabulates and analyzes census and other data as requested by local agencies. **Founded:** 1983.

21268 ■ Center for Interuniversity Research in Quantitative Economics (CIREQ)
3150 Jean Brillant St.
Montreal, QC, Canada H3T 1N8
Ph: (514)343-6557
Co. E-mail: cireq@umontreal.ca
URL: http://cireqmontreal.com/en
Contact: Emanuela Cardia, Director
E-mail: emanuela.cardia@umontreal.ca
Facebook: www.facebook.com/CIREQ
X (Twitter): x.com/cireqmtl
Description: Joint research activity of McGill University, Concordia University, and the University of Montreal but operated under an independent board of governors. **Scope:** Deals with theoretical and applied econometrics, decision theory, macroeconomics policies and financial markets as well as environmental problems. **Founded:** 2002. **Publications:** *Interuniversity Research Centre on Quantitative Economics Annual report*; *Interuniversity Research Centre on Quantitative Economics Research papers*. **Educational Activities:** CIREQ Montreal Econometrics Conference.

21269 ■ Center for the Study of Economics (CSE)
407 Nassau St.
Princeton, NJ 08540-4647
Ph: (215)266-4877
URL: http://www.urbantoolsconsult.org
Facebook: www.facebook.com/UrbantoolsCSE
X (Twitter): x.com/urbantools
Description: Conducts objective research in property tax reform, land value taxation, and certain aspects of unemployment, recession, and inflation. Compiles statistics. **Scope:** A major tool for strengthening the development market in cities, reduce taxes for productive citizens and businesses and provide a progressive fair and equitable source of public revenue. **Founded:** 1980. **Publications:** *Incentive Taxation* (Annual). **Geographic Preference:** National.

21270 ■ Centre for the Study of Living Standards (CSLS) [Centre d'Étude des Niveaux de Vie (CENV)]
170 Laurier Ave. West Ste. 604
Ottawa, ON, Canada K1P 5V5
Ph: (613)233-8891
Co. E-mail: info@csls.ca
URL: http://www.csls.ca
Contact: Dr. Andrew Sharpe, Executive Director
E-mail: andrew.sharpe@csls.ca
Facebook: www.facebook.com/csls
Linkedin: www.linkedin.com/company/centre-for-the-study-of-living-standards
X (Twitter): x.com/cslsottawa
Description: Independent, nonprofit research organization. Offers database development (occasionally). **Scope:** Trends in and determinants of productivity, living standards and economic and social well being. **Founded:** 1995. **Publications:** *CSLS Research Reports* (Irregular); *International Productivity Monitor* (Semiannual).

21271 ■ Chapman University - A. Gary Anderson Center for Economic Research (ACER)
One University Dr.
Orange, CA 92866
URL: http://www.chapman.edu/research/institutes-and-centers/anderson-center/index.aspx
Contact: Dr. Raymond Sfeir, Director
E-mail: sfeir@chapman.edu
Description: Integral unit of George L. Argyros School of Business and Economics, Chapman University. Offers consulting services. **Scope:** Economics and business in the U.S. and California, as well as in Orange County, Los Angeles County, and the Inland Empire in California. **Founded:** 1978. **Publications:** *Economic & Business Review* (Semiannual); *Local business surveys*; *ACER Newsletter*; *ACER Working papers*.

21272 ■ East Tennessee State University College of Business and Technology - Bureau of Business and Economic Research
227 Sam-Wilson Hall
Johnson City, TN 37614
URL: http://www.etsu.edu/cbat/economics/bureau-research.php
Contact: Jon L. Smith, Director, Research
E-mail: smitjl01@etsu.edu
Description: Integral unit of the College of Business at East Tennessee State University. Offers business development program; economic feasibility (impact) studies; global research; implementation of pay systems; regional development information. **Scope:** Regional business conditions and the economic development of northeast Tennessee and the Tri-Cities Metropolitan Statistical Area (MSA) (Johnson City, Kingsport, and Bristol). Assists faculty and students in research efforts. **Founded:** 1967. **Publications:** *East Tennessee Business Indicators* (Annual); *Labor Market Report*; *Tri-Cities Retail Sales Report* (8/year).

21273 ■ Fort Lewis College - Office of Business and Economic Research (OBER)
1000 Rim Dr.
Durango, CO 81301
Co. E-mail: askit@fortlewis.edu
URL: http://www.fortlewis.edu/ober
Contact: Tom Stritikus, President
Description: Integral unit of School of Business Administration, Fort Lewis College. Conducts contract research and serves as a clearinghouse linking college faculty and the business community. **Scope:** Economics and local economic conditions. **Founded:** 1990. **Publications:** *Four Corners Economic Quarterly* (Quarterly). **Educational Activities:** OBER Southwest Business Forum (Annual), Provides the local community an overview of the local, state, and national international economies.

21274 ■ Georgia Southern University - Center for Business Analytics and Economic Research (CBAER)
1332 Southern Dr.
Statesboro, GA 30458
Ph: (912)478-0872
Co. E-mail: dhalaby@georgiasouthern.edu
URL: http://research.georgiasouthern.edu/big/big-programs/cbaer
Contact: Ben McKay, Assistant Director
E-mail: bpmckay@georgiasouthern.edu
Description: Integral unit of Georgia Southern University. Offers consulting and assistance for local businesses and communities. **Scope:** Local economic development, economic forecasting, regional economics, and public finance.

21275 ■ Georgia State University - J. Mack Robinson College of Business - Economic Forecasting Center (EFC)
35 Broad St. NW Ste. 200
Atlanta, GA 30303
Ph: (404)413-7260
Fax: (404)413-7264
Co. E-mail: efc@gsu.edu
URL: http://efc.robinson.gsu.edu
Contact: Dr. Rajeev Dhawan, Director
E-mail: rdhawan@gsu.edu
Facebook: www.facebook.com/economicforecastcentergsu
X (Twitter): x.com/EFC_GSU
Description: Integral unit of J. Mack Robinson College of Business, Georgia State University. Entitles sponsors to all data collected or produced by the Center and to one or two private meetings yearly with the Center director. **Scope:** National, regional, and state economic analysis and forecasting. Studies include econometric descriptions of the United States, the Southeast, Georgia, and the Atlanta metropolitan area, including short-term interest rates, long-term bond issues, foreign competition, and currency stability. The Center's objective is to provide economic commentary and analysis to the public and to the business community in particular. **Founded:** 1973. **Publications:** *Forecast of Georgia and Atlanta* (Quarterly); *Forecast of the Nation* (Quarterly); *Southeast States Indicators* (Quarterly). **Educational Activities:** EFC Economic Forecasting Conference (Quarterly); EFC Sponsors' Seminar (Quarterly).

21276 ■ Hawaii Department of Business, Economic Development, and Tourism - Research and Economic Analysis Div. (READ)
No. 1 Capitol District Bldg., 250 S Hotel St.
Honolulu, HI 96813
URL: http://dbedt.hawaii.gov/economic
Contact: Dr. Eugene Tian, Chief Economist
E-mail: xtian@dbedt.hawaii.gov
Description: Integral unit of Hawaii Department of Business, Economic Development, and Tourism. **Scope:** Business, economic development, tourism. **Publications:** *Construction and Hawaii's Economy*; *Quarterly Statistical and Economic Report* (Quarterly); *State of Hawaii Data Book* (Semiannual); *Hawaii Business Abroad* (Irregular).

21277 ■ Indiana University - Kelley School of Business - Indiana Business Research Center (IBRC)
1309 E 10th St.
Bloomington, IN 47405
Co. E-mail: ibrc@iu.edu
URL: http://ibrc.kelley.iu.edu
Contact: Carol O. Rogers, Director
E-mail: rogersc@iu.edu
Facebook: www.facebook.com/IUibrc
Linkedin: www.linkedin.com/company/indiana-business-research-center
X (Twitter): x.com/IUibrc
Description: Collects and analyses business and economic data in the state. Information is accessible through the Indiana Information Retrieval System at libraries, universities, and public agencies. Puts out two bimonthly publications. Presents a Business Outlook Panel annually in several cities. **Scope:** Indiana's economic development, population trends, state and local economic indicators, and information technology. **Founded:** 1925. **Publications:** *Indiana Business Review* (Quarterly); *InContext* (Bimonthly); *Indiana Business Review (IBR)* (Quarterly).

21278 ■ Jacksonville State University - Center for Economic Development and Business Research (CEDBR)
700 Pelham Rd. N
Jacksonville, AL 36265
Ph: (256)782-5324
Co. E-mail: techsupport@jsu.edu
URL: http://www.jsu.edu/ced
Contact: Jennifer Green, Director
E-mail: jngreen@jsu.edu
Description: Integral unit of School of Business at Jacksonville State University. Maintains a small business development center; State Data Center affiliate. **Scope:** Industrial needs analysis for cities and counties and business research, including retail and service studies. Special projects include economic development strategies for Alabama counties and marketing plan considerations for local governments, including Best Fit Studies. **Founded:** 1984. **Publications:** *JSU Economic Update* (Monthly); *CED Monographs*.

21279 ■ North Dakota State University - Institute for Business and Industry Development (IBID)
Dept. 7000
311 Morrill Hall
Fargo, ND 58108-6050
URL: http://www.ag.ndsu.edu/manufacturing
Contact: David Lehman, Site Manager
E-mail: david.lehman@ndsu.edu
Description: Integral unit of College of Agriculture, Food Systems and Natural Resources, North Dakota State University. Offers engineering extension services. **Scope:** Business and community economic development. **Founded:** 1989.

21280 ■ Princeton University - Woodrow Wilson School of Public and International Affairs - Research Program in Development Studies (RPDS)
Robertson Hall Princeton University
Princeton, NJ 08544
Co. E-mail: shiggins@princeton.edu
URL: http://spia.princeton.edu/departments/research-program-development-studies
Contact: Amaney A. Jamal, Dean
Description: Economic development, particularly in health and microeconomics. **Scope:** Research include interests in labor and development economics with special focus on human capital, crime and gender-violence. Other research includes focusing on the political economy in developing countries. **Founded:** 1967. **Publications:** *Working Paper Series* (Periodic). **Educational Activities:** RPDS Research Seminars in Economic Development for Staff and Graduate Students of the School.

21281 ■ Simon Fraser University Faculty of Environment - Centre for Sustainable Development (CSD)
8888 University Dr.
Burnaby, BC, Canada V5A 1S6
URL: http://www.sfu.ca/sustainabledevelopment.html
Contact: Dr. Yildiz Atasoy, Director
E-mail: yatasoy@sfu.ca
Description: Integral unit of Faculty of Environment, Simon Fraser University. Offers CED-NET, a worldwide discussion group of CED participants. **Scope:** Community economic development through access to knowledge, programs, markets, and funds. **Founded:** 1989.

21282 ■ Texas A&M International University - Texas Center for Border Economic and Enterprise Development (TCBEED)
5201 University Blvd. PLG 216
Laredo, TX 78041
Ph: (956)326-2546
Fax: (956)326-2544
Co. E-mail: texascenter@tamiu.edu
URL: http://texascenter.tamiu.edu
Contact: Dr. Daniel Covarrubias, Director
E-mail: dcova@tamiu.edu
Description: Integral unit of Texas AandM International University. Data accessible by Internet. **Scope:** International trade and border economic enterprise and development. **Founded:** 1989. **Educational Activities:** TCBEED Maquila visits; USIA delegations.

21283 ■ University of Alberta - Faculty of Arts - Department of Economics - Institute for Public Economics (IPE)
Edmonton, AB, Canada
Co. E-mail: ipe@ualberta.ca
URL: http://sites.ualberta.ca/~ipe/IPE/IPE.html
Contact: Dr. Corinne Langinier, Director
E-mail: corinne.langinier@ualberta.ca
URL(s): www.ualberta.ca/economics/institute-for-public-economics/index.html

Description: Integral unit of the Department of Economics, University of Alberta. **Scope:** Public economics, including the public sector and its influence on the economy and society. **Publications:** *IPE Working papers*.

21284 ■ University of Colorado at Boulder Department of Economics - Carl McGuire Center for International Studies
256 University of Colorado Boulder Rm. 121
Boulder, CO 80309-0256
Ph: (303)735-5500
URL: http://www.colorado.edu/economics/seminars-research/mcguire-center
Description: Separately incorporated unit affiliated with and under primary control of University of Colorado at Boulder. **Scope:** Organized within the Economics Department, the Center conducts research and graduate training in a broad range of topics relating to international economics, including international trade and finance, international trade negotiations, monetary theory and policy, economic development, and macroeconomics. Offers students in international economics exposure to interdisciplinary study involving the University's programs in international politics, conflict and peace studies, and international business. **Founded:** 1985.

21285 ■ University of Connecticut - Connecticut Center for Economic Analysis (CCEA)
2100 Hillside Rd.
Storrs, CT 06269-1240
URL: http://ccea.uconn.edu
Description: Integral unit of University of Connecticut. **Scope:** Economic analysis, including state and local finance, economic impact, policy analysis, cluster analysis, assessment of fiscal structure, dynamic REMI forecasting, econometrics, benchmarking, labor, and health economics. **Founded:** 1992. **Publications:** *The Connecticut Economy*. **Educational Activities:** CCEA Outlook, Features forecast of state employment and gross output.

21286 ■ University of Maryland at College Park Department of Economics - Center for International Economics
Mitchell Bldg 7999 Regents Dr.
College Park, MD 20742
URL: http://www.umd.edu/centers-and-institutes
Contact: Sebnem Kalemli-Ozcan, Director
E-mail: kalemli@umd.edu
Description: Integral unit of Economics Department, University of Maryland at College Park. **Scope:** International economics. **Founded:** 1993. **Educational Activities:** Center for International Economics Conferences (Annual); Center for International Economics Graduate Training Program; Professional Training Program in International Economics.

21287 ■ University of North Texas - Center for Economic Development and Research
1155 Union Cir. No. 310469
Denton, TX 76203-5017
Ph: (940)565-4049
URL: http://digital.library.unt.edu/explore/partners/UNTCEDR
Description: Research unit of University of North Texas. **Scope:** Applied economics, business, and public policy, particularly in the areas of economic development, fiscal analysis, energy policy, economic forecasting, and public policy. **Founded:** 1989. **Publications:** *Perspectives* (Semiannual).

21288 ■ University of South Carolina - Darla Moore School of Business - Division of Research
SC
URL: http://sc.edu/study/colleges_schools/moore/research_and_centers/division_of_research
Contact: Douglas P. Woodward, Director

E-mail: woodward@moore.sc.edu

21289 ■ University of Texas at Austin - IC2 Institute - Bureau of Business Research (BBR)
2815 San Gabriel St.
Austin, TX 78705
URL: http://ic2.utexas.edu
Contact: Dr. Bruce Kellison, Director
E-mail: bkellison@ic2.utexas.edu
Description: Publishes in-house research projects and outside book manuscripts presenting business end economic research that ordinarily could not be published without subsidy. Also publishes newsletters. Reaches market through direct mail. Does not accept unsolicited manuscripts. **Scope:** Economics and business in Texas, including economic development and planning, natural resources. **Founded:** 1926. **Publications:** *Directory of Texas Wholesalers* (Biennial); *Directory of Texas Manufacturers* (Annual); *Natural Fibers Information Center (NFIC)*; *Texas Business Review*; *Texas Industrial Expansion* (Monthly); *Texas Business Review* (Bimonthly). **Educational Activities:** Bureau of Business Research Conferences, Offer exemplary teaching and training programs.

21290 ■ University of Wisconsin - Superior - Northern Center for Community and Economic Development (NCCED)
801 N 28th St.
Superior, WI 54880
Ph: (715)394-8206
Fax: (715)394-8097
Co. E-mail: helpdesk@uwsuper.edu
URL: http://www.uwsuper.edu/acaddept/sbe/economics/center.cfm
Contact: Mark Maclean, Director
E-mail: mmaclean@uwsuper.edu
Description: Integral unit of University of Wisconsin-Superior. Offers consulting services. **Scope:** Regional and local economic development, including area economic profiles surveys, and statistical analyses. **Founded:** 1984. **Educational Activities:** NCCED Training, Offer exemplary teaching and training programs.

21291 ■ Washington Policy Center (WPC)
9 S Washington St Ste. 212
Spokane, WA 99201
Ph: (206)937-9691
Fax: (206)624-8038
Co. E-mail: wpc@washingtonpolicy.org
URL: http://www.washingtonpolicy.org
Contact: Liv Finne, Director
E-mail: lfinne@washingtonpolicy.org
Facebook: www.facebook.com/washington.policy.center
Linkedin: www.linkedin.com/company/washington-policy-center
X (Twitter): x.com/WAPolicyCenter
YouTube: www.youtube.com/channel/UCTljIqVt94OrqtCyNkRIRqg
Description: Independent, nonprofit think tank. **Scope:** Free-market economic policy issues at the local, state, and national level. **Founded:** 1986. **Publications:** *Policy briefs*; *Environmental Watch* (Monthly); *Policy notes*. **Educational Activities:** WPC Forums. **Awards:** WPC Internships.

21292 ■ Williams College - Center for Development Economics (CDE)
1065 Main St.
Williamstown, MA 01267
Ph: (413)597-2148
URL: http://cde.williams.edu
Description: Integral unit of Williams College. **Scope:** Deals with problems of economic development, emphasizing exter nal trade and finance policies, domestic resource and investment policies, industrialization and technology strategies, and developing countries. **Founded:** 1960. **Publications:** *Research Memorandum Series*. **Educational Activities:** CDE Seminar.

Education and Training

START-UP INFORMATION

21293 ■ *"2007 Top Colleges for Entrepreneurs"* in *Entrepreneur (Vol. 35, November 2007, No. 11, pp. 82)*
Pub: Entrepreneur Media Inc.
Contact: Dan Bova, Director
E-mail: dbova@entrepreneur.com
Ed: Nichole L. Torres. **Description:** Education in entrepreneurship is being pursued by many students and it is important to understand what entrepreneurship program fits you. Aspiring entrepreneurs should also ask about the program's focus. Considerations searched for by students regarding the particular school they chose to study entrepreneurship are discussed. **Availability:** Online.

21294 ■ *"Austin, Aggies and Innovation"* in *Austin Business Journal (Vol. 32, April 6, 2012, No. 5, pp. A1)*
Pub: American City Business Journals, Inc.
Contact: Mike Olivieri, Executive Vice President
Ed: Christopher Calnan. **Description:** Texas A and M University System director for new ventures, Jamie Rhodes, has been using his experience as an entrepreneur and angel investor to work with the university's professors, researchers, and new entrepreneurs on commercialization opportunities. Rhodes has a goal to create startups based on research produced at Texas A and M. **Availability:** Online.

21295 ■ *"Can You Say $1 Million? A Language-Learning Start-Up Is Hoping That Investors Can"* in *Inc. (Vol. 33, November 2011, No. 9, pp. 116)*
Pub: Inc. Magazine
Ed: April Joyner. **Description:** Startup, Verbling is a video platform that links language learners and native speakers around the world. The firm is working to raise money to hire engineers in order to build the product and redesign their Website. **Availability:** Online.

21296 ■ *"Campus CEOs: Young and the Restless"* in *Business Journal Portland (Vol. 30, February 21, 2014, No. 50, pp. 4)*
Pub: American City Business Journals, Inc.
Contact: Mike Olivieri, Executive Vice President
Released: Weekly. **Price:** $4, Introductory 4-week offer(Digital & Print). **Description:** A number of startups in Portland, Oregon were created by young entrepreneurs while still attending college. The University of Oregon and Portland State University are developing courses designed to launch the entrepreneurial ambitions of their students. **Availability:** Print; Online.

21297 ■ *"Franchises with an Eye on Chicago"* in *Crain's Chicago Business (Vol. 34, March 14, 2011, No. 11, pp. 20)*
Pub: Crain Communications Inc.
Contact: Barry Asin, President
Ed: Kevin McKeough. **Description:** Profiles of franchise companies seeking franchisees for the Chicago area include: Extreme Pita, a sandwich shop; Hand and Stone, offering massage, facial and waxing services; Molly Maid, home-cleaning service; Primrose Schools, private accredited schools for children 6 months to 6 hears and after-school programs; Protect Painters, residential and light-commercial painting contractor; and Wingstop, a restaurant offering chicken wings in nine flavors, fries and side dishes. **Availability:** Online.

21298 ■ *"Katharine Grayson: Three Questions with John Brownlee, CEO of Vidscrip.com"* in *Business Journal (Vol. 32, June 27, 2014, No. 5, pp. 6)*
Pub: American City Business Journals, Inc.
Contact: Mike Olivieri, Executive Vice President
Description: John Brownlee, CEO of vidscrip.com, discusses the Minneapolis, Minnesota startup's deal with Partners HealthCare and what it means for the business. Partners HealthCare is using the vidscrip technology to create educational videos for patients. **Availability:** Print; Online.

21299 ■ *"Open English Touted as Startup Worth Emulating"* in *South Florida Business Journal (Vol. 34, January 24, 2014, No. 27, pp. 30)*
Pub: American City Business Journals, Inc.
Contact: Mike Olivieri, Executive Vice President
Released: Weekly. **Price:** $8, Introductory 4-week offer(Digital & Print). **Description:** Open English, a language education company, received more than $150 million in investments from venture capitalists. The firm's cloud-based platform is still in its infancy, but the startup's success has shown that entrepreneurs can generate money and grow their businesses in Florida. Open English is the only online English school that offers live classes with native English-speaking teachers. **Availability:** Print; Online.

21300 ■ *"The Startup of Something Big"* in *Philadelphia Business Journal (Vol. 33, July 11, 2014, No. 22, pp. 4)*
Pub: American City Business Journals, Inc.
Contact: Mike Olivieri, Executive Vice President
Released: Weekly. **Price:** $4, Introductory 4-week offer(Digital only). **Description:** Philadelphia is slowly emerging as America's leading innovation district. The South Bank Campus is the city's game changer as University of Pennsylvania and Drexel University, along with others are seeking to harness the merging of innovation and academic pursuits that ultimately translate into new business development. **Availability:** Print; Online.

21301 ■ *"Texas State Seeks Startups"* in *Austin Business Journal (Vol. 32, April 20, 2012, No. 7, pp. 1)*
Pub: American City Business Journals, Inc.
Contact: Mike Olivieri, Executive Vice President
Ed: Sandra Zaragoza. **Description:** Texas State University is set to open a new business incubator for technology startups. The incubator will have secure wet labs, clean rooms and office space. **Availability:** Online.

21302 ■ *"UM-Dearborn to Launch Program for Entrepreneurs"* in *Crain's Detroit Business (Vol. 24, April 14, 2008, No. 15, pp. 7)*
Pub: Crain Communications Inc.
Contact: Barry Asin, President
Ed: Chad Halcom. **Description:** Starting this fall the University of Michigan-Dearborn will begin its Product Realization and Technology Commercialization Program for entrepreneurs and innovators with lab-tested, high-technology products. Ultimately, 20 businesses will each work with the university in creating a customer base, commercializing a new high-tech product or process and connecting with venture capitalists who may invest in the new companies. **Availability:** Online.

ASSOCIATIONS AND OTHER ORGANIZATIONS

21303 ■ Association to Advance Collegiate Schools of Business (AACSB) [AACSB International]
777 S Harbour Island Blvd. Ste. 750
Tampa, FL 33602
Ph: (813)769-6500
Co. E-mail: events@aacsb.edu
URL: http://www.aacsb.edu
Contact: Caryn L. Beck-Dudley, President
Facebook: www.facebook.com/AACSB
Linkedin: www.linkedin.com/company/aacsb-international
X (Twitter): x.com/aacsb
Description: Represents educational institutions, businesses, and other entities devoted to the advancement of management education. Works to advance quality management education worldwide through accreditation. **Founded:** 1916. **Publications:** *AACSB LINK* (Biweekly); *International Business Education in the 1990s: A Global Perspective* (Irregular); *Achieving Quality and Continuous Improvement Through Self-Evaluation and Peer Review* (Annual); *eNewsline* (Monthly); *Salary Survey* (Annual); *AACSB--The International Association for Management Education--Membership Directory* (Annual); *Global Salary Survey Report* (Annual); *AACSB Insights* (Bimonthly). **Educational Activities:** SITRA Technological Conference; AACSB International Conference & Annual Meeting (ICAM) (Annual). **Geographic Preference:** Multinational.

21304 ■ Association of Arts Administration Educators (AAAE)
3560 Willow Dr., APT No.115, Plover
Plover, WI 54467
Ph: (715)204-9628
Co. E-mail: hello@artsadministration.org

URL: http://artsadministration.org
Contact: Diane Claussen, President
E-mail: dclauss2@depaul.edu
Facebook: www.facebook.com/aaaeducators
Linkedin: www.linkedin.com/company/aaaeducators
X (Twitter): x.com/AAAEducators
Instagram: www.instagram.com/artsadminedu
Description: Enhances the quality of arts administration education, preparing students for careers in visual, performance, literary, media, and arts service organizations. Assesses the expansion of programmatic goals to include cooperative projects with national arts service organizations and other professional and academic groups. **Founded:** 1979. **Publications:** *Guide to Arts Administration Training and Research* (Triennial). **Geographic Preference:** National.

21305 ■ Association for Talent Development (ATD) - Library
1640 King St.
 Alexandria, VA 22313-1443
Ph: (703)683-8100
Free: 800-628-2783
Fax: (703)683-1523
Co. E-mail: customercare@td.org
URL: http://www.td.org
Contact: Tony Bingham, President
Facebook: www.facebook.com/ATD
Linkedin: www.linkedin.com/company/15989
X (Twitter): x.com/ATD
Instagram: www.instagram.com/atdnational
Pinterest: www.pinterest.com/ATDofficial
Description: Supports the talent development profession by providing trusted content in the form of research, books, webcasts, events, and education programs. **Scope:** Management; leadership. **Services:** Library open to members only. **Founded:** 1943. **Holdings:** 170 monographs; 100 books; 100 newspapers. **Publications:** *American Society Training and Development Buyer's Guide and Consultant Directory* (Annual); *Technical Training Basics*; *ASTD Buyer's Guide & Consultant Directory* (Annual); *TD at Work* (Monthly); *Learning Circuits* (Monthly); *TD Magazine* (Monthly); *Member Information Exchange (MIX)*; *TRAINET*; *ATD Buyer's Guide*; *ATD Buyer's Guide*; *American Society for Training and Development--Training Video Directory*; *Who's Who in Training and Development* (Annual). **Educational Activities:** ATD International Conference and Exposition (Annual); ATD TechKnowledge Conference (Annual); TechKnowledge Conference and Exposition (Annual). **Awards:** ATD BEST Award (Annual); Awards in the Advancing Workplace Learning and Performance; ATD Excellence in Practice Awards (Annual); Gordon M. Bliss Memorial Award (Annual); ATD Dissertation Award (Annual); ASTD Talent Development Thought Leader Award (Annual); ATD Torch Award (Annual). **Geographic Preference:** Multinational.

21306 ■ Business Professionals of America (BPA)
700 Morse Rd., Ste. 201
 Columbus, OH 43214
Ph: (614)895-7277
Fax: (614)895-1165
URL: http://www.bpa.org
Contact: Sophia Silva, President
E-mail: presidentssilva@gmail.com
Facebook: www.facebook.com/
 businessprofessionalsofamerica
Linkedin: www.linkedin.com/company/business
 -professionals-of-america
X (Twitter): x.com/National_BPA
YouTube: www.youtube.com/
 businessprofessionalsameric
Description: High school and postsecondary career and technical, business, and office education students. Seeks to develop leadership abilities, interest in the American business system, and competency in office occupations within the framework of career and technical education. Conducts projects in safety, citizenship, and economic awareness involvement. **Founded:** 1966. **Educational Activities:** Business Professionals of America National Leadership Conference (Annual). **Awards:** BPA Merit Scholar Award (Annual); BPA Recruiter of the Year Award (Annual); BPA Membership Explosion Award; BPA Social Media Award; The Professional Cup of BPA (Annual); BPA Diplomat Torch Award (Annual); BPA Statesman Torch Award (Annual); BPA Ambassador Torch Award; BPA Chapter Activities Award of Excellence; BPA Quality Chapter Distinction (Annual); BPA Marketing and Public Relations Award (Annual); BPA Executive Torch Award; National Technical Honor Society Scholarships (Annual). **Geographic Preference:** National.

21307 ■ Canadian Accredited Independent Schools (CAIS)
PO Box 56
 Jordan, ON, Canada L0R1S0
Ph: (905)684-5658
Co. E-mail: tnolan@cais.ca
URL: http://www.cais.ca
Contact: Anand Mahadevan, Executive Director
E-mail: anand@cais.ca
Linkedin: www.linkedin.com/company/canadian-accre
 dited-independent-schools-cais
X (Twitter): x.com/CAIS_Schools
Instagram: www.instagram.com/cais_schools
Description: Private schools. Promotes excellence in independent education. Represents members' interests. **Founded:** 1981. **Publications:** *Canadian Accredited Independent School--School Directory* (Biennial). **Geographic Preference:** National.

21308 ■ Canadian Federation of University Women (CFUW)
815 St Laurent Blvd, Suite 230
 Ottawa, ON, Canada K1K 3A7
Ph: (613)234-8252
Co. E-mail: memberservices@cfuw-fcfdu.ca
URL: http://www.cfuw.org
Contact: Joy Hurst, President
Facebook: www.facebook.com/cfuw.fcfdu
X (Twitter): x.com/CFUWFCFDU
Instagram: www.instagram.com/cfuwfcfdu
YouTube: www.youtube.com/channel/UC1t_06P
 1lINjxkExDamY46w
Description: Women graduates from accredited universities from around the world. Promotes continuing education for women. Fosters communication and fellowship among members. Advocates for status of women and human rights and equality rights. **Founded:** 1919. **Publications:** *The Communicator* (Periodic). **Awards:** Canadian Home Economics Association Fellowship (CHEA) (Annual); Elizabeth and Rachel Massey Award (Annual); Dr. Alice E. Wilson Awards (Annual); Beverley Jackson Fellowship (Annual); Bourse Georgette LeMoyne Award (Annual); CFUW Memorial Fellowship (Annual); CFUW Aboriginal Women's Award (Annual); Margaret Dale Philip Award (Annual); Dr. Margaret McWilliams Pre-Doctoral Fellowship (Annual); École Polytechnique Commemorative Awards (Annual). **Geographic Preference:** National.

21309 ■ *Canadian Journal of Learning and Technology*
204, 260 Dalhousie
 Ottawa, ON, Canada K1N 7E4
Ph: (613)241-0018
Fax: (613)241-0019
Co. E-mail: hello@cnie-rcie.ca
URL: http://e.cnie-rcie.ca
Contact: David Macdonald, President
URL(s): cjlt.ca/index.php/cjlt
X (Twitter): x.com/cjltrcat
Released: Semiannual **Description:** Features papers on all aspects of educational technology and learning. **Availability:** Print; PDF; Online; Download.

21310 ■ Canadian Network for Innovation in Education (CNIE) [Reseau canadien pour l'innovation en education]
204, 260 Dalhousie
 Ottawa, ON, Canada K1N 7E4
Ph: (613)241-0018
Fax: (613)241-0019
Co. E-mail: hello@cnie-rcie.ca
URL: http://e.cnie-rcie.ca
Contact: David Macdonald, President
Facebook: www.facebook.com/CNIE.RCIE
X (Twitter): x.com/cnie_rcie
YouTube: www.youtube.com/channel/
 UCIHSUimVjjpm5Q9qElBv2LQ
Description: Promotes advancement in the field of distance education. Encourages use of new technologies in distance education. **Founded:** 1983. **Publications:** *Canadian Journal of Learning and Technology (CJLT)* (3/year); *Online Learning* (Quarterly); *Canadian Journal of Learning and Technology* (Semiannual); *International Journal of E-Learning & Distance Education (IJEDE)* (Semiannual). **Awards:** CNIE Awards of Excellence (Irregular); CNIE Leadership Award (Annual). **Geographic Preference:** National.

21311 ■ A Commitment to Training and Employment for Women (ACTEW)
215 Spadina Ave., Ste. 350
 Toronto, ON, Canada M5T 2C7
Ph: (416)599-3590
Fax: (416)599-2043
Co. E-mail: info@actew.org
URL: http://www.ohrc.on.ca/zh-hant/node/8932
Description: Serves as umbrella organization of agencies, networks, and groups working on the local level to support existing education and training opportunities for women (particularly lower income, refugee, and older women). Encourages the creation of new programs. Conducts research, lobbying, and advocacy. **Geographic Preference:** National.

21312 ■ Community College Business Officers (CCBO)
PO Box 80994
 Charleston, SC 29416
Ph: (434)293-2825
Co. E-mail: info@ccbo.org
URL: http://www.ccbo.org
Contact: Chris Wodka, President
Description: Represents business officers. Works to support business officers. **Founded:** 1983. **Awards:** CCBO Exemplary Practices Award (Annual); CCBO Outstanding Business Officer and Outstanding Chief Business Officer Awards (Annual). **Geographic Preference:** National.

21313 ■ Consortium for Entrepreneurship Education
Charleston, WV
Ph: (301)859-0337
Co. E-mail: info@entre-ed.org
URL: http://www.entre-ed.org
Contact: Chad Rieflin, President
E-mail: chad@entre-ed.org
Facebook: www.facebook.com/Entrepreneurship.Ed
X (Twitter): x.com/entretalk
YouTube: www.youtube.com/channel/UCbE
 tcHfmcuOIDXyVzj_AfgA
Pinterest: www.pinterest.com/EntreEdPin
Description: Provides advocacy, leadership, networking, technical assistance, and resources nationally across all levels and disciplines of education, promoting quality practices and programs. **Founded:** 1980. **Publications:** *EntrepreNews and Views* (Quarterly). **Educational Activities:** Entrepreneurship Education FORUM (Annual). **Awards:** Entrepreneurship Education FORUM Scholarships. **Geographic Preference:** Regional.

21314 ■ Kapor Center
2148 Broadway
 Oakland, CA 94612
Ph: (510)488-6600
URL: http://www.kaporcenter.org
Contact: Allison Scott, Chief Executive Officer
Facebook: www.facebook.com/KaporCenter
Linkedin: www.linkedin.com/company/kapor-center
X (Twitter): x.com/KaporCenter
Instagram: www.instagram.com/kaporcenter
YouTube: www.youtube.com/user/KaporCenter
Description: Works to remove barriers to science, technology, engineering, and math (STEM) education and tech careers for underrepresented people of color.

GENERAL SMALL BUSINESS TOPICS   Education and Training ■ 21329

21315 ■ National Black MBA Association Inc. - Chicago Chapter
PO Box 8513
Chicago, IL 60680
Ph: (312)458-9161
Co. E-mail: partnerships@ccnbmbaa.org
URL: http://www.chicagochapternbmbaa.org
Contact: Stacy Crook, President
E-mail: scrook@ccnbmbaa.org
URL(s): nbmbaa.org/nbmbaa-chicago-chapter
Facebook: www.facebook.com/groups/chicagoblackmba
Linkedin: www.linkedin.com/company/national-black-mba-association-chicago-chapter
X (Twitter): x.com/chicagoblackmba
Instagram: www.instagram.com/nbmbaa_chicagochapter

Description: Creates educational opportunities to form professional and economic growth of African-Americans. Develops partnerships to its members and provides educational programs to increase the awareness on business field. **Founded:** 1970. **Publications:** *National Black MBA Association-Newsletter*, *Black MBA* (Semiannual). **Educational Activities:** NBMBAA Annual Conference and Exposition (Annual). **Awards:** CEIBS scholarship (Annual). **Geographic Preference:** Local; National.

21316 ■ National Business Education Association (NBEA)
1908 Association Dr., Ste. B
Reston, VA 20191
Ph: (703)860-8300
Fax: (703)620-4483
Co. E-mail: nbea@nbea.org
URL: http://nbea.org/?
Contact: Lori Hauf, President
Facebook: www.facebook.com/NBEAofficial
X (Twitter): x.com/NBEA

Description: Teachers of business in secondary and postsecondary schools and colleges; administrators and researchers; businesspersons interested in business education. Offers training, job listings, and the National Business Honor Society. **Founded:** 1892. **Publications:** *Journal of Applied Research in Business Instruction (JARBI)*; *National Business Education Yearbook* (Annual); *Keying In* (Quarterly); *NBEA Yearbook* (Annual); *Business Education Forum-- Professional Leadership Roster Issue* (Quarterly); *Business Education Forum: Official Publication of the National Business Education Association* (Quarterly). **Educational Activities:** National Business Education Association Convention (Annual). **Awards:** Distinguished Service Award for Outstanding Contribution to Business Education by an Administrator or Supervisor of Business Education (Annual); NBEA College/University Teacher of the Year (Annual); NBEA Distinguished Service Award for Outstanding Contribution to Business Education by an Administrator or Supervisor of Business Education (Annual); The John Robert Gregg Award (Annual); NBEA Post-Secondary Teacher of the Year (Annual); NBEA Middle School/Secondary Business Teacher of the Year Award (Annual). **Geographic Preference:** National.

21317 ■ Nitem Foundation
15, 1527 Sofia center
Sofia, Bulgaria
Ph: 359 2 943 19 99
Co. E-mail: office@nitem-bg.com
URL: http://www.nitem-bg.com
Facebook: www.facebook.com/NitemCompany
X (Twitter): x.com/NitemBG

Description: A not-for-profit organization that commits its resources to address issues of global social and environmental concern, particularly those that have a major impact and changing through education and support entrepreneurship. **Founded:** 2002.

21318 ■ *Online Learning*
204, 260 Dalhousie
Ottawa, ON, Canada K1N 7E4
Ph: (613)241-0018
Fax: (613)241-0019
Co. E-mail: hello@cnie-rcie.ca
URL: http://e.cnie-rcie.ca

Contact: David Macdonald, President
URL(s): olj.onlinelearningconsortium.org/index.php/olj/index
Released: Quarterly **Description:** Journal for practitioners in online education. Covers excellent research in online learning. **Availability:** PDF; Download; Online.

EDUCATIONAL PROGRAMS

21319 ■ ACCS - Advanced Cisco Campus Switching (Onsite)
Seminar Information Service Inc. (SIS)
250 El Camino Real., Ste. 112
Tustin, CA 92780
Ph: (714)508-0340
Free: 877-736-4636
Fax: (714)734-8027
Co. E-mail: info@seminarinformation.com
URL: http://www.seminarinformation.com
Contact: Catherine Bellizzi, President
URL(s): www.seminarinformation.com

Description: Covers Catalyst 6000 Series Architecture; Catalyst 2948G-L3 Configuration; Layer 2 and Layer3 Forwarding; Switching Quality of Service Fundamentals and Configuration; Dynamic and Private VLANs; VLAN Access Control Lists; MLS and CEF Operation; High Availability Options for the 6000 Series; FlexWAN Configuration and Operation; and Catalyst 6000 Hybrid to Native IOS Conversion. **Audience:** Professionals. **Principal Exhibits:** Covers Catalyst 6000 Series Architecture; Catalyst 2948G-L3 Configuration; Layer 2 and Layer3 Forwarding; Switching Quality of Service Fundamentals and Configuration; Dynamic and Private VLANs; VLAN Access Control Lists; MLS and CEF Operation; High Availability Options for the 6000 Series; FlexWAN Configuration and Operation; and Catalyst 6000 Hybrid to Native IOS Conversion.

21320 ■ Adobe Acrobat I (Onsite)
URL(s): www.eeicom.com

Description: Covers creating PDF documents, including using hyperlinks, bookmarks, sound clips, and security. **Audience:** Industry professionals. **Principal Exhibits:** Covers creating PDF documents, including using hyperlinks, bookmarks, sound clips, and security.

21321 ■ Adobe After Effects I (Onsite)
URL(s): www.eeicom.com

Description: Covers using After Effects to create digital composites, smooth 2-D animations, and elaborate special effects. **Audience:** Industry professionals. **Principal Exhibits:** Covers using After Effects to create digital composites, smooth 2-D animations, and elaborate special effects.

21322 ■ Adobe FrameMaker I (Onsite)
URL(s): www.eeicom.com

Description: Covers paragraph designs, color use, graphics, headers and footers, tables, and advanced editing techniques. **Audience:** Industry professionals. **Principal Exhibits:** Covers paragraph designs, color use, graphics, headers and footers, tables, and advanced editing techniques.

21323 ■ Adobe FrameMaker II (Onsite)
URL(s): www.eeicom.com

Description: Covers cross-references, footnotes, creating a book file, hyperlinks, and exporting to HTML and PDF. **Audience:** Industry professionals. **Principal Exhibits:** Covers cross-references, footnotes, creating a book file, hyperlinks, and exporting to HTML and PDF.

21324 ■ Adobe Illustrator I (Onsite)
URL(s): www.eeicom.com

Description: Covers basic graphic design features, including creating geometric shapes and free forms, using type, creating graphs, and using the manipulation tools. **Audience:** Industry professionals. **Principal Exhibits:** Covers basic graphic design features, including creating geometric shapes and free forms, using type, creating graphs, and using the manipulation tools.

21325 ■ Adobe Illustrator II (Onsite)
URL(s): www.eeicom.com

Description: Covers some advanced features of Illustrator, including custom brush patterns, blending modes, effects and styles, and image maps. **Audience:** Industry professionals. **Principal Exhibits:** Covers some advanced features of Illustrator, including custom brush patterns, blending modes, effects and styles, and image maps.

21326 ■ Adobe Illustrator III (Onsite)
URL(s): www.eeicom.com

Description: Covers one- and two-point perspective, shadows, geometric depth, and masking and pathfinders. **Audience:** Industry professionals. **Principal Exhibits:** Covers one- and two-point perspective, shadows, geometric depth, and masking and pathfinders.

21327 ■ Adobe InDesign CS4 Master Class for Designers Training (Onsite)
URL(s): www.eeicom.com

Description: Master Adobe InDesign CS4's styles, text processing capabilities, table-creation tools, automation features, and in-document creativity enhancements to free up countless hours from smaller tasks and concentrate on designing. **Audience:** Designers. **Principal Exhibits:** Master Adobe InDesign CS4's styles, text processing capabilities, table-creation tools, automation features, and in-document creativity enhancements to free up countless hours from smaller tasks and concentrate on designing.

21328 ■ Adobe InDesign with InCopy for Workgroups Training (Onsite)
URL(s): www.eeicom.com

Description: Learn a professional writing and editing program that tightly integrates with Adobe InDesign for a complete solution, including assigning editors to work on parts of pages, spreads, or entire documents in parallel with designers, significantly decreasing the production time for projects. **Audience:** Industry professionals. **Principal Exhibits:** Learn a professional writing and editing program that tightly integrates with Adobe InDesign for a complete solution, including assigning editors to work on parts of pages, spreads, or entire documents in parallel with designers, significantly decreasing the production time for projects.

21329 ■ Advanced PC Configuration, Troubleshooting and Data Recovery: Hands-On (Onsite)
Seminar Information Service Inc. (SIS)
250 El Camino Real., Ste. 112
Tustin, CA 92780
Ph: (714)508-0340
Free: 877-736-4636
Fax: (714)734-8027
Co. E-mail: info@seminarinformation.com
URL: http://www.seminarinformation.com
Contact: Catherine Bellizzi, President
URL(s): www.seminarinformation.com

Description: Learn how to: Recover lost files and directories; Revive non-bootable floppies and hard disks; Create emergency rescue disks to recover crashed Windows systems; Detect, isolate and contain damage from virus programs; Create full disk images for complete backups; Remove unwanted start-up programs from the Registry; Examine system status with Windows XP Computer Management tools; Install and configure a simple TCP/IP network. **Audience:** Industry professionals. **Principal Exhibits:** Learn how to: Recover lost files and directories; Revive non-bootable floppies and hard disks; Create emergency rescue disks to recover crashed Windows systems; Detect, isolate and contain damage from virus programs; Create full disk images for complete backups; Remove unwanted start-up programs from the Registry; Examine system status with Windows XP Computer Management tools; Install and configure a simple TCP/IP network.

21330 ■ Advertising Research (Onsite)
Seminar Information Service Inc. (SIS)
　250 El Camino Real., Ste. 112
　Tustin, CA 92780
Ph: (714)508-0340
Free: 877-736-4636
Fax: (714)734-8027
Co. E-mail: info@seminarinformation.com
URL: http://www.seminarinformation.com
Contact: Catherine Bellizzi, President
URL(s): www.seminarinformation.com

Description: Provides a practical and a comprehensive framework for classifying various advertising research methods based on what they measure, how they measure it and how good they are at it. Participants will be able to evaluate and select among the numerous procedures used in practice to facilitate key advertising decisions. **Audience:** Industry professionals. **Principal Exhibits:** Provides a practical and a comprehensive framework for classifying various advertising research methods based on what they measure, how they measure it and how good they are at it. Participants will be able to evaluate and select among the numerous procedures used in practice to facilitate key advertising decisions.

21331 ■ Air Conditioning & Refrigeration (Onsite)
TPC Trainco Inc.
　225 E Robinson St., Ste. 570
　Orlando, FL 32801
Free: 877-978-7246
Co. E-mail: sales@tpctraining.com
URL: http://live.tpctraining.com
URL(s): live.tpctraining.com/public-seminars/hvac-training/air-conditioning-refrigeration

Description: Course designed for anyone who needs to understand basic operation, maintenance, and troubleshooting of air conditioning and refrigeration systems in order to improve efficiencies and uptime at their industrial plants and large building facilities. **Audience:** Industry professionals. **Principal Exhibits:** Course designed for anyone who needs to understand basic operation, maintenance, and troubleshooting of air conditioning and refrigeration systems in order to improve efficiencies and uptime at their industrial plants and large building facilities.

21332 ■ AMA's PMP Exam Prep Express (Onsite)
American Management Association (AMA)
　1601 Broadway
　New York, NY 10019
Ph: (212)586-8100
Free: 800-262-9699
Fax: (212)903-8168
Co. E-mail: customerservice@amanet.org
URL: http://www.amanet.org
Contact: Manny Avramidis, President
URL(s): www.amanet.org/training/seminars/onsite/pmp-exam-prep-express.aspx

Price: $2,445, Non-members; $2,195, Members AMA; $1,889, Members GSA. **Description:** Three-day seminar to increase the probability of obtaining your PMP. **Audience:** Project managers, program managers, and project team leaders. **Principal Exhibits:** Three-day seminar to increase the probability of obtaining your PMP.

21333 ■ Arc Flash Protection & Electrical Safety 70E
TPC Trainco Inc.
　225 E Robinson St., Ste. 570
　Orlando, FL 32801
Free: 877-978-7246
Co. E-mail: sales@tpctraining.com
URL: http://live.tpctraining.com
URL(s): live.tpctraining.com/public-seminars/electrical-training/fundamentals/arc-flash-electrical-safety-nfpa-70e

Description: Training course designed to save lives, prevent disabling injuries, and prevent damage to plants, buildings and equipment. Participants learn about personal safety for working on or around electrical systems and equipment, how to use proper materials and procedures for doing electrical work, and the potential consequences for themselves and others if they don't. **Audience:** Electricians, maintenance supervisors, and machine operators. **Principal Exhibits:** Training course designed to save lives, prevent disabling injuries, and prevent damage to plants, buildings and equipment. Participants learn about personal safety for working on or around electrical systems and equipment, how to use proper materials and procedures for doing electrical work, and the potential consequences for themselves and others if they don't.

21334 ■ Assertiveness Training (Onsite)
URL(s): www.amanet.org/assertiveness-training

Price: $2,345, Non-members; $2,095, Members AMA; $1,889, Members GSA. **Description:** Three-day seminar to enhance your assertiveness skills at all levels in the organization. **Audience:** Associates, business professionals, team leaders and individual contributors. **Principal Exhibits:** Three-day seminar to enhance your assertiveness skills at all levels in the organization.

21335 ■ Basic Electricity for the Non Electrician (Onsite)
TPC Trainco Inc.
　225 E Robinson St., Ste. 570
　Orlando, FL 32801
Free: 877-978-7246
Co. E-mail: sales@tpctraining.com
URL: http://live.tpctraining.com
URL(s): live.tpctraining.com/public-seminars/electrical-training/fundamentals/basic-electrical-training

Description: Understanding and working with industrial electricity. **Audience:** Mechanics, HVAC technicians, and machine operators. **Principal Exhibits:** Understanding and working with industrial electricity.

21336 ■ Basic Problem Solving Techniques (Onsite)
Seminar Information Service Inc. (SIS)
　250 El Camino Real., Ste. 112
　Tustin, CA 92780
Ph: (714)508-0340
Free: 877-736-4636
Fax: (714)734-8027
Co. E-mail: info@seminarinformation.com
URL: http://www.seminarinformation.com
Contact: Catherine Bellizzi, President
URL(s): www.seminarinformation.com

Description: With the help of several qualitative, quantitative, and creative problem solving methods participants develop their ability to recognize and solve problems through their own efforts. **Audience:** Managers, and professionals. **Principal Exhibits:** With the help of several qualitative, quantitative, and creative problem solving methods participants develop their ability to recognize and solve problems through their own efforts.

21337 ■ Basics of Commercial Contracting (Onsite)
Seminar Information Service Inc. (SIS)
　250 El Camino Real., Ste. 112
　Tustin, CA 92780
Ph: (714)508-0340
Free: 877-736-4636
Fax: (714)734-8027
Co. E-mail: info@seminarinformation.com
URL: http://www.seminarinformation.com
Contact: Catherine Bellizzi, President
URL(s): www.seminarinformation.com/qqbaqm/basics-of-commercial-contracting

Description: Learn the key practical and legal principles applicable to business dealings, as well as a thorough understanding of the Uniform Commercial Code (UCC). **Audience:** Business industry professionals. **Principal Exhibits:** Learn the key practical and legal principles applicable to business dealings, as well as a thorough understanding of the Uniform Commercial Code (UCC).

21338 ■ Best Practices in Java Programming: Hands-On (Onsite)
Seminar Information Service Inc. (SIS)
　250 El Camino Real., Ste. 112
　Tustin, CA 92780
Ph: (714)508-0340
Free: 877-736-4636
Fax: (714)734-8027
Co. E-mail: info@seminarinformation.com
URL: http://www.seminarinformation.com
Contact: Catherine Bellizzi, President
URL(s): www.seminarinformation.com/qqbtlg/best-practices-in-java-programming-hands-on

Description: Learn how to: Apply Java best practices to increase productivity and build fast, secure and reliable applications; Optimize the compilation, deployment and testing of software applications; Solve architectural problems with proven design patterns and advanced language features; Code securely in Java and authenticate with industry-standard security frameworks; Maximize software performance; Improve the reliability of threaded applications; Extend application functionality non-intrusively. **Audience:** Developers, architects and java programmers. **Principal Exhibits:** Learn how to: Apply Java best practices to increase productivity and build fast, secure and reliable applications; Optimize the compilation, deployment and testing of software applications; Solve architectural problems with proven design patterns and advanced language features; Code securely in Java and authenticate with industry-standard security frameworks; Maximize software performance; Improve the reliability of threaded applications; Extend application functionality non-intrusively. **Telecommunication Services:** info@seminarinformation.com.

21339 ■ Boiler Operation, Maintenance & Safety (Onsite)
TPC Trainco Inc.
　225 E Robinson St., Ste. 570
　Orlando, FL 32801
Free: 877-978-7246
Co. E-mail: sales@tpctraining.com
URL: http://live.tpctraining.com
URL(s): live.tpctraining.com/public-seminars/hvac-training/boiler-operation-maintenance-safety-training

Description: Seminar designed to teach building and facility maintenance personnel how to service their own boiler safely reducing the need for outside service contractors, while at the same time increases your confidence and comfort level in operating and maintaining your own broilers. **Audience:** Building maintenance personnel, technicians and engineers . **Principal Exhibits:** Seminar designed to teach building and facility maintenance personnel how to service their own boiler safely reducing the need for outside service contractors, while at the same time increases your confidence and comfort level in operating and maintaining your own broilers.

21340 ■ Building Applications with Microsoft Access 2007: Hands-On (Onsite)
Seminar Information Service Inc. (SIS)
　250 El Camino Real., Ste. 112
　Tustin, CA 92780
Ph: (714)508-0340
Free: 877-736-4636
Fax: (714)734-8027
Co. E-mail: info@seminarinformation.com
URL: http://www.seminarinformation.com
Contact: Catherine Bellizzi, President
URL(s): www.seminarinformation.com/details.cfm?qc=qqbtnb

Description: Learn how to: Develop distributable applications with Microsoft Access 2007; Incorporate user specifications to enhance application functionality; Customize applications by dynamically setting properties and executing methods; Assemble expressions into VBA statements using variables and intrinsic functions; Control program flow with loops and decision-making logic; Apply Data Access Objects (DAO) to incorporate business rules; Centralize the error handling process. **Audience:** Industry professionals. **Principal Exhibits:** Learn how to: Develop distributable applications with Microsoft Access 2007; Incorporate user specifications to enhance application functionality; Customize applications by dynamically setting properties and executing methods; Assemble expressions into VBA statements using variables and intrinsic functions; Control program flow with loops and decision-making logic; Apply Data Access Objects (DAO) to incorporate business rules; Centralize the error handling process.

21341 ■ Business Process Reengineering for Competitive Advantage (Onsite)
Seminar Information Service Inc. (SIS)
 250 El Camino Real., Ste. 112
 Tustin, CA 92780
Ph: (714)508-0340
Free: 877-736-4636
Fax: (714)734-8027
Co. E-mail: info@seminarinformation.com
URL: http://www.seminarinformation.com
Contact: Catherine Bellizzi, President
URL(s): www.seminarinformation.com

Description: Learn how to: Select, organize and implement a business reengineering project using CLAMBRE/UML; Achieve competitive advantage by capitalizing on technology opportunities and the application of UML tools; Maximize customer satisfaction by matching process design to customer needs; Identify typical symptoms of business process dysfunction; Redesign workflow and structure successfully within the business; Ensure best practice through the application of business patterns. **Audience:** Industry professionals. **Principal Exhibits:** Learn how to: Select, organize and implement a business reengineering project using CLAMBRE/UML; Achieve competitive advantage by capitalizing on technology opportunities and the application of UML tools; Maximize customer satisfaction by matching process design to customer needs; Identify typical symptoms of business process dysfunction; Redesign workflow and structure successfully within the business; Ensure best practice through the application of business patterns.

21342 ■ C Programming: Hands-On (Onsite)
Seminar Information Service Inc. (SIS)
 250 El Camino Real., Ste. 112
 Tustin, CA 92780
Ph: (714)508-0340
Free: 877-736-4636
Fax: (714)734-8027
Co. E-mail: info@seminarinformation.com
URL: http://www.seminarinformation.com
Contact: Catherine Bellizzi, President
URL(s): www.seminarinformation.com/qqbtkn/c-programming-hands-on

Description: Learn how to create, compile and run C programs using Visual Studio 2005; write and understand C language constructs, syntax and classes; leverage the architecture and namespaces of the .NET Framework library; manage the common language infrastructure (CLI) to integrate C with Visual Basic 2005 and C; develop .NET components in C for desktop and distributed multi-tier applications. **Audience:** C programmers, developers and engineers. **Principal Exhibits:** Learn how to create, compile and run C programs using Visual Studio 2005; write and understand C language constructs, syntax and classes; leverage the architecture and namespaces of the .NET Framework library; manage the common language infrastructure (CLI) to integrate C with Visual Basic 2005 and C; develop .NET components in C for desktop and distributed multi-tier applications.

21343 ■ C++ Programming for Non-C Programmers (Onsite)
Seminar Information Service Inc. (SIS)
 250 El Camino Real., Ste. 112
 Tustin, CA 92780
Ph: (714)508-0340
Free: 877-736-4636
Fax: (714)734-8027
Co. E-mail: info@seminarinformation.com
URL: http://www.seminarinformation.com
Contact: Catherine Bellizzi, President
URL(s): www.seminarinformation.com/qqbvuh/c++-programming-for-non-c-programmers

Description: Provides an accelerated introduction to the most essential components of the C language on the first day, followed by four days focus on object-oriented programming with C. **Audience:** Programmers. **Principal Exhibits:** Provides an accelerated introduction to the most essential components of the C language on the first day, followed by four days focus on object-oriented programming with C.

21344 ■ Certified Ethical Hacker (Onsite)
Seminar Information Service Inc. (SIS)
 250 El Camino Real., Ste. 112
 Tustin, CA 92780
Ph: (714)508-0340
Free: 877-736-4636
Fax: (714)734-8027
Co. E-mail: info@seminarinformation.com
URL: http://www.seminarinformation.com
Contact: Catherine Bellizzi, President
URL(s): ww.seminarinformation.com

Description: Learn to footprint organizations, perform port scanning, and exploit a variety of systems and architectures, including hands-on labs. You'll also receive the CEH study guide, Certified Ethical Hacker Exam Prep, CDs packed with security tools, templates, and white papers, practice exam questions, and an exam voucher. **Audience:** Security consultants, auditors, and firewall/IDS personnel. **Principal Exhibits:** Learn to footprint organizations, perform port scanning, and exploit a variety of systems and architectures, including hands-on labs. You'll also receive the CEH study guide, Certified Ethical Hacker Exam Prep, CDs packed with security tools, templates, and white papers, practice exam questions, and an exam voucher.

21345 ■ Chilled Water Systems (Onsite)
TPC Trainco Inc.
 225 E Robinson St., Ste. 570
 Orlando, FL 32801
Free: 877-978-7246
Co. E-mail: sales@tpctraining.com
URL: http://live.tpctraining.com
URL(s): live.tpctraining.com/public-seminars/hvac-training/chilled-water-systems

Description: Learn to control your systems and properly maintain them, getting the most out of them. **Audience:** Students. **Principal Exhibits:** Learn to control your systems and properly maintain them, getting the most out of them.

21346 ■ CMC The Project Planning Workshop
URL(s): www.cmcoutperform.com

Description: Two-day seminar covers the applicable tools, templates and proven practices to plan real life work projects. **Audience:** Project managers. **Principal Exhibits:** Two-day seminar covers the applicable tools, templates and proven practices to plan real life work projects.

21347 ■ Creative Problem Solving and Strategic Thinking (Onsite)
URL(s): www.pryor.com

Description: Learn an innovative approach to problem solving. **Audience:** Professionals. **Principal Exhibits:** Learn an innovative approach to problem solving.

21348 ■ Critical Thinking Skills-Strategic Planning in Action (Onsite)
Seminar Information Service Inc. (SIS)
 250 El Camino Real., Ste. 112
 Tustin, CA 92780
Ph: (714)508-0340
Free: 877-736-4636
Fax: (714)734-8027
Co. E-mail: info@seminarinformation.com
URL: http://www.seminarinformation.com
Contact: Catherine Bellizzi, President
URL(s): www.seminarinformation.com

Description: Seminar provides participants with tools, techniques and the critical thinking skills to identify their critical measures of success, the requirements of internal and external customers, including the strengths and weaknesses of their staff. **Audience:** Experienced managers, and supervisors . **Principal Exhibits:** Seminar provides participants with tools, techniques and the critical thinking skills to identify their critical measures of success, the requirements of internal and external customers, including the strengths and weaknesses of their staff.

21349 ■ Dealing with Competing Demands
URL(s): cmcoutperform.com/files/CMC%20Fall%20Catalogue%202011.pdf

Description: Covers the skills necessary to manage your objectives with success, including prioritizing, realistic objectives, effective use of communication to meet your goals, and utilize control stress. **Audience:** All professionals. **Principal Exhibits:** Covers the skills necessary to manage your objectives with success, including prioritizing, realistic objectives, effective use of communication to meet your goals, and utilize control stress. **Telecommunication Services:** cmcinfo@cmcoutperform.com

21350 ■ Defending Windows Networks (Onsite)
Seminar Information Service Inc. (SIS)
 250 El Camino Real., Ste. 112
 Tustin, CA 92780
Ph: (714)508-0340
Free: 877-736-4636
Fax: (714)734-8027
Co. E-mail: info@seminarinformation.com
URL: http://www.seminarinformation.com
Contact: Catherine Bellizzi, President
URL(s): www.seminarinformation.com

Description: Lab-intensive to illustrate defense techniques against real-world threats, instead of simply addressing software security features, including how attacks are performed, how they can compromise a Windows Server Network Infrastructure, and how you can lock down the network. **Audience:** IT professionals, business industry professionals. **Principal Exhibits:** Lab-intensive to illustrate defense techniques against real-world threats, instead of simply addressing software security features, including how attacks are performed, how they can compromise a Windows Server Network Infrastructure, and how you can lock down the network.

21351 ■ Deploying Intrusion Detection Systems: Hands-On (Onsite)
Seminar Information Service Inc. (SIS)
 250 El Camino Real., Ste. 112
 Tustin, CA 92780
Ph: (714)508-0340
Free: 877-736-4636
Fax: (714)734-8027
Co. E-mail: info@seminarinformation.com
URL: http://www.seminarinformation.com
Contact: Catherine Bellizzi, President
URL(s): www.seminarinformation.com

Description: Learn how to: Detect and respond to network- and host-based intruder attacks; Integrate intrusion detection systems (IDS) into your current network topology; Analyze IDS alerts using the latest tools and techniques; Identify methods hackers use to attack systems; Recognize detection avoidance schemes; Stop attackers with Intrusion Prevention Systems (IPSs). **Audience:** Industry professionals. **Principal Exhibits:** Learn how to: Detect and respond to network- and host-based intruder attacks; Integrate intrusion detection systems (IDS) into your current network topology; Analyze IDS alerts using the latest tools and techniques; Identify methods hackers use to attack systems; Recognize detection avoidance schemes; Stop attackers with Intrusion Prevention Systems (IPSs).

21352 ■ Deploying Virtual Server and Workstation Technology: Hands-On (Onsite)
Seminar Information Service Inc. (SIS)
 250 El Camino Real., Ste. 112
 Tustin, CA 92780
Ph: (714)508-0340
Free: 877-736-4636
Fax: (714)734-8027
Co. E-mail: info@seminarinformation.com
URL: http://www.seminarinformation.com
Contact: Catherine Bellizzi, President
URL(s): www.seminarinformation.com

Description: Learn how to: Implement VMware and Microsoft virtual machine (VM) technologies; Combine Windows and Linux workstations and servers on a single platform; Leverage VMs to build testing, support and training environments; Partition physical servers to decrease operating costs; Migrate from physical to virtual machines; Manage VMs throughout the enterprise. **Audience:** Industry professionals. **Principal Exhibits:** Learn how to: Implement VMware and Microsoft virtual machine (VM) technologies; Combine Windows and Linux workstations and servers on a single platform; Leverage VMs to build testing, support and training environments; Partition physical servers to decrease operating costs; Migrate from physical to virtual machines; Manage VMs throughout the enterprise.

21353 ■ Designing and Building Great Web Pages: Hands-On (Onsite)
Seminar Information Service Inc. (SIS)
  250 El Camino Real., Ste. 112
  Tustin, CA 92780
Ph: (714)508-0340
Free: 877-736-4636
Fax: (714)734-8027
Co. E-mail: info@seminarinformation.com
URL: http://www.seminarinformation.com
Contact: Catherine Bellizzi, President
URL(s): www.seminarinformation.com

Description: Learn to build powerful Web content that effectively conveys your message; Create graphical content using Photoshop CS2, Fireworks 8 and Flash 8; Develop Web page content with FrontPage and Dreamweaver 8; Generate complex Web pages using Cascading Style Sheets, tables and layers; and Enhance Web pages with special effects and DHTML. **Audience:** IT professionals, designing and building web industry professionals. **Principal Exhibits:** Learn to build powerful Web content that effectively conveys your message; Create graphical content using Photoshop CS2, Fireworks 8 and Flash 8; Develop Web page content with FrontPage and Dreamweaver 8; Generate complex Web pages using Cascading Style Sheets, tables and layers; and Enhance Web pages with special effects and DHTML.

21354 ■ Developing Effective Software Estimation Techniques (Onsite)
Seminar Information Service Inc. (SIS)
  250 El Camino Real., Ste. 112
  Tustin, CA 92780
Ph: (714)508-0340
Free: 877-736-4636
Fax: (714)734-8027
Co. E-mail: info@seminarinformation.com
URL: http://www.seminarinformation.com
Contact: Catherine Bellizzi, President
URL(s): www.seminarinformation.com

Description: Learn how to prepare a software project estimate through an iterative process; Develop an initial estimate using the expert judgment method; Apply historical data for greater precision in an estimate; Refine the size or scope estimate using a component-based method; Perform Function Point calculations to determine the magnitude of a project; Translate a size or scope estimate into a time, schedule and cost estimate. **Audience:** Industry professionals, IT. **Principal Exhibits:** Learn how to prepare a software project estimate through an iterative process; Develop an initial estimate using the expert judgment method; Apply historical data for greater precision in an estimate; Refine the size or scope estimate using a component-based method; Perform Function Point calculations to determine the magnitude of a project; Translate a size or scope estimate into a time, schedule and cost estimate.

21355 ■ Developing Effective Training
Seminar Information Service Inc. (SIS)
  250 El Camino Real., Ste. 112
  Tustin, CA 92780
Ph: (714)508-0340
Free: 877-736-4636
Fax: (714)734-8027
Co. E-mail: info@seminarinformation.com
URL: http://www.seminarinformation.com
Contact: Catherine Bellizzi, President
URL(s): www.seminarinformation.com

Description: Provides less experienced trainers with an overview of the training process and shows them how to make each element yield effective learning results. **Audience:** Industry professionals. **Principal Exhibits:** Provides less experienced trainers with an overview of the training process and shows them how to make each element yield effective learning results.

21356 ■ Developing SQL Queries for SQL Server: Hands-On (Onsite)
Seminar Information Service Inc. (SIS)
  250 El Camino Real., Ste. 112
  Tustin, CA 92780
Ph: (714)508-0340
Free: 877-736-4636
Fax: (714)734-8027
Co. E-mail: info@seminarinformation.com
URL: http://www.seminarinformation.com
Contact: Catherine Bellizzi, President
URL(s): www.seminarinformation.com/qqbtlv/developing-sql-queries-for-sql-server-hands-on

Description: Learn how to develop complex and robust SQL queries for SQL Server 2005 and SQL Server 2000; Query multiple tables with inner joins, outer joins and self joins; Transform data with built-in functions; Summarize data using aggregation and grouping; Execute analytic functions to calculate ranks; Build simple and correlated sub-queries. **Audience:** Those who are developing systems using SQL Server databases, or who are using SQL to extract and analyze data from SQL Server databases. **Principal Exhibits:** Learn how to develop complex and robust SQL queries for SQL Server 2005 and SQL Server 2000; Query multiple tables with inner joins, outer joins and self joins; Transform data with built-in functions; Summarize data using aggregation and grouping; Execute analytic functions to calculate ranks; Build simple and correlated sub-queries.

21357 ■ Digital Photography Techniques (Onsite)
URL(s): www.eeicom.com

Description: Covers using a digital camera, and manipulating digital pictures with Photoshop. **Audience:** Industry professionals. **Principal Exhibits:** Covers using a digital camera, and manipulating digital pictures with Photoshop.

21358 ■ EEI Communications Adobe Director I

Description: Covers how to create interactive training applications, electronic marketing pieces, and presentations utilizing Macromedia Director. **Audience:** Industry professionals. **Principal Exhibits:** Covers how to create interactive training applications, electronic marketing pieces, and presentations utilizing Macromedia Director. **Telecommunication Services:** train@eeicom.com.

21359 ■ EEI Communications Adobe Director II
URL(s): www.eeicom.com

Description: Seminar introduces Lingo, Director's programming language. **Audience:** Industry professionals. **Principal Exhibits:** Seminar introduces Lingo, Director's programming language. **Telecommunication Services:** train@eeicom.com.

21360 ■ EEI Communications Adobe Flash I (Onsite)
URL(s): www.eeicom.com

Description: Covers the basics of Flash including creating animation on the Web that downloads fast and takes up less file space. **Audience:** Adobe flash users and industry professionals. **Principal Exhibits:** Covers the basics of Flash including creating animation on the Web that downloads fast and takes up less file space. **Telecommunication Services:** train@eeicom.com.

21361 ■ EEI Communications Adobe Flash II (Onsite)
URL(s): www.eeicom.com

Description: Covers advanced techniques including planning, organizing, and creating a Flash project. **Audience:** Adobe flash users and industry professionals. **Principal Exhibits:** Covers advanced techniques including planning, organizing, and creating a Flash project. **Telecommunication Services:** train@eeicom.com.

21362 ■ EEI Communications Adobe InDesign I (Onsite)
URL(s): www.eeicom.com

Description: Covers basic techniques for creating graphic-intensive documents including editing master pages, placeholder frames, applying color, and flowing and threading text. **Audience:** Adobe InDesign users and industry professionals. **Principal Exhibits:** Covers basic techniques for creating graphic-intensive documents including editing master pages, placeholder frames, applying color, and flowing and threading text. **Telecommunication Services:** train@eeicom.com.

21363 ■ EEI Communications Adobe InDesign II (Onsite)
URL(s): www.eeicom.com

Description: Covers techniques for creating graphic-intensive documents including typography, decorative and special font features, exporting documents, importing and linking graphics, drawing straight and curved segments, and advanced frame techniques. **Audience:** Adobe InDesign users and industry professionals. **Principal Exhibits:** Covers techniques for creating graphic-intensive documents including typography, decorative and special font features, exporting documents, importing and linking graphics, drawing straight and curved segments, and advanced frame techniques. **Telecommunication Services:** info@eeicom.com.

21364 ■ EEI Communications Adobe Photoshop I (Onsite)
URL(s): www.eeicom.com

Description: Covers the basic photo manipulation features of Photoshop. **Audience:** Adobe photoshop users and industry professionals. **Principal Exhibits:** Covers the basic photo manipulation features of Photoshop. **Telecommunication Services:** train@eeicom.com.

21365 ■ EEI Communications Adobe Photoshop II (Onsite)
URL(s): www.eeicom.com

Description: Covers intermediate techniques including channel and masking, paths, layering, spot techniques, proper file formatting, and gamuts and color transition issues. **Audience:** Adobe photoshop users and industry professionals. **Principal Exhibits:** Covers intermediate techniques including channel and masking, paths, layering, spot techniques, proper file formatting, and gamuts and color transition issues. **Telecommunication Services:** train@eeicom.com.

21366 ■ EEI Communications Adobe Photoshop III: Tips and Tricks (Onsite)
URL(s): www.eeicom.com

Description: Covers advanced Photoshop techniques and effects. **Audience:** Adobe photoshop users and industry professionals. **Principal Exhibits:** Covers advanced Photoshop techniques and effects. **Telecommunication Services:** train@eeicom.com.

21367 ■ EEI Communications Adobe Premiere I (Onsite)
URL(s): www.eeicom.com

Description: Covers an introduction to video capture and video editing utilizing Premiere. **Audience:** Industry professionals. **Principal Exhibits:** Covers an introduction to video capture and video editing utilizing Premiere. **Telecommunication Services:** train@eeicom.com.

21368 ■ EEI Communications Advanced Grammar Roundtable (Onsite)
EEI Communications
  66 Canal Center Plz., Ste. 200
  Alexandria, VA 22314

Ph: (703)683-0683
Fax: (703)683-4915
Co. E-mail: info@eeicommunications.com
URL: http://eei-alex.com
URL(s): www.eeicom.com
Description: Discuss various philosophies about grammar, the origins of grammar rules and the case against "rule-based" grammar, diagram sentences, review grammar concepts as needed, examine particles, determiners and interrupters, examine the difference between an absolute phrase and a descriptive one. **Audience:** Industry professionals. **Principal Exhibits:** Discuss various philosophies about grammar, the origins of grammar rules and the case against "rule-based" grammar, diagram sentences, review grammar concepts as needed, examine particles, determiners and interrupters, examine the difference between an absolute phrase and a descriptive one.

21369 ▪ EEI Communications Introduction to Windows
URL(s): www.eeicom.com
Description: Covers introduction to the PC and the basics of Windows. **Audience:** Industry professionals. **Principal Exhibits:** Covers introduction to the PC and the basics of Windows. **Telecommunication Services:** train@eeicom.com.

21370 ▪ EEI Communications Macromedia Authorware I
URL(s): www.eeicom.com
Description: Covers how to utilize Authorware to develop presentations, quizzes, interactive hypertext, Help systems, and glossaries. **Audience:** Industry professionals. **Principal Exhibits:** Covers how to utilize Authorware to develop presentations, quizzes, interactive hypertext, Help systems, and glossaries. **Telecommunication Services:** train@eeicom.com.

21371 ▪ EEI Communications Microsoft Access 2007 - I (Onsite)
URL(s): www.eeicom.com
Description: Covers basic database concepts using Access. **Audience:** Microsoft Access users and industry professionals. **Principal Exhibits:** Covers basic database concepts using Access. **Telecommunication Services:** train@eeicom.com.

21372 ▪ EEI Communications Microsoft Access 2007 - II (Onsite)
URL(s): www.eeicom.com
Description: Covers database concepts including table design and relationships, advanced query, functions, and form and report techniques. **Audience:** Microsoft Access users and industry professionals. **Principal Exhibits:** Covers database concepts including table design and relationships, advanced query, functions, and form and report techniques. **Telecommunication Services:** train@eeicom.com.

21373 ▪ EEI Communications Microsoft PowerPoint 2007 - I (Onsite)
URL(s): www.eeicom.com
Description: Covers creating slides and electronic presentations utilizing PowerPoint. **Audience:** Microsoft application users and industry professionals. **Principal Exhibits:** Covers creating slides and electronic presentations utilizing PowerPoint. **Telecommunication Services:** train@eeicom.com.

21374 ▪ EEI Communications Microsoft Word 2007 - I (Onsite)
URL(s): www.eeicom.com
Description: Covers how to create basic documents using Word. **Audience:** Microsoft Word users and industry professionals. **Principal Exhibits:** Covers how to create basic documents using Word. **Telecommunication Services:** train@eeicom.com.

21375 ▪ EEI Communications Microsoft Word 2007 - II (Onsite)
URL(s): www.eeicom.com
Description: Covers techniques including creating styles and sections, newspaper-style layouts, creating charts, and adding clip art. **Audience:** Microsoft Word users and industry professionals. **Principal Exhibits:** Covers techniques including creating styles and sections, newspaper-style layouts, creating charts, and adding clip art. **Telecommunication Services:** train@eeicom.com.

21376 ▪ EEI Communications Microsoft Word 2007 - III (Onsite)
URL(s): www.eeicom.com
Description: Covers advanced Word skills including running, recording, and running macros, creating custom toolbars, creating online forms, working with master documents, and creating table of contents and indexes. **Audience:** Microsoft Word users and industry professionals. **Principal Exhibits:** Covers advanced Word skills including running, recording, and running macros, creating custom toolbars, creating online forms, working with master documents, and creating table of contents and indexes. **Telecommunication Services:** train@eeicom.com.

21377 ▪ EEI Communications QuarkXPress I
URL(s): www.eeicom.com
Description: Covers basic desktop publishing skills including creating and saving documents, formatting text and paragraphs, and manipulating graphics. **Audience:** Industry professionals and users. **Principal Exhibits:** Covers basic desktop publishing skills including creating and saving documents, formatting text and paragraphs, and manipulating graphics. **Telecommunication Services:** train@eeicom.com.

21378 ▪ EEI Communications QuarkXPress II
URL(s): www.eeicom.com
Description: Covers desktop publishing skills including paragraph and character style sheets, libraries, master pages, tracking and kerning, and processing colors. **Audience:** QuarkXPress users and industry professionals. **Principal Exhibits:** Covers desktop publishing skills including paragraph and character style sheets, libraries, master pages, tracking and kerning, and processing colors. **Telecommunication Services:** train@eeicom.com.

21379 ▪ EEI Communications QuarkXPress III
URL(s): www.eeicom.com
Description: Covers advanced desktop publishing skills including building table of contents and indexes, creating PostScript files, working with books, and synchronizing documents. **Audience:** QuarkXPress users and industry professionals. **Principal Exhibits:** Covers advanced desktop publishing skills including building table of contents and indexes, creating PostScript files, working with books, and synchronizing documents. **Telecommunication Services:** info@eeicom.com.

21380 ▪ EEI Communications Writing the Perfect Business E-Mail (Onsite)
URL(s): www.eeicom.com
Description: Seminar that covers e-mails that get read and are understood, including keeping it short and simple, make it useful, spelling, grammar, and other problems, controlling emotion, writing attachments that get read, progress reports, instructions, and evaluations and recommendations. **Audience:** Writers and editors. **Principal Exhibits:** Seminar that covers e-mails that get read and are understood, including keeping it short and simple, make it useful, spelling, grammar, and other problems, controlling emotion, writing attachments that get read, progress reports, instructions, and evaluations and recommendations.

21381 ▪ Effective Training Techniques for Group Leaders (Onsite)
Seminar Information Service Inc. (SIS)
250 El Camino Real., Ste. 112
Tustin, CA 92780
Ph: (714)508-0340
Free: 877-736-4636
Fax: (714)734-8027
Co. E-mail: info@seminarinformation.com
URL: http://www.seminarinformation.com
Contact: Catherine Bellizzi, President
URL(s): www.seminarinformation.com/details.cfm?qc=qqadnm
Description: Provides group leaders precise and practical methods to train their employees. Leaders also learn to spot worker training needs and provide effective on-the-job training. **Audience:** Group leaders. **Principal Exhibits:** Provides group leaders precise and practical methods to train their employees. Leaders also learn to spot worker training needs and provide effective on-the-job training.

21382 ▪ Electrical Ladder Drawings, Schematics & Diagrams (Onsite)
TPC Trainco Inc.
225 E Robinson St., Ste. 570
Orlando, FL 32801
Free: 877-978-7246
Co. E-mail: sales@tpctraining.com
URL: http://live.tpctraining.com
URL(s): live.tpctraining.com/public-seminars/electrical-training/electrical-controls/electrical-ladder-drawings-schematics-and-diagrams
Description: Training will include exercises where participants create schematic diagrams based on circuit descriptions, as well as interpreting schematic drawings so that they can provide verbal or written circuit descriptions and an understanding of several types of drawings and diagrams including Block, Pictorial, One-line, Wiring, Terminal, and Schematic. **Audience:** Engineers, electricians, plant and facility managers and mechanics. **Principal Exhibits:** Training will include exercises where participants create schematic diagrams based on circuit descriptions, as well as interpreting schematic drawings so that they can provide verbal or written circuit descriptions and an understanding of several types of drawings and diagrams including Block, Pictorial, One-line, Wiring, Terminal, and Schematic.

21383 ▪ Electrical Troubleshooting & Preventive Maintenance (Onsite)
TPC Trainco Inc.
225 E Robinson St., Ste. 570
Orlando, FL 32801
Free: 877-978-7246
Co. E-mail: sales@tpctraining.com
URL: http://live.tpctraining.com
URL(s): live.tpctraining.com/public-seminars/electrical-training/fundamentals/electrical-troubleshooting-preventive-maintenance
Description: Two-day seminar designed for anyone who needs to sharpen their electrical troubleshooting skills in order to increase efficiencies and uptime at their industrial plant or building facility. **Audience:** Electricians, Mechanic, HVAC Technicians and students. **Principal Exhibits:** Two-day seminar designed for anyone who needs to sharpen their electrical troubleshooting skills in order to increase efficiencies and uptime at their industrial plant or building facility.

21384 ▪ Electronic Editing (Onsite)
URL(s): www.eeicom.com
Description: Seminar that covers marking copy using style sheets, tracking changes and comparing documents, using the "search and replace" function, analyzing global changes, writing macros to make repetitive tasks simpler, checking references against citations, and develop a systematic approach to electronic manuscripts. **Audience:** Editors and writers, public. **Principal Exhibits:** Seminar that covers marking copy using style sheets, tracking changes and comparing documents, using the "search and replace" function, analyzing global changes, writing macros to make repetitive tasks simpler, checking references against citations, and develop a systematic approach to electronic manuscripts.

21385 ▪ Forensic Photoshop (Onsite)
URL(s): www.eeicom.com
Description: Designed for law enforcement and Homeland Security personnel that outlines the processes for using Photoshop in a forensic environment. **Audience:** General public, professionals. **Principal Exhibits:** Designed for law enforcement and Homeland Security personnel that outlines the processes for using Photoshop in a forensic environment.

21386 ■ Functional Gage Design (Onsite)
Seminar Information Service Inc. (SIS)
　250 El Camino Real., Ste. 112
　Tustin, CA 92780
Ph: (714)508-0340
Free: 877-736-4636
Fax: (714)734-8027
Co. E-mail: info@seminarinformation.com
URL: http://www.seminarinformation.com
Contact: Catherine Bellizzi, President
URL(s): www.seminarinformation.com/details.cfm?qc=qqaydw

Description: Learn about Gage design principles/tolerances; Ways to avoid commonly used but improper gaging and inspection techniques; Inspection machines; Substitute systems; Surface plate inspection and more. **Audience:** Managers of engineering, quality control and inspection departments, design engineers, product engineers, mechanical engineers. **Principal Exhibits:** Learn about Gage design principles/tolerances; Ways to avoid commonly used but improper gaging and inspection techniques; Inspection machines; Substitute systems; Surface plate inspection and more.

21387 ■ Generators & Emergency Power (Onsite)
TPC Trainco Inc.
　225 E Robinson St., Ste. 570
　Orlando, FL 32801
Free: 877-978-7246
Co. E-mail: sales@tpctraining.com
URL: http://live.tpctraining.com
URL(s): www.tpctrainco.com/public-seminars/electrical-training/emergency-power/generators-emergency-power-training

Description: Learn what you can do, and should do with generators, to make sure your facility will keep running even when the electricity to your facility doesn't. **Audience:** Facility managers, building owners, maintenance managers, building engineers and maintenance technicians. **Principal Exhibits:** Learn what you can do, and should do with generators, to make sure your facility will keep running even when the electricity to your facility doesn't.

21388 ■ Hands-On UNIX and Linux Tools and Utilities (Onsite)
Seminar Information Service Inc. (SIS)
　250 El Camino Real., Ste. 112
　Tustin, CA 92780
Ph: (714)508-0340
Free: 877-736-4636
Fax: (714)734-8027
Co. E-mail: info@seminarinformation.com
URL: http://www.seminarinformation.com
Contact: Catherine Bellizzi, President
URL(s): www.seminarinformation.com/qqapyk/hands-on-unix-and-linux-tools-and-utilities

Description: Become an expert builder and user of UNIX/Linux tools and utilities, including how to employ standard, programmable text filters to manipulate text and data, build shell scripts to automate routine tasks, and achieve significant productivity gains by matching the mix of tools to the task at hand. **Audience:** Systems and database administrators, software engineers and programmers. **Principal Exhibits:** Become an expert builder and user of UNIX/Linux tools and utilities, including how to employ standard, programmable text filters to manipulate text and data, build shell scripts to automate routine tasks, and achieve significant productivity gains by matching the mix of tools to the task at hand.

21389 ■ How to Conduct Your Own Energy Audit (Onsite)
TPC Trainco Inc.
　225 E Robinson St., Ste. 570
　Orlando, FL 32801
Free: 877-978-7246
Co. E-mail: sales@tpctraining.com
URL: http://live.tpctraining.com
URL(s): www.tpctrainco.com

Description: Two-day hands-on seminar shows you how to find quick and inexpensive ways to immediately cut energy costs at your plant or facility. **Audience:** Industry professionals. **Principal Exhibits:** Two-day hands-on seminar shows you how to find quick and inexpensive ways to immediately cut energy costs at your plant or facility.

21390 ■ HVAC Electrical Controls & Air Distribution (Onsite)
TPC Trainco Inc.
　225 E Robinson St., Ste. 570
　Orlando, FL 32801
Free: 877-978-7246
Co. E-mail: sales@tpctraining.com
URL: http://live.tpctraining.com
URL(s): live.tpctraining.com/public-seminars/hvac-training/hvac-electrical-controls-air-distribution

Description: Learn how to "control" their controls, and how to use fundamental air distribution principles for achieving consistent HVAC comfort and efficiency in buildings, plants and facilities. **Audience:** Supervisors, building owners, managers, building maintenance technicians and engineers. **Principal Exhibits:** Learn how to "control" their controls, and how to use fundamental air distribution principles for achieving consistent HVAC comfort and efficiency in buildings, plants and facilities.

21391 ■ Improving Editing Skills (Onsite)
URL(s): www.eeicom.com

Description: Covers the editorial issues such as active and passive voice, lists, redundancy, and sentence construction. **Audience:** Editors and writers. **Principal Exhibits:** Covers the editorial issues such as active and passive voice, lists, redundancy, and sentence construction.

21392 ■ Installing, Configuring, and Troubleshooting Microsoft SQL Server
Seminar Information Service Inc. (SIS)
　250 El Camino Real., Ste. 112
　Tustin, CA 92780
Ph: (714)508-0340
Free: 877-736-4636
Fax: (714)734-8027
Co. E-mail: info@seminarinformation.com
URL: http://www.seminarinformation.com
Contact: Catherine Bellizzi, President
URL(s): www.seminarinformation.com

Description: Learn to manage your database projects efficiently, knowledgeable and effectively. **Audience:** IT and IS professionals, database administrators, computer and database support personnel, database programmers, network administrators, SQL report generators, data security managers, data warehousing specialists, and business intelligence managers. **Principal Exhibits:** Learn to manage your database projects efficiently, knowledgeable and effectively.

21393 ■ Instrumentation, Process Measurement & Control (Onsite)
TPC Trainco Inc.
　225 E Robinson St., Ste. 570
　Orlando, FL 32801
Free: 877-978-7246
Co. E-mail: sales@tpctraining.com
URL: http://live.tpctraining.com
URL(s): live.tpctraining.com/on-site-training/specialty-on-site-training-topics/instrumentation-process-measurement-and-control

Description: Learn why it is necessary to measure what is going on with your systems and equipment, how to measure it, and what those measurements may mean in terms of action that should be taken to eliminate future downtime and unnecessary expense. **Audience:** Electricians, mechanics, and engineers. **Principal Exhibits:** Learn why it is necessary to measure what is going on with your systems and equipment, how to measure it, and what those measurements may mean in terms of action that should be taken to eliminate future downtime and unnecessary expense.

21394 ■ Integrating Forms and Databases on the Web (Onsite)
URL(s): www.eeicom.com

Description: Covers the basics of integrating a database with the world wide web using a Microsoft Access database, active server pages, or Microsoft's Internet Information Server. **Audience:** Industry professionals. **Principal Exhibits:** Covers the basics of integrating a database with the world wide web using a Microsoft Access database, active server pages, or Microsoft's Internet Information Server.

21395 ■ Introduction to System and Network Security (Onsite)
Seminar Information Service Inc. (SIS)
　250 El Camino Real., Ste. 112
　Tustin, CA 92780
Ph: (714)508-0340
Free: 877-736-4636
Fax: (714)734-8027
Co. E-mail: info@seminarinformation.com
URL: http://www.seminarinformation.com
Contact: Catherine Bellizzi, President
URL(s): www.seminarinformation.com/qqaxen/introduction-to-system-and-network-security

Description: Learn to analyze your exposure to information assurance threats and protect your organization's systems and data; Reduce your susceptibility to an attack by deploying firewalls, data encryption and other countermeasures; Manage risks emanating from inside the organization and from the Internet; Protect network users from hostile applications and viruses; Identify the security risks that need to be addressed within your organization. **Audience:** Industry professionals. **Principal Exhibits:** Learn to analyze your exposure to information assurance threats and protect your organization's systems and data; Reduce your susceptibility to an attack by deploying firewalls, data encryption and other countermeasures; Manage risks emanating from inside the organization and from the Internet; Protect network users from hostile applications and viruses; Identify the security risks that need to be addressed within your organization.

21396 ■ Inventory Control for Maintenance (Onsite)
TPC Trainco Inc.
　225 E Robinson St., Ste. 570
　Orlando, FL 32801
Free: 877-978-7246
Co. E-mail: sales@tpctraining.com
URL: http://live.tpctraining.com
URL(s): live.tpctraining.com/on-site-training/specialty-on-site-training-topics/inventory-control-for-maintenance

Description: Focus on building an inventory management system that will lead to better control through optimization of inventory quantities, organization of inventory and access to inventory. **Audience:** Maintenance, operations and purchasing managers and personnel. **Principal Exhibits:** Focus on building an inventory management system that will lead to better control through optimization of inventory quantities, organization of inventory and access to inventory.

21397 ■ Java for Non-Programmers (Onsite)
URL(s): www.eeicom.com

Description: Covers the basics of Java and how to use it for developing websites. **Audience:** Industry professionals. **Principal Exhibits:** Covers the basics of Java and how to use it for developing websites.

21398 ■ Maintenance Welding (Onsite)
TPC Trainco Inc.
　225 E Robinson St., Ste. 570
　Orlando, FL 32801
Free: 877-978-7246
Co. E-mail: sales@tpctraining.com
URL: http://live.tpctraining.com
URL(s): live.tpctraining.com/on-site-training/specialty-on-site-training-topics/maintenance-welding

Description: Learn welding techniques, welding processes, metal and filler selection, cutting processes, new fabrications, troubleshooting defects, welding repair, personal safety, managing costs, record keeping and more. **Audience:** Welders, maintenance and repair personnel, multi-craft technicians, fabricators, maintenance supervisors and managers, and inspectors. **Principal Exhibits:** Learn welding techniques, welding processes, metal and filler selection, cutting processes, new fabrications, troubleshooting defects, welding repair, personal safety, managing costs, record keeping and more.

21399 ■ Managing Stress Productively (Onsite)
Seminar Information Service Inc. (SIS)
  250 El Camino Real., Ste. 112
  Tustin, CA 92780
Ph: (714)508-0340
Free: 877-736-4636
Fax: (714)734-8027
Co. E-mail: info@seminarinformation.com
URL: http://www.seminarinformation.com
Contact: Catherine Bellizzi, President
URL(s): www.seminarinformation.com

Description: Learn to deal with the pressures of work and to meet the challenges of stress-related problems. **Audience:** Individuals who are experiencing work-related stress, and industry professionals. **Principal Exhibits:** Learn to deal with the pressures of work and to meet the challenges of stress-related problems.

21400 ■ Mastering Microsoft Project (Onsite)
Seminar Information Service Inc. (SIS)
  250 El Camino Real., Ste. 112
  Tustin, CA 92780
Ph: (714)508-0340
Free: 877-736-4636
Fax: (714)734-8027
Co. E-mail: info@seminarinformation.com
URL: http://www.seminarinformation.com
Contact: Catherine Bellizzi, President
URL(s): www.seminarinformation.com/details.cfm?qc=qqbrfh

Description: Learn how to import tasks into your project from any source; how to pull resources from Microsoft Outlook Active Directory and other sources; merge multiple projects into a single master project; and take advantage of templates and Wizards that can reduce your project planning time. **Audience:** Industry professionals. **Principal Exhibits:** Learn how to import tasks into your project from any source; how to pull resources from Microsoft Outlook Active Directory and other sources; merge multiple projects into a single master project; and take advantage of templates and Wizards that can reduce your project planning time.

21401 ■ Mastering QuickBooks Seminars and QuickBooks Classes (Onsite)
Seminar Information Service Inc. (SIS)
  250 El Camino Real., Ste. 112
  Tustin, CA 92780
Ph: (714)508-0340
Free: 877-736-4636
Fax: (714)734-8027
Co. E-mail: info@seminarinformation.com
URL: http://www.seminarinformation.com
Contact: Catherine Bellizzi, President
URL(s): www.seminarinformation.com/qqbvef/mastering-quickbooks-seminars-and-quickbooks-classes

Description: Discover how QuickBooks can make you and your business more successful. **Audience:** New users. **Principal Exhibits:** Discover how QuickBooks can make you and your business more successful.

21402 ■ Microsoft Access 2003: A Comprehensive Hands-On Introduction - Building a Foundation for Client/Server Database Applications (Onsite)
Seminar Information Service Inc. (SIS)
  250 El Camino Real., Ste. 112
  Tustin, CA 92780
Ph: (714)508-0340
Free: 877-736-4636
Fax: (714)734-8027
Co. E-mail: info@seminarinformation.com
URL: http://www.seminarinformation.com
Contact: Catherine Bellizzi, President
URL(s): www.seminarinformation.com

Description: Learn how to: Design robust relational database applications using Microsoft Access 2003; Develop client/server database front-ends; Build database applications quickly using Form, Table, Report and Query wizards; Link to ODBC and OLE-DB data sources to leverage enterprise security; Create and integrate macros into your applications; Implement advanced Access reporting features. **Audience:** Industry professionals. **Principal Exhibits:** Learn how to: Design robust relational database applications using Microsoft Access 2003; Develop client/server database front-ends; Build database applications quickly using Form, Table, Report and Query wizards; Link to ODBC and OLE-DB data sources to leverage enterprise security; Create and integrate macros into your applications; Implement advanced Access reporting features.

21403 ■ Microsoft Access 2007: A Comprehensive Hands-On Introduction (Onsite)
Seminar Information Service Inc. (SIS)
  250 El Camino Real., Ste. 112
  Tustin, CA 92780
Ph: (714)508-0340
Free: 877-736-4636
Fax: (714)734-8027
Co. E-mail: info@seminarinformation.com
URL: http://www.seminarinformation.com
Contact: Catherine Bellizzi, President
URL(s): www.seminarinformation.com/qqbtnb/microsoft-access-2007-a-comprehensive-hands-on

Description: Learn how to: Utilize Microsoft Access 2007 to design robust database applications; Apply Form, Table, Report and Query wizards to quickly build database applications; Create and integrate macros into your applications; Quickly modify forms and reports with selective filtering, sorting and grouping; Implement advanced Access reporting features; Link to SharePoint and SQL Server data systems. **Audience:** Industry professionals. **Principal Exhibits:** Learn how to: Utilize Microsoft Access 2007 to design robust database applications; Apply Form, Table, Report and Query wizards to quickly build database applications; Create and integrate macros into your applications; Quickly modify forms and reports with selective filtering, sorting and grouping; Implement advanced Access reporting features; Link to SharePoint and SQL Server data systems.

21404 ■ Microsoft Excel 2007 - I (Onsite)
URL(s): www.eeicom.com
Facebook: www.facebook.com/EEICommunications

Description: Covers the basics of creating simple spreadsheets, including absolute and relative formulas, formatting cells and cell ranges, control pages, working with multiple sheets, and using templates. **Audience:** Industry professionals. **Principal Exhibits:** Covers the basics of creating simple spreadsheets, including absolute and relative formulas, formatting cells and cell ranges, control pages, working with multiple sheets, and using templates.

21405 ■ Microsoft FrontPage (Onsite)
URL(s): www.eeicom.com

Description: Covers using FrontPage to develop websites. **Audience:** Industry professionals. **Principal Exhibits:** Covers using FrontPage to develop websites.

21406 ■ Microsoft Office
Fred Pryor Seminars & CareerTrack
  5700 Broadmoor, Ste. 300
  Mission, KS 66202
Free: 800-780-8476
Fax: (913)967-8849
Co. E-mail: customerservice@pryor.com
URL: http://www.pryor.com
Contact: Janet Turner, Contact
E-mail: dmca@pryor.com
URL(s): www.pryor.com/training-categories/microsoft-office

Frequency: Irregular. **Description:** Covers using Microsoft Office. **Audience:** Business professionals. **Principal Exhibits:** Covers using Microsoft Office.

21407 ■ Microsoft Project 2007 - I (Onsite)
URL(s): www.eeicom.com
Facebook: www.facebook.com/EEICommunications

Description: Covers using Project to successfully manage projects, including using Gantt charts, resource leveling, and establishing task dependencies. **Audience:** Industry professionals. **Principal Exhibits:** Covers using Project to successfully manage projects, including using Gantt charts, resource leveling, and establishing task dependencies.

21408 ■ Microsoft Project: Managing Multiple and Complex Projects (Onsite)
Seminar Information Service Inc. (SIS)
  250 El Camino Real., Ste. 112
  Tustin, CA 92780
Ph: (714)508-0340
Free: 877-736-4636
Fax: (714)734-8027
Co. E-mail: info@seminarinformation.com
URL: http://www.seminarinformation.com
Contact: Catherine Bellizzi, President
URL(s): www.seminarinformation.com/qqbfge/microsoft-project-introduction-structuring-projects-to

Description: Learn how to: Leverage Microsoft Project Professional tools and techniques in a multi-project environment; Reorganize large or complex projects into master and subprojects; Optimize resource assignments across projects and resolve over allocations; Track schedule, completeness and budget on complex projects and for distributed teams; Connect project managers, teams and data across the organization; Integrate third-party applications to facilitate data sharing and accessibility. **Audience:** Industry professionals. **Principal Exhibits:** Learn how to: Leverage Microsoft Project Professional tools and techniques in a multi-project environment; Reorganize large or complex projects into master and subprojects; Optimize resource assignments across projects and resolve over allocations; Track schedule, completeness and budget on complex projects and for distributed teams; Connect project managers, teams and data across the organization; Integrate third-party applications to facilitate data sharing and accessibility.

21409 ■ Motor Selection, Maintenance, Testing & Replacement
TPC Trainco Inc.
  225 E Robinson St., Ste. 570
  Orlando, FL 32801
Free: 877-978-7246
Co. E-mail: sales@tpctraining.com
URL: http://live.tpctraining.com
URL(s): www.tpctrainco.com

Description: Seminar designed for anyone whose work is affected by motors at their facility, whether they are mechanics doing the work, a supervisor in charge of fixing problems, or purchasing agents responsible for saving money. **Audience:** Mechanics, foremen, supervisors, purchasing agents, and HVAC technicians. **Principal Exhibits:** Seminar designed for anyone whose work is affected by motors at their facility, whether they are mechanics doing the work, a supervisor in charge of fixing problems, or purchasing agents responsible for saving money.

21410 ■ Moving Ahead: Breaking Behavior Patterns That Hold You Back (Onsite)
American Management Association (AMA)
  1601 Broadway
  New York, NY 10019
Ph: (212)586-8100
Free: 800-262-9699
Fax: (212)903-8168
Co. E-mail: customerservice@amanet.org
URL: http://www.amanet.org
Contact: Manny Avramidis, President
URL(s): www.amanet.org/training/seminars/onsite/moving-ahead-breaking-behavior-patterns-that-hold-you-back.aspx

Price: $2,195, Non-members; $1,995, Members; $1,795, General Services Administration (GSA). **Description:** Covers resolution techniques for bad workplace behaviors. **Audience:** General managers, supervisors, team leaders and anyone who has a negative behavior pattern that has created a bad professional image and impeded his or her career success. **Principal Exhibits:** Covers resolution techniques for bad workplace behaviors.

21411 ■ Online Marketing and Search Engine Optimization

URL(s): www.eeicom.com

Description: Covers how to increase traffic to your online site to market your products and services using the Web, including creating and implementation of your plan, setting a budget, redesigning Web site for search engine optimization, tips and tricks, promotion hints, tips, and advice, and how to measure your Internet marketing results. **Audience:** Marketing professionals. **Principal Exhibits:** Covers how to increase traffic to your online site to market your products and services using the Web, including creating and implementation of your plan, setting a budget, redesigning Web site for search engine optimization, tips and tricks, promotion hints, tips, and advice, and how to measure your Internet marketing results.

21412 ■ Personal Success Strategies (Onsite)

Seminar Information Service Inc. (SIS)
  250 El Camino Real., Ste. 112
  Tustin, CA 92780
Ph: (714)508-0340
Free: 877-736-4636
Fax: (714)734-8027
Co. E-mail: info@seminarinformation.com
URL: http://www.seminarinformation.com
Contact: Catherine Bellizzi, President
URL(s): www.seminarinformation.com

Description: Develop a plan to eliminate weaknesses that inhibit success and replace them with positive actions. **Audience:** Individuals who wish to modify behaviors, professionals. **Principal Exhibits:** Develop a plan to eliminate weaknesses that inhibit success and replace them with positive actions.

21413 ■ PLC Programming & Applications (Onsite)

TPC Trainco Inc.
  225 E Robinson St., Ste. 570
  Orlando, FL 32801
Free: 877-978-7246
Co. E-mail: sales@tpctraining.com
URL: http://live.tpctraining.com
URL(s): live.tpctraining.com/public-seminars/elec trical-training/electrical-controls/plc-programming -applications

Description: Provides skills needed to organize, plan, write, enter, test, and document SLC500 programs using the basic programming instructions and RSLogix software. **Audience:** Apprentice and experienced electricians, instrumentation technicians, and building maintenance personnel. **Principal Exhibits:** Provides skills needed to organize, plan, write, enter, test, and document SLC500 programs using the basic programming instructions and RSLogix software.

21414 ■ PLCs for Non-Programmers (Onsite)

TPC Trainco Inc.
  225 E Robinson St., Ste. 570
  Orlando, FL 32801
Free: 877-978-7246
Co. E-mail: sales@tpctraining.com
URL: http://live.tpctraining.com
URL(s): live.tpctraining.com/public-seminars/elec trical-training/electrical-controls/plcs-for-non -programmers

Description: Seminar designed for maintenance technicians, electricians, or other non-programmers who need a general understanding of automation and Programmable Logic Controllers. **Audience:** Apprentice and experienced electricians, instrumentation technicians, and all building maintenance personnel. **Principal Exhibits:** Seminar designed for maintenance technicians, electricians, or other non-programmers who need a general understanding of automation and Programmable Logic Controllers.

21415 ■ Plumbing & Pipefitting for Plants & Buildings (Onsite)

TPC Trainco Inc.
  225 E Robinson St., Ste. 570
  Orlando, FL 32801
Free: 877-978-7246
Co. E-mail: sales@tpctraining.com
URL: http://live.tpctraining.com
URL(s): live.tpctraining.com/on-site-training/specialty -on-site-training-topics/plumbing-pipefitting-for-plan ts-and-buildings

Description: Covers the necessary requirements to follow code and safety regulations while providing the student with a practical foundation to quickly identify problems and solve them on their own, whether it's a low-pressure water supply line problem, drippy valve or a clogged drain trap. **Audience:** Plumbing and pipefitting professionals. **Principal Exhibits:** Covers the necessary requirements to follow code and safety regulations while providing the student with a practical foundation to quickly identify problems and solve them on their own, whether it's a low-pressure water supply line problem, drippy valve or a clogged drain trap.

21416 ■ Power Excel: Making Better Decisions (Onsite)

Seminar Information Service Inc. (SIS)
  250 El Camino Real., Ste. 112
  Tustin, CA 92780
Ph: (714)508-0340
Free: 877-736-4636
Fax: (714)734-8027
Co. E-mail: info@seminarinformation.com
URL: http://www.seminarinformation.com
Contact: Catherine Bellizzi, President
URL(s): www.seminarinformation.com

Description: Learn how to: Leverage advanced features of Microsoft Excel to facilitate business decisions; Perform 'what-if' analysis for developing budget and project plans; Predict potential business developments using trend analysis; Consolidate and process multidimensional worksheets; Summarize and analyze large amounts of data using PivotTables and Excel features; Automate Excel processes and enhance worksheet models; Generate interactive Web-based worksheet models. **Audience:** Industry professionals. **Principal Exhibits:** Learn how to: Leverage advanced features of Microsoft Excel to facilitate business decisions; Perform 'what-if' analysis for developing budget and project plans; Predict potential business developments using trend analysis; Consolidate and process multidimensional worksheets; Summarize and analyze large amounts of data using PivotTables and Excel features; Automate Excel processes and enhance worksheet models; Generate interactive Web-based worksheet models.

21417 ■ Predictive Maintenance and Condition Monitoring (Onsite)

TPC Trainco Inc.
  225 E Robinson St., Ste. 570
  Orlando, FL 32801
Free: 877-978-7246
Co. E-mail: sales@tpctraining.com
URL: http://live.tpctraining.com
URL(s): live.tpctraining.com/public-seminars/plan t-management/predictive-maintenance-and-condi tion-monitoring

Description: Provides the fundamentals of PdM and condition monitoring applicable to plants, facilities, and manufacturing lines. **Audience:** Maintenance, operations, purchasing managers and personnel. **Principal Exhibits:** Provides the fundamentals of PdM and condition monitoring applicable to plants, facilities, and manufacturing lines.

21418 ■ Preparing for the Project Management Professional PMP Exam (Onsite)

Seminar Information Service Inc. (SIS)
  250 El Camino Real., Ste. 112
  Tustin, CA 92780
Ph: (714)508-0340
Free: 877-736-4636
Fax: (714)734-8027
Co. E-mail: info@seminarinformation.com
URL: http://www.seminarinformation.com
Contact: Catherine Bellizzi, President
URL(s): www.seminarinformation.com/qqbtjx/ preparing-for-the-project-management-professional -pmp

Description: Learn how to: Prepare to pass the PMP(r) exam; Navigate the process groups and knowledge areas of the PMBOK(r) Guide 3rd Edition; Identify and map the inputs and outputs of the PMBOK(r) Guide processes; Align your project management knowledge with PMBOK(r) Guide terminology and definitions; Analyze PMBOK(r) Guide tools and techniques essential for PMP(r) exam success; Improve your exam-taking techniques through PMP(r)-style practice questions; Create a personalized plan for self-study to focus your efforts after the course. **Audience:** Experienced project managers. **Principal Exhibits:** Learn how to: Prepare to pass the PMP(r) exam; Navigate the process groups and knowledge areas of the PMBOK(r) Guide 3rd Edition; Identify and map the inputs and outputs of the PMBOK(r) Guide processes; Align your project management knowledge with PMBOK(r) Guide terminology and definitions; Analyze PMBOK(r) Guide tools and techniques essential for PMP(r) exam success; Improve your exam-taking techniques through PMP(r)-style practice questions; Create a personalized plan for self-study to focus your efforts after the course.

21419 ■ Programming Boot Camp (Onsite)

URL(s): www.eeicom.com

Description: Covers basic concepts of scripting languages and tools, including JavaScript and Visual Basic. **Audience:** Industry professionals. **Principal Exhibits:** Covers basic concepts of scripting languages and tools, including JavaScript and Visual Basic.

21420 ■ Programming Microsoft Access 2003: Hands-On - Building Database Applications with Access and VBA (Onsite)

Seminar Information Service Inc. (SIS)
  250 El Camino Real., Ste. 112
  Tustin, CA 92780
Ph: (714)508-0340
Free: 877-736-4636
Fax: (714)734-8027
Co. E-mail: info@seminarinformation.com
URL: http://www.seminarinformation.com
Contact: Catherine Bellizzi, President
URL(s): www.seminarinformation.com

Description: Learn how to: Develop applications with Microsoft Access 2003 using Visual Basic for Applications (VBA); Identify and populate event properties to satisfy design specifications; Modify object properties and invoke object methods to customize applications; Create VBA statements using variables and built-in functions; Build loops and decision logic; Apply Data Access Objects (DAO) to incorporate business rules; Integrate Access with external applications through automation. **Audience:** Industry professionals. **Principal Exhibits:** Learn how to: Develop applications with Microsoft Access 2003 using Visual Basic for Applications (VBA); Identify and populate event properties to satisfy design specifications; Modify object properties and invoke object methods to customize applications; Create VBA statements using variables and built-in functions; Build loops and decision logic; Apply Data Access Objects (DAO) to incorporate business rules; Integrate Access with external applications through automation.

21421 ■ Pump Repair & Maintenance (Onsite)

TPC Trainco Inc.
  225 E Robinson St., Ste. 570
  Orlando, FL 32801
Free: 877-978-7246
Co. E-mail: sales@tpctraining.com
URL: http://live.tpctraining.com
URL(s): live.tpctraining.com/public-seminars/me chanical-and-industrial-training/pump-repair-main tenance

Description: Learn common sense pump maintenance and repair techniques to keep facilities and equipment up and running. **Audience:** Multi-craft technicians, maintenance technicians, plumbers and pipefitters and pump system engineers. **Principal Exhibits:** Learn common sense pump maintenance and repair techniques to keep facilities and equipment up and running.

21422 ■ Pumps & Pump Systems: Specification, Installation & Operation (Onsite)
TPC Trainco Inc.
225 E Robinson St., Ste. 570
Orlando, FL 32801
Free: 877-978-7246
Co. E-mail: sales@tpctraining.com
URL: http://live.tpctraining.com
URL(s): live.tpctraining.com/public-seminars/mechanical-and-industrial-training/pumps-pump-systems-specification-installation-operation

Description: From the pump and pump system, to the people who operate, maintain and design the pump system, this seminar will teach students how to identify the real problems causing pump failure, and how to avoid repeating those problems in the future. **Audience:** Maintenance technicians. **Principal Exhibits:** From the pump and pump system, to the people who operate, maintain and design the pump system, this seminar will teach students how to identify the real problems causing pump failure, and how to avoid repeating those problems in the future.

21423 ■ Resume Writing (Onsite)
URL(s): www.eeicom.com
Description: Learn to create an exceptional resume that helps you compete successfully for the job you want, as well as how to customize your resume and cover letter for each targeted employer in just a few strokes. **Audience:** General public, professionals. **Principal Exhibits:** Learn to create an exceptional resume that helps you compete successfully for the job you want, as well as how to customize your resume and cover letter for each targeted employer in just a few strokes.

21424 ■ Search Engine Optimization Training
URL(s): www.eeicom.com
Description: Learn how to increase traffic to your Web site and get your products and services visible on the Web. **Audience:** Professionals, students. **Principal Exhibits:** Learn how to increase traffic to your Web site and get your products and services visible on the Web.

21425 ■ Speed Reading with Evelyn Wood Reading Dynamics
Fred Pryor Seminars & CareerTrack
5700 Broadmoor, Ste. 300
Mission, KS 66202
Free: 800-780-8476
Fax: (913)967-8849
Co. E-mail: customerservice@pryor.com
URL: http://www.pryor.com
Contact: Janet Turner, Contact
E-mail: dmca@pryor.com
URL(s): www.pryor.com/mkt_info/seminars/desc/rd.asp

Description: Learn Evelyn Wood's basic concepts, how to increase your reading rate, note-taking, studying and listening skills and develop better memory, recall and comprehension. **Audience:** Administrative professionals. **Principal Exhibits:** Learn Evelyn Wood's basic concepts, how to increase your reading rate, note-taking, studying and listening skills and develop better memory, recall and comprehension.

21426 ■ Steam Systems Maintenance, Safety & Optimization (Onsite)
TPC Trainco Inc.
225 E Robinson St., Ste. 570
Orlando, FL 32801
Free: 877-978-7246
Co. E-mail: sales@tpctraining.com
URL: http://live.tpctraining.com
URL(s): live.tpctraining.com/on-site-training/specialty-on-site-training-topics/steam-systems-maintenance-safety-optimization

Description: This course will teach you how to keep your steam system working efficiently and how to fix common problems and work safely reducing energy loss. **Audience:** Boiler operators, technicians and mechanics, plant engineers, steam drive equipment operators and energy management personnel. **Principal Exhibits:** This course will teach you how to keep your steam system working efficiently and how to fix common problems and work safely reducing energy loss.

21427 ■ Style Summit (Onsite)
URL(s): www.eeicom.com
Description: Covers simplifying the editorial process, including issues such as nouns used as verbs (E-mail me), e-jargon and acronyms, and informal usages that seem to break the rules (like vs. such as; more vs. over). **Audience:** Industry professionals. **Principal Exhibits:** Covers simplifying the editorial process, including issues such as nouns used as verbs (E-mail me), e-jargon and acronyms, and informal usages that seem to break the rules (like vs. such as; more vs. over).

21428 ■ Technical Writing: A Comprehensive Hands-On Introduction (Onsite)
Seminar Information Service Inc. (SIS)
250 El Camino Real., Ste. 112
Tustin, CA 92780
Ph: (714)508-0340
Free: 877-736-4636
Fax: (714)734-8027
Co. E-mail: info@seminarinformation.com
URL: http://www.seminarinformation.com
Contact: Catherine Bellizzi, President
URL(s): www.seminarinformation.com/qqbtkf/technical-writing-a-comprehensive-hands-on-introduction

Description: Learn how to: Write clear, effective technical = documents, including user manuals and technical reports; Assess your target audience and develop documents to meet their needs; Choose the appropriate writing style to communicate to specialized audiences; Build effective sentences, paragraphs and sections that explain information clearly; Employ diagrams, tables, charts and other graphical tools effectively; Create informative and interesting content that your readers will comprehend and utilize. **Audience:** Technical writers. **Principal Exhibits:** Learn how to: Write clear, effective technical = documents, including user manuals and technical reports; Assess your target audience and develop documents to meet their needs; Choose the appropriate writing style to communicate to specialized audiences; Build effective sentences, paragraphs and sections that explain information clearly; Employ diagrams, tables, charts and other graphical tools effectively; Create informative and interesting content that your readers will comprehend and utilize. **Telecommunication Services:** info@seminarinformation.com.

21429 ■ Troubleshooting Mechanical Drive Systems & Rotating Equipment (Onsite)
TPC Trainco Inc.
225 E Robinson St., Ste. 570
Orlando, FL 32801
Free: 877-978-7246
Co. E-mail: sales@tpctraining.com
URL: http://live.tpctraining.com
URL(s): live.tpctraining.com/on-site-training/specialty-on-site-training-topics/troubleshooting-mechanical-drive-systems-rotating-equipment

Description: Provide a new perspective on troubleshooting mechanical and rotating equipment and learn about basic mechanical applications, failures, life expectancy and maintenance shafts, bearings, couplings, chains, sprockets, bushings, gears, belts, sheaves and other mechanical components. You'll learn what data to measure, track and trend so that when equipment fails you can get quick answers to what is wrong, as well as fix the real problems with your equipment and not just the symptoms. **Audience:** Maintenance technicians, mechanics, HVAC technicians, electricians and machine operators. **Principal Exhibits:** Provide a new perspective on troubleshooting mechanical and rotating equipment and learn about basic mechanical applications, failures, life expectancy and maintenance shafts, bearings, couplings, chains, sprockets, bushings, gears, belts, sheaves and other mechanical components. You'll learn what data to measure, track and trend so that when equipment fails you can get quick answers to what is wrong, as well as fix the real problems with your equipment and not just the symptoms.

21430 ■ Understanding & Troubleshooting Hydraulics (Onsite)
TPC Trainco Inc.
225 E Robinson St., Ste. 570
Orlando, FL 32801
Free: 877-978-7246
Co. E-mail: sales@tpctraining.com
URL: http://live.tpctraining.com
URL(s): live.tpctraining.com/public-seminars/mechanical-and-industrial-training/understanding-troubleshooting-hydraulics

Description: Provides the basic building blocks and information you need to become proficient in working with industrial hydraulics and fluid power, whether a small mobile unit or large industrial installation. **Audience:** Mechanics, fluid power technicians, machine operators, plant and facility managers and building engineers. **Principal Exhibits:** Provides the basic building blocks and information you need to become proficient in working with industrial hydraulics and fluid power, whether a small mobile unit or large industrial installation.

21431 ■ Uninterruptable Power Supply (UPS) Maintenance and Readiness (Onsite)
TPC Trainco Inc.
225 E Robinson St., Ste. 570
Orlando, FL 32801
Free: 877-978-7246
Co. E-mail: sales@tpctraining.com
URL: http://live.tpctraining.com
URL(s): live.tpctraining.com/on-site-training/specialty-on-site-training-topics/uninterruptible-power-supply-ups-maintenance

Description: Seminar designed for personnel responsible for the UPS systems in industrial plants, public facilities, and commercial buildings. **Audience:** Electricians, maintenance technicians, maintenance managers, supervisors, plant and building engineers. **Principal Exhibits:** Seminar designed for personnel responsible for the UPS systems in industrial plants, public facilities, and commercial buildings.

21432 ■ Variable Frequency Drives (Onsite)
TPC Trainco Inc.
225 E Robinson St., Ste. 570
Orlando, FL 32801
Free: 877-978-7246
Co. E-mail: sales@tpctraining.com
URL: http://live.tpctraining.com
URL(s): live.tpctraining.com/public-seminars/electrical-training/electrical-controls/variable-frequency-drives

Description: Learn how to troubleshoot common VFD problems, take care of your own equipment, and avoid costly repairs or service repairs, including how to identify hazards associated with working on VFDs, an understanding of the importance of safe work practices, recognition of the main components of a VFD system, and the different methods of controlling a VFD. **Audience:** Industry professionals. **Principal Exhibits:** Learn how to troubleshoot common VFD problems, take care of your own equipment, and avoid costly repairs or service repairs, including how to identify hazards associated with working on VFDs, an understanding of the importance of safe work practices, recognition of the main components of a VFD system, and the different methods of controlling a VFD.

21433 ■ Visual Design I (Onsite)
URL(s): www.eeicom.com

Description: Covers the history of type, typography's role in visual communication, structural line, space and kinetic lines, the elements of line, shape and space, and typography and type anatomy. **Audience:** Professional digital artist, general public. **Principal Exhibits:** Covers the history of type, typography's role in visual communication, structural line, space and kinetic lines, the elements of line, shape and space, and typography and type anatomy.

21434 ■ Visual Design II (Onsite)
URL(s): www.eeicom.com
Description: Covers the principles of texture and the diverse approaches to the element of value. Explore monochromatic, analogous and complementary combinations from Itten's color wheel. **Audience:** Digital professional, and students. **Principal Exhibits:** Covers the principles of texture and the diverse approaches to the element of value. Explore monochromatic, analogous and complementary combinations from Itten's color wheel.

21435 ■ Visual Design III (Onsite)
URL(s): www.eeicom.com
Description: Covers the compositional elements of line, plane, and form combined with neutral tones, and the Bauhaus and Constructivist theory as it relates to compositional tension and movement created by design. **Audience:** Digital professional and Students. **Principal Exhibits:** Covers the compositional elements of line, plane, and form combined with neutral tones, and the Bauhaus and Constructivist theory as it relates to compositional tension and movement created by design.

21436 ■ Visual Design IV (Onsite)
URL(s): www.eeicom.com
Description: With focus on the works of Malevich and Escher as a foundation, learn the attributes of shape in positive and negative space, organic and geometric differences, metamorphosis, and symbolism. **Audience:** Digital professional, and students. **Principal Exhibits:** With focus on the works of Malevich and Escher as a foundation, learn the attributes of shape in positive and negative space, organic and geometric differences, metamorphosis, and symbolism.

21437 ■ Water Treatment for Boilers, Chillers & Cooling Towers (Onsite)
TPC Trainco Inc.
225 E Robinson St., Ste. 570
Orlando, FL 32801
Free: 877-978-7246
Co. E-mail: sales@tpctraining.com
URL: http://live.tpctraining.com
URL(s): live.tpctraining.com/on-site-training/specialty-on-site-training-topics/water-treatment-for-boilers-chillers-and-cooling-towers
Description: One-day seminar to take the mystery out of creating, and stabilizing high water quality for your HVAC systems. **Audience:** Building maintenance personnel, engineers and plant maintenance technicians. **Principal Exhibits:** One-day seminar to take the mystery out of creating, and stabilizing high water quality for your HVAC systems.

21438 ■ WBENC Energy Executive Program
URL(s): www.wbenc.org/programs/wbenc-energy-executive-program
Frequency: Irregular. **Description:** A program designed to provide professional development for women in the Energy industry. **Principal Exhibits:** A program designed to provide professional development for women in the Energy industry.

21439 ■ The Women's Conference
Fred Pryor Seminars & CareerTrack
5700 Broadmoor, Ste. 300
Mission, KS 66202
Free: 800-780-8476
Fax: (913)967-8849
Co. E-mail: customerservice@pryor.com
URL: http://www.pryor.com
Contact: Janet Turner, Contact
E-mail: dmca@pryor.com

URL(s): www.pryor.com/training-seminars/womens-conference
Frequency: Irregular. **Description:** Covers the following topics: enhancing your career and professional development; expert communication skills just for women; and the women's professional toolbox. **Audience:** Industry professionals. **Principal Exhibits:** Covers the following topics: enhancing your career and professional development; expert communication skills just for women; and the women's professional toolbox.

REFERENCE WORKS

21440 ■ 35 Free Small Business Classes for Business Owners
URL(s): www.mydegreeguide.com/open-courses/35-open-courses-small-business-owners/
Description: Covers 35 of the top free courses available for entrepreneurs and small business startups. **Availability:** Online.

21441 ■ "The 2007 Black Book" in Hawaii Business (Vol. 53, December 2007, No. 6, pp. 43)
Description: Brief biographies of 364 top executives in Hawaii are presented. Information on their educational achievement, membership in associations, hobbies, family, present position and the company they work for are supplied. **Availability:** Print; Online.

21442 ■ "2010 Book of Lists" in Business Courier (Vol. 26, December 26, 2009, No. 36, pp. 1)
Price: $49.95. **Description:** Rankings of companies and organizations within the business services, education, finance, health care, hospitality and tourism, real estate, and technology industries in the Cincinnati, Ohio-Northern Kentucky area are presented. Rankings are based on sales, business size, or other statistics. **Availability:** PDF; Online.

21443 ■ "Advantage Tutoring Center Helps Students of All Levels" in Bellingham Business Journal (Vol. February 2010, pp. 16)
Pub: Sound Publishing Inc.
Contact: Josh O'Connor, President

Ed: Ashley Mitchell. **Description:** Profile of the newly opened Advantage Tutoring, owned by Mary and Peter Morrison. The center offers programs ranging from basic homework help to subject-specific enrichment.

21444 ■ "All Fired Up!" in Small Business Opportunities (November 2008)
Description: Profile of Brixx Wood Fired Pizza, which has launched a franchising program due to the amount of interest the company's founders received over the years; franchisees do not need experience in the food industry or pizza restaurant service business in order to open a franchise of their own because all franchisees receive comprehensive training in which they are educated on all of the necessary tools to effectively run the business. **Availability:** Print; Online.

21445 ■ "Alpharetta Seeding Startups To Encourage Job Growth" in Atlanta Business Chronicle (June 20, 2014, pp. 3A)
Pub: American City Business Journals, Inc.
Contact: Mike Olivieri, Executive Vice President
Description: The City of Alpharetta is witnessing several incubators and accelerators that will create the physical and educational infrastructure to convert ideas into sustainable businesses. This will help startups develop a go-to-market strategy, prepare for FDA certification and insurance reimbursement as well as see that the company reaches a point where it can attract private equity or venture capital. **Availability:** Print; Online.

21446 ■ "American Indian College Fund to Support Environmental Science and Sustainability Programs, Fellowships, and Internships" in Ecology, Environment & Conservation Business (April 12, 2014, pp. 21)
Pub: NewsRX LLC.
Contact: Kalani Rosell, Contact

Description: Tribal colleges serve communities facing environmental issues, such as water quality, energy development, depletion of natural resources, and agricultural management. The American Indian College Fund has created a new Environmental Science and Sustainability Project of $1.35 million grant money to support tribal colleges and universities in select states that underwrite environmental science and sustainability programs of studies. Details of the project are included. **Availability:** Online.

21447 ■ "The Americans Are Coming" in The Economist (Vol. 390, January 3, 2009, No. 8612, pp. 44)
Description: Student recruitment consultancies, which help place international students at universities in other countries and offer services such as interpreting or translating guidelines, are discussed; American universities who have shunned these agencies in the past; the result has been that America underperforms in relation to its size with a mere 3.5 percent of students on its campuses that are from abroad. **Availability:** Print; Online.

21448 ■ "Applications for Law School Drop" in Philadelphia Business Journal (Vol. 28, June 8, 2012, No. 17, pp. 1)
Pub: Baltimore Business Journal
Contact: Rhonda Pringle, President
E-mail: rpringle@bizjournals.com

Description: Law School Admissions Council data for the past two years show the number of applicants have dropped by 25 percent ant the number of people who took the Law School Admissions Test fell by 26 percent. The numbers reflect the national trend that shows the struggling job market has affected decisions to go to law school. **Availability:** Print; Online.

21449 ■ "Applying to Colleges? Consultants Can Demystify the Process" in Palm Beach Post (September 3, 2011)
Pub: McClatchy Tribune Information Services
Contact: Patrick J. Talamantes, President

Ed: Susan Salisbury. **Released:** September 03, 2011. **Description:** More parents are turning to college consultants to help guide them through the process of applying to and choosing the right college or university. These specialized consultants assist with every detail for several years and students can reach them 24/7; costs can vary from several hundred dollars to $10,000 depending on services. **Availability:** Online.

21450 ■ "Apprenticeship: Earn While You Learn" in Occupational Outlook Quarterly (Vol. 54, Fall 2010, No. 3, pp. 24)
Description: Paid training, or apprenticeships, are examined. Registered apprenticeship programs conform to certain guidelines and industry-established training standards and may be run by businesses, trade or professional associations, or partnerships with business and unions. **Availability:** Online.

21451 ■ "Aquatic Medications Engender Good Health" in Pet Product News (Vol. 64, November 2010, No. 11, pp. 47)
Ed: Madelaine Heleine. **Description:** Pet supply manufacturers and retailers have been exerting consumer education and preparedness efforts to help aquarium hobbyists in tackling ornamental fish disease problems. Aquarium hobbyists have been also assisted in choosing products that facilitate aquarium maintenance before disease attacks their pet fish. **Availability:** Online.

21452 ■ ATD Buyer's Guide (Internet only)
Pub: Association for Talent Development
Contact: Tony Bingham, President
URL(s): webcasts.td.org/get-listed

Price: $1,800, for 1 year; $3,240, for 2 year; $3,672, for 3 year. **Description:** Database covers businesses and individual consultants offering products, services, and equipment for sale to persons in corporate training and human resource development. **Entries include:** Company name, contact information and name, profile, list of products and services. **Arrangement:** Alphabetical. **Indexes:** Subject, geographical, industry focus. **Availability:** Online.

21453 ■ *"Barshop Leading 'Paradigm Shift' In Aging Research"* in *San Antonio Business Journal (Vol. 28, September 12, 2014, No. 31, pp. 4)*
Pub: American City Business Journals, Inc.
Contact: Mike Olivieri, Executive Vice President
Released: September 12, 2014. **Price:** $4, Introductory 4-week offer(Digital & Print). **Description:** The National Institute of Health has given a $7.5 million five-year grant to University of Texas Health Science at San Antonio's Barshop Insitute for Longevity and Aging Studies. The funding was awarded to help researchers accelerate the discoveries of commercial drugs that slow the aging process. **Availability:** Print; Mailing list; Online.

21454 ■ *"The Bell Tolls for Thee"* in *Canadian Business (Vol. 81, March 3, 2008, No. 3, pp. 36)*
Description: Bell Canada has formed the Canadian Coalition for Tomorrow's IT Skills to solve the shortage of technology talent in the country. Canada's total workforce has only around 4%, or 600,000 people employed in information technology-related fields. The aims of the Bell-led coalition, which is supported by different industry associations and 30 corporations, are investigated. **Availability:** Print; Online.

21455 ■ *"Best Foot Forward"* in *Canadian Business (Vol. 80, October 22, 2007, No. 21, pp. 115)*
Description: Jeremy Shinewald's mbaMission admissions consulting business helps prospective MBA students with essay writing, mock interview preparation and school selection. The consulting fee for application to one school is $2,250. Details of the business schools' MBA programs and tuition fees are explored. **Availability:** Online.

21456 ■ *"The Big Idea: No, Management Is Not a Profession"* in *Harvard Business Review (Vol. 88, July-August 2010, No. 7-8, pp. 52)*
Pub: Harvard Business Publishing
Contact: Diane Belcher, Managing Director
Ed: Richard Barker. **Price:** $8.95, PDF. **Description:** An argument is presented that management is not a profession, as it is less focused on mastering a given body of knowledge than it is on obtaining integration and collaboration skills. Implications for teaching this new approach are also examined. **Availability:** Online; PDF.

21457 ■ *"Bond Hill Cinema Site To See New Life"* in *Business Courier (Vol. 27, October 29, 2010, No. 26, pp. 1)*
Pub: Business Courier
Ed: Dan Monk. **Description:** Avondale, Ohio's Corinthian Baptist Church will redevelop the 30-acre former Showcase Cinema property to a mixed-use site that could feature a college, senior home, and retail. Corinthian Baptist, which is one of the largest African-American churches in the region, is also planning to relocate the church. **Availability:** Print; Online.

21458 ■ *"Breaking from Tradition Techstyle"* in *Providence Business News (Vol. 28, March 17, 2014, No. 50, pp. 1)*
Pub: American City Business Journals, Inc.
Contact: Mike Olivieri, Executive Vice President
Released: March 15, 2014. **Description:** Providence, Rhode Island's Techstyle Haus is being constructed by a group of students from Brown University. The textile house features a flexible exterior that uses high-performance materials and solar cells. Techstyle Haus is one of two entries from the U.S. competing in the Solar Decathlon Europe 2014. **Availability:** Print; Online.

21459 ■ *"Bridging the Academic-Practitioner Divide in Marketing Decision Models"* in *Journal of Marketing (Vol. 75, July 2011, No. 4, pp. 196)*
Pub: American Marketing Association
Contact: Bennie F. Johnson, Chief Executive Officer
Ed: Gary L. Lilien. **Description:** A study to determine the reason for the relatively low level of practical use of the many marketing models is presented. Changing the incentive and reward systems for marketing academics, practitioners, and intermediaries can bring about adoption and implementation improvements. Those changes could be beneficial by bridging the academic-practitioner divide. **Availability:** PDF.

21460 ■ *"Bridging the Talent Gap Through Partnership and Innovation"* in *Canadian Business (Vol. 81, October 27, 2008, No. 18, pp. 88)*
Description: Research revealed that North America is short by more than 60,000 qualified networking professionals. Businesses, educators and communities are collaborating in order to address the shortfall. **Availability:** Print; Online.

21461 ■ *"Brown Lab Image of R.I. Innovation"* in *Providence Business News (Vol. 28, February 24, 2014, No. 47, pp. 1)*
Pub: American City Business Journals, Inc.
Contact: Mike Olivieri, Executive Vice President
Released: February 22, 2014. **Description:** The Advanced Baby Imaging Lab at Brown University in Rhode Island is studying infant brain development using magnetic resonance imaging (MRI). The lab is attracting attention from researchers from Europe and California who see potential in Sean C. Deoni's technique to take an MRI of an infant without using sedation. **Availability:** Print; Online.

21462 ■ *Business Black Belt: Develop the Strength, Flexibility and Agility to Run Your Company*
Price: $15.99. **Description:** Manual offering insights that will enable anyone to become successful in small business. Seventy short chapters included topics such as attitude, management, marketing, selling, employees, money, MBAs, lawyers, consultants, and investors. **Availability:** Print.

21463 ■ *"CADD Microsystems Launches the CADD Community, Partners with Global eTraining to Provide Online, On-Demand Training for Autodesk Software"* in *Computer Business Week (August 28, 2014, pp. 24)*
Pub: NewsRX LLC.
Contact: Kalani Rosell, Contact
Description: A new online customer-only portal the integrates on-demand training, applications and extension, videos and additional value-added content for customers only was developed by CADD Microsystems. The Autodesk Platinum Partner calls this training program, CADD Community. **Availability:** Online.

21464 ■ *"Cancer-Fighting Entrepreneurs"* in *Austin Business Journal (Vol. 31, August 5, 2011, No. 22, pp. 1)*
Pub: Austin Business Journal
Contact: Rachel McGrath, Director
E-mail: rmcgrath@bizjournals.com
Ed: Sandra Zaragoza. **Description:** Cancer Prevention and Research Institute of Texas has invested $10 million in recruiting known faculty to the University of Texas. The move is seen to bolster Austin's position as a major cancer research market. The institute has awarded grants to researchers Jonghwan Kim, Guangbin Dong and Kyle Miller. **Availability:** Print; Online.

21465 ■ *"Capital One and Count Me In for Women's Economic Independence to Launch Program to Support Women Veteran-Owned Small Businesses Across the U.S."* in *Investment Weekly News (June 23, 2012, pp. 210)*
Description: Capital One Financial Corporation partnered with Count Me In for Women's Economic Independence to help create a new small business training program for women veteran business owners. The not-for-profit providers of business education and resources for women is commited to helping women veterans to succeed. **Availability:** Print; Online.

21466 ■ *"Capitalizing On Our Intellectual Capital"* in *Harvard Business Review (Vol. 90, May 2012, No. 5, pp. 42)*
Pub: Harvard Business Review Press
Contact: Moderna V. Pfizer, Contact
Ed: Iqbal Quadir. **Price:** $6, hardcopy and PDF. **Description:** By managing education as an export, the US can benefit not only from revenue received from tuition, but also from the relationships forged with foreign students. The students will import the networks and technologies they used while in the US and their education levels will help create global growth. **Availability:** Print; Online; PDF.

21467 ■ *"Captain Planet"* in *(Vol. 90, June 2012, No. 6, pp. 112)*
Pub: Harvard Business Review Press
Contact: Moderna V. Pfizer, Contact
Ed: Paul Polman, Adi Ignatius. **Price:** $8.95, hardcopy black and white. **Description:** Paul Polman, chief executive officer of Unilever N.V., discusses his company's sustainable living plan, which integrates social responsibility with corporate objectives. Topics include sustainable sourcing, abolishing quarterly reporting in favor of long-term perspectives, the impact of the 2008 global economic crisis, and turning a company into a learning organization. **Availability:** Print; Online; PDF.

21468 ■ *"Cengage Learning Makes Boston Its Headquarters"* in *Boston Business Journal (Vol. 34, April 25, 2014, No. 12, pp. 6)*
Pub: American City Business Journals, Inc.
Contact: Mike Olivieri, Executive Vice President
Released: April 14, 2014. **Description:** Cengage Learning's office in Boston, Massachusetts will become the company's new corporate headquarters. The educational publishing firm, which has more than 400 employees in Boston, is also expected to develop new digital products for higher education. **Availability:** Print; Mailing list; Online.

21469 ■ *"The CEO of Anglo American On Getting Serious About Safety"* in *(Vol. 90, June 2012, No. 6, pp. 43)*
Pub: Harvard Business Review Press
Contact: Moderna V. Pfizer, Contact
Ed: Cynthia Carroll. **Price:** $8.95, PDF and hardcover black and white. **Description:** The author discusses her decision to shut down Anglo American PLC's platinum mine, the world's largest, for a complete overhaul of the firm's safety procedures. This involved a thorough retraining of the mine's workforce, replacing nearly all of the managers, and promoting the changes throughout the rest of the industry. **Availability:** Print; PDF; Online.

21470 ■ *"The China Connection"* in *Crain's Chicago Business (Vol. 31, March 24, 2008, No. 12, pp. 26)*
Ed: Samantha Stainburn. **Description:** Interview with Ben Munoz who studied abroad in Beijing, China for three months to study international economics, e-commerce and global leadership. **Availability:** Print; Online.

21471 ■ *"Cincinnati Business Committee's Tom Williams: Future is Now"* in *Business Courier (Vol. 27, August 13, 2010, No. 15, pp. 1)*
Pub: Business Courier
Ed: Lucy May. **Description:** Tom Williams, chairman of the Cincinnati Business Committee (CBC), maintains that politicians and business leaders must cooperate to ensure the competitiveness of the city for the 21st Century. Under Williams' leadership, the CBC has put emphasis on initiatives related to government efficiency, economic development, and public education. Williams' views on a proposed inland port are given. **Availability:** Print; Online.

21472 ■ Classes to Consider Taking When Starting a Business
URL(s): www.kabbage.com/resource-center/start/classes-to-consider-taking-when-starting-a-business/
Description: One of the best ways to get a better understanding of the needs of a new business is to take classes that can help you succeed in any industry. This article provides suggested areas of study to ensure that you are able to get your small business off on the right foot. Availability: Online.

21473 ■ "The Colt Effect" in Hawaii Business (Vol. 53, January 2008, No. 7, pp. 30)
Pub: PacificBasin Communications
Contact: Chuck Tindle, Director
E-mail: chuckt@pacificbasin.net
Ed: David K. Choo. Description: Participation at the Bowl Championship Games can help the University of Hawaii financially. Playing at a prominent sports event could provoke donations from alumni and increase enrollment at the university. Examples of universities that earned generous income by becoming a part of prestigious sporting events are presented. Availability: Online.

21474 ■ "Computer Science for All: Can Schools Pull It Off?" in Education Week (February 19, 2018)
URL(s): www.edweek.org/ew/articles/2018/02/20/computer-science-for-all-can-schools-pull.html
Ed: Benjamin Herold. Released: February 18, 2018. Description: The White House has backed a vision to get more computer-science courses and technology into the classrooms, in order to get more kids interested in the subject. However, there is debate on whether the new initiative should focus on preparing students for jobs or to teach them new ways to think. Also, there is the practical challenge of getting the tech into the classroom and keeping it updated. Availability: Online.

21475 ■ "Continuing Education Courses Every Business Owner Should Consider" in Legal Zoom (February 22, 2023)
URL(s): www.legalzoom.com/articles/continuing-education-courses-every-business-owner-should-consider
Ed: Kylie Ora Lobell. Released: February 22, 2023. Description: Continuing education courses are very useful in keeping up with new trends when it comes to management, marketing, e-commerce, and many other aspects that will keep your business running smoothly. Availability: Online.

21476 ■ "Contractors Debate Maximizing Green Opportunities, Education" in Contractor (Vol. 56, November 2009, No. 11, pp. 3)
Ed: Robert P. Mader. Description: Attendees at the Mechanical Service Contractors Association convention were urged to get involved with their local U.S. Green Building Council chapter by one presenter. Another presenter says that one green opportunity for contractors is the commissioning of new buildings. Availability: Print; Online.

21477 ■ "Could UNC Charlotte Be Home to Future Med School?" in Charlotte Business Journal (Vol. 25, July 23, 2010, No. 18, pp. 1)
Pub: Charlotte Business Journal
Contact: Robert Morris, Editor
E-mail: rmorris@bizjournals.com
Ed: Jennifer Thomas. Description: University of North Carolina, Charlotte chancellor Phil Dubois is proposing that a medical school be established at the campus. The idea began in 2007 and Dubois' plan is for students to spend all four years in Charlotte and train at the Carolinas Medical Center. Availability: Print; Online.

21478 ■ "Craning for Workers: Seattle Is Full of Cranes, but Not Enough Operators" in Puget Sound Business Journal (Vol. 35, August 15, 2014, No. 17, pp. 4)
Pub: American City Business Journals, Inc.
Contact: Mike Olivieri, Executive Vice President
Released: August 15, 2014. Description: The U.S. Department of Labor statistics show that Washington State has 15, 510 laborers in 2013. However, construction companies are having difficulty hiring skilled workers, particularly as apprentices. The Associated General Contractors of Washington's expansion of training slots for crane and other heave equipment operators is discussed. Availability: Print; Online.

21479 ■ "A Crash Course in Global Relations" in Canadian Business (Vol. 87, July 2014, No. 7, pp. 77)
Description: Teach Away Inc. is a global education firm based in Toronto, Ontario that recruits English-speaking teachers to work abroad. The firm's revenues have grown by 1,621 percent from 2008 to 2013, placing it in the 37th spot on the 2014 Profit ranking of fastest growing companies in Canada. Availability: Online.

21480 ■ "Crew Training Changes Tactics" in Memphis Business Journal (Vol. 33, March 16, 2012, No. 49, pp. 1)
Pub: Baltimore Business Journal
Contact: Rhonda Pringle, President
E-mail: rpringle@bizjournals.com
Ed: Cole Epley. Description: Teamwork and communication training services firm Crew Training International Inc. has revamped its strategy and executive board as it moved from small to mid-tier status. The recalibration of strategy comes along with a renovation at the headquarters in southeast Memphis, Tennessee. Availability: Print; Online.

21481 ■ "Culinary School Puts a Food Truck on the Road" in St. Louis Post-Dispatch (March 21, 2012)
Ed: Joe Bonwich. Description: Le Food Truck is a teach tool to help students learn about the fast-growing food truck market. Tony Hedger, instructor at L'Ecole Culinaire, a career college located in Laude, Missouri, coordinated the new program. The school also operates the Presentation Room, a restaurant used as part of the classroom. Availability: Print; Online.

21482 ■ "Day-Care Center Owner to Argue Against Liquor Store Opening Nearby" in Chicago Tribune (March 13, 2008)
Pub: Tribune News Service
Contact: Jack Barry, Vice President, Operations
E-mail: jbarry@tribpub.com
Ed: Matthew Walberg. Description: NDLC's owner feels that Greenwood Liquors should not be granted its liquor license due to the claim that the NDLC is not only a day-care center but also a school that employs state-certified teachers. Availability: Print; Online.

21483 ■ "Deal Made for Pontiac Home of Film Studio" in Crain's Detroit Business (Vol. 25, June 1, 2009, No. 22, pp. 3)
Pub: Crain Communications Inc.
Contact: Barry Asin, President
Ed: Daniel Duggan. Description: Details of the $75 million movie production and training facility in Pontiac, Michigan are revealed. Availability: Print; Online.

21484 ■ "Deep Thoughts: Getting Employees to Think Better Requires a Bit of Creative Thinking Itself" in Canadian Business (March 17, 2008)
Description: Discusses the reason a company needs to make their employees understand that ideas are the stuff of life. For employees to be more creative, they need to cultivate spark moments, play with possibilities, and venture into the unknown. Availability: Print; Online; PDF.

21485 ■ "Design program in Athletic Footwear" in Occupational Outlook Quarterly (Vol. 55, Fall 2011, No. 3, pp. 21)
Description: The Fashion Institute of Technology offers the only certificate program in performance athletic footwear design in the U.S. The program focuses on conceptualizing and sketching shoe designs and covers ergonomic, anatomical, and material considerations for athletic footwear design. Availability: Print; Online.

21486 ■ "Digital-Physical Mashups: To Consumers, the Real and Virtual Worlds Are One. The Same Should Go For Your Company" in Harvard Business Review (Vol. 92, September 2014, No. 9, pp. 84)
Pub: Harvard Business Publishing
Contact: Diane Belcher, Managing Director
Price: $8.95. Description: By merging their physical and virtual operations, companies can provide a seamless experience for customers, boosting competitive advantage. These include strengthening customer/engagement links, approaching innovation through complementary expertise, and ensure that chief executive officers possess adequate technological knowledge. Availability: Online; PDF.

21487 ■ "Dispelling Rocky Mountain Myths Key to Wellness" in Employee Benefit News (Vol. 25, November 1, 2011, No. 14, pp. 12)
Pub: SourceMedia LLC
Contact: Gemma Postlethwaite, Chief Executive Officer
Ed: Andrea Davis. Description: Andrew Sykes, chairman of Health at Work Wellness Actuaries, states that it is a myth that Colorado is ranked as the healthiest state in America. Sykes helped implement a wellness programs at Brighton School District in the Denver area.

21488 ■ "Don't Shoot the Messenger: A Wake-Up Call For Academics" in Academy of Management Journal (Vol. 50, No. 5, October 1, 2007, pp. 1020)
Pub: Academy of Management
Contact: Sharon Alvarez, President
Ed: David E. Guest. Description: Author evaluates two well-known publications: HR Magazine and People Management, to emphasize the role of U.S. academics in communicating management practice. Availability: Electronic publishing; PDF; Download; Online.

21489 ■ "Downtowns Must Court Young, CEOs for Cities President Says" in Crain's Detroit Business (Vol. 24, October 6, 2008, No. 40, pp. 18)
Description: It is important to produce more college graduates, and keep them in Michigan, according to CEOs for Cities President Carol Coletta when she spoke to a session at the West Michigan Regional Policy Conference which was held in September in Grand Rapids. Ways in which city leaders can connect students to communities, resulting in employees who have vested interest in the region, are also discussed.

21490 ■ "Dozens 'Come Alive' in Downtown Chicago" in Green Industry Pro (July 2011)
Ed: Gregg Wartgow. Description: Highlights from the Come Alive Outside training event held in Chicago, Illinois July 14-15, 2011 are shared. Nearly 80 people representing 38 landscape companies attended the event that helps contractors review their services and find ways to sell them in new and various ways. Availability: Online.

21491 ■ "East Coast Solar" in Contractor (Vol. 57, February 2010, No. 2, pp. 17)
Ed: Dave Yates. Description: U.S. Department of Energy's Solar Decathlon lets 20 college student-led teams from around the world compete to design and build a solar-powered home. A mechanical contractor discusses his work as an advisor during the competition. Availability: Print; Online.

21492 ■ "The Economics of Well-Being: Have We Found a Better Gauge of Success Than GDP?" in Harvard Business Review (Vol. 90, January-February 2012, No.1-2, pp. 78)
Pub: Harvard Business Review Press
Contact: Moderna V. Pfizer, Contact

Ed: Justin Fox. **Price:** $8.95. **Description:** Gross domestic product is no longer a valid means of determining national success. GDP does not take into account factors such as unpaid housework and sustainability. Other metrics may be more accurate and encompassing, including life expectancy, individual freedom, and educational achievement. **Availability:** Online; PDF.

21493 ■ *"An Educated Play on China"* in *Barron's (Vol. 88, June 30, 2008, No. 26, pp. M6)*
Pub: Dow Jones & Company Inc.
Contact: Almar Latour, Chief Executive Officer
Ed: Mohammed Hadi. **Description:** New Oriental Education & Technology Group sells English-language courses to an increasingly competitive Chinese workforce that values education. The shares in this company have been weighed down by worries on the impact of the Beijing Olympics on enrollment and the Sichuan earthquake. These shares could be a great way to get exposure to the long-term growth in China. **Availability:** Online.

21494 ■ *"Elkhart Education Foundation to Open Supply Store for Teachers"* in *The Elkart Truth (June 5, 2019)*
URL(s): www.elkharttruth.com/news/elkhart-education-foundation-to-open-supply-store-for-teachers/article_828c0fea-d97f-5e41-b31e-806d82ec034c.html
Released: June 05, 2019. **Description:** The Elkhart Education Foundation has recognized that teachers often spend hundreds of their own dollars buying classroom supplies. To help alleviate that spending, the foundation is creating a teacher store where teachers can get any supplies and items they need for their classes. **Availability:** Online.

21495 ■ *"Embry-Riddle Aeronautical University Opening Alliance Campus"* in *Dallas Business Journal (Vol. 35, May 25, 2012, No. 37, pp. 1)*
Pub: Baltimore Business Journal
Contact: Rhonda Pringle, President
E-mail: rpringle@bizjournals.com
Ed: Matt Joyce. **Description:** Embry-Riddle Aeronautical University is set to open a campus at Fort Worth Alliance Airport. The plan is part of the university's efforts to supply the workforce demands of the aviation and aerospace sectors. Comments from university officials are also included.

21496 ■ *"EMU, Spark Plan Business Incubator for Ypsilanti"* in *Crain's Detroit Business (Vol. 23, October 15, 2007, No. 42, pp. 3)*
Pub: Crain Communications Inc.
Contact: Barry Asin, President
Ed: Chad Halcom. **Description:** Eastern Michigan University is seeking federal grants and other funding for a new business incubator program that would be in cooperation with Ann Arbor Spark. The site would become a part of a network of three Spark incubator programs with a focus on innovation in biotechnology and pharmaceuticals. **Availability:** Print; Online.

21497 ■ *"Encouraging Study in Critical Languages"* in *Occupational Outlook Quarterly (Vol. 55, Summer 2011, No. 2, pp. 23)*
Description: Proficiency in particular foreign languages is vital to the defense, diplomacy, and security of the United States. Several federal programs provide scholarships and other funding to encourage high school and college students to learn languages of the Middle East, China, and Russia. **Availability:** Print; Online.

21498 ■ *"The End of RIM"* in *Canadian Business (Vol. 85, August 13, 2012, No. 13, pp. 22)*
Ed: Joe Castaldo. **Description:** The potential implications of the collapse of Research in Motion (RIM) on the Canadian technology sector are examined. The country is expected to lose its biggest training ground for technology talent without RIM, but the company's decline will not stop Canadians from trying to build and sustain multinational technolgy companies. **Availability:** Print; Online.

21499 ■ *"Endowments for Colleges Hit Hard in '09"* in *Milwaukee Business Journal (Vol. 27, February 12, 2010, No. 20, pp. A1)*
Pub: The Business Journal
Contact: Heather Ladage, President
E-mail: hladage@bizjournals.com
Ed: Corrinne Hess. **Description:** Southeast Wisconsin college endowments declined by as much as 35 percent in 2009 due to the economic downturn. A list of 2009 endowments to colleges in southeast Wisconsin and their percent change from 2008 is presented. **Availability:** Print; Online.

21500 ■ *"Energy Exec Bankrolls Big-Budget UT Film"* in *Austin Business Journal (Vol. 34, June 6, 2014, No. 16, pp. A8)*
Pub: American City Business Journals, Inc.
Contact: Mike Olivieri, Executive Vice President
Released: Weekly. **Price:** $4, introductory 4-week offer(Digital only). **Description:** Bud Brigham, CEO of the energy firm Brigham Resources is bankrolling the film, "My All American" that focuses on University of Texas football coach Darrell K. Royal. The film is about his bond with star player Freddie Steinmark during the 1969 national championship season. Through this film, Brigham hopes to establish himself in Hollywood and dreams of being as big as Disney. **Availability:** Print; Online.

21501 ■ *"Enriching the Ecosystem: A Four-Point Plan for Linking Innovation, Enterprises, and Jobs"* in *Harvard Business Review (Vol. 90, March 2012, No. 3, pp. 140)*
Pub: Harvard Business Review Press
Contact: Moderna V. Pfizer, Contact
Ed: Rosabeth Moss Kanter. **Price:** $8.95, hardcopy black and white. **Description:** The four goals for enriching the ecosystem include: linking venture creation and knowledge creation to speed up the idea-to-enterprise transition; revitalizing small-, medium-, and large-sized firms via partnerships; improving matches between education and employment opportunities; and bringing together leaders across different sectors to create regional strategies. **Availability:** Print; PDF; Online.

21502 ■ *"Etextbook Space Heats Up"* in *Information Today (Vol. 28, November 2011, No. 10, pp. 10)*
Pub: Information Today Inc.
Contact: Thomas H. Hogan, President
Ed: Paula J. Hane. **Description:** The use of etextbooks is expected to grow with the use of mobile devices and tablets. A new group of activists is asking students, faculty members and others to sign a petition urging higher education leaders to prioritize affordable textbooks or free ebooks over the traditional, expensive new books required for classes.

21503 ■ *"Etextbooks: Coming of Age"* in *Information Today (Vol. 28, September 2011, No. 8, pp. 1)*
Pub: Information Today Inc.
Contact: Thomas H. Hogan, President
Ed: Amanda Mulvihill. **Description:** National average for textbooks costs was estimated at $1,137 annually at a 4-year public college for the 2010-2011 school year. Amazon reported selling 105 etextbooks for every 100 print books, while Barnes and Noble announced that their etextbooks were outselling print 3 to 1.

21504 ■ *"EVMS Gets Grant to Train Providers for Elder Care"* in *Virginian-Pilot (October 29, 2010)*
Pub: The Virginian-Pilot
Contact: Kevin Goyette, Director
E-mail: kgoyette@dailypress.com
Ed: Elizabeth Simpson. **Description:** Eastern Virginia Medical School received a federal grant to train health providers in elder care. Details of the program are provided. **Availability:** Online.

21505 ■ *"Executive Training"* in *Black Enterprise (Vol. 37, December 2006, No. 5, pp. 70)*
Description: Roy N. Gundy Jr. was preparing to introduce a new strategic plan within his division and understood that his plan may fail if not executed properly. He discusses his experience in the Wharton School's executive education workshop Implementing Strategy, at the University of Pennsylvania and gives tips on putting strategy into action. **Availability:** Print; Online.

21506 ■ *"Expanding the Entrepreneur Class"* in *Harvard Business Review (Vol. 90, July-August 2012, No. 7-8, pp. 40)*
Pub: Harvard Business Review Press
Contact: Moderna V. Pfizer, Contact
Ed: Carl Schramm. **Price:** $6, PDF and hardcover black and white. **Description:** Two programs for encouraging entrepreneurship are highlighted. One offers trained facilitators who help participants move through iterations to produce viable business models. Another provides college juniors and seniors with instruction and advice from successful businesspeople. **Availability:** Print; PDF; Online.

21507 ■ *"Experts Strive to Educate on Proper Pet Diets"* in *Pet Product News (Vol. 64, November 2010, No. 11, pp. 40)*
Ed: Joan Hustace Walker. **Description:** Pet supply manufacturers have been bundling small mammal food and treats with educational sources to help retailers avoid customer misinformation. This action has been motivated by the customer's quest to seek proper nutritional advice for their small mammal pets. **Availability:** Online.

21508 ■ *"Exploring Supportive and Developmental Career Management Through Business Strategies and Coaching"* in *Human Resource Management (Vol. 51, January-February 2012, No. 1, pp. 99-120)*
Pub: John Wiley & Sons, Inc.
Contact: Christina Van Tassell, Executive Vice President Chief Financial Officer
Ed: Jesse Segers, Ilke Inceoglu. **Released:** January 26, 2012. **Description:** Coaching and other career practices that are part of supportive and developmental career management are examined. Such practices are found to be most present in organizations with a prospector strategy. **Availability:** Print; PDF; Online.

21509 ■ *"Face Time: Fastenal founder Bob Kierlin and CEO Will Oberton"* in *Business Journal (Vol. 31, January 31, 2014, No. 36, pp. 9)*
Pub: American City Business Journals, Inc.
Contact: Mike Olivieri, Executive Vice President
Released: Weekly. **Price:** $4, Introductory 4-week offer(Digital & Print). **Description:** Fastenal founder, Bob Kierline, keeps hiring standards high in order to promote his firm's growth. He also said Fastenal's School of Business employs 40 licensed teachers. Their CEO, Will Oberton, said the company has done a better job in customer relations than its competitors. **Availability:** Print; Online.

21510 ■ *"Facilitating and Rewarding Creativity During New Product Development"* in *Journal of Marketing (Vol. 75, July 2011, No. 4, pp. 53)*
Pub: American Marketing Association
Contact: Bennie F. Johnson, Chief Executive Officer
Ed: James E. Burroughs, Darren W. Dahl, C. Page Moreau, Amitava Chattopadhay, Gerald J. Gorn. **Description:** A study to determine the effects of rewards to creativity in the process of new product development is presented. The findings show that the effect of rewards can be made positive if combined with appropriate creativity training. **Availability:** PDF.

21511 ■ *"Falcons' Blank Kicking Off 'Westside Works' Job Training Program"* in *Atlanta Business Chronicle (May 30, 2014, pp. 6A)*
Pub: American City Business Journals, Inc.
Contact: Mike Olivieri, Executive Vice President

Description: Arthur Blank, owner of the Atlanta Falcons, is kicking off 'Westside Works', an initiative to build a world-class football/soccer stadium in Atlanta and transform the adjacent communities. Westside Works, a partnership between The Arthur M. Blank Family Foundation, the Construction Education Foundation of Georgia, and Integrity CDC will provide construction jobs for at least 100 men and women from the Westside neighborhoods in the next 12 months. The program will also provide job training, skills assessment, adult education programs, interview preparedness, and job placement. **Availability:** Print; Online.

21512 ■ *"Feds to Pay University Hospital $20M"* in *Business Courier (Vol. 27, July 23, 2010, No. 12, pp. 3)*
Pub: Business Courier

Ed: James Ritchie. **Description:** The U.S. government is set to pay University Hospital and medical residents who trained there $20 million as part of a tax dispute settlement. Around 1,000 former residents are to receive tax refunds. But the hospital must provide the U.S. Internal Revenue Service with extensive documentation. **Availability:** Print; Mailing list; Online.

21513 ■ *"Fighting The Good Fight - Against Hate"* in *Inc. (Vol. 33, October 2011, No. 8, pp. 8)*

Description: Rob Roy, former Navy SEAL, runs SOT-G a firm that offers an 80-hour leadership training course inspired by military combat preparations. Details of the program are outlined. **Availability:** Online.

21514 ■ *"Finding Life Behind the Numbers"* in *Crain's Chicago Business (Vol. 31, March 24, 2008, No. 12, pp. 25)*
Pub: Crain Communications Inc.
Contact: Barry Asin, President

Ed: Samantha Stainburn. **Description:** Interview with Phillip Capodice who is a graduate student at DePaul University's Kellstadt Graduate School of Business and studied abroad in Lima, Peru where he visited a number of companies including some who are trade partners with the United States. **Availability:** Online.

21515 ■ *"Finishing High School Leads to Better Employment Prospects"* in *Occupational Outlook Quarterly (Vol. 55, Summer 2011, No. 2, pp. 36)*
Pub: U.S. Department of Labor Bureau of Labor Statistics
Contact: Amrit Kohli, Director
E-mail: kohli.amrit@bls.gov

Description: Students who drop out of high school are more likely to face unemployment than those who finish. Statistical data included. **Availability:** PDF; Online.

21516 ■ *"The Firm: The Story of McKinsey and Its Secret Influence on American Business"*
Pub: Simon & Schuster Adult Publishing Group
Contact: Jonathan Karp, President

Released: September 30, 2014. **Price:** $20, paperback, plus $1.55 shipping charges. **Description:** Profile of McKinsey & Company, the most influential and controversial business consulting firm in the United States. McKinsey consultants have ushered in waves of structural, financial, and technological change to America's best organizations; they've reorganized the power structure within the White House; and they have revolutionized business schools. **Availability:** E-book; Print.

21517 ■ *"Five New Scientists Bring Danforth Center $16 Million"* in *Saint Louis Business Journal (Vol. 32, October 7, 2011, No. 6, pp. 1)*
Pub: Saint Louis Business Journal
Contact: Robert Bobroff, President
E-mail: rbobroff@bizjournals.com

Ed: E.B. Solomont. **Description:** Donald Danforth Plant Science Center's appointment of five new lead scientists has increased its federal funding by $16 million. Cornell University scientist Tom Brutnell is one of the five new appointees. **Availability:** Print; Online.

21518 ■ *"Florida Hospital, UCF Affiliation in Danger?"* in *Orlando Business Journal (Vol. 29, September 21, 2012, No. 29, pp. 1)*
Pub: Baltimore Business Journal
Contact: Rhonda Pringle, President
E-mail: rpringle@bizjournals.com

Description: Florida Hospital is said to be considering the possibility of terminating its affiliation agreement with the University of Central Florida's (UCF) College of Medicine that ends June 30, 2018. Two of the reasons for the move include UCF's plans for a teaching hospital and a new graduate medical education program that could place Florida Hospital into competition with UCF. **Availability:** Print; Online.

21519 ■ *"For-Profit Medical School Ramping Up for Business"* in *Sacramento Business Journal (Vol. 30, February 21, 2014, No. 52, pp. 6)*
Pub: American City Business Journals, Inc.
Contact: Mike Olivieri, Executive Vice President

Description: California Northstate University got full accreditation for the College of Pharmacy at Elk Grove in summer 2013 and hopes to start classes in August or September 2014. The university is in talks to acquire a second building in the area worth $15 million. **Availability:** Online.

21520 ■ *"Forward Motion"* in *Green Industry Pro (July 2011)*

Ed: Gregg Wartgow. **Description:** Several landscape contractors have joined this publication's Working Smarter Training Challenge over the last year. This process is helping them develop ways to improve work processes, boost morale, drive out waste, reduce costs, improve customer service, and be more competitive. **Availability:** Print; Online.

21521 ■ *"Future Autoworkers will Need Broader Skills"* in *Crain's Detroit Business (Vol. 25, June 8, 2009, No. 23, pp. 13)*
Pub: Crain Communications Inc.
Contact: Barry Asin, President

Ed: Ryan Beene. **Description:** Auto industry observers report that new workers in the industry will need advanced skills and educational backgrounds in engineering and technical fields because jobs in the factories will become more technology-based and multidisciplinary. **Availability:** Online.

21522 ■ *"The Future Is Another Country; Higher Education"* in *The Economist (Vol. 390, January 3, 2009, No. 8612, pp. 43)*

Description: Due to the growth of the global corporation, more ambitious students are studying at universities abroad; the impact of this trend is discussed. **Availability:** Print; Online.

21523 ■ *"Ga. PMA Launches Online Education Program"* in *Contractor (Vol. 56, October 2009, No. 10, pp. 8)*

Description: Plumbing & Mechanical Association of Georgia launched an online program that covers technical and business management that will help contractors run their businesses. Future courses will include math for plumbers, graywater systems, and recession-proofing your business. **Availability:** Print; Online.

21524 ■ *"The Gender Wage Gap: What Local Firms Plan To Do About It"* in *Orlando Business Journal (Vol. 30, May 2, 2014, No. 45, pp. 4)*
Pub: American City Business Journals, Inc.
Contact: Mike Olivieri, Executive Vice President

Released: Weekly. **Price:** $8, introductory 4-week offer(Digital & Print). **Description:** Reports show that women in Orlando, Florida earn 20 percent less than men. The gender wage gap trend in the city can be attributed to bias and women working in lower-wage positions. Graphs that present information on income gap by education and income gap by industry are also given. **Availability:** Print; Online.

21525 ■ *"Giving Biotech Startups a Hand"* in *Philadelphia Business Journal (Vol. 28, January 8, 2010, No. 47, pp. 1)*
Pub: Philadelphia Business Journal
Contact: Sierra Quinn, Director
E-mail: squinn@bizjournals.com

Ed: John George. **Description:** Elkins Park, Pennsylvania-based BioStrategy Partners is a virtual life sciences incubator that is seeking to improve the dull ranking of Philadelphia in the small business vitality index of life sciences. BioStrategy provides technology and business development services to startup life sciences companies and university-based research projects. **Availability:** Online.

21526 ■ *"Global Business Speaks English: Why You Need a Language Strategy Now"* in *Harvard Business Review (Vol. 90, May 2012, No. 5, pp. 116)*
Pub: Harvard Business Review Press
Contact: Moderna V. Pfizer, Contact

Ed: Tsedal Neeley. **Price:** $8.95. **Description:** English is rapidly becoming the language of businesses regardless of where they are located. To improve efficiency, the author advocates implementing an English-only policy. However, this must be conducted with sufficient training and support, and appropriate cultural sensitivity. **Availability:** PDF; Online.

21527 ■ *"Globalization: Canada Tomorrow"* in *Canadian Business (Vol. 80, October 8, 2007, No. 20, pp. 14)*

Description: An assessment of Canada's future in terms of its educational, social, and economic environment is presented. Concerns regarding the country's educational system such as the declining interest in science and technology and the possible lack of teachers in the future are discussed. In terms of its social and economic aspects, the need to support entrepreneurs and other qualified people is explained. **Availability:** Online.

21528 ■ *"Grant Program Boosting Biomedical Research"* in *Providence Business News (Vol. 28, February 24, 2014, No. 47, pp. 3)*
Pub: American City Business Journals, Inc.
Contact: Mike Olivieri, Executive Vice President

Released: February 22, 2014. **Description:** The role played by the Institutional Development Award Network of Biomedical Research Excellence (INBRE) is boosting biomedical research in Rhode Island. According to researcher, Niall G. Howlett, procuring startup funding through INBRE led to receiving other grants and working with graduate students who have the potential to become part of the biomedical workforce. **Availability:** Print; Online.

21529 ■ *"Grant Could Help Schools Harness Wind"* in *Dallas Business Journal (Vol. 37, April 11, 2014, No. 31, pp. 8)*
Pub: American City Business Journals, Inc.
Contact: Mike Olivieri, Executive Vice President

Released: Weekly. **Price:** $4, introductory 4-week offer(Digital only); $4, introductory 4-week offer(Digital & Print). **Description:** Five universities led by Texas A&M have received a $2.2 million grant from the Texas Emerging Technologies Fund for use in wind technology research. The research will focus on turbines that feature bigger blades to capture more wind. Technology developed by the universities will eventually be handed to the state. **Availability:** Print; Online.

21530 ■ *"Groomers Eye Profit Growth Through Services"* in *Pet Product News (Vol. 64, December 2010, No. 12, pp. 26)*

Ed: Kathleen M. Mangan. **Description:** Pet groomers can successfully offer add-on services by taking into account insider customer knowledge, store image, and financial analysis in the decision-making process. Many pet groomers have decided to add services such as spa treatments and training due to a slump in the bathing and grooming business. How some pet groomers gained profitability through add-on services is explored. **Availability:** Online.

21531 ■ *"Ground Forces: Insurance Companies Should Help Agents to Build the Skills and Relationships that Translate Into More Business"* in *Best's Review (Vol. 113, September 2012, No. 5, pp. 25)*
Description: The economic challenges of the past few years required insurance agents and financial professionals to better trained. Insurance companies should help their agents build skills and relationships in order to grow. **Availability:** Print; Online.

21532 ■ *"Group Thinking"* in *Business Strategy Review (Vol. 23, Spring 2012, No. 1, pp. 48)*
Description: Conflicts and decision making in groups has long been a subject of fascination for Randall Peterson, Professor of Organizational Behavior at London Business School. He talks to Business Strategy Review about what ignited his interest and his latest research and thinking. **Availability:** Print; Online.

21533 ■ *"GSK Creating Pathways From Academia to Industry"* in *Philadelphia Business Journal (Vol. 33, March 7, 2014, No. 4, pp. 8)*
Pub: American City Business Journals, Inc.
Contact: Mike Olivieri, Executive Vice President
Released: Weekly. **Price:** $4, introductory 4-week offer(Digital & Print). **Description:** The Discovery Fast Track Challenge program of GlaxoSmithKline will expand in 2014 to include scientists in North America and Europe. Scientists will be asked to submit information about their innovative drug research proposals and the winner could be offered a deal with the Discovery Partnerships with Academia team. **Availability:** Print; Online.

21534 ■ *"Health Science Center's Capital Campaign Will Boost Local Research"* in *San Antonio Business Journal (Vol. 28, March 14, 2014, No. 5, pp. 8)*
Pub: American City Business Journals, Inc.
Contact: Mike Olivieri, Executive Vice President
Description: The University of Texas Health Science Center at San Antonio's Campaign for the Future of fundraising project has been completed. The Health Science Center is expected to use the money to support research at the South Texas Medical Center. The capital campaign will allow the Health Science Center to become one of the most prominent universities in the U.S. **Availability:** Print; Online.

21535 ■ *"Healthy Start for Medical Kiosks; Lions Kick in $20K"* in *Crain's Detroit Business" (Vol. 28, June 11, 2012, No. 24, pp. 18)*
Pub: Crain Communications Inc.
Contact: Barry Asin, President
Ed: Jay Greene. **Description:** Detroit Lions Charities has given Henry Ford Health System's school-based and community health program money to purchase nine interactive health kiosks. These kiosks will be provided by Medical Imagineering LLC, a spinoff of Henry Ford's Innovation Institute and installed in elementary and middle schools in Detroit. **Availability:** Print; Online.

21536 ■ *"Henry Mintzberg: Still the Zealous Skeptic and Scold"* in *Strategy and Leadership (Vol. 39, March-April 2011, No. 2, pp. 4)*
Pub: Emerald Group Publishing Limited
Contact: Erika Valenti, President
Ed: Robert J. Allio. **Description:** Henry Mintzberg, professor at the McGill University in Montreal, Canada, shares his thoughts on issues such as inappropriate methods in management education and on trends in leadership and management. Mintzberg believes that US businesses are facing serious management and leadership challenges. **Availability:** Download; Online.

21537 ■ *"Higher-Ed Finally in Session"* in *Business Journal Portland (Vol. 30, February 7, 2014, No. 49, pp. 4)*
Pub: American City Business Journals, Inc.
Contact: Mike Olivieri, Executive Vice President
Released: February 07, 2014. **Price:** $4, Introductory 4-Week Offer(Digital & Print). **Description:** Oregon lawmakers and voters are set to consider several proposals on how higher education is funded, including free community college and free college for a percentage of future earnings. State Treasurer, Ted Wheeler, is proposing a large endowment that would pay for scholarships and vocational training. **Availability:** Print; Online.

21538 ■ *"Hire Education: An Emerging Cohort"* in *Canadian Business (Vol. 79, September 11, 2006, No. 18, pp. 114)*
Pub: LNRS Data Services Limited
Contact: Mark Vickers Kelsey, Director
Ed: Erin Pooley. **Description:** Study results showing the perceptions of students while considering full-time employment and the attributes they look for in their future employers are presented. **Availability:** Online.

21539 ■ *"Hiring Unpaid Interns: Failing To Comply With Labor Laws Can Lead to Legal Trouble"* in *Black Enterprise (Vol. 44, June 2014, No. 10, pp. 22)*
Pub: Earl G. Graves Ltd.
Contact: Earl Graves, Jr., President
Description: Before hiring an intern for a small business it is critical to study the Department of Labor's legal criteria, determine whether the internship should be paid or unpaid, weigh the pros and cons, focus on the training aspect, and work with local colleges.

21540 ■ *"His Brother's Keeper: A Mentor Learns the True Meaning of Leadership"* in *Black Enterprise (Vol. 37, December 2006, No. 5, pp. 69)*
Pub: Earl G. Graves Ltd.
Contact: Earl Graves, Jr., President
Ed: Laura Egodigwe. **Description:** Interview with Keith R. Wyche of Pitney Bowes Management Services, which discusses the relationship between a mentor and mentee as well as sponsorship. **Availability:** Online.

21541 ■ *"Home Instead Senior Care of Seacoast and Southern New Hampshire"* in *New Hampshire Business Review (Vol. 34, April 6, 2012, No. 7, pp. 45)*
Description: Portsmouth, New Hampshire-based Home Instead Senior Care of Seacoast and Southern New Hampshire launched a specialized training program for professional and family caregivers designed to help them improve the quality of life for those living with dementia and the families who support them. **Availability:** Online.

21542 ■ *"Hopkins' Security, Reputation Face Challenges in Wake of Slaying"* in *Baltimore Business Journal (Vol. 28, August 6, 2010, No. 13)*
Pub: Baltimore Business Journal
Contact: Rhonda Pringle, President
E-mail: rpringle@bizjournals.com
Ed: Gary Haber. **Description:** The slaying of Johns Hopkins University researcher Stephen Pitcairn has not tarnished the reputation of the elite school in Baltimore, Maryland among students. Maintaining Hopkins' reputation is important since it is Baltimore's largest employer with nearly 32,000 workers. Insights on the impact of the slaying among the Hopkins' community are also given.

21543 ■ *"How Busy Executives Manage to Live a Balanced Life"* in *Influencive(March 20, 2019)*
URL(s): www.influencive.com/how-busy-executives-manage-to-live-a-balanced-life/

Ed: Kiara Williams. **Released:** March 20, 2019. **Description:** Discusses how those in the C-suite are able to run corporations while also maintaining some balance in their personal lives. **Availability:** Online.

21544 ■ *"How I Became a Serial Entrepreneur"* in *Baltimore Business Journal (Vol. 31, April 18, 2014, No. 51, pp. 26)*
Pub: American City Business Journals, Inc.
Contact: Mike Olivieri, Executive Vice President
Description: Dr. Lisa Beth Ferstenberg, a physician by training, teaches a course at the Maryland Center for Entrepreneurship in Columbia to help CEOs attract prospective investors. Dr. Ferstenberg is also the chief medical officer at Sequella Inc. She reflects on the kind of personality required to become a successful entrepreneur and the mistakes entrepreneurs make in raising capital funding. **Availability:** Print; Online.

21545 ■ *"How to Survive This Mess"* in *Crain's Chicago Business (Vol. 31, April 14, 2008, No. 15, pp. 18)*
Pub: Crain Communications Inc.
Contact: Barry Asin, President
Ed: Christina Le Beau. **Description:** Small business owners can make it through a possible recession with preparations such as reviewing their balance sheet and cash flow every week and spotting trends then reacting quickly to them. **Availability:** Online.

21546 ■ *"How To Prevent Cyber Crime At Your Biz"* in *Birmingham Business Journal (Vol. 31, March 14, 2014, No. 11, pp. 10)*
Pub: American City Business Journals, Inc.
Contact: Mike Olivieri, Executive Vice President
Released: Weekly. **Price:** $4, introductory 4-week offer(Digital only). **Description:** Ways businesses can prevent cyber attacks are prevented. Employees should be educated to be aware of cyber crimes. Policies on confidentiality and privacy should also be established in business organizations. **Availability:** Print; Online.

21547 ■ *"Human Resource Management: Challenges for Graduate Education"* in *Business Horizons (Vol. 51, March-April 2008, No. 2, pp. 151)*
Pub: Elsevier Advanced Technology Publications
Ed: James C. Wimbush. **Description:** Human resource management education at the master's and doctoral degree levels is discussed. There is an ever-increasing need to produce human resource managers who understand the value of human resource management as a strategic business contributor. **Availability:** PDF; Online.

21548 ■ *"IMPACT Fitness Boot Camp Training Now Approved for NESTA Credits for Personal Trainer Certification"* in *Marketing Weekly News (January 28, 2012)*
Description: Intense Mixed Performance Accelerated Cross Training (IMPACT) helps personal trainers impact their clients' lives as well as their own income. However, the IMPACT fitness certification program now qualifies trainers for continuing education credits through the National Exercise & Sports Trainers Assocation's (NESTA) Personal Fitness Trainer program. The online IMPACT fitness training and business systems helps personal trainers create a successful fitness business in any 30x30 foot space. **Availability:** Online.

21549 ■ *"Innovation Station"* in *Canadian Business (Vol. 80, October 8, 2007, No. 20, pp. 42)*
Description: Study and teaching of entrepreneurship at the University of Waterloo is discussed. Research projects in the university are expected to be influential in Canada's economic development. In spite of the success of these studies, financing is still a problem for the university, especially in technological innovations. **Availability:** Online.

21550 ■ "Innovators Critical in Technical Economy" in Crain's Cleveland Business (Vol. 28, November 5, 2007, No. 44, pp. 10)
Pub: Crain Communications Inc.
Contact: K. C. Crain, President
Ed: Peter Rea. **Description:** Discusses the importance to attract, develop and retain talented innovators on Ohio's economy. Also breaks down the four fronts on which the international battle for talent is being waged. **Availability:** Online.

21551 ■ "Interning Your Way to the Right Career" in Business Review Albany (Vol. 41, June 20, 2014, No. 12, pp. 9)
Pub: American City Business Journals, Inc.
Contact: Mike Olivieri, Executive Vice President
Released: Weekly. **Price:** $4, introductory 4-week offer(Digital only). **Description:** The degree boom has made it increasingly important for students to participate in internship programs in order to stand out. Internship programs also provide companies with several benefits. **Availability:** Print; Online.

21552 ■ "Invest in Energy-Efficient Equipment for Your Pet Store" in Pet Product News (Vol. 66, September 2012, No. 9, pp. 72)
Ed: Leila Meyer. **Description:** Aquatic retailers can achieve business growth by offering lighting products, pumps, heaters, filters, and other aquarium supplies that would help customers realize energy efficiency. Aside from offering an education in energy efficiency as a customer service opportunity, retailers are encouraged to determine what supplies are crucial in helping customers achieve energy usage goals. **Availability:** Online.

21553 ■ "Is Amazon Training Its Workers or Creating a College Alternative?" in Inside Higher Ed (July 17, 2019)
URL(s): www.insidehighered.com/digital-learning/article/2019/07/17/perspectives-field-amazons-big-dollar-entry-training-workers
Ed: Doug Lederman. **Released:** July 17, 2019. **Description:** Amazon is making a huge investment in its employees by spending $700 million on their training. In the past, most companies would outsource the training but Amazon is taking care of this in-house and educating their employees themselves. **Availability:** Online.

21554 ■ "Is Business Ethics Getting Better? A Historical Perspective" in Business Ethics Quarterly (Vol. 21, April 2011, No. 2, pp. 2)
Ed: Joanne B. Ciulla. **Released:** Volume 21, Issue 2. **Description:** The question 'Is Business Ethics Getting Better?' as a heuristic for discussing the importance of history in understanding business and ethics is answered. The article uses a number of examples to illustrate how the same ethical problems in business have been around for a long time. It describes early attempts at the Harvard School of Business to use business history as a means of teaching students about moral and social values. In the end, the author suggests that history may be another way to teach ethics, enrich business ethics courses, and develop the perspective and vision in future business leaders. **Availability:** Online.

21555 ■ "Is Culinary School Still Worth It? Four Chefs Weigh In" in Food&Wine (November 14, 2017)
URL(s): www.foodandwine.com/lifestyle/culinary-school-worth-it-four-chefs-weigh-in
Ed: Gowri Chandra. **Released:** November 14, 2017. **Description:** Culinary school is often expensive and it begs the question: Is it worth attending? That depends on what your individual goals are because these schools can and do open doors into the industry. Other options are explored, such as receiving training in a kitchen and apply those skills to the job. **Availability:** Online.

21556 ■ "Is Formal Ethics Training Merely Cosmetic? A Study of Ethics Training and Ethical Organizational Culture" in Business Ethics Quarterly (Vol. 24, January 2014, No. 1, pp. 85)
Pub: Business Ethics Quarterly
Contact: Dawn Elm, Executive Director
E-mail: drelm@stthomas.edu
Description: U.S. Organizational Sentencing Guidelines provide firms with incentives to develop formal ethics programs that promote ethical organizational cultures and thereby decrease corporate offenses. An examination of the effects of training on ethical organizational culture is discussed. **Availability:** Online.

21557 ■ "Is It Ever OK to Break a Promise? A Student Must Decide Whether to Leave the Company that Sponsored His MBA for a Dream Job" in Harvard Business Review (Vol. 92, September 2014, No. 9, pp. 119)
Pub: Harvard Business Publishing
Contact: Diane Belcher, Managing Director
Price: $8.95. **Description:** A fictitious decision making scenario is presented, with contributors providing advice. One notes that change, requiring people to adapt and, in some cases, alter contracts. Another states that the original contract should be honored and that other opportunities are likely to present themselves to the student considering leaving the firm that sponsored his MBA. **Availability:** Online; PDF.

21558 ■ "A Jobs Compact for America's Future: Badly Needed Investments In Human Capital Are Not Being Made. What We Can Do - Together - To Jump-Start the Process?" in Harvard Business Review (Vol. 90, March 2012, No. 3, pp. 64)
Pub: Harvard Business Review Press
Contact: Moderna V. Pfizer, Contact
Ed: Thomas A. Kochan. **Price:** $8.95. **Description:** Obstacles to strengthening US human capital are a lack of focus on obtaining both high wages and high productivity, and a lack of value placed on human capital as a competitive advantage. Business schools are well positioned to address these obstacles via curricula, programs, and partnerships. **Availability:** Online; PDF.

21559 ■ "Knocking On the World's Door" in Business Journal Portland (Vol. 31, March 28, 2014, No. 4, pp. 4)
Pub: American City Business Journals, Inc.
Contact: Mike Olivieri, Executive Vice President
Released: Weekly. **Price:** $4, introductory 4-week offer(Digital & Print). **Description:** A list of things that the City of Portland, Oregon should do to achieve world-class status is provided. Portland must welcome companies as a site selection, build infrastructure, consider the economic and recreational potential of the Willamette River, allocate more education budget and provide greater access to capital. **Availability:** Print; Online.

21560 ■ "Knox County Schools Debate Outsourcing Janitorial Services" in (March 29, 2011)
Description: Custodial services of Knox County Schools in Tennessee may be outsourced in move to save money for the school district. Details of the proposed program are included. **Availability:** Print; Online.

21561 ■ "Law School Not Such a Great Idea?" in Philadelphia Business Journal (Vol. 33, February 28, 2014, No. 3, pp. 8)
Pub: American City Business Journals, Inc.
Contact: Mike Olivieri, Executive Vice President
Released: Weekly. **Price:** $4, introductory 4-week offer(Digital & Print). **Description:** Several law schools in Philadelphia, Pennsylvania saw a 31.5 percent decline in combined first-year enrollment from 2000-2014. The University of Pennsylvania gained less than one percent during the period, while Widener University's Hidener Campus had the biggest drop from 181 first-year students in 2009-2010 to just 74 in 2013-2014. **Availability:** Print; Online.

21562 ■ The Leadership Challenge: How to Make Extraordinary Things Happen in Organizations
Pub: Jossey-Bass
Ed: James M. Kouzes, Barry Z. Posner. **Released:** 7th edition. **Price:** $34.95, hardcover; $34.95, hardcover. **Description:** According to research by the authors, people can make extraordinary things happen by liberating the leader within everyone around them. This handbook gives practical tips to aspire leaders in retail, manufacturing, government, community, church and school settings. **Availability:** E-book; Print.

21563 ■ "Leadership Development In the Age of the Algorithm" in (Vol. 90, June 2012, No. 6, pp. 86)
Pub: Harvard Business Review Press
Contact: Moderna V. Pfizer, Contact
Ed: Marcus Buckingham. **Price:** $8.95. **Description:** Guidelines to tailor leadership training to specific individuals include assessing the leadership type for each person, identifying the top leaders for each type, creating practices that are effective for each type, delivering those practices to others, and integrate user feedback to fine-tune the process. **Availability:** Online; PDF.

21564 ■ "Learning Before Earning" in Pittsburgh Business Times (Vol. 34, August 15, 2014, No. 4, pp. 12)
Pub: American City Business Journals, Inc.
Contact: Mike Olivieri, Executive Vice President
Description: The importance of the Master in Business Administration (MBA) degree in the contemporary U.S. job market, specifically whether the cost of an MBA education is justified in the current economy is discussed. Experts assert that an MBA does not guarantee a job and recommend that undergraduate students join the workforce for a few years before entering and MBA program. **Availability:** Online.

21565 ■ Learning While Working: Structuring Your On-the-Job Training
Ed: Paul Smith. **Released:** July 10, 2018. **Price:** $42.95, Paperback; $42.95, E-book. **Description:** A guide to providing the focus and structure your employees need to receive on-the-job training that develop top-tier talent for your business. **Availability:** E-book; Print.

21566 ■ "Liberty Tax Service is Registering Students for Fall Tax Preparation Courses" in Economics Week (August 3, 2012)
Description: Liberty Tax Service is enrolling for fall income tax preparation classes across the nation. The ten-week school teaches students strategies and advantages for personal tax savings. Liberty Tax Service offers a three-tier skill certification examination for its preparers. **Availability:** Online.

21567 ■ "The Life Changers" in Canadian Business (Vol. 81, October 27, 2008, No. 18, pp. 86)
Description: The first season of 'The Life Changers' was produced in September 2007 to feature stories about research and development (R&D) efforts by universities in Atlantic Canada. The program addresses the need to inform the public about university R&D and its outcomes. **Availability:** Print; Online.

21568 ■ "Lobster Mania Hits China: They Just Had to Get Used to the Claws" in Canadian Business (Vol. 85, July 16, 2012, No. 11-12, pp. 10)
Ed: Joe Castaldo. **Description:** Canadian lobster exports to China have tripled to almost $30 million annually since 2010 as a result of marketing efforts by Maritimes governments including pitching lobster to cooking shows and organizing training sessions for Chinese chefs. Canadian exporters must decide whether their lobster is a premium product or a commodity product to solidify its image in China. **Availability:** Print; Online.

21569 ■ "The Long View: Roberta Bondar's Unique Vision of Science, The Need for Education, and More" in Canadian Business (Vol. 81, October 27, 2008, No. 18)
Pub: Rogers Media Inc.
Contact: Neil Spivak, Chief Executive Officer

GENERAL SMALL BUSINESS TOPICS   Education and Training ■ 21587

Ed: Alex Mlynek. Description: Roberta Bondar believes that energy and renewable energy is a critical environmental issue faced by Canada today. Bondar is the first Canadian woman and neurologist in space. Availability: Online.

21570 ■ "Loss of Rutgers Name Causing a Stir for Law School" in Philadelphia Business Journal (Vol. 28, April 20, 2012, No. 10, pp. 1)
Pub: Baltimore Business Journal
Contact: Rhonda Pringle, President
E-mail: rpringle@bizjournals.com
Description: The plan to merge Rutgers University-Camden with Rowan University is being opposed by those from Rutgers who feel they will have problems recruiting students if they lose the Rutgers brand. Rowan on the other hand, is more known in the South Jersey area only. Availability: Print; Online.

21571 ■ "Lower Unemployment Hasn't Offset Total Losses" in Sacramento Business Journal (Vol. 31, May 23, 2014, No. 13, pp. 6)
Pub: American City Business Journals, Inc.
Contact: Mike Olivieri, Executive Vice President
Released: Weekly. Price: $4, Introductory 4-week offer(Digital & Print). Description: The decline in Sacramento, California's unemployment rate has not reduced the city's economic losses. Unemployment in the area has decreased by 7.5 percent in April 2014. Meanwhile, educational and health services are expected to be the job growth sectors in the next 12 months. Availability: Print; Online.

21572 ■ "Macomb County, OU Eye Business Incubator" in Crain's Detroit Business (Vol. 24, February 11, 2008, No. 6, pp. 1)
Pub: Crain Communications Inc.
Contact: Barry Asin, President
Ed: Chad Halcom. Description: Officials in Macomb County, Michigan are discussing plans to create a defense-themed business incubator in the county. Macomb County was awarded $282,000 in federal budget appropriation for the project. Availability: Print; Online.

21573 ■ "Managing the Facebookers; Business" in The Economist (Vol. 390, January 3, 2009, No. 8612, pp. 10)
Pub: Economist Newspaper Ltd.
Contact: Lara Boro, Chief Executive Officer
Description: According to a report from PricewaterhouseCoopers, a business consultancy, workers from Generation Y, also known as the Net Generation, are more difficult to recruit and integrate into companies that practice traditional business acumen. 61 percent of chief executive managers say that they have trouble with younger employees who tend to be more narcissistic and more interested in personal fulfillment with a need for frequent feedback and an over-precise set of objectives on the path to promotion which can be hard for managers who are used to a different relationship with their subordinates. Older bosses should prepare to make some concessions to their younger talent since some of the issues that make them happy include cheaper online ways to communicate and additional coaching, both of which are good for business. Availability: Online.

21574 ■ "Marketing Scholarship 2.0" in Journal of Marketing (Vol. 75, July 2011, No. 4, pp. 225)
Pub: American Marketing Association
Contact: Bennie F. Johnson, Chief Executive Officer
Ed: Richard J. Lutz. Released: Volume: 75 issue: 4. Description: A study of the implications of changing environment and newer collaborative models for marketing knowledge production and dissemination is presented. Crowdsourcing has become a frequently employed strategy in industry. Academic researchers should collaborate more as well as the academe and industry, to make sure that important problems are being investigated. Availability: PDF.

21575 ■ "Mass. STEM Approach and R.I. Model?" in Providence Business News (Vol. 28, March 10, 2014, No. 49, pp. 1)
Pub: American City Business Journals, Inc.
Contact: Mike Olivieri, Executive Vice President
Released: March 08, 2014. Description: Rhode Island is in the process of developing an educational system that prepares students to excel in science, technology, engineering and math (STEM). Educational services in the state are examining the Massachusetts educational program in order to generate ideas. Availability: Print; Online.

21576 ■ "A Master Chef's Recipe for Business Success" in Business Strategy Review (Vol. 23, Spring 2012, No. 1, pp. 65)
Description: Often called the world's greatest chef, Ferran Adria, longtime owner of El Built, Spain's three-star Michelin rated revolutionary restaurant, is now embarking on a new venture: the El Built Foundation, a place where chefs can create, interact, and discuss their ideas with researchers from other disciplines. He recently spoke at London Business School as part of his tour of a number of select universities to invite students to enter a competition to design an innovative business model for the new Foundation. Availability: Print; Online.

21577 ■ "MBAs for Hire, By the Hour" in Entrepreneur (August 2014)
Pub: Entrepreneur Media Inc.
Contact: Dan Bova, Director
E-mail: dbova@entrepreneur.com
Description: HourlyNerd started from a classroom project by Pat Petitti and Rob Biederman at Harvard Business School in Boston, Massachusetts in 2003. the temporary-staffing firm recruits business students to act as consultants to small businesses that hire them. Consultants must come from one of the top 40 Master of Business Administration Programs in the U.S. in order to bid on a project. The firm receives 15 percent of the project fee from the hiring company while the business consultants pay 5 percent to the company. Availability: Online.

21578 ■ "Meet the Next Big Name in Residential Construction" in Houston Business Journal (Vol. 44, February 21, 2014, No. 42, pp. 8)
Pub: American City Business Journals, Inc.
Contact: Mike Olivieri, Executive Vice President
Released: Weekly. Price: $4, introductory 4-week offer(Digital only). Description: Hillwood Communities of Dallas, Texas will break ground on the Pomona master-planned community in Manvel, 20 miles south of downtown Houston. The development will include 2,100 single-family homes ranging from $250,000 to $400,000, a new elementary school and a new junior high school. Availability: Print; Online.

21579 ■ "Meet University of Texas' New Business Mind" in Austin Business Journal (Vol. 31, May 13, 2011, No. 10, pp. A1)
Pub: Austin Business Journal
Contact: Rachel McGrath, Director
E-mail: rmcgrath@bizjournals.com
Ed: Sandra Zaragoza. Description: University of Texas (UT) chief commercialization officer, Dr. Richard Miller, has opened a satellite office in Silicon Valley, California in the hopes of luring Californian investors to the science and technology at UT. The satellite office is just one of Miller's efforts to reshape and widen the commercialization of UT-Austin. Insights into Miller's long-term view approach to commercialization are also covered. Availability: Online.

21580 ■ "Mercyhurst Rolls Out Culinary Cab Food Truck" in Erie Times-News (June 19, 2012)
Ed: Erica Erwin. Description: Mercyhurst University's food service company launched a Culinary Cab, or food truck, offering a variety of food choices to the campus community. Details of Parkhurst Dining Services plan for the mobile restaurant are outlined.

21581 ■ "Negotiating Tips" in Black Enterprise (Vol. 37, December 2006, No. 5, pp. 70)
Pub: Earl G. Graves Ltd.
Contact: Earl Graves, Jr., President
Ed: Marcia A. Reed-Woodard. Description: Sekou Kaalund, head of strategy, mergers & acquisitions at Citigroup Securities & Fund Services, states that "Negotiation skills are paramount to success in a business environment because of client, employee, and shareholder relationships". He discusses how the book by George Kohlrieser, Hostage at the Table: How Leaders Can Overcome Conflict, Influence Others, and Raise Performance, has helped him negotiate more powerfully and enhance his skills at conflict-resolution. Availability: Online.

21582 ■ "Never Stop Learning: Education Opportunities for Small Business Owners" in The Bottom Line Blog (Sept. 10, 2019)
URL(s): www.nationalfunding.com/blog/small-business-owner-courses/
Ed: Stephanie Vozza. Released: September 10, 2019. Description: Provides information on how to identify areas for improvement as a small business owner and how to find education opportunities to help you continue to grow and gain skills to boost your business savvy. Availability: Online.

21583 ■ "A New Approach to Learning Centers" in Scholastic
URL(s): www.scholastic.com/teachers/articles/teaching-content/new-approach-learning-centers/
Description: A discussion of setting up learning centers within a classroom, which often include technology and the Internet. Availability: Online.

21584 ■ "New Biz Mixes Paint, Wine; Will It Yield Green?" in Crain's Detroit Business (Vol. 30, September 8, 2014, No. 36, pp. 6)
Pub: Crain Communications Inc.
Contact: Barry Asin, President
Description: Profile of Leanna Haun, owner of Picasso's Grapevine in downtown Clarkston, Michigan. Haun describes her business as one part wine, one part paint, and one part entertainment. Sessions include as many as ten people who are given instruction to paint a picture while enjoying wine and conversation with others. Availability: Print; Online.

21585 ■ "New Generation Deans Lead Atlanta Area Business Schools Into the Future" in Atlanta Business Chronicle (July 25, 2014, pp. 3A)
Pub: American City Business Journals, Inc.
Contact: Mike Olivieri, Executive Vice President
Released: Weekly. Price: $4, introductory 4-week offer(Digital only). Description: An interview with five business school deans from Georgia share their views on the future of business education, changing business education needs, and other issues affecting the Atlanta area business schools. The growing demands for greater global competences, good communication skills across various cultures, and other challenges faced by the students and employers are discussed. Other topics include the role of women in the corporate world. Availability: Print; Online.

21586 ■ "New Stem Cell Research Awareness Org Launched in Austin" in Austin Business Journal (Vol. 31, June 3, 2011, No. 13, pp. 1)
Pub: Austin Business Journal
Contact: Rachel McGrath, Director
E-mail: rmcgrath@bizjournals.com
Ed: Sandra Zaragoza. Description: MedRebels Foundation was launched in February 2011 with the goal of providing millions of dollars for research funding, education and advocacy for adult stem cell-focused medicine. The foundation, whose major contributor is SpineSmith LP, is a collaboration of other adult stem cell-related companies and nonprofit partners. It hopes to raise $200,000 by the end of 2011. Availability: Print; Online.

21587 ■ "Next Generation Security Awareness" in Security Management (Vol. 56, September 2012, No. 9, pp. 32)
Description: Carnegie Mellon University (CMU) has purchased Wombat Security Technologies' PhishGuru to reduce the phishing attacks. CMU also purchased Wombat's two educational games, Anti-Phishing and

Anti-Phishing Phyllis, partly due to the PhishGuru's success. Insights on the software-as-a-service solution are also given.

21588 ■ "No More Ivory Towers: Local Colleges and Universities are Here to Help Your Business" in Orlando Business Journal (Vol. 30, February 28, 2014, No. 36, pp. 4)
Pub: American City Business Journals, Inc.
Contact: Mike Olivieri, Executive Vice President
Released: Weekly. **Price:** $8, Introductory 4-week offer(Digital & Print). **Description:** A number of school leaders in Central Florida share their views on partnering with the business community, boosting science and technology graduates, benefits of a private college, economic development efforts and fixing the higher education construction gridlock. Local universities and colleges have a combined economic impact of $15 billion each year. **Availability:** Print; Online.

21589 ■ "NSU Seeks Private Partners For New $80M Research Building" in South Florida Business Journal (Vol. 34, February 21, 2014, No. 31, pp. 4)
Pub: American City Business Journals, Inc.
Contact: Mike Olivieri, Executive Vice President
Released: Weekly. **Price:** $8, Introductory 4-week offer(Digital & Print). **Description:** The $80 million Center for Collaborative Research at Nova Southeastern University hopes to become the largest incubator and wet laboratory space in Broward County, Florida. The center had its groundbreaking on February 13, 2014, and will be open for lease to private companies when it is ready in 22 months. **Availability:** Print; Online.

21590 ■ "Nurturing Talent for Tomorrow" in Restaurants and Institutions (Vol. 118, September 15, 2008, No. 14, pp. 90)
Description: Hormel Foods Corporation and The Culinary Institute of America (CIA) have teamed to develop The Culinary Enrichment and Innovation Program that supports future culinary leaders by providing creative and competitive staff development. Sixteen students attend four three-day sessions at the CIA's campus in Hyde Park, New York; sessions include classroom teaching, one-on-one interaction with leading culinarians, and hands-on kitchen time.

21591 ■ "Oakland County to Survey Employers on Needed Skills" in Crain's Detroit Business (Vol. 24, April 14, 2008, No. 15, pp. 30)
Pub: Crain Communications Inc.
Contact: Barry Asin, President
Ed: Chad Halcom. **Description:** In an attempt to aid educators and attract talent, Oakland County plans to collect data from 1,000 local employers on workforce skills they need now or will need soon. **Availability:** Online.

21592 ■ "On Their Own: Bronx High School Students Open a Bank Branch" in Black Enterprise (Vol. 38, February 2008, No. 7, pp. 42)
Pub: Earl G. Graves Ltd.
Contact: Earl Graves, Jr., President
Ed: Jessica Jones. **Description:** Students at Fordham Leadership Academy for Business and Technology in New York City opened a student-run bank branch at their high school. The business paid high school seniors $11 per hour to work as tellers. Students were also taught interviewing basics. **Availability:** Online.

21593 ■ "One Hundred Years of Excellence in Business Education: What Have We Learned?" in Business Horizons (January-February 2008)
Pub: Elsevier Advanced Technology Publications
Ed: Frank Acito, Patricia M. McDougall, Daniel C. Smith. **Description:** Business schools have to be more innovative, efficient and nimble, so that the quality of the next generation of business leaders is improved. The Kelley School of Business, Indiana University has long been a leader in business education. The trends that influence the future of business education and useful success principles are discussed. **Availability:** PDF; Online.

21594 ■ "One Laptop Per Child Weighs Going For-Profit" in Boston Business Journal (Vol. 31, May 20, 2011, No. 17, pp. 1)
Pub: Boston Business Journal
Contact: Carolyn M. Jones, President
E-mail: cmjones@bizjournals.com
Ed: Mary Moore. **Released:** Weekly. **Price:** $4, Print. **Description:** Nonprofit organization One Laptop Per Child is thinking of shifting into a for-profit structure in order to raise as much as $10 million in capital to achieve its goal of distributing more XO laptops to poor children worldwide. The organization has distributed 2 million computers since 2008 with Uruguay, Peru and Rwanda as its biggest markets. **Availability:** Print; Online.

21595 ■ "Online Small Business Training Courses" in The Balance Small Business (Nov. 20, 2019)
URL(s): www.thebalancesmb.com/online-business-training-for-small-business-owners-2951646
Ed: Alyssa Gregory. **Released:** November 20, 2019. **Description:** Provides information on five free online small business training sites that provide an introduction to online programs as well as additional business resources. **Availability:** Online.

21596 ■ "Online Training Requires Tools, Accessories" in Contractor (Vol. 56, September 2009, No. 9, pp. 67)
Ed: Larry Drake. **Description:** Importance of the right equipment and tools to members of the United States plumbing industry undergoing online training is discussed. Portable devices such as BlackBerrys and I-phones could be used for online training. The use of headphones makes listening easier for the trainee. **Availability:** Print; Online.

21597 ■ "Opinion: Prison Farms are Closing, but the Manure Remains" in Canadian Business (Vol. 83, August 17, 2010, No. 13-14, pp. 9)
Pub: Rogers Media Inc.
Contact: Neil Spivak, Chief Executive Officer
Ed: Steve Maich. **Description:** The explanation given by Canada's government ministers on planned closure of the prison farms and scrapping of the long form census are designed by mixing of spin, argument and transparent justification. The defense should have been plausible but the ministers could not handle the simple questions about statistics and prison job training with pretense. **Availability:** Online.

21598 ■ "Organic Food Industry Goes to College" in USA Today (April 9, 2012)
Ed: Chuck Raasch. **Description:** With the organic food industry growing the US Department of Agriculture is has pumped $117 million into organic research in the last three years. According to a recent report by the Organic Farming Research Foundation (OFRF), the number of states committing land for organic research has nearly doubled from 2003 to 2011. Universities offering academic programs in organic farming rose from none to nine. The OFRF supports organic farmers and producers. **Availability:** Online.

21599 ■ "The Outcome of an Organization Overhaul" in Black Enterprise (Vol. 41, December 2010, No. 5)
Pub: Earl G. Graves Ltd.
Contact: Earl Graves, Jr., President
Ed: Tamara E. Holmes. **Description:** Savvy business owners understand the need for change in order to stay competitive and be successful. This article examines how to manage change as well as what strategies can help employees to get with the program faster. **Availability:** Online.

21600 ■ "Overqualified. Underemployed" in Philadelphia Business Journal (Vol. 33, August 1, 2104, No. 25, pp. 14)
Pub: American City Business Journals, Inc.
Contact: Mike Olivieri, Executive Vice President
Description: Overqualified workers often find themselves in employment situations where their education, experience and skills are beyond the requirements of the job. The implications of underemployment for the worker, the organization and the overall U.S. economy are discussed. **Availability:** Print; Online.

21601 ■ "Owner of Skin Care Business Offers Westfield State Scholarships If Ex-President Drops Lawsuit" in Boston Business Journal (Vol. 34, April 25, 2014, No. 12, pp. 5)
Pub: American City Business Journals, Inc.
Contact: Mike Olivieri, Executive Vice President
Description: John Walsh, CEO of Elizabeth Grady Company, has offered $100,000 in scholarships if Westfield State University President, Evan Dobelle, drops his lawsuits against the university. Dobelle decided to sue the school after he was placed on paid leave by three trustees. **Availability:** Print; Online.

21602 ■ "The People Puzzle; Re-Training America's Workers" in The Economist (Vol. 390, January 3, 2009, No. 8612, pp. 32)
Description: With thousands of workers losing their jobs, America is now facing the task of getting them back to work. With an overall unemployment rate of 6.7 percent, the federal government has three main ways for leading workers back to employment: training them for new jobs, providing unemployment insurance in order to replace lost wages during the period of job-hunting; and matching employers who desire a skill with workers who have that skill. Specialized staffing agencies provide employers and potential employees with the help necessary to find a job in some of the more niche markets. **Availability:** Online.

21603 ■ "Perfecting Customer Services" in Pet Product News (Vol. 64, November 2010, No. 11, pp. 18)
Ed: Alison Bour. **Description:** Pet supply retailers are encouraged to emphasize customer experience and sales representatives' knowledge of the store's product offerings to foster repeat business. Employee protocols could be implemented to improve customer interaction. Other guidelines on developing a pet supply retail environment that advances repeat business are presented. **Availability:** Online.

21604 ■ "Pet Store Fish Provide Clue to How Alzheimer's Disease May Start" in Marketwired (July 9, 2012)
Pub: Comtex News Network Inc.
Contact: Kan Devnani, President
Released: August 07, 2012. **Description:** Western University of Health Sciences in Pomona, California researchers report that studies with zebrafish provided an important clue to understanding how Alzheimer's disease starts. Details of the study are included. **Availability:** Print; Online.

21605 ■ "Pet Store Pro Adds New Curriculum" in Pet Product News (Vol. 66, February 2012, No. 2, pp. 2012)
Description: Pet Store Pro, the Pet Industry Distributors Association's free online training program, is going to launch chapters of a curriculum intended to assist pet store managers learn effective approaches to motivate employees and boost profitability. Other management-level chapters to be added by Pet Store Pro throughout 2012 are listed. **Availability:** Print; Online.

21606 ■ "Physics for Females" in Occupational Outlook Quarterly (Vol. 55, Summer 2011, No. 2, pp. 22)
Description: Free resources to help females investigate careers in medical physics and health physics are available from the American Physical Society. The booklet is designed for girls in middle and high school and describes the work of 15 women who use physics to solve medical mysteries, discover planets, research new materials, and more. **Availability:** Print; Online.

GENERAL SMALL BUSINESS TOPICS — Education and Training ■ 21624

21607 ■ *"Plenty of Jobs, Will Workers Follow?"* in *Providence Business News* (Vol. 28, January 27, 2014, No. 43, pp. 1)
Pub: American City Business Journals, Inc.
Contact: Mike Olivieri, Executive Vice President
URL(s): pbn.com/plenty-of-jobs-will-workers-follow9 4642

Description: Electric Boat announced a plan to hire 650 employees in 2014 for its facility at Quonset Business Park in North Kingstown, Rhode Island. However, meeting the hiring goals will be a challenge because of smaller educational pipeline for welders, electricians, shipfitters, and pipefitters. Rhode Island's internship programs to fill the skills gap are also discussed. **Availability:** Online.

21608 ■ *"The Preparation Gap: Teacher Education for Middle School Mathematics in Six Countries"* in *Hawaii Business* (Vol. 53, February 2008, No. 8, pp. 37)
Pub: PacificBasin Communications
Contact: Chuck Tindle, Director
E-mail: chuckt@pacificbasin.net

Ed: Ashley Hamershock. **Description:** Discussion of the educational gap in Hawaii's workforce is being addressed by educational workshops that aim to improve students' knowledge in science, technology, math, and engineering, and prepare them for their entry into the workforce. Education beyond high school is required for jobs to be filled in the coming years. **Availability:** PDF; Online.

21609 ■ *"Programs Provide Education and Training"* in *Contractor* (Vol. 56, September 2009, No. 9, pp. 56)

Ed: William Feldman, Patti Feldman. **Description:** Opportunity Interactive's Showroom v2 software provides uses computer graphics to provide education and training on HVAC equipment and systems. It can draw heat pump balance points for a specific home. Meanwhile, Simutech's HVAC Training Simulators provide trainees with 'hands-on' HVACR training. **Availability:** Print; Online.

21610 ■ *Python and Algorithmic Thinking for the Complete Beginner: Learn to Think Like a Programmer*
Ed: Aristides S. Bouras. **Released:** June 19, 2019. **Price:** $42.74, Paperback; $9.99, E-Book. **Description:** A complete guide on how to learn Python programming. This book is designed for anyone who does not know anything about programming, but who wishes to learn at their own pace. **Availability:** E-book; Print.

21611 ■ *"Real-Life Coursework for Real-Life Business People"* in *Women In Business* (Vol. 63, Summer 2011, No. 2, pp. 22)
Pub: American Business Women's Association
Contact: Rene Street, Executive Director

Ed: Leigh Elmore. **Released:** June 22, 2011. **Description:** American Business Women's Association National Women's Leadership Conference provides members with academic business training courses. Members can take a variety of MBA-level courses that are taught by University of Kansas School of Business professors. Courses include marketing, management, leadership and communication and decision making. **Availability:** Print; Online.

21612 ■ *"Recovery on Tap for 2010?"* in *Orlando Business Journal* (Vol. 26, January 1, 2010, No. 31, pp. 1)
Pub: Orlando Business Journal
Contact: Julie Swyers, Director
E-mail: jswyers@bizjournals.com

Ed: Melanie Stawicki Azam, Richard Bilbao, Christopher Boyd, Anjali Fluker. **Description:** Economic forecasts for Central Florida's leading business sectors in 2010 are presented. These sectors include housing, film and TV, sports business, law, restaurants, aviation, tourism and hospitality, banking and finance, commercial real estate, retail, health care, insurance, higher education, and manufacturing. According to some local executives, Central Florida's economy will slowly recover in 2010. **Availability:** Online.

21613 ■ *"Region to Be Named Innovation Hub"* in *Business Courier* (Vol. 27, July 2, 2010, No. 9, pp. 1)
Pub: Business Courier

Ed: Dan Monk. **Description:** The selection of Cincinnati's consumer-marketing cluster as a 'Hub of Innovation' by the Ohio Department of Development could boost Cincinnati's chances of receiving $100 million in grants from Ohio's Third Frontier program and other funding sources. Implications of the University of Cincinnati's designation as a Center of Excellence in Advanced Transportation and Aerospace are also discussed. **Availability:** Print; Online.

21614 ■ *"Research, Treatment to Expand"* in *Philadelphia Business Journal* (Vol. 28, June 22, 2012, No. 19, pp. 1)
Pub: Baltimore Business Journal
Contact: Rhonda Pringle, President
E-mail: rpringle@bizjournals.com

Description: Fox Chase Cancer Center and Temple University Health System have been planning several projects once their merger is completed. Their plans include the construction of a unit for cancer patients on the third floor of the Founder's Building at Jeanes Hospital and a granting mechanism to fund research collaborations. **Availability:** Print; Online.

21615 ■ *"Rethinking School: For the U.S. To Remain Competitive, Its Students Need To Learn Vastly More, Much More Quickly"* in *Harvard Business Review* (Vol. 90, March 2012, No. 3, pp. 76)
Pub: Harvard Business Review Press
Contact: Moderna V. Pfizer, Contact

Ed: Stacey Childress. **Price:** $8.95, hardcover. **Description:** Improving primary education is a key component to future US economic growth. The article emphasizes the importance of personalized learning and educational technology to enhance academic achievement. **Availability:** PDF; Online.

21616 ■ *"Revisiting Rep Coping Strategies"* in *Agency Sales Magazine* (Vol. 39, December 2009, No. 11, pp. 32)

Description: Independent manufacturer's representatives should become a well-rounded and complete businessman with continued education. The new type of representative is a problem solver and the resource for answering questions. Employing the concept of synergistic selling is also important to salespeople. **Availability:** Online.

21617 ■ *"RhodeMap for State Won't Focus on Finding a 'Big Fix'"* in *Providence Business News* (Vol. 29, June 23, 2014, No. 12, pp. 4)
Pub: American City Business Journals, Inc.
Contact: Mike Olivieri, Executive Vice President

Released: June 22, 2014. **Description:** Rhode Island Department of Administration Associate Director, Kevin Flynn, asserts that the new comprehensive plan for land use and economic development, RhodeMap RI, is not focused on one single big fix to solve the state's economic problems. Flynn notes that RhodeMap RI will address various social disparities, including education and income. **Availability:** Print; Online.

21618 ■ *"The Right Time for REITs"* in *Barron's* (Vol. 88, July 14, 2008, No. 28, pp. 32)
Pub: Dow Jones & Company Inc.
Contact: Almar Latour, Chief Executive Officer

Ed: Mike Hogan. **Description:** Discusses the downturn in U.S. real estate investment trusts so these are worth considering for investment. Several Websites that are useful for learning about real estate investment trusts for investment purposes are presented. **Availability:** Online.

21619 ■ *"Rosewood Site Faces Big Cleanup Before Stevenson Can Expand"* in *Baltimore Business Journal* (Vol. 27, February 6, 2010, No. 40, pp. 1)
Pub: Baltimore Business Journal
Contact: Rhonda Pringle, President
E-mail: rpringle@bizjournals.com

Ed: Daniel J. Sernovitz. **Description:** Environmental assessment report states that Maryland's Rosewood Center for the Developmentally Disabled has significant amounts of toxic chemicals, which could impact Stevenson University's decision to purchase the property. Senator Robert A. Zirkin believes that the state should pay for the cleanup, which is expected to cost millions. **Availability:** Print; Online.

21620 ■ *"San Antonio Researchers Develop New Laser-Based Imaging System"* in *San Antonio Business Journal* (Vol. 26, August 24, 2012, No. 30, pp. 1)
Pub: Baltimore Business Journal
Contact: Rhonda Pringle, President
E-mail: rpringle@bizjournals.com

Description: Researchers at the University of Texas Health Science Center at San Antonio in Texas have developed an optical sensor-dependent medical imaging system, which is ready for commercialization. The laser-based imaging system is expected to improve non-invasive imaging for medical diagnostics. **Availability:** Print; Online.

21621 ■ *"School for Tech Skills"* in *San Antonio Business Journal* (Vol. 28, September 5, 2014, No. 30, pp. 4)
Pub: American City Business Journals, Inc.
Contact: Mike Olivieri, Executive Vice President

Released: Weekly. **Price:** $4, introductory 4-week offer(Digital & Print). **Description:** The Alamo Academies program is a nonprofit partnership between Alamo Colleges, local high schools, local industry groups and the City of San Antonio, Texas aimed at creating skilled workers. The program has been recognized by the Texas Higher Education Coordinating Board for meeting the state's goal of reducing the skills gap in the workforce. **Availability:** Print; Online.

21622 ■ *"SCO Expanding to Meet Optometry Growth"* in *Memphis Business Journal* (Vol. 33, March 2, 2012, No. 47, pp. 1)
Pub: Baltimore Business Journal
Contact: Rhonda Pringle, President
E-mail: rpringle@bizjournals.com

Ed: Christopher Sheffield. **Description:** Southern College of Optometry (SCO) has begun construction of a $9.4 million expansion that will provide new classrooms, a flexible state-of-the-art lecture hall, and a glass atrium and grand hall. The project was designed to secure SCO's position among the top US optometry school as demand for its graduates grow. **Availability:** Print; Online.

21623 ■ *"The Secret Behind Building Your Own Apps? It's Not As Hard As You Think"* in *Mashable* (October 20, 2019)
URL(s): mashable.com/shopping/oct-20-the-complete-javascript-course-pcmag/

Ed: Haley Henschel. **Released:** October 20, 2019. **Description:** The most popular programming language, JavaScript, is being offered as an online class with a steep discount. On-demand video training and articles are included, and the user will receive real-world experience by completed three apps. **Availability:** Online.

21624 ■ *"Selling With Strengths; Talent Trumps Training"* in *Gallup Management Journal* (March 24, 2011)

Released: April 03, 2011. **Description:** What are the strengths of salespeople, and how can organizations develop them? What do great sales managers do differently? The authors of, 'Strengths Based Selling' answer these questions and others, including: why money is overrated as a motivator. **Availability:** Print; Online.

21625 ■ *"The Service Imperative"* in *Business Horizons* (Vol. 51, January-February 2008, No. 1, pp. 39)
Pub: Elsevier Advanced Technology Publications
Ed: Mary Jo Bitner, Stephen W. Brown. Description: The importance of services is growing in developing countries like India and China, but little attention is given to service research, education and innovation. The 'service imperative' seeks to promote the advancement of services. The scope, objectives and philosophy of the service imperative platform are outlined. Availability: Online.

21626 ■ *"Sewing Is a Life Skill; Teaching To Sew Is An Art"* in *Virginia-Pilot* (August 31, 2010)
Pub: The Virginian-Pilot
Contact: Kevin Goyette, Director
E-mail: kgoyette@dailypress.com
Ed: Jamesetta M. Walker. Description: In conjunction with National Sewing Month, the American Sewing Guild is sponsoring a two-day workshop featuring Stephanie Kimura. Availability: Print; Online.

21627 ■ *"Sharing's Not Just for Start-ups: What Marriott, GE, and Other Traditional Companies are Learning About the Collaborative Economy"* in *Harvard Business Review* (Vol. 92, September 2014, No. 9, pp. 23)
Pub: Harvard Business Publishing
Contact: Diane Belcher, Managing Director
Ed: Rachel Botsman. Price: $6. Description: The collaborative economy answers five basic problems companies face: redundancy, broken trust, limited access, waste, and complexity. Online matches eliminate redundancy; peer-to-peer networks boost trust; online training answers access issues; online services can market what other entities are not utilizing (i.e. excess space); and other services can streamline or provide alternative solutions for complex processes. Availability: Online; PDF.

21628 ■ *"Skill Seekers"* in *South Florida Business Journal* (Vol. 34, February 7, 2014, No. 29, pp. 15)
Pub: American City Business Journals, Inc.
Contact: Mike Olivieri, Executive Vice President
Description: Executives talk about the need for schools to help businesses find talent to hire. Robin Sandler of Charter School USA reveals that the organization's 'Leading Edge' program allows teachers to participate in leadership opportunities, while Mason Jackson of WorkForce One Employment Solutions believes that schools need to customize the curriculum in order to support internships. Availability: Print; Online.

21629 ■ *"Spinout Success: New Leadership Steps In At UW's C4C"* in *Puget Sound Business Journal* (Vol. 35, June 27, 2014, No. 10, pp. 11)
Pub: American City Business Journals, Inc.
Contact: Mike Olivieri, Executive Vice President
Description: University of Washington's Center for Commercialization vice provost, Vikram Jandhyala, talks about his new position with the school. Jandhyala says he plans to build more synergy between the medical school and engineering and between social sciences and computer science. He also says the medical and software industry need to grow to accommodate the volume of data crossing and stored within the Internet. Availability: Online.

21630 ■ *StartingUp Now Facilitator Guide*
Price: $29.95. Description: Guide for those teaching entrepreneurship using StartingUp Now; the guide provides 24 lesson plans for each of the 24 steps/chapters in the book. Availability: Print.

21631 ■ *"State Moves to Improve Child Care"* in *Providence Business News* (Vol. 29, April 7, 2014, No. 1, pp. 1)
Pub: American City Business Journals, Inc.
Contact: Mike Olivieri, Executive Vice President
URL(s): pbn.com/state-moves-to-improve-child-care96248

Description: Rhode Island Department of Human Services has been helping to administer BrightStars contracts to child care centers, home-based providers and educational programs to help ensure the availability of high quality child care to the workforce. Part of the BrightStars funding came from the $50 million Race to the Top grant. Insights on BrightStars rating systems are also given.

21632 ■ *"Steel Yard Eyes Funding Balance"* in *Providence Business News* (Vol. 29, May 26, 2014, No. 8, pp. 1)
Pub: American City Business Journals, Inc.
Contact: Mike Olivieri, Executive Vice President
Released: May 24, 2014. Description: Steel Yard is looking for new revenue to sustain its expansion as a nonprofit, metalwork training organization based in Providence, Rhode Island. The organization is applying for money from a proposed state funding pool of $590,000 for the first time to be used in 2014-2015 fiscal year. Availability: Print; Online.

21633 ■ *"Students' Mounting Interest in Taxidermy"* in *Sanilac County News* (November 24, 2019)
URL(s): sanilaccountynews.mihomepaper.com/articles/students-mounting-interest-in-taxidermy/
Ed: Steven Kovac. Released: November 24, 2019. Description: Sanilac County offers an unusual class for high school students — taxidermy. Here, students learn the art of preparing, stuffing, and mounting the skins of animals. Often, the students themselves hunted the animals and in class they diligently work on preserving the carcasses with a hands-on approach to the topic. Availability: Online.

21634 ■ *"Survey: Don't Expect Big Results From Stimulus"* in *Crain's Detroit Business* (Vol. 25, June 1, 2009, No. 22)
Pub: Crain Communications Inc.
Contact: Barry Asin, President
Ed: Nancy Kaffer, Chad Halcom. Description: In a recent survey, Michigan business owners, operators or managers showed that 48 percent of respondents oppose the President's stimulus package and believe it will have little or no effect on the economy. Availability: Print.

21635 ■ *"The Sustainability Agenda: Ioannia Ioannou"* in *Business Strategy Review* (Vol. 25, Summer 2014, No. 2, pp. 16)
Released: June 02, 2014. Description: How should academics keep up to date with issues such as corporate responsibility? Ioannis Ioannou of the London School of Business advocates a more interventionist approach to this issue. Availability: Print; PDF; Online.

21636 ■ *"Tackling Tuition Increases Head On"* in *Pittsburgh Business Times* (Vol. 34, July 25, 2014, No. 1, pp. 6)
Pub: American City Business Journals, Inc.
Contact: Mike Olivieri, Executive Vice President
Description: The University of Pittsburgh has tried to contain tuition increases after the state cut funding by about $70 million in the 2012 budget year. The measures include a one-time-only early retirement program offered in 2012, greater focus on sustainability and cutting energy costs, and streamlining operations and sharing services. Availability: Print; Online.

21637 ■ *"Taking on 911 - and Making a New Tech Biz In the Process"* in *Orlando Business Journal* (Vol. 30, January 24, 2014, No. 31, pp. 3)
Pub: American City Business Journals, Inc.
Contact: Mike Olivieri, Executive Vice President
Released: Weekly. Price: $8, introductory 4-week offer(Digital & Print). Description: Central Florida-based TapShield LLC is on the path to growth. The firm has developed a mobile application that enables University of Florida students to coordinate with police. Meanwhile, TapShield is in negotiations with large companies for similar deals. Availability: Print; Online.

21638 ■ *"Teachable Moments: Worth Every Penny"* in *Pet Product News* (Vol. 64, December 2010, No. 12, pp. 34)
Ed: Cheryl Reeves. Description: Pet bird retailers can attain both outreach to customers and enhanced profitability by staging educational events such as the annual Parrot Palooza event of Burlington, New Jersey-based Bird Paradise. Aside from attracting a global audience, Parrot Palooza features seminars, workshops, classes, and bird-related contests. Availability: Print; Online.

21639 ■ *"Teaching Sales: Great Sales Professionals are Scarce and Getting Scarcer. Why Aren't Universities Working Harder to Create More?"* in (Vol. 90, July-August 2012, No. 7-8, pp. 94)
Pub: Harvard Business Review Press
Contact: Moderna V. Pfizer, Contact
Ed: Suzanne Fogel, David Hoffmeister, Richard Rocco, Daniel P. Strunk. Price: $8.95, PDF and hardcover black and white. Description: Partnerships between industry and business schools can improve the quality of new sales education programs, increasing access to funding and talent. Industry input to school curricula and scholarly research informing business decisions will produce mutual benefits. Availability: Print; PDF; Online.

21640 ■ *"Technology in the Classroom: What the Research Tells Us"* in *Inside Higher Ed* (December 12, 2018)
URL(s): www.insidehighered.com/digital-learning/views/2018/12/12/what-research-tells-us-about-using-technology-classroom-opinion
Ed: Aaron S. Richmond, Jordan D. Troisi. Released: December 12, 2018. Description: Takes a look at how technology introduced into the classroom is being used and whether or not it is helping or harming education. Availability: Online.

21641 ■ *"Tooling Firm Thinks Being In U.P. Gives It Upper Hand"* in *Crain's Detroit Business* (Vol. 30, October 13, 2014, No. 41, pp. 21)
Pub: Crain Communications Inc.
Contact: Barry Asin, President
Description: Extreme Tool & Engineering is located in a remote region of Michigan's Upper Peninsula. The firm's employees average age is 28 and owner, Mike Zacharias, believes that combination contributes to the mold maker's success. He believes in the power of youth and reinvesting in training. Despite the economic challenges of the area, he employs nearly 80 workers. Availability: Online.

21642 ■ *"Trade Craft: Take Pride in Your Trade, Demand Excellence"* in *Contractor* (Vol. 56, October 2009, No. 10, pp. 24)
Ed: Al Schwartz. Description: There is a need for teaching, developing, and encouraging trade craft. An apprentice plumber is not only versed in the mechanical aspects of the trade but he also has a working knowledge of algebra, trigonometry, chemistry, and thermal dynamics. Contractors should be demanding on their personnel regarding their trade craft and should only keep and train the very best people they can hire. Availability: Print; Online.

21643 ■ *"Train Now to Get the Competitive Edge"* in *Contractor* (Vol. 56, October 2009, No. 10, pp. 58)
Ed: Merry Beth Hall. Description: Due to the harsh economic climate, mechanical contractors would be well-served to train their employees while they have time to take them out of the field. This will help ensure that they are not behind when the economic recovery happens. Suggestions on how to choose the best type of training are presented. Availability: Print; Online.

21644 ■ *"Training Essential For Growth; It Doesn't Have To Cost Much"* in *Crain's Detroit Business* (Vol. 24, January 21, 2008, No. 3, pp. 14)
Pub: Crain Communications Inc.
Contact: Barry Asin, President

Ed: Sheena Harrison. Description: Employee training is essential for small companies to achieve growth. Availability: Print; Online.

21645 ■ "Tufts Wins Grant for K-2 Coding Education" in TuftsNow (October 21, 2019)
URL(s): now.tufts.edu/articles/tufts-wins-grant-k-2-co
ding-education

Ed: Angela Nelson. Released: October 21, 2019. Description: A four-year, $4 million grant was awarded to Tufts professor Marina Umaschi Bers to collaborate with the Norfolk Public Schools in order to train 450 early childhood teachers in technology and bring the ScratchJr app to the students.The researchers involved are looking at ways to best teach computer science and coding as another language in order to develop a free, publicly available K-2 computer science curriculum. Availability: Online.

21646 ■ "TWU Offers Course in Project Management" in Bellingham Business Journal (Vol. February 2010, pp. 4)
Pub: Sound Publishing Inc.
Contact: Josh O'Connor, President

Ed: Lance Henderson. Description: Trinity Western University in Bellinham, Washington is offering a new certification program in project management. Students who take and pass the certification examination of the International Project Management Institutes will lead to positions in many industries. Details of the program are provided.

21647 ■ "UA, BP Test Unmanned Aircraft" in Alaska Business Monthly (Vol. 27, October 2011, No. 10, pp. 8)
Pub: Alaska Business Publishing Company Inc.
Contact: Charles Bell, Vice President, Sales and Marketing
E-mail: cbell@akbizmag.com

Ed: Nancy Pounds. Description: University of Alaska Fairbanks Geophysical Institute and BP Exploration Alaska tested the oil-spill capabilities of an unmanned aircraft. The aircraft will be used to gather 3-D ariel data to aid in oil-spill cleanup. Availability: Online.

21648 ■ "UB Program Offers Free Tax Preparation" in Buffalo News (January 29, 2012)

Ed: Jonathan D. Epstein. Description: University of Buffalo's Schhol of Management in New York is offering free tax preparation for low-income individuals and families. The program is available on North and South campuses and is designed to help these people save money and collect all refunds in which they are eligible. Availability: Online.

21649 ■ "University of Texas Deans Serious about Biz" in Austin Business Journal (Vol. 31, May 20, 2011, No. 11, pp. 1)
Pub: Austin Business Journal
Contact: Rachel McGrath, Director
E-mail: rmcgrath@bizjournals.com

Ed: Sandra Zaragoza. Description: Dean Thomas Gilligan of the University of Texas, McCombs School of Business and engineering school Dean Gregory Fenves have partnered to develop a joint engineering and business degree. Their partnership has resulted in an undergraduate course on initiating startups. Availability: Print; Online.

21650 ■ "Urban League Training Program Finds Jobs for Cincinnati's 'Hard to Serve" in Business Courier (Vol. 27, July 2, 2010, No. 9, pp. 1)
Pub: Business Courier

Ed: Lucy May. Description: Stephen Tucker, director of workforce development for the Urban League of Greater Cincinnati, is an example of how ex-offenders can be given chances for employment after service jail sentences. How the Urban Leagues' Solid Opportunities for Advancement job training program helped Tucker and other ex-offenders is discussed. Availability: Print; Online.

21651 ■ "URI Centre Seen as Bridge From Campus to Employment" in Providence Business News (Vol. 29, June 30, 2014, No. 13, pp. 4)
Pub: American City Business Journals, Inc.
Contact: Mike Olivieri, Executive Vice President
URL(s): pbn.com/uri-center-seen-as-bridge-from
-campus-to-employment98182

Description: Kimberly S. Washor is the first director of University of Rhode Island's (URIs) new Centre for Career and Experiential Education that combines the missions of Experiential Learning and Community Engagement along with Career Services and Employer Relations. By joining the two offices, URI is implementing a new database that will meet the needs of both career and internship advising, where adviser will be able to track industry human resource partners. Telecommunication Services: Daddona@pbn.com.

21652 ■ "Using Technology as a Learning Tool, Not Just the Cool New Thing" in Educause
URL(s): www.educause.edu/research-and-publica
tions/books/educating-net-generation/using
-technology-learning-tool-not-just-cool-new-thing

Description: Discusses the goals of this generation in the classroom in regards to technology, with the emphasis on college-level courses. Availability: Online.

21653 ■ "USM Focuses on Turning Science Into New Companies, Cash" in Boston Business Journal (Vol. 29, July 1, 2011, No. 8, pp. 1)
Pub: Boston Business Journal
Contact: Carolyn M. Jones, President
E-mail: cmjones@bizjournals.com

Ed: Alexander Jackson. Description: University System of Maryland gears up to push for its plan for commercializing its scientific discoveries which by 2020 could create 325 companies and double the $1.4 billion the system's eleven schools garner in yearly research grants. It is talking with University of Utah and University Maryland, Baltimore to explore ways to make this plan a reality. Availability: Print; Online.

21654 ■ "UTSA Entrepreneur Program Receives Federal Designation" in San Antonio Business Journal (Vol. 28, June 6, 2014, No. 17, pp. 7)
Pub: American City Business Journals, Inc.
Contact: Mike Olivieri, Executive Vice President

Released: Weekly. Price: $4, Introductory 4-week offer(Digital & Print). Description: The National Science Foundation has designated the University of Texas at San Antonio (UTSA) as an Innovation Corps Site because of its strong entrepreneurial system through the Center for Innovation and Technology Entrepreneurship. The UTSA expects to see an increase in entrepreneurial activity and successful technology commercialization with such designation. Availability: Print; Online.

21655 ■ "UW Wary of WSU's Wish for Spokane Medical School" in Puget Sound Business Journal (Vol. 35, May 9, 2014, No. 3, pp. 9)
Pub: American City Business Journals, Inc.
Contact: Mike Olivieri, Executive Vice President

Description: University of Washington leaders believe that opening a medical school in Washington State University's (WSU) Spokane Campus will create more competition for state funding. However, WSU officials claim that the demand for new doctors demonstrates the need for a second school. Availability: Online.

21656 ■ "Veterans Train to Use Military Skills In Civilian Workforce" in South Florida Business Journal (Vol. 34, April 18, 2014, No. 39, pp. 10)
Pub: American City Business Journals, Inc.
Contact: Mike Olivieri, Executive Vice President

Released: Weekly. Price: $8, Introductory 4-week offer(Digital & Print). Description: United Way of Broward County has launched the Mission United program that offers a one-stop shop of information and resources to meet the needs of military veterans. Mission United aims to reduce the jobless rate among veterans by creating two programs to help veterans and connect them with potential employers who are hiring. Details of the job training program is explored. Availability: Print; Online.

21657 ■ "The View from the Field: Six Leaders Offer Their Perspectives On Sales Success" in (Vol. 90, July-August 2012, No. 7-8, pp. 101)
Pub: Harvard Business Review Press
Contact: Moderna V. Pfizer, Contact

Ed: Jim Koch, James Farley, Susan Silbermann, Duncan Mac Naughton, Phil Guido, Suresh Goklaney. Price: $8.95. Description: Six business leaders provide their perspectives on successful selling. Common themes include engaging customers and seeking their input, personalizing their services, ensuring accountability, implementing community outreach, being mindful of cultural and regulatory issues, providing unique offerings, incorporating experiential learning, and properly identifying a customer's needs. Availability: Online; PDF.

21658 ■ "Vision for Camden in Better Focus" in Philadelphia Business Journal (Vol. 30, September 30, 2011, No. 33, pp. 1)
Pub: Philadelphia Business Journal
Contact: Sierra Quinn, Director
E-mail: squinn@bizjournals.com

Ed: Natalie Kostelni. Description: More than $500 million worth of projects aimed at redeveloping the downtown and waterfront areas of Camden, New Jersey are being planned. These include the construction of residential, commercial, and education buildings. Availability: Online.

21659 ■ "A Well-Crafted Employee Handbook Can Make Work Run More Smoothly" in Idaho Business Review (September 17, 2014)
Pub: BridgeTower Media
Contact: Adam Reinebach, President

Description: An employee handbook will provide a complaint process, provide company management flexibility and clarity and keep a company out of legal problems. Training, compensation, benefits, security, health, performance appraisals, and safety issues must be covered. Human resource managers and other mangers should cover basics to help communicate with workers.

21660 ■ "What 126 Studies Say About Education Technology" in MIT News (February 26, 2019)
URL(s): news.mit.edu/2019/mit-jpal-what-126-studies
-tell-us-about-education-technology-impact-0226

Released: February 26, 2019. Description: Within the education sphere, technology used in classrooms has boomed. However, there are times when technology can actually harm student learning due to inequality in the classroom. Also, just having the equipment doesn't necessarily mean that grades improve, it just means that the student learns how to use that particular piece of technology. Availability: Online.

21661 ■ "What Business Schools Can Learn From the Medical Profession" in Harvard Business Review (Vol. 90, January-February 2012, No.1-2, pp. 38)
Pub: Harvard Business Review Press
Contact: Moderna V. Pfizer, Contact

Ed: Nitin Nohria. Price: $6. Description: The author recommends closing the knowing-doing gap by applying health care feedback methods to business school instruction. Hospital residents receive feedback after making their rounds; so too should business school students and faculty assemble on a regular basis so that they can discuss what they are learning. Availability: Online; PDF.

21662 ■ "What's Working Now: In Providing Jobs for North Carolinians" in Business North Carolina (Vol. 28, February 2008, No. 2, pp. 16)
Pub: Business North Carolina
Contact: Peggy Knaack, Manager
E-mail: pknaack@businessnc.com

Ed: Edward Martin, Frank Maley. **Description:** Individuals previously employed in the furniture, tobacco, or textile manufacturing sectors have gone back to school to be trained in new sectors in the area such as life sciences, finances and other emerging sectors. **Availability:** Online.

21663 ■ "Where Can a Small Business Owner Get Education and Training" in Financing Solutions (June 21, 2021)
URL(s): financingsolutionsnow.com/where-can-a-small-business-owner-get-education-and-training/

Released: June 21, 2021. **Description:** Provides popular and insightful business owner training resources for small business owners and entrepreneurs. **Availability:** Online.

21664 ■ "Where New Economy Initiative Grants Have Gone" in Crain's Detroit Business (Vol. 25, June 1, 2009, No. 22, pp. M014)
Pub: Crain Communications Inc.
Contact: Barry Asin, President

Ed: Sherri Begin Welch. **Description:** Listing of grants totaling $20.5 million focusing on talent development, attraction and retention; innovation and entrepreneurship; and shifting to a culture that values learning, work and innovation, is presented. **Availability:** Online; PDF.

21665 ■ "Why Does Firm Reputation In Human Resource Policies Influence College Students? The Mechanisms Underlying Job Pursuit Intentions" in Human Resource Management (Vol. 51, January-February 2012, No. 1, pp. 121-142)
Pub: John Wiley & Sons, Inc.
Contact: Christina Van Tassell, Executive Vice President Chief Financial Officer

Ed: Julie Holliday Wayne, Wendy J. Casper. **Released:** January 26, 2012. **Description:** The effects of reputational information about human resource practices of companies on college students seeking employment are examined. The reputation of firms in compensation, work-family, and diversity efforts are found to increase intentions to pursue employment in these firms. **Availability:** Print; PDF; Online.

21666 ■ "Why I Stopped Firing Everyone and Started Being a Better Boss" in Inc. (Vol. 34, September 2012, No. 7, pp. 86)
Pub: Mansueto Ventures L.L.C.
Contact: Stephanie Mehta, Chief Executive Officer

Ed: April Joyner. **Released:** August 28, 2012. **Description:** Indigo Johnson, former Marine, discusses her management style when starting her business. She fired employees regularly. Johnson enrolled in a PhD program in leadership and established a better hiring program and learned to utilize her workers' strengths. **Availability:** Print; Online.

21667 ■ "Why Top Young Managers Are In a Nonstop Job Hunt" in Harvard Business Review (Vol. 90, July-August 2012, No. 7-8, pp. 28)
Pub: Harvard Business Review Press
Contact: Moderna V. Pfizer, Contact

Ed: Monika Hamori, Jie Cao, Burak Koyuncu. **Price:** $6. **Description:** Managers are moving from firm to firm in part because companies are not addressing formal training, coaching, and mentoring needs. While these are costly, companies might benefit from the investment, as managers may tend to stay longer in firms where they are provided. **Availability:** Online; PDF.

21668 ■ "A Woman's Advantage" in Black Enterprise (Vol. 38, December 2007, No. 5, pp. 86)
Pub: Earl G. Graves Ltd.
Contact: Earl Graves, Jr., President

Ed: Marcia A. Reed-Woodard. **Description:** Leadership development is essential for any small business. Simmons College's Strategic Leadership for Women educational course offers a five-day program for professional women teaching powerful strategies to perform, compete, and win in the workplace. **Availability:** Online.

21669 ■ "Women as 21st Century Leaders" in Women In Business (Vol. 63, Summer 2011, No. 2, pp. 26)
Pub: American Business Women's Association
Contact: Rene Street, Executive Director

Ed: Leigh Elmore. **Description:** American Business Women's Association and Park University have partnered to provide a leadership training program to attendees of the 2011 National Women's Leadership Conference. The courses will incorporate introduction to concepts, development of critical thinking skills and direct application through exercises. Comments from executives are also included. **Availability:** Online.

21670 ■ "Women and Higher Education" in Montly Labor Review (Vol. 133, September 2010, No. 9, pp. 70)
Pub: U.S. Department of Labor Bureau of Labor Statistics
Contact: Amrit Kohli, Director
E-mail: kohli.amrit@bls.gov

Description: The increase in people going to college has been mostly among women. Statistical data included. **Availability:** Online; PDF.

21671 ■ "Work Less, Earn More" in Canadian Business (Vol. 80, March 12, 2007, No. 6, pp. 30)

Description: Expert advice on ways to work efficiently to complete the job instead of extending work hours is presented. **Availability:** Online.

21672 ■ "The World Is Your Oyster" in Canadian Business (Vol. 80, October 22, 2007, No. 21, pp. 140)

Description: Business graduates are not that keen on working abroad. Fortune 500 companies are requiring executives to have a multi-country focus. The skill required for jobs abroad, as well as employment opportunities are discussed.

21673 ■ "The World is Their Classroom" in Crain's Chicago Business (Vol. 31, March 24, 2008, No. 12, pp. 24)

Ed: Samantha Stainburn. **Released:** January 17, 2017. **Description:** Due to globalization more business students are studying abroad; 89 percent of eligible students in its executive MBA program went overseas in 2007 compared to 15 percent ten years ago. **Availability:** Print; Online.

21674 ■ "Young Entrepreneur Gets Some Recognition and Some Help for College" in Philadelphia Inquirer (August 30, 2010)
Pub: The Philadelphia Inquirer
Contact: Elizabeth H. Hughes, Chief Executive Officer

Ed: Susan Snyder. **Description:** Profile of Zachary Gosling, age 18, who launched an online auction Website from his bedroom, using advertising and sponsorship funds rather than charging fees to users.

21675 ■ "Young Money"
Pub: Grand Central Publishing
Contact: Michael Pietsch, Chairman

Released: February 18, 2014. **Price:** $27, hardcover. **Description:** How the financial crisis of 2008 changed a generation and remade Wall Street is discussed. The author spent three years following eight entry-level workers at Goldman Sachs, Bank of America Merrill Lynch and other leading investment firms. These young bankers are exposed to the exhausting workloads, huge bonuses, and recreational drugs that have always characterized Wall Street life, but as they get their education and training, they face questions about ethics, prestige and the value of their work. **Availability:** E-book; Print; Audio.

21676 ■ "Zions Offers Step-by-Step Small Business Guidance" in Idaho Business Review (September 1, 2014)
Pub: BridgeTower Media
Contact: Adam Reinebach, President

Description: Zions bank provides small business guidance to clients through its Zions Bank Idaho Business Resource Center. The program helps entrepreneurs learn the basic rules of running a small business. Free courses teach the essentials of finance, marketing and selling, .

TRADE PERIODICALS

21677 ■ *The Chemical Educator*
Pub: The Chemical Educator
Contact: Kimberly Newell LeMaster, Office Manager
URL(s): chemeducator.org/about.htm

Ed: Yehudit Judy Dori, Hugh Cartwright, Raymond Chang. **Released:** Annual **Price:** $179.95, Institutions for 1 year; $34.95, Individuals for 1 year; $20, for single issue. **Description:** Online journal for chemical educators with a print archive version. **Availability:** Print; PDF; Online.

21678 ■ *Teach Magazine: Education for Today and Tomorrow*
Pub: TEACH Magazine
Contact: Wili Liberman, Publisher Editor
URL(s): teachmag.com/latest-issue
Facebook: www.facebook.com/teachmag

Released: Quarterly **Price:** $1,100, for Canada, continental united states (includes Alaska and Hawaii); $6.99, Single issue. **Description:** Educational publication featuring reproducible teaching units. **Availability:** Print; Online.

VIDEO/AUDIO MEDIA

21679 ■ *Side Hustle to Small Business: Taking the Stage: Courage, Confidence, and Charisma*
URL(s): www.hiscox.com/side-hustle-to-small-business/shavonne-davis-acting-mrs-davis-podcast-season-3

Ed: Sanjay Parekh. **Released:** December 14, 2022. **Description:** Podcast features a former teacher who offers after-school theater programs, classes, workshops, and educational consulting.

TRADE SHOWS AND CONVENTIONS

21680 ■ **AASBO Annual Conference and Exposition**
Arizona Association of School Business Officials (AASBO)
2100 N Central Ave., Ste. 202
Phoenix, AZ 85004
Ph: (602)253-5576
Fax: (602)253-5764
Co. E-mail: asba-information@azsba.org
URL: http://www.aasbo.org
Contact: Karla Walter, President
URL(s): www.aasbo.org/page/Conferences

Frequency: Annual. **Description:** Exhibits relating to the business of schools. **Audience:** Industry professionals. **Principal Exhibits:** Exhibits relating to the business of schools. **Telecommunication Services:** ahawthorne@aasbo.org.

21681 ■ **ABSEL Conference**
Association for Business Simulation and Experiential Learning (ABSEL)
320 Stanley Ave.
Greenwood, SC 29649
Ph: (864)388-8775
Co. E-mail: mfekula@lander.edu

URL: http://absel.org
Contact: Mick Fekula, Executive Director
E-mail: mfekula@lander.edu
URL(s): bsel.org/programme/
Frequency: Annual. **Audience:** Academicians, industry professionals, and students. Dates and Locations: 2025 Mar 12-14 Drury Plaza Hotel, Orlando, FL. **Telecommunication Services:** debgood@katz.pitt.edu.

21682 ■ Business Extravaganza
Madera Chamber of Commerce
120 N E St.
Madera, CA 93638
Ph: (559)673-3563
URL: http://maderachamber.com
Contact: Debi Bray, President
E-mail: dbray@maderachamber.com
URL(s): maderachamber.com/?tribe_events=madera-business-extravaganza-home-expo
Frequency: Annual. **Description:** Promotes business and community development in Madera District, CA. **Audience:** Business professionals. **Principal Exhibits:** Promotes business and community development in Madera District, CA.

21683 ■ Business Professionals of America National Leadership Conference
National Geographic
1145 17th St. NW
Washington, DC 20036
Ph: (202)835-0021
Free: 888-966-8687
URL: http://www.nationalgeographic.com
Contact: Gary E. Knell, President
URL(s): bpa.org/nlc
Frequency: Annual. **Description:** Leadership conference for business professionals. **Audience:** Business professionals, students, alumni, advisors, and business teachers. **Principal Exhibits:** Leadership conference for business professionals. Dates and Locations: 2025 May 07-11 Orlando, FL; 2026 May 06-10 Nashville, TN; 2027 May 05-9 Denver, CO; 2028 May 10-14 Orlando, FL; 2029 May 09-13 Washington, DC. **Telecommunication Services:** mgordon@bpa.org.

21684 ■ CAG Conference
California Association for the Gifted (CAG)
2345 Searl Pky.
Hemet, CA 92543
Free: 888-315-5350
Co. E-mail: admin@cagifted.org
URL: http://www.cagifted.org
Contact: Krisa Muller, President
URL(s): cagifted.org/events/#conferences
Frequency: Annual. **Audience:** Educators and parents of gifted children.

21685 ■ California Council for the Social Studies Conference
California Council for the Social Studies (CCSS)
PO Box 1187
Weimar, CA 95736
Ph: (916)318-6800
Co. E-mail: info@ccss.org
URL: http://www.ccss.org
Contact: Dawniell Black, Contact
E-mail: msdkblack@gmail.com
URL(s): www.ccss.org/conference2024
Frequency: Annual. **Description:** Social studies education for all students at all grade levels. **Audience:** Social studies educators, school administrators, professional development providers, and publishers. **Principal Exhibits:** Social studies education for all students at all grade levels. **Telecommunication Services:** info@ccss.org.

21686 ■ Educational Conference
Institute for Credentialing Excellence (ICE)
2001 K St., NW 3rd Fl. N
Washington, DC 20006
Ph: (202)367-1165
Fax: (202)367-2165
Co. E-mail: info@credentialingexcellence.org
URL: http://www.credentialingexcellence.org
Contact: B. Denise Roosendaal, Executive Director
E-mail: droosendaal@credentialingexcellence.org
URL(s): www.credentialingexcellence.org/ICE-Exchange/Save-the-Date
Frequency: Annual. **Description:** Organizations conducting certification programs for occupations and professionals and trade associations representing these professionals. **Audience:** Credentialing professionals in both the public and private sectors. **Principal Exhibits:** Organizations conducting certification programs for occupations and professionals and trade associations representing these professionals. **Telecommunication Services:** registration@credentialingexcellence.org.

21687 ■ ICA Annual Conference
International Communication Association (ICA)
1500 21st St. NW
Washington, DC 20036
Ph: (202)955-1444
Co. E-mail: membership@icahdq.org
URL: http://www.icahdq.org
Contact: Laura Sawyer, Executive Director
E-mail: lsawyer@icahdq.org
URL(s): www.icahdq.org/mpage/ica24
Frequency: Annual. **Description:** Communications study equipment, supplies, and services. **Audience:** Industry professionals. **Principal Exhibits:** Communications study equipment, supplies, and services. Dates and Locations: 2025 Jun 12-16 Denver, CO; 2026; 2027 Chicago, IL. **Telecommunication Services:** membership@icahdq.org.

21688 ■ Mathematical Association of America, Texas Section Conference
Mathematical Association of America - Texas Section
c/o Samuel Ivy University of Mary Hardin-Baylor
PO Box 8420
Belton, TX 76513
Co. E-mail: mhughes@umhb.edu
URL: http://sections.maa.org/texas
Contact: David Ivy, Director
E-mail: sivy@umhb.edu
URL(s): sections.maa.org/texas/tumc
Frequency: Annual. **Description:** Promotes the study of mathematics. **Audience:** Mathematicians and members. **Principal Exhibits:** Promotes the study of mathematics.

21689 ■ Michigan Association for Computer Users in Learning Conference
Michigan Association for Computer Users in Learning (MACUL)
520 S Creyts Rd.
Lansing, MI 48917
Ph: (517)882-1403
Fax: (517)882-2362
Co. E-mail: macul@macul.org
URL: http://macul.org
Contact: Mark Smith, Executive Director
E-mail: msmith@macul.org
URL(s): maculconference.org
Frequency: Annual; held in March. **Audience:** Educators and students. Dates and Locations: 2025 Mar 19-21 Detroit, MI; 2026 Mar 18-20 Grand Rapids, MI; 2027 Mar 17-19 Detroit, MI. **Telecommunication Services:** msmith@macul.org.

21690 ■ NACUBO Annual Meeting
National Association of College and University Business Officers (NACUBO)
1110 Vermont Ave. NW Ste. 800
Washington, DC 20005
Ph: (202)861-2500
Free: 800-462-4916
Co. E-mail: membership@nacubo.org
URL: http://www.nacubo.org
Contact: Kim Ford, Manager, Business Development
URL(s): www.nacubo.org/Events/2024/NACUBO-2024-Annual-Meeting
Price: $850, Pre-registered, members; $1,090, Pre-registered, non-members; $1,105, Onsite registered, members; $1,345, Onsite registered, non-members. **Frequency:** Annual; held in july. **Description:** Exhibits relating to business and financial administration in higher education. **Audience:** Professionals. **Principal Exhibits:** Exhibits relating to business and financial administration in higher education. Dates and Locations: 2025 Jul 26-29 Gaylord National Resort & Convention Center, Washington, DC. **Telecommunication Services:** annualmeeting@nacubo.org.

21691 ■ National Business Education Association Convention
National Business Education Association (NBEA)
1908 Association Dr., Ste. B
Reston, VA 20191
Ph: (703)860-8300
Fax: (703)620-4483
Co. E-mail: nbea@nbea.org
URL: http://nbea.org/?
Contact: Lori Hauf, President
URL(s): nbea.org/page/2025Convention
Frequency: Annual. **Description:** Event will be a hybrid format with in-person and virtual options. **Audience:** Business teachers from middle schools, high schools, community colleges and universities. **Principal Exhibits:** Event will be a hybrid format with in-person and virtual options. Dates and Locations: 2025 Oct 21-24 Hyatt Regency Cincinnati, Cincinnati, OH. **Telecommunication Services:** events@nbea.org.

21692 ■ National Conference on Education
AASA, The School Superintendents Association
1615 Duke St.
Alexandria, VA 22314
Ph: (703)528-0700
Fax: (703)841-1543
Co. E-mail: info@aasa.org
URL: http://www.aasa.org/home
Contact: Valerie Truesdale, Executive Director
E-mail: vtruesdale@aasa.org
URL(s): www.aasa.org/professional-learning/national-conference-on-education
Frequency: Annual. **Description:** Conference focuses on educating and connecting superintendents. **Audience:** Industry professionals. **Principal Exhibits:** Conference focuses on educating and connecting superintendents. Dates and Locations: 2025 Mar 06-08 New Orleans, LA; 2026 Feb 12-14 Nashville, TN; 2027 Feb 25-27 Atlanta, GA. **Telecommunication Services:** aasance@aasa.org.

21693 ■ National Council of Teachers of Mathematics Annual Convention
National Council of Teachers of Mathematics (NCTM)
1906 Association Dr.
Reston, VA 20191-1502
Ph: (703)620-9840
Free: 800-235-7566
Fax: (703)476-2970
Co. E-mail: nctm@nctm.org
URL: http://www.nctm.org
Contact: Trena L. Wilkerson, President
E-mail: twilkerson@nctm.org
URL(s): www.nctm.org/tmf/library/view/71425.html
Frequency: Annual. **Description:** Computer hardware and software, textbooks, workbooks, math games, and videos. **Audience:** Mathematics educators, supervisors, administrators, and general public. **Principal Exhibits:** Computer hardware and software, textbooks, workbooks, math games, and videos.

21694 ■ National Head Start Association Conference
National Head Start Association (NHSA)
1651 Prince St.
Alexandria, VA 22314
Ph: (703)739-0875
Free: 866-677-8724
Co. E-mail: info@nhsa.org
URL: http://nhsa.org
Contact: Damon Carson, Chairman
URL(s): nhsa.org/conference/national-head-start-conference
Price: $545, Members; $655, Non-members. **Frequency:** Annual. **Description:** Discuss the latest developments, innovations, and obstacles in early learning and to inspire ideas for turning challenges into opportunities. **Audience:** Executive directors,

directors, administrators, managers, teachers, policy council members, and parents. **Principal Exhibits:** Discuss the latest developments, innovations, and obstacles in early learning and to inspire ideas for turning challenges into opportunities. Dates and Locations: 2025 May 19-22 Columbus, OH. **Telecommunication Services:** kpruitt@nhsa.org.

21695 ■ National Science Teachers Association Conference
National Science Teachers Association (NSTA)
1840 Wilson Blvd.
Arlington, VA 22201
Ph: (703)524-3646
Fax: (703)243-7177
Co. E-mail: executive@nsta.org
URL: http://www.nsta.org
Contact: Dr. Julie A. Luft, President
URL(s): www.nsta.org/national-conference-science-education-new-orleans-2024

Frequency: Semiannual; held in fall and spring. **Description:** Offer the latest in science content, teaching strategy, and research to enhance and expand your professional growth. **Audience:** Science teachers, science supervisors, administrators, scientists, business and industry representatives. **Principal Exhibits:** Offer the latest in science content, teaching strategy, and research to enhance and expand your professional growth. Dates and Locations: 2025 Mar 26-29 Philadelphia, PA. **Telecommunication Services:** conferences@nsta.org.

21696 ■ NCFR Annual Conference
National Council on Family Relations (NCFR)
661 LaSalle St., Ste. 200
Saint Paul, MN 55114
Free: 888-781-9331
Co. E-mail: info@ncfr.org
URL: http://www.ncfr.org
Contact: Dr. Bethany L. Letiecq, President
E-mail: bletiecq@gmu.edu
URL(s): www.ncfr.org/ncfr-2024

Frequency: Annual; held each November. **Description:** Opportunity to learn about the latest in research, practice, and teaching in the family field. **Audience:** Researchers, demographers, marriage and family therapists, parent/family educators, university faculty, students, social workers, public health workers, extension specialists and faculty, clergy, counselors, and k-12 teachers. **Principal Exhibits:** Opportunity to learn about the latest in research, practice, and teaching in the family field. Dates and Locations: 2025 Nov 19-22 Baltimore Marriott Waterfront Hotel, Baltimore, MD; 2026 Nov 18-21 Hilton Minneapolis, Minneapolis, MN. **Telecommunication Services:** info@ncfr.org.

21697 ■ NCTE Annual Convention
National Council of Teachers of English (NCTE)
2427 Bond St.
University Park, IL 60484
Ph: (217)328-3870
Free: 877-369-6283
Fax: (217)328-9645
Co. E-mail: customerservice@ncte.org
URL: http://ncte.org
Contact: Tonya B. Perry, President
URL(s): convention.ncte.org

Frequency: Annual. **Description:** English education materials and related equipment, supplies, and services. **Audience:** Educators, experts, authors, administrators, publishers, and others. **Principal Exhibits:** English education materials and related equipment, supplies, and services. Dates and Locations: 2025 Nov 20-23 Colorado Convention Center, Denver, CO. **Telecommunication Services:** ncteevents@ncte.org.

21698 ■ NSBA Annual Conference and Exhibition
National School Boards Association (NSBA)
1680 Duke St., FL2
Alexandria, VA 22314-3493
Ph: (703)838-6722
Fax: (571)470-5108
Co. E-mail: info@nsba.org
URL: http://www.nsba.org

Contact: Dr. John Heim, Chief Executive Officer
URL(s): www.nsba.org/Events/NSBA-2025-Annual-Conference-and-Exposition

Frequency: Annual. **Description:** Equipment, supplies, and services for in U.S. public schools. **Audience:** Local school board members, superintendents, and education leaders. **Principal Exhibits:** Equipment, supplies, and services for in U.S. public schools. Dates and Locations: 2025 Apr 04-06 Atlanta, GA. **Telecommunication Services:** info@nsba.org.

21699 ■ SSSP Annual Meetings
Society for the Study of Social Problems (SSSP)
901 McClung Twr., University of Tennessee
Knoxville, TN 37996-0490
Ph: (865)689-1531
Fax: (865)689-1534
Co. E-mail: sssp@utk.edu
URL: http://www.sssp1.org
URL(s): www.sssp1.org/index.cfm/m/944/2024_Annual_Meeting

Frequency: Annual; mostly held in August. **Description:** Meeting discusses topics in social problems to achieve social justice. **Audience:** Students, professors, activists and private sector professionals. **Principal Exhibits:** Meeting discusses topics in social problems to achieve social justice. Dates and Locations: 2026. **Telecommunication Services:** mkoontz3@utk.edu.

21700 ■ Winter Academic Conference
EBSCO Information Services
10 Estes St.
Ipswich, MA 01938
Ph: (978)356-6500
Free: 800-653-2726
Co. E-mail: information@ebsco.com
URL: http://www.ebsco.com
Contact: Tim Collins, Chief Executive Officer
URL(s): www.ama.org/events/academic/2024-ama-winter-academic-conference

Frequency: Annual. **Audience:** Marketing scholars. Dates and Locations: 2025 Feb 14-16 Sheraton Phoenix Downtown, Phoenix, AZ. **Telecommunication Services:** customersuppot@ama.org.

CONSULTANTS

21701 ■ American English Academy (AEA) [American English College]
111 N Atlantic Blvd., Ste. 112
Monterey Park, CA 91754
Ph: (626)457-2800
Fax: (626)457-2808
Co. E-mail: info@aec.edu
URL: http://www.aec.edu
Facebook: www.facebook.com/americanenglishcollege
Linkedin: www.linkedin.com/company/american-english-college
Instagram: www.instagram.com/americanenglishcollege
YouTube: www.youtube.com/channel/UC6eS1MpXLDagYdZVZWWJO6A

Description: Specializes in providing on-site English language and communication development for corporations and individuals. Also develops and delivers training in speaking, writing, pronunciation, grammar, and idioms with an emphasis on business communication. Offers individual, small group, intensive, and long-distance learning. Programs tailor-made for each client. **Scope:** Specializes in providing on-site English language and communication development for corporations and individuals. Also develops and delivers training in speaking, writing, pronunciation, grammar, and idioms with an emphasis on business communication. Offers individual, small group, intensive, and long-distance learning. Programs tailor-made for each client. **Founded:** 1983.

21702 ■ Art Munin Consulting
c/o Assistant Dean of Students Office
Depaul University
Chicago, IL 60614-3673
Ph: (773)316-2276

Co. E-mail: art@artmunin.com
URL: http://www.artmunin.com
Contact: Dr. Art Munin, Owner
E-mail: art@artmunin.com
X (Twitter): twitter.com/ArtMunin

Description: Consulting firm committed to advancing multicultural education and imparting advocacy, the firm runs workshops and seminars that expand the opportunities to engage people in conversations about diversity and social justice. **Publications:** "Would they still have written if they knew I had to go home and tell my wife?," 2009; "The leadership bookshelf," 2009; "Improving the campus environment for bi/multiracial students," Peter Lang Publishing, 2009; "Empathy: Love the sinner, hate the sin. About Campus," 2007; "Factors influencing the ally development of college students". **Training:** White Privilege 101; Locating Justice; Targeting the Majority in Diversity Education; Art of War - Targeting the Majority in Multicultural Education; Higher Education: The Gate-Keeper to the Middle Class; Who Are Our Transgendered Students?; The Basics of Diversity Training; Retreats; Ethics and Leadership: Making Choices for Social Justice; Color by Number.

21703 ■ Blackmon Roberts Group Inc. (BRG)
902 S Florida Ave., Ste. 205
Lakeland, FL 33803-1116
Ph: (863)802-1280
Free: 877-450-3237
Fax: (863)802-1290
Co. E-mail: info@blackmonroberts.com
URL: http://www.blackmonroberts.com
Contact: Sylvia Blackmon Roberts, President

Description: Firm provides strategic and innovative solutions and industry expertise, public planning and management consulting services such as transportation and public planning, business management, and non-profit management. **Scope:** Firm provides strategic and innovative solutions and industry expertise, public planning and management consulting services such as transportation and public planning, business management, and non-profit management. **Founded:** 1992.

21704 ■ Business Culture Consultants
PO Box 3067
Burlington, VT 05408
Ph: (802)658-4111
URL: http://businesscultureconsultants.com
Contact: Flip Brown, Contact
E-mail: flip.brown@icloud.com

Description: Firm provides training for professional development. **Scope:** Firm provides training for professional development. **Founded:** 2000.

21705 ■ Business Improvement Architects (BIA)
633 Lakelands Ave.
Innisfil, ON, Canada L9S 4E5
Co. E-mail: info@bia.ca
URL: http://bia.ca
Contact: Rowena Lamy, Consultant
E-mail: rlamy@bia.ca
Facebook: www.facebook.com/BusinessImprovementArchitects
Linkedin: www.linkedin.com/company/business-improvement-architects

Description: Provider of the following services, strategic planning, leadership development, innovation and project and quality management. Specialize in strategic planning, change management, leadership assessment and development of skills. **Scope:** Provider of the following services, strategic planning, leadership development, innovation and project and quality management. Specialize in strategic planning, change management, leadership assessment and development of skills. **Founded:** 1989. **Publications:** "Avoiding Pit falls to Innovation"; "Create a New Dimension of Performance with Innovation"; "The Power of Appreciation in Leadership"; "Why It Makes Sense To Have a Strategic Enterprise Office"; "Burning Rubber at the Start of Your Project"; "Accounting for Quality"; "How Pareto Charts Can Help You Improve the Quality of Business Processes"; "Managing Resistance to Change". **Training:** The Innovation

Process From Vision to Reality, San Diego, Oct, 2007; Critical Thinking, Kuala Lump or, Sep, 2007; Critical Thinking, Brunei, Sep, 2007; Delivering Project Assurance, Auckland, Jun, 2007; From Crisis to Control: A New Era in Strategic Project Management, Prague, May, 2007; What Project Leaders Need to Know to Help Them Sleep Better At Night, London, May, 2007; Innovation Process. From Vision To Reality, Orlando, Apr, 2007. **Special Services:** Project Planning Tool™.

21706 ■ Charter School Business Management (CSBM)
237 W 35th St., Ste. 301
New York, NY 10001
Free: 888-710-2726
Co. E-mail: info@csbm.com
URL: http://csbm.com
Contact: Karen Daniels, President
Facebook: www.facebook.com/CharterSchoolBusinessManagement
Linkedin: www.linkedin.com/company/charter-school-business-management-inc

Description: Firm aims to support the charter school movement by creating and maintaining a foundation of finance, operations, human resources, and compliance at each school it serves. **Scope:** Firm aims to support the charter school movement by creating and maintaining a foundation of finance, operations, human resources, and compliance at each school it serves. **Founded:** 2006.

21707 ■ Competitive Edge Inc.
PO Box 724705
Atlanta, GA 31139
Ph: (770)487-6460
Fax: (770)319-0313
Co. E-mail: info@competiveedgeinc.com
URL: http://www.competitiveedgeinc.com
Contact: Judy Suiter, Founder

Description: Firm provides cutting-edge services such as effective selections, coaching, and training. **Scope:** Firm provides cutting-edge services such as effective selections, coaching, and training. **Founded:** 1981. **Publications:** "Beteenden och drivkrafter"; "Energizing People: Unleashing The Power of DISC"; "The Ripple Effect: How the Global Model of Endorsement Opens Doors to Success"; "The Journey - Quotes to keep your boat afloat"; "The Universal Language DISC Reference Manual"; "Exploring Values: Releasing the Power of Attitudes"; "Competitive Products Review Book"; "The Mother Of All Minds"; "The Sea of Change: Solutions for Navigating the Disconnects in the Workplace". **Training:** How to Recruit and Retain High Performing Employees; The Importance of Values Matching For Sales Selection; How to Build a High Performance Team; Dynamic Communication Skills; Creating Nurturing Customer Relationships; Your Attitude Is Showing; Sales Strategy Index; Validity Study.

21708 ■ Daniel Bloom and Associates Inc. (DBAI)
11517 128th Ave. N
Largo, FL 33778
Ph: (727)581-6216
URL: http://dbaiconsulting.com
Contact: Daniel T. Bloom, Chief Executive Officer

Description: Human resources management consultant with a specialization in corporate relocation. Offers clients a turn key service aimed at meeting the unique relocation needs of their employees. Develops and implements training programs within the relocation industry. **Scope:** Human resources management consultant with a specialization in corporate relocation. Offers clients a turn key service aimed at meeting the unique relocation needs of their employees. Develops and implements training programs within the relocation industry. **Founded:** 1980. **Publications:** "Where Have All the Elders Gone," Aug, 2002; "Recoup Your Hiring Investment," Brainbuzz.com, Aug, 2000; "Managing Your Lump Sum Program," Brainbuzz.com, Jun, 2000; "Buyer Value Options," Brainbuzz.com, Apr, 2000; "Just Get Me There". **Training:** Chaos in the Workplace: Multiple Generational Interactions; Training Effectiveness: Is the Cost Justified?; Human Capital Resource Management: A Six-Sigma Based Approach to Paving Your Way to the Table; Welcome to My World.

21709 ■ Don Phin, Esq.
114 C. Ave., No. 200
Coronado, CA 92118
Ph: (619)852-4580
URL: http://www.donphin.com
Contact: Don Phin, Contact
E-mail: don@donphin.com
Linkedin: www.linkedin.com/in/donphin
X (Twitter): x.com/donphin12
YouTube: www.youtube.com/donphin

Description: Firm is engaged in consulting services on training, coaching and mentoring for the individuals and small businesses. **Scope:** Firm is engaged in consulting services on training, coaching and mentoring for the individuals and small businesses. **Founded:** 1983. **Publications:** "Doing Business Right!"; "HR That Works!"; "Lawsuit Free! How to Prevent Employee Lawsuits"; "Building Powerful Employment Relationships!"; "Victims, Villains and Heroes: Managing Emotions in The Workplace". **Training:** Doing Business Right!; HR That Works!; Building Powerful Employment Relationships; Lawsuit Free!.

21710 ■ Full Voice
9912B Holmes Rd., Ste. 237
Kansas City, MO 64131-4206

Description: Vocal performance training firm offering consulting services and personal training sessions in the implementation of effective vocal communication techniques for the development of business relationships and career enhancement. **Scope:** Vocal performance training firm offering consulting services and personal training sessions in the implementation of effective vocal communication techniques for the development of business relationships and career enhancement. **Publications:** "You Can Sound Like You Know What You're Saying". **Training:** You Can Sound Like You Know What You're Saying; The Psychology of Vocal Performance; Security. . .the Ability to Accept Change; Knowing. . .the Key to Relaxed Public Communication; The Effective Voice for Customer Service Enhancement; You Can Speak With Conviction; How To Make Yours a Championship Team; Functional English For Foreign Trade. **Special Services:** FULL VOICE™.

21711 ■ National Pediculosis Association (NPA)
1005 Boylston St., Ste. 343
Newton, MA 02461
Ph: (617)905-0176
Co. E-mail: npa@headlice.org
URL: http://www.headlice.org/comb
Contact: Deborah Altschuler, President
X (Twitter): x.com/TheLiceMeister

Description: Parents, physicians, school nurses, and individuals representing hospitals and county health departments. Works to eliminate the incidence, particularly among children, of pediculosis (head lice). Conducts public education campaign to make pediculosis control a public health priority; acts as consumer advocate to ensure the quality and safety of products for treating pediculosis and scabies; encourages scientific research to discover methods of treatment that minimize the use of pesticides, which may harm pregnant and nursing women as well as infants and children. Provides consultations to schools, camps, and other organizations. **Scope:** Consultants in head lice and scabies management, treatment, prevention, and education. Specializes in monitoring health policy administration in schools and trends in the treatment of head lice. Emphasis is on educational activities. Industries served: schools, health professionals, medical professionals, child care centers, health departments, hospitals, HMO's, clinics, libraries, parents, PTA's, camps, military bases, and churches. **Founded:** 1983. **Publications:** "All out Comb out". **Geographic Preference:** National; Multinational.

21712 ■ Next Step Business Education Ltd.
Thornhill, ON, Canada

Description: Continuous improvement and training specialists. Helps set-up and facilitate your teams to solve problems, improve processes and implement new practices, using the kaizen or kaizen-blitz, continuous improvement workshop method. **Scope:** Continuous improvement and training specialists. Helps set-up and facilitate your teams to solve problems, improve processes and implement new practices, using the kaizen or kaizen-blitz, continuous improvement workshop method. **Founded:** 1985. **Training:** Food Safety Management Programs; The Visual Factory; 5S Methodology; Value Stream Mapping; Focused Factory; Set-Up Reduction; Lean Strategy; Problem Solving; ERP or MRP II; Sales & Operations Planning; Competing to Win; TEAMWORK; GAMEShare; Effective Meetings; High Performance Culture.

21713 ■ Organized Business Techniques, Inc.
13 Fountain Dr.
Valhalla, NY 10595
Contact: Marie T. Rossi, Chief Executive Officer

Description: Training programs consulting firm. **Scope:** Training programs consulting firm. **Founded:** 1984.

21714 ■ Tamayo Consulting Inc.
662 Encinitas Blvd., Ste. 236
Encinitas, CA 92024
Ph: (760)479-1352
URL: http://www.tamayoconsulting.com
Contact: Jennifer Dreyer, President

Description: It Provides training and consulting services. And also it specializes in leadership and team development. Industries served: private, non-profit, government, educational. **Scope:** It Provides training and consulting services. And also it specializes in leadership and team development. Industries served: private, non-profit, government, educational. **Training:** Presentation AdvantEdge Program; Lead point Development Program; Supervisor Development Programs.Identify Presentation Objectives; Implement 360-degree presentation assessment; conduct baseline-coaching session; Develop coaching plan; Staying connected.

FRANCHISES AND BUSINESS OPPORTUNITIES

21715 ■ Canadian School of Natural Nutrition (CSNN)
10909 Yonge St., Unit 216
Richmond Hill, ON, Canada L4C 3E3
URL: http://csnn.ca
Contact: Danielle Perrault, Founder
Facebook: www.facebook.com/CSNNNational
Linkedin: www.linkedin.com/school/canadian-school-of-natural-nutrition-national
X (Twitter): x.com/csnn
YouTube: www.youtube.com/wwwcsnnca

Description: private vocational school offering adult education leading to professional designations: RHN-Reg. Holistic Nutritionist, and RECP-Reg, ElderCare Practitioner. Franchisees are licensed to distribute CSNN curriculum material to students through classroom education. CSNN offers two programs: Natural Nutrition and Elder Care. CSNN is privately owned, incorporated as 3393291 Canada Inc. **No. of Franchise Units:** 4. **No. of Company-Owned Units:** 10. **Founded:** 1994. **Franchised:** 1996. **Equity Capital Needed:** $70,000 Canadian Capital. **Franchise Fee:** $12,000. **Training:** Ongoing.

21716 ■ Club Scientific, LLC
PO Box 1194
Jackson, MI 49204
Free: 800-379-8302
Co. E-mail: info@clubscientific.com
URL: http://www.clubscientific.com
Facebook: www.facebook.com/ClubScientificCorporate
X (Twitter): x.com/clubscientific_
Instagram: www.instagram.com/clubscientific

Description: Firm provides science enrichment programs to children through interactive experiments, adventures and entertainment. **Founded:** 1997. **Financial Assistance:** Yes **Training:** Provides 4 days training at headquarters, 4 days at franchisee's location and ongoing support.

21717 ■ Drama Kids International, Inc. (DKI)
405 E Market St.
  Leesburg, VA 20176
Ph: (703)726-1226
URL: http://dramakids.com
Facebook: www.facebook.com/dramakids
X (Twitter): x.com/DramaKidsIntl
YouTube: www.youtube.com/user/DramaKidsIntl

Description: After-school developmental drama program. Curriculum uses fun and creative drama activities so kids ages 5-17 act confidently and speak clearly. **No. of Franchise Units:** 56. **Founded:** 1985. **Franchised:** 1989. **Equity Capital Needed:** $33,550-38,950. **Franchise Fee:** $29,000. **Royalty Fee:** 8-9%. **Financial Assistance:** Yes **Training:** Provides training for the kids to perform drama.

21718 ■ Eye Level Learning Centers
2nd Fl., Daekyo America, Ste. 105 Challenger Rd.
  Ridgefield Park, NJ 07660
Free: 888-835-1212
URL: http://m.myeyelevel.com/Indonesia/index.do
Facebook: www.facebook.com/eyeleveleducation

Description: Supplemental education. **No. of Franchise Units:** 125. **No. of Company-Owned Units:** 513. **Founded:** 1976. **Franchised:** 1976. **Equity Capital Needed:** $52,000-$91,000. **Franchise Fee:** $12,000. **Royalty Fee:** $15/student. **Training:** Offers 16 hours training at headquarters, at franchisee's location and ongoing.

21719 ■ Fastrackids International, Ltd.
6950 E Belleview Ave., Ste. 320
  Greenwood Village, CO 80111
Ph: (303)224-0200
Free: 888-576-6888
Fax: (303)224-0222
Co. E-mail: info@fastrackids.com
URL: http://www.fastrackids.com
Facebook: www.facebook.com/FasTracKidsInternational
Linkedin: www.linkedin.com/company/fastrackids-international
X (Twitter): x.com/FasTracKidsINTL
Instagram: www.instagram.com/intl_fastrackids
YouTube: www.youtube.com/user/FasTracKids

Description: An accelerated learning system for children. **No. of Franchise Units:** 150. **Founded:** 1998. **Franchised:** 1998. **Equity Capital Needed:** $33,800-$183,500. **Franchise Fee:** $22,000. **Training:** Provides initial training, periodic regional seminars, an annual international conference, sales/telemarketing assistance, and classroom facilitation tips.

21720 ■ Frozen Ropes Training Centers
24 Old Black Meadow Rd.
  Chester, NY 10918
Ph: (845)469-7331
Fax: (845)469-6742
Co. E-mail: info@frozenropes.com
URL: http://www.frozenropes.com
Contact: Tony Abbatine, Director
Facebook: www.facebook.com/FrozenRopesUSA
X (Twitter): x.com/FrozenRopesUSA
Instagram: www.instagram.com/frozenropesusa
YouTube: www.youtube.com/user/FrozenRopesCorporate

Description: Operator of national training center for frozen ropes baseball and softball. **Founded:** 1994.

21721 ■ Ho Math & Chess Learning Centre
Vancouver, BC, Canada
URL: http://www.homathchess.com/web-page_4.html
Contact: Frank Ho, Director
E-mail: fho1928@gmail.com

Description: Math and chess learning center. **Founded:** 1995. **Royalty Fee:** None. **Training:** 1 week training provided at headquarters.

21722 ■ KidzArt
833 Laurence Ave., Ste. B
  Jackson, MI 49202
Ph: (517)784-5000
Free: 800-379-8302
Co. E-mail: info@kidzart.com
URL: http://www.kidzart.com
Facebook: www.facebook.com/kidzart
Linkedin: www.linkedin.com/company/kidzart-art-innovators
X (Twitter): x.com/kidzartceo
Instagram: www.instagram.com/kidzartcorporate

Description: Firm offers children products and educational services. **Founded:** 1998. **Franchised:** 2002. **Franchise Fee:** $65,000-$250,000. **Financial Assistance:** Yes **Training:** Offers 1 week business/operations training and cutting edge franchisee support; conferences, monthly training calls, one on one quick start coaching and ongoing support.

21723 ■ Kumon North America Inc.
Kumon North America Inc.
  Meadows Office Complex 301 Rte. 17 N, 12th Fl.
  Rutherford, NJ 07070
Ph: (201)928-0444
Fax: (201)928-0044
Co. E-mail: communications@kumon.com
URL: http://www.kumon.com
Contact: Hidenori Ikegami, President
Facebook: www.facebook.com/kumon
Linkedin: www.linkedin.com/company/kumon
X (Twitter): x.com/Kumon_NA
Instagram: www.instagram.com/kumonnorthamerica
YouTube: www.youtube.com/channel/UCiuM9mlCeYLXwiGhSTIZCAg

Description: Firm is a provider of after-school math and reading enrichment programs. **Founded:** 1958. **Equity Capital Needed:** $150,000 and liquid capital of $70,000. **Franchise Fee:** $1,000. **Training:** Kumon has offices worldwide to provide training, support and onsite consultation to franchisee's.

21724 ■ LearningRx Inc.
6385 Corporate Dr.
  Colorado Springs, CO 80919
Ph: (719)550-8263
Free: 866-BRA-IN01
Co. E-mail: contact@learningrx.com
URL: http://www.learningrx.com
Contact: Teri Miller, Director
Facebook: www.facebook.com/learningrx
Linkedin: www.linkedin.com/company/learningrx
X (Twitter): x.com/LearningRxCO1
Instagram: www.instagram.com/learningrx_coloradosprings
YouTube: www.youtube.com/user/LearningRxCO01

Description: Firm provides brain training, learning disabilities, education. **Founded:** 2002.

21725 ■ The Mad Science Group (MSG)
8360 Bougainville St., Ste. 201
  Montreal, QC, Canada H4P 2G1
Ph: (514)344-4181
Free: 800-586-5231
Fax: (514)344-6695
Co. E-mail: info@madscience.org
URL: http://www.madscience.org
Facebook: www.facebook.com/MadScience
X (Twitter): x.com/madsciencegroup
Instagram: www.instagram.com/madsciencegroup
YouTube: www.youtube.com/user/MadScienceGroup

Description: Mad Science is a service company specializing in fun hands on educational science for children. We send trained instructors with all required materials and supplies to conduct onsite activities to schools and other organizations dealing with kids. Our franchisees are sales marketing oriented individuals who enjoy a hands-on owner operated business that enriches children and contributes to the community. **No. of Franchise Units:** 200. **Founded:** 1985. **Franchised:** 1995. **Equity Capital Needed:** $10,000-$23,500 franchise fee, $25,000 equipment package; $20,000-$30,000 working capital. **Franchise Fee:** $10,000-$23,500. **Financial Assistance:** Yes **Training:** 6 day training at corporate headquarters followed by 5 day training onsite.

21726 ■ Mathnasium Learning Centers
5120 W Goldleaf Cir., Ste. 400
  Los Angeles, CA 90056-1661
Free: 877-601-6284
Co. E-mail: marketing@mathnasium.com
URL: http://www.mathnasium.com
Contact: Henry Moore, Director
Facebook: www.facebook.com/mathnasium
X (Twitter): x.com/mathnasium
YouTube: www.youtube.com/c/mathnasium

Description: Mathnasium provides the most effective mathematics in education available to grade school children after school, in an attractive neighborhood learning center environment. The Mathnasium Method, developed over 30 years of hands-on experience, is engaging for students and builds confidence as it builds real understanding. Created to address a real need in the market by a team with unparalleled success in the industry, the business model is strong and the opportunity is now. **No. of Franchise Units:** 389. **No. of Company-Owned Units:** 2. **Founded:** 2002. **Franchised:** 2003. **Equity Capital Needed:** $82,250-$136,000 initial investment range. **Franchise Fee:** $37,000. **Training:** Initial training 1 week online followed by 1 week in person at corporate headquarters. Support continues with ongoing training, in-the-field regional managers and monthly conference calls.

21727 ■ Online Trading Academy
Al Khaleej Training and Education Co.
  17780 Fitch, Ste. 200
  Irvine, CA 92614
Ph: 966 9 20024824
URL: http://www.alkhaleej.com.sa
Contact: Eyal Shahar, Chief Executive Officer
Facebook: www.facebook.com/OnlineTradingAcademy
Linkedin: www.linkedin.com/company/online-trading-academy
X (Twitter): x.com/TradingAcademy
YouTube: www.youtube.com/tradingacademy

Description: Stock-trading instruction. **No. of Franchise Units:** 16. **Founded:** 1998. **Franchised:** 2004. **Equity Capital Needed:** $209,800-$388,000. **Franchise Fee:** $80,000-$200,000. **Royalty Fee:** 10%. **Training:** Provides trading and investing education for any markets or asset class.

21728 ■ Oxford Learning Centers Inc.
747 Hyde Park Rd., Ste. 230
  London, ON, Canada N6H 3S3
Ph: (226)646-9422
Co. E-mail: info@oxfordlearning.com
URL: http://www.oxfordlearning.com
Contact: Kala Challis, Manager
Facebook: www.facebook.com/OxfordLearning
X (Twitter): x.com/oxfordlearning
Instagram: www.instagram.com/oxfordlearningcentres
YouTube: www.youtube.com/user/OxfordLearning

Description: Provider of supplemental education and tutoring services. **Founded:** 1984. **Equity Capital Needed:** 50000. **Franchise Fee:** $109,600-$243,000. **Royalty Fee:** 0.1. **Training:** Provides 2 weeks training and ongoing support.

21729 ■ Parisi Speed School
516-B Commerce St.
  Franklin Lakes, NJ 07417
Ph: (201)847-1939
Free: 888-438-3278
Co. E-mail: info@parisischool.com
URL: http://www.parisischool.com
Contact: George Stephens, Managing Director
Facebook: www.facebook.com/ParisiSchool
X (Twitter): x.com/ParisiSpeed
YouTube: www.youtube.com/user/ParisiSpeedSchool1

Description: Youth performance training. **No. of Franchise Units:** 44. **No. of Company-Owned Units:** 5. **Founded:** 1992. **Franchised:** 2005. **Equity Capital Needed:** $132,500-$300,100. **Franchise Fee:** $29,900. **Royalty Fee:** $1,000/month.

21730 ■ Parmasters Golf Training Centers
1500 W Georgia St., 14th Fl.
Vancouver, BC, Canada V6G 2Z6
URL: http://www.franchising.com/linksgolfcafe
Description: Provider of golf training services. **Founded:** 2009.

21731 ■ Spirit of Math Schools
101-1446 Don Mills Rd.
Toronto, ON, Canada M3B 3N3
Ph: (416)223-1985
Fax: (416)946-1902
Co. E-mail: info@spiritofmath.com
URL: http://spiritofmath.com
Contact: Kim Langen, Chief Executive Officer
Facebook: www.facebook.com/spiritofmath
Linkedin: www.linkedin.com/company/spirit-of-math-schools-inc.
X (Twitter): x.com/spiritofmath
Instagram: www.instagram.com/spiritofmath
YouTube: www.youtube.com/channel/UC8SmLw79583CVc8yynBmlvA
Description: Offers an after-school classroom program for high performing students. It develops as skill-based understanding of math focusing on problem solving, co-operation and numeric skills and produces some of the top math students in the nation. **No. of Franchise Units:** 13. **No. of Company-Owned Units:** 13. **Founded:** 1995. **Franchised:** 2006. **Equity Capital Needed:** $32,000-$70,000. **Franchise Fee:** $39,000. **Training:** A comprehensive training and support program is provided.

21732 ■ Thinkertots
191-17 35th Ave.
Flushing, NY 11358
Description: Educational parent/child classes. **No. of Franchise Units:** 4. **No. of Company-Owned Units:** 1. **Founded:** 1998. **Franchised:** 2005. **Equity Capital Needed:** $42,000-$160,000. **Franchise Fee:** $15,000-$25,000. **Training:** Employs multiple intelligence strategies to help promote development of Logical thinking & problem solving skill in children.

21733 ■ The Whole Child Learning Company
2200 Kraft Dr., Ste. 1350
Blacksburg, VA 24060
Ph: (540)443-9252
Fax: (540)242-3214
Co. E-mail: info@wholechild.com
URL: http://www.wholechild.com
Description: Firm provides educational enrichment programs for children. **Founded:** 1996. **Financial Assistance:** Yes **Training:** Yes.

21734 ■ Young Rembrandts - The Power Of Drawing
23 N Union St.
Elgin, IL 60123
Ph: (847)742-6966
Co. E-mail: info@youngrembrandts.com
URL: http://www.youngrembrandts.com
Contact: Bette Fetter, Founder
Facebook: www.facebook.com/YoungRembrandts1
Linkedin: www.linkedin.com/company/young-rembrandts
X (Twitter): x.com/YoungRembrandts
Instagram: www.instagram.com/youngrembrandts
YouTube: www.youtube.com/youngrembrandts
Pinterest: www.pinterest.com/youngrembrandts
Description: Teaches drawing, the fundamental skill of visual arts to children ages 3 1/2 to 12. **No. of Franchise Units:** 80. **Founded:** 1988. **Franchised:** 2001. **Equity Capital Needed:** Liquid $50,000; $100,000 net. **Franchise Fee:** $31,500. **Training:** Provides sales, marketing, the Young & Rembrandts method, classroom training.

PUBLICATIONS

21735 ■ AACSB Insights
777 S Harbour Island Blvd. Ste. 750
Tampa, FL 33602
Ph: (813)769-6500
Co. E-mail: events@aacsb.edu
URL: http://www.aacsb.edu
Contact: Caryn L. Beck-Dudley, President
URL(s): www.aacsb.edu/insights/publications/bized-archives
Ed: Tricia Bisoux, Sharon Shinn. **Released:** Bi-monthly **Description:** Magazine covering trends in business education. **Availability:** Online; PDF.

21736 ■ Business Education Forum: Official Publication of the National Business Education Association
1908 Association Dr., Ste. B
Reston, VA 20191
Ph: (703)860-8300
Fax: (703)620-4483
Co. E-mail: nbea@nbea.org
URL: http://nbea.org/?
Contact: Lori Hauf, President
URL(s): nbealibrary.org
Released: Quarterly **Description:** Business education journal covering articles on accounting, basic business, communication, international business, marketing, methods, and technology. **Availability:** Online.

21737 ■ Handbook of Research on Serious Games as Educational, Business and Research Tools
701 E Chocolate Ave.
Hershey, PA 17033
Ph: (717)533-8845
Free: 866-342-6657
Fax: (717)533-8661
Co. E-mail: cust@igi-global.com
URL: http://www.igi-global.com
Contact: Jan Travers, Director
URL(s): www.igi-global.com/book/handbook-research-serious-games-educational/58271
Price: $580, for hardcover + e-book; $37.50, for On-Demand (individual chapters); $480, for hardcover; $480, for e-book. **Description:** Published by IGI Global. Collects research on the most recent technological developments in all fields of knowledge or disciplines of computer games development, including planning, design, development, marketing, business management, users and behavior. **Availability:** E-book; Print; PDF.

21738 ■ Kaplan Financial Education (KFE)
Kaplan Financial Education (KFE)
Hawthorne, NY 10532
Ph: (608)779-8301
Free: 877-731-5061
Fax: (608)779-5877
Co. E-mail: kfeducation@kaplan.com
URL: http://ecampus.smartpros.com
Contact: John M. Fleming, Director
Linkedin: www.linkedin.com/company/kaplan-financial-education
Description: Provider of education and training on accounting, financial services, legal and ethics, health and safety and information technology. **Founded:** 1938. **Publications:** "Accounting Today Lists Top 100 Technology Products for 2005," Dec, 2004; "SOX Compliance Cost Estimates Soar 62% in 04," Aug, 2004; "Smart Pros Top 10 Bestselling Titles in 2003," Dec, 2003; "Judge Approves Wal-Mart Class-Action Case," Jun, 2004; "Plan Would Pay Tax Whistleblowers," Jun, 2004; "Accounting Educators Fight to Keep Two Journals," Apr, 2003; "IMA Ethics Hotline Now Open to All Financial Professionals," Oct, 2002. **Training:** IFRS, Chicago, May, 2010; Taxation of Financial Products, New York, Apr, 2010; Income Tax Accounting, Dec, 2009; Financial Planning Attitude and Time Management; The National Public Accountant, May, 2002. **Special Services:** SmartPros®.

COMPUTERIZED DATABASES

21739 ■ Health & Wellness InSite
Type: Full-text.

LIBRARIES

21740 ■ Association for Talent Development (ATD) - Library
1640 King St.
Alexandria, VA 22313-1443
Ph: (703)683-8100
Free: 800-628-2783
Fax: (703)683-1523
Co. E-mail: customercare@td.org
URL: http://www.td.org
Contact: Tony Bingham, President
Facebook: www.facebook.com/ATD
Linkedin: www.linkedin.com/company/15989
X (Twitter): x.com/ATD
Instagram: www.instagram.com/atdnational
Pinterest: www.pinterest.com/ATDofficial
Description: Supports the talent development profession by providing trusted content in the form of research, books, webcasts, events, and education programs. **Scope:** Management; leadership. **Services:** Library open to members only. **Founded:** 1943. **Holdings:** 170 monographs; 100 books; 100 newspapers. **Publications:** American Society Training and Development Buyer's Guide and Consultant Directory (Annual); Technical Training Basics; ASTD Buyer's Guide & Consultant Directory (Annual); TD at Work (Monthly); Learning Circuits (Monthly); TD Magazine (Monthly); Member Information Exchange (MIX); TRAINET; ATD Buyer's Guide; ATD Buyer's Guide; American Society for Training and Development--Training Video Directory; Who's Who in Training and Development (Annual). **Educational Activities:** ATD International Conference and Exposition (Annual); ATD TechKnowledge Conference (Annual); TechKnowledge Conference and Exposition (Annual). **Awards:** ATD BEST Award (Annual); Awards in the Advancing Workplace Learning and Performance; ATD Excellence in Practice Awards (Annual); Gordon M. Bliss Memorial Award (Annual); ATD Dissertation Award (Annual); ASTD Talent Development Thought Leader Award (Annual); ATD Torch Award (Annual). **Geographic Preference:** Multinational.

RESEARCH CENTERS

21741 ■ Center for Entrepreneurial Studies and Development, Inc. (CESD)
62 Morrill Way, Ste. 200
Evansdale Crossing
Morgantown, WV 26506
URL: http://www.thecesdgroup.org
Contact: Carl Hadsell, President
Description: Firm promotes advancement of education, research and economic development for improving productivity in manufacturing organizations. **Scope:** Business operations improvement, employee training, management, and systems development. Operations improvement studies focus on quality control, materials handling systems, cost reduction, work standards development, facilities utilization and planning, work methods, inventory control systems, and computer applications. Employee training focuses on supervisory development, quality training, and problem solving. Management studies focus on management development programs, organization development, steering committee development, facilitation, incentives, and small business organizations. Systems studies focus on business plan development. **Founded:** 1981.

21742 ■ Center for Occupational Research and Development (CORD)
4901 Bosque Blvd., Ste. 200
Waco, TX 76710
Ph: (254)772-8756
Co. E-mail: info@cord.org
URL: http://www.cord.org
Contact: Hope Cotner, President
URL(s): dr.cord.org
Description: Independent, nonprofit education, research, and development organization. Provides innovative changes in education to prepare students for better chances in career and higher education. Assists educators in secondary schools and colleges through new curricula, teaching strategies, professional development and partnerships with community leaders. Initiates developments in curriculum design, learning tools and creating applications in educational technology and conducting educational research and

evaluation. Offers consulting and coordination services. Forms networks and partnerships. **Founded:** 1979. **Publications:** *CORD Newsletter*; *White papers*; *Rigor and Relevance: A New Vision for Career and Technical Education*; *Teacher Professional Development: It's Not an Event, It's a Process*; *Teaching Mathematics Contextually*; *Technology to Improve Texas Education*. **Geographic Preference:** National.

21743 ■ Indiana University Bloomington - Center for Evaluation and Education Policy (CEEP)
201 N Rose Ave.
 Bloomington, IN 47405
Co. E-mail: soeceep@indiana.edu
URL: http://www.education.indiana.edu/research/centers/ceep.html
Contact: Christopher Lubienski, Director
E-mail: clubiens@iu.edu
Facebook: www.facebook.com/soeceep
X (Twitter): x.com/soeceep
Description: Integral unit of Indiana University Bloomington. **Scope:** Program evaluation and policy research, primarily on education issues but also in healthcare. **Founded:** 1990. **Publications:** *Policy Bulletins* (Monthly); *Education Policy Briefs*; *Special reports* (Occasionally).

21744 ■ Indiana University Bloomington - Center for Postsecondary Research (CPR)
201 North Rose Ave.
 Bloomington, IN 47405
Ph: (812)856-5824
Co. E-mail: cpr@indiana.edu
URL: http://cpr.indiana.edu
Contact: Thomas Nelson Laird, Officer
E-mail: tflaird@iu.edu
Description: Integral unit of Indiana University Bloomington, promoting student success and institutional effectiveness through research and service to postsecondary institutions and related agencies. **Scope:** Policy issues and issues related to student learning and personal development, including student engagement, student persistence and attrition, institutional advancement, enrollment management and marketing, program evaluation, institutional culture, student learning and personal development, and equity and access in higher education. **Founded:** 1986. **Publications:** *National Survey of Student Engagement* (Annual).

21745 ■ Indiana University Bloomington - Center for the Study of Institutions, Population, and Environmental Change (CIPEC)
c/o Ostrom Workshop
 513 N Park Ave.
 Bloomington, IN 47408-3799
URL: http://environment.indiana.edu/centers-institutes-preserve/index.html
Description: Integral unit of Indiana University Bloomington. **Scope:** Processes of change in forest environments as mediated by institutional arrangements, demographic factors, and other major human driving forces. **Founded:** 1996.

21746 ■ Indiana University-Purdue University at Indianapolis - Center for the Study of Religion and American Culture (CSRAC)
425 University Blvd., Rm. 417
 Indianapolis, IN 46202-5140
Ph: (317)274-8409
Fax: (317)278-3354
Co. E-mail: raac@iupui.edu
URL: http://raac.iupui.edu
X (Twitter): x.com/csraac
Description: Integral unit of Indiana University-Purdue University at Indianapolis. **Scope:** Promotes relationship between religion and aspects of American culture, and how religion has shaped American politics, justice, and society. **Founded:** 1989. **Publications:** *News from the Center for the Study of Religion and American Culture* (Semiannual); *Religion and American Culture: A Journal of Interpretation* (3/year).

21747 ■ Indiana University-Purdue University at Indianapolis (IUPUI) - CyberLab
IUPUI SELB101, 350 N Blackford St.
 Indianapolis, IN 46202
Ph: (317)274-3463
Co. E-mail: cyberlab@iupui.edu
URL: http://cyberlab.iupui.edu/index.html
Contact: Ali Jafari, Contact
E-mail: jafari@iupui.edu
X (Twitter): x.com/IUPUICyberLab
Description: Integral unit of Indiana University-Purdue University at Indianapolis. **Scope:** Worldwide web applications in teaching and learning, especially course management portals, campus portals, agent-based learning environment, and intelligent user interfaces. **Founded:** 1996.

21748 ■ Indiana University-Purdue University at Indianapolis - Peirce Edition Project (PEP)
425 University Blvd. IUPUI
 Indianapolis, IN 46202-5140
Ph: (317)274-2033
Co. E-mail: cpeirce@iupui.edu
URL: http://peirce.iupui.edu
Description: Integral unit of Indiana University-Purdue University at Indianapolis. **Scope:** American philosophy and culture, focusing on the writings of scientist and philosopher Charles S. Peirce. **Founded:** 1975. **Publications:** *Peirce Project News* (Periodic); *Writings of Charles S. Peirce: A Chronological Edition*. **Educational Activities:** Indianapolis Peirce Seminar Series (Irregular), Aims to enable visiting scholars to present their work to a specialized audience that has a strong interest in the work of Charles S. Peirce.

21749 ■ Indiana University-Purdue University Indianapolis Physics Department - Nuclear Magnetic Resonance Center (NMR)
402 N Blackford St.
 Indianapolis, IN 46202
URL: http://science.iupui.edu/chemistry/research/centers-partners.html
Description: Integral unit of Physics Department, Indiana University-Purdue University at Indianapolis. **Scope:** Structure-function relationships of biological macromolecules, using the techniques of nuclear magnetic resonance (NMR). The research is interdisciplinary, bringing together researchers from the School of Science and the School of Medicine. **Founded:** 1992.

21750 ■ Massachusetts Institute of Technology - Center for Biomedical Innovation (CBI)
77 Massachusetts Ave., Bldg. E19-604
 Cambridge, MA 02139-4307
Ph: (617)324-9640
Co. E-mail: cbi@mit.edu
URL: http://cbi.mit.edu
Contact: Stacy Springs, Executive Director
E-mail: ssprings@mit.edu
Description: Integral unit of MIT Sloan School of Management, Massachusetts Institute of Technology. **Scope:** Research focuses on biomanufacturing process innovation for producing antibodies, vaccines, viral vectors, and cell therapies, analytical technologies, data analytics, advanced modeling, and manufacturing. **Founded:** 2005.

21751 ■ Massachusetts Institute of Technology - Japan Program
1 Amherst St., Bldg., E40-Fl.4
 Cambridge, MA 02139
URL: http://misti.mit.edu/mit-japan
Contact: April Julich Perez, Executive Director
E-mail: ajulich@mit.edu
X (Twitter): x.com/MITJapan_MISTI
Description: Integral unit of Massachusetts Institute of Technology. **Scope:** Studies focus on Japan and Asia, in particular Japanese foreign policy with regard to China, Asian energy and security, the changing role of Japan's technology at home and abroad. **Founded:** 1981. **Publications:** *MIT Japan Science, Technology & Management Report*; *Japan Program Newsletter* (Monthly); *Sponsor Update* (Quarterly); *Working Papers Series*.

21752 ■ Powers Research and Training Institute
Miami, FL
Ph: (305)494-9304
Co. E-mail: icoachyou@gmail.com
URL: http://wisdomwands.com/NancyPowers.Com
Contact: Nancy M. Powers, President
E-mail: nancy@nancypowers.com
Description: Independent consultant and trainer offer custom-designed programs, topics and exercises include brain storming ideas coach, formulating solutions to problems and developing action plans to achieve goals, weekly sessions of intimate think tank groups, facilitated by success coaches keep action plans on target and cover plans for every area of life career, health, spiritual, personal, family, and relationships. **Scope:** Independent consultant and trainer offer custom-designed programs, topics and exercises include brain storming ideas coach, formulating solutions to problems and developing action plans to achieve goals, weekly sessions of intimate think tank groups, facilitated by success coaches keep action plans on target and cover plans for every area of life career, health, spiritual, personal, family, and relationships. **Publications:** "How a Success Coach Can Give You the Edge to Succeed"; "Do You Need a Success Coach to Grow Your Business?"; "The Real Secrets to Success"; "The Top Ten Ways to Avoid Failing in Your Business"; "The Top Seven Ways to Avoid Failing in Your Business"; "How to Be a Simply Irresistible Salesperson!"; "Are You a Coaching Candidate?"; "Money, What Role Does Money Play in Your Life?"; "What Was the Most Important Thing You Learned From Your Coach?". **Training:** Selling with Integrity; How to Effortlessly Attract Without Selling; Customer Service- Moments of Magic with Your Customers; Life Planning, Team: Covisioning For Results; Mastering Communication Strategies; Empowering Belief Strategies; The Power Of Irresistible Attraction; Customized Programs.

21753 ■ Rice University - Center for Education
6100 Main St.
 Houston, TX 77005-1827
Co. E-mail: education@rice.edu
URL: http://centerforeducation.rice.edu
Contact: Courtney Tardy, Director
E-mail: ctardy@rice.edu
Description: Integral unit of Rice University. **Scope:** Teacher development, reorganization of schools, student evaluation methods, and educational policy and urban schools. **Founded:** 1988. **Publications:** *CenterPiece*.

21754 ■ Rice University - Center for Languages and Intercultural Communication (CLIC)
6100 Main St.
 Houston, TX 77005
Ph: (713)348-5844
Co. E-mail: clicadmin@rice.edu
URL: http://clic.rice.edu
Description: Integral unit of Rice University. **Scope:** Language teaching and learning. **Founded:** 1997.

21755 ■ University of Connecticut - Institute for Teaching and Learning (ITL)
Gulley Hall 352 Mansfield Rd., Unit 1086
 Storrs, CT 06269-1086

URL: http://academicvision.uconn.edu/a-path-toward-excellence-in-teaching-effectiveness/center-for-excellence-in-teaching-learning
Description: Integral unit of University of Connecticut. Offers consulting; instructional design. **Scope:** Teaching and learning methods, pedagogy, media use and distance learning, and technology use in the classroom and online. **Founded:** 1996. **Publications:** *The Journal of Graduate Teaching Assistant Development*; *TA Handbook*.

21756 ■ University of Toronto - Ontario Institute for Studies in Education - International Centre for Educational Change (ICEC)
252 Bloor St. W
Toronto, ON, Canada M5S 1V6
Ph: (416)978-1161
Fax: (416)926-4741
Co. E-mail: icec@oise.utoronto.ca
URL: http://icec.oise.utoronto.ca
Contact: Stephen Anderson, Director (Acting)
E-mail: sanderson@oise.utoronto.ca
Description: Integral unit of the Ontario Institute for Studies in Education, University of Toronto; offers practical field development, professional development activities, and consulting. **Scope:** Processes of educational change, including scheduling, teaching, curriculum, caring, assessment and decision-making; large-scale reform efforts, large-scale assessment, evaluation of programs and policies. **Founded:** 1997.

Electronic Commerce/E-Business

START-UP INFORMATION

21757 ■ *101 Internet Businesses You Can Start from Home: How to Choose and Build Your Own Successful E-Business*
Pub: Maximum Press
Ed: Susan Sweeney. **Released:** Third edition. **Description:** Guide for starting and growing an Internet business; information for developing a business plan, risk levels, and promotional techniques are included.

21758 ■ *"Amazon Selling Secrets: How to Make an Extra $1K - $10K a Month Selling Your Own Products on Amazon"*
Released: July 06, 2014. **Price:** $8.99. **Description:** Secrets for finding and selling popular items on Amazon.com are shared. The tools, resources and system for earning extra money each month selling on Amazon are presented.

21759 ■ *The Complete Idiot's Guide to Starting an eBay® Business*
Pub: Penguin Publishing Group
Released: April 03, 2012. **Price:** $19.95, paperback; $12.99, e-book. **Description:** Guide for starting an eBay business includes information on products to sell, how to price merchandise, and details for working with services like PayPal, and how to organize fulfillment services. **Availability:** E-book; Print.

21760 ■ *"Consumer Startup Hub Set for Downtown" in Atlanta Business Chronicle (June 13, 2014, pp. 3A)*
Pub: American City Business Journals, Inc.
Contact: Mike Olivieri, Executive Vice President
Description: Michael Tavani, co-founder of Scoutmob, believes that Atlanta is fast becoming the hub for consumer- and design-focused startups. He is planning to locate his consumer-focused startup, Switchyards, in a 1920s building downtown, which will become a hive for mobile app, media, and ecommerce startups. **Availability:** Print; Online.

21761 ■ *eBay Business the Smart Way*
Released: 3rd edition. **Description:** eBay commands ninety percent of all online auction business. Computer and software expert and online entrepreneur shares information to help online sellers get started and move merchandise on eBay. Tips include the best ways to build credibility, find products to sell, manage inventory, create a storefront Website, and more. **Availability:** Print; PDF.

21762 ■ *The eBay Business Start-Up Kit: With 100s of Live Links to All the Information & Tools You Need*
Pub: Nolo
Contact: Chris Braun, President
Ed: Richard Stim. **Description:** Interactive kit that provides in-depth information and practical advice in launching an eBay business. **Availability:** Print.

21763 ■ *"How to Open and Operate a Financially Successful Florist and Floral Business Online and Off"*
Pub: Atlantic Publishing Co.
Contact: Dr. Heather L. Johnson, Contact
Released: Revised second edition. **Description:** A concise and easy to follow guide for opening a retail florist or floral business online or a traditional brick and mortar store. Knowledge shared includes: cost control systems, retail math and competitive pricing, legal concerns, tax reporting requirements and reporting, profit and loss statements, management skills, sales advertising, and marketing techniques, customer service, direct sales, internal marketing ideas, and more. **Availability:** CD-ROM; Print; Online.

21764 ■ *How to Start a Home-Based Mail Order Business*
Ed: Georganne Fiumara. **Released:** June 01, 2011. **Price:** Paperback. **Description:** Step-by-step guide for starting and growing a home-based mail order business. Information about equipment, pricing, online marketing, are included along with worksheets and checklists for planning. **Availability:** Print; Online.

21765 ■ *How to Start a Home-Based Online Retail Business*
Ed: Jeremy Shepherd. **Released:** November 08, 2011. **Price:** paperback, softback. **Description:** Information for starting an online retail, home-based business is shared. **Availability:** E-book; Print.

21766 ■ *How to Start an Internet Sales Business Without Making the Government Mad*
Pub: Lulu Press Inc.
Ed: Dan Davis. **Released:** October 01, 2011. **Price:** $19.95, paperback; $14.38, PDF; $14.38, e-book. **Description:** Small business guide for launching an Internet sales company. Topics include business structure, licenses, and taxes. **Availability:** E-book; Print; PDF.

21767 ■ *"Leading Digital: Turning Technology into Business Transformation"*
Pub: Harvard Business Review Press
Contact: Moderna V. Pfizer, Contact
Released: October 14, 2014. **Price:** $32, Hardcover/Hardcopy. **Description:** Mobile technology, analytics, social media, sensors, and cloud computing have changed the entire business environment in every industry. A guide to help any small startup business in any industry gain strategic advantage using digital, including where to invest in digital technologies and how to lead the transformation. The guide teaches how to engage better with customers, digitally enhance operations, create a digital vision, and govern digital activities. **Availability:** E-book; Print.

21768 ■ *"Modern Meal Offers Recipe Inspiration, Curation and Home Delivery" in Orlando Business Journal (Vol. 30, April 4, 2014, No. 41, pp. 3)*
Pub: American City Business Journals, Inc.
Contact: Mike Olivieri, Executive Vice President
Released: Weekly. **Price:** $8, introductory 4-week offer(Digital & Print). **Description:** Modern Meal LLC's CEO, Mark Hudgins, works to get people to the dinner table for a good meal. The social network with a Pinterest look is in early-beta-launch and users are trying out the features by curating recipes from popular cooking Websites and looking at recipes of other users. Modern' Meal's plan to tap into the e-grocery market is also discussed. **Availability:** Print; Online.

21769 ■ *"Open English Touted as Startup Worth Emulating" in South Florida Business Journal (Vol. 34, January 24, 2014, No. 27, pp. 30)*
Pub: American City Business Journals, Inc.
Contact: Mike Olivieri, Executive Vice President
Released: Weekly. **Price:** $8, Introductory 4-week offer(Digital & Print). **Description:** Open English, a language education company, received more than $150 million in investments from venture capitalists. The firm's cloud-based platform is still in its infancy, but the startup's success has shown that entrepreneurs can generate money and grow their businesses in Florida. Open English is the only online English school that offers live classes with native English-speaking teachers. **Availability:** Print; Online.

21770 ■ *Scrapbooking for Profit: Cashing in on Retail, Home-Based and Internet Opportunities*
Pub: Allworth Press
Contact: Tad Crawford, Founder
Ed: Rebecca Pittman. **Released:** June 01, 2005. **Price:** $16.95, paperback; $19.99, Ebook; $19.95, Paperback. **Description:** Eleven strategies for starting a scrapbooking business, including brick-and-mortar stores, home-based businesses, and online retail and wholesale outlets. **Availability:** E-book; Print.

INCUBATORS/RESEARCH AND TECHNOLOGY PARKS

21771 ■ **Plug and Play - Energy**
440 N Wolfe Rd.
Sunnyvale, CA 94085
URL: http://www.plugandplaytechcenter.com/industries/energy
Description: An accelerator for startups in the energy tech industry. Provides support with venture and angel partners, mentorship, a data center, office space, and networking opportunities. This program has a focus on the following: e-Mobility and EV charging, hydrogen, grid scale storage, smart home and IoT, cybersecurity, retail and customer engagement platforms, renewable and distributed energy resources, asset management and predictive analytics, and supply chain optimization.

EDUCATIONAL PROGRAMS

21772 ■ **Developing Web E-Commerce Applications**
URL(s): www.eeicom.com

GENERAL SMALL BUSINESS TOPICS

Electronic Commerce/E-Business ■ 21791

Description: Experienced Web producers will learn how to build a shopping cart/order management system for secure transaction processing using the scripting languages ColdFusion and PHP. **Audience:** IT professionals. **Principal Exhibits:** Experienced Web producers will learn how to build a shopping cart/order management system for secure transaction processing using the scripting languages ColdFusion and PHP.

REFERENCE WORKS

21773 ■ *"3Par: Storing Up Value"* in *Barron's* (Vol. 90, August 30, 2010, No. 35, pp. 30)
Pub: Barron's Editorial & Corporate Headquarters
Ed: Mark Veverka. **Description:** Dell and Hewlett Packard are both bidding for data storage company 3Par. The acquisition would help Dell and Hewlett Packard provide customers with a one-stop shop as customers move to a private cloud in the Internet. **Availability:** Online.

21774 ■ *"10 Advantages of E-Commerce for Consumers & Businesses"* in *become Blog* (July 21, 2020)
URL(s): www.become.co/blog/ecommerce-advan tages-consumers-businesses/
Ed: Nici Pillemer. **Released:** July 21, 2020. **Description:** Discusses advantages of utilizing e-commerce for your small business. **Availability:** Online.

21775 ■ *"11 Minutes That Rocked the Sneaker World"* in *Business Journal Portland* (Vol. 30, February 14, 2014, No. 50, pp. 8)
Pub: American City Business Journals, Inc.
Contact: Mike Olivieri, Executive Vice President
Released: Weekly. **Price:** $4, Introductory 4-week offer(Digital & Print). **Description:** The sale of the Nike Air Yeezy 2, the latest shoes from a partnership with artist Kanye West, sparked a social media debate on the importance of limited edition shoes for the Nike brand. The shoes sold out in 11 minutes and made their way to eBay for as much as $10,000. **Availability:** Print; Online.

21776 ■ *15 Advantages of Ecommerce for Small Businesses*
URL(s): salvadorbriggman.com/advantages-of -ecommerce-for-small-businesses/
Description: Covers key advantages of running your own e-commerce store over having a physical storefront. **Availability:** Online.

21777 ■ *"2015 Marketing Calendar for Real Estate Pros: Own It"*
Pub: CreateSpace
Released: October 14, 2014. **Price:** $9.56, paperback. **Description:** Real estate agents, mortgage loan agents, and new home builders and site and listing agents are shown how to use low-cost, high yield, proven marketing techniques to create digital real estate listings, find more customers, and sell more homes. Advice for building a brand and public relations; attracting renters and buyers; developing a good Website; and a digital marketing plan are explained. **Availability:** Print.

21778 ■ *Advanced Selling for Dummies*
Released: 2011. **Description:** This book explores topics such as: visualizing success (includes exercises), investing and reinvesting in your own success, harnessing media and multi-media outlets, calculating risks that stretch your limits, creating lasting relationships, finding balance to avoid burnout and more. This guide is for salespeople who have already read 'Selling for Dummies' and now want forward-thinking, advanced strategies for recharging and reenergizing their careers and their lives. Blogging, Internet leads and virtual assistants are also discussed. **Availability:** emobi; Online; Electronic publishing.

21779 ■ *"All Hail: How Taxi Companies Stay Competitive in an Evolving Marketplace"* in *SmartcitiesDive* (March 28, 2019)
URL(s): www.smartcitiesdive.com/news/taxi-compa nies-ride-hailing-competitition/551449/

Ed: Katie Pyzyk. **Released:** March 28, 2019. **Description:** It's no surprise that Uber an Lyft have taken a good deal of market share from the traditional taxi business, so how do taxis still make a living? By adapting the same business model as Uber and Lyft, several taxi cab companies are still profitable and gaining back that market share. **Availability:** Online.

21780 ■ *"Amazon Launches a Personal Shopper Service That Sends Monthly Curated Clothing Boxes"* in *The Verge* (July 31, 2019)
URL(s): www.theverge.com/2019/7/31/20748632/ amazon-personal-shopper-prime-wardrobe-service -style-subscription-box
Ed: Ashley Carman. **Released:** July 31, 2019. **Description:** Amazon launched a new fashion service called Personal Shopper by Prime Wardrobe. Prime members who sign up will need to answer a survey about their fit and trend preferences and will then receive a curated box of clothing. Up to eight pieces will be included and the member can preview it before it ships and they will only pay for what they keep. Services costs $4.99 a month. **Availability:** Online.

21781 ■ *"American Chemistry Council Launches Flagship Blog"* in *Ecology,Environment & Conservation Business* (October 29, 2011, pp. 5)
Pub: PR Newswire Association LLC.
Description: American Chemistry Council (ACC) launched its blog, American Chemistry Matters, where interactive space allows bloggers to respond to news coverage and to discuss policy issues and their impact on innovation, competitiveness, job creation and safety. **Availability:** Online.

21782 ■ *"Ann Arbor Google's Growth Dips: Few Worried about High-tech Firm's Future"* in *Crain's Detroit Business* (Vol. 25, June 8, 2009, No. 23, pp. 3)
Pub: Crain Communications Inc.
Contact: Barry Asin, President
Ed: Bill Shea. **Description:** Global recession has slowed the growth of Google Inc. Three years ago, when Google moved to Ann Arbor, Michigan it estimated it would provide 1,000 new jobs within five years, so far the firm employs 250. **Availability:** Online; PDF.

21783 ■ *"Another California Firm Moving to Austin"* in *Austin Business Journal* (Vol. 31, May 6, 2011, No. 9, pp. 1)
Pub: Austin Business Journal
Contact: Rachel McGrath, Director
E-mail: rmcgrath@bizjournals.com
Ed: Christopher Calnan. **Description:** Main Street Hub Inc. is planning to build a facility in Austin, Texas. The company helps businesses manage their online reputations. Main Street has selected Aquila Commercial LLC as its real estate broker. **Availability:** Print; Online.

21784 ■ *"App Helps Consumers Spot Suspicious Charges"* in *Black Enterprise* (Vol. 44, June 2014, No. 10, pp. 34)
Pub: Earl G. Graves Ltd.
Contact: Earl Graves, Jr., President
Description: BiliGuard is a mobile app used to track activity on credit and debit card accounts. The app allows users to notify a merchant as soon as they see an unfamiliar charge. BiliGuard can also alert users to fees. **Availability:** Online.

21785 ■ *"Are Offline Pushes Important to E-Commerce?"* in *DM News* (Vol. 31, September 14, 2009, No. 23, pp. 10)
Pub: Haymarket Media Inc.
Contact: Kevin Costello, Chief Executive Officer
Description: With the importance of Internet marketing and the popularity of ecommerce increasing experts debate the relevance of more traditional channels of advertising. **Availability:** Online.

21786 ■ *"Are You Ready To Do It Yourself? Discipline and Self-Study Can Help You Profit From Online Trading"* in *Black Enterprise* (February 1, 2008)
Pub: Earl G. Graves Ltd.
Contact: Earl Graves, Jr., President
Ed: Steve Garmhausen. **Description:** Steps to help individuals invest in stocks online is given by an expert broker. Discount brokerage houses can save money for online investors. **Availability:** Online.

21787 ■ *"Art of the Online Deal"* in *Farm Industry News* (March 25, 2011)
Pub: Informa Business Media, Inc.
Contact: Charlie McCurdy, President
Description: Farmers share advice for shopping online for machinery; photos, clean equipment, the price, equipment details, and online sources topped their list. **Availability:** Print; Online.

21788 ■ *"As Technology Changes, So Must African American Business"* in *Black Enterprise* (Vol. 41, August 2010, No. 1, pp. 61)
Pub: Earl G. Graves Ltd.
Contact: Earl Graves, Jr., President
Ed: Sonya A. Donaldson. **Description:** Social media is essential to compete in today's business environment, especially for African American firms. **Availability:** Online.

21789 ■ *"Auctions and Bidding: A Guide for Computer Scientists"* in *ACM Computing Surveys* (Vol. 43, Summer 2011, No. 2, pp. 10)
Pub: Association for Computing Machinery
Contact: Yannis Ioannidis, President
Ed: Simon Parsons, Juan A. Rodriguez-Aguilar, Mark Klein. **Released:** Volume 43 Issue 2. **Price:** $10, Members; $15, Nonmembers; $5, Students. **Description:** There are various actions: single dimensional, multi-dimensional, single-sided, double-sided, first-price, second-price, English, Dutch, Japanese, sealed-bid, and these have been extensively discussed and analyzed in economics literature. This literature is surveyed from a computer science perspective, primarily from the viewpoint of computer scientists who are interested in learning about auction theory, and to provide pointers into the economics literature for those who want a deeper technical understanding. In addition, since auctions are an increasingly important topic in computer science, the article also looks at work on auctions from the computer science literature. The aim is to identify what both bodies of work tell us about creating electronic auctions. **Availability:** Download; PDF.

21790 ■ *"Austin Group-Buying Site Hones In on Hispanics"* in *Austin Business Journal* (Vol. 31, July 1, 2011, No. 17, pp. 1)
Pub: Austin Business Journal
Contact: Rachel McGrath, Director
E-mail: rmcgrath@bizjournals.com
Ed: Vicky Garza. **Description:** Descuentl Libre is a new group-buying site from Austin, Texas that targets the Hispanic market, offering discounts of practical items and family-friendly activities. The Hispanic market constitutes 17 percent of the U.S. population and spends $23 billion yearly online. **Availability:** Online.

21791 ■ *"Baltimore Ravens Back to Business as NFL Lockout Ends"* in *Baltimore Business Journal* (Vol. 29, July 29, 2011, No. 12, pp. 1)
Pub: Boston Business Journal
Contact: Carolyn M. Jones, President
E-mail: cmjones@bizjournals.com
Ed: Scott Dance. **Description:** The Baltimore Ravens football team has been marketing open sponsorship packages following the end of the National Football League lockout. Team officials are working to get corporate logos and slogans on radio and television commercials and online advertisements. **Availability:** Print; Online.

21792 ■ *"The Bankrate Double Play, Bankrate Is Having Its Best Quarter Yet" in Barron's (Vol. 88, March 24, 2008, No. 12, pp. 27)*
Pub: Dow Jones & Company Inc.
Contact: Almar Latour, Chief Executive Officer
Ed: Neil A. Martin. **Description:** Shares of Bankrate may rise as much as 25 percent from their level of $45.08 a share due to a strong cash flow and balance sheet. The company's Internet business remains strong despite weakness in the online advertising industry and is a potential takeover target. **Availability:** Online.

21793 ■ *"Baseline Metrics CEOs Need for Online Brand Oversight" in South Florida Business Journal (Vol. 34, May 23, 2014, No. 44, pp. 16)*
Pub: American City Business Journals, Inc.
Contact: Mike Olivieri, Executive Vice President
Released: Weekly. **Price:** $8, Introductory 4-week offer(Digital & Print). **Description:** Chief executive officers have the option to use metrics that will allow them to monitor their online brands. Social media engagement is an effective customer service metric because it presents a clear assessment of a business social media prowess. Reputation management software, on the other hand, ranks a firm's weekly, hourly, and daily sentiments online. **Availability:** Print; Online.

21794 ■ *"BayTSP, NTT Data Corp. Enter Into Reseller Pact to Market Online IP Monitoring" in Professional Services Close-Up (Sept. 11, 2009)*
Description: Due to incredible interest from distributors and content owners across Asia, NTT Data Corp. will resell BayTSP's online intellectual property monitoring, enforcement, business intelligence and monetization services in Japan.

21795 ■ *"BDC Launches New Online Business Advice Centre" in Marketwired (July 13, 2010)*
Pub: Comtex News Network Inc.
Contact: Kan Devnani, President
Description: The Business Development Bank of Canada (BDC) offers entrepreneurs the chance to use their new online BDC Advice Centre in order to seek advice regarding the challenges of entrepreneurship. Free online business tools and information to help both startups and established firms are also provided. **Availability:** Print; Online.

21796 ■ *"Being All a-Twitter" in Canadian Business (Vol. 81, December 8, 2008, No. 21, pp. 22)*
Description: Marketing experts suggest that advertising strategies have to change along with new online social media. Companies are advised to find ways to incorporate social software because workers and customers are expected to continue its use. **Availability:** Print; Online.

21797 ■ *The Big Switch: Rewiring the World, from Edison to Google*
Pub: W.W. Norton & Company Ltd.
Contact: Stanley Kubrick, Director
Ed: Nicholas Carr. **Released:** June 10, 2013. **Price:** $16.95, paperback; $26.95, hardcover. **Description:** Companies such as Google, Microsoft, and Amazon.com are building huge centers in order to create massive data centers. Together these centers form a giant computing grid that will deliver the digital universe to scientific labs, companies and homes in the future. This trend could bring about a new, darker phase for the Internet, one where these networks could operate as a fearsome entity that will dominate the lives of individuals worldwide. **Availability:** Print.

21798 ■ *"Bitcoin 'Killer App' Or the Currency of the Future?" in Providence Business News (Vol. 28, January 6, 2014, No. 40, pp. 1)*
Pub: American City Business Journals, Inc.
Contact: Mike Olivieri, Executive Vice President
URL(s): pbn.com/bitcoin-killer-app-or-the-currency-of-the-future94158
Description: The Providence Bitcoin Meetup has gathered several technology experts to discuss Bitcoin, the popular digital currency. However, software developers, engineers and entrepreneurs see Bitcoin as the next killer app for the Internet and is changing how information and data is stored, shared and verified. The Bitcoin's impact in Rhode Island is examined. **Availability:** Online. **Telecommunication Services:** Anderson@pbn.com.

21799 ■ *"Book Yourself Solid: The Fastest, Easiest, and Most Reliable System for Getting More Clients Than You Can Handle"*
Pub: John Wiley & Sons, Inc.
Contact: Christina Van Tassell, Executive Vice President Chief Financial Officer
Released: 3rd edition. **Price:** $22, paperback; $14.99, E-book. **Description:** Self-promotion is essential for successful selling. Strategies, techniques, and skills necessary for success are presented, covering social media marketing strategies for service professionals; pricing models and sales strategies to simplify selling; new networking and outreach plans that take only minutes a day; and new product launches ideas and tactics. **Availability:** E-book; Print.

21800 ■ *"Boom and Bust in the Book Biz" in Canadian Business (Vol. 83, August 17, 2010, No. 13-14, pp. 16)*
Pub: Rogers Media Inc.
Contact: Neil Spivak, Chief Executive Officer
Ed: Jordan Timm. **Description:** Electronic book marketplace is booming with Amazon.com's e-book sales for the Kindle e-reader exceeding the hardcover sales. Kobo Inc. has registered early success with its Kobo e-reader and has partnered with Hong Kong telecom giant on an e-book store. **Availability:** Print; Online.

21801 ■ *"Brands' Mass Appeal" in ADWEEK (Vol. 51, June 14, 2010, No. 24)*
Ed: Brian Morrissey. **Description:** Engineering/science crowdsourced projects tend to result from posting and/or publishing interim results as well as from other talents building upon those results to produce even better results. However, the author does not see the same results in the creative world. **Availability:** Online.

21802 ■ *"Brite-Strike Tactical Launches New Internet Marketing Initiatives" in Marketwired (September 15, 2009)*
Pub: Comtex News Network Inc.
Contact: Kan Devnani, President
Description: Brite-Strike Tactical Illumination Products, Inc. has enlisted the expertise of Internet marketing guru Thomas J. McCarthy to help revamp the company's Internet campaign. An outline of the Internet marketing strategy is provided. **Availability:** Print; Online.

21803 ■ *"Buyout Rumors Have Rackspace Back in the News" in San Antonio Business Journal (Vol. 28, September 12, 2014, No. 31, pp. 6)*
Pub: American City Business Journals, Inc.
Contact: Mike Olivieri, Executive Vice President
Description: Louisiana-based CenturyLink Inc. has offered to buyout San Antonio, Texas-based Rackspace Hosting in order to boost its Internet and cloud services. The latest stock market valuation of Rackspace was at $5.33 billion. The potential impact of the CenturyLink and Rackspace merger deal on the managed hosting services market is also analyzed. **Availability:** Online.

21804 ■ *"CADD Microsystems Launches the CADD Community, Partners with Global eTraining to Provide Online, On-Demand Training for Autodesk Software" in Computer Business Week (August 28, 2014, pp. 24)*
Pub: NewsRX LLC.
Contact: Kalani Rosell, Contact
Description: A new online customer-only portal the integrates on-demand training, applications and extension, videos and additional value-added content for customers only was developed by CADD Microsystems. The Autodesk Platinum Partner calls this training program, CADD Community. **Availability:** Online.

21805 ■ *"Campaigner Survey: 46 Percent of Small Businesses Use Email Marketing" in Wireless News (November 21, 2009)*
Description: Almost half (46 percent) of small businesses surveyed by Campaigner's 2009 State of Small Business Online Marketing, say that they rely on email marketing to help them find new customers, keep existing ones and grow their businesses. The survey also found that 36 percent of small businesses plan to begin using email marketing over the next year. The trend to utilize Internet marketing tools is allowing small businesses to grow faster and generate higher revenues than those that are not using these mediums. **Availability:** Print; Online.

21806 ■ *"Capturing Generation Y: Ready, Set, Transform" in Credit Union Times (Vol. 21, July 14, 2010, No. 27, pp. 20)*
Ed: Senthil Kumar. **Description:** The financial services sector recognizes that Generation Y will have a definite impact on the way business is conducted in the future. The mindset of Generation Y is social and companies need to use networking tools such as Facebook in order to reach this demographic. **Availability:** Online.

21807 ■ *"Chafee Eyes Tax On Travel Sites" in Providence Business News (Vol. 28, March 24, 2014, No. 51, pp. 1)*
Pub: American City Business Journals, Inc.
Contact: Mike Olivieri, Executive Vice President
URL(s): pbn.com/chafee-eyes-tax-on-travel-sites95903
Description: Rhode Island Governor, Lincoln D. Chafee's 2015 budget will include new tax rules for travel Websites. State officials claim the new regulations will deal with a loophole that has allowed travel Websites to pay less in taxes. Many hotels enter into partnerships with travel Websites in order to sell rooms in bulk. **Availability:** Online. **Telecommunication Services:** Anderson@pbn.com.

21808 ■ *"The China Connection" in Crain's Chicago Business (Vol. 31, March 24, 2008, No. 12, pp. 26)*
Ed: Samantha Stainburn. **Description:** Interview with Ben Munoz who studied abroad in Beijing, China for three months to study international economics, e-commerce and global leadership. **Availability:** Print; Online.

21809 ■ *"Chipotle Mexican Grill Adds Alexa for Reorders of Favorite Meals" in Nation's Restaurant News (November 21, 2019)*
URL(s): www.nrn.com/fast-casual/chipotle-mexican-grill-adds-alexa-reorders-favorite-meals
Ed: Nancy Luna. **Released:** November 21, 2019. **Description:** Chipotle has added Amazon's voice ordering assistant, Alexa, to its list of ways consumers can order. However, there are limitations since it's only set up to reorder meals for delivery once a Chipotle loyalty member links their profile to the Alexa app. **Availability:** Online.

21810 ■ *"Click Your Chicken" in Canadian Business (Vol. 87, October 2014, No. 10, pp. 11)*
Released: October 2014. **Description:** A number of business ideas, products and strategies are ranked from the ingenious to the extremely bizarre. A mobile Web startup called FarmLogs helps farmers track everything from soil conditions to weather to profit forecasts. Kentucky Fried Chicken restaurants awards top Twitter fans in Japan with USB drive, a mouse and a keyboard designed with chicken parts.

21811 ■ *"ClickFuel Unveils Internet Marketing Tools for Small Businesses" in Marketwired (October 19, 2009)*
Pub: Comtex News Network Inc.
Contact: Kan Devnani, President

GENERAL SMALL BUSINESS TOPICS

Description: ClickFuel, a firm that manages, designs and tracks marketing campaigns has unveiled a full software suite of affordable services and technology solutions designed to empower small business owners and help them promote and grow their businesses through targeted Internet marketing campaigns. **Availability:** Online.

21812 ■ *Clicking Through: A Survival Guide for Bringing Your Company Online*
Released: First edition. **Description:** Summary of legal compliance issues faced by small companies doing business on the Internet, including copyright and patent laws.

21813 ■ *"Cloud City: An Industry - and a Region - On the Rise" in Puget Sound Business Journal (Vol. 34, February 28, 2014, No. 46, pp. 4)*
Pub: American City Business Journals, Inc.
Contact: Mike Olivieri, Executive Vice President
Description: Seattle, Washington is experiencing an influx of the world's most innovative cloud companies. Businesses are shifting their applications from in-house servers or private data center into public cloud infrastructure, which is less expensive than buying the servers and managing the data systems. Seattle software companies are taking advantage of this trend and developing products. **Availability:** Online.

21814 ■ *"Cloudy Future for VMware?" in Barron's (Vol. 90, September 13, 2010, No. 37, pp. 21)*
Pub: Barron's Editorial & Corporate Headquarters
Ed: Jonathan R. Laing. **Description:** VMWare dominated the virtualization market for years, but it may be ending as it faces more competition from rivals that offer cloud computing services. The company's stocks are also expensive and are vulnerable to the smallest mishap. **Availability:** Online.

21815 ■ *"Complete Discovery Source, Inc. (CDS) Receives Minority Owned Business Certification" in Marketwired (December 14, 2010)*
Pub: Comtex News Network Inc.
Contact: Kan Devnani, President
Description: Complete Discovery Source Inc. (CDS) was granted Minority-Owned Business Enterprise status by the New York State Department of Economic Development. The certification provides CDS, an end-to-end eDiscovery services provider, with access to contracting opportunities with 130 government agencies throughout New York state. **Availability:** Print; Online.

21816 ■ *The Complete Guide to Google Adwords: Secrets, Techniques, and Strategies You Can Learn to Make Millions*
Pub: Atlantic Publishing Co.
Contact: Dr. Heather L. Johnson, Contact
Released: 2012. **Description:** Google AdWords, when it launched in 2002 signaled a fundamental shift in what the Internet was for so many individuals and companies. Learning and understanding how Google AdWords operates and how it can be optimized for maximum exposure, boosting click through rates, conversions, placement, and selection of the right keywords, can be the key to a successful online business. **Availability:** Print; Online.

21817 ■ *"Consumer Trust in E-Commerce Web Sites: a Meta-Study" in ACM Computing Surveys (Vol. 43, Fall 2011, No. 3, pp. 14)*
Pub: Association for Computing Machinery
Contact: Yannis Ioannidis, President
Ed: Patricia Beatty, Ian Reay, Scott Dick, James Miller. **Released:** Volume 43 Issue 3. **Price:** $10, Members; $15, Nonmembers; $5, Students. **Description:** Trust is at once an elusive, imprecise concept, and a critical attribute that must be engineered into e-commerce systems. Engineering trust is examined. **Availability:** Download; PDF.

21818 ■ *"Contagious: Why Things Catch On"*
Pub: Simon & Schuster, Inc.
Contact: Jonathan Karp, President

Released: March 2013. **Price:** $26, after_pricing-text. **Description:** Wharton marketing professor, Jonah Berger, reveals the science of successful word-of-mouth and social media marketing that provides greater results than traditional advertising. **Availability:** Print.

21819 ■ *Content Rich: Writing Your Way to Wealth on the Web*
Released: 1st Edition. **Description:** A definitive search engine optimization (SEO) copywriting guide for search engine rankings and sales conversion. It includes topics not covered in other books on the subject and targets the small to medium sized business looking for ways to maximize online marketing activities as well as designers and Web developers seeking to incorporate more SEO techniques into design and content.

21820 ■ *"Conversations with Customers" in Business Journal Serving Greater Tampa Bay (Vol. 31, December 31, 2010, No. 1, pp. 1)*
Pub: Tampa Bay Business Journal
Contact: Ian Anderson, President
E-mail: ianderson@bizjournals.com
Description: Tampa Bay, Florida-based businesses have been using social media to interact with customers. Forty percent of businesses have been found to have at least one social media platform to reach customers and prospects. **Availability:** Print; Online.

21821 ■ *"Copyright Clearance Center (CCC) Partnered with cSubs" in Information Today (Vol. 28, November 2011, No. 10, pp. 14)*
Description: Copyright Clearance Center (CCC) partnered with cSubs to integrate CCC's point-of-content licensing solution RightsLink Basic directly into cSubs workflow. The partnership will allow cSubs' customers a user-friendly process for obtaining permissions. Csubs is a corporate subscription management service for books, newspapers, and econtent. **Availability:** Online.

21822 ■ *"The Copyright Evolution" in Information Today (Vol. 28, November 2011, No. 10, pp. 1)*
Pub: Information Today Inc.
Contact: Thomas H. Hogan, President
Ed: Nancy Davis Kho. **Description:** For information professionals, issues surrounding copyright compliance have traditionally been on the consumption side. However, today, content consumption is only half the program because blogging, tweeting, and commenting is a vital part of more standard duties for workers as corporations aim to create authentic communications with customers.

21823 ■ *"CradlePoint Is Adding Workers, Seeking More Space" in Idaho Business Review (September 3, 2014)*
Pub: BridgeTower Media
Contact: Adam Reinebach, President
Price: $11.99, Print, Digital & Mobile(1 Month); 149, Print, Digital & Mobile(1 Year); 99, Digital & Mobile Only(1 Year); $99, Digital & Mobile Only(For 1 Year); $9.95, Print, Digital & Mobile (For 1 Month Intro Rate); $149, Print, Digital & Mobile(For 1 Year). **Description:** CradlePoint makes networking routers and software, focusing on security for businesses. The firm is hiring new workers at a rate higher than predicted and is seeking new office space in downtown Boise, Idaho. CradlePoint is a major player in the growing wireless service and cloud platform market and is growing faster than its competitors. **Availability:** Print; Online.

21824 ■ *Crossing the Chasm: Marketing and Selling Disruptive Products to Mainstream Customers*
Pub: HarperCollins Publishers L.L.C.
Contact: Brian Murray, President
Ed: Geoffrey A. Moore. **Released:** 3rd edition. **Price:** $21.99, paperback; $11.99, e-book. **Description:** A guide for marketing in high-technology industries, focusing on the Internet. **Availability:** E-book; Print.

Electronic Commerce/E-Business ■ 21831

21825 ■ *"Crowd Control" in Washington Business Journal (Vol. 33, August 15, 2014, No. 17, pp. 8)*
Pub: American City Business Journals, Inc.
Contact: Mike Olivieri, Executive Vice President
Description: Washington DC's Department of Insurance, Securities and Banking issued a proposal that would create the legal framework by which companies can raise cash through crowdfunding. The DC proposal would allow District-based businesses to crowdfund from District-based backers. The advantages and drawbacks to the plan are examined. **Availability:** Online.

21826 ■ *"Crowdfund Your Way to Millions: LeVar Burton's Kickstarter Campaign Raises $1 Million In Less Than 12 Hours" in Black Enterprise (Vol. 45, July-August 2014, No. 1, pp. 61)*
Pub: Earl G. Graves Ltd.
Contact: Earl Graves, Jr., President
Description: Kickstarted is a viable option for funding a small business. Actor, LeVar Burton launched a Kickstarter campaign to help revive the learning show Reading Rainbow and raised $1 million in less than 12 hours. Information about six crowdfunding sites are listed, including: Kickstarter, Angellist, Rockethub, Crowdtilt, Indiegogo, and Rallyme.

21827 ■ *"Crowdsourcing their Way into One Big Mess" in Brandweek (Vol. 51, October 25, 2010, No. 38, pp. 26)*
Description: The Gap, was counting on crowdsourcing to provide feedback for its new logo, but it did not prove positive for the retailer. However, a massive outcry of negative opinion, via crowdsourcing, may not always equal valid, constructive criticism. **Availability:** Online.

21828 ■ *"Custom Picture Framing Is Too Expensive — and Framebridge Has a Fix for That" in Forbes (January 4, 2019)*
URL(s): www.forbes.com/sites/pamdanziger/2019/01/04/custom-picture-framing-is-too-expensive-framebridge-has-a-fix-for-that/#7c5100ff2489
Ed: Pamela N. Danziger. **Released:** January 04, 2019. **Description:** After Susan Tynan tried to get several posters custom framed and found out how expensive that was, she founded an online frame shop called Framebridge, which will frame pictures for a fraction of the price. The demand in cheaper framing options has caused smaller shops to close, while online stores and bigger chains are taking up more of the market. **Availability:** Online.

21829 ■ *"Cyber Thanksgiving Online Shopping a Growing Tradition" in Marketing Weekly News (December 12, 2009, pp. 137)*
Pub: Investment Weekly News
Description: According to e-commerce analysts, Thanksgiving Day is becoming increasingly important to retailers in terms of online sales. Internet marketers are realizing that consumers are already searching for Black Friday sales and if they find deals on the products they are looking for, they are highly likely to make their purchase on Thanksgiving Day instead of waiting. **Availability:** Online.

21830 ■ *Designing Websites for Every Audience*
Description: Twenty-five case studies targeting six difference audiences are used to help a business design, or make over, a Website. **Availability:** E-book.

21831 ■ *"Digital Marketing: Integrating Strategy and Tactics with Values, A Guidebook for Executives, Managers, and Students"*
Pub: Routledge, Taylor & Francis Group
Released: First edition. **Price:** $59.95, Paperback-$47.96; $190, Hardback - $152; $29.98, e-book. **Description:** Guidebook filled with information on the latest digital marketing tactics and strategic insights to help small businesses generate sustainable growth and achieve competitive advantage through digital

integration. A five-step program: mindset, model, strategy, implementation, and sustainability is explained. **Availability:** E-book; Print.

21832 ■ *"Do-It-Yourself Portfolio Management"* in Barron's (Vol. 89, July 13, 2009, No. 28, pp. 25)
Pub: Dow Jones & Company Inc.
Contact: Almar Latour, Chief Executive Officer
Ed: Mike Hogan. **Description:** Services of several portfolio management web sites are presented. These web sites include MarketRiders E.Adviser, TD Ameritrade and E. **Availability:** Online.

21833 ■ *"DocuSign Raises $85 Million for Electronic Signatures"* in San Francisco Business Times (Vol. 28, March 7, 2014, No. 33, pp. 6)
Pub: American City Business Journals, Inc.
Contact: Mike Olivieri, Executive Vice President
Released: Weekly. **Description:** DocuSign, the market leader in electronic signatures, reported that it was able to raise another $85 million in capital. The company is expected to file an initial public offering in 2014 or 2015. CFO, Mike Dinsdale, shares that the firm also wants to expand internationally. **Availability:** Print; Online.

21834 ■ *"Dollar General Selects GSI Commerce to Launch Its eCommerce Business"* in Benzinga.com (October 29, 2011)
Pub: Benzinga.com
Contact: Jason Raznick, Founder
Description: Dollar General Corporation chose GSI Commerce, a leading provider of ecommerce and interactive marketing solutions, to launch its online initiative. GSI Commerce is an eBay Inc. company. **Availability:** Online.

21835 ■ *E-Commerce for Small Business: Starting Out*
URL(s): online.csp.edu/resources/article/ecommerce-for-small-business/
Description: Explores why small businesses should understand the importance of taking advantage of e-commerce to increase their bottom line. Provides information on how to start an online storefront and next steps. **Availability:** Online.

21836 ■ *"E-Commerce's Impact on Small Business in the Age of COVID-19"* in The National Law Review (Feb. 22, 2021)
URL(s): www.natlawreview.com/article/e-commerce-s-impact-small-business-age-covid-19
Ed: Morris A. Ellison. **Released:** February 22, 2021. **Description:** Discusses retail trends for in-person and online business as well as the importance of employing the flexibility of a blended approach for your small business during the age of Covid-19. **Availability:** Online.

21837 ■ *EBay Income: How ANYONE of Any Age, Location, and/or Background Can Build a Highly Profitable Online Business with eBay*
Pub: Atlantic Publishing Co.
Contact: Dr. Heather L. Johnson, Contact
Description: A complete overview of eBay is given and guides any small company through the entire process of creating the auction and auction strategies, photography, writing copy, text and formatting, multiple sales, programming tricks, PayPal, accounting, creating marketing, merchandising, managing email lists, advertising plans, taxes and sales tax, best time to list items and for how long, sniping programs, international customers, opening a storefront, electronic commerce, buy-it now pricing, keywords, Google marketing and eBay secrets.

21838 ■ *"Elanco Challenges Bayer's Advantage, K9 Advantix Ad Claims"* in Pet Product News (Vol. 64, November 2010, No. 11, pp. 11)
Description: Elanco Animal Health has disputed Bayer Animal Health's print and Web advertising claims involving its flea, tick, and mosquito control products Advantage and K9 Advantix. The National Advertising Division of the Council of Better Business Bureaus recommended the discontinuation of ads, while Bayer Animal Health reiterated its commitment to self-regulation. **Availability:** Online.

21839 ■ *Electronic Commerce*
Ed: Gary P. Schneider, Bryant Chrzan, Charles McCormick. **Released:** 12th edition. **Price:** $29.49, e-book. **Description:** E-commerce can open the door to more opportunities than ever before for small business. Packed with real-world examples and cases, the book delivers comprehensive coverage of emerging online technologies and trends and their influence on the electronic marketplace. It details how the landscape of online commerce is evolving, reflecting changes in the economy and how business and society are responding to those changes. Balancing technological issues with the strategic business aspects of successful e-commerce, the new edition includes expanded coverage of international issues, social networking, mobile commerce, Web 2.0 technologies, and updates on spam, phishing, and identity theft. **Availability:** Print.

21840 ■ *Emerging Business Online: Global Markets and the Power of B2B Internet Marketing*
Pub: FT Press
Ed: Lara Fawzy, Lucas Dworski. **Released:** First edition. **Price:** $39.99, Members, watermarked. **Description:** An introduction into ebocube (emerging business online), a comprehensive proven business model for Internet B2B marketing in emerging markets. **Availability:** E-book; Print; Online; PDF; Electronic publishing.

21841 ■ *"Empowered"* in Harvard Business Review (Vol. 88, July-August 2010, No. 7-8, pp. 94)
Pub: Harvard Business Publishing
Contact: Diane Belcher, Managing Director
Ed: Josh Bernoff, Ted Schadler. **Price:** $8.95, PDF. **Description:** HERO concept (highly empowered and resourceful operative) which builds a connection between employees, managers, and IT is outlined. The resultant additional experience and knowledge gained by employees improves customer relationship management. **Availability:** Online; PDF.

21842 ■ *"Endeca Gears Up for Likely IPO Bid"* in Boston Business Journal (Vol. 31, July 1, 2011, No. 23, pp. 1)
Pub: Boston Business Journal
Contact: Carolyn M. Jones, President
E-mail: cmjones@bizjournals.com
Ed: Kyle Alspach. **Released:** Weekly. **Price:** $4. **Description:** Endeca Inc. is readying itself for its plans to register as a public company. The search engine technology leader is enjoying continued growth with revenue up by 30 percent in 2010 while its expansion trend makes it an unlikely candidate for an acquisition. **Availability:** Print; Online.

21843 ■ *"Etextbook Space Heats Up"* in Information Today (Vol. 28, November 2011, No. 10, pp. 10)
Pub: Information Today Inc.
Contact: Thomas H. Hogan, President
Ed: Paula J. Hane. **Description:** The use of etextbooks is expected to grow with the use of mobile devices and tablets. A new group of activists is asking students, faculty members and others to sign a petition urging higher education leaders to prioritize affordable textbooks or free ebooks over the traditional, expensive new books required for classes.

21844 ■ *"Etextbooks: Coming of Age"* in Information Today (Vol. 28, September 2011, No. 8, pp. 1)
Pub: Information Today Inc.
Contact: Thomas H. Hogan, President
Ed: Amanda Mulvihill. **Description:** National average for textbooks costs was estimated at $1,137 annually at a 4-year public college for the 2010-2011 school year. Amazon reported selling 105 etextbooks for every 100 print books, while Barnes and Noble announced that their etextbooks were outselling print 3 to 1.

21845 ■ *The Everything Store: Jeff Bezos and the Age of Amazon*
Pub: Little, Brown and Company
Contact: Judy Clain, Editor-in-Chief
Released: October 15, 2013. **Price:** $28, hardcover; $30, audiobook CD; $24.98, audiobook downloadable; $12.99, e-book; $18, paperback; $30, hardcover(large print); $28. **Description:** Amazon.com started as a bookseller, a company delivering books through the mail. Today, the online store, offers a limitless selection of goods at competitively low prices. Profile of entrepreneur Jeff Bezos that outlines his endless pursuit of new markets and risky new ventures to transform retail. **Availability:** audiobook; CD-ROM; E-book; Print.

21846 ■ *"Evolutionary Psychology in the Business Sciences"*
Pub: Springer Publishing Co.
Contact: Bernhard Springer, Founder
Released: First edition. **Description:** All individuals operating in the business sphere share a common biological heritage, including consumers, employers, employees, entrepreneurs, or financial traders, to name a few. The evolutionary behavioral sciences and specific business contexts including marketing, consumer behavior, advertising, innovation and creativity and invention, intertemporal choice, negotiations, competition and cooperation in organizational settings, sex differences in workplace patterns, executive leadership, business ethics, store and office design, behavioral decision making, and electronic communications and commerce are all addressed. **Availability:** E-book; Print.

21847 ■ *Exploring E-Commerce*
URL(s): www.entrepreneur.com/article/159680
Description: Presents information on why considering an online presence for your small business is a great idea to boost sales and provides a guide to how to begin. **Availability:** Online.

21848 ■ *The Facebook Effect: The Inside Story of the Company That Is Connecting the World*
Ed: David Kirkpatrick. **Released:** 2011. **Price:** $18, paperback; $13.99, e-book. **Description:** There's never been a Website like Facebook: more than 350 million people have accounts, and if the growth rate continues, by 2013 every Internet user worldwide will have his or her own page. No one's had more access to the inner workings of the phenomenon than Kirkpatrick, a senior tech writer at Fortune magazine. Written with the full cooperation of founder Mark Zuckerberg, the book follows the company from its genesis in a Harvard dorm room through its successes over Friendster and MySpace, the expansion of the user base, and Zuckerberg's refusal to sell. **Availability:** E-book; Print.

21849 ■ *"Facebook, Google, LinkedIn Line Up In Patent Case Before Supreme Court"* in San Francisco Business Times (Vol. 28, March 28, 2014, No. 36)
Pub: American City Business Journals, Inc.
Contact: Mike Olivieri, Executive Vice President
Released: Weekly. **Description:** The U.S. Supreme Court is set to hear a case involving Alice Corporation Pty. Ltd. and CLS Bank International in a dispute over a patented computer-implemented escrow service. The case has larger implications to tech companies concerning whether a business method can be patented if it is made electronic. **Availability:** Print; Online.

21850 ■ *Facebook Marketing: Leveraging Facebook's Features for Your Marketing Campaigns*
Pub: Que Publishing
Ed: Justin R. Levy. **Released:** Third edition. **Price:** $18.21, e-book; $16.18, paperback. **Description:** Detailed steps are given in order to develop, use,

and create awareness for any business. The book provides detailed instructions, along with case studies from known brands, for launching marketing campaigns on Facebook. **Availability:** E-book; Print.

21851 ■ *"Facebook Purchased Push Pop Press"* in *Information Today* (Vol. 28, October 2011, No. 9, pp. 12)

Description: Facebook purchased Push Pop Press, a digital publishing company that developed a multi-touch interface for ebook publishing on the iPad.

21852 ■ *"Feds Finalize I-9 Form Rules Allowing Electronic Storage"* in *HR Specialist* (Vol. 8, September 2010, No. 9, pp. 5)

Pub: Capitol Information Group Inc.
Contact: Allie Ash, Chief Executive Officer

Description: U.S. Department of Homeland Security issued regulations that give employers more flexibility to electronically sing and store I-9 employee verification forms. **Availability:** Print; PDF; Online.

21853 ■ *"Fifty Percent of Global Online Retail Visits Were to Amazon, eBay and Alibaba in June 2011"* in *Benzinga.com* (October 29, 2011)

Pub: Benzinga.com
Contact: Jason Raznick, Founder

Description: Current statistics and future forecasts through the year 2015 for Amazon, eBay and Alibaba are explored. **Availability:** Online.

21854 ■ *"For Apple, It's Showtime Again"* in *Barron's* (Vol. 90, August 30, 2010, No. 35, pp. 29)

Pub: Barron's Editorial & Corporate Headquarters

Ed: Eric J. Savitz. **Description:** Speculations on what Apple Inc. will unveil at its product launch event are presented. These products include a possible new iPhone Nano, a new update to its Apple TV, and possibly a deal with the Beatles to distribute their songs over iTunes. **Availability:** Online.

21855 ■ *"ForeSee Finds Satisfaction On Web Sites, Bottom Line"* in *Crain's Detroit Business* (Vol. 24, February 25, 2008, No. 8, pp. 3)

Pub: Crain Communications Inc.
Contact: Barry Asin, President

Ed: Tom Henderson. **Description:** Ann Arbor-based ForeSee Results Inc. evaluates user satisfaction on Web sites. The company expects to see an increase of 40 percent in revenue for 2008 with plans to expand to London, Germany, Italy and France by the end of 2009.

21856 ■ *"Formula One Makes Room(s) for Aspiring Entrepreneur in Austin"* in *Austin Business Journal* (Vol. 31, July 1, 2011, No. 17, pp. 1)

Pub: Austin Business Journal
Contact: Rachel McGrath, Director
E-mail: rmcgrath@bizjournals.com

Ed: Vicky Garza. **Description:** Formula One fan and graphic designer Danielle Crespo cashes in on the June 17, 2012 racing event in Austin, Texas via hosting a Website that allows users to book hotel rooms. She invested less than $100 and long hours on this enterprise which now has 74,000-plus visitors. **Availability:** Print; Online.

21857 ■ *"Free Speech Vs. Privacy in Data Mining"* in *Information Today* (Vol. 28, September 2011, No. 8, pp. 22)

Pub: Information Today Inc.
Contact: Thomas H. Hogan, President

Ed: George H. Pike. **Description:** The U.S. Constitution does not explicitly guarantee the right of privacy. Organizations and businesses that require obtaining and disseminating information can be caught in the middle of privacy rights. The long-term impact on data mining, Internet marketing, and Internet privacy issues are examined.

21858 ■ *"Friendly Ice Cream Corporation"* in *Ice Cream Reporter* (Vol. 23, August 20, 2010, No. 9, pp. 8)

Description: Friendly Ice Cream Corporation appointed Andrea M. McKenna as vice president of marketing and chief marketing officer. **Availability:** Print; Online.

21859 ■ *"The Future of Work"* in *Black Enterprise* (Vol. 41, August 2010, No. 1, pp. 65)

Pub: Earl G. Graves Ltd.
Contact: Earl Graves, Jr., President

Ed: Annya M. Lott. **Description:** Technology, globalization, and outsourcing will continue to shape the future of work. Social media is a means for small companies to market goods and services. **Availability:** Online.

21860 ■ *"Generation Y Chooses the Mobile Web"* in *PR Newswire* (November 24, 2010)

Pub: PR Newswire Association LLC.

Description: Generation Y individuals between the ages of 18 - 27 use their mobile phones to browse the Internet more often than a desktop or laptop computer, according to a survey conducted by Opera, a Web browser company. **Availability:** Print; Online.

21861 ■ *"Geo-Location Technology Linking Stores, Shoppers"* in *Providence Business News* (Vol. 29, May 5, 2014, No. 5, pp. 1)

Pub: American City Business Journals, Inc.
Contact: Mike Olivieri, Executive Vice President

Released: May 03, 2014. **Description:** Jewelry maker, Alex and Ani LLC of Cranston, Rhode Island, outfitted their 40 retail stores in the U.S. with Bluetooth Low Energy systems called iBeacons to communicate directly with customers' mobile phones when they are in or near the store. The company claims that its stores have not received any negative feedback on hyperlocal messaging since the program started in summer 2013. **Availability:** Online.

21862 ■ *Global E-Commerce: Impacts of National Environment and Policy*

Pub: Cambridge University Press
Contact: Peter Phillips, Chief Executive Officer

Released: September 01, 2011. **Description:** Global assessment of the impact of e-business on companies as well as countries.

21863 ■ *"Google Places a Call to Bargain Hunters"* in *Advertising Age* (Vol. 79, September 29, 2008, No. 36, pp. 13)

Pub: Crain Communications, Inc.
Contact: Jessica Botos, Manager, Marketing
E-mail: jessica.botos@crainsnewyork.com

Ed: Abbey Klaassen. **Description:** Google highlighted application developers who have created tools for its Android mobile phone in the device's unveiling; applications such as ShopSavvy and CompareEverywhere help shoppers to find bargains by allowing them to compare prices in their local areas and across the web. **Availability:** Online.

21864 ■ *"Google's Next Stop: Below 350?"* in *Barron's* (Vol. 88, March 10, 2008, No. 10, pp. 17)

Pub: Dow Jones & Company Inc.
Contact: Almar Latour, Chief Executive Officer

Ed: Jacqueline Doherty. **Description:** Share prices of Google Inc. are expected to drop from their level of $433 each to below $350 per share. The company is expected to miss its earnings forecast for the first quarter of 2008, and its continued aggressive spending on non-core areas will eventually bring down earnings. **Availability:** Online.

21865 ■ *"Grooming Your Online Persona"* in *Women In Business* (Vol. 62, June 2010, No. 2, pp. 36)

Description: Employees' use of online social networks could become a basis on how their employers, clients, or business partners would judge them. Personal details, pictures and other online data should be filtered to avoid inappropriate or uncomfortable situations and distinguish personal from professional or work life. **Availability:** Online.

21866 ■ *Groundswell: Winning in a World Transformed by Social Technologies*

Pub: Harvard Business Review Press
Contact: Moderna V. Pfizer, Contact

Ed: Charlene Li, Josh Bernoff. **Released:** June 09, 2011. **Price:** $22, paperback/softbound. **Description:** Individuals are using online social technologies such as blogs, social networking sites, YouTube, and podcasts to discuss products and companies, write their own news, and find their own deals. When consumers you've never met are rating your company's products in public forums with which you have no experience or influence, your company is vulnerable. This book teaches the tools and data necessary to turn this treat into an opportunity. **Availability:** E-book; Print.

21867 ■ *"Haagen-Dazs Recruits Shop Owners through Facebook"* in *Ice Cream Reporter* (Vol. 23, November 20, 2010, No. 12, pp. 1)

Description: Haagen-Dazs Shoppe Company is using Facebook, the leading social media, to recruit new franchises. **Availability:** Print; Online.

21868 ■ *"Harness the Internet to Boost Equipment Sales"* in *Indoor Comfort Marketing* (Vol. 70, July 2011, No. 7, pp. 24)

Description: Advice is given to increase HVAC/R equipment sales using the Internet. **Availability:** Online.

21869 ■ *"Hatching Twitter: A True Story of Money, Power, Friendship, and Betrayal"*

Pub: Portfolio Hardcover
Contact: Adrian Zackheim, President

Released: September 05, 2013. **Price:** $18, paperback; $2.18, paperback(100 used from $2.18); $4.28, paperback(55 new from $4.28); $4.39, kindle; $12.99, hardcover; $1.96, hardcover(73 used from $1.96); $8.59, hardcover(9 new from $8.59); $17.50, hardcover(2 collectible from $17.50). **Description:** The first full coverage story covering the four founders of Twitter: Evan Williams, Biz Stone, Jack Dorsey, and Noah Glass, who went from ordinary engineers to wealthy celebrities and entrepreneurs. The story explores their pursuits for money, influence, publicity, and control as Twitter grew larger and more powerful. **Availability:** E-book; Print; Audio.

21870 ■ *"Health-Care Highway"* in *Saint Louis Business Journal* (Vol. 32, October 14, 2011, No. 7, pp. 1)

Pub: Saint Louis Business Journal
Contact: Robert Bobroff, President
E-mail: rbobroff@bizjournals.com

Ed: Angela Mueller. **Description:** Around $2.6 billion will be invested in health care facilities along the Highway 64/40 corridor in St. Louis, Missouri. Mercy Hospital is planning to invest $19 million in a virtual care center. St. Elizabeth's Hospital on the other hand, will purchase 105 acres in the corridor. **Availability:** Print; Online.

21871 ■ *"Helping Customers Fight Pet Waste"* in *Pet Product News* (Vol. 64, November 2010, No. 11, pp. 52)

Ed: Sandy Robins. **Description:** Pet cleaning products manufacturers have been enjoying high sales figures by paying attention to changing pet ownership trends and environmental awareness. Meanwhile, the inclusion of user-friendly features in these products has also been boosted by the social role of pets and the media attention to pet waste. How manufacturers have been responding to this demand is explored. **Availability:** Print; Online.

21872 ■ *"Here's How You Boycott Amazon"* in *Puget Sound Business Journal* (Vol. 35, June 13, 2014, No. 8, pp. 12)

Pub: American City Business Journals, Inc.
Contact: Mike Olivieri, Executive Vice President

Description: Critic, Kimberly Mills, says she boycotted Amazon.com because of its lack of corporate philanthropy and poor working conditions. She also boycotted the firm by purchasing directly from the listed company Websites when purchasing retail products, instead of buying directly from Amazon's site. Other online retailers are increasing customer services corporate social responsibility. **Availability:** Online.

21873 ■ *"Horse Race: Putting the App in Apple" in Inc. (Vol. 30, November 2008, No. 11)*
Pub: Mansueto Ventures L.L.C.
Contact: Stephanie Mehta, Chief Executive Officer
Ed: Nitasha Tiku. **Description:** Aftermarket companies are scrambling to develop games and widgets for Apple's iPhone. Apple launched a kit for developers interested in creating iPhone-specific software along with the App Store, and an iTunes spinoff. Profiles of various software programs that may be used on the iPhone are given. **Availability:** Online.

21874 ■ *"Hospital Communication Goes Mobile" in Providence Business News (Vol. 29, July 7, 2014, No. 14, pp. 12)*
Pub: American City Business Journals, Inc.
Contact: Mike Olivieri, Executive Vice President
Released: July 05, 2014. **Description:** Software company, Care Thread, has designed a mobile health records application that allows providers to share patient e-medical records over a secure network. Care Thread signed a contract for the system with Eastern Connecticut Health Network and Boston's Brigham and Women's Hospital as well as a deal with health care management firm Beacon Partners Inc. to sell and implement the app across the U.S. **Availability:** Print; Online.

21875 ■ *Housecleaning Business: Organize Your Business - Get Clients and Referrals - Set Rates and Services*
Ed: Laura Jorstad, Melinda Morse. **Price:** Paperback,softback. **Description:** This book shares insight into starting a housecleaning business. It shows how to develop a service manual, screen clients, serve customers, select cleaning products, competition, how to up a home office, using the Internet to grow the business and offering green cleaning options to clients. **Availability:** E-book; Print.

21876 ■ *"How Good Advice 'Online' Can Attract Customers" in Indoor Comfort Marketing (Vol. 70, August 2011, No. 8, pp. 20)*
Pub: Spray Technology & Marketing
Contact: Ava Caridad, Director, Editorial
E-mail: acaridad@spraytm.com
Ed: Richard Rutigilano. **Description:** Online marketing tips for heating and cooling small businesses are explained.

21877 ■ *"How I Did It: Best Buy's CEO On Learning to Love Social Media" in Harvard Business Review (Vol. 88, December 2010, No. 12, pp. 43)*
Pub: Harvard Business Publishing
Contact: Diane Belcher, Managing Director
Ed: Brian J. Dunn. **Price:** $8.95, PDF. **Description:** Effective utilization of online social networks to enhance brand identity, connect with consumers, and address bad publicity scenarios is examined. **Availability:** Online; PDF.

21878 ■ *"How I Did It: Jack Ma, Alibaba.com" in Inc. (January 2008, pp. 94-102)*
Ed: Rebecca Fannin. **Description:** Profile of Jack Ma, who started as a guide and interpreter for Western tourists in Hangzhou. Ma used the Internet to build Alibaba.com, China's largest business-to-business site and one of the hottest IPOs in years. **Availability:** Online.

21879 ■ *How to Make Money with Social Media: An Insider's Guide to Using New and Emerging Media to Grow Your Business*
Ed: Jamie Turner, Reshma Shah, PhD. **Released:** 2nd edition. **Description:** Marketers, executives, entrepreneurs are shown more effective ways to utilize Internet social media to make money. This guide brings together both practical strategies and proven execution techniques for driving maximum value from social media marketing. **Availability:** E-book; Print.

21880 ■ *"How to Manage Successful Crowdsourcing Projects" in eWeek (September 29, 2010)*
Ed: Lukas Biewald. **Released:** September 29, 2010. **Description:** The advantages, challenges and pitfalls faced when using crowdsourcing to improve a business are outlined. Crowdsourcing helps to eliminate the need to rely on an internal workforce and the need to forecast task volume. **Availability:** Online.

21881 ■ *How to Open and Operate a Financially Successful Bookstore on Amazon and Other Web Sites: With Companion CD-ROM*
Pub: Atlantic Publishing Co.
Contact: Dr. Heather L. Johnson, Contact
Description: This book was written for every used book aficionado and bookstore owner who currently wants to take advantage of the massive collection of online resources available to start and run your own online bookstore business.

21882 ■ *How to Price Products - 7 Competitive Pricing Strategies to Make a Profit*
URL(s): www.godaddy.com/garage/how-to-price-products/
Released: April 28, 2021. **Description:** Lists 7 steps to establish a competitive pricing strategy for your e-commerce business. **Availability:** Online.

21883 ■ *How to Start a Home-Based Landscaping Business*
Ed: Owen E. Dell. **Released:** 7th edition. **Price:** $21.95, paperback(£14.95); $9.99, e-book(£6.95); $18.95; Electronic Book. **Description:** Guide to starting and running a home-based landscaping business. **Availability:** E-book; Print.

21884 ■ *"How To Be a Twitter Ninja" in Canadian Business (Vol. 87, October 2014, No. 10, pp. 51)*
Description: Robert Palmer, public relations manager at WestJet, shares some rules when it comes to customer engagement on Twitter. He emphasizes the importance of communication when dealing with customer complaints as quickly as possible. **Availability:** Print; Online.

21885 ■ *"How To Get a Loan the Web 2.0 Way" in Black Enterprise (Vol. 41, December 2010, No. 5, pp. 23)*
Pub: Earl G. Graves Ltd.
Contact: Earl Graves, Jr., President
Ed: John Simons. **Description:** People are turning to online peer-to-peer network for personal loans as banks are lending less money. **Availability:** Online.

21886 ■ *"How-To Workshops in St. Charles Teach Sewing, Styles" in St. Louis Post-Dispatch (September 14, 2010)*
Pub: St. Louis Post-Dispatch LLC.
Contact: Gilbert Bailon, Editor
E-mail: gbailon@post-dispatch.com
Ed: Kalen Ponche. **Description:** Profile of DIY Style Workshop in St. Charles, Missouri, where sewing, designing and teaching is offered. The shop is home base for DIY Style, a Website created by mother and daughter to teach younger people how to sew. **Availability:** Online.

21887 ■ *How to Use the Internet to Advertise, Promote, and Market Your Business or Web Site: With Little or No Money*
Pub: Atlantic Publishing Co.
Contact: Dr. Heather L. Johnson, Contact
Ed: Bruce C. Brown. **Released:** Revised third edition. **Description:** Information is given to help build, promote, and make money from your Website or brick and mortar store using the Internet, with minimal costs.

21888 ■ *How Your Small Business Can Benefit from E-Commerce*
URL(s): www.businessblogshub.com/2017/03/how-your-small-business-can-benefit-from-e-commerce/
Description: Details how small businesses have found success with online e-commerce and provides information on the benefits of e-commerce for your small business. **Availability:** Online.

21889 ■ *"Hunhu Healthcare Gets Some Mayo Help" in Business Journal (Vol. 32, August 29, 2014, No. 14, pp. 4)*
Pub: American City Business Journals, Inc.
Contact: Mike Olivieri, Executive Vice President
Description: Hunhu Healthcare Inc. has signed a licensing agreement with Mayo Clinic to develop mobile and Web applications that will enable patients to communicate with the company's network using social networking tools. The firm is expected to charge a monthly fee for the service. **Availability:** Print; Online.

21890 ■ *"I Hear You're Interested In A..." in Inc. (January 2008, pp. 40-43)*
Ed: Leah Hoffmann. **Description:** Four tips to help any small business generate sales leads online are examined. **Availability:** Online.

21891 ■ *I'm on LinkedIn - Now What?*
Pub: Happy About
Contact: Ric Vatner, Chief Executive Officer
Ed: Jason Alba. **Released:** Fourth edition. **Price:** $19.95, paperback; $14.95; $9.99. **Description:** Designed to help get the most out of LinkedIn, the popular business networking site and follows the first edition and includes the latest and great approaches using LinkedIn. With over 32 million members there is a lot of potential to find and develop relationships to help in your business and personal life, but many professionals find themselves wondering what to do once they sign up. This book explains the different benefits of the system and recommends best practices (including LinkedIn Groups) so that you get the most out of LinkedIn. **Availability:** E-book; Print; PDF; DVD; Electronic publishing; Download; Online.

21892 ■ *"Information Technology Changes Roles, Highlights Hiring Needs" in South Florida Business Journal (Vol. 34, February 14, 2014, No. 30, pp. 3)*
Pub: American City Business Journals, Inc.
Contact: Mike Olivieri, Executive Vice President
Released: Weekly. **Price:** $8, Introductory 4-week offer(Digital & Print). **Description:** Results of the Steven Douglas Associates survey of 218 senior and mid-level information technology executives in South Florida are presented. About 75 percent of the respondents cited cloud services, mobile technologies, big data and enterprise reporting planning as having the most profound impact on their roles. The challenges they face with the expected hiring growth are also examined. **Availability:** Print; Online.

21893 ■ *Information Technology for the Small Business: How to Make IT Work For Your Company*
Description: Basics of information technology to help small companies maximize benefits are covered. Topics include pitfalls to avoid, email and Internet use, data backup, recovery and overall IT organization.

21894 ■ *"InnoCentive Announces Next Generation Crowdsourcing Platform" in Marketwired (June 15, 2010)*
Pub: Comtex News Network Inc.
Contact: Kan Devnani, President
Description: InnoCentive, Inc., a world leader in open innovation, is launching InnoCentive@Work3, a third generation of its @Work enterprise platform for collaborative-driven innovation for companies. The product will help clients solve critical business and technical issues by tapping information both inside and outside of a company. **Availability:** Online.

GENERAL SMALL BUSINESS TOPICS

Electronic Commerce/E-Business ■ 21915

21895 ■ *"Innovation Central: Tech, Tweets, and Trolls"* in Inc. (Vol. 36, September 2014, No. 7, pp. 102)
Pub: Mansueto Ventures L.L.C.
Contact: Stephanie Mehta, Chief Executive Officer
Description: Results of a survey regarding the ways small business is using technology to grow their businesses is presented. Information covers social media applications, government software patents, trends impacting small business, and the most innovative technology companies. **Availability:** Print; Online.

21896 ■ *"Intentional Networking: Your Guide to Word of Mouth Marketing Greatness"*
Pub: CreateSpace
Released: October 28, 2014. **Price:** $10.55, kindle; paperback ; $7.84, paperback. **Description:** Business owners and salespeople know the power of word of mouth marketing to increase sales. Networking, email communications, social media and referrals are techniques to help build revenue. **Availability:** Print.

21897 ■ *"Israeli Spam Law May Have Global Impact"* in Information Today (Vol. 26, February 2009, No. 2, pp. 28)
Pub: Information Today Inc.
Contact: Thomas H. Hogan, President
Ed: David Mirchin. **Description:** Israels new law, called Amendment 40 of the Communications Law, will regulate commercial solicitations including those sent without permission via email, fax, automatic phone dialing systems, or short messaging technologies. **Availability:** PDF; Online.

21898 ■ *"It's 2019 and Faxing Is Still a Thing"* in Quartz (February 6, 2019)
URL(s): qz.com/1544122/its-2019-and-faxing-is-still-a-thing/
Ed: Jonathan Coopersmith. **Released:** February 06, 2019. **Description:** The fax machine was supposed to be outdated technology, but surprisingly it is still popular and being used. Businesses are still faxing and legal documents are still being faxed instead of adapting new technology to accept electronic signatures. Since a lot of users already have the old technology, they are reluctant to update and spend money on something that they don't really need. **Availability:** Online.

21899 ■ *"Jab, Jab, Jab, Right Hook: How to Tell Your Story in a Noisy Social World"*
Pub: Harper Business
Contact: Hollis Heimbouch, Senior Vice President Publisher
Released: November 26, 2013. **Price:** $23.99, hardcover. **Description:** Author and social media expert shares advice on ways to connect with customers and beat the competition. Social media strategies for marketers and managers need to convert Internet traffic to sales. Communication is the key to online sales that are adapted to high quality social media platforms and mobile devices. **Availability:** E-book; Print.

21900 ■ *"Jo-Ann Fabric and Craft Stores Joins ArtFire.com to Offer Free Online Craft Marketplace"* in Marketwired (January 26, 2010)
Pub: Comtex News Network Inc.
Contact: Kan Devnani, President
Description: Jo-Ann Fabric and Craft Stores has entered into a partnership with ArtFire.com which will provide sewers and crafters all the tools they need in order to make and sell their products from an online venue. **Availability:** Print; Online.

21901 ■ *"Joe Wikert, General Manager, O'Reilly Technology Exchange"* in Information Today (Vol. 26, February 2009, No. 2, pp. 21)
Description: Joe Wikert, general manager of O'Reilly Technology Exchange discusses his plans to develop a free content model that will evolve with future needs. O'Reilly's major competitor is Google. Wikert plans to expand the firm's publishing program to include print, online, and in-person products and services. **Availability:** Online.

21902 ■ *"Kodak Offers Cloud-Based Operating Option"* in American Printer (Vol. 128, June 1, 2011, No. 6)
Description: Kodak partnered with VMware to offer its first Virtual Operating Environment option for Kodak Unified Workflow Solutions. The new feature enables cost savings, increased efficiency and failover protection. **Availability:** Online.

21903 ■ *"Kuno Creative to Present the Three Steps of a Successful B2B Social Media Campaign"* in Business Tech & Wireless (August 25, 2011)
Pub: Close-Up Media Inc.
Contact: Caroline S. Moore, President
E-mail: cms@closeupmedia.com
Released: August 24, 2011. **Description:** Kuno Creative, an inbound marketing agency, will host Three Steps of a Successful B2B Social Media Campaign. The firm is a provider of Website development, branding, marketing strategy, public relations, Internet marketing, and inbound marketing. **Availability:** Print; Online.

21904 ■ *"Lavante, Inc. Joins Intersynthesis, Holistic Internet Marketing Company"* in Marketwired (November 5, 2009)
Pub: Comtex News Network Inc.
Contact: Kan Devnani, President
Description: Lavante, Inc., the leading provider of on-demand vendor information and profit recovery audit solutions for Fortune 1000 companies has chosen Intersynthesis, a new holistic Internet marketing firm, as a provider of pay for performance services. Lavante believes that Intersynthesis' expertise and knowledge combined with their ability to develop integrated strategies, will help them fuel more growth. **Availability:** Print; Online.

21905 ■ *"Lawyers Object to New Online Court Fees"* in Sacramento Business Journal (Vol. 31, August 8, 2014, No. 24, pp. 3)
Pub: American City Business Journals, Inc.
Contact: Mike Olivieri, Executive Vice President
Description: Lawyers and consumer advocates have complained that the Sacramento County Superior Court's new fee system for online access to online court records hinders access to justice. However, court administrators argue that the charging of fees will only help offset the online record system's maintenance costs. **Availability:** Print; Online.

21906 ■ *"Legislating the Cloud"* in Information Today (Vol. 28, October 2011, No. 9, pp. 1)
Pub: Information Today Inc.
Contact: Thomas H. Hogan, President
Ed: Kurt Schiller. **Description:** Internet and telecommunications industry leaders are asking for legislation to address the emerging market in cloud computing. Existing communications laws do not adequately govern the modern Internet.

21907 ■ *"Lights, Camera, Action: Tools for Creating Video Blogs"* in Inc. (Volume 32, December 2010, No. 10, pp. 57)
Pub: Mansueto Ventures L.L.C.
Contact: Stephanie Mehta, Chief Executive Officer
Ed: John Brandon. **Description:** A video blog is a good way to spread company news, talk about products, and stand out among traditional company blogs. New editing software can create two- to four-minute blogs using a webcam and either Windows Live Essentials, Apple iLife 2011, Powerdirector 9 Ultra, or Adobe Visual Communicator 3. **Availability:** Online.

21908 ■ *"LivingSocial's New 'Glue'"* in Washington Business Journal (Vol. 33, May 2, 2014, No. 2, pp. 10)
Pub: American City Business Journals, Inc.
Contact: Mike Olivieri, Executive Vice President
Description: LivingSocial Inc. CFO, John Bax, shares his views on the confluence of forces that shaped the company's first quarter results. Bax reports the company is pouring resources into the creation of a new retail merchant solution platform to help market products and services. Bax named the project Glue because it is geared to encouraging customer loyalty to merchants along with repeat business. **Availability:** Print; Online.

21909 ■ *"Looking To Leap?"* in Black Enterprise (Vol. 38, January 2008, No. 6, pp. 64)
Pub: Earl G. Graves Ltd.
Contact: Earl Graves, Jr., President
Ed: Tennille M. Robinson. **Description:** Websites and organizations providing resources for any young entrepreneur wishing to start a new business are outlined.

21910 ■ *"A Love of Likes: What's a Facebook Nod Worth to a Business? Serious Sales Growth, Say Some"* in Boston Business Journal (Vol. 31, July 8, 2011, No. 24, pp. 1)
Pub: Boston Business Journal
Contact: Carolyn M. Jones, President
E-mail: cmjones@bizjournals.com
Ed: Lisa Van der Pool. **Description:** An increasing number of companies in Boston, Massachusetts have been keen on getting Facebook 'likes' from people. Business owners realize that Facebook 'likes' could generate sales and based on some studies, equate to specific dollar values.

21911 ■ *Low-Budget Online Marketing for Small Business*
Pub: Self-Counsel Press Inc.
Contact: Diana Douglas, Governor
Ed: Holly Berkley. **Released:** 3rd edition. **Price:** C$21.95; $20.95; $20.95; C$21.95; C$12.99; C$21.95. **Description:** Low-budget advertising campaigns are presented to help market any small business. **Availability:** CD-ROM; Print; Download; Electronic publishing; PDF.

21912 ■ *"Making It Click: Annual Ranking Of the Best Online Brokers"* in Barron's (Vol. 88, March 17, 2008, No. 11, pp. 31)
Pub: Dow Jones & Company Inc.
Contact: Almar Latour, Chief Executive Officer
Ed: Theresa W. Carey. **Description:** Listing of 23 online brokers that are evaluated based on their trade experience, usability, range of offerings, research amenities, customer service and access, and costs. TradeStation Securities takes the top spot followed by thinkorswim by just a fraction. **Availability:** Online.

21913 ■ *"Managing Yourself: What's Your Personal Social Media Strategy?"* in Harvard Business Review (Vol. 88, November 2010, No. 11, pp. 127)
Pub: Harvard Business Publishing
Contact: Diane Belcher, Managing Director
Ed: Soumitra Dutta. **Price:** $8.95, PDF. **Description:** Identification of four distinct sectors and how they interrelate to social media is given. The sectors are personal and private; professional and private; personal and public; and professional and public. Appropriate topics and types of social media are discussed for each. **Availability:** Online; PDF.

21914 ■ *"Marketing in the Digital World: Here's How to Craft a Smart Online Strategy"* in Black Enterprise (Vol. 40, July 2010, No. 12, pp. 47)
Pub: Earl G. Graves Ltd.
Contact: Earl Graves, Jr., President
Ed: Sonya A. Donaldson. **Description:** Social media is an integral part of any small business plan in addressing marketing, sales, and branding strategies.

21915 ■ *"Marketing Scholarship 2.0"* in Journal of Marketing (Vol. 75, July 2011, No. 4, pp. 225)
Pub: American Marketing Association
Contact: Bennie F. Johnson, Chief Executive Officer
Ed: Richard J. Lutz. **Released:** Volume: 75 issue: 4. **Description:** A study of the implications of changing environment and newer collaborative models for marketing knowledge production and dissemination is presented. Crowdsourcing has become a frequently

employed strategy in industry. Academic researchers should collaborate more as well as the academe and industry, to make sure that important problems are being investigated. **Availability:** PDF.

21916 ■ **Marketing Without Money for Small and Midsize Businesses: 300 FREE and Cheap Ways to Increase Your Sales**
Price: $11.25. **Description:** Three hundred practical low-cost or no-cost strategies to increase sales, focusing on free advertising, free marketing assistance, and free referrals to the Internet. **Availability:** Print; Online.

21917 ■ *"Media Terminology"* in *MarketingMagazine* (Vol. 115, September 27, 2010, No. 13, pp. 80)
Pub: Rogers Media Inc.
Contact: Neil Spivak, Chief Executive Officer
Description: Media terminology is provided. **Availability:** Print; PDF; Online.

21918 ■ *"Message to the Masses"*
Pub: BK Royston Publishing
Contact: Julia A. Royston, Publisher
E-mail: julia@bkroystonpublishing.com
Description: Information is offered to help explore ways to get your message to your audience so they not only hear your words, they understand their meaning. Marketing tips for using social media, blogs, the elevator pitch and more are featured. **Availability:** Video; CD-ROM; E-book; Print; Audio.

21919 ■ *"Messaging Apps: What the New Face of Social Media Means for Brands"* in *New Generation Latino Consortium* (December 2010)
Ed: Gary Fackler. **Description:** Latina bloggers carve out a new niche in social media that helps preserve their unique cultural identities. **Availability:** Online.

21920 ■ *"Microsoft Releases Office Security Updates"* in *Mac World* (Vol. 27, November 2010, No. 11, pp. 66)
Description: Office for Mac and Mac Business Unit are Microsoft's pair of security- and stability-enhancing updates for Office 2008 and Office 2004. The software will improve the stability and compatibility and fixes vulnerabilities that would allow attackers to overwrite Mac's memory with malicious code. **Availability:** Online.

21921 ■ *"MoneyGram Hopes Digital Push Will Click With Customers"* in *Dallas Business Journal* (Vol. 37, July 4, 2014, No. 43, pp. 17)
Pub: American City Business Journals, Inc.
Contact: Mike Olivieri, Executive Vice President
Released: Weekly. **Price:** $4, introductory 4-week offer(Digital only). **Description:** Reports on MoneyGram's recent release of a digital monitoring system, which will allow it to work more closely with customers, is profiled. This digital monitoring system will aggregate data from social media platforms and enable the company to identify customer needs and trends across the money transfer industry. It will help MoneyGram outshine its rivals in the money transfer business. **Availability:** Print; Online.

21922 ■ *"More Leading Retailers Using Omniture Conversion Solutions to Boost Sales and Ecommerce Performance"* in *Marketwired* (September 22, 2009)
Pub: Comtex News Network Inc.
Contact: Kan Devnani, President
Description: Many retailers are utilizing Omniture conversion solutions to improve the performance of their ecommerce businesses; recent enhancements to Omniture Merchandising and Omniture Recommendations help clients drive increased conversion to their Internet ventures.

21923 ■ *"My Favorite Tool for Managing Expenses"* in *Inc.* (Volume 32, December 2010, No. 10, pp. 60)
Pub: Inc. Magazine

Ed: J.J. McCorvey. **Description:** Web-based service called Expensify is outlined. The service allows companies to log expenses while away from the office using the service's iPhone application. **Availability:** Online.

21924 ■ **Negative Effects of E-Commerce**
URL(s): onhike.com/negative-effects-of-e-commerce/117254/
Released: July 05, 2021. **Description:** Includes information on the benefits of e-commerce for your small business and focuses on the negative effects that e-commerce may have on both consumers and retailers. **Availability:** Online.

21925 ■ *"New Sales. Simplified: The Essential Handbook for Prospecting and New Business Development"*
Pub: HarperCollins Leadership
Contact: Donald Miller, Chief Executive Officer
Released: September 04, 2012. **Price:** $19.99, Paperback. **Description:** The constant flow of new accounts is essential for any small business to grow and thrive. A proven formula for prospecting; customer-focused selling; proactive telephone calling that leads to face-to-face meetings; the use of email, voicemail, and social media; prevent the buyer's anti-salesperson response; build a rapport; winning sales; communicating with clients; plan time for business development activities; and more. **Availability:** E-book; Print; Audio; Download.

21926 ■ *"New Wave of Business Security Products Ushers in the Kaspersky Anti-Malware Protection System"* in *Internet Wire* (October 26, 2010)
Description: Kaspersky Anti-Malware System provides anti-malware protection that requires minimal in-house resources for small businesses. The system offers a full range of tightly integrated end-to-end protection solutions, ensuring unified protection across an entire network, from endpoint and mobile device protection to file server, mail server, network storage and gateway protection. It provides flexible centralized management, immediate threat visibility and a level of responsiveness not seen in other anti-malware approaches. **Availability:** Print; Online.

21927 ■ *"A New Way to Tell When to Fold 'Em"* in *Barron's* (Vol. 88, July 7, 2008, No. 27, pp. 27)
Pub: Dow Jones & Company Inc.
Contact: Almar Latour, Chief Executive Officer
Ed: Theresa W. Carey. **Description:** Overview of the Online trading company SmartStops, a firm that aims to tell investors when to sell the shares of a particular company. The company's Web site categorizes stocks as moving up, down, or sideways, and calculates exit points for individual stocks based on an overall market trend. **Availability:** Online.

21928 ■ *"The Next Frontier"* in *San Francisco Business Times* (Vol. 28, February 28, 2014, No. 32, pp. 4)
Pub: American City Business Journals, Inc.
Contact: Mike Olivieri, Executive Vice President
Description: The growth of the electronic payments business in San Francisco, California has captured the interest of venture capitalists, entrepreneurs, and other investors. Social media companies like Facebook and Google are expected to expand into electronic payments. Telecommunication companies are also investing in promising startups and joint ventures. **Availability:** Print; Online.

21929 ■ *"Next-Level E-Commerce"* in *Entrepreneur* (June 2014)
Pub: Entrepreneur Media Inc.
Contact: Dan Bova, Director
E-mail: dbova@entrepreneur.com
Description: BloomReach's SNAP software enables consumers to see the products they want upon arriving at an e-commerce Website. The software does this by evaluating the users' intent and preferences based on previous site usage. The enterprise-level software, which costs retailers at least $7,500/month, aims to use big data to help consumers choose products based on their intent. The cloud-based service indexes every page on a client's site and automatically generates appropriate content for visitors. The use of machine learning reduces lag time between application and positive results. **Availability:** Print; Online.

21930 ■ *"'Nobody Knows What To Do' To Make Money on the Web"* in *Barron's* (Vol. 88, March 17, 2008, No. 11, pp. 40)
Pub: Dow Jones & Company Inc.
Contact: Almar Latour, Chief Executive Officer
Ed: Mark Veverka. **Description:** Attendees of the South by Southwest Interactive conference failed to get an insight on how to make money on the Web from former Walt Disney CEO Michael Eisner when Eisner said there's no proven business model for financing projects. Eisner said he finances his projects with the help of his connections to get product-placement deals. **Availability:** Online.

21931 ■ *"Nowspeed and OneSource to Conduct Webinar: How to Develop Social Media Content That Gets Results"* in *Marketwired* (December 14, 2009)
Pub: Comtex News Network Inc.
Contact: Kan Devnani, President
Description: OneSource, a leading provider of global business information, and Nowspeed, an Internet marketing agency, will conduct a webinar titled "How to Develop Social Media Content That Gets Results" in order to provide marketers insight into how to develop and optimize effective social media content to get consumer results that translate into purchases and lead generation. **Availability:** Print; Mailing list; Online.

21932 ■ *"Old Spice Guy (Feb.-July 2010)"* in *Canadian Business* (Vol. 83, August 17, 2010, No. 13-14, pp. 23)
Pub: Rogers Media Inc.
Contact: Neil Spivak, Chief Executive Officer
Ed: Andrew Potter. **Description:** Old Spice Guy was played by ex-football player and actor Isaiah Mustafa who made the debut in the ad for Old Spice Red Zone body wash that was broadcast during Super Bowl XLIV in February 2010. Old Spice Guy has become one of social marketing success but was cancelled in July when online viewership started to wane. **Availability:** Print; Online.

21933 ■ *"Oliver Russell Acquiring Social Good Network"* in *Idaho Business Review* (August 29, 2014)
Pub: BridgeTower Media
Contact: Adam Reinebach, President
Description: Oliver Russell, owner of a Boise advertising firm, is acquiring the assets of startup Social Good Network, an online fundraising firm that was turned down for additional funding beyond its seed funding. Details of the deal and future plans are discussed.

21934 ■ *"The One Thing You Must Get Right When Building a Brand"* in *Harvard Business Review* (Vol. 88, December 2010, No. 12, pp. 80)
Pub: Harvard Business Publishing
Contact: Diane Belcher, Managing Director
Ed: Patrick Barwise, Sean Meehan. **Price:** $8.95, PDF. **Description:** Four uses for new media include: communicating a clearly defined customer promise, creating trust via delivering on the promise, regularly improving on the promise, and innovating past what is familiar. **Availability:** Online; PDF.

21935 ■ *"Online Book Sales Surpass Bookstores"* in *Information Today* (Vol. 28, September 2011, No. 8, pp. 11)
Pub: Information Today Inc.
Contact: Thomas H. Hogan, President
Ed: Cindy Martine. **Description:** Online book sales outpaced bookstore purchases in the United States, signaling a shift in the US book industry. Statistical data included.

21936 ■ *"Online Directories: Your Silent Sales Staff"* in *South Florida Business Journal* (Vol. 34, June 20, 2014, No. 48, pp. 14)
Pub: American City Business Journals, Inc.
Contact: Mike Olivieri, Executive Vice President
Released: Weekly. **Price:** $8, introductory 4-week offer(Digital only). **Description:** The benefits of using online business directories as an extension of the physical sales personnel are explained. Business owners who plan to use online directories to their advantage need to check their listings and links at least once a year and whenever there is a change to the business. **Availability:** Print; Online.

21937 ■ *"Online Forex Broker Tadawul FX Intros Arabic Website"* in *Services Close-Up* (June 23, 2011)
Pub: Close-Up Media Inc.
Contact: Caroline S. Moore, President
E-mail: cms@closeupmedia.com
Description: Online forex broker, Tadawul FX, launched its Arabic language Website, noting that the Middle East is a key market for the investment firm. **Availability:** Online.

21938 ■ *"Online Security Crackdown"* in *Chain Store Age* (Vol. 84, July 2008, No. 7, pp. 46)
Ed: Samantha Murphy. **Description:** Online retailers are beefing up security on their Websites. Cyber thieves use retail systems in order to gain entry to consumer data. David's Bridal operates over 275 bridal showrooms in the U.S. and has a one-stop wedding resource for new brides planning weddings. **Availability:** Online.

21939 ■ *"Online Translation Service Aids Battlefield Troops"* in *Product News Network* (August 30, 2011)
Pub: Thomas Publishing Company
Contact: Tony Uphoff, President
E-mail: tuphoff@thomaspublishing.com
Description: Linquist online service, LinGo Link provides real-time interpreter support to military troops overseas. Interpreters skilled in multiple languages and dialects are used in various areas and in multiple instances without requiring physical presence. The service is available through commercial cellular or WiFi services or tactical communications network. The system accommodates exchange of audio, video, photos, and text during conversations via smartphones and mobile peripheral devices. **Availability:** Online.

21940 ■ *"The Open Mobile Summit Opens in San Francisco Today: John Donahoe CEO eBay to Keynote"* in *Benzinga.com* (November 2, 2011)
Pub: Benzinga.com
Contact: Jason Raznick, Founder
Description: eBay's CEO, John Donahoe was keynote speaker at the 4th Annual Open Mobile Summit held in San Francisco, California. eBay is one of the 130 companies participating as speakers at the event.

21941 ■ *"PC Connection Acquires Cloud Software Provider"* in *New Hampshire Business Review* (Vol. 33, March 25, 2011, No. 6, pp. 8)
Description: Merrimack-based PC Connection Inc. acquired ValCom Technology, a provider of cloud-based IT service management software. Details of the deal are included. **Availability:** Print; Online.

21942 ■ *"People; E-Commerce, Online Games, Mobile Apps"* in *Advertising Age* (Vol. 80, October 19, 2009, No. 35, pp. 14)
Pub: Crain Communications, Inc.
Contact: Jessica Botos, Manager, Marketing
E-mail: jessica.botos@crainsnewyork.com
Ed: Nat Ives. **Description:** Profile of People Magazine and the ways in which the publisher is moving its magazine forward by exploring new concepts in a time of declining newsstand sales and advertising pages; among the strategies are e-commerce such as the brand People Style Watch in which consumers are able highlight clothing and jewelry and then connect to retailers' sites and a channel on Taxi TV, the network of video-touch screens in New Your City taxis. **Availability:** Online.

21943 ■ *"Plan Your Future with My Next Move"* in *Occupational Outlook Quarterly* (Vol. 55, Summer 2011, No. 2, pp. 22)
Description: My Next Move, an online tool offering a variety of user-friendly ways to browse more than 900 occupations was created by the National Center for O NET Development for the US Department of Labor's Employment and Training Administration. Clicking on an occupation presents a one-page profile summarizing key information for specific careers. **Availability:** Print; Online.

21944 ■ *"Play By Play: These Video Products Can Add New Life to a Stagnant Website"* in *Black Enterprise* (Vol. 41, December 2010, No. 5)
Pub: Earl G. Graves Ltd.
Contact: Earl Graves, Jr., President
Ed: Marcia Wade Talbert. **Description:** Web Visible, provider of online marketing products and services, cites video capability as the fastest-growing Website feature for small business advertisers. Profiles of various devices for adding video to a Website are included. **Availability:** Online.

21945 ■ *"Points of Light Sells MissionFish to eBay"* in *Non-Profit Times* (Vol. 25, May 15, 2011, No. 7, pp. May 15, 2011)
Description: eBay purchased MissionFish, a subsidiary of Points of Light Institute for $4.5 million. MissionFish allows eBay sellers to give proceeds from sales to their favorite nonprofit organization and helps nonprofits raise funds by selling on eBay. **Availability:** Print; Online.

21946 ■ *"The Power of Negative Thinking"* in *Inc.* (Volume 32, December 2010, No. 10, pp. 43)
Pub: Inc. Magazine
Ed: Jason Fried. **Description:** A Website is software and most businesses have and need a good Website to generate business. Understanding for building a powerful Website is presented. **Availability:** Online.

21947 ■ *"The Power of Online"* in *Advertising Age* (Vol. 85, October 13, 2014, No. 21, pp. 4)
Pub: Crain Communications Inc.
Contact: Barry Asin, President
Description: According to Shop.org, online sales could increase by as much as 11 percent this holiday season. Retailers are not only focusing on when customers will start holiday shopping, but whether they will use online stores or shop at brick-and-mortar stores. Many retailers are expanding their online services using digital showrooms on their Websites. **Availability:** Online.

21948 ■ *"Powering Intelligent Commerce: eCommera Rebrands as OrderDynamics, Helping Retailers Activate Commerce from First Interaction to Fulfillment"* in *Computer Business Week* (August 28, 2014, pp. 20)
Pub: NewsRX LLC.
Contact: Kalani Rosell, Contact
Description: OrderDynamics, a new global brand created by eCommera, is profiled. The firm will continue to provide an integrated suite of software-as-a-service (SaaS) big data products and service that power intelligent commerce for retailers and brands around the world. Details of the integration of the new brand are included. **Availability:** Online.

21949 ■ *"The Pre-Tail Revolution"* in *Canadian Business* (Vol. 87, October 2014, No. 10, pp. 10)
Description: A number of products that succeeded in security support from crowdfunding platforms, Kickstarter and Indiegogo, and those that failed are presented. Included are the do-it-yourself computer kit Kano, Bluetooth speakers Edge.sound, three-dimensional printer The Micro, Coolest Cooler the insect control device BugASalt, hexacopter Hexo+, and the Ubuntu Edge. **Availability:** Print; Online.

21950 ■ *"Pro Livestock Launches Most Comprehensive Virtual Sales Barn for Livestock and Breed Stock"* in *Benzinga.com* (October 29, 2011)
Description: Pro Livestock Marketing launched the first online sales portal for livestock and breed stock. The firm has designed a virtual sales barn allowing individuals to purchase and sell cattle, swine, sheep, goats, horses, rodeo stock, show animals, specialty animals, semen and embryos globally. It is like an eBay for livestock and will help ranchers and farmers grow. **Availability:** Print; PDF; Online.

21951 ■ *"Promotional Marketing: How to Create, Implement & Integrate Campaigns That Really Work"*
Pub: Kogan Page
Released: Sixth edition. **Description:** Promotional marketing helps companies stay ahead of competition to gain new customers and keep existing ones. The guide includes new developments in the field of marketing, examining the use of digital media such as mobile devices and phones, interactive television, and Web-based advertising, as well as ways to research and evaluate promotional marketing campaigns. **Availability:** Online; PDF.

21952 ■ *"Promotions Create a Path to Better Profit"* in *Pet Product News* (Vol. 64, December 2010, No. 12, pp. 1)
Ed: Joan Hustace Walker. **Description:** Pet store retailers can boost small mammal sales by launching creative marketing and promotions such as social networking and adoption days.

21953 ■ *"Protect Your Domain Name From Cybersquatters"* in *Idaho Business Review* (September 1, 2014)
Pub: BridgeTower Media
Contact: Adam Reinebach, President
Description: Cybersquatting is the practice of registering, trafficking in or using domain names with the intent to profit from the goodwill of recognizable trade names or trademarks of other companies. Companies can protect their Website domain by following these steps: register domain names, promptly renew registrations, maintain proper records, obtain additional top-level domains, and monitor your site for cybersquatters.

21954 ■ *"Providers Ride First Wave of eHealth Dollars"* in *Boston Business Journal* (Vol. 31, June 10, 2011, No. 20, pp. 1)
Pub: Boston Business Journal
Contact: Carolyn M. Jones, President
E-mail: cmjones@bizjournals.com
Ed: Julie M. Donnelly. **Released:** Weekly. **Description:** Health care providers in Massachusetts implementing electronic medical records technology started receiving federal stimulus funds. Beth Israel Deaconess Medical Center was the first hospital to qualify for the funds. **Availability:** Print.

21955 ■ *"Punta Gorda Interested in Wi-Fi Internet"* in *Charlotte Observer* (February 1, 2007)
Description: Punta Gorda officials are developing plans to provide free wireless Internet services to businesses and residents. **Availability:** Online.

21956 ■ *"Putting SogoTrade Through Its Paces"* in *Barron's* (Vol. 89, July 27, 2009, No. 30, pp. 27)
Pub: Dow Jones & Company Inc.
Contact: Almar Latour, Chief Executive Officer
Ed: Theresa W. Carey. **Description:** SogoTrade options platform streams options quotes in real time and lets users place a trade in several ways. The site also features notable security tactics and is a reasonable choice for bargain-seekers. OptionsXpress' Xtend platform lets users place trades and get real time quotes. **Availability:** Online.

21957 ■ "Q&A with Google's Patrick Pichette" in Canadian Business (Vol. 81, October 13, 2008, No. 17, pp. 6)
Description: Patrick Pichette finds challenge in taking over the finances of an Internet company that has a market cap of about $140 billion. He feels, however, that serving as Google's chief financial officer is nothing compared to running Bell Canada Enterprises (BCE). Pichette's other views on Google and BCE are presented. **Availability:** Print; Online.

21958 ■ "Reinventing Marketing to Manage the Environmental Imperative" in Journal of Marketing (Vol. 75, July 2011, No. 4, pp. 132)
Pub: American Marketing Association
Contact: Bennie F. Johnson, Chief Executive Officer
Ed: Philip Kotler. **Description:** Marketers must now examine their theory and practices due to the growing recognition of finite resources and high environmental costs. Companies also need to balance more carefully their growth goals with the need to purse sustainability. Insights on the rise of demarketing and social marketing are also given. **Availability:** PDF.

21959 ■ "Renren Partners With Recruit to Launch Social Wedding Services" in Benzinga.com (June 7, 2011)
Pub: PR Newswire Association LLC.
Description: Renren Inc., the leading real name social networking Internet platform in China has partnered with Recruit Company Limited, Japan's largest human resource and classified media group to form a joint venture to build a wedding social media catering to the needs of engaged couples and newlyweds in China.

21960 ■ "Retail Product Management: Buying and Merchandising"
Pub: Routledge, Taylor & Francis Group
Released: Third edition. **Description:** Due to the rise in Internet use, retailers are facing challenges associated with more informed buyers, technological advances, and the competitive environment. Retail ethics are also examined.

21961 ■ "The Return of the Infomercial" in Canadian Business (Vol. 83, September 14, 2010, No. 15, pp. 19)
Pub: Rogers Media Inc.
Contact: Neil Spivak, Chief Executive Officer
Ed: James Cowan. **Description:** Infomercials or direct response ads have helped some products succeed in the marketplace. The success of infomercials is due to the cheap advertising rates, expansion into retail stores and the products' oddball appeal. Insights into the popularity of infomercial products on the Internet and on television are given. **Availability:** Online.

21962 ■ "Ride-Share Field Has New Player" in Providence Business News (Vol. 29, April 21, 2014, No. 3, pp. 1)
Pub: American City Business Journals, Inc.
Contact: Mike Olivieri, Executive Vice President
URL(s): pbn.com/ride-share-field-has-new-player9 6580
Description: Lyft is Providence, Rhode Island's newest ride-sharing service. State officials continue to look for ways to regulate Internet vehicle services, taxis and limousines. Nearly all of Lyft's drivers are part-time employees using their own personal vehicles.

21963 ■ "Rise Interactive, Internet Marketing Agency, Now Offers Social Media Services" in Marketwired (November 4, 2009)
Pub: Comtex News Network Inc.
Contact: Kan Devnani, President
Description: Profile of Rise Interactive, a full-service Internet marketing agency which has recently added social media to its list of offerings; the agency touts that its newest service gives their clients the power to have ongoing communication with current and potential customers on the sites they are most actively visiting. **Availability:** Print; Online.

21964 ■ "ROIonline Announces Streaming Video Products" in Marketing Weekly News (December 5, 2009, pp. 155)
Pub: Investment Weekly News
Description: ROIonline LLC, an Internet marketing firm serving business-to-business and the industrial marketplace, has added streaming video options to the Internet solutions it offers its clients; due to the huge increase of broadband connections, videos are now commonplace on the Internet and can often convey a company's message in a must more efficient, concise and effective way that will engage a website's visitor thus delivering a high return on a company's investment. **Availability:** Print; Mailing list; Online.

21965 ■ "Ryan Gilbert Wants SBA To Mean Speedy Business Administration" in Philadelphia Business Journal (Vol. 33, May 9, 2014, No. 13, pp. 8)
Pub: American City Business Journals, Inc.
Contact: Mike Olivieri, Executive Vice President
Released: May 23, 2014. **Description:** Ryan Gilbert, CEO of San Francisco, California-based Better Finance explains that his company uses its financial technology, SmartBiz, to help banks expedite Small Business Administration (SBA) loans. Better Finance, formerly known as BillFloat, helps small business owners receive SBA 7(a) loans between $5,000 and $150,000 within five business days instead of several week, offering easy online access to SBA loans at low interest rates. **Availability:** Print; Online.

21966 ■ "Same-Day Delivery's Second Act" in Inc. (Vol. 36, March 2014, No. 2, pp. 87)
Pub: Mansueto Ventures L.L.C.
Contact: Stephanie Mehta, Chief Executive Officer
Description: New technology is helping electronic commerce to be reliable and profitable while offering same day delivery. Profiles of delivery services competing for retail contracts include Instacart, Zookal, Postmates, to name a few. Statistical data included. **Availability:** Online.

21967 ■ The Savvy Gal's Guide to Online Networking: Or What Would Jane Austen Do?
Pub: Booklocker.com Inc.
Ed: Diane K. Danielson, Lindsey Pollak. **Description:** It is a truth universally acknowledged that a woman in search of a fabulous career must be in want of networking opportunities. Or so Jane Austen would say if she were writing, or more likely, blogging today. So begins the must-read guide to networking in the 21st Century. Authors and networking experts share the nuts, bolts and savvy secrets that businesswomen need in order to use technology to build professional relationships. **Availability:** Print; Online; PDF.

21968 ■ "Scientific American Builds Novel Blog Network" in Information Today (Vol. 28, September 2011, No. 8, pp. 12)
Pub: Information Today Inc.
Contact: Thomas H. Hogan, President
Ed: Kurt Schiller. **Description:** Scientific American launched a new blog network that joins a diverse lineup of bloggers cover various scientific topics under one banner. The blog network includes 60 bloggers providing insights into the ever-changing world of science and technology.

21969 ■ "Search and Discover New Opportunities" in DM News (Vol. 31, December 14, 2009, No. 29, pp. 13)
Pub: Haymarket Media Inc.
Contact: Kevin Costello, Chief Executive Officer
Ed: Chantal Tode. **Description:** Although other digital strategies are gaining traction in Internet marketing, search marketing continues to dominate this advertising forum. Companies like American Greetings, which markets e-card brands online, are utilizing social networking sites and affiliates to generate a higher demand for their products. **Availability:** Print; Online.

21970 ■ "The Secret to Keeping a School Supplies Store Open in the Amazon Era" in The New York Times (September 13, 2018)
URL(s): www.nytimes.com/2018/09/13/nyregion/the -secret-to-keeping-a-school-supplies-store-open-in -the-amazon-era.html
Ed: Fabrice Robinet. **Released:** September 13, 2018. **Description:** Amazon has once again helped cause the demise of a once-booming business — the teacher supply store. Thousands used to be open around the country, but nowadays there are only a few hundred. Still, those that are still around do well because of the customer service they provide, plus it's once stop shopping for teachers and they can see all of the merchandise in one setting. **Availability:** Online.

21971 ■ "Securing our Cyber Status" in San Antonio Business Journal (Vol. 28, May 16, 2014, No. 14, pp. 4)
Pub: American City Business Journals, Inc.
Contact: Mike Olivieri, Executive Vice President
Released: Weekly. **Price:** $4, introductory 4-week offer(Digital & Print). **Description:** The San Antonio Chamber of Commerce commissioned Deloitte to conduct a study on the local cyber security sector of San Antonio, Texas. Industry insiders are looking forward to securing the status of San Antonio as a top tier cyber city with the results of the study research. **Availability:** Print; Online.

21972 ■ Selling Online: Canada's Bestselling Guide to Becoming a Successful E-Commerce Merchant
Description: Helps individuals build online retail enterprises; this updated version includes current tools, information and success strategies, how to launch an online storefront, security, marketing strategies, and mistakes to avoid. **Availability:** Online.

21973 ■ The SEO Manifesto: A Practical and Ethical Guide to Internet Marketing and Search Engine Optimization
Description: Comprehensive guide for each phase of launching an online business; chapters include checklists, process descriptions, and examples.

21974 ■ "Shellshocked: Dealing With Cyber Insecurity" in Philadelphia Business Journal (Vol. 33, June 13, 2014, No. 18, pp. 4)
Pub: American City Business Journals, Inc.
Contact: Mike Olivieri, Executive Vice President
Description: The threat of cyber theft or data breach is increasing globally as technology becomes advanced and more companies start storing their important data electronically. Therefore, the importance of cyber security has increased. Although big businesses suffer more from data breaches, small companies can also take a beating if data breach happens. A survey found that small businesses were wary of spending money on security issues; good investment in IT and creating a privacy policy will help companies fight cyber threats. **Availability:** Online.

21975 ■ "Silverpop Recognised for Email Marketing Innovations by Econsultancy" in Marketing Weekly News (January 23, 2010, pp. 124)
Pub: Investment Weekly News
Description: Econsultancy, a respected source of insight and advice on digital marketing and e-commerce, recognized Silverpop, the world's only provider of both marketing automation solutions and email marketing specifically tailored to the unique needs of B2C and B2B marketers at Econsultancy's 2009 Innovation Awards. **Availability:** Online.

21976 ■ "Skype Ltd. Acquired GroupMe" in Information Today (Vol. 28, October 2011, No. 9, pp. 12)
Description: Skype Ltd. acquired GroupMe, a group messaging company that allows users to form impromptu groups where they can text message,

share data, and make conference calls for free and is supported on Android, iPhone, BlackBerry, and Windows phones. **Availability:** Print; Online.

21977 ■ *"Small Budget, Big Impact" in Small Business Opportunities (Summer 2010)*
Pub: Harris Publishing, Inc.
Contact: Janet Chase, Contact
Description: Ways to use social media to get in from of a target audience for small businesses are examined. **Availability:** Online.

21978 ■ *Small Business Ecommerce: How to Go Digital in a Big Market*
URL(s): www.bigcommerce.com/articles/ecommerce/small-business-ecommerce/
Description: Presents information on the importance of small businesses having an e-commerce component, describes 3 types of e-commerce solutions and things to consider when selecting the small business e-commerce platform for your company. **Availability:** Online.

21979 ■ *The Social Media Bible: Tactics, Tools, and Strategies for Business Success*
Pub: John Wiley & Sons, Inc.
Contact: Christina Van Tassell, Executive Vice President Chief Financial Officer
Ed: Lon Safko. **Released:** Third edition. **Price:** $29.95, paperback; $19.99, E-Book. **Description:** Information is given to build or transform a business into social media, where customers, employees, and prospects connect, collaborate, and champion products and services in order to increase sales and to beat the competition. **Availability:** E-book; Print.

21980 ■ *"Social Media Conference NW 2010" in Bellingham Business Journal (Vol. February 2010, pp. 3)*
Pub: Sound Publishing Inc.
Contact: Josh O'Connor, President
Ed: Lance Henderson. **Description:** Center for Economic Vitality (CEV) and the Technology Alliance Group (TAG) will host the 2010 Social Media Conference at the McIntyre Hall Performing Arts & Conference Center in Mt. Vernon, Washington. The event will provide networking opportunities for attendees.

21981 ■ *"Social Media By the Numbers: Social-Media Marketing Is All the Rage" in Inc. (Vol. 33, November 2011, No. 9, pp. 70)*
Pub: Inc. Magazine
Ed: J.J. McCorvey, Issie Lapowsky. **Description:** Six strategies to help small businesses use social media sites such as Facebook and Twitter to promote their companies are presented. **Availability:** Online.

21982 ■ *"Social Networks in the Workplace: The Risk and Opportunity of Business 2.0" in Strategy & Leadership (Vol. 38, July-August 2010, No. 4, pp. 50-53)*
Pub: Emerald Inc.
Ed: Daniel Burrus. **Description:** The opinions of futurist Daniel Burrus on a novel trend called 'Business 2.0', which involves the use of social networking applications as business tools, are presented. His suggestion that personal social networking technology can be used by businesses to improve collaboration, problem solving, and leadership communications to achieve continuous value innovation is discussed. **Availability:** Online.

21983 ■ *"Social Safety, Thanks to New App" in Providence Business News (Vol. 29, July 21, 2014, No. 16, pp. 10)*
Pub: American City Business Journals, Inc.
Contact: Mike Olivieri, Executive Vice President
URL(s): pbn.com/social-safety-thanks-to-new-app98633
Description: Middletown-based Vizsafe Inc. has developed the Vizsafe application (app) for public safety and community engagement and is offering it to police departments and to citizens at no cost. Vizsafe president and CEO, Peter Mottur, asserts that the 24/7 crowdsourcing platform is available to smartphone users and can be used as an additional safety resource by individuals and emergency responders. **Telecommunication Services:** Miller@pbn.com.

21984 ■ *"Sounders Kicking Ball to Fans" in Puget Sound Business Journal (Vol. 29, November 28, 2008, No. 32, pp. 1)*
Ed: Greg Lamm. **Description:** Major League Soccer expansion team, Seattle Sounders FC, hopes to build fan support leading to its inaugural season 2009-2010 by tapping online social networks. The club launched fan clubs with actual powers over its decision making and Websites similar to Facebook. **Availability:** Print; Online.

21985 ■ *"Spanish Company to Offer Free Wi-Fi In Miami-Dade County" in South Florida Business Journal (Vol. 34, April 25, 2014, No. 40)*
Pub: American City Business Journals, Inc.
Contact: Mike Olivieri, Executive Vice President
Released: Weekly. **Description:** GOWEX a Madrid-based company, is offering free Wi-Fi access at 400 public spots in Miami, Florida. The firm will sell advertising over the Wi-Fi network. It has offered similar free access to users in New York, NY and in San Francisco, CA. **Availability:** Print; Online.

21986 ■ *"Spinout Success: New Leadership Steps In At UW's C4C" in Puget Sound Business Journal (Vol. 35, June 27, 2014, No. 10, pp. 11)*
Pub: American City Business Journals, Inc.
Contact: Mike Olivieri, Executive Vice President
Description: University of Washington's Center for Commercialization vice provost, Vikram Jandhyala, talks about his new position with the school. Jandhyala says he plans to build more synergy between the medical school and engineering and between social sciences and computer science. He also says the medical and software industry need to grow to accommodate the volume of data crossing and stored within the Internet. **Availability:** Online.

21987 ■ *"Start: Punch Fear in the Face, Escape Average and Do Work that Matters"*
Pub: Ramsey Press
Contact: Dave Ramsey, Chief Executive Officer
Released: April 22, 2013. **Price:** $22.99, Hardcover. **Description:** Three things have occurred that have changed the predictable stages of success. Boomers have started second and third careers. Technology has given access to unprecedented number of people who are building online empires, thus changing their lives. The days of success first, significance later have ended. All stages must be experienced but there are only two paths in life: average and awesome. Tips for building an awesome life or business are included. **Availability:** Print.

21988 ■ *"Sylvie Collection Offers a Feminine Perspective and Voice in Male Dominated Bridal Industry" in Benzinga.com (October 29, 2011)*
Description: Bridal jewelry designer Sylvie Levine has created over 1,000 customizable styles of engagement rings and wedding bands and is reaching out to prospective new brides through a new Website, interactive social media campaign and monthly trunk show appearances. **Availability:** Online.

21989 ■ *"Target to Power New Toys 'R' Us Online Business" in Reuters (October 8, 2019)*
URL(s): www.reuters.com/article/us-target-toys-r-us/target-to-power-new-toys-r-us-online-business-idUSKBN1WN1GG
Released: October 08, 2019. **Description:** Target announced a partnership with Tru Kids, which is the parent of the Toys 'R' Us brand, in order to run their toy website, ToysRUs.com. Consumers have the option to complete their purchase at Target.com. **Availability:** Online.

21990 ■ *"ThredUp Is Helping Big Stores Sell Recyled Clothes" in Quartzy (August 21, 2019)*
URL(s): qz.com/quartzy/1692050/thredup-is-giving-retailers-a-plug-and-play-platform-to-sell-used-clothes/
Ed: Marc Bain. **Released:** August 21, 2019. **Description:** ThredUp has announced its new program, Resale-As-A-Servie (RAAS), which will allow big box clothes retailers to sell directly from its used clothing inventory. **Availability:** Online.

21991 ■ *"Three Ways to Power Up Mobile Marketing" in South Florida Business Journal (Vol. 34, July 18, 2014, No. 52, pp. 12)*
Pub: American City Business Journals, Inc.
Contact: Mike Olivieri, Executive Vice President
Released: Weekly. **Price:** $8, introductory 4-week offer(Digital only). **Description:** A number of strategies that companies can apply to prepare for the future reality of mobile marketing are provided. Companies are encouraged to start the change to accommodate the new mobile world as mobile traffic data is projected to increase in record numbers and mobile connected devices will reach over 10 billion by 2007. **Availability:** Print; Online.

21992 ■ *"Tim Tebow Foundation to Hold Pink 'Cleats for a Cure' Auction" in Travel & Leisure Close-Up (October 20, 2011)*
Pub: Close-Up Media Inc.
Contact: Caroline S. Moore, President
E-mail: cms@closeupmedia.com
Description: Tim Tebow Foundation partnered with XV Enterprises to hold the 'Cleats for a Cure' auction on eBay. Tebow is auctioning off a pair of pink cleans he wore during the Denver Broncos vs. Tennessee Titans game October 3, 2010. All funds will go toward finding a cure for breast cancer. **Availability:** Print; Online.

21993 ■ *"Tool-o-Rama" in Barron's (Vol. 90, September 6, 2010, No. 36)*
Pub: Barron's Editorial & Corporate Headquarters
Ed: Theresa W. Carey. **Description:** New trading tool features from several online brokers are discussed. The new features from Fidelity, ChoiceTrade, JunoTrade and TradeKing are examined. Investors can now screen exchanged traded funds in the same way as stocks with Fidelity, while ChoiceTrade can run in any browser without the need to install additional plug-ins. **Availability:** Online.

21994 ■ *"Top E-Commerce Challenges Facing SMBs" in Business News Daily (Feb. 18, 2022)*
URL(s): www.businessnewsdaily.com/6028-small-ecommerce-challenges.html
Ed: Jennifer Post. **Released:** February 18, 2022. **Description:** An article for e-commerce business owners about facing and overcoming common e-commerce challenges. **Availability:** Online.

21995 ■ *"Travel Tech: 4 Gadgets for Running Your Business on the Fly" in Entrepreneur (May 2014)*
Pub: Entrepreneur Media Inc.
Contact: Dan Bova, Director
E-mail: dbova@entrepreneur.com
Description: The Goal Zero Sherpa 100 Power Pack includes two USB ports, a 12-volt plug and a proprietary laptop port that can fill a MacBook Air's battery faster on a single charge. The Nomad ChargeKey is lightweight, flexible and allows users to connect their spent smartphones to any full-size USB outlet. The Jawbone Era Bluetooth headset features a sleek carrying case that also functions as a battery-powered charger. The Belkin WeMo Insight Switch is a mobile wall plug that connects to a Wi-Fi and links to smartphones through an application. **Availability:** Online.

21996 ■ *"Try a Little Social Media" in American Printer (Vol. 128, June 1, 2011, No. 6)*
Description: Social media helps keep Ussery Printing on customers radar. Jim David, VP of marketing

21997 ■ *"TW Trade Shows to Offer Seminars On Niche Selling, Social Media"* in *Travel Weekly* (Vol. 69, October 4, 2010, No. 40, pp. 9)
Pub: NorthStar Travel Media
Description: Travel Weekly's Leisure World 2010 and Fall Home Based Travel Agent Show focused on niche selling, with emphasis on all-inclusives, young consumers, groups, incentives, culinary vacations, and honeymoon or romance travel. **Availability:** Print; Online.

21998 ■ *"Twitter Hack: Made in Japan? User Says Attack Showed Security Flaw"* in *Houston Chronicle* (September 24, 2010, pp. 3)
Description: Details of the attack on Twitter caused by a Japanese computer hacker are revealed. **Availability:** Print; Mailing list; Online.

21999 ■ *"Ultimate Guide to Google AdWords: How to Access 100 Million People in 10 Minutes"*
Pub: Entrepreneur Media Inc.
Contact: Dan Bova, Director
E-mail: dbova@entrepreneur.com
Released: 5th edition. **Price:** $24.95, paperback. **Description:** The Google AdWords experts and analytics specialist present the techniques, tools, and tricks for using Google AdWords. The experts help small businesses to write advertising and Web site copy design, work in difficult markets, advertise, increase search engine presence, bid strategies for online auctions, financial budgeting and more. **Availability:** Print.

22000 ■ *"Up To Code? Website Eases Compliance Burden for Entrepreneurs"* in *Black Enterprise* (Vol. 38, March 1, 2008, No. 8, pp. 48)
Pub: Earl G. Graves Ltd.
Contact: Earl Graves, Jr., President
Ed: Robin White-Goode. **Description:** Business.gov is a presidential E-government project created to help small businesses easily find, understand, and comply with laws and regulations pertaining to a particular industry. **Availability:** Online.

22001 ■ *"UPMC Develops Own Billing Solutions"* in *Pittsburgh Business Times* (Vol. 33, January 17, 2014, No. 27, pp. 6)
Pub: American City Business Journals, Inc.
Contact: Mike Olivieri, Executive Vice President
Description: How University of Pittsburgh Medical Center (UPMC) Health System transformed its accounts payable department by passing its process to a subsidiary, Prodigo Solutions, is discussed. UPMC moved suppliers and purchasers to a shared electronic platform and created a digital marketplace. The system's no purchase order, no pay policy has reduced the number of rogue purchases. **Availability:** Online.

22002 ■ *"Uptick in Clicks: Nordstrom's Online Sales Surging"* in *Puget Sound Business Journal* (Vol. 29, August 22, 2008, No. 18, pp. 1)
Description: Nordstrom Inc.'s online division grew its sales by 15 percent in the second quarter of 2008, compared to 2007's 4.3 percent in overall decline. The company expects their online net sales to reach $700 million in 2008 capturing eight percent of overall sales. **Availability:** Print; Online.

22003 ■ *"Vision Statement: Mapping the Social Internet"* in *Harvard Business Review* (Vol. 88, July-August 2010, No. 7-8, pp. 32)
Pub: Harvard Business Publishing
Contact: Diane Belcher, Managing Director
Ed: Mikolaj Jan Piskorski, Tommy McCall. **Price:** $6, PDF. **Description:** Chart compares and contrasts online social networks in selected countries. **Availability:** Online; PDF.

22004 ■ *"Vistaprint Survey Indicates that Online Marketing Taking Hold Among Small Businesses"* in *Marketwired* (December 10, 2009)
Pub: Comtex News Network Inc.
Contact: Kan Devnani, President
Description: According to a comprehensive survey from Vistaprint N.V., small businesses are very likely to increase their use of Internet marketing strategies such as paid and organic search, email marketing, social media networking and custom websites over the next year. Trends continue to show that more small businesses are indeed adapting to the changing marketplace and are more willing to diversify their marketing strategies than ever before. **Availability:** Print; Online.

22005 ■ *"Web-Based Marketing Excites, Challenges Small Business Use"* in *Colorado Springs Business Journal* (January 20, 2010)
Pub: BridgeTower Media
Contact: Adam Reinebach, President
Ed: Becky Hurley. **Description:** Business-to-business and consumer-direct firms alike are using the fast-changing Web technologies to increase sales, leads and track consumer behavior but once a company commits to an Online marketing plan, experts believe, they must be prepared to consistently tweak and overhaul content and distribution vehicles in order to keep up. **Availability:** Online.

22006 ■ *"Web to Print"* in *American Printer* (Vol. 128, August 1, 2011, No. 8)
Description: Jerry Kennelly, CEO and founder of Tweak.com believes that Web-to-Design is middleware with no content. His firm offers an easy to use interface that flows right into the printer's workflow with no additional costs. **Availability:** Online.

22007 ■ *"Web Translation Made Simple"* in *Inc.* (Vol. 33, October 2011, No. 8, pp. 44)
Pub: Inc. Magazine
Ed: Adam Baer. **Description:** Smartling is a Web-based service that translates sites into more than 50 foreign languages. The software will begin translation right after setting up the account. **Availability:** Online.

22008 ■ *"What the Future Holds for Consumers"* in *Black Enterprise* (Vol. 41, August 2010, No. 1, pp. 47)
Pub: Earl G. Graves Ltd.
Contact: Earl Graves, Jr., President
Ed: Sheiresa Ngo. **Description:** The way people purchase goods and service has changed with technology. With an increased focus on security (as well as privacy and fairness) the U.S. Congress began regulating the credit card industry with the Fair Credit Reporting Act of 1970 and the Credit Card Accountability, Responsibility, and Disclosure (CARD) Act of 2009. **Availability:** Online.

22009 ■ *"What Marketers Misunderstand about Online Reviews: Managers Must Analyze What's Really Driving Buying Decisions - and Adjust Their Strategies Accordingly"* in *Harvard Business Review* (Vol. 92, January-February 2014, No. 1-2, pp. 23)
Pub: Harvard Business Press
Contact: Gabriela Allmi, Regional Manager
E-mail: gabriela.allmi@hbsp.harvard.edu
Price: $6, hardcopy black and white. **Description:** Companies may overestimate the influence of online reviews, as consumers do not turn to reviews for certain products and services (for example, habitual low-involvement purchases such as groceries). Others' opinions matter more for purchases such as independent restaurants and electronics. **Availability:** Print; PDF; Online.

22010 ■ *"What Online Brokers Are Doing To Keep Their Customers' Accounts Safe"* in *Barron's* (Vol. 88, March 10, 2008, No. 10, pp. 37)
Pub: Dow Jones & Company Inc.
Contact: Almar Latour, Chief Executive Officer
Ed: Theresa W. Carey. **Description:** Online brokerage firms employ different methods to protect the accounts of their customers from theft. These methods include secure Internet connections, momentary passwords, and proprietary algorithms. **Availability:** Online.

22011 ■ *"What's Your Social Media Strategy?"* in *Black Enterprise* (Vol. 41, November 2010, No. 4, pp. 75)
Pub: Earl G. Graves Ltd.
Contact: Earl Graves, Jr., President
Ed: Denise A. Campbell. **Description:** Advice for using social media sites such as Twitter, Facebook and LinkedIn as a professional networking tool is given. **Availability:** Online.

22012 ■ *Why Every Small Business Should Engage in E-Commerce?*
URL(s): www.coverwallet.com/business-tips/advantages-of-ecommerce-for-small-business
Description: Discusses the importance of creating a strong online presence via e-commerce activities to facilitate growth and expand the scope of your business. **Availability:** Online.

22013 ■ *"Why LinkedIn is the Social Network that Will Never Die"* in *Advertising Age* (Vol. 81, December 6, 2010, No. 43, pp. 2)
Pub: Crain Communications, Inc.
Contact: Jessica Botos, Manager, Marketing
E-mail: jessica.botos@crainsnewyork.com
Ed: Irina Slutsky. **Description:** Despite the popularity of Facebook, LinkedIn in will always be a source for professionals who wish to network. **Availability:** Online.

22014 ■ *"Why Some Get Shafted By Google Pricing"* in *Advertising Age* (Vol. 79, July 14, 2008, No. 7, pp. 3)
Pub: Crain Communications, Inc.
Contact: Jessica Botos, Manager, Marketing
E-mail: jessica.botos@crainsnewyork.com
Ed: Abbey Klaassen. **Description:** Google's search advertising is discussed as well as the company's pricing structure for these ads. **Availability:** Online.

22015 ■ *"Why We'll Never Escape Facebook"* in *Canadian Business* (Vol. 83, June 15, 2010, No. 10, pp. 28)
Pub: Rogers Media Inc.
Contact: Neil Spivak, Chief Executive Officer
Ed: James Cowan, Tamara Shopsin, Jason Fulford. **Description:** Facebook users are growing in numbers despite criticism of the site's privacy policies that have put the onus of keeping anonymous to the user. Facebook's business model and its growing influence on the Internet are discussed. **Availability:** Online.

22016 ■ *"Why You Need a New-Media 'Ringmaster"* in *Harvard Business Review* (Vol. 88, December 2010, No. 12, pp. 78)
Pub: Harvard Business Publishing
Contact: Diane Belcher, Managing Director
Ed: Patrick Spenner. **Price:** $8.95, PDF. **Description:** The concept of ringmaster is applied to brand marketing. This concept includes integrative thinking, lean collaboration skills, and high-speed decision cycles. **Availability:** Online; PDF.

22017 ■ *Wikinomics: How Mass Collaboration Changes Everything*
Pub: Penguin Publishing Group
Ed: Don Tapscott, Anthony D. Williams, Anthony D. Williams. **Released:** September 28, 2010. **Price:** $16.93, paperback; $8.99, e-book; $12.77, audio; $17, paperback; $13.99. **Description:** Research and information about the every changing world of the Internet is provided to help small businesses. **Availability:** E-book; Print; Electronic publishing.

22018 ■ *"Will mCommerce Make Black Friday Green?"* in *Retail Merchandiser* (Vol. 51, September-October 2011, No. 5, pp. 8)
Description: Retailers speculate the possibilities of mobile commerce and are implementing strategies at their stores. Consumers using mobile devices ac-

counted for only 0.1 percent of visits to retail Websites on Black Friday 2009 and rose to 5.6 percent in 2010; numbers are expected to rise for 2011. **Availability:** Print; Online.

22019 ■ *"Women Clicking to Earn Virtual Dollars" in Sales and Marketing Management (November 11, 2009)*
Ed: Stacy Straczynski. **Description:** According to a new report from Internet marketing firm Q Interactive, women are increasingly playing social media games where they are able to click on an ad or sign up for a promotion to earn virtual currency. Research is showing that this kind of marketing may be a potent tool, especially for e-commerce and online stores. **Availability:** Print; Online.

22020 ■ *"WordStream Announces a Pair of Firsts for SEO & PPC Keyword Research Tools" in Marketwired (November 10, 2009)*
Pub: Comtex News Network Inc.
Contact: Kan Devnani, President
Description: WordSteam, Inc., a provider of pay-per-click (PPC) and search engine optimization (SEO) solutions for continuously expanding and optimizing search marketing efforts has released two new features in their flagship Keyword Management solution; these tools will allow marketers to analyze data from paid search, organic search and estimated totals from keyword suggestion tools side-by-side. **Availability:** Print; Online.

22021 ■ *"Xtium Has Its Head in the Clouds" in Philadelphia Business Journal (Vol. 30, September 23, 2011, No. 32, pp. 1)*
Pub: Philadelphia Business Journal
Contact: Sierra Quinn, Director
E-mail: squinn@bizjournals.com
Ed: Peter Key. **Description:** Philadelphia-based cloud computing firm Xtium LLC received an $11.5 million first-round investment from Boston-Massachusetts-based OpenView Venture Partners. Catering to midsize businesses and unit of bigger firms, Xtium offers disaster-recovery, hosting, and managed-information-technology-infrastructure services. **Availability:** Online.

22022 ■ *"The Yahoo Family Tree" in Conde Nast Portfolio (Vol. 2, June 2008, No. 6, pp. 34)*
Pub: Conde Nast Publications
Contact: Agnes Chu, President
Ed: Blaise Zerega. **Description:** Yahoo, founded in 1994 by Stanford students Jerry Yang and David Filo, is still an Internet powerhouse. The company's history is also outlined as well as the reasons in which Microsoft desperately wants to acquire the firm. **Availability:** Print.

22023 ■ *"Yammer Gets Serious" in Inc. (Volume 32, December 2010, No. 10, pp. 58)*
Pub: Inc. Magazine
Ed: Eric Markowitz. **Description:** Yammer, an internal social network for companies, allows coworkers to share ideas and documents in real-time. Details of this service are included. **Availability:** Online.

22024 ■ *Your First Year in Real Estate: Making the Transition from Total Novice to Successful Professional*
Released: Second edition. **Price:** $22, paperback; $9.99, e-book. **Description:** Zeller helps new realtors to select the right company, develop mentor and client relationships, using the Internet and social networking to stay ahead of competition, to set and reach career goals, to stay current in the market, and more. **Availability:** E-book; Print.

22025 ■ *"The Zero Marginal Cost Society: The Internet of Things, the Collaborative Commons, and the Eclipse of Capitalism"*
Pub: Palgrave Macmillan
Released: April 04, 2014. **Price:** $18.99, paperback; $9.99, e-book; $29.99, hardcover. **Description:** The emerging Internet of things is speeding society to an ear of nearly free goods and services, causing the rise of a global Collaborative Commons and the eclipse of capitalism. Entrepreneurial dynamism of competitive markets that drives productivity up and marginal costs down, enabling businesses to reduce the price of their goods and services to win consumers and market share is slowly dying. **Availability:** E-book; Print.

VIDEO/AUDIO MEDIA

22026 ■ *How I Built This: Food52: Amanda Hesser*
URL(s): wondery.com/shows/how-i-built-this/episode/10386-food52-amanda-hesser-2021
Ed: Guy Raz. **Released:** March 20, 2023. **Description:** Podcast explains how a food writer gave up her dream job to become an entrepreneur, and how she pivoted when that fizzled to launch Food52.

CONSULTANTS

22027 ■ **BIA/Kelsey**
14901 Bogle Dr., Ste. 101
Chantilly, VA 20151
Ph: (703)818-2425
Co. E-mail: info@bia.com
URL: http://www.bia.com
Contact: Tom Buono, Chief Executive Officer
Facebook: www.facebook.com/biakelsey
Linkedin: www.linkedin.com/company/biaadvisorysrvs
X (Twitter): x.com/BIAAdvisorySvcs
YouTube: www.youtube.com/user/BIAmediacenter
Description: Publishes market and industry reports for the communications industry. Does not accept unsolicited manuscripts. Reaches market through commission representatives, direct mail, reviews and listings and distributors. **Scope:** A provider of research and fact-based analysis focusing on local advertising and electronic commerce. **Founded:** 1983. **Publications:** "Penetration of Online Media Surpasses Traditional Media for First Time Among Small-Business Advertisers," Aug, 2009; "Rapid Adoption of Advanced Mobile Devices Driving Increased Mobile Local Search Activity, According to The Kelsey Group," Nov, 2008; "Online Consumer Generated Reviews Have Significant Impact on Offline Purchase Behavior," Nov, 2007. **Training:** Drilling Down on Local: Marketplaces, The Westin Seattle, Seattle, Washington, Apr, 2008; The Future of Local Search in Europe, London, Jun, 2007; DDC2006?Directory Driven Commerce Conference, Hyatt Century Plaza, LA, Sep, 2006; Drilling Down on Local: Targeting the On-Demand Marketplace, 2005.

22028 ■ **Dominari Holdings Inc.**
1 Rockefeller Plz., 11th Fl.
New York, NY 10020
Ph: (703)992-9325
Co. E-mail: info@aikidopharma.com
URL: http://aikidopharma.com
Contact: Anthony C. Hayes, Chief Executive Officer
Linkedin: www.linkedin.com/spherix
X (Twitter): twitter.com/spherix
Description: An intellectual property company engaged in the ownership, acquisition, development, and monetization of patents, as well as the obtaining of existing rights to already issued patents and pending patent intellectual property assets from inventors and patent owners. Focuses on offering a diversified commercialization platform for protected technologies, with an emphasis on wireless communications and telecommunications sectors, including antenna technology, Wi-Fi, base station functionality, and cellular. **Founded:** 1967. **Publications:** "Viking found no life on Mars, and, just as important, it found why there can be no life". **Special Services:** Naturlose®.

22029 ■ **Organic Inc.**
5353 Grosvenor Blvd.
Los Angeles, CA 90066
Co. E-mail: friends@organic.com
URL: http://www.organic.com
Linkedin: www.linkedin.com/company/organic
Description: Firm provides interaction services between clients and consumers to derive better solutions. **Scope:** Strategic consulting, e-business, marketing solutions, e-commerce website creation, customer service and fulfillment.

PUBLICATIONS

22030 ■ *Handbook of Research on E-Business Standards and Protocols: Documents, Data and Advanced Web Technologies*
701 E Chocolate Ave.
Hershey, PA 17033
Ph: (717)533-8845
Free: 866-342-6657
Fax: (717)533-8661
Co. E-mail: cust@igi-global.com
URL: http://www.igi-global.com
Contact: Jan Travers, Director
URL(s): www.igi-global.com/book/handbook-research-business-standards-protocols/58279
Released: Latest Issue February, 2012. **Price:** $470, for hardcover; $565, for hardcover + e-book; $37.50, for on demand (individual chapters); $470, for e-book. **Description:** Published by IGI Global. Contains an overview of new achievements in the field of e-business standards and protocols, offers in-depth analysis of and research on the development and deployment of cutting-edge applications, and provides insight into future trends. **Availability:** E-book; Print; PDF.

22031 ■ *Journal of Internet and e-business Studies (JIEBS)*
630 Freedom Business Ctr. Dr., 3rd Fl.
King of Prussia, PA 19406
Fax: (215)867-9992
Co. E-mail: contact@ibimapublishing.com
URL: http://www.ibimapublishing.com
URL(s): ibimapublishing.com/journals/journal-of-internet-and-e-business-studies
Released: Annual; last edition; volume 2024. **Description:** Peer-reviewed journal publishing research, analyses, case studies and reviews relating to internet and electronic business. **Availability:** Print; Online; PDF.

22032 ■ *Plunkett's E-Commerce & Internet Business Almanac*
PO Box 541737
Houston, TX 77254-1737
Ph: (713)932-0000
Fax: (713)932-7080
Co. E-mail: customersupport@plunkettresearch.com
URL: http://www.plunkettresearch.com
Contact: Jack W. Plunkett, Chief Executive Officer
URL(s): www.plunkettresearch.com/printed-book-ebook-plunkett-industry-almanac/?Industry=ecommerce-internet-technology-market-research
Released: Latest edition 2024. **Price:** $399.99, for 2024 eBook or Print. **Description:** Contains comprehensive information on current trends and developments in electronic commerce and Internet business. **Availability:** E-book; Print; Online. **Type:** Full-text; Numeric; Statistical; Directory.

22033 ■ *Social Implications and Challenges of E-Business*
701 E Chocolate Ave.
Hershey, PA 17033
Ph: (717)533-8845
Free: 866-342-6657
Fax: (717)533-8661
Co. E-mail: cust@igi-global.com
URL: http://www.igi-global.com
Contact: Jan Travers, Director
URL(s): www.igi-global.com/book/social-implications-challenges-business/912
Released: Last Updated March, 2007. **Price:** $165, for hardcover; $165, for eBook; $195, for hardcover and eBook; $37.50, for on demand. **Description:** Published by the Business Science Reference division of IGI Global. Explores the profound social implications and challenges of e-business, investigates how the rapid development of the Internet and e-business shapes, and is shaped, by various social forces; and highlights the enormous difficulties and challenges involved in applying e-business technologies and principles in public services and other non-business activities. **Availability:** E-book; Print; PDF; Download.

Employee Motivation/Team Building

EDUCATIONAL PROGRAMS

22034 ■ Administrative Professionals Retreat
National Seminars Training L.L.C. (NST)
  14502 W 105th St.
  Lenexa, KS 66215
Free: 800-349-1935
Co. E-mail: info@findaseminar.com
URL: http://www.findaseminar.com/tpd/Padge
  tt-Thompson-Seminars.asp
URL(s): www.findaseminar.com/event1.asp?eventID
  =8754
Description: A two-day seminar for administrative professionals. **Audience:** Administrative professionals and assistants. **Principal Exhibits:** A two-day seminar for administrative professionals.

22035 ■ Advanced Issues in Employee Relations
Seminar Information Service Inc. (SIS)
  250 El Camino Real., Ste. 112
  Tustin, CA 92780
Ph: (714)508-0340
Free: 877-736-4636
Fax: (714)734-8027
Co. E-mail: info@seminarinformation.com
URL: http://www.seminarinformation.com
Contact: Catherine Bellizzi, President
URL(s): www.seminarinformation.com
Description: Key topics include coaching managers to more effectively manage high performing employees who consistently demonstrate one serious performance failing, collaborating with managers to assist them in focusing on performance issues without being influenced by employees' personal circumstances, working with managers on dealing more effectively with strong negative employee reactions to direction or feedback, and addressing managers' behavior that is inappropriate and potentially high risk. **Audience:** Industry professionals. **Principal Exhibits:** Key topics include coaching managers to more effectively manage high performing employees who consistently demonstrate one serious performance failing, collaborating with managers to assist them in focusing on performance issues without being influenced by employees' personal circumstances, working with managers on dealing more effectively with strong negative employee reactions to direction or feedback, and addressing managers' behavior that is inappropriate and potentially high risk.

22036 ■ AMA Developing Your Personal Brand and Professional Image
American Management Association (AMA)
  1601 Broadway
  New York, NY 10019
Ph: (212)586-8100
Free: 800-262-9699
Fax: (212)903-8168
Co. E-mail: customerservice@amanet.org
URL: http://www.amanet.org
Contact: Manny Avramidis, President
URL(s): www.amanet.org/training/articles/projecting-a
  -positive-professional-image.aspx
Frequency: Continuous. **Description:** Covers creating a self-image, including look, dress, and behavior, to project a positive image in your current position and to advance to new positions. **Audience:** Anyone who is interested in advancing their career by demonstrating more credibility, poise and presence in business interactions, team meetings, presentations and customer interactions both locally and internationally. **Principal Exhibits:** Covers creating a self-image, including look, dress, and behavior, to project a positive image in your current position and to advance to new positions. **Telecommunication Services:** customerservice@amanet.org.

22037 ■ AMA Greater Productivity Through Improved Work Processes: A Guide for Administrative Professionals (Onsite)
URL(s): www.amanet.org
Description: Covers increasing productivity and efficiency, dealing with change, improving your work, and assisting in improving various aspects of the organization. **Audience:** Administrative professionals. **Principal Exhibits:** Covers increasing productivity and efficiency, dealing with change, improving your work, and assisting in improving various aspects of the organization. **Telecommunication Services:** customerservice@amanet.org.

22038 ■ AMA Partnering with Your Boss: Strategic Skills for Administrative Professionals
American Management Association (AMA)
  1601 Broadway
  New York, NY 10019
Ph: (212)586-8100
Free: 800-262-9699
Fax: (212)903-8168
Co. E-mail: customerservice@amanet.org
URL: http://www.amanet.org
Contact: Manny Avramidis, President
URL(s): www.amanet.org/training/seminars/Par
  tnering-with-Your-Boss-Strategic-Skills-for-Adminis
  trative-Professionals.aspx
Frequency: Continuous. **Description:** Covers skills for setting goals, prioritizing, making decisions, building relationships, and communicating in such a way as to represent your boss authoritatively and gain respect in the workplace. **Audience:** Senior administrative support staff, executive secretaries, administrative assistants, staff assistants and executive assistants. **Principal Exhibits:** Covers skills for setting goals, prioritizing, making decisions, building relationships, and communicating in such a way as to represent your boss authoritatively and gain respect in the workplace. **Telecommunication Services:** customerservice@amanet.org.

22039 ■ AMA's Myers-Briggs Type Indicator (MBTI) Certification Program
URL(s): www.amanet.org
Description: Updated MBTI program that focuses on team building, leadership, and individual development. **Audience:** HR professionals, training and OD specialists, career counselors, and line managers. **Principal Exhibits:** Updated MBTI program that focuses on team building, leadership, and individual development.

22040 ■ Assertive Management (Onsite)
Seminar Information Service Inc. (SIS)
  250 El Camino Real., Ste. 112
  Tustin, CA 92780
Ph: (714)508-0340
Free: 877-736-4636
Fax: (714)734-8027
Co. E-mail: info@seminarinformation.com
URL: http://www.seminarinformation.com
Contact: Catherine Bellizzi, President
URL(s): www.seminarinformation.com
Description: Develop the qualities necessary for successful, assertive management. Participants gain confidence and skill in being 'pro-active' in communicating with others, including how to use positive, win-win approaches and to defuse emotionally charged situations in order to work more effectively with their fellow workers, supervisors and subordinates. **Audience:** Supervisors and managers. **Principal Exhibits:** Develop the qualities necessary for successful, assertive management. Participants gain confidence and skill in being 'pro-active' in communicating with others, including how to use positive, win-win approaches and to defuse emotionally charged situations in order to work more effectively with their fellow workers, supervisors and subordinates. **Telecommunication Services:** info@seminarinformation.com.

22041 ■ Basic Problem Solving Techniques (Onsite)
Seminar Information Service Inc. (SIS)
  250 El Camino Real., Ste. 112
  Tustin, CA 92780
Ph: (714)508-0340
Free: 877-736-4636
Fax: (714)734-8027
Co. E-mail: info@seminarinformation.com
URL: http://www.seminarinformation.com
Contact: Catherine Bellizzi, President
URL(s): www.seminarinformation.com
Description: With the help of several qualitative, quantitative, and creative problem solving methods participants develop their ability to recognize and solve problems through their own efforts. **Audience:** Managers, and professionals. **Principal Exhibits:** With the help of several qualitative, quantitative, and creative problem solving methods participants develop their ability to recognize and solve problems through their own efforts.

22042 ■ Building Better Work Relationships: New Techniques for Results-oriented Communication
American Management Association (AMA)
  1601 Broadway
  New York, NY 10019
Ph: (212)586-8100
Free: 800-262-9699
Fax: (212)903-8168

Co. E-mail: customerservice@amanet.org
URL: http://www.amanet.org
Contact: Manny Avramidis, President
URL(s): www.amanet.org/building-better-work-rela tionships-new-techniques-for-results-oriente d-communication
Price: $2,445, Non-members; $2,195, Members AMA; $1,984, Members GSA. **Frequency:** Continuous. **Description:** Covers effective work relationships, communication and perceptions, investigating emotions and emotional intelligence, relationship building, relational communication and listening and more. **Audience:** People who want to build better work relationships, maximize impact, increase productivity, and drive results by applying effective communication and relationship management. **Principal Exhibits:** Covers effective work relationships, communication and perceptions, investigating emotions and emotional intelligence, relationship building, relational communication and listening and more.

22043 ■ Business Conversation for Sales and Service (Onsite)
Seminar Information Service Inc. (SIS)
 250 El Camino Real., Ste. 112
 Tustin, CA 92780
Ph: (714)508-0340
Free: 877-736-4636
Fax: (714)734-8027
Co. E-mail: info@seminarinformation.com
URL: http://www.seminarinformation.com
Contact: Catherine Bellizzi, President
URL(s): www.seminarinformation.com/details.cfm?qc =qqbmve
Description: Participants will learn practical tips and practice conversation. Build common ground with colleagues, customers, and senior managers, including methods to develop a repertoire of topics, make skillful transitions, develop confidence and draw people to you. **Audience:** Business professionals. **Principal Exhibits:** Participants will learn practical tips and practice conversation. Build common ground with colleagues, customers, and senior managers, including methods to develop a repertoire of topics, make skillful transitions, develop confidence and draw people to you.

22044 ■ CMC Leadership and Team Development for Managerial Success
URL(s): cmcoutperform.com/leadership-team -development-managerial-success
Price: $1,845, Members; $1,995, Non-members. **Description:** Covers how to work in a horizontal mode of operation, including when to manage and when to lead your team, distinguishing the three team types, principles that make teams work, differentiating team content and process, and diagnosing work teams. **Audience:** Executives, managers, team leaders and business professionals. **Principal Exhibits:** Covers how to work in a horizontal mode of operation, including when to manage and when to lead your team, distinguishing the three team types, principles that make teams work, differentiating team content and process, and diagnosing work teams. **Telecommunication Services:** cmcinfo@cmctraining.org.

22045 ■ Coaching and Teambuilding Skills for Managers and Supervisors (Onsite)
Seminar Information Service Inc. (SIS)
 250 El Camino Real., Ste. 112
 Tustin, CA 92780
Ph: (714)508-0340
Free: 877-736-4636
Fax: (714)734-8027
Co. E-mail: info@seminarinformation.com
URL: http://www.seminarinformation.com
Contact: Catherine Bellizzi, President
URL(s): www.seminarinformation.com/details.cfm?qc =qqayxm
Description: Gain team building expertise guaranteed to make your team more cohesive, motivated, and productive. **Audience:** Managers and supervisors. **Principal Exhibits:** Gain team building expertise guaranteed to make your team more cohesive, motivated, and productive.

22046 ■ Criticism & Discipline Skills for Managers and Supervisors (Onsite)
URL(s): www.pryor.com/training-seminars/criticism -discipline-skills-managers-supervisors
Description: Learn proven techniques for managing difficult employees without incurring resentment, making enemies, or destroying relationships, including how to discipline employees who have a bad attitude, are chronically tardy, miss work often, refuse to take responsibility and challenge your authority. **Audience:** Industry professionals. **Principal Exhibits:** Learn proven techniques for managing difficult employees without incurring resentment, making enemies, or destroying relationships, including how to discipline employees who have a bad attitude, are chronically tardy, miss work often, refuse to take responsibility and challenge your authority.

22047 ■ Effective Communication and Motivation (Onsite)
Seminar Information Service Inc. (SIS)
 250 El Camino Real., Ste. 112
 Tustin, CA 92780
Ph: (714)508-0340
Free: 877-736-4636
Fax: (714)734-8027
Co. E-mail: info@seminarinformation.com
URL: http://www.seminarinformation.com
Contact: Catherine Bellizzi, President
URL(s): www.seminarinformation.com
Description: Gives managerial personnel a sound understanding of the principles of effective communication and the skill to recognize and to resolve communication breakdowns in the workplace. Participants learn to apply communication skills to problem solving, employee relations and performance appraisal. **Audience:** General public, industry professionals. **Principal Exhibits:** Gives managerial personnel a sound understanding of the principles of effective communication and the skill to recognize and to resolve communication breakdowns in the workplace. Participants learn to apply communication skills to problem solving, employee relations and performance appraisal.

22048 ■ The Effective Facilitator
URL(s): cmcoutperform.com
Description: Covers achieving positive results in group settings such as meetings, project teams, and group work projects. **Audience:** Facilitators. **Principal Exhibits:** Covers achieving positive results in group settings such as meetings, project teams, and group work projects. **Telecommunication Services:** cmcinfo@cmcoutperform.com.

22049 ■ The Effective Facilitator: Maximizing Involvement and Results
American Management Association (AMA)
 1601 Broadway
 New York, NY 10019
Ph: (212)586-8100
Free: 800-262-9699
Fax: (212)903-8168
Co. E-mail: customerservice@amanet.org
URL: http://www.amanet.org
Contact: Manny Avramidis, President
URL(s): www.amanet.org/training/seminars/The-Effec tive-Facilitator-Maximizing-Involvement-and-Results .aspx
Price: $2,445, Non-members; $2,195, Members; $1,984, General Services Administration (GSA). **Frequency:** Continuous. **Description:** Covers achieving positive results in group settings such as meetings, project teams, and group work projects. Held in Chicago, IL; Atlanta, GA; Arlington, VA; and Washington, DC. Also available live online. **Audience:** Managers and internal consultants. **Principal Exhibits:** Covers achieving positive results in group settings such as meetings, project teams, and group work projects. Held in Chicago, IL; Atlanta, GA; Arlington, VA; and Washington, DC. Also available live online.

22050 ■ Effective Project Communications, Negotiations and Conflict (Onsite)
URL(s): www.eeicom.com
Description: Learn what you need to know to lead projects through their initiation, planning, execution, and control phases, including the skills needed to find common ground, overcome resistance, resolve disputes, and gain commitment to project management efforts. **Audience:** Industry professionals, administrative. **Principal Exhibits:** Learn what you need to know to lead projects through their initiation, planning, execution, and control phases, including the skills needed to find common ground, overcome resistance, resolve disputes, and gain commitment to project management efforts.

22051 ■ Enhancing Your Management Skills (Onsite)
Seminar Information Service Inc. (SIS)
 250 El Camino Real., Ste. 112
 Tustin, CA 92780
Ph: (714)508-0340
Free: 877-736-4636
Fax: (714)734-8027
Co. E-mail: info@seminarinformation.com
URL: http://www.seminarinformation.com
Contact: Catherine Bellizzi, President
URL(s): www.seminarinformation.com/qqbsee/ enhancing-your-management-skills
Description: Learn the critical success factors for driving results through goal alignment, coaching for performance, building trust, and driving committed action through stronger leadership. Receive practical, state-of-the-art tools and techniques for holding conversations that set clear expectations, provide focused feedback, create a motivational environment, and build commitment for needed change. **Audience:** Industry professionals. **Principal Exhibits:** Learn the critical success factors for driving results through goal alignment, coaching for performance, building trust, and driving committed action through stronger leadership. Receive practical, state-of-the-art tools and techniques for holding conversations that set clear expectations, provide focused feedback, create a motivational environment, and build commitment for needed change.

22052 ■ Enhancing Your People Skills
Seminar Information Service Inc. (SIS)
 250 El Camino Real., Ste. 112
 Tustin, CA 92780
Ph: (714)508-0340
Free: 877-736-4636
Fax: (714)734-8027
Co. E-mail: info@seminarinformation.com
URL: http://www.seminarinformation.com
Contact: Catherine Bellizzi, President
URL(s): www.seminarinformation.com
Description: Build awareness and skill in the areas of team dynamics, group problem solving, and group decision making. The critical structural and behavioral dimensions of building and leading an effective work team or task force are fully explored. You will develop leadership skills applicable to many areas, but especially suited to self-directed work teams, employee participation teams, interdepartmental task groups, and other group situations where combined efforts are needed to reach optimal performance levels. **Audience:** General public. **Principal Exhibits:** Build awareness and skill in the areas of team dynamics, group problem solving, and group decision making. The critical structural and behavioral dimensions of building and leading an effective work team or task force are fully explored. You will develop leadership skills applicable to many areas, but especially suited to self-directed work teams, employee participation teams, interdepartmental task groups, and other group situations where combined efforts are needed to reach optimal performance levels.

22053 ■ Essential Skills for the First-Time Manager or Supervisor (Onsite)
URL(s): www.pryor.com
Description: Gain all the skills and insights you need to lead with confidence and conviction, including how to start producing results right away, what it takes to get productivity from people who aren't used to you being the boss. **Audience:** Manager and supervisor.

Principal Exhibits: Gain all the skills and insights you need to lead with confidence and conviction, including how to start producing results right away, what it takes to get productivity from people who aren't used to you being the boss.

22054 ■ Fred Pryor Seminars & CareerTrack
The Exceptional Assistant
Fred Pryor Seminars & CareerTrack
5700 Broadmoor, Ste. 300
Mission, KS 66202
Free: 800-780-8476
Fax: (913)967-8849
Co. E-mail: customerservice@pryor.com
URL: http://www.pryor.com
Contact: Janet Turner, Contact
E-mail: dmca@pryor.com
URL(s): www.pryor.com/training-seminars/exceptional-assistant

Frequency: Irregular. **Description:** Covers the necessary skills for success, including prioritizing, problem solving, political and people skills, managing time and resources, crises and decision making. **Audience:** Administrative professionals. **Principal Exhibits:** Covers the necessary skills for success, including prioritizing, problem solving, political and people skills, managing time and resources, crises and decision making.

22055 ■ How to Be a Dynamic Trainer (Onsite)
Seminar Information Service Inc. (SIS)
250 El Camino Real., Ste. 112
Tustin, CA 92780
Ph: (714)508-0340
Free: 877-736-4636
Fax: (714)734-8027
Co. E-mail: info@seminarinformation.com
URL: http://www.seminarinformation.com
Contact: Catherine Bellizzi, President
URL(s): www.seminarinformation.com

Description: Learn how to motivate reluctant learners and how to engage learners to get them to participate. **Audience:** Trainers, training managers, HR professionals, team leaders, supervisors, managers and educators. **Principal Exhibits:** Learn how to motivate reluctant learners and how to engage learners to get them to participate.

22056 ■ How to Be a Highly Successful Team Leader (Onsite)
Seminar Information Service Inc. (SIS)
250 El Camino Real., Ste. 112
Tustin, CA 92780
Ph: (714)508-0340
Free: 877-736-4636
Fax: (714)734-8027
Co. E-mail: info@seminarinformation.com
URL: http://www.seminarinformation.com
Contact: Catherine Bellizzi, President
URL(s): www.seminarinformation.com

Description: Intensive two-day workshop that teaches the many dimensions of effective leadership and develop the skills needed to lead your team to maximum performance. **Audience:** New team leaders. **Principal Exhibits:** Intensive two-day workshop that teaches the many dimensions of effective leadership and develop the skills needed to lead your team to maximum performance.

22057 ■ Leadership Skills: Building Success Through Teamwork (Onsite)
Seminar Information Service Inc. (SIS)
250 El Camino Real., Ste. 112
Tustin, CA 92780
Ph: (714)508-0340
Free: 877-736-4636
Fax: (714)734-8027
Co. E-mail: info@seminarinformation.com
URL: http://www.seminarinformation.com
Contact: Catherine Bellizzi, President
URL(s): www.seminarinformation.com/qqbtjm/leadership-skills-building-success-through-teamwork

Description: Learn how to: Develop your teams to maximize their strengths and enhance productivity; Optimize organization and work design for success in service delivery teams; Motivate your team with effective performance measurement; Integrate your role as a leader into your management style; Leverage the complementary skills and styles of your team; Eliminate barriers and chokepoints that block teamwork; Apply a diverse and multilevel approach to minimize communication breakdowns. **Audience:** Industry professionals. **Principal Exhibits:** Learn how to: Develop your teams to maximize their strengths and enhance productivity; Optimize organization and work design for success in service delivery teams; Motivate your team with effective performance measurement; Integrate your role as a leader into your management style; Leverage the complementary skills and styles of your team; Eliminate barriers and chokepoints that block teamwork; Apply a diverse and multilevel approach to minimize communication breakdowns.

22058 ■ Leading Effective Teams II - Communicating with Your Teammates (Onsite)
Seminar Information Service Inc. (SIS)
250 El Camino Real., Ste. 112
Tustin, CA 92780
Ph: (714)508-0340
Free: 877-736-4636
Fax: (714)734-8027
Co. E-mail: info@seminarinformation.com
URL: http://www.seminarinformation.com
Contact: Catherine Bellizzi, President
URL(s): www.seminarinformation.com

Description: Leaders learn their communication style and how it relates to their team members, as well as how to motivate through communication. **Audience:** Members, industry professionals. **Principal Exhibits:** Leaders learn their communication style and how it relates to their team members, as well as how to motivate through communication.

22059 ■ Leading High Performance Teams
Seminar Information Service Inc. (SIS)
250 El Camino Real., Ste. 112
Tustin, CA 92780
Ph: (714)508-0340
Free: 877-736-4636
Fax: (714)734-8027
Co. E-mail: info@seminarinformation.com
URL: http://www.seminarinformation.com
Contact: Catherine Bellizzi, President
URL(s): www.seminarinformation.com/qqbmxs/leading-high-performing-project-teams

Description: Builds awareness and skill in the areas of team dynamics, group problem solving, and group decision making. You will develop leadership skills applicable to many areas, but especially suited to self-directed work teams, employee participation teams, interdepartmental task groups, and other group situations where combined efforts are needed to reach optimal performance levels. **Audience:** Team leaders and project managers. **Principal Exhibits:** Builds awareness and skill in the areas of team dynamics, group problem solving, and group decision making. You will develop leadership skills applicable to many areas, but especially suited to self-directed work teams, employee participation teams, interdepartmental task groups, and other group situations where combined efforts are needed to reach optimal performance levels. **Telecommunication Services:** Info@seminarinformation.com.

22060 ■ Making Successful Business Decisions: Getting it Right the First Time (Onsite)
Seminar Information Service Inc. (SIS)
250 El Camino Real., Ste. 112
Tustin, CA 92780
Ph: (714)508-0340
Free: 877-736-4636
Fax: (714)734-8027
Co. E-mail: info@seminarinformation.com
URL: http://www.seminarinformation.com
Contact: Catherine Bellizzi, President
URL(s): www.seminarinformation.com

Description: Learn how to make intelligent decisions with limited time and information, how to convert conflicting opinions into useful insights, foster efficient and effective group decision making, and ensure decisions are implemented by the organization. **Audience:** Managers, professionals. **Principal Exhibits:** Learn how to make intelligent decisions with limited time and information, how to convert conflicting opinions into useful insights, foster efficient and effective group decision making, and ensure decisions are implemented by the organization.

22061 ■ Management Skills for an IT Environment (Onsite)
Seminar Information Service Inc. (SIS)
250 El Camino Real., Ste. 112
Tustin, CA 92780
Ph: (714)508-0340
Free: 877-736-4636
Fax: (714)734-8027
Co. E-mail: info@seminarinformation.com
URL: http://www.seminarinformation.com
Contact: Catherine Bellizzi, President
URL(s): www.seminarinformation.com/qqbuun/management-skills-for-an-it-environment

Description: Learn how to apply a proven management model for leading technical staff to excellence; identify key success criteria for leadership in an IT environment; leverage emotion to optimize communication and performance; motivate and empower technical professionals to achieve results; delegate proactively to focus on strengths of IT teams and build accountability. **Audience:** IT managers. **Principal Exhibits:** Learn how to apply a proven management model for leading technical staff to excellence; identify key success criteria for leadership in an IT environment; leverage emotion to optimize communication and performance; motivate and empower technical professionals to achieve results; delegate proactively to focus on strengths of IT teams and build accountability.

22062 ■ Managing Today's IT and Technical Professionals (Onsite)
Seminar Information Service Inc. (SIS)
250 El Camino Real., Ste. 112
Tustin, CA 92780
Ph: (714)508-0340
Free: 877-736-4636
Fax: (714)734-8027
Co. E-mail: info@seminarinformation.com
URL: http://www.seminarinformation.com
Contact: Catherine Bellizzi, President
URL(s): www.seminarinformation.com/details.cfm?qc=qqakqt

Description: Learn how to strengthen, motivate and inspire any group or team. **Audience:** Technical professionals, experienced managers. **Principal Exhibits:** Learn how to strengthen, motivate and inspire any group or team.

22063 ■ Managing in Tough Times (Onsite)
Seminar Information Service Inc. (SIS)
250 El Camino Real., Ste. 112
Tustin, CA 92780
Ph: (714)508-0340
Free: 877-736-4636
Fax: (714)734-8027
Co. E-mail: info@seminarinformation.com
URL: http://www.seminarinformation.com
Contact: Catherine Bellizzi, President
URL(s): www.seminarinformation.com

Description: Learn how to demonstrate authentic and strong leadership to create an atmosphere of confidence and trust in tough times, share your vision and display confidence that the problems your team currently faces will be solved, and minimize stress and maximize productivity and performance during difficult times. **Audience:** Industry professionals, managers. **Principal Exhibits:** Learn how to demonstrate authentic and strong leadership to create an atmosphere of confidence and trust in tough times, share your vision and display confidence that the problems your team currently faces will be solved, and minimize stress and maximize productivity and performance during difficult times.

GENERAL SMALL BUSINESS TOPICS

22064 ■ Project Leadership: Building High-Performance Teams (Onsite)
Seminar Information Service Inc. (SIS)
  250 El Camino Real., Ste. 112
  Tustin, CA 92780
Ph: (714)508-0340
Free: 877-736-4636
Fax: (714)734-8027
Co. E-mail: info@seminarinformation.com
URL: http://www.seminarinformation.com
Contact: Catherine Bellizzi, President
URL(s): www.seminarinformation.com/qqbtkk/projec t-leadership-building-high-performance-teams
Description: Learn how to: Develop the leadership skills to build and sustain high-performing project teams; Develop effective team performance through the Leadership Services Model; Build a strong team identity through vision, purpose and commitment; Foster positive and productive team communication and define ground rules; Protect the team and convert conflicts into advantages that promote high performance; Maximize your leadership abilities when you return to your organization. **Audience:** Team leaders and project managers. **Principal Exhibits:** Learn how to: Develop the leadership skills to build and sustain high-performing project teams; Develop effective team performance through the Leadership Services Model; Build a strong team identity through vision, purpose and commitment; Foster positive and productive team communication and define ground rules; Protect the team and convert conflicts into advantages that promote high performance; Maximize your leadership abilities when you return to your organization.

22065 ■ Responding to Conflict: Creating Resolution and Cooperation (Onsite)
Seminar Information Service Inc. (SIS)
  250 El Camino Real., Ste. 112
  Tustin, CA 92780
Ph: (714)508-0340
Free: 877-736-4636
Fax: (714)734-8027
Co. E-mail: info@seminarinformation.com
URL: http://www.seminarinformation.com
Contact: Catherine Bellizzi, President
URL(s): www.seminarinformation.com
Description: Learn how to: Effectively handle conflict using a powerful conflict resolution method; Anticipate the causes of conflict and respond proactively; Manage strong emotions in a conflict situation; Remove barriers to cooperation; Create productive outcomes and reach a final agreement; Embrace conflict as an opportunity for team and organizational growth. **Audience:** Business professionals. **Principal Exhibits:** Learn how to: Effectively handle conflict using a powerful conflict resolution method; Anticipate the causes of conflict and respond proactively; Manage strong emotions in a conflict situation; Remove barriers to cooperation; Create productive outcomes and reach a final agreement; Embrace conflict as an opportunity for team and organizational growth. **Telecommunication Services:** info@seminarinformation.com.

22066 ■ Sparking Innovation and Creativity (Onsite)
Seminar Information Service Inc. (SIS)
  250 El Camino Real., Ste. 112
  Tustin, CA 92780
Ph: (714)508-0340
Free: 877-736-4636
Fax: (714)734-8027
Co. E-mail: info@seminarinformation.com
URL: http://www.seminarinformation.com
Contact: Catherine Bellizzi, President
URL(s): www.seminarinformation.com/qqbupu/spark ing-innovation-and-creativity
Description: Innovative problem-solving skills to overcome negative thinking habits within the organization to reach the company's goals and objectives. **Audience:** All employees. **Principal Exhibits:** Innovative problem-solving skills to overcome negative thinking habits within the organization to reach the company's goals and objectives.

22067 ■ Strategic Planning: From Vision-to-Action
URL(s): cmcoutperform.com/strategic-planning-from -vision-to-action
Price: C$1,845, Members; C$1,995, Non-members.
Description: Covers the strategic planning process, identifying threats and opportunities for your company, and developing strategies and action plans. **Audience:** Business leaders who currently play a role in their organization's strategic planning process and professionals wishing to strengthen their skills in order to become more effective leaders or to prepare for more senior roles. **Principal Exhibits:** Covers the strategic planning process, identifying threats and opportunities for your company, and developing strategies and action plans. **Telecommunication Services:** cmcinfo@cmcoutperform.com.

22068 ■ Total Productive Maintenance (TPM) & 5S (Onsite)
TPC Trainco Inc.
  225 E Robinson St., Ste. 570
  Orlando, FL 32801
Free: 877-978-7246
Co. E-mail: sales@tpctraining.com
URL: http://live.tpctraining.com
URL(s): live.tpctraining.com/public-seminars/plan t-management/total-productive-maintenance-tpm -training
Description: Two-day seminar that focuses on getting managers, maintenance personnel and equipment users all working together to prevent equipment problems and reduce expenditures. **Audience:** Managers, maintenance personnel and equipment users. **Principal Exhibits:** Two-day seminar that focuses on getting managers, maintenance personnel and equipment users all working together to prevent equipment problems and reduce expenditures.

REFERENCE WORKS

22069 ■ "3 Signs Your Employees Hate Their Jobs (and What to Do About It)" in Business News Daily (March 6, 2023)
URL(s): www.businessnewsdaily.com/signs -employees-hate-their-job
Ed: Max Freedman. **Released:** March 06, 2023. **Description:** A good business owner is also astute about their employees' happiness within the workplace. Provided are actions owners can take to ensure a good working environment that will keep employees at your business instead of heading for the door. **Availability:** Online.

22070 ■ 4 Team-Building Techniques That Work for Small Business
URL(s): www.ondeck.com/resources/4-team-building -techniques-work-small-business
Ed: Kimberly Solarz. **Description:** Discusses the nuances of creating a cohesive team for your small business and provides team-building techniques that are enjoyable and effective. **Availability:** Online.

22071 ■ "5 Conversations: How to Transform Trust, Engagement and Performance at Work"
Pub: Panoma Press
Contact: Daniel Steven Priestley, Director
Released: 2nd edition. **Description:** Engaged employees help to create successful businesses. The importance of authentic, two-way, human conversations to build relationships, trust, and engagement is stressed to develop a motivated workforce. **Availability:** Print.

22072 ■ "5 Ways to Motivate Small Business Staff" in ZenBusiness (Dec. 13, 2021)
URL(s): www.zenbusiness.com/blog/5-ways-motivate -small-business-staff/
Ed: Tiffany Rowe. **Released:** December 13, 2021. **Description:** Discusses the importance of keeping your small business employees engaged and productive and offers five incentives to explore that will keep your staff motivated. **Availability:** Online.

22073 ■ "6 Methods to Overcome Challenges at Work" in sweetbutfearless.com(October 15, 2020)
URL(s): www.sweetbutfearless.com/blog/6-methods -to-overcome-challenges-at-work-change
Description: Challenges often arise throughout the work day, with some more intense than others. Here, tips are given to get through these moments with success. **Availability:** Online.

22074 ■ "6 Tips for Open-Office Etiquette" in Business News Daily (March 7, 2023)
URL(s): www.businessnewsdaily.com/10913-open -office-etiquette.html
Ed: Kiely Kuligowski. **Released:** March 07, 2023. **Description:** Open offices are becoming more prevalent, so learning some tips to function within one will be beneficial to anyone who works in this type of space. **Availability:** Online.

22075 ■ "8 Motivation Tricks to Inspire Your Employees" in Small Business Trends (January 25, 2023)
URL(s): smallbiztrends.com/2020/11/motivation-tricks -for-employees.html
Ed: Jayson DeMers. **Released:** January 25, 2023. **Description:** Discusses several ways small business owners can motivate their employees. **Availability:** Online.

22076 ■ "10 Effective Methods for Measuring Employee Happiness" in Small Business Trends (August 23,2022)
URL(s): smallbiztrends.com/2021/06/measuring-em ployee-happiness.html
Released: August 23, 2022. **Description:** Cultivating happy employees helps small businesses out on the in the long run because these employees tend to stick around much longer. Listed in this article are tips for gauging how satisfied your employees are working at your small business. **Availability:** Online.

22077 ■ "11 Ways to Reward Hardworking Employees (and Encourage More Exemplary Behavior)" in Small Business Trends (January 15, 2023)
URL(s): smallbiztrends.com/2023/01/ways-to-rewar d-hardworking-employees.html
Released: January 15, 2023. **Description:** Every small businesses should spend some time identifying hard workers and rewarding them for their company contributions. The number one suggestion? Giving a raise. This article provides other ideas as well. **Availability:** Online.

22078 ■ 12 Reasons Why Team Building Works
URL(s): www.teambonding.com/6-reasons-for-team -building/
Ed: Amanda Deiratani. **Released:** September 13, 2021. **Description:** Discusses the benefits of team building for your small business and provides 12 reasons to start team building. **Availability:** Online.

22079 ■ "12 Secrets to Keeping Employees Happy without a Raise" in Business News Daily (March 20, 2023)
URL(s): www.businessnewsdaily.com/6084-employee -happiness-without-raise.html
Ed: Simone Johnson. **Released:** March 20, 2023. **Description:** Sometimes small businesses cannot provide raises, so oftentimes owners will need to get creative and find other ways to keep and engage their hard-working employees. **Availability:** Online.

22080 ■ "12 Steps to Take after Receiving Negative Feedback about Your Company Culture" in Small Business Trends (February 19, 2023)
URL(s): smallbiztrends.com/2023/02/steps-to-take-af ter-receiving-negative-feedback-regarding-the -companys-culture.html
Released: February 19, 2023. **Description:** A guide on how to work through negative feedback about your small business. **Availability:** Online.

22081 ■ Employee Motivation/Team Building

22081 ■ *"15 Small Business Team-Building Ideas"* **in Constant Contact Blog (Feb. 7 2022)**
URL(s): blogs.constantcontact.com/small-business-team-building-ideas/
Ed: Alaina Brandenburger. **Released:** February 07, 2022. **Description:** Discusses the importance of team building for your small business. Includes information on how productivity and cohesion can benefit your company and provides 15 small business team-building ideas. **Availability:** Online.

22082 ■ *"16 Cool Job Perks That Keep Employees Happy"* **in Business News Daily (March 7, 2023)**
URL(s): www.businessnewsdaily.com/5134-cool-job-benefits.html
Ed: Katharine Paljug. **Released:** March 07, 2023. **Description:** Describes job perks that will make your employees appreciate working for your small business. **Availability:** Online.

22083 ■ *"16 Creative and Cheap Ways to Say 'Thank You'"* **in HR Specialist (Vol. 8, September 2010, No. 9, pp. 8)**
Pub: Capitol Information Group Inc.
Contact: Allie Ash, Chief Executive Officer
Released: October 14, 2010. **Description:** Tips for starting an employee appreciation program for a small company are presented. **Availability:** Print; PDF; Online.

22084 ■ *20 Quick Team Building Activities for Small Business Leaders*
URL(s): getsling.com/blog/quick-team-building-activities/
Description: Provides 20 quick team building activities to keep your employees engaged and working well together. **Availability:** Online.

22085 ■ *"20 Tips and Tricks for Zoom - before, during and after Meetings"* **in krisp(October 1, 2022)**
URL(s): krisp.ai/blog/zoom-tips/
Ed: Alexandra Cote. **Released:** October 01, 2022. **Description:** Tips on how to have successful Zoom meetings. Now that more corporations have embraced work-from-home, Zoom is one of the most needed tools to keep communication flowing between employees and to customers. **Availability:** Online.

22086 ■ *"24 Team Building Exercises and Games Your Team Will Enjoy"* **in Small Business Trends (February 13, 2023)**
URL(s): smallbiztrends.com/2022/11/team-building-exercises.html
Ed: Kevin Ocasio. **Released:** February 13, 2023. **Description:** Describes various team bonding events that small business can use to build compatibility amongst team members. **Availability:** Online.

22087 ■ *"40 Virtual Event Ideas"* **in Small Business Trends (February 24, 2022)**
URL(s): smallbiztrends.com/2021/11/virtual-event-ideas.html
Ed: Annie Pilon. **Released:** February 24, 2022. **Description:** With the advent of work from home situations and the software that makes that possible, many companies are embracing virtual events for their employees such as webinars, live chats, and even live concerts. **Availability:** Online.

22088 ■ *"56% of Employees Believe Too Many Meetings Affecting Job Performance"* **in Small Business Trends (August 10, 2021)**
URL(s): smallbiztrends.com/2021/07/meetings-affecting-job-performance.html
Ed: Michael Guta. **Released:** August 10, 2021. **Description:** Its been noted that the amount of meetings has gone up over the decades and according to a recent poll, the majority of workers think it is too much. The article discusses the results of the poll. **Availability:** Online.

22089 ■ *"The Advantage: Why Organizational Health Trumps Everything Else in Business (J-B Lencioni Series)"*
Pub: Jossey-Bass
Released: February 01, 2012. **Price:** $28.95, hardcover. **Description:** A comprehensive examination of the unique advantage organizational health provides any small business and sets them apart from their competition. A healthy organization is whole, consistent and complete, is free of politics and confusion, and provides an environment where star performers want to stay. **Availability:** E-book; Print.

22090 ■ *"The Alliance: Managing Talent in the Networked Age"*
Pub: Harvard Business Review Press
Contact: Moderna V. Pfizer, Contact
Released: July 08, 2014. **Price:** $30, Hardcover/Hardcopy. **Description:** It is suggested that management see their workers as allies instead of family or free agents in order to create a realistic loyalty pact between employer and employee. Both sides need to trust each other for the company to succeed and the employee to further their career with the firm. **Availability:** E-book; Print.

22091 ■ *"Altus Jobs Founders' Unique Operating System Generates Success"* **in Orlando Business Journal (Vol. 30, April 11, 2014, No. 42, pp. 3)**
Pub: American City Business Journals, Inc.
Contact: Mike Olivieri, Executive Vice President
Released: Weekly. **Price:** $8, introductory 4-week offer(Digital & Print). **Description:** Maitland, Florida-based Altus Jobs founders, Saum Sharifi and Augusto Guevara, have credited their unique operating sytem with their quick success in recruiting talent, specializing in high level engineering positions. The system allows employees to work from 9:30 a.m. to 3:30 p.m. in their casual office and motivates them to show entrepreneurship by offering commission on top of base salary. **Availability:** Print; Online.

22092 ■ *"The Anatomy of a High Potential"* **in Business Strategy Review (Vol. 21, Autumn 2010, No. 3, pp. 52)**
Ed: Doug Ready, Jay Conger, Linda Hill, Emily Stecker. **Released:** September 22, 2010. **Description:** Companies have long been interested in identifying high potential employees, but few firms know how to convert top talent into game changers, or people who can shape the future of the business. The authors have found the 'x factors' that can make a high-potential list into a strong competitive advantage. **Availability:** Print; Electronic publishing; PDF; Online.

22093 ■ *"The Art of Appreciation"* **in Business Horizons (November-December 2007, pp. 441)**
Ed: Catherine M. Dalton. **Released:** November 01, 2011. **Description:** The art of appreciation is an art less and less practices by employees. Employers should lead by example and practice this art to inspire employees to do the same. **Availability:** Print; Online.

22094 ■ *"Baltimore GM Plant Moves Forward"* **in Baltimore Business Journal (Vol. 32, July 4, 2014, No. 9, pp. 18)**
Pub: American City Business Journals, Inc.
Contact: Mike Olivieri, Executive Vice President
Released: Weekly. **Price:** $4, introductory 4-week offer(Digital only). **Description:** General Motors (GM) plant at White Marsh represents traditional and modern manufacturing, attracting young employees with the use of advanced technology, but still retaining its loyal, veteran workforce. Most workers at the plant's Allison Transmission facility have been with GM for 25 years or more, while the adjacent facility making electric motors for the Chevy Spark EV is primarily made up of workers in their late 20s. **Availability:** Print; Online.

22095 ■ *Be a Brilliant Business Writer: Write Well, Write Fast, and Whip the Competition*
Released: October 05, 2010. **Price:** $14.99, paperback; $5.99. **Description:** Tools for mastering the art of persuasive writing in every document created, from email and client letters to reports and presentations, this book will help any writer convey their message with clarity and power, increase productivity by reducing rewrites, and provide the correct tone for navigating office politics. **Availability:** E-book; Print.

22096 ■ *"Be Nice at Work - Everybody's Watching"* **in Puget Sound Business Journal (Vol. 34, April 4, 2014, No. 51, pp. 10)**
Pub: American City Business Journals, Inc.
Contact: Mike Olivieri, Executive Vice President
Description: Employees can become great co-workers by acknowledging their colleagues, respecting others, avoiding gossip, expressing gratitude and being helpful. Staying positive will also allow staff to deal with demanding bosses and challenging co-workers. **Availability:** Online.

22097 ■ *"Before Happiness: The 5 Hidden Keys to Achieving Success, Spreading Happiness, and Sustaining Positive Change"*
Released: 2013. **Price:** $26, hardcover; 6.99, e-book. **Description:** Harvard trained researcher explains proven strategies for changing attitudes to positive include, the most valuable reality to see a broader range of ideas and solutions; success mapping, setting goals around things that matter to you most; the x-spot, using success accelerants to propel you more quickly towards goals; noise-canceling, boost the signal pointing to opportunities and possibilities others miss; and positive inception, transferring your skills to your team, employees and everyone around you. **Availability:** CD-ROM; E-book; Print.

22098 ■ *"Biblical Secrets to Business Success"*
Pub: CreateSpace
Released: October 02, 2014. **Price:** paperback. **Description:** Bob Diener share insight into his journey as an entrepreneur. He focuses on tough issues like: how to treat employees, how to please customers, whether or not to cut corners, whether to follow temptation of an unethical deal, and provides solutions to these dilemmas. He recommends abiding by the Bible's rules of business in order to prosper long term. **Availability:** Print.

22099 ■ *"Blach Builds on Teamwork"* **in Silicon Valley/San Jose Business Journal (Vol. 30, August 24, 2012, No. 22, pp. 1)**
Pub: Baltimore Business Journal
Contact: Rhonda Pringle, President
E-mail: rpringle@bizjournals.com
Description: Blach Construction chief executive, Mike Blach, has grown the firm into a top contractor in San Jose, California. The construction company's earnings have increased to $98 million in 2011. **Availability:** Print; Online.

22100 ■ *Bottom-Line Training: Performance-Based Results*
Pub: Training Education Management
Contact: Dr. Donald J. Ford, President
Ed: Donald J. Ford. **Released:** Second edition. **Price:** $29. **Description:** Training is critical to any successful enterprise. The key to any successful training program involves defining and constantly focusing on the desired results of the program. The author provides a training model based on five phases, known as ADDIE: analysis, design, development, implementation and evaluation. **Availability:** Print.

22101 ■ *"Boundaries for Leaders (Enhanced Edition): Results, Relationships, and Being Ridiculously In Charge"*
Pub: Harper Business
Contact: Hollis Heimbouch, Senior Vice President Publisher
Released: April 16, 2013. **Price:** $15.97, Default Title; $16.99. **Description:** Clinical psychologist and author explains how the best business leaders set boundaries within their organizations, with their teams and themselves, to improve performance and increase customer and employee satisfaction. Practical advice is given to manage teams, coach direct reports, and create an organization with strong ethics and culture. **Availability:** E-book; Print.

GENERAL SMALL BUSINESS TOPICS

Employee Motivation/Team Building ■ 22121

22102 ■ *"Breaking Bad: Rid Yourself of Negative Habits"* in *Black Enterprise* (Vol. 40, July 2010, No. 12, pp. 104)
Pub: Earl G. Graves Ltd.
Contact: Earl Graves, Jr., President
Ed: Renita Burns. **Description:** Tardiness, procrastination, chronic complaining are among the bad habits that can make people bad employees; tips for breaking these habits are outlined. **Availability:** Online.

22103 ■ *"Brief: Janitorial Company Must Pay Back Wages"* in *Buffalo News* (September 24, 2011)
Description: Knights Facilities Management, located in Michigan, provides grounds maintenance and janitorial services at the Ralph Wilson Stadium in Buffalo, New York. The US Department of Labor ordered the firm to pay $22,000 in back wages and damages to 26 employees for overtime and minimum wage compensation. Details of the company's violation of the Fair Labor Standards Act are included. **Availability:** Online.

22104 ■ *"Bring Out the Best in Your Team"* in *Harvard Business Review* Vol. 92, September 2014, No. 9, pp. 26)
Pub: Harvard Business Publishing
Contact: Diane Belcher, Managing Director
Price: $6. **Description:** Social influence often impacts team decision making, as more outgoing members tend to dominate discussion. To replace social influence with informational influence, have team members state at the beginning what knowledge they have regarding the task at hand. **Availability:** Online; PDF.

22105 ■ *"Building the Right Culture Can Add Huge Value"* in *South Florida Business Journal* (Vol. 34, May 9, 2014, No. 42, pp. 20)
Pub: American City Business Journals, Inc.
Contact: Mike Olivieri, Executive Vice President
Released: Weekly. **Price:** $8, Introductory 4-week offer(Digital & Print). **Description:** Corporate culture has become an afterthought in many companies and this might be the result of viewing operating results purely from a financial perspective. However, it is the people who work for the companies that create value and they would become more effective by defining the culture. The benefits of creating a positive culture are also discussed. **Availability:** Print; Online.

22106 ■ *"Business Team Building Activities"* in *Chron*
URL(s): smallbusiness.chron.com/business-team-building-activities-695.html
Ed: Kyra Sheahan. **Description:** Discusses the importance of having team-building activities in your small business toolbox to help employees learn to work together toward a common goal. **Availability:** Online.

22107 ■ *"Can People Collaborate Effectively While Working Remotely? Vint Cerf, Co-Creator of the Internet, On How Employees Can Work Together More Productively In An Age When Many Can Work Almost Anywhere"* in *Gallup Business Journal* (March 13, 2014)
Pub: Gallup, Inc.
Contact: Jon Clifton, Chief Executive Officer
Description: Vint Cerf, co-creator of the Internet, discusses ways that employees can work more productively when technology allows them to work from almost anywhere. **Availability:** Online.

22108 ■ *"Candor, Criticism, Teamwork"* in *Harvard Business Review* (Vol. 90, January-February 2012, No.1-2, pp. 40)
Pub: Harvard Business Review Press
Contact: Moderna V. Pfizer, Contact
Ed: Keith Ferrazzi. **Price:** $6. **Description:** To ensure honest and effective feedback, meetings should be broken up into smaller groups. Individuals should be selected to be advocates of candor, and techniques for caring criticism should be taught, such as identifying a problem but then suggesting ways to correct it. **Availability:** Online; PDF.

22109 ■ *"Celebrate Success. Embrace Innovation"* in *Black Enterprise* (Vol. 37, February 2007, No. 7, pp. 145)
Description: 2007 Women of Power Summit provides networking opportunities, empowerment sessions, and nightly entertainment. More than 500 executive women of color are expected to attend this inspiring summit in Phoenix, February 7-10. **Availability:** Print; Online.

22110 ■ *"Chameleonic or Consistent? A Multilevel Investigation of Emotional Labor Variability and Self-Monitoring"* in *Academy of Management Journal* (Vol. 55, August 1, 2012, No. 4, pp. 905)
Pub: Academy of Management
Contact: Sharon Alvarez, President
Ed: Brent A. Scott, Christopher M. Barnes, David T. Wagner. **Description:** The importance of emotional labor variability in association with job satisfaction and work withdrawal is examined. Results indicate that surface acting variability is linked to lower levels of job satisfaction and higher levels of work withdrawal and that self-monitoring influences the impact of surface acting variability on job satisfaction and work withdrawal. **Availability:** Electronic publishing; Download; PDF; Online.

22111 ■ *"Chameloeonic or Consistent? A Multilevel Investigation of Emotional Labor Variability and Self-Monitoring"* in *Academy of Management Journal* (Vol. 55, August 2012, No. 4, pp. 905)
Released: Volume 55. No 4. **Price:** $30, PDF and download. **Description:** The importance of emotional labor variability in association with job satisfaction and work withdrawal is examined. Results indicate that surface acting variability is linked to lowe levels of job satisfaction and higher levels of work withdrawal and that self-monitoring influences the impact of surface acting variability on job satisfactionand work withdrawal. **Availability:** Print; Download; PDF; Online.

22112 ■ *"Cloud Computing for a Crowd"* in *CIO* (Vol. 24, October 2, 2010, No. 1, pp. 16)
Pub: CIO
Ed: Stephanie Overby. **Description:** Information about a project which aimed to implement a cloud-based crowdsourcing platform and innovation-management process is provided. Chubb Group of Insurance Companies wanted to mine revenue-generating ideas from its 10,400 employees and hundreds of thousands of external agents. The company hosted its first innovation event using its new system in October 2008. **Availability:** Online.

22113 ■ *"Coffee Breaks Don't Boost Productivity After All"* in *Harvard Business Review* (Vol. 90, May 2012, No. 5, pp. 34)
Pub: Harvard Business Review Press
Contact: Moderna V. Pfizer, Contact
Ed: Charlotte Fritz. **Price:** $6. **Description:** Research shows no statistical correlation between taking a short break at work and one's fatigue and vitality levels. However, a link was found between personal productivity and assisting a coworker. Employees detach from work more successfully during long breaks rather than short ones. **Availability:** Online; PDF.

22114 ■ *"Column: Good Decisions. Bad Outcomes"* in *Harvard Business Review* (Vol. 88, December 2010, No. 12, pp. 40)
Pub: Harvard Business Publishing
Contact: Diane Belcher, Managing Director
Ed: Dan Ariely. **Price:** $6, PDF. **Description:** Suggestions are provided for developing and implementing improved reward systems that in turn produce better decision-making processes. These include documenting critical assumptions and changing mind sets. **Availability:** Online; PDF.

22115 ■ *"Column: Work Pray Love"* in *Harvard Business Review* (Vol. 88, December 2010, No. 12, pp. 38)
Pub: Harvard Business Publishing
Contact: Diane Belcher, Managing Director
Ed: Rosabeth Moss Kanter. **Price:** $6, PDF. **Description:** It is recommended to reinvest in values in order to promote better employee-company engagement and performance. **Availability:** Online; PDF.

22116 ■ *"Coming Through When It Matters Most: How Great Teams Do Their Best Work Under Pressure"* in *Harvard Business Review* (Vol. 90, April 2012, No. 4, pp. 82)
Pub: Harvard Business Review Press
Contact: Moderna V. Pfizer, Contact
Ed: Heidi K. Gardner. **Price:** $8.95, hardcover. **Description:** Teamwork can be enhanced by measuring each member's contribution more deliberately, and by examining every new item of information. This way, teams avoid performance pressure that constricts creativity and innovation. **Availability:** PDF; Online.

22117 ■ *"Communication Technology and Inclusion Will Shape the Future of Remote Work"* in *Business News Daily* (March 6, 2023)
URL(s): www.businessnewsdaily.com/8156-future-of-remote-work.html
Ed: Natalie Hamingson. **Released:** March 06, 2023. **Description:** Working from home has skyrocketed in popularity as more companies embrace this practice. Business owners are learning to adapt this practice as it leads to higher job satisfaction for their employees. **Availability:** Online.

22118 ■ *"Conquering the Seven Summits of Sales: From Everest to Every Business, Achieving Peak Performance"*
Pub: Harper Business
Contact: Hollis Heimbouch, Senior Vice President Publisher
Released: October 07, 2014. **Price:** $4.99, e-book; $6.19, hardcover; $0.10, hardcover(39 used from $0.10); $3.75, hardcover(19 new from $3.75); $9.10, kindle. **Description:** Sales professionals are taught to overcome their perceived limitations and strive for success. The guide shows how to define goals, build the right team, commit to a vision, time management, and tracking of progress. **Availability:** E-book; Print.

22119 ■ *"Conscious Capitalism: Liberating the Heroic Spirit of Business"*
Released: January 07, 2014. **Price:** $12.47, e-book; $16.79, paperback. **Description:** Conscious Capitalism companies include Whole Foods Market, Southwest Airlines, Costco, Google, Patagonia, The Container Store, UPS and others. These firms under the four specific tenants to success: higher purpose, stakeholder integration, conscious leadership, and conscious culture and management. These companies are able to create value for all stakeholders, including customers, employees, suppliers, investors, society, and the environment. A new preface by the authors is included. **Availability:** E-book; Print.

22120 ■ *"The Consequences of Tardiness"* in *Modern Machine Shop* (Vol. 84, August 2011, No. 3, pp. 34)
Description: Five point addressing motivating factors behind employees who are tardy and those who choose to be on time in the workplace are shared. **Availability:** Online.

22121 ■ *"Corporate Responsibility"* in *Professional Services Close-Up* (July 2, 2010)
Description: List of firms awarded the inaugural Best Corporate Citizens in Government Contracting by the Corporate Responsibility Magazine is presented. The list is based on the methodology of the Magazine's Best Corporate Citizen's List, with 324 data points of publicly-available information in seven categories which include: environment, climate change, human rights, philanthropy, employee relations, financial performance, and governance. **Availability:** Online.

22122 ■ **"Counting on Engagement at Ernst & Young"** in *Workforce Management (Vol. 88, November 16, 2009, No. 12, pp. 25)*
Pub: Crain Communications Inc.
Contact: Barry Asin, President
Ed: Ed Frauenheim. **Description:** Employee engagement has been difficult to maintain through the recession but firms such as Ernst & Young have found that the effort to keep their employees loyal has paid off. **Availability:** Print; Online.

22123 ■ **"Creating Sustainable Performance: If You Give Your Employees the Chance To Learn and Grow, They'll Thrive - And So Will Your Organization"** in *Harvard Business Review (Vol. 90, January-February 2012, No.1-2, pp. 92)*
Pub: Harvard Business Review Press
Contact: Moderna V. Pfizer, Contact
Ed: Christine Porath, Gretchen Spreitzer. **Price:** $8.95. **Description:** Identification of four key factors that increase employee morale and productivity are outlined. These are: providing decision-making capability, sharing information, reducing incivility, and offering performance feedback. All four factors are needed to produce improvements. **Availability:** Online; PDF.

22124 ■ **"Creativity, Inc.: Overcoming the Unseen Forces That Stand in the Way of True Inspiration"**
Pub: Penguin Random House
Contact: Nihar Malaviya, Chief Executive Officer
Released: April 08, 2014. **Price:** $28, hardcover, plus shipping charges; $2.99, e-book; $35, CD, plus shipping charges; $17.50, audiobook download; $16.89, Hardcover; $15.79, Paperback; $28.33, Audible Audiobook. **Description:** Ed Catmull, co-founder of Pixar Animation Studios, reaches out to managers who want to lead their employees to greater heights. Pixar has dominated the world of animated films for twenty years. Catmull addresses philosophies that protect the creative process and defy convention to inspire employees and create a successful small business. **Availability:** CD-ROM; E-book; Print; Audio.

22125 ■ **"Crew Training Changes Tactics"** in *Memphis Business Journal (Vol. 33, March 16, 2012, No. 49, pp. 1)*
Pub: Baltimore Business Journal
Contact: Rhonda Pringle, President
E-mail: rpringle@bizjournals.com
Ed: Cole Epley. **Description:** Teamwork and communication training services firm Crew Training International Inc. has revamped its strategy and executive board as it moved from small to mid-tier status. The recalibration of strategy comes along with a renovation at the headquarters in southeast Memphis, Tennessee. **Availability:** Print; Online.

22126 ■ **"Cultural Due Diligence"** in *Canadian Business (Vol. 80, April 23, 2007, No. 9, pp. 60)*
Description: The factors to be considered by job seekers during judging good workplace with relation to corporate culture are presented. **Availability:** Download; PDF; Online.

22127 ■ **"Culture Club: Effective Corporate Cultures"** in *Canadian Business (Vol. 79, October 9, 2006, No. 20, pp. 115)*
Pub: Rogers Media Inc.
Contact: Neil Spivak, Chief Executive Officer
Ed: Calvin Leung. **Description:** Positive impacts of an effective corporate culture on the employees' productivity and the performance of the business are discussed. **Availability:** Online.

22128 ■ **"Customer Retention is Proportionate to Employee Retention"** in *Green Industry Pro (Vol. 23, September 2011)*
Description: Presented in a question-answer format, information is provided to help retain customers as well as keeping workers happy. **Availability:** Online.

22129 ■ **"The Darwinian Workplace: New Technology Is Helping Employers Systematically Shift More Work To Their Best Employees"** in *Harvard Business Review (Vol. 90, May 2012, No. 5, pp. 25)*
Pub: Harvard Business Review Press
Contact: Moderna V. Pfizer, Contact
Ed: Serguei Netessine, Valery Yakubovich. **Price:** $6. **Description:** The winners-take-all model is a productivity-based system that shifts work and incentives to a firm's most productive employees. Challenges such as unpredictable pay swings, excessive competition, and unfair comparisons are addressed. **Availability:** Online; PDF.

22130 ■ **"Deep Thoughts: Getting Employees to Think Better Requires a Bit of Creative Thinking Itself"** in *Canadian Business (March 17, 2008)*
Description: Discusses the reason a company needs to make their employees understand that ideas are the stuff of life. For employees to be more creative, they need to cultivate spark moments, play with possibilities, and venture into the unknown. **Availability:** Print; Online; PDF.

22131 ■ **"Defend Your Research: It's Not 'Unprofessional' to Gossip at Work"** in *Harvard Business Review (Vol. 88, September 2010, No. 9, pp. 28)*
Pub: Harvard Business Publishing
Contact: Diane Belcher, Managing Director
Ed: Giuseppe Labianca. **Price:** $6, PDF. **Description:** Gossip can be of value to a company as an exchange of information and its use as a diagnostic tool can enable managers to address problems promptly and even head them off. **Availability:** Online; PDF.

22132 ■ **"Determining Your Food Truck Employee Needs"** in *Mobile-Cuisine.com (September 8, 2020)*
Ed: Richard Myrick. **Released:** September 08, 2020. **Description:** Detailed information on determining food truck employee wants and needs. **Availability:** Online.

22133 ■ **"Discipline In Your Business"** in *South Florida Business Journal (Vol. 34, June 6, 2014, No. 46, pp. 10)*
Pub: American City Business Journals, Inc.
Contact: Mike Olivieri, Executive Vice President
Released: Weekly. **Price:** $8, introductory 4-week offer(Digital only). **Description:** Ways a business can maintain a disciplined response to market conditions and achieve success are discussed. Organizations are advised to set clear goals, communicate these goals, and establish clear lines of accountability. The importance of compensation to motivate staff is also explained. **Availability:** Print; Online.

22134 ■ **"The Discomfort Zone: How Leaders Turn Difficult Conversations Into Breakthroughs"**
Released: October 13, 2014. **Price:** $21.95, Nonmembers, paperback; $19.76, Members, paperback; $18.95, paperback; $17.06, paperback; $18.95, Nonmembers, electronic publishing; $13.27, Members, electronic publishing; $18.95, Nonmembers, PDF e-book; $13.27, Members, PDF e-book. **Description:** Top leadership coach provides a model for using the Discomfort Zone, which leads people to think through problems, see situations more strategically, and transcend their limitations. The author draws on recent findings in the neuroscience of learning and provides exercises and case studies to use discomfort in business conversations and communication to create lasing changes and a more motivated workforce. **Availability:** E-book; Print; PDF; Electronic publishing.

22135 ■ **"Does Rudeness Really Matter? The Effects of Rudeness on Task Performance and Helpfulness"** in *Academy of Management Journal (Vol. 50, No. 5, October 1, 2007, pp. 1181)*
Pub: Academy of Management
Contact: Sharon Alvarez, President
Ed: Christine L. Porath, Amir Erez. **Description:** Study assessing the effect of impoliteness on performance and helpfulness showed rude behavior lowered performance levels and also decreased attitude of helpfulness. **Availability:** Electronic publishing; Download; PDF; Online.

22136 ■ **"The Don't Do Lists"** in *Inc. (Vol. 33, October 2011, No. 8, pp. 65)*
Pub: Inc. Magazine
Ed: Jennifer Alsever, Adam Bluestein. **Description:** Ten business leaders and experts share their don't do lists, the things that should be avoided when going on sales calls, planning business lunches, motivating employees and more are presented. **Availability:** Online.

22137 ■ **"Don't Leave Employees on the Outside Looking In"** in *Canadian Business (Vol. 83, July 20, 2010, No. 11-12, pp. 13)*
Description: Managers should be careful with employee's tendencies to use the word 'they' when problems occur since this shows that employees are not associating themselves with their company. Employees should be involved in the development of the company and improving the flow of information is important in overcoming this communication challenge. **Availability:** Print; Online.

22138 ■ **"Doria Camaraza on the Best Advice She's Ever Received 'Leave Your Ego at the Door"** in *South Florida Business Journal (Vol. 34, June 20, 2014, No. 43, pp. 13)*
Pub: American City Business Journals, Inc.
Contact: Mike Olivieri, Executive Vice President
Description: Doria Camaraza, senior vice president and general manager of American Express Service Centers in Fort Lauderdale, Mexico and Argentina, share advice for successfully running service centers for the credit card company. She describes ways in which she inspires creativity and drive, while promoting employee team building with her workers. **Availability:** Print; Online.

22139 ■ **"Downturn Tests HCL's Pledge to Employees"** in *Workforce Management (Vol. 88, November 16, 2009, No. 12, pp. 23)*
Pub: Crain Communications Inc.
Contact: Barry Asin, President
Ed: Ed Frauenheim. **Description:** HCL Technologies has kept its promise to keep from laying any employees off during the recession which served as a test for the tech firm's Employee First program, which seeks to give workers greater income security as well as a stronger voice in the firm. **Availability:** Online.

22140 ■ **"Dream Town Launches Organic Food Delivery for Its Employees"** in *Internet Wire (June 28, 2012)*
Pub: Comtex News Network Inc.
Contact: Kan Devnani, President
Description: Local organics were spotlighted by Chicago real estate online firm, Dream Team, who held a special event for its employees and special guests at the Landmark Century Cinema. Robert Kenner's Food Inc. presented Irv and Shelly's Fresh Picks. Dream Team is committed to helping first time home buyers. **Availability:** Print; Online.

22141 ■ **"The Dynamic DUO"** in *Canadian Electronics (Vol. 23, February 2008, No. 1, pp. 24)*
Description: Citronics Corporation not only aims to proved a good working environment for its employees, it also values the opinions of its personnel. Citronics had its employees test different workbenches before finally purchasing thirty-five of Lista's Align adjustable height workstation, which combines flexibility with aesthetics. The design of the Alin workbench is described. **Availability:** Print; Online.

22142 ■ **"Dynamically Integrating Knowledge in Teams: Transforming Resources Into Performance"** in *Academy of Management Journal (Vol. 55, August 1, 2012, No. 4, pp. 998)*
Pub: Academy of Management
Contact: Sharon Alvarez, President

Ed: Heidi K. Gardner, Francesca Gino, Bradley R. Staats. **Description:** A method for developing a knowledge-integration capability to dynamically integrate the resources of team members into higher performance is proposed. Results suggest that the development of this capability is aided by the use of relational, structural, and experiential resources while uncertainty plays a moderating role in these relationships. **Availability:** Electronic publishing; Download; PDF; Online.

22143 ■ *"Easing the Global (and Costly) Problem of Workplace Stress; Stress Is Reportedly the Leading Cause of Long-Term Sickness for Workers Around the World. But Relief Is In Sight"* in Gallup Business Journal (March 27, 2014)
Pub: Gallup, Inc.
Contact: Jon Clifton, Chief Executive Officer
Description: Stress is considered the leading cause of long-term illness for workers globally. According to an employee engagement survey, workplace stress can be reduced through engagement. **Availability:** Online.

22144 ■ *"The Effects of Perceived Corporate Social Responsibility on Employee Attitudes"* in Business Ethics Quarterly (Vol. 24, April 2014, No. 2, pp. 165)
Pub: Business Ethics Quarterly
Contact: Dawn Elm, Executive Director
E-mail: drelm@stthomas.edu
Description: The impact on employee attitudes and their perceptions of how others outside the organization are treated (i.e., corporate social responsibility) above and beyond the impact of how employees are directly treated by organizations is addressed. Results of a study of 827 employees in 18 organizations show that employee perceptions of corporation social responsibility (CSR) are positively related to organizational commitment with the relationship being partially mediated by work meaningfulness and perceived organizational support (POS) and job satisfaction with work meaningfulness partially mediating the relationship but not POS. **Availability:** Download; PDF; Online.

22145 ■ *"Eight Tips For Leaders On Protecting the Team"* in Puget Sound Business Journal (Vol. 35, August 22, 2014, No. 18, pp. 13)
Pub: American City Business Journals, Inc.
Contact: Mike Olivieri, Executive Vice President
Description: Advice on ways to protect corporate teams is given. Unnecessary information and processes should be filtered to avoid distraction of the team. Team action plans must be prioritized. **Availability:** Print; Online.

22146 ■ *"Empathy, Engagement the 'Secret Sauce' for Post-Pandemic Leadership Success"* in Minority Business Entrepreneur (Vol. 39, Fall, 2022, No. 4, pp. 48-49)
URL(s): digital.mbemag.com/?m=53732&i=769780&p=48&ver=html5
Ed: Merilee Kern. **Released:** 2022. **Description:** A big shift occurred during the COVID pandemic when it comes to employees and keeping them engaged with the job. A lot of employees expect to find more purpose and meaning in their jobs and it's much easier to leave an unsatisfying job these days than it was in the past.

22147 ■ *"The Employee Brand: Is Yours an All-Star?"* in Business Horizons (September-October 2007, pp. 423)
Pub: Elsevier Technology Publications
Contact: Kumsal Bayazit, Chief Executive Officer
Ed: W. Glynn Mangold, Sandra Jeanquart Miles. **Description:** Employees can influence the brand image either positively or negatively. The typology presented provides guidelines on how employees can reflect a company's brand image. Classifications of organizations into all-star rookies, injured reserves, or strike-out kings are also discussed. **Availability:** Online.

22148 ■ *"Empowered"* in Harvard Business Review (Vol. 88, July-August 2010, No. 7-8, pp. 94)
Pub: Harvard Business Publishing
Contact: Diane Belcher, Managing Director
Ed: Josh Bernoff, Ted Schadler. **Price:** $8.95, PDF. **Description:** HERO concept (highly empowered and resourceful operative) which builds a connection between employees, managers, and IT is outlined. The resultant additional experience and knowledge gained by employees improves customer relationship management. **Availability:** Online; PDF.

22149 ■ *"The End of Clock-Punching"* in Canadian Business (Vol. 83, September 14, 2010, No. 15, pp. 96)
Pub: Rogers Media Inc.
Contact: Neil Spivak, Chief Executive Officer
Ed: Lyndsie Bourgon. **Description:** Workplace consultant Peter Hadwen is pushing for the transformation of Canada's government departments into results-only work environments (ROWE). ROWE does not require employees to show up to work at a certain time as long as they are meeting goals and achieving results in their jobs. Details of studies regarding ROWE in US companies are examined. **Availability:** Online.

22150 ■ *"Examining the Real Costs of Remote Work"* in Small Business Trends (September 11, 2022)
URL(s): smallbiztrends.com/2022/09/the-real-costs-of-remote-work.html
Ed: Gabrielle Pickard-Whitehead. **Released:** September 11, 2022. **Description:** With the advent of the pandemic, many offices switched to remote work. Now that offices are opening back up, not everyone wants to return. While there are many benefits to working at home there are a few drawbacks, which are discussed here. **Availability:** Online.

22151 ■ *"Executive Summary: Codeines and Coding"* in Business Strategy Review (Vol. 23, Spring 2012, No. 1, pp. 82)
Description: Adam Powell, Sergei Savin, and Nicos Savva, 'Physician Workload and Hospital Reimbursement: Overworked Servers Generate Lower Income', working paper, August 2011 is examined. **Availability:** Online.

22152 ■ *"Experts Share How to Create Company Culture That Gets Results"* in Small Business Trends (October 29, 2022)
URL(s): smallbiztrends.com/2022/10/how-to-create-company-culture-that-gets-results.html
Ed: Annie Pilon. **Released:** October 29, 2022. **Description:** The culture within a company is a big deal since employees are required to spend the majority of their day there. Having a culture that is positive helps your current employees stay engaged and it can also attract top talent when you are hiring. **Availability:** Online.

22153 ■ *"Explaining Organizational Responsiveness to Work-Life Balance Issues: the Role of Business Strategy and High-Performance Work Systems"* in Human Resource Management (Vol. 51, May- June 2012, No. 3, pp. 407-432)
Pub: John Wiley & Sons, Inc.
Contact: Christina Van Tassell, Executive Vice President Chief Financial Officer
Ed: Jing Wang, Anil Verma. **Released:** May 25, 2012. **Description:** The effects of business strategies and high-performance work systems on the adoption of work-life balance programs are examined. Results indicate a mediating role of high-performance work systems in the relationship between business strategies and the adoption of work-life balance programs. **Availability:** Print; PDF; Online.

22154 ■ *"Facilitating and Rewarding Creativity During New Product Development"* in Journal of Marketing (Vol. 75, July 2011, No. 4, pp. 53)
Pub: American Marketing Association
Contact: Bennie F. Johnson, Chief Executive Officer
Ed: James E. Burroughs, Darren W. Dahl, C. Page Moreau, Amitava Chattopadhay, Gerald J. Gorn. **Description:** A study to determine the effects of rewards to creativity in the process of new product development is presented. The findings show that the effect of rewards can be made positive if combined with appropriate creativity training. **Availability:** PDF.

22155 ■ *"Family Dollar Reaches Preliminary Class Action Settlement"* in Benzinga.com (September 12, 2012)
Pub: Benzinga.com
Contact: Jason Raznick, Founder
Description: Family Dollar Stores Inc. has reached a preliminary settlement with New York store managers. The settlement provides 1,700 managers a maximum payment of $14 million. A profile of the Family Dollar Stores company is also included. **Availability:** Print; Online.

22156 ■ *"Forward Motion"* in Green Industry Pro (July 2011)
Ed: Gregg Wartgow. **Description:** Several landscape contractors have joined this publication's Working Smarter Training Challenge over the last year. This process is helping them develop ways to improve work processes, boost morale, drive out waste, reduce costs, improve customer service, and be more competitive. **Availability:** Print; Online.

22157 ■ *"Friends With (Health) Benefits"* in Canadian Business (Vol. 87, July 2014, No. 7, pp. 32)
Description: The benefits of turning professional working relationships into real friendships and strong personal bonds are explained. The decision to create warm and respectful culture in the company will pay a lot of dividends in long-term employee motivation and team work. **Availability:** Print; Online.

22158 ■ *"Gain the 'Come Alive Outside' Selling Edge"* in Green Industry Pro (July 2011)
Ed: Jim Paluch. **Description:** Marketing the 'Come Alive Outside' slogan can help landscapers to increase their market share by identifying and applying these elements to each customer as well as their workers. **Availability:** Online.

22159 ■ *"Generalizing Newcomers' Relational and Organizational Identifications: Processes and Prototypicality"* in Academy of Management Journal (Vol. 55, August 1, 2012, No. 4, pp. 949)
Pub: Academy of Management
Contact: Sharon Alvarez, President
Ed: David M. Sluss, Robert E. Ployhart, M. Glenn Cobb, Blake E. Ashforth. **Description:** The process in which newcomers identify themselves with a supervisor and with the employing organization is examined. Results suggest that relational identification with a supervisor converges with organizational identification through effective, cognitive and behavioral mechanisms yet only when the relational other is perceived to be prototypical. **Availability:** Electronic publishing; Download; PDF; Online.

22160 ■ *"Getting Drowned Out by the Brainstorm"* in Canadian Business (Vol. 83, June 15, 2010, No. 10, pp. 91)
Pub: Rogers Media Inc.
Contact: Neil Spivak, Chief Executive Officer
Ed: Joe Castaldo. **Description:** A study reveals that people generate more ideas when they do it alone rather than as part of a brainstorming group. The limited range of ideas is due to the fixation of group members on the first idea that gets offered. **Availability:** Online.

22161 ■ *"Getting to 'Us'"* in Harvard Business Review (Vol. 92, September 2014, No. 9, pp. 38)
Pub: Harvard Business Publishing
Contact: Diane Belcher, Managing Director

Price: $6. **Description:** Employee motivation and satisfaction can be enhanced through leadership that presents a shared goal that emphasizes kinship and relationship to others, rather than citing a common enemy. **Availability:** Online; PDF.

22162 ■ *"Gilt Groupe's CEO On Building a Team of A Players"* in *Harvard Business Review (Vol. 90, January-February 2012, No.1-2, pp. 43)*
Pub: Harvard Business Review Press
Contact: Moderna V. Pfizer, Contact
Ed: Kevin Ryan. **Description:** The author stresses the role of human capital in a firm's success, and the importance of employment references in determining a candidate's talents. Key questions include whether the reference would hire the person, whether people enjoy working with him or her, and what areas could use improvements.

22163 ■ *"Glenmede at Liberty To Show Off Space"* in *Philadelphia Business Journal (Vol. 32, January 24, 2014, No. 50, pp. 8)*
Pub: American City Business Journals, Inc.
Contact: Mike Olivieri, Executive Vice President
Released: Weekly. **Price:** $4, introductory 4-week offer(Digital & Print). **Description:** Glenmede Trust Company decided to undertake a full office renovation after renewing its lease at One Liberty Place. The investment company decided to replace drywall with glass and more informal meeting places be constructed. The firm, which focuses on employee engagement, aims to improve the work environment. **Availability:** Print; Online.

22164 ■ *Go Put Your Strengths to Work*
Pub: Free Press/Simon and Schuster Inc.
Contact: Jonathan Karp, President
Ed: Marcus Buckingham. **Description:** A guide to being more productive, focused and creative at work. **Availability:** Video; Online.

22165 ■ *"Go Team! Why Building a Cohesive Organization Is a Necessary Exercise"* in *Black Enterprise (Vol. 38, February 2008, No. 7, pp. 66)*
Pub: Earl G. Graves Ltd.
Contact: Earl Graves, Jr., President
Ed: Angeli R. Rasbury. **Description:** Tips to help manage successful as well as productive teams are outlined for small business managers. **Availability:** Online.

22166 ■ *"HBR Case Study: When the Longtime Star Fades"* in *Harvard Business Review (Vol. 88, September 2010, No. 9, pp. 117)*
Pub: Harvard Business Publishing
Contact: Diane Belcher, Managing Director
Ed: Jimmy Guterman. **Price:** $8.95, PDF. **Description:** A fictitious aging employee scenario is presented, with contributors offering advice. The scenario focuses on an older employee's match with a rapidly changing industry; suggestions include consolidating a niche business around the employee, and also engaging the older employee in solving the productivity issue. **Availability:** Online; PDF.

22167 ■ *"Healthy Workers = A Healthy Company"* in *Minority Business Entrepreneur (Vol. 39, Fall, 2022, No. 4, pp. 18-19)*
URL(s): digital.mbemag.com/?m=53732&i=769780&p=18&ver=html5
Ed: James Harold Webb. **Price:** $7.95. **Description:** Discusses how a wellness program in your company benefits your employees. **Availability:** Print; Online.

22168 ■ *"A Heart for Software; Led by Its Upbeat CEO, Menlo Spreads Joy of Technology"* in *Crain's Detroit Business (Vol. 30, October 13, 2014, No. 41, pp. 1)*
Pub: Crain Communications Inc.
Contact: Barry Asin, President
Description: Profile of Rich Sheridan, one of the most prominent names in IT in Ann Arbor, Michigan. Sheridan believes in common-sense solutions and manages his workers to be empowered employees to come up with their own solutions to software coding issues, and he is a consummate salesman and marketer. He runs his company so it goes beyond understanding what the user needs, and managing a great team, to being the front man selling his goods and services. **Availability:** Print; Online.

22169 ■ *"The Hidden Advantages of Quiet Bosses"* in *Harvard Business Review (Vol. 88, December 2010, No. 12, pp. 28)*
Pub: Harvard Business Publishing
Contact: Diane Belcher, Managing Director
Ed: Adam M. Grant, Francesca Gino, David A. Hofmann. **Price:** $6, PDF. **Description:** Research on organizations behavior indicates that, while extroverts most often become managers, introvert managers paired with proactive employees make a highly efficient and effective combination. **Availability:** Online; PDF.

22170 ■ *"Holiday Shopping Meets Social Media"* in *Employee Benefit News (Vol. 25, December 1, 2011, No. 15)*
Pub: SourceMedia LLC
Contact: Gemma Postlethwaite, Chief Executive Officer
Ed: Rob J. Thurston. **Description:** Offering employees access to discount shopping using social media sites for Christmas bonuses, could be the gift that keeps on giving.

22171 ■ *"How to Avoid Quiet Quitting and Lead a Successful Small Business Team"* in *Small Business Trends (February 4, 2023)*
URL(s): smallbiztrends.com/2023/02/how-to-avoid-quiet-quitting.html
Ed: Annie Pilon. **Released:** February 04, 2023. **Description:** Quite quitting is becoming more prevalent within the workforce and this article aims to help small business owners avoid this situation with their employees. **Availability:** Online.

22172 ■ *"How to Build a Great Employee Benefits Package"* in *Business News Daily (February 21, 2023)*
URL(s): www.businessnewsdaily.com/9494-small-business-benefits-package.html
Ed: Andreas Rivera. **Description:** Small business owners may need to start providing a benefits package to entice quality employees. Details about what to included are discussed. **Availability:** Online.

22173 ■ *How to Build a Winning Sales Team: Tips and Strategies*
URL(s): www.barnesandnoble.com/w/how-to-build-a-winning-sales-team-tips-and-strategies-james-dickson/1143168176?ean=2940185841747
Ed: James Dickson. **Released:** March 04, 2023. **Price:** $4.99, e-book. **Description:** Increasing growth and revenue is usually the main goal of a business, so having a successful sales team will make all the difference. Learn how to develop a sales team with the tips and tools provided in this book. **Availability:** E-book.

22174 ■ *"How to Divorce Your Office Spouse"* in *Canadian Business (Vol. 83, June 15, 2010, No. 10, pp. 74)*
Pub: Rogers Media Inc.
Contact: Neil Spivak, Chief Executive Officer
Ed: Jacqueline Nelson. **Description:** A work spouse or the platonic relationship between male and female coworkers can increase productivity in some cases, but these friendships can become complicated due to power struggles and sexual tension. When this type of relationship goes sour, it is advised to tell the spouse honestly how you feel. **Availability:** Online.

22175 ■ *"How Employees' Strengths Make Your Company Stronger; Employees Who Use Their Strengths Are More Engaged, Perform Better, Are Less Likely To Leave -- and Boost Your Bottom Line"* in *Gallup Business Journal (February 20, 2014)*
Pub: Gallup, Inc.
Contact: Jon Clifton, Chief Executive Officer
Description: The best way for organizations to maximize their workers' strengths is through their managers. When staff members know and use their strongest skills, they are more engaged and will perform better, have a higher sense of well being, are less likely to seek employment elsewhere, while increasing the firm's bottom line. **Availability:** Online.

22176 ■ *How Entrepreneurs Can Motivate Workers*
URL(s): smallbusiness.chron.com/entrepreneurs-can-motivate-workers-51927.html
Ed: Lisa McQuerrey. **Description:** Discusses ways in which entrepreneurs can keep workers enthused and dedicated. **Availability:** Online.

22177 ■ *"How to Get a Workplace Wellness Program for Your Office"* in *Entrepreneurs (June 2014)*
Pub: Entrepreneur Media Inc.
Contact: Dan Bova, Director
E-mail: dbova@entrepreneur.com
Description: Workplace wellness programs can be started by checking with insurers who may provide program and activity suggestions promotional materials or other resources. Teaming up with others is encouraged. For instance, employees from various departments or nearby companies can get flu shots or blood pressure screening. Management should also get involved in these programs, because it will then be known among employees that wellness is taken seriously. It is also important that workplace wellness programs are kept safe and legally sound. **Availability:** Online.

22178 ■ *"How Great Leaders Think: The Art of Reframing"*
Pub: Jossey-Bass
Released: July 01, 2014. **Price:** $30, hardcover. **Description:** More complex thinking is the key to better leadership. A guide to help leaders understand four major aspects of organizational life: structure, people, politics, and culture is given. The book's lessons include: how to use structural tools to organize teams and organizations for better results, how to build motivation and morale by aligning organizations and people, how to map the terrain and build a power base to navigate the political dynamics of organizations, and how to develop a leadership story that shapes culture, provides direction, and inspires commitment to excellence. **Availability:** E-book; Print.

22179 ■ *"How to Make Remote Team Collaboration More Successful"* in *Blog.vantagecircle.com(January 3, 2023)*
URL(s): blog.vantagecircle.com/remote-team-collaboration/
Ed: Braja Deepon Roy. **Released:** January 03, 2023. **Description:** With working from home being the new reality for many companies, staff will need to learn how to function as an effective team with all new digital technology instead of old-fashioned face-to-face meetings.

22180 ■ *"How to Manage and Motivate a Remote Workforce during a Crisis"* in *Legal Zoom (February 17, 2023)*
URL(s): www.legalzoom.com/articles/how-to-manage-and-motivate-a-remote-workforce-during-a-crisis
Ed: Diane Faulkner. **Released:** February 17, 2023. **Description:** Your small business may face some sort of crisis at one point, such as the one presented by the COVID-19 pandemic. This article gives advice on how to keep your employees motivated and focused. **Availability:** Online.

22181 ■ *"How to Manage the New Expectations of the Younger Workforce"* in *Entrepreneur (March 21, 2023)*
URL(s): www.entrepreneur.com/leadership/how-to-manage-the-new-expectations-of-the-younger-workforce/447205
Ed: Cheri Beranek. **Released:** March 21, 2023. **Description:** With a smaller workforce to choose from, employers are now being confronted with a workforce that has different expectations than previ-

ous generations had. This article discusses what's changed and what procedures workplaces need to adjust. **Availability:** Online.

22182 ■ *"How to Retain That 'Small Business' Feel as Your Company Grows"* in *Small Business Trends (December 9, 2021)*
URL(s): smallbiztrends.com/2021/12/small-business-feel-while-company-grows.html
Released: December 09, 2021. **Description:** Many businesses thrive when their culture is based on a small business feel. However, how does a business retain that concept when the business starts expanding and becoming more corporate? Included are tips to make sure the culture that made your business successful is retained. **Availability:** Online.

22183 ■ *"How Small Business Can Motivate Employees"* on StartupBros website
URL(s): startupbros.com/how-small-business-can-motivate-employees-to-boost-productivity/
Ed: Mark Feldman. **Description:** Discusses what makes employee motivation challenging, how managers can help, and how to implement motivation methods to improve employee productivity for your small business. **Availability:** Online.

22184 ■ *"How To Earn Loyalty From Millenials"* in *Birmingham Business Journal (Vol. 31, February 28, 2014, No. 9, pp. 16)*
Pub: American City Business Journals, Inc.
Contact: Mike Olivieri, Executive Vice President
Released: Weekly. **Price:** $4, Introductory 4-week offer(Digital only). **Description:** Advice for earning loyalty from millennial employees is offered. Management need to create an environment where mistakes are openly admitted and employees should be encouraged to give back to causes that matter most to them. **Availability:** Print; Online.

22185 ■ *"How to Turn Employee Conflict Into a Positive, Productive Force"* in *HR Specialist (Vol. 8, September 2010, No. 9, pp. 6)*
Pub: Capitol Information Group Inc.
Contact: Allie Ash, Chief Executive Officer
Description: Ways to help manage a team of workers are presented, focusing on ways to avoid conflict within the group are discussed. **Availability:** Print; Online; PDF.

22186 ■ *"Increasing HR's Strategic Participation: the Effect of HR Service Quality and Contribution Expectations"* in *Human Resource Management (Vol. 51, January-February 2012, No. 1, pp. 3-23)*
Pub: John Wiley & Sons, Inc.
Contact: Christina Van Tassell, Executive Vice President Chief Financial Officer
Ed: Jin Feng Uen, David Ahlstrom, Shu-Yuan Chen, Pai-Wei Tseng. **Released:** January 26, 2012. **Description:** The impact of human resources service quality and human resources contribution expectations on the strategic participation of human resources in organizations is examined. Human resource professionals are found to increase the organizational value of human resources through improving quality and addressing the needs of potential internal customers. **Availability:** Print; PDF; Online.

22187 ■ *"Innovation Despite Reorganization"* in *Journal of Business Strategy (Vol. 35, May-June 2014, No. 3, pp. 18-25)*
Pub: Emerald Group Publishing Limited
Contact: Erika Valenti, President
Description: Innovation can be sustained through a downsizing event. The articles shows how prevailing formal and informal networks can be used for reestablishing connections between employees after a company is downsized. **Availability:** Download; Online.

22188 ■ *"Is Remote Working Really Impeding Collaboration and Communication?"* in *Reworked(September 21, 2021)*
URL(s): www.reworked.co/digital-workplace/is-remote-working-really-impeding-collaboration-and-communication/
Ed: David Roe. **Released:** September 20, 2021. **Description:** The pandemic all but forced many offices into a remote work situation, which some were not ready for and many companies and employees found to be disruptive and a detriment to their work. However, as remote work progressed through the months, solutions were developed through technology, communication, and deeper collaboration between business units. **Availability:** Online.

22189 ■ *"It's Not the How or the What but the Who: Succeed by Surrounding Yourself with the Best"*
Pub: Harvard Business Review Press
Contact: Moderna V. Pfizer, Contact
Released: June 03, 2014. **Price:** $32, Hardcover/Hardcopy. **Description:** Surrounding yourself with the best matters in every aspect of life and can mean the difference between success and failure. The author draws upon years of experience in global executive search and talent development, as well as the latest management and psychology research, to help improve the choices management makes about employees and mentors, business partners and friends, top corporate leaders and elected officials. **Availability:** E-book; Print.

22190 ■ *"Jenna Bush Hager: Forging Her Own Career and Identity"* in *Women in Business (Vol. 66, Summer 2014, No. 1, pp. 10)*
Ed: Leigh Elmore. **Description:** Jenna Bush Hager, daughter of former United States President George W. Bush, believes that women who are entering the workforce need to look for mentors who can help them grow. Hager, who works as a correspondent for the "Today" show, also thinks that women employees should become part of a team. **Availability:** Print; Online.

22191 ■ *"The Job Survival Equation"* in *Women in Business (Vol. 65, Winter 2013, No. 3, pp. 36)*
Description: How combining skills and a positive attitude can improve job survivability after a layoff is discussed. The attitude side of survivability is said to be more difficult than improving one's set of skills, because people do not always see themselves as others see them. **Availability:** Online.

22192 ■ *"Justice In Self-Managing Teams: the Role of Social Networks In the Emergence of Procedural Justice Climates"* in *Academy of Management Journal (Vol. 55, June 1, 2012, No. 3, pp. 685)*
Pub: Academy of Management
Contact: Sharon Alvarez, President
Ed: Quinetta M. Roberson, Ian O. Williamson. **Description:** The effect of social network content and structure on organizational justice in self-managing teams is studied using data from 79 project teams. Findings show that team instrumental network density has positive impact on procedural justice climate strength. Low team functional background diversity was also found to strengthen this relationship. **Availability:** Electronic publishing; Download; PDF; Online.

22193 ■ *"Labor and Management: Working Together for a Stable Future"* in *Alaska Business Monthly (Vol. 27, October 2011, No. 10, pp. 130)*
Pub: Alaska Business Publishing Company Inc.
Contact: Charles Bell, Vice President, Sales and Marketing
E-mail: cbell@akbizmag.com
Ed: Nicole A. Bonham Colby. **Description:** Alaska unions and employers are working to ensure a consistent flow of skilled Alaska workers as current the current workforce reaches retirement age. **Availability:** Print; Online.

22194 ■ *"The Last Word Dirty Work Required"* in *Workforce Management (Vol. 88, November 16, 2009, No. 12, pp. 34)*
Pub: Crain Communications Inc.
Contact: Barry Asin, President
Ed: John Hollon. **Description:** Due to salary freezes, pay cuts, layoffs, buyouts and a number of other stress factors brought about by the recession, employee engagement has been difficult to maintain by managers. **Availability:** Online.

22195 ■ *"Lead Like It Matters...Because It Does: Practical Leadership Tools to Inspire and Engage Your People and Create Great Results"*
Released: First Edition. **Price:** $33; $33. **Description:** The Ripple Effect method for increasing employee engagement, reducing turnover, and driving overall business success will help any manager or entrepreneur to lead his company. Important practices like eliminating wasted meetings, addressing conflict, and aligning decisions with business needs are addressed. **Availability:** E-book; Print; Online.

22196 ■ *"Leaders Eat Last Deluxe: Why Some Teams Pull Together and Others Don't"*
Pub: Penguin Publishing Group
Released: May 23, 2017. **Price:** $7.99, e-book; $17, paperback ; $28, hardcover ; $10.99, enhanced e-book . **Description:** Author of "Start with Why" returns to help create happier and healthier organizations. Sinek helps us to understand the biology of trust and cooperation and why they are critical to success and fulfillment. He believes that organizations that develop environments filled with trust and cooperation thrive and outperform competition because employees love working there. **Availability:** enhanced e-book ; E-book; Print.

22197 ■ *"The Leadership Equation: 10 Practices That Build Trust, Spark Innovation, and Create High-Performing Organizations"*
Pub: Greenleaf Book Group Press
Contact: Tanya Hall, Chief Executive Officer
Released: September 30, 2014. **Price:** $18.95, U.S., paperback. **Description:** Entrepreneur and business consultant draws upon his work with corporations, government agencies, and nonprofit organizations and their human resource departments to explain the workings of high-performing organizations with his equation: Trust + Spark = Leadership Culture. He describes the ten more important practices for building trust and spark that improves team performance, the business unit, and the entire organization. **Availability:** Print.

22198 ■ *"Leadership: Growing Pains"* in *Canadian Business (Vol. 80, November 19, 2007, No. 23, pp. 41)*
Pub: Rogers Media Inc.
Contact: Neil Spivak, Chief Executive Officer
Ed: Lauren McKeon. **Description:** Employee promotions must be done with consideration to the effects of ill-prepared leadership, which include high worker turnover, low morale, and ineffective management. Organizations must handle the transition period involved in promotion by setting clear expectations, providing guidelines on approaching different situations, and by welcoming the promoted employees; impacts are further analyzed. **Availability:** Online.

22199 ■ *"Leadership Is a Conversation: How To Improve Employee Engagement and Alignment In Today's Flatter, More Networked Organizations"* in *Harvard Business Review (Vol. 90, June 2012, No. 6, pp. 76)*
Pub: Harvard Business Review Press
Contact: Moderna V. Pfizer, Contact
Ed: Boris Groysberg, Michael Slind. **Description:** A two-way flow of communication is essential in promoting and maintaining employee motivation. Key points are establishing intimacy through gaining trust, interactivity via dialogue, inclusion by expanding employee roles, and intentionality through establishing an agenda.

22200 ■ *"Lessons from Turnaround Leaders"* in *Strategy and Leadership (Vol. 39, May-June 2011, No. 3, pp. 36-43)*
Pub: Emerald Group Publishing Limited
Contact: Erika Valenti, President

Ed: David P. Boyd. **Description:** A study analyzes the cases of some successful turnaround leaders to present a strategic model to help firms tackle challenges such as employee inertia, competition and slow organizational renewal. It describes a change model consisting of five major steps to be followed by firms with environmental uncertainty for the purpose. **Availability:** Download; Online.

22201 ■ *"Let's Go Team: When a Retail Professional Leads by Example, Everyone Benefits" in Black Enterprise (Vol. 41, November 2010, No. 4)*
Pub: Earl G. Graves Ltd.
Contact: Earl Graves, Jr., President
Ed: Aisha I. Jefferson. **Description:** Profile of Derek Jenkins, senior vice president of Target Stores Northeast Region is presented. Jenkins oversees the management of 450 retail stores with nearly 75,000 workers. He shares insight into managing by making sure every interaction with his team counts.

22202 ■ *"Life's Work: Interview with Alain Ducasse" in Harvard Business Review (Vol. 92, May 2014, No. 5, pp. 136)*
Pub: Harvard Business Press
Contact: Gabriela Allmi, Regional Manager
E-mail: gabriela.allmi@hbsp.harvard.edu
Price: $8.95. **Description:** Alain Ducasse believes supervision is secondary to shared experience, and emphasizes the importance of communicating with employees to engage them and enable them to perform well. Job satisfaction is dependent on individual growth, appropriate compensation, and harmony. **Availability:** PDF; Online.

22203 ■ *"Life's Work: Ben Bradlee" in Harvard Business Review (Vol. 88, September 2010, No. 9, pp. 128)*
Pub: Harvard Business Publishing
Contact: Diane Belcher, Managing Director
Ed: Alison Beard. **Price:** $8.95, PDF. **Description:** Newspaper publisher Ben Bradlee discusses factors that lead to success, including visible supervisors, enthusiasm, appropriate expansion, and the importance in truth in reporting. **Availability:** Online; PDF.

22204 ■ *"Linking HRM and Knowledge Transfer Via Individual-Level Mechanisms" in Human Resource Management (Vol. 51, May-June 2012, No. 3, pp. 387-405)*
Pub: John Wiley & Sons, Inc.
Contact: Christina Van Tassell, Executive Vice President Chief Financial Officer
Ed: Dana B. Minbaeva, Kristina Makela, Larissa Rabbiosi. **Released:** May 25, 2012. **Description:** The relationship between human resource management and knowledge transfer and the role of individual-level mechanisms in this relationship are examined. Results indicate that individual-level perceptions of organizational commitment to knowledge sharing and extrinsic motivation affect internal knowledge exchange among employees. **Availability:** Print; PDF; Online.

22205 ■ *"Managerial Rudeness: Bad Attitudes Can Demoralize Your Staff" in Black Enterprise (Vol. 37, January 2007, No. 6, pp. 58)*
Pub: Earl G. Graves Ltd.
Contact: Earl Graves, Jr., President
Ed: Chauntelle Folds. **Description:** Positive leadership in the managerial realm leads to a more productive workplace. Managers who are negative, hostile, arrogant, rude or fail to accept any responsibility for their own mistakes find that employees will not give their all on the job. **Availability:** Online.

22206 ■ *The Manager's Guide to Rewards: What You Need to Know to Get the Best of-and-from-Your Employees*
Availability: E-book.

22207 ■ *Managing the Older Worker: How to Prepare for the New Organizational Order*
Pub: Harvard Business Press
Contact: Gabriela Allmi, Regional Manager

E-mail: gabriela.allmi@hbsp.harvard.edu
Ed: Peter Cappelli, Bill Novelli. **Description:** Your organization needs older workers more than ever: They transfer knowledge between generations, transmit your company's values to new hires, make excellent mentors for younger employees, and provide a 'just in time' workforce for special projects. **Availability:** Print; Audio.

22208 ■ *"The Moderating Effects of Organizational Context On the Relationship Between Voluntary Turnover and Organizational Performance: Evidence from Korea" in Human Resource Management (Vol. 51, January-February 2012, No. 1, pp. 47-70)*
Pub: John Wiley & Sons, Inc.
Contact: Christina Van Tassell, Executive Vice President Chief Financial Officer
Ed: Kiwook Kwon, Kweontaek Chung, Hyuntak Roh, Clint Chadwick, John J. Lawler. **Released:** January 26, 2012. **Description:** The ability of organizational context to moderate the relationship between voluntary employee turnover and organizational performance is examined using data from South Korean firms. The effects of employee involvement practices, investment in employee training and development, and the availability of potential workers on this relationship are studied. **Availability:** Print; PDF; Online.

22209 ■ *"Money Isn't Enough: 6 Incentives to Motivate Your Employees" in Business News Daily (March 17, 2023)*
URL(s): www.businessnewsdaily.com/10731-money-not-enough.html
Ed: Bassam Kaado. **Released:** March 17, 2023. **Description:** Discusses ways to motivate your employees with something other than a raise. **Availability:** Online.

22210 ■ *"Music and Its Effect on Productivity" in Business News Daily (March 7, 2023)*
URL(s): www.businessnewsdaily.com/11294-music-effect-on-productivity.html
Ed: Skye Schooley. **Released:** March 07, 2023. **Description:** If you are looking to create a positive environment and boost productivity, consider adding music in your small business. This article explains the effects music has on people and their work. **Availability:** Online.

22211 ■ *"Negotiating Tips" in Black Enterprise (Vol. 37, December 2006, No. 5, pp. 70)*
Pub: Earl G. Graves Ltd.
Contact: Earl Graves, Jr., President
Ed: Marcia A. Reed-Woodard. **Description:** Sekou Kaalund, head of strategy, mergers & acquisitions at Citigroup Securities & Fund Services, states that "Negotiation skills are paramount to success in a business environment because of client, employee, and shareholder relationships". He discusses how the book by George Kohlrieser, Hostage at the Table: How Leaders Can Overcome Conflict, Influence Others, and Raise Performance, has helped him negotiate more powerfully and enhance his skills at conflict-resolution. **Availability:** Online.

22212 ■ *"The New Science of Building Great Teams: The Chemistry of High-Performing Groups Is No Longer a Mystery" in Harvard Business Review (Vol. 90, April 2012, No. 4, pp. 60)*
Pub: Harvard Business Review Press
Contact: Moderna V. Pfizer, Contact
Ed: Alex Pentland. **Description:** Body language and tone of voice are key to the dynamics of a team that works well together. Face-to-face communication is the most valuable. Energy, engagement, and exploration delineate how team members contribute, communicate with other team members, and communicate with other teams respectively.

22213 ■ *"Nine Paradoxes of Problem Solving" in Strategy and Leadership (Vol. 39, May-June 2011, No. 3, pp. 25-31)*
Pub: Emerald Group Publishing Limited
Contact: Erika Valenti, President
Ed: Alex Lowy. **Description:** Nine frequently-occurring inherent paradoxes in corporate decision making for solving complex problems are identified. The methods with which these paradoxes and their influence can be recognized and dealt with for firm leaders and management team members to better understand and solve the problems are discussed. **Availability:** Download; Online.

22214 ■ *"No Place Like Home? An Identity Strain Perspective On Repatriate Turnover" in Academy of Management Journal (Vol. 55, April 1, 2012, No. 2, pp. 399)*
Pub: Academy of Management
Contact: Sharon Alvarez, President
Ed: Maria L. Kraimer, Margaret A. Shaffer, David A. Harrison, Hong Ren. **Description:** Identity theory is invoked to investigate why employees returning from an international assignment may leave their organizations. Identity strain is attributed to the relation between prior job embeddedness during expatriation and strength of one's identity as an international employee of repatriation. Implications on international role transitions and turnover mechanisms are discussed. **Availability:** Electronic publishing; Download; PDF; Online.

22215 ■ *"The Office Christmas Party and Legal Liability" in Legal Zoom (March 23, 2023)*
URL(s): www.legalzoom.com/articles/the-office-christmas-party-and-legal-liability
Ed: Ann MacDonald. **Released:** March 23, 2023. **Description:** Discusses some of the settings that could get a small business owner in legal trouble during the annual office Christmas party. Also includes alternatives and rules to have in order to avoid compromising situations. **Availability:** Online.

22216 ■ *"On the Edge: The Art of High-Impact Leadership"*
Released: January 07, 2014. **Price:** $30, audiobook CD; $13.99, e-book; $24.98, audiobook downloadable; $27, hardcover. **Description:** Alison Levine provides insights into leadership garnered from her various expeditions from Mount Everest to the South Pole. Levine believes that leadership principles that apply in extreme adventure sport also apply in today's extreme business environment. She discusses your survival as well as the survival of the team. **Availability:** CD-ROM; E-book; Print.

22217 ■ *"Open For Business" in Baltimore Business Journal (Vol. 30, June 22, 2012, No. 7, pp. 1)*
Ed: James Briggs. **Description:** The demand for offices with open floor plans has risen as companies look to improve collaboration while cutting costs. Incorporating glass walls and low desks to open office design allow the flow of natural light, which in turn, reduces energy bills. How companies are addressing the challenge of maintaining privacy in an open office design are also discussed. **Availability:** Print; Online.

22218 ■ *"Optimizing the Power of Your Employees through Diversity and Inclusion" in Minority Business Entrepreneur (Vol. 39, Fall, 2022, No. 4, pp. 10-11)*
URL(s): digital.mbemag.com/?m=53732&i=769780&p=1&ver=html5
Ed: Celeste W. Warren. **Price:** $7.95. **Description:** Explains how diversity and inclusion can benefit your company's culture and help make your company a success. **Availability:** Print; Online.

22219 ■ *The Orange Revolution: How One Great Team Can Transform an Entire Organization*
Pub: Simon & Schuster, Inc.
Contact: Jonathan Karp, President

Ed: Adrian Gostick, Chester Elton. **Released:** September 2010. **Price:** $25, hardcover; $16.99. **Description:** Based on a 350,000-person study by the Best Companies Group, as well as research into exceptional teams at leading companies, including Zappos.com, Pepsi Beverages Company, and Madison Square Garden, the authors have determined a key set of characteristics displayed by members of breakthrough teams, and have identified a set of rules great teams live by, which generate a culture of positive teamwork and led to extraordinary results. Using specific stories from the teams they studied, they reveal in detail how these teams operate and how managers can transform their own teams into such high performers by fostering: stronger clarity of goals, greater trust among team members, more open and honest dialogue, stronger accountability for all team members, and purpose-based recognition of team member contributions. **Availability:** E-book; Print.

22220 ■ *"The Outcome of an Organization Overhaul" in Black Enterprise (Vol. 41, December 2010, No. 5)*
Pub: Earl G. Graves Ltd.
Contact: Earl Graves, Jr., President
Ed: Tamara E. Holmes. **Description:** Savvy business owners understand the need for change in order to stay competitive and be successful. This article examines how to manage change as well as what strategies can help employees to get with the program faster. **Availability:** Online.

22221 ■ *"Pay or Play: Do Nice (Sales) Guys Finish Last?" in Agency Sales Magazine (Vol. 39, August 2009, No. 8, pp. 8)*
Description: How positive interpersonal relationships among salespersons, program coordinators, and other business-related professions will pay in terms of business success is presented. Business people should know the ideal customers, promise only what they can do, refer out when needed, and follow through with any stated promise. Further insight into these ideas is presented. **Availability:** Online.

22222 ■ *"Pep Talk: Marketing An Independent Film" in Black Enterprise (Vol. 40, July 2010, No. 12, pp. 104)*
Pub: Earl G. Graves Ltd.
Contact: Earl Graves, Jr., President
Ed: Tennille M. Robinson. **Description:** Advice for maintaining motivation in any small business is given. **Availability:** Online.

22223 ■ *"The Performer: Soulpepper Theatre Company's Albert Shultz" in Canadian Business (Vol. 83, August 17, 2010, No. 13-14, pp. 71)*
Pub: Rogers Media Inc.
Contact: Neil Spivak, Chief Executive Officer
Ed: Steve Maich. **Description:** Soulpepper Theater Company founder and actor/director Albert Schultz shares the key ingredient to his success both artistically and commercially. Schultz believes his success was a combination of passion and persistence, as well as team building. He believes his entrepreneurial impulse came when he began thinking of making opportunities instead of taking them.

22224 ■ *"Pet Store Pro Adds New Curriculum" in Pet Product News (Vol. 66, February 2012, No. 2, pp. 2012)*
Description: Pet Store Pro, the Pet Industry Distributors Association's free online training program, is going to launch chapters of a curriculum intended to assist pet store managers learn effective approaches to motivate employees and boost profitability. Other management-level chapters to be added by Pet Store Pro throughout 2012 are listed. **Availability:** Print; Online.

22225 ■ *"Pete Carroll's Winning Rule: Protect Your Team" in Puget Sound Business Journal (Vol. 35, July 25, 2014, No. 14, pp. 12)*
Pub: American City Business Journals, Inc.
Contact: Mike Olivieri, Executive Vice President
Released: Weekly. **Price:** $4, Introductory 4-week offer(Digital & Print). **Description:** Seattle Seahawks coach, Pete Carroll, has three simple rules for team success and the first rule is to always protect the team. The rule is also important in every workplace because it will help align the workers attention to their behavior. Seven ways to protect the team are outlined. **Availability:** Print; Online.

22226 ■ *"Power Play" in Harvard Business Review (Vol. 88, July-August 2010, No. 7-8, pp. 84)*
Pub: Harvard Business Publishing
Contact: Diane Belcher, Managing Director
Ed: Jeffrey Pfeffer. **Price:** $8.95, PDF. **Description:** Guidelines include in-depth understanding of resources at one's disposal, relentlessness that still provides opponents with opportunities to save face, and a determination not to be put off by the processes of politics. **Availability:** Online; PDF.

22227 ■ *"The Power of Self Leadership" in Minority Business Entrepreneur (Vol. 39, Fall, 2022, No. 4, pp. 46-47)*
URL(s): digital.mbemag.com/?m=53732&i=769780&p=46&ver=html5
Ed: Jacqueline M. Baker. **Price:** $7.95. **Description:** Discusses developing employees as self leaders. **Availability:** Print; Online.

22228 ■ *"Powerlessness Corrupts" in Harvard Business Review (Vol. 88, July-August 2010, No. 7-8, pp. 36)*
Pub: Harvard Business Publishing
Contact: Diane Belcher, Managing Director
Ed: Rosabeth Moss Kanter. **Price:** $6, PDF. **Description:** Studies show that individuals who perceive that they are being treated poorly and denied sufficient freedom for a certain level of autonomy are more likely to act negatively. **Availability:** Online; PDF.

22229 ■ *"Prepare to Take on Life's Challenges" in Minority Business Entrepreneur (Vol. 39, Fall, 2022, No. 4, pp. 20-21)*
URL(s): digital.mbemag.com/?m=53732&i=769780&p=20&ver=html5
Price: $7.95. **Description:** Challenges constantly arise within our lives, whether it's at work or at home. Tips are given here to help deal with the unexpected so as to not lose focus become overwhelmed. **Availability:** Print; Online.

22230 ■ *"Principles for Creating Growth in Challenging Times" in Agency Sales Magazine (Vol. 39, September-October 2009, No. 9, pp. 35)*
Description: Creating a productive environment is one vital key for businesses to utilize during the challenging times that arise due to a weak economy; other important factors include maintaining a good relationship with the staff, responding appropriately to challenges and keeping a sense of humor.

22231 ■ *"Problem Solving Requires Total Team Approach" in Green Industry Pro (Vol. 23, September 2011)*
Ed: Bob Coulter. **Description:** Working Smarter Training Challenge teaches that leaders are able to carry out solutions directly into their organization, develop skills and drive business results in key areas by creating a culture of energized workers who are able to take ownership of their performance as well as the performance of the company as a whole. **Availability:** Online.

22232 ■ *"The Profits of Good Works" in Barron's (Vol. 92, September 17, 2012, No. 38, pp. 14)*
Description: The nonprofit organization B Lab is responsible for certifying companies as socially conscious and environmentally friendly. B Lab examines the impact of companies on workers, communities, and the environment as well as their internal governance. **Availability:** Online.

22233 ■ *"Proud Out Loud" in Canadian Business (Vol. 80, April 23, 2007, No. 9, pp. 52)*
Description: The role of accomplishments of employees in improving workplace conditions is presented. **Availability:** Online.

22234 ■ *"Quitting Your Job Might Be Tougher Than You Think" in Canadian Business (Vol. 85, July 16, 2012, No. 11-12, pp. 71)*
Ed: Matthew McClearn. **Description:** Employees who are planning to resign should consider the notice period, the time it will take for employers to find a replacement and the reason for leaving. Departing employees can use their knowledge and skills to compete directly with their former employer, but they should be wary of unfair competition. **Availability:** Online.

22235 ■ *Reality-Based Leadership: Ditch the Drama, Restore Sanity to the Workplace, & Turn Excuses into Results*
Pub: Jossey-Bass
Ed: Cy Wakeman. **Released:** August 01, 2010. **Price:** $27.95, hardcover; $27.95, hardcover. **Description:** Recent polls show that 71 percent of workers think about quitting their jobs every day. That number would be shocking if people actually were quitting. Worse, they go to work, punching time clocks and collecting pay checks, while checked out emotionally. Cy Wakeman reveals how to be the kind of leader who changes the way people think about and perceive their circumstances, one who deals with the facts, clarifies roles, gives clean and direct feedback, and insists that everyone do the same without drama or defensiveness. **Availability:** E-book; Print.

22236 ■ *"Reconsidering Pay Dispersion's Effect On the Performance of Interdependent Work: Reconciling Sorting and Pay Inequality" in Academy of Management Journal (Vol. 55, June 1, 2012, No. 3, pp. 585)*
Pub: Academy of Management
Contact: Sharon Alvarez, President
Ed: Charlie O. Trevor, Greg Reilly, Barry Gerhart. **Description:** The use of pay dispersion in interdependent work settings to secure valued employee inputs is investigated. Results show that the strategy positively affects interdependent team performance. Potential constraints on the sorting perspective on pay dispersion are also studied. **Availability:** Electronic publishing; Download; PDF; Online.

22237 ■ *Remote Not Distant: Design a Company Culture That Will Help You Thrive in a Hybrid Workplace*
Ed: Gustavo Razzetti. **Released:** June 07, 2022. **Price:** $7.99, e-book; $26.31, hardcover. **Description:** With the advent of work at home and hybrid offices, many companies are being forced to adapt away from their obsolete ideas of what working in an office means. This book acts as a guide to help business owners design a modern work environment that works for the business and for their employees. **Availability:** E-book; Print.

22238 ■ *"Research Highlights Disengaged Workforce" in Workforce Management (Vol. 88, November 16, 2009, No. 12, pp. 22)*
Pub: Crain Communications Inc.
Contact: Barry Asin, President
Ed: Ed Frauenheim. **Description:** Most researchers have documented a drop in employee engagement during the recession due to such factors as layoffs, restructuring and less job security. **Availability:** Online.

22239 ■ *"Retiring Baby Boomers and Dissatisfied Gen-Xers Cause..Brain Drain" in Agency Sales Magazine (Vol. 39, November 2009, No. 10)*
Description: Due to the impending retirement of the baby boomers a critical loss of knowledge and experience in businesses will result. Creating a plan to address this loss of talent centered on the development of the younger generation is discussed.

22240 ■ "A Reverse-Innovation Playbook: Insights From a Company That Developed Products For Emerging Markets and Then Brought Them Back Home" in *Harvard Business Review* (Vol. 90, April 2012, No. 4, pp. 120)
Pub: Harvard Business Review Press
Contact: Moderna V. Pfizer, Contact

Ed: Vijay Govindarajan. **Price:** $8.95, hardcover. **Description:** An overview is presented on the organizational change implemented by Harman International Industries Inc. to create products for emerging markets and ensure that they would be accepted in already established middle markets. Components include setting radical goals, selecting team leaders with no competing interests, and leveraging global resources. **Availability:** PDF; Online.

22241 ■ "RIM Rocks Out: Billionaire Bosses Sponsor a Free Concert for Deserving Staff" in *Canadian Business* (Vol. 80, Winter 2007, No. 24)

Description: Jim Balsillie and Mike Lazaridis of Research in Motion Ltd. (RIM) rented out the Air Canada Centre in Toronto to give their employees a free concert that features performances by the Tragically Hip and Van Halen on November 15, 2007. RIM has sponsored concerts by Aerosmith, Tom Cochrane, and the Barenaked Ladies in past parties that only shows how far the company goes in terms of employee appreciation.

22242 ■ "The Risks and Rewards of Speaking Up: Managerial Responses to Employee Voice" in *Academy of Management Journal* (Vol. 55, August 1, 2012, No. 4, pp. 851)
Pub: Academy of Management
Contact: Sharon Alvarez, President

Ed: Ethan R. Burris. **Description:** The ways in which managers respond to suggestions made by employees is examined. Positive and negative managerial reactions to employees speaking up depend on whether the type of voice exhibited is challenging or supportive as well as on the psychological mechanisms of loyalty and threat. **Availability:** Download; Electronic publishing; PDF; Online.

22243 ■ Rituals for Virtual Meetings: Creative Ways to Engage People and Strengthen Relationships
URL(s): www.wiley.com/en-us/Rituals+for+Virtual+Meetings%3A+Creative+Ways+to+Engage+People+and+Strengthen+Relationships-p-9781119755999

Ed: Kursat Ozenc, Glenn Fajardo. **Released:** January 2021. **Price:** $17, e-book; $29, paperback. **Description:** Online meetings are becoming the norm for businesses, but sometimes it's difficult to achieve the desired outcome from meeting virtually due to limitations. This book explains how to break through these roadblocks. **Availability:** E-book; Print.

22244 ■ "The Secret Strategy for Meaningful Sales Meetings" in *Agency Sales Magazine* (Vol. 39, December 2009, No. 11, pp. 40)

Description: Sales meetings can be made more meaningful by focusing on the end results that the meeting seeks to achieve. Describing the changed behavior that is sought from the sales force and working backwards from there also help make a sales meeting more meaningful. **Availability:** Online.

22245 ■ "Seven Things Great Employers Do (That Others Don't); Unusual, Innovative, and Proven Tactics To Create Productive and Profitable Working Environments" in *Gallup Business Journal* (April 15, 2014)
Pub: Gallup, Inc.
Contact: Jon Clifton, Chief Executive Officer

Price: $8.95. **Description:** Seven unusual, innovative, and proven tactics that create productive and profitable working environments are examined through researching 32 companies. These firms represented many industries, including healthcare, financial services, hospitality, manufacturing, and retail throughout the world. **Availability:** Print; PDF; Online.

22246 ■ "Shared Leadership In Teams: An Investigation of Antecedent Conditions and Performance" in *Academy of Management Journal* (Vol. 50, No. 5, October 1, 2007, pp. 1217)
Pub: Academy of Management
Contact: Sharon Alvarez, President

Ed: Jay B. Carson, Paul E. Tesluk, Jennifer A. Marrone. **Description:** Study assessed the advantages of distribution of leadership among team members rather than on a single person revealed advantages that ranged from support and shared functions along with higher ratings from clients on their performance. **Availability:** Electronic publishing; Download; PDF; Online.

22247 ■ Shop Class as Soulcraft
Pub: Penguin Publishing Group

Ed: Matthew B. Crawford. **Released:** April 27, 2010. **Price:** $19.93, hardcover; $13.31, paperback; $14.99, audio. **Description:** A philosopher and mechanic argues for the satisfaction and challenges of manual work. **Availability:** E-book; Print.

22248 ■ "Should Managers Focus on Performance or Engagement? Gallup Examined this Question and Found That the Answer Isn't as 'Either/Or' as Many Companies Might Think" in *Gallup Business Journal* (August 5, 2014)
Pub: Gallup, Inc.
Contact: Jon Clifton, Chief Executive Officer

Description: A Gallup survey of over 8,000 employees were asked whether managers should focus on performance or engagement. High performance managers create an engaging work environment promoting peak performance in three ways. **Availability:** Print; Online.

22249 ■ "Size Does Matter" in *International Journal of Globalisation and Small Business* (Vol. 4, September 21, 2010, No. 1, pp. 61)

Ed: Julia Connell, Ranjit Voola. **Description:** Examination of how members of an Australian-based manufacturing and engineering cluster share knowledge through networking as a means to improve competitive advantage. **Availability:** Online.

22250 ■ "Sleeping with Your Smartphone: How to Break the 24/7 Habit and Change the Way You Work"
Pub: Harvard Business Review Press
Contact: Moderna V. Pfizer, Contact

Released: May 29, 2012. **Price:** $30, Hardcover/Hardcopy. **Description:** Harvard Business School professor, Leslie Perlow, reveals ways to become more productive after disconnecting from your smartphone. A six-person team was used in an experiment at The Boston Consulting Group, an elite management consulting firm, where teams changed the way they worked and became more efficient and effective by disconnecting. The team was better able to perform and recruit new talent. A step-by-step guide is offered to change your team. **Availability:** E-book; Print.

22251 ■ "Small Business Post–COVID-19: Motivational Needs through Uncertain Times" in *SAGE Journals* (Aug. 14, 2020)
URL(s): journals.sagepub.com/doi/full/10.1177/0886368720945134

Ed: Dean Stefanie Ertel. **Released:** August 14, 2020. **Description:** Discusses the effects on your small business in a post-Covid-19 world. Includes research on employee needs, employee empowerment, and how your small business can thrive based not on what you do, but why you do it. **Availability:** Online.

22252 ■ "A Social Context Model of Envy and Social Undermining" in *Academy of Management Journal* (Vol. 55, June 1, 2012, No. 3, pp. 643)
Pub: Academy of Management
Contact: Sharon Alvarez, President

Ed: Michelle K. Duffy, Kristin L. Scott, Jason D. Shaw, Bennett J. Tepper, Karl Aquino. **Description:** The relationship between envy and social undermining is investigated using the case of hospital employees. Results show that the impact of envy on social undermining through moral disengagement is higher when social identification ith coworkers is low. The indirect effect of envy is also greater in teams with high team undermining norms and low team identification. **Availability:** Electronic publishing; Download; PDF; Online.

22253 ■ The Social Media Bible: Tactics, Tools, and Strategies for Business Success
Pub: John Wiley & Sons, Inc.
Contact: Christina Van Tassell, Executive Vice President Chief Financial Officer

Ed: Lon Safko. **Released:** Third edition. **Price:** $29.95, paperback; $19.99, E-Book. **Description:** Information is given to build or transform a business into social media, where customers, employees, and prospects connect, collaborate, and champion products and services in order to increase sales and to beat the competition. **Availability:** E-book; Print.

22254 ■ "Spying on Your Employees? Better Understand the Law First" in *Business News Daily* (March 9, 2023)
URL(s): www.businessnewsdaily.com/6685-employee-monitoring-privacy.html

Ed: Max Freedman. **Released:** March 09, 2023. **Description:** With the advent of technology in the workplace, it's becoming easier to track and even spy on your employees to make sure they are staying on task. However, there are certain privacy laws you could be breaking. **Availability:** Online.

22255 ■ "Start Filling Your Talent Gap - Now" in *Business Strategy Review* (Vol. 21, Spring 2010, No. 1, pp. 56)

Ed: Alan Bird, Lori Flees, Paul DiPaola. **Released:** March 22, 2010. **Description:** As businesses steer their way out of turbulence, they have a unique opportunity to identify their leadership supply and demand and then to close the talent gap in their organization. Authors explain how to take immediate steps to build the right team now and lay the groundwork for a long-term approach for nurturing talent within the organization. **Availability:** Online; Electronic publishing.

22256 ■ "Steps to Motivate Your Employees" in *business.com* (Aug. 18, 2020)
URL(s): www.business.com/articles/tips-for-motivating-employees/

Ed: Jennifer Post. **Released:** August 18, 2020. **Description:** Provides tips to keep your small business employees motivated and excited about the work they do. **Availability:** Online.

22257 ■ "Stress-Test Your Strategy: the 7 Questions to Ask" in *Harvard Business Review* (Vol. 88, November 2010, No. 11, pp. 92)
Pub: Harvard Business Publishing
Contact: Diane Belcher, Managing Director

Ed: Robert Simons. **Price:** $8.95, PDF. **Description:** Seven questions organizations should use to assess crisis management capabilities are: who is the primary customer, how do core values prioritize all parties, what performance variables are being tracked, what strategic boundaries have been set, how is creative tension being produced, how committed are workers to assisting each other, and what uncertainties are causing worry?. **Availability:** Online; PDF.

22258 ■ "Striving for Self-Verification During Organizational Entry" in *Academy of Management Journal* (Vol. 55, June 2012, No. 2, pp. 360)
Pub: Academy of Management
Contact: Sharon Alvarez, President

Ed: Daniel M. Cable, Virginia S. Kay. **Description:** How striving for self-verification relates with self-disclosure, self-monitoring, and core self-evaluations is explored. Striving refers to bringing others to know who a person is during the organizational entry process. Relations to the validity of interviewers' evaluations, job seekers' ability to find satisfying work, and supervisors' evaluations of newcomers' performance are given. **Availability:** Electronic publishing; Download; PDF; Online.

22259 ■ "The Sustainable Supply Chain" in Harvard Business Review (Vol. 88, October 2010, No. 10, pp. 70)
Pub: Harvard Business Publishing
Contact: Diane Belcher, Managing Director

Ed: Steven Prokesch. **Price:** $8.95, PDF. **Description:** Peter Senge, founder of the Society for Organizational Learning, emphasizes the importance of assessing the system as a whole under which one is operating, and learning how to work with individuals with which one has not worked previously. He also points to nongovernmental organizations to provide assistance and legitimacy. **Availability:** Online; PDF.

22260 ■ Switch: How to Change Things When Change Is Hard
Pub: Broadway Business

Ed: Chip Heath, Dan Heath. **Released:** February 16, 2010. **Price:** $29, U.S., hardcover; $17.50, U.S., e-book. **Description:** Change is difficult for everyone. This book helps business leaders to motivate employees as well as to help everybody motive themselves and others. **Availability:** E-book; Print; Download; Audio.

22261 ■ Take Command: Lessons in Leadership: How to Be a First Responder in Business"
Released: 2018. **Price:** $25. **Description:** What do elite members of the military, first responders in a disaster zone, and successful business leaders have in common? Clarity of mind and purpose in the midst of chaos. Cofounder and CEO of Team Rubicon and former Marine Sniper Jake Wood, teaches the lessons in leadership and teamwork to help managers and entrepreneurs succeed in this hyper-competitive business environment today.

22262 ■ "Team Too Big for Regular One-on-Ones? Try These 11 Communication Strategies Instead" in Small Business Trends (December 18, 2022)
URL(s): smallbiztrends.com/2022/12/alternative-communication-strategies.html
Released: December 18, 2022. **Description:** It's important to meet with your employees one on one but that can get complicated if your team grows too big! Presented in this article are tips to mitigate this issue. **Availability:** Online.

22263 ■ "Teamwork On the Fly: How To Master the New Art of Teaming" in Harvard Business Review (Vol. 90, April 2012, No. 4, pp. 72)
Pub: Harvard Business Review Press
Contact: Moderna V. Pfizer, Contact

Ed: Amy C. Edmondson. **Price:** $8.95. **Description:** Description of the concept of 'teaming' or flexible teamwork is given. Teaming brings together expertise from disparate fields and forms temporary groups to identify innovations and address unanticipate problems. Project management and team leadership are important components of success. **Availability:** Online; PDF.

22264 ■ "There's Always Something Unexpected" in South Florida Business Journal (Vol. 34, June 6, 2014, No. 46, pp. 13)
Pub: American City Business Journals, Inc.
Contact: Mike Olivieri, Executive Vice President
Released: Weekly. **Price:** $8, introductory 4-week offer(Digital only). **Description:** Hannah Granade, CEO of Advantix Systems, likes how her job allows her to build the business and bring people together. The company, that provides cooling and dehumidification systems for industrial and commercial applications, encourages creative thinking by building an open culture. **Availability:** Print; Online.

22265 ■ The Thin Book of Naming Elephants: How to Surface Undiscussables for Greater Organizational Success
Pub: Thin Book Publishing Co.
Contact: Sue Annis Hammond, Founder
E-mail: sue@thinbook.com

Ed: Sue Annis Hammond, Andrea B. Mayfield. **Description:** Organizational success is of upmost importance to today's entrepreneurs and organizations. The hierarchal system in which people are afraid to speak up in organizations is discussed. The points of view and inability to see things from an overall perspective can cause insecurity among employees. The three elephants present in every organization include: arrogance, hubris, and screamers and the damage caused by these elephants in any organization is examined. **Availability:** E-book.

22266 ■ Training & Development for Dummies
Pub: John Wiley & Sons, Inc.
Contact: Christina Van Tassell, Executive Vice President Chief Financial Officer
URL(s): www.wiley.com/en-us/Training+%
26+Development+For+Dummies%2C+2nd+Edition
-p-9781119896029

Ed: Elaine Biech. **Released:** 2nd edition. **Price:** $18, e-book; $29.99, paperback. **Description:** Retaining your most valuable talent in your workplace is crucial and this guide will help you develop the skills and programs to keep your top employees. Training and development is crucial for team growth and there are various ways to complete these programs, which are outlined in this book. **Availability:** E-book; Print.

22267 ■ "Truffles & Trifles' Marci Arthur Plans YouTube Channel, Cookbook" in Orlando Business Journal (Vol. 30, May 2, 2014, No. 45, pp. 3)
Pub: American City Business Journals, Inc.
Contact: Mike Olivieri, Executive Vice President
Released: Weekly. **Price:** $8, introductory 4-week offer(Digital & Print). **Description:** Marci Arthur, founder of Truffles & Trifles Cooking School, plans to create a YouTube channel and publish a cookbook. Arthur believes that the survival of her business can be attributed to the devotion and integrity of her employees. Reports show that the school has been receiving donations from sponsors such as Wolf Appliances and Sub-Zero. **Availability:** Print; Online.

22268 ■ "Tsingtao's Chairman On Jump-Starting a Sluggish Company" in Harvard Business Review (Vol. 90, April 2012, No. 4, pp. 41)
Pub: Harvard Business Review Press
Contact: Moderna V. Pfizer, Contact

Ed: Jin Zhiguo. **Description:** The key challenge Tsingtao Brewery Company Ltd. faced was the focus on pleasing corporate superiors, rather than the firm's customers. By inventing a new model, the brewery was able to boost both employee productivity and product quality. First half profits and revenue for 2011 grew more than 20 percent over the previous year.

22269 ■ "Turn the Great Resignation into a Great Employee Retention Strategy" in Minority Business Entrepreneur (Vol. 39, Fall, 2022, No. 4, pp. 16-17)
URL: digital.mbemag.com/?m=53732&i=769780&p=16&ver=html5
Ed: Rod Robertson. **Released:** 2022. **Price:** $7.95, print. **Description:** Tips on retaining employees. **Availability:** Print; Online.

22270 ■ Ubuntu!: An Aspiring Story About an African Tradition of Teamwork and Collaboration
Pub: Broadway Business

Ed: Bob Nelson, Stephen Lundin. **Released:** March 30, 2010. **Price:** $23, paperback; $9. **Description:** The African tradition of teamwork and collaboration is used to demonstrate these skills to small business leaders. **Availability:** E-book; Print; Download; Audio.

22271 ■ "Vacation, All I Ever Wanted" in Entrepreneur (August 2014)
Pub: Entrepreneur Media Inc.
Contact: Dan Bova, Director
E-mail: dbova@entrepreneur.com
Description: Small business owners can maximize the value of spending time away from work. Paid vacations boost employee productivity and the same effect can also be experienced by owners. Vacation expenses can be managed with creativity and careful planning according to Matt Kepnes, author of 'How to Travel the World on $50 a Day: Travel Cheaper, Longer, Smarter'. The three main vacation expenses that business owners should carefully plan include lodging, transportation, and food and entertainment. **Availability:** Print; Online.

22272 ■ "The Value of Conversations With Employees; Talk Isn't Cheap" in Gallup Management Journal (June 30, 2011)
Ed: Jessica Tyler. **Released:** June 30, 2011. **Description:** When managers have meaningful exchanges with their employees, they don't only show they care, they also add value to their organization's bottom line. **Availability:** Print; Online.

22273 ■ "The Virgin Way"
Description: Sir Richard Branson, founder of Virgin Group, shares his own style of leadership. He teaches how fun, family, passion, and the dying art of listening are key ingredients to what his employees describe as the "Virgin Way". The entrepreneur reveals insights into his forty years of starting and building his airline company.

22274 ■ "Virtue and Vice" in Entrepreneur (September 2014)
Pub: Entrepreneur Media Inc.
Contact: Dan Bova, Director
E-mail: dbova@entrepreneur.com
Description: Socially responsible investments (SRI) are popular in the U.S., but many claim that vice funds offer better returns. Vice fund proponents argue that any profitable company deserves a place in a good investment portfolio. SRI proponents emphasize investments that benefit the society. Analysts note that investors who restrict their investment landscape by selecting only vice funds or only SRI funds may lead to lower returns. Other specialized funds attract activist investors supporting advocacies like gender equality or a positive work environment. **Availability:** PDF; Online.

22275 ■ "Voices: More Important than Results" in Business Strategy Review (Vol. 21, Summer 2010, No. 2, pp. 81)
Ed: Bert De Reyck, Zeger Degraeve. **Released:** June 24, 2010. **Description:** Managing only for results leads to crises. It is important to reward people for the decisions they make, not just for the results they create. **Availability:** Print; Online.

22276 ■ "Want To Increase Hospital Revenues? Engage Your Physicians. When Doctors Are Frustrated, Patient Care and Hospital Revenues Suffer. Here's How to Boost Physicians' Engagement -- and the Bottom Line" in Gallup Business Journal (June 5, 2014)
Pub: Gallup, Inc.
Contact: Jon Clifton, Chief Executive Officer
Description: Hospitals need to engage their doctors in order to be successful for both patient care and the bottom line. Four key practices to drive physician engagement are outlined. **Availability:** Print.

22277 ■ "A Well-Crafted Employee Handbook Can Make Work Run More Smoothly" in Idaho Business Review (September 17, 2014)
Pub: BridgeTower Media
Contact: Adam Reinebach, President
Description: An employee handbook will provide a complaint process, provide company management flexibility and clarity and keep a company out of legal problems. Training, compensation, benefits, security, health, performance appraisals, and safety issues

must be covered. Human resource managers and other mangers should cover basics to help communicate with workers.

22278 ■ *"What Employees Worldwide Have in Common"* **in Gallup Management Journal (September 22, 2011)**
Description: According to a Gallup study, workplace conditions are strongly tied to personal wellbeing, regardless of geographic region. The employee study covered 116 countries. **Availability:** Print; Online.

22279 ■ *"What Your Employees Need to Know; They Probably Don't Know How They're Performing"* **in Gallup Management Journal (April 13, 2011)**
Ed: Steve Crabtree. **Released:** April 13, 2011. **Description:** Personalized feedback and recognition aren't just extras that make workers feel good about themselves they are critical predictors of positive performance. **Availability:** Print; Online.

22280 ■ *"What Your Workplace Wellness Programs are Missing; Companies Can Benefit From Taking a Holistic Approach To Their Employees. Here's How"* **in Gallup Business Journal (July 7, 2014)**
Pub: Gallup, Inc.
Contact: Jon Clifton, Chief Executive Officer
Description: Companies should take a holistic approach to their employees' well being when addressing physical wellness in their workforce. Although employers are working to improve the physical wellness of workers, including weight loss, smoking cessation, and stress management, five essential elements: purpose, social, financial, community and physical issues would round out a good program. **Availability:** Print.

22281 ■ *"What's More Important: Talent or Engagement? A Study With Retailer ANN INC. Seeks To Find the Essential Ingredients To High-Performing Managers and Employees"* **in Gallup Business Journal (April 22, 2014)**
Pub: Gallup, Inc.
Contact: Jon Clifton, Chief Executive Officer
Description: ANN INC. is a leading women's clothing retailer that is exploring the necessary steps to achieving both high-performing managers and employees. The firm found that hiring people with the right talent and engaging them will maximize performance. **Availability:** Online.

22282 ■ *"When Emotional Reasoning Trumps IQ"* **in Harvard Business Review (Vol. 88, September 2010, No. 9, pp. 27)**
Pub: Harvard Business Publishing
Contact: Diane Belcher, Managing Director
Ed: Roderick Gilkey, Ricardo Caceda, Clinton Kilts. **Price:** $6, PDF. **Description:** Strategic reasoning was found to be linked more closely to areas of the brain associated with intuition and emotion, rather than the prefrontal cortex, which is typically thought to be the center of such activity. Implications for management skills are discussed. **Availability:** Online; PDF.

22283 ■ *"When Key Employees Clash: How Should a Business Owner Handle a Conflict Between Two Senior Managers?"* **in Harvard Business Review (Vol. 90, June 2012, No. 6, pp. 135)**
Pub: Harvard Business Review Press
Contact: Moderna V. Pfizer, Contact
Ed: H. Irving Grousbeck. **Price:** $8.95. **Description:** A fictitious employee conflict scenario is presented, with contributors providing suggestions for an effective management plan. The key component is ensuring that both employees receive the coaching and support necessary to enable them to perceive their roles more clearly and to build trust. **Availability:** Online; PDF.

22284 ■ *"When R&D Spending Is Not Enough: The Critical Role of Culture When You Really Want to Innovate"* **in Human Resource Management (Vol. 49, July-August 2010, No. 4, pp. 767-792)**
Pub: John Wiley & Sons, Inc.
Contact: Christina Van Tassell, Executive Vice President Chief Financial Officer
Ed: Sheng Wang, Rebecca M. Guidice, Judith W. Tansky, Zhong-Ming Wang. **Released:** July 19, 2010. **Description:** A study was conducted to examine the effect of contextual contingencies on innovation. Findings indicate that Chinese manufacturers with cultures emphasizing innovation and teamwork more effectively utilize financial resources in the innovation process. Results also show that a culture emphasizing outcomes and stability leads to lower levels innovation irrespective of investments. **Availability:** Print; PDF; Online.

22285 ■ *"Why Creating Organizational Change Is So Hard; Resistance To Change Is Entrenched In Most Companies. Here's How To Overcome Obstacles and Create Change That Lasts"* **in Gallup Business Journal (May 22, 2014)**
Pub: Gallup, Inc.
Contact: Jon Clifton, Chief Executive Officer
Description: Poorly defined objectives, politics, and unclear metrics are come of the obstacles to implementing meaningful change in any organization. Employees are motivated to change if leaders provide hope and inspiration. Ways that companies can overcome barriers to change are examined. **Availability:** Print; Online.

22286 ■ *"Why Does Firm Reputation In Human Resource Policies Influence College Students? The Mechanisms Underlying Job Pursuit Intentions"* **in Human Resource Management (Vol. 51, January-February 2012, No. 1, pp. 121-142)**
Pub: John Wiley & Sons, Inc.
Contact: Christina Van Tassell, Executive Vice President Chief Financial Officer
Ed: Julie Holliday Wayne, Wendy J. Casper. **Released:** January 26, 2012. **Description:** The effects of reputational information about human resource practices of companies on college students seeking employment are examined. The reputation of firms in compensation, work-family, and diversity efforts are found to increase intentions to pursue employment in these firms. **Availability:** Print; PDF; Online.

22287 ■ *"Why Good Jobs Are Good for Retailers: Some Companies Are Investing In Their Workers and Reaping Healthy Profits"* **in Harvard Business Review (Vol. 90, January-February 2012, No.1-2, pp. 124)**
Pub: Harvard Business Review Press
Contact: Moderna V. Pfizer, Contact
Ed: Zeynep Ton. **Price:** $8.95. **Description:** Four key operational practices can help retailers sever the trade-off between investing in employees and maintaining low prices. These are: offering fewer promotions and SKUs, cross-training workers rather than varifying their number to match customer traffic, eliminating waste while preserving staff, and empowering workers to make prompt decisions. **Availability:** Online; PDF.

22288 ■ *"Why I Stopped Firing Everyone and Started Being a Better Boss"* **in Inc. (Vol. 34, September 2012, No. 7, pp. 86)**
Pub: Mansueto Ventures L.L.C.
Contact: Stephanie Mehta, Chief Executive Officer
Ed: April Joyner. **Released:** August 28, 2012. **Description:** Indigo Johnson, former Marine, discusses her management style when starting her business. She fired employees regularly. Johnson enrolled in a PhD program in leadership and established a better hiring program and learned to utilize her workers' strengths. **Availability:** Print; Online.

22289 ■ *"Why Motivating People Doesn't Work...and What Does: The New Science of Leading, Energizing, and Engaging"*
Released: September 30, 2014. **Price:** $20.95, Nonmembers, PDF e-book; $18.86, Members, electronic publishing; $20.95, Nonmembers, paperback; $18.86, Members, paperback; $24.95, Nonmembers, hardcover; $22.46, Members, hardcover; $20.95, Nonmembers, electronic publishing; $14.67, Members, electronic publishing; $18.95, PDF e-book; $14.67, Members, PDF e-book. **Description:** Leadership researcher, consultant, and business coach, Susan Fowler, shares the latest research on the nature of human motivation to present a tested model and course of action to help Human Resource leaders and managers guide workers towards motivation that will not only increase productivity and engagement but will provide employees with a sense of purpose and fulfillment. **Availability:** E-book; Print; PDF; Electronic publishing.

22290 ■ *"Why People Believe Things That Aren't True inside Your Company"* **in Small Business Trends (October 3, 2022)**
URL(s): smallbiztrends.com/2022/10/illusionary-truth-effect.html
Released: October 03, 2022. **Description:** A discussion of how workplace leaders can use four strategies to prevent workplace misinformation from spreading. **Availability:** Online.

22291 ■ *"Why To Embrace Positive Leadership"* **in Birmingham Business Journal (Vol. 31, February 7, 2014, No. 6, pp. 14)**
Pub: American City Business Journals, Inc.
Contact: Mike Olivieri, Executive Vice President
Released: Weekly. **Price:** $4, introductory 4-week offer(Digital only). **Description:** The benefits achieved from managers' adoption of positive leadership are discussed. Positive leadership motivates employees to achieve higher performance levels. Tips to achieve positive leadership are listed. **Availability:** Print; Online.

22292 ■ *"Why Your Company Must Be Mission-Driven; A Clear Mission Inspires Employee Engagement, Fosters Customer Engagement, and Helps Boost Company Performance -- Among Other Benefits"* **in Gallup Business Journal (March 6, 2014)**
Pub: Gallup, Inc.
Contact: Jon Clifton, Chief Executive Officer
Description: It is stressed that executives need a clear mission in order to engage their workers, foster customer engagement, and to help boost their firm's performance. **Availability:** Print; Online.

22293 ■ *"Winners Dream: A Journey from Corner Store to Corner Office"*
Pub: Simon & Schuster Adult Publishing Group
Contact: Jonathan Karp, President
Released: October 14, 2014. **Price:** $28.99, hardcover, plus $2.24 shipping charges. **Description:** Bill McDermott, CEO of the world's largest business software company, SAP, profiles his career. He discusses his career moves, sales strategies, employee incentives to create high performance teams, and the competitive advantages of optimism and hard work. The entrepreneur offers a blueprint for success and the knowledge that the real dream is the journey, not the preconceived destination. **Availability:** E-book; Print; Download; Audio.

22294 ■ *"Winners & Losers"* **in Canadian Business (Vol. 85, July 16, 2012, No. 11-12, pp. 22)**
Description: Canadian Pacific Railway's 4,800 locomotive engineers and conductors walked out in protest of the proposed work rules and pension cuts. Shareholders rejected a $25-million bonus and retention payout to Astral Media chief executive officer Ian Greenburg. The Dragon spacecraft of Space Exploration Technologies delivered supplies and experiments to the International Space Station. **Availability:** Print.

22295 ■ *"Work/Life Balance"* **in Dallas Business Journal (Vol. 37, June 20, 2014, No. 41, pp. 4)**
Pub: Routledge, Taylor & Francis Group
Description: Younger generations of corporate employees are increasingly looking for a more engaged workplace community. Research firm, Quantum Workplace, identifies several trends that help to attract and retain employees, including jobs that align with the workers' own values, growth op-

portunities within the firm, social interactions with co-workers, and employee health benefits. **Availability:** Print; Online.

22296 ■ *"Your First 100 Days on Your New Job" in Women In Business (Vol. 63, Spring 2011, No. 1, pp. 28)*
Pub: American Business Women's Association
Contact: Rene Street, Executive Director
Ed: Diane Stafford. **Released:** March 22, 2011.
Description: The first 100 days on the job are crucial if the person's permanent hiring is conditional on surviving a probationary period. The new hire must do more than just master the job's technical details to maximize the chance of success. Details of some basic tips to fit into the corporate culture and get along with coworkers are also discussed. **Availability:** Print; Online.

TRADE PERIODICALS

22297 ■ *Teamwork*
Pub: Dartnell Corporation
URL(s): www.dartnellcorp.com/newsletters/teamwork.php
Released: Monthly **Price:** $179, Individuals online only. **Description:** Focuses on successful teamwork in manufacturing and corporate businesses. Recurring features include columns titled What Would You Do?, Test Yourself and See, and Teamwork in Action. **Availability:** Online.

VIDEO/AUDIO MEDIA

22298 ■ *Harnessing Gen Z in the Workplace: 5 Strategies for Impact Leaders*
URL(s): www.awarepreneurs.com/podcast/330-gen-z-in-the-workplace
Ed: Paul Zelizer. **Released:** April 15, 2024. **Description:** Podcast discusses understanding and engaging Gen Z in the workplace.

22299 ■ *The How of Business: Debra Corey - Employee Recognition*
URL(s): www.thehowofbusiness.com/453-debra-corey-employee-recognition
Ed: Henry Lopez. **Released:** January 02, 2023.
Description: Podcast explains how employee recognition leads to employee retention.

22300 ■ *The How of Business: Employee Development Program for Small Business*
URL(s): www.thehowofbusiness.com/episode-330-laura-tolhoek
Ed: Henry Lopez. **Released:** September 14, 2020.
Description: Podcast discusses the components of an effective employee development program.

22301 ■ *How to Create a Healthy Company Culture in Your Small Business with Dana Kaye*
URL(s): beingboss.club/podcast/how-to-create-a-healthy-company-culture-in-your-small-business
Ed: Emily Thompson. **Released:** May 22, 2023.
Description: Podcast defines company culture and why it's important, describes a boss's role in shaping culture, and explains how to navigate conflicts with personal and company values.

22302 ■ *Nurture Small Business: Unlocking Employee Passion: Strategies for a Resilient Workplace*
Ed: Denise Cagan. **Released:** January 29, 2024.
Description: Podcast discusses how to recognize and foster employee motivation.=.

22303 ■ *Nurture Small Business: Unlocking Leadership Excellence with Emotional Intelligence*
URL(s): nurturesmallbusiness.buzzsprout.com/900445/13551073-unlocking-leadership-excellence-with-emotional-intelligence
Ed: Denise Cagan. **Released:** September 18, 2023.
Description: Podcast discusses the role of emotional intelligence in leadershipl .

22304 ■ *Think Business: How to Revolutionize Employee Experience and Boost Business Growth with Ryan Englin*
URL(s): thinktyler.com/podcast_episode/boost-business-growth-ryan-englin
Ed: Tyler Martin. **Released:** October 23, 2023.
Description: Podcast explains why employee experience is important, how to attract talent, the importance of small gestures in recruitment, and why a strong company culture can make a difference.

22305 ■ *This Is Small Business: How a Small Business Owner Can Do More for Their Employees*
URL(s): www.smallbusiness.amazon/podcast-episodes/ep-53-how-a-small-business-owner-can-do-more-for-their-employees
Ed: Andrea Marquez. **Released:** April 16, 2024.
Description: Podcast considers whether doing more for your employees can improve the bottom line.

22306 ■ *Women Amplified: Improv Your Work: Unlocking Creativity and Collaboration*
URL(s): www.conferencesforwomen.org/improv-your-work-unlocking-creativity-and-collaboration
Ed: Celeste Headlee. **Description:** Podcast how the rules of improv comedy can reinvigorate the workplace and turn it into a hub of creativity and empowerment.

22307 ■ *Women Amplified: Juggling Team Engagement & Balance*
URL(s): www.conferencesforwomen.org/juggling-team-enagement-balance-thats-a-good-question
Ed: Celeste Headlee. **Description:** Podcast discusses the juggling act of keeping a team engaged with a hands-off leadership style.

CONSULTANTS

22308 ■ **Advisory Management Services Inc.**
9600 E 129th St.
Kansas City, MO 64149
Contact: William H. Wood, President
Description: A management consulting and training firm specializing in employee relations, management and staff training, organizational development, strategic planning and continuous quality improvement. **Scope:** A management consulting and training firm specializing in employee relations, management and staff training, organizational development, strategic planning and continuous quality improvement. **Founded:** 1979.

22309 ■ **The Axelrod Group Inc.**
723 Laurel Ave.
Wilmette, IL 60091
Ph: (847)251-7361
Co. E-mail: info@axelrodgroup.com
URL: http://axelrodgroup.com
Contact: Hank Queen, Vice President, Engineering
Instagram: www.instagram.com/axelrodgroup
YouTube: www.youtube.com/channel/UCMH3hhExucz6EuaiSJCQr-Q
Description: Provider of organizational development consulting services in conference model approach to redesign, strategic planning, organization assessment, self-directed work teams, cultural change, team development and management, and their clients include major corporations and non-profit organizations. **Scope:** Provider of organizational development consulting services in conference model approach to redesign, strategic planning, organization assessment, self-directed work teams, cultural change, team development and management, and their clients include major corporations and non-profit organizations. **Founded:** 1981. **Publications:** "Large Group Interventions"; "Future Search"; "Real Time Strategic Change"; "The Path of Least Resistance for Managers"; "Open Space Technology"; "Flawless Consulting"; "Leadership and the New Science"; "The Birth of the Chaordic Age"; "Beyond the Wall of Resistance"; "Beat the Odds and Succeed in Organizational Change," Consulting to Management Magazine, Jun, 2006; "You Don't Have to Do it Alone," Oct, 2004; "Terms of Engagement," Barrett-Koehler Publishers; "The Conference Model"; "Harnessing Complexity"; "The Philosophy Behind Our Systems"; "Considerations Before You Build a Collaborative Process"; "Making Teams Work"; "Purpose is the Cornerstone"; "How to Build Relationships"; "How to Maximize Information Sharing"; "How to Promote Equity and Fairness"; "How to Create Freedom and Autonomy"; "The Handbook of Large Group Methods"; "The Change Handbook"; "The Intelligence Advantage: Organizing for Complexity"; "Investors Business Daily Leaders and Success: Top 10 Secrets to Success"; "Terms of Engagement: An Interview with Dick Axelrod," Per dido Magazine; "The Beauty of the Beast". **Training:** Conference Model Professional Skills; Team Development; Creating Team Based Organizations; Conflict Management for Managers; Working Together; Communications Skills for Improving Productivity and Relationships; Designing for Engagement; Terms of Engagement.

22310 ■ **Business Development Group Inc. (BDG)**
29255 Laurel Wood Dr., No. 202
Southfield, MI 48034
Ph: (248)358-0121
URL: http://www.busdevgroup.com
Contact: Shernon Harriyton, Director
Description: Consulting firm with expertise in leadership development, strategic thinking, organizational transformation, team-based work systems, organizational learning, rapid change, knowledge management, competitive intelligence, crisis management, merger and acquisition integration, product integration and new product development. **Scope:** Consulting firm with expertise in leadership development, strategic thinking, organizational transformation, team-based work systems, organizational learning, rapid change, knowledge management, competitive intelligence, crisis management, merger and acquisition integration, product integration and new product development. **Publications:** "Navigating in the Sea of Change," Competitive Intelligence Review Journal; "The Influence of Cultural Aspects of Strategic Information, Analysis and Delivery"; "What Leadership Needs From Competitive Intelligence Professionals," Journal of Association for Global and Strategic Information. **Training:** Process of Self-Design for the Evolving Organization; Large System Change Intervention; Self Assessment and the Transformational Process; The Knowledge Exchange - Shared Practices Workshop.

22311 ■ **CFI Group USA L.L.C.**
3916 Ranchero Dr.
Ann Arbor, MI 48108
Ph: (734)930-9090
Fax: (734)930-0911
Co. E-mail: info@cfigroup.se
URL: http://cfigroup.com
Contact: Sheri Petras, Chief Executive Officer
Facebook: www.facebook.com/CFIGroup
Linkedin: www.linkedin.com/company/cfi-group
X (Twitter): x.com/cfigroup
Description: Management consulting firm helps its clients worldwide to maximize shareholder value by optimizing customer and employee satisfaction, their clients span from a variety of industries including manufacturing, telecommunication, retail and government. **Scope:** Management consulting firm helps its clients worldwide to maximize shareholder value by optimizing customer and employee satisfaction, their clients span from a variety of industries including manufacturing, telecommunication, retail and government. **Founded:** 1988. **Publications:** "Customer Satisfaction and Stock Prices: High Returns, Low Risk," American Marketing Association, Jan, 2006; "Customer Satisfaction Index Climbs," The Wall Street Journal, Feb, 2004; "What's Next? Customer Service is Key to Post-Boom Success," The Bottom Line, Mar, 2003; "Boost Stock Performance, Nation's Economy," Quality Progress, Feb, 2003.

22312 ■ **Cole Financial Service Inc.**
1321 Joliet Pl.
Detroit, MI 48207

22313 ■ Employee Motivation/Team Building

Description: Services: Office management and computer consultant. **Scope:** A full service human capital development firm providing services in recruiting, coaching, retaining, developing and retiring. Works with front line staff, managers and executive level decision makers that set strategy. Industries served: Engineering, construction, government and other business entities. **Founded:** 1983. **Training:** How to Run Your Own Business; 25Ways to stay in Business 25Years; How to Tap Your Potential and Discover Your GENIUS; The Job Ladder Steps to SUCCESS; Making and Keeping a Budget; Records Retention and Disposal; Take Control of Your Life; Time and Priority Management; TQM - Total Quality Management; Leadership 101; Leadership 201; Diversity Agent or Opponent A Personal Development Workshop; Coaching in a Diverse Workplace.

22313 ■ Competitive Edge Inc.
PO Box 724705
Atlanta, GA 31139
Ph: (770)487-6460
Fax: (770)319-0313
Co. E-mail: info@competitiveedgeinc.com
URL: http://www.competitiveedgeinc.com
Contact: Judy Suiter, Founder

Description: Firm provides cutting-edge services such as effective selections, coaching, and training. **Scope:** Firm provides cutting-edge services such as effective selections, coaching, and training. **Founded:** 1981. **Publications:** "Beteenden och drivkrafter"; "Energizing People: Unleashing The Power of DISC"; "The Ripple Effect: How the Global Model of Endorsement Opens Doors to Success"; "The Journey - Quotes to keep your boat afloat"; "The Universal Language DISC Reference Manual"; "Exploring Values: Releasing the Power of Attitudes"; "Competitive Products Review Book"; "The Mother Of All Minds"; "The Sea of Change: Solutions for Navigating the Disconnects in the Workplace". **Training:** How to Recruit and Retain High Performing Employees; The Importance of Values Matching For Sales Selection; How to Build a High Performance Team; Dynamic Communication Skills; Creating Nurturing Customer Relationships; Your Attitude Is Showing; Sales Strategy Index; Validity Study.

22314 ■ The Cradlerock Group
500 Summer St., Ste. 205
Stamford, CT 06905
Ph: (203)324-0088
Co. E-mail: info@cradlerock.com
URL: http://cradlerock.com
Contact: Linnea Conley, Contact

Description: Firm provides team performance, leadership development, and interpersonal effectiveness learning solutions, the company offers customized management training, executive retreats, annual meetings, individual coaching, comprehensive corporate learning initiatives, outsourced logistical support services and leadership curriculum that supports everyone from first-time managers to senior executives. **Founded:** 1984. **Training:** Team Start; Who Are We?; Who's On First?; Getting Past Stuck; Team Skills; Group Skills; Effective Team Leadership; Leading Global Teams; 360Coaching; The Other Diversity; Harnessing Change; The Art of Sale.

22315 ■ Delta Systems
5621 Somerset Dr.
Brooklyn, MI 49230
Ph: (517)592-5463
Fax: (517)592-5463
Co. E-mail: renee@4deltasystems.com
URL: http://www.4deltasystems.com
Contact: Renee Merchant, Contact
E-mail: renee@4deltasystems.com

Description: Organizational development consultant specializing in team-building training and keynote speeches. Industries served: manufacturing, automotive suppliers, and nuclear power plants. **Scope:** Organizational development consultant specializing in team-building training and keynote speeches. Industries served: manufacturing, automotive suppliers, and nuclear power plants. **Publications:** "Teamwork Case"; "Changes, Choices, and Commitment"; "Make Teamwork a Way of Life"; "Checkered Flag Teams: Driving Your Workplace Into the Winners Circle"; "Success is a Team Effort"; "CARStyles™ - A Communication Style Model"; "Face Posters"; "CAR Styles Communication Model and Assessment". **Training:** Team Leader Training; Fast Cycle Time and Process Improvement; Change Leadership; Revitalizing Mature Teams; Fast Problem Solving; Pit Crew Challenge; Leadership Skills for Non-Supervisory People; Fast Start Teamwork; The Pit Crew Challenge.

22316 ■ Eastern Point Consulting Group Inc.
75 Oak St.
Newton, MA 02465
Ph: (617)965-4141
URL: http://www.eastpt.com
Contact: Katherine Herzog, President

Description: Firm specializes in bringing practical solutions to complex challenges and provides consulting and training in managing diversity, comprehensive sexual-harassment policies and programs, organizational development, benchmarks 360-degree skills assessment, executive coaching, strategic human resource planning, team building, leadership development for women, mentoring programs, and gender issues in the workplace. **Scope:** Firm specializes in bringing practical solutions to complex challenges and provides consulting and training in managing diversity, comprehensive sexual-harassment policies and programs, organizational development, benchmarks 360-degree skills assessment, executive coaching, strategic human resource planning, team building, leadership development for women, mentoring programs, and gender issues in the workplace. **Training:** Leadership Development for Women.

22317 ■ Employee Development Systems Inc. (EDSI)
7300 S Alton Way, Ste. 5J
Centennial, CO 80112
Free: 800-282-3374
Fax: (303)221-0704
Co. E-mail: info@edsiusa.com
URL: http://employeedevelopmentsystems.com
Contact: Suzanne Updegraff, Chief Executive Officer
Facebook: www.facebook.com/pages/Employee+Development+Systems,+Inc./132086156812546
Linkedin: www.linkedin.com/company/employee-development-systems-inc.
X (Twitter): x.com/edsiusa
YouTube: www.youtube.com/user/shermanupdegraff

Description: Firm provides result-oriented training programs to increase productivity, effectiveness and performance, and also programs that address professional presence, personal effectiveness or performance management. **Scope:** Firm provides result-oriented training programs to increase productivity, effectiveness and performance, and also programs that address professional presence, personal effectiveness or performance management. **Founded:** 1979. **Publications:** "Company Connection Life Changing Lessons"; "Why People Skills are Still Being Taught at Work"; "Leading With Credibility Manage Up"; "Words of Peter Drucker"; "Coaching for Results". **Training:** Increasing Personal Effectiveness; Communicating to Manage Performance; Pro-Action: Responding to Change; Just-in-Time Training: Working Successfully in a Changing Environment, Challenging the Status Quo for Continuous Improvement, Assertive Communication and Reaching Agreement; Learning in the 21st Century, Apr, 2007.

22318 ■ Interminds & Federer Resources Inc.
PO Box 438
Pasadena, CA 91102
Ph: (512)261-0761
Co. E-mail: yesyoucan@interminds.com
URL: http://www.interminds.com

Description: Firm specializes in feasibility studies, startup businesses, small business management, mergers and acquisitions, joint ventures, divestitures, interim and crisis management, turnarounds, production planning, team building, appraisals, and valuations. **Scope:** Firm specializes in feasibility studies, startup businesses, small business management, mergers and acquisitions, joint ventures, divestitures, interim and crisis management, turnarounds, production planning, team building, appraisals, and valuations. **Founded:** 1985. **Publications:** "Yes You Can: How To Be A Success No Matter Who You Are Or Where You're From".

22319 ■ Interpersonal Communication Programs Inc. (ICP)
30772 Southview Dr., Ste. 200
Evergreen, CO 80439
Ph: (303)674-2051
Free: 800-328-5099
Fax: (303)674-4283
Co. E-mail: thrive@comskills.com
URL: http://www.thrivesphere.com
Contact: Phyllis A. Miller, President

Description: Firm provides counseling resources for marriage and couples communication, instructor and facilitator training, tools and materials to help individuals, couples, and groups. **Publications:** "CC I & II texts"; "Collaborative Marriage Skills and Thriving Together in the Skills Zone"; "Core communication"; "Alive and Aware"; "Straight Talk," Connecting With Self and Others. **Training:** Collaborative Team Skills for Intact Work Groups; Core Communication: Skills and Processes for Managers, Supervisors and Employees; Couple communication I and II. **Special Services:** Awareness Wheel®; Styles of Communication®; Listening Cycle®; Styles of Communication®.

22320 ■ The Ken Blanchard Cos.
125 State Pl.
Escondido, CA 92029
Ph: (760)489-5005
Free: 800-728-6000
Co. E-mail: contact@kenblanchard.com
URL: http://www.kenblanchard.com
Contact: Scott Blanchard, President
Facebook: www.facebook.com/TheKenBlanchardCompanies
Linkedin: www.linkedin.com/company/the-ken-blanchard-companies
Instagram: www.instagram.com/kenblanchardcompanies
YouTube: www.youtube.com/user/KenBlanchardCos

Description: Provider of public speaking training and development programs. **Scope:** Full service management development-training company known for development of the one minute manager concept. Develops and sells quality products and services that enhance management and leadership skills. Offers seminars, workshops, in house consulting, videos, audio tapes, slides, books, instruments and games. Areas of expertise include management training, team building, attitude and needs assessment, productivity improvement, motivation, and corporate development. Industries served: health, hospitality, financial, food service, telecommunications, retail, utilities, associations, aerospace, automotive, military, education, manufacturing, and government agencies. **No. of Franchise Units:** 750. **Founded:** 1979. **Publications:** "Who Killed Change? Solving the Mystery of Leading People Through Change," 2009; "Helping People Win at Work: A Business Philosophy Called Don't Mark My Paper, Help Me Get An A," 2009; "Leading at a Higher Level," 2009; "The One Minute Entrepreneur," 2008; "Coaching in Organizations," 2008; "Know Can Do! Put Your Know-How Into Action," Oct, 2007; "Hamster Revolution, The: Stop Info Glut-Reclaim Your Life!"; "Leading at a Higher Level: Blanchard on Leadership and Creating High Performing Organizations"; "The Simple Truths of Service"; "Building High Performing Teams"; "Leadership Training for Supervisors"; "Legendary Service"; "The One Minute Manager"; "Whale Done!"; "The Power of Ethical Management"; "Managing By Values"; "The Leader Within"; "Leverage Your Best, Ditch the Rest"; "High Five". **Training:** Situational Leadership II; Situational Team Leadership; The One Minute Manager; Leadership and The One Minute Manager; Putting The One Minute Manager to Work; Ethical Management; Situational Frontline Leadership; The Magic of Situational Self Leadership; Discovering Self and Others; Coaching Essentials for Leaders; Legendary Service; Whale Done!; Gung-ho!.

22321 ■ LDG Associates
333 C St.
  San Diego, CA 92101
Ph: (344)344-2487
Co. E-mail: info@ldgcre.com
URL: http://www.ldgcre.com
Contact: Barrett Geenen, Partner
E-mail: bgeenen@ldgcre.com
Facebook: www.facebook.com/ldgcommercial
X (Twitter): x.com/LDG_Commercial
Instagram: www.instagram.com/ldgcommercial

Description: Consultants in leadership training and development, coaching, 360 degree feedback and team building. Specialize in helping leaders build effective teams. Leaders learn specific skills to help them achieve individual and organizational objectives. Industries served medical manufacturing, aerospace, electrical manufacturing, manufacturing, petroleum and government agencies. **Scope:** Consultants in leadership training and development, coaching, 360 degree feedback and team building. Specialize in helping leaders build effective teams. Leaders learn specific skills to help them achieve individual and organizational objectives. Industries served medical manufacturing, aerospace, electrical manufacturing, manufacturing, petroleum and government agencies. **Founded:** 1988. **Training:** Leadership Styles and Strategies; Influencing Styles and Strategies; Organizing Yourself and Others; Team Building; 360 Degree Feed back; Executive Coaching; Stress Management; Leadership 2000; Team Building 2000.

22322 ■ MAA Consulting Inc.
PO Box 703
  Perrysburg, OH 43551
Ph: (419)352-7782
Fax: (419)354-8781
Co. E-mail: maa@wcnet.org
URL: http://www.wcnet.org/~maa/about.htm
Contact: Dr. Glenn H. Varney, President

Description: Firm provides professional consulting services and serves various industries including energy, health care, auto parts manufacturers, chemical, financial, petroleum, and government agencies. **Publications:** "Caribbean Island Survival II"; Alaskan Adventure"; Task Force"; "Group Process Questionnaire"; "Acceleration"; "Contracting for Change"; "The Discipline of Change Management," 2005; "An Operational Definition of Odc," 2004; "Cases in Organization Development," 1999; "Measuring and Improving Teamwork," 1998; "Name Recognition of Master Level Graduate Programs in Organization Development and Change," 1998; "A Critical Examination of a Failed Attempt to Implement Self-Directed Work Teams," 1996; "Organization Development," 1996; "Rethinking the Knowledge Worker: Where Have All the Workers Gone," 1995; "The Primary Determinant of Successful Application of Self-Directed Work Teams," 1994; "Helping a Team Find All the Answers," 1991; "The Caster Case," 1990; "Teamwork Survey and Planning Guide," 1990. **Training:** Implementing Self-Directed Work Teams; SDWT Simulation; Managing Team Productivity; Navigating the Mine Fields of Change.

22323 ■ Miller, Leiby & Associates P.C.
32 Broadway, 13th Fl.
  New York, NY 10004
Ph: (212)227-4200
Fax: (212)504-8369
URL: http://www.millerleiby.com
Contact: Doron Leiby, Partner
Facebook: www.facebook.com/MillerLeibyAssociatesPc
Linkedin: www.linkedin.com/company/1269719
Instagram: www.instagram.com/millerleiby

Description: Firm is engaged in legal counsel for individuals and businesses. **Scope:** Firm is engaged in legal counsel for individuals and businesses. **Training:** Objectives and standards/recruiting for boards of directors.

22324 ■ Murray Dropkin & Associates
390 George St.
  New Brunswick, NJ 08901
URL: http://dropkin.com
Contact: Murray Dropkin, Contact

Description: Firm specializes in feasibility studies, business management, business process reengineering, team building, healthcare, and housing. **Scope:** Firm specializes in feasibility studies, business management, business process reengineering, team building, healthcare, and housing. **Publications:** "Bookkeeping for Nonprofits," Jossey Bass, 2005; "Guide to Audits of Nonprofit Organizations," PPC; "The Nonprofit Report," Warren, Gorham & Lamont; "The Budget Building Book for Nonprofits," Jossey-Bass; "The Cash Flow Management Book for Nonprofits," Jossey-Bass.

22325 ■ Partnerwerks Inc.
1401 Lavaca St. No. 557
  Austin, TX 78701
Ph: (210)201-4438
Co. E-mail: info@christopheravery.com
URL: http://www.christopheravery.com
Contact: Christopher Avery, President

Description: Firm provides management services on a contract or fee basis. **Scope:** Firm provides management services on a contract or fee basis. **Founded:** 1991. **Publications:** "Teamwork Is An Individual Skill: Getting Your Work Done When Sharing Responsibility," Berrett-Kohler, 2001; "The Leaders Guide". **Training:** Leadership: Simply Solve the Real Problem, Jun, 2010; Project Team Leadership; Managing Teams; Team Planning.

22326 ■ Performance Consulting Associates, Inc. (PCA)
3700 Crestwood Pky., Ste. 100
  Duluth, GA 30096
Ph: (770)717-2737
Co. E-mail: info@pcaconsulting.com
URL: http://pcaconsulting.com
Contact: Richard deFazio, President
Linkedin: www.linkedin.com/company/pcaconsulting

Description: Firm provides asset management solutions, business process optimization, and much more. **Scope:** Firm provides asset management solutions, business process optimization, and much more. **Founded:** 1976. **Publications:** "Does Planning Pay," Plant Services, Nov, 2000; "Asset Reliability Coordinator," Maintenance Technology, Oct, 2000; "Know What it is You Have to Maintain," Maintenance Technology, May, 2000; "Does Maintenance Planning Pay," Maintenance Technology, Nov, 2000.; "What is Asset Management?"; "Implementing Best Business Practices".

22327 ■ Performance Technologies Inc. (PTC)
1 Oakwood Ave., Ste. 562
  Dayton, OH 45409
Ph: (937)409-1419
Co. E-mail: info@perf-tec.com
URL: http://www.perf-tec.com
Contact: Michael Boland, President

Description: A consulting/training firm that designs and instills sales, leadership and management skills, processes and tools that strengthens overall organizational effectiveness. Services include: organizational transformation, creation of vision, values and operating philosophy, business analysis, impact analysis, innovation technology, succession planning and process mapping. Training services include: Advanced sales strategies, sales coaching and management, training processes, management effectiveness, leadership development, performance management, measurement and assessment. **Scope:** A consulting/training firm that designs and instills sales, leadership and management skills, processes and tools that strengthens overall organizational effectiveness. Services include: organizational transformation, creation of vision, values and operating philosophy, business analysis, impact analysis, innovation technology, succession planning and process mapping. Training services include: Advanced sales strategies, sales coaching and management, training processes, management effectiveness, leadership development, performance management, measurement and assessment. **Founded:** 1982. **Publications:** "Get- Real Selling".

22328 ■ Pilot Consulting Corporation
29 Wildhorse Trl.
  Crested Butte, CO 81225
Ph: (970)349-1250
Fax: (970)349-1251
URL: http://www.pilotconsulting.com
Contact: Chris Cappy, President
E-mail: ccappy@pilotconsulting.com

Description: Firm specializes in the implementation of strategy, management of transition and development of leadership in companies. **Scope:** Firm specializes in the implementation of strategy, management of transition and development of leadership in companies. **Founded:** 1995. **Publications:** "Leading Beyond the Walls". **Training:** Facilitative Leadership Training.

22329 ■ Positive Impact Consulting
9845 Horn Rd., Ste. 120
  Sacramento, CA 95827
Ph: (916)366-3000
URL: http://positiveimpact.com
Contact: Cheri Douglas, Contact
E-mail: cheri@positiveimpact.com

Description: Firm provides consulting and management transformation services for organizations. **Founded:** 1985.

22330 ■ Profit Associates Inc.
26 Hunters Forest Dr.
  Charleston, SC 29414
Free: 800-688-6304
URL: http://www.profit-associates.com
Contact: Bob Rogers, Managing Director
E-mail: bobrog@awod.com

Description: Firm offers executive coaching and on-site management consulting services for small- to medium-sized businesses and provides strategic business and production planning, funding, change management, marketing and public relations, profit and expense control, employee productivity and incentive services for clients in manufacturing, distribution, construction, software, healthcare, and transportation industries. **Training:** Essential Elements of a Good Incentive Program; Why Look at Management Re-engineering; The Profit & Expense Control Process; The Executive Coaching Alternative.

22331 ■ Steve Wilson and Co.
3800 Embassy Pkwy., Ste. 300
  Akron, OH 44333

Description: Firm engaged in team building, staff development and personal growth, consultant presents the way humor works and awakens new ways of relating to ourselves and others. Consultant carries designation of certified speaking professional and is one of seven persons worldwide certified in I Power program instruction. **Scope:** Firm engaged in team building, staff development and personal growth, consultant presents the way humor works and awakens new ways of relating to ourselves and others. Consultant carries designation of certified speaking professional and is one of seven persons worldwide certified in I Power program instruction. **Founded:** 1999. **Publications:** "Good Hearted Living"; "Birthrights: Your Essence, Purpose & Self-Esteem"; "Toilet Paper, Toothpaste, and Tuna Noodle Casserole"; "The Steve Wilson Report"; "The Art of Mixing Work and Play," Sep, 1992; "Super Humor Power," Oct, 1992; "Remarried with Children," May, 1992; "Eat Dessert First," May, 1990; "CHILL!". **Training:** Creating Positive Working Environments™; Putting Humor to Work at Work; Pulling Together Instead of Falling Apart; Winning over Customers from Hell; The Play shop Lab™; Humor For the Health of It; I-Power; Don't Postpone Joy™; Laughing Matters in the Classroom; The Art of Mixing Work and Play™; and Managing Stress Through Humor.

22332 ■ Tamayo Consulting Inc.
662 Encinitas Blvd., Ste. 236
Encinitas, CA 92024
Ph: (760)479-1352
URL: http://www.tamayoconsulting.com
Contact: Jennifer Dreyer, President
Description: It Provides training and consulting services. And also it specializes in leadership and team development. Industries served: private, non-profit, government, educational. **Scope:** It Provides training and consulting services. And also it specializes in leadership and team development. Industries served: private, non-profit, government, educational. **Training:** Presentation AdvantEdge Program; Lead point Development Program; Supervisor Development Programs.Identify Presentation Objectives; Implement 360-degree presentation assessment; conduct baseline-coaching session; Develop coaching plan; Staying connected.

FRANCHISES AND BUSINESS OPPORTUNITIES

22333 ■ Turbo Leadership Systems Ltd. (TLS)
36280 NE Willsonville Rd.
Newberg, OR 97132
Free: 800-574-4373
Fax: (503)625-2699
Co. E-mail: turbo@turbols.com
URL: http://turboleadershipsystems.com
Contact: Larry W. Dennis, President
E-mail: larry@turbols.com
Description: Management training and team building training. **Scope:** Provider of improvement programs that creates synergistic teamwork, impacts culture, and much more. **Founded:** 1985. **Publications:** "Empowering Leadership"; "How to Turbo Charge You"; "Repeat Business"; "Making Moments Matter, Information"; "The Turbo Charger"; "15 Leadership Principles and Ronald Reagan"; "Motorcycle Meditations"; "Repeat Business"; "Empowering Leadership"; "Communication For Results"; "The Great Baseball Cap". **Training:** Yes.

PUBLICATIONS

22334 ■ "How to Retain Generation Y Employees?" in Journal of Small Business Strategy (March 4, 2021)
URL(s): libjournals.mtsu.edu/index.php/jsbs/article/view/1979
Ed: Rosa Maria Fuchs, Oswaldo Morales, Juan Timana. **Description:** A study of employees belonging to Generation Y and their perceptions to work-life balance. **Availability:** PDF.

RESEARCH CENTERS

22335 ■ Riegel and Emory Human Resource Research Center
1014 Greene St.
Columbia, SC 29208
URL: http://sc.edu/study/colleges_schools/moore/research_and_centers/centers/riegel_and_emory_human_resources_center/index.php
Contact: Paul D. Bliese, Contact
E-mail: paul.bliese@moore.sc.edu
Description: Separately incorporated, nonprofit organization affiliated with the School of Business, University of South Carolina at Columbia. **Scope:** Aims to increase cooperation in the workplace and to preserve the values of the free market system. **Founded:** 1982. **Publications:** Values Research Project Reprint Series.

22336 ■ University of North Carolina at Chapel Hill - Kenan-Flagler Business School - Frank Hawkins Kenan Institute of Private Enterprise
300 Kenan Dr., Ste. 300
Chapel Hill, NC 27599
Ph: (919)962-8201
Co. E-mail: unckenaninstitute@gmail.com
URL: http://kenaninstitute.unc.edu
Contact: Kim Allen, Executive Director
E-mail: kim_allen@kenan-flagler.unc.edu
Facebook: www.facebook.com/kenaninstitute
Linkedin: www.linkedin.com/company/kenan-institute-of-private-enterprise
X (Twitter): x.com/kenaninstitute
YouTube: www.youtube.com/user/UNCKenanInstitute
Description: National center for private enterprise research focusing on entrepreneurial development, new venture management, and coursework development. **Scope:** Free enterprise, including job creation, changing labor-force skill needs, factors affecting business competitiveness and employment growth, international trade and privatization, management in the financial services industry, policy issues relating to financial services, financial services markets, offshore sourcing in manufacturing, manufacturing quality, manufacturing forecasting, human resources supervision, team building, compensation, management development, and multidisciplinary research on global economic change and international marketing. **Founded:** 1985. **Educational Activities:** Carolina Challenge Star Program; Carolina Entrepreneurial Initiative; International Executive Series and MBA Enterprise Corps.

22337 ■ University of Southern California - Marshall School of Business - Center for Effective Organizations
1149 South Hill St., Ste. 500
Los Angeles, CA 90015
Ph: (213)740-9814
Fax: (213)740-4354
Co. E-mail: ceo@usc.edu
URL: http://ceo.usc.edu
Facebook: www.facebook.com/CenterForEffectiveOrganizations
Linkedin: www.linkedin.com/company/ceousc
X (Twitter): x.com/CEOusc
YouTube: www.youtube.com/channel/UCZ4JJQmwWLBPJkt5hv3iKtw
Description: Integral unit of Marshall School of Business, University of Southern California. **Scope:** Center offers expertise of faculty on critical organizational issues that involve the design and management of complex organizations. Issues include: performance appraisal, careers, organizational learning, job design, knowledge work teams, team performance management and organizational change. Primarily serves human resources executives. **Founded:** 1979. **Publications:** "Beyond HR: The New Science of Human Capital," Harvard Business School Press, 2007; "Achieving Strategic Excellence: An Assessment of Human Resource Organizations," Stanford University Press, 2006; "America at Work: Choices and Challenges," Palgrave-Macmillan, 2006; "Built to Change: How to Achieve Sustained Organizational Effectiveness," Jossey-Bass, 2006. **Training:** Becoming an Organizational Playmaker: Influence Skills for HR Leaders, Mar, 2013; Advanced Topics in Organization Design Workshop, Jun, 2013; Employee Resource Group Leadership Summit, Jun, 2013; Data Coaching Workshop, Jun, 2013; THREE - The HR Emerging Executive, Sep, 2013; Beyond Change Management: Accelerating Transformations and Building Agile Organizations, Oct, 2013; Strategic Partnership with Impact, Oct, 2013; Strategic Organization Design Workshop, Nov, 2013. **Educational Activities:** Strategic Organization Design Workshop (Biennial).

Employee Theft

ASSOCIATIONS AND OTHER ORGANIZATIONS

22338 ■ **International Association of Professional Security Consultants (IAPSC)**
136 Everett Rd.
Albany, NY 12205
Ph: (415)536-0288
Co. E-mail: iapsc@iapsc.org
URL: http://iapsc.org
Contact: Michael Silva, President
Facebook: www.facebook.com/International-Association-of-Professional-Security-Consultants-105968860944868
X (Twitter): x.com/IAPSCIAPSC
Instagram: www.instagram.com/iapsc
Description: Promotes understanding and cooperation among members and industries or individuals requiring such services. Seeks to enhance members' knowledge through seminars, training programs and educational materials. **Founded:** 1984. **Publications:** *International Association of Professional Security Consultants--Directory*; *IAPSC Consultants Directory* (Annual); *IAPSC News* (Semimonthly). **Educational Activities:** International Association of Professional Security Consultants Convention (Annual); How to Succeed as a Professional Security Consultant. **Awards:** The IAPSC Charles A. Sennewald Distinguished Service Accolade (Irregular). **Geographic Preference:** National.

REFERENCE WORKS

22339 ■ *"5 Employee Theft Prevention Strategies"* by U.S. Chamber of Commerce
URL(s): www.uschamber.com/co/run/human-resources/preventing-employee-theft
Description: Discusses types of employee theft and prevention strategies for small business owners to utilize. **Availability:** Online.

22340 ■ *"7 Ways to Protect Your Small Business from Fraud and Cybercrime"* in Merchants Insurance Group Blog (Jan. 27, 2022)
URL(s): www.merchantsgroup.com/blog/7-ways-to-protect-your-small-business-from-fraud-and-cybercrime/
Released: January 27, 2022. **Description:** Discusses fraud and cybercrime prevention resources for your small business. **Availability:** Online.

22341 ■ *"8 Ways Employees Commit Time Theft"* in Business News Daily (Nov. 19, 2021)
URL(s): www.businessnewsdaily.com/16177-employee-time-theft.html
Released: November 19, 2021. **Description:** Describes eight ways in which small business employees steal company time and how to ensure this doesn't happen to your business. **Availability:** Online.

22342 ■ *"The Danger from Within: The Biggest Threat to Your Cybersecurity May Be an Employee or a Vendor"* in Harvard Business Review (Vol. 92, September 2014, No. 9, pp. 94)
Pub: Harvard Business Publishing
Contact: Diane Belcher, Managing Director
Price: $8.95. **Description:** Corporate computer crimes involving insiders are on the rise. To reduce vulnerability, firms should incorporate employees into the watchdog process, perform regular audits of distributors and suppliers, and implement security procedures involving both management and information technology personnel. **Availability:** Online; PDF.

22343 ■ *"Detecting and Combating Employee Theft"* in Wolters Kluwer Expert Insights (Mar 20, 2020)
URL(s): www.wolterskluwer.com/en/expert-insights/detecting-and-combating-employee-theft
Released: March 20, 2020. **Description:** Discusses how employers can detect employee theft and how to properly handle suspicions within the workplace. Provides information on anti-theft policies. **Availability:** Online.

22344 ■ *"Employee Theft: Identify & Prevent Fraud Embezzlement & Pilfering"* in ZenBusiness (Aug. 11, 2021)
URL(s): www.zenbusiness.com/blog/employee-theft-embezzlement/
Released: August 11, 2021. **Description:** Provides tips on spotting and eliminating employee theft in your small business. **Availability:** Online.

22345 ■ *"How to Detect and Prevent Employee Fraud"* in Contractor (Vol. 56, October 2009, No. 10, pp. 57)
Ed: James R. Leichter. **Description:** Mechanical contractors can prevent employee fraud by handing out a detailed employment policy manual to their employees and making sure that their invoices are numbered. It is also highly advised to have bank statements reconciled by a third party. **Availability:** Print; Online.

22346 ■ *"How to Spot Employee Theft and What You Can Do About It"* in Insperity Blog
URL(s): www.insperity.com/blog/spot-employee-theft-can/
Description: Discusses the varying degrees of employee theft and the importance of not leaving one person in charge of the finances. Provides 3 tasks needed to keep a system of checks and balances in place. **Availability:** Online.

22347 ■ *"Preventing Theft and Embezzlement Within Small Businesses"* in Greater Fayetteville Business Journal (Jan. 31, 2022)
URL(s): bizfayetteville.com/insights/adam-hall-cpa/preventing-theft-and-embezzlement-within-small-businesses/622
Released: January 31, 2022. **Description:** Discusses the susceptibility of small businesses to embezzlement and other nefarious activities due to the level of trust that typically exists in a small business environment. Provides key things that small business owners can do to safeguard against theft. **Availability:** Online.

22348 ■ *"Retailers Report 'Shrinkage' - Disappearance of Inventory - on the Rise"* in Arkansas Business (Vol. 26, September 28, 2009, No. 39, pp. 17)
Pub: Arkansas Business Publishing Group
Contact: Mitch Bettis, President
Ed: Mark Friedman. **Description:** According to a National Retail Security Survey report released last June, retailers across the country have lost about $36.5 billion in shrinkage, most of it at the hands of employees and shoplifters alike. Statistical data included. **Availability:** Online.

22349 ■ *"Small Businesses Are Especially Susceptible to Employee Theft. Here's How to Protect Yourself and Your Company"* Inc. (March 21, 2019)
URL(s): www.inc.com/associated-press/simple-ways-to-protect-your-small-business-from-employee-theft.html
Released: March 21, 2019. **Description:** Provides examples of workplace theft and how to put practices and systems in place to prevent wrongdoing at your small business. **Availability:** Online.

22350 ■ *"What to Do If You Suspect Employee Theft at Your Business"* in Insureon Small Business Blog
URL(s): www.insureon.com/blog/what-to-do-if-you-suspect-employee-theft-at-your-business
Description: Provides information on types of employee theft, what to do when you suspect employee theft, and insurance policy information to protect your small business. **Availability:** Online.

22351 ■ *"What Has Sergey Wrought?"* in Barron's (Vol. 89, July 13, 2009, No. 28, pp. 8)
Pub: Dow Jones & Company Inc.
Contact: Almar Latour, Chief Executive Officer
Ed: Alan Abelson. **Description:** Sergey Aleynikov is a computer expert that once worked for Goldman Sachs but he was arrested after he left the company and charged with theft for bringing with him the code for the company's proprietary software for high-frequency trading. The stock market has been down for four straight weeks as of July 13, 2009 which reflects the reality of how the economy is still struggling. **Availability:** Online.

22352 ■ *"Your Employees Are Probably Stealing From You. Here Are Five Ways To Put An End To It."* in Forbes (Dec. 28, 2018)
URL(s): www.forbes.com/sites/ivywalker/2018/12/28/your-employees-are-probably-stealing-from-you-here-are-five-ways-to-put-an-end-to-it/?sh=4180f0dc3386

22353 ■ Employee Theft

Released: December 28, 2018. **Description:** Describes how small business owners may have a false sense of security about their employees. Provides information on things to consider to protect your business from employee fraud and abuse. **Availability:** Online.

CONSULTANTS

22353 ■ AlixPartners LLP
2000 Town Ctr., Ste. 2400
Southfield, MI 48075
Ph: (248)358-4420
Fax: (248)358-1969
URL: http://www.alixpartners.com
Contact: Jeremy Borys, Director
E-mail: jborys@alixpartners.com
Facebook: www.facebook.com/AlixPartners
X (Twitter): x.com/AlixPartnersLLP
Description: Firm engages in performance improvement, investigations, disputes, risk, turnaround, restructuring, digital, organization and transformative leadership. **Founded:** 1981. **Publications:** "Managing Along the Cutting Edge," Newsweek, Feb, 2009; "Mitigating Fcpa Risks When Doing Business in China," Bloomberg Corporate Law Journal, Feb, 2009; "Crisis Management Alix partners," Consulting Magazine, 2008; "Getting The Most Out Of IT C Suite Survey"; "Vestar Minority Deal Turns Into Turnaround"; "The Impact of US Style Regulation in Europe"; "The Corporate Superheroes Who Support Strapped Businesses in Their Hour of Need," the Daily Telegraph, Dec, 2008; "Changes to Claim Objection Rules Go Effective," Dec, 2007; "Squeeze Makes Life Harder," Financial Times, Oct, 2007; "Dialing for Dollars and Other Tactics for Finding Cash for the Estate," Abi Journal, Oct, 2007; "Don't Blame the Tool," Sep, 2007; "Claims Chats Guide to Claims Settlement Letters," Abi Journal, Aug, 2007; "Managing it Through Tough Times," Architecture and Governance, Jul, 2007; "Marketers Must Learn New Brand Imperatives," Cpg Matters, Jun, 2007. **Training:** A Business Perspective on Bankruptcy and Insolvency; How to Avoid Corporate Bankruptcy; The Accountant's Role in Bankruptcy and Insolvency. **Educational Activities:** Winter Leadership Conference (Annual).

22354 ■ Assets Protection Inc. (API)
421 E Blvd.
Essex, MD 21221
URL: http://www.assetsprotectioninc.com
Description: Firm provides professional loss prevention assistance, development, maintenance of security programs for businesses of all size in retail and manufacturing. **Scope:** Firm provides professional loss prevention assistance, development, maintenance of security programs for businesses of all size in retail and manufacturing.

22355 ■ Executive Management Services Inc. (EMS)
500 Locust Valley Rd.
Greensburg, PA 15601
Ph: (724)836-2424
Fax: (724)836-4305
URL: http://www.emsinc.com
Contact: David A. Bego, President
Description: Firm provides commercial, educational, manufacturing and medical cleaning solutions and also offers security, maintenance and exterior care services. **Scope:** Firm provides commercial, educational, manufacturing and medical cleaning solutions and also offers security, maintenance and exterior care services. **Founded:** 1987.

22356 ■ Haynes Associates L.L.C.
1021 Temple St.
Charleston, WV 25312
Contact: Richard A. Haynes, Contact
Description: Security management consultant. Offers the following services security surveys and audits, security readiness for labor disputes, investigations, security training and awareness programs, special projects. Industries served: Mining, petroleum, law enforcement, private security companies and government agencies. **Scope:** Security management consultant. Offers the following services security surveys and audits, security readiness for labor disputes, investigations, security training and awareness programs, special projects. Industries served: Mining, petroleum, law enforcement, private security companies and government agencies. **Founded:** 1980. **Publications:** "Let's Talk Security," Kanawha Valley Business Monthly; "The SWAT Cyclopedia" Aug, 1999. **Training:** Personal Protection Workshop: Workplace Violence.

RESEARCH CENTERS

22357 ■ Centre International de Criminologie Comparée (CICC) [International Centre for Comparative Criminology]
University of Montreal
Pavillon Lionel-Groulx
3150, rue Jean-Brillant
Ste. C-4086
Montreal, QC, Canada H3T 1N8
Ph: (514)343-7065
Fax: (514)343-2269
Co. E-mail: cicc@umontreal.ca
URL: http://www.cicc-iccc.org/fr
Contact: Rémi Boivin, Director
Facebook: www.facebook.com/CICCUdeM
Linkedin: www.linkedin.com/in/cicc-centre-in
teruniversitaire-77266861
X (Twitter): x.com/CICCTweet
Instagram: www.instagram.com/panoptique_cicc
YouTube: www.youtube.com/user/CICCTV
Description: Initiates comparative studies and the training of professional personnel and research workers in the field of criminal justice. Disseminates cross-cultural experience and resources; encourages the exchange of information on research and penal reform. Conducts studies on topics such as the adaptation of traditional systems of criminal justice to the demands of modern industrial societies. Organizes refresher courses for practitioners; participants evaluate the criminal justice system of many countries with a view toward initiating reforms in their own system. Conducts seminars on subjects such as crime, and deviance, adolescent delinquency, domestic violence, development of delinquent behavior, enforcement of penal norms, social image of crime, and victimology. **Scope:** Criminal phenomenon as it exists in Quebec and Canada, including prevention of delinquency and protection of youth; delinquency that persists from adolescence to adulthood; female delinquency; victimology, white collar criminality (fraud, forgery, and counterfeiting and business crimes); crimes of violence (terrorism, group violence, and armed robbery); public reaction to various forms of deviance and criminality; functioning of the justice system, including functioning of the juvenile and adult courts; services for the execution of punishment (probation and pre-sentence reports); community participation in measures regarding criminals and delinquents; and clinical criminology and forensic psychiatry. **Founded:** 1969. **Publications:** *CICC Annual report* (Annual); *CICC-Hebdo* (Weekly); *CICC-Info*; *Proceedings* Collaborates in the publication of four specialized reviews: *Criminologie* (Semiannual); *ICCC Research Reports*; *Annual reports* (Annual); *Revue Criminologie* (Semiannual). **Awards:** CICC Postdoctoral Fellowships Program (Annual); CICC Postdoctoral Fellowship (Annual). **Geographic Preference:** Multinational.

22358 ■ Vera Institute of Justice - Library
34 35th St., Ste. 4-2A
Brooklyn, NY 11232
Ph: (212)334-1300
Fax: (212)941-9407
Co. E-mail: contactvera@vera.org
URL: http://www.vera.org
Contact: Nicholas Turner, President
E-mail: nturner@vera.org
Facebook: www.facebook.com/verainstitute
X (Twitter): x.com/verainstitute
Instagram: www.instagram.com/verainstitute
YouTube: www.youtube.com/channel/UCdUfqPJeOB
_bHFdx1lhR0jQ
Description: Seeks to make government policies and practices more fair and humane. Encourages just practices in public services and aims to improve the quality of urban life. **Scope:** Effects of community policing, alternatives to incarceration programs in New York City courts, the introduction of European dayfines into U.S. criminal courts, speed of felony case processing in New York City, alcohol and drug treatment strategies for parolees in New York City, mental health care in the justice system, policing, relationships between employment and crime, juveniles and the court system, immigration, violence against women, and indigent defense. **Founded:** 1961. **Holdings:** Figures not available. **Publications:** *Federal Sentencing Reporter* (5/year); *Research Department Monographs*; *Research Department Reports*. **Geographic Preference:** National.

Entrepreneurial Traits/Skills

START-UP INFORMATION

22359 ■ *"$44M Father/Son Biz Involved in Major Orlando Projects"* in *Orlando Business Journal (Vol. 31, July 18, 2014, No. 3, pp. 3)*
Pub: American City Business Journals, Inc.
Contact: Mike Olivieri, Executive Vice President
Released: Weekly. **Price:** $8, Introductory 4-week offer(Digital & Print). **Description:** Sy and mark Israel, father-son duo of Universal Engineering Sciences, speak about the projects that have been their largest challenges. They also highlight the advice they would give to a family business or a new business startup. **Availability:** Print; Online.

22360 ■ *"The $100 Startup: Reinvent the Way You Make a Living, Do What You Love, and Create a New Future"*
Released: August 05, 2012. **Description:** Chris Guillebeau shows how to turn good ideas into income in order to pursue a life of adventure and the ability to give back to society. He believes entrepreneurship is about finding the intersection between our expertise and what people will buy. **Availability:** Print; Online.

22361 ■ *The 250 Questions Every Self-Employed Person Should Ask*
Ed: Mary Mihaly. **Released:** 2010. **Description:** Comprehensive information is given for anyone wishing to start their own business.

22362 ■ *"2007 Top Colleges for Entrepreneurs"* in *Entrepreneur (Vol. 35, November 2007, No. 11, pp. 82)*
Pub: Entrepreneur Media Inc.
Contact: Dan Bova, Director
E-mail: dbova@entrepreneur.com
Ed: Nichole L. Torres. **Description:** Education in entrepreneurship is being pursued by many students and it is important to understand what entrepreneurship program fits you. Aspiring entrepreneurs should also ask about the program's focus. Considerations searched for by students regarding the particular school they chose to study entrepreneurship are discussed. **Availability:** Online.

22363 ■ *"Alex Gomez on Leaving Medical School to Launch a Startup"* in *South Florida Business Journal (Vol. 34, May 9, 2014, No. 42, pp. 19)*
Pub: American City Business Journals, Inc.
Contact: Mike Olivieri, Executive Vice President
Description: New Wave Health Care Ventures managing partners, Alex Gomez, shares his views about leaving medical school to launch his startup. Gomez says he always had the spirit of an entrepreneur and business excites him. He knows what he is looking for in investing at startup companies because of his experience with New Wave Surgical Corporation. **Availability:** Print; Online.

22364 ■ *"Allied Brokers of Texas Looking to Fill Private Lending Gap"* in *San Antonio Business Journal (Vol. 26, March 23, 2012, No. 8, pp. 1)*
Pub: Baltimore Business Journal
Contact: Rhonda Pringle, President
E-mail: rpringle@bizjournals.com
Description: San Antonio, Texas-based Allied Brokers of Texas has announced the expansion of its services to offer private lending. The move would provide direct private financing of $250,000 to $5 million to entrepreneurs looking to buy or sell a small business. Insights into the firm's new subsidiary, Allied Lending Services, are also offered. **Availability:** Print; Online.

22365 ■ *"Angel Investing Network Launches"* in *Washington Business Journal (Vol. 31, August 31, 2012, No. 19, pp. 1)*
Pub: Baltimore Business Journal
Contact: Rhonda Pringle, President
E-mail: rpringle@bizjournals.com
Description: Dan Mindus, investment director for Virginia's CIT GAP Funds, is launching a network of angel investors, venture capitalists and entrepreneurs. The network, which is expected to have 45 to 50 investors, is in the final stages of formation and could be a source of funds for startups in Washington, DC. **Availability:** Print; Online.

22366 ■ *"Austin, Aggies and Innovation"* in *Austin Business Journal (Vol. 32, April 6, 2012, No. 5, pp. A1)*
Pub: American City Business Journals, Inc.
Contact: Mike Olivieri, Executive Vice President
Ed: Christopher Calnan. **Description:** Texas A and M University System director for new ventures, Jamie Rhodes, has been using his experience as an entrepreneur and angel investor to work with the university's professors, researchers, and new entrepreneurs on commercialization opportunities. Rhodes has a goal to create startups based on research produced at Texas A and M. **Availability:** Online.

22367 ■ *"Austin Welcomes New Program for Entrepreneurs"* in *Austin Business JournalInc. (Vol. 29, February 12, 2010, No. 29, pp. 1)*
Pub: Austin Business Journal
Contact: Rachel McGrath, Director
E-mail: rmcgrath@bizjournals.com
Ed: Christopher Calnan. **Description:** Nonprofit group Economic Development Catalyst Organization (ECDO) is formalizing its BizLaunch mentoring program, which was stated in 2009. The program aims to offer support networks to entrepreneurs and assistance regarding early-stage venture capital. **Availability:** Print; Online.

22368 ■ *"Beyond Bootstrapping"* in *Inc. (Vol. 36, September 2014, No. 7, pp. 64)*
Pub: Mansueto Ventures L.L.C.
Contact: Stephanie Mehta, Chief Executive Officer
Price: $15, Nonmembers. **Description:** Dave Lerner, serial entrepreneur, angel investor, B-school professor, and author, explains the challenges entrepreneurs face when self-funding their startup business. **Availability:** PDF; Online.

22369 ■ *"Breaking Barriers"* in *Baltimore Business Journal (Vol. 30, June 29, 2012, No. 8, pp. 1)*
Ed: Jack Lambert. **Description:** Many Hispanic entrepreneurs have been struggling to start businesses in Baltimore, Maryland. Many necessary documents are available only in English. Hispanic businesses are seen to spark future economic growth in Baltimore. **Availability:** Print; Online.

22370 ■ *"Breakthrough: How to Build a Million Dollar Business by Helping Others Succeed"*
Pub: CreateSpace
Released: October 23, 2014. **Price:** $3.72, paperback. **Description:** Instruction for starting and growing a thriving business from home is provided. The book teaches how to listing to the small voice within, follow your instincts, deliver effective presentations, attract customers who require your products or services, host home meetings, develop leadership skills, discover purpose, and clarify your entrepreneurial visions and goals. **Availability:** Print.

22371 ■ *Brewing Up a Business: Adventures in Beer from the Founder of Dogfish Head Craft Brewery*
Pub: John Wiley & Sons, Inc.
Contact: Christina Van Tassell, Executive Vice President Chief Financial Officer
Ed: Sam Calagione. **Released:** 2nd Edition. **Price:** $18.95, paperback; $12.99, E-book. **Description:** Author shares nontraditional success secrets. Calgione began his business with a home brewing kit and grew it into Dogfish Head Craft Beer, the leading craft brewery in the U.S. **Availability:** E-book; Print.

22372 ■ *Canadian Small Business Kit for Dummies*
Ed: Margaret Kerr, JoAnn Kurtz, Andrew Dagys. **Released:** 4th edition. **Price:** $26.60, paperback; $39.99, paperback. **Description:** Resources include information on changes to laws and taxes for small businesses in Canada. **Availability:** Print; Online.

22373 ■ *Careers for Self-Starters and Other Entrepreneurial Types*
Released: Second Edition. **Description:** Advice to entrepreneurs wishing to start their own small company. Tips for turning hobbies into job skills are included. **Availability:** Print.

22374 ■ *"Campus CEOs: Young and the Restless"* in *Business Journal Portland (Vol. 30, February 21, 2014, No. 50, pp. 4)*
Pub: American City Business Journals, Inc.
Contact: Mike Olivieri, Executive Vice President
Released: Weekly. **Price:** $4, Introductory 4-week offer(Digital & Print). **Description:** A number of startups in Portland, Oregon were created by young entrepreneurs while still attending college. The University of Oregon and Portland State University

are developing courses designed to launch the entrepreneurial ambitions of their students. **Availability:** Print; Online.

22375 ■ *"CrowdFunding Made Simple Conference at University of Utah Ignites Ecosystem of Entrepreneurs and Investors"* in Economics Week (June 29, 2012)
Description: The first national conference on crowdfunding was held at the University of Utah Guest House and Conference Center May 31 through June 1, 2012. The event, CrowdFunding Made Simple, gathered entrepreneurs, business owners, professional service providers, investors, government officials and students to provide understanding and potential of crowdfunding, including information on the Jumpstart Our Business Startups (JOBS) Act. **Availability:** Print; Online.

22376 ■ *"Do Cool Sh*t: Quit Your Day Job, Start Your Own Business, and Live Happily Ever After"*
Pub: Harper Business
Contact: Hollis Heimbouch, Senior Vice President Publisher
Released: January 20, 2015. **Price:** $16.61, hardcover; $11.97, paperback; $11.49, e-book; $3.13, kindle; $0.05, hardcover(99 used from $0.05); $8, hardcover(44 new from $8.00); $2, paperback(76 used from $2.00); $5.47, paperback(64 new from $5.47). **Description:** Serial social entrepreneur, angel investor, and woman business leader, Miki Agrawal, teaches how to start and run a successful new business. She covers all issues from brainstorming, to raising money to getting press without any connections, and still have time to enjoy life. She created WILD, a farm-to-table pizzeria in New York City and Las Vegas. She also partnered in a children's multimedia company called Super Sprowtz--a story-driven nutrition program for children, and she launched a patented high-tech underware business called THINX. Agrawal also discusses the growth in her businesses. **Availability:** E-book; Print.

22377 ■ *The E-Myth Enterprise: How to Turn a Great Idea into a Thriving Business*
Pub: HarperCollins Publishers L.L.C.
Contact: Brian Murray, President
Ed: Michael E. Gerber. **Released:** August 03, 2010. **Price:** $14.99, trade pb. **Description:** This book explores the requirement needed to start and run a successful small business. **Availability:** CD-ROM; E-book; Print.

22378 ■ *"Entrepreneurial StrengthsFinder"*
Pub: Gallup, Inc.
Contact: Jon Clifton, Chief Executive Officer
Released: 2020. **Description:** The psychology of the entrepreneur is investigated. Research performed by Gallup shows that decisions and actions, influenced by the personality of the entrepreneur, affect the survival and growth of any small business. The book answers essential questions for anyone thinking about starting a new business or for those already managing a startup. Advice is offered to help grow a new venture. **Availability:** Print.

22379 ■ *Entrepreneur's Information Sourcebook*
Ed: Susan C. Awe. **Released:** January 16, 2012. **Description:** A comprehensive source for those looking to start their own business, which contains information on creating a business plan, marketing and advertising, taxes, and many more relevant topics. Also contains sources for further research.

22380 ■ *"Entrepreneurs: Search Party"* in Business Strategy Review (Vol. 21, Autumn 2010, No. 3, pp. 30)
Ed: Georgina Peters. **Released:** September 22, 2010. **Description:** Entrepreneurs tend to be fixated on coming up with a foolproof idea for a new business and then raising money to start it. Raising startup funds is difficult, but it doesn't have to be that way. Search funds offer an innovative alternative, and the results are often impressive. **Availability:** Electronic publishing; Online.

22381 ■ *"Entrepreneurs Take Different Paths, but Arrive at Same Place"* in Business Journal Portland (Vol. 30, February 14, 2014, No. 50, pp. 6)
Pub: American City Business Journals, Inc.
Contact: Mike Olivieri, Executive Vice President
Released: Weekly. **Price:** $4, Introductory 4-week offer(Digital & Print). **Description:** Several young entrepreneurs in Portland, Oregon describe how they started their own businesses while attending college. They discuss the challenges of balancing their studies and their companies. **Availability:** Print; Online.

22382 ■ *Entrepreneurship*
Pub: John Wiley & Sons, Inc.
Contact: Christina Van Tassell, Executive Vice President Chief Financial Officer
Ed: William D. Bygrave, Andrew Zacharakis. **Released:** Fourth edition. **Price:** $75.95, paperback. **Description:** Information for starting a new business is shared, focusing on marketing and financing a product or service. **Availability:** Print.

22383 ■ *Entrepreneurship and the Creation of Small Firms: Empirical Studies of New Ventures*
Pub: Edward Elgar Publishing Inc.
Contact: Edward Elgar, Founder Chairman
Ed: Carin Holmquist, Johan Wiklund. **Released:** 2010. **Description:** Study focuses on the important issue of new venture creation. Using a variety of data sources, methods and theories, the authors demonstrate the factors that aid or hinder new venture creation in a number of settings.

22384 ■ *Entrepreneurship: Successfully Launching New Ventures*
Ed: Bruce Barringer, Duane Ireland. **Released:** July 20, 2019. **Price:** $230.20. **Description:** Guide to help any entrepreneur successfully launch a new venture. **Availability:** Print.

22385 ■ *Escape from Cubicle Nation: From Corporate Prisoner to Thriving Entrepreneur*
Pub: Berkley Books
Contact: Ivan Held, President
Ed: Pamela Slim. **Released:** April 30, 2009. **Price:** $18.50, Paperback. **Description:** Insight is offered to help anyone wishing to leave their corporate position and start their own small business. **Availability:** E-book; Print.

22386 ■ *"Faces: Q&A with Kevin Huyck, Chef/Owner of R.A. MacSammy's Food Truck Specializing in Mac and Cheese"* in Saint Paul Pioneer Press (March 28, 2012)
Ed: Kathie Jenkins. **Description:** Profile of 48 year old Kevin Huyck, chef and owner of his R.A. MacSammy food truck. Huyck specializes in serving a variety of macaroni and cheese dishes. He wanted to own his own restaurant but did not have the capital for such an investment at the time and hopes to expand with either another food truck or possibly a restaurant that features mac and cheese dishes. **Availability:** Online.

22387 ■ *"Find a Customer To Validate Your Idea"* in South Florida Business Journal (Vol. 34, May 2, 2014, No. 41, pp. 15)
Pub: American City Business Journals, Inc.
Contact: Mike Olivieri, Executive Vice President
Released: Weekly. **Price:** $8, Introductory 4-week offer(Digital only). **Description:** Venture Hive founder, Susan Amat, share her views on her mission to nurture the entrepreneurial ecosystem from South Florida to the Americas. Amat says Venture Hive is a safe space where world-class technologists can learn to scale their businesses. Amat is a 40 Under 40 honoree, a White House Champion of Change, chair of Startup Florida, an Emerging Leader and a Woman to Watch. **Availability:** Print; Online.

22388 ■ *"The Food Truck Handbook: Start, Grow, and Succeed in the Mobile Food Business"*
Pub: John Wiley & Sons, Inc.
Contact: Christina Van Tassell, Executive Vice President Chief Financial Officer
Released: March 2012. **Price:** $19.95, paperback; $12.99, e-book. **Description:** Food truck businesses have grown so much in popularity, there are actually food truck competitions and was once a television show featuring them. A practical, step-by-step handbook is offered to help an entrepreneur start a mobile food delivery service. Information includes tips on choosing vending locations, opening and closing checklists; creation of a business plan with budget and finding vendor services, daily operation issues; common operating mistakes; and insight into delivery high quality food. **Availability:** E-book; Print.

22389 ■ *"Former Boxer Lou Savarese Fits Into New Business Role"* in Houston Business Journal (Vol. 40, January 8, 2010, No. 35, pp. 1)
Pub: Houston Business Journal
Contact: Bob Charlet, President
E-mail: bcharlet@bizjournals.com
Ed: Greg Barr. **Description:** Lou Savarese explains how the lessons he learned as a professional boxer help him to manage his new business venture, a gym called Savarese Fight Gym. Customers who desire to learn boxing and to stay fit like a boxer comprise the fitness center's target market. **Availability:** Print; Online.

22390 ■ *"Former WCVB Anchor Bianca De la Garza Discusses the Launch of Her New Media Venture"* in Boston Business Journal (Vol. 34, June 6, 2014, No. 18, pp. 4)
Pub: American City Business Journals, Inc.
Contact: Mike Olivieri, Executive Vice President
Released: June 02, 2014. **Description:** News anchor, Bianca de la Garza says career advancement prompted her to form Lucky Gal Productions LLC. She said her entrepreneurial pursuit will develop a television show focusing on lifestyle and entertainment. De la Garza admits she will miss her co-anchor job at WCVB-TV's morning show, 'EyeOpener'. **Availability:** Print; Online.

22391 ■ *How I Made It: 40 Successful Entrepreneurs Reveal How They Made Millions*
Pub: Kogan Page Ltd.
Contact: Christina Lindeholm, Manager, Sales
Ed: Rachel Bridge. **Released:** Second edition. **Description:** Inspiration is given to anyone wishing to become a successful entrepreneur. **Availability:** Print; Electronic publishing.

22392 ■ *How to Make Big Money in Your Own Small Business: Unexpected Rules Every Small Business Owner Needs to Know*
Ed: Jeffrey J. Fox, Jeffrey J. Fox. **Released:** May 12, 2004. **Price:** $16.95; C$24.95; $16.95; C$24.95; $16.95; C$24.95. **Description:** Former sales and marketing pro offers advice on growing a small business. **Availability:** Print.

22393 ■ *"Innovative Ability and Entrepreneurial Activity: Two Factors to Enhance 'Quality of Life"* in Journal of Business & Industrial Marketing (Vol. 29, July 2014, No. 6)
Pub: Emerald Group Publishing Limited
Contact: Erika Valenti, President
Description: Examination of how aspects of knowledge economy covered by the KEI (Knowledge Economy Index) and those of entrepreneurial activity covered by the GEI (Global Entrepreneurship Index) affect QOL (quality of Life) in a country. KEI, GEI, and QOL data gathered from different countries was analyzed using correlation and regression analyses. It was observed that KEI and GEI feature a momentous effect on QOL, while innovation index and total early stage entrepreneurship improve it. **Availability:** Download; Online.

22394 ■ *International Entrepreneurship: Starting, Developing, and Managing a Global Venture*
Pub: SAGE Publications
Contact: Tracey Ozmina, President

Ed: Robert D. Hisrich. **Released:** Third edition. **Price:** $95, paperback. **Description:** International entrepreneurship combines the aspects of domestic entrepreneurship along with other disciplines, including anthropology, economics, geography, history, jurisprudence, and language. **Availability:** Print; Online.

22395 ■ *"The Introvert's Guide to Entrepreneurship: How to Become a Successful Entrepreneur as an Introvert"*
Pub: CreateSpace
Released: October 17, 2014. **Price:** $4.27, kindle; $12.99, paperback . **Description:** The five main strengths and the five harmful weaknesses for an introvert wishing to become an entrepreneur are listed. Three key strategies to help an introvert run his new company are examined. Five key attributes of a good business partner are considered. Management tips are also shared for introverted leaders. **Availability:** Print.

22396 ■ *"Lean Branding"*
Pub: O'Reilly Media Inc.
Contact: Tim O'Reilly, Chief Executive Officer
E-mail: tim@oreilly.com
Released: September 01, 2014. **Description:** Branding your startup is essential to any small business success. A toolkit is provided to help build dynamic brands that generate conversion. Over 100 do-it-yourself branding tactics and case studies as well as step-by-step instructions for building and measuring 25 essential brand strategy ingredients, from logo design to demonstration day pitches. **Availability:** E-book.

22397 ■ *Lean In: Women, Work, and the Will to Lead*
Pub: Knopf Doubleday Publishing Group
Contact: Nan A. Talese, Contact
E-mail: ddaypub@randomhouse.com
Ed: Sheryl Sandberg. **Released:** March 11, 2013. **Description:** The chief operating officer at Facebook examines women's progress in achieving leadership roles and provides solutions to help women fully achieve their goals. **Availability:** Print.

22398 ■ *Legal Guide for Starting & Running a Small Business*
Pub: Nolo
Contact: Chris Braun, President
Ed: Fred S. Steingold. **Released:** 18th Edition. **Price:** $27.99, e-book. **Description:** Legal issues any small business owner needs to know for starting and running a successful business are outlined. **Availability:** Handheld; E-book; Print; Electronic publishing; PDF.

22399 ■ *"Live & Learn: Gordon Stollery" in Canadian Business (Vol. 81, December 19, 2007, No. 1, pp. 76)*
Pub: Rogers Media Inc.
Contact: Neil Spivak, Chief Executive Officer
Ed: Michelle Magnan. **Description:** Gordon Stollery of Highpine Oil and Gas Ltd. talks about being a hard-rock geologist and his move to start his oil and gas business. Other aspects of his business career are discussed. **Availability:** Print; Online.

22400 ■ *"Looking To Leap?" in Black Enterprise (Vol. 38, January 2008, No. 6, pp. 64)*
Pub: Earl G. Graves Ltd.
Contact: Earl Graves, Jr., President
Ed: Tennille M. Robinson. **Description:** Websites and organizations providing resources for any young entrepreneur wishing to start a new business are outlined.

22401 ■ *The Marketing Plan Handbook*
Ed: Robert W. Bly. **Released:** 2015. **Description:** A beginner's guide to understanding customers and their needs to help form a solid marketing plan for your business. Designed to help your small business outpace your competitors, this book will help you understand the market for your products and develop steps to achieve success. Comes with assignments and examples.

22402 ■ *"Moms Mean Business: A Guide to Creating a Successful Company and Happy Life as a Mom Entrepreneur"*
Pub: Career Press Inc.
Released: October 20, 2014. **Price:** $15.99, Trade Paperback,plus S&H. **Description:** Currently, more women are starting new businesses than men and there are 9 million women-owned businesses in the United States; most of these women are also moms. A guide to help women start and run a successful home-based business is presented. **Availability:** Print.

22403 ■ *"Mount Laurel Woman Launches Venture Into Children's Used Clothing" in Philadelphia Inquirer (September 17, 2010)*
Pub: The Philadelphia Inquirer
Contact: Elizabeth H. Hughes, Chief Executive Officer
Ed: Maria Panaritis. **Description:** Profile of Jennifer Frisch, stay-at-home mom turned entrepreneur. Frisch started a used-clothing store Once Upon a Child after opening her franchised Plato's Closet, selling unwanted and used baby clothing and accessories at her new shop, while offering used merchandise to teens at Plato's Closet.

22404 ■ *"The New CEO: 185 Easy-To-Set-Up Businesses for Youth and Adult Entrepreneurs"*
Pub: CreateSpace
Released: September 09, 2014. **Price:** $7.12, paperback. **Description:** Regardless of age, this book will help anyone wishing to launch and run a small business. **Availability:** E-book; Print.

22405 ■ *New Venture Creation: Entrepreneurship for the 21st Century with Online Learning Center Access Card*
Released: Tenth edition. **Price:** $169.06, hardcover-,softcover. **Description:** A handbook for students that explores all the concepts necessary for successfully launching a new enterprise. **Availability:** Print.

22406 ■ *Niche and Grow Rich*
Description: Consultants share insight to entrepreneurs wishing to find a profitable niche market. Authors write that good niche businesses are easy to start and easy to defend from competitors. They also report that finding a successful niche can attract and maintain good customers who are willing to pay more for unique goods and services.

22407 ■ *"No. 64: Scaling the Business Meant Rebuilding a Bridge" in Inc. (Vol. 36, September 2014, No. 7, pp. 48)*
Pub: Mansueto Ventures L.L.C.
Contact: Stephanie Mehta, Chief Executive Officer
Released: September 2014. **Description:** Profile of Susan Meitner, mortgage industry veteran who founded Centennial Lending Group, a mortgage lending institution. Meitner and her family helped raise the needed $2.5 million to launch the firm in order to provide loans to new customers. **Availability:** Print; Online.

22408 ■ *"No. 407: What I Learned in the Military, and What I Had to Unlearn" in Inc. (Vol. 36, September 2014, No. 7, pp. 80)*
Pub: Mansueto Ventures L.L.C.
Contact: Stephanie Mehta, Chief Executive Officer
Released: September 2014. **Description:** Profile of William Bailey, who served in the U.S. Army as information manager at the U.S. Military Academy at West Point. Bailey discusses his startup firm, Rapier Solutions, a government contractor providing IT, logistics, and social-work expertise. The firm has developed a new survivor outreach system for the U.S. Army. **Availability:** Print; Online.

22409 ■ *"No. 479: SeaSnax Seaweed Snacks" in Inc. (Vol. 36, September 2014, No. 7, pp. 44)*
Pub: Mansueto Ventures L.L.C.
Contact: Stephanie Mehta, Chief Executive Officer

Released: September 2014. **Description:** SeaSnax make a perfect snack for children's lunchboxes. These crispy sheets of seaweed made the 500 Inc. list of outstanding entrepreneurial startups and are now sold in Whole Food Stores. **Availability:** Print; Online.

22410 ■ *"Office For One: The Sole Proprietor's Survival Guide"*
Pub: CreateSpace
Released: January 12, 2014. **Price:** $12.95, Paperback; $6.42, kindle; $3.95, Paperback. **Description:** Over thirty experts offer advice to any entrepreneur wishing to start a business by themselves. Tips and advice on tuning out negativity, maintaining balance and boundaries, handling legal issues and financial challenges, finding and keeping customers, marketing on a small budge, networking, cracking the media code, growing a sustainable vision, and addressing burnouts. **Availability:** Print.

22411 ■ *"One of the Best Ways to Build Wealth...Is to Take Equity In a Company" in Business Journal (Vol. 31, May 2, 2014, No. 49, pp. 9)*
Pub: American City Business Journals, Inc.
Contact: Mike Olivieri, Executive Vice President
Released: Weekly. **Price:** $4, introductory 4-week offer(Digital only). **Description:** Entrepreneur Abir Sen reveals that he was not planning to start a business after selling Bloom Health, but he soon discovered that he wanted to do something productive. He believes that the traditional model of employer-paid health care insurance is dying. His opinion on health care entrepreneurial activity in Minnesota is also examined. **Availability:** Print; Online.

22412 ■ *"'Passion Is the Key to Accomplishment"' in South Florida Business Journal (Vol. 35, August 15, 2014, No. 3, pp. 11)*
Pub: American City Business Journals, Inc.
Contact: Mike Olivieri, Executive Vice President
Released: Weekly. **Price:** $8, introductory 4-week offer(Digital only). **Description:** Metro 1 president and CEO, Tony Cho, made his name by shaping neighborho9ods and large-scale urban projects in Miami, Florida. Cho says he got his first job when he was 11 years old working with a maintenance crew. Cho started his real estate firm during the economic downturn and believes surviving during the recession is his greatest entrepreneurial accomplishment to date. **Availability:** Print; Online.

22413 ■ *"Paul Hawken and Other Top Lumnaries to Participate in Green Business BASE CAMP in Los Angeles" in Benzinga.com (April 19, 2012)*
Pub: Benzinga.com
Contact: Jason Raznick, Founder
Ed: Aaron Wise. **Description:** Paul Hawken, environmentalist, entrepreneur and author, is one of many people participating in the Green Business BASE CAMP, a four-day workshop for green business and cleantech entrepreneurs. The event will be held in Los Angeles, California from May 31 through June 3, 2012. Insider guidance will be offered to early-stage entrepreneurs seeking to compete within this sector. **Availability:** Online.

22414 ■ *"Places for People Who Want to Make Things" in Philadelphia Business Journal (Vol. 28, May 4, 2012, No. 23, pp. 1)*
Pub: Baltimore Business Journal
Contact: Rhonda Pringle, President
E-mail: rpringle@bizjournals.com
Released: Weekly. **Description:** Entrepreneurs in Philadelphia, Pennsylvania have been opening businesses and nonprofits for people who have the urge to work in wood, sculpt or even make robots. Their sudden proliferation has provided people who like making things with their hands but can't afford the tools or don't have the space in which to do it where they live. **Availability:** Print; Online.

22415 ■ "The Responsible Entrepreneur: Four Game-Changing Archetypes for Founders, Leaders, and Impact Investors"
Pub: Jossey-Bass

Released: July 14, 2014. Description: Responsible entrepreneurs are special people who are able to transform industries as well as society. They challenge and refine cultural assumptions, laws, regulations, along with the processes of governance. They think beyond the status quo of entrepreneurship. Sanford provides the makings for this new type of business leadership, describing the ways in which any entrepreneur can achieve a higher level of work. Four archetypes are cover to help managers and entrepreneurs start and scale any business venture.

22416 ■ "SABER Research Institute's Steve Nivin" in San Antonio Business Journal (Vol. 28, April 4, 2014, No. 8, pp. 6)
Pub: American City Business Journals, Inc.
Contact: Mike Olivieri, Executive Vice President

Released: Weekly. Price: $4, Introductory 4-week offer(Digital only). Description: SABER Research Institute director and chief economist, Steve Nivin, shares his views on the potential expansion of Google Fiber's broadband Internet network to San Antonio, Texas. Nivin says Google Fiber should encourage entrepreneurs to start businesses in San Antonio. He also says the chances of fast growth companies being created in the city is enhanced with Google Fiber. Availability: Print; Online.

22417 ■ Seed-Stage Venture Investing: An Insider's Guide to Start-Ups for Scientists, Engineers, and Investors
Ed: William L. Robbins, Jonathan Lasch. Released: 2011. Description: Ideas for starting, funding, and managing technology-based firms, also known as, venture capitalists, are featured.

22418 ■ "Self-Employment: What To Know To Be Your Own Boss" in Occupational Outlook Quarterly (Vol. 58, Summer 2014, No. 2, pp. 2)
Pub: Government Publishing Office
Contact: Hugh Nathanial Halpern, Director

Description: Information is presented to help would-be entrepreneurs decide if self-employment is for them. The challenges, rewards, and fastest growth sectors are discussed. Whether to incorporate or not is examined, as well as the skills and knowledge to become a successful small business owner is explored. Availability: Print; Online.

22419 ■ "The Self Starting Entrepreneurs Handbook"
Pub: CreateSpace

Released: September 24, 2014. Price: $17.99; $11.03, paperback. Description: Information for starting a business is provided. Advice is given for writing a business plan, naming your new business, obtaining a business license if required, and building a marketing strategy for entrepreneurs. Availability: Print.

22420 ■ "Should You Choose a Lump-Sum Pension Payout? Here's How Entrepreneur Ramona Harper Decided" in Black Enterprise (Vol. 44, June 2014, No. 10, pp. 27)
Pub: Earl G. Graves Ltd.
Contact: Earl Graves, Jr., President

Description: Entrepreneur, Ramona Harper, chose a lump sum payout of her pension in order to start a new business. She used $110,000 to start her accessories boutique and put the remaining money into a small business 401(k), which helped her avoid a large tax. Tips to help individuals decide the best way to collect their pension are provided. Availability: Online.

22421 ■ "Slow-Down Startups Hot" in Austin Business JournalInc. (Vol. 28, September 12, 2008, No. 26, pp. 1)
Pub: Austin Business Journal
Contact: Rachel McGrath, Director
E-mail: rmcgrath@bizjournals.com

Ed: Sandra Zaragoza. Description: A number of entrepreneurs from Austin, Texas are starting their own small business despite the economic slowdown. The Small Business Development Program in Austin has seen a 50 percent increase in the demand for its services in 2008 as compared to demand in 2007. Other details about the entrepreneurship trend are discussed. Availability: Print; Online.

22422 ■ Small Business for Dummies
Pub: John Wiley & Sons, Inc.
Contact: Christina Van Tassell, Executive Vice President Chief Financial Officer

Ed: Eric Tyson, Jim Schell. Released: 5th Edition. Price: $24.99, paperback; $16.99, E-book. Description: Guidebook for anyone wanting to start or grow a small business; topics include information financing, budgeting, marketing, management and more. Availability: E-book; Print.

22423 ■ Small Business Entrepreneur: Launching a New Venture and Managing a Business on a Day-to-Day Basis
Released: February 2006. Price: $19.95. Description: Comprehensive guide examining the management skills required to launch and run a small business.

22424 ■ The Small Business Start-Up Kit
Pub: Nolo
Contact: Chris Braun, President

Ed: Peri Pakroo. Released: 12th edition. Price: $20.99, E-book. Description: Entrepreneurial advice for launching a new business. Topics include compliance with state regulations, sole proprietorships, partnerships, corporations, limited liability companies, as well as accounting and tax information. Availability: E-book; Print; Electronic publishing; PDF.

22425 ■ Small Business Survival Guide
Released: First edition. Description: Small business expert provides strategies to start a company and survive in the 21st Century. He shows small business owners how to succeed despite challenges that can defeat any firm. His advice covers suppliers; customers and contractors; competitors and creditors; spouses, family and friends; as well as the ways lawyers, accountants and other can steal an entrepreneur's success. Ennico also describes how startups can comply with local regulations. Availability: E-book; Print.

22426 ■ Soul Proprietor: 101 Lessons from a Lifestyle Entrepreneur
Price: $9.95. Description: More than 100 tips and stores to inspire and guide any would-be entrepreneur to earn a living from a favorite hobby or passion. Availability: E-book; Online.

22427 ■ "Staking Claim as Hub for Design" in Providence Business News (Vol. 28, March 17, 2014, No. 50, pp. 1)
Pub: American City Business Journals, Inc.
Contact: Mike Olivieri, Executive Vice President
URL(s): pbn.com/staking-claim-as-hub-for-design9 5764

Description: Providence, Rhode Island is expected to have two startup accelerators in 2014, even though the city lacks a large technology and venture capital presence. The Providence Design Forward accelerator is a partnership with Rhode Island School of Design and will focus on architecture and interior design entrepreneurship. It is modeled after Boston's MassChallenge. Availability: Online.

22428 ■ Start Business in California, 3E
Description: Information required for starting any business in California.

22429 ■ "Start-Up! So You Want to Be an Entrepreneur. So You Want to Be Rich"
Released: September 25, 2014. Price: $14.99. Description: Entrepreneur offers a guide for startups. Jim Lewis shares the innovative thinking that helped him launch, grow and sell two successful high-tech companies.

22430 ■ Start Your Own Business
Pub: Entrepreneur Media Inc.
Contact: Dan Bova, Director
E-mail: dbova@entrepreneur.com

Ed: Rieva Lesonsky. Released: Eighth edition. Description: Author and the staff of Entrepreneur Magazine provide business resources and information for starting a successful business. The book guides you through the first three years of ownership and provides work sheets and checklists.

22431 ■ Starting a Successful Business in Canada
Pub: Self-Counsel Press Inc.
Contact: Diana Douglas, Governor

Ed: Jack D. James. Released: Updated 18th Edition. Price: C$12.99; C$12.99; C$24.95. Description: Provides a framework for entrepreneurs launching a new business in Canada. Availability: E-book; Print; Download; PDF; Electronic publishing.

22432 ■ "Starting Up All Over Again: Alex Bogusky Backs Bootcamp for Advertising Startup" in Denver Business Journal (Vol. 65, February 7, 2014, No. 39, pp. 8)
Pub: American City Business Journals, Inc.
Contact: Mike Olivieri, Executive Vice President

Released: February 7, 2014. Description: Once called the Elvis of advertising, Alex Bogusky is now launching a new startup named 'Boomtown' with an aim to cultivate a new generation of advertising, marketing, design, and media related tech companies. The end goal of boomtown will be to figure out the trend in which media as well as the relationship between brands and people is going.

22433 ■ StartingUp Now Facilitator Guide
Price: $29.95. Description: Guide for those teaching entrepreneurship using StartingUp Now; the guide provides 24 lesson plans for each of the 24 steps/chapters in the book. Availability: Print.

22434 ■ "The Startup Blueprint: The Young Entrepreneur's Step-by-Step Guide To Starting Your Own Business"
Pub: CreateSpace

Released: October 21, 2014. Description: Careful planning and smart execution is required to start a new business. More than 90 percent of new business fail with the first three years. Practical tips and advice are offered to help young entrepreneurs successfully start a new business. Availability: Print.

22435 ■ "Startup Communities: Building an Entrepreneurial Ecosystem in Your City"
Pub: John Wiley & Sons, Inc.
Contact: Christina Van Tassell, Executive Vice President Chief Financial Officer

Released: September 2012. Price: $17.99, e-book; $26.95, hardcover. Description: A guide for building supportive entrepreneurial communities that drive innovation and small business energy. Brad Feld, entrepreneur turned-venture capitalist describes what it takes to create an entrepreneurial community in any city, at any time. He details the four critical principles required to form a sustainable startup community. Availability: O-book; E-book; Print; Online; PDF.

22436 ■ "StartX Med Prescribed for Innovation" in Silicon Valley/San Jose Business Journal (Vol. 30, June 8, 2012, No. 11, pp. 1)
Pub: Baltimore Business Journal
Contact: Rhonda Pringle, President
E-mail: rpringle@bizjournals.com

Description: StartX Med is a program started by entrepreneur Divya Nag along with Stanford student-led nonprofit StartX to help medical startups. Under the program, entrepreneurs will have access to wet and dry laboratory space, animal testing and information related to US Food and Drug Adminstration regulations. Availability: Print; Online.

22437 ■ "Take the Money and Run" in Entrepreneur (September 2014)
Released: February 08, 2011. **Description:** Startup founders are encouraged to ask for more than they think they will need when raising capital. The tendency to think small when it comes to capital or staging rounds to preserve ownership is a mistake for founders. Securing a large amount of capital in the first round could help save the time and costs associated with raising the next round of funds. Venture capitalists welcome founders who ask for more money because they prefer to go bigger on a single bet and their focus is always on valuation. **Availability:** Online.

22438 ■ Technology Ventures: From Idea to Enterprise
Pub: McGraw-Hill Higher Education
Contact: Michael Ryan, President
Ed: Richard C. Dorf, Thomas H. Byers, Andrew Nelson. **Released:** Fifth edition. **Price:** $130.66; $80. **Description:** Textbook examining technology entrepreneurship on a global basis; technology management theories are explored. **Availability:** E-book; Print.

22439 ■ "TEDx Talk Puts the Pieces Together" in Philadelphia Business Journal (Vol. 33, April 4, 2014, No. 8, pp. 6)
Pub: American City Business Journals, Inc.
Contact: Mike Olivieri, Executive Vice President
Description: Gabriel Investments managing partner, Richard Vague, shares his views about entrepreneurs wanting to start a company. Vague says they should be relentless because it takes a long time to start and run a business and it is a challenge to recruit customers and grow rapidly. He also states his experience as an entrepreneur enables him to give advice and put things into perspective for the people he mentors. **Availability:** Online.

22440 ■ "Think of Start-Ups as Shots On Goal" in (Vol. 90, June 2012, No. 6, pp. 38)
Pub: Harvard Business Review Press
Contact: Moderna V. Pfizer, Contact
Ed: Robert E. Litan. **Price:** $6. **Description:** The importance of start-up businesses to the nation's economic recovery is emphasized. Comprehensive legislation is necessary to improve start-up access to opportunity and talent. **Availability:** PDF; Online.

22441 ■ The Toilet Paper Entrepreneur: The Tell-It-Like-It-Is Guide to Cleaning Up In Business, Even If You Are At the End of Your Roll
Pub: Obsidian Launch L.L.C.
Contact: Kelsey Ayres, President
Ed: Mike Michalowicz. **Description:** The founder of three multimillion-dollar companies, including Obsidian Launch, a company that partners with first-time entrepreneurs to grow their concepts into industry leaders. **Availability:** Print; Online.

22442 ■ "The Toughest Sell: Women Hate to Buy Swimsuits, So Firms Try New Tack" in Inc. (Vol. 36, September 2014, No. 7, pp. 69)
Pub: Mansueto Ventures L.L.C.
Contact: Stephanie Mehta, Chief Executive Officer
Description: Finding top talent for a new startup company is challenging. It is suggested that entrepreneurs should sell the challenges faced by the new firm when hiring new workers. Startup recruiting is examined. **Availability:** Print; Online.

22443 ■ "Troy Patent Law Firm Launches Rent-Free Tech Incubator" in Crain's Detroit Business (Vol. 25, June 8, 2009, No. 23, pp. 4)
Pub: Crain Communications Inc.
Contact: Barry Asin, President
Ed: Tom Henderson. **Description:** Young Basile Hanlon MacFarlane & Helmholdt PC, a patent law firm located in Troy, Michigan has created a small, rent-free technology incubator on site. The incubator will be called North Woodward Tech Incubator and has room for four or five startups. The incubator is for the earliest or pre-seed stage for entrepreneurs who have not yet gotten significant investment capital. **Availability:** Online.

22444 ■ "UM-Dearborn to Launch Program for Entrepreneurs" in Crain's Detroit Business (Vol. 24, April 14, 2008, No. 15, pp. 7)
Pub: Crain Communications Inc.
Contact: Barry Asin, President
Ed: Chad Halcom. **Description:** Starting this fall the University of Michigan-Dearborn will begin its Product Realization and Technology Commercialization Program for entrepreneurs and innovators with lab-tested, high-technology products. Ultimately, 20 businesses will each work with the university in creating a customer base, commercializing a new high-tech product or process and connecting with venture capitalists who may invest in the new companies. **Availability:** Online.

22445 ■ "Why High Confidence Is Crucial for Entrepreneurs; It Helps Them Start Businesses, Persist In the Face of Ambiguity and Failure, and Remain Poised In Meeting Challenges" in Gallup Business Journal (July 17, 2014)
Pub: Gallup, Inc.
Contact: Jon Clifton, Chief Executive Officer
Description: Confidence is the key for entrepreneurs when starting new businesses, it helps them persist in the face of ambiguity and failure and to remain ready to meet any challenges.

22446 ■ You Can Do It Too: The 20 Essential Things Every Budding Entrepreneur Should Know
Pub: Kogan Page Ltd.
Contact: Christina Lindeholm, Manager, Sales
Ed: Rachel Bridge. **Released:** April 03, 2010. **Price:** $23.67, paperback / softback. **Description:** Collective wisdom of successful entrepreneurs in the form of twenty essential elements to focus on when starting a new company is illustrated by real-life entrepreneurial stories. **Availability:** E-book; Print; Online.

22447 ■ Your Million-Dollar Idea: From Concept to Marketplace
Description: Self-taught entrepreneur provides a 12-step plan to make a new product or service a profitable reality.

22448 ■ "Zero to One: Notes on Startups, or How to Build the Future"
Released: September 16, 2014. **Price:** $28, hardcover; $14.99, e-book; $30, CD; $15, audiobook download. **Description:** Entrepreneur and investor, Peter Thiel, covers new frontiers and new inventions yet to be discovered. Progress can be achieved in more industries than information technology, but thinking for one's self is critical to any entrepreneur in order to start and build a new venture. Tomorrow's leaders will avoid competition and create a unique business that will stand on its own. **Availability:** E-book; Print; Download; Audio.

ASSOCIATIONS AND OTHER ORGANIZATIONS

22449 ■ Applied Business and Entrepreneurship Association International (ABEAI)
PO Box 83731
　Portland, OR 97283
Ph: (503)943-7220
Fax: (503)943-8041
Co. E-mail: abeai@up.edu
URL: http://abeai.org
Description: Provides a scholarly forum for the exchange of research papers and ideas among faculty members and practitioners in business and entrepreneurship.

22450 ■ ATHENA International
2425 E Grand River Ave.
　Lansing, MI 48912
Ph: (312)580-0111
Co. E-mail: communications@athenainternational.org
URL: http://www.athenainternational.org
Contact: Traci Corey, President
Facebook: www.facebook.com/ATHENAInternational
Linkedin: www.linkedin.com/company/athena-international
X (Twitter): x.com/ATHENAleaders
Instagram: www.instagram.com/athena_international
Description: Supports, develops and honors women leaders. Inspires women to achieve their full potential. Creates balance in leadership worldwide. **Founded:** 1982. **Publications:** The ATHENAIAN (3/year). **Awards:** The ATHENA Leadership Award (Annual). **Geographic Preference:** Local.

22451 ■ Canadian Innovation Centre (CIC)
Waterloo Research & Technology Park Accelerator Centre
295 Hagey Blvd., Ste. 15
　Waterloo, ON, Canada N2L 6R5
Ph: (519)885-5870
Fax: (519)513-2421
Co. E-mail: info@innovationcentre.ca
URL: http://innovationcentre.ca
Contact: Josie Graham, Chief Executive Officer
E-mail: jgraham@innovationcentre.ca
Linkedin: www.linkedin.com/company/canadian-innovation-centre
X (Twitter): x.com/innovationctre
Description: Offers Invention Assistance Program, which assesses all aspects of an invention and aids in its development. **Scope:** Privately incorporated organization associated with University of Waterloo. Offers Invention Assistance Program, which assesses all aspects of an invention and aids in its development. Provides market research assistance to small, medium, and large companies. **Founded:** 1980. **Publications:** "Getting Going on Innovation part 3 in a series of 4: How a Gating System Can Boost Your Innovation Success," 2008; "Aligning the stages of the commercialization process"; "Overestimating the importance of licensing in fostering the Entrepreneurial University"; "Creating a New Model for Technology Commercialization in the Canadian Context"; "The role of Incubators and Contract research Organizations in growing new biotechnology companies"; "The role of Incubators within a University Environment"; "How the Inno-Gate System Can Boost Your Rates of Innovation Success"; "How entrepreneurs-in-residence increase seed investment rates"; "Technology incubators: Facilitating technology transfer or creating regional wealth"; "Pitchers Bible," Oct, 2007; "Making the Pitch - A Guide," Oct, 2006; "What should I include in my pitch? - A Guide," Oct, 2006. **Training:** Big Companies Can't Innovate; Innovation Awareness Seminar, Mar, 2008; First Steps Seminar, Jun, 2006; Government Assistance: Financing and Risk Solutions in Trying Times; First Steps for Innovators, 2006; Services for Innovation Partners; Innovation Workshop, Jun, 2006; Increasing the Rate of Commercialization of technological innovation: the catalytic role of the commerce agent, Jul, 2006; CFA Workshop; The Role of Universities and Colleges in Creating Canada's Wealth, Feb, 2005; Increasing the commercialization yield of Canada's innovation Efforts by Establishing Customer Pull, Jan, 2005; BCIP Presentation, Nov, 2004. **Geographic Preference:** National.

22452 ■ Center for Micro-Entrepreneurial Training
10028 Rustic Ridge Ct.
　Orlando, FL 32832
Co. E-mail: team@tcmet.org
URL: http://tcmet.org
Contact: Adm. (Ret.) Joseph A. A. Simmons, Chief Executive Officer
Description: Provides entrepreneurial training that prepares women and black and brown entrepreneurs with the skills needed to succeed in business.

22453 ■ Chinese Entrepreneur Association (CEA)
PO Box 2752
　Acton, MA 01720

Co. E-mail: info@ceaa.org
URL: http://www.ceaa.org
Contact: Frank W. Lee, Executive Officer
Description: Provides networking opportunities for members and associates interested in creating business in the infotechnology/biotechnology areas. Provides a platform for the training and exchange of knowledge in the discovery, development, manufacturing, and marketing of high tech products. **Founded:** 1999. **Geographic Preference:** Multinational.

22454 ■ Christian Entrepreneurs Association (CEA)
751 N Canyons Pkwy.
Livermore, CA 94551
Ph: (925)292-2331
Co. E-mail: info@ceasf.org
URL: http://ceasf.org
Facebook: www.facebook.com/ceasf
Linkedin: www.linkedin.com/company/christian-entrepreneurs-association
X (Twitter): x.com/ceasfbay
Description: Seeks to educate and support business owners to "live out their Christian faith more fully in their work and business.". **Founded:** 2000.

22455 ■ Elite Entrepreneur Organization
9545 Wilshire Blvd.
Beverly Hills, CA 90212
Ph: (310)560-5603
URL: http://www.eliteentrepreneurorganization.org
Contact: Delila Pouldar, President
Facebook: www.facebook.com/EliteEntrepreneurSociety
Instagram: www.instagram.com/eliteentrepreneurorganization
Description: Global business network that seeks to support small- and large-business owners by providing leadership-development programs and other resources designed for business growth. **Founded:** 2011.

22456 ■ Enactus Canada
920 Yonge St., Ste. 800
Toronto, ON, Canada M4W 3C7
Ph: (416)304-1566
URL: http://enactus.ca
Contact: Allyson Hewitt, President
E-mail: allyson@enactus.ca
Facebook: www.facebook.com/enactuscanada
X (Twitter): x.com/Enactus_Canada
Instagram: www.instagram.com/enactuscanada
YouTube: www.youtube.com/user/EnactusCanada
Description: Young people, business owners, or engaged in entrepreneurial activities. Promotes growth and development of members' business interests. Provides support and services to businesses owned by young people; encourages communication and mutual support among collegiate entrepreneurs. **Founded:** 1987. **Awards:** Enactus Canada Most Improved Award (Annual); Student Leader of the Year (Annual); Alumnus/Alumna of the Year Award (Annual); Most Supportive Business Advisory Board Member of the Year Award; Most Supportive Dean or Department Chair of the Year Award; Student Leader of the Year Award (Annual); Alumnus or Alumna of the Year (Annual); Most Supportive Business Advisory Board Member of the Year (Annual); Most Supportive Dean or Department Chair of the Year (Annual). **Geographic Preference:** National.

22457 ■ Entrepreneurs' Organization At Large - U.S. Central Chapter (EO)
OH
URL: http://www.eonetwork.org/atlarge-uscentral
Description: Provides local resources to members which includes networking events, mentorship, live forums, and leadership development. Industries represented in this chapter include: Computer/Services, Computer/Software, Consulting, Education/Training, Food/Beverage, and Marketing/PR. **Founded:** 2016.

22458 ■ Entrepreneurs' Organization - New York Chapter (EO)
151 W 19th St., 5th Fl.
New York, NY 10011
Co. E-mail: eonewyorkadmin@eonyc.org
URL: http://eonyc.org
Contact: Domenic Romano, President
E-mail: eo@romanolaw.com
URL(s): www.eonetwork.org/newyork
Facebook: www.facebook.com/EONewYork
Description: Supports entrepreneurs and business owners in Connecticut. Members must be founders, owners, or controlling shareholders of a company grossing more than $1 million annually. **Founded:** 1998.

22459 ■ Global Entrepreneurship Network (GEN)
1201 Wilson Blvd., 27
Arlington, VA 22209
URL: http://www.genglobal.org
Contact: Jonathan Ortmans, President
Facebook: www.facebook.com/unleashingideas
Linkedin: www.linkedin.com/company/genhq
X (Twitter): x.com/unleashingideas
Instagram: www.instagram.com/genhq
YouTube: www.youtube.com/user/Unleashingideas
Description: Operates programs around the world that promote collaboration and initiatives between entrepreneurs, investors, researchers, and policymakers in an effort to create jobs, provide education, and strengthen economic growth. **Founded:** 2008.

22460 ■ Global Entrepreneurship Research Association
London Business School
Regents Pk.
London NW1 4SA, United Kingdom
Co. E-mail: info@gemconsortium.org
URL: http://www.gemconsortium.org
Contact: Jose Ernesto Amoros, Chairman
Facebook: www.facebook.com/GEMonitor
Linkedin: www.linkedin.com/company/global-entrepreneurship-monitor
X (Twitter): x.com/gemnow
Description: Produces the Global Entrepreneurship Monitor, a collection of information, reports, and stories that aim to enhance the understanding of entrepreneurship around the world.

22461 ■ The Indus Entrepreneurs (TIE)
3964 Rivermark Plz. No. 113
Santa Clara, CA 95054
Ph: (408)567-0700
Fax: (408)567-0700
Co. E-mail: global@tie.org
URL: http://tie.org
Contact: Vijay Menon, Executive Director
Facebook: www.facebook.com/TiEGlobal1
Linkedin: www.linkedin.com/company/tieglobal1
X (Twitter): x.com/tieglobal
YouTube: www.youtube.com/user/TheTieNetwork
Description: Advocates for the advancement of entrepreneurship and the exchange of ideas. Works in fostering entrepreneurship and nurturing entrepreneurs; providing a networking platform for members; and helping members integrate with the mainstream community. **Founded:** 1994. **Geographic Preference:** Regional.

22462 ■ National Entrepreneurs Association
18444 W 10 Mile Rd., Ste. 103
Southfield, MI 48075
Ph: (248)416-7278
Co. E-mail: supportstaff@nationalentrepreneurs.org
URL: http://www.nationalentrepreneurs.org
Contact: ZaLonya Allen, PhD, President
Facebook: www.facebook.com/NationalEntrepreneursAssociation
Linkedin: www.linkedin.com/company/national-entrepreneurs-association
X (Twitter): x.com/NationalEntrep1
YouTube: www.youtube.com/channel/UC0MiAnMYBpFHWeGZ_Z2Cquw
Description: Empowers entrepreneurs to grow and sustain successful business through networking and education programs. **Founded:** 2018.

22463 ■ National Federation of Filipino American Associations (NaFFAA)
1612 K St. NW, Ste. 600
Washington, DC 20006
Ph: (202)262-0772
Co. E-mail: info@naffaa.org
URL: http://naffaa.org
Contact: Brendan Flores, President
Facebook: www.facebook.com/NaFFAA.National
X (Twitter): x.com/NaFFAA_National
Instagram: www.instagram.com/naffaa.national
Description: Filipino American individuals and organizations. Seeks to promote the interests and well-being of the 3 million Filipinos and Filipino Americans residing in the United States by getting them involved as leaders and participants in United States society. Major programs include citizenship and leadership development, voter education, entrepreneurial training, and community development. **Founded:** 1997. **Geographic Preference:** National.

22464 ■ Network for Teaching Entrepreneurship (NFTE)
120 Wall St., 18th Fl.
New York, NY 10005
Ph: (212)232-3333
Co. E-mail: nfte@nfte.com
URL: http://www.nfte.com
Contact: J. D. LaRock, President
Facebook: www.facebook.com/NFTE
Linkedin: www.linkedin.com/company/network-for-teaching-entrepreneurship
X (Twitter): x.com/NFTE
Instagram: www.instagram.com/nfte
YouTube: www.youtube.com/user/NFTEGlobal
Description: Devoted to teaching entrepreneurship education to low-income young people, ages 11 through 18. **Founded:** 1987. **Geographic Preference:** Multinational.

MINORITY BUSINESS ASSISTANCE PROGRAMS

22465 ■ Innovate Coalition
c/o SUEGO
1015 15th St. NW
Washington, DC 20005
Free: 888-944-6461
Co. E-mail: info@innovatecoalition.org
Contact: Steven A. Rodriguez, Contact
Linkedin: www.linkedin.com/company/incohq
X (Twitter): twitter.com/incohq
Description: Seeks to support underrepresented entrepreneurs across the world by catalyzing, connecting, and accelerating inclusive innovation. Offers entrepreneurship programming and event experiences designed to inspire, educate, and connect. **Founded:** 2014.

EDUCATIONAL PROGRAMS

22466 ■ Is Entrepreneurship Right for You?
URL(s): cwewbc.ecenterdirect.com/events/977133
Description: This online seminar hosted by the Center for Women and Entrepreneurship discusses key points about entrepreneurs and and how they run their businesses. Also gives out a self assessment to help attendees determine if they are a good fit for this type of business. **Audience:** Women small business owners and entrepreneurs. **Principal Exhibits:** This online seminar hosted by the Center for Women and Entrepreneurship discusses key points about entrepreneurs and and how they run their businesses. Also gives out a self assessment to help attendees determine if they are a good fit for this type of business.

22467 ■ WBENC Lift Financial Center of Excellence
URL(s): www.wbenc.org/programs/wbenc-lift-financial-center-of-excellence

GENERAL SMALL BUSINESS TOPICS

Frequency: Irregular. **Description:** Educational program to educate women entrepreneurs on financial business support and funding opportunities. **Principal Exhibits:** Educational program to educate women entrepreneurs on financial business support and funding opportunities.

22468 ■ WBENC Women & Pride
URL(s): www.wbenc.org/programs/women-and-pride
Frequency: Irregular. **Description:** A program to help provide support and development for LGBTQ+ entrepreneurs and corporate professionals. **Principal Exhibits:** A program to help provide support and development for LGBTQ+ entrepreneurs and corporate professionals.

22469 ■ Women of Color Program
URL(s): www.wbenc.org/programs/women-of-color-program
Frequency: Irregular. **Description:** Outreach and development for women of color entrepreneurs. **Principal Exhibits:** Outreach and development for women of color entrepreneurs.

REFERENCE WORKS

22470 ■ "4 Traits That Have Helped Small Businesses Survive the Pandemic" in Entrepreneur (Sept. 21, 2021)
URL(s): www.entrepreneur.com/article/386923
Ed: Tina Orem. **Released:** September 21, 2021. **Description:** Presents 4 characteristics that small businesses have that kept people coming during the pandemic and how you can ensure that your small business has the flexibility to incorporate these traits. **Availability:** Online.

22471 ■ "5 Characteristics of Successful Entrepreneurs" in Investopedia (March 13, 2021)
URL(s): www.investopedia.com/articles/personal-finance/101014/10-characteristics-successful-entrepreneurs.asp
Ed: Shobhit Seth. **Released:** March 13, 2021. **Description:** Looks at characteristics of existing successful entrepreneurs and key takeaways to ensure your own entrepreneurial success. **Availability:** Online.

22472 ■ 5 Entrepreneurial Skills to Master (Absolutely!) As an Entrepreneur
URL(s): impactified.com/self-coaching/entrepreneurship-101/5-entrepreneurial-skills-to-master-as-an-entrepreneur/
Description: Discusses what it takes to be an entrepreneur, how to go beyond the classical technical skills of an entrepreneur, and how to improve entrepreneurial skills. Includes 5 essential skills every entrepreneur should have. **Availability:** Online.

22473 ■ "5 Skills Every Entrepreneur Should Have" in Investopedia (Apr 5, 2021)
URL(s): www.investopedia.com/articles/personal-finance/080615/5-skills-every-entrepreneur-needs.asp
Ed: Evan Tarver. **Released:** April 05, 2021. **Description:** Discusses specific skills that an entrepreneur should have to ensure a successful lauch to their small business. **Availability:** Online.

22474 ■ 6 Vital Entrepreneur Skills for a Successful Small Business
URL(s): www.morebusiness.com/6-vital-entrepreneur-skills-for-a-successful-small-business/
Description: Presents information on important skills every entrepreneur should hone. **Availability:** Online.

22475 ■ 10 Business Skills All Entrepreneurs Need to Develop
URL(s): www.oberlo.com/blog/business-skills-to-start-online-store
Released: November 02, 2020. **Description:** Breaks down 3 essential business skills for entrepreneurs to develop. **Availability:** Online.

22476 ■ "10 Common Leadership Mistakes You're Probably Making" in Business News Daily (March 2, 2023)
URL(s): www.businessnewsdaily.com/8517-common-leadership-mistakes.html
Ed: Sammi Caramela. **Released:** March 02, 2023. **Description:** It can be easy to be caught up in bad habits that aren't professional, so follow these tips about how business professionals should conduct themselves and become that leader your employees will appreciate. **Availability:** Online.

22477 ■ "10 Talents That Drive Entrepreneurial Success; Gallup Has Identified the Behaviors We Have Consistently Observed In Highly Successful Entrepreneurs" in Gallup Business Journal (May 6, 2014)
Pub: Gallup, Inc.
Contact: Jon Clifton, Chief Executive Officer
Description: Behaviors observed in highly successful entrepreneurs are defined. The ten talents of successful entrepreneurs are listed. **Availability:** PDF; Online.

22478 ■ "12 Business Skills You Need to Master" in business.com (Jan. 31, 2022)
URL(s): www.business.com/articles/12-business-skills-you-need-to-master/
Ed: Terry Hill. **Released:** January 31, 2022. **Description:** Discusses the challenges in running a successful small business and presents essential soft skills that are necessary to learn to help you succeed. **Availability:** Online.

22479 ■ 12 Characteristics & Personality Traits Great Entrepreneurs Share
URL(s): blog.hubspot.com/sales/entrepreneur-personality-traits
Ed: Lestraundra Alfred. **Description:** Discusses the varying factors that contribute to the success of an entrepreneur with a focus on personality traits that successful entrepreneurs have in common. **Availability:** Online.

22480 ■ "15 Entrepreneur Characteristics to Develop" on Indeed Career Guide (Apr 1, 2021)
URL(s): www.indeed.com/career-advice/finding-a-job/entrepreneur-characteristics
Released: April 01, 2021. **Description:** Presents the qualities needed for successful entrepreneurship and how you can improve those that are not naturally present in your personality. **Availability:** Online.

22481 ■ "26 Great Business Ideas for Entrepreneurs" in Business News Daily (March 8, 2023)
URL(s): www.businessnewsdaily.com/2747-great-business-ideas.html
Ed: Tejas Vemparala. **Released:** March 08, 2023. **Description:** If you are thinking about entrepreneurship, check into these ideas to launch a small business. **Availability:** Online.

22482 ■ 42 Home-Based Businesses You Can Start Today
URL(s): www.businesstown.com/42-home-based-businesses-you-can-start-today/
Ed: Bob Adams. **Description:** Provides a quiz to help entrepreneurs understand what type of home-based business suits your personality. Offers 42 home-based business ideas and provides eight steps to getting started. **Availability:** Online.

22483 ■ "100 Brilliant Companies" in Entrepreneur (May 2014)
Pub: Entrepreneur Media Inc.
Contact: Dan Bova, Director
E-mail: dbova@entrepreneur.com
Description: Entrepreneur magazine annually selects 100 companies, ideas, innovations and applications which the editors feel offer unique, simple and high-tech solutions to various everyday problems. These may include design developments, innovations in wearable gadgets, travel applications and other new ideas which represent 21st Century breakthroughs and thinking outside the box. The list is divided into ten categories, including Fashion, The Human Factor, and Travel and Transportation. **Availability:** Online.

22484 ■ "The 2007 Black Book" in Hawaii Business (Vol. 53, December 2007, No. 6, pp. 43)
Description: Brief biographies of 364 top executives in Hawaii are presented. Information on their educational achievement, membership in associations, hobbies, family, present position and the company they work for are supplied. **Availability:** Print; Online.

22485 ■ "Advice at Entrepreneurs Event: Make Fast Decisions, See Trends" in Crain's Detroit Business (Vol. 30, July 28, 2014, No. 30, pp. 4)
Pub: Crain Communications Inc.
Contact: Barry Asin, President
Description: Crain's entrepreneurial event was held a The Henry Ford in Dearborn, Michigan. Panelists at the event advised entrepreneurs to make fast decisions and to be aware of small business trends in order to be successful. George Matick Chevrolet was honored. Details of the event are covered. **Availability:** PDF; Online.

22486 ■ "Albuquerque Entrepreneurs Selected As Top Participants in USHCC Foundation Green Builds Business Program" in Marketing Weekly News (April 21, 2012)
Description: Five winners of the 2012 Green Builds Business program was announced by the United States Hispanic Chamber of Commerce Foundation (USHCCF). These winners will receive a combined 24 hours of one-on-one green coaching with Bill Roth, the Green Business Coach for Entrepreneur.com and Founder of Earth 2017. Details are included. **Availability:** Print; Online.

22487 ■ "Altus Jobs Founders' Unique Operating System Generates Success" in Orlando Business Journal (Vol. 30, April 11, 2014, No. 42, pp. 3)
Pub: American City Business Journals, Inc.
Contact: Mike Olivieri, Executive Vice President
Released: Weekly. **Price:** $8, introductory 4-week offer(Digital & Print). **Description:** Maitland, Florida-based Altus Jobs founders, Saum Sharifi and Augusto Guevara, have credited their unique operating sytem with their quick success in recruiting talent, specializing in high level engineering positions. The system allows employees to work from 9:30 a.m. to 3:30 p.m. in their casual office and motivates them to show entrepreneurship by offering commission on top of base salary. **Availability:** Print; Online.

22488 ■ The AMA Handbook of Project Management
Pub: HarperCollins Leadership
Contact: Donald Miller, Chief Executive Officer
Ed: Paul C. Dinsmore, Jeannette Cabanis-Brewin. **Released:** Fifth edition. **Price:** $22.99, E-book. **Description:** A comprehensive reference presenting the critical concepts and theories all project managers must master using essays and advice from the field's top professionals. **Availability:** E-book; Print.

22489 ■ "Another Determinant of Entrepreneurship: The Belief in Witchcraft and Entrepreneurship" in International Journal of Entrepreneurship and Small Business (Vol. 10, July 6, 2010)
Ed: Felix Pauligard Ntep, Wilton Wilton. **Description:** Interviews were carried out with entrepreneurs of Douala, Cameroon. These entrepreneurs believe that witchcraft existed and could bring harm to them or their enterprises. **Availability:** Download; PDF; Online.

22490 ■ "The Apprentice Entrepreneur"
Pub: CreateSpace
Released: October 09, 2014. **Price:** $2.04, Paperback. **Description:** An autobiography of an amateur entrepreneur and his journey to succeed in the business world is presented. **Availability:** Print.

Entrepreneurial Traits/Skills

22491 ■ *"The Art of War for Women"* in *Hawaii Business (Vol. 54, July 2008, No. 1, pp. 23)*
Pub: PacificBasin Communications
Contact: Chuck Tindle, Director
E-mail: chuckt@pacificbasin.net
Ed: Chin-Ning Chu. **Description:** Business consultant Chi-Ning Chu talks about her new book 'The Art of War for Women: Sun Tzu's Ancient Strategies and Wisdom for Winning at Work', which discusses how women can more effectively win in business. She also shares her thoughts about the advantages that women have, which they can use in businesses decisions.

22492 ■ *"Backtalk with Terrie M. Williams"* in *Black Enterprise (Vol. 38, December 2007, No. 5, pp. 204)*
Pub: Earl G. Graves Ltd.
Contact: Earl Graves, Jr., President
Ed: Tennille M. Robinson. **Description:** Profile of Terrie M. Williams, president of a public relations agency as well as founder of a youth empowerment organization called Stay Strong Foundation. Williams reflects on her bouts with depression and how the disease impacts sufferers and talks about her book that will inspire others dealing with depression. **Availability:** Online.

22493 ■ *"Baltimore Entrepreneur Develops an Event-Themed Wish List App"* in *Baltimore Business Journal (Vol. 32, July 25, 2014, No. 12, pp. 7)*
Pub: American City Business Journals, Inc.
Contact: Mike Olivieri, Executive Vice President
Released: Weekly. **Price:** $4, introductory 4-week offer(Digital only). **Description:** Baltimore-based entrepreneur Patrick Nagle has developed an online event-themed gift registry named Glist, a mobile application (app) and Website that assists in gift buying. Glist allows users to photograph items they want, put them on the online birthday wish list, or 'glist', and share the registries via social media. **Availability:** Print; Online.

22494 ■ *"Baltimore's Co-Working Spaces Introduces New Kind of Cubicle Culture"* in *Baltimore Business Journal (Vol. 29, August 19, 2011, No. 15, pp. 1)*
Pub: Boston Business Journal
Contact: Carolyn M. Jones, President
E-mail: cmjones@bizjournals.com
Ed: Alexander Jackson. **Description:** Beehive Baltimore offers a co-working space where independent freelancers and entrepreneurs can work. There are two other companies that provide the same service and the value of these services to these professional is that it provides them with an office that is both convenient and affordable aside from letting them network with peers.

22495 ■ *"Barriers to Small Business Creations in Canada"* in *International Journal of Entrepreneurship and Small Business*
Description: Studies of Hatala (2005) and Choo and Wong (2006) related to the barriers to new venture creations in Canada are examined. **Availability:** Print; Online.

22496 ■ *"BDC Launches New Online Business Advice Centre"* in *Marketwired (July 13, 2010)*
Pub: Comtex News Network Inc.
Contact: Kan Devnani, President
Description: The Business Development Bank of Canada (BDC) offers entrepreneurs the chance to use their new online BDC Advice Centre in order to seek advice regarding the challenges of entrepreneurship. Free online business tools and information to help both startups and established firms are also provided. **Availability:** Print; Online.

22497 ■ *"Be a Better Manager: Live Abroad"* in *Harvard Business Review (Vol. 88, September 2010, No. 9, pp. 24)*
Pub: Harvard Business Publishing
Contact: Diane Belcher, Managing Director
Ed: William W. Maddux, Adam D. Galinsky, Carmit T. Tadmor. **Price:** $6, PDF. **Description:** Interrelationship between international experience and entrepreneurship is discussed. Individuals with international experience are likelier to be promoted and to develop new products and businesses. **Availability:** Online; PDF.

22498 ■ *"Because 10 Million Zumba Lovers Can't Be Wrong"* in *Inc. (Volume 32, December 2010, No. 10, pp. 106)*
Pub: Mansueto Ventures L.L.C.
Contact: Stephanie Mehta, Chief Executive Officer
Ed: Christine Lagorio. **Released:** December 01, 2010. **Description:** Profile of partners, Alberto Perez, Alberto Perlman, and Alberto Aghion, founders of Zumba, a form of dance used for fitness. **Availability:** Online.

22499 ■ *"Best Places to Work; No. 2 Tasty Catering Inc."* in *Crain's Chicago Business (Vole 35, April 2, 2012, No. 14, pp. 18)*
Pub: Crain Communications Inc.
Contact: Barry Asin, President
Ed: Sachiko Yoshitsugu. **Description:** Tasty Catering Inc., located in Elk Grove Village, Illinois was rated Number 2 in Crain's Best Places to Work category. The event planning and catering firm offers a family style lunch to employees weekly. CEO Tom Walters enjoys this meal with his workers. The company offers an educational program called Tasty Catering University that provides up to 30 hours of paid class time in courses ranging from English to business. **Availability:** Online.

22500 ■ *"Biblical Secrets to Business Success"*
Pub: CreateSpace
Released: October 02, 2014. **Price:** paperback. **Description:** Bob Diener share insight into his journey as an entrepreneur. He focuses on tough issues like: how to treat employees, how to please customers, whether or not to cut corners, whether to follow temptation of an unethical deal, and provides solutions to these dilemmas. He recommends abiding by the Bible's rules of business in order to prosper long term. **Availability:** Print.

22501 ■ *The Big Payback: The History of the Business of Hip-Hop*
Ed: Dan Charnas. **Released:** November 01, 2011. **Price:** $17, paperback; $13.99. **Description:** The complete history of hip-hop music is presented, by following the money and the relationship between artist and merchant. In its promise of economic security and creative control for black artist-entrepreneurs, it is the culmination of dreams of black nationalists and civil rights leaders. **Availability:** E-book; Print.

22502 ■ *"'Bill Feinberg on Building the Model of Success - 'Strive for 100 Percent Satisfaction'"* in *South Florida Business Journal (Vol. 34, June 27, 2014, No. 49, pp. 13)*
Pub: American City Business Journals, Inc.
Contact: Mike Olivieri, Executive Vice President
Released: Weekly. **Price:** $8, introductory 4-week offer(Digital only). **Description:** Allied Kitchen & Bath president and CEO, Bill Feinberg, is profiled. The entrepreneur discusses his advocacy for helping to find a cure for leukemia and lymphoma. He enjoys cooking and traveling with family. **Availability:** Print; Online.

22503 ■ *"Bitcoin 'Killer App' Or the Currency of the Future?"* in *Providence Business News (Vol. 28, January 6, 2014, No. 40, pp. 1)*
Pub: American City Business Journals, Inc.
Contact: Mike Olivieri, Executive Vice President
URL(s): pbn.com/bitcoin-killer-app-or-the-currency-of-the-future94158
Description: The Providence Bitcoin Meetup has gathered several technology experts to discuss Bitcoin, the popular digital currency. However, software developers, engineers and entrepreneurs see Bitcoin as the next killer app for the Internet and is changing how information and data is stored, shared and verified. The Bitcoin's impact in Rhode Island is examined. **Availability:** Online. **Telecommunication Services:** Anderson@pbn.com.

22504 ■ *"Blindspot: Hidden Biases of Good People"*
Pub: Ballantine/ Del Rey/Fawcett/Ivy Books
Contact: Matt Shatz, Contact
E-mail: mshatz@randomhouse.com
Released: February 12, 2013. **Price:** $14, paperback; $14.50, Hardcover. **Description:** Perceptions of social groups that shape our likes and dislikes and our judgments about people's character, abilities and potential include exposure to and attitudes about age, gender, race, ethnicity, religion, social class, sexuality, disability status, and nationality are examined. Hidden biases impact everyone, including business leaders, entrepreneurs and managers in decision making. **Availability:** E-book; Print.

22505 ■ *"Boar Market: Penny-Wise Consumers Favoring Pork"* in *Crain's Chicago Business (Vol. 31, April 14, 2008, No. 15, pp. 4)*
Pub: Crain Communications Inc.
Contact: Barry Asin, President
Ed: Bruce Blythe. **Description:** Interview with Alan Cole who is the president of Cedar Hill Associates Inc. and who discusses ways in which his company is taking advantage of the record highs of oil and natural gas as well as his overall outlook on the market. **Availability:** Online.

22506 ■ *Bottom-Line Training: Performance-Based Results*
Pub: Training Education Management
Contact: Dr. Donald J. Ford, President
Ed: Donald J. Ford. **Released:** Second edition. **Price:** $29. **Description:** Training is critical to any successful enterprise. The key to any successful training program involves defining and constantly focusing on the desired results of the program. The author provides a training model based on five phases, known as ADDIE: analysis, design, development, implementation and evaluation. **Availability:** Print.

22507 ■ *Break the Rules!: The Six Counter-Conventional Mindsets of Entrepreneurs That Can Help Anyone Change the World*
URL(s): www.wiley.com/en-us/Break+the+Rules%21%3A+The+Six+Counter+Conventional+Mindsets+of+Entrepreneurs+That+Can+Help+Anyone+Change+the+World-p-9781394153015
Ed: John Mullins. **Released:** January 2023. **Price:** $17, e-book; $29, hardcover. **Description:** Dr. John Mullins discusses how successful entrepreneurs often portray six mindsets that set them apart from other business owners. Learn about these mindsets and how to apply them to your business. **Availability:** E-book; Print.

22508 ■ *"Breaking Through"* in *Inc. (January 2008, pp. 90-93)*
Ed: Mike Hofman. **Description:** Entrepreneur Keith R. McFarland, shares insight into why most successful companies eventually plateau, while others keep on growing. **Availability:** Online.

22509 ■ *"Brief: Make a Bigger Impact by Saying Less"*
Pub: John Wiley & Sons, Inc.
Contact: Christina Van Tassell, Executive Vice President Chief Financial Officer
Released: February 23, 2014. **Price:** $24, hardcover; $15.99, e-book. **Description:** Communication is key to any business success. Today, busy executives demand respect and manage their time more efficiently than ever. The author addresses the challenges of inattention, interruptions, and impatience faced by professionals and to help leaders gain the strength required to eliminate wasteful words and stand out from others when communicating. **Availability:** E-book; Print.

22510 ■ "Bringing Manufacturing Concerns to Springfield" in Crain's Chicago Business (Vol. 31, March 31, 2008, No. 13, pp. 6)
Pub: Crain Communications Inc.
Contact: Barry Asin, President
Ed: Paul Merrion. **Description:** Profile of the new executive vice-president of Tooling & Manufacturing Assn., Paul Merrion, a man who plans to grow TMA's membership with an aggressive legislative agenda in Springfield. **Availability:** Online.

22511 ■ "The Buck Stops Here" in Canadian Business (Vol. 81, November 10, 2008, No. 19, pp. 25)
Ed: Sarka Halas. **Description:** Reputation strategist Leslie Gaines-Ross says that minimizing the damage followed by the identification of what went wrong are the first steps that companies need to take when trying to salvage their reputation. Gaines-Ross states that it is up to the CEO to ensure the company's speedy recovery and they need to be at the forefront of the process. **Availability:** Online.

22512 ■ "Building Black-Owned Bigger" in Crain's Chicago Business (November 11, 2021)
URL(s): www.chicagobusiness.com/equity/chicagos-black-owned-businesses-look-scale
Ed: Cassandra West. **Released:** November 12, 2021. **Description:** Profiling several black-owned businesses and their successes. Also discusses how black-owned businesses are growing revenue, creating jobs, and entering high-growth sectors. **Availability:** Online.

22513 ■ Building Wealth in China: 36 True Stories of Chinese Millionaires and How They Made Their Fortunes
Released: April 27, 2010. **Price:** $7.99, e-book. **Description:** Thirty-six of China's most successful and innovative entrepreneurs discuss valuable lessons for growing a business in China. **Availability:** E-book.

22514 ■ Built to Last: Successful Habits of Visionary Companies
Pub: HarperCollins Publishers L.L.C.
Contact: Brian Murray, President
Ed: James C. Collins, Jerry I. Porras. **Released:** August 30, 2011. **Price:** $14.99, e-book; $18.99, paperback; $32.50, hardcover; $29.95, audiobook CD abridged. **Availability:** audiobook; E-book; Print.

22515 ■ Business Black Belt: Develop the Strength, Flexibility and Agility to Run Your Company
Price: $15.99. **Description:** Manual offering insights that will enable anyone to become successful in small business. Seventy short chapters included topics such as attitude, management, marketing, selling, employees, money, MBAs, lawyers, consultants, and investors. **Availability:** Print.

22516 ■ Business Fairy Tales
Ed: Cecil W. Jackson. **Description:** The seven most-common business schemes are uncovered.

22517 ■ Business Management for Entrepreneurs
Released: Third Edition. **Description:** Lack of good management skills are usually the reason for any small company to fail. This book introduces entrepreneurs and managers of small to medium-sized firms to all functions required to manage successfully. **Availability:** Print; Download; PDF.

22518 ■ Business as Usual
Description: Founder of The Body Shop shares her story and gives her opinion on everything from cynical cosmetic companies to destructive consultants.

22519 ■ Business Warrior: Strategy for Entrepreneurs
Price: $9.99. **Description:** Advice to help entrepreneurs understand competitive strategies in order to succeed, focusing on sales, marketing, and personnel management. **Availability:** Print; Download; PDF.

22520 ■ "Calendar" in Crain's Detroit Business (Vol. 24, March 10, 2008, No. 10, pp. 21)
Pub: Crain Communications Inc.
Contact: Barry Asin, President
Description: Listing of events in the Detroit area include conferences addressing entrepreneurialism, economic development, and women business ownership. **Availability:** Print; Online.

22521 ■ "Can He Win the Patent Game?" in Globe & Mail (February 20, 2006, pp. B1)
Ed: Simon Avery, Paul Waldie. **Description:** A profile on managerial abilities of chief executive officer Jim Balsillie of Research In Motion Ltd., who will face the patent case with NTP Inc., is presented. **Availability:** Online.

22522 ■ Canadian Small Business Kit for Dummies
Ed: Margaret Kerr, JoAnn Kurtz, Andrew Dagys. **Released:** 4th edition. **Price:** $26.60, paperback; $39.99, paperback. **Description:** Resources include information on changes to laws and taxes for small businesses in Canada. **Availability:** Print; Online.

22523 ■ Careers for Homebodies & Other Independent Souls
Ed: Jan Goldberg. **Released:** Second Edition. **Description:** The books offers insight into choosing the right career for individuals. Jobs range from office to outdoors, job markets, and levels of education requirements. **Availability:** Print; Online.

22524 ■ "Carving Passion, Talent Help Couple Craft Business on Wood-Rich Land" in Crain's Cleveland Business (October 8, 2007)
Pub: Crain Communications Inc.
Contact: K. C. Crain, President
Ed: Sharon Schnall. **Description:** Profile of Woodcarved Art Gallery & Studio, a family-owned business which includes several ventures of the husband-and-wife team, Jim Stadtlander and Diane Harto. **Availability:** Online.

22525 ■ Cash In a Flash
Released: December 28, 2010. **Price:** $13.68, hardcover; $22.50. **Description:** Proven, practical advice and techniques are given to help entrepreneurs make money quickly using skills and resources known to generate permanent and recurring income. **Availability:** E-book; Print; Audio; Online.

22526 ■ "The Caterer Interview - Patrick Harbour and Nathan Jones" in Caterer & Hotelkeeper (October 28, 2011, No. 288)
Description: Profiles of Patrick Harbour and Nathan Jones who quit their jobs to start their own catering business. The partners discuss their business strategy when launching their boutique catering firm and ways they are adapting to the slow economy in order to remain successful. **Availability:** Print; Mailing list; Online.

22527 ■ "Celebrate Self Improvement Month with These Tips and Resources for Entrepreneurs" in Small Business Trends (September 2, 2022)
URL(s): smallbiztrends.com/2022/09/celebrate-self-improvement-month-with-these-tips.html
Ed: Annie Pilon. **Released:** September 02, 2022. **Description:** Self Improvement Month is in September, which is a great time for small business owners to reflect upon and improve their mindset. **Availability:** Online.

22528 ■ "Celebrate Success. Embrace Innovation" in Black Enterprise (Vol. 37, February 2007, No. 7, pp. 145)
Description: 2007 Women of Power Summit provides networking opportunities, empowerment sessions, and nightly entertainment. More than 500 executive women of color are expected to attend this inspiring summit in Phoenix, February 7-10. **Availability:** Print; Online.

22529 ■ "The Center of Success: Author Explores How Confidence Can Take You Further" in Black Enterprise (Vol. 38, March 1, 2008, No. 8)
Pub: Earl G. Graves Ltd.
Contact: Earl Graves, Jr., President
Ed: Ayana Dixon. **Description:** Motivational speaker and author, Valorie Burton, provides a 50-question confidence quotient assessment to help business owners and managers develop confidence in order to obtain goals. **Availability:** Online.

22530 ■ "CEO Forecast: With Cloudy Economy, Executives Turn to Government Contracting" in Hispanic Business (January-February 2009, pp. 34, 36)
Ed: Jessica Haro, Richard Kaplan. **Description:** As economic uncertainty fogs the future, executives turn to government contracts in order to boost business. Revenue sources, health care challenges, environmental consulting and remediation services, as well as technological strides are discussed. **Availability:** Print; Online.

22531 ■ "Challenges, Responses and Available Resources: Success in Rural Small Businesses" in Journal of Small Business and Entrepreneurship (Vol. 23, Winter 2010, No. 1)
Pub: Canadian Council for Small Business and Entrepreneurship
Contact: John MacRitchie, President
Ed: Lynne Siemens. **Description:** Rural communities and their residents are exploring the potential of small business and entrepreneurship to address the economic changes they are facing. While these rural areas present many opportunities, business people in these areas face challenges which they must navigate to operate successfully. **Availability:** Download; PDF; Online.

22532 ■ The Checklist Manifesto: How to Get Things Right
Ed: Atul Gawande. **Released:** January 4, 2011. **Price:** $32, hardcover; $16, paperback; $9.99, e-book; $34.99, CD-ROM; $9.99, hardcover(4 Collectible from $9.99); $2.87, hardcover(180 Used from $2.87); $7.76, hardcover(84 New from $7.76); $13.60, Paperback; $3.61, Paperback(191 Used from $3.61); $9.64, Paperback(90 New from $9.64); $8.99, Paperback(3 Collectible from $8.99); $25.09, Audio CD; $15.94, Audio CD; $19.29, Audio CD. **Description:** How tragic errors can be sharply reduced with a piece of paper, hand-drawn boxes, and a pencil. **Availability:** CD-ROM; E-book; Print; Audio.

22533 ■ China's Rational Entrepreneurs: The Development of the New Private Business Sector
Pub: Routledge, Taylor & Francis Group
Ed: Barbara Krug. **Released:** First edition. **Description:** Difficulties faced by entrepreneurs in China are discussed, including analysis for understanding their behavior and relations with local governments in order to secure long-term business success.

22534 ■ "The Classless Workplace: The Digerati and the New Spirit of Technocapitalism" in WorkingUSA (Vol. 11, June 2008, No. 2, pp. 181)
Description: Article argues the formation of a new type of economic actor at the intersection of a new capitalism and a new technology: The Dierati. The discourse in based on the analysis of the popular magazine Wired, which registers the culture of contemporary technocapitalism. The suggestion that the new persona of the digerati is constructed as a rejection of the ethics, which dominated the Fordist workplace and Fordist society: Hierarchy and differentiation between workers, on the one hand and capitalists and managers, on the other hand. The transformation of these two categories, workers and capitalists into the digerati worker and the digerati entrepreneur, is described. Set within the context of the structural transformations of capitalism from Fordism to post-Fordism, the article shows the ideological

22535 ■ Entrepreneurial Traits/Skills

fit of the new ethics of the digerati to the new working arrangements of post-Fordist capitalism, characterized by more privatizes, flexible, and precarious working arrangements. **Availability:** Print; Online.

22535 ■ "Code Name: Inventors: Go from Golden Idea to Agent of Invention" in Black Enterprise (Vol. 41, November 2010, No. 4, pp. 78)
Pub: Earl G. Graves Ltd.
Contact: Earl Graves, Jr., President
Ed: Renita Burns. **Description:** Profile of Andre Woolery, inventor of a magnetic wristband that holds small nails, screws, drill bits, and small tools, allowing handymen to keep essential tools at hand while working. **Availability:** Online.

22536 ■ "Conference Calendar" in Marketing to Women (Vol. 21, April 2008, No. 4, pp. 7)
Description: Listing of current conferences and events concerning women, marketing and business. **Availability:** Print; PDF; Download; Online.

22537 ■ Connect with SmartBook: Online Access for Canadian Entrepreneurship and Small Business Management
Ed: D. Wesley Balderson. **Released:** 10th Edition. **Price:** C$89, connect with smartbook; C$143.95, print text plus connect with smartbook; C$133.95, print text; C$89, Digital(Connect with SmartBook); C$143.95, Print (Print text + Connect with SmartBook); C$133.95, Print text. **Description:** Successful entrepreneurship and small business management is shown through the use of individual Canadian small business experiences. **Availability:** Print; Online.

22538 ■ Corporate Entrepreneurship & Innovation
Ed: Michael H. Morris, Donald F. Kuratko, Jeffrey G. Covin. **Released:** 3rd edition. **Price:** $22.49, e-book; $279.95, hardcover. **Description:** Innovation is the key to running a successful small business. The book helps entrepreneurs to develop the skills and business savvy to sustain a competitive edge. **Availability:** E-book; Print.

22539 ■ "Corporate Responsibility" in Professional Services Close-Up (July 2, 2010)
Description: List of firms awarded the inaugural Best Corporate Citizens in Government Contracting by the Corporate Responsibility Magazine is presented. The list is based on the methodology of the Magazine's Best Corporate Citizen's List, with 324 data points of publicly-available information in seven categories which include: environment, climate change, human rights, philanthropy, employee relations, financial performance, and governance. **Availability:** Online.

22540 ■ Creativity and Innovation: Breaking New Ground..Without Breaking the Bank
Description: Advice is given to help small business owners be creative in order to compete in their sector. **Availability:** Print; Download.

22541 ■ "Crucible: Losing the Top Job - And Winning It Back" in Harvard Business Review (Vol. 88, October 2010, No. 10, pp. 136)
Pub: Harvard Business Publishing
Contact: Diane Belcher, Managing Director
Ed: Alison Beard. **Price:** $8.95, PDF. **Description:** Michael Mack chronicles the changes in perspectives that occurred when he was fired from Garden Fresh, a restaurant firm he co-owned. Once again at the company helm, he is now more receptive to outside input and acknowledges the importance of work-life balance. **Availability:** Online; PDF.

22542 ■ "Customized Before Custom Was Cool" in Green Industry Pro (July 2011)
Ed: Gregg Wartgow. **Description:** Profile of Turf Care Enterprises and owner Kevin Vogeler, who discusses his desire to use more natural programs using little or no chemicals in 1986. At that time, that sector represented 20 percent of his business, today it shares 80 percent. **Availability:** Online.

22543 ■ "Data: Nearly 80% of Black Entrepreneurs Believe They Run Thriving Businesses, Yet Gaining Access to Capital Still a Hurdle" in Black Enterprise(February 24, 2023)
URL(s): www.blackenterprise.com/data-nearly-80-of-black-entrepreneurs-believe-they-run-thriving-businesses-yet-gaining-access-to-capital-still-a-hurdle/
Ed: Jeffrey McKinney. **Released:** February 24, 2023. **Description:** After navigating a world-wide pandemic, many Black entrepreneurs are focused on building up their businesses and creating generational wealth while also supporting other Black-owned businesses. Even with these commitments, issues obtaining financing have been encountered. Tips for circumventing these hurdles are discussed. **Availability:** Online.

22544 ■ Dead on Arrival: How the Anti-Business Backlash is Destroying Entrepreneurship in America and What We Can Still Do About It!
Released: August 01, 2017. **Price:** $26.99, hardcover; $9.99, e-book; $24.99, digital audiobook unabridged; $15.99, paperback. **Description:** Bernie Marcus, Home Depot leader, addresses regulations hurting small businesses in America. **Availability:** E-book; Print.

22545 ■ "Defend Your Research: The Early Bird Really Does Get the Worm" in Harvard Business Review (Vol. 88, July-August 2010, No. 7-8, pp. 30)
Pub: Harvard Business Publishing
Contact: Diane Belcher, Managing Director
Ed: Christoph Randler. **Price:** $6, PDF. **Description:** Research indicates that those who identify themselves as 'morning people' tend to be more proactive, and thus have a career-development advantage over those who identify themselves as 'night people'. Implications of the research are also discussed. **Availability:** Online; PDF.

22546 ■ "Describing the Entrepreneurial Profile: The Entrepreneurial Aptitude Test (TAI)" in International Journal of Entrepreneurship and Small Business (Vol. 11, November 1, 2010)
Ed: Serena Cubico, Elisa Bortolani, Giuseppe Favretto, Riccardo Sartori. **Description:** An illustration of metric characteristics and selected research applications of an instrument that can be used to define aptitude for an entrepreneurial profile (created in the 1990s) is examined. The entrepreneurial aptitude test (TAI) describes entrepreneurial potential with regard to eight factors. **Availability:** PDF; Online.

22547 ■ "Developing a Small Business Educational Program for Growing Rural Businesses" in Journal of Small Business Strategy (Vol. 31, December 1, 2021, No. 4, 50-56)
Ed: Timothy L. Pett, John Francis, Wendy Veatch. **Released:** November 16, 2021. **Description:** Discusses the research on educational programs to start new businesses in rural communities. **Availability:** PDF; Online.

22548 ■ "Digging Deep for Gold: David Iben, Manager, Nuveen Tradewinds Value Opportunities Fund" in Barron's (Vol. 88, March 24, 2008, No. 12, pp. 49)
Pub: Dow Jones & Company Inc.
Contact: Almar Latour, Chief Executive Officer
Ed: Suzanne McGee. **Description:** David Iben, manager of the Nuveen Tradewinds Value Opportunities Fund, looks for value in companies and industries where the consensus of analysts is negative. He started investing in gold stocks well before gold prices started to rise. **Availability:** Online.

22549 ■ Disciplined Entrepreneurship Workbook
Pub: John Wiley & Sons, Inc.

Contact: Christina Van Tassell, Executive Vice President Chief Financial Officer
URL(s): www.wiley.com/en-us/Disciplined+Entrepreneurship+Workbook-p-9781119365792
Ed: Bill Aulet. **Released:** March 2017. **Price:** $17; $28, paperback. **Description:** Used in conjunction with the book Disciplined Entrepreneurship, this workbook will help you grasp key concepts of startup success. **Availability:** E-book; Print.

22550 ■ "Disrupt Yourself: Four Principles for Finding the Career Path You Really Want" in Harvard Business Review (Vol. 90, July-August 2012, No. 7-8, pp. 147).
Pub: Harvard Business Review Press
Contact: Moderna V. Pfizer, Contact
Ed: Whitney Johnson. **Description:** The four principles are: target needs that need to be met more effectively; identify one's own disruptive strengths; step down or step aside to aside to achieve growth; and allow one's strategy to emerge.

22551 ■ Divas Doing Business: What the Guidebooks Don't Tell You About Being A Woman Entrepreneur
Pub: Nouveau Connoisseurs Corporation
Contact: Monique Hayward, President
Ed: Monique Hayward. **Description:** A must-read for any woman who's currently running a business or is thinking of starting one.

22552 ■ Divine Wisdom at Work: 10 Universal Principles for Enlightened Entrepreneurs
Description: Entrepreneurial advice for managing a small enterprise is given using inspiration, anecdotes and exercises. **Availability:** Print.

22553 ■ "The Don't Do Lists" in Inc. (Vol. 33, October 2011, No. 8, pp. 65)
Pub: Inc. Magazine
Ed: Jennifer Alsever, Adam Bluestein. **Description:** Ten business leaders and experts share their don't do lists, the things that should be avoided when going on sales calls, planning business lunches, motivating employees and more are presented. **Availability:** Online.

22554 ■ "Don't Quit When The Road Gets Bumpy" in Women Entrepreneur (November 25, 2008)
Description: Discusses techniques four women entrepreneurs are utilizing to keep their businesses successful despite the credit crunch and the economic downturn.

22555 ■ "The Doodle Revolution: Unlock the Power to Think Differently"
Pub: Portfolio Hardcover
Contact: Adrian Zackheim, President
Released: January 09, 2014. **Price:** $21, hardcover; $15.99, e-book. **Description:** Powerhouse minds like Albert Einstein, John F. Kennedy, Marie Curie, Thomas Edison, and Henry Ford were all doodlers. Doodling has led to countless discoveries in science, technology, medicine, architecture, literature, and art. Brown guides us through basic doodling to the info-doodle, in other words, a higher level of thinking and empowerment for anyone, especially entrepreneurs and managers. **Availability:** E-book; Print.

22556 ■ "Driving Passion" in Small Business Opportunities (April 2008)
Pub: Harris Publishing, Inc.
Contact: Janet Chase, Contact
Ed: Chuck Green. **Description:** Profile of Joe Assell, founder of Golftec, a company offering golf instruction that uses the latest technology with professional teachers. **Availability:** Print; Online.

22557 ■ Driving With No Brakes: How a Bunch of Hooligans Built the Best Travel Company in the World
Pub: Grand Circle Corp.
Ed: Alan Lewis, Harriet Lewis. **Released:** 2010. **Description:** Inspirational book about how two courageous leaders built a remarkable company that can

thrive in change and succeed in an unpredictable world. Important lessons for any business leader trying to create value in the 21st Century are included. **Availability:** Print.

22558 ■ *"The Duty of Wealth: Canadian Business Leaders on Nepotism and Philanthropy" in Canadian Business (Vol. 80, Winter 2007, No. 24)*
Description: Fifty-one percent of the respondents in a survey of business leaders say that the decision to allow adult children to join a family firm should be based on the circumstances at the time. He CEOs that were surveyed also believed that billionaires should donate an average of forty percent of their estates and keep the rest for their family.

22559 ■ *Eco Barons: The New Heroes of Environmental Activism*
Pub: Ecco Books
Contact: Daniel Halpern, Founder
Ed: Edward Humes. **Price:** $18.99, hardcover . **Description:** Profiles of business leaders who have dedicated their lives to saving the planet from ecological devastation. **Availability:** E-book; Print; Download.

22560 ■ *Economic Freedom and the American Dream*
Pub: Palgrave Macmillan
Ed: Joseph Shaanan. **Released:** 2010. **Price:** $80, Hardcover; $75, softcover; $59.99, e-book. **Description:** An exploration into the effects of economic freedom on American in several areas such as markets, politics, and opportunities for would-be entrepreneurs. **Availability:** E-book; Print.

22561 ■ *"Eight Bucks an Hour" in South Florida Business Journal (Vol. 34, July 11, 2014, No. 51, pp. 13)*
Pub: American City Business Journals, Inc.
Contact: Mike Olivieri, Executive Vice President
Released: Weekly. **Price:** $8, introductory 4-week offer(Digital only). **Description:** Tips on ways to improve entrepreneurial selling behavior are listed. A number of potential activities that entrepreneurs can and should be doing to build business include cold calling, attending networking events, and creating business alliances. **Availability:** Print; Online.

22562 ■ *"Empathy: An Entrepreneur's Killer App" in Women Entrepreneur (February 3, 2009)*
Description: It is just as important to treat employees with courtesy and respect during bad economic times as it is in a good economy. Employers sometimes take advantage of such bad economic times since they realize that employees are grateful to have a job and cannot just quit and easily find work elsewhere. The importance of empathy in a company's leadership personnel is discussed. **Availability:** Online.

22563 ■ *Employee Management for Small Business*
Pub: Self-Counsel Press Inc.
Contact: Diana Douglas, Governor
Ed: Lin Grensing-Pophal. **Released:** Third edition. **Price:** C$12.99, EPUB. **Description:** Management tools to help entrepreneurs maintain an effective human resources plan for a small company. **Availability:** E-book; Print; PDF; Download.

22564 ■ *Encyclopedia of Small Business*
Ed: Arsen Darnay, Monique D. Magee, Kevin Hillstrom. **Released:** 5th edition. **Price:** $881. **Description:** Concise encyclopedia of small business information. **Availability:** E-book; Print.

22565 ■ *"Engineering Business Success: Essential Lessons In Building A Thriving Company"*
Released: September 01, 2014. **Description:** The structure of success is examined offering detail about business systems. As an engineer and businessperson, the author, discusses business opportunities and how so many businesses fail. He believes seizing the responsibility to serve your industry, your clients, and our stakeholders is key to any successful business venture. Entrepreneurial enthusiasm is also explored.

22566 ■ *Enterprise and Small Business: Principles, Practice and Policy*
Pub: Pearson Education Inc.
Contact: Andy Bird, Chief Executive Officer
Ed: Sara Carter, Dylan Jones-Evans. **Released:** 3rd edition. **Description:** Introduction to small business, challenges of a changing environment, and the nature of entrepreneurship are among the issues covered. **Availability:** E-book; Print; Online; Download.

22567 ■ *The Entrepreneur Next Door: Discover the Secrets to Financial Independence*
Description: Traits required to become a successful entrepreneur are highlighted.

22568 ■ *"Entrepreneur Quiz: Is Starting a Business Right for You?" in Small Business Trends (October 17, 2019)*
URL(s): smallbiztrends.com/2019/10/entrepreneur-quiz.html
Ed: Anita Campbell. **Released:** October 17, 2019. **Description:** Not sure if entrepreneurship is the right path you want to take? Take this quiz and see if the results match up with your business goals. **Availability:** Online.

22569 ■ *"Entrepreneur Says Spirituality Has Been a Key to Her Success" in Business First Columbus (Vol. 25, October 17, 2008, No. 8, pp. 1)*
Description: Profile of Carolyn Williams Francis, CEO of Williams Interior Designs Inc. She outlines her mantra for success in her furniture design business, but emphasizes that faith has taken her business to greater heights.

22570 ■ *Entrepreneurial Finance*
Pub: Pearson Education Inc.
Contact: Andy Bird, Chief Executive Officer
Ed: Philip J. Adelman, Alan M. Marks. **Released:** Sixth edition. **Description:** Financial aspects of running a small business are covered; topics include sole proprietorships, partnerships, limited liability companies, and private corporations. **Availability:** Print; Download; Online.

22571 ■ *"Entrepreneurial Orientation and Firm Performance: The Unique Impact of Innovativeness, Proactiveness, and Risk-taking" in Journal of Small Business and Entrepreneurship (Vol. 23, Winter 2010, No. 1)*
Pub: Canadian Council for Small Business and Entrepreneurship
Contact: John MacRitchie, President
Ed: Patrick M. Kreisera, Justin Davis. **Description:** The article develops a theoretical model of the relationship between firm-level entrepreneurship and firm performance. This model is intended to further clarify the consequences of an 'entrepreneurial orientation', paying particular attention to the differential relationship that exists between the three sub-dimensions of entrepreneurial orientation and firm performance. Included in the theoretical model are other important variables (such as organizational structure and environmental characteristics) that may impact the EO-performance relationship. Propositions are developed regarding the various configurations of the sub-dimensions of EO and organizational structure that would be most appropriate in a given environmental context. Future research may also benefit from considering the important role that organizational strategy and life cycle stage play in this model. The implications of this model for both researchers and managers are discussed.

22572 ■ *Entrepreneurial Small Business*
Pub: McGraw-Hill Higher Education
Contact: Michael Ryan, President
Ed: Jerome A. Katz, Richard P. Green. **Released:** Seventh edition. **Price:** $57, e-book; $70, print. **Description:** Students are able to get a clear vision of small enterprise in today's business climate. The textbook helps focus on the goal of having personal independence with financial security as an entrepreneur. **Availability:** Print.

22573 ■ *The Entrepreneur's Almanac: Fascinating Figures, Fundamentals and Facts You Need to Run and Grow Your Business*
Description: Reference containing a collection of tips, ideas and wisdom required to run and grow a successful business. Short articles, anecdotes, powerful lists and checklists, charts, and profiles of successful entrepreneurs are included.

22574 ■ *The Entrepreneur's Edge: Finding Money, Making Money, Keeping Money*
Released: August 01, 2016. **Price:** $20.99, bound softcover; $3.99, e-book. **Description:** Advice for starting, running and growing a new business is given. **Availability:** E-book; Print.

22575 ■ *"Entrepreneurs and Gamblers: Shared Traits" in Entrepreneur (Sept. 8, 2017)*
URL(s): www.entrepreneur.com/en-za/starting-a-business/entrepreneurs-and-gamblers-shared-traits/330977
Ed: Jeff Broth. **Released:** September 08, 2017. **Description:** Describes the traits that successful business owners and gamblers may share and why it should come as no surprise that some of the most successful entrepreneurs are also big gamblers. **Availability:** Online.

22576 ■ *Entrepreneurship*
Pub: McGraw-Hill Higher Education
Contact: Michael Ryan, President
Ed: Robert D. Hisrich, Michael P. Peters, Dean A. Shepherd. **Released:** 10th edition. **Price:** $169.06, hardcopy. **Description:** Advice is offered to entrepreneurs in formulating, planning, and implementing a business plan. **Availability:** Print.

22577 ■ *Entrepreneurship: A Process Perspective*
Ed: Robert A. Baron, Scott A. Shane. **Released:** 2nd Edition. **Description:** Entrepreneurial process covering team building, finances, business plan, legal issues, marketing, growth and exit strategies. **Availability:** Print.

22578 ■ *Entrepreneurship: A Small Business Approach*
Pub: McGraw-Hill Higher Education
Contact: Michael Ryan, President
Ed: Charles E. Bamford, Garry D. Bruton. **Released:** Sixth edition. **Description:** This text takes a hands-on, problem-based learning approach that works through real problems faced by entrepreneurs and small business owners. **Availability:** Print.

22579 ■ *Entrepreneurship for Dummies*
Pub: John Wiley & Sons, Inc.
Contact: Christina Van Tassell, Executive Vice President Chief Financial Officer
Ed: Kathleen Allen. **Released:** 2nd edition. **Price:** $29.99, paperback; $18, e-book. **Description:** A guide to help entrepreneurs get their business up and running. Includes sections on starting a business from beginning to end, testing products, legal requirements, securing funding, and much more. **Availability:** E-book; Print.

22580 ■ *"Entrepreneurship and Service Innovation" in Journal of Business & Industrial Marketing (Vol. 29, July 2014, No. 6)*
Pub: Emerald Group Publishing Limited
Contact: Erika Valenti, President
Description: An overview of entrepreneurship and service innovation and the association between entrepreneurial orientation, innovation, and entrepreneurship or new entry. Analysis of secondary data was performed and observed that EO (entrepreneurial orientation), innovation, and entrepreneurship feature a triadic connect. EO supports innovation, innovation endorses new venture creation, and it in turn commercializes innovations. **Availability:** Download; Online.

22581 ■ Entrepreneurship and Small Business Development in the Former Soviet Bloc

Description: Examination of entrepreneurship and small business in Russia and other key countries of Eastern Europe, showing how far small businesses have developed in the region. **Availability:** Online; PDF.

22582 ■ Entrepreneurship: Theory, Process, and Practice

Ed: Donald F. Kuratko. **Released:** Ninth edition. **Price:** $22.99, e-book; $44.49, rental,wholesale price $210,retail $279.95 . **Description:** Understanding the process of entrepreneurship. **Availability:** E-book; Print.

22583 ■ The Essential Entrepreneur: What It Takes to Start, Scale, and Sell a Successful Business

Pub: John Wiley & Sons, Inc.
Contact: Christina Van Tassell, Executive Vice President Chief Financial Officer
URL(s): www.wiley.com/en-us/The+Essential+Entrepreneur%3A+What+It+Takes+to+Start%2C+Scale%2C+and+Sell+a+Successful+Business-p-9781119984559

Released: November 2022. **Price:** $13, e-book; $21.99, paperback. **Description:** Take your business to the next level with the tips included in this guide. **Availability:** E-book; Print.

22584 ■ Everything is Possible: Life and Business Lessons from a Self-Made Billionaire and the Founder of Slim-Fast

Released: First edition. **Description:** A profile of the founder of Slim-Fast nutritional diet drink used to help people lose weight. **Availability:** E-book.

22585 ■ "Evolutionary Psychology in the Business Sciences"

Pub: Springer Publishing Co.
Contact: Bernhard Springer, Founder

Released: First edition. **Description:** All individuals operating in the business sphere share a common biological heritage, including consumers, employers, employees, entrepreneurs, or financial traders, to name a few. The evolutionary behavioral sciences and specific business contexts including marketing, consumer behavior, advertising, innovation and creativity and invention, intertemporal choice, negotiations, competition and cooperation in organizational settings, sex differences in workplace patterns, executive leadership, business ethics, store and office design, behavioral decision making, and electronic communications and commerce are all addressed. **Availability:** E-book; Print.

22586 ■ "Ex-Medical Student Stages Career In Event Planning: Barcelona Owner Makes Inroads with Luxury Car Dealerships" in Los Angeles Business Journal (Vol. 34, June 18, 2012, No. 25, pp. 10)

Pub: CBJ L.P.
Contact: Terri Cunningham, Contact

Description: Barcelona Enterprises started as a company designing menus for restaurants, organizing food shows, to planning receptions for luxury car dealers. The fim will be launching the first Las Vegas Chocolate Festival & Pastry Show in July 2012. Presently, the company runs 24 wine and food festivals, organizes events for an upscale dog shampoo maker, and sports car dealerships. **Availability:** Print; Online.

22587 ■ "Executive Summary: How Smart Firms Create Productive Ties" in Business Strategy Review (Vol. 23, Spring 2012, No. 1, pp. 83)

Description: Benjamin L. Hallen and Kathleen M. Eisenhardt wrote, 'Catalyzing Strategies and Efficient Tie Formation: How Entrepreneurial Firms Obtain Investment Ties', May 3, 2011. The report is examined. **Availability:** Online.

22588 ■ "Expanding the Entrepreneur Class" in Harvard Business Review (Vol. 90, July-August 2012, No. 7-8, pp. 40)

Pub: Harvard Business Review Press
Contact: Moderna V. Pfizer, Contact
Ed: Carl Schramm. **Price:** $6, PDF and hardcover black and white. **Description:** Two programs for encouraging entrepreneurship are highlighted. One offers trained facilitators who help participants move through iterations to produce viable business models. Another provides college juniors and seniors with instruction and advice from successful businesspeople. **Availability:** Print; PDF; Online.

22589 ■ "Expanding Middleby's Food Processing Biz" in Crain's Chicago Business (Vol. 31, April 21, 2008, No. 16, pp. 6)

Pub: Crain Communications Inc.
Contact: Barry Asin, President
Ed: David Sterrett. **Description:** Profile of the executive vice-president of the food processing company, Middleby Corp, whose business plan is to develop new products, begin looking for acquisitions and simplify operations in order to expand the firm. **Availability:** Online.

22590 ■ The Facebook Effect: The Inside Story of the Company That Is Connecting the World

Ed: David Kirkpatrick. **Released:** 2011. **Price:** $18, paperback; $13.99, e-book. **Description:** There's never been a Website like Facebook: more than 350 million people have accounts, and if the growth rate continues, by 2013 every Internet user worldwide will have his or her own page. No one's had more access to the inner workings of the phenomenon than Kirkpatrick, a senior tech writer at Fortune magazine. Written with the full cooperation of founder Mark Zuckerberg, the book follows the company from its genesis in a Harvard dorm room through its successes over Friendster and MySpace, the expansion of the user base, and Zuckerberg's refusal to sell. **Availability:** E-book; Print.

22591 ■ "A Failed Promise: A Dream Job Gone..or Just Delayed?" in Restaurant Business (Vol. 107, September 2008, No. 9, pp. 34)

Description: Profile of Jeremy Lycan, executive chef who taught at the California Culinary Academy. Lycan tells of accepting a position as executive chef from his mentor, and later started his own restaurant. **Availability:** Online.

22592 ■ "The Family Tools" in Canadian Business (Vol. 80, March 26, 2007, No. 7, pp. 14)

Description: A few strategies for running family businesses successfully are presented.

22593 ■ "Fearless Leaders: Sharpen Your Focus: How the New Science of Mindfulness Can Help You Reclaim Your Confidence"

Pub: Waterfront Digital Press
Released: First edition. **Description:** Executive coaches explain the principles that make managers and entrepreneurs and business leaders fearless. **Availability:** Print.

22594 ■ Female Entrepreneurship in East and South-East Asia: Opportunities and Challenges

Ed: Philippe Debroux. **Released:** 2010. **Description:** A detailed study of female entrepreneurship in Asia, where public authorities are slowly realizing the importance of women as workers and entrepreneurs. **Availability:** E-book; Print.

22595 ■ Fierce Leadership

Price: Paperback. **Description:** A bold alternative to the worst 'best' practices of business in the 21st Century. **Availability:** Print.

22596 ■ "Filling the Gap" in Canadian Business (Vol. 80, March 12, 2007, No. 6, pp. 62)

Ed: Andrew Wahl. **Released:** October 09, 2016. **Description:** The chief executive officer of GAP, Bruce Poon Tip, shares his experience and efforts in the growth of the company to a leading position in Canada. **Availability:** Print; Online.

22597 ■ Find. Build. Sell.: How I Turned a $100 Backyard Bar into a $100 Million Pub Empire

URL(s): www.wiley.com/en-us/Find+Build+Sell+%3A+How+I+Turned+a+%24100+Backyard+Bar+into+a+%24100+Million+Pub+Empire-p-9780730399865

Ed: Stepehn J. Hunt. **Released:** February 2022. **Price:** $13, e-book; $22, paperback. **Description:** Stephen J. Hunt tells the story of how he turned his backyard beer garden into a huge pub industry. Learn about developing your passion into a business. **Availability:** E-book; Print.

22598 ■ "Five Lessons in Entrepreneurship from the Worlds of Trading and Gambling" in Entrepreneur (Aug. 21, 2017)

URL(s): www.entrepreneur.com/en-in/news-and-trends/five-lessons-in-entrepreneurship-from-the-worlds-of-trading/299047

Released: August 21, 2017. **Description:** Describes the parallels between trading and gambling on one hand and traditional entrepreneurship on the other. **Availability:** Online.

22599 ■ "Floral-Design Kiosk Business Blossoming" in Colorado Springs Business Journal (September 24, 2010)

Pub: Dolan Media Newswires

Ed: Monica Mendoza. **Description:** Profile of Shellie Greto and her mother Jackie Martin who started a wholesale flower business in their garage. The do-it-yourself floral arrangement firm started a kiosk business in supermarkets called Complete Design. **Availability:** Online.

22600 ■ "For Giving Us a Way To Say Yes To Solar: Lynn Jurich and Edward Fenster" in Inc. (Volume 32, December 2010, No. 10, pp. 110)

Pub: Mansueto Ventures L.L.C.
Contact: Stephanie Mehta, Chief Executive Officer
Ed: Leigh Buchanan. **Released:** December 01, 2010. **Description:** Profile of entrepreneurs Lynn Jurich and Edward Fenster, cofounders of SunRun. The firm installs solar panels at little or no cost and homeowners sign 20-year contracts to buy power at a fixed price. **Availability:** Online.

22601 ■ "For His Bigness of Heart: Larry O'Toole: Gentle Giant Moving, Somerville, Massachusetts" in Inc. (Volume 32, December 2010)

Pub: Mansueto Ventures L.L.C.
Contact: Stephanie Mehta, Chief Executive Officer
Ed: Leigh Buchanan. **Released:** December 01, 2010. **Description:** Profile of Larry O'Toole, owners of Gentle Giant Moving Company, where his company charges more, but in return consumers receive a higher quality service. **Availability:** Online.

22602 ■ "Former Dell Exec Turns Entrepreneur, Buys Travel Agency" in Austin Business Journal (Vol. 34, May 9, 2014, No. 12, pp. 9)

Pub: American City Business Journals, Inc.
Contact: Mike Olivieri, Executive Vice President
Released: Weekly. **Price:** $4, Introductory 4-week offer(Digital & Print). **Description:** Robin Goad, former sales executive for Dell Inc., is buying Tramex Travel of Austin, Texas. She hopes to reinvent the travel agency into a corporate powerhouse it once was when she worked there in the 1990s before working for Dell. **Availability:** Print; Online.

22603 ■ "The Formula for Growth: Through a Mixture of Vision and Partnerships, Leon Richardson has ChemicoMays in Expansion Mode" in Black Enterprise (Vol. 44, June 2014, No. 10, pp. 66)

Pub: Earl G. Graves Ltd.
Contact: Earl Graves, Jr., President

Description: Profile of Leon Richardson, who has his family-owned business poised for growth. At the age of 13, Leon helped his family in their convenience store located in West Haven, Connecticut. He has gone from managing storefronts to overseeing a chemical management business during his entrepreneurial career.

22604 ▪ *"Formula for Success: Dispelling the Age-Old Myths"* **in Agency Sales Magazine (Vol. 39, July 2009, No. 7, pp. 26)**
Description: Common misperceptions about selling and salespeople include the idea that anyone can be successful in selling if they work hard enough and that successful salespeople are born that way. In fact, top performers take risks and they invest in themselves. **Availability:** Online.

22605 ▪ *The Foundations of Female Entrepreneurship: Enterprise, Home and Household in London, c. 1800-1870*
Pub: Routledge, Taylor & Francis Group
Ed: Alison Kay. **Released:** First edition. **Description:** This book argues that active business did not exclude women from 1747 to 1880, although careful representation was necessary and this has obscured the similarities of women's businesses to those of many male business owners.

22606 ▪ *"Four Lessons in Adaptive Leadership"* **in Harvard Business Review (Vol. 88, November 2010, No. 11, pp. 86)**
Pub: Harvard Business Publishing
Contact: Diane Belcher, Managing Director
Ed: Michael Useem. **Price:** $8.95, PDF. **Description:** Four key factors to effective leadership are presented. These are establishing a personal link, making sound and timely decisions, developing a common purpose while avoiding personal gain, and ensuring that objectives are clear without micromanaging those implementing them. **Availability:** Online; PDF.

22607 ▪ *"From the Battlefield to the Boardroom"* **in Business Horizons (Vol. 51, March-April 2008, No. 2, pp. 79)**
Pub: Elsevier Advanced Technology Publications
Ed: Catherine M. Dalton. **Description:** Effective intelligence gathering, a thorough understanding of the mission, efficient use of resources, and strategic leadership are vital to achieving success in business as well as in the battlefield. Examples of effective leadership in the battle of Gettysburg are cited. **Availability:** Online.

22608 ▪ *"From Rapper to Fashion Designer, Philly 12-Year-Old Builds Brand Using Instagram"* **in WHYY (December 19, 2018)**
URL(s): whyy.org/articles/from-rapper-to-fashion-designer-philly-12-year-old-builds-his-brand-using-instagram/
Ed: Unique Ratcliff. **Released:** December 19, 2018. **Description:** Trey Brown is a 12-year-old fashion designer, motivational speaker, and Instagram influencer residing in Philadelphia. His clothing brand is SPERGO, which ships around the world, and is successful in part due to his ability to use Intagram. **Availability:** Online.

22609 ▪ *"Game On at Jordan's New Spot"* **in Crain's Chicago Business (Vol. 34, October 24, 2011, No. 42, pp. 34)**
Pub: Crain Communications Inc.
Contact: Barry Asin, President
Ed: Laura Bianchi. **Description:** Michael Jordan partnered with Cornerstone Restaurant Group to launch Michael Jordan's Steakhouse in Chicago. Details are included. **Availability:** Online.

22610 ▪ *"General Brock's Lessons for Modern CEOs"* **in Canadian Business (Vol. 85, June 11, 2012, No. 10, pp. 17)**
Ed: Peter Shawn Taylor. **Description:** Modern day executives can learn the characteristics of a great leader from Sir Isaac Brock, who helped win the War of 1812 for Canada. Brock refused to accept defeat, took steps to deal with his weaknesses and was always at the front when decisive action was necessary. **Availability:** Print; Online.

22611 ▪ *"Generation Entrepreneur"* **in Business Strategy Review (Vol. 25, Summer 2014, No. 2, pp. 41)**
Released: June 02, 2014. **Description:** The early days of entrepreneurial ventures are often recorded in rose-tinted retrospect. In this special section, ideas, hopes, dreams and fears of entrepreneurs in the early stages of their journeys are featured. **Availability:** Print; PDF; Online.

22612 ▪ *Get Your Business to Work!: 7 Steps to Earning More, Working Less and Living the Life You Want*
Pub: BenBella Books Inc.
Contact: Aida Herrera, Director
E-mail: aida@benbellabooks.com
Ed: George Hedley. **Released:** May 01, 2014. **Price:** $17.95, paperback; $9.99, E-Book (EPUB). **Description:** Complete step-by-step guide for the small business owner to realize profits, wealth and freedom. **Availability:** E-book; Print.

22613 ▪ *"Getting Inventive With..Ed Spellman"* **in Crain's Cleveland Business (Vol. 28, October 22, 2007, No. 42, pp. 18)**
Pub: Crain Communications Inc.
Contact: K. C. Crain, President
Ed: Kimberly Bonvissuto. **Description:** Profile featuring Ed Spellman, a mechanical engineer who decided to quit his job at Invacare Corp., a medical equipment manufacturer and distributor, in order to devote his full attention to promoting his numerous inventions, including the DV-Grip, a vehicle mount for portable DVD players. **Availability:** Online.

22614 ▪ *"Globalization: Canada Tomorrow"* **in Canadian Business (Vol. 80, October 8, 2007, No. 20, pp. 14)**
Description: An assessment of Canada's future in terms of its educational, social, and economic environment is presented. Concerns regarding the country's educational system such as the declining interest in science and the possible lack of teachers in the future are discussed. In terms of its social and economic aspects, the need to support entrepreneurs and other qualified people is explained. **Availability:** Online.

22615 ▪ *"The Globe: A Cautionary Tale for Emerging Market Giants"* **in Harvard Business Review (Vol. 88, September 2010, No. 9, pp. 99)**
Pub: Harvard Business Publishing
Contact: Diane Belcher, Managing Director
Ed: J. Stewart Black, Allen J. Morrison. **Price:** $8.95. **Description:** Key factors that negatively affected Japan corporate growth and organizational effectiveness include: devotion to established path, isolated domestic markets, homogeneous executive teams, and a non-contentious labor force. Solutions include leadership development programs, multicultural input, and cross-cultural training. **Availability:** Online; PDF.

22616 ▪ *"Go Beyond Visionary. Be a Leader: Having a Grand Vision Isn't Enough to Build Your Business. You Have to Take the Reins and Actually Run Your Startup"* **in Inc. (Vol. 36, February 2014, No. 1, pp. 43)**
Pub: Mansueto Ventures L.L.C.
Contact: Stephanie Mehta, Chief Executive Officer
Released: February 01, 2014. **Description:** Entrepreneurs must be visionaries, leaders and focus on running and growing their small business. Tips for going from visionary to leader include building trust with talented people, determining what's important, and being transparent. Vision is the reason you started your firm, leadership will be the reason for its success. **Availability:** Print; Online.

22617 ▪ *The Go-Giver: A Little Story About a Powerful Business Idea*
Pub: Penguin Publishing Group
Ed: Bob Burg, John David Mann. **Released:** October 20, 2015. **Price:** $16.95, hardcover; $17.99; 11.95, audio. **Description:** Story of an ambitious young man named Joe who yearns for success. The book is a heartwarming tale that brings new relevance to the old proverb, "Give and you shall receive". **Availability:** E-book.

22618 ▪ *"Go Green Or Go Home"* **in Black Enterprise (Vol. 41, August 2010, No. 1, pp. 53)**
Pub: Earl G. Graves Ltd.
Contact: Earl Graves, Jr., President
Ed: Robinson M. Tennille. **Description:** The green economy has become an essential part of every business, however, small business owners need to learn how to participate, including minority owned entrepreneurs. **Availability:** Online.

22619 ▪ *Going to Extremes: How Like Minds Unite and Divide*
Ed: Cass R. Sustein. **Released:** July 09, 2009. **Description:** Solutions to marketplace problems are examined.

22620 ▪ *"A Good Book Is Worth a Thousand Blogs"* **in Barron's (Vol. 88, July 14, 2008, No. 28, pp. 42)**
Pub: Dow Jones & Company Inc.
Contact: Almar Latour, Chief Executive Officer
Ed: Gene Epstein. **Description:** Nine summer book suggestions on economics are presented. The list includes 'The Revolution' by Ron Paul, 'The Forgotten Man' by Amity Shales, 'The Commitments of Traders Bible' by Stephen Briese, and 'Economic Facts and Fallacies' by Thomas Sowell. **Availability:** Online.

22621 ▪ *Goventure: Live the Life of an Entrepreneur*
Description: Challenges of operating a small business are presented with more than 6,000 graphics, audio, and interactive video. **Availability:** CD-ROM.

22622 ▪ *The Growing Business Handbook: Inspiration and Advice from Successful Entrepreneurs and Fast Growing UK Companies*
Pub: Kogan Page Ltd.
Contact: Christina Lindeholm, Manager, Sales
Ed: Adam Jolly. **Released:** 17th edition. **Price:** $90, hardback; $90, e-book. **Description:** Tips for growing and running a successful business are covered, focusing on senior managers in middle market and SME companies. **Availability:** E-book; Print.

22623 ▪ *"Halls Give Hospital Drive $11 Million Infusion"* **in The Business Journal-Serving Metropolitan Kansas City (Vol. 26, July 18, 2008)**
Description: Don Hall, chairman of Hallmark Cards Inc., and eight family members have announced that they will give $11 million to Children's Mercy Hospitals and Clinics for its $800 million expansion plan. Hall Family Foundation president Bill Hall that contributions such as that for Children's Mercy reflect the charitable interests of the foundation's board and founders. The possible impacts of the Hall's donation are analyzed.

22624 ▪ *The Halo Effect: And the Eight Other Business Delusions That Deceive Managers*
Pub: Free Press/Simon and Schuster Inc.
Contact: Jonathan Karp, President
Ed: Phil Rosenzweig. **Released:** June 17, 2014. **Description:** Nine common business delusions, including the halo effect (which the author describes as the need to attribute positive qualities to successful individuals and companies), are illustrated using case studies of Lego, Cisco, and Nokia to show how adhering to myths can be bad for any business.

22625 ▪ *Happy About Joint-Venturing: The 8 Key Critical Factors of Success*
Pub: Happy About
Contact: Ric Vatner, Chief Executive Officer

Ed: Valerie Orsoni-Vauthey. **Price:** $19.95, paperback,(with 15% discount only ($16.96); $14.95, eBook,(with 20% discount only $11.95). **Description:** An overview of joint venturing is presented. **Availability:** E-book; Print; PDF.

22626 ■ *"Harvey Mackay: How to Stop the Fear of Success From Holding You Back"* in *South Florida Business Journal* (Vol. 34, May 30, 2014, No. 45, pp. 20)
Pub: American City Business Journals, Inc.
Contact: Mike Olivieri, Executive Vice President
Released: May 18, 2014. **Description:** Advice is given to help entrepreneurs overcome the fear of success. **Availability:** Print; Online.

22627 ■ *"Hatching Twitter: A True Story of Money, Power, Friendship, and Betrayal"*
Pub: Portfolio Hardcover
Contact: Adrian Zackheim, President
Released: September 05, 2013. **Price:** $18, paperback; $2.18, paperback(100 used from $2.18); $4.28, paperback(55 new from $4.28); $4.39, kindle; $12.99, hardcover; $1.96, hardcover(73 used from $1.96); $8.59, hardcover(9 new from $8.59); $17.50, hardcover(2 collectible from $17.50). **Description:** The first full coverage story covering the four founders of Twitter: Evan Williams, Biz Stone, Jack Dorsey, and Noah Glass, who went from ordinary engineers to wealthy celebrities and entrepreneurs. The story explores their pursuits for money, influence, publicity, and control as Twitter grew larger and more powerful. **Availability:** E-book; Print; Audio.

22628 ■ *Heart: Building a Great Brand in the Digital Age*
Pub: CreateSpace
Released: September 29, 2014. **Price:** $3.70, paperback. **Description:** Business leader and consultant who works with designers, contractors and service providers in the green industry helps business owners develop and implement company systems and increase revenue. His is a third-generation horticulturist and small business owner and share the challenges of being an entrepreneur. **Availability:** Print.

22629 ■ *"The High-Intensity Entrepreneur"* in *Harvard Business Review* (Vol. 88, September 2010, No. 9, pp. 74)
Pub: Harvard Business Publishing
Contact: Diane Belcher, Managing Director
Ed: Anne S. Habiby, Deirdre M. Coyle, Jr. **Price:** $8.95, PDF. **Description:** Examination of the role of small companies in promoting global economic growth is presented. Discussion includes identifying entrepreneurial capability. **Availability:** Online; PDF.

22630 ■ *"His Brother's Keeper: A Mentor Learns the True Meaning of Leadership"* in *Black Enterprise* (Vol. 37, December 2006, No. 5, pp. 69)
Pub: Earl G. Graves Ltd.
Contact: Earl Graves, Jr., President
Ed: Laura Egodigwe. **Description:** Interview with Keith R. Wyche of Pitney Bowes Management Services, which discusses the relationship between a mentor and mentee as well as sponsorship. **Availability:** Online.

22631 ■ *"Home Depot Co-Founder Ken Langone Talks About Business"* in *Atlanta Business Chronicle* (April 11, 2014)
Pub: American City Business Journals, Inc.
Contact: Mike Olivieri, Executive Vice President
Description: Ken Langone spoke on April 7, 2014 at Fairfield University in Connecticut. He is one of the co-founders of Home Depot home improvement chain. He provided the funds to start the chain in 1978 after Arthur Blank and Bernie Marcus were let go from their jobs at Handy Dan. **Availability:** Print; Online.

22632 ■ *Hoover's Vision*
Released: 1st edition. **Description:** Founder of Bookstop Inc. and Hoover's Inc. provides a plan to turn an enterprise into a success by showing entrepreneurs how to address inputs with an open mind in order to see more than what other's envision. Hoover pushes business owners to create and feed a clear and consistent vision by recognizing the importance of history and trends, then helps them find the essential qualities of entrepreneurial leadership. **Availability:** Print.

22633 ■ *Hoover's Vision: Original Thinking for Business Success*
Ed: Gary Hoover. **Released:** First edition. **Description:** Three keys to business success are to observe and understand other people, serve others while making their lives better, and develop a business style that expresses your5 own passions while serving others. **Availability:** Print.

22634 ■ *How to Get Rich*
Ed: Felix Dennis. **Released:** 2013. **Price:** $8.16, paperback. **Description:** The author, publisher of Maxim, The Week, and Stuff magazines, discusses the mistakes he made running his companies. He didn't understand that people who buy computer gaming magazines wanted a free game with each copy, as one of his rivals was offering. And he laments not diversifying into television and exploiting the Internet. **Availability:** E-book; Print.

22635 ■ *"How Great Leaders Think: The Art of Reframing"*
Pub: Jossey-Bass
Released: July 01, 2014. **Price:** $30, hardcover. **Description:** More complex thinking is the key to better leadership. A guide to help leaders understand four major aspects of organizational life: structure, people, politics, and culture is given. The book's lessons include: how to use structural tools to organize teams and organizations for better results, how to build motivation and morale by aligning organizations and people, how to map the terrain and build a power base to navigate the political dynamics of organizations, and how to develop a leadership story that shapes culture, provides direction, and inspires commitment to excellence. **Availability:** E-book; Print.

22636 ■ *"How I Became a Serial Entrepreneur"* in *Baltimore Business Journal* (Vol. 31, April 18, 2014, No. 51, pp. 26)
Pub: American City Business Journals, Inc.
Contact: Mike Olivieri, Executive Vice President
Description: Dr. Lisa Beth Ferstenberg, a physician by training, teaches a course at the Maryland Center for Entrepreneurship in Columbia to help CEOs attract prospective investors. Dr. Ferstenberg is also the chief medical officer at Sequella Inc. She reflects on the kind of personality required to become a successful entrepreneur and the mistakes entrepreneurs make in raising capital funding. **Availability:** Print; Online.

22637 ■ *"How I Did It: Jack Ma, Alibaba.com"* in *Inc.* (January 2008, pp. 94-102)
Ed: Rebecca Fannin. **Description:** Profile of Jack Ma, who started as a guide and interpreter for Western tourists in Hangzhou. Ma used the Internet to build Alibaba.com, China's largest business-to-business site and one of the hottest IPOs in years. **Availability:** Online.

22638 ■ *"How I Did It: Mel Zuckerman, Chairman, Canyon Ranch"* in *Inc.* (December 2007, pp. 140-142)
Ed: Daniel McGinn. **Description:** Profile of Mel Zuckerman, who tells how transformed his life as a middle-aged, overweight homebuilder to a healthy addition to the fitness and spa industry with his posh Canyon Ranch retreats. **Availability:** Online.

22639 ■ *"How Ivanah Thomas Founded a $5 Million Business - While Working Nights"* in *Orlando Business Journal* (Vol. 30, April 18, 2014, No. 43, pp. 3)
Pub: American City Business Journals, Inc.
Contact: Mike Olivieri, Executive Vice President
Released: Weekly. **Price:** $8, introductory 4-week offer(Digital & Print). **Description:** Caring First Inc. founder, Ivanah Thomas, says her drive to serve people in their home rather than them being institutionalized lead to the establishment of her firm. She added that she ran the home care business by herself during its early years. Thomas also stated her social status posed challenges for the company. **Availability:** Print; Online.

22640 ■ *How to Make Money with Social Media: An Insider's Guide to Using New and Emerging Media to Grow Your Business*
Ed: Jamie Turner, Reshma Shah, PhD. **Released:** 2nd edition. **Description:** Marketers, executives, entrepreneurs are shown more effective ways to utilize Internet social media to make money. This guide brings together both practical strategies and proven execution techniques for driving maximum value from social media marketing. **Availability:** E-book; Print.

22641 ■ *How to Persuade and Influence People: Powerful Techniques to Get your Own Way More Often*
Pub: John Wiley & Sons, Inc.
Contact: Christina Van Tassell, Executive Vice President Chief Financial Officer
Ed: Philip Hesketh. **Released:** September 2010. **Price:** $26, paperback; $16.99, e-book. **Description:** Seven psychological reasons behind why and how people are persuaded and how to use these reasons to your advantage in both your personal and business life. **Availability:** E-book; Print.

22642 ■ *How to Run Your Business Like a Girl: Successful Strategies from Entrepreneurial Women Who Made It Happen*
Description: Tour of three women entrepreneurs and their successful companies.

22643 ■ *How to Start and Run Your Own Corporation: S-Corporations For Small Business Owners*
Pub: HCM Publishing
Ed: Peter I. Hupalo. **Description:** Basics of corporate business structure are explained. Topics include discovering the best business structure for your company; how to decided between an S-Corporation and LLC; choosing the state in which to incorporate, how to form a corporation, angel investing, special issues for one-person corporations, the role of bylaws and corporate minutes, board of directors, taxes, workers' compensation issues, retirement plans, and more. **Availability:** Print.

22644 ■ *How to Succeed As a Lifestyle Entrepreneur*
Availability: Print; Online.

22645 ■ *"How to Survive This Mess"* in *Crain's Chicago Business* (Vol. 31, April 14, 2008, No. 15, pp. 18)
Pub: Crain Communications Inc.
Contact: Barry Asin, President
Ed: Christina Le Beau. **Description:** Small business owners can make it through a possible recession with preparations such as reviewing their balance sheet and cash flow every week and spotting trends then reacting quickly to them. **Availability:** Online.

22646 ■ *"How Tender Green Turns Top Chefs Into Fast-Food Cooks: a Quick-Serve Chain Lures Kitchen Starts by Treating Them Like Entrepreneurs"* in *Inc.* (Vol. 36, March 2014, No. 2, pp. 28)
Pub: Mansueto Ventures L.L.C.
Contact: Stephanie Mehta, Chief Executive Officer
Released: March 2014. **Description:** Chefs Erik Oberholtzer, David Dressier and Matt Lyman launched Tender Greens, a series of quick-service restaurants serving fresh organic dishes made from local produce, cheeses and meats. The three partners set out to hire fine-dining chefs to run each location. The used their entrepreneurial skills to inspire great chefs into entrepreneur type control by allowing them to run their restaurant individually, including operations, culture and menu items. Tender Greens has

grown to 12 locations with an estimated $40 million annual revenue. Their business vision and strategy is examined. **Availability:** Print; Online.

22647 ■ *"How To Overcome the Jitters and Not Choke"* in *South Florida Business Journal* (Vol. 34, July 25, 2014, No. 53, pp. 10)
Pub: American City Business Journals, Inc.
Contact: Mike Olivieri, Executive Vice President
Released: Weekly. **Price:** $8, introductory 4-week offer(Digital only). **Description:** Recommended tips for controlling performance anxiety are presented. The fear of failure for entrepreneurs is paralyzing and prevents owners from taking necessary risks to succeed. **Availability:** Print; Online.

22648 ■ *How: Why How We Do Anything Means Everything*
Pub: John Wiley & Sons, Inc.
Contact: Christina Van Tassell, Executive Vice President Chief Financial Officer
Ed: Dov L. Seidman. **Released:** Expanded edition. **Price:** $27.95, hardcover; $18.99, E-book. **Description:** Author shares his unique approach to building successful companies using case studies, anecdotes, research, and interviews to help entrepreneurs succeed in the 21st Century. **Availability:** E-book; Print.

22649 ■ *"How Your Stories of Failure Create Better Business Success"* in *Forbes* (March 1, 2023)
URL(s): www.forbes.com/sites/jodiecook/2023/03/01/how-your-stories-of-failure-create-better-business-success/?sh=7acb80ff4ae1
Ed: Jodie Cook. **Released:** March 01, 2023. **Description:** A discussion on how business failures can be channeled into success. How we perceive our mistakes can be a great learning opportunity and way to create better mental health. **Availability:** Online.

22650 ■ *I Can't Believe I Get Paid to Do This*
Ed: Stacey Mayo. **Description:** This book is targeted to anyone unhappy in their current position. It is designed to help everyone feel good about their job.

22651 ■ *"In My Shoes: A Memoir"*
Pub: Portfolio Hardcore
Contact: Adrian Zackheim, President
Released: October 01, 2013. **Price:** $3.48, kindle; $32.80, hardcover; $0.25, hardcover(49 used from $0.25); $25.60, hardcover (6 new from $25.60); $8.86, paperback; $1.55, paperback(93 used from $1.55); $4.01, paperback(49 new from $4.01). **Description:** Profile of Tamara Mellon, woman entrepreneur who built Jimmy Choo into a premier name in the global fashion industry. She addresses her family life, her battles with anxiety and depression, as well as time spend in rehabilitation. She shares her entire life story from her work as a young editor at Vogue to her partnership with shoemaker, Jimmy Choo to her public relationships. She confides what it was like working with an obstinate business partner but also her ability to understand what customers want. **Availability:** E-book; Print; Audio.

22652 ■ *"Info Junkie: Karen Eng"* in *Crain's Chicago Business* (Vol. 34, October 24, 2011, No. 42, pp. 35)
Pub: Crain Communications Inc.
Contact: Barry Asin, President
Ed: Christina Le Beau. **Description:** Greg Colando, president of Flor Inc., an eco-friendly carpet company located I Chicago discusses his marketing program to increase sales. **Availability:** Online.

22653 ■ *"Infomercial King on TeleBrands, Going Broke, Making Millions"* in *Philadelphia Business Journal* (Vol. 33, July 11, 2014, No. 22, pp. 3)
Pub: American City Business Journals, Inc.
Contact: Mike Olivieri, Executive Vice President
Released: Weekly. **Price:** $4, Introductory 4-week offer(Digital only). **Description:** Ajit "A.J." Khubani is CEO of TeleBrands, the Fairfield, New Jersey company that brings to the American mainstream market novelty products by using infomercials, including AmberVision sunglasses and PedEgg. Though the marketing/advertising firm is worth $1 billion, Khubani's entrepreneurship career has gone through ups and downs and he has been close to bankruptcy three times. **Availability:** Print; Online.

22654 ■ *"Innovation Station"* in *Canadian Business* (Vol. 80, October 8, 2007, No. 20, pp. 42)
Description: Study and teaching of entrepreneurship at the University of Waterloo is discussed. Research projects in the university are expected to be influential in Canada's economic development. In spite of the success of these studies, financing is still a problem for the university, especially in technological innovations. **Availability:** Online.

22655 ■ *The Innovators: How a Group of Hackers, Geniuses, and Geeks Created the Digital Revolution*
Pub: Simon & Schuster, Inc.
Contact: Jonathan Karp, President
Released: October 2014. **Price:** $17.99, paperback; $29.99, abridged compact disk; $13.99, e-book; $29.99, unabridged audio download; $49.99, abridged audio download; $29.99, unabridged compact disk, plus shipping charges; 13.99, trade paperback. **Description:** Profiles of the individuals who created the computer and the Internet are provided describing the talents of certain inventors and entrepreneurs who are able to turn their business visions and goals into realities, while others have failed. The author begins with Ada Lovelace, Lord Byron's daughter, who pioneered computer programming back in the 1840s and continues by exploring the minds of Vannevar Bush, Alan Turing, John von Neumann, J.C.R. Licklider, Doug Englebart, Robert Noyce, Bill Gates, Steve Wozniak, Steve Jobs, Tim Berners-Lee and Larry Page. **Availability:** CD-ROM; E-book; Print; Audio.

22656 ■ *"The Innovator's Solution: Creating and Sustaining Successful Growth"*
Pub: Harvard Business Review Press
Contact: Moderna V. Pfizer, Contact
Released: November 19, 2013. **Price:** $35, Hardcover/Hardcopy. **Description:** Even in today's hyper-accelerated business environment any small company can transform their business. Advice on business decisions crucial to achieving truly disruptive growth and purpose guidelines for developing their own disruptive growth engine is given. The forces that cause managers to make bad decisions as they plan new ideas for their company are identified and new frameworks to help develop the right conditions, at the right time, for a disruption to succeed. Managers and business leaders responsible for innovation and growth will benefit their business and their teams with this information. **Availability:** E-book; Print.

22657 ■ *Instant Income: Strategies That Bring in the Cash*
Pub: McGraw-Hill Professional
Ed: Janet Switzer. **Released:** First Edition. **Price:** $24. **Description:** Book covers small business advertising techniques, marketing, joint ventures, and sales. **Availability:** Print.

22658 ■ *Instinct: Tapping Your Entrepreneurial DNA to Achieve Your Business Goals*
Description: Research shows that entrepreneurs may attribute their success to genetics. **Availability:** Online.

22659 ■ *"The Intel Trinity: How Robert Noyce, Gordon Moore, and Andy Grove Built the World's Most Important Company"*
Pub: Harper Business
Contact: Hollis Heimbouch, Senior Vice President Publisher
Released: July 15, 2014. **Price:** $34.99, hardcover; $11.74, e-book; $4.34, kindle; $19.42, hardcover; $4.30, hardcover(69 used from $4.30); $15.17, hardcover(56 new from $15.17); $19.99, hardcover(1 collectible from $19.99); $31.74, paperback; $22.95, paperback(10 used from $22.95); $19.13, paperback(4 new from $19.13). **Description:** A complete history of Intel Corporation, the essential company of the digital age, is presented. After over four decades Intel remains the most important company in the world, a defining company of the global digital economy. The inventors of the microprocessor that powers nearly every intelligent electronic device worldwide are profiled. These entrepreneurs made the personal computer, Internet, telecommunications, and personal electronics all possible. The challenges and successes of the company and its ability to maintain its dominance, its culture and its legacy are examined. **Availability:** E-book; Print; Online.

22660 ■ *International Handbook of Entrepreneurship and HRM*
Pub: Edward Elgar Publishing Inc.
Contact: Edward Elgar, Founder Chairman
Ed: Rowena Barrett, Susan Mayson. **Released:** 2008. **Description:** Conceived on the basis that there is a growing recognition of the interplay between human resource management and entrepreneurship, this volume offers insights into the role of HRM and entrepreneurial firms.

22661 ■ *"Into the Groove: Fine-Tune Your Biz By Getting Into the Good Habit Groove"* in *Small Business Opportunities* (Spring 2008)
Description: Profile of Ty Freyvogel and his consulting firm Freyvogel Communications. Freyvogel serves the telecommunications need of Fortune 500 and mid-sized businesses.

22662 ■ *"Intrepid Souls: Meet a Few Who've Made the Big Leap"* in *Crain's Chicago Business* (Vol. 31, November 10, 2008, No. 45, pp. 26)
Description: Advice is given from entrepreneurs who have launched businesses in the last year despite the economic crisis. Among the types of businesses featured are a cooking school, a child day-care center, a children's clothing store and an Internet-based company. **Availability:** Online.

22663 ■ *"It Was a Very Good Year..To Be Ted Rogers"* in *Canadian Business* (Vol. 80, Winter 2007, No. 24, pp. 121)
Description: Ted Rogers had a banner year in 2007 as Rogers Communications Inc. (RCI) took in huge profits from its phone and wireless business and his personal wealth grew sixty-seven percent to $7.6 billion. Rogers has record of betting on technologies that get the best returns relative to the investment in the marketplace such as its use of the GSM network and its cable hybrid fiber coaxial network.

22664 ■ *It's Not Who You Know - It's Who Knows You!: The Small Business Guide to Raising Your Profits by Raising Your Profile*
Pub: John Wiley & Sons, Inc.
Contact: Christina Van Tassell, Executive Vice President Chief Financial Officer
Ed: David Arvin. **Released:** 2nd edition. **Price:** $8.69, hardcover. **Description:** When it comes to promoting a small business or a brand, it is essential to know how valuable high-profile attention can be. But for most small companies, the cost of hiring an outside firm to increase attention can be too expensive. **Availability:** Print; Online.

22665 ■ *"I've Always Been an Entrepreneur"* in *South Florida Business Journal* (Vol. 34, June 13, 2014, No. 47, pp. 11)
Pub: American City Business Journals, Inc.
Contact: Mike Olivieri, Executive Vice President
Released: June 13, 2014. **Price:** $4, Introductory 4-Week Offer(Digital & Print). **Description:** Modernizing Medicine CEO, Daniel Cane, says he started doing business at age six when he opened a lemonade stand. His firm helps physicians increase efficiencies in their practices while improving both business and treatment outcomes. He surrounds himself with talented people, which is what he likes most about his job. Cane added that dividing time between work and family is difficult for entrepreneurs. **Availability:** Print; Online.

22666 ■ **"J.C. Penney Head Shops for Shares"** in *Barron's* (Vol. 88, July 7, 2008, No. 27, pp. 29)
Pub: Dow Jones & Company Inc.
Contact: Almar Latour, Chief Executive Officer
Ed: Teresa Rivas. **Description:** Myron Ullman III, chairman and chief executive officer of J.C. Penney, purchased $1 million worth of shares of the company. He now owns 393,140 shares of the company and an additional 1,282 on his 401(k) plan. **Availability:** Online.

22667 ■ *The King of Vodka: The Story of Pyotr Smirnov and the Upheaval of an Empire*
Pub: HarperCollins Publishers L.L.C.
Contact: Brian Murray, President
Ed: Linda Himelstein. **Released:** November 30, 2010. **Price:** $15.99, paperback. **Description:** Biography of Pyotr Smirnov and how his determination took him from serf to the head of Smirnov Vodka. Smirnov's marketing techniques are defined and show how he expanded the drink worldwide. **Availability:** E-book; Print; Online.

22668 ■ **"Koneco Building Services Inc. to Add Theme Park Division"** in *Orlando Business Journal* (Vol. 30, April 25, 2014, No. 44, pp. 3)
Pub: American City Business Journals, Inc.
Contact: Mike Olivieri, Executive Vice President
Released: Weekly. **Price:** $8, introductory 4-week offer(Digital & Print). **Description:** Koneco Building Services Inc. operations director, Ernie Falco and sales director Wolf Adler, discuss plans to add a theme park division to the Florida-based facility maintenance firm. They offer advice to other entrepreneurs and share the sacrifices they made as their business was growing. **Availability:** Print; Online.

22669 ■ **"Labor of Love"** in *Green Industry Pro* (Vol. 23, March 2011, No. 3, pp. 14)
Ed: Gregg Wartgow. **Description:** Profile of CLS Landscape Management in Chino, California and its owner who started the company when he was 21 years old. Kevin Davis built his landscape firm into a $20 million a year business without using any dedicated salesperson. **Availability:** Online.

22670 ■ *Launchpad Republic: America's Entrepreneurial Edge and Why It Matters*
Pub: John Wiley & Sons, Inc.
Contact: Christina Van Tassell, Executive Vice President Chief Financial Officer
URL(s): www.wiley.com/en-us/Launchpad+Republic%3A+America%27s+Entrepreneurial+Edge+and+Why+It+Matters-p-9781119900054
Ed: Howard Wolk, John Landry. **Released:** July 2022. **Price:** $18, e-book; $29.95, hardcover. **Description:** A history of entrepreneurship in the U.S. and how that systems is critical to today's startups. **Availability:** E-book; Print.

22671 ■ **"Laurent Beaudoin Interview: Deja Vu"** in *Canadian Business* (Vol. 81, July 22, 2008, No. 12-13, pp. 38)
Pub: Rogers Media Inc.
Contact: Neil Spivak, Chief Executive Officer
Ed: Joe Castaldo. **Description:** Laurent Beaudoin has retired as chief executive officer for Bombardier Inc.'s, a manufacturer of regional and business aircraft, but kept a role in the firm as a non-executive chairman. Beaudoin first resigned from the company in 1999, but had to return in 2004 to address challenging situations faced by the company. Beaudoin's views on management and the company are presented. **Availability:** Online.

22672 ■ **"Lead Like It Matters...Because It Does: Practical Leadership Tools to Inspire and Engage Your People and Create Great Results"**
Released: First Edition. **Price:** $33; $33. **Description:** The Ripple Effect method for increasing employee engagement, reducing turnover, and driving overall business success will help any manager or entrepreneur to lead his company. Important practices like eliminating wasted meetings, addressing conflict, and aligning decisions with business needs are addressed. **Availability:** E-book; Print; Online.

22673 ■ *Lead Upwards: How Startup Joiners Can Impact New Ventures, Build Amazing Careers, and Inspire Great Teams*
Pub: John Wiley & Sons, Inc.
Contact: Christina Van Tassell, Executive Vice President Chief Financial Officer
URL(s): www.wiley.com/en-us/Lead+Upwards%3A+How+Startup+Joiners+Can+Impact+New+Ventures%2C+Build+Amazing+Careers%2C+and+Inspire+Great+Teams-p-9781119833352
Ed: Sarah E. Brown. **Released:** April 2022. **Price:** $15, e-book; $25, hardcover. **Description:** This guide helps develop leadership skills for startup executives. **Availability:** E-book; Print.

22674 ■ *The Leadership Challenge: How to Make Extraordinary Things Happen in Organizations*
Pub: Jossey-Bass
Ed: James M. Kouzes, Barry Z. Posner. **Released:** 7th edition. **Price:** $34.95, hardcover; $34.95, hardcover. **Description:** According to research by the authors, people can make extraordinary things happen by liberating the leader within everyone around them. This handbook gives practical tips to aspire leaders in retail, manufacturing, government, community, church and school settings. **Availability:** E-book; Print.

22675 ■ **"Leadership Development In the Age of the Algorithm"** in (Vol. 90, June 2012, No. 6, pp. 86)
Pub: Harvard Business Review Press
Contact: Moderna V. Pfizer, Contact
Ed: Marcus Buckingham. **Price:** $8.95. **Description:** Guidelines to tailor leadership training to specific individuals include assessing the leadership type for each person, identifying the top leaders for each type, creating practices that are effective for each type, delivering those practices to others, and integrate user feedback to fine-tune the process. **Availability:** Online; PDF.

22676 ■ **"Learning Charisma: Transform Yourself Into the Person Others Want to Follow"** in *Harvard Business Review* (Vol. 90, June 2012, No. 6, pp. 127)
Pub: Harvard Business Review Press
Contact: Moderna V. Pfizer, Contact
Ed: John Antonakis, Marika Fenley, Sue Liechti. **Price:** $8.95, hardcopy black and white. **Description:** Chrismatic leadership tactics include gestures, facial expressions, and an animated voice, all of which can enhance the receptiveness of a given message. Tips include engaging listeners and distilling points, and demonstrating passion, authority, and integrity. **Availability:** Print; Online; PDF.

22677 ■ **"Lessons Learned From Animals, Part II"** in *South Florida Business Journal* (Vol. 35, September 19, 2014, No. 8, pp. 11)
Pub: American City Business Journals, Inc.
Contact: Mike Olivieri, Executive Vice President
Description: Advice on how to achieve business growth is given. Striving to be in environments that offer mental, spiritual and physical growth to entrepreneurs is encouraged. Businesses should be consistent in practices that promote business growth. **Availability:** Online.

22678 ■ **"Lessons from Turnaround Leaders"** in *Strategy and Leadership* (Vol. 39, May-June 2011, No. 3, pp. 36-43)
Pub: Emerald Group Publishing Limited
Contact: Erika Valenti, President
Ed: David P. Boyd. **Description:** A study analyzes the cases of some successful turnaround leaders to present a strategic model to help firms tackle challenges such as employee inertia, competition and slow organizational renewal. It describes a change model consisting of five major steps to be followed by firms with environmental uncertainty for the purpose. **Availability:** Download; Online.

22679 ■ *Liespotting: Proven Techniques to Detect Deception*
Pub: St. Martins Press/Macmillan
Ed: Pamela Meyer. **Released:** September 13, 2011. **Price:** $15.99, paperback; $25.99, hardcover. **Description:** Liespotting links three disciplines: facial recognition training, interrogation training, and a comprehensive survey of research in the field - into a specialized body of information developed specifically to help business leaders detect deception and get the information they need to successfully conduct their most important interactions and transactions. **Availability:** Paperback; E-book; Print.

22680 ■ **"Life's Work: Ben Bradlee"** in *Harvard Business Review* (Vol. 88, September 2010, No. 9, pp. 128)
Pub: Harvard Business Publishing
Contact: Diane Belcher, Managing Director
Ed: Alison Beard. **Price:** $8.95, PDF. **Description:** Newspaper publisher Ben Bradlee discusses factors that lead to success, including visible supervisors, enthusiasm, appropriate expansion, and the importance in truth in reporting. **Availability:** Online; PDF.

22681 ■ **"Life's Work: James Dyson"** in *Harvard Business Review* (Vol. 88, July-August 2010, No. 7-8, pp. 172)
Pub: Harvard Business Publishing
Contact: Diane Belcher, Managing Director
Ed: Alison Beard. **Price:** $8.95. **Description:** The founder of appliance company Dyson Ltd. discusses the role of making mistakes in learning and innovation, and emphasizes the importance of hands-on involvement to make a company successful. **Availability:** Online; PDF.

22682 ■ **"Life's Work: Manolo Blahnik"** in *Harvard Business Review* (Vol. 88, December 2010, No. 12, pp. 144)
Pub: Harvard Business Publishing
Contact: Diane Belcher, Managing Director
Ed: Alison Beard. **Price:** $8.95, PDF. **Description:** Shoe designer Manolo Blahnik recounts his beginnings in the shoe industry and the influence art has had on his work, as well as balancing art and commerce. He also discusses the importance of quality materials and craftsmanship and the benefits of managing an independent, family-owned business. **Availability:** Online; PDF.

22683 ■ **"Life's Work: Oliver Sacks"** in *Harvard Business Review* (Vol. 88, November 2010, No. 11, pp. 152)
Pub: Harvard Business Publishing
Contact: Diane Belcher, Managing Director
Ed: Lisa Burrell. **Price:** $8.95, PDF. **Description:** Neurologist and author Oliver Sacks discusses whether different types of minds tend toward certain skills, physician-patient communication, and his own perspectives from being a patient himself. **Availability:** Online; PDF.

22684 ■ **"Lifestyle Entrepreneurship and Innovation in Rural Areas: The Case of Tourism Entrepreneurs"** in *Journal of Small Business Strategy* (Vol. 31, December 1, 2021, No. 4, 40-49)
URL(s): libjournals.mtsu.edu/index.php/jsbs/article/view/2132
Ed: Alvaro Dias, Graca M. Silva. **Released:** November 16, 2021. **Description:** Discusses the research on lifestyle entrepreneurs and their role in rural communities. **Availability:** PDF; Online.

22685 ■ **"A Lifetime of Giving: Food Bank CEO Fights Hunger One Mouth At a Time"** in *Black Enterprise* (Vol. 41, November 2010, No. 4, pp. 86)
Pub: Earl G. Graves Ltd.
Contact: Earl Graves, Jr., President

Ed: Tamara E. Holmes. Description: Profile of Valerie Traore, CEO of Food Bank of South Jersey. Traore stresses the importance of volunteerism that she learned from her grandparents. Hunger relief became her passion when she served as a temp office worker for the Maryland Food Bank in Baltimore. She earned her Bachelor's of Science in management and has dedicated herself to a career in nonprofit service. Availability: Online.

22686 ■ "A Light Bulb Came On, and It Was Energy Efficient" in Globe & Mail (January 27, 2007, pp. B3)
Description: A brief profile of Edward Weinstein, chief executive officer of the Montreal-based family-run lighting firm Globe Electric Co., is presented The firm's management strategies are described. Availability: Online.

22687 ■ Linchpin: Are You Indispensable?
Pub: Portfolio
Contact: Adrian Zackheim, President
Ed: Seth Godin. Released: January 26, 2010. Price: $18, paperback; $26.95, hardcover; $9.99, e-book. Description: The best way to get what you're worth, according to the author, is to exert emotional labor, to be seen as indispensable, and to produce interactions that organizations and people care about. Availability: E-book; Print.

22688 ■ "Live and Learn" in Canadian Business (Vol. 80, April 23, 2007, No. 9, pp. 76)
Description: Paul Anka, a musician, feels that ground work is essential before establishing a company. Availability: Print; Online.

22689 ■ "Donald Tarlton" in Canadian Business (Vol. 80, March 26, 2007, No. 7, pp. 70)
Pub: Rogers Media Inc.
Contact: Neil Spivak, Chief Executive Officer
Ed: Andy Holloway. Description: Donald Tarlton, owner of Donald K Donald Entertainment Group, shares few things about his childhood and career. Availability: Print; Online.

22690 ■ "Live & Learn: François Joly" in Canadian Business (Vol. 79, September 11, 2006, No. 18, pp. 146)
Pub: Rogers Media Inc.
Contact: Neil Spivak, Chief Executive Officer
Ed: Andy Holloway. Description: President and chief operating officer of Desjardins Financial Security, Francois Joly speaks about his interests and emphasizes the need to be passionate about work. Availability: Online.

22691 ■ "Live & Learn: Ian Delaney" in Canadian Business (Vol. 81, Summer 2008, No. 9, pp. 168)
Pub: Rogers Media Inc.
Contact: Neil Spivak, Chief Executive Officer
Ed: Joe Castaldo. Description: Interview with Ian Delaney who is the executive vice president of chemical company Sherritt International Corp.; Delaney previously worked as chief executive for a holding company owned by Peter Munk. Details of his beliefs, profession and family life are discussed. Availability: Online.

22692 ■ "Laurent Beaudoin" in Canadian Business (Vol. 80, April 9, 2007, No. 8, pp. 68)
Pub: Rogers Media Inc.
Contact: Neil Spivak, Chief Executive Officer
Ed: Thomas Watson. Description: Chief executive officer of Bombardier Inc., Laurent Beaudoin, talks about his personal life and career. Availability: Print; Online.

22693 ■ "Live and Learn: Penny Chapman" in Canadian Business (Vol. 79, July 17, 2006, No. 14-15, pp. 75)
Pub: Rogers Media Inc.
Contact: Neil Spivak, Chief Executive Officer

Ed: Erin Pooley. Description: Interview with Penny Chapman, president of Chapman's Ice Cream, who speaks about her journey from rags to riches. Availability: Online.

22694 ■ "Live & Learn: Philip Kives, Founder and CEO of K-Tel" in Canadian Business (Vol. 79, October 23, 2006, No. 21, pp. 160)
Pub: Rogers Media Inc.
Contact: Neil Spivak, Chief Executive Officer
Ed: Joe Castaldo. Description: Philip Kives, founder and chief executive officer of K-Tel International Inc. discusses his professional achievements. Availability: Online.

22695 ■ "Live & Learn: Thomas D'Aquino" in Canadian Business (Vol. 80, November 19, 2007, No. 23, pp. 92)
Pub: Rogers Media Inc.
Contact: Neil Spivak, Chief Executive Officer
Ed: Calvin Leung. Description: Thomas D'Aquino is the CEO and president of the Canadian Council of Chief Executives since 1981. D'Aquino thinks he has the best job in Canada because he can change the way policies are made and the way people think. Details of his career as a lawyer and CEO and his views on Canada's economy are provided. Availability: Print; Online.

22696 ■ "The Long Game" in Business Strategy Review (Vol. 21, Summer 2010, No. 2, pp. 36)
Ed: Stuart Crainer. Released: June 24, 2010. Description: Profile of Alibaba.com and its CEO David Wei. Availability: Print; PDF; Online.

22697 ■ "The Lords of Ideas" in Business Strategy Review (Vol. 21, Autumn 2010, No. 3, pp. 57)
Ed: Stuart Crainer. Released: September 22, 2010. Description: True originators of modern strategy are profiled. Availability: Print; Electronic publishing; PDF; Online.

22698 ■ "Lots More Mr. Nice Guy" in Canadian Business (Vol. 80, October 22, 2007, No. 21, pp. 58)
Description: Galen Weston Jr., executive chairman of Loblaw and heir to the Weston family business, has his hands full running the company. Details of his turnaround strategies and ambitious plans to increase profitability of the business are discussed.

22699 ■ "Lynn Johnson, President: Dowland-Bach" in Alaska Business Monthly (Vol. 27, October 2011, No. 10, pp. 11)
Pub: Alaska Business Publishing Company Inc.
Contact: Charles Bell, Vice President, Sales and Marketing
E-mail: cbell@akbizmag.com
Ed: Peg Stomierowski. Description: Profile of Lynn C. Johnson cofounder of Dowland-Bach Corporation, a manufacturing and distribution company is presented. The firms primary products are wellhead control and chemical injection systems for corrosion control, UL industrial control panels, and specialty stainless steel sheet metal fabrication. Availability: Print; Online.

22700 ■ Make It in America: How International Companies and Entrepreneurs Can Successfully Enter and Scale in U.S. Markets
Pub: John Wiley & Sons, Inc.
Contact: Christina Van Tassell, Executive Vice President Chief Financial Officer
URL(s): www.wiley.com/en-us/Make+It+in+America%3A+How+International+Companies+and+Entrepreneurs+Can+Successfully+Enter+and+Scale+in+U+S+Markets-p-9781119885146
Ed: Matthew Lee Sawyer. Released: November 2022. Price: $18, e-book; $30, hardcover. Description: Includes case studies of international companies who successfully launched inside the U.S. Availability: E-book; Print.

22701 ■ Making Difficult Decisions: How to Be Decisive and Get the Business Done
Pub: John Wiley & Sons, Inc.
Contact: Christina Van Tassell, Executive Vice President Chief Financial Officer
Ed: Peter Shaw. Released: February 28, 2010. Price: $29.95, paperback; $19.99, e-book. Description: Experience of others can help entrepreneurs and managers make difficult business decisions. The strategies set forth in this book have been used successfully in public, private and voluntary sectors. Availability: E-book; Print.

22702 ■ The Management of Small and Medium Enterprises
Pub: Routledge, Taylor & Francis Group
Released: First edition. Description: Investigation into the underlying mechanisms and practices of management within small and medium enterprises is provided.

22703 ■ "Many in Tech Look to Push More Community Involvement, But Not in Traditional Ways" in Boston Business Journal (Vol. 31, August 5, 2011, No. 28, pp. 1)
Pub: Boston Business Journal
Contact: Carolyn M. Jones, President
E-mail: cmjones@bizjournals.com
Ed: Mary Moore. Released: Weekly. Price: $4, Introductory 4-Week Offer(Digital Only). Description: Entrepreneurs and venture capitalists in Boston have launched Technology Underwriting Greater Good, the tech industry's answer to the criticism that they are not charitable. The foundation finances nonprofits that aid young people through entrepreneurship, education and life experience. Other tech firms in Boston doing charitable works are discussed. Availability: Print; Online.

22704 ■ Marketing for Entrepreneurs
Pub: FT Press
Ed: Jurgen Wolff. Released: 1st edition. Description: This text identifies marketing as the entire process of researching, creating, distributing and selling a product or service. It isn't about theory and metrics, rather it is a practical guide that starts with the basics of all marketing aspects. Availability: Print.

22705 ■ Marketing that Works: How Entrepreneurial Marketing Can Add Sustainable Value to Any Sized Company
Pub: Wharton School Publishing
Ed: Leonard M. Lodish, Howard Morgan, Shellye Archambeau. Released: 2nd edition. Price: $57.49, book plus e-book bundle price; $99.98, book plus e-book bundle list price; $39.99, book; $49.99, e-book(water marked). Description: Entrepreneurial marketing techniques are shared in order to help a new company position and target products and services. Availability: E-book; Print; Electronic publishing; PDF.

22706 ■ "Marketing: You Are On the Air: Radio and TV Producers Are Looking For Shows Starring Smart CEOs" in Inc. (December 2007, pp. 67-69)
Ed: Sarah Goldstein. Description: Many successful entrepreneurs are being hired to host television and radio shows in order to share business expertise. Availability: Print; Online.

22707 ■ "Master of His Domain" in Canadian Business (Vol. 81, December 8, 2008, No. 21, pp. S17)
Description: L'Oreal Canada chief executive Javier San Juan believes in being close to consumers and travels to one of his company's fifteen locations in Canada about once a month. San Juan's job is to build the L'Oreal brand in Canada. Availability: Online.

22708 ■ Mastering Business Negotiation: A Working Guide to Making Deals and Resolving Conflict
Pub: Jossey-Bass

Ed: Roy J. Lewicki, Alexander Hiam. **Released:** 2011. **Description:** Provides extensive insight into practical strategies and ideas for conducting business negotiations. **Availability:** Print; Electronic publishing; Online.

22709 ■ *"Meet the Class of 2014, In their Own Words"* in *South Florida Business Journal (Vol. 34, June 27, 2014, No. 49, pp. 18)*
Pub: American City Business Journals, Inc.
Contact: Mike Olivieri, Executive Vice President

Released: Weekly. **Price:** $8, introductory 4-week offer(Digital & Print). **Description:** Several business leaders and entrepreneurs under the age of 40 who have achieved success and contributed to their community are presented. The honorees of the 40 Under 40 Class of 2014 share their views about personal and professional lives and social responsibilities to their communities. **Availability:** Print; Online.

22710 ■ *"Megachurch Movie Mogul"* in *Dallas Business Journal (Vol. 37, June 6, 2014, No. 39, pp. 4)*
Pub: American City Business Journals, Inc.
Contact: Mike Olivieri, Executive Vice President

Description: Ordained minister and entrepreneur T.D. Jakes hopes to use the faith-based filmmaking business in Dallas-Fort Worth, Texas as a ministry tool while making huge profits. Jakes says Christian filmmaking represents about 60 percent of his revenue at TDJ Enterprises. **Availability:** Database; Online.

22711 ■ *"Michigan Means Growth: Sustaining Growth Through Thick and Thin: Michigan Companies Sustain Growth with Well-Timed Access to Capital"* in *Inc. (Vol. 36, September 2014, No. 7, pp. 164)*
Pub: Mansueto Ventures L.L.C.
Contact: Stephanie Mehta, Chief Executive Officer

Description: Successful companies possess flexibility, foresight and resources to turn adversity into opportunity. The small businesses in Michigan who have sustained experienced sales growth despite the recession of 2007. The Michigan Economic Development Corporation has introduced three initiatives to help Michigan businesses grow, including venture capital, collateral support and loan participation through the State Small Business Credit Initiative, and cash incentives for businesses looking to invest in urban communities or grow jobs. **Availability:** Print; Online.

22712 ■ *Microfranchising: Creating Wealth at the Bottom of the Pyramid*
Pub: Edward Elgar Publishing Inc.
Contact: Edward Elgar, Founder Chairman

Released: 2007. **Description:** Ideas from researchers and social entrepreneurs discusses the movement that moves microfranchising into a mechanism for sustainable poverty reduction on a scale to match microfinance.

22713 ■ *Minority Women Entrepreneurs: How Outsider Status Can Lead to Better Business Practices*
Ed: Mary Godwyn, Donna Stoddard. **Released:** September 08, 2017. **Description:** Minority women in the US start businesses at a faster rate then non-minority men and women. This book explores their success and how they use their outside status to develop business practices that benefit not only their company, but their communities. **Availability:** E-book.

22714 ■ *"More Power to Your Presentation"* in *Business Strategy Review (Vol. 21, Spring 2010, No. 1, pp. 50)*
Ed: Roly Grimshaw. **Released:** March 22, 2010. **Description:** You might wonder what similarities there can be between a Russian oligarch and an entrepreneur. When it comes to persuading people to invest, there are plenty. **Availability:** Online; Electronic publishing.

22715 ■ *"More Than a Feeling"* in *Entrepreneur (Vol. 36, April 2008, No. 4, pp. 10)*
Description: It is said that emotion has no place when it comes to business matters, but it may not be the case as entrepreneurs and other people in business feel passionate about what they do. Emotions can help bring out a positive outlook in them. Other details on the topic are discussed. **Availability:** Online.

22716 ■ *"Mover and Sheika"* in *Conde Nast Portfolio (Vol. 2, June 2008, No. 6, pp. 104)*
Ed: John Arlidge. **Description:** Profile of Princess Sheika Lubna who is the first female foreign trade minister in the Middle East, the United Arab Emirates biggest business envoy, paving the way for billions in new investment, and also a manufacturer of her own perfume line. **Availability:** Online.

22717 ■ *My Big Idea: 30 Successful Entrepreneurs Reveal How They Found Inspiration*
Pub: Kogan Page Ltd.
Contact: Christina Lindeholm, Manager, Sales
Ed: Rachel Bridge. **Released:** First edition. **Description:** Thirty successful entrepreneurs share insight into starting and running a small business. **Availability:** E-book; Print.

22718 ■ *"My Day"* in *Business Strategy Review (Vol. 21, Autumn 2010, No. 3, pp. 77)*
Ed: Julie Meyer. **Description:** Julie Meyer shots to prominence as cofounder of the entrepreneurial network, First Tuesday. The firm was sold for $50 million in 2000. **Availability:** PDF; Online.

22719 ■ *"My Inglorious Road to Success"* in *Harvard Business Review (Vol. 88, July-August 2010, No. 7-8, pp. 38)*
Pub: Harvard Business Publishing
Contact: Diane Belcher, Managing Director
Ed: Warren Bennis. **Price:** $6, PDF. **Description:** The author discusses the intersection of fortune and opportunity in his career success, and emphasizes the important role of awareness when taking advantage of both. **Availability:** Online; PDF.

22720 ■ *Navigating Your Way to Business Success: An Entrepreneur's Journey*
Ed: Kathryn B. Freeland. **Released:** January 01, 2010. **Price:** $24.95, hardcover. **Description:** Learn first-hand from a successful entrepreneur about assessing skills and talent, envisioning your company, planning a path to success, and then tapping into available government agencies to make your business become a reality. **Availability:** Print.

22721 ■ *Never Eat Alone: And Other Secrets to Success, One Relationship at a Time*
Released: June 03, 2014. **Price:** $28; $13.99. **Description:** Business networking strategies are offered. **Availability:** E-book; Print.

22722 ■ *"New Project? Don't Analyze - Act: Entrepreneurs Take Small, Quick Steps To Get Initiatives Off the Ground. You Can Do the Same In Your Organization"* in *Harvard Business Review (Vol. 90, March 2012, No. 3, pp. 154)*
Pub: Harvard Business Review Press
Contact: Moderna V. Pfizer, Contact
Ed: Leonard A. Schlesinger, Charles F. Kiefer, Paul B. Brown. **Description:** Guidelines for acting on a new project include using the means at hand, securing only the commitments needed for the next step, staying within an acceptable loss range, focusing on producing early results, and managing expectations.

22723 ■ *"The Next Frontier"* in *San Francisco Business Times (Vol. 28, February 28, 2014, No. 32, pp. 4)*
Pub: American City Business Journals, Inc.
Contact: Mike Olivieri, Executive Vice President
Description: The growth of the electronic payments business in San Francisco, California has captured the interest of venture capitalists, entrepreneurs, and other investors. Social media companies like Facebook and Google are expected to expand into electronic payments. Telecommunication companies are also investing in promising startups and joint ventures. **Availability:** Print; Online.

22724 ■ *Non-Standard Employment under Globalization: Flexible Work and Social Security in the Newly Industrializing Countries*
Pub: Palgrave Macmillan
Ed: Koichi Usami. **Released:** First edition. **Description:** Expansion of non-standard employment under globalization is being recognized in all of the newly industrialized countries. The book examines deregulation of labor markets, social protection for nonstandard workers, and social security reforms in accordance with the transformation of employment.

22725 ■ *"Noodles Founder Becomes Colorado's Chief Marketing Officer"* in *Denver Business Journal (Vol. 64, August 24, 2012, No. 14, pp. 1)*
Pub: Baltimore Business Journal
Contact: Rhonda Pringle, President
E-mail: rpringle@bizjournals.com

Description: Governor John Hickenlooper has hired Aaron Kennedy to become the first chief marketing officer of the state of Colorado. The founder of restaurant, Noodles & Company will begin his job on August 6, 2012 of creating a state brand to attract more entrepreneurs and businesses entrepises to invest in Colorado. **Availability:** Print; Online.

22726 ■ *"No. 123: Protecting People, From the Bronx to the Beltway"* in *Inc. (Vol. 36, September 2014, No. 7, pp. 106)*
Pub: Mansueto Ventures L.L.C.
Contact: Stephanie Mehta, Chief Executive Officer
Released: August 20, 2014. **Description:** Profile of Michael S. Rogers, founder of Securityhunter, located in Baltimore, Maryland. The firm installs security systems for military bases and government agencies. The company developed a security system that was used to protect Colin Powell while traveling. **Availability:** Print; Online.

22727 ■ *"No. 423: How a Date Led To al Bowling Juggernaut"* in *Inc. (Vol. 36, September 2014, No. 7, pp. 42)*
Pub: Mansueto Ventures L.L.C.
Contact: Stephanie Mehta, Chief Executive Officer
Released: September 2014. **Description:** Profile of Tom Shannon, entrepreneur who got the idea to buy a bowling alley following a date with a girl. The New York City-based Bowlmor is a 262-location bowling and entertainment venue that recently became an AMF bowling company. **Availability:** Print; Online.

22728 ■ *"The Obstacle Is the Way: The Timeless Art of Turning Trials into Triumph"*
Pub: Portfolio Hardcover
Contact: Adrian Zackheim, President
Released: May 01, 2014. **Price:** $9.99, e-book; $25, hardcover; $16.96, hardcover; $9.38, hardcover(73 used from $9.38); $12.14, hardcover(66 new from $12.14); $89.99, hardcover(2 collectible from $89.99). **Description:** The formula for success is taking any obstacle and turning it into a business opportunity. Successful leaders throughout history are profiled to show how any entrepreneur can succeed. **Availability:** E-book; Print.

22729 ■ *"Off the Wall: Keith Collins' Larger-Than-Life Designs"* in *Black Enterprise (Vol. 37, February 2007, No. 7, pp. 138)*
Pub: Earl G. Graves Inc.
Contact: Earl Graves, Jr., President
Ed: Sonia Alleyne. **Description:** Profile of Keith Collins, an entrepreneur who makes carpets for the likes of Jay Leno, Nicolas Cage, Arnold Schwarzenegger, Janet Jackson, and Will Smith. Collins is passionate about this ancient art form and saw a future in it despite the negative feedback from those around him. **Availability:** Online.

22730 ■ "The Office: Do Not Disturb" in Inc. (November 2007, pp. 144)

Ed: Leigh Buchanan. **Description:** The importance for any CEO to be accessible to his employees is stressed. **Availability:** Online.

22731 ■ "Oil Markets: A Nasty Russian Tale" in Canadian Business (Vol. 81, March 3, 2008, No. 3, pp. 85)

Pub: Rogers Media Inc.
Contact: Neil Spivak, Chief Executive Officer

Ed: Andrew Nikiforuk. **Description:** Billionaires Alex Shnaider and Michael Shtaif entered a partnership for an oil venture which ended in a slew of litigations. Cases of breach of contract, injurious falsehood and other related lawsuits were filed against Shnaider. Details of the lawsuits and the other parties involved in the disputes are presented. **Availability:** Online.

22732 ■ "Out of This World" in Black Enterprise (November 2007)

Pub: Earl G. Graves Ltd.
Contact: Earl Graves, Jr., President

Ed: Anthony Calypso. **Description:** Profile of Noah Samara, CEO of WorldSpace Inc. who raised $1 billion to help create the technological architecture for satellite radio. **Availability:** Online.

22733 ■ Outliers: The Story of Success

Pub: Little, Brown and Company
Contact: Judy Clain, Editor-in-Chief

Ed: Malcolm Gladwell. **Released:** November 18, 2008. **Price:** $18.99, trade paper. **Description:** The book explores reasons for individual success. **Availability:** Large print; CD-ROM; E-book; Print; Download; Audio.

22734 ■ "An Overview of Rural Entrepreneurship and Future Directions " in Journal of Small Business Strategy (Vol. 31, December 1, 2021, No. 4, pp. 1-4)

URL(s): libjournals.mtsu.edu/index.php/jsbs/article/view/2129/1269

Ed: Dennis Barber, III, Michael L. Harris, Jeffrey Jones. **Released:** December 01, 2021. **Description:** Discusses the research accomplished on rural entrepreneurship ventures. **Availability:** PDF; Online.

22735 ■ The Oz Principle

Released: May 04, 2010. **Price:** $17, paperback. **Description:** The role of personal and organizational accountability in getting business results is profiled. **Availability:** E-book; Print.

22736 ■ "Panera Breadwinner Tries on Tattu Designer Jeans" in Houston Business Journal (Vol. 40, December 18, 2009, No. 32, pp. 1)

Pub: Houston Business Journal
Contact: Bob Charlet, President
E-mail: bcharlet@bizjournals.com

Ed: Allison Wollam. **Description:** Chuck Cain, the franchisee who introduced Panera Bread to Houston, Texas has partnered with tax accountant Jim Jacobsen to introduce custom-make Tattu Jeans. As more Tattu Jeans outlets are being planned, Cain is using entrepreneurial lessons learned from Panera Bread in the new venture. Both Panera Bread and Tattu Jeans were opened by Cain during economic downturns. **Availability:** Print; Online.

22737 ■ "Perfecting the Process: Creating a More Efficient Organization on Your Terms" in Black Enterprise (Vol. 41, October 2010, No. 3)

Pub: Earl G. Graves Ltd.
Contact: Earl Graves, Jr., President

Ed: Tamara E. Holmes. **Description:** More than ever, entrepreneurs need to identify new ways of doing business in a cost-effective manner in order to expand their companies, while remaining true to their customer demands. **Availability:** Online.

22738 ■ "The Performer: Soulpepper Theatre Company's Albert Shultz" in Canadian Business (Vol. 83, August 17, 2010, No. 13-14, pp. 71)

Pub: Rogers Media Inc.
Contact: Neil Spivak, Chief Executive Officer

Ed: Steve Maich. **Description:** Soulpepper Theater Company founder and actor/director Albert Schultz shares the key ingredient to his success both artistically and commercially. Schultz believes his success was a combination of passion and persistence, as well as team building. He believes his entrepreneurial impulse came when he began thinking of making opportunities instead of taking them.

22739 ■ Personal Success and the Bottom Line

Description: Retired certified public accountant provides a primer for those wishing to achieve a balance between career and their personal life. **Availability:** Print.

22740 ■ "Personality Traits You Need to Start a Business" in Business News Daily (Oct. 12, 2021)

URL(s): www.businessnewsdaily.com/3124-personality-traits-start-a-business.html

Ed: Katharine Paljug. **Released:** October 12, 2021. **Description:** Presents qualities that are beneficial to have if you want to be your own boss. **Availability:** Online.

22741 ■ "Peter Bynoe Trades Up" in Black Enterprise (Vol. 38, July 2008, No. 12, pp. 30)

Pub: Earl G. Graves Ltd.
Contact: Earl Graves, Jr., President

Description: Chicago-based Loop Capital Markets L.L.C. has named Peter Bynoe managing director of corporate finance. Bynoe was previously a senior partner at the law firm DLA Piper U.S. L.L.P., where he worked on stadium deals.

22742 ■ "Peter French Tapped to Lead Cafe Commerce" in San Antonio Business Journal (Vol. 28, May 30, 2014, No. 16, pp. 6)

Pub: American City Business Journals, Inc.
Contact: Mike Olivieri, Executive Vice President

Description: Entrepreneur Peter French was appointed as the first president of Café Commerce, the new one-stop small business development center in San Antonio, Texas. French is bringing his diverse business experience and entrepreneurial mindset to the business center. **Availability:** Print; Online.

22743 ■ "Philanthropy Good For Business" in Crain's Detroit Business (Vol. 24, February 18, 2008, No. 7, pp. 14)

Pub: Crain Communications Inc.
Contact: Barry Asin, President

Ed: Sheena Harrison. **Description:** Profile of Burce McCully, founder of Dynamic Edge Inc., and his views on philanthropy as a key to any small company's success. The Ann Arbor, Michigan information technology firm has volunteered and raised funds for many causes since 1999 when the company was founded. **Availability:** Print; Online.

22744 ■ "Phillip Frost: 'Technology Is the Future" in South Florida Business Journal (Vol. 34, June 20, 2014, No. 48, pp. 16)

Pub: American City Business Journals, Inc.
Contact: Mike Olivieri, Executive Vice President

Released: Weekly. **Price:** $8, introductory 4-week offer(Digital only). **Description:** Entrepreneur, Phillip Frost, shares his strategies and perspectives on the business climate of Miami, Florida. He describes investment strategy for the diverse holdings of Opko Health and his criteria for buying companies and licensing technologies. **Availability:** Print; Online.

22745 ■ "Pioneering Strategies for Entrepreneurial Success" in Business Horizons (Vol. 51, January-February 2008, No. 1, pp. 21)

Pub: Elsevier Advanced Technology Publications

Ed: Candida G. Brush. **Price:** $8.95, hardcopy black and white. **Description:** Entrepreneurs are known for new products, services, processes, markets and industries. In order to achieve success, they have to develop a clear vision, creatively manage finances, and use social skills to persuade others to commit to the venture. Pioneering strategies and their implementation are examined. **Availability:** Print; PDF; Online.

22746 ■ The Platinum Rule for Small Business Success

Description: Rules for running a successful and profitable small business are shared. **Availability:** E-book.

22747 ■ "Politicians Who Really Get Business: Meet Four of the Entrepreneurs Running for Congress" in Inc. (Vol. 34, September 2012, No. 7, pp. 21)

Ed: Ryan Underwood. **Description:** Businessman Mitt Romney is running for President of the United States. Profiles of three entrepreneurs running for Congress and one for the Senate in the 2012 elections include: John Dennis (Rep.), 12th District, California; Jim Graves (Dem.), 6th District, Minnesota; Thomas Massie (Rep.), 4th District, Kentucky; and Linda McMahon (Rep.), US Senate, Connecticut. **Availability:** Online.

22748 ■ Power Ambition Glory: The Stunning Parallels between Great Leaders of the Ancient World and Today... and the Lessons You Can Learn

Ed: Steve Forbes, John Prevas. **Released:** 2010. **Price:** $4.99, e-book. **Description:** An examination into the lives of the ancient world's greatest leaders and the lessons they have for today's business leaders. **Availability:** E-book; Print.

22749 ■ "Power Cues: The Subtle Science of Leading Groups, Persuading Others, and Maximizing Your Personal Impact"

Pub: Harvard Business Review Press
Contact: Moderna V. Pfizer, Contact

Released: May 13, 2014. **Price:** $30, hardcover. **Description:** Renowned speaking coach and communication expert, Nick Morgan, shows how humans are programmed to respond to the nonverbal cues of others. He teaches business leaders and entrepreneurs how to take control of their communications in order to communicate more effectively while commanding influence. **Availability:** E-book; Print.

22750 ■ The Power of Many: Values for Success in Business and in Life

Ed: Meg Whitman, Joan O'C Hamilton. **Released:** 2010. **Price:** $15.99, paperback; $14.99, e-book. **Description:** Meg Whitman discusses the important values for success in business and in life: integrity, accountability, authenticity and courage. **Availability:** E-book; Print.

22751 ■ "The Power of Noticing: What the Best Leaders See"

Pub: Simon & Schuster Adult Publishing Group
Contact: Jonathan Karp, President

Released: August 05, 2014. **Price:** $17.99, paperback, plus $1.55 shipping charges. **Description:** A guide to help entrepreneurs and managers gain the advantage in negotiations, decision making, and leadership skills. Instruction is given to see and evaluate information that others overlook. **Availability:** E-book; Print; Download; Audio.

22752 ■ The Power of Pull: How Small Moves, Smartly Made, Can Set Big Things in Motion

Ed: John Hagel, III, John Seely Brown, Lang Davison. **Released:** April 13, 2010. **Price:** $11.99; C$14.99. **Description:** Examination of how we can effectively address the most pressing challenges in a rapidly changing and increasingly interdependent world is addressed. New ways in which passionate thinking, creative solutions, and committed action can and will make it possible for small businesses owners to seize opportunities and remain in step with change. **Availability:** E-book; Print.

22753 ■ *The Power of Social Innovation: How Civic Entrepreneurs Ignite Community Networks for Good*
Pub: John Wiley & Sons, Inc.
Contact: Christina Van Tassell, Executive Vice President Chief Financial Officer
Ed: Stephen Goldsmith, Tim Burke, Gigi Georges. **Released:** March 01, 2010. **Price:** $44, Hardcover; $35.99, E-Book; $44, hardcover. **Description:** This seminal book provides tools for civic entrepreneurs to create healthier communities and promote innovative solutions to public and social problems. It shows how to effectively tackle the intractable issues facing the country. **Availability:** E-book; Print.

22754 ■ *Prescriptive Entrepreneurship*
Pub: Edward Elgar Publishing Inc.
Contact: Edward Elgar, Founder Chairman
Ed: James O. Fiet. **Released:** 2008. **Description:** In the only known program of prescriptive entrepreneurship, the author provides a marked contrast to the standard descriptive focus of entrepreneurship studies.

22755 ■ *"Priority: In Memoriam" in Inc. (December 2007, pp. 25-26, 28, 30)*
Ed: Ryan McCarthy. **Description:** Profiles of entrepreneurs who died in 2007; these individuals helped to create some major business trends in the last fifty years, from the advent of socially responsible business to development of quality manufacturing. **Availability:** Online.

22756 ■ *"Profile: Charles Handy" in Business Strategy Review (Vol. 21, Summer 2010, No. 2, pp. 86)*
Ed: Stuart Crainer. **Description:** In a new series, profiles of a major thinker who has made a significant difference in how organizations are managed and how business careers are shaped are presented. **Availability:** PDF; Online.

22757 ■ *Profit First for Minority Business Enterprises*
Ed: Susanne Mariga. **Released:** May 25, 2021. **Description:** Explains the Profit First systems to help entrepreneurs succeed in their chosen business path. **Availability:** Print.

22758 ■ *"The Profit Recipe: Top Restaurant Trends and How to Use Them to Boost Your Profits"*
Pub: CreateSpace
Released: September 26, 2014. **Price:** $17.50, paperback; $8.08, kindle; $10.74, paperback. **Description:** Restaurant entrepreneur shares information about food industry trends that will help make a food business more profitable. **Availability:** Print.

22759 ■ *"Program for Women Entrepreneurs: Tips for Surviving this Economy" in Crain's Detroit Business (Vol. 25, June 22, 2009, No. 25)*
Pub: Crain Communications Inc.
Contact: Barry Asin, President
Description: Michigan Leadership Institute for Women Entrepreneurs will hold its third and final program, "Tough Times are Temporary, but Tough People are Permanent" at the Davenport University in Livonia, Michigan. **Availability:** Online.

22760 ■ *Progress-Driven Entrepreneurs, Private Equity Finance and Regulatory Issues*
Pub: Palgrave Macmillan
Ed: Zuhayr Mikdashi. **Released:** 2010. **Description:** Durable business performance is critically dependent on a stakeholder's strategy along with accessible entrepreneurial financing availability within macroeconomic and economic regulatory environments. **Availability:** E-book; Print.

22761 ■ *The Psychology of Entrepreneurship*
Pub: Taylor & Francis Group Limited
Contact: Christoph Chesher, Executive Director
Released: August 16, 2012. **Price:** $35.19, paperback, plus shipping charges; $64.79, hardback, plus shipping charges; $21, e-book; $22.80, 12 Month Rental-eBook; $19, 6 Month Rental- eBook. **Description:** Psychology as the basis for understanding successful entrepreneurship is used to discuss how these small firms impact international social and economic well-being and how they are the main source of job creation, market innovation, and economic growth in most societies. **Availability:** E-book; Print.

22762 ■ *"The Pumpkin Plan: A Simple Strategy to Grow a Remarkable Business in Any Field"*
Pub: Portfolio Hardcover
Contact: Adrian Zackheim, President
Released: September 22, 2022. **Price:** $17.95, paperback. **Description:** One million new businesses are started every year in America and nearly 80 percent of them fail within the first five years. Entrepreneur, Mike Michalowicz discovered the inspiration he needed to successfully grow his business when reading an article about a pumpkin farmer who was committed to growing giant pumpkins. Michalowicz applied the same process to his small business and transformed his company into a multimillion dollar success. The pumpkin plan includes: planting the right seeds, wedding out the losers, and nurturing the winners. **Availability:** Print.

22763 ■ *"Q&A: Chuck Hughes, Celebrity Chef" in Canadian Business (Vol. 85, July 16, 2012, No. 11-12, pp. 65)*
Ed: Nancy Won. **Description:** Celebrity chef Chuck Hughes feels blessed for the opportunity to work on a new cookbook based on the 'Chuck's Day Off' series and to start filming for a new U.S. show called 'Chuck Eats the Street'. For Hughes, cooking at the restaurant is the most rewarding and fulfilling job of all the things he does. **Availability:** Print; Online.

22764 ■ *"Quality Performance of SMEs in a Developing Economy: Direct and Indirect Effects of Service Innovation and Entrepreneurial Orientation" in Journal of Business & Industrial Marketing (Vol. 29, July 2014, No. 6)*
Pub: Emerald Group Publishing Limited
Contact: Erika Valenti, President
Description: A study was conducted to investigate the effects of innovation and EO (entrepreneurial orientation) on organizational performance in Asian small enterprise context. Strategic management literature and the relationship between EO, innovation, and quality performance was tested. The results indicated that a noteworthy direct and indirect positive relationship exists between EO dimensions, innovation, and quality performance. **Availability:** Download; Online.

22765 ■ *Race and Entrepreneurial Success: Black-, Asian-, and White-Owned Businesses in the United States*
Pub: The MIT Press
Ed: Robert W. Fairlie, Alicia M. Robb. **Released:** 2008. **Description:** Trends in minority small business ownership are explored, focusing on the importance of human capital, financial capital, and family business background in successful business ownership. **Availability:** E-book; Print; PDF.

22766 ■ *"Real Estate Reinventions: Black Lotus Brewing Co." in Crain's Detroit Business (Vol. 23, October 1, 2007, No. 40, pp. 13)*
Pub: Crain Communications Inc.
Contact: Barry Asin, President
Ed: Leah Boyd. **Description:** Profile of Black Lotus Brewing Company and owner, Mike Allan who converted a drug store location into a brewery while restoring the building's original architecture. **Availability:** Print; Online.

22767 ■ *The Real Leadership Lessons of Steve Jobs*
Pub: Harvard Business Review Press
Contact: Moderna V. Pfizer, Contact
Ed: Walter Isaacson. **Price:** $8.95, hardcover. **Description:** Fourteen separate leadership practices of Steve Jobs are listed. These include focus, simplify, assume end-to-end responsibility, leapfrog when behind, place products ahead of profits, engage in face-to-face, understood both the details and the big picture, blend the sciences with the humanities, push for perfection, and stay hungry. **Availability:** PDF; Online.

22768 ■ *Reality-Based Leadership: Ditch the Drama, Restore Sanity to the Workplace, & Turn Excuses into Results*
Pub: Jossey-Bass
Ed: Cy Wakeman. **Released:** August 01, 2010. **Price:** $27.95, hardcover; $27.95, hardcover. **Description:** Recent polls show that 71 percent of workers think about quitting their jobs every day. That number would be shocking if people actually were quitting. Worse, they go to work, punching time clocks and collecting pay checks, while checked out emotionally. Cy Wakeman reveals how to be the kind of leader who changes the way people think about and perceive their circumstances, one who deals with the facts, clarifies roles, gives clean and direct feedback, and insists that everyone do the same without drama or defensiveness. **Availability:** E-book; Print.

22769 ■ *"Red McCombs, Partner Rolling Out New Venture Capital Fund" in San Antonio Business Journal (Vol. 26, April 20, 2012, No. 12, pp. 1)*
Pub: Baltimore Business Journal
Contact: Rhonda Pringle, President
E-mail: rpringle@bizjournals.com
Description: Entrepreneur Red McCombs has partnered with businessman Chase Fraser to create a new venture capital fund. This new fund will focus on technology startups in the automotive sector. **Availability:** Print; Online.

22770 ■ *"Reinventing the Cheeseburger" in Inc. (November 2007, pp. 124-125)*
Ed: Chris Lydgate. **Description:** Profile of Burgerville's Tom Mears, who turned his drive-through burger restaurant green. **Availability:** Online.

22771 ■ *"Reinventing Management" in Harvard Business Review (Vol. 88, July-August 2010, No. 7-8, pp. 167)*
Description: Review of the book, 'Reinventing Management' is presented. **Availability:** Online.

22772 ■ *"The Reinvention of Management" in Strategy and Leadership (Vol. 39, March-April 2011, No. 2, pp. 9)*
Pub: Emerald Group Publishing Limited
Contact: Erika Valenti, President
Ed: Stephen Denning. **Description:** An examination found that critical changes in management practice involves five shifts. These shifts involve the firm's goals, model of coordination, the role of managers and values practiced. Other findings of the study are discussed. **Availability:** Download; Online.

22773 ■ *Remarkable Leadership: Unleashing Your Leadership Potential One Skill at a Time*
Released: 2011. **Description:** Handbook for anyone wishing to be an outstanding business leader; the framework and a mechanism for learning new things and applying current knowledge in a practical to any business situation is outlined. **Availability:** Print; Online; Electronic publishing.

22774 ■ *"A Renewed Sisterhood" in Women in Business (Vol. 64, Summer 2012, No. 2, pp. 6)*
Ed: Rene Street. **Description:** The American Business Women's Association (ABWA) regional conference highlighted a new sense of enthusiasm and sisterhood as well as effective visioning exercise and breakout sessions. The ABWA National Women's Leadership Conference in October 2012 will feature

the graduates of the Kansas University MBA Essentials Program and keynote speakers Bob Eubanks and Francine Ward. **Availability:** Online.

22775 ■ *The Resilient Founder: Lessons in Endurance from Startup Entrepreneurs*
Pub: John Wiley & Sons, Inc.
Contact: Christina Van Tassell, Executive Vice President Chief Financial Officer
URL(s): www.wiley.com/en-us/The+Resilient+Founder%3A+Lessons+in+Endurance+from+Startup+Entrepreneurs-p-9781119839736

Ed: Mahendra Ramsinghani. **Released:** December 2021. **Price:** $17, e-book; $28, hardcover. **Description:** Discusses the psychology behind entrepreneurs. **Availability:** E-book; Print.

22776 ■ *"Reviving Entrepreneurship: Policy Decisions in 12 Areas Could Nurture - Or Cripple - America's Greatest Asset"* in *Harvard Business Review (Vol. 90, March 2012, No. 3, pp. 116)*
Pub: Harvard Business Review Press
Contact: Moderna V. Pfizer, Contact

Ed: Josh Lerner, William A. Sahlman. **Price:** $8.95, hardcover. **Description:** Government policies should address entrepreneurship as a process, rather than an act. Several key areas for policymaking include basic and translational science, supply and quality of human capital, information availability, tax treatment of rewards and risks, intellectual property rights, workforce healthcare, and mobility of financial and human capital. **Availability:** PDF; Online.

22777 ■ *Rework*
Ed: Jason Fried, David Heinemeier Hansson. **Released:** 2010. **Price:** $19.62, hardcover; $14.99, e-book; $9, audiobook. **Description:** Works to help entrepreneurs and business owners to rethink strategy, customers, and getting things accomplished. **Availability:** E-book; Print.

22778 ■ *The Rhythm of Success: How an Immigrant Produced His Own American Dream*
Pub: Penguin Publishing Group

Ed: Emilio Estefan. **Description:** Emilio Estefan, husband to singer Gloria Estefan and founder of the Latin pop legend Miami Sound Machine, is the classic example of the American dream. He shares his guiding principles that entrepreneurs need to start and grow a business. **Availability:** E-book; Print.

22779 ■ *"Riding High"* in *Small Business Opportunities (November 2008)*
Description: Profile of David Sanborn who found a way to turn his passion for biking into a moneymaking opportunity by opening his own bicycle shops; Sanborn's goal is to become the largest independent bike retailer in the United States.

22780 ■ *"The Right Remedy: Entrepreneur's Success Is a Matter of Life and Death"* in *Black Enterprise (Vol. 38, February 2008, No. 7, pp. 46)*
Pub: Earl G. Graves Ltd.
Contact: Earl Graves, Jr., President

Ed: Tamara E. Holmes. **Description:** Profile of Leah Brown, whose company conducts clinical trials to determine if specific drugs will relieve particular symptoms. Her company will also visit physician's offices to make certain doctors are following proper protocol for a clinical trial or will collect data from patients. **Availability:** Online.

22781 ■ *"Road Warriors: How To Survive Business Travel"* in *Crain's Detroit Business (Vol. 24, February 4, 2008, No. 5, pp. 11)*
Pub: Crain Communications Inc.
Contact: Barry Asin, President

Ed: Maureen McDonald. **Description:** Entrepreneurs share tips that help save time and energy at airports when traveling for business. **Availability:** Print; Online.

22782 ■ *"Robert S. McNamara and the Evolution of Modern Management"* in *Harvard Business Review (Vol. 88, December 2010, No. 12, pp. 86)*
Pub: Harvard Business Publishing
Contact: Diane Belcher, Managing Director

Ed: Phil Rosenzweig. **Price:** $8.95, PDF. **Description:** A chronicle of the emergence and development of Robert S. McNamara's management skills and perspectives, focusing on the role of his idealism. Lessons learned during the course of the Vietnam Ware are also delineated. **Availability:** Online; PDF.

22783 ■ *"Roger Hickel Contracting: Smoothing the Road for Owners"* in *Alaska Business Monthly (Vol. 27, October 2011, No. 10, pp. 114)*
Pub: Alaska Business Publishing Company Inc.
Contact: Charles Bell, Vice President, Sales and Marketing
E-mail: cbell@akbizmag.com

Ed: Gail West. **Description:** Profile of Roger Hickel and his contracting company that reports nearly $60 million annually in gross revenue. The firm focuses on customer service. **Availability:** Print; Online.

22784 ■ *"Roger Rechler Played Major Role in Long Island's Evolution"* in *Commercial Property News (March 17, 2008)*
Description: Profile of Roger Rechler, real estate developer on Long Island, New York, is presented. Rechler, who died in March 2008, was instrumental in the development, ownership and operations of the largest commercial real estate portfolio on Long Island. **Availability:** Online.

22785 ■ *"The Romance of Good Deeds: A Business with a Cause Can Do Good in the World"* in *Inc. (Volume 32, December 2010, No. 10, pp. 47)*
Pub: Inc. Magazine

Ed: Meg Cadoux Hirshberg. **Description:** Entrepreneurship and family relationships are discussed. When a small business has a passion for philanthropy it can help any marriage by creating even greater passion for each other. **Availability:** Online.

22786 ■ *"Rural Entrepreneurship Success Factors: An Empirical Investigation in an Emerging Market"* in *Journal of Small Business Strategy (Vol. 31, December 1, 2021, No. 4, pp. 5-19)*
URL(s): libjournals.mtsu.edu/index.php/jsbs/article/view/2130

Ed: Prince Gyimah, Robert N. Lussier. **Released:** November 16, 2021. **Description:** Discusses the research accomplished on rural small businesses and their economic development on the a global level. **Availability:** PDF; Online.

22787 ■ *"Sage Advice"* in *Canadian Business (Vol. 80, October 22, 2007, No. 21, pp. 70)*
Description: Seymour Schulich, one of Canada's richest men and generous philanthropist, wrote the book, "Get Smarter: Life and Business Lessons". The business book sold more than 50,000 copies and now sits on Canada's bestseller's list. Its popularity is attributed to the marketing efforts of the entrepreneur and author. **Availability:** Print; Online.

22788 ■ *The Secret Language of Competitive Intelligence: How to See Through and Stay Ahead of Business Disruptions, Distortions, Rumors, and Smoke*

22789 ■ *Secrets of Next-Level Entrepreneurs: 11 Powerful Lessons to Thrive in Business and Lead a Balanced Life*
Pub: John Wiley & Sons, Inc.
Contact: Christina Van Tassell, Executive Vice President Chief Financial Officer
URL(s): www.wiley.com/en-us/Secrets+of+Next+Level+Entrepreneurs%3A+11+Powerful+Lessons+to+Thrive+in+Business+and+Lead+a+Balanced+Life-p-9781394185382

Ed: Alex Brueckmann. **Released:** March 2023. **Price:** $28, hardcover. **Description:** Learn how to maintain a life-work balance with the insights and resources given in this book. It is possible to start and run a successful business, but to also have time for other important aspects of your life. **Availability:** Print.

22790 ■ *"SEEing an Opportunity: Golden's Eyewear Chain Has a National Vision"* in *Crain's Detroit Business (Vol. 24, January 7, 2008, No. 1)*
Pub: Crain Communications Inc.
Contact: Barry Asin, President

Ed: Sheena Harrison. **Description:** Richard Golden, who recently sold D.O.C. Optics Corporation is planning to build a new national eyewear chain called SEE Inc., which stands for Selective Eyewear Elements. SEE will sell expensive-looking glasses at lower prices than designer styles. **Availability:** Online.

22791 ■ *"Shared Leadership In Teams: An Investigation of Antecedent Conditions and Performance"* in *Academy of Management Journal (Vol. 50, No. 5, October 1, 2007, pp. 1217)*
Pub: Academy of Management
Contact: Sharon Alvarez, President

Ed: Jay B. Carson, Paul E. Tesluk, Jennifer A. Marrone. **Description:** Study assessed the advantages of distribution of leadership among team members rather than on a single person revealed advantages that ranged from support and shared functions along with higher ratings from clients on their performance. **Availability:** Electronic publishing; Download; PDF; Online.

22792 ■ *"Shining a Light on Entrepreneurial Opportunities"* in *San Antonio Business Journal (Vol. 28, July 11, 2014, No. 22, pp. 4)*
Pub: American City Business Journals, Inc.
Contact: Mike Olivieri, Executive Vice President

Released: Weekly. **Price:** $4, Introductory 4-week offer(Digital & Print). **Description:** Café Commerce is a small business and entrepreneurship development program launched by the City of San Antonio in partnership with microlender Accion Texas. The goal of the new resource center is to make entrepreneurship easier by complementing existing programs and serving as a platform to introduce new ones to the business community. **Availability:** Print; Online.

22793 ■ *"Should I Stay or Should I Go?"* in *Entrepreneur (August 2014)*
Pub: Entrepreneur Media Inc.
Contact: Dan Bova, Director
E-mail: dbova@entrepreneur.com

Description: The timing of meeting clients in person is critical to the success of a business venture. Entrepreneurs can save time and money if they know when it is worth seeing the client in person. For Jackie Kimzey of the Institute for Innovation and Entrepreneurship, the best time for a face-to-face meeting with clients is when a business relationship is starting to flourish. Kimzey advises entrepreneurs to consider their budget, the amount of time they have been working together, and the importance of the client to the business. **Availability:** Print; Online.

22794 ■ *"Sisters Partner to Open Beauty Supply Store"* in *The Philadelphia Tribune (August 27, 2019)*
URL(s): www.phillytrib.com/news/business/sisters-partner-to-open-beauty-supply-store/article_51b223fd-401c-5c44-ae7b-8086d8802161.html

Ed: Ayana Jones. **Released:** August 27, 2019. **Description:** Two sisters with extensive backgrounds in cosmetology are opening a new beauty supply store in an area where independent shops like this are owned by Korean Americans. This store will serve the Black community and give back to the area. **Availability:** Online.

22795 ■ *Small Business: An Entrepreneur's Plan*
Pub: Nelson Education Ltd.
Contact: Steve Brown, President

Ed: Ronald A. Knowles. **Released:** 7th Canadian edition. **Price:** $111.95, paperback; $67.95, e-book. **Description:** Entrepreneur's guide to planning a small business. **Availability:** E-book; Print.

22796 ■ Small Business Management in Canada

Released: 8th edition. **Price:** $243.27. **Description:** Small business management in Canada. **Availability:** E-book; Print.

22797 ■ Small Business Revolution: How Owners and Entrepreneurs Can Succeed

Pub: John Wiley & Sons, Inc.
Contact: Christina Van Tassell, Executive Vice President Chief Financial Officer
URL(s): www.wiley.com/en-us/Small+Business +Revolution%3A+How+Owners+and+En trepreneurs+Can+Succeed-p-9781119802648

Ed: Barry C. McCarthy. **Released:** September 2021. **Price:** $15, e-book; $25, hardcover. **Description:** A small business manual how-to along with relatable work stories from CEO Barry C. McCarthy. **Availability:** E-book; Print.

22798 ■ "Smartcuts: How Hackers, Innovators, and Icons Accelerate Success"

Pub: Harper Business
Contact: Hollis Heimbouch, Senior Vice President Publisher

Released: September 09, 2014. **Price:** $26.99, hardcover; $11.24, e-book; $20.99, digital audiobook unbridged; $15.99, paperback. **Description:** Entrepreneur and journalist describes how some startups go from zero to billions in months by analyzing the lives of the entrepreneurs and their successful companies. He reveals that they do it like computer hackers, they use lateral thinking to rethink convention and break rules that aren't really rules. **Availability:** E-book; Print.

22799 ■ "So You Want to Start a Brewery? The Lagunitas Story"

Pub: Chicago Review Press Inc.
Contact: Cynthia Sherry, Publisher
E-mail: csherry@chicagoreviewpress.com

Released: October 01, 2014. **Price:** $17.95, trade paper, estimate shipping and sales tax; C$21.95, trade paper, estimate shipping and sales tax; $12.99, pdf, estimate shipping and sales tax; C$17.99, pdf, estimate shipping and sales tax; $12.99, epub, estimate shipping and sales tax; C$17.99, epub, estimate shipping and sales tax; $12.99, mob. **Description:** Profile of Tony Magee, who founded a brewery in 1993, based in Petaluma, California. The entrepreneur describes the business story of his firm, Lagunitas Brewing Company that makes craft bee that he says defies categorization. **Availability:** E-book; Print; Electronic publishing; PDF; Online.

22800 ■ Social Entrepreneurship For Dummies

Pub: John Wiley & Sons, Inc.
Contact: Christina Van Tassell, Executive Vice President Chief Financial Officer

Ed: Mark Durieux, PhD, Robert Stebbins, PhD. **Released:** April 2010. **Price:** $16.99, E-book; $24.99, paperback. **Description:** Discover ways to bring social entrepreneurship to a small company in today's business environment. Today, a company is not measured by financial performance alone, but also on social entrepreneurship. **Availability:** E-book; Print.

22801 ■ Social Entrepreneurship: What Everyone Needs to Know

Ed: David Bornstein, Susan Davis. **Released:** May 27, 2010. **Description:** In development circles, there is now a widespread consensus that social entrepreneurs represent a far better mechanism to respond to needs than we have ever had before, a decentralized and emergent force that remains the best hope for solutions.

22802 ■ "Souled Out" in Canadian Business (Vol. 81, March 3, 2008, No. 3, pp. 35)

Description: According to a survey of over 100 entrepreneurs, 78 percent responded that selling their business was emotionally draining for them. Greig Clark, for example, says that one of the toughest times of his life was selling College Pro Painters, after putting 18 years into that business. The economic impacts of selling out are also examined. **Availability:** Online.

22803 ■ "Speed Traps: Every Fast-Growth Company Eventually Runs Into At Least One of These All-Too-Common Obstacles. How You Handle Them Can Make the Difference Between Success and a High-Speed Smashup" in Inc. (Vol. 34, September 2012, No. 7, pp. 53)

Pub: Mansueto Ventures L.L.C.
Contact: Stephanie Mehta, Chief Executive Officer

Ed: Kimberly Weisul. **Released:** September 01, 2012. **Description:** Obstacles encountered by fast growing companies and suggestions to avoid falling into these traps are covered. According to a recent study conducted by Gary Kunkle, an economist and research fellowwith Edward Lowe Foundation's Institute for Exceptional Growth Companies, shows that fast growing companies share the same issues, which are different from those of industry peers or businesses of the same size. **Availability:** Print; Online.

22804 ■ "Spreading Your Wings" in Canadian Business (Vol. 81, March 17, 2008, No. 4, pp. 31)

Ed: Megan Harman. **Released:** February 09, 2017. **Description:** Financing from angel investors is one avenue that should be explored by startups. Angel investors are typically affluent individuals who invest their own money. Angel investors usually want at least 10 times their initial investment within eight years but they benefit the businesses through their help in decision-making and the industry expertise they provide. **Availability:** Download; Online.

22805 ■ "Start or Buy? It's a Tough Question for Eager Entrepreneurs" in Crain's Cleveland Business (Vol. 28, October 8, 2007, No. 40, pp. 24)

Pub: Crain Communications Inc.
Contact: K. C. Crain, President

Ed: David Prizinsky. **Description:** Discusses different approaches to becoming a small business owner. **Availability:** Online.

22806 ■ Start, Run, & Grow a Successful Small Business

Pub: Toolkit Media Group

Ed: John L. Duoba, Joel Handelsman, Alice H. Magos, Catherine Gordon. **Released:** Sixth edition. **Availability:** Print.

22807 ■ Start Small, Finish Big

Released: December 15, 2012. **Description:** Fred DeLuca is profiled; after founding the multi-billion dollar chain of Subway sandwich restaurants, DeLuca is committed to helping microentrepreneurs, people who start successful small businesses with less than $1,000. **Availability:** Print; Online.

22808 ■ "Staying Engaged: Location, Location" in Black Enterprise (Vol. 38, February 2008, No. 7, pp. 64)

Pub: Earl G. Graves Ltd.
Contact: Earl Graves, Jr., President

Ed: Marcia A. Reed-Woodard. **Description:** Rules to help business leaders construct networking contacts in order to maximize professional success are outlined. **Availability:** Online.

22809 ■ "Street Bistro Brings Food Truck Treats to Bangor" in Bangor Daily News (June 26, 2012)

Ed: Emily Burnham. **Description:** Chef Kim Smith launched her food truck, Street Bistro in Bangor, Maine. Smith took a year off after closing her two restaurants called Unbridled Bistro and Bennett's Market. Smith and her husband purchased a Snap-On truck and redesigned it into a kitchen. Menu items range from French to Tex-Mex to Thai to American. **Availability:** Video; Online.

22810 ■ Strengths Based Leadership

Pub: Gallup, Inc.
Contact: Jon Clifton, Chief Executive Officer

Ed: Tom Rath, Barry Conchie. **Price:** $19.99. **Description:** Three keys to being a more effective leader. **Availability:** Print; Online.

22811 ■ "Stress-Test Your Strategy: the 7 Questions to Ask" in Harvard Business Review (Vol. 88, November 2010, No. 11, pp. 92)

Pub: Harvard Business Publishing
Contact: Diane Belcher, Managing Director

Ed: Robert Simons. **Price:** $8.95, PDF. **Description:** Seven questions organizations should use to assess crisis management capabilities are: who is the primary customer, how do core values prioritize all parties, what performance variables are being tracked, what strategic boundaries have been set, how is creative tension being produced, how committed are workers to assisting each other, and what uncertainties are causing worry?. **Availability:** Online; PDF.

22812 ■ "Strivers and High Fliers" in Dallas Business Journal (Vol. 37, February 7, 2014, No. 22, pp. 4)

Pub: American City Business Journals, Inc.
Contact: Mike Olivieri, Executive Vice President

Released: February 08, 2014. **Price:** $4, print. **Description:** The winners of the 2014 Minority Business Leader Award in Dallas, Texas, all share significant entrepreneurial traits like taking the lessons they learned as a child in their careers. Each of the award winners have achieved success using very particular and personal sets of benchmarks. **Availability:** Print; Online.

22813 ■ Supermaker: Crafting Business on Your Own Terms

Released: September 08, 2020. **Description:** A guide for entrepreneurs who are interested in starting a small business, especially crafting or maker-centered. Sections on branding, product development, social media marketing, scaling, PR, and customer engagement are included. **Availability:** E-book.

22814 ■ Switch: How to Change Things When Change Is Hard

Pub: Broadway Business

Ed: Chip Heath, Dan Heath. **Released:** February 16, 2010. **Price:** $29, U.S., hardcover; $17.50, U.S., e-book. **Description:** Change is difficult for everyone. This book helps business leaders to motivate employees as well as to help everybody motive themselves and others. **Availability:** E-book; Print; Download; Audio.

22815 ■ "Synthesis: From Lone Hero to a Culture of Leadership" in Harvard Business Review (Vol. 88, November 2010, No. 11, pp. 146)

Pub: Harvard Business Publishing
Contact: Diane Belcher, Managing Director

Ed: Charles J. Palus, John B. McGuire. **Released:** November 30, 2010. **Description:** Review of the book, 'Working Together: Why Great Partnerships Succeed', is given. **Availability:** Print; Online.

22816 ■ "Take Command: Lessons in Leadership: How to Be a First Responder in Business"

Released: 2018. **Price:** $25. **Description:** What do elite members of the military, first responders in a disaster zone, and successful business leaders have in common? Clarity of mind and purpose in the midst of chaos. Cofounder and CEO of Team Rubicon and former Marine Sniper Jake Wood, teaches the lessons in leadership and teamwork to help managers and entrepreneurs succeed in this hyper-competitive business environment today.

22817 ■ "A Tale of Two Brothers" in Canadian Business (Vol. 80, March 26, 2007, No. 7, pp. 18)
Description: The successful business strategies followed by Tyler Gompf and Kirby Gompf, owners of Tell Us About Us Inc., are presented. **Availability:** Online.

22818 ■ The Talent Masters: Why Smart Leaders Put People Before Numbers
Released: November 09, 2010. **Price:** $27.50, hardcover; $7.99, e-book; $20, audiobook download. **Description:** This book helps leaders recognize talent in their employees, and to put that talent to work to help achieve business success. **Availability:** E-book; Print.

22819 ■ "Talk, Inc.: How Trusted Leaders Use Conversation to Power Their Organizations" in Canadian Business (Vol. 85, August 13, 2012, No. 13, pp. 59)
Ed: Boris Groysberg, Michael Slind. **Price:** $32. **Description:** Review of the book entitled, "Talk, Inc.: How Trusted Leaders Use Conversation to Power Their Organizations". As the title states, this book will help business leaders deliver their messages concisely and effectively. **Availability:** E-book; Print; Online.

22820 ■ "Tao of Downfall: the Failures of High-profile Entrepreneurs in the Chinese Economic Reform" in International Journal of Entrepreneurship and Small Business (Vol. 11, August 31, 2010, No. 2, pp. 121)
Ed: Wenxian Zhang, Ilan Alon. **Description:** Through historical reviews and case studies, this research seeks to understand why some initially successful entrepreneurs failed in the economic boom of past decades. Among various factors contributing to their downfall are a unique political and business environment, fragile financial systems, traditional cultural influences and personal characteristics. **Availability:** Online.

22821 ■ "Tap Into Food Truck Trend to Rev Up Sales, Build Buzz" in Nation's Restaurant News (Vol. 45, February 7, 2011, No. 3, pp. 18)
Ed: Brian Sacks. **Description:** Food truck trend is growing, particularly in New York City, Philadelphia, Washington DC, and Los Angeles, California. Man entrepreneurs are using a mobile food component to market their food before opening a restaurant. **Availability:** Print; Online.

22822 ■ "Tastee-Freez Celebrates 60th Anniversary" in Ice Cream Reporter (Vol. 23, July 20, 2010, No. 8, pp. 2)
Description: Tastee-Freez founders, Leo Moranz (inventor) and Harry Axene, an inventor partnered to market the soft-serve pump and freezer for serving frozen treats back in 1950. **Availability:** Print; Online.

22823 ■ "Technology-Market Combinations and the Identification of Entrepreneurial Opportunities: an Investigation of the Opportunity-Individual Nexus" in Academy of Management Journal (Vol. 55, August 1, 2012, No. 4, pp. 753)
Pub: Academy of Management
Contact: Sharon Alvarez, President
Ed: Denis A. Gregoire, Dean A. Shepherd. **Description:** The effects of differences among opportunity ideas on entrepreneurs' opportunity beliefs are investigated. Results indicate that the formation of opportunity beliefs is influenced by the superficial and structural similarities of technology-market combinations and individual differences pay a significant role in moderating these relationships. **Availability:** Download; Electronic publishing; PDF; Online.

22824 ■ "Tell Me Why" in Business Strategy Review (Vol. 25, Summer 2014, No. 2, pp. 50)
Released: June 02, 2014. **Description:** Successful entrepreneurs constantly ask why their ideas will or won't work to help with business visions and goals. **Availability:** Print; PDF; Online.

22825 ■ The Ten Laws of Enduring Success
Released: March 01, 2011. **Price:** $15, paperback; $4.99, e-book. **Description:** A new meaning for success is described by financial expert, Maria Bartiromo, with advice on how to adapt with the changing times. **Availability:** E-book; Print.

22826 ■ "There's Risk, Reward for Business in Baltimore's Edgier Areas: Taking a Chance" in Baltimore Business Journal (Vol. 28, July 16, 2010, No. 10, pp. 1)
Pub: Baltimore Business Journal
Contact: Rhonda Pringle, President
E-mail: rpringle@bizjournals.com
Ed: Scott Dance. **Description:** North Avenue in Baltimore, Maryland is considered a rough neighborhood due to the dangers of prostitution and drug dealing. However, some entrepreneurs have taken the risk of building their businesses on North Avenue as revitalization efforts grow. One of the challenges for businesses in rough neighborhoods is bringing customers to their stores or offices. **Availability:** Print.

22827 ■ "These Are the Women Who Really Mean Business" in Canadian Business (Vol. 87, October 2014, No. 10, pp. 67)
Description: A list of the top 100 women entrepreneurs in Canada are ranked, based on sales, three-year revenue growth rate, and profitability of their businesses is presented. Included in the list are Janet Stimpson of White House Design Company, Inc.; builder, Allison Grafton of Rockwood Custom Homes Inc.; and Janet Jing Di Zhang of Vancouver, BC of New Immigrants Information Services Inc. **Availability:** Online.

22828 ■ The Thin Book of Naming Elephants: How to Surface Undiscussables for Greater Organizational Success
Pub: Thin Book Publishing Co.
Contact: Sue Annis Hammond, Founder
E-mail: sue@thinbook.com
Ed: Sue Annis Hammond, Andrea B. Mayfield. **Description:** Organizational success is of upmost importance to today's entrepreneurs and organizations. The hierarchal system in which people are afraid to speak up in organizations is discussed. The points of view and inability to see things from an overall perspective can cause insecurity among employees. The three elephants present in every organization include: arrogance, hubris, and screamers and the damage caused by these elephants in any organization is examined. **Availability:** E-book.

22829 ■ "Think Again: What Makes a Leader?" in Business Strategy Review (Vol. 21, Autumn 2010, No. 3, pp. 64)
Ed: Rob Goffee, Gareth Jones. **Released:** September 29, 2010. **Description:** Leadership cannot be faked and all the self-help books in the world won't make you a leader - but there are four characteristics any leader must possess and they are outlined. **Availability:** Print; PDF; Online.

22830 ■ Third Shift Entrepreneur: Keep Your Day Job, Build Your Dream Job
Pub: John Wiley & Sons, Inc.
Contact: Christina Van Tassell, Executive Vice President Chief Financial Officer
URL(s): www.wiley.com/en-us/Third+Shift+Entrepreneur%3A+Keep+Your+Day+Job%2C+Build+Your+Dream+Job-p-9781119708360
Ed: Todd Connor. **Released:** April 2021. **Price:** $17, e-book; $28, hardcover. **Description:** Conveys techniques entrepreneurs can use to start a business. **Availability:** E-book; Print.

22831 ■ "Tips for Entrepreneurs Pitching to Investors" in Legal Zoom (March 14, 2023)
URL(s): www.legalzoom.com/articles/tips-for-entrepreneurs-pitching-to-investors
Ed: Sandra Beckwith. **Released:** March 14, 2023. **Description:** Startups often need initial funding to get the business off the ground, and entrepreneurs should brush up on these tips to in order to maximize their success in the investor saying yes. **Availability:** Online.

22832 ■ "Tips From a Turnaround Expert" in Business Owner (Vol. 35, July-August 2011, No. 4, pp. 8)
Description: The book, 'The Six Month Fix: Adventures in Rescuing Failing Companies' by Gary Sutton is summarized. It provides lessons for finding and building profits in failing firms. **Availability:** Print; Online.

22833 ■ "To Build for the Future, Reach Beyond the Skies" in Canadian Business (Vol. 83, June 15, 2010, No. 10, pp. 11)
Pub: Rogers Media Inc.
Contact: Neil Spivak, Chief Executive Officer
Ed: Richard Branson. **Description:** Richard Branson says that tackling an engineering challenge or a scientific venture is a real adventure for an entrepreneur. Branson discusses Virgin's foray into the aviation business and states that at Virgin, they build for the future. **Availability:** Print; Online.

22834 ■ "To Live and Thrive in L.A." in Canadian Business (Vol. 81, October 13, 2008, No. 17, pp. 78)
Description: Toronto entrepreneur Shereen Arazm thrived in Los Angeles, California as the queen of nightlife. Arazm holds or has held ownership stakes in bars, nightspots and restaurants that include the Geisha House, Concorde, Shag, Parc and Central, and Terroni L.A. **Availability:** Online.

22835 ■ "To Sell Is Human: The Surprising Truth About Moving Others"
Pub: Riverhead Books
Contact: Geoffrey Kloske, President
Released: December 31, 2012. **Description:** The U.S. Bureau of Labor Statistics reports that one in nine Americans form the work sales force. Whether an employee or an entrepreneur, everyone is selling something. The entrepreneur is looking for funders to invest. Pink describes the six successors to the elevator pitch, the three rules for understanding another's perspective, the five frames that can make a message clearer and more persuasive, and more. **Availability:** Print.

22836 ■ "Too Much Information?" in Black Enterprise (Vol. 37, December 2006, No. 5, pp. 59)
Pub: Earl G. Graves Ltd.
Contact: Earl Graves, Jr., President
Ed: James C. Johnson. **Description:** African American business owners often face the dilemma of whether or not to divulge their minority status when soliciting new customers and financial institutions. The quality of the products or services is always the key factor and race should never define one's business; however, it is appropriate to market oneself as a minority- or women-owned business, especially if the company is in an industry where those clients are offered top-tier contracts. **Availability:** Online.

22837 ■ "Tough Times for the Irving Clan" in Canadian Business (Vol. 83, August 17, 2010, No. 13-14, pp. 14)
Pub: Rogers Media Inc.
Contact: Neil Spivak, Chief Executive Officer
Ed: Dean Jobb. **Description:** The death of John E. Irving and reported health problems of his nephew Kenneth Irving was a double blow to the billionaire Irving clan. Kenneth suddenly left his job as CEO of Fort Reliance, holding company for Irving Oil and new energy ventures, wherein the explanation was for personal reasons. **Availability:** Online.

22838 ■ "The Trust Edge: How Top Leaders Gain Faster Results, Deeper Relationships"
Pub: Free Press Inc.
Contact: Craig Aaron, President
Released: October 09, 2012. **Price:** $28, hardcover; $14.99, ebook; $17, unabridged audio download; $29.99, unabridged compact disk. **Description:** David Horsager provides the eight Pillars of Trust to business leaders, including managers and entrepreneurs. Those eight trusts are based on research and are practical for today's leaders. They include: clarity,

compassion, character, competency, commitment, connection, contribution, and consistency. **Availability:** CD-ROM; E-book; Print; Audio.

22839 ■ *Ubuntu!: An Aspiring Story About an African Tradition of Teamwork and Collaboration*
Pub: Broadway Business
Ed: Bob Nelson, Stephen Lundin. **Released:** March 30, 2010. **Price:** $23, paperback; $9. **Description:** The African tradition of teamwork and collaboration is used to demonstrate these skills to small business leaders. **Availability:** E-book; Print; Download; Audio.

22840 ■ *The Unicorn's Shadow: Combating the Dangerous Myths that Hold Back Startups, Founders, and Investors*
URL(s): www.amazon.com/Unicorns-Shadow-Combating-Dangerous-Investors/dp/1613630964/
Ed: Ehtan Mollick. **Released:** June 23, 2020. **Price:** $17.99, paperback; $17.09, e-book. **Description:** Examines what is likely to cause success for startups and encourages entrepreneurs to not focus so much on the "unicorns" of startups — the Googles, Ubers, and other high-profile companies that made it big. **Availability:** E-book; Print.

22841 ■ *"Unretirement: How Baby Boomers are Changing the Way We Think About Work, Community, and the Good Life"*
Released: 1st edition. **Price:** $16.20, paperback; $23.40, hardback; $14.40, ebook. **Description:** Baby boomers are transforming American economics and society in a positive way. Because boomers are living longer in better health and are extending their work lives, may times with new careers, entrepreneurial ventures, and socially responsible volunteering service. This trend will enrich the American workplace, economy, and the society as a whole for future generations. **Availability:** E-book; Print; Online.

22842 ■ *"Unveiling the Secrets Behind Hispanic Business' 100 Fastest-Growing Companies"* in *Hispanic Business* (Vol. 30, July-August 2008, No. 7-8, pp. 22)
Ed: Michael Bowker. **Description:** CEO's of the five fastest growing Hispanic-owned companies discuss the success of their companies; most of them attribute their success to proper investment and diversification, effective innovations and seeing growth opportunities where others see roadblocks. **Availability:** Online.

22843 ■ *"Up To Code? Website Eases Compliance Burden for Entrepreneurs"* in *Black Enterprise* (Vol. 38, March 1, 2008, No. 8, pp. 48)
Pub: Earl G. Graves Ltd.
Contact: Earl Graves, Jr., President
Ed: Robin White-Goode. **Description:** Business.gov is a presidential E-government project created to help small businesses easily find, understand, and comply with laws and regulations pertaining to a particular industry. **Availability:** Online.

22844 ■ *"UTSA Entrepreneur Program Receives Federal Designation"* in *San Antonio Business Journal* (Vol. 28, June 6, 2014, No. 17, pp. 7)
Pub: American City Business Journals, Inc.
Contact: Mike Olivieri, Executive Vice President
Released: Weekly. **Price:** $4, Introductory 4-week offer(Digital & Print). **Description:** The National Science Foundation has designated the University of Texas at San Antonio (UTSA) as an Innovation Corps Site because of its strong entrepreneurial system through the Center for Innovation and Technology Entrepreneurship. The UTSA expects to see an increase in entrepreneurial activity and successful technology commercialization with such designation. **Availability:** Print; Online.

22845 ■ *"Valuation: Confusing and Misunderstood"* in *Business Owner* (Vol. 35, July-August 2011, No. 4, pp. 10)
Description: Business valuation is explained to help small business owners realize the value of their company. **Availability:** Print; Online.

22846 ■ *The Value Equation: A Business Guide to Wealth Creation for Entrepreneurs, Leaders & Investors*
Pub: John Wiley & Sons, Inc.
Contact: Christina Van Tassell, Executive Vice President Chief Financial Officer
URL(s): www.wiley.com/en-us/The+Value+Equation%3A+A+Business+Guide+to+Wealth+Creation+for+Entrepreneurs%2C+Leaders+%26+Investors-p-9781119875642
Ed: Christopher H. Volk. **Released:** May 2022. **Price:** $18, e-book; $29.95, hardcover. **Description:** Explains the nature of businesses and how they end up providing wealth for entrepreneurs. **Availability:** E-book; Print.

22847 ■ *Values-Centered Entrepreneurs and Their Companies*
Pub: Routledge, Taylor & Francis Group
Ed: David Y. Choi, Edmund Gray. **Released:** First edition. **Description:** A new brand of entrepreneurs has arrived on the business scene, carrying with them a new set of values. They possess a sense of social responsibility, the need to protect the planet, and to do the right thing for all stakeholders.

22848 ■ *Values and Opportunities in Social Entrepreneurship*
Pub: Palgrave Macmillan
Released: 2010. **Price:** $89, hardcover; $120, hardcover; $64.99, e-book; $84.99, Softcover. **Description:** Social entrepreneurship has grown as a research field. This book discusses social entrepreneurship as well as the identification and exploitation of social venturing opportunities. **Availability:** E-book; Print; PDF; Electronic publishing.

22849 ■ *"Veteran-owned Business: EPG Security Group"* in *Business Journal* (Vol. 31, May 16, 2014, No. 51, pp. 10)
Pub: American City Business Journals, Inc.
Contact: Mike Olivieri, Executive Vice President
Released: Weekly. **Price:** $4, introductory 4-week offer(Digital only). **Description:** Profile of Erik Bergling, a former Marine, and owner of EPG Security Group. The firm provides security guards for special events, music venues, and executive protection. Bergling was forced to retire early from the Marines due to a hip injury. **Availability:** Print; Online.

22850 ■ *"The Virgin Way"*
Description: Sir Richard Branson, founder of Virgin Group, shares his own style of leadership. He teaches how fun, family, passion, and the dying art of listening are key ingredients to what his employees describe as the "Virgin Way". The entrepreneur reveals insights into his forty years of starting and building his airline company.

22851 ■ *"Watchful Eye: Entrepreneur Protects Clients and His Bottom Line"* in *Black Enterprise* (Vol. 38, March 1, 2008, No. 8, pp. 46)
Pub: Earl G. Graves Ltd.
Contact: Earl Graves, Jr., President
Ed: Tennille M. Robinson. **Description:** Profile of Elijah Shaw, founder of Icon Services Corporation, a full service security and investigative service; Shaw shares his plans to protect clients while growing his business. **Availability:** Online.

22852 ■ *"The Way of the Seal: Think Like an Elite Warrior to Lead and Succeed"*
Pub: Trusted Media Brands Inc.
Contact: Marty Moe, President
Released: 2013. **Description:** Ex-Navy Commander, Mark Divine, teaches how to lead from the front so others will work for you. He reveals exercises, meditations, and focusing techniques train your mind for mental toughness, emotional resilience and uncanny intuition. His experience in America's elite forces provides a guide for business leaders to succeed. **Availability:** Print; Online.

22853 ■ *"Wealth and Jobs: the Broken Link"* in *Harvard Business Review* (Vol. 88, November 2010, No. 11, pp. 44)
Pub: Harvard Business Publishing
Contact: Diane Belcher, Managing Director
Ed: Nitin Nohria. **Price:** $6, PDF. **Description:** Rebuilding the link between business and job creation to shore up the middle class is advocated. A blend of government policies and business strategies that foster entrepreneurship and innovation are essential. **Availability:** Online; PDF.

22854 ■ *"The Weeks Ahead"* in *Crain's New York Business* (Vol. 24, January 7, 2008, No. 1, pp. 26)
Description: Listing of events in the Detroit area include conferences addressing entrepreneurialism, economic development, and women business ownership. **Availability:** Print; Online.

22855 ■ *A Whack on the Side of the Head: How You Can Be More Creative*
Ed: Roger von Oech. **Released:** 25th anniversary edition. **Price:** $17, paperback. **Description:** The author, a consultant, shares insight into increasing entrepreneurial creativity. **Availability:** Print.

22856 ■ *"What Kind of Golfer Are You?"* in *Baltimore Business Journal* (Vol. 29, May 4, 2012, No. 53, pp. 1)
Ed: Gary Haber. **Description:** Businesspeople playing golf are classified into different profiles according to style. These profiles also describe the behavior of businessmen during and after playing golf. **Availability:** Print; Online.

22857 ■ *"What Kind of Leader Are You?"* in *Inc.* (Vol. 36, September 2014, No. 7, pp. 76)
Pub: Mansueto Ventures L.L.C.
Contact: Stephanie Mehta, Chief Executive Officer
Description: Ranking of leadership skills for entrepreneurs and managers is presented, with being a visionary leading each category. **Availability:** Print; Online.

22858 ■ *What Works: A Comprehensive Framework to Change the Way We Approach Goal Setting*
Pub: John Wiley & Sons, Inc.
Contact: Christina Van Tassell, Executive Vice President Chief Financial Officer
URL(s): www.wiley.com/en-us/What+Works%3A+A+Comprehensive+Framework+to+Change+the+Way+We+Approach+Goal+Setting-p-9781119906070
Ed: Tara McMullin. **Released:** October 2022. **Price:** $16, e-book; $26, hardcover. **Description:** A guide on goal setting for work and for your personal life. **Availability:** E-book; Print.

22859 ■ *What Works: Success in Stressful Times*
Ed: Hamish McRae. **Released:** August 04, 2011. **Price:** $14.95, paperback; $5.99, e-book. **Description:** Exploration of success stories from across the glove, and what Michelle Obama referred to as 'the flimsy difference between success and failure.' Why do some initiatives take off while others flounder? How have communities managed to achieve so much while others struggle? What distinguishes the good companies from the bad? What lessons can be learned from the well-ordered Mumbai community made famous by 'Slumdog Millionaire'? Why have Canadian manners helped Whistler become the most popular ski resort in North America?. **Availability:** E-book; Print.

22860 ■ *"Where Are They Now?"* in *Canadian Business* (Vol. 79, October 9, 2006, No. 20, pp. 71)
Ed: Jeff Sanford, Zena Olijnyk, Andrew Wahl, Andy Holloway, John Gray. **Description:** The profile of the top chief executive officers of Canada for the year 2005 is discussed. **Availability:** Online.

22861 ■ *Who's Got Your Back*
Pub: Broadway Books

Contact: Sally McPherson, Editor Publisher Manager, Sales

Ed: Keith Ferrazzi. Released: 1st edition. Description: Achieving goals by building close relationships with a small circle of trusted individuals.

22862 ■ *"Why Business Focus Is a Crucial Entrepreneurial Talent; Successful Entrepreneurs are Profit-Oriented and Judge the Value of Decisions and Relationships By Their Effect On Business"* in *Gallup Business Journal (June 10, 2014)*
Pub: Gallup, Inc.
Contact: Jon Clifton, Chief Executive Officer

Description: Entrepreneurial traits and skills are highlighted. Successful business owners focus on profit and understand the value of an opportunity, relationship, or a decision can impact their business. It is critical, while focusing on profit, to never underestimate the value of a customer. Availability: Print; Online.

22863 ■ *"Why Entrepreneurs Matter More Than Innovators"* in *Gallup Management Journal (November 22, 2011)*
Ed: Jim Clifton. Released: November 22, 2011. Description: In the race to create good jobs, leaders are not paying enough attention to cultivating talented entrepreneurs, rather they invest too much attention on innovation. Availability: Print; Online.

22864 ■ *"Why Is It So Hard To Find Good People? The Problem Might Be You"* in *Inc. (Vol. 33, November 2011, No. 9, pp. 100)*
Description: Entrepreneurs sometimes struggle to find good workers. A recent survey shows hiring as their top concern. Four common mistakes that can occur during the hiring process our outlined. Availability: Online.

22865 ■ *"Why Successful Entrepreneurs Are Effective Delegators; Shifting from a Do-It-Yourself Executive Style to a More Hands-Off Approach is Essential When They're Growing a Business"* in *Gallup Business Journal (August 26, 2014)*
Pub: Gallup, Inc.
Contact: Jon Clifton, Chief Executive Officer

Description: It is critical for entrepreneurs to step away from a do-it-yourself executive style to a more hands-off approach when a company begins to grow. Availability: Print; Online.

22866 ■ *"Wilderness Leadership - On the Job: Five Principles From Outdoor Exploration That Will Make You a Better Manager"* in *Harvard Business Review (Vol. 90, April 2012, No. 4, pp. 127)*
Pub: Harvard Business Review Press
Contact: Moderna V. Pfizer, Contact

Ed: John Kanengieter, Aparna Rajagopal-Durbin. Description: Five principles of wilderness leadership are: practicing leadership, leading from everywhere, behaving well, remaining calm, and disconnecting to connect. Key points include knowing when to offer leadership to another member, and taking a break from technological devices that can distract from critical thinking.

22867 ■ *"Winners Dream: A Journey from Corner Store to Corner Office"*
Pub: Simon & Schuster Adult Publishing Group
Contact: Jonathan Karp, President

Released: October 14, 2014. Price: $28.99, hardcover, plus $2.24 shipping charges. Description: Bill McDermott, CEO of the world's largest business software company, SAP, profiles his career. He discusses his career moves, sales strategies, employee incentives to create high performance teams, and the competitive advantages of optimism and hard work. The entrepreneur offers a blueprint for success and the knowledge that the real dream is the journey, not the preconceived destination. Availability: E-book; Print; Download; Audio.

22868 ■ *"Women as 21st Century Leaders"* in *Women In Business (Vol. 63, Summer 2011, No. 2, pp. 26)*
Pub: American Business Women's Association
Contact: Rene Street, Executive Director

Ed: Leigh Elmore. Description: American Business Women's Association and Park University have partnered to provide a leadership training program to attendees of the 2011 National Women's Leadership Conference. The courses will incorporate introduction to concepts, development of critical thinking skills and direct application through exercises. Comments from executives are also included. Availability: Online.

22869 ■ *Women Entrepreneurs in The Global Marketplace*
Pub: Edward Elgar Publishing Inc.
Contact: Edward Elgar, Founder Chairman

Ed: Andrea E. Smith-Hunter. Released: 2013. Description: Focus is on women entrepreneurs; information includes human capital, network structures and financial capital, with comparative analysis across racial lines.

22870 ■ *"Women's Initiative for Self Employment Honors Home Instead Senior Care Owner as 2012 Woman Entrepreneur of the Year"* in *Marketwired (September 11, 2012)*
Pub: Comtex News Network Inc.
Contact: Kan Devnani, President

Ed: Michelle Rogers. Description: Women's Initiative for Self Employment has bestowed its 2012 Woman Entrepreneur of the Year award on Michelle Rogers, owner of Home Instead Senior Care. The Women's Initiative is a nonprofit organization celebrating eight female business owners in the Silicon Valley Region annually. Home Instead Senior Care provides in-home care for seniors in the Bay Area of northern California. Availability: Online.

22871 ■ *Working for Yourself: Law & Taxes for Independent Contractors, Freelancers & Consultants*
Pub: Nolo
Contact: Chris Braun, President

Ed: Stephen Fishman. Released: 12th Edition. Price: $27.99, e-book(downloadable); $34.99, book and e-book; $27.99, E-book. Description: In-depth information is shared for contractors, freelancers and consultants involving business law and small business taxes. Availability: E-book; Print; Electronic publishing; PDF.

22872 ■ *"World's Best CEOs"* in *Barron's (Vol. 88, March 24, 2008, No. 12, pp. 33)*
Pub: Dow Jones & Company Inc.
Contact: Almar Latour, Chief Executive Officer

Ed: Andrew Bary. Description: Listing of the 30 best chief executive officers worldwide which was compiled through interviews with investors and analysts, analysis of financial and stock market performance, and leadership and industry stature.

22873 ■ *"Worth His Salt"* in *Hawaii Business (Vol. 53, January 2008, No. 7, pp. 45)*
Pub: PacificBasin Communications
Contact: Chuck Tindle, Director
E-mail: chuckt@pacificbasin.net

Ed: Jolyn Okimoto Rosa. Description: Bryan Zada owns three PretzelMaker franchises, whose total loss amounted to $40,000 in 2003. Zada believes that listening to employees was one of the key steps in turning the business around. The efforts made to improve the franchises' products are also given. Availability: Online.

22874 ■ *"Young Millionaires"* in *Entrepreneur (Vol. 35, October 2007, No. 10, pp. 76)*
Pub: Entrepreneur Media Inc.
Contact: Dan Bova, Director
E-mail: dbova@entrepreneur.com

Ed: Jason Ankeny. Description: Young successful entrepreneurs of 2007 were chosen to talk about their success story and their business strategies in the past and those for the future. Among those featured are Kelly Flatley, Brendan Synnott, Herman Flores, Myles Kovacs, Haythem Haddad, Jim Wetzel, Lance Lawson, Jacob DeHart, Jake Nickell, Tim Vanderhook, Chris Vanderhook, Russell Vanderhook, Megan Duckett, Brad Sugars, John Vechey, Brian Fiete, Jason Kapalka, Nathan Jones, Devon Rifkin, Ryan Black, Ed Nichols, Jeremy Black, Amy Smilovic, Bob Shallenberger, and John Cavanagh.

22875 ■ *"The Zero Marginal Cost Society: The Internet of Things, the Collaborative Commons, and the Eclipse of Capitalism"*
Pub: Palgrave Macmillan

Released: April 04, 2014. Price: $18.99, paperback; $9.99, e-book; $29.99, hardcover. Description: The emerging Internet of things is speeding society to an ear of nearly free goods and services, causing the rise of a global Collaborative Commons and the eclipse of capitalism. Entrepreneurial dynamism of competitive markets that drives productivity up and marginal costs down, enabling businesses to reduce the price of their goods and services to win consumers and market share is slowly dying. Availability: E-book; Print.

22876 ■ *"Zions Offers Step-by-Step Small Business Guidance"* in *Idaho Business Review (September 1, 2014)*
Pub: BridgeTower Media
Contact: Adam Reinebach, President

Description: Zions bank provides small business guidance to clients through its Zions Bank Idaho Business Resource Center. The program helps entrepreneurs learn the basic rules of running a small business. Free courses teach the essentials of finance, marketing and selling, .

VIDEO/AUDIO MEDIA

22877 ■ *The Best Small Business Show: Are You Entrepreneurship Material?*
URL(s): richgee.libsyn.com/300-are-you-entrepreneurship-material

Ed: Rich Gee. Released: June 19, 2023. Description: Podcast asks how to know if you have what it takes to be an entrepreneur.

22878 ■ *The Best Small Business Show: If You Own a Business, You're a Salesperson*
URL(s): richgee.libsyn.com/182-if-you-own-a-business-youre-a-salesperson

Ed: Rich Gee. Released: March 15, 2021. Description: Podcast observes that all entrepreneurs are also salespeople.

22879 ■ *The Best Small Business Show: They're Fooling You - The Entrepreneurship Myth*
URL(s): richgee.libsyn.com/305-theyre-fooling-you-the-entrepreneurship-myth

Ed: Rich Gee. Released: July 24, 2023. Description: Podcast discusses entrepreneurship myths.

22880 ■ *The Big Enough Approach to Entrepreneurship with Lee LeFever*
URL(s): www.eofire.com/podcast/leelefever

Ed: Jon Lee Dumas. Released: April 18, 2024. Description: Podcast discusses the benefits of a long-term scalable business model.

22881 ■ *Building Brick by Brick with Torrey C Butler*
URL(s): www.eofire.com/podcast/torreycbutler

Ed: Jon Lee Dumas. Released: November 22, 2023. Description: Podcast explains how the most important investment for entrepreneurs is in themselves, how to stay focused on the goal, how a beginning entrepreneur can stand out, and how to remain persistent.

22882 ■ *Dedicated to Helping Serious and Committed Entrepreneurs with Jay Rodgers*
URL(s): www.eofire.com/podcast/jayrodgers

Ed: Jon Lee Dumas. Released: November 27, 2023. Description: Podcast profiles and discusses reasons for becoming an entrepreneur.

22883 ■ *Elevated Entrepreneurship: Gino Wickman: The Six Essential Traits for Entrepreneurship*
URL(s): mikemichalowicz.com/podcast/gino-wickman
Ed: Mike Michalowiicz. **Released:** June 29, 2020. **Description:** Podcast discusses useful traits and mistakes to avoid for entrepreneurs.

22884 ■ *Entrepreneurial Thought Leaders: Building from Values*
URL(s): ecorner.stanford.edu/podcasts/patrick-schmitt-and-jenny-xia-spradling-freewill-building-from-values
Ed: Tobey Corey. **Released:** April 27, 2022. **Description:** Podcast explains how entrepreneurs can use company values, such as kindness, to drive fundraising and growth.

22885 ■ *Entrepreneurial Thought Leaders: Clara Shih (Salesforce AI) - What No One Tells You About Entrepreneurship*
URL(s): stvp.stanford.edu/podcasts/what-no-one-tells-you-about-entrepreneurship
Ed: Ravi Belani. **Released:** March 06, 2024. **Description:** Podcast offers unconventional advice for entrepreneurs.

22886 ■ *Entrepreneurial Thought Leaders: Finding Fulfillment in Entrepreneurship*
URL(s): ecorner.stanford.edu/podcasts/justin-kan-twitch-finding-fulfillment-in-entrepreneurship
Ed: Ravi Belani. **Released:** October 06, 2021. **Description:** Podcast offers a conversation with the co-founder of Twitch, who suggests that entrepreneurial satisfaction is found by enjoying the process as much as the outcome.

22887 ■ *Entrepreneurial Thought Leaders: From Customer to Co-CEO*
URL(s): ecorner.stanford.edu/podcasts/elise-densborn-splendid-spoon-from-customer-to-co-ceo
Ed: Emily Ma. **Released:** January 25, 2023. **Description:** Podcast explains how passion for a brand or an industry can be a starting point for entrepreneurial experience.

22888 ■ *Entrepreneurial Thought Leaders: Lessons from a Stanford Success*
URL(s): ecorner.stanford.edu/podcasts/nikil-viswanathan-alchemy-lessons-from-a-stanford-success
Description: Nikil Viswanathan shares the key entrepreneurial lessons he's learned and suggest that you can build a world-changing company and have fun doing it.

22889 ■ *Entrepreneurial Thought Leaders: Seizing Global Success*
URL(s): ecorner.stanford.edu/podcasts/jorge-rios-bridgefy-seizing-global-opportunities
Ed: Ravi Belani. **Released:** May 04, 2022. **Description:** Podcast suggests how to discover new opportunities by thinking beyond borders.

22890 ■ *Entrepreneurial Thought Leaders: Sharon Prince (Grace Farms Foundation) - Designing from Values*
URL(s): stvp.stanford.edu/podcasts/sharon-prince-grace-farms-foundation-designing-from-values
Ed: Ravi Belani. **Released:** April 17, 2024. **Description:** Podcast discusses how a startup reflects your vision and values.

22891 ■ *Entrepreneurial Thought Leaders: Shiza Shahid (Our Place) - A Meaningful Entrepreneurial Path*
URL(s): stvp.stanford.edu/podcasts/shiza-shahid-our-place-a-meaningful-entrepreneurial-path
Ed: Ravi Belani. **Released:** February 28, 2024. **Description:** Podcast discusses how a meaningful mission can shape your entrepreneurial journey.

22892 ■ *Entrepreneurial Thought Leaders: The Power of Scrappiness*
URL(s): ecorner.stanford.edu/podcasts/deb-liu-ances-try-the-power-of-scrappiness
Released: April 19, 2023. **Description:** Podcast explains how a scrappy attitude and a willingness to learn can lead to success.

22893 ■ *Entrepreneurial Thought Leaders: The Truth about Entrepreneurship*
URL(s): ecorner.stanford.edu/podcasts/frederic-kerrest-okta-the-truth-about-entrepreneurship
Released: May 03, 2023.

22894 ■ *HBR Ideacast: A Roadmap for Today's Entrepreneurs*
URL(s): hbr.org/podcast/2024/04/a-roadmap-for-today-entrepreneurs
Ed: Alison Beard. **Released:** April 09, 2024. **Description:** Podcast discusses trends and changes in entrepreneurship and outlines steps for launching a new venture.

22895 ■ *How ADHD Can Hinder and Help Entrepreneurs with Dave Delaney*
URL(s): www.eofire.com/podcast/davedelaney3
Ed: Jon Lee Dumas. **Released:** October 10, 2024. **Description:** Podcast explains entrepreneurship and ADHD often go hand in hand because entrepreneurs are intelligent, creative risk-takers. .

22896 ■ *How to Avoid the Top 3 Things that Take Entrepreneurs Out of the Game with Shawn Stevenson*
URL(s): www.eofire.com/podcast/shawnstevenson4
Ed: Jon Lee Dumas. **Released:** December 27, 2023. **Description:** Podcast discusses the three things that take entrepreneurs out of the game: depression, infectious illness, and injury.

22897 ■ *The How of Business: Entrepreneurial Leap - Finding the Right Business for You*
URL(s): www.thehowofbusiness.com/episode-348-entrepreneurial-leap-right-business
Ed: Henry Lopez. **Released:** January 06, 2021. **Description:** Podcast offers insights into finding the right business for you, including industry, type of business, and size of business.

22898 ■ *The How of Business: Entrepreneurship Skills with Dan Sullivan*
URL(s): www.thehowofbusiness.com/episode-158-dan-sullivan
Released: October 30, 2017. **Description:** Podcast discusses skills small business owners can develop to be more successful.

22899 ■ *The How of Business: Taking Your Entrepreneurial Leap with Gino Wickman*
URL(s): www.thehowofbusiness.com/episode-339-gion-wickman
Ed: Henry Lopez. **Released:** November 02, 2020. **Description:** Podcast discusses whether entrepreneurship is right for you.

22900 ■ *The How of Business: The 6 Essential Traits of Successful Entrepreneurs*
URL(s): www.thehowofbusiness.com/episode-346-e-leap-confirm
Ed: Henry Lopez. **Released:** December 28, 2020. **Description:** Podcast discusses essentials traits for entrepreneurs.

22901 ■ *The How of Business: Walid Azami - Entrepreneurship for Creatives*
URL(s): www.thehowofbusiness.com/463-walid-azami-entrepreneurship-for-creatives
Ed: Henry Lopez. **Released:** March 13, 2023. **Description:** Podcast explains how all small businesses represent a form of creative expression.

22902 ■ *How I Built This: Achieving Greater Things with Adam Grant*
URL(s): wondery.com/shows/how-i-built-this/episode/10386-achieving-greater-things-with-adam-grant
Ed: Guy Raz. **Released:** March 21, 2024. **Description:** Podcast offers insights on what great entrepreneurs have in common, fostering collaboration, and cultivating untapped potential. .

22903 ■ *How I Built This: Creating a Creative Community with Tina Roth-Eisenberg of CreativeMornings*
URL(s): wondery.com/shows/how-i-built-this/episode/10386-cultivating-a-creative-community-with-tina-roth-eisenberg-of-creativemorningsati
Ed: Guy Raz. **Released:** July 01, 2023. **Description:** Podcast explains how a design career evolved into an unintentional path to entrepreneurship; also discusses why community and collaboration are key.

22904 ■ *How I Built This: Leatherman Tool Group: Tim Leatherman*
URL(s): www.npr.org/2022/01/28/1076433969/leatherman-tool-group-tim-leatherman
Ed: Guy Raz. **Released:** January 31, 2022. **Description:** Podcast explains how the founder of Leatherman Tools waited seven years before making a first sale.

22905 ■ *How I Built This: Xero Shoes: Steven Sashen and Lena Phoenix*
URL(s): wondery.com/shows/how-i-built-this/episode/10386-xero-shoes-steven-sashen-and-lena-phoenix
Ed: Guy Raz. **Released:** March 13, 2023. **Description:** Podcast outlines the obstacles Xero shoes faced, from manufacturing meltdowns and a mountain of debt to anxious investors, a trade war with China, and an appearance on Shark Tank ending in an insulting offer.

22906 ■ *How to Succeed as an Entrepreneur in Dance and Arts with Roger Lee*
URL(s): www.eofire.com/podcast/rogerlee
Ed: Jon Lee Dumas. **Released:** April 10, 2024. **Description:** Podcast outlines the value (and challenges) of artistic entrepreneurship.

22907 ■ *Midwest Moxie: Coffee Meetings and Phishing Attacks: Taralinda Willis and Norman Sadeh*
Released: March 11, 2022. **Description:** Podcast discusses how two entrepreneurs built their startups into successful businesses.

22908 ■ *Midwest Moxie: Grain Elevators and Specialty Meds: Jake Joraanstad and Julia Regan*
URL(s): www.wuwm.com/podcast/midwest-moxie/2023-02-26/grain-elevators-and-specialty-meds-jake-joraanstad-and-julia-regan
Released: February 26, 2023. **Description:** Podcast discusses how entrepreneurs with different perspectives seized upon an opportunity to digitize a paper process.

22909 ■ *Midwest Moxie: Nuclear Fusion and the Era of Abundant Energy: Greg Piefer*
URL(s): www.wuwm.com/podcast/midwest-moxie/2023-03-19/nuclear-fusion-and-the-ear-of-abundant-energy-greg-piefer
Ed: Kathleen Gallagher. **Released:** March 19, 2023. **Description:** Podcast discusses the transition to a fusion-fueled era of abundant energy.

22910 ■ *Midwest Moxie: Protecting the Wellbeing of Youth Athletes: Tyrre Burks*
URL(s): www.wuwm.com/podcast/midwest-moxie/2023-04-02/protecting-the-wellbeing-of-youth-athletes-tyrre-burks
Ed: Kathleen Gallagher. **Released:** April 02, 2023. **Description:** Podcast discusses how an entrepreneur with a sports scheduling app ended up with an insurance company.

22911 ■ *Midwest Moxie: Redefining Flavor and Live Event Streaming: Matt Rubin and Gordon Daily*
URL(s): www.wuwm.com/podcast/midwest-moxie/2023-03-05/redefining-flavor-and-live-event-streaming-matt-rubin-and-gordon-daily
Ed: Kathleen Gallagher. **Released:** March 05, 2023. **Description:** Podcast discusses how entrepreneurs use their tech skills to grow businesses.

GENERAL SMALL BUSINESS TOPICS   Entrepreneurial Traits/Skills ■ 22936

22912 ■ Navigating Entrepreneurship's Unexpected Challenges with Caitlin Saenz
URL(s): www.eofire.com/podcast/caitlinsaenz
Ed: Jon Lee Dumas. **Released:** June 12, 2024. **Description:** Podcast discusses how to handle the uncertainties of entrepreneurship and the importance of grit.

22913 ■ Nurture Small Business: Outsmarting Burnout: Strategies for Sustainable Success
URL(s): nuturesmallbusiness.buzzsprout.com/900445/episodes/15423649-outsmarting-burnout-strategies-for-sustainable-success
Ed: Denise Cagan. **Released:** July 16, 2024. **Description:** Podcast explores methods to remedy entrepreneurial burnout.

22914 ■ Overnight Success. Don't Kid Yourself with Todd Sawyer
URL(s): www.eofire.com/podcast/toddsawyer
Ed: Jon Lee Dumas. **Released:** August 28, 2024. **Description:** Podcast explains dispels the myth of overnight success. It requires work, a willingness to do jobs others don't want, and taking responsibility for your actions.

22915 ■ Profit First Nation: Don't Be the Hub
URL(s): www.profitfirstnation.com/episodes/ep-142-dont-be-the-hub
Ed: Danielle Mulvey. **Released:** October 17, 2023. **Description:** Podcast discusses the adverse effects of entrepreneurs at the epicenter of the organization and how to break free of the hub-and-spoke model.

22916 ■ Side Hustle to Small Business: Do Not Wait Around to Jump into Entrepreneurship
URL(s): www.hiscox.com/side-hustle-to-small-business/racheal-allen-podcast-season-3
Ed: Sanjay Parekh. **Released:** July 19, 2023. **Description:** Podcast discusses operational efficiency, avoiding burnout, and the essentials of entrepreneurship.

22917 ■ Side Hustle to Small Business: Helping Girls Overcome Barriers to Become Entrepreneurs
URL(s): www.hiscox.com/side-hustle-to-small-business/ebony-peay-ramirez-build-her-world-podcast-season-3
Ed: Sanjay Parekh. **Released:** November 01, 2023. **Description:** Podcast features the founder of an online platform aimed at helping girls aged 9-13 build entrepreneurial skills.

22918 ■ Side Hustle to Small Business: How Joe Koufman Built a Career as a Business Matchmaker
URL(s): www.hiscox.com/side-hustle-to-small-business/joe-koufman-setup-podcast-season-4
Ed: Sanjay Parekh. **Released:** July 03, 2024. **Description:** Podcast explains how a matchmaker uses his skills to pair business brands with marketing agencies.

22919 ■ Side Hustle to Small Business: How Your Perspective on Entrepreneurship Can Evolve Over Time
URL(s): sidehustletosmallbusiness.podbean.com/e/how-your-perspective-on-entrepreneurshp-can-evolve-over-time
Ed: Sanjay Parekh. **Released:** October 09, 2024. **Description:** Podcast discusses the transition to entrepreneurship.

22920 ■ Side Hustle to Small Business: Leveraging Existing Skills to Launch a Business
URL(s): www.hiscox.com/side-hustle-to-small-business/bryson-tarbet-music-teacher-podcast-season-4
Ed: Sanjay Parekh. **Released:** September 11, 2024. **Description:** Podcast features an elementary school teacher turned entrepreneur.

22921 ■ Side Hustle to Small Business: Moving from Wall Street to Three-Time Entrepreneur
URL(s): www.hiscox.com/side-hustle-to-small-business/yong-soo-chung-podcast-season-3
Ed: Sanjay Parekh. **Released:** May 10, 2023. **Description:** Podcast features a conversation with a serial entrepreneur.

22922 ■ Side Hustle to Small Business: Passion to Profit: Transforming Hobbies into Side Hustles
URL(s): www.hiscox.com/side-hustle-to-small-business/should-your-hobby-become-your-side-hustle-podcast-season-4
Ed: Sanjay Parekh. **Released:** April 17, 2024. **Description:** Podcast discusses turning hobbies into thriving businesses.

22923 ■ The Small Business School Podcast: The Visibility Journey
URL(s): podcasts.apple.com/us/podcast/the-visibility-journey-with-danielle-joworski/id1695210366?i=1000641285283
Ed: Staci Millard. **Released:** January 11, 2024. **Description:** Podcasts discusses the impact of--and strategies for--visiblity on financial success for small businesses.

22924 ■ Surviving Year One As an Entrepreneur
URL(s): www.startuphustlepodcast.com/surviving-year-one-as-an-entrepreneur
Ed: Lauren Conway. **Released:** October 04, 2023. **Description:** Podcast discusses navigating your first year as an entrepreneur.

22925 ■ Think Business: Coding, Coping, and Conquering with Jeremy Nagel
URL(s): thinktyler.com/podcast_episode/coping-conquering-jeremy-nagel
Released: March 11, 2024. **Description:** Podcast explores how neurodivergence can fuel the entrepreneurial spirit.

22926 ■ Think Business: Mastering the Waves of Entrepreneurship with Rodic Lenhart
URL(s): thinktyler.com/podcast_episode/entrepreneurship-rodric-lenhart
Ed: Tyler Martin. **Released:** November 13, 2023. **Description:** Podcast discusses knowing your business purpose, aligning with the business mission with personal purpose, dedication to your business, and making the right decisions for your business.

22927 ■ Think Business: Turning Loss into Leadership with Business Expert Robert Poole
URL(s): thinktyler.com/podcast_episode/business-expert-robert-poole
Ed: Tyler Martin. **Released:** December 04, 2023. **Description:** Podcast discusses accountability in entrepreneurship, business as a team sport, and the power of a mindset shift in business.

22928 ■ Think Business with Tyler: Mastering Obstacles and Conquering Challenges in Entrepreneurship with Bryan Clayton
URL(s): thinktyler.com/podcast_episode/challenges-bryan-clayton
Ed: Tyler Martin. **Released:** July 10, 2023. **Description:** Podcast discusses how you constantly need to level up for the next obstacle and the next big challenge in entrepreneurship.

22929 ■ Think Business with Tyler: Mind Strategies for Entrepreneurs with Troy Lavinia
URL(s): thinktyler.com/podcast_episode/mind-entrepreneurs-troy-lavinia
Ed: Tyler Martin. **Released:** September 30, 2024. **Description:** Podcast discusses spiritual well-being for entrepreneurs.

22930 ■ Think Business with Tyler: Overcoming Challenges and Embracing Failure in Entrepreneurship with Kerry-Ann Powell
URL(s): thinktyler.com/podcast_episode/challenges-failure-kerry-ann-powell
Ed: Tyler Martin. **Released:** May 01, 2023. **Description:** Podcast discusses the challenges of entrepreneurship, the importance of scaling at your own pace, aligning your business vision with your life plan, and how to keep going during tough times.

22931 ■ Think Business with Tyler: The Role of Mindset and Optimism in Entrepreneurial Success with Matt Drinkhahn
URL(s): thinktyler.com/podcast_episode/mindset-and-optimism-matt-drinkhahn
Released: July 17, 2023. **Description:** Podcast discusses the dark side of perfectionism, why mindset makes a difference in business, how to remain focused on goals, and the importance of eternal optimism.

22932 ■ This Is Small Business: Do You Have What It Takes to Own a Small Business?
URL(s): www.smallbusiness.amazon/podcast-episodes/ep-49-do-you-have-what-it-takes-to-own-your-own-business
Ed: Andrea Marquez. **Released:** March 19, 2024. **Description:** Podcast discusses what qualities are needed in an entrepreneur.

22933 ■ The Top 5 Characteristics of Successful Social Entrepreneurs with Cory Ames
URL(s): www.awarepreneurs.com/podcast/311-social-entrepreneur-success
Ed: Paul Zelizer. **Released:** November 07, 2023. **Description:** Podcast discusses characteristics of successful social entrepreneurs, including the importance of transparency, avoiding distractions, and the value of mentorship.

22934 ■ Waiting for the Perfect Time Might Be Delaying Your Dreams
URL(s): www.hiscox.com/side-hustle-to-small-business/angel-hendrix-nc-solution-group-podcast-season-3
Ed: Sanjay Parekh. **Released:** December 07, 2022. **Description:** Podcast features a conversation with a realtor/notary.

TRADE SHOWS AND CONVENTIONS

22935 ■ Inc. 5000
URL(s): events.inc.com/inc5000-2021
Frequency: Annual. **Description:** Key topics sessions on entrepreneurship and running a business. **Principal Exhibits:** Key topics sessions on entrepreneurship and running a business. **Telecommunication Services:** events@inc.com.

CONSULTANTS

22936 ■ Beacon Management-Management Consultants
Pompano Beach, FL 33069
Co. E-mail: md@beaconmgmt.com
URL: http://www.beaconmgmt.com
Contact: Michael J. Donnelly, Consultant Managing Director Principal

Description: Provider of management consulting services such as strategic and business planning, market intelligence, decision support services, corporate finance, and much more. **Scope:** Provider of management consulting services such as strategic and business planning, market intelligence, decision support services, corporate finance, and much more. **Founded:** 1985. **Publications:** "Sun-Sentinel Article," Oct, 2012.

22937 ■ Entrepreneurial Traits/Skills

22937 ■ Invanti
2702 S Twyckenham Dr.
South Bend, IN 46614
URL: http://www.invanti.co
Description: Helps aspiring entrepreneurs navigate which problems are the most important to solve. **Scope:** Helps aspiring entrepreneurs navigate which problems are the most important to solve.

22938 ■ Jennifer Cramer Lewis
Vancouver, BC, Canada
URL: http://jennifercramerlewis.com
Contact: Jennifer Cramer Lewis, Founder
E-mail: jennifer@jennifercramerlewis.com
Facebook: www.facebook.com/
  jennifercramerlewispersonal
Linkedin: www.linkedin.com/in/jennifercramerlewis
Description: Business and relationship turnaround expert for ambitious female entrepreneurs. Offers experience in Finance, Real Estate, Management, and Investing. **Scope:** Business and relationship turnaround expert for ambitious female entrepreneurs. Offers experience in Finance, Real Estate, Management, and Investing.

22939 ■ Pinpoint Tactics Business Consulting
5525 West Blvd.
  Vancouver, BC, Canada V6M 3W6
Ph: (604)263-4698
Co. E-mail: info@pinpointtactics.com
URL: http://www.pinpointtactics.com
Contact: Sandy Huang, President
Facebook: www.facebook.com/PinpointTactics
X (Twitter): x.com/pinpointtactics
Description: Firm provides business consulting services such as marketing programs, small business launch program, strategic business program, market research, and much more. **Scope:** Firm provides business consulting services such as marketing programs, small business launch program, strategic business program, market research, and much more.

22940 ■ Third Sector New England Inc. (TSNE)
89 S St., Ste. 700
  Boston, MA 02111
Ph: (617)523-6565
Fax: (617)523-2070
Co. E-mail: info@tsne.org
URL: http://www.tsne.org
Contact: Miki C. Akimoto, President
X (Twitter): x.com/tsne
YouTube: www.youtube.com/channel/UCZBLAMY
  6D9WLEhyMvvFBC-A
Description: Provider of management and leadership resources to non-profits. **Scope:** Provider of management and leadership resources to non-profits. **Founded:** 1959. **Publications:** "Executive Directors Guide"; "Creative Disruption: Sabbaticals for Capacity Building and Leadership Development in the Nonprofit Sector"; "A Step-by-Step Guide to Achieving Diversity in the Workplace"; "Valuing Our Nonprofit Workforce 2010: A Compensation Survey of and for Nonprofits in Massachusetts and Adjoining Communities"; "Shared Services: A Guide to Collaborative Solutions for Nonprofits"; "TSNe-Bulletin". **Training:** Supporting Nonprofits and Communities Through the Rough Times.

PUBLICATIONS

22941 ■ *American Inventors, Entrepreneurs, and Business Visionaries*
132 W 31st., 16 Fl.
  New York, NY 10001
Ph: (212)896-4268
Free: 800-322-8755
Fax: (800)678-3633
Co. E-mail: info@infobase.com
URL: http://www.infobase.com
Contact: Paul Skordilis, President
URL(s): www.infobasepublishing.com/Bookdetail
  .aspx?ISBN=0816081468&Ebooks=0
Released: Published October, 2010. **Price:** $95, for hardcover. **No. of Listings:** 300. **Description:** Covers the range of people from early inventors who were also entrepreneurs. From Thomas Edison to Bill Gates. Includes 51 black and white photographs. **Entries include:** Short description of the person's importance, the person's birth date and information, and chronological life story. **Availability:** E-book; Print.

22942 ■ *"Entrepreneurial passion: A systematic review and research opportunities" in Journal of Small Business Strategy (August 11, 2021)*
Ed: Younggeun Lee, Pol Herrmann. **Released:** August 11, 2021. **Description:** Summarizes empirical findings on the topic of how various types of passion influences entrepreneurs and their work. **Availability:** PDF.

22943 ■ *Small Business Institute Journal*
URL(s): www.sbij.org/index.php/SBIJ
Description: Publishes scholarly research articles regarding small business management, entrepreneurship, and field based learning.

22944 ■ *"Young Latino Business Owners Getting Helping Hand Amid Hispanic Heritage Month" in Business 2 Community (October 6, 2021)*
URL(s): www.business2community.com/small-business/young-latino-business-owners-getting-helping
  -hand-amid-hispanic-heritage-month-02434741
Ed: Merilee Kern. **Released:** October 06, 2021. **Description:** Discusses two business leaders who help facilitate young entrepreneurs of Hispanic heritage by hosting summits and other events in order to give a boost to that particular community of small businesses. **Availability:** Online.

INTERNET DATABASES

22945 ■ DreamBuilder
URL(s): dreambuilder.org
Description: Provides online educational programs for women small business owners and entrepreneurs. **Availability:** Online.

22946 ■ Entrepreneur's Reference Guide to Small Business Information
101 Independence Ave., SE
  Washington, DC 20540
Ph: (202)707-9779
Co. E-mail: visit@loc.gov
URL: http://www.loc.gov
Contact: Carla Hayden, Librarian
URL(s): guides.loc.gov/entrepreneurs-reference
  -guide
Description: Contains links to books, directories, online resources, and databases for those interested in running their own business. **Availability:** Online.

22947 ■ Small Business Financing: A Resource Guide
URL(s): guides.loc.gov/small-business-financing
Description: Provides links to online resources to conduct research on financing options for small businesses and entrepreneurs. Covers the following topics: types of financing, financing by situation, financial management, and avoiding scams. **Availability:** Online.

22948 ■ Small Business Hub: A Research Guide for Entrepreneurs
URL(s): guides.loc.gov/small-business-hub
Description: An online guide with links for further research into running a small business. Topics cover a large selection of useful information for entrepreneurs for all stages of setting up a business. Includes resources on planning, finance, location, registering, marketing, managing, growing, and exiting the business. **Availability:** Online.

22949 ■ Women in Business and the Workforce
URL(s): guides.loc.gov/women-business-workforce
Description: Includes links to primary and secondary resources about women in business, industry, commerce, and entrepreneurship. Provides research into the history of women in the workforce along with reports and statistics. **Availability:** Online.

LIBRARIES

22950 ■ Canadian Federation of Independent Business (CFIB) - Research Library
401-4141 Yonge St.
  Toronto, ON, Canada M2P 2A6
Co. E-mail: cfib@cfib.ca
URL: http://www.cfib-fcei.ca/en
Contact: Dan Kelly, President
Facebook: www.facebook.com/CFIB
Linkedin: www.linkedin.com/company/canadian-fe
  deration-of-independent-business
X (Twitter): x.com/CFIBNews
Instagram: www.instagram.com/cfib_fcei
YouTube: www.youtube.com/user/cfibdotca
Description: Promotes economic well-being of members and seeks to maintain a healthy domestic business climate. **Scope:** Business. **Founded:** 1971. **Holdings:** Figures not available. **Publications:** *Mandate* (Quarterly); *Business Barometer* (Monthly). **Geographic Preference:** National.

RESEARCH CENTERS

22951 ■ Baylor University - Center for Private Enterprise
1311 S 5th St.
  Waco, TX 76706
URL: http://orgchart.web.baylor.edu/academic-affairs/
  hankamer-school-business/economics
Contact: Kimberly Mencken, Lecturer
E-mail: kimberly_mencken@baylor.edu
Description: Integral unit of Hankamer School of Business at Baylor University. **Scope:** Pedagogical methods for teaching economics in high school and college levels, development of new active learning lessons for kindergarten through college economics. **Founded:** 1978.

22952 ■ Boston University - Institute for Technology Entrepreneurship and Commercialization (ITEC)
595 Commonwealth Ave.
  Boston, MA 02215
URL: http://www.bu.edu/ubx/about-us/leadership
Contact: Peter Russo, Director
Description: Integral unit of Boston University. **Scope:** Entrepreneurship, global entrepreneurship in healthcare, clean energy, and information systems, women entrepreneurs, management policy, and marketing. **Founded:** 2006. **Publications:** *ITEC Newsletter* (Monthly).

22953 ■ Lehigh University Small Business Development Center (LUSBDC) - Library
416 E 5th St.
  Bethlehem, PA 18015
Ph: (610)758-3980
Fax: (610)758-5205
Co. E-mail: insbdc@lehigh.edu
URL: http://sbdc.lehigh.edu
Contact: Brett Smith, Director
E-mail: bds206@lehigh.edu
Linkedin: www.linkedin.com/in/lehighsbdc
X (Twitter): x.com/lehighsbdc
Description: Represents and promotes the small business sector. Provides management assistance to current and prospective small business owners. Helps to improve management skills and expand the products and services of members. **Scope:** Problems faced by small businesses, the impact of the general economy on the formation and operation of small business, and characteristics on entrepreneurs. **Services:** Library open to the public on a limited schedule. **Founded:** 1978. **Holdings:** Books. **Publications:** *Export Planning Guide*; *Financing Guide for Northampton*; *Financing Your Business*; *Lehigh and*

Berks County; *Lehigh Valley Business Support Services*; *Market Planning Guide*. **Educational Activities:** First Step Seminar. **Geographic Preference:** Local.

22954 ■ Massachusetts Institute of Technology (MIT) - The Entrepreneur Forum
1 Broadway, 14th Fl.
 Cambridge, MA 02142-1187
Co. E-mail: team@theeforum.org
URL: http://theeforum.org
Contact: Joe Laurin, Contact
Facebook: www.facebook.com/theeforumorg
Linkedin: www.linkedin.com/company/theentrepreneurforum
YouTube: www.youtube.com/channel/UCqOxHzqUh12eLi5GHUCXvIQ
Description: Global organization seeking to make a difference and achieving global outcomes for participants in the entrepreneurial ecosystem. **Founded:** 1978. **Geographic Preference:** Local.

22955 ■ New York University - Leonard N. Stern School of Business - Berkley Center for Entrepreneurial Studies (BCES)
44 West Fourth St.
 New York, NY 10012
URL: http://www.stern.nyu.edu/experience-stern/about/departments-centers-initiatives/academic-departments/finance/resources
Description: Integral unit of Leonard N. Stern School of Business at New York University. **Scope:** Factors that promote entrepreneurship and lead to the creation of new wealth and business revenues; business venturing within established firms. Topics include the major pitfalls and obstacles to start-ups, securing of venture capital, psychology and sociology of entrepreneurship, valuation and management of new ventures, technological innovation and new product development, emerging and creative industries, and cross-cultural environments that stimulate entrepreneurship. **Founded:** 1984. **Publications:** *Case series*; *BCES Working papers*. **Educational Activities:** BCES Business Plan Competition; BCES Conferences; BCES Entrepreneur in Residence Program; BCES Forums and workshops. **Awards:** Harold Price Entrepreneurship Award (Annual); Rennert Entrepreneurial Prize (Annual); Gloria Appel Award (Annual).

22956 ■ Southern Methodist University - Cox School of Business - Caruth Institute for Entrepreneurship
3150 Binkley, Ste. 203
 Dallas, TX 75205
Ph: (214)768-3330
Co. E-mail: caruth@smu.edu
URL: http://www.smu.edu/cox/Centers-and-Institutes/caruth-institute-for-entrepreneurship
Contact: Simon Mak, Executive Director
E-mail: smak@smu.edu
Linkedin: www.linkedin.com/company/smu-caruth-institute
Description: Research and educational activity of Edwin L. Cox School of Business, Southern Methodist University. **Scope:** Entrepreneurs as managers. **Founded:** 1970. **Publications:** *Caruth Institute of Entrepreneurship Newsletter* (Monthly). **Educational Activities:** Caruth Institute for Entrepreneurship Southwest Venture Forum (Bimonthly); Caruth Institute for Entrepreneurship Bimonthly Breakfast Meeting (Bimonthly). **Awards:** The Dallas 100 Entrepreneur Awards (Annual).

22957 ■ University of British Columbia - Sauder School of Business - W. Maurice Young Centre Entrepreneurship and Venture Capital Research
Henry Angus Bldg.
 2053 Main Mall
 Vancouver, BC, Canada V6T 1Z2
Co. E-mail: darren.dahl@sauder.ubc.ca
URL: http://www.sauder.ubc.ca/thought-leadership/research-outreach-centres/w-maurice-young-centre-entrepreneurship-and-venture-capital-research
Contact: Marc-David Seidel, Director
E-mail: seidel@mail.ubc.ca
Description: Promotes learning and research related to entrepreneurship, and encourages dialogue and cooperation between the university, business, policy makers and other stakeholders. The center creates new knowledge of entrepreneurship and venture capital, advances entrepreneurial business activity and promotes economic growth. Its research covers theoretical, empirical, experimental and field studies of entrepreneurship. The center shares this research through workshops, symposia, and internship programs. **Scope:** Entrepreneurship and venture capital. **Publications:** *Industry reports*. **Educational Activities:** Entrepreneurship Luncheon.

Entrepreneurship on the Web

START-UP INFORMATION

22958 ■ *"8 Ways to Make Your Crowdfunding Campaign Stand Out"* in **Entrepreneur (June 2014)**
Pub: Entrepreneur Media Inc.
Contact: Dan Bova, Director
E-mail: dbova@entrepreneur.com
Description: Business experts offer some tips to launch a successful crowdfunding campaign for startups. Entrepreneurs should create a solid plan and reach out to prospective backers before launching their campaigns. Richard Swart of the University of California, suggest hosting launch parties, organizing round table discussions, and establishing a presence at community events to garner support. A series of small campaigns builds brand loyalty over time and provides fans with additional opportunities to support the startup at different stages.

22959 ■ *"Begslist.org Launches Crowdfunding On Its Website"* in **Computer Business Week (August 2, 2012)**
Description: Donation Website called Begslist has added crowdfunding to its site. Crowdfunding and begging are popular among small startups wishing to procure funding for their new companies. **Availability:** Online.

22960 ■ *"CrowdFunding Platform, START.ac, Announces It Is Expanding Its International Scope From the US, Canada and the UK to 36 Countries Including Australia, India, Israel, Italy and Africa"* in **Benzinga.com (July 11, 2012)**
Pub: Benzinga.com
Contact: Jason Raznick, Founder
Ed: Aaron Wise. **Description:** START.ac is expanding its CrowdFunding site to include 36 countries and increasing its scope to include business startups, teen projects, as well as medical products. START.ac projects are in the fundraising stage at this point, with 23 percent located outside the United States. **Availability:** Online.

22961 ■ *"Crowdfunding Site Targets Jan. Launch"* in **Crain's Detroit Business (July 9, 2012)**
Pub: Crain Communications Inc.
Contact: Barry Asin, President
Ed: Meghana Keshavan. **Description:** Michigan based RelayFund Inc. incorporates social media with fundraising private equity form small businesses. Before the JOBS Act legislation, it was difficult for small firms to raise money. Crowdfunding connects groups of investors with small startup businesses. **Availability:** Print; Online.

22962 ■ *"Equity 'Crowdfunding' Platform, RelayFund, Launched by Michigan Investor Group"* in **Economics Week (July 20, 2012)**
Description: RelayFund was launched by a group of Michigan venture capitalists, entrepreneurs, and investment bankers to link small investors with startup firms under the new JOBS (Jumpstart Our Business Startups) Act. Crowdfunding is money raised for charities, projects or pre-selling products or services and allows online micro investments for startup companies.

22963 ■ *"Kickstarter Funds the Future; Crowdfunding Services Such as Kickstarter Have Been Hailed as a New Way To Get Started In Business and Cut Out the Traditional Money Men"* in **Telegraph Online (August 24, 2012)**
Pub: Telegraph Media Group Limited
Contact: Nick Hugh, Chief Executive Officer
Ed: Monty Munford. **Description:** More than 530 crowdfunding services are expected to his the net by the end of the year. Crowdfunding helps companies raise money from investors for specific projects. A musician was able to raise over $1 million to fund a new record. **Availability:** Online.

22964 ■ *"Leading Digital: Turning Technology into Business Transformation"*
Pub: Harvard Business Review Press
Contact: Moderna V. Pfizer, Contact
Released: October 14, 2014. **Price:** $32, Hardcover/Hardcopy. **Description:** Mobile technology, analytics, social media, sensors, and cloud computing have changed the entire business environment in every industry. A guide to help any small startup business in any industry gain strategic advantage using digital, including where to invest in digital technologies and how to lead the transformation. The guide teaches how to engage better with customers, digitally enhance operations, create a digital vision, and govern digital activities. **Availability:** E-book; Print.

22965 ■ *"Legal Matters: 'Crowdfunding' a Boon for Entrepreneurs, If They Clear Regulatory Hurdles"* in **Finance and Commerce (July 17, 2012)**
Pub: BridgeTower Media
Contact: Adam Reinebach, President
Ed: Dan Heilman. **Description:** Part of the Jumpstart Our Business Startups Act (JOBS) is crowdfunding, which allows the funding of a company by selling small parts of equity to a group of investors. Kickstarter, a Website for raising funds for business entitites, is primarily used for film and book projects. Most businesses cannot adopt Kickstarter's model because of the legality of receiving investor funds without offering security.

22966 ■ *"MicroVentures: New Crowdfunding Game Makes Startups the Stars, Prepares Players for a New Kind of Investing"* in **Health & Beauty Close-Up (July 31, 2012)**
Description: MicroVentures created the MicroVentures Investor Challenge as a game on Facebook. The game features real startups such as AirBnB, Etsy, and Pinterest and players invest in these firms. The game has real startups face off in six weekly rounds and the players act as venture capitalists. One startup and one investor will win the game. **Availability:** Print; Online.

22967 ■ *"Modern Meal Offers Recipe Inspiration, Curation and Home Delivery"* in **Orlando Business Journal (Vol. 30, April 4, 2014, No. 41, pp. 3)**
Pub: American City Business Journals, Inc.
Contact: Mike Olivieri, Executive Vice President
Released: Weekly. **Price:** $8, introductory 4-week offer(Digital & Print). **Description:** Modern Meal LLC's CEO, Mark Hudgins, works to get people to the dinner table for a good meal. The social network with a Pinterest look is in early-beta-launch and users are trying out the features by curating recipes from popular cooking Websites and looking at recipes of other users. Modern' Meal's plan to tap into the e-grocery market is also discussed. **Availability:** Print; Online.

22968 ■ *"No. 381: Metallica and Other Forms of Hardware"* in **Inc. (Vol. 36, September 2014, No. 7, pp. 107)**
Pub: Mansueto Ventures L.L.C.
Contact: Stephanie Mehta, Chief Executive Officer
Released: August 20, 2014. **Description:** Profile of Mikhail Orlov, who stayed in American instead of fighting a war he did not believe in while living in Chechnya, Russia. Orlov discovered his entrepreneurial spirit when he began importing Russian army surplus gear. He operates his startup online store selling guns, ammo, and hunting accessories. **Availability:** Print; Online.

22969 ■ *"Open English Touted as Startup Worth Emulating"* in **South Florida Business Journal (Vol. 34, January 24, 2014, No. 27, pp. 30)**
Pub: American City Business Journals, Inc.
Contact: Mike Olivieri, Executive Vice President
Released: Weekly. **Price:** $8, Introductory 4-week offer(Digital & Print). **Description:** Open English, a language education company, received more than $150 million in investments from venture capitalists. The firm's cloud-based platform is still in its infancy, but the startup's success has shown that entrepreneurs can generate money and grow their businesses in Florida. Open English is the only online English school that offers live classes with native English-speaking teachers. **Availability:** Print; Online.

22970 ■ *"PeoplesVC Becomes the 1st Stock-Based Crowdfunding Site to Open Its Doors to Investors"* in **Investment Weekly (June 23, 2012)**
Description: Peoples VC is the first equity-based crowdfunding site to invite public investors to set up individual crowdfunding investment accounts. Equity-based crowdfunding allows funders to receive stock in return for their investment into companies. In the past, this process was only available to venture capitalists and accredited investors. **Availability:** Print; Online.

22971 ■ *"SEC, NASAA Tell Small Businesses: Wait To Join the 'Crowd': Crowdfunding Is 'Not Yet Legal Until the Commission Appoints Rules', Says SEC's Kim"* in *Investment Advisor* (Vol. 3, August 2012, No. 8, pp. 13)
Ed: Melanie Waddell. **Description:** Securities and Exchange Commission along with state regulators have advised small businesses and entrepreneurs to wait until the SEC has produced rules governing crowdfunding practices. Until that happens, federal and state securities laws prohibit publicly accessible Internet securities offerings. An overview of crowdfunding and the JOBS Act is included. **Availability:** Online.

ASSOCIATIONS AND OTHER ORGANIZATIONS

22972 ■ **Association for Entrepreneurship USA (AFEUSA)**
666 Dundee Rd., Ste. 1603
Northbrook, IL 60062
Free: 844-750-5927
Fax: (888)289-7001
Co. E-mail: info@afeusa.org
URL: http://afeusa.org
Contact: Jack Diehl, President
Facebook: www.facebook.com/AFEUSA
X (Twitter): x.com/AFE_USA_Org
Description: Seeks to serve, support, represent, and promote entrepreneurship for those have (or wish for) the freedom of successfully operating their own business.

22973 ■ **Collegiate Entrepreneurs' Organization (CEO)**
401 W Kennedy Blvd., Box 2F
Tampa, FL 33606-1490
Ph: (813)258-7236
Co. E-mail: ceo@c-e-o.org
URL: http://www.c-e-o.org
Contact: Becky Gann, Treasurer
Facebook: www.facebook.com/ceoentorg
Linkedin: www.linkedin.com/company/collegiate-entrepreneurs-organization
X (Twitter): x.com/ceoorg
Instagram: www.instagram.com/ceoorg
YouTube: www.youtube.com/user/CEOORG
Description: Operates a network of chapters on university/college campuses throughout North America in an effort to inform, support, and inspire college students to be entrepreneurial and seek opportunity through venture creation. **Founded:** 1983.

22974 ■ **The Entrepreneurship Institute (TEI)**
4449 E Way
Columbus, OH 43219
Ph: (614)934-1540
URL: http://www.tei.net
Description: Provides encouragement and assistance to entrepreneurs who operate companies with revenue in excess of $1 million. Unites financial, legal, and community resources to help foster the success of companies. Promotes sharing of information and interaction between members. Operates President's forums and projects which are designed to improve communication between businesses, develop one-to-one business relationships between small and mid-size businesses and local resources, provide networking, and stimulate the growth of existing companies. **Founded:** 1976. **Educational Activities:** The Entrepreneurship Institute Meeting. **Geographic Preference:** National.

22975 ■ **G20 Young Entrepreneurs' Alliance (G20 YEA)**
c/o the Centre for Social Innovation
326-192 Spadina Ave.
Toronto, ON, Canada M5T 2C2
Co. E-mail: admin@g20yea.com
URL: http://www.g20yea.com
Facebook: www.facebook.com/G20YEA
Linkedin: www.linkedin.com/company/g20-yea
X (Twitter): x.com/g20_yea
Instagram: www.instagram.com/g20yea
YouTube: www.youtube.com/channel/UC6eWxfXjmuYUEXMxI7VXguQ
Description: Young entrepreneurs and their supporting organizations around the world. Seeks to support young entrepreneurs at the local, national, and international level, and to promote an environment in which entrepreneurs can grow businesses, create jobs, change lives, and ensure future economic prosperity. Meets each year in advance of the G20 Summit to champion the importance of young entrepreneurs to the G20 member nations and to share members' examples and practices. **Founded:** 2010.

22976 ■ **National Association of Entrepreneurship (NAE)**
OH
Free: 800-497-6950
Co. E-mail: info@naeonline.org
URL: http://naeonline.org
Description: Seeks to advance free enterprise by providing and expanding opportunities for U.S. emerging mid-market companies to grow and succeed in a competitive global economy. Offers peer connectivity, institutional partnerships, and relevant information and education.

22977 ■ **National Entrepreneurs Association (NEA)**
18444 W 10 Mile Rd., No. 103
Southfield, MI 48075
Ph: (248)416-7278
Co. E-mail: supportstaff@nationalentrepreneurs.org
URL: http://www.nationalentrepreneurs.org
Contact: ZaLonya Allen, President
Facebook: www.facebook.com/National-Entrepreneurs-Association-137536660415863
Linkedin: www.linkedin.com/company/national-entrepreneurs-association
X (Twitter): x.com/NationalEntrep1
YouTube: www.youtube.com/channel/UC0MiAnMYBpFHWeGZ_Z2Cquw
Description: Provides networking and education opportunities to help entrepreneurs create and operate their business successfully.

INCUBATORS/RESEARCH AND TECHNOLOGY PARKS

22978 ■ **Richi Foundation [Richi Childhood Cancer Foundation]**
705 Adams St.
Holliston, MA 01746
Co. E-mail: contact@richifoundation.org
URL: http://www.richifoundation.org
Contact: Ricardo García, President
Facebook: www.facebook.com/RichiFoundation
Linkedin: www.linkedin.com/company/richi-childhood-cancer-foundation
X (Twitter): x.com/RichiE_RCCF
Description: An initiative whose mission is to boost Life Sciences startups from around the world by connecting them with Boston's unique innovation ecosystem. **Founded:** 2013.

EDUCATIONAL PROGRAMS

22979 ■ **Building XML Web Services with Java- Hands-On (Onsite)**
Seminar Information Service Inc. (SIS)
250 El Camino Real., Ste. 112
Tustin, CA 92780
Ph: (714)508-0340
Free: 877-736-4636
Fax: (714)734-8027
Co. E-mail: info@seminarinformation.com
URL: http://www.seminarinformation.com
Contact: Catherine Bellizzi, President
URL(s): www.seminarinformation.com/qqbtmk/building-xml-web-services-with-java-hands-on
Description: Learn how to: Develop and deploy Web services with Java and XML; Describe the functionality of Web services using WSDL; Write interoperable SOAP-based services and clients using JAX-RPC; Generate Java source files for services from WSDL and XML schemas; Customize SOAP messages using SAAJ; Implement strategies to secure your Web services; Locate Web services in XML registries using JAXR. **Audience:** Java programmers, professionals and general public. **Principal Exhibits:** Learn how to: Develop and deploy Web services with Java and XML; Describe the functionality of Web services using WSDL; Write interoperable SOAP-based services and clients using JAX-RPC; Generate Java source files for services from WSDL and XML schemas; Customize SOAP messages using SAAJ; Implement strategies to secure your Web services; Locate Web services in XML registries using JAXR. **Telecommunication Services:** info@seminarinformation.com.

22980 ■ **Building XML Web Services with .NET: Hands-On (Onsite)**
Seminar Information Service Inc. (SIS)
250 El Camino Real., Ste. 112
Tustin, CA 92780
Ph: (714)508-0340
Free: 877-736-4636
Fax: (714)734-8027
Co. E-mail: info@seminarinformation.com
URL: http://www.seminarinformation.com
Contact: Catherine Bellizzi, President
URL(s): www.seminarinformation.com
Description: Learn how to: Develop highly scalable distributed applications with XML Web services; Process XML documents with System.Xml library classes; Describe and publish Web services using standard protocols (SOAP, WSDL); Leverage ASP.NET for rapid development and monitoring of Web services; Build high-performance multithreaded and Web clients; Secure XML Web services using encryption and authentication. **Audience:** Industry professionals. **Principal Exhibits:** Learn how to: Develop highly scalable distributed applications with XML Web services; Process XML documents with System.Xml library classes; Describe and publish Web services using standard protocols (SOAP, WSDL); Leverage ASP.NET for rapid development and monitoring of Web services; Build high-performance multithreaded and Web clients; Secure XML Web services using encryption and authentication.

22981 ■ **Cascading Style Sheets CSS for Web Page Development (Onsite)**
Seminar Information Service Inc. (SIS)
250 El Camino Real., Ste. 112
Tustin, CA 92780
Ph: (714)508-0340
Free: 877-736-4636
Fax: (714)734-8027
Co. E-mail: info@seminarinformation.com
URL: http://www.seminarinformation.com
Contact: Catherine Bellizzi, President
URL(s): www.seminarinformation.com/qqbtln/cascading-style-sheets-css-for-web-page-development
Description: Learn how to: Develop fast, efficient, accessible and attractive Web pages using CSS; Generate table page layouts with pure CSS; Structure site layout and content to make your site faster and more maintainable; Apply best practices to develop cross-browser compatible Web pages and avoid pitfalls; Implement menu designs for effective site navigation; Create Web sites that meet Section 508 and W3C accessibility standards. **Audience:** Web establishers, web designers and web developers and general public. **Principal Exhibits:** Learn how to: Develop fast, efficient, accessible and attractive Web pages using CSS; Generate table page layouts with pure CSS; Structure site layout and content to make your site faster and more maintainable; Apply best practices to develop cross-browser compatible Web pages and avoid pitfalls; Implement menu designs for effective site navigation; Create Web sites that meet Section 508 and W3C accessibility standards. **Telecommunication Services:** info@seminarinformation.com.

22982 ■ **Cisco Networking Introduction: Hands-On (Onsite)**
Seminar Information Service Inc. (SIS)
250 El Camino Real., Ste. 112
Tustin, CA 92780
Ph: (714)508-0340

Free: 877-736-4636
Fax: (714)734-8027
Co. E-mail: info@seminarinformation.com
URL: http://www.seminarinformation.com
Contact: Catherine Bellizzi, President
URL(s): www.seminarinformation.com

Description: Learn how to: Successfully install and configure Cisco routers and switches to build internetworks; Create Cisco device configurations from scratch; Configure IP routing protocols; Troubleshoot complex IP routing problems; Perform software and hardware upgrades; Effectively manage and maintain Cisco routers with SNMP. **Audience:** Industry professionals. **Principal Exhibits:** Learn how to: Successfully install and configure Cisco routers and switches to build internetworks; Create Cisco device configurations from scratch; Configure IP routing protocols; Troubleshoot complex IP routing problems; Perform software and hardware upgrades; Effectively manage and maintain Cisco routers with SNMP.

22983 ■ Database Design for Web Development
URL(s): www.eeicom.com

Description: Web designers learn how to design and structure a database efficiently. **Audience:** Programmer, IT professionals. **Principal Exhibits:** Web designers learn how to design and structure a database efficiently.

22984 ■ Developing AJAX Web Applications: Hands-On - Enhancing the Web User Experience (Onsite)
Seminar Information Service Inc. (SIS)
250 El Camino Real., Ste. 112
Tustin, CA 92780
Ph: (714)508-0340
Free: 877-736-4636
Fax: (714)734-8027
Co. E-mail: info@seminarinformation.com
URL: http://www.seminarinformation.com
Contact: Catherine Bellizzi, President
URL(s): www.seminarinformation.com

Description: Learn how to: Develop AJAX-powered interactive and dynamic Web sites; Design accessible interfaces for cross-browser compatibility; Integrate frameworks for data exchange on multiple server environments; Leverage toolkits to rapidly create rich user-friendly interfaces; Optimize and strengthen code to build stable applications; Protect vital information from interception. **Audience:** Professionals and general public. **Principal Exhibits:** Learn how to: Develop AJAX-powered interactive and dynamic Web sites; Design accessible interfaces for cross-browser compatibility; Integrate frameworks for data exchange on multiple server environments; Leverage toolkits to rapidly create rich user-friendly interfaces; Optimize and strengthen code to build stable applications; Protect vital information from interception.

22985 ■ Developing a Web Site: Hands-On (Onsite)
Seminar Information Service Inc. (SIS)
250 El Camino Real., Ste. 112
Tustin, CA 92780
Ph: (714)508-0340
Free: 877-736-4636
Fax: (714)734-8027
Co. E-mail: info@seminarinformation.com
URL: http://www.seminarinformation.com
Contact: Catherine Bellizzi, President
URL(s): www.seminarinformation.com/qqayzx/developing-a-web-site-hands-on

Description: Learn how to: Establish, configure and maintain an intranet or Internet Web site; Develop and publish Web pages using HyperText Markup Language (HTML); Create image maps to allow easy navigation of your Web site; Configure a Web server; Capture, retrieve and display information via a database; Produce dynamic Web pages using server-side and client-side scripts. **Audience:** Web programmers, developers and designers. **Principal Exhibits:** Learn how to: Establish, configure and maintain an intranet or Internet Web site; Develop and publish Web pages using HyperText Markup Language (HTML); Create image maps to allow easy navigation of your Web site; Configure a Web server; Capture, retrieve and display information via a database; Produce dynamic Web pages using server-side and client-side scripts. **Telecommunication Services:** info@seminarinformation.com.

22986 ■ EEI Communications Internet Marketing
URL(s): www.eeicom.com

Description: Covers how businesses can use the Internet to market products, including increasing traffic to your site, and measuring results. **Audience:** Industry professionals. **Principal Exhibits:** Covers how businesses can use the Internet to market products, including increasing traffic to your site, and measuring results. **Telecommunication Services:** train@eeicom.com.

22987 ■ EEI Communications Web Design
URL(s): www.eeicom.com

Description: Covers various aspects of graphic interface design for World Wide Web sites, including site conception; navigational and schematic design; processes from delivery of content to page layout for HTML; editorial, informational, and navigational graphics; and related topics. **Audience:** Designers, programmers, and production specialists. **Principal Exhibits:** Covers various aspects of graphic interface design for World Wide Web sites, including site conception; navigational and schematic design; processes from delivery of content to page layout for HTML; editorial, informational, and navigational graphics; and related topics. **Telecommunication Services:** train@eeicom.com.

22988 ■ EEI Communications Writing for the Web I (Onsite)
URL(s): www.eeicom.com

Description: Covers how to write and edit for sites on the World Wide Web, including understanding the Web's strengths and limitations, providing your audience the information it needs, organizing information with flowcharts and site maps, and using techniques of multimedia writing. **Audience:** Editors, graphic/web designers, desktop publishers, writers, content managers, and communications experts. **Principal Exhibits:** Covers how to write and edit for sites on the World Wide Web, including understanding the Web's strengths and limitations, providing your audience the information it needs, organizing information with flowcharts and site maps, and using techniques of multimedia writing. **Telecommunication Services:** train@eeicom.com.

22989 ■ EEI Communications (X)HTML and CSS I (Onsite)
URL(s): eeicom.com

Description: Covers the fundamentals of Web page design, including formatting text, using graphics in a Web page, creating links, making simple tables in HTML, and avoiding common page design flaws. **Audience:** Web developers and programmers. **Principal Exhibits:** Covers the fundamentals of Web page design, including formatting text, using graphics in a Web page, creating links, making simple tables in HTML, and avoiding common page design flaws. **Telecommunication Services:** train@eeicom.com.

22990 ■ EEI Communications (X)HTML and CSS II (Onsite)
URL(s): www.eeicom.com

Description: Covers intermediate Web page design techniques, including creating forms, including radio buttons and check boxes, creating transparent and interlaced GIFs, using tables for page layout, and creating client-side image maps. **Audience:** Web developers and programmers. **Principal Exhibits:** Covers intermediate Web page design techniques, including creating forms, including radio buttons and check boxes, creating transparent and interlaced GIFs, using tables for page layout, and creating client-side image maps. **Telecommunication Services:** train@eeicom.com.

22991 ■ EEI Communications (X)HTML and CSS III (Onsite)
URL(s): www.eeicom.com

Description: Covers advanced Web page development techniques, including using frames, animated GIFs, cascading style sheets, and Java Script. **Audience:** Web developers and programmers. **Principal Exhibits:** Covers advanced Web page development techniques, including using frames, animated GIFs, cascading style sheets, and Java Script. **Telecommunication Services:** train@eeicom.com.

22992 ■ SharePoint I (Onsite)
URL(s): www.eeicom.com

Description: Learn how to simplify team collaboration using Windows SharePoint Services. **Audience:** Industry professionals. **Principal Exhibits:** Learn how to simplify team collaboration using Windows SharePoint Services.

22993 ■ SharePoint II (Onsite)
URL(s): www.eeicom.com

Description: Learn skills to design, maintain, and publish a custom SharePoint site. **Audience:** Industry professionals, administrative. **Principal Exhibits:** Learn skills to design, maintain, and publish a custom SharePoint site.

22994 ■ SharePoint III (Onsite)
URL(s): www.eeicom.com

Description: Learn how to create and make modifications that can be applied to all users on the site or to individual users using Microsoft SharePoint controls, as well as how to apply personalization to Web pages so that when users modify pages and controls. **Audience:** Industry professionals. **Principal Exhibits:** Learn how to create and make modifications that can be applied to all users on the site or to individual users using Microsoft SharePoint controls, as well as how to apply personalization to Web pages so that when users modify pages and controls.

22995 ■ Webinars with a WOW Factor: Creating Memorable Meeting Across the Globe (Onsite)
Seminar Information Service Inc. (SIS)
250 El Camino Real., Ste. 112
Tustin, CA 92780
Ph: (714)508-0340
Free: 877-736-4636
Fax: (714)734-8027
Co. E-mail: info@seminarinformation.com
URL: http://www.seminarinformation.com
Contact: Catherine Bellizzi, President
URL(s): www.seminarinformation.com/qqbvka/webinars-that-work

Description: Discover techniques that will make your material come to life on the screen and over the phone. **Audience:** Veteran and apprentice trainers. **Principal Exhibits:** Discover techniques that will make your material come to life on the screen and over the phone.

REFERENCE WORKS

22996 ■ "2015 Marketing Calendar for Real Estate Pros: Own It"
Pub: CreateSpace

Released: October 14, 2014. **Price:** $9.56, paperback. **Description:** Real estate agents, mortgage loan agents, and new home builders and site and listing agents are shown how to use low-cost, high yield, proven marketing techniques to create digital real estate listings, find more customers, and sell more homes. Advice for building a brand and public relations; attracting renters and buyers; developing a good Website; and a digital marketing plan are explained. **Availability:** Print.

22997 ■ "Bank of America Fights To Keep Top Spot in Mobile Banking" in Charlotte Business Journal (Vol. 27, June 15, 2012, No. 13, pp. 1)
Pub: American City Business Journals, Inc.
Contact: Mike Olivieri, Executive Vice President

GENERAL SMALL BUSINESS TOPICS

Released: Weekly. Price: $20, Introductory 12-week offer(Digital & Print). Description: Bank of America has been fighting to maintain its lead in mobile banking services. Financial institutions, payment processors and e-commerce firms have started offering mobile banking services. Availability: Print; Online.

22998 ■ *"Crowdfunding Author Thinks Google Will Beat Facebook to the Punch on InvestP2P Acquisition" in GlobeNewswire (July 17, 2012)*
Pub: Comtex News Network Inc.
Contact: Kan Devnani, President
Description: Author, Mark Kanter, explores the potentials of crowdfunding Websites, especially InvestP2P (aka: peer to peer lending) in his new book, "Street Smart CEO". Invest P2P has social networking tools built into its system. Kanter predicts Google to acquire InvestP2P.

22999 ■ *"CrowdFunding Made Simple Conference at University of Utah Ignites Ecosystem of Entrepreneurs and Investors" in Economics Week (June 29, 2012)*
Description: The first national conference on crowdfunding was held at the University of Utah Guest House and Conference Center May 31 through June 1, 2012. The event, CrowdFunding Made Simple, gathered entrepreneurs, business owners, professional service providers, investors, government officials and students to provide understanding and potential of crowdfunding, including information on the Jumpstart Our Business Startups (JOBS) Act. Availability: Print; Online.

23000 ■ *"Digital Marketing: Integrating Strategy and Tactics with Values, A Guidebook for Executives, Managers, and Students"*
Pub: Routledge, Taylor & Francis Group
Released: First edition. Price: $59.95, Paperback-$47.96; $190, Hardback - $152; $29.98, e-book.
Description: Guidebook filled with information on the latest digital marketing tactics and strategic insights to help small businesses generate sustainable growth and achieve competitive advantage through digital integration. A five-step program: mindset, model, strategy, implementation, and sustainability is explained. Availability: E-book; Print.

23001 ■ *"Equity Crowdfunding Platform Initial Crowd Offering, Inc. Closes Equity Financing with Third-Party Investor" in GlobeNewswire (July 18, 2012)*
Description: Initial Crowd Offering Inc. closed third-party equity financing round hat provided capital to finish development of its equity crowdfunding portal to the Website. A private angel investor provided development costs to promote the firm's marketing program. Discussion on equity crowdfunding is included. Availability: Print; PDF; Online.

23002 ■ *The Everything Store: Jeff Bezos and the Age of Amazon*
Pub: Little, Brown and Company
Contact: Judy Clain, Editor-in-Chief
Released: October 15, 2013. Price: $28, hardcover; $30, audiobook CD; $24.98, audiobook downloadable; $12.99, e-book; $18, paperback; $30, hardcover(large print); $28. Description: Amazon.com started as a bookseller, a company delivering books through the mail. Today, the online store, offers a limitless selection of goods at competitively low prices. Profile of entrepreneur Jeff Bezos that outlines his endless pursuit of new markets and risky new ventures to transform retail. Availability: audiobook; CD-ROM; E-book; Print.

23003 ■ *"FutureDash Launches IndieGoGo Crowdfunding Campaign for the EnergyBuddy Home Energy Monitoring System" in Benzinga.com (June 21, 2012)*
Pub: Benzinga.com
Contact: Jason Raznick, Founder
Ed: Aaron Wise. Description: FutureDash launched its campaign on IndieGoGo to promote its home energy monitoring system called EnergyBuddy. The system monitors the amount of electricity being used in the home or building. Information and control is available through an iPhone, iPad, Android smartphone or computer screen or anywhere on a secure Internet connection. Availability: Online.

23004 ■ *"H&R Block Launches One-of-a-Kind Tax Preparation Solution: Block Live" in Investment Weekly News (February 4, 2012, pp. 384)*
Pub: Comtex News Network Inc.
Contact: Kan Devnani, President
Description: Block Live, H&R Blocks latest offering, allows taxpayers to have their tax return prepared by an H&R Block tax professional in real time usng an online video conferencing or chat venue. H&R Block is offering a $100 discount for those using virtual tax preparation service. Details of the new program are provided. Availability: Online.

23005 ■ *"Hoop Culture Opens Showroom, Expands Reach Globally" in Orlando Business Journal (Vol. 30, February 28, 2014, No. 36, pp. 3)*
Pub: American City Business Journals, Inc.
Contact: Mike Olivieri, Executive Vice President
Released: Weekly. Description: Hoop Culture Inc. president, Mike Brown, shares how the online basketball apparel retailer/wholesaler online store has expanded globally. He mentions that Orlando, Florida is one of their biggest markets. Availability: Print; Online.

23006 ■ *"Information Technology Changes Roles, Highlights Hiring Needs" in South Florida Business Journal (Vol. 34, February 14, 2014, No. 30, pp. 3)*
Pub: American City Business Journals, Inc.
Contact: Mike Olivieri, Executive Vice President
Released: Weekly. Price: $8, Introductory 4-week offer(Digital & Print). Description: Results of the Steven Douglas Associates survey of 218 senior and mid-level information technology executives in South Florida are presented. About 75 percent of the respondents cited cloud services, mobile technologies, big data and enterprise reporting planning as having the most profound impact on their roles. The challenges they face with the expected hiring growth are also examined. Availability: Print; Online.

23007 ■ *"Initial Crowd Offering, Inc. Announces Launch of Equity Crowdfunding Intermediary Site" in GlobeNewswire (June 21, 2012)*
Pub: Comtex News Network Inc.
Contact: Kan Devnani, President
Description: Initial Crowd Offering is the IPO for small and emerging businesses and is the most current process to invest and raise capital. The site allows direct, real-time investments in exchange for equity ownership. Availability: Print; PDF; Online.

23008 ■ *"A Neat SocialTrade" in Barron's (Vol. 92, July 23, 2012, No. 30, pp. 23)*
Pub: Dow Jones & Company Inc.
Contact: Almar Latour, Chief Executive Officer
Ed: Theresa W. Carey. Description: SocialTrade is a Website that allows users to exchange ideas and data with each other through video. Online broker DittoTrade launched a mobile applications that allows investors to connect to other traders and follow their trades. Availability: Online.

23009 ■ *"Online Directories: Your Silent Sales Staff" in South Florida Business Journal (Vol. 34, June 20, 2014, No. 48, pp. 14)*
Pub: American City Business Journals, Inc.
Contact: Mike Olivieri, Executive Vice President
Released: Weekly. Price: $8, introductory 4-week offer(Digital only). Description: The benefits of using online business directories as an extension of the physical sales personnel are explained. Business owners who plan to use online directories to their advantage need to check their listings and links at least once a year and whenever there is a change to the business. Availability: Print; Online.

23010 ■ *"Putting Down Roots" in Entrepreneur (August 2014)*
Released: October 28, 2016. Description: Entrepreneur Justin Hartfield and partner Doug Francis created Weedmaps.com, an online portal for marijuana dispensaries, after California legalized the sale of medical marijuana. Hartfield is looking forward to a billion-dollar business once the federal prohibition of marijuana is ended. Local dispensaries pay a monthly subscription of $420 to appear on the site while doctors pay $295 to be featured on the site. Harfield is seeking partnerships with laboratories that will provide marijuana testing and other services. Availability: Online.

23011 ■ *"Spanish Company to Offer Free Wi-Fi In Miami-Dade County" in South Florida Business Journal (Vol. 34, April 25, 2014, No. 40)*
Pub: American City Business Journals, Inc.
Contact: Mike Olivieri, Executive Vice President
Released: Weekly. Description: GOWEX a Madrid-based company, is offering free Wi-Fi access at 400 public spots in Miami, Florida. The firm will sell advertising over the Wi-Fi network. It has offered similar free access to users in New York, NY and in San Francisco, CA. Availability: Print; Online.

23012 ■ *"Truffles & Trifles' Marci Arthur Plans YouTube Channel, Cookbook" in Orlando Business Journal (Vol. 30, May 2, 2014, No. 45, pp. 3)*
Pub: American City Business Journals, Inc.
Contact: Mike Olivieri, Executive Vice President
Released: Weekly. Price: $8, introductory 4-week offer(Digital & Print). Description: Marci Arthur, founder of Truffles & Trifles Cooking School, plans to create a YouTube channel and publish a cookbook. Arthur believes that the survival of her business can be attributed to the devotion and integrity of her employees. Reports show that the school has been receiving donations from sponsors such as Wolf Appliances and Sub-Zero. Availability: Print; Online.

23013 ■ *"Ultimate Guide to Google AdWords: How to Access 100 Million People in 10 Minutes"*
Pub: Entrepreneur Media Inc.
Contact: Dan Bova, Director
E-mail: dbova@entrepreneur.com
Released: 5th edition. Price: $24.95, paperback. Description: The Google AdWords experts and analytics specialist present the techniques, tools, and tricks for using Google AdWords. The experts help small businesses to write advertising and Web site copy design, work in difficult markets, advertise, increase search engine presence, bid strategies for online auctions, financial budgeting and more. Availability: Print.

23014 ■ *"What Makes a Great Tweet" in Harvard Business Review (Vol. 90, May 2012, No. 5, pp. 36)*
Pub: Harvard Business Review Press
Contact: Moderna V. Pfizer, Contact
Ed: Kurt Luther, Michael Bernstein, Paul Andre. Price: $6, PDF. Description: A chart uses readership approval percentages to identify the most effective uses of Twitter. Best tweets include amusing random thoughts and self promotion; worst include complaints and presence maintenance. Availability: Online; PDF.

23015 ■ *"The Zero Marginal Cost Society: The Internet of Things, the Collaborative Commons, and the Eclipse of Capitalism"*
Pub: Palgrave Macmillan
Released: April 04, 2014. Price: $18.99, paperback; $9.99, e-book; $29.99, hardcover. Description: The emerging Internet of things is speeding society to an ear of nearly free goods and services, causing the rise of a global Collaborative Commons and the eclipse of capitalism. Entrepreneurial dynamism of competitive markets that drives productivity up and marginal costs down, enabling businesses to reduce

the price of their goods and services to win consumers and market share is slowly dying. **Availability:** E-book; Print.

VIDEO/AUDIO MEDIA

23016 ■ *Planet Money: The Economics of the Influencer Industry and Its Pitfalls*
URL(s): www.npr.org/2023/05/03/1173799326/influencer-industry-content-creators-career
Ed: Robert Smith. **Released:** May 23, 2023. **Description:** Reflects on the promises and perils of the influencer.

23017 ■ *Working: How a Professional Pen Expert Makes a Living*
URL(s): slate.com/podcsats/working/2023/09/pen-and-stationary-expert-hobby-career
Released: September 17, 2023. **Description:** Podcast explains how a pen and stationery enthusiast turned his hobby into a career. Also discusses how to schedule your days as a freelancer.

RESEARCH CENTERS

23018 ■ Prosperity Now
1200 G St. NW Ste. 400
Washington, DC 20005
Ph: (202)408-9788
Co. E-mail: hello@prosperitynow.org
URL: http://www.prosperitynow.org
Contact: Gary Cunningham, Co-President Co-Chief Executive Officer
Facebook: www.facebook.com/ProsperityNow.org
Linkedin: www.linkedin.com/company/prosperity-now
X (Twitter): x.com/prosperitynow
Instagram: www.instagram.com/prosperitynow
YouTube: www.youtube.com/user/CFEDorg
Description: Provides assistance to public and private organizations concerned with increasing economic opportunity of individuals through the encouragement and support of enterprise development; serves as a forum for the exchange of ideas. Strives to research, develop, and disseminate entrepreneurial policy initiatives at the local, state, and federal levels. Conducts consulting services and compiles statistics. **Scope:** Offers expertise in economic research. Offers services as identify promising ideas, test and refine them in communities to find out what works, craft policies and products to help good ideas reach scale, and foster new markets to achieve greater economic impact. **Founded:** 1979. **Publications:** "Children's Savings Accounts and Financial Aid"; "Linking Youth Savings and Entrepreneurship". **Training:** Fighting Poverty: The Role of Asset Building in Public Policy; IDAS and Microenterprise; Self-Sustaining IDA Initiatives; Serving Multi-Cultural Markets; Asset Purchase Effective Practices; Policy Proposals, Opportunities, and Barriers for Youth Savings. **Educational Activities:** Prosperity Summit (Biennial). **Geographic Preference:** National.

23019 ■ University of California, Los Angeles - Anderson School of Management - Harold and Pauline Price Center for Entrepreneurial Studies
110 Westwood Plz., Rm. C305
Los Angeles, CA 90095-1481
Ph: (310)825-2985
Fax: (310)206-9102
Co. E-mail: price.center@anderson.ucla.edu
URL: http://www.anderson.ucla.edu/centers/price-center-for-entrepreneurship-and-innovation
Contact: Dr. Alfred E. Osborne, Jr., Director
E-mail: al.osborne@anderson.ucla.edu
Description: Integral unit of John E. Anderson Graduate School of Management, University of California, Los Angeles operating under its own board of advisors. **Scope:** Center for entrepreneurial studies. **Founded:** 1995. **Educational Activities:** Research grants for selected faculty members for entrepreneurially related work; Venture Fellows Program.

23020 ■ University of South Florida - Small Business Development Center (SBDC)
3802 Spectrum Blvd., Ste. 201
Tampa, FL 33612
Ph: (813)905-5800
URL: http://sbdctampabay.com/tampa
Contact: Kris Manning, Manager
Facebook: www.facebook.com/usfsbdc
Linkedin: www.linkedin.com/company/usfsbdc
X (Twitter): x.com/usfsbdc
YouTube: www.youtube.com/user/usfsbdc
Description: Integral unit of College of Business Administration at University of South Florida. Offers counseling. **Scope:** Small business operations, entrepreneurship, and success and failure factors for small business development and management, including developing business plans, marketing strategy, and loan packages. **Founded:** 1980. **Publications:** *Entrepreneurial Training Schedule* (Monthly); *Minding Your Own Business* (3/year). **Educational Activities:** SBDC Entrepreneurship seminars, Offer exemplary teaching programs.; SBDC Government contracting trade fair, Offer exemplary teaching programs.; SBDC Seminars on Small Business Management, Offer exemplary teaching programs.; SBDC Small Business Trade Conference (Annual), Offer exemplary teaching and training programs.; SBDC Women Executive Forum, Offer exemplary teaching programs.

Environmentally Responsible Business Practices

START-UP INFORMATION

23021 ■ "Green Clean Machine" in Small Business Opportunities (Winter 2010)
Pub: Harris Publishing, Inc.
Contact: Janet Chase, Contact
Description: Eco-friendly maid franchise plans to grow its $62 million sales base. Profile of Maid Brigade, a green-cleaning franchise is planning to expand across the country. **Availability:** Print; Online.

23022 ■ "Sustainable Advantage" in Inc. (Vol. 36, September 2014, No. 7, pp. 86)
Pub: Mansueto Ventures L.L.C.
Contact: Stephanie Mehta, Chief Executive Officer
Price: $8.95, hardcopy black and white. **Description:** Four startup companies committed to providing sustainable, eco-friendly products and services while protecting the environment and bettering human health are profiled. Holganix(TM) offers organic lawn care products; Motiv Power Systems electrifies large vehicles; Clean Energy Collective Solar Power builds lareg community solar panel arrays; and Protein Bar offers healthy alternatives to fast food in its chain of restaurants. The company also works with nonprofits focused on wellness and education and has created 167 Learning Gardens nationwide. **Availability:** Print; PDF; Online.

ASSOCIATIONS AND OTHER ORGANIZATIONS

23023 ■ Association Canadienne des Ressources Hydriques (ACRH) [Canadian Water Resources Association (CWRA)]
PO Box 93
 Parson, BC, Canada V0A 1L0
Ph: (613)237-9363
Co. E-mail: info@cwra.org
URL: http://cwra.org
Contact: Jeffrey Hirvonen, President
E-mail: president@cwra.org
Linkedin: www.linkedin.com/company/cwra
X (Twitter): x.com/CWRA_Flows
Instagram: www.instagram.com/cwranational
Description: Corporations, government agencies, public libraries, and individuals with an interest in water resources. Seeks to increase public awareness and understanding of water resources; serves as a forum for the exchange of information relating to their management and use. Encourages governments at all levels to recognize the importance of water as a resource and supports formulation of appropriate water use policies. Conducts educational programs. **Founded:** 1947. **Publications:** *Canadian Water Resources Journal* (Quarterly); *CWRA Water News* (Quarterly). **Educational Activities:** CWRA National Conference (Annual). **Awards:** Dillon Consulting Scholarship (Annual); Ken Thompson Scholarship (Annual); Hoskin Scientific Student Poster Award (Annual); Harker/Cameron Women in Water Scholarship (Annual); Ken Thomson Scholarship (Annual). **Geographic Preference:** National.

23024 ■ Association of Clean Water Administrators (ACWA)
1634 Eye St. NW Ste. 750
 Washington, DC 20006
Ph: (202)756-0605
Fax: (202)793-2600
Co. E-mail: srolland@acwa-us.org
URL: http://www.acwa-us.org
Contact: Julia Anastasio, Executive Director
E-mail: janastasio@acwa-us.org
X (Twitter): x.com/cleanwateracwa
Description: Administrators of state and interstate governmental agencies responsible for prevention, abatement, and control of water pollution. Promotes coordination among state agency programs and those of the Environmental Protection Agency, Congress, and other federal agencies. **Founded:** 1961. **Publications:** *List of State Water Pollution Control Administrators* (Annual). **Geographic Preference:** National.

23025 ■ Association of Environmental and Resource Economists (AERE)
222 S Westmonte Dr., Ste. 111
 Altamonte Springs, FL 32714
Ph: (407)774-7880
Fax: (407)774-6440
Co. E-mail: info@aere.org
URL: http://www.aere.org
Contact: Karen Fisher-Vanden, President
E-mail: kaf26@psu.edu
X (Twitter): x.com/aereorg
Description: Professionals, economists, and individuals from universities and governmental agencies interested in resource and environmental issues. **Founded:** 1979. **Publications:** *AERE Newsletter* (Semiannual); *Review of Environmental Economics and Policy (REEP)* (Semiannual). **Awards:** AERE Publication of Enduring Quality Award (Annual). **Geographic Preference:** National.

23026 ■ Canadian Association on Water Quality (CAWQ) [Association canadienne sur la qualite de l'eau (ACQE)]
155-2 King St W Unit No.258
 Hamilton, ON, Canada L8P 4S0
Ph: (289)780-0378
Free: 833-426-7825
URL: http://www.cawq.ca
Contact: Elsayed Elbeshbishy, President
E-mail: elsayed.elbeshbishy@ryerson.ca
Description: Corporations, learned societies, universities, organizations, and individuals. Promotes research on water quality and water pollution. Furthers the exchange of information and practical application of such research for public benefit. **Founded:** 1967. **Publications:** *Water Quality Research Journal of Canada* (Quarterly). **Awards:** Philip H. Jones Award (Annual). **Geographic Preference:** National.

23027 ■ Canadian Environmental Network [Reseau canadien de l'environment (RCEN)]
136F Billings Ave.
 Ottawa, ON, Canada K1H 5K9
Co. E-mail: info@rcen.ca
URL: http://www.rcen.ca/en/home
Contact: Jade Scognamillo, Executive Director
Facebook: www.facebook.com/CanadianEnvironmentalNetwork
Linkedin: www.linkedin.com/company/canadian-environmental-network-rcen-
X (Twitter): x.com/rcen
Instagram: www.instagram.com/canadianenvironmentalnetwork
Description: Environmental organizations. Seeks to advance the projects and activities of members. Promotes ecologically sustainable development. Serves as a clearinghouse on environmental issues; provides support and assistance to members. **Founded:** 1977. **Publications:** *Canadian Environmental Network News*. **Geographic Preference:** Multinational.

23028 ■ Canadian Water Resources Journal
PO Box 93
 Parson, BC, Canada V0A 1L0
Ph: (613)237-9363
Co. E-mail: info@cwra.org
URL: http://cwra.org
Contact: Jeffrey Hirvonen, President
E-mail: president@cwra.org
URL(s): cwra.org/resources/publicationswww.tandfonline.com/journals/tcwr20
Ed: Chris Spence, Jim Buttle. **Released:** Quarterly **Price:** $709, Institutions for print and online or print 2023; $628, Institutions for online. **Description:** Publishes research articles on water resources. **Availability:** Print; PDF; Online.

23029 ■ Conseil Canadien du Compost [Compost Council of Canada]
16, rue Northumberland St.
 Toronto, ON, Canada M6H 1P7
Ph: (416)535-0240
Free: 877-571-4769
Fax: (866)902-7272
Co. E-mail: info@compost.org
URL: http://www.compost.org
Facebook: www.facebook.com/compost.council
X (Twitter): x.com/compostcanada
Description: Advances composting and compost usage across Canada. Serves as the central resource and network for the composting industry in Canada. Contributes to the environmental sustainability of communities. Sponsors International Composting Awareness Week; "Plant a Row Grow a Row". **Founded:** 1991. **Publications:** *Compost Council of Canada Communique*. **Geographic Preference:** National.

23030 ■ Ecology Action Centre (EAC) - Library [Centre d'Action Écologique]
2705 Fern Ln.
 Halifax, NS, Canada B3K 4L3

Ph: (902)429-2202
Fax: (902)405-3716
Co. E-mail: info@ecologyaction.ca
URL: http://www.ecologyaction.ca
Facebook: www.facebook.com/EcologyActionCentre
Linkedin: www.linkedin.com/company/ecology-action-centre
X (Twitter): x.com/ecologyaction

Description: Works to develop solutions to ecological problems. Fosters communication between members. **Scope:** Environmental issues, including acid rain, deforestation, hazardous wastes, recycling, nuclear power, ecosystem stability, species extinction, global warming, pesticides, and waste management. **Founded:** 1971. **Holdings:** Figures not available. **Publications:** *Between the Issues Newsletter* (3/year). **Geographic Preference:** Multinational.

23031 ■ Enviro Business Guide
PO Box 23
Bluffton, AB, Canada T0C 0M0
Ph: (403)843-6563
Co. E-mail: info@recycle.ab.ca
URL: http://recycle.ab.ca
Contact: Don Hughes, President
E-mail: don.hughes@hughesenvironmentalservices.net
URL(s): recycle.ab.ca/enviro-businesses
Availability: Print.

23032 ■ Environmental Design Research Association (EDRA) - Library
PO Box 43023
Washington, DC 20010
Ph: (507)339-4620
Co. E-mail: headquarters@edra.org
URL: http://www.edra.org
Contact: Deni Ruggeri, Executive Director
E-mail: jeremy@heritagestudies.org
Facebook: www.facebook.com/edra.org
Linkedin: www.linkedin.com/company/environmental-design-research-association
X (Twitter): x.com/edratweets

Description: Represents design professionals, social scientists, students, educators, and environmental managers. Advances the art and science of environmental design research. Improves understanding of the relationships between people and their surroundings. Works to create environments responsive to human needs. Promotes design and building processes that incorporate more information about user requirements. Examines the effects of designed environments on family organization, worker productivity, and the recovery rate of hospital patients. Encourages the education of designers, clients, and users about the behavioral consequences of designed environments. **Scope:** Environmental design, focusing on understanding the relationships between people and their environments and creating environments responsive to human needs. Also examines the effects of designed environments on family organizations, worker productivity, and recovery rates of hospital patients. Research also includes conservation of energy and other limited resources. Specific areas of research include environmental cognition, cultural issues in design, post-occupancy evaluation, community psychology, childhood environments, disabilities environments, and interior design research. **Services:** Interlibrary loan (members only). **Founded:** 1968. **Holdings:** Books; journals; documents; technical papers; multimedia materials. **Publications:** *Design Research News* (Quarterly); *EDRA Proceedings*. **Educational Activities:** EDRA Annual conference (Annual). **Awards:** EDRA Career Award (Annual); EDRA Student Design Awards (Annual); EDRA Great Places Awards (Annual). **Geographic Preference:** National.

23033 ■ Environmental & Energy Technology Council of Maine (E2TECH)
ThinkTank Coworking
Pepperell Ctr., 40 Main St.
Biddeford, ME 04005
Ph: (207)423-8260
Co. E-mail: info@e2tech.org
URL: http://e2tech.org
Contact: Martin Grohman, Executive Director
E-mail: marty@e2tech.org
Facebook: www.facebook.com/E2TechMaine
Linkedin: www.linkedin.com/company/e2tech-maine
X (Twitter): x.com/e2techmaine
Instagram: www.instagram.com/e2techmaine
YouTube: www.youtube.com/channel/UCuM47PYOZ0MMwcb48WoKIqQ

Description: Group of individuals, businesses, and organizations with the goal of building and growing Maine's clean technology in the energy sector. Provides networking opportunities, education, lectures, and technology projects for interested members.

23034 ■ Environmental Entrepreneurs (E2)
1152 15th St. NW
Washington, DC 20005
Co. E-mail: info@e2.org
URL: http://www.e2.org
Contact: Bob Keefe, Executive Director
Facebook: www.facebook.com/e2.org
Linkedin: www.linkedin.com/grps
X (Twitter): x.com/e2org

Description: Represents business people who believe in protecting the environment while building economic prosperity. Serves as a champion on the economic side of good environmental policy by taking an economically sound approach to environmental issues. Focuses on environmental policies that drive economic growth in a healthy direction. **Founded:** 2000. **Publications:** *Environmental Entrepreneurs Update* (Monthly). **Geographic Preference:** National.

23035 ■ Environmental Entrepreneurs Mountain West Chapter
CO
URL: http://e2.org/chapters/mountain-west
Contact: Whitney Painter, Director

Description: Represents individual business leaders who advocate for good environmental policy while building economic prosperity. Provides information about pressing environmental issues to members. Tackles environmental issues through bipartisan efforts. **Founded:** 2007. **Geographic Preference:** Regional.

23036 ■ Environmental Entrepreneurs Northern California Chapter
111 Sutter St., 20th Fl.
San Francisco, CA 94104
URL: http://www.e2.org/chapters/northern-california
Contact: David Rosenheim, Director

Description: Represents individual business leaders who advocate for good environmental policy while building economic prosperity. Provides information about pressing environmental issues to members. Tackles environmental issues through bipartisan efforts. **Founded:** 2000. **Geographic Preference:** Local.

23037 ■ Green Exchange
2545 W Diversey Ave.
Chicago, IL 60647
Ph: (312)275-6000
Co. E-mail: info@greenexchange.com
URL: http://www.greenexchange.com
Facebook: www.facebook.com/GxChicago
X (Twitter): x.com/gxchicago
Instagram: www.instagram.com/gxchicago

Description: A center for innovation in the green economy, Green Exchange serves as a living showcase for green design and practices. **Founded:** 2006.

23038 ■ Green Hotels Association (GHA)
1611 Mossy Stone Dr.
Houston, TX 77077-4109
Ph: (713)789-8889
Fax: (713)789-9786
Co. E-mail: green@greenhotels.com
URL: http://greenhotels.com/index.php
Contact: Patricia Griffin, President
X (Twitter): x.com/#!/GreenHotelsAssn

Description: Encourages, promotes and supports ecological consciousness in the hospitality industry. **Founded:** 1993. **Publications:** *Greening Newsletter* (Bimonthly); *Membership Conservation Guidelines and Ideas*. **Geographic Preference:** Multinational.

23039 ■ Municipal Waste Association (MWA)
10C Shared Space, 42 Carden St.
Guelph, ON, Canada N1H 3A2
Ph: (519)837-6863
Co. E-mail: mwa@municipalwaste.ca
URL: http://municipalwaste.ca
Contact: David Douglas, Chairman

Description: Promotes more effective and environmentally sustainable removal of solid wastes. Facilitates sharing of municipal waste management, reduction, recycling, and reuse information and facilities. **Founded:** 1987. **Publications:** *For R Information* (Quarterly). **Awards:** MWA Promotion and Education Campaign Award (Annual). **Geographic Preference:** National.

23040 ■ National Association of Clean Air Agencies (NACAA)
1530 Wilson Blvd., Ste. 320
Arlington, VA 22209
Ph: (571)970-6678
Co. E-mail: 4cleanair@4cleanair.org
URL: http://www.4cleanair.org
Contact: Frank Kohlasch, President
E-mail: frank.kohlasch@state.mn.us
X (Twitter): x.com/weare4cleanair

Description: State, local and territorial air pollution program administrators and members of their staffs. Provides an opportunity for state and local officials who are responsible for implementing air pollution control programs established under the Clean Air Act to share air quality-related experiences and to discuss problems. Encourages communication and cooperation among federal, state, and local regulatory agencies. **Founded:** 1968. **Geographic Preference:** National.

23041 ■ National Association of Clean Water Agencies (NACWA)
1130 Connecticut Ave., NW, Ste. 1050
Washington, DC 20036
Ph: (202)833-2672
Fax: (888)267-9505
Co. E-mail: info@nacwa.org
URL: http://www.nacwa.org
Contact: Adam Krantz, Chief Executive Officer
E-mail: akrantz@nacwa.org
Facebook: www.facebook.com/NACWAOfficial
Linkedin: www.linkedin.com/company/nacwa
X (Twitter): x.com/nacwa
YouTube: www.youtube.com/nacwaorg

Description: Public waste water treatment facilities, consulting firms and other private and public organization. Advances knowledge in the management of metropolitan sewerage agencies and develop more effective public service by encouraging the establishment of sound sewage collection, treatment and disposal policies. **Founded:** 1970. **Publications:** *Clean Water Advocate* (Semiannual); *NACWA Annual Report* (Annual). **Educational Activities:** National Environmental Policy Forum (Annual); Winter/Summer Technical Conference (Annual). **Awards:** NACWA Environment Award (Annual); NACWA Excellence in Management Award (Annual); NACWA Public Service Award (Annual); NACWA Peak Performance Platinum Award (Annual); NACWA Peak Performance Gold Award (Annual); NACWA Peak Performance Silver Award (Annual); NACWA Distinguished Service Award (Annual); NACWA President's Award (Annual); NACWA Special Recognition Award (Annual); NACWA Water Resources Utility of the Future Award (Periodic); NACWA Research & Technology Award (Annual); NACWA Operations & Environmental Performance Award (Annual); NACWA Member Agency Public Service Award (Annual); NACWA Public Information & Education Award (Annual). **Geographic Preference:** National.

GENERAL SMALL BUSINESS TOPICS

23042 ■ National Environmental, Safety and Health Training Association (NESHTA)
584 Main St.
  South Portland, ME 04106
Ph: (207)771-9020
Co. E-mail: neshta@neshta.org
URL: http://neshta.org
Contact: Sharon L. Flory, President
Description: Professional society for environmental training professionals organized to promote competency and standards. Seeks to encourage communication among individual trainers, training institutions, and governmental agencies, promote environmental personnel training and education and set minimum standards for training and education programs. Sponsors research programs. Conducts a national certification program for environmental trainers. **Founded:** 1977. **Publications:** CET Information and Examination Guide; NESHTA eNews (Periodic). **Educational Activities:** NESHTA Conference (Annual). **Awards:** NESHTA Environmental Education Award (Annual). **Geographic Preference:** Multinational.

23043 ■ Nitem Foundation
15, 1527 Sofia center
  Sofia, Bulgaria
Ph: 359 2 943 19 99
Co. E-mail: office@nitem-bg.com
URL: http://www.nitem-bg.com
Facebook: www.facebook.com/NitemCompany
X (Twitter): x.com/NitemBG
Description: A not-for-profit organization that commits its resources to address issues of global social and environmental concern, particularly those that have a major impact and changing through education and support entrepreneurship. **Founded:** 2002.

23044 ■ Pellet Fuels Institute (PFI)
2150 N 107th St., Ste. 205
  Seattle, WA 98133
Ph: (206)209-5277
Co. E-mail: office@pelletheat.org
URL: http://www.pelletheat.org
Contact: Tim Portz, Executive Director
E-mail: tim@pelletheat.org
X (Twitter): x.com/pelletfuel
Description: Promotes the increased use of pellets, briquettes, chips, and other renewable fiber fuels. Supports lobbying efforts promoting fiber fuels. Acts as an information clearinghouse among members. **Founded:** 1985. **Publications:** PFI Newsletter. **Geographic Preference:** National.

23045 ■ Pembina Institute
No. 802, 322 - 11 Ave., SW
  Calgary, AB, Canada T2R 0C5
Ph: (403)269-3344
Fax: (587)606-6423
Co. E-mail: news@pembina.org
URL: http://www.pembina.org
Contact: Chris Severson-Baker, Executive Director
E-mail: executivedirector@pembina.org
Facebook: www.facebook.com/pembina.institute
Linkedin: www.linkedin.com/company/pembina-institute
X (Twitter): x.com/pembina
YouTube: www.youtube.com/user/PembinaInstitute
Description: Promotes increased public awareness of environmental and development issues. **Scope:** Provide research, analysis and recommendations to inform policies and practices related to energy. **Founded:** 1986. **Publications:** Pembina Institute Annual report (Annual); Electronic newsletter (Monthly). **Geographic Preference:** Multinational.

23046 ■ Planetary Association for Clean Energy Inc. (PACE) - Library [Societe Planetaire pour l'Assainissement de l'Energie, Inc.]
100 Bronson Ave., Ste. 1001
  Ottawa, ON, Canada K1R 6G8
Ph: (613)236-6265
URL: http://pacenet.homestead.com
Contact: Chesley W. Carter, Chairperson
Description: Researchers, individuals, corporations, and institutions worldwide seeking to facilitate research, development, demonstration, and evaluation of clean energy systems. Defines clean energy systems as those that utilize natural sources, and are inexpensive, non-polluting, and universally applicable. Concerns include the bioeffects of low-level electromagnetics, bioenergetics, new energy technology, decontamination of nuclear and toxic wastes, production of clean water from ambient air, and pesticide and fertilizer-free ultra-productive agricultural practices. Tests and recommends products that facilitate the implementation of clean energy systems. Serves as a consultant to governments and other agencies. Maintains speaker's bureau. **Scope:** Clean energy. **Founded:** 1976. **Holdings:** Figures not available. **Geographic Preference:** Multinational.

23047 ■ Pollution Probe (PP)
130 Queens Quay E Ste. 902 W Twr.
  Toronto, ON, Canada M5A 0P6
Ph: (416)926-1907
Free: 877-926-1907
Co. E-mail: pprobe@pollutionprobe.org
URL: http://www.pollutionprobe.org
Contact: Christopher Hilkene, Chief Executive Officer
E-mail: chilkene@pollutionprobe.org
Facebook: www.facebook.com/PollutionProbe
Linkedin: www.linkedin.com/company/pollution-probe
X (Twitter): x.com/pollutionprobe
Instagram: www.instagram.com/pollutionprobe
YouTube: www.youtube.com/PollutionProbe
Description: Works to define environmental problems through research; seeks to raise public awareness of environmental issues through education; lobbies for environmental protection and remediation before government agencies and industrial associations. Focuses on smog and climate change, reduction and elimination of mercury in water, child health and the environment, indoor air quality, and water quality. **Scope:** Environmental problems. **Founded:** 1969. **Publications:** Pollution Probe Reports; Probe-Abilities (Quarterly); Probe Post: Canada's Environmental Magazine (Quarterly); P2 - Exclusive Donor Newsletter (Quarterly). **Geographic Preference:** National.

23048 ■ *RCA Connector*
PO Box 23
  Bluffton, AB, Canada T0C 0M0
Ph: (403)843-6563
Co. E-mail: info@recycle.ab.ca
URL: http://recycle.ab.ca
Contact: Don Hughes, President
E-mail: don.hughes@hughesenvironmentalservices.net
URL(s): recycle.ab.ca/newsyear/2024
Released: Monthly **Availability:** Print; Online.

23049 ■ Recycling Council of Alberta (RCA)
PO Box 23
  Bluffton, AB, Canada T0C 0M0
Ph: (403)843-6563
Co. E-mail: info@recycle.ab.ca
URL: http://recycle.ab.ca
Contact: Don Hughes, President
E-mail: don.hughes@hughesenvironmentalservices.net
Facebook: www.facebook.com/RecyclingCouncilOfAlberta
Linkedin: www.linkedin.com/company/recycling-council-of-alberta
X (Twitter): x.com/3RsAB
Instagram: www.instagram.com/recyclingcouncilab
Description: Promotes and facilitates waste reduction, recycling and resource conservation in the province of Alberta. **Founded:** 1987. **Publications:** RCA Connector (Monthly); Enviro Business Guide. **Awards:** R's of Excellence (Annual); Rs of Excellence Awards (Annual). **Geographic Preference:** State.

23050 ■ Resource Efficient Agricultural Production - Canada (REAPC)
Centennial Ctr., CCB13
  21, 111 Lakeshore Rd.
  Sainte-Anne-de-Bellevue, QC, Canada H9X 3V9
Ph: (514)398-7743
Fax: (514)398-7972
Co. E-mail: info@reap-canada.com
URL: http://www.reap-canada.com
Contact: Roger Samson, Executive Director
Description: Promotes development and implementation of environmentally sustainable and economically viable agricultural techniques in Canada and internationally. Conducts research and disseminates results in areas including ecology, energy, agri-fibre, and food production. **Founded:** 1986. **Educational Activities:** International Agriculture Program. **Geographic Preference:** Multinational.

23051 ■ Saskatchewan Environmental Society (SES)
Offices No. 204 & No. 205a€"220 20th St. W
  Saskatoon, SK, Canada S7K 3N9
Ph: (306)665-1915
Co. E-mail: info@environmentalsociety.ca
URL: http://environmentalsociety.ca
Contact: Margret Asmuss, President
Facebook: www.facebook.com/environmentalsociety
Linkedin: www.linkedin.com/company/saskatchewan-environmental-society
X (Twitter): x.com/skenvsociety
Instagram: www.instagram.com/skenvsociety
YouTube: www.youtube.com/user/EnvironmentalSociety
Description: Seeks to support and encourage the creation of a global community in which all needs are met in sustainable ways. **Founded:** 1970. **Publications:** SES Newsletter (Quarterly). **Geographic Preference:** National.

23052 ■ Society Promoting Environmental Conservation (SPEC) - Library
2305 W 7th Ave.
  Vancouver, BC, Canada V6K 1Y4
Ph: (604)736-7732
Co. E-mail: admin@spec.bc.ca
URL: http://www.spec.bc.ca
Contact: Jennifer Henry, Executive Director
Facebook: www.facebook.com/SPEC.bc.ca
X (Twitter): x.com/specbc
Instagram: www.instagram.com/specbc
YouTube: www.youtube.com/user/specbc
Description: Promotes environmental research, advocacy, and education. **Scope:** Urban living. **Founded:** 1969. **Holdings:** Figures not available. **Publications:** SPECTRUM (Quarterly). **Geographic Preference:** Multinational.

23053 ■ *Water Quality Research Journal of Canada*
155-2 King St W Unit No.258
  Hamilton, ON, Canada L8P 4S0
Ph: (289)780-0378
Free: 833-426-7825
URL: http://www.cawq.ca
Contact: Elsayed Elbeshbishy, President
E-mail: elsayed.elbeshbishy@ryerson.ca
URL(s): iwaponline.com/wqrj
Released: Quarterly **Price:** $1,034, Institutions for online. **Description:** Contains research papers on all aspects of water pollution. **Availability:** Print; PDF; Online.

23054 ■ *Women & Environments International* (WEI)
192 Spadina Ave., Ste. 400
  Toronto, ON, Canada M5T 2C2
Ph: (416)928-0880
Fax: (416)644-0116
Co. E-mail: office@womenshealthyenvironments.ca
URL: http://www.womenshealthyenvironments.ca
Contact: Kanisha Acharya-Patel, Executive Director
URL(s): www.womenshealthyenvironments.ca/partnerswww.yorku.ca/weimag/index.html
Released: Semiannual **Price:** $7, Single issue for back issues; $11, for back issue double; $5, for photocopies of out-of-print issues. **Availability:** Print; PDF; Online.

23055 ■ Women's Healthy Environments Network (WHEN)
192 Spadina Ave., Ste. 400
Toronto, ON, Canada M5T 2C2
Ph: (416)928-0880
Fax: (416)644-0116
Co. E-mail: office@womenshealthyenvironments.ca
URL: http://www.womenshealthyenvironments.ca
Contact: Kanisha Acharya-Patel, Executive Director
Facebook: www.facebook.com/WHENonlinex
X (Twitter): x.com/WHENonline
Description: Represents women experts in environmental studies and issues. Works to implement community development projects to improve the environment. Advocates environmental protection, anti-discriminatory zoning practices, and the development of affordable housing. **Founded:** 1994. **Publications:** *Women & Environments International (WEI)* (Semiannual). **Geographic Preference:** National.

23056 ■ Yukon Conservation Society (YCS) - Library
302 Hawkins St.
Whitehorse, YT, Canada Y1A 1X6
Ph: (867)668-5678
Co. E-mail: coservices@yukon.ca
URL: http://www.yukonconservation.org
Contact: Kim Melton, Director
Facebook: www.facebook.com/yukonconservationsociety
X (Twitter): x.com/YukonConservati
Instagram: www.instagram.com/yukonconservation
Description: Seeks to protect Canada's natural environment; particularly that of the Yukon region. Encourages the conservation of Yukon wilderness, wildlife and natural resources. **Scope:** Canada's natural environment, particularly that of the Yukon region. **Founded:** 1968. **Holdings:** Figures not available. **Publications:** *Walk Softly*. **Awards:** Ted Parnell Scholarship (Annual). **Geographic Preference:** National.

INCUBATORS/RESEARCH AND TECHNOLOGY PARKS

23057 ■ NextEnergy
461 Burroughs St.
Detroit, MI 48202
Ph: (313)833-0100
Facebook: www.facebook.com/nextenergymi
Linkedin: www.linkedin.com/company/nextenergy-mi
Description: Works with innovators to accelerate smarter, cleaner, more accessible solutions for communities and cities. **Founded:** 2002.

23058 ■ Third Derivative Institute
22830 Two Rivers Rd.
Basalt, CO 81621
Description: Works to accelerate the rate of climate innovation through an inclusive ecosystem approach, which rapidly finds, funds, and scales climate tech globally. Joint venture between Rocky Mountain Insitute (RMI) and New Energy Nexus. **Founded:** 2020.

EDUCATIONAL PROGRAMS

23059 ■ ASTM Phase I & Phase II Environmental Site Assessment Processes (Onsite)
Seminar Information Service Inc. (SIS)
250 El Camino Real., Ste. 112
Tustin, CA 92780
Ph: (714)508-0340
Free: 877-736-4636
Fax: (714)734-8027
Co. E-mail: info@seminarinformation.com
URL: http://www.seminarinformation.com
Contact: Catherine Bellizzi, President
URL(s): www.seminarinformation.com/qqbrwl/astm-phase-i-and-phase-ii-environmental-site-assessment
Description: Gain an understanding how to use the standards and how the standards affect the way you do business. The 'Innocent Landowner Defense' under the Comprehensive Environmental Response, Compensation and Liability Act (CERCLA) and why due diligence is necessary will be covered. **Audience:** Industry professionals. **Principal Exhibits:** Gain an understanding how to use the standards and how the standards affect the way you do business. The 'Innocent Landowner Defense' under the Comprehensive Environmental Response, Compensation and Liability Act (CERCLA) and why due diligence is necessary will be covered.

23060 ■ Climatic Test Techniques (Onsite)
Seminar Information Service Inc. (SIS)
250 El Camino Real., Ste. 112
Tustin, CA 92780
Ph: (714)508-0340
Free: 877-736-4636
Fax: (714)734-8027
Co. E-mail: info@seminarinformation.com
URL: http://www.seminarinformation.com
Contact: Catherine Bellizzi, President
URL(s): www.seminarinformation.com/qqalqq/climatic-test-techniques
Description: An introduction to climatic testing with an overview of field test measurement and analysis, with primary emphasis on understanding the physics of each environment, and available measurement and control techniques. **Audience:** Environmental engineering specialists . **Principal Exhibits:** An introduction to climatic testing with an overview of field test measurement and analysis, with primary emphasis on understanding the physics of each environment, and available measurement and control techniques.

23061 ■ Comprehensive 5-Day Training Program For Energy Managers (Onsite)
Seminar Information Service Inc. (SIS)
250 El Camino Real., Ste. 112
Tustin, CA 92780
Ph: (714)508-0340
Free: 877-736-4636
Fax: (714)734-8027
Co. E-mail: info@seminarinformation.com
URL: http://www.seminarinformation.com
Contact: Catherine Bellizzi, President
URL(s): www.seminarinformation.com
Description: Provides detailed coverage of all of the six training areas specified for energy managers in the Energy Policy Act, and offers a comprehensive learning and problem-solving forum for those who want a broader understanding of the latest energy cost reduction techniques and strategies. **Audience:** Managers. **Principal Exhibits:** Provides detailed coverage of all of the six training areas specified for energy managers in the Energy Policy Act, and offers a comprehensive learning and problem-solving forum for those who want a broader understanding of the latest energy cost reduction techniques and strategies.

23062 ■ Crude Oil: Sampling, Testing, and Evaluation (Onsite)
Seminar Information Service Inc. (SIS)
250 El Camino Real., Ste. 112
Tustin, CA 92780
Ph: (714)508-0340
Free: 877-736-4636
Fax: (714)734-8027
Co. E-mail: info@seminarinformation.com
URL: http://www.seminarinformation.com
Contact: Catherine Bellizzi, President
URL(s): www.seminarinformation.com/details.cfm?qc=qqbruu
Description: Learn how to obtain representative samples of crude oil using automatic and manual methods. Learn the test methods available for obtaining the basic data necessary to determine quantity for custody transfer purposes and conformance to expected quality. **Audience:** Laboratory technicians and chemists. **Principal Exhibits:** Learn how to obtain representative samples of crude oil using automatic and manual methods. Learn the test methods available for obtaining the basic data necessary to determine quantity for custody transfer purposes and conformance to expected quality.

23063 ■ DOT Hazardous Materials Training (Onsite)
Seminar Information Service Inc. (SIS)
250 El Camino Real., Ste. 112
Tustin, CA 92780
Ph: (714)508-0340
Free: 877-736-4636
Fax: (714)734-8027
Co. E-mail: info@seminarinformation.com
URL: http://www.seminarinformation.com
Contact: Catherine Bellizzi, President
URL(s): www.seminarinformation.com/details.cfm?qc=qqaubm
Description: DOT is changing virtually all of the rules for hazardous materials containers, labeling, shipping papers, placards, and shipping names. Learn how to comply with the regulations. **Audience:** Shipping supervisors, purchasing managers, traffic managers, plant managers, shipping clerks, dispatchers, purchasing agents, drivers, and compliance managers. **Principal Exhibits:** DOT is changing virtually all of the rules for hazardous materials containers, labeling, shipping papers, placards, and shipping names. Learn how to comply with the regulations.

23064 ■ Energy Auditing 101: Identifying Cost Saving Opportunities in Plants & Buildings (Onsite)
Seminar Information Service Inc. (SIS)
250 El Camino Real., Ste. 112
Tustin, CA 92780
Ph: (714)508-0340
Free: 877-736-4636
Fax: (714)734-8027
Co. E-mail: info@seminarinformation.com
URL: http://www.seminarinformation.com
Contact: Catherine Bellizzi, President
URL(s): www.seminarinformation.com
Description: Seminar designed to provide you with the knowledge you need to identify where energy consumption can be reduced, and utilize the latest methods and technologies to accomplish real savings, with emphasis on providing useful calculation methods and practical examples. **Audience:** Industry professionals, managers, admin. **Principal Exhibits:** Seminar designed to provide you with the knowledge you need to identify where energy consumption can be reduced, and utilize the latest methods and technologies to accomplish real savings, with emphasis on providing useful calculation methods and practical examples.

23065 ■ Fundamentals of Carbon Reduction (Onsite)
Seminar Information Service Inc. (SIS)
250 El Camino Real., Ste. 112
Tustin, CA 92780
Ph: (714)508-0340
Free: 877-736-4636
Fax: (714)734-8027
Co. E-mail: info@seminarinformation.com
URL: http://www.seminarinformation.com
Contact: Catherine Bellizzi, President
URL(s): www.seminarinformation.com
Description: First step for organizations that want to become more environmentally-friendly, including how to conduct a 'carbon audit' and how to begin a carbon reduction program. **Audience:** Professionals. **Principal Exhibits:** First step for organizations that want to become more environmentally-friendly, including how to conduct a 'carbon audit' and how to begin a carbon reduction program.

23066 ■ Gasoline: Specifications, Testing, and Technology (Onsite)
Seminar Information Service Inc. (SIS)
250 El Camino Real., Ste. 112
Tustin, CA 92780
Ph: (714)508-0340
Free: 877-736-4636
Fax: (714)734-8027
Co. E-mail: info@seminarinformation.com
URL: http://www.seminarinformation.com
Contact: Catherine Bellizzi, President
URL(s): www.seminarinformation.com/qqatlt/gasoline-specifications-testing-and-technology

Description: Covers the properties and specifications of gasoline and how they affect its performance in a spark ignition engine, including a tour of a gasoline testing laboratory. **Audience:** Petroleum company employees, regulatory personnel, and fuel marketing personnel. **Principal Exhibits:** Covers the properties and specifications of gasoline and how they affect its performance in a spark ignition engine, including a tour of a gasoline testing laboratory.

23067 ■ Hazardous Waste Management: The Complete Course

Seminar Information Service Inc. (SIS)
250 El Camino Real., Ste. 112
Tustin, CA 92780
Ph: (714)508-0340
Free: 877-736-4636
Fax: (714)734-8027
Co. E-mail: info@seminarinformation.com
URL: http://www.seminarinformation.com
Contact: Catherine Bellizzi, President
URL(s): www.seminarinformation.com/qqajxq/hazardous-waste-management-the-complete-course

Description: Covers how to meet your annual training requirement and learn a systematic approach to understanding and complying with the latest state and federal regulations. **Audience:** Environmental coordinators, hazardous waste managers and plant managers. **Principal Exhibits:** Covers how to meet your annual training requirement and learn a systematic approach to understanding and complying with the latest state and federal regulations.

23068 ■ Marine Fuels: Specifications, Testing, Purchase & Use

Seminar Information Service Inc. (SIS)
250 El Camino Real., Ste. 112
Tustin, CA 92780
Ph: (714)508-0340
Free: 877-736-4636
Fax: (714)734-8027
Co. E-mail: info@seminarinformation.com
URL: http://www.seminarinformation.com
Contact: Catherine Bellizzi, President
URL(s): www.seminarinformation.com/qqaadj/marine-fuels-specifications-testing-purchase-and-use

Description: Learn how the properties of marine fuels affect fuel handling, combustion, and cost, including a detailed understanding of fuel quality requirements, and why they are necessary for good handling and combustion performance. **Audience:** Supervisors and managers in laboratory operations. **Principal Exhibits:** Learn how the properties of marine fuels affect fuel handling, combustion, and cost, including a detailed understanding of fuel quality requirements, and why they are necessary for good handling and combustion performance.

23069 ■ Risk-Based Corrective Action RBCA Applied at Petroleum Release Sites (Onsite)

Seminar Information Service Inc. (SIS)
250 El Camino Real., Ste. 112
Tustin, CA 92780
Ph: (714)508-0340
Free: 877-736-4636
Fax: (714)734-8027
Co. E-mail: info@seminarinformation.com
URL: http://www.seminarinformation.com
Contact: Catherine Bellizzi, President
URL(s): www.seminarinformation.com/qqbcej/risk-based-corrective-action-rbca-applied-at-petroleum

Description: Receive the same RBCA training your state regulators are receiving from the organization that developed the RBCA standard from RBCA process overview and risk assessment to fate and transport and policy decisions. **Audience:** Environmental engineers, underground storage tank owners, managers, attorneys and insurance underwriters, and petroleum marketers. **Principal Exhibits:** Receive the same RBCA training your state regulators are receiving from the organization that developed the RBCA standard from RBCA process overview and risk assessment to fate and transport and policy decisions.

REFERENCE WORKS

23070 ■ "3 Proven Sustainability Practices for Small Businesses" in Hazardous Waste Experts Blog (March 3, 2015)

Released: March 03, 2015. **Description:** It may feel like a monumental task to become a 'green' company, but small businesses can certainly be a part of this burgeoning movement of corporate social responsibility (CSR). This article details how small businesses can start with small steps. **Availability:** Online.

23071 ■ "3 Ways Entrepreneurs Can Implement Sustainable Practices in 2022" in Forbes (Jan. 30, 2022)

URL(s): www.forbes.com/sites/rhettpower/2022/01/30/3-ways-entrepreneurs-can-implement-sustainable-practices-in-2022/?sh=1cbae33a129a

Released: January 30, 2022. **Description:** Discusses the challenges involved in implementing sustainable business practices and offers tips on how small businesses can start small as they focus their efforts on utilizing sustainable business practices. **Availability:** Online.

23072 ■ "4 Strategies for Sustainable Businesses" in MIT Management Sloan School Ideas Made to Matter (Nov. 30, 2021)

URL(s): mitsloan.mit.edu/ideas-made-to-matter/4-strategies-sustainable-business

Released: November 30, 2021. **Description:** Discusses the importance of adopting sustainable business practices. Offers four guiding principles to help business leaders set sustainability strategies for their small business. **Availability:** Online.

23073 ■ "5 Sustainable Businesses in 2020 & Their Best Practices" in FlyGreen Blog (February 26, 2020)

Released: February 26, 2020. **Description:** Discusses how a business can become sustainable and details five companies with great sustainability processes and their best practices. **Availability:** Online.

23074 ■ "8 Sustainable Business Practices - Are You Doing Your Part?" in Thriving Small Business (May 29, 2019)

Ed: Patricia Lotich. **Released:** May 29, 2019. **Description:** The increasingly popular green approach to business practices is what sustainability is all about. This article details eight sustainable business practices examples that small businesses can utilize. **Availability:** Online.

23075 ■ "10 Ways to Make Your Small Business More Sustainable" in Looka (July 7, 2021)

URL(s): looka.com/blog/make-your-small-business-sustainable/

Released: July 07, 2021. **Description:** Discusses the growing practice of small business sustainability and provides ten ways to make your small business more sustainable. **Availability:** Online.

23076 ■ "23 Green Business Ideas for Eco-Minded Entrepreneurs" in Business News Daily (Dec. 21, 2021)

URL(s): www.businessnewsdaily.com/5102-green-business-ideas.html

Released: December 21, 2021. **Description:** Discusses environmentally sound business practices and provides eco-friendly business ideas that can make money and save the planet at the same time. **Availability:** Online.

23077 ■ "39 Green Business Ideas for Sustainable Entrepreneurs" in Just Business (October 22, 2020)

Ed: Meredith Wood. **Released:** October 22, 2020. **Description:** An eco-friendly business, or "green business" is one that demonstrates a commitment to an environmentally sustainable future. This article provides 39 sustainable business ideas for entrepreneurs to consider. **Availability:** Online.

23078 ■ "45 Green Business Ideas for Aspiring Entrepreneurs" in LegalZoom (Oct. 12, 2021)

URL(s): www.legalzoom.com/articles/45-green-business-ideas-for-aspiring-entrepreneurs

Released: October 12, 2021. **Description:** Discusses the impact that green businesses have on a community and provides green business ideas for entrepreneurs looking to start an eco-friendly business. **Availability:** Online.

23079 ■ "2010: Important Year Ahead for Waterfront" in Bellingham Business Journal (Vol. March 2010, pp. 2)

Description: A tentative timeline has been established for the environmental impact statement (EIS) slated for completion in May 2010. The plan for the Waterfront District includes detailed economic and architectural analysis of the feasibility of reusing remaining structures and retaining some industrial icons. **Availability:** Print; Online.

23080 ■ "2011 FinOvation Awards" in Farm Industry News (January 19, 2011)

Pub: Informa Business Media, Inc.
Contact: Charlie McCurdy, President

Ed: Karen McMahon, Jodie Wehrspann. **Description:** The 2011 FinOvation Award winners are announced, covering new products that growers need for corn and soybean crops. Winners range from small turbines and a fuel-efficient pickup to a Class 10 combine and drought-tolerant hybrids. **Availability:** Online.

23081 ■ "2011 a Record Year for New Wind Energy Installations in Canada" in CNW Group (September 26, 2011)

Pub: CNW Group Ltd.

Description: Canada reports a record for new wind energy projects in 2011 with about 1,338 MW of newly installed wind energy capacity expected to come on line, compared to 690 MW installed in 2010. Statistical data included. **Availability:** Print; Online.

23082 ■ "Abt Electronics and Appliances Announces the Second Annual Earth Day Recycle Drive" in Ecology, Environment & Conservation Business (May 3, 2014, pp. 3)

Pub: NewsRX LLC.
Contact: Kalani Rosell, Contact

Description: Abt Electronics and Appliances is the largest independent, single-store appliance and electronics retailer in the U.S. In honor of Earth Day, Abt has partnered with the City of Chicago to help local residents recycle e-waste, such as electronics and appliances, in an environmentally friendly way for the second year in a row. **Availability:** Online.

23083 ■ "Acciona Windpower to Supply 3-Megawatt Turbines to Prince Edward Island Energy" in Professional Close-Up (September 11, 2012)

Description: Acciona Windpower and Prince Edward Island Energy Corporation (PEIEC) have partnered to supply turbines for the Hermanville & Clear Springs Wind Project that will provide 10 Acciona Windpower AW3000/116 wind turbine generators with capacity of 3 megawatts and a rotor diameter of 116 meters. Acciona will operate and maintain the turbines for the first 15 years.

23084 ■ "ACE Commits $300,000 to Support Environmental Conservation Initiatives and Green Business Entrepreneurs" in Insurance Business Weekly (March 2, 2012, pp. 13)

Pub: NewsRX LLC.
Contact: Kalani Rosell, Contact

Description: ACE Charitable Foundation has committed to a two-year, $300,000 funding of The Conservation Fund for new initiatives that protect key watersheds, expand wildlife migration corridors and investment in local green economies in the United States. **Availability:** Online.

23085 ■ "Acing the Test" in Contractor (Vol. 57, January 2010, No. 1, pp. 32)
Pub: Informa USA, Inc.
Contact: Stephen A. Carter, Chief Executive Officer
Ed: Robert P. Mader. **Released:** January 01, 2010. **Description:** A ward winning mechanical system retrofitting of a middle school in Ohio is discussed. The school now operates at 37,800 Btu/sq. ft and reduced a significant amount of pollutants from being emitted into the environment.

23086 ■ "Actiontec and Verizon Team Up for a Smarter Home" in Ecology,Environment & Conservation Business (November 5, 2011, pp. 3)
Pub: Comtex News Network Inc.
Contact: Kan Devnani, President
Description: Verizon is implementing Actiontec Electronics' SG200 Service Gateway as a basic component of its Home Monitoring and Control service. This new smart home service allows customers to remotely check their homes, control locks and appliances, view home-energy use and more using a smartphone, PC, or FiOS TV. **Availability:** Online.

23087 ■ "Adventures at Hydronicahh" in Contractor (Vol. 56, September 2009, No. 9, pp. 52)
Ed: Mark Eatherton. **Released:** Part 6. **Description:** Installations of the heating system of a lakeview room are described. The room's radiant windows are powered by electricity from a solar PV array and a propane-powered hydrogen fuel cell. The system will be programmed to use the most energy available. **Availability:** Print; Online.

23088 ■ "Agana To Bottle Rain for Whole Foods" in Austin Business Journal (Vol. 32, March 30, 2012, No. 4, pp. 1)
Pub: American City Business Journals, Inc.
Contact: Mike Olivieri, Executive Vice President
Ed: Vicky Garza. **Description:** Agana Rainwater has signed a deal to bottle rainwater for Whole Foods Market Inc. Rainwater bottling is seen as a conservation tools as it does not deplete the lake or aquifer. **Availability:** Online.

23089 ■ "AgraQuest Deal Signals Growth for Biopesticide Makers" in Sacramento Business Journal (Vol. 29, July 13, 2012, No. 20, pp. 1)
Pub: Baltimore Business Journal
Contact: Rhonda Pringle, President
E-mail: rpringle@bizjournals.com
Description: Industry observes claim that biotechnology irm Bayer CropScience's upcoming acquisition of AgraQuest Inc. could signal the growth of biopesticide manufacturing chemical methods for agricultural crop protection could then be complemented with environmentally friendly approaches allowed by biopesticides. **Availability:** Print; Online.

23090 ■ "Agricultural Community Implements Green Technologies, Building Team" in Contractor (Vol. 56, September 2009, No. 9, pp. 5)
Ed: Candace Roulo. **Description:** John DeWald and Associates has initiated a residential development project which uses green technologies in Illinois. The community features a community center, organic farm and recreational trails. Comments from executives are also provided. **Availability:** Print; Online.

23091 ■ "Alberta Carbon Capture Strategy Falters: Alberta's Favoured Emissions-Control Plan is Falling Apart" in Canadian Business (Vol. 85, June 11, 2012, No. 10, pp. 13)
Ed: Matthew McClearn. **Description:** The emissions-control plan of Alberta suffered a major setback following cancellations of major carbon capture and storage (CCS) pilot projects. Project Pioneer was cancelled because the saving did not justify the operating costs while discontinuation of Heartland Area Redwater Project was due to the uncertainty surrounding the province's changing CCS rules. **Availability:** Print; Online.

23092 ■ "Albuquerque Entrepreneurs Selected As Top Participants in USHCC Foundation Green Builds Business Program" in Marketing Weekly News (April 21, 2012)
Description: Five winners of the 2012 Green Builds Business program was announced by the United States Hispanic Chamber of Commerce Foundation (USHCCF). These winners will receive a combined 24 hours of one-on-one green coaching with Bill Roth, the Green Business Coach for Entrepreneur.com and Founder of Earth 2017. Details are included. **Availability:** Print; Online.

23093 ■ "Alcoa: 'Going Where No Materials Scientist Has Gone Before'" in Pittsburgh Business Times (Vol. 33, July 18, 2014, No. 53, pp. 5)
Pub: American City Business Journals, Inc.
Contact: Mike Olivieri, Executive Vice President
Released: Weekly. **Price:** $4, introductory 4-week offer(Digital & Print). **Description:** Alcoa Inc. has signed a $1.1 billion supply agreement with Pratt & Whitney to build the forging for aluminum jet-engine fan blades as well as other parts made with aluminum lithium. This partnership brings together Alcoa's proprietary alloys and unique manufacturing processes with Pratt & Whitney's design, thus forging an aluminum fan blade that is lighter and enables better fuel efficiency. **Availability:** Print; Online.

23094 ■ Alex James: Slowing Down Fast Fashion
Released: 2016. **Description:** A critical look at the fashion industry and the impact it has had on society and the environment. **Availability:** Streaming.

23095 ■ "Allowing Ethanol Tax Incentive to Expire Would Risk Jobs, RFA's Dinneen Says" in Farm Industry News (November 3, 2010)
Pub: Informa Business Media, Inc.
Contact: Charlie McCurdy, President
Ed: Lynn Grooms. **Price:** $4, Print and Online; Special Offers only for 4 weeks. **Description:** Jobs would be at risk if the ethanol tax incentive expires. **Availability:** Print; Online.

23096 ■ "Alstom Launches the ECO 122 - 2.7MW Wind Turbine for Low Wind Sites" in CNW Group (September 28, 2011)
Pub: CNW Group Ltd.
Description: Alstom is launching its new ECO 122, a 2.7MW onshore wind turbine that combines high power and high capacity factor (1) to boost energy yield in low wind regions around the world. The ECO 122 will produce about 25 percent increased wind farm yield that current turbines and fewer turbines would be installed in areas. **Availability:** Print; Online.

23097 ■ "Altera Ranks Among Top 25 Greenest Companies in U.S." in Ecology, Environment & Conservation Business (August 9, 2014, pp. 2)
Pub: NewsRX LLC.
Contact: Kalani Rosell, Contact
Description: Altera Corporation was ranked 24 on the Newsweek Magazine 2014 Green Rankings of over 500 companies in the United States. These rankings are one of the world's most recognized assessments of corporate sustainability and environmental impact. Eight specific indicators were used, including conservation and sustainability efforts in the areas of energy, carbon, water, and waste productivity. **Availability:** Online.

23098 ■ "Alternative Energy Calls for Alternative Marketing" in Indoor Comfort Marketing (Vol. 70, June 2011, No. 6, pp. 8)
Pub: Spray Technology & Marketing
Contact: Ava Caridad, Director, Editorial
E-mail: acaridad@spraytm.com
Ed: Richard Rutigliano. **Released:** June 01, 2011. **Description:** Advice for marketing solar energy products and services is given. **Availability:** Print; Online.

23099 ■ "Alternative Energy Is a Major Topic at Agritechnica 2011" in Farm Industry News (November 16, 2011)
Pub: Informa Business Media, Inc.
Contact: Charlie McCurdy, President
Ed: Mark Moore. **Description:** Sustainable agricultural systems were a hot topic at this year's Agritechnia 2011, held in Germany. Germany is a leader in the development of on-farm biogas systems. **Availability:** Online.

23100 ■ "Alternative Fuels Take Center Stage at Houston Auto Show" in Houston Business Journal (Vol. 44, January 31, 2014, No. 39, pp. 8)
Pub: American City Business Journals, Inc.
Contact: Mike Olivieri, Executive Vice President
Released: January 31, 2014. **Price:** $4, Introductory 4-Week Offer(Digital & Print). **Description:** An energy summit was held at the Houston Auto Show in Texas on January 22, 2014, where energy executives discussed new technology and initiatives. They considered the market for electric and natural gas-fueled vehicles as well as other options including hydrogen, fuel cells, and biofuels. **Availability:** Print; Online.

23101 ■ "American Chemistry Council Launches Flagship Blog" in Ecology,Environment & Conservation Business (October 29, 2011, pp. 5)
Pub: PR Newswire Association LLC.
Description: American Chemistry Council (ACC) launched its blog, American Chemistry Matters, where interactive space allows bloggers to respond to news coverage and to discuss policy issues and their impact on innovation, competitiveness, job creation and safety. **Availability:** Online.

23102 ■ "American Farmland Trust Profiles In Stewardship, How California Farmers and Ranchers are Producing a Better Environment" in Ecology, Environment & Conservation Business (January 4, 2014, pp. 2)
Pub: PR Newswire Association LLC.
Description: Forty-five Profiles In Stewardship were presented by the American Farmland Trust showing how farmers and ranchers in 25 California counties are improving the environment by adopting conservation practices that serve examples for others to follow in order to promote sound farming practices and improve the environment by protecting land, air and water.

23103 ■ "Answers About Commercial Wind Farms Could Come from Downstate" in Erie Times-News (September 27, 2011)
Pub: Erie Times News
Contact: Christopher Millette, Managing Editor
E-mail: cmillette@timesnews.com
Ed: Valerie Myers. **Description:** Texas-based Pioneer Green Energy is measuring wind and leasing land in North East Township, Pennsylvania. The firm plans to build a 7,000-acre wind farm along wine-country ridges. About 70 turbines would harness wind in order to generate electricity that would be sold into the eastern power grid. **Availability:** Online.

23104 ■ "Areva Diversifies Further Into Wind" in Wall Street Journal Eastern Edition (November 29, 2011, pp. B7)
Pub: Dow Jones & Company Inc.
Contact: Almar Latour, Chief Executive Officer
Ed: Max Colchester, Noemie Bisserbe. **Description:** French engineering company Areva SA is diversifying and moving away from nuclear energy projects. One sign of that is its recent discussion to construct 120 wind turbines to be located at two German wind farms. Such a deal, if signed, would be worth about US$1.59 billion. **Availability:** Online.

23105 ■ "Art Institute of Chicago Goes Green" in Contractor (Vol. 56, July 2009, No. 7, pp. 1)
Ed: Candace Roulo. Description: Art Institute of Chicago's Modern Wing museum addition will receive a certification that makes them one of the most environmentally sound museum expansions in the U.S. A modified variable-air-volume system is being used to meet temperature and humidity requirements in the building and it also has a double curtain wall to capture summer heat. Availability: Print; Online.

23106 ■ "As Costs Skyrocket, More U.S. Cities Stop Recycling" in The New York Times (March 16, 2019)
URL(s): www.nytimes.com/2019/03/16/business/local-recycling-costs.html
Ed: Michael Corkery. Description: After China stopped buying recyclable material from the US in 2018 due to it being mixed in with too much actual trash, many communities across the nation are canceling their recycling programs. With fewer buyers, recycling companies are charging cities more, and these communities have to pass down the cost somehow, either by raising taxes or cutting other services. Many just close their recycling centers, and it's having a detrimental impact the environment. Availability: Online.

23107 ■ "Austin to Buy $1.1B of Wind Power from Two" in Austin Business Journal (Vol. 31, August 19, 2011, No. 24, pp. A1)
Pub: Austin Business Journal
Contact: Rachel McGrath, Director
E-mail: rmcgrath@bizjournals.com
Ed: Vicky Garza. Description: Austin City Council is set to approve contracts to purchase wind energy from Duke Energy Corporation and MAP Royalty Inc. The city will get 200MW from Duke and 91MW from MAP and the total contract is estimated to be worth $1.1 million. Availability: Print; Online.

23108 ■ "Auto Show Aims to Electrify" in Crain's Detroit Business (Vol. 26, January 11, 2010, No. 2, pp. 1)
Pub: Crain Communications Inc.
Contact: Barry Asin, President
Ed: Ryan Beene. Description: Overview of the North American International Auto show include sixteen production and concept vehicles including eight from the Detroit 3. High-tech battery suppliers as well as hybrid and electric vehicles will highlight the show. Availability: Print; Online.

23109 ■ "Automaker Foundations Run Leaner" in Crain's Detroit Business (Vol. 26, January 11, 2010, No. 2, pp. 1)
Pub: Crain Communications Inc.
Contact: Barry Asin, President
Ed: Sherri Welch. Description: Overview of the Detroit automobile industry includes restoring profitability, smarter marketing strategies and philanthropy. Each company comprising the Big 3 is examined, as is their vision for the future. Availability: Print; Online.

23110 ■ "AV Concept Expands Into Green Energy Storage" in Wireless News (January 25, 2010)
Description: Electronics distributor and manufacturer AV Concept Holdings Limited announced a marketing partnership with Boston-Power, a provider of lithium-ion batteries, with a focus in the Chinese and Korean markets. Availability: Online.

23111 ■ "Avoid the Stress of Traffic and Pollution with House Call Doctor Los Angeles" in Ecology, Environment & Conservation Business (May 24, 2014)
Pub: NewsRX LLC.
Contact: Kalani Rosell, Contact
Description: Record levels of air pollution in the Los Angeles, California area pose serious risks to those suffering from illness or injury. Michael Farzam and his team at House Call Doctor Los Angeles provides telephone medicine for those unable or unwilling to visit a physician in person. The mobile doctor in Los Angeles offers individuals throughout the area with concierge care without leaving home. Availability: Online.

23112 ■ "Award Win Highlights Slingsby's Green Credentials" in Ecology,Environment & Conservation Business (August 20, 2011, pp. 3)
Description: Slingsby, an industrial and commercial equipment supplier, was joint winner with Hallmark Cards of the Baildon Business in the Community's Yorkshire and Humber Long Term Environmental Improvement Award. The firm cites its commitment to reducing environmental impact. Availability: Print; PDF; Online.

23113 ■ "BARS+TONE Achieves Green Business Certification by the City and County of San Francisco" in Benzinga.com (April 26, 2012)
Pub: Benzinga.com
Contact: Jason Raznick, Founder
Ed: Aaron Wise. Description: City and County of San Francisco, California presented a Green Business certification to BARS+TONE, a creative video agency. The certification is part of an ongoing effort to reduce environmental impact. Availability: Online.

23114 ■ "Be Wary of Dual-Flush Conversion Kits" in Contractor (Vol. 56, September 2009, No. 9, pp. 66)
Ed: John Koeller, Bill Gauley. Description: Recommendation of untested dual-flush conversion devices for tank-type toilets in the United States has been questioned. The products are being advertised as having the ability to convert single-flush to a dual-flush toilet. No evidence of water conservation from using such devices has been recorded. Availability: Print; Online.

23115 ■ "BETC Backers Plot Future" in Business Journal Portland (Vol. 27, December 10, 2010, No. 41, pp. 1)
Pub: Portland Business Journal
Contact: Andy Giegerich, Managing Editor
E-mail: agiegerich@bizjournals.com
Ed: Erik Siemers. Description: A coalition of clean energy groups and industrial manufacturers have spearheaded a campaign aimed at persuading Oregon legislators that the state's Business Energy Tax Credit (BETC) is vital in job creation. Oregon's BETC grants tax credits for 50 percent of an eligible renewable or clean energy project's cost. However, some legislators propose BETC's abolition. Availability: Print; Online.

23116 ■ "Beware of E15 Gasoline" in Rental Product News (Vol. 33, October 2011)
Ed: Curt Bennink. Description: Environmental Protection Agency (EPA) set a new regulation that grants partial waivers to allow gasoline containing up to 15 percent ethanol (E15) to be introduced into commerce for use in model year 2001 and newer light-duty motor vehicles, subject to certain conditions. Availability: Online.

23117 ■ "Beyond Green – Ways to Make Your Business More Sustainable in 2022" in Success Consciousness
URL(s): www.successconsciousness.com/blog/wellness/beyond-green-ways-to-make-your-business-more-sustainable/
Description: Discusses the imperative nature of utilizing sustainable business practices to remain in the game. Provides recommendations on how to make your small business more sustainable. Availability: Online.

23118 ■ "Beyond Meat (R) Completes Largest Financing Round to Date" in Ecology, Environment & Conservation Business (August 16, 2014, pp. 4)
Pub: NewsRX LLC.
Contact: Kalani Rosell, Contact
Description: Beyond Meat (R) is the first company to recreate meat from plants and is dedicated to improving human health, positively impacting climate change, conserving natural resources and respecting animal welfare. The firm has completed its Series D financing round, which will also help the company promote consumer awareness and increase capacity at its manufacturing facility to meet demand. Availability: Online.

23119 ■ "Biodiesel Poised to Regain Growth" in Farm Industry News (January 21, 2011)
Pub: Informa Business Media, Inc.
Contact: Charlie McCurdy, President
Ed: Lynn Grooms. Description: According to Gary Haer, vice president of sales and marketing for Renewable Energy Group, the biodiesel industry is positioned to regain growth in 2011 with the reinstatement of the biodiesel blendersa tax credit of $1 per gallon. Availability: Print; Online.

23120 ■ "Bioheat - Alternative for Fueling Equipment" in Indoor Comfort Marketing (Vol. 70, May 2011, No. 5, pp. 14)
Description: Profile of Worley and Obetz, supplier of biofuels used as an alternative for fueling industry equipment. Availability: Print; Online.

23121 ■ "Bitumen Oilsands: Slick Science" in Canadian Business (Vol. 81, September 15, 2008, No. 14-15, pp. 55)
Pub: Rogers Media Inc.
Contact: Neil Spivak, Chief Executive Officer
Ed: Andrew Nikiforuk. Description: N-Solv Corp's John Nenniger has discovered a better alternative to steam-assisted gravity drainage methods for extracting bitumen. Nenniger's technique also relies on gravity but replaces steam with propane, which leaves behind impurities like asphaltenes and heavy metals that are too dirty to burn. Availability: Print; Mailing list; Online.

23122 ■ "Blackwater Is LEED Golden for Port of Portland Building" in Contractor (Vol. 56, October 2009, No. 10, pp. 3)
Ed: Robert P. Mader. Description: Worrel Water Technologies' Tidal Wetlands Living Machine recycles blackwater from the toilets and sends it right back to flush the toilets. The Technology is being installed in the new headquarters of the Port of Portland which aims to get awarded a gold certificate from the Leadership in Energy and Environmental Design. Availability: Print; Online.

23123 ■ "Boatyard Expansion 8-Year Odyssey" in Providence Business News (Vol. 28, March 31, 2014, No. 52, p. 1)
Pub: American City Business Journals, Inc.
Contact: Mike Olivieri, Executive Vice President
Released: March 29, 2014. Description: Bristol Marine owner, Andy Tyska, has found it challenging to operate and improve the boatyard due to lack of available coastal land and restrictive environmental regulations. Tyska made a large investment in plans for expanding the property he purchased in 1998. Tyska discusses the challenges faced while trying to improve his boatyard. Availability: Print; Online.

23124 ■ "Boeing Partnership to Preserve Thousands of Acres of Threatened Wetlands in South Carolina" in Ecology, Environment & Conservation Business (August 2, 2014, pp. 3)
Pub: NewsRX LLC.
Contact: Kalani Rosell, Contact
Description: U.S. Army Corps of Engineers approved Boeing's comprehensive wetlands mitigation plan to preserve about 4,000 acres of land, including more than 2,000 acres of wetlands near the Francis Marion National Forest in South Carolina Lowcountry. Boeing worked in partnership with federal, state and local agencies and conservation organizations to identify the tracts for preservation in order to achieve conservation goals of regional and national significance. Availability: Online.

23125 ■ "Bonefish Grill Debuts New Cocktail to Benefit Conservation Foundation" in *Ecology, Environment & Conservation Business* (May 17, 2014, pp. 5)
Pub: NewsRX LLC.
Contact: Kalani Rosell, Contact
Description: Bonefish Grill has introduced the Ocean Trust Tropic Heat Martini to support the Ocean Trust, an ocean conservation foundation. The new drink contains house-made infused pineapple Absolut vodka, with fresh mango and a thin slice of jalapeno and served at their restaurants nationwide. **Availability:** Online.

23126 ■ "Boston Cab Association Gets 2012 Green Business Award" in *Professional Close-Up* (April 28, 2012)
Description: Boston Cab Association was awarded the 2012 Green Business Award for its conversion to all hybrid vehicles in its fleet. The company was the first to commit to the purchase of hybrids in 2006 as part of the City of Boston's Clean Air Cab program. **Availability:** Online.

23127 ■ "Buy the Pants, Save the Planet?" in *Globe & Mail* (February 5, 2007, pp. B1)
Description: The marketing campaign of the clothing company Diesel S.p.A. is discussed. The company has based its latest collection of T-shirt designs on the problem of global warming. **Availability:** Online.

23128 ■ "Caber Engineering Helps to Reduce Canada's Carbon Footprint" in *Ecology,Environment & Conservation Business* (July 16, 2011, pp. 7)
Description: Calgary-based Caber Engineering Inc. will assist in the engineering design of the Alberta Carbon Trunk Line (ACTL). The ACTL is Alberta's first sizable commercial carbon capture and storage project focusing on the reduction of environmental impacts while being economically beneficial. **Availability:** Online.

23129 ■ "Calendar" in *Crain's Detroit Business* (Vol. 24, March 10, 2008, No. 10, pp. 21)
Pub: Crain Communications Inc.
Contact: Barry Asin, President
Description: Listing of events in the Detroit area include conferences addressing entrepreneurialism, economic development, and women business ownership. **Availability:** Print; Online.

23130 ■ "Canada in 2020 Energy: Mr. Clean" in *Canadian Business* (Vol. 81, October 27, 2008, No. 18, pp. 74)
Pub: Rogers Media Inc.
Contact: Neil Spivak, Chief Executive Officer
Ed: Rachel Pulfer. **Description:** Profile of Nicholas Parker, co-founder of Cleantech Group LLC, a pioneer in clean technology investing. Cleantech, now a global industry, accounts for 10 percent of all venture capital investments made by U.S. companies in 2007. **Availability:** Print; Online.

23131 ■ "Canada's Largest Bakery Officially Opened Today" in *Ecology,Environment & Conservation Business* (October 15, 2011, pp. 7)
Description: Maple Leaf Foods opened Canada's largest commercial bakery in Hamilton, Ontario. The firm's 385,000 square foot Trillium bakery benefits from efficient design flow and best-in-class technologies. **Availability:** Print; Online.

23132 ■ "Canadian Hydronics Businesses Promote 'Beautiful Heat" in *Indoor Comfort Marketing* (Vol. 70, September 2011, No. 9, pp. 20)
Pub: Spray Technology & Marketing
Contact: Ava Caridad, Director, Editorial
E-mail: acaridad@spraytm.com
Released: September 01, 2011. **Description:** Canadian hydronics companies are promoting their systems as beautiful heat. Hydronics is the use of water as the heat-transfer medium in heating and cooling system. **Availability:** Print; Online.

23133 ■ "Canadian Wind Farm Sued Due to Negative Health Effects" in *PC Magazine Online* (September 22, 2011)
Pub: PC Magazine
Contact: Dan Costa, Editor-in-Chief
E-mail: dan_costa@pcmag.com
Ed: Andrew Webster. **Description:** Suncor Energy is being sued by a family in Ontario, Canada. The family claims that Suncor's wind turbines have created health problems for them, ranging from vertigo and sleep disturbance to depression and suicidal thoughts. The family's home is over 1,000 meters from the eight wind turbines, and according to Ontario officials, wind turbines must be a minimum of 550 meters from existing homes. **Availability:** Online.

23134 ■ "CanWEA Unveils WindVision for BC: 5,250 MW of Wind Energy by 2025" in *CNW Group* (October 4, 2011)
Pub: CNW Group Ltd.
Description: Wind industry leaders are asking British Columbia, Canada policy makers to created conditions to further develop and integrate wind energy in accordance with greenhouse gas emission targets and projected economic growth. Statistical data included. **Availability:** PDF; Online.

23135 ■ "Carbon Capture and Storage: Grave Concerns" in *Canadian Business* (Vol. 81, July 21 2008, No. 11, pp. 25)
Ed: Andrew Nikiforuk. **Released:** January 01, 2017. **Description:** Air pollution control regulations to reduce greenhouse gasses have been implemented by the Canadian government. The federal government is planning to construct a carbon funeral industry that will store the global warming gases, however the expenditure for the project will be shifted to the taxpayers. Details of the Bruce Peachy's initiative on how to reduce GHGs are presented. **Availability:** Print; Online.

23136 ■ "Caribou Coffee Kick-Starts Spring Planting with New Grounds for Your Ground Program in Time for Earth Day" in *Ecology, Environment and Conservation Business* (May 3, 2014, pp. 5)
Pub: NewsRX LLC.
Contact: Kalani Rosell, Contact
Description: Caribou Coffee is providing customers and local gardening clubs in Minnesota free used espresso ground for their gardens. The Grounds for Your Grounds program allows customers to pick up five-pound recycled bags of used grounds from retail locations for use in their home garden or community garden. The firm is committed to supporting local gardens and gardening organizations with existing reusable resource-espresso grounds. **Availability:** Online.

23137 ■ "Carrington Co. LLC Revolutionizes the Hot Tea Market with First-Ever, Organic Tea in Eco-Friendly Packaging" in *Ecology, Environment & Conservation Business* (May 3, 2014, pp. 6)
Pub: NewsRX LLC.
Contact: Kalani Rosell, Contact
Description: Carrington Company makes organic non-genetically modified products including flax seeds, hemp, chia, and organic coconut oil and teas. The firm is launching its Carrington Organics Tea to its lineup of healthy products, packed in a 100 percent eco-friendly packaging that will fully and safely biodegrade when composted. It is the first tea available packaged in fully recyclable packaging. **Availability:** Online.

23138 ■ "Cascades Awarded 'Innovative Product of the Year' and 'Environmental Strategy of the Year' by Pulp & Paper International PPI" in *Ecology, Environment & Conservation Business* (January 4, 2014, pp. 4)
Pub: NewsRX LLC.
Contact: Kalani Rosell, Contact
Description: Cascades Tissue Group was awarded 'Innovative Product of the Year' for its bathroom and facial tissues made from unbleached recycled fiber, the first of its kind in the U.S. Cascades also won the 'Environmental Strategy of the Year' based on its commitment to reducing its ecological impact through continuous improvement of processes, unique recycling infrastructure, and use of recycled fibers in packaging and tissue products. Pulp and Paper recognizes companies for these efforts annually. **Availability:** Print; Online.

23139 ■ "Case IH Announces Strategy to Meet 2014 Clean Air Standards" in *Farm Industry News* (September 15, 2011)
Pub: Informa Business Media, Inc.
Contact: Charlie McCurdy, President
Ed: Jodie Wehrspann. **Description:** Case IH will meet EPA's stringent engine emissions limits imposed in 2014, called Tier 4. The limits call for a 90 percent reduction in particulate matter and nitrogen oxides (NOx) over the Tier 3 requirements from a few years ago. **Availability:** Print; Online.

23140 ■ "Cash for Appliances Targets HVAC Products, Water Heaters" in *Contractor* (Vol. 56, October 2009, No. 10, pp. 1)
Ed: Candace Roulo. **Description:** States and territories would need to submit a full application that specifies their implementation plans if they are interested in joining the Cash for Appliances program funded by the American Recovery and Reinvestment Act. The Department of Energy urges states to focus on heating and cooling equipment, appliances and water heaters since these offer the greatest energy savings potential. **Availability:** Print; Online.

23141 ■ "Catch the Wind Announces Filing of Injunction Against Air Data Systems LLC and Philip Rogers" in *CNW Group* (September 30, 2011)
Pub: CNW Group Ltd.
Description: Catch the Wind, providers of laser-based wind sensor products and technology, filed an injunction against Optical Air Data Systems (OADS) LLC and its former President and CEO Philip L. Rogers. The complaint seeks to have OADS and Rogers return tangible and intangible property owned by Catch the Wind, which the firm believes to be critical to the operations of their business. **Availability:** Online.

23142 ■ "Catch the Wind to Hold Investor Update Conference Call on October 18, 2011" in *CNW Group* (October 4, 2011)
Pub: CNW Group Ltd.
Description: Catch the Wind Ltd., providers of laser-based wind sensor products and technology, held a conference call for analysts and institutional investors. The high-growth technology firm is headquartered in Manassas, Virginia. **Availability:** Print; Online.

23143 ■ "CE2 Carbon Capital and Dogwood Carbon Solutions Partner with Missouri Landowners to Generate High Quality Carbon Offsets from 300,000 Acres of Forest" in *Nanotechnolgy Business Journal* (January 25, 2010)
Pub: Investment Weekly News
Description: Dogwood Carbon Solutions, a developer of agriculture and forestry based conservation projects, has partnered with CE2 Carbon Capital, one of the largest investors and owners of U.S. carbon commodities and carbon emissions reduction projects, to develop high-quality carbon offsets from over 30,000 acres of privately-owned non-industrial forest in the Ozark mountain region of Arkansas and Missouri. **Availability:** Print; Online.

23144 ■ "CEO Forecast: With Cloudy Economy, Executives Turn to Government Contracting" in *Hispanic Business* (January-February 2009, pp. 34, 36)
Ed: Jessica Haro, Richard Kaplan. **Description:** As economic uncertainty fogs the future, executives turn to government contracts in order to boost business.

Revenue sources, health care challenges, environmental consulting and remediation services, as well as technological strides are discussed. **Availability:** Print; Online.

23145 ▪ *"The CEO Poll: Fuel for Thought II Canadian Business Leaders on Energy Policy"* in *Canadian Business (Vol. 81, September 15, 2008, No. 14-15, pp. 12)*
Pub: Rogers Media Inc.
Contact: Neil Spivak, Chief Executive Officer
Ed: Joe Castaldo. **Description:** Most Canadian business leaders worry about the unreliability of the oil supply but feel that Canada is in a better position to benefit from the energy supply crisis than other countries. Many respondents also highlighted the need to invest in renewable energy sources. **Availability:** Online.

23146 ▪ *"Certification Experts Germanischer Lloyd Wind Energy Assist NaiKun's Offshore Wind Project"* in *Marketwired (May 14, 2007)*
Pub: Comtex News Network Inc.
Contact: Kan Devnani, President
Description: Germanischer Lloyd Wind Energy (GL Wind) will examine, inspect, and provide quality management services for the engineering, design, and construction of the offshore wind project planned by NaiKun Wind Development Inc. in northwest British Columbia. **Availability:** Online.

23147 ▪ *"Charged Up for Sales"* in *Charlotte Business Journal (Vol. 25, October 15, 2010, No. 30, pp. 1)*
Description: Li-Ion Motors Corporation is set to expand its production lines of electric cars in Sacramento, California. The plan is seen to create up to 600 jobs. The company's total investment is seen to reach $500 million. **Availability:** Print; Online.

23148 ▪ *"Chicago Public Schools District Builds Green"* in *Contractor (Vol. 56, October 2009, No. 10, pp. 5)*
Ed: Candace Roulo. **Description:** Chicago Public Schools district has already built six U.S. Green Building Council LEED certified schools and one addition in five years and will continue to build new green buildings. The district has an Environmental Action Plan that strives to reduce energy usage, improve indoor air quality, and reduce contribution to climate change. **Availability:** Print; Online.

23149 ▪ *"China's Transition to Green Energy Systems: The Economics of Home Solar Water Heaters and Their Popularization in Dezhou City"* in *Energy Policy (Vol. 39, October 2011, No. 10, pp. 5909-5919)*
Ed: Wei Li, Guojun Song, Melanie Beresford, Ben Ma. **Released:** 2011. **Description:** The economics of home solar water heaters and their growing popularity in Dezhous City, China is discussed. **Availability:** PDF; Online.

23150 ▪ *"Christmas Trees Keep Giving in St. Louis Area"* in *St. Louis Post-Dispatch (January 11, 2012)*
Pub: Tribune News Service
Contact: Jack Barry, Vice President, Operations
E-mail: jbarry@tribpub.com
Ed: Jonah Newman. **Description:** Missouri state law prohibiting disposing of Christmas trees into area lakes has forced citizens to find new ways to use their old trees. Saint Louis and other municipalities offers ways to recycle Christmas trees while creating a good habitat for fish. Cities have sunk a portion of the trees, then created mulch and is offered free to residents. **Availability:** Online.

23151 ▪ *"Clean-Tech Focus Sparks Growth"* in *Philadelphia Business Journal (Vol. 28, January 15, 2010, No. 48, pp. 1)*
Pub: Philadelphia Business Journal
Contact: Sierra Quinn, Director
E-mail: squinn@bizjournals.com
Ed: Peter Key. **Description:** Keystone Redevelopment Group and economic development organization Ben Franklin Technology Partners of Southeastern Pennsylvania have partnered in supporting the growth of new alternative energy and clean technology companies. Keystone has also been developing the Bridge Business Center. **Availability:** Online.

23152 ▪ *"'Climate Positive Now' a Welcome Message of Sustainability"* in *Woodworking Network (November 19, 2021)*
URL(s): www.woodworkingnetwork.com/news/woodworking-industry-news/climate-positive-now-welcome-message-sustainability
Ed: Larry Adams. **Released:** November 19, 2021. **Description:** A positive trend of using sustainable wood materials is being voiced by consumers and designers. Furniture makers are listening and looking for leads on materials that are branded as climate positive.

23153 ▪ *Clothing Poverty: The Hidden World of Fast Fashion and Second-Hand Clothes*
Ed: Andrew Brooks. **Released:** March 15, 2015. **Price:** $21.95, Paperback; $14.95, E-Book. **Description:** A journey around the world exploring where our clothes come from and how the fashion industry perpetuates poverty around the world. **Availability:** E-book; Print.

23154 ▪ *"Co-Op Launches Revolving Loan Program for Farmers"* in *Bellingham Business Journal (Vol. February 2010, pp. 3)*
Pub: Sound Publishing Inc.
Contact: Josh O'Connor, President
Ed: Lance Henderson. **Description:** Community Food Co-op's Farm Fund received a $12,000 matching grant from the Sustainable Whatcom Fund of the Whatcom Community Foundation. The Farm Fund will create a new revolving loan program for local farmers committed to using sustainable practices.

23155 ▪ *"Coal Train Crush Feared"* in *Puget Sound Business Journal (Vol. 33, July 6, 2012, No. 11, pp. 1)*
Pub: Baltimore Business Journal
Contact: Rhonda Pringle, President
E-mail: rpringle@bizjournals.com
Ed: Steve Wilhelm. **Description:** Coal exports are seen to take up more rail capacity in Washington. The issue was raised in connection with the proposed Gateway Pacific Terminal at Cherry Point. The planned terminal has been opposed by environmental groups. **Availability:** Print; Online.

23156 ▪ *"Combo Dorm-Field House Built to Attain LEED Gold"* in *Contractor (Vol. 56, September 2009, No. 9, pp. 1)*
Ed: Candace Roulo, Robert P. Mader. **Description:** North Central College in Illinois has built a new dormitory that is expected to attain Leadership in Energy and Environmental Design Gold certification from the United States Green Building Council. The structure features a geo-exchange heat pump system and radiant floor heat. A description of the facility is also provided. **Availability:** Print; Online.

23157 ▪ *"Coming Soon: Electric Tractors"* in *Farm Industry News (November 21, 2011)*
Pub: Informa Business Media, Inc.
Contact: Charlie McCurdy, President
Ed: Jodie Wehrspann. **Description:** The agricultural industry is taking another look at electric farm vehicles. John Deere Product Engineering Center said that farmers can expect to see more diesel-electric systems in farm tractors, sprayers, and implements. **Availability:** Online.

23158 ▪ *"Commercial Water Efficiency Initiatives Announced"* in *Contractor (Vol. 56, November 2009, No. 11, pp. 5)*
Ed: Robert P. Mader. **Description:** Plumbing engineers John Koeller and Bill Gauley are developing a testing protocol for commercial toilets. The team said commercial toilets should have a higher level of flush performance than residential toilets for certification. The Environmental Protection Agency's WaterSense program wants to expand the program into the commercial/institutional sector. **Availability:** Print; Online.

23159 ▪ *"CommScope and Comsearch to Showcase Innovative Wind Power Solutions at WINDPOWER 2012 in Atlanta"* in *Benzinga.com (May 31, 2012)*
Pub: Benzinga.com
Contact: Jason Raznick, Founder
Ed: Aaron Wise. **Description:** CommScope Inc. and its subsidiary CommScope will highlight their complete wind power solution products during the WINDPOWER 2012 Conference and Exhibition in Atlanta, Georgia this year. CommScope's wind power products include fiber optic cabling solutions, while Comsearch offers wind energy services that address the siting challenges resulting from complex telecommunications issues. **Availability:** Print; PDF; Online.

23160 ▪ *"The Comprehensive Business Case for Sustainability"* in *Harvard Business Review (October 21, 2016)*
Released: October 21, 2016. **Description:** This article discusses the benefits of placing sustainability practices at the top of your small business list. **Availability:** Online.

23161 ▪ *"Conscious Capitalism: Liberating the Heroic Spirit of Business"*
Released: January 07, 2014. **Price:** $12.47, e-book; $16.79, paperback. **Description:** Conscious Capitalism companies include Whole Foods Market, Southwest Airlines, Costco, Google, Patagonia, The Container Store, UPS and others. These firms under the four specific tenants to success: higher purpose, stakeholder integration, conscious leadership, and conscious culture and management. These companies are able to create value for all stakeholders, including customers, employees, suppliers, investors, society, and the environment. A new preface by the authors is included. **Availability:** E-book; Print.

23162 ▪ *"Consumers Like Green, But Not Mandates"* in *Business Journal-Milwaukee (Vol. 28, December 10, 2010, No. 10, pp. A1)*
Pub: The Business Journal
Contact: Heather Ladage, President
E-mail: hladage@bizjournals.com
Ed: Sean Ryan. **Description:** Milwaukee, Wisconsin consumers are willing to spend more on green energy, a survey has revealed. Respondents also said they will pay more for efficient cars and appliances. Support for public incentives for homeowners and businesses that reduce energy use has also increased. **Availability:** Print; Online.

23163 ▪ *"Consumers Want to Learn More About Green Business Efforts Despite Deep Doubt"* in *Benzinga.com (May 1, 2012)*
Pub: Benzinga.com
Contact: Jason Raznick, Founder
Ed: Aaron Wise. **Released:** May 01, 2012. **Description:** According to the third annual Gibbs & Soell Sense & Sustainability Study, 21 percent of Americans think the majority of businesses are working toward sustainable development, while 71 percent of consumer desire more knowledge about things corporations are doing to become sustainable and green. A majority of respondents believe the media is more likely to report green business when they can report bad news. **Availability:** Online.

23164 ▪ *"Contractors Debate Maximizing Green Opportunities, Education"* in *Contractor (Vol. 56, November 2009, No. 11, pp. 3)*
Ed: Robert P. Mader. **Description:** Attendees at the Mechanical Service Contractors Association convention were urged to get involved with their local U.S. Green Building Council chapter by one presenter. Another presenter says that one green opportunity for contractors is the commissioning of new buildings. **Availability:** Print; Online.

23165 ▪ *"Convert New Customers to Long Term Accounts"* in *Indoor Comfort Marketing (Vol. 70, February 2011, No. 2, pp. 22)*
Description: Marketing to new customers and suggestions for retaining them is covered. **Availability:** Online.

23166 ■ "Corporate Park Retrofits for Water Savings" in Contractor (Vol. 56, October 2009, No. 10, pp. 5)
Description: Merrit Corporate Park in Norwalk, Connecticut has been interested in improving building efficiency and one of their buildings has been retrofitted with water-efficient plumbing systems which will allow them to save as much as two million gallons of water. ADP Service Corp. helped the park upgrade their plumbing system. Availability: Online.

23167 ■ Corporate Radar: Tracking the Forces That Are Shaping Your Business
Description: Ways for a business to assess the forces operating in the external environment that can affect the business and solutions to protect from outside threats. Availability: Print.

23168 ■ "Corporate Responsibility" in Professional Services Close-Up (July 2, 2010)
Description: List of firms awarded the inaugural Best Corporate Citizens in Government Contracting by the Corporate Responsibility Magazine is presented. The list is based on the methodology of the Magazine's Best Corporate Citizen's List, with 324 data points of publicly-available information in seven categories which include: environment, climate change, human rights, philanthropy, employee relations, financial performance, and governance. Availability: Online.

23169 ■ "Cost Remains Top Factor In Considering Green Technology" in Canadian Sailings (June 30, 2008)
Description: Improving its environmental performance remains a priority in the shipping industry; however, testing new technologies can prove difficult due to the harsh conditions that ships endure as well as installation which usually requires a dry dock. Availability: Online.

23170 ■ "Cover Story: Minnesota Firms Plug Into Solar" in Business Journal (Vol. 31, April 25, 2014, No. 48, pp. 10)
Pub: American City Business Journals, Inc.
Contact: Mike Olivieri, Executive Vice President
Released: April 25, 2014. Price: $4, Introductory 4-week offer(Digital & Print). Description: Minneapolis, Minnesota-based companies have been benefiting from the increase in solar energy projects. Xcel Energy Inc.'s demand for more power is expected to lure national solar companies to the city. Meanwhile, Geronimo Energy is planning a $250 million solar project in the state. Availability: Print; Online.

23171 ■ "Crude Awakening" in Canadian Business (Vol. 81, October 27, 2008, No. 18, pp. 14)
Description: Jim Grays believes that a global liquid fuels crisis is coming and hopes the expected transition from oil dependence will be smooth. Charles Maxwell, on the other hand, predicts that a new world economy will arrive in three waves. Views of both experts are examined. Availability: Print; Online.

23172 ■ "Customized Before Custom Was Cool" in Green Industry Pro (July 2011)
Ed: Gregg Wartgow. Description: Profile of Turf Care Enterprises and owner Kevin Vogeler, who discusses his desire to use more natural programs using little or no chemicals in 1986. At that time, that sector represented 20 percent of his business, today it shares 80 percent. Availability: Online.

23173 ■ "David Robinson Column" in Buffalo News (October 2, 2011)
Pub: The Buffalo News, Inc.
Contact: Tom Wiley, President
E-mail: twiley@buffnews.com
Ed: David Robinson. Description: New York Power Authority ceased development of an offshore wind farm project. Wind farming in the waters of Lake Erie or Lake Ontario would be too costly. Details of the project are discussed. Availability: Online.

23174 ■ "A Day Late and a Dollar Short" in Indoor Comfort Marketing (Vol. 70, March 2011, No. 3, pp. 30)
Description: A discussion involving futures options and fuel oil prices is presented. Availability: Online.

23175 ■ "DEM Says River Needs Cleanup" in Providence Business News (Vol. 28, January 6, 2014, No. 40, pp. 1)
Pub: American City Business Journals, Inc.
Contact: Mike Olivieri, Executive Vice President
Released: January 04, 2014. Description: Rhode Island's Department of Environmental Management (DEM) called a meeting to gather information for its Ten Mile River water-quality-restoration plan. DEM announced the failure of the Ten Mile River and its impoundments to meet state water quality standards. The government grant received by Attleboro for the cleanup efforts is examined. Availability: Print; Online.

23176 ■ "Denton to Consider Texas' First Fracking Ban" in Dallas Business Journal (Vol. 37, July 11, 2014, No. 44, pp. 12)
Pub: American City Business Journals, Inc.
Contact: Mike Olivieri, Executive Vice President
Released: June 11, 2014. Price: $4, Introductory 4-Week Offer(Digital & Print). Description: The process of hydraulic fracturing or fracking and its disadvantages is discusses, focusing on Denton City Council's plan to declare the first fracking ban in Texas. The ban is expected to make oil and gas companies to file legal challenges. It is reported that Denton residents had to be relocated after oil well were re-drilled and transformed into deeper and horizontal Barnett Shale natural gas wells. Availability: Print; Online.

23177 ■ "Despite Economic Upheaval Generation Y is Still Feeling Green: RSA Canada Survey" in CNW Group (October 28, 2010)
Pub: CNW Group Ltd.
Description: Canadian Generation Y individuals believe it is important for their company to be environmentally-friendly and one-third of those surveyed would quit their job if they found their employer was environmentally irresponsible, despite the economy. Availability: Online.

23178 ■ "Detroit Hosts Conferences on Green Building, IT, Finance" in Crain's Detroit Business (Vol. 25, June 1, 2009, No. 22, pp. 9)
Pub: Crain Communications Inc.
Contact: Barry Asin, President
Ed: Tom Henderson. Description: Detroit will host three conferences in June 2009, one features green technology, one information technology and the third will gather black bankers and financial experts from across the nation. Availability: Online.

23179 ■ "DeWind Delivering Turbines to Texas Wind Farm" in Professional Services Close-Up (September 25, 2011)
Description: DeWind Company has begun shipment of turbines to the 20 MW Frisco Wind Farm located in Hansford County, Texas. DeWind is a subsidiary of Daewoo Shipbuilding and Marine Engineering Company. Details of the project are discussed. Availability: Online.

23180 ■ "Dog Marketplace: Pet Waste Products Pick Up Sales" in Pet Product News (Vol. 66, September 2012, No. 9, pp. 58)
Ed: Sandi Cain. Description: Pet supplies manufacturers are developing dog waste pickup bags and other convenient cleanup tools characterized by environment-friendliness and fashion. The demand for these cleanup tools has been motivated by dog owners' desire to minimize their and their dogs' environmental footprints. Availability: Online.

23181 ■ "Dow Champions Innovative Energy Solutions for Auto Industry at NAIAS" in Business of Global Warming (January 25, 2010, pp. 7)
Description: This year's North American International Auto Show in Detroit will host the "Electric Avenue" exhibit sponsored by the Dow Chemical Company. The display will showcase the latest in innovative energy solutions from Dow as well as electric vehicles and the technology supporting them. This marks the first time a non-automotive manufacturer is part of the main floor of the show. Availability: Print; PDF; Online.

23182 ■ "Drop in the Bucket Makes a lot of Waves" in Globe & Mail (March 22, 2007, pp. B1)
Ed: Greg Keenan. Description: The concern of several auto makers in Canada over the impact of providing heavy rebates to customers buying energy-efficient cars is discussed. Availability: Online.

23183 ■ "DTE Energy Foundation Expands 'Greening' Programs at Michigan Festivals" in Ecology, Environment & Conservation Business (June 28, 2014, pp. 3)
Pub: NewsRX LLC.
Contact: Kalani Rosell, Contact
Description: DTE Energy Foundation is expanding its support for its 'Greening' or recycling programs to the GrandJazz Fest in Grand Rapids and the Lakeshore Art Festival in Michigan. The Foundation already supports recycling programs at the Detroit Jazz Festival and the National Cherry Festival in Traverse City. The foundation is committed to reduce the carbon footprint at these events by recycling plastic, aluminum cans, glass and other materials. Availability: Online.

23184 ■ "East Coast Solar" in Contractor (Vol. 57, February 2010, No. 2, pp. 17)
Ed: Dave Yates. Description: U.S. Department of Energy's Solar Decathlon lets 20 college student-led teams from around the world compete to design and build a solar-powered home. A mechanical contractor discusses his work as an advisor during the competition. Availability: Print; Online.

23185 ■ Eco Barons: The New Heroes of Environmental Activism
Pub: Ecco Books
Contact: Daniel Halpern, Founder
Ed: Edward Humes. Price: $18.99, hardcover. Description: Profiles of business leaders who have dedicated their lives to saving the planet from ecological devastation. Availability: E-book; Print; Download.

23186 ■ "Ecovative Moves Beyond Packaging" in Business Review Albany (Vol. 41, August 1, 2014, No. 19, pp. 12)
Description: Ecovative Design of Green Island, NY has started making new packaging materials to add to its biodegradable product line, including the Myco Board, a material similar to particleboard. Clients range from computer manufacturers to furniture retailers. Availability: Print; Online.

23187 ■ "Editorial: Find Private Money for FutureGen Plant" in Crain's Chicago Business (Vol. 34, September 12, 2011, No. 37, pp. 18)
Pub: Crain Communications Inc.
Contact: Barry Asin, President
Description: FutureGen is a clean-coal power plant being developed in Southern Illinois. The need for further funding is discussed. Availability: Print.

23188 ■ "Eleni Reed: C&W Gets Green Star" in Crain's New York Business (Vol. 24, January 6, 2008, No. 1, pp. 25)
Pub: Crain Communications, Inc.
Contact: Jessica Botos, Manager, Marketing
E-mail: jessica.botos@crainsnewyork.com
Ed: Theresa Agovino. Description: Cushman & Wakefield Inc. has hired Eleni Reed as director of sustainability strategies; the real estate firm wants to ensure that the 500 million square feet of office space it manages around the globe meets environmental standards.

23189 ■ "Elon Musk's Solar Firm Is Nearly Doubling Its Massachusetts Workforce" in Boston Business Journal (Vol. 34, May 30, 2014, No. 17, pp. 3)
Pub: American City Business Journals, Inc.
Contact: Mike Olivieri, Executive Vice President
Released: Weekly. **Description:** SolarCity is planning to add 100 jobs to its Massachusetts operations. The solar panel firm opened a second operations center in the state. State business incentives have enabled the company to expand presence in the area. **Availability:** Print; Online.

23190 ■ "Emissions: Cloudy Skies" in Canadian Business (Vol. 81, October 27, 2008, No. 18, pp. 101)
Pub: Rogers Media Inc.
Contact: Neil Spivak, Chief Executive Officer
Ed: Andrew Wahl. **Description:** Canada's federal government is expected to implement its regulations on greenhouse-gas emissions by January 1, 2010, but companies are worried because the plan took so long and some details are yet to be revealed. Corporate Canada wants a firm, long-range plan similar to the European Union Emissions Trading Scheme in dealing with greenhouse-gas emissions. **Availability:** Online.

23191 ■ "Encore Container, Manufacturer of Plastic Drums and IBC Totes, Leads the Way in Environmental Sustainability" in Ecology, Environment & Conservation Business (January 25, 2014, pp. 33)
Pub: NewsRX LLC.
Contact: Kalani Rosell, Contact
Description: Encore Container, a leading reconditioner of IBC totes and manufacturer and reconditioner of plastic drums describes its efforts to promote environmental sustainability within the company: container reconditioning, plastic and steel recycling, water conservation and waste minimization. **Availability:** Online.

23192 ■ "Energy Consulting Company to Expand" in Austin Business JournalInc. (Vol. 28, November 7, 2008, No. 34, pp. A1)
Pub: Austin Business Journal
Contact: Rachel McGrath, Director
E-mail: rmcgrath@bizjournals.com
Ed: Kate Harrington. **Description:** CLEAResult Consulting Inc. is planning to increase its workforce and move its headquarters to a larger office. The company has posted 1,000 percent increase in revenues. The company's adoption of best practices and setting of benchmark goals are seen as the reason for its growth. **Availability:** Print; Online.

23193 ■ "Energy Efficiency Ordinance Softened" in Austin Business JournalInc. (Vol. 28, October 3, 2008, No. 29)
Pub: Austin Business Journal
Contact: Rachel McGrath, Director
E-mail: rmcgrath@bizjournals.com
Ed: Jean Kwon. **Description:** City of Austin has eliminated mandatory energy efficiency upgrades to single-family housing as a condition for selling or renting homes or buildings. The new law proposes that an energy performance audit be conducted on single-family homes before being sold and the results of the audit disclosed to perspectives buyers. **Availability:** Print; Online.

23194 ■ "Enriching the Ecosystem: A Four-Point Plan for Linking Innovation, Enterprises, and Jobs" in Harvard Business Review (Vol. 90, March 2012, No. 3, pp. 140)
Pub: Harvard Business Review Press
Contact: Moderna V. Pfizer, Contact
Ed: Rosabeth Moss Kanter. **Price:** $8.95, hardcopy black and white. **Description:** The four goals for enriching the ecosystem include: linking venture creation and ecosystem creation to speed up the idea-to-enterprise transition; revitalizing small-, medium-, and large-sized firms via partnerships; improving matches between education and employment opportunities; and bringing together leaders across different sectors to create regional strategies. **Availability:** Print; PDF; Online.

23195 ■ Environmental Guide to the Internet
Contact: Carol Briggs Erickson, Author
URL(s): rowman.com/ISBN/9780805876439
Ed: Carol Briggs-Erickson, Toni Murphy. **Released:** Latest edition 4th. **Price:** $106, Individuals Paperback. **Description:** Covers 1,200 resources covering the environment on the Internet, including organizations, products, and resources, including discussion groups, electronic journals, newsgroups, and discussion groups. **Entries include:** Name, online address, description, e-mail address. **Arrangement:** Categories. **Availability:** Print.

23196 ■ "Environmental Working Group Names Whole Foods Market (R) Leading National Retailer for 'Green' Sunscreen" in Ecology, Environment & Conservation Business (June 14, 2014, pp. 5)
Pub: NewsRX LLC.
Contact: Kalani Rosell, Contact
Description: Whole Foods Market has been named as the leading retailer selling the largest selection of 'green' rated sunscreen to shoppers. **Availability:** Online.

23197 ■ "EPA Finalizes WaterSense for Homes" in Contractor (Vol. 57, January 2010, No. 1, pp. 70)
Ed: Robert P. Mader. **Description:** U.S. Environmental Protection Agency released its "final" version of the WaterSense for Homes standard. The standard's provisions that affect plumbing contractors include the specification that everything has to be leak tested and final service pressure cannot exceed 60 psi. **Availability:** Print; Online.

23198 ■ "EPA Grants E15 Waiver for 2001-2006 Vehicles" in Farm Industry News (January 21, 2011)
Pub: Informa Business Media, Inc.
Contact: Charlie McCurdy, President
Ed: Lynn Grooms. **Description:** U.S. Environmental Protection Agency waived a limitation on selling gasoline that contains more than 10 percent ethanol for model year 2001-2006 cars and light trucks, allowing fuel to contain up to 15 percent ethanol (E15) for these vehicles. **Availability:** Online.

23199 ■ "EPA to Tighten Energy Star Standards for 2011" in Contractor (Vol. 56, September 2009, No. 9, pp. 6)
Description: United States Environmental Protection Agency will tighten standards for its Energy Star for Homes program in 2011. The green trend in the construction industry has been cited as reason for the plan. The agency is adding requirements for energy-efficient equipment and building techniques. **Availability:** Print; Online.

23200 ■ "ESolar Partners With Penglai on Landmark Solar Thermal Agreement for China" in Business of Global Warming (January 25, 2010, pp. 8)
Description: Penglai Electric, a privately-owned Chinese electrical power equipment manufacturer, and eSolar, a global provider of cost-effective and reliable solar power plants, announced a master licensing agreement in which eSolar will build at least 2 gigawatts of solar thermal power plants in China over the next 10 years. **Availability:** Print; Online.

23201 ■ "Family Takes Wind Turbine Companies to Court Over Gag Clauses on Health Effects of Turbines" in CNW Group (September 12, 2011)
Pub: CNW Group Ltd.
Description: Shawn and Trisha Drennan are concerned about the negative experiences other have had with wind turbines close to their homes, including adverse health effects. The couple's home will be approximately 650 meters from the Kingsbridge II wind farm project in Ontario, Canada. **Availability:** Online.

23202 ■ Fashionopolis: The Price of Fast Fashion and the Future of Clothes
Ed: Dana Thomas. **Released:** September 03, 2019. **Price:** $22.49, Hardcover; $14.99, E-Book. **Description:** Investigates the impact the fashion and clothing industry has had on the environment and in society. Also studies companies and people who are leading the way in producing sustainable clothing. **Availability:** E-book; Print.

23203 ■ "Federal Buildings to Achieve Zero-Net Energy by 2030" in Contractor (Vol. 56, December 2009, No. 12, pp. 5)
Ed: Candace Roulo. **Description:** United States president Barack Obama has issued sustainable goals for federal buildings. Federal agencies are also required to increase energy efficiency, conserve water and support sustainable communities. Obama has also announced a $3.4 billion investment in a smart energy creed. **Availability:** Print; Online.

23204 ■ "Financial Benefits of an Eco-Friendly Business" in Green Business Bureau (June 17, 2019)
Released: June 17, 2019. **Description:** Discusses how small businesses can reap the plentiful financial rewards of taking their business in an eco-friendly direction. **Availability:** Online.

23205 ■ "First Sustainability Standard for Household Portable and Floor Care Appliances Developed to Identify Environmentally Responsible Products" in Ecology, Environment & Conservation Business (September 13, 2014, pp. 39)
Pub: NewsRX LLC.
Contact: Kalani Rosell, Contact
Description: the Association of Home Appliance Manufacturers (AHAM), CSA Group, and the UL Environment released the AHAM 7002-2014/CSA SPE-7002-14/UL 7002, Sustainability Standard for Household Portable and Floor Care Appliances. This is the first voluntary sustainability standards for these appliances and is the third in a unit of product sustainability standards under development by the group. These standards are intended for use by manufacturers, governments, retailers, and others to identify products conforming to these standards in six key areas: materials, manufacturing and operations, energy consumption during use, end-of-life, consumables, and innovation. **Availability:** Online.

23206 ■ "First Suzlon S97 Turbines Arrive in North America for Installation" in PR Newswire (September 28, 2011)
Pub: PR Newswire Association LLC.
Description: Suzlon Energy Ltd., the world's fifth largest manufacturer of wind turbines, will install its first S97 turbine at the Amherst Wind Farm Project. These turbines will be installed on 90-meter hub height towers and at full capacity, will generate enough electricity to power over 10,000 Canadian homes. **Availability:** Online.

23207 ■ "First Venture Reports Proprietary Yeasts Further Reduce Ethyl Carbamate in Sake" in Canadian Corporate News (May 16, 2007)
Description: First Ventures Technologies Corp., a biotechnology company that develops and commercializes advanced yeast products, confirmed that two of their proprietary yeasts used in the making of sake have yielded reductions in ethyl carbamate compared to previous sake brewing trials.

23208 ■ The Flaw of Averages: Why We Underestimate Risk in the Face of Uncertainty
Pub: John Wiley & Sons, Inc.
Contact: Christina Van Tassell, Executive Vice President Chief Financial Officer
Ed: Sam L. Savage. **Released:** March 26, 2012. **Price:** $19.95, paperback; $27.95, hardcover; $12.99, E-Book. **Description:** Personal and business plans are based on uncertainties on a daily basis. The common avoidable mistake individuals make in

23209 ■ **"For Giving Us a Way To Say Yes To Solar: Lynn Jurich and Edward Fenster"** in *Inc.* (Volume 32, December 2010, No. 10, pp. 110)
Pub: Mansueto Ventures L.L.C.
Contact: Stephanie Mehta, Chief Executive Officer
Ed: Leigh Buchanan. **Released:** December 01, 2010.
Description: Profile of entrepreneurs Lynn Jurich and Edward Fenster, cofounders of SunRun. The firm installs solar panels at little or no cost and homeowners sign 20-year contracts to buy power at a fixed price. **Availability:** Online.

23210 ■ **"For One Homebuilder, It's Pretty Easy Being Green, Even in Houston"** in *Houston Business Journal* (Vol. 44, April 11, 2014, No. 49, pp. 7)
Pub: American City Business Journals, Inc.
Contact: Mike Olivieri, Executive Vice President
Released: Weekly. **Price:** $4, introductory 4-week offer(Digital only). **Description:** Frankel Building Group vice president, Scott Frankel, says new housing projects in Houston, Texas have been getting bigger. He also said that industry members are facing the problem of lack of residential lots in the region. Frankel added that the company builds its homes to LEED-certified standards. **Availability:** Print; Online.

23211 ■ **"Former Tech Execs Want to Tap Building Trend in Austin"** in *Austin Business Journal* (Vol. 31, May 13, 2011, No. 10, pp. A1)
Pub: Austin Business Journal
Contact: Rachel McGrath, Director
E-mail: rmcgrath@bizjournals.com
Ed: Cody Lyon. **Description:** Falcon Containers moved to a 51-acre site in Far East Austin, Texas and started construction of a 2,500-square-foot headquarters made from eight 40-foot shipping containers. Falcon's CEO Stephen Shang plans to use his headquarters building as a showroom to attract upscale, urban hipsters. Insights on the construction's environmental and social impact are shared. **Availability:** Print; Online.

23212 ■ **"Fossil Fuel, Renewable Fuel Shares Expected to Flip Flop"** in *Farm Industry News* (April 29, 2011)
Pub: Informa Business Media, Inc.
Contact: Charlie McCurdy, President
Ed: Lynn Grooms. **Description:** Total energy use of fossil fuels is predicted to fall 5 percent by the year 2035, with renewable fuel picking it up. **Availability:** Online.

23213 ■ **"The Freshest Ideas Are in Small Grocery Stores"** in *The New York Times* (July 31, 2018)
URL(s): www.nytimes.com/2018/07/31/dining/grocery-store.html
Released: July 31, 2018. **Description:** Smaller grocery stores are starting to make headway in the industry, as consumers' shopping habits change. More younger customers are interested in "food experiences" and shop more than once a week while looking for curated items and more innovations. Smaller stores are complying and are able to give their customers what they want, which is often a zero waste store and healthier options. **Availability:** Online.

23214 ■ **"From Scarcity to Plenty"** in *Inc.* (Vol. 36, March 2014, No. 2, pp. 76)
Pub: Mansueto Ventures L.L.C.
Contact: Stephanie Mehta, Chief Executive Officer
Description: Profile of Mom's Organic Market which started in Scott Nash's mom's garage. Nash describes the healthy food choices offered at the store as well as its Environmental Restoration program which addressed issues including carbon offsets, recycling, and composting. **Availability:** Print; Online.

23215 ■ **"FSU's OGZEB Is Test Bed for Sustainable Technology"** in *Contractor* (Vol. 56, October 2009, No. 10, pp. 1)
Ed: Candace Roulo. **Description:** Florida State University has one of 14 off-grid zero emissions buildings (OGZEB) in the U.S.; it was built to research sustainable and alternative energy systems. The building produces electricity from 30 photovoltaic panels and it also has three AET water heating solar panels on the roof. **Availability:** Print; Online.

23216 ■ **"Fuel King: The Most Fuel-Efficient Tractor of the Decade is the John Deere 8295R"** in *Farm Industry News* (November 10, 2011)
Pub: Informa Business Media, Inc.
Contact: Charlie McCurdy, President
Description: Farm Industry News compiled a list of the most fuel-efficient tractors with help from the Nebraska Tractor Test Lab, with the John Deere 8295R PTO winner of the most fuel-efficient tractor of the decade. **Availability:** Print; Online.

23217 ■ **"Funeral Directors Get Creative As Boomers Near Great Beyond"** in *Advertising Age* (Vol. 79, October 13, 2008, No. 38, pp. 30)
Pub: Crain Communications, Inc.
Contact: Jessica Botos, Manager, Marketing
E-mail: jessica.botos@crainsnewyork.com
Ed: Lenore Skenazy. **Description:** Despite the downturn in the economy, the funeral business is thriving due to the number of baby boomers who realize the importance of making preparations for their death. Marketers are getting creative in their approach and many companies have taken into consideration the need for a more environmental friendly way to dispose of bodies and thus have created innovative businesses that reflect this need. **Availability:** Online.

23218 ■ **"GE Announces New Projects, Technology Milestone and New Service Program at AWEA Windpower 2012"** in *News Bites US* (June 6, 2012)
Description: General Electric announced plans at the AWEA Windpower 2012 for its two new wind turbine projects to be located in Michigan and Iowa. Details of these new wind turbine projects are included. **Availability:** Online.

23219 ■ **"GE Milestone: 1,000th Wind Turbine Installed in Canada"** in *CNW Group* (October 4, 2011)
Pub: CNW Group Ltd.
Description: GE installed its 1,000th wind turbine in Canada at Cartier Wind Energy's Gros Morne project in the Gaspesie Region of Quebec, Canada. As Canada continues to expand its use of wind energy, GE plans to have over 1,100 wind turbines installed in the nation by the end of 2011. **Availability:** Online.

23220 ■ **"General Electric Touts Going Green for Business Fleet Services"** in *America's Intelligence Wire* (June 1, 2012)
Description: General Capital Fleet Services if featuring alternative-fuel vehicles in Eden Prairie for its corporate customers. GE Capital is the world's largest fleet management service and is offering its customers the first of its kind service that allows corporate lease customers to test drive alternative fuel cars from 20 different manufacturers. **Availability:** Print; Online.

23221 ■ **"Germans Win Solar Decathlon Again"** in *Contractor* (Vol. 56, November 2009, No. 11, pp. 1)
Ed: Robert P. Mader. **Description:** Students from Technische Universtat Darmstadt won the U.S. Department of Energy's Solar Decathlon by designing and building the most attractive and efficient solar-powered home. The winner's design produced a surplus of power even during three days of rain and photovoltaic panels covered nearly every exterior surface. **Availability:** Print; Online.

23222 ■ **"Getting the Bioheat Word Out"** in *Indoor Comfort Marketing* (Vol. 70, September 2011, No. 9, pp. 32)
Description: Ways to market advanced liquid fuels to the public are outlined. **Availability:** Print; Online.

23223 ■ **"Getting Green Certification for Your Products"** in *Legal Zoom* (March 22, 2023)
URL(s): www.legalzoom.com/articles/getting-green-certification-for-your-products
Ed: Stephanie Morrow. **Released:** March 22, 2023.
Description: There are several options when it comes to getting your products from your small business certified as Green. Listed are sources to contact to receive your certification so you can start advertising your environmentally-friendly products to the public. **Availability:** Online.

23224 ■ **"GIV Mobile Announces New Partnership with American Forests, the Oldest National Nonprofit Conservation Organization in the Country"** in *Ecology, Environment & Conservation Business* (January 25, 2014, pp. 34)
Pub: PR Newswire Association LLC.
Description: GIV Mobile has partnered with American Forests to restore and protect urban and rural forests in the nation. GIV is the first consumer conscious wireless network and operates on the 4G network of T-Mobile USA cellular service. **Availability:** Online.

23225 ■ **"The Global Environment Movement is Bjorn Again"** in *Canadian Business* (Vol. 83, September 14, 2010, No. 15, pp. 11)
Pub: Rogers Media Inc.
Contact: Neil Spivak, Chief Executive Officer
Ed: Steve Maich. **Description:** Danish academic Bjorn Lomborg is in favor of decisive action to combat climate change in his new book and was given front page treatment by a London newspaper. Environmentalist groups see this as a victory since Lomborg had not previously considered climate change an immediate issue. **Availability:** Online.

23226 ■ **"Global Environmental Consulting Market Set to Surge"** in *Environmental Analyst* (May 14, 2021)
Released: May 14, 2021. **Description:** The environmental consulting market took a dip during the COVID-19 pandemic, but is set to soar in the coming years as society turns more and more towards caring for the planet. **Availability:** Online.

23227 ■ **"GM's Volt Woes Cast Shadow on E-Cars"** in *Wall Street Journal Eastern Edition* (November 28, 2011, pp. B1)
Pub: Dow Jones & Company Inc.
Contact: Almar Latour, Chief Executive Officer
Ed: Sharon Terlep. **Description:** The future of electric cars is darkened with the government investigation by the National Highway Traffic Safety Administration into General Motor Company's Chevy Volt after two instances of the car's battery packs catching fire during crash tests conducted by the Agency. **Availability:** Online.

23228 ■ **"Go Green Or Go Home"** in *Black Enterprise* (Vol. 41, August 2010, No. 1, pp. 53)
Pub: Earl G. Graves Ltd.
Contact: Earl Graves, Jr., President
Ed: Robinson M. Tennille. **Description:** The green economy has become an essential part of every business, however, small business owners need to learn how to participate, including minority owned entrepreneurs. **Availability:** Online.

23229 ■ *Good Green Guide for Small Businesses: How to Change the Way Your Business Works for the Better*
Pub: A. and C. Black
Contact: Jenny Ridout, Director
Released: First edition. **Description:** Guide for small businesses to take an environmental audit of their company and shows how to minimize the impact of office essentials such as utilities, insulation, recycling

and waste, electrical equipment, water systems, lighting options, food and drink, and office cleaning arrangements and products. **Availability:** Print.

23230 ■ *"Got to be Smarter than the Average Bear" in Contractor (Vol. 56, September 2009, No. 9, pp. 82)*

Ed: Robert P. Mader. **Description:** International Association of Plumbing and Mechanical Officials Green Technical Committee has debated the need for contractors to have certifications in installing green plumbing. Some have argued that qualifications would discourage homeowners from improving their properties. Comments from executives are also included. **Availability:** Print; Online.

23231 ■ *"Governor Candidates Differ on Oregon's Green Streak" in Business Journal Portland (Vol. 27, October 22, 2010, No. 34, pp. 1)*

Pub: Portland Business Journal
Contact: Andy Giegerich, Managing Editor
E-mail: agiegerich@bizjournals.com

Ed: Andy Giegerich. **Description:** The views of Oregon gubernatorial candidates Chris Dudley and John Kitzhaber on the state's economy and on environmental policies are presented. Both Dudley, who is a Republican, and his Democratic challenger believe that biomass could help drive the state's economy. Both candidates also pledged changes in Oregon's business energy tax credit (BETC) program.

23232 ■ *"Grainger Show Highlights Building Green, Economic Recovery" in Contractor (Vol. 57, February 2010, No. 2, pp. 3)*

Ed: Candace Roulo. **Description:** Chief U.S. economist told attendees of the Grainger's 2010 Total MRO Solutions National Customer Show that the economic recovery would be subdued. Mechanical contractors who attended the event also learned about building sustainable, green products, and technologies, and economic and business challenges. **Availability:** Print; Online.

23233 ■ *"Green Business Owners Share Secrets of Success In This Business Guide" in PRNewsChannel.com (March 1, 2012)*

Pub: Comtex News Network Inc.
Contact: Kan Devnani, President

Description: Business guide to help companies become sustainable and work to be a green business. **Availability:** Online.

23234 ■ *"Green Business Plan Competition" in Chemical & Engineering News (Vol. 90, July 9, 2012, No. 28, pp. 34)*

Pub: American Chemical Society Philadelphia Section
Contact: Dr. David Cichowicz, Director

Ed: Stephen K. Ritter. **Description:** Startup anticorrosion coatings firm AnCatt Inc. won the inaugural chemistry business plan competition at the Green Chemistry & Engineering Conference held in July 2012 in Washington, DC. AnCatt was honored for its conducting-polymer-based anticorrosion paint system aimed at replacing chormate, lead, and cadmium paint pigments. **Availability:** Online.

23235 ■ *"Green and Clean" in Retail Merchandiser (Vol. 51, July-August 2011, No. 4, pp. 56)*

Description: Green Valley Grocery partnered with Paragon Solutions consulting firm to make their stores environmentally green. **Availability:** Print; Online.

23236 ■ *"Green Cleaning - It's Your Business" in Cleaning Business Today (April 3, 2019)*

Ed: Cloud Conrad. **Released:** April 03, 2019. **Description:** Information on how to run an environmentally friendly green cleaning business. **Availability:** Online.

23237 ■ *"Green Collar: Green Buildings Support Job Creation, Workforce Transformation and Economic Recovery" in Environmental Design and Construction (Vol. 15, July 2012, No. 7, pp. 31)*

Pub: BNP Media
Contact: Harper Henderson, Owner Co-Chief Executive Officer

Ed: Maggie Comstock. **Description:** Despite construction being at an all-time low, green building construction has maintained its hold on nonresidential buildings. It has even shown growth in some sectors and accounts for over one-third of all nonresidential design and construction jobs and is expected to show further growth through 2014. Statistical details included.

23238 ■ *The Green Guide for Business: The Ultimate Environment for Businesses of All Sizes*

Pub: Profile Books Limited
Contact: Stephen Brough, Co-Founder

Ed: Chris Goodball, Roger East, Hannah Bullock. **Released:** March 09, 2010. **Description:** Everyone wants to go green these days, but for small businesses that's easier said than done. How do you measure a company's carbon footprint? Are dryers or hand towels more eco-friendly? Recycled paper or FSC-certified? All these questions and more are explored. **Availability:** E-book.

23239 ■ *"Green Housing for the Rest of Us" in Inc. (November 2007, pp. 128-129)*

Ed: Nitasha Tiku. **Description:** Profile of Full Spectrum NY, real estate developer firm, offering residences at the Kalahari, a green high-rise with state-of-the-art features at a reasonable price. **Availability:** Online.

23240 ■ *"Green Ideas for Making Your Business Environmentally Sustainable" in The Balance Small Business (February 10, 2020)*

Ed: Susan Ward. **Released:** February 10, 2020. **Description:** Discusses the positive impact making your business environmentally sustainable can have on revenue. Provides tips on moving toward eco-friendly business practices to attract a growing audience of green consumers. **Availability:** Online.

23241 ■ *"Green It Like You Mean It" in Special Events Magazine (Vol. 28, February 1, 2009, No. 2)*

Description: Eco-friendly party planners offer advice for planning and hosting green parties or events. Tips include information for using recycled paper products, organic food and drinks. The Eco Nouveau Fashion Show held by Serene Star Productions reused old garments to create new fashions as well as art pieces from discarded doors and window frames for the show; eco-friendly treats and gift bags were highlighted at the event.

23242 ■ *"Green Light" in The Business Journal-Portland (Vol. 25, July 11, 2008, No. 18, pp. 1)*

Description: Ecos Consulting, a sustainability consulting company based in Portland, Oregon, is seeing a boost in revenue as more businesses turn to sustainable practices. The company's revenue rose by 50 percent in 2007 and employees increased from 57 to 150. Other details about Ecos' growth are discussed. **Availability:** Print; Online.

23243 ■ *"Green Manufacturer Scouts Sites in Greater Cincinnati" in Business Courier (Vol. 27, July 23, 2010, No. 12, pp. 1)*

Pub: Business Courier

Ed: Dan Monk. **Description:** CresaPartners is searching for a manufacturing facility in Cincinnati, Ohio. The company is set to tour about ten sites in the area. **Availability:** Print; Online.

23244 ■ *"Green Rules To Drive Innovation: Charging for Carbon Can Inspire Conservation, Fuel Competition, and Enhance Competitiveness" in Harvard Business Review (Vol. 90, March 2012, No. 3, pp. 120)*

Pub: Harvard Business Review Press
Contact: Moderna V. Pfizer, Contact

Ed: Daniel C. Esty, Steve Charnovitz. **Price:** $8.95. **Description:** Along with carbon emissions charges, other green policy recommendations include expanding domestic renewable power and the use of natural gas, increasing federal funding of clean-energy research, utilizing incentive-based approaches to encourage the adoption of renewable energy, and implementing the World Trade Organization's Doha negotiations on sustainable development. **Availability:** Online; PDF.

23245 ■ *"The Green Trap" in Canadian Business (Vol. 80, April 9, 2007, No. 8, pp. 19)*

Description: Expert advice to companies on investing in environmental-friendly measures is presented. **Availability:** Online.

23246 ■ *"Greenhouse Announces Reverse Merger With Custom Q, Inc." in Investment Weekly (January 30, 2010, pp. 338)*

Pub: Investment Weekly News

Description: In accordance with an Agreement and Plan of Share Exchange, GreenHouse Holdings, Inc., an innovative green solutions provider, has gone public via a reverse merger with Custom Q, Inc. **Availability:** Print; Online.

23247 ■ *Greening Your Small Business: How to Improve Your Bottom Line, Grow Your Brand, Satisfy Your Customers and Save the Planet*

Price: $19.95. **Description:** A definitive resource for anyone who wants their small business to be cutting-edge, competitive, profitable, and eco-conscious. Stories from small business owners address every aspect of going green, from basics such as recycling waste, energy efficiency, and reducing information technology footprint, to more in-depth concerns such as green marketing and communications, green business travel, and green employee benefits.

23248 ■ *"GreenTech Gears Up for Production" in Memphis Business Journal (Vol. 33, April 6, 2012, No. 52, pp. 1)*

Pub: Baltimore Business Journal
Contact: Rhonda Pringle, President
E-mail: rpringle@bizjournals.com

Description: GreenTech Automotive has broken ground for construction of a new production facility in Tunica, Tennessee. The company will focus its manufacturing operations in the new facility. **Availability:** Print; Online.

23249 ■ *"Groups Seek Donations to Recycle Christmas Trees" in The Register-Guard (January 7, 2012, pp. B11)*

Description: Groups wishing to recycle used Christmas trees in the Eugene, Oregon area are listed. Some of the groups offer incentives as well as free pickup. Contact information for each group is provided. **Availability:** Print; Online.

23250 ■ *"A Growing Concern" in Canadian Business (Vol. 79, October 9, 2006, No. 20, pp. 90)*

Description: With rich dividends being harvested by companies producing ethanol, after ethanol became a petrol additive, is discussed. **Availability:** Online.

23251 ■ *Guerrilla Marketing Goes Green: Winning Strategies to Improve Your Profits and Your Planet*

Pub: John Wiley & Sons, Inc.
Contact: Christina Van Tassell, Executive Vice President Chief Financial Officer

Ed: Jay Conrad Levinson, Shel Horowitz, Jay Conrad Levinson. **Released:** 2010. **Description:** The latest tips on green marketing and sustainable business strategies are shared. **Availability:** E-book; Print; Electronic publishing; Online.

23252 ■ *"Habitat, Home Depot Expand Building Program" in Contractor (Vol. 56, September 2009, No. 9, pp. 16)*

Description: Habitat for Humanity International and The Home Depot Foundation are planning to expand their Partners in Sustainable Building program. The program will provide funds to help Habitat affiliates build 5,000 homes. Comments from executives are also included. **Availability:** Print; Online.

23253 ■ *"Harpoon Brewery Wins Boston Green Business Award for Sustainability and EnerNOC Energy Management Programs" in Investment Weekly News (May 12, 2012, No. 543)*

Description: Harpoon Brewery was awarded a 2012 Boston Green Business Award by Mayor Thomas Menino of Boston, Massachusetts. The brewery was cited for having an exceptional sustainability program that includes waste reduction, responsible chemical usage, and operational efficiency measures combined with energy management initiatives with EnerNOC. EnerNOC is a leading provider of energy management applications for commercial, industrial, and institutional energy users, including Harpoon. **Availability:** Online.

23254 ■ *"Healthy Foods Drive Dining Choices" in National Restaurant Association (July 25, 2017)*
URL(s): restaurant.org/Articles/News/Batch2_201901/State-of-the-Industry-Healthy-foods-drive-dining-c
Released: July 25, 2017. **Description:** According to the State of the Industry report compiled by the National Restaurant Association, diners want healthier options and this influences where they dine out. Locally sources and environmentally friendly food is also important to diners, especially if they are from the younger generations. **Availability:** Online.

23255 ■ *"Helping Customers Fight Pet Waste" in Pet Product News (Vol. 64, November 2010, No. 11, pp. 52)*
Ed: Sandy Robins. **Description:** Pet cleaning products manufacturers have been enjoying high sales figures by paying attention to changing pet ownership trends and environmental awareness. Meanwhile, the inclusion of user-friendly features in these products has also been boosted by the social role of pets and the media attention to pet waste. How manufacturers have been responding to this demand is explored. **Availability:** Print; Online.

23256 ■ *"Hey, You Can't Do That" in Green Industry Pro (Vol. 23, September 2011)*
Ed: Rod Dickens. **Description:** Manufacturers of landscape equipment are making better use of energy resources, such as the use of fuel-injection systems instead of carburetors, lightweight materials, better lubricants, advanced battery technology, and innovative engine designs. **Availability:** Online.

23257 ■ *"High Energy: Gaurdie Banister Joins Aera As President and CEO" in Black Enterprise (Vol. 38, July 2008, No. 12, pp. 30)*
Pub: Earl G. Graves Ltd.
Contact: Earl Graves, Jr., President
Ed: Brenda Porter. **Description:** Gaurdie Banister Jr. has been appointed president and CEO of Aera Energy L.L.C., becoming one of the first African Americans in the nation to run a major energy corporation. His plans for the firm include utilizing new, sophisticated technologies in order to unlock the 3-1/2 billion barrels of resources the company has on their books in a safe and environmentally friendly way. He also hopes to increase production and maintain cost leadership.

23258 ■ *"The High Price of Fast Fashion" in The Wall Street Journal (August 29, 2019)*
URL(s): www.wsj.com/articles/the-high-price-of-fast-fashion-11567096637
Ed: Dana Thomas. **Released:** August 29, 2019. **Description:** Examines the impact fast fashion has on the environment and in society. Fast fashion comes from designers who steal ideas from fashion runways and "reinterpret" the piece and produce it as cheap as possible. To do this, the poorest labor in third-world countries is used, which is a problem due to labor-rights violations. Clothes that do not sell are discarded into the environment, and since many of these items are synthetic, they are not biodegradable. **Availability:** Online.

23259 ■ *Housecleaning Business: Organize Your Business - Get Clients and Referrals - Set Rates and Services*
Ed: Laura Jorstad, Melinda Morse. **Price:** Paperback, softback. **Description:** This book shares insight into starting a housecleaning business. It shows how to develop a service manual, screen clients, serve customers, select cleaning products, competition, how to up a home office, using the Internet to grow the business and offering green cleaning options to clients. **Availability:** E-book; Print.

23260 ■ *"How Bad Is It?" in Hawaii Business (Vol. 54, July 2008, No. 1, pp. 35)*
Pub: PacificBasin Communications
Contact: Chuck Tindle, Director
E-mail: chuckt@pacificbasin.net
Ed: Jolyn Okimoto Rosa. **Description:** Donald G. Horner, chief executive officer of First Hawaiian Bank, says that the current Hawaiian economic situation is a cyclical slowdown. Maurice Kaya, an energy consultant, says the slowdown is due to overdependence on imported fuels. Other local leaders, such as Constance H. Lau, also discuss their view on the current economic situation in Hawaii.

23261 ■ *"How to Be Environmentally Sustainable As a Small to Medium Size Business" in noissue.com (August 8, 2018)*
Ed: Beth Owens. **Released:** August 20, 2018. **Description:** Big companies dominate when it comes to news about utilizing environmentally sustainable initiatives. This article details steps small businesses can take to reduce your footprint and to save money. **Availability:** Online.

23262 ■ *"How Coffee Producers Can Adapt to Climate Change" in Perfect Daily Grind (November 7, 2019)*
URL(s): www.perfectdailygrind.com/2019/11/how-coffee-producers-can-adapt-to-climate-change/
Ed: Sarah Charles. **Released:** November 07, 2019. **Description:** Examines how climate change can and will affect coffee producers since most growers are smaller farms and the crop needs a specific temperature and rainfall pattern. Pest and diseases are also detrimental to coffee crops and climate change has released these outbreaks as well. Included are suggestions to help offset damage from climate change. **Availability:** Online.

23263 ■ *"How Green Is The Valley?" in Barron's (Vol. 88, July 4, 2008, No. 28, pp. 13)*
Description: San Jose, California has made a good start towards becoming a leader in alternative energy technology through the establishment of United Laboratories' own lab in the city. The certification process for photovoltaic cells will be dramatically shortened with this endeavor. **Availability:** Print.

23264 ■ *"How I Did It: Timberland's CEO On Standing Up to 65,000 Angry Activists" in Harvard Business Review (Vol. 88, September 2010, No. 9, pp. 39)*
Pub: Harvard Business Publishing
Contact: Diane Belcher, Managing Director
Ed: Jeff Swartz. **Price:** $8.95, PDF. **Description:** Timberland Company avoided a potential boycott by taking a two-way approach. It addressed a supplier issue that posed a threat to the environment, and launched an email campaign to keep Greenpeace activists informed of the development of a new supplier agreement. **Availability:** Online; PDF.

23265 ■ *"How to Reuse Or Recycle Your Old Tech: eWaste Is on the Rise but You Can Help Combat It By Using Old PCs and Electronics in Different Ways" in PC Magazine (Vol. 31, February 2012, No. 2, pp. 108)*
Description: US recycling businesses employ 30,000 workers to recycle 3.5 million tons of electronic waste, that does not include the number of devices that go to landfills. Simple and cheap ways to recycle or put old electronics to work are examined. **Availability:** Online.

23266 ■ *"How Small Businesses Can Make a Big Environmental Impact" in Sustainability Times (May 28, 2021)*
URL(s): www.sustainability-times.com/expert/how-small-businesses-can-make-a-big-environmental-impact/
Released: May 28, 2021. **Description:** Discusses the importance for small businesses to choose sustainable vendors to ensure eco-friendly business practices. **Availability:** Online.

23267 ■ *"How to... Harness Green Power" in The Caterer (July 20, 2012, No. 325)*
Pub: LNRS Data Services Limited
Contact: Mark Vickers Kelsey, Director
Description: Roger and Emma Stevens discuss their success as at winning the Considerate Hoteliers Association's award for Best Green Marketing Initiative. The couple discusses their restaurant and its partnership with tow nearby guesthouses. **Availability:** Online.

23268 ■ *"Hyatt Joins Other Big Hotel Chains by Pledging to Eliminate Small Plastic Bottles" in Skift (November 12, 2019)*
URL(s): skift.com/2019/11/12/hyatt-joins-other-big-hotel-chains-by-pledging-to-eliminate-small-plastic-bottles/
Ed: Nancy Trejos. **Released:** November 12, 2019. **Description:** While trying to go green and eliminate unnecessary waste, Hyatt is joining Marriott and IHG by not offering single-use plastic bottles of shampoo, conditioner, shower gel, and lotion. **Availability:** Online.

23269 ■ *"IAPMO GTC Debates Supplement" in Contractor (Vol. 56, September 2009, No. 9, pp. 3)*
Ed: Robert P. Mader. **Description:** Green Technical Committee of the International Association of Plumbing and Mechanical Officials is developing a Green Plumbing and Mechanical Supplement. The supplement provides for installation of systems by licensed contractors and installers. Comments from officials are also presented. **Availability:** Print; Online.

23270 ■ *"IAPMO GTC Votes to Limit Showers to 2.0-GPM" in Contractor (Vol. 56, September 2009, No. 9, pp. 1)*
Description: Green Technical Committee of the International Association of Plumbing and Mechanical Officials has voted to limit showers to 2.0 GPM. It is also developing a Green Plumbing and Mechanical Supplement. Comments from executives are also supplied. **Availability:** Print; Online.

23271 ■ *"ICC Works on Prescriptive Green Construction Code" in Contractor (Vol. 56, October 2009, No. 10, pp. 1)*
Ed: Robert P. Mader. **Description:** International Code Council launched an initiative to create a green construction code that focuses on existing commercial buildings. The initiative's timeline will include public meetings leading up to a final draft that will be available in 2010. **Availability:** Print; Online.

23272 ■ *Inclusive Sustainability*
URL(s): www.kornferry.com/insights/featured-topics/diversity-equity-inclusion/inclusive-sustainability-download-pdf
Released: January 20, 2022. **Description:** A downloadable paper that discusses why the environment, social, and governance spotlight should be on diversity, equity, and inclusion. **Availability:** Download.

23273 ■ *"Independence Station Utilizes Sustainable Technologies" in Contractor (Vol. 56, September 2009, No. 9, pp. 3)*
Ed: Candace Roulo. **Description:** Independence Station building in Oregon is seen to receive the most LEED points ever awarded by the United States Green Building Council. The building will use an ice-based cooling storage system, biofuel cogeneration system and phovoltaic system. Other building features and dimensions are also supplied. **Availability:** Print; Online.

GENERAL SMALL BUSINESS TOPICS   Environmentally Responsible Business Practices ■ 23297

23274 ■ *"IndieCompanyDk Offers Eco-Friendly Furniture That Stands Out"* in *Ecology, Environment & Conservation Business (September 6, 2014, pp. 39)*
Pub: NewsRX LLC.
Contact: Kalani Rosell, Contact
Description: A new manufacturer of eco-friendly furniture and interiors, IndieCompanyDk, is offering a new concept in sustainable furniture design, using exclusive and affordable smooth designs, which maintain the natural and raw look of quality reclaimed materials. **Availability:** Online.

23275 ■ *"Industry Escalates Lobbying Efforts For Loan Program"* in *Crain's Detroit Business (Vol. 24, September 22, 2008, No. 38, pp. 22)*
Pub: Crain Communications Inc.
Contact: Barry Asin, President
Ed: Jay Greene, Ryan Beene, Harry Stoffer. **Description:** Auto suppliers such as Lear Corp., which is best known for vehicle seating, also supplies high-voltage wiring for Ford hybrids and is developing other hybrid components. These suppliers are joining automakers in lobbying for the loan program which would promote the accelerated development of fuel-efficient vehicles. **Availability:** Print; PDF; Online.

23276 ■ *"Info Junkie: Karen Eng"* in *Crain's Chicago Business (Vol. 34, October 24, 2011, No. 42, pp. 35)*
Pub: Crain Communications Inc.
Contact: Barry Asin, President
Ed: Christina Le Beau. **Description:** Greg Colando, president of Flor Inc., an eco-friendly carpet company located I Chicago discusses his marketing program to increase sales. **Availability:** Online.

23277 ■ *"Invest in Energy-Efficient Equipment for Your Pet Store"* in *Pet Product News (Vol. 66, September 2012, No. 9, pp. 72)*
Ed: Leila Meyer. **Description:** Aquatic retailers can achieve business growth by offering lighting products, pumps, heaters, filters, and other aquarium supplies that would help customers realize energy efficiency. Aside from offering an education in energy efficiency as a customer service opportunity, retailers are encouraged to determine what supplies are crucial in helping customers achieve energy usage goals. **Availability:** Online.

23278 ■ *"Iogen in Talks to Build Ethanol Plant in Canada"* in *Globe & Mail (March 21, 2007, pp. B7)*
Ed: Shawn McCarthy. **Description:** Ottawa based Iogen Corp. is planning to construct a cellulosic ethanol plant in Saskatchewan region. The company will be investing an estimated $500 million for this purpose. **Availability:** Print; Online.

23279 ■ *"Is Mulcair Good for Business?"* in *Canadian Business (Vol. 85, June 11, 2012, No. 10, pp. 20)*
Ed: Sarah Barmak. **Description:** Some of the pronouncements made by New Democratic Party leader Thomas Mulcair suggest that he may be both a friend and an enemy of the Canadian business community. He expressed supportto the energy sector and endorsed lower taxes but also commented on the negative effect of oilsands development. **Availability:** Online.

23280 ■ *"Keene: Nominations are Being Sought by the Keene Cities for Climate Protection Committee for the Monadnock Green Business of the Year Award"* in *New Hampshire Business Review (Vol. 34, February 24, 2012, No. 4, pp. 7)*
Released: February 24, 2012. **Description:** Nominations are being sought by the Keene Cities for Climate Protection Committee for the Monadnock Green Business of the Year Award. The award recognizes socially and environmentally responsible companies in the region that have developed innovative practices or programs while contributing to the economic growth of the area.

23281 ■ *"Keeping the Faith in Fuel-Tech"* in *Barron's (Vol. 88, March 24, 2008, No. 12, pp. 20)*
Pub: Dow Jones & Company Inc.
Contact: Almar Latour, Chief Executive Officer
Ed: Christopher C. Williams. **Description:** Shares of air pollution control company Fuel-Tech remain on track to reach $40 each from their $19 level due to a continued influx of contracts. The stock has suffered from lower-than-expected quarterly earnings and tougher competition but stand to benefit from increased orders. **Availability:** Online.

23282 ■ *"Kohler Building Earns LEED Silver Certification"* in *Contractor (Vol. 56, September 2009, No. 9, pp. 12)*
Description: United States Green Building Council has awarded Kohler Co. with the Silver Leadership in Energy and Environmental Design Status. The award has highlighted the company's work to transform its building into a more environmentally efficient structure. A description of the facility is also provided. **Availability:** Print; Online.

23283 ■ *"Kroger Releases Annual Sustainability Report"* in *Ecology, Environment & Conservation Business (July 26, 2014, pp. 46)*
Pub: NewsRX LLC.
Contact: Kalani Rosell, Contact
Description: Kroger Company published its eighth annual sustainability report. The company is committed to reducing water consumption in its grocery stores by 5 percent in 2014. The report also provides a progress report on moving retail locations toward 'zero waste' and sourcing 100 percent certified palm oil. Statistical data included. **Availability:** Online.

23284 ■ *"Large Homes can be Energy Efficient Too"* in *Contractor (Vol. 56, October 2009, No. 10, pp. 5)*
Ed: Candace Roulo. **Description:** Eco Estate at Briggs Chaney subdivision in Silver Spring, Maryland has model houses that use sustainable technologies and products and the homes that will be built on the subdivision will feature some of the technologies featured on the model home. The energy efficient HVAC system of the model homes are discussed. **Availability:** Print; Online.

23285 ■ *"Let's Put On a Show"* in *Inc. (November 2007, pp. 127)*
Ed: Elaine Appleton Grant. **Description:** Profile of Jeff Baker, CEO of Image 4, designer of trade show exhibits. Baker shares details of the firm's commitment to being green. **Availability:** Online.

23286 ■ *"A Light Bulb Came On, and It Was Energy Efficient"* in *Globe & Mail (January 27, 2007, pp. B3)*
Description: A brief profile of Edward Weinstein, chief executive officer of the Montreal-based family-run lighting firm Globe Electric Co., is presented The firm's management strategies are described. **Availability:** Online.

23287 ■ *"Lining Up at the Ethanol Trough (Ethanol Production in Canada)"* in *Globe & Mail (January 25, 2007, pp. B2)*
Ed: Eric Reguly. **Description:** The future of ethanol production in Canada is discussed; alternate fuel market is expected to reach 35 billion gallons by 2017. **Availability:** Online.

23288 ■ *"Long Live Rock"* in *Inc. (November 2007, pp. 130)*
Ed: Nitasha Tiku. **Description:** Profile of a family business using chemistry to recycle concrete products. **Availability:** Print; Online.

23289 ■ *"The Long View: Roberta Bondar's Unique Vision of Science, The Need for Education, and More"* in *Canadian Business (Vol. 81, October 27, 2008, No. 18)*
Pub: Rogers Media Inc.
Contact: Neil Spivak, Chief Executive Officer

Ed: Alex Mlynek. **Description:** Roberta Bondar believes that energy and renewable energy is a critical environmental issue faced by Canada today. Bondar is the first Canadian woman and neurologist in space. **Availability:** Online.

23290 ■ *"Magpower May Build Solar Panels in Pflugerville"* in *Austin Business Journal (Vol. 31, May 13, 2011, No. 10, pp. A1)*
Pub: Austin Business Journal
Contact: Rachel McGrath, Director
E-mail: rmcgrath@bizjournals.com
Ed: Christopher Calnan. **Description:** RRE Austin Solar LLC CEO Doven Mehta has revealed plans to partner with Portugal-based Magpower SA, only if Austin energy buys electricity from planned solar energy farm in Pflugerville. Austin Energy has received 100 bids from 35 companies to supply 200 megawatts of solar- and wind-generated electricity. **Availability:** Print; Online.

23291 ■ *"Make Sustainability Part of Your Business Model"* in *Business News Daily (February 21, 2023)*
URL(s): www.businessnewsdaily.com/11240-buil d-sustainability-business-model.html
Ed: Kiely Kuligowski. **Released:** February 21, 2023. **Description:** Explains how small businesses can reduce their impact on the environment with sustainable practices. **Availability:** Online.

23292 ■ *"Malarkey Using Upcycled Plastics in Shingles"* in *Roofing Contractor (December 28, 2018)*
URL(s): www.roofingcontractor.com/articles/9 3334-malarkey-using-upcycled-plastics-in-shingles
Released: December 28, 2018. **Description:** Malarkey Roofing Products is going ot offer NEX polymer modified asphalt in all of its roofing shingles, keeping many materials out of the landfill. The company is focused on using upcycled materials to keep unnecessary waste from entering the environment. **Availability:** Online.

23293 ■ *"Manufacturers Become Part of Coalition"* in *Contractor (Vol. 56, July 2009, No. 7, pp. 40)*
Description: Bradford White Water Heaters, Rheem Water Heating, Rinnai America Corp., and A.O. Smith Water Heaters have joined the Consortium for Energy Efficiency in the Coalition for Energy Star Water Heaters. The coalition seeks to increase the awareness of Energy Star water heaters. **Availability:** Print; Online.

23294 ■ *"Market Takes Shape for Emissions Credits"* in *Globe & Mail (April 16, 2007, pp. B3)*
Ed: Shawn McCarthy. **Description:** The effort of Canadian companies to prepare for emissions trading after the government imposes climate change regulations is discussed. **Availability:** Online.

23295 ■ *"MFG Wind Launched at AWEA WindPower 2012 Conference and Exhibition"* in *Marketing Weekly News (June 23, 2012, pp. 169)*
Description: American Wind Energy Association's Conference & Exhibition was held in Atlanta, Georgia. The Molded Fiber Glass Companies (MFG) introduced MFG Wind, a new brand that stands for comprehensive wind-focused set of capabilities that it is bringing to the marketplace.

23296 ■ *"Mixing Business and Pleasure On the Green"* in *Black Enterprise (Vol. 41, October 2010, No. 3, pp. 65)*
Description: Glow Golf, sponsored by Glow Sports, will offer instruction to 150 female corporate executives and entrepreneurs to learn the fundamentals of the game of golf. **Availability:** Print; Online.

23297 ■ *The Necessary Revolution: Working Together to Create a Sustainable World*
Pub: Broadway Business
Ed: Peter M. Senge, Bryan Smith, Nina Kruschwitz, Joe Laur, Sara Schley. **Released:** April 06, 2010. **Price:** $20, paperback. **Description:** The book

outlines various examples for companies to implement sustainable change and go green in the process. **Availability:** E-book; Print; Audio; Online.

23298 ■ *"The New Alchemists" in Canadian Business (Vol. 81, October 27, 2008, No. 18, pp. 22)*
Description: Ethanol industry expects second-generation ethanol or cellulosic biofuels to provide ecologically friendly technologies than the ethanol made from food crops. Government and industries are investing on producing cellulosic biofuels. **Availability:** Print; Online.

23299 ■ *"A New Alliance For Global Change" in Harvard Business Review (Vol. 88, September 2010, No. 9, pp. 56)*
Pub: Harvard Business Publishing
Contact: Diane Belcher, Managing Director
Ed: Bill Drayton, Valeria Budinich. **Price:** $8.95, PDF.
Description: Collaboration between social organizations and for-profit firms through the development of hybrid value chains to target complex global issues is promoted. While social organizations offer links to communities and consumers, firms provide financing and scale expertise. **Availability:** Online; PDF.

23300 ■ *"New Book Takes Alternate View on Ontario's Wind Industry" in CNW Group (September 19, 2011)*
Pub: CNW Group Ltd.
Description: Dirty Business: The Reality Behind Ontario's Rush to Wind Power, was written by editor and health care writer Jane Wilson of Ottawa, Ontario, Canada along with contributing editor Parker Gallant. The book contains articles and papers on the wind business, including information on illnesses caused from the environmental noise. **Availability:** Print; Online.

23301 ■ *"A New Day is Dawning" in Indoor Comfort Marketing (Vol. 70, August 2011, No. 8, pp. 18)*
Description: New trends in the HVAC/R industry regarding biofuels and bioheat are explored. **Availability:** Online.

23302 ■ *"New Hydronic Heating Technologies Work" in Contractor (Vol. 57, January 2010, No. 1, pp. 58)*
Ed: Carol Fey. **Released:** January 01, 2010. **Description:** Technology behind hydronic heating systems is reviewed. These technologies include radiant and geothermal hydronic heating. System requirements for installing these greener forms of heating are discussed.

23303 ■ *"New No. 1 at Element 8: Angel Group Brings on New Executive Director" in Puget Sound Business Journal (Vol. 35, September 19, 2014, No. 22, pp. 6)*
Pub: American City Business Journals, Inc.
Contact: Mike Olivieri, Executive Vice President
Description: Element 8 executive director, Kristi Growdon, says the company continues to find investment opportunities in the Pacific Northwest's clean technology sector. She also said the agricultural sector is a potentially lucrative investment destination. Growdon added that the company bases decisions on clean technology. **Availability:** Online.

23304 ■ *"A New World" in Canadian Business (Vol. 80, October 8, 2007, No. 20, pp. 136)*
Description: Effects of climate change in Canada's economy are presented. A report published by Natural Resources Canada's Climate Change Impacts and Adaptation Program shows severe weather events such as droughts and storms will cause severe economic problems. Canada's infrastructure could also be affected by the rise in sea level over the next century. **Availability:** Print; Online.

23305 ■ *"The Next Great Canadian Idea: Peripiteia Generator" in Canadian Business (Vol. 81, July 21, 2008, No. 11, pp. 45)*
Pub: Rogers Media Inc.
Contact: Neil Spivak, Chief Executive Officer

Ed: Sharda Prashad. **Description:** Thane Heins has invented a generator that produces energy in an isolated system which contradicts the law of conservation of energy. Perepiteia generator is referred to as a 'perpetual motion machine.' Other inventions slated for the Canadian invention competition include Rob Matthies' batteries and Frank Naumann's Smart Trap. **Availability:** Online.

23306 ■ *"Next Stage of Green Building will be Water Efficiency" in Contractor (Vol. 56, July 2009, No. 7, pp. 41)*
Description: One market report says that water efficiency and conservation will become critical factors in green design, construction, and product selection in the next five years from 2009. The report outlines how critical it will be for the construction industry to address responsible water practices in the future. **Availability:** Print; Online.

23307 ■ *"Nothing But Green Skies" in Inc. (November 2007, pp. 115-120)*
Ed: Alison Stein Wellner. **Description:** Profile of Enterprise Rent-A-Car, one of the largest family-owned businesses in the U.S. Andy Taylor, CEO, discusses the company's talks about the idea of offering carbon off-sets for a few years. **Availability:** Print; Online.

23308 ■ *"NStar Feels the Heat" in Cape Cod Times (September 30, 2011)*
Pub: Cape Cod Media Group
Contact: Anne Brennan, Executive Editor
E-mail: abrennan@capecodonline.com
Ed: Patrick Cassidy. **Description:** Massachusetts energy officials wish to delay a merger between NStar and Northeast Utilities until it is clear how the partnership would meet the state's green energy goals. Governor Deval Patrick supports the proposed Nantucket Sound wind farm. **Availability:** Online.

23309 ■ *"Nuclear Renaissance" in Canadian Business (Vol. 83, August 17, 2010, No. 13-14, pp. 46)*
Description: Nuclear energy has come back into the public's favor in Canada because it has virtually no emissions and is always available anytime of the day. Canada's nuclear industry has also achieved an incomparable record of safe, economic and reliable power generation in three provinces for 48 years. **Availability:** Online.

23310 ■ *"One Thing You Can Do: Brew a Greener Cup of Coffee" in The New York Times (March 27, 2019)*
URL(s): www.nytimes.com/2019/03/27/climate/nyt-climate-newsletter-coffee.html
Ed: Tik Root, Somini Sengupta. **Released:** March 27, 2019. **Description:** Practical tips on making coffee that lowers the environmental impact. There are beans that can be bought and used that are sourced with care, and ditching those single-serve pods. Cutting back on electricity and using a press is also a good idea. **Availability:** Online.

23311 ■ *"Open For Business" in Baltimore Business Journal (Vol. 30, June 22, 2012, No. 7, pp. 1)*
Ed: James Briggs. **Description:** The demand for offices with open floor plans has risen as companies look to improve collaboration while cutting costs. Incorporating glass walls and low desks to open office design allow the flow of natural light, which in turn, reduces energy bills. How companies are addressing the challenge of maintaining privacy in an open office design are also discussed. **Availability:** Print; Online.

23312 ■ *"Out of Juice?" in Canadian Business (Vol. 81, October 27, 2008, No. 18, pp. 32)*
Description: Alternative energy experts suggest Canada should be more aggressive and should make major policy changes on energy alternatives despite an Ernst & Young research that rated the country high on renewable energy. **Availability:** Print; Online.

23313 ■ *Overdressed: The Shockingly High Cost of Cheap Fashion*
Ed: Elizabeth L. Cline. **Released:** August 27, 2013. **Price:** $12.82, Paperback; 12.99, E-Book. **Description:** Explores the impact cheap fashion has on our planet and society. With stores producing these clothes to keep up with the newest trends, people find it easier to discard clothes and pay for new, than to fix up what they already have. What is this costing our wallets and out environment?. **Availability:** E-book; Print.

23314 ■ *"Overheating Taking Place? Pay Attention to Details.." in Indoor Comfort Marketing (Vol. 70, March 2011, No. 3)*
Description: Boiler facts are outlined to help the small HVAC company when servicing customers. **Availability:** PDF; Online.

23315 ■ *"An Overview of Energy Consumption of the Globalized World Economy" in Energy Policy (Vol. 39, October 2011, No. 10, pp. 5920-2928)*
Ed: Z. M. Chen, G. Q. Chen. **Released:** October 01, 2011. **Description:** Energy consumption and its impact on the global world economy is examined. **Availability:** Print; Online.

23316 ■ *"Paul Hawken and Other Top Lumnaries to Participate in Green Business BASE CAMP in Los Angeles" in Benzinga.com (April 19, 2012)*
Pub: Benzinga.com
Contact: Jason Raznick, Founder
Ed: Aaron Wise. **Description:** Paul Hawken, environmentalist, entrepreneur and author, is one of many people participating in the Green Business BASE CAMP, a four-day workshop for green business and cleantech entrepreneurs. The event will be held in Los Angeles, California from May 31 through June 3, 2012. Insider guidance will be offered to early-stage entrepreneurs seeking to compete within this sector. **Availability:** Online.

23317 ■ *"Pennsylvania DEP To Conduct Natural Gas Vehicle Seminar" in Travel & Leisure Close-Up (October 8, 2012)*
Description: Pennsylvania Department of Environmental Protection is holding a Natural Gas Vehicle seminar at the Bayfront Convention Center in Erie, PA, as well as other locations throughout the state. The seminars will help municipal and commercial fleet owners make better informed decisions when converting fleets from compressed natural gas and liquefied natural gas. **Availability:** Print; Online.

23318 ■ *"Planned CO2 Regulations Could Hit Region Hard" In Pittsburgh Business Times (Vol. 33, June 6, 2014, No. 47, pp. 9)*
Pub: American City Business Journals, Inc.
Contact: Mike Olivieri, Executive Vice President
Released: Weekly. **Price:** $4, introductory 4-week offer(Digital only). **Description:** The U.S. Environmental Protection Agency's (EPA's) proposed rules to cut carbon dioxide (CO2) emissions by 30 percent over 16 years could have an adverse impact on southwestern Pennsylvania. The draft regulations, announced June 2, 2014, will affect the Pennsylvania region's power-generation sector as well as its coal industry, thereby impacting the regional economy. **Availability:** Print; Online.

23319 ■ *"Power Ranger" in Inc. (November 2007, pp. 131)*
Ed: Nitasha Tiku. **Description:** Surveyor software is designed to power down computers when not in use, in order to save energy. **Availability:** Online.

23320 ■ *"Pre-Certified LEED Hotel Prototype Reduces Energy Use, Conserves Water" in Contractor (Vol. 57, January 2010, No. 1, pp. 3)*
Pub: Informa USA, Inc.
Contact: Stephen A. Carter, Chief Executive Officer
Ed: Candace Roulo. **Released:** January 01, 2010. **Description:** Marriott International Inc.'s LEED pre-certified prototype hotel will reduce a hotel's energy

and water consumption by 25 percent and save owners approximately $100,000. Their Courtyard Settler's Ridge in Pittsburgh will be the first hotel built based on the prototype.

23321 ■ *"PrintCity Shares Guide for Carbon Footprinting"* in *American Printer (Vol. 128, June 1, 2011, No. 6)*
Description: PrintCity Alliance published its new report, 'Carbon Footprint & Energy Reduction for Graphic Industry Value Chain.' The report aims to help improve the environmental performance of printers, converters, publishers, brand owners and their suppliers. **Availability:** Online.

23322 ■ *"Prioritizing the Planet: 11 Ways Small Businesses Can Become More Eco-Friendly"* in *GreenBiz (Nov. 10, 2020)*
URL(s): www.greenbiz.com/article/prioritizing-plane t-11-ways-small-businesses-can-become-more-eco -friendly
Released: November 10, 2020. **Description:** Discusses sustainability in small businesses, current carbon footprints, and eleven ways small businesses can change to have the most impact. **Availability:** Online.

23323 ■ *"Professional Grooming Marketplace: Cash In On Green Products and Services"* in *Pet Product News (Vol. 66, September 2012, No. 9, pp. 84)*
Ed: Lizett Bond. **Description:** Pet grooming salons can build customer reputation by providing sustainable and environment-friendly products and services. Energy efficiency and electricity conservation can also be focused upon as pet grooming salons aspire for green marketing goals. **Availability:** Online.

23324 ■ *"The Profits of Good Works"* in *Barron's (Vol. 92, September 17, 2012, No. 38, pp. 14)*
Description: The nonprofit organization B Lab is responsible for certifying companies as socially conscious and environmentally friendly. B Lab examines the impact of companies on workers, communities, and the environment as well as their internal governance. **Availability:** Online.

23325 ■ *"Provinces Tackle E-Waste Problem"* in *Canadian Electronics (Vol. 23, June-July 2008, No. 4, pp. 1)*
Pub: Action Communication Inc.
Ed: Ken Manchen. **Description:** Canadian provinces are implementing measures concerning the safe and environmentally friendly disposal of electronic waste. Alberta, British Columbia, Nova Scotia, and Saskatchewan impose an e-waste recycling fee on electronic equipment purchases. **Availability:** Online.

23326 ■ *"PSC Approves $130M TECO Solar Project"* in *Tampa Bay Business Journal (Vol. 30, December 18, 2009, No. 52, pp. 1)*
Pub: Tampa Bay Business Journal
Contact: Ian Anderson, President
E-mail: ianderson@bizjournals.com
Ed: Michael Hinman. **Description:** Florida's Public Service Commission has endorsed Tampa Electric Company's plan to add 25 megawatts of solar energy to its portfolio. TECO's plan needed the approval by PSC to defray additional costs for the project through ratepayers. **Availability:** Print; Online.

23327 ■ *"PSC Decision Could Help Bolster a Solar Market Supernova"* in *Tampa Bay Business Journal (Vol. 29, November 6, 2009, No. 46, pp. 1)*
Pub: Tampa Bay Business Journal
Contact: Ian Anderson, President
E-mail: ianderson@bizjournals.com
Ed: Michael Hinman. **Description:** Florida's Public Service Commission (PSC) decision on a power purchase agreement that could add 25 megawatts of solar energy on Tampa Electric Company's offerings is presented. The decision could support the growing market for suppliers and marketers of renewable energy such as Jabil Circuit Inc., which manufactures photovoltaic modules. Details of the agreement are discussed. **Availability:** Print; Online.

23328 ■ *"PSEG Queen Creek Solar Farm in Arizona Begins Commercial Operation"* in *Benzinga.com (October 4, 2012)*
Description: PSEG Solar Source will launch the commercial operation of the 25.2 megawatt DC (19 megawatt AC) Queen Creek Solar Farm in Queen Creek, Arizona. The Salt River Project (SRP) has a 20-year agreement to acquire acquire all of the solar energy generated by the project. More details are included.

23329 ■ *"PSI Repair Services to Showcase at Windpower Conference and Exhibition"* in *Entertainment Close-Up (May 19, 2012)*
Description: Subsidiary of Phillips Service Industries, PSI Repair Services, will highlight its off-warranty repair support for wind energy operations at the Windpower 2012 Conference and Exhibition. **Availability:** Online.

23330 ■ *"Reagan HQ In Limbo"* in *Austin Business Journal (Vol. 32, April 6, 2012, No. 5, pp. A1)*
Pub: American City Business Journals, Inc.
Contact: Mike Olivieri, Executive Vice President
Ed: Vicky Garza. **Description:** Reagan National Advertising has been awaiting the Austin City Council decision on whether it would be allowed to build a new headquarters that was on the drawing board for more than five years. However, approval of Reagan's plan would cut down several trees and that would violate the Heritage tree ordinance. **Availability:** Online.

23331 ■ *"Recession Creating Surge in Business for Auto Recyclers"* in *Business Journal-Serving Phoenix & the Valley of the Sun (Vol. 31, November 12, 2010, No. 10, pp. 1)*
Pub: Phoenix Business Journal
Contact: Alex McAlister, Director
E-mail: amcalister@bizjournals.com
Ed: Patrick O'Grady. **Description:** Automotive parts recyclers in Arizona are benefiting from the challenging national economic conditions as well as from the green movement. Recyclers revealed that customers prefer recycled parts more because they are cheaper and more environmentally friendly. Other information about the automotive parts recycling industry is presented. **Availability:** Print; Online.

23332 ■ *"Recycling 202: How to Take Your Recycling Practices to the Next Level"* in *Black Enterprise (Vol. 41, September 2010, No. 2, pp. 38)*
Pub: Earl G. Graves Ltd.
Contact: Earl Graves, Jr., President
Ed: Tamara E. Holmes. **Description:** Consumer Electronics Association and other organizations, manufacturers and retailers list ways to recycle all household items. **Availability:** Online.

23333 ■ *"Reducing the Book's Carbon Footprint"* in *American Printer (Vol. 128, July 1, 2011, No. 7)*
Description: Green Press Initiative's Book Industry Environmental Council is working to achieve a 20 percent reduction in the book industry's carbon footprint by 2020. The Council is made up of publishers, printers, paper suppliers, and non-governmental organizations. **Availability:** Online.

23334 ■ *"Reinventing the Cheeseburger"* in *Inc. (November 2007, pp. 124-125)*
Ed: Chris Lydgate. **Description:** Profile of Burgerville's Tom Mears, who turned his drive-through burger restaurant green. **Availability:** Online.

23335 ■ *"Reinventing Marketing to Manage the Environmental Imperative"* in *Journal of Marketing (Vol. 75, July 2011, No. 4, pp. 132)*
Pub: American Marketing Association
Contact: Bennie F. Johnson, Chief Executive Officer
Ed: Philip Kotler. **Description:** Marketers must now examine their theory and practices due to the growing recognition of finite resources and high environmental costs. Companies also need to balance more carefully their growth goals with the need to purse sustainability. Insights on the rise of demarketing and social marketing are also given. **Availability:** PDF.

23336 ■ *"Renewable Energy Adoption in an Ageing Population: Heterogeneity in Preferences for Micro-Generation Technology Adoption"* in *Energy Policy (Vol. 39, October 2011, No. 10, pp. 6021-6029)*
Ed: Ken Willis, Riccardo Scarpa, Rose Gilroy, Neveen Hamza. **Released:** October 01, 2011. **Description:** Attitudes and impacts of renewable energy adoption on an aging population is examined. **Availability:** Print; Online.

23337 ■ *"Renewable Energy Market Opportunities: Wind Testing"* in *PR Newswire (September 22, 2011)*
Pub: PR Newswire Association LLC.
Description: Global wind energy test systems markets are discussed. Research conducted covers both non-destructive test equipment and condition monitoring equipment product segments.

23338 ■ *"Repairing - Not Recycling - Is the First Step to Tackling E-Waste From Smartphones. Here's Why."* in *World Economic Forum (July 19, 2021)*
Ed: Mo Chatterji. **Released:** July 19, 2021. **Description:** While smartphones have gained popularity throughout the years, so has the electronic waste from these devices. Recycling may not be the only answer unless the phone has truly reached the end of usefulness. Instead, repairing smartphones is making more sense because the process doesn't produce as much carbon emissions as recycling, and is therefore more environmentally friendly.

23339 ■ *"Research and Markets Offers Report on US Business Traveler's Green, New Technology Views"* in *Airline Industry Information (July 30, 2012)*
Description: The US Business Traveler Expectations of Green and Technology Initiatives in Hotels in 2012 contains comprehensive analysis on US business travelers views on green and technology initiative and socially responsible measures geared towards the business traveler. **Availability:** Print; Online.

23340 ■ *Resource and Environmental Management in Canada*
Ed: Bruce Mitchell. **Released:** Third edition. **Description:** Discusses resource management in Canada, focusing on business and industry, environmental groups, First Nations, the public, local communities with resource-based economies.

23341 ■ *"Return to Wild for R.I. Oysters?"* in *Providence Business News (Vol. 29, August 25, 2014, No. 21, pp. 1)*
Pub: American City Business Journals, Inc.
Contact: Mike Olivieri, Executive Vice President
Released: August 23, 2014. **Description:** The Nature Conservancy is working to return wild oyster populations that have almost disappeared from Rhode Island waters and to restore the region's nearly extinct oyster reefs. The group's Oysters Gone Wild project collects hundreds of tons of oyster shells from participating Rhode Island restaurants and returns them into protected waters to build new oyster reefs. **Availability:** Mailing list; Online.

23342 ■ *"ReVenture Plan Appears Close to Landing Key N.C. Legislative Deal"* in *Charlotte Business Journal (Vol. 25, July 9, 2010, No. 16, pp. 1)*
Pub: Charlotte Business Journal
Contact: Robert Morris, Editor
E-mail: rmorris@bizjournals.com
Ed: John Downey. **Description:** North Carolina lawmakers acted on special legislation that would boost development of Forsite Development 667-acre

ReVenture Energy Park. The legislation could also improve chances that Duke Energy Carolinas will contract to purchase the power from the planned 50-megawatt biomass power plant located at the park. How utilities would benefit from the legislation is also discussed. **Availability:** Print; Online.

23343 ■ *"R.I. Lags in Solar Incentives"* in *Providence Business News (Vol. 29, May 26, 2014, No. 8, pp. 1)*
Pub: American City Business Journals, Inc.
Contact: Mike Olivieri, Executive Vice President
Released: May 24, 2014. **Description:** The state of Rhode Island has offered less in government renewable energy incentives than its neighboring states and has yet to experience the growth of residential solar energy projects. The Rhode Island Renewable Energy Fund allocated $800,000 to the small scale solar program in 2014. **Availability:** Print; Online.

23344 ■ *"Richard Faulk Covers Climate in Copenhagen"* in *Houston Business Journal (Vol. 40, December 25, 2009, No. 33, pp. 1)*
Pub: Houston Business Journal
Contact: Bob Charlet, President
E-mail: bcharlet@bizjournals.com
Ed: Ford Gunter. **Description:** Houston environmental attorney Richard Faulk talks to the United Nations Climate Change Conference in Copenhagen, Denmark. Faulk believes the conference failed due to political differences between countries like US and China. Faulk believed the discussion of developed and developing countries on verification and limits on carbon emissions is something good that came from the conference. **Availability:** Print; Online.

23345 ■ *"The Rise of 'Zero-Waste' Grocery Stores"* in *Smithsonian.com (February 15, 2019)*
URL(s): www.smithsonianmag.com/innovation/rise-zero-waste-grocery-stores-180971495/
Ed: Emily Matchar. **Released:** February 15, 2019. **Description:** Plastic waste that ends up in landfills and oceans is starting to take a major toll on the environment. Some grocers are mindful of this and have introduced zero waste stores, where food is sold in bulk with consumers bringing their own containers, instead of wrapping everything in plastic. **Availability:** Online.

23346 ■ *"Rosewood Site Faces Big Cleanup Before Stevenson Can Expand"* in *Baltimore Business Journal (Vol. 27, February 6, 2010, No. 40, pp. 1)*
Pub: Baltimore Business Journal
Contact: Rhonda Pringle, President
E-mail: rpringle@bizjournals.com
Ed: Daniel J. Sernovitz. **Description:** Environmental assessment report states that Maryland's Rosewood Center for the Developmentally Disabled has significant amounts of toxic chemicals, which could impact Stevenson University's decision to purchase the property. Senator Robert A. Zirkin believes that the state should pay for the cleanup, which is expected to cost millions. **Availability:** Print; Online.

23347 ■ *"Rough Headwinds"* in *Boston Business Journal (Vol. 30, November 12, 2010, No. 42, pp. 1)*
Pub: Boston Business Journal
Contact: Carolyn M. Jones, President
E-mail: cmjones@bizjournals.com
Ed: Kyle Alspach. **Description:** Views of residents, as well as key information on First Wind's plan to install wind power turbines in Brimfield, Massachusetts are presented. Residents believe that First Wind's project will devalue properties, compromise quality of life, and ruin the rural quality of Brimfield. First Wind expects to produce 2,000 megawatts of power from wind by 2020. **Availability:** Online.

23348 ■ *"Sacramento Businesses Must Cut Water Use 20 Percent"* in *Sacramento Business Journal (Vol. 30, January 17, 2014, No. 47, pp. 5)*
Pub: American City Business Journals, Inc.
Contact: Mike Olivieri, Executive Vice President
Released: Weekly. **Price:** $4, introductory 4-week offer(Digital & Print). **Description:** The Sacramento, California City, California Council's decision to reduce water use by 20 percent could have a big impact on businesses. Hotels and restaurants are among the biggest commercial users of water, while golf courses generally use well water. The need for businesses to purchase more efficient fixtures is also discussed. **Availability:** Print; Online.

23349 ■ *"Sales of What's Under Feet Add Up Fast"* in *Pet Product News (Vol. 66, September 2012, No. 9, pp. S8)*
Description: Pet supplies retailers and manufacturers have been emphasizing the type of substances in creating new approaches to developing environment-friendly natural litters and beddings for small mammals and cats. Some of these approaches are highlighted, along with marketing strategies retailers have implemented. **Availability:** Print; Online.

23350 ■ *"Saving the Planet: A Tale of Two Strategies: Thomas Malthus Advised Restraint; Robert Solow Promotes Innovation. Let's Pursue Both To Solve the Environmental Crisis"* in *Harvard Business Review (Vol. 90, April 2012, No. 4, pp. 48)*
Pub: Harvard Business Review Press
Contact: Moderna V. Pfizer, Contact
Ed: Roger Martin, Alison Kemper. **Price:** $8.95, hardcover. **Description:** Theories of economists Thomas Malthus and Robert Solow are merged to address specific environmental problems. Malthusian restraint includes fuel economy, refillable bottles, and recycling. Solovian innovation includes water supply chlorination, solar cooking, and geothermal energy. **Availability:** PDF; Online.

23351 ■ *"Seafood Sustainability — Consumer Preference Study"* in *Fresh Seafood (November 12, 2018)*
URL(s): www.fresh-seafood.net/2018/11/seafood-sustainability-consumer-preference-study/
Released: November 12, 2018. **Description:** A recent study in a paper, "Measuring willingness to pay for environmental attributes in seafood," determined that consumers are willing to pay a premium for sustainable seafood. Americans consume about 15 pounds of seafood each per year, and labels with information about sustainability do affect their purchase decisions. **Availability:** Online.

23352 ■ *"The Second Most Fuel-Efficient Tractor of the Decade: John Deere 8320R"* in *Farm Industry News (November 10, 2011)*
Pub: Informa Business Media, Inc.
Contact: Charlie McCurdy, President
Description: John Deere's 8320R Tractor was ranked second in the Farm Industry News listing of the top 40 most fuel-efficient tractors of the decade, following the winner, John Deere's 8295R PTO tractor. **Availability:** Online.

23353 ■ *"Should I or Shouldn't I?"* in *Indoor Comfort Marketing (Vol. 70, February 2011, No. 2, pp. 30)*
Description: Investment tips are shared for investing in futures options. **Availability:** Print; Online.

23354 ■ *"Six Arkansas Construction Projects Get LEED Certification"* in *Arkansas Business (Vol. 29, July 23, 2012, No. 30, pp. 19)*
Pub: Arkansas Business Publishing Group
Contact: Mitch Bettis, President
Ed: Lance Turner. **Description:** State of Arkansas has bestowed its Leadership in Energy and Environmental Design certification on 55 projects throughout the state. Six projects are identified and described. A list of all projects is included. **Availability:** Online.

23355 ■ *"Sizing Up Bentley"* in *Barron's (Vol. 92, September 17, 2012, No. 38, pp. 16)*
Description: The energy efficiencies of cars produced by Bentley Motors have shown little improvement over time. The company needs to invest in improving the fuel efficiencies of its vehicles to attract new customers and remain competitive. **Availability:** Online.

23356 ■ *"Sky Harvest Windpower Corp. - Operational Update"* in *Investment Weekly News (March 10, 2012, pp. 744)*
Pub: PR Newswire Association LLC.
Description: Sky Harvest Windpower Corporation is rebranding its focus on gas and power activities both nationally and internationally. The firm's Canadian projects are outlined as well as its commitment to purse the Green Options Partners Program in 2012. **Availability:** Online.

23357 ■ *"Small Business Grants Available for Environmental Upgrades"* in *Small Business Trends(December 24, 2022)*
URL(s): smallbiztrends.com/2022/12/small-business-grants-environmental-upgrades.html
Ed: Annie Pilon. **Released:** December 24, 2022. **Description:** Small businesses wishing to become more environmentally friendly should investigate these grants that are discussed in this article. **Availability:** Online.

23358 ■ *"The Small Business Guide to Sustainable Business Practices"* in *Cultivating Capital*
URL(s): www.cultivatingcapital.com/sustainable-business-practices/
Description: Small business guide to sustainable business practices. **Availability:** Online.

23359 ■ *"Small Changes Can Mean Big Energy Savings"* in *Crain's Cleveland Business (Vol. 28, November 5, 2007, No. 44, pp. 21)*
Pub: Crain Communications Inc.
Contact: K. C. Crain, President
Ed: Harriet Tramer. **Description:** Many Northeast Ohio businesses are taking their cues from the residential real estate market to draw and capitalize on interest in energy efficiency and is regularly taken into account by local architects. **Availability:** Online.

23360 ■ *"Small Wind Power Market to Double by 2015 at $634 Million"* in *Western Farm Press (September 30, 2011)*
Description: Small wind power provides cost-effective electricity on a highly localized level, in both remote settings as well as in conjunction with power from the utility grid. Government incentives are spurring new growth in the industry. **Availability:** Online.

23361 ■ *"Star Power Versus (Somewhat) Green Power"* in *Globe & Mail (January 18, 2007, pp. B2)*
Ed: Konrad Yakabuskl. **Description:** The views of the Canadian actor Roy Dupuis on the trends of energy consumption by Quebeckers are presented, along with statistics of energy consumption in the Quebec region. **Availability:** Online.

23362 ■ *"State Investment Goes Sour"* in *Business Journal Portland (Vol. 26, December 4, 2009, No. 39, pp. 1)*
Pub: Portland Business Journal
Contact: Andy Giegerich, Managing Editor
E-mail: agiegerich@bizjournals.com
Ed: Erik Siemers. **Description:** Oregon might recoup only $500,000 of a $20 million loan to Vancouver-based Cascade Grain Products LLC. Cascade Grain's ethanol plant in Clatskanie, OR will be put into auction under the supervision of a bankruptcy court. **Availability:** Print; Online.

23363 ■ *"Stock Car Racing"* in *Canadian Business (Vol. 81, September 15, 2008, No. 14-15, pp. 29)*
Description: Some analysts predict a Chapter 11-style tune-up making GM and Ford a speculative turnaround stock. However, the price of oil could make or break the shares of the Big Three U.S. automobile manufacturers and if oil goes up too high then a speculative stock to watch is an electric car company called Zenn Motor Co. **Availability:** Online.

23364 ■ *"Store Front: Invest in Energy-Efficient Equipment for Your Pet Store"* in *Pet Product News* (Vol. 66, September 2012, No. 9, pp. 43)

Ed: Leila Meyer. **Description:** Developments in energy-efficient lighting, heating, and air conditioning have allowed pet supplies stores to conduct upgrades that result in savings. Pet supplies stores have also been impressing customers by obtaining Energy Start or LEED certification. **Availability:** Print; Online.

23365 ■ *"The Superpower Dilemma"* in *Canadian Business* (Vol. 83, August 17, 2010, No. 13-14, pp. 42)

Description: Canada has been an energy superpower partly because it controls the energy source and the production means, particularly of fossil fuels. However, Canada's status as superpower could diminish if it replaces petroleum exports with renewable technology for using sources of energy available globally. **Availability:** Online.

23366 ■ *"Sustainability: Is It a Good Choice for Small Companies?"* in *Inquiries Journal* 2010, Vol. 2, No. 10

Ed: Jennifer L. Miller. **Description:** Sustainability is a good choice for companies, the environment, and society. This article discusses the importance of sustainability and how to ensure your small business or entrepreneurship is utilizing sustainable practices. **Availability:** Online.

23367 ■ *"Sustainability Is Top Priority for GreenTown Chicago"* in *Contractor* (Vol. 56, November 2009, No. 11, pp. 1)

Ed: Candace Roulo. **Description:** GreenTown Chicago 2009 conference tackled energy-efficient practices and technologies, green design and building, and sustainable policies. Water conservation was also a topic at the conference and one mayor who made a presentation said that reducing the water loss in the system is a priority in the city's endeavor. **Availability:** Print; Online.

23368 ■ *"Sustainable Is Attainable"* in *Cvent Blog* (October 16, 2019)

URL(s): www.cvent.com/en/blog/events/sustainable-attainable

Ed: Madison Layman. **Released:** October 16, 2019. **Description:** Podcast episode discussing environmentally conscious event planning. Learn how to make events more "green", from sourcing eco-friendly hotels and venues to waste reduction. **Availability:** Online.

23369 ■ *"Suzlon S88-Powered Wind Farm in Minnesota Secures Long-Term Financing"* in *PR Newswire* (September 21, 2011)

Pub: PR Newswire Association LLC.

Description: Suzlon Energy Limited is the world's fifth largest manufacturer of wind turbines. Owners of the Grant County Wind Farm in Minnesota have secured a long-term financing deal for the ten Suzlon S88 2.1 MW wind turbines that generate enough electricity to power 7,000 homes.

23370 ■ *"Taxis Are Set to Go Hybrid"* in *Philadelphia Business Journal* (Vol. 30, September 16, 2011, No. 31, pp. 1)

Pub: Philadelphia Business Journal
Contact: Sierra Quinn, Director
E-mail: squinn@bizjournals.com

Ed: Natalie Kostelni. **Description:** Taxis are going hybrid in several major states such as New York, California and Maryland where it is mandated, but it is yet to happen in Philadelphia, Pennsylvania with the exception of one taxi company. Freedom Taxi is awaiting Philadelphia Parking Authority's sign off. **Availability:** Online.

23371 ■ *"Taylor Tests Land Grant Program"* in *Austin Business Journal* (Vol. 31, June 3, 2011, No. 13, pp. 1)

Pub: Austin Business Journal
Contact: Rachel McGrath, Director
E-mail: rmcgrath@bizjournals.com

Ed: Vicky Garza. **Description:** Taylor Economic Development Corporation implemented a land grant program called Build On Our Lot to lure businesses to Taylor City, Austin, Texas. They are targeting small businesses, especially those in the renewable energy, advanced manufacturing, technical services and food products. Program details are included. **Availability:** Print; Online.

23372 ■ *"Thirsty? Now There's a Water Cooler to Suit Every Taste"* in *Inc.* (Vol. 33, October 2011, No. 8, pp. 43)

Description: Brita's Hydration Station is a wall-mounted unit with a touch-free sensor for dispensing water. This water cooler cuts down on landfill waste and offers special features. **Availability:** Print; Online.

23373 ■ *"Three Megatrends to Help Your Business Compete in 2014"* in *South Florida Business Journal* (Vol. 34, January 3, 2014, No. 24, pp. 10)

Pub: American City Business Journals, Inc.
Contact: Mike Olivieri, Executive Vice President

Released: Weekly. **Price:** $8, Introductory 4-week offer(Digital & Print). **Description:** Businesses can improve their competitive edge in 2014 by adapting several mega small business trends in marketing and communications. Brands can use brand bridging to get customers attention, use wearable technology to increase their value, and adapt environmental sustainability and corporate social responsibility to keep their customers. **Availability:** Print; Online.

23374 ■ *"Timken Features Solutions at AWEA WINDPOWER 2012"* in *PR Newswire* (June 3, 2012)

Pub: PR Newswire Association LLC.

Description: The Timken Company plans to highlight its products and aftermarket solutions for the wind industry at the AWEA WINDPOWER 2012 Conference and Exhibition. Timken products help to maximize the performance of wind energy equipment. **Availability:** Online.

23375 ■ *"Tire CEOs Focus on Sustainability"* in *Modern Tire Dealer* (November 22, 2019)

URL(s): www.moderntiredealer.com/news/736494/tire-ceos-focus-on-sustainability

Released: November 22, 2019. **Description:** The Global Platform for Sustainable Natural Rubber (GPSNR) is being supported by the CEOs of 11 global tire manufacturers, with the goal of improving the socioeconomic and environmental performance of the natural rubber value chain. **Availability:** Online.

23376 ■ *"Too Much Precaution About Biotech Corn"* in *Barron's* (Vol. 88, March 17, 2008, No. 11, pp. 54)

Pub: Dow Jones & Company Inc.
Contact: Almar Latour, Chief Executive Officer

Ed: Mark I. Schwartz. **Description:** In the U.S., 90 percent of cultivated soybeans are biotech varietals as well as 60 percent of the corn. Farmers have significantly reduced their reliance on pesticides in the growing of biotech corn. Biotech cotton cultivation has brought hundreds of millions of dollars in net financial gains to farmers. The European Union has precluded the cultivation or sale of biotech crops within its border. **Availability:** Online.

23377 ■ *"Toolmakers' New Tack: Firms' Goal -- Advance Wind-Turbine Technology"* in *Crain's Detroit Business* (Vol. 25, June 8, 2009,)

Pub: Crain Communications Inc.
Contact: Barry Asin, President

Ed: Ryan Beene, Amy Lane. **Description:** MAG Industrial Automation Systems LLC and Dowding Machining Inc. have partnered to advance wind-turbine technology. The goal is to cut costs of wind energy to the same level as carbon-based fuel. **Availability:** Print; Online.

23378 ■ *"The Ultimate Guide to Green Practices for Your Small Business"* in *Small Business Trends* (April 27, 2017)

Released: April 27, 2017. **Description:** Adopting greener workplace practices that prioritize creating a more sustainable business is becoming a leading concern for small businesses. This article discusses how crafting sustainable practices can help businesses save money on things like energy bills as well as ensures a business adapts a more environmentally-responsible reputation. **Availability:** Online.

23379 ■ *"Ultra Low Sulfur Diesel: The Promise and the Reality"* in *Indoor Comfort Marketing* (Vol. 70, July 2011, No. 7, pp. 22)

Description: Impacts of ultra low sulfur diesel are examined.

23380 ■ *"Unilever to Sustainably Source All Paper and Board Packaging"* in *Ice Cream Reporter* (Vol. 23, July 20, 2010, No. 8, pp. 1)

Description: Unilever, a leader in the frozen dessert market, has developed a new sustainable paper and board packaging sourcing policy that will reduce environmental impact by working with suppliers to source 75 percent of paper and board packaging from sustainably managed forests or from recycled material. Unilever is parent company to Breyers, Haagen-Dazs, Klondike, Popsicle and other ice cream brands.

23381 ■ *"Uranium Energy Corp Provides an Update on Its Goliad Operations"* in *Canadian Corporate News* (May 16, 2007)

Description: Complaints against Uranium Energy Corp. and its Goliad Project in South Texas have been dismissed. The Railroad Commission of Texas (RRC), the regulatory authority which oversees mineral exploration in Texas, concluded that Uranium Energy Corp.'s drilling activities on the Goliad Project have not contaminated certain water wells or the related aquifer. **Availability:** Print; Online.

23382 ■ *"Valener Announces that Gaz Metro has Achieved a Key Step in Acquiring CVPS"* in *CNW Group* (September 30, 2011)

Pub: CNW Group Ltd.

Description: Valener Inc., which owns about 29 percent of Gaz Metro Ltd. Partnership, announced that Gaz Metro welcomes the sale of Central Vermont Public Service Corporation (CVPS). Valener owns an indirect interest of 24.5 percent in the wind power projects jointly developed by Beaupre Eole General Partnership and Boralex Inc. on private lands in Quebec. Details of the deal are included. **Availability:** Print; Online.

23383 ■ *Values-Centered Entrepreneurs and Their Companies*

Pub: Routledge, Taylor & Francis Group

Ed: David Y. Choi, Edmund Gray. **Released:** First edition. **Description:** A new brand of entrepreneurs has arrived on the business scene, carrying with them a new set of values. They possess a sense of social responsibility, the need to protect the planet, and to do the right thing for all stakeholders.

23384 ■ *"Volunteers Needed"* in *Canadian Business* (Vol. 81, October 27, 2008, No. 18, pp. 60)

Description: Emissions-targeting regulations focus on the biggest polluters, missing out on other companies that leave carbon footprints in things such as shipping and travel. Some companies in Canada have initiated programs to offset their carbon emissions. Critics claim that offsetting does not reduce emissions and the programs merely justify pollution.

23385 ■ *"Volvo: Logistics Agreement to Reduce Environmental Impact"* in *Ecology, Environment & Conservation Business* (July 19, 2014, pp. 28)

Pub: NewsRX LLC.
Contact: Kalani Rosell, Contact

Description: Scandinavian Logistics Partners AB (Scanlog) will sell surplus capacity in rail transport from Belgium to Sweden to the Volvo Group. The partnership benefits both costs and environmental impact. The Volvo group is committed to optimizing transport of their manufactured cars and trucks. **Availability:** Online.

23386 ■ *Wardrobe Crisis: How We Went from Sunday Best to Fast Fashion*

Ed: Clare Press. **Released:** February 20, 2018. **Price:** $10.95, Paperback; $12.99, E-Book. **Description:** Throughout history, everyone knew where their clothes came from — they made it themselves or a local person was hired. In our modern times, our clothes are made around the world, with an emphasis on discarding our clothes soon after we buy them. Explores famous fashion icons and the entire fashion industry. **Availability:** E-book; Print.

23387 ■ *"Water Conservation Helps GC's Building Attain LEED Gold Status" in Contractor (Vol. 56, September 2009, No. 9, pp. 5)*

Description: Green contractor Marshall Erdman has built a new office building using green design. The facility is seen to become a prime Leadership in Energy and Environmental Design (LEED) building model. Details of the building's design and features are also provided. **Availability:** Print; Online.

23388 ■ *"Water Efficiency Bills Move Through Congress" in Contractor (Vol. 56, July 2009, No. 7, pp. 20)*

Ed: Kevin Schwalb. **Description:** National Association, a plumbing-heating-cooling contractor, was instrumental in drafting the Water Advanced Technologies for Efficient Resource Use Act of 2009 and they are also backing the Water Accountability Tax Efficiency Reinvestment Act. The first bill promotes WaterSense-labeled products while the other promotes water conservation through tax credits. **Availability:** Print; Online.

23389 ■ *"Water Woes Force Big Brewers to Tighten the Tap" in Idaho Business Review (June 11, 2014)*

Pub: BridgeTower Media
Contact: Adam Reinebach, President

Description: As drought or wildfires threated watersheds, large brewers across the nation are seeking to reduce their water-to-beer ratio in order to conserve the nation's water supply. Craft beer makers have expanded to its highest level since the 1870s. Statistical data included.

23390 ■ *"Wave of Resale, Consignment Shops Pop Up In Springs" in Gazette (March 19, 2012)*

Ed: Bill Radford. **Description:** The depressed economy has spurred the growth of consignment shops across the nation. Colorado Springs, Colorado area urges people to shop at these resale locations because they promote green initiatives by recycling goods. WeeCycle, Knit Wits, Once Upon a Child and Re-Generation, Moutain Equipment Recyclers, and Gearonimo, are among the established consignment stores in the area. **Availability:** Print.

23391 ■ *"What Is Corporate Social Responsibility?' in Business News Daily (June 26, 2020)*

Ed: Skye Schooley. **Released:** June 26, 2020. **Description:** Corporate social responsibility (CSR) is a type of business self-regulation with the aim of being socially accountable. This article discusses how small businesses can benefit from using CSR in multiple ways and also provides four types of corporate responsibility your business can practice. **Availability:** Online.

23392 ■ *"What Is a Geothermal Heat Pump" in Indoor Comfort Marketing (Vol. 70, August 2011, No. 8, pp. 14)*

Description: Examination of geothermal heat pumps is provided, citing new trends in the industry. **Availability:** Print; Online.

23393 ■ *"What Keeps Global Leaders Up at Night" in Harvard Business Review (Vol. 90, April 2012, No. 4, pp. 32)*

Pub: Harvard Business Review Press
Contact: Moderna V. Pfizer, Contact

Price: $6. **Description:** A chart uses colored squares to portray economic, environmental, geopolitical, societal, and technological concerns of industry leaders, and ranks them according to likelihood and impact. **Availability:** PDF; Online.

23394 ■ *"What's In That Diaper?' in Inc. (November 2007, pp. 126)*

Ed: Nitasha Tiku. **Description:** Profile of Jason and Kimberly Graham-Nye, inventors of the gDiaper, consisting of a washable cotton elastine outer pant and an insert made of fluffed wood pulp and viscose rayon, both harvested from trees certified by the Sustainable Forestry Initiative. **Availability:** Online.

23395 ■ *Why All Businesses Should Embrace Sustainability*

Released: November 2016. **Description:** Sustainability is a business approach to creating long-term value by taking into consideration how a given organization operates in the ecological, social and economic environment. This article discusses corporations who have made strong commitments to sustainability and provides practical recommendations to improve sustainability practices. **Availability:** Online.

23396 ■ *"Why the Ethanol King Loves Driving his SUV" in Globe & Mail (January 29, 2007, pp. B17)*

Ed: Gordon Pitts. **Description:** Ken Field, chairman of Canada's leading ethanol manufacturer GreenField Ethanol, talks about the cars he drives, the commercial use of cellulose, ethanol's performance as an alternative to gasoline and about the plans of his firm to go public. **Availability:** Online.

23397 ■ *"Why Sustainable Business Practices Are Better for Business and for the Planet" in Intuit: Official Blog (Nov. 3, 2021)*

URL(s): www.intuit.com/blog/social-responsibility/sustainable-business-practices-for-small-businesses/

Released: November 03, 2021. **Description:** Details seven ways in which small businesses can reduce their environmental impact, build resiliency, pursue cost savings, and engage customers. **Availability:** Online.

23398 ■ *"Why You Should Become an Environmentally Friendly Company" in Hiscox Blog*

Description: Small businesses thrive on efficiency as far as financial decisions and business processes go. It makes sense for small businesses to also consider the positive impact of becoming eco-friendly. This article details the benefits and also provides tips to go green. **Availability:** Online.

23399 ■ *"Will Home Buyers Pay for Green Features?' in Contractor (Vol. 56, October 2009, No. 10, pp. 70)*

Ed: Robert P. Mader. **Description:** National Association of Home Builders commissioned a survey which shows that homeowners are interested in green as long as they do not have to pay much for it. The association did not allow a board member to read the survey which raises questions about how the questions were phrased and how the sample was selected. **Availability:** Print; Online.

23400 ■ *"Wind Farm Is Planned for Yolo Farmland" in Sacramento Business Journal (Vol. 29, September 21, 2012, No. 30, pp. 1)*

Pub: Baltimore Business Journal
Contact: Rhonda Pringle, President
E-mail: rpringle@bizjournals.com

Ed: Melanie Turner. **Description:** Austin, Texas-based Pioneer Green Energy LLC has been planning to build as many as 400 wind turbines in Yolo County, California that could potentially generate up to 600 megawatts. The company has already raised $20 and it is expected to formally propose the project in early 2013. The economic impact on the farmers and landowners in the region is explored. **Availability:** Online.

23401 ■ *"Wind Gets Knocked Out of Energy Farm Plan" in Buffalo News (September 28, 2011)*

Description: New York Power Authority formally killed the proposal for a wind energy farm off the shores of Lake Erie and Lake Ontario. The Authority cited high subsidy costs would be required to make the wind farm economically feasible. Details of the proposal are outlined. **Availability:** Online.

23402 ■ *"WindPower Solutions Announces Its Best In Class 'Next Gen' 85kw Wind Turbine" in Marketwired (June 6, 2012)*

Pub: Comtex News Network Inc.
Contact: Kan Devnani, President

Description: WinPower Innovations Inc.'s subsidiary, WindPower Solutions, unveiled its next generation 85kw wind turbines that are available for sale. They are perfect for remote locations where there is a lot of wind and can be used locally or the site owner, if near the power grid, could sell the energy to the market. **Availability:** Online.

23403 ■ *"Women Up: Kathleen Ligocki of Harvest Power Inc." in Boston Business Journal (Vol.. 34, April 11, 2014, No. 10)*

Pub: American City Business Journals, Inc.
Contact: Mike Olivieri, Executive Vice President

Released: Weekly. **Price:** $4, introductory 4-week offer(Digital & Print). **Description:** Kathleen Ligocki is the CEO of Harvest Power Inc. of Massachusetts. The company diverts organic waste destined for landfills and produces green energy and soil enrichment products. The company was founded in 2008 and reported sales of over $130 million in 2013. **Availability:** Print; Online.

23404 ■ *"Wood Increasingly Used in School Construction" in Arkansas Business (Vol. 29, July 23, 2012, No. 30, pp. 11)*

Pub: Arkansas Business Publishing Group
Contact: Mitch Bettis, President

Ed: Jan Cottingham. **Description:** Arkansas state guidelines have increased the use of wood in school building construction. Wood is believed to provide strength and durability along with cost effectiveness and environmental benefits. **Availability:** Online.

23405 ■ *"WQA's Leadership Conference Tackles Industry Issues" in Contractor (Vol. 56, October 2009, No. 10, pp. 3)*

Ed: Candace Roulo. **Description:** Water Quality Association's Mid-Year Leadership Conference held in Bloomingdale, Illinois in September 2009 tackled lead regulation, water softeners, and product efficiency. The possibility of a WQA green seal was discussed by the Water Sciences Committee and the Government Relations Committee meeting. **Availability:** Online.

23406 ■ *"Xerox Diverts Waste from Landfills" in Canadian Electronics (Vol. 23, February 2008, No. 1, pp. 1)*

Description: Xerox Corporation revealed that it was able to divert more than two billion pounds of electronic waste from landfills through waste-free initiatives. The company's program, which was launched in 1991, covers waste avoidance in imaging supplies and parts reuse. Environmental priorities are also integrated into manufacturing operations. **Availability:** Print; Online; PDF.

23407 ■ *"Yates Helps Turn Log Home Green" in Contractor (Vol. 56, November 2009, No. 11, pp. 1)*

Description: Dave Yates of F.W. Behler Inc. helped homeowners from James Creek, Pennsylvania achieve energy efficiency on the heating system of their log cabin. The mechanical system installed on the cabin had high-temp "THW" water-to-water geothermal system by ClimateMaster, two twin-coil indirect water heaters, and several pre-assembled, pre-engineered Hydronex panels by Watts Radiant. **Availability:** Print; Online.

23408 ■ *"Yates Turns Log Home Green - Part Three"* in *Contractor (Vol. 57, January 2010, No. 1, pp. 5)*
Released: January 12, 2010. **Description:** Dave Yates of F.W. Behler Inc. discusses remodeling a log home's HVAC system with geo-to-radiant heat and thermal-solar systems. The solar heater's installation is discussed.

23409 ■ *"You're a What? Wind Turbine Service Technician"* in *Occupational Outlook Quarterly (Vol. 54, Fall 2010, No. 3, pp. 34)*
Pub: U.S. Department of Labor Bureau of Labor Statistics
Contact: Amrit Kohli, Director
E-mail: kohli.amrit@bls.gov
Ed: Drew Liming. **Description:** Profile of Brandon Johnson, former member of the Air Force, found a career as a wind turbine service technician. **Availability:** Online; PDF.

23410 ■ *"Yudelson Challenges San Antonio Groups"* in *Contractor (Vol. 56, October 2009, No. 10, pp. 6)*
Description: Green building consultant and author Jerry Yudelson made a presentation for the Central Texas Green Building Council and Leadership San Antonio where he discussed the European approach to sustainability and how it can be used for designing green buildings. Yudelson also discussed how to use sustainable practices for planning 25 years into the future. **Availability:** Print; Online.

23411 ■ *"Zalondo Commits to Carbon Neutrality"* in *FashionUnited (October 30, 2019)*
URL(s): fashionunited.com/news/business/
Ed: Huw Hughes. **Released:** October 30, 2019. **Description:** The online fashion house Zalondo is planning on helping to meet the goals of the Paris climate agreement by committing to a net-zero carbon footprint. This will entail operations, deliveries, and returns. **Availability:** Online.

23412 ■ *Zero Waste Grocery Guide*
URL(s): www.litterless.com/wheretoshop
Description: An online database of where to grocery shop for bulk food that doesn't come in packaging. These stores encourage shoppers to bring their own containers to maintain a zero waste lifestyle. **Availability:** Online.

STATISTICAL SOURCES

23413 ■ *Environmental Consulting Industry in the US - Market Research Report*
URL(s): www.ibisworld.com/united-states/market-research-reports/environmental-consulting-industry/
Price: $925. **Description:** Downloadable report analyzing the current and future trends in the environmental consulting industry. **Availability:** Download.

23414 ■ *Remediation & Environmental Cleanup Services Industry in the US - Market Research Report*
URL(s): www.ibisworld.com/united-states/market-research-reports/remediation-environmental-cleanup-services-industry/
Price: $925. **Description:** Downloadable report analyzing data about current and future trends in the remediation and environmental cleanup services industry. **Availability:** Download.

23415 ■ *Waste Collection Services Industry in the US - Market Research Report*
URL(s): www.ibisworld.com/united-states/market-research-reports/waste-collection-services-industry/
Price: $925. **Description:** Downloadable report analyzing current and future trends in the waste collection industry. **Availability:** Download.

23416 ■ *Waste Treatment & Disposal Services Industry in the US - Market Research Report*
URL(s): www.ibisworld.com/united-states/market-research-reports/waste-treatment-disposal-services-industry/
Price: $925. **Description:** Downloadable report analyzing current and future trends in the waste treatment industry. **Availability:** Download.

TRADE PERIODICALS

23417 ■ *Cal/EPA*
Pub: Inside Washington Publishers
Contact: Robert Woolard, Contact
URL(s): insideepa.com/topics/issue-inside-calepa
Description: Reports on environmental legislation, regulation, and litigation. **Availability:** Print.

23418 ■ *Composting News*
Pub: McEntee Media Corp.
URL(s): compostingnews.com
Facebook: www.facebook.com/CompostingNews
X (Twitter): x.com/CompostingNews
Released: Monthly **Price:** $83, Individuals for one year; $140, Individuals for two years. **Description:** Covers news and trends in the composting industry. Also reports on compost product prices. Recurring features include letters to the editor, interviews, news of research, a calendar of events, reports of meetings, and notices of publications available. **Availability:** Print; Download; Online.

23419 ■ *Water Policy Report*
Pub: Inside Washington Publishers
Contact: Robert Woolard, Contact
URL(s): iwpnews.com/index.html#products
Released: Biweekly **Price:** $730, U.S. for per year; $730, Canada for per year; $780, Elsewhere for per year. **Description:** Reports on federal water quality programs and policies. Covers topics such as drinking water, toxics, enforcement, monitoring, and state/EPA relations. **Availability:** Online.

VIDEO/AUDIO MEDIA

23420 ■ *Animal Free Dairy: Making Cheese without Cows with Irina Gerry*
URL(s): www.awarepreneurs.com/podcast/331-animal-free-dairy
Ed: Paul Zelizer. **Released:** April 23, 2024. **Description:** Podcast discusses creating animal-free dairy products with a precision fermentation food tech company.

23421 ■ *Be the SOLution: Building Community and Sharing Resources with Megan Bott*
URL(s): www.awarepreneurs.com/podcast/337-building-community
Ed: Paul Zelizer. **Released:** June 04, 2024. **Description:** Podcast discusses finding values-aligned companies and inclusive access to community solar initiatives in New Mexico.

23422 ■ *Braden Cadenelli - Brining Sustainable Practices to the Food Industry*
URL(s): podcast.imanet.org/187
Ed: Adam Larson. **Released:** June 20, 2022. **Description:** Podcast features Braden Cadenelli, a professional baker and pastry chef who runs test kitchens for Puratos. Discusses sustainable solutions that deliver value to customers and eliminates waste to landfills.

23423 ■ *Building a Community of Climate Entrepreneurs in New Mexico with Wart Hendon*
URL(s): www.awarepreneurs.com/podcast/340-climate-entrepreneurship
Ed: Paul Zelizer. **Released:** August 20, 2024. **Description:** Podcast offers a conversation the founder of a VC firm emphasizing sustainability and resilience.

23424 ■ *Clean Energy Trends: Driving Innovation*
URL(s): omny.fm/shows/startup-hustle/clean-energy-trends-driving-innovation
Ed: Matt DeCoursey. **Released:** September 21, 2023. **Description:** Podcast discusses the evolving climate tech landscape, the role of public-private collaborations in energy, and the obstacles facing clean energy initiatives. Features Tim Hade, co-founder and Chief Development Officer of Scale Microgrid Solutions.

23425 ■ *Disruptors for Good: Biofuel Cells and the Future of Sustainable Batteries*
URL(s): share.transistor.fm/s/b7ac6d88
Released: March 14, 2023. **Description:** Podcast discusses biofuel cells as an effective way to reduce waste and provide an efficient source of energy.

23426 ■ *Disruptors for Good: Regenerative Farming, Ethical Supply Chains, and Future of Plastic Bottles*
URL(s): share.transistor.fm/s/a2929b45
Released: May 01, 2023. **Description:** Podcast discussed regenerative farming, ethical supply chains, and the future of plastic bottles.

23427 ■ *Entrepreneurial Thought Leaders: Engineering Green Materials*
URL(s): ecorner.stanford.edu/podcasts/john-felts-cruz-foam-engineering-green-materials
Ed: Tobey Corey. **Released:** May 25, 2022. **Description:** Podcast offers tips on how to pitch to investors, build scalable solutions, and producing alternative packaging solutions for a cleaner environment.

23428 ■ *Entrepreneurial Thought Leaders: Opportunities in Climate Tech*
URL(s): ecorner.stanford.edu/podcasts/julia-collins-planet-fwd-opportunities-in-climate-tech
Released: May 17, 2023. **Description:** Podcast explains that to bulid a sustainable future, we need to focus on decarbonization and that the tech market offers opportunities for that.

23429 ■ *How I Built This: Reimagining Seafood Production with Aryé Elfenbein and Justin Kolbeck of Wildtype*
URL(s): wondery.com/shows/how-i-built-this/episode/10386-reimagining-seafood-production-with-arye-elfenbein-and-justin-kolbeck-of-wildtype-2022
Ed: Guy Raz. **Released:** June 29, 2023. **Description:** Podcast explains how a cardiologist and a diplomat started a business with the hope of revolutionizing the seafood production industry by using stem cells to cultivate sushi-grade salmon without harming fish.

23430 ■ *How I Built This: Stasher and Modern Twist: Kat Nouri*
URL(s): www.npr.org/2021/11/19/1057486872/stasher-and-modern-twist-kat-nouri
Ed: Guy Raz. **Released:** November 22, 2021. **Description:** Podcast explains how a mother who was concerned about the amount of single-use plastic she was using for school lunches decided to make durable food storage bags out of silicone.

23431 ■ *How I Built This: Tapping the Heat Beneath Your Feet with Kathy Hannun of Dandelion Energy*
URL(s): wondery.com/shows/how-i-built-this/episode/10386-tapping-the-heat-beneath-your-feet-with-kathy-hannun-of-dandelion-energyion
Ed: Guy Raz. **Released:** June 08, 2023. **Description:** Podcast discusses how Dandelion energy made geothermal energy accessible for heating and cooling.

23432 ■ *How I Built This: Unlocking the Renewable Energy Revolution with Ramay Swaminathan of Malta Inc.*
URL(s): wondery.com/shows/how-i-built-this/episode/10386-unlocking-the-renewable-energy-revolution-with-ramya-swaminathan-of-malta-inc

Ed: Guy Raz. **Released:** October 05, 2023. **Description:** Podcast explains how Malta Inc. founder got into the renewable energy business.

23433 ■ **How I Built This: When Your Dinner is Printed with Eshchar Ben-Shitrit of Redefine Meat**
URL(s): wondery.com/shows/how-i-built-this/episode/10386-when-your-dinner-is-printed-with-eshchar-ben-shitrit-of-redefine-meat
Ed: Guy Raz. **Released:** September 28, 2023. **Description:** Podcast offers a discussion with the founder of Redefine Meat, a company that commercialized 3D-printed, plant-based steaks.

23434 ■ **Midwest Moxie: Helping Workplace Resources Find Their Next Use: Garry Cooper**
URL(s): www.wuwm.com/podcast/midwest-moxie/2023-11-12/helping-workplace-resources-find-their-next-use-garry-cooper
Ed: Kathleen Gallagher. **Released:** November 12, 2023. **Description:** Podcast discusses Chicago-based digital resource exchange to find uses for used industrial and IT equipment, building materials, and furniture.

23435 ■ **Midwest Moxie: Pea Protein and Novel Battery Materials: Nicole Atchison and Francis Wang**
URL(s): www.wuwm.com/podcast/midwest-moxie/2023-04-09/pea-protein-and-novel-battery-materials-nicole-atchison-and-francis-wang
Ed: Kathleen Gallagher. **Released:** April 29, 2023. **Description:** Podcast discusses entrepreneurs building a more sustainable future.

23436 ■ **Planet Money: Green Energy Gridlock**
URL(s): www.npr.org/2023/05/16/1176462647/green-energy-transmission-queue-power-grid-wind-solar
Released: May 24, 2023. **Description:** Discusses the hurdles of trying to build a wind farm on a reservation in South Dakota.

23437 ■ **Rethinking Agriculture as a Climate Solution with Carlos Parea**
URL(s): www.awarepreneurs.com/podcast/344-agriculture-climate
Ed: Paul Zelizer. **Released:** September 17, 2024. **Description:** Podcast discusses an entrepreneur's transition to sustainable agriculture.

23438 ■ **This Is Small Business: How to Grow a Sustainable Business**
URL(s): www.smallbusiness.amazon/podcast-episodes/ep-43-how-to-grow-a-sustainable-business
Ed: Andrea Marquez. **Released:** December 12, 2023. **Description:** Podcast discussed how to navigate eco-friendly regulations and still thrive in a competitive market.

23439 ■ **Vertical Integration and Sustainability in the Hospitality Industry with Levar Jackson**
URL(s): www.awarepreneurs.com/podcast/343-hospitality-sustainability
Ed: Paul Zelizer. **Released:** September 10, 2024. **Description:** Podcast discusses challenges and innovation in hospitality sustainability.

TRADE SHOWS AND CONVENTIONS

23440 ■ **Air & Waste Management Association Annual Conference & Exhibition (ACE)**
AECOM
13355 Noel Rd., Ste. 400
Dallas, TX 75240
Ph: (972)788-1000
Co. E-mail: info@aecom.com
URL: http://www.aecom.com
Contact: Lara Poloni, President
URL(s): www.awma.org/ace2024

Frequency: Annual. **Description:** Instrumentation, environmental control products, and services. **Audience:** Industry professionals. **Principal Exhibits:** Instrumentation, environmental control products, and services. **Telecommunication Services:** jkeefer@awma.org.

23441 ■ **IOA World Congress and Exhibition**
International Ozone Association (IOA)
1521 I St.
Sacramento, CA 95814
Ph: (480)529-3787
Co. E-mail: support@ioa-pag.org
URL: http://www.ioa-pag.org
Contact: Nick Burns, President
URL(s): ww.ioa-ea3g.org/congress/

Frequency: Biennial. **Description:** Advanced oxidation, air treatment and building remediation, biofiltration, bromate formation and control, system and component design, drinking water treatment, emerging contaminants, microorganism inactivation, ozone generation, regulatory perspectives, ultrapure water, wastewater treatment. **Audience:** Engineers, scientists, and end users of ozone and active oxygen species. **Principal Exhibits:** Advanced oxidation, air treatment and building remediation, biofiltration, bromate formation and control, system and component design, drinking water treatment, emerging contaminants, microorganism inactivation, ozone generation, regulatory perspectives, ultrapure water, wastewater treatment. Dates and Locations: 2025 Aug 25-28 Omni Atlanta Hotel, Atlanta, GA. **Telecommunication Services:** ioa@esip.univ-poitiers.fr.

23442 ■ **Lions Clubs International Convention**
The International Association of Lions Clubs
300 W 22nd St.
Oak Brook, IL 60523-8842
Ph: (630)571-5466
URL: http://www.lionsclubs.org/en
Contact: Brian Sheehan, President
URL(s): lionscon.lionsclubs.org

Frequency: Annual. **Description:** Exhibits relating to community service, including environmental, social, and health related problems. **Audience:** Lions Clubs members. **Principal Exhibits:** Exhibits relating to community service, including environmental, social, and health related problems. Dates and Locations: 2025 Jul 04-08 Mexico City; 2026 Jul 03-07 Atlanta, GA; 2027 Jul 02-06 Washington, DC; 2028 Jun 23-27. **Telecommunication Services:** convention@lionsclubs.org.

23443 ■ **Michigan Green Industry Association Trade Show**
Michigan Green Industry Association (MGIA)
30600 Telegraph Rd., Ste. 3360
Bingham Farms, MI 48025
Ph: (248)646-4992
Fax: (248)646-4994
Co. E-mail: facebook@landscape.org
URL: http://www.landscape.org
Contact: Michelle Atkinson, Executive Director
E-mail: michelle@landscape.org
URL(s): www.landscape.org/tradeshow

Frequency: Annual. **Audience:** General public and trade professionals.

23444 ■ **Plastics Recycling Conference**
URL(s): www.plasticsrecycling.com
Facebook: www.facebook.com/ResourceRecycling
X (Twitter): twitter.com/rrecycling

Description: Provides networking and seminars on the latest in plastics recycling. A tradeshow of innovative products is also held. **Principal Exhibits:** Provides networking and seminars on the latest in plastics recycling. A tradeshow of innovative products is also held. **Telecommunication Services:** nfo@plasticsrecycling.com.

23445 ■ **Re/focus Sustainability & Recycling Summit**
URL(s): events.plasticsindustry.org/2021Refocus

Frequency: Annual. **Description:** Recycling topic seminars for those in plastic manufacturing industry. **Principal Exhibits:** Recycling topic seminars for those in plastic manufacturing industry.

23446 ■ **Waste Management Symposia**
URL(s): www.wmsym.org/conference-information/wm2022

Frequency: Annual. **Description:** Conference geared towards finding solutions for the management and disposal of radioactive waste and the decommissioning of nuclear facilities. Provides an exhibit. **Principal Exhibits:** Conference geared towards finding solutions for the management and disposal of radioactive waste and the decommissioning of nuclear facilities. Provides an exhibit.

23447 ■ **Waste360 Business Leadership Forum**
URL(s): www.wasteexpo.com/en/conference-and-events/Waste360BusinessLeadershipForum.html

Frequency: Annual. **Description:** Provides seminars and resources for small to midsized environmental services with the goal of growing their businesses. **Principal Exhibits:** Provides seminars and resources for small to midsized environmental services with the goal of growing their businesses.

CONSULTANTS

23448 ■ **Versar, Inc.**
Versar, Inc.
1025 Vermont Ave., NW Ste. 500
Washington, DC 20005
Ph: (703)750-3000
Fax: (703)642-6825
Co. E-mail: mjones@versar.com
URL: http://www.versar.com
Contact: James M. Jaska, Chief Executive Officer
Facebook: www.facebook.com/VersarInc
Linkedin: www.linkedin.com/company/versar
X (Twitter): x.com/VersarInc

Description: Provider of environmental and engineering services including EIS preparation and services for the management of wetlands, endangered species, cultural resources, and hazardous waste issues. **Scope:** Provider of environmental and engineering services including EIS preparation and services for the management of wetlands, endangered species, cultural resources, and hazardous waste issues. **Founded:** 1969. **Publications:** "A comparison of pectoral fin contact between two different wild dolphin populations. Behavioral Processes," 2009; "DON as a source of bio available nitrogen for phytoplankton," 2007; "Distribution of Molidae in the Northern Gulf of Mexico," 2007.

PUBLICATIONS

23449 ■ **Green Technologies and Business Practices: An IT Approach**
701 E Chocolate Ave.
Hershey, PA 17033
Ph: (717)533-8845
Free: 866-342-6657
Fax: (717)533-8661
Co. E-mail: cust@igi-global.com
URL: http://www.igi-global.com
Contact: Jan Travers, Director
URL(s): www.igi-global.com/book/green-technologies-business-practices/64894

Price: $180, for hardcover; $37.50, for on demand (individual chapters); $215, for hardcover + e-book; $180, for e-book. **Description:** Published by IGI Global. An international platform that brings together academics, researchers, lecturers, policy makers, practitioners, and persons in decision-making positions from all backgrounds who ultimately share new theories, research findings and case studies, together enhancing understanding and collaboration of green issues in business and the role of information technologies and also analyze recent developments in theory and practice. **Availability:** E-book; Print; PDF; Download.

23450 ■ Hydro Energy Businesses in the World
PO Box 460813
 Glendale, CO 80246
Ph: (303)229-4841
Fax: (408)705-2031
Co. E-mail: energy@mtt.com
URL: http://www.mtt.com
URL(s): energy.sourceguides.com/businesses/byP/hydro/hRP.shtml

Description: Contains detailed directory listings and contact information for dozens of hydro energy businesses in operation throughout the world. Includes business name, address, phone and fax numbers, and online contact addresses. Includes brief descriptions of product lines, services offered, and business type. Covers businesses providing large hydro energy systems (more than 50 KW) and smaller hydro energy systems (less than 50 KW); large and small hydro energy system components; and large and small hydroelectric turbines. Provides keyword search functions. **Availability:** Print. **Type:** Directory.

23451 ■ Organization & Environment: The Journal of Business Sustainability (O&E)
2455 Teller Rd.
 Thousand Oaks, CA 91320
Contact: Tracey Ozmina, President
URL(s): journals.sagepub.com/home/oaec

Ed: Michael Russo. **Released:** Quarterly **Price:** $1,450, Institutions for backfile lease, e-access plus backfile (all online content); $1,318, Institutions for backfile purchase, e-access (content through 1998); $1,318, Institutions for online only; $151, Individuals for online only. **Description:** Journal covering research on the management of organizations and its implications for the sustainability and flourishing of the social, natural, and economic environment in which they exist. **Availability:** Print; PDF; Online.

23452 ■ Photovoltaic Module Retail Businesses in the World
PO Box 460813
 Glendale, CO 80246
Ph: (303)229-4841
Fax: (408)705-2031
Co. E-mail: energy@mtt.com
URL: http://www.mtt.com
URL(s): energy.sourceguides.com/businesses/byP/solar/pvM/pvM.shtml

Description: Contains 811 directory listings of retail businesses throughout the world that supply photovoltaic modules and associated energy equipment. Includes business name, address, phone number, fax number, e-mail address, and web site address. Includes brief descriptions of product lines, services offered, and business type. Provides keyword search functions. **Availability:** Online. **Type:** Directory.

23453 ■ Renewable Energy Businesses in the World
PO Box 460813
 Glendale, CO 80246
Ph: (303)229-4841
Fax: (408)705-2031
Co. E-mail: energy@mtt.com
URL: http://www.mtt.com

URL(s): energy.sourceguides.com/businesses/index.shtml

Description: Contains more than 28,734 directory listings and associated contact data for renewable energy businesses and related companies in operation throughout the world. Includes company name, address, telephone number, fax number, e-mail address, and web site address. Provides description of business type, product types, and services provided. Searchable by location, business type, company name, and keyword. **Availability:** Online. **Type:** Directory.

INTERNET DATABASES

23454 ■ Corporate Social Responsibility (CSR): A Resource Guide
URL(s): guides.loc.gov/corporate-social-responsibility
Description: Provides links to online resources concerning the history of corporate social responsibility to the current day. Also contains links to company and facility information, government resources, journals, and print materials. **Availability:** Online.

23455 ■ Green Business: Sources of Information
URL(s): www.loc.gov/rr/business/green/intro.html
Description: Online resources to research the Green Business industry. **Availability:** Online.

LIBRARIES

23456 ■ Environmental Bankers Association (EBA) - Library
2900 Delk Rd., Ste. 700
 Marietta, GA 30067
Ph: (678)619-5045
Fax: (678)229-2777
Co. E-mail: eba@envirobank.org
URL: http://www.envirobank.org
Contact: David Lambert, President
E-mail: president@envirobank.org
Facebook: www.facebook.com/EnviroBankOrg
X (Twitter): x.com/envirobankorg
Instagram: www.instagram.com/envirobankers

Description: Banks and financial services organizations, law firms, consultants, and insurers interested in environmental risk management and liability issues. Aims to help members preserve net income and assets from environmental liability issues resulting from lending and trust activities. Updates members on environmental risk management programs, auditing procedures, legislation and government regulation, environmental banking case law, and environmental insurance/risk management procedures. **Scope:** Environmental Policy Development; Environmental Risk Evaluation; and Environmental Risk Mitigation. **Services:** Library open for reference use only. **Founded:** 1994. **Holdings:** 50 books, periodicals and clippings. **Educational Activities:** Environmental Bankers Association Meeting. **Geographic Preference:** National.

RESEARCH CENTERS

23457 ■ Colorado State University - Industrial Assessment Center (IAC)
1374 Campus Delivery
 Fort Collins, CO 80523

Co. E-mail: help@engr.colostate.edu
URL: http://www.engr.colostate.edu/IAC
Contact: John Mizia, Director
E-mail: john.mizia@colostate.edu

Description: Integral unit of Colorado State University. Offers pollution prevention, energy conservation and productivity improvement to industry. **Scope:** Pollution prevention and energy conservation in manufacturing. **Founded:** 1984.

23458 ■ Tarleton State University - Texas Institute for Applied Environmental Research (TIAER)
201 St. Felix St.
 Stephenville, TX 76401
Ph: (254)968-9567
Fax: (254)968-9336
Co. E-mail: tiaerinfo@tarleton.edu
URL: http://www.tarleton.edu/tiaer
Contact: Dr. Ali Saleh, Director
E-mail: saleh@tarleton.edu
Facebook: www.facebook.com/TarletonTIAER

Description: Integral unit of Tarleton State University. **Scope:** Environmental issues of state and national significance, focusing on the interface between the private sector and government as environmental policy is developed and implemented. **Founded:** 1991.

23459 ■ University of California, Davis - Information Center for the Environment (ICE)
One Shields Ave.
 Davis, CA 95616
URL: http://ice.ucdavis.edu
Contact: James F. Quinn, Director
E-mail: jfquinn@ucdavis.edu

Description: Integral unit of University of California, Davis, functioning as a cooperative effort of environmental scientists at the University and collaborators at over thirty private, state, federal, and international environmental organizations. **Scope:** Environmental protection. **Founded:** 1991.

23460 ■ University of Florida - M. E. Rinker, Sr. School of Construction Management - Powell Center for Construction and Environment
341 Rinker Hall
573 Newell Dr.
 Gainesville, FL 32611
URL: http://www.cce.ufl.edu
Contact: Dr. Robert J. Ries, Director
E-mail: rries@ufl.edu

Description: Integral unit of M. E. Rinker, Sr. School of Construction Management, University of Florida. Offers continuing education courses. **Scope:** Researches on environmental problems associated with planning and architecture activities, and the determination of the optimum materials and methods for use in minimizing environmental damage. **Publications:** Powell Center for Construction and Environment Conference proceedings; Powell Center for Construction and Environment Research reports. **Educational Activities:** Powell Center for Construction and Environment Conferences; Powell Center for Construction and Environment Workshops.

Ethics

ASSOCIATIONS AND OTHER ORGANIZATIONS

23461 ■ **Conseil National d'Éthique en Recherche chez l'humain (NCEHR) [National Council on Ethics in Human Research (NCEHR)]**
774 Promenade Echo Dr.
Ottawa, ON, Canada K1S 3W9
Ph: (613)730-6225
Fax: (613)730-8251
URL: http://www.ncehr-cnerh.org
Contact: Dr. Henry Dinsdale, President
Description: Encourages high ethical standards research involving human subjects. Consults with universities, government agencies and businesses engaged in human research; recommends standards for research projects using human subjects. Conducts educational programs. **Founded:** 1989. **Geographic Preference:** National.

23462 ■ **National Ethics Association (NEA)**
8430 Enterprise Cir., Ste. 200
Lakewood Ranch, FL 34202
Free: 800-282-1831
Co. E-mail: info@ethics.net
URL: http://www.ethics.net
Facebook: www.facebook.com/NationalEthicsAssociation
Linkedin: www.linkedin.com/company/national-ethics-association
Description: Helps businesses serve their customers by providing educational resources and content that encourages and promotes ethics in business and beyond. **Founded:** 2001.

23463 ■ **Society for Business Ethics (SBE)**
North Michigan Ave.
Chicago, IL
Co. E-mail: admin@sbeonline.org
URL: http://sbeonline.org
Contact: Christopher Wong Michaelson, President
Facebook: www.facebook.com/societyforbusinessethics
Linkedin: www.linkedin.com/company/society-for-business-ethics
X (Twitter): x.com/sbeonline
Description: Philosophy and theology professors, business school professors, and business executives. Facilitates information exchange regarding research and activities in business ethics. **Founded:** 1980. **Publications:** *Society For Business Ethics Newsletter* (3/year). **Educational Activities:** Society for Business Ethics Annual Conference (Annual). **Geographic Preference:** Multinational.

REFERENCE WORKS

23464 ■ *"1 in 4 Food Delivery Drivers Admit to Eating Your Food"* in NPR (July 30, 2019)
URL(s): www.npr.org/2019/07/30/746600105/1-in-4-food-delivery-drivers-admit-to-eating-your-food
Released: June 30, 2019. **Description:** Results from a recent US Foods survey found that 54% of respondents, who are drivers for food delivery apps such as DoorDash, admit to being tempted by the smell of customers' food and half actually took a bite. To help solve this problem customers want tamper-evident stickers on their food containers. Other delivery services are stepping up and creating strategies to prevent this in the first place. **Availability:** Online.

23465 ■ *"6 Ways Integrity Can Improve Your Business"* in ZenBusiness (Aug. 11, 2021)
URL(s): www.zenbusiness.com/blog/business-integrity/
Ed: Donald Lee Sheppard. **Released:** August 11, 2021. **Description:** Discusses the importance of business integrity and provides six ways in which integrity can improve your business. **Availability:** Online.

23466 ■ *"21 Percent of Fish is Mislabeled in Restaurant and Stores"* in U.S. News & World Report (March 8, 2019)
URL(s): www.usnews.com/news/health-news/articles/2019-03-08/report-21-percent-of-fish-is-mislabeled-in-restaurants-and-stores
Ed: Alexa Lardieri. **Released:** March 08, 2019. **Description:** The conservation group Oceana's study on seafood concluded that about one-fifth of fish in restaurants is mislabeled. Sea bass and snapper were the most commonly mislabeled and were actually giant perch or nile tilapia and lavender jobfish. **Availability:** Online.

23467 ■ *"Accountants Get the Hook"* in Canadian Business (Vol. 80, October 22, 2007, No. 21, pp. 19)
Description: Chartered Accountants of Ontario handed down the decision on Douglas Barrington, Anthony Power and Claudio Russo's professional misconduct case. The three accountants of Deloitte & Touche LLP must pay C$100,000 in fines and C$417,000 in costs. Details of the disciplinary case are presented. **Availability:** Print; Online.

23468 ■ *"Are Business Ethics Important for Profitability?"* in Investopedia (May 27, 2021)
URL(s): www.investopedia.com/ask/answers/040715/how-important-are-business-ethics-running-profitable-business.asp
Ed: Melissa Horton. **Released:** March 27, 2021. **Description:** Discusses the importance of business ethics as it relates to the success of your small business and how you can employ ethical policies. **Availability:** Online.

23469 ■ *"Beware of Credit 'Repair' Companies, Consumer Watchdogs Say"* in The New York Times (May 10 2019)
URL(s): www.nytimes.com/2019/05/10/your-money/credit-repair-companies-complaints.html
Ed: Ann Carrns. **Released:** May 10, 2019. **Description:** A warning about credit repair companies that may be targeting people struggling with loans and bad credit. These companies are illegally charging for upfront credit reapir, which is against the law. Deceptive practices are also occurring and misleading consumers as well. **Availability:** Online.

23470 ■ *"Biblical Secrets to Business Success"*
Pub: CreateSpace
Released: October 02, 2014. **Price:** paperback. **Description:** Bob Diener share insight into his journey as an entrepreneur. He focuses on tough issues like: how to treat employees, how to please customers, whether or not to cut corners, whether to follow temptation of an unethical deal, and provides solutions to these dilemmas. He recommends abiding by the Bible's rules of business in order to prosper long term. **Availability:** Print.

23471 ■ *"Biovail Hits SAC With $4.6 Billion Suit"* in Globe & Mail (February 23, 2006, pp. B1)
Ed: Shawn McCarthy. **Description:** The details of Biovail Corp.'s securities fraud case against SAC Management LLC are presented. **Availability:** Online.

23472 ■ *"Blood Diamonds are Forever"* in Canadian Business (Vol. 83, August 17, 2010, No. 13-14, pp. 59)
Description: The failed case against Donald McKay who was found in possession of rough diamonds in a raid by Royal Canadian Mounted Police has raised doubts about Kimberley Process (KP) attempts to stop the illicit global trade in diamonds. KP has managed to reduce total global trade of blood diamonds by 1 percent in mid-2000. **Availability:** Print; Online.

23473 ■ *The Board Book: An Insider's Guide for Directors and Trustees*
Pub: W.W. Norton & Company Ltd.
Contact: Stanley Kubrick, Director
Ed: William G. Bowen. **Released:** May 06, 2008. **Price:** $16.95, paperback; $26.95, hardcover. **Description:** A primer for all directors and trustees that provides suggestions for getting back to good-governance basics in business. **Availability:** Print.

23474 ■ *"Boards That Lead: When to Take Charge, When to Partner, and When to Stay Out of the Way"*
Pub: Harvard Business Review Press
Contact: Moderna V. Pfizer, Contact
Released: December 10, 2013. **Price:** $35, Hardcover/Hardcopy. **Description:** As boards take a more active role in decision making at companies, leadership at the top is being redefined. Boardroom veterans describe the successes and pitfalls of this new leadership style and explain how to define the central idea of the company, ensure that the right CEO is in place and potential successors are identified, recruit directors who add value, root out board dysfunction, select a board leader who bridges the divide between management and the board, and to set a high bar on ethics and risk. **Availability:** E-book; Print.

GENERAL SMALL BUSINESS TOPICS
Ethics ■ 23493

23475 ■ *"Boundaries for Leaders (Enhanced Edition): Results, Relationships, and Being Ridiculously In Charge"*
Pub: Harper Business
Contact: Hollis Heimbouch, Senior Vice President Publisher
Released: April 16, 2013. **Price:** $15.97, Default Title; $16.99. **Description:** Clinical psychologist and author explains how the best business leaders set boundaries within their organizations, with their teams and themselves, to improve performance and increase customer and employee satisfaction. Practical advice is given to manage teams, coach direct reports, and create an organization with strong ethics and culture. **Availability:** E-book; Print.

23476 ■ *"Bridging Diverging Perspectives and Repairing Damaged Relationships in the Aftermath of Workplace Transgressions"* in *Business Ethics Quarterly (Vol. 24, July 2014, No. 3, pp. 443)*
Pub: Business Ethics Quarterly
Contact: Dawn Elm, Executive Director
E-mail: drelm@stthomas.edu
Description: Workplace transgressions elicit a variety of opinions about their meaning and what is required to address them. This diversity in views makes it difficult for managers to identify a mutually satisfactory response and to enable repair of the relationships between the affected parties. A conceptual model is developed for understanding how to bridge these diverging perspectives and foster relationship repair. **Availability:** Online.

23477 ■ *Business Fairy Tales*
Ed: Cecil W. Jackson. **Description:** The seven most-common business schemes are uncovered.

23478 ■ *Business Psychology and Organizational Behaviour*
URL(s): www.routledge.com/Business-Psychology-and-Organizational-Behaviour/McKenna/p/book/9781138182646#
Ed: Eugene McKenna. **Released:** May 27, 2020. **Price:** $70.95, Paperback; $63.85, eBook. **Description:** A graduate and undergraduate textbook discussing theories and research findings on behaviors exhibited within a work environment. **Availability:** E-book; Print.

23479 ■ *"The Case for Treating the Sex Trade As an Industry"* in *Canadian Business (Vol. 83, October 12, 2010, No. 17, pp. 9)*
Pub: Rogers Media Inc.
Contact: Neil Spivak, Chief Executive Officer
Ed: Steve Maich. **Description:** It is believed that the worst aspects of prostitution in Canada are exacerbated by the fact that it must take place in secret. The laws that deal with the market for sex have led to an unsafe working environment. Prostitutes believe their industry needs to be sanctioned and regulated rather than ignored and reviled. **Availability:** Online.

23480 ■ *"Citi Ruling Could Chill SEC, Street Legal Pacts"* in *Wall Street Journal Eastern Edition (November 29, 2011, pp. C1)*
Pub: Dow Jones & Company Inc.
Contact: Almar Latour, Chief Executive Officer
Ed: Jean Eaglesham, Chad Bray. **Description:** A $285 million settlement was reached between the Securities and Exchange Commission and Citigroup Inc. over allegations the bank misled investors over a mortgage-bond deal. Now, Judge Jed S. Rakoff has ruled against the settlement, a decision that will affect the future of such attempts to prosecute Wall Street fraud. Rakoff said that the settlement was "neither fair, nor reasonable, nor adequate, nor in the public interest." **Availability:** Online.

23481 ■ *"The Classless Workplace: The Digerati and the New Spirit of Technocapitalism"* in *WorkingUSA (Vol. 11, June 2008, No. 2, pp. 181)*
Description: Article argues the formation of a new type of economic actor at the intersection of a new capitalism and a new technology: The Dierati. The discourse in based on the analysis of the popular magazine Wired, which registers the culture of contemporary technocapitalism. The suggestion that the new persona of the digerati is constructed as a rejection of the ethics, which dominated the Fordist workplace and Fordist society: Hierarchy and differentiation between workers, on the one hand and capitalists and managers, on the other hand. The transformation of these two categories, workers and capitalists into the digerati worker and the digerati entrepreneur, is described. Set within the context of the structural transformations of capitalism from Fordism to post-Fordism, the article shows the ideological fit of the new ethics of the digerati to the new working arrangements of post-Fordist capitalism, characterized by more privatizes, flexible, and precarious working arrangements. **Availability:** Print; Online.

23482 ■ *"Column: It's Time to Take Full Responsibility"* in *Harvard Business Review (Vol. 88, October 2010, No. 10, pp. 42)*
Pub: Harvard Business Publishing
Contact: Diane Belcher, Managing Director
Ed: Rosabeth Moss Kanter. **Price:** $6, PDF. **Description:** A case for corporate responsibility is cited, focusing on long-term impact and the effects of public accountability. **Availability:** Online; PDF.

23483 ■ *"Corporate Responsibility"* in *Professional Services Close-Up (July 2, 2010)*
Description: List of firms awarded the inaugural Best Corporate Citizens in Government Contracting by the Corporate Responsibility Magazine is presented. The list is based on the methodology of the Magazine's Best Corporate Citizen's List, with 324 data points of publicly-available information in seven categories which include: environment, climate change, human rights, philanthropy, employee relations, financial performance, and governance. **Availability:** Online.

23484 ■ *"CR Magazine Taps ITT As a 'Best Corporate Citizen' in Government Contracting"* in *Profesisonal Services Close-Up (July 30, 2010)*
Description: ITT Corporation was named by Corporate Responsibility Magazine as a Best Corporate Citizen in Government Contracting. The list recognizes publicly-traded companies that exemplify transparency and accountability while serving the U.S. government. **Availability:** Print.

23485 ■ *"Crime and Punishment"* in *Canadian Business (Vol. 81, December 24, 2007, No. 1, pp. 21)*
Description: Cmpass Inc.'s survey of 137 Canadian chief executive officers showed that they want tougher imposition of sentences on white-collar criminals, as they believe that the weak enforcement of securities laws gives an impression that Canada is a country where it is easy to get away with fraud. **Availability:** Online.

23486 ■ *"Critics Target Bribery Law"* in *Wall Street Journal Eastern Edition (November 28, 2011, pp. B1)*
Pub: Dow Jones & Company Inc.
Contact: Almar Latour, Chief Executive Officer
Ed: Joe Palazzolo. **Description:** Concern about how the Foreign Corrupt Practices Act, the United States' anti-bribery law, is enforced has drawn the focus of corporate lobbyists. Corporations have paid some $4 billion in penalties in cases involving the law, which prohibits companies from paying foreign officials bribes. The US Chamber of Commerce believes amending the act should be a priority. **Availability:** Online.

23487 ■ *"Crucible: Battling Back from Betrayal"* in *Harvard Business Review (Vol. 88, December 2010, No. 12, pp. 130)*
Pub: Harvard Business Publishing
Contact: Diane Belcher, Managing Director
Ed: Daniel McGinn. **Price:** $8.95, PDF. **Description:** Stephen Greer's scrap metal firm, Hartwell Pacific, lost several million dollars due to a lack of efficient and appropriate inventory audits, accounting procedures, and new-hire reference checks for his foreign operations. Greer believes that balancing growth with control is a key component of success. **Availability:** Print; PDF.

23488 ■ *"A Culture of Ethical Behavior Is Essential to Business Success"* in *Business News Daily (Aug. 30, 2021)*
URL(s): www.businessnewsdaily.com/9424-business-ethical-behavior.html
Ed: Sean Peek. **Released:** August 30, 2021. **Description:** Discusses the research that shows that ethical business operations are important to success, while unethical behavior can negatively impact your small business. Also provides information on the importance of creating a code of ethics for your small business. **Availability:** Online.

23489 ■ *"Decent Termination: A Moral Case for Severance Pay"* in *Business Ethics Quarterly (Vol. 24, April 2014, No. 2, pp. 203)*
Pub: Business Ethics Quarterly
Contact: Dawn Elm, Executive Director
E-mail: drelm@stthomas.edu
Description: People are often involuntarily laid off from their jobs through no fault of their own. Employees who are dismissed in this manner cannot always legitimately hold employers accountable for these miserable situations because the decision to implement layoffs is often the best possible outcome given the context. Even in circumstances in which layoffs qualify as 'necessary evils', morality demands that employers respect the dignity of those whose employment is involuntarily terminated. This paper argues that to preserve the dignity of the employees involuntarily terminated, in most cases employers have a substantial reason to offer a special unemployment benefit or severance pay. **Availability:** Online.

23490 ■ *"Defend Your Research: People Often Trust Eloquence More Than Honesty"* in *Harvard Business Review (Vol. 88, November 2010, No. 11, pp. 36)*
Pub: Harvard Business Publishing
Contact: Diane Belcher, Managing Director
Ed: Todd Rogers, Michael I. Norton. **Price:** $6, PDF. **Description:** The article shows how deftly side-stepping a question in an eloquent manner generates a more positive response in an audience than does a direct answer that is ineffectively delivered. Implications for both politics and business are discussed. **Availability:** Online; PDF.

23491 ■ *"The Downfall of Trustify"* in *PInow.com (November 11, 2019)*
URL(s): www.pinow.com/articles/2779/the-downfall-of-trustify
Ed: Stephanie Irvine. **Released:** November 11, 2019. **Description:** Profile of Trustify, Inc., a start-up company founded in 2015 that helped people hire private investigators online. It's popularity was fueled by its forward-thinking business model, but quickly died out within a few years due to financial troubles, hiring unlicensed investigators, and taking on cases that normally shouldn't be investigated. **Availability:** Online.

23492 ■ *The Economics of Integrity: From Dairy Farmers to Toyota, How Wealth Is Built on Trust and What That Means for Our Future*
Ed: Anna Bernasek. **Released:** February 23, 2010. **Price:** $3.99. **Description:** Integrity is built over time and the importance of trust in starting and building business relationships is stressed. **Availability:** E-book.

23493 ■ *"Effects of a Lack of Ethics on a Business Environment"* in *Chron (March 11, 2019)*
URL(s): smallbusiness.chron.com/effects-lack-ethics-business-environment-23332.html
Ed: Stacy Zeiger. **Released:** March 11, 2019. **Description:** Discusses the importance of ethical behavior in business and provides information on the types of problems lack of ethics can bring to your small business. **Availability:** Online.

Ethics

23494 ■ Ethical Pitfalls for Professional Organizers
Ed: Debbie Stanley. **Released:** January 01, 2020. **Price:** $19.95. **Description:** Presents a strategic and organized approach for professional organizers to understanding ethics, mitigating risk, avoiding harm, and encouraging honor. **Availability:** E-book; Print.

23495 ■ "The Ethics of Price Discrimination" in Business Ethics Quarterly (Vol. 21, October 2011, No. 4, pp. 633)
Ed: Juan M. Elegido. **Released:** Volume 21, Issue 4. **Description:** Price discrimination is the practice of charging different customers different prices for the same product. Many people consider price discrimination unfair, but economists argue that in many cases price discrimination is more likely to lead to greater welfare than is the uniform pricing alternative, sometimes even for every party in the transaction. **Availability:** Online.

23496 ■ Ethics and a Successful Small Business: Can You Have Both?
URL(s): www.hiveage.com/blog/ethics-an d-successful-small-business/#
Description: Provides examples of ethical issues your small business may face and how you can deal with issues early and honestly. **Availability:** Online.

23497 ■ "Evolutionary Psychology in the Business Sciences"
Pub: Springer Publishing Co.
Contact: Bernhard Springer, Founder
Released: First edition. **Description:** All individuals operating in the business sphere share a common biological heritage, including consumers, employers, employees, entrepreneurs, or financial traders, to name a few. The evolutionary behavioral sciences and specific business contexts including marketing, consumer behavior, advertising, innovation and creativity and invention, intertemporal choice, negotiations, competition and cooperation in organizational settings, sex differences in workplace patterns, executive leadership, business ethics, store and office design, behavioral decision making, and electronic communications and commerce are all addressed. **Availability:** E-book; Print.

23498 ■ "Extortion: How Politicians Extract Your Money, Buy Votes, and Line Their Own Pockets"
Pub: Mariner Books
Released: October 22, 2013. **Price:** $12.79, Paperback. **Description:** Politicians and lawmakers have developed a new set of legislative tactics designed to extort wealthy industries and donors into huge contributions. This money is then funneled into the pockets of their friends and family members. Schweizer reveals the secret 'fees' each political party charges politicians for top committee assignments; how fourteen members of Congress received hundreds of thousands of dollars using a self-loan loophole; how PAC money is used to bankroll their lavish lifestyles; and more. The first time these unethical issues have been reported to the public. **Availability:** E-book; Print.

23499 ■ "From the Editors: Plagiarism Policies and Screening at AMJ" in Academy of Management Journal (Vol. 55, August 2012, No. 4, pp. 749)
Pub: Academy of Management
Contact: Sharon Alvarez, President
Description: The plagiarism policies and practices of the Academy of Management Journal (AMJ) based on the Committee on Publications Ethics and AOM guidelines are described. The function of the Cross-Check software tool for screening manuscripts for plagiarism is explained. **Availability:** Download; Electronic publishing; PDF; Online.

23500 ■ "FTC Sues Owner of Online Dating Service Match.com For Using Fake Love Interest Ads to Trick Consumers into Paying for a Match.com Subscription" in Federal Trade Commission (September 25, 2019)
URL(s): www.ftc.gov/news-events/press-releases/20 19/09/ftc-sues-owner-online-dating-service-ma tchcom-using-fake-love
Released: September 25, 2019. **Description:** The FTC has sued Match.com over unfair business practices, resulting in consumers being tricked into buying paid subscriptions to Match.com. Users need a paid subscription to Match.com in order to respond to messages they may receive from potential suitors, and those with free accounts were sent ads by the company in an effort to get them to sign up and pay for a paid account. **Availability:** Online.

23501 ■ Guerrilla Marketing Goes Green: Winning Strategies to Improve Your Profits and Your Planet
Pub: John Wiley & Sons, Inc.
Contact: Christina Van Tassell, Executive Vice President Chief Financial Officer
Ed: Jay Conrad Levinson, Shel Horowitz, Jay Conrad Levinson. **Released:** 2010. **Description:** The latest tips on green marketing and sustainable business strategies are shared. **Availability:** E-book; Print; Electronic publishing; Online.

23502 ■ A Guide to Business Ethics: How to Navigate Ethical Issues in Small Business
URL(s): www.womply.com/blog/a-guide-to-business-e thics-how-to-navigate-ethical-issues-in-small-busi ness/
Description: A guide to business ethics. Provides information on how to navigate ethical issues, how to create a code of ethics, and common ethical dilemmas and solutions for your small business. **Availability:** Online.

23503 ■ "Hello, and Goodbye" in Entrepreneur (June 2014)
Released: December 19, 2015. **Description:** Companies must implement strategies to ensure the creation of an ethical workplace. They must be able to deal with clients that experience problems and try to bully their counterparts as a result. Executive search firms must be responsible for compensating new executive hires by helping them find new jobs. Businesses must communicate to their employees about their importance as a way of making them feel appreciated and, thus, contribute to ethical behavior. **Availability:** Online.

23504 ■ How to Start a Home-Based Senior Care Business: Develop a Winning Business Plan
Ed: James L. Ferry. **Released:** Second edition. **Price:** paperback; softback; Electronic Book. **Description:** Everything needed to know in order to start and run a profitable, ethical, and satisfying senior care business from your home. Information covers writing a good business plan, marketing services to families, creating a fee structure, and developing a network of trusted caregivers and service providers. **Availability:** E-book; Print.

23505 ■ "How To Detect a Liar (Even One as Big as Bernie Madoff)" in South Florida Business Journal (Vol. 34, May 2, 2014, No. 41, pp. 16)
Pub: American City Business Journals, Inc.
Contact: Mike Olivieri, Executive Vice President
Released: Weekly. **Description:** Ways to avoid pitfalls of con artists is discussed. To detect a deception and unethical behavior requires paying attention and watch out for signs of lying because awkward speech patterns are a good indicator of deception. Liars are more likely to repeat the questions of their target victim or rephrase it when they answer. **Availability:** Print; Online.

23506 ■ "In the Afternoon, the Moral Slope Gets Slipperier" in Harvard Business Review (Vol. 92, May 2014, No. 5, pp. 34)
Pub: Harvard Business Publishing
Contact: Diane Belcher, Managing Director
Price: $6. **Description:** Research indicates that psychological stress accumulated as the day goes on can make individuals cognitively weaker, and therefore more susceptible to engaging in unethical behavior. **Availability:** Online; PDF.

23507 ■ "Individual and Organizational Reintegration After Ethical or Legal Transgressions: Challenges and Opportunities" in Business Ethics Quarterly (Vol. 24, July 2014, No. 3, pp. 315)
Pub: Business Ethics Quarterly
Contact: Dawn Elm, Executive Director
E-mail: drelm@stthomas.edu
Description: Individual and organizational reintegration in the aftermath of transgressions that violate ethical and legal boundaries are explored. **Availability:** Download; PDF; Online.

23508 ■ "Internal Auditor Wants Ethics Review of City's Billy Casper Golf Contract" in Business Courier (Vol. 27, September 10, 2010, No. 19, pp. 1)
Pub: Business Courier
Ed: Dan Monk. **Description:** Mark Ashworth, an internal auditor from Cincinnati, Ohio is pushing for an ethics review of management contract for seven city-owned golf courses. Ashworth wants the Ohio Ethics Commission to investigate family ties between a superintendent for the Cincinnati Recreation Commission and Billy Casper Golf. **Availability:** Print; Online.

23509 ■ "Is Business Ethics Getting Better? A Historical Perspective" in Business Ethics Quarterly (Vol. 21, April 2011, No. 2, pp. 335)
Ed: Joanne B. Ciulla. **Released:** Volume 21, Issue 2. **Description:** The question 'Is Business Ethics Getting Better?' as a heuristic for discussing the importance of history in understanding business and ethics is answered. The article uses a number of examples to illustrate how the same ethical problems in business have been around for a long time. It describes early attempts at the Harvard School of Business to use business history as a means of teaching students about moral and social values. In the end, the author suggests that history may be another way to teach ethics, enrich business ethics courses, and develop the perspective and vision in future business leaders. **Availability:** Online.

23510 ■ "Is Formal Ethics Training Merely Cosmetic? A Study of Ethics Training and Ethical Organizational Culture" in Business Ethics Quarterly (Vol. 24, January 2014, No. 1, pp. 85)
Pub: Business Ethics Quarterly
Contact: Dawn Elm, Executive Director
E-mail: drelm@stthomas.edu
Description: U.S. Organizational Sentencing Guidelines provide firms with incentives to develop formal ethics programs that promote ethical organizational cultures and thereby decrease corporate offenses. An examination of the effects of training on ethical organizational culture is discussed. **Availability:** Online.

23511 ■ "Is It Ever OK to Break a Promise? A Student Must Decide Whether to Leave the Company that Sponsored His MBA for a Dream Job" in Harvard Business Review (Vol. 92, September 2014, No. 9, pp. 119)
Pub: Harvard Business Publishing
Contact: Diane Belcher, Managing Director
Price: $8.95. **Description:** A fictitious decision making scenario is presented, with contributors providing advice. One notes that change, requiring people to adapt and, in some cases, alter contracts. Another states that the original contract should be honored and that other opportunities are likely to present themselves to the student considering leaving the firm that sponsored his MBA. **Availability:** Online; PDF.

23512 ■ Liespotting: Proven Techniques to Detect Deception
Pub: St. Martins Press/Macmillan
Ed: Pamela Meyer. **Released:** September 13, 2011. **Price:** $15.99, paperback; $25.99, hardcover. **Description:** Liespotting links three disciplines: facial recognition training, interrogation training, and a comprehensive survey of research in the field - into a specialized body of information developed specifi-

cally to help business leaders detect deception and get the information they need to successfully conduct their most important interactions and transactions. **Availability:** Paperback; E-book; Print.

23513 ■ *"Life's Work: Ben Bradlee" in Harvard Business Review (Vol. 88, September 2010, No. 9, pp. 128)*
Pub: Harvard Business Publishing
Contact: Diane Belcher, Managing Director
Ed: Alison Beard. **Price:** $8.95, PDF. **Description:** Newspaper publisher Ben Bradlee discusses factors that lead to success, including visible supervisors, enthusiasm, appropriate expansion, and the importance in truth in reporting. **Availability:** Online; PDF.

23514 ■ *"Life's Work: Interview With Kareem Abdul-Jabbar" in Harvard Business Review (Vol. 90, January-February 2012, No.1-2, pp. 156)*
Pub: Harvard Business Review Press
Contact: Moderna V. Pfizer, Contact
Ed: Alison Beard. **Description:** Former basketball player Kareem Abdul-Jabbar believes that a solid work ethic and practice always wins over lazy, undeveloped talent. Although he was known as a strictly-focused athlete, he now feels he relates to others on a more personal level than before. His interests in history and writing have made him a multidimensional individual.

23515 ■ *"Macy's, Home to $8,000 Mink Jackets, Will Stop Selling Fur Products by 2021" in The New York Times (October 21, 2019)*
URL(s): www.nytimes.com/2019/10/21/business/macys-fur-sales.html
Ed: Sapna Maheshwari. **Released:** October 21, 2019. **Description:** Macy's and Bloomingdale's department stores will stop selling fur by 2021, leading to the closure of 34 Fur Vaults at Macy's and 22 Maximilian salons at Bloomingdale's. The chain is taking on this change due to consumers who are buying less furs due to animal welfare concerns. **Availability:** Online.

23516 ■ *"Medicare Fraudsters Turn to Pharmacies" in South Florida Business Journal (Vol. 32, June 15, 2012, No. 47, pp. 1)*
Pub: Baltimore Business Journal
Contact: Rhonda Pringle, President
E-mail: rpringle@bizjournals.com
Description: U.S. Department of Health and Human Services, Office of Inspector General reports indicate that 2,637 retail pharmacies, or 4.4 percent of all pharmacies, had dubious Part D practices in 2009. However, the Miami area led the nation with 19.4 percent of its retail pharmacies submitting dubious claims as unethical frauds turn them in. **Availability:** Print; Online.

23517 ■ *"Messing with Corporate Heads? Psychological Contracts and Leadership Integrity" in Journal of Business Strategy (Vol. 35, May-June 2014, No. 3, pp. 38-46)*
Pub: Emerald Group Publishing Limited
Contact: Erika Valenti, President
Description: A model of leadership, i.e. the leadership psychological contract (LPC) and investigation of the contribution of psychological contract (PC) to the leadership domain is investigated. Contemporary literature on leadership and PC is reviewed and it was observed that the LPC is a predictive model consisting of three dependent variables namely trust, fairness, and fulfillment of expectations. The LPC model seeks to augment the value of ethical and effective leadership approaches.

23518 ■ *"Millions of Senior Citizens Swindled by Financial Fraud" in Black Enterprise (Vol. 41, September 2010, No. 2, pp. 24)*
Pub: Earl G. Graves Ltd.
Contact: Earl Graves, Jr., President
Description: One of every five citizens over the age of 65 have been victims of financial fraud. Statistical data included.

23519 ■ *"The Moral Legitimacy of NGOs as Partners of Corporations" in Business Ethics Quarterly (Vol. 21, October 2011, No. 4, pp. 579)*
Ed: Dorothea Baur, Guido Palazzo. **Description:** Partnerships between companies and NGOs have received considerable attention in CSR in the past years. However, the role of NGO legitimacy in such partnerships has thus far been neglected. The article argues that NGOs assume a status as special stakeholders of corporations which act on behalf of the common good. This role requires a particular focus on their moral legitimacy. An introduction to the conceptual framework analyzing the moral legitimacy of NGOs along three dimensions, building on the theory of deliberative democracy. **Availability:** PDF; Online.

23520 ■ *"'No Snitch' Culture in American Business" in Business Owner (Vol. 35, September-October 2011, No. 5, pp. 7)*
Description: It is important to make known the fact that a businessman is performing unethical or illegal activities in his firm. **Availability:** Online.

23521 ■ *"Now That's Rich" in Canadian Business (Vol. 80, February 12, 2007, No. 4, pp. 92)*
Description: The effort of chief executive officer of Stelco Inc. Rodney Mott in resolving the issue of financial loss of the company by taking up backdating options for share price is discussed. **Availability:** Print; Online.

23522 ■ *"One-Time Area Trust Executive Finds Trouble in N.H." in The Business Journal-Serving Metropolitan Kansas City (September 12, 2008)*
Description: About 200 investors, some from Missouri's Kansas City area, claim that they had conducted business with Noble Trust Co. The trust company was placed under New Hampshire Banking Department's conservatorship after $15 million was discovered to be missing from its account. It is alleged that the money was lost in a Colorado Ponzi scheme. **Availability:** Print; Online.

23523 ■ *"Organizational Virtue Orientation and Family Firms" in Business Ethics Quarterly (Vol. 21, April 2011, No. 2, pp. 257)*
Ed: G. Tyge Payne, Keith H. Brigham, J. Christian Broberg, Todd W. Moss, Jeremy C. Short. **Released:** Quarterly; Volume 21, issue 2. **Description:** The concept of organizational virtue orientation (OVO) and the differences between family and non-family firms on six organizational virtue dimensions of Integrity, Empathy, Warmth, Courage, Conscientiousness, and Zeal are examined. **Availability:** PDF; Online.

23524 ■ *"Paging Dr. Phil" in Canadian Business (Vol. 79, September 25, 2006, No. 19, pp. 21)*
Description: Increasing corporate crimes in software industry is discussed by focusing on recent case of Hewlett and Packard. **Availability:** Print; Mailing list; Online.

23525 ■ *The Power of Many: Values for Success in Business and in Life*
Ed: Meg Whitman, Joan O'C Hamilton. **Released:** 2010. **Price:** $15.99, paperback; $14.99, e-book. **Description:** Meg Whitman discusses the important values for success in business and in life: integrity, accountability, authenticity and courage. **Availability:** E-book; Print.

23526 ■ *"Practices, Governance, and Politics: Applying MacIntyre's Ethics to Business" in Business Ethics Quarterly (Vol. 24, April 2014, No. 2, pp. 229)*
Pub: Business Ethics Quarterly
Contact: Dawn Elm, Executive Director
E-mail: drelm@stthomas.edu
Description: An argument to apply MacIntyre's positive moral theory to business ethics is problematic due to the cognitive closure of MacIntyre's concept of practice. The paper begins by outlining the notion of a practice, before turning Moore's attempt to provide a MacIntyrean account of corporate governance. It argues that Moore's attempt is mismatched with MacIntyre's account of moral education. Because the notion of practices resists general application it is argued that a negative application, which focuses on regulation, is more plausible. Large-scale regulation, usually thought anti-ethical to MacIntyre's advocacy of small-scale politics, has the potential to facilitate practice-based work and reveals that MacIntyre's own work can be used against his pessimism about the modern order. Furthermore, the conception of regulation can show how management is more amenable to ethical understanding than MacIntyre's work is often taken to imply.

23527 ■ *"A Property Rights Analysis of Newly Private Firms" Opportunities for Owners to Appropriate Rents and Partition Residual Risks" in Business Ethics Quarterly (Vol. 21, July 2011, No. 3, pp. 445)*
Ed: Marguerite Schneider, Alix Valenti. **Description:** A key factor in the decision to convert a publicly owned company to private status is the expectation that value will be create, providing the firm with rent. These rents have implications regarding the property rights of the firm's capital-contributing constituencies. The article identifies and analyzes the types of rent associated with the newly private firm. Compared to public firms, going private allows owners the potential to partition part of the residual risk to bond holders and employees, rendering them to be co-residual risk bearers with owners. **Availability:** Download; PDF; Online.

23528 ■ *"Regulator Issues Warning On Reverse Mortgage Loans" in Retirement Advisor (Vol. 13, October 2012, No. 10, pp. 28)*
Description: Reverse mortgages were first introduced in 1961 and are becoming popular now with aging baby boomers. The new Consumer Financial Protection Bureau warns the public to look closing before entering a reverse mortgage contract. The National Ethics Association encourages financial advisors to use the same caution and offers advise for advisors to help educate their clients about reverse mortgages. **Availability:** Print; Online.

23529 ■ *"A Responsive Approach to Organizational Misconduct: Rehabilitation, Reintegration, and the Reduction of Reoffense" in Business Ethics Quarterly (Vol. 24, July 2014, No. 3, pp. 343)*
Pub: Business Ethics Quarterly
Contact: Dawn Elm, Executive Director
E-mail: drelm@stthomas.edu
Description: Examination of ways regulators, prosecutors, and courts might support and encourage the efforts of organizations to not only reintegrate after misconduct, but to also improve their conduct in a way that reduces their likelihood of re-offense (rehabilitation). An experiment in creative sentencing in Alberta, Canada that aimed to try to change the behavior of an industry by publicly airing the root causes of a failure of one of the industry's leaders is examined. A model for a responsive and restorative approach to organizational misconduct that balances the punitive role of regulators and courts with new roles in supporting and overseeing rehabilitation are observed. **Availability:** Online.

23530 ■ *"Retail Product Management: Buying and Merchandising"*
Pub: Routledge, Taylor & Francis Group
Released: Third edition. **Description:** Due to the rise in Internet use, retailers are facing challenges associated with more informed buyers, technological advances, and the competitive environment. Retail ethics are also examined.

23531 ■ *"Ringgold Computer Repair Owner Accused of Swindling Customers" in Chattanooga Times/Free Press (February 15, 2012)*
Availability: Online.

23532 ■ "Scott Rothstein Ponzi Reveals Ethics Issues in Jewelry Biz" in South Florida Business Journal (Vol. 33, September 14, 2012, No. 7, pp. 1)

Pub: Baltimore Business Journal
Contact: Rhonda Pringle, President
E-mail: rpringle@bizjournals.com

Description: JR Dunn Jewelers of Florida is suing New York jewelry company JB International for an 8.91 carat diamond it claims is tainted because it was allegedly sold offby Ponzi schemer Scott Rothstein or his wife Kimberly. Dunn is being sued for $748,000 in the bankruptcy of Rothstein Rosenfelt Adler, Rothstein's former law firm. **Availability:** Print; Online.

23533 ■ "Search Engine Optimization is Becoming a Must for Businesses, But Unethical Companies Can Hurt Worse than Help" in Idaho Business Review (August 3, 2012)

Ed: Sean Olson. **Description:** Search engine optimization increases presence on the Internet for any small business wishing to market a service or product. It is critical to choose an ethical company that has experience in creating Web sites that will get noticed. **Availability:** Print; Online.

23534 ■ The SEO Manifesto: A Practical and Ethical Guide to Internet Marketing and Search Engine Optimization

Description: Comprehensive guide for each phase of launching an online business; chapters include checklists, process descriptions, and examples.

23535 ■ Small Business Ethics Policies

URL(s): www.kabbage.com/resource-center/manage/small-business-ethics-policies/

Description: Discusses the importance of moral and ethical codes and provides tips to keep in mind when putting together your own business code of ethics. **Availability:** Online.

23536 ■ "Soldiers as Consumers: Predatory and Unfair Business Practices Harming the Military Community"

Pub: CreateSpace

Released: October 05, 2014. **Price:** $9.81, paperback. **Description:** Soldiers, airmen, sailors, and marines are young consumers and are appealing targets for unscrupulous businesses. There are lending organizations that prey upon our military offering products to help them bridge financial problems. Unethical elements of these loans includes higher interest rates and/or high fees or waivers of certain rights in fine print of contracts. A Federal Law called the Military Lending Act is supposed to protect service members from this kind of abuse, but the law only covers loans with terms of six months or less. **Availability:** Print.

23537 ■ "Stan Chesley Fighting Kentucky Disbarment" in Business Courier (Vol. 27, September 10, 2010, No. 19, pp. 1)

Pub: Business Courier

Ed: Jon Newberry. **Description:** Stan Chesley, a Cincinnati attorney, has been accused of making false statements to the courts and bar officials, self-dealing in violation of the bar's conflict of interest rules, and failing to adequately inform clients. Kentucky Bar Association officials will seek to have Chesley permanently disbarred. **Availability:** Print; Online.

23538 ■ "A Startup's Guide to Business Ethics and Social Responsibility" in Embroker Blog (Aug. 23, 2021)

URL(s): www.embroker.com/blog/business-ethics-and-social-responsibility/

Released: August 23, 2021. **Description:** A guide for startups to utilize as they incorporate business ethics and social responsibility policies in their small business plans. **Availability:** Online.

23539 ■ Technology Ethics for Small Businesses

URL(s): www.gaebler.com/Small-Business-Technology-Ethics.htm

Description: Provides do's and don'ts to implementing ethical business practices. **Availability:** Online.

23540 ■ "The Ten Commandments of Legal Risk Management" in Business Horizons (Vol. 51, January-February 2008, No. 1, pp. 13)

Pub: Elsevier Advanced Technology Publications

Ed: Michael B. Metzger. **Description:** Effective legal risk management is tightly linked with ethical and good management, and managers' behaviors have to be professional and based on ethically defensible principles of action. Basic human tendencies cannot be used in justifying questionable decisions in court. Guidelines for legal risk management are presented. **Availability:** Print; Online.

23541 ■ "Toward a Theory of Stakeholder Salience in Family Firms" in Business Ethics Quarterly (Vol. 21, April 2011, No. 2, pp. 235)

Ed: Ronald K. Mitchell, Bradley R. Agle, James J. Chrisman, Laura J. Spence. **Released:** Volume 21, Issue 2. **Description:** The notion of stakeholder salience based on attributes (e.g. power, legitimacy, urgency) is applied in the family business setting. **Availability:** Online.

23542 ■ Trade-Off: The Ever-Present Tension Between Quality and Conscience

Released: August 17, 2010. **Price:** $15. **Description:** The tension between fidelity (the quality of a consumer's experience) and convenience (the ease of getting and paying for a product) are shown to be the forces that determine the success or failure of new products and services in the marketplace.

23543 ■ "Trial of Enron Ex-Bosses to Begin Today" in Globe & Mail (January 30, 2006, pp. B1)

Description: The details of the case against former executives Kenneth L. Lay and Jeffrey Skilling of Enron Corp. are presented. **Availability:** Online.

23544 ■ "Two Major Credit Reporting Agencies Have Been Lying to Consumers" in The Atlantic (January 4, 2017)

URL(s): www.theatlantic.com/business/archive/2017/01/credit-scores-cfpb/512162/

Ed: Gillian B. White. **Released:** January 04, 2017. **Description:** The Consumer Financial Protection Bureau found that Equifax and Tansunion have been deceiving consumers and must pay $23 million in fines and restitution. **Availability:** Online.

23545 ■ "UIC Medical Ethicist Faces Life-and-Death Decisions Daily" in Crain's Chicago Business (Vol. 34, October 24, 2011, No. 42, pp. 31)

Pub: Crain Communications Inc.
Contact: Barry Asin, President

Ed: Lisa Bertagnoli. **Description:** Technology has enabled doctors to provide more and better methods for helping patients, however end of life issues faced by medical ethicists are discussed. **Availability:** Print.

23546 ■ Values-Centered Entrepreneurs and Their Companies

Pub: Routledge, Taylor & Francis Group

Ed: David Y. Choi, Edmund Gray. **Released:** First edition. **Description:** A new brand of entrepreneurs has arrived on the business scene, carrying with them a new set of values. They possess a sense of social responsibility, the need to protect the planet, and to do the right thing for all stakeholders.

23547 ■ "Voice: Rebuilding Trust" in Business Strategy Review (Vol. 21, Summer 2010, No. 2, pp. 79-80)

Ed: David De Cremer. **Released:** June 24, 2010. **Description:** The financial world's attempts to rebuild trust are charted. Three steps to jump-start that process are outlined. **Availability:** Print; PDF; Online.

23548 ■ "Voices: Breaking the Corruption Habit" in Business Strategy Review (Vol. 21, Autumn 2010, No. 3, pp. 67)

Ed: David De Cremer. **Released:** September 22, 2010. **Description:** In times of crisis, it seems natural that people will work together for the common good. David De Cremer cautions that, on the contrary, both economic and social research prove otherwise. He proposes steps for organizations to take to prevent corrupt behaviors. **Availability:** Print; Electronic publishing; PDF; Online.

23549 ■ "When You Need Strong Millennials in Your Workplace" in Agency Sales Magazine (Vol. 39, November 2009, No. 10, pp. 22)

Description: Millennials are bringing a new set of skills and a different kind of work ethics to the workplace. This generation is used to receiving a great deal of positive feedback and they expect to continue receiving this on the job. Expectations should be made clear to this generation and long-term career plans and goals should also be discussed with them. **Availability:** Online.

23550 ■ "Why Business Ethics Needs Rhetoric: an Aristotelian Perspective" in Business Ethics Quarterly (Vol. 24, January 2014, No. 1, pp. 119)

Pub: Business Ethics Quarterly
Contact: Dawn Elm, Executive Director
E-mail: drelm@stthomas.edu

Description: If the ultimate purpose of ethical argument is to persuade people to act a certain way, the point of doing business ethics is to persuade others about what constitutes proper ethical behavior. **Availability:** Online.

23551 ■ Why Should Small Business Owners Think About Ethics?

URL(s): articles.bplans.com/why-should-small-business-owners-think-about-ethics/

Ed: Alison Napolitano. **Description:** Presents information on why small business owners should worry about business ethics. **Availability:** Online.

23552 ■ "Young Money"

Pub: Grand Central Publishing
Contact: Michael Pietsch, Chairman

Released: February 18, 2014. **Price:** $27, hardcover. **Description:** How the financial crisis of 2008 changed a generation and remade Wall Street is discussed. The author spent three years following eight entry-level workers at Goldman Sachs, Bank of America Merrill Lynch and other leading investment firms. These young bankers are exposed to the exhausting workloads, huge bonuses, and recreational drugs that have always characterized Wall Street life, but as they get their education and training, they face questions about ethics, prestige and the value of their work. **Availability:** E-book; Print; Audio.

TRADE PERIODICALS

23553 ■ Business Ethics: The Magazine of Corporate Responsibility

Pub: Business Ethics
Contact: Michael Connor, Editor Publisher
URL(s): business-ethics.com
X (Twitter): x.com/BizEthicsMag

Ed: Michael Connor. **Released:** Quarterly **Description:** Business newsletter. **Availability:** Print; Online.

23554 ■ Ethics Resources

Pub: Santa Clara University Markkula Center for Applied Ethics
Contact: Don Heider, Executive Director
URL(s): www.scu.edu/ethics/ethics-resources

Description: Covers ethics in fields of education, business, biotech, healthcare, and technology. Recurring features include interviews, news of research, and book reviews. **Availability:** Print.

GENERAL SMALL BUSINESS TOPICS Ethics ■ 23574

VIDEO/AUDIO MEDIA

23555 ■ *AI for Creatives: Navigating the Ethics of Technology with Tasha L. Harrison*
URL(s): beingboss.club/podcast/ai-for-creatives-navigating-the-ethics-of-technology
Ed: Emily Thompson. **Released:** April 25, 2023. **Description:** Podcast discusses the intersection of technology and ethics; explains how to harness the power of AI while staying true to your values.

23556 ■ *BS-Free Service Business Show: Ethics over Easy: Succeed without the Shady Shortcuts*
URL(s): bsfreebusiness.com/ethics-over-easy
Ed: Maggie Patterson. **Released:** October 28, 2024. **Description:** Podcast explains why the ethics of staying true to your values will create lasting success.

23557 ■ *BS-Free Service Business Show: The State of "Ethical" Business 2024*
URL(s): duped.online/2024/03/04/ethical-business-2024
Released: March 18, 2024. **Description:** Podcast highlights the status of ethical business practices in 2024.

23558 ■ *Entrepreneurial Thought Leaders: Ethical Crypto Innovation*
URL(s): ecorner.stanford.edu/podcasts/dante-disparte-circle-ethcial-crypto-innovation
Ed: Ravi Belani. **Released:** December 07, 2022. **Description:** Podcast offers advice for an ethical and innovative future for blockchain and crypto-based companies.

23559 ■ *Entrepreneurial Thought Leaders: How to Build an Ethical Company*
URL(s): ecorner.stanford.edu/podcasts/nicole-diaz-snap-inc-how-to-build-an-ethical-company
Ed: Tom Byers. **Released:** June 02, 2021. **Description:** Podcast explains how ethics is a strategic imperative, not a nice-to-have extra.

23560 ■ *Entrepreneurial Thought Leaders: OpenAI*
URL(s): ecorner.stanford.edu/podcasts/ilya-sutskever-openai-inside-openai
Released: April 26, 2023. **Description:** Podcast asks how to approach ethics, growth, and innovation.

23561 ■ *Entrepreneurial Thought Leaders: Responsible AI Innovation*
URL(s): ecorner.stanford.edu/podcasts/rahul-roy-chowdhury-grammarly-responsible-ai-innovatioin
Released: May 31, 2023. **Description:** Podcast discusses building ethical AI tools and encourages aspiring entrepreneurs to engage in that conversation.

23562 ■ *Entrepreneurship and Ethics: Ethics in Venture Capital*
URL(s): ecorner.stanford.edu/podcasts/ethics-in-venture-capital
Ed: Tom Byers. **Released:** November 09, 2020. **Description:** Podcast asks venture capitalists how the VC community can incentivize ethical leadership in the companies they fund and manage.

23563 ■ *Entrepreneurship and Ethics: Facing a Crisis with Principles*
URL(s): ecorner.stanford.edu/podcasts/facing-a-crisis-with-principles
Ed: Tom Byers. **Released:** May 01, 2020. **Description:** Podcasts discusses who clear principles can help leaders and companies weather a storm.

23564 ■ *Entrepreneurship and Ethics: Teaching Ethical Entrepreneurship*
URL(s): ecorner.stanford.edu/podcasts/teaching-ethical-entrepreneurship
Ed: Tom Byers. **Released:** September 01, 2020. **Description:** Podcast asks what if entrepreneurship placed ethics at the same level of importance as product-market fit and fundraising.

23565 ■ *Entrepreneurship and Ethics: The Ethics of Emerging Technologies*
URL(s): ecorner.stanford.edu/podcasts/the-ethics-of-emerging-technologies
Ed: Tom Byers. **Released:** July 01, 2020. **Description:** Podcast asks what "ethics of innovation" looks like and suggests that efforts in biomedical research and computer science offer clues.

23566 ■ *Entrepreneurship and Ethics: Theranos Whistleblower Erika Cheung on Incentivizing Ethics*
URL(s): ecorner.stanford.edu/podcasts/theranos-whistleblower-erika-cheung-on-incentivizing-ethics
Ed: Tom Byers. **Released:** June 01, 2020. **Description:** Podcasts asks Theranos whistleblower how she found the courage to do so and why she's starting a nonprofit focused on creating ethical toolkits for entrepreneurs.

TRADE SHOWS AND CONVENTIONS

23567 ■ Rotary International Convention
Rotary International (RI)
1 Rotary Ctr.
1560 Sherman Ave.
Evanston, IL 60201-3698
Ph: (847)866-3000
Free: 866-976-8279
Co. E-mail: rotarysupportcenter@rotary.org
URL: http://www.rotary.org/en
Contact: Jennifer Jones, President
URL(s): convention.rotary.org
Frequency: Annual; mostly held in June or May. **Description:** Exhibits relating to community development, professional and business ethical standards, and international understanding. **Audience:** Members. **Principal Exhibits:** Exhibits relating to community development, professional and business ethical standards, and international understanding. Dates and Locations: 2025 Jun 21-25 Calgary, AB; 2026 Jun 13-17 Taipei; 2027 Jun 05-09 Honolulu, HI; 2028; 2029 May 26-30 Minneapolis, MN; 2030 May 25-29 Chicago, IL. **Telecommunication Services:** ri.registration@rotary.org.

23568 ■ Society for Business Ethics Annual Conference
Society for Business Ethics (SBE)
North Michigan Ave.
Chicago, IL
Co. E-mail: admin@sbeonline.org
URL: http://sbeonline.org
Contact: Christopher Wong Michaelson, President
URL(s): sbeonline.org/conference/2024-annual-conference
Frequency: Annual. **Description:** Exhibits demonstrating research and activities in business ethics. **Audience:** Industry professionals. **Principal Exhibits:** Exhibits demonstrating research and activities in business ethics. **Telecommunication Services:** programchair@sbeonline.org.

CONSULTANTS

23569 ■ Siebrand-Wilton Associates Inc. (S-WA)
PO Box 193
Rocky Hill, NJ 08553-0193
URL: http://www.s-wa.com
Contact: John S. Sturges, Principal
Description: Firm provides nationwide human resources consulting support and also offers executive coaching and counseling, benefit plan design, and other related services. **Founded:** 1986. **Publications:** "Should Government or Business Try to Save Medicare," HR News; "Executive Temping," HR Horizons; "When is an Employee Truly an Employee," HR Magazine; "Examining Your Insurance Carrier," HR Magazine.

PUBLICATIONS

23570 ■ *Business Ethics Journal Review (BEJR)*
2123 Berkmar Dr.
Charlottesville, VA 22901-1423
Ph: (434)220-3300
Free: 800-444-2419
Fax: (434)220-3301
Co. E-mail: order@pdcnet.org
URL: http://www.pdcnet.org
Contact: George Leaman, Director
E-mail: leaman@pdcnet.org
URL(s): businessethicsjournalreview.cawww.pdcnet.org/bejr/Business-Ethics-Journal-Review
Facebook: www.facebook.com/BusinessEthicsJournalReview
X (Twitter): x.com/BEJReview
Ed: Alexei Marcoux, Chris MacDonald. **Released:** Irregular **Description:** Peer-reviewed, academic, open access journal publishing commentaries on current issues in the field of business ethics. **Availability:** PDF; Online.

23571 ■ *Business Ethics Quarterly*
University Printing House
Shaftesbury Rd.
Cambridge CB2 8BS, United Kingdom
Ph: 44 1223 358331
Co. E-mail: information@cambridge.org
URL: http://www.cambridge.org
Contact: Peter Phillips, Chief Executive Officer
URL(s): www.cambridge.org/core/journals/business-ethics-quarterly
X (Twitter): x.com/BEQJournal
Released: Quarterly; January, April, July, October. **Price:** $557, Institutions for print; $632, Institutions for print + online; $494, Institutions for online. **Description:** Peer-reviewed scholarly journal covering business ethics studies. **Availability:** Print; Download; PDF; Online.

LIBRARIES

23572 ■ Ethics Centre CA Library
18 King Street East, Suite 1400
Toronto, ON, Canada M5C 1C4
Ph: (416)368-7525
Fax: (416)369-0515
Co. E-mail: info@ethicscentre.ca
URL: http://ethicscentre.ca
Contact: Rose Genele, Chief Executive Officer
Linkedin: www.linkedin.com/company/ethicscentre-ca
X (Twitter): x.com/ethicscentre
Description: Operates as a clearinghouse on business ethics issues for individuals, students and the media looking for resources, information and speakers on business ethics issues. **Founded:** 1988.

23573 ■ University of South Florida, Saint Petersburg - Nelson Poynter Memorial Library and Special Collections
140 7th Ave. S
Saint Petersburg, FL 33701-5016
URL: http://lib.stpetersburg.usf.edu/home
Contact: Alexandra Vargas-Minor, Contact
E-mail: acv@usf.edu
Scope: Educational material. **Services:** Inte+P89rlibrary loan; copying; library open to the public by appointment. **Founded:** 1968. **Subscriptions:** e-journals books; bound periodical volumes; reports; archival material; audio/visual materials.

RESEARCH CENTERS

23574 ■ Josephson Institute of Ethics
8117 W Manchester Ave., No. 830
Playa del Rey, CA 90293
Ph: (310)846-4829
Co. E-mail: awade@jiethics.org
URL: http://josephsoninstitute.org
Contact: Michael Josephson, President
Facebook: www.facebook.com/JIBusinessEthics
Linkedin: www.linkedin.com/company/josephson-institute

YouTube: www.youtube.com/user/josephsoninstitute
Description: Independent, nonprofit organization. Offers radio commentaries. **Scope:** Ethical decision making and behavior, focusing on improving the ethical quality of personal, corporate, and governmental conduct by stimulating moral aspirations, reinforcing the motivation and abilities necessary to perceive the ethical dimensions of choices, and formulating optimal ethical responses. **Founded:** 1987. **Publications:** *Ethics in Action*; *Good Ideas Books—The Power of Character*. **Educational Activities:** Aspen Summit Conference; Josephson Institute of Ethics Character Counts!, Youth education project.; Character Development Seminars; Ethics in the Workplace training; Pursuing Victory with Honor, Sportsmanship campaign.; Character Counts! Coalition Meeting.

23575 ■ San Jose State University - Institute for Social Responsibility, Ethics, and Education (ISREE)
1 Washington Sq., FO 201
San Jose, CA 95192-0096
Ph: (408)924-1000
Co. E-mail: admissions@sjsu.edu
URL: http://www.sjsu.edu/philosophy/initiatives/ISREE
Contact: Bo Mou, Contact
E-mail: bmou@email.sjsu.edu
Description: Integral unit of San Jose State University. **Scope:** Educational institution for social responsibility, including professional and business ethics. **Founded:** 1987. **Educational Activities:** Lecture series, corporate roundtables, seminars, training session, and workshops.

23576 ■ Western Michigan University - Center for the Study of Ethics in Society
1903 W Michigan Ave.
Kalamazoo, MI 49008-5328
Ph: (269)387-4397
Fax: (269)387-4389
URL: http://www.wmich.edu/ethics
Contact: Dr. Sandra L. Borden, Director
Facebook: www.facebook.com/wmuethics
Linkedin: www.linkedin.com/company/wmu-ethics-center
X (Twitter): x.com/WMU_ETHICS
YouTube: www.youtube.com/channel/UCekE2CrJlxzQnRh3LPvWf2Q
Description: Interdisciplinary research and education activity of Western Michigan University. Offers consulting services. **Scope:** Applied and professional ethics in all fields. **Founded:** 1985. **Publications:** *Occasional papers* (Quarterly). **Educational Activities:** Center for the Study of Ethics in Society Colloquia; Center for the Study of Ethics in Society Public presentations (Annual), 20 per academic year.

Family-Owned Business

START-UP INFORMATION

23577 ■ *"Aubry & Kale Walch, Herbivorous Butcher"* in *Business Journal* (Vol. 32, August 29, 2014, No. 14, pp. 6)
Pub: American City Business Journals, Inc.
Contact: Mike Olivieri, Executive Vice President
Released: August 29, 2014. **Description:** Kale and Aubry Walch, founders of family-owned The Herbivorous Butcher, reveal that the process of formulating recipes for their shop took years. Aubry said that she and her brother used to make fake meats for themselves. Their plan to open a full-scale vegan butcher shop is also discussed. **Availability:** Print; Online.

23578 ■ *"Dining Notes: The Salty Fig is Jacksonville's Newest Food Truck"* in *Florida Times-Union* (July 13, 2012)
Ed: Gary T. Mills. **Description:** Jeff and John Stanford has selected locations throughout the city of Jacksonville, Florida to operate the food truck operation called, The Salty Fig. The brothers serve New American Southern style food along with a bar drink menu. The Salty Fig is named after the trees the boys enjoyed at their grandparent's home. **Availability:** Online.

23579 ■ *"Military Vet Uses SBA Program to Help Fund His Business"* in *Philadelphia Business Journal* (Vol. 33, May 9, 2014, No. 13, pp. 6)
Pub: American City Business Journals, Inc.
Contact: Mike Olivieri, Executive Vice President
Released: Weekly. **Description:** Colonel Richard Elam and his wife Kimberly, both with the Florida Army National Guard, secured funding through the Small Business Administration's (SBA's) Veterans Advantage program to launch iPlay, which rents mobile entertainment equipment such as rock walls and laser-tag setups for group events. The capital access initiative, launched in January 2014, waives the origination fee for SBA Express loans to qualified veteran entrepreneurs. **Availability:** Print; Online.

23580 ■ *"No. 359: FlexGround: Recreational Surfaces"* in *Inc.* (Vol. 36, September 2014, No. 7, pp. 130)
Pub: Mansueto Ventures L.L.C.
Contact: Stephanie Mehta, Chief Executive Officer
Released: September 2014. **Description:** FlexGround was co-founded by Bill Stafford and his father, Bill Stafford Sr. The company makes flooring used on playgrounds that provides both grip and safety padding. FlexGround flowing is poured into place like concrete, but feels like a mix of a rubber mat and a trampoline and maintains its thickness no matter how high the traffic. **Availability:** Print; Online.

23581 ■ *"Should You Go Into Business With Your Spouse?"* in *Women Entrepreneur* (September 1, 2008)
Description: Things to consider before starting a business with one's spouse are discussed. Compatible work ethics, clear expectations of one another, long-term goals for the company and the status of the relationship are among the things to consider before starting a business endeavor with a spouse. **Availability:** Online.

23582 ■ *"Street Bistro Brings Food Truck Treats to Bangor"* in *Bangor Daily News* (June 26, 2012)
Ed: Emily Burnham. **Description:** Chef Kim Smith launched her food truck, Street Bistro in Bangor, Maine. Smith took a year off after closing her two restaurants called Unbridled Bistro and Bennett's Market. Smith and her husband purchased a Snap-On truck and redesigned it into a kitchen. Menu items range from French to Tex-Mex to Thai to American. **Availability:** Video; Online.

ASSOCIATIONS AND OTHER ORGANIZATIONS

23583 ■ **Family Business Coalition (FBC)**
PO Box 722
Washington, DC 20044
Ph: (202)787-1399
Co. E-mail: info@familybusinesscoalition.org
URL: http://www.familybusinesscoalition.org
Contact: Alex Ayers, Executive Director
E-mail: alex@familybusinesscoallition.org
Facebook: www.facebook.com/FamBizCoalition
X (Twitter): x.com/FamBizCoalition
Description: Advocates for the protection of family businesses across the U.S. Monitors legislation that affects family businesses. **Founded:** 2012. **Geographic Preference:** National.

23584 ■ **Family Firm Institute (FFI) - Library**
101 Federal St., Ste. 1900
Boston, MA 02110
Ph: (617)482-3045
Fax: (617)482-3049
Co. E-mail: ffi@ffi.org
URL: http://www.ffi.org
Contact: Judy Green, President
Facebook: www.facebook.com/FFIGlobal
Linkedin: www.linkedin.com/company/the-family-firm-institute
X (Twitter): x.com/FFIGlobal
Description: Works to assist family firms by increasing the interdisciplinary skills of family business advisors, educators, researchers and consultants. **Scope:** Small business. **Founded:** 1986. **Holdings:** Figures not available. **Publications:** *Practitioner* (Weekly); *FFI Conference Proceedings*; *FFI Yellow Pages*; *Update* (Monthly). **Awards:** Interdisciplinary Award (Annual); Barbara Hollander Award (Annual); FFI International Award (Annual); FFI Best Doctoral Dissertation (Annual); FFI Best Unpublished Research Paper (Annual); Interdisciplinary Achievement Award (Annual); Richard Beckhard Practice Award (Annual). **Geographic Preference:** National.

23585 ■ **Family Office Association**
500 W Putnam Ave., Ste. 400
Greenwich, CT 06830
Ph: (203)570-2898
Co. E-mail: angelo@familyofficeassociation.com
URL: http://familyofficeassociation.com
Contact: Angelo Robles, Chief Executive Officer
Facebook: www.facebook.com/familyofficeassociation
X (Twitter): x.com/familyoffice
Instagram: www.instagram.com/familyofficeassociation
YouTube: www.youtube.com/user/FamilyOffice
Description: Supports single-family businesses. Provides educational and networking opportunities.

23586 ■ **Focus on the Family (FOTF)**
8605 Explorer Dr.
Colorado Springs, CO 80920-1051
Free: 800-232-6459
Co. E-mail: help@focusonthefamily.com
URL: http://www.focusonthefamily.com
Contact: Jim Daly, President
Linkedin: www.linkedin.com/company/focus-on-the-family
X (Twitter): x.com/focusfamily
YouTube: www.youtube.com/user/FocusOnTheFamilyUSA
Pinterest: www.pinterest.com/focusonthefamily
Description: Promotes Judeo-Christian and strong family values. Disseminates information on marriage, parenting, and other subjects related to family life. Produces fourteen different radio programs, aired in 96 countries. **Founded:** 1977. **Publications:** *Boundless*; *Breakaway*; *Clubhouse* (Monthly); *Citizen* (Daily); *Breakaway Magazine* (Monthly); *Teachers in Focus Magazine*; *Focus on the Family Citizen*; *Focus on the Family Citizen*; *LifeWise*; *Physician Magazine: A Publication of Focus on the Family* (Bimonthly); *Plugged In* (Monthly); *Focus on the Family Clubhouse* (Monthly); *Clubhouse Jr.* (Monthly). **Educational Activities:** Focus on the Family Pillars; Focus on the Family Counseling Enrichment Program; Crisis Pregnancy Center Directors Conference. **Geographic Preference:** Multinational.

23587 ■ **Prairie Family Business Association (PFBA)**
4801 N Career Ave.
Beacom School of Business
University of S Dakota
Sioux Falls, SD 57107
Ph: (605)274-9530
Co. E-mail: fba@usd.edu
URL: http://fambus.org
Contact: Stephanie Larscheid, Executive Director
E-mail: stephanie.larscheid@usd.edu
Facebook: www.facebook.com/prairiefamilybusiness
Linkedin: www.linkedin.com/company/prairie-family-business-association
X (Twitter): x.com/prairiefambus
Instagram: www.instagram.com/prairiefamilybusiness
YouTube: www.youtube.com/user/ThePFBA/featured

Description: Seeks to support and assist family businesses in South Dakota, North Dakota, Minnesota, Iowa, and Nebraska by providing high quality education and collaboration. **Founded:** 1993.

EDUCATIONAL PROGRAMS

23588 ■ **Kennesaw State University - Coles College of Business - Cox Family Enterprise Center**
1000 Chastain Rd.
Kennesaw, GA 30144
URL: http://www.kennesaw.edu/coles/intranet/staff-awards/committee.php
Contact: Nancy Heller, Office Manager
Description: Four-day course covering family business. Topics include: strategic and family business planning, leadership and management, conflict resolutions, total quality management (TQM), working with boards and other advisors, family and business values, and succession.

REFERENCE WORKS

23589 ■ *"5 Business Lessons From Bob's Burgers"* in *Business News Daily (March 20, 2023)*
URL(s): www.businessnewsdaily.com/8104-bobs-burgers-business-advice.html
Ed: Brittney Morgan. **Released:** March 20, 2023.
Description: Small business owners can take away some lessons from the show Bob's Burgers. Even thought it's fiction, the portrayal of running a family business can provide some inspiration. **Availability:** Online.

23590 ■ *"5 Challenges for Family-Owned Businesses"* in *SCORE Blog (April 16, 2018)*
URL(s): www.sba.gov/blog/5-challenges-family-owned-businesses
Ed: Barbara Weltman. **Released:** April 16, 2018.
Description: Discusses 5 unique challenges that family-owned businesses face and what you can do about them. **Availability:** Online.

23591 ■ *"12 Family Business Ideas—Plus Tips for Starting a Family Business"* in *NerdWallet (Oct. 22, 2020)*
URL(s): www.nerdwallet.com/article/small-business/family-business-ideas
Ed: Christine Aebischer. **Released:** October 22, 2020. **Description:** Offers twelve family business ideas to inspire those who are interested in starting their own family-owned business. Also includes tips for starting a family business. **Availability:** Online.

23592 ■ *"$44M Father/Son Biz Involved in Major Orlando Projects"* in *Orlando Business Journal (Vol. 31, July 18, 2014, No. 3, pp. 3)*
Pub: American City Business Journals, Inc.
Contact: Mike Olivieri, Executive Vice President
Released: Weekly. **Price:** $8, Introductory 4-week offer(Digital & Print). **Description:** Sy and mark Israel, father-son duo of Universal Engineering Sciences, speak about the projects that have been their largest challenges. They also highlight the advice they would give to a family business or a new business startup. **Availability:** Print; Online.

23593 ■ *"50 Family Small Business Ideas"* in *Small Business Trends (July 5, 2021)*
URL(s): smallbiztrends.com/2016/11/family-business-ideas.html
Ed: Annie Pilon. **Released:** November 24, 2016.
Description: Starting a family business can be a popular way to make a living. This article provides a list of potential family business opportunities. **Availability:** Online.

23594 ■ *"Advantage Tutoring Center Helps Students of All Levels"* in *Bellingham Business Journal (Vol. February 2010, pp. 16)*
Pub: Sound Publishing Inc.
Contact: Josh O'Connor, President
Ed: Ashley Mitchell. **Description:** Profile of the newly opened Advantage Tutoring, owned by Mary and Peter Morrison. The center offers programs ranging from basic homework help to subject-specific enrichment.

23595 ■ *"All In The Family: Weston Undergoes a Shakeup"* in *Canadian Business (Vol. 79, September 22, 2006, No. 19, pp. 75)*
Pub: Rogers Media Inc.
Contact: Neil Spivak, Chief Executive Officer
Ed: Zena Olijnyk. **Description:** Continuing ownership of Weston dynasty on Canada's largest chain Loblaw Co. is discussed. **Availability:** Online.

23596 ■ *"Auction Company Grows with Much Smaller Sites"* in *Automotive News (Vol. 86, October 31, 2011, No. 6488, pp. 23)*
Pub: Crain Communications Inc.
Contact: Barry Asin, President
Ed: Arlena Sawyers. **Description:** Auction Broadcasting Company has launched auction sites and is expanding into new areas. The family-owned business will provide auctions half the size traditionally used. The firm reports that 40 percent of the General Motors factory-owned vehicles sold on consignment were purchased by online buyers, up 30 percent over 2010. **Availability:** Online.

23597 ■ *"Avoid the Traps That Can Destroy Family Businesses: An Emerging Set of Best Practices Can Turn the Age-Old Problem of Generational Succession Into an Opportunity To Thrive"* in *Harvard Business Review (Vol. 90, January-February 2012, No.1, pp. 25)*
Pub: Harvard Business Review Press
Contact: Moderna V. Pfizer, Contact
Ed: George Stalk, Henry Foley. **Price:** $6, hardcopy black and white. **Description:** Tips to efffective succession planning in family-owned businesses include proper screening and training for family members, managing family-member entry with company growth, and appointing non-family mentors to provide cross training. **Availability:** Print; PDF; Online.

23598 ■ *"Bellingham Boatbuilder Norstar Yachts Maintains Family Tradition"* in *Bellingham Business Journal (Vol. February 2010, pp. 12)*
Description: Profile of Norstar Yachts and brothers Gary and Steve Nordtvedt who started the company in 1994. The company recently moved its operations to a 12,000 square foot space in the Fairhaven Marine Industrial Park. **Availability:** Print; Online.

23599 ■ *"Better Than New Runs on Tried-and-True Model"* in *Bellingham Business Journal (Vol. February 2010, pp. 16)*
Pub: Sound Publishing Inc.
Contact: Josh O'Connor, President
Ed: Ashley Mitchell. **Description:** Profile of family owned Better Than New clothing store that sells overstock items from department stores and clothing manufacturers. The stores location makes it easy to miss and its only advertising is a large sign posted outside. This is the sixth store owned by the couple, Keijeo and Sirba Halmekanqas.

23600 ■ *"Bienvenido, Mercadito"* in *Washington Business Journal (Vol. 33, September 12, 2014, No. 21, pp. 8)*
Pub: American City Business Journals, Inc.
Contact: Mike Olivieri, Executive Vice President
Released: Weekly. **Price:** $4, introductory 4-week offer(Digital & Print). **Description:** Restaurateur, Alfredo Sandoval, partnered with brothers Felipe and Patricio to open Mercadito, an upscale casual Mexican restaurant at the Marriott Marquis Hotel in Washington DC. The restaurant is geared to attract customers between 25 and 40 years of age. **Availability:** Print; Online.

23601 ■ *"Business Succession Planning From an Estate Planner's Perspective"* in *New Jersey Law Review (December 7, 2007)*
Pub: New Jersey Law Journal

Ed: Robert W. Cockren, Elga A. Goodman. **Description:** Ninety percent of American businesses are family-owned. The importance of estate planning for family-owned or controlled firms is covered. **Availability:** Online.

23602 ■ *"Carving Passion, Talent Help Couple Craft Business on Wood-Rich Land"* in *Crain's Cleveland Business (October 8, 2007)*
Pub: Crain Communications Inc.
Contact: K. C. Crain, President
Ed: Sharon Schnall. **Description:** Profile of Wood-carved Art Gallery & Studio, a family-owned business which includes several ventures of the husband-and-wife team, Jim Stadtlander and Diane Harto. **Availability:** Online.

23603 ■ *"Changing Prescriptions"* in *Business North Carolina (Vol. 28, March 2008, No. 3, pp. 52)*
Description: Profile of Moose Drug Company, founded by Archibald Walter Moose in 1882. Family owners share how they focus on pharmacoeconomics (cost-benefit analyses of drugs or drug therapy) and customer service. **Availability:** Print; Online.

23604 ■ *"Common Mistakes Family-Owned Businesses Make"*
URL(s): www.legalnature.com/guides/common-mistakes-family-owned-businesses-make
Description: Discusses common mistakes that family-owned businesses make. Topics include: not setting up a clear hierarchy, mixing business and personal finances, forcing children to participate in the business, failing to have a succession plan, skipping important essentials, and failing to protect your business legally. **Availability:** Online.

23605 ■ *"Concrete Company Makes Lasting Impression in Valley"* in *Silicon Valley/San Jose Business Journal (Vol. 30, August 10, 2012, No. 20, pp. 1)*
Pub: Baltimore Business Journal
Contact: Rhonda Pringle, President
E-mail: rpringle@bizjournals.com
Ed: Gloria Wang Shawber. **Description:** Joseph J. Albanese Inc. has made a lasting impression on projects throughout Silicon Valley for nearly 60 years. President and CEO, John Albanese, started his family owned concrete company as concrete contractors and it was often selected as the subcontractor for various general contractors in the valley. **Availability:** Print; Online.

23606 ■ *"Consulting to Family Businesses: Contracting, Assessment, and Implementation"*
Pub: John Wiley & Sons, Inc.
Contact: Christina Van Tassell, Executive Vice President Chief Financial Officer
URL(s): www.wiley.com/en-us/Consulting+to+Family+Businesses%3A+Contracting%2C+Assessment%2C+and+Implementation-p-9780787962494
Ed: Jane Hilburt-Davis, William G. Dyer. **Released:** September 2002. **Price:** $65, paperback. **Description:** Running a family business takes a certain skill- and mindset that differs from standard business practices due to family expectations and having to make decisions that affect just not your co-workers but your family members. Discussed are strategies and approaches to take while dealing with this type of dynamic. **Availability:** Print.

23607 ■ *"Davis Family Expands Cable Empire"* in *St. Louis Business Journal (Vol. 32, June 15, 2012, No. 43, pp. 1)*
Pub: Baltimore Business Journal
Contact: Rhonda Pringle, President
E-mail: rpringle@bizjournals.com
Description: Missouri-based Fidelity Communications has become a standout in the $98 billion cable industry through low-profile management of the Davis family, with the help of John Colbert. Fidelity has made five acquisitions since 1992 and has grown its subscriber base to more than 115,000 customers or revenue generating units. **Availability:** Print; Online.

23608 ■ "The Duty of Wealth: Canadian Business Leaders on Nepotism and Philanthropy" in Canadian Business (Vol. 80, Winter 2007, No. 24)
Description: Fifty-one percent of the respondents in a survey of business leaders say that the decision to allow adult children to join a family firm should be based on the circumstances at the time. He CEOs that were surveyed also believed that billionaires should donate an average of forty percent of their estates and keep the rest for their family.

23609 ■ Family Business
Pub: Cengage Learning, Inc.
Contact: Michael E. Hansen, Chief Executive Officer
Ed: Ernesto J. Poza. **Released:** 2014. **Price:** $69.99, ETextbook. **Description:** Family-owned businesses face unique challenges in today's economy. This book provides the next generation of knowledge and skills required for profitable management and leadership in a family enterprise. **Availability:** E-book; Print.

23610 ■ Family Business Models: Practical Solutions for the Family Business
Pub: Palgrave Macmillan
Ed: Alberto Gimeno, Gemma Baulenas, Joan Coma-Cros. **Released:** First edition. **Description:** A unique new model for understanding family businesses gives readers the potential to build better managed and more stable family firms and to plan for a success future.

23611 ■ "Family Business Research: A Strategic Reflection" in International Journal of Entrepreneurship and Small Business (Vol. 12, December 3, 2010, No. 1)
Ed: A. Bakr Ibrahim, Jean B. McGuire. **Description:** Assessment of the growing field of family business and suggestions for an integrated framework. The paper addresses a number of key issues facing family business research. **Availability:** PDF; Download.

23612 ■ "Family Feud: Pawn Shop Empire Stalls with Transition to Second Generation" in Billings Gazette (December 19, 2010)
Pub: The Billings Gazette
Ed: Jan Falstad. **Description:** Profile of Ben L. Brown Sr. and his pawn shop located in Billings, Montana is presented. Brown discusses his plan to transition his business to his children. **Availability:** Print; Online.

23613 ■ Family-Owned Businesses
URL(s): www.referenceforbusiness.com/encyclopedia/Fa-For/Family-Owned-Businesses.html
Description: Discusses the pros and cons of family-owned business, the importance of establishing roles and business and succession planning. **Availability:** Online.

23614 ■ "Family-Owned Train Service Offers a Ride for Your Raft" in Idaho Business Review (June 11, 2014)
Pub: BridgeTower Media
Contact: Adam Reinebach, President
Description: Payette River Flyer's run between Smith's Ferry and Cascade is part of Thunder Mountain's Line new rail service that allows rafters to leave their vehicles at Smith's Ferry and load whitewater gear onto the train. The train provides a scenic ride along the Payette River. Details of this family-operated tourist train service is profiled.

23615 ■ "The Family Tools" in Canadian Business (Vol. 80, March 26, 2007, No. 7, pp. 14)
Description: A few strategies for running family businesses successfully are presented.

23616 ■ Family Wars
Pub: Kogan Page
Ed: Nigel Nicholson, Grant E. Gordon. **Released:** First edition. **Description:** Family feuding, sibling rivalries, and petty jealousies are among the greatest issues faced by family owned companies. Family Wars explores behind the scenes issues of some of the largest family-run firms in the world, and shows how family in-fighting has threatened their downfall. Ford, Gucci, McCain, Guinness, Fallo, and Restone are among the families discussed. Advice is given to anyone involved in a family business and offers suggestions to avoid problems. **Availability:** E-book; Print.

23617 ■ "A Family's Fortune" in Canadian Business (Vol. 80, Winter 2007, No. 24, pp. 103)
Price: $23. **Description:** James Richardson started as a tailor before moving into the grain business because his clients paid him in sacks of wheat and barley. The James Richardson and Sons Ltd. entered the radio business in 1927 but later sold it off in 1951. **Availability:** Print; Online.

23618 ■ "Former NFL Player Tackles a New Restaurant Concept" in Inc. (Vol. 33, September 2011, No. 7, pp. 32)
Pub: Inc. Magazine
Ed: Nadine Heintz. **Description:** Matt Chatham, former NFL player, launched SkyCrepers, a chain of fast-serve crepe shops with his wife Erin. Chatham entered Babson College's MBA program after retiring from football. **Availability:** Online.

23619 ■ "Get On the Shelf: Selling Your Product In Retail Stores" in Black Enterprise (Vol. 44, February 2014, No. 6, pp. 18)
Pub: Earl G. Graves Ltd.
Contact: Earl Graves, Jr., President
Description: Profile of Arsha and Charles Jones, Washington DC natives, who are selling their Capital City Mumbo Sauce to local retailers as well as big box retailers. The husband and wife team share tips for getting your product into retail establishments.

23620 ■ "Gray Matters: An Aging Workforce Has Mass. Companies Scrambling to Deal with 'Silver Tsunami'" in Austin Business Journal (Vol. 34, May 30, 2014, No. 15, pp. 8)
Pub: American City Business Journals, Inc.
Contact: Mike Olivieri, Executive Vice President
Description: Profiles of Seniors Real Estate Inc. Institute founders Nikki and Bruce Buckelew are presented. Nikki has focused on providing real estate agents with training and Webinars. Their career achievements are also included. **Availability:** Print; Online.

23621 ■ "'Groundhog Day' B&B Likely Will Be Converted Into One In Real Life" in Chicago Tribune (October 21, 2008)
Pub: Tribune News Service
Contact: Jack Barry, Vice President, Operations
E-mail: jbarry@tribpub.com
Ed: Carolyn Starks. **Description:** Everton Martin and Karla Stewart Martin have purchased the Victorian house that was featured as a bed-and-breakfast in the 1993 hit move "Groundhog Day"; the couple was initially unaware of the structure's celebrity status when they purchased it with the hope of fulfilling their dream of owning a bed-and-breakfast. **Availability:** Print; Online.

23622 ■ "Halls Give Hospital Drive $11 Million Infusion" in The Business Journal-Serving Metropolitan Kansas City (Vol. 26, July 18, 2008)
Description: Don Hall, chairman of Hallmark Cards Inc., and eight family members have announced that they will give $11 million to Children's Mercy Hospitals and Clinics for its $800 million expansion plan. Hall Family Foundation president Bill Hall that contributions such as that for Children's Mercy reflect the charitable interests of the foundation's board and founders. The possible impacts of the Hall's donation are analyzed.

23623 ■ "Healthful, Organic Food is the Name of the Game at Renee's" in AZ Daily Star (May 10, 2012)
Pub: McClatchy Tribune Information Services
Contact: Patrick J. Talamantes, President
Ed: Kristen Cook. **Description:** Profile of Renee's Organic Oven offer organic and locally grown foods at their restaurant. The eatery is owned by husband and wife team, Steve and Renee Kreager. **Availability:** Online.

23624 ■ How are Family-Owned Businesses Different Than Other Businesses?
URL(s): www.lovelawfirmpllc.com/library/how-are-family-owned-business-different-than-other-businesses-.cfm
Ed: Francine Love. **Description:** Discusses how family-owned businesses are different from other businesses and how employing a mediator to provide unbiased advice and counsel may be important for your family-owned business. **Availability:** Online.

23625 ■ "How to... Harness Green Power" in The Caterer (July 20, 2012, No. 325)
Pub: LNRS Data Services Limited
Contact: Mark Vickers Kelsey, Director
Description: Roger and Emma Stevens discuss their success as at winning the Considerate Hoteliers Association's award for Best Green Marketing Initiative. The couple discusses their restaurant and its partnership with tow nearby guesthouses. **Availability:** Online.

23626 ■ "How-To Workshops in St. Charles Teach Sewing, Styles" in St. Louis Post-Dispatch (September 14, 2010)
Pub: St. Louis Post-Dispatch LLC.
Contact: Gilbert Bailon, Editor
E-mail: gbailon@post-dispatch.com
Ed: Kalen Ponche. **Description:** Profile of DIY Style Workshop in St. Charles, Missouri, where sewing, designing and teaching is offered. The shop is home base for DIY Style, a Website created by mother and daughter to teach younger people how to sew. **Availability:** Online.

23627 ■ "Husband-Wife Team Opens Somali Interpreting Business in Willmar, Minn." in West Central Tribune (May 22, 2012)
Ed: Linda Vanderwerf. **Description:** Profile of husband and wife team who launched an interpreting service in Somali. Details of the business are included. **Availability:** Online.

23628 ■ ""I'm Kind of a Vanilla Guy': Steve Herrell Shares Confessions and Memories in His New Book, 'Ice Cream and Me'" in Masslive.com(January 3, 2022)
URL(s): www.masslive.com/business/2022/01/im-kind-of-a-vanilla-guy-steve-herrell-shares-confessions-and-memories-in-his-new-book-ice-cream-and-me.html
Ed: Jim Kinney. **Released:** January 03, 2022. **Description:** Profile of Steve Herrell, founder of Herrell's Ice Cream & Sweet Bakery, who self-published a book about running his family business. **Availability:** Online.

23629 ■ In-N-Out Burger: A Behind-the-Counter Look at the Fast-Food Chain That Breaks All the Rules
Pub: HarperCollins Publishers L.L.C.
Contact: Brian Murray, President
Ed: Stacy Perman. **Released:** December 10, 2010. **Price:** $14.99, paperback; $8.24, e-book. **Description:** Business analysis of the factors that helped In-N-Out Burgers, a family owned burger chain in California, along with a history of its founding family, the Synders. **Availability:** E-book; Print.

23630 ■ "In a Twist, Pretzel Vendors Will Be Selling Pizza: Wetzels to Launch Blaze Fast-Fire'd Concept with Two SoCal Locations" in Los Angeles Business Journal (Vol. 34, June 4, 2012, No. 23, pp. 12)
Pub: CBJ L.P.
Contact: Terri Cunningham, Contact
Ed: Bethany Firnhaber. **Description:** Rick and Elise Wetzel, cofounders of Wetzel's Pretzels is launching its new restaurants featuring fast-casual pizza. The concept is of an assembly line process where customers can make 11-inch personalized pizzas with

toppings like artichokes, gorgonzola cheese, roasted red peppers and arugula. The pizzas bake in two minutes. **Availability:** Online.

23631 ■ *"JK Lasser's New Rules for Estate, Retirement, and Tax Planning"*
Pub: John Wiley & Sons, Inc.
Contact: Christina Van Tassell, Executive Vice President Chief Financial Officer
Released: 6th Edition. **Price:** $24.95, paperback; $16.99, E-book. **Description:** The authoritative guide to estate, retirement and tax planning is fully updated and reflects the new changes and legal updates. Estate planning section covers: planning, taxation, investing, wills, executors, trusts, life insurance, retirement planning, Social Security, business planning, succession, asset protection and family limited partnerships. **Availability:** E-book; Print.

23632 ■ *"Life's Work: Manolo Blahnik" in Harvard Business Review (Vol. 88, December 2010, No. 12, pp. 144)*
Pub: Harvard Business Publishing
Contact: Diane Belcher, Managing Director
Ed: Alison Beard. **Price:** $8.95, PDF. **Description:** Shoe designer Manolo Blahnik recounts his beginnings in the shoe industry and the influence art has had on his work, as well as balancing art and commerce. He also discusses the importance of quality materials and craftsmanship and the benefits of managing an independent, family-owned business. **Availability:** Online; PDF.

23633 ■ *"Long Live Rock" in Inc. (November 2007, pp. 130)*
Ed: Nitasha Tiku. **Description:** Profile of a family business using chemistry to recycle concrete products. **Availability:** Print; Online.

23634 ■ *"Lots More Mr. Nice Guy" in Canadian Business (Vol. 80, October 22, 2007, No. 21, pp. 58)*
Description: Galen Weston Jr., executive chairman of Loblaw and heir to the Weston family business, has his hands full running the company. Details of his turnaround strategies and ambitious plans to increase profitability of the business are discussed.

23635 ■ *"Marketing is Everything, But Timing Helps" in Idaho Business Review (September 9, 2014)*
Pub: BridgeTower Media
Contact: Adam Reinebach, President
Description: Profile of Ladd Family Pharmacy, founded by husband and wife Kip and Elaine, who borrowed money from Idaho Banking Company to start their pharmacy. The firm has expanded from three workers in 2008 to 22 to date and reported $6.2 million in revenue for 2013.

23636 ■ *"Mars Advertising's Orbit Grows as Other Ad Segments Fall" in Crain's Detroit Business (Vol. 25, June 1, 2009, No. 22, pp. 10)*
Pub: Crain Communications Inc.
Contact: Barry Asin, President
Ed: Bill Shea. **Description:** An electrical fire burned at Mars Advertising's headquarters in Southfield, Michigan. The company talks about its plans for regrouping and rebuilding. The family firm specializes in in-store marketing that targets consumers already in the buying mode. **Availability:** Print; Online.

23637 ■ *"Minnesota State Fair Vendors Accept Big Risks for Big Rewards" in Business Journal (Vol. 32, August 22, 2014, No. 13, pp. 10)*
Pub: American City Business Journals, Inc.
Contact: Mike Olivieri, Executive Vice President
Released: Weekly. **Price:** $4, introductory 4-week offer(Digital & Print). **Description:** Food and beverage concessionaires compete for booths at the Minnesota State Fair and there are many vendors that wait for years to get one, especially a large booth with room for tables and a beer garden. The State Fair has been a good business opportunity and a family bonding experience for most of the vendors. **Availability:** Video; Print; Online.

23638 ■ *The Mom & Pop Store: How the Unsung Heroes of the American Economy Are Surviving and Thriving*
Ed: Robert Spector. **Description:** The history of small independent retail enterprises and how mom and pop stores in the U.S. continue to thrive through customer service and renewed community support for local businesses. **Availability:** Audio.

23639 ■ *"MPI Expansion Goes Back to Family Roots" in Crain's Detroit Business (Vol. 25, June 1, 2009, No. 22, pp. M007)*
Pub: Crain Communications Inc.
Contact: Barry Asin, President
Ed: Sherri Begin Welch. **Description:** William Parfet, grandson of Upjohn Company founder, is expanding MPI Research's clinical and early clinical research operations into two buildings in Kalamazoo, land which was once part of his grandfather's farm. **Availability:** Print; PDF; Online.

23640 ■ *"Muirhead Farmhouse B&B Owners Get Hospitality Wright" in Chicago Tribune (July 31, 2008)*
Pub: Tribune News Service
Contact: Jack Barry, Vice President, Operations
E-mail: jbarry@tribpub.com
Ed: Glenn Jeffers. **Description:** Profile of the Muirhead Farmhouse, a bed-and-breakfast owned by Mike Petersdorf and Sarah Muirhead Petersdorf; Frank Lloyd Wright designed the historic farmhouse which blends farm life and history into a unique experience that is enhanced by the couple's hospitality. **Availability:** Online.

23641 ■ *"Nothing But Green Skies" in Inc. (November 2007, pp. 115-120)*
Ed: Alison Stein Wellner. **Description:** Profile of Enterprise Rent-A-Car, one of the largest family-owned businesses in the U.S. Andy Taylor, CEO, discusses the company's talks about the idea of offering carbon off-sets for a few years. **Availability:** Print; Online.

23642 ■ *"No. 156: Divorced, But Still Running the Company Together" in Inc. (Vol. 36, September 2014, No. 7, pp. 78)*
Pub: Mansueto Ventures L.L.C.
Contact: Stephanie Mehta, Chief Executive Officer
Released: September 2014. **Description:** Co-founders, Lacy Starling and Tony Coutsoftides, of Legion Logistics discuss the challenges of running their family-owned business after their divorce. **Availability:** Print; Online.

23643 ■ *"Oberweis Tests Home Ice Cream Delivery" in Ice Cream Reporter (Vol. 21, November 20, 2008, No. 12, pp. 1)*
Description: Oberwies Dairy launched its Treat Delivery Program in the Saint Louis area. The program allows customers to order milkshakes, ice cream cones, sundaes and scoops of ice cream and they are delivered to their home or office. Oberweis is a fourth generation family run business. **Availability:** Print; Online.

23644 ■ *"Organizational Virtue Orientation and Family Firms" in Business Ethics Quarterly (Vol. 21, April 2011, No. 2, pp. 257)*
Ed: G. Tyge Payne, Keith H. Brigham, J. Christian Broberg, Todd W. Moss, Jeremy C. Short. **Released:** Quarterly; Volume 21, issue 2. **Description:** The concept of organizational virtue orientation (OVO) and the differences between family and non-family firms on six organizational virtue dimensions of Integrity, Empathy, Warmth, Courage, Conscientiousness, and Zeal are examined. **Availability:** PDF; Online.

23645 ■ *"Organizing the Family-Run Business" in Small Business Opportunities (Get Rich At Home 2010)*
Pub: Harris Publishing, Inc.
Contact: Janet Chase, Contact
Ed: Gene Siciliano. **Description:** The good, the bad and the ugly of succession planning for any small business is spotlighted. **Availability:** Online.

23646 ■ *"Perry's Goes Organic" in Ice Cream Reporter (Vol. 22, December 20, 2008, No. 1, pp. 1)*
Description: Family-owned Perry's Ice Cream is starting a new line of organic ice cream in both vanilla and chocolate flavors. All Perry's products are made with milk and cream from local dairy farmers. **Availability:** Print; Online.

23647 ■ *"A Pioneer of Paying With Plastic" in Crain's Chicago Business (Vol. 31, April 28, 2008, No. 17, pp. 39)*
Pub: Crain Communications Inc.
Contact: Barry Asin, President
Ed: Phuong Ly. **Description:** Profile of Perfect Plastic Printing Corp., a family-owned company which manufactures credit cards, bank cards and gift cards and whose sales hit $50.1 million last year, a 16 percent jump from 2006. **Availability:** Online.

23648 ■ *"Please Pass the Mayo" in Crain's Chicago Business (Vol. 31, April 28, 2008, No. 17, pp. 32)*
Pub: Crain Communications Inc.
Contact: Barry Asin, President
Ed: Samantha Stainburn. **Description:** Fort Dearborn Co. has come a long way since it started as on one-press print shop; the family-owned company was struggling to keep up with the technology of making consumer product labels for curvy bottles of products like V8 V-Fusion juice and in 2006 sold off to Genstar Capital LLC which has pushed for acquisitions; last year, Fort Derborn bought its biggest competitor, Renaissance Mark Inc., doubling its size and adding spirit and wine makers to its client roster. **Availability:** Online.

23649 ■ *"Printing Company Edwards Brothers Grapples With a Shrinking Market" in Crain's Detroit Business (Vol. 26, Jan. 4, 2010)*
Pub: Crain Communications Inc.
Contact: Barry Asin, President
Ed: Bill Shea. **Description:** Overview of the publishing industry, which has seen a huge decline in revenue; Edwards Brothers, Inc., a family printing business that was founded 117 years ago is struggling due to a variety of factors, many of which are explored. **Availability:** Print; Online.

23650 ■ *Protecting the Legacy of Family-Owned MSME Businesses – Advancing Economic Growth & Job Creation*
URL(s): www.ifac.org/knowledge-gateway/contribu ting-global-economy/discussion/protecting-legacy -family-owned-msme-businesses-advancing-eco nomic-growth-job-creation
Released: May 25, 2021. **Description:** Discusses the role that family businesses play as an economic portion of small and medium-sized enterprises and includes information on challenges these businesses face. **Availability:** Online.

23651 ■ *Race and Entrepreneurial Success: Black-, Asian-, and White-Owned Businesses in the United States*
Pub: The MIT Press
Ed: Robert W. Fairlie, Alicia M. Robb. **Released:** 2008. **Description:** Trends in minority small business ownership are explored, focusing on the importance of human capital, financial capital, and family business background in successful business ownership. **Availability:** E-book; Print; PDF.

23652 ■ *"The Real Estate Success Formula: 19 Proven Strategies to Making Money in Real Estate"*
Pub: CreateSpace
Released: September 28, 2014. **Price:** $19.99, paperback; $1.07, kindle; $99, paperback. **Description:** Nineteen proven strategies for selling real estate are provided by husband and wife real estate team. The book teaches how to buy, hold and sell

houses quickly without using your money or your credit. Tactics for marketing, systematizing and managing your real estate business are outlined. **Availability:** Print.

23653 ■ *"The Romance of Good Deeds: A Business with a Cause Can Do Good in the World"* in Inc. (Volume 32, December 2010, No. 10, pp. 47)
Pub: Inc. Magazine
Ed: Meg Cadoux Hirshberg. **Description:** Entrepreneurship and family relationships are discussed. When a small business has a passion for philanthropy it can help any marriage by creating even greater passion for each other. **Availability:** Online.

23654 ■ *"Rudy's Tortillas Wraps Up Expansion Plan in Carrollton"* in Dallas Business Journal (Vol. 35, August 31, 2012, No. 51, pp. 1)
Pub: Baltimore Business Journal
Contact: Rhonda Pringle, President
E-mail: rpringle@bizjournals.com
Ed: Candace Carlisle. **Released:** Weekly. **Description:** Rudy's Tortillas Corporation, a 67-year old family business based in Dallas, Texas, is moving into a new plant on Belt Line Road, Carrollton. The expansion will also involve the hiring of 150 new workers and enable the company to expand its operations. Rudy's will spend $14 million dollars on construction and equipment on the new tortilla plant. **Availability:** Print; Online.

23655 ■ *Running a Family-Owned Business: Challenges and Benefits*
URL(s): www.ondeck.com/resources/running-a-family-owned-business-challenges-and-benefits
Ed: Katie Tregurtha. **Description:** Presents information on the challenges and opportunities that come with running a family-owned busienss. **Availability:** Online.

23656 ■ *"Savvy Solutions"* in Black Enterprise (Vol. 41, November 2010, No. 4, pp. 42)
Description: Society of Children's Book Writers and Illustrators offers members many benefits, including directories of agencies looking for new writers of books. **Availability:** Online.

23657 ■ *"Sawatdee Rethinks Express Eatery Model"* in Business Journal (Vol. 31, January 10, 2014, No. 33, pp. 4)
Pub: American City Business Journals, Inc.
Contact: Mike Olivieri, Executive Vice President
Released: Weekly. **Price:** $4, Introductory 4-week offer(Digital & Print). **Description:** The two Sawatdee Express restaurants owned by Supenn Harrison closed their uptown and downtown locations in Minneapolis, Minnesota in December 2013. Harrison and her family own six other traditional, sit-down models of the Sawatdee restaurants. **Availability:** Print; Online.

23658 ■ *Small Business Survival Guide*
Released: First edition. **Description:** Small business expert provides strategies to start a company and survive in the 21st Century. He shows small business owners how to succeed despite challenges that can defeat any firm. His advice covers suppliers; customers and contractors; competitors and creditors; spouses, family and friends; as well as the ways lawyers, accountants and other can steal an entrepreneur's success. Ennico also describes how startups can comply with local regulations. **Availability:** E-book; Print.

23659 ■ *"Social Networking: Growing Pains"* in Canadian Business (Vol. 81, July 22, 2008, No. 12-13, pp. 35)
Pub: Rogers Media Inc.
Contact: Neil Spivak, Chief Executive Officer
Ed: Alex Mlynek. **Description:** Laughing Stock Vineyards' Cynthia Enns and David Enns plan to target young buyers by using social media. The Enns however, are concerned that targeting younger buyers may affect Laughing Stock's image as a premium brand. Additional information regarding the company's future plans is presented. **Availability:** Print; Online.

23660 ■ *"Solutions to Family Business Problems"* in Contractor (Vol. 56, October 2009, No. 10, pp. 51)
Ed: Irving L. Blackman. **Description:** Several common business problems that family owned firms face are presented together with their solutions. These problems include giving the children stock bonus options while another discusses the tax burden when a father wants to transfer the business to his son. **Availability:** Print; Online.

23661 ■ *"Spouses Plan for the Return of the Company Doctor"* in Philadelphia Business Journal (Vol. 33, May 2, 2014, No. 12, pp. 4)
Pub: American City Business Journals, Inc.
Contact: Mike Olivieri, Executive Vice President
Released: Weekly. **Price:** $4, introductory 4-week offer(Digital only). **Description:** Nephrologist, Scott Bralow and primary care physician, Vick Bralow, started a company called Affordable Care Options in Philadelphia, Pennsylvania. The couple's company will provide physicians to the workplace to monitor the health of employees for a monthly fee. **Availability:** Print; Online.

23662 ■ *"Stockerts Open Repair Business"* in Dickinson Press (July 13, 2010)
Pub: The Dickinson Press
Contact: Joy Schoch, Business Manager
Description: Ed Stockert is opening his new appliance repair firm in Dickinson, North Dakota with his wife Anna.

23663 ■ *"A Tale of Two Brothers"* in Canadian Business (Vol. 80, March 26, 2007, No. 7, pp. 18)
Description: The successful business strategies followed by Tyler Gompf and Kirby Gompf, owners of Tell Us About Us Inc., are presented. **Availability:** Online.

23664 ■ *"Termite Trouble"* in Arkansas Business (Vol. 28, March 28, 2011, No. 13, pp. 5)
Description: Thomas Pest Control of Little Rock, Arkansas has had liens placed against it by the Internal Revenue Service. The owner's daughter took over the business after her father passed away and is trying to rectify the situation. **Availability:** Online.

23665 ■ *Tips for Starting a Successful Family Business*
URL(s): www.nationwide.com/lc/resources/small-business/articles/starting-family-business
Description: Starting a family business takes time and careful consideration. This article details things to know before starting a family business. **Availability:** Online.

23666 ■ *"To Sell or Not To Sell"* in Inc. (December 2007, pp. 80)
Ed: Patrick J. Sauer. **Description:** Owner of a private equity discusses the challenges he faces when deciding to sell his family's business. **Availability:** Online.

23667 ■ *"Toward a Theory of Stakeholder Salience in Family Firms"* in Business Ethics Quarterly (Vol. 21, April 2011, No. 2, pp. 235)
Ed: Ronald K. Mitchell, Bradley R. Agle, James J. Chrisman, Laura J. Spence. **Released:** Volume 21, Issue 2. **Description:** The notion of stakeholder salience based on attributes (e.g. power, legitimacy, urgency) is applied in the family business setting. **Availability:** Online.

23668 ■ *"Variations in R&D Investments of Family and Nonfamily Firms: Behavioral Agency and Myopic Loss Aversion Perspectives"* in Academy of Management Journal (Vol. 55, August 1, 2012, No. 4, pp. 976)
Pub: Academy of Management
Contact: Sharon Alvarez, President
Ed: James J. Chrisman, Pankaj C. Patel. **Description:** The variability in the behavior of family firms is analyzed using the behavioral agency model and the myopic loss aversion framework. Results show that family firms tend to invest less in research and development than nonfamily businesses but the variability of their investments is influenced by family goals and economic goals of the firm. **Availability:** Electronic publishing; Download; PDF; Online.

23669 ■ *"We Do: Copreneurs Simultaneously Build Happy Marriages and Thriving Enterprises"* in Black Enterprise (Vol. 38, February 1, 2008)
Pub: Earl G. Graves Ltd.
Contact: Earl Graves, Jr., President
Ed: Krissah Williams. **Description:** Of the 2.7 million businesses in the U.S. that are equally owned by male-female partnerships, about 79,000 are black-owned. One couple shares their experiences of working and growing their business together.

23670 ■ *"Wegmans Adding 1,600-Plus Jobs Here Over the Next Year"* in Boston Business Journal (Vol. 34, February 14, 2014, No. 2, pp. 3)
Pub: American City Business Journals, Inc.
Contact: Mike Olivieri, Executive Vice President
Description: Wegmans, a family-owned grocery chain, is planning to add the most jobs of any firm in Massachusetts in 2014. The company will create more than 1,600 full- and part-time positions by opening three stores. Bill Congdon, Wegmans' New England division manager, reveals that the company is also planning to open a store in the city of Boston. **Availability:** Print; Online.

23671 ■ *"West Palm Beach Bed and Breakfast is a Labor of Love"* in Palm Beach Post (April 7, 2012)
Pub: McClatchy Tribune Information Services
Contact: Patrick J. Talamantes, President
Ed: Susan Salisbury. **Released:** April 07, 2012. **Description:** Profile of Cheryl and Kirk Grantham, husband and wife team who run a bed and breakfast in West Palm Beach, Florida. The couple discusses their move to the community and why they decided to open their inn. Their property offers five bed and breakfast guest suites along with another five suites in an Art Deco building. Cheryl talks about her love for entertaining along with the four diamond rating of their establishment. **Availability:** Print; Online.

23672 ■ *What's the Best Entity Type for a Family Business?*
URL(s): www.cpapracticeadvisor.com/small-business/article/21138308/whats-the-best-entity-type-for-a-family-business
Released: May 15, 2020. **Description:** Provides information on choosing the best entity type for your family business. **Availability:** Online.

23673 ■ *When Family Businesses are Best: The Parallel Planning Process for Family Harmony and Business Success*
Pub: Palgrave Macmillan
Ed: Randel S. Carlock, John L. Ward. **Released:** First edition. **Description:** An exploration into effective planning and communication to help small businesses grow into multi-generation family enterprises. **Availability:** E-book; Print.

VIDEO/AUDIO MEDIA

23674 ■ *Elevated Entrepreneurship: Ryan Langford: The Entrepreneurial Family*
URL(s): mikemichalowicz.com/podcast/ryan-langford
Ed: Mike Michalowiicz. **Released:** May 05, 2020. **Description:** Podcast discusses being an entrepreneurial family.

23675 ■ *Side Hustle to Small Business: Family Ties and Enterprise: Navigating Family Business Dynamics*
URL(s): www.hiscox.com/side-hustle-to-small-business/family-businesses-podcast-season-4

Ed: Sanjay Parekh. **Released:** March 06, 2024. **Description:** Podcast features two entrepreneurs navigating family businesses.

23676 ■ Side Hustle to Small Business: How Andy O'Brien Is Redefining Work in a Family Business
URL(s): www.hiscox.com/side-hustle-to-small-business/andy-obrien-actioncoach-cenral-texas-podcast-season-4
Ed: Sanjay Parekh. **Released:** March 13, 2024. **Description:** Podcast explains how outsourcing tasks and setting clear communications boundaries redefined a family business. .

23677 ■ Small Business Radio Show: What You Must Know to Successfully Run a Family Business
URL(s): barrymoltz.com/small-business-radio-show
Ed: Barry Moltz. **Description:** Podcast discusses the unique challenges of running a family business.

TRADE SHOWS AND CONVENTIONS

23678 ■ NCFR annual conference
National Council on Family Relations Family and Health Section (FH)
661 LaSalle St., Ste. 200
Saint Paul, MN 55114
Ph: (763)781-9331
Free: 888-781-9331
Co. E-mail: info@ncfr.org
URL: http://www.ncfr.org/membership/member-groups/sections/families-health-section
Contact: Amber J. J. Seidel, Chairman
E-mail: ajs49@psu.edu
URL(s): www.ncfr.org/ncfr-2024
Frequency: Annual. **Description:** A section of the National Council on Family Relations. **Audience:** Researchers, practitioners, program evaluators, policymakers, and community members. **Principal Exhibits:** A section of the National Council on Family Relations. Dates and Locations: 2025 Nov 19-22 Baltimore Marriott Waterfront Hotel, Baltimore, MD; 2026 Nov 18-21 Hilton Minneapolis, Minneapolis, MN; 2028 Nov 15-18 Hilton Minneapolis, Minneapolis, MN. **Telecommunication Services:** finance@ncfr.org.

23679 ■ Religion and Family Life Section of the National Council on Family Relations Conference
National Council on Family Relations Religion and Family Life Section
661 LaSalle St., Ste. 200
Saint Paul, MN 55114
URL: http://www.ncfr.org/membership/member-groups/sections/religion-spirituality-family-section
Contact: Andrew Rose, Chairman
E-mail: andrew.rose@ttu.edu
URL(s): www.ncfr.org/index.php/future-conferences
Frequency: Annual; usually November. **Description:** A section of the National Council on Family Relations. **Audience:** Researchers, demographers, marriage and family therapists, parent/family educators, university faculty, students, social workers, public health workers, extension specialists and faculty, ECFE teachers, clergy, counselors, and K-12 teachers. **Principal Exhibits:** A section of the National Council on Family Relations.

CONSULTANTS

23680 ■ Family Business Institute Inc. (FBI)
3520 Ridge View Ct.
Marietta, GA 30068
Ph: (770)952-4085
URL: http://www.family-business-experts.com
Contact: Don A. Schwerzler, Founder
Description: Firm engages in business consulting and professional services. **Scope:** Assists families in business to achieve personal, family and organizational goals. **Founded:** 1995. **Publications:** "Professional Intervention in the Family Owned Business"; "Building Consensus in a Family Business"; "Professionalizing Family Business Management".

23681 ■ Family Business Network
3670 Trousdale Pkwy
Los Angeles, CA 90089
Fax: (213)740-6406
Co. E-mail: management.studies@marshall.usc.edu
URL: http://www.marshall.usc.edu/web/FamilyBusiness.cfm
Facebook: www.facebook.com/uscmarshall
Linkedin: www.linkedin.com/school/usc-marshall-school-of-business
X (Twitter): twitter.com/uscmarshall
Instagram: www.instagram.com/uscmarshall
Description: Acts as a resource for families and their businesses, providing a forum for information about management, growth, continuity and strategy. Offers continuing educational resources. Brings owners and managers of mid-sized family companies together in interactive forums to address common issue sand work through transitions, develop strategic vision and enact strategic plans for the business and for the family. **Scope:** Acts as a resource for families and their businesses, providing a forum for information about management, growth, continuity and strategy. Offers continuing educational resources. Brings owners and managers of mid-sized family companies together in interactive forums to address common issue sand work through transitions, develop strategic vision and enact strategic plans for the business and for the family.

23682 ■ Family Business USA
400 W N St., 1406
Raleigh, NC 27603
Free: 877-609-1918
URL: http://www.familybusinessusa.com
Contact: Henry Hutcheson, President
Facebook: www.facebook.com/FamilyBusinessUSA
Description: Firm provides family business consulting services including succession plans, successor development, next generation mentoring, managing family conflicts, employment policies and compensation plans. **Scope:** Firm provides family business consulting services including succession plans, successor development, next generation mentoring, managing family conflicts, employment policies and compensation plans.

23683 ■ Management Growth Institute (MGI)
27 Chelmsford Rd.
Rochester, NY 14618-1727
Contact: Kathleen Barry Albertini, Contact
Description: Firm offers assistance in the specification, design, and implementation of management development programs, their clients include individuals, small businesses, national trade associations and government agencies. **Scope:** Firm offers assistance in the specification, design, and implementation of management development programs, their clients include individuals, small businesses, national trade associations and government agencies. **Publications:** "Cost Reduction Is Your Company the Target," InFocus Magazine, Apr, 2010; "Fall-I hired this great person," The Canadian Mover, Dec, 2009; "Profit Strategies," Direction Magazine, Jul, 2009; "Customer Loyalty," InFocus Magazine, Jul, 2009; "Cash Management," The Portal Magazine, Jul, 2009; "What is Customer Loyalty," In FOCUS Magazine, Dec, 2008; "Strategies to Improve Profits," Aug, 2008; "A Question of Management," Moving World. **Training:** Profit Enhancement; Family-Owned Businesses; Strategic Planning; Survival and Growth in a Down Economy.

23684 ■ Profit Planning Consultants
617 Fields Dr.
Lafayette Hill, PA 19444
Contact: Martin Feinberg, Owner
Description: Strengthening the family firm, increasing the value of business and preserving the heritage, provides full range of management services to independently-owned companies. Services cover such areas as operations analysis, planning and budgeting, marketing and sales, organizational development, succession planning and much more. **Scope:** Strengthening the family firm, increasing the value of business and preserving the heritage, provides full range of management services to independently-owned companies. Services cover such areas as operations analysis, planning and budgeting, marketing and sales, organizational development, succession planning and much more. **Training:** How to Enter International Markets; Time Management; Leadership, Professional Selling Skills; Managing a Family Owned Business; Profit Opportunities for Your Business; Family vs. Business; Doubling Your Net Profit; Transferring Management in a Family Owned Business.

23685 ■ ReGENERATION Partners
3811 Turtle Creek Blvd., Ste. 1830
Dallas, TX 75219
Ph: (214)559-3999
URL: http://familybusinessregeneration.com
Contact: Elle Hansen, Managing Partner
Facebook: www.facebook.com/ReGENPartners
Linkedin: www.linkedin.com/company/regeneration-partners
X (Twitter): x.com/regenpartners
Description: Firm provides business expertise growth strategies, competitive planning, crisis intervention, dispute resolution, interim and bridge management, strategic planning, and much more. **Scope:** Firm provides business expertise growth strategies, competitive planning, crisis intervention, dispute resolution, interim and bridge management, strategic planning, and much more. **Founded:** 1995. **Publications:** "When Siblings Share Leadership," May, 2007; "The End of a 1400-Year-Old Business," Apr, 2007; "Building a Family Business to Last," Mar, 2007; "Dealing with Death in a Family Business," Feb, 2007; "Best Practices for Family Business," Dec, 2006; "Resolving Family Business Conflicts," Nov, 2006; "Coping with Family-Business Ills," Oct, 2006; "Should You Join the Family Business," Sep, 2006; "A Transfer Tsunami for Family Biz," Jun, 2006; "When Kids Play the Guilt Card," Apr, 2006.

23686 ■ Schneider Consulting Group Inc.
2801 E 4th Ave.
Denver, CO 80206
Contact: Frank S. Schneider, Contact
Description: Firm assists family-owned and privately-held business transition to the next generation and or to a more professionally managed company, turn around consulting for small and medium-sized companies. **Scope:** Firm assists family-owned and privately-held business transition to the next generation and or to a more professionally managed company, turn around consulting for small and medium-sized companies. **Founded:** 1987. **Training:** Family Business Council; Impact of the Energy Renaissance.

PUBLICATIONS

23687 ■ Family Business Review: Journal of the Family Firm Institute (FBR)
2455 Teller Rd.
Thousand Oaks, CA 91320
Contact: Tracey Ozmina, President
URL(s): journals.sagepub.com/home/FBR
X (Twitter): x.com/FBRJournal
Ed: Donald O. Neubaum. **Released:** Quarterly **Price:** $854, Institutions for backfile lease, combined plus backfile (current volume print & all online content); $738, Institutions for backfile lease, e-access plus backfile (all online content); $660, Institutions for backfile purchase, e-access (content through 1998); $209, Institutions for single print issue; $58, Individuals for single print issue; $179, Individuals for print

GENERAL SMALL BUSINESS TOPICS

and online; $776, Institutions for print and online; $660, Institutions for online only; $760, Institutions for print only. **Description:** Interdisciplinary, scholarly journal focused on the exploration of the dynamics of family-controlled enterprises of all sizes. **Availability:** Print; PDF; Download; Online.

23688 ■ *"Family Human Capital and the Championing of Innovation in Small Firms" in Journal of Small Business Strategy (November 19, 2021)*
URL(s): ibjournals.mtsu.edu/index.php/jsbs/article/view/1633
Ed: Richard L. Gottschall, Jeremy Alan Woods.
Description: Discusses the results from a study that examines family members in small businesses and their business-level activities and the outcomes that were reported concerning innovation and the adoption of these innovative practices. **Availability:** PDF.

23689 ■ *"Marketing Strategies in Family Firms" in Journal of Small Business Strategy (April 13, 2021)*
URL(s): libjournals.mtsu.edu/index.php/jsbs/article/view/2010
Ed: Manuel Alonso Dos Santos, Orlando Llanos Contreras, Raj V. Mahto. **Released:** April 13, 2021.
Description: Explores why family firms do not apply marketing theories and branding concepts. **Availability:** PDF.

VENTURE CAPITAL FIRM

23690 ■ *Elevated Entrepreneurship: Experiences of Running a Family-Owned Business with Chris Prefontaine*
URL(s): mikemichalowicz.com/podcast/experiences-of-running-a-family-owned-business-with-chris-prefontaine
Ed: Mike Michalowiicz. **Released:** June 17, 2019.
Description: Podcast explains how a family can work together without entangling personal lives with business lives.

Financial Management

START-UP INFORMATION

23691 ■ *"Beyond Bootstrapping" in Inc. (Vol. 36, September 2014, No. 7, pp. 64)*
Pub: Mansueto Ventures L.L.C.
Contact: Stephanie Mehta, Chief Executive Officer
Price: $15, Nonmembers. **Description:** Dave Lerner, serial entrepreneur, angel investor, B-school professor, and author, explains the challenges entrepreneurs face when self-funding their startup business.
Availability: PDF; Online.

23692 ■ *How to Start a Bankruptcy Forms Processing Service*
Released: First edition. **Description:** Due to the increase in bankruptcy filings, attorneys are outsourcing related jobs in order to reduce overhead.

23693 ■ *"Office For One: The Sole Proprietor's Survival Guide"*
Pub: CreateSpace
Released: January 12, 2014. **Price:** $12.95, Paperback; $6.42, kindle; $3.95, Paperback. **Description:** Over thirty experts offer advice to any entrepreneur wishing to start a business by themselves. Tips and advice on tuning out negativity, maintaining balance and boundaries, handling legal issues and financial challenges, finding and keeping customers, marketing on a small budge, networking, cracking the media code, growing a sustainable vision, and addressing burnouts. **Availability:** Print.

ASSOCIATIONS AND OTHER ORGANIZATIONS

23694 ■ **American Finance Association (AFA)**
1655 E Campus Center Dr.
Salt Lake City, UT 84112
Ph: (201)299-4719
Co. E-mail: membership@afajof.org
URL: http://afajof.org
Contact: Kathleen Weiss Hanley, Executive Secretary Treasurer
E-mail: kwh315@lehigh.edu
Description: College and university professors of economics and finance, bankers, treasurers, analysts, financiers and others interested in financial problems; libraries and other institutions. Seeks to improve public understanding of financial problems and to provide for exchange of analytical ideas. Areas of special interest include: corporate finance, investments, banking and international and public finance. **Founded:** 1939. **Educational Activities:** AFA Annual Meeting (Annual). **Awards:** Fischer Black Prize (Biennial); Amundi Pioneer Prizes (Annual); Brattle Group Prizes in Corporate Finance (Annual). **Geographic Preference:** National.

23695 ■ **Association for Financial Professionals (AFP)**
4520 East-West Hwy., Ste. 800
Bethesda, MD 20814
Ph: (301)907-2862
Fax: (301)907-2864
Co. E-mail: customerservice@afponline.org
URL: http://www.afponline.org
Contact: James A. Kaitz, President
Linkedin: www.linkedin.com/company/association-for-financial-professionals
X (Twitter): x.com/afponline
YouTube: www.youtube.com/afponline
Description: Seeks to establish a national forum for the exchange of concepts and techniques related to improving the management of treasury and the careers of professionals through research, education, publications and recognition of the treasury management profession through a certification program. Conducts educational programs. Operates career center. **Founded:** 1976. **Publications:** *AFP Exchange: Turning Knowledge Into Performance*. **Educational Activities:** AFP Conference (Annual). **Awards:** AFP Pinnacle Award (Annual). **Geographic Preference:** National; Local.

23696 ■ **CAIA Association (CAIAA)**
11 Amity St.
Amherst, MA 01002
Ph: (413)253-7373
Co. E-mail: info@caia.org
URL: http://caia.org
Contact: John L. Bowman, President
Facebook: www.facebook.com/CAIA-Association-126663167435874
Linkedin: www.linkedin.com/company/caia-association
X (Twitter): x.com/calaassoclation
Instagram: www.instagram.com/caiaassociation
Description: Seeks to establish the Chartered Alternative Investment Analyst designation as the educational standard for the alternative investment industry. Advocates for high standards of professional conduct in the field of alternative investment analysis. **Founded:** 2002. **Publications:** *The Journal of Alternative Investments* (Quarterly). **Geographic Preference:** Multinational.

23697 ■ **Financial Women's Association (FWA)**
580 Fifth Ave., Ste. 820
New York, NY 10036
Ph: (212)533-2141
Co. E-mail: fwaoffice@fwa.org
URL: http://www.fwa.org
Contact: Annette Stewart, President
Facebook: www.facebook.com/fwany1956
Linkedin: www.linkedin.com/company/financial-women's-association
X (Twitter): x.com/FWANY
Instagram: www.instagram.com/fwanyc
Description: Promotes the professional development and advancement of all women through education, mentorship, scholarships, networking, and alliances across the financial community. **Founded:** 1956.

23698 ■ **Healthcare Financial Management Association (HFMA)**
4 Broad Plain
Bristol BS2 0JP, United Kingdom
Ph: 44 117 929-478-9
Co. E-mail: info@hfma.org.uk
URL: http://www.hfma.org.uk
Contact: Owen Harkin, President
Facebook: www.facebook.com/HFMAUK
X (Twitter): x.com/HFMA_UK
Instagram: www.instagram.com/hfma_uk
Description: Any qualified accountant and/or financial employee working in the NHS. Promotes professional standards of financial practice in the management and audit of the NHS. **Publications:** *NHS Health Authorities*; *NHS Trust*. **Geographic Preference:** National.

23699 ■ **Managed Funds Association (MFA)**
1301 Pennsylvania Ave., NW, Ste. 350
Washington, DC 20004
Ph: (202)730-2600
Co. E-mail: info@managedfunds.org
URL: http://www.managedfunds.org
Contact: Bryan Corbett, President
Linkedin: www.linkedin.com/company/managed-funds-association
X (Twitter): x.com/mfaupdates
YouTube: www.youtube.com/channel/UCxzsT9hBjzCkQpQ81vGZvZw
Description: Alternative investment professionals including hedge fund managers, fund of funds managers, service providers, and others associated with non-regulated investment funds. **Founded:** 1991. **Geographic Preference:** National.

23700 ■ **Wisconsin Association for Financial Professionals (WIAFP)**
N78W8120 Topview Trl.
Cedarburg, WI 53012-3412
Co. E-mail: info@wiafp.org
URL: http://wiafp.wildapricot.org
Contact: Shaun Hampton, President
E-mail: shaunhampton@northwesternmutual.com
Linkedin: www.linkedin.com/company/wisconsin-association-for-financial-professionals-wiafp
Description: Provides a forum for the exchange of ideas and techniques in the field of financial and treasury management. Promotes the finance and treasury profession through the education and professional development of its members. **Founded:** 1978. **Geographic Preference:** State.

EDUCATIONAL PROGRAMS

23701 ■ **Advanced Auditing for In-Charge Auditors (Onsite)**
Seminar Information Service Inc. (SIS)
250 El Camino Real., Ste. 112
Tustin, CA 92780
Ph: (714)508-0340
Free: 877-736-4636
Fax: (714)734-8027

Co. E-mail: info@seminarinformation.com
URL: http://www.seminarinformation.com
Contact: Catherine Bellizzi, President
URL(s): www.seminarinformation.com

Description: Learn all of the elements involved in traditional and operational auditing from the unique perspective of the in-charge position, while reviewing concepts such as audit program flexibility, risk assessment, priority setting during fieldwork, and effective oral and written communications of audit findings. **Audience:** Financial, operational IT and external auditors . **Principal Exhibits:** Learn all of the elements involved in traditional and operational auditing from the unique perspective of the in-charge position, while reviewing concepts such as audit program flexibility, risk assessment, priority setting during fieldwork, and effective oral and written communications of audit findings.

23702 ■ Advanced Collection Strategies (Onsite)

Seminar Information Service Inc. (SIS)
250 El Camino Real., Ste. 112
Tustin, CA 92780
Ph: (714)508-0340
Free: 877-736-4636
Fax: (714)734-8027
Co. E-mail: info@seminarinformation.com
URL: http://www.seminarinformation.com
Contact: Catherine Bellizzi, President
URL(s): www.seminarinformation.com/details.cfm?qc=qqbvad

Description: Learn the secrets to getting what's owed while complying with strict debtor protection laws, including strategies for defending against collection harassment claims should they arise. **Audience:** Attorneys, in-house counsel, creditors, third-party debt collectors and debt buyers. **Principal Exhibits:** Learn the secrets to getting what's owed while complying with strict debtor protection laws, including strategies for defending against collection harassment claims should they arise.

23703 ■ Advanced Financial Forecasting and Modeling Workshop

Canadian Management Centre (CMC)
150 King St. W Ste. 271
Toronto, ON, Canada M5H 1J9
Ph: (416)214-5678
Free: 877-262-2519
Fax: (416)214-6047
Co. E-mail: cmcinfo@cmcoutperform.com
URL: http://cmcoutperform.com
Contact: Chris Peacock, Director
URL(s): cmcoutperform.com/live-online

Price: $2,500, Members; $2,799, Non-members. **Description:** This highly interactive course helps you build more powerful and accurate forecasting models that fast-track decision making and improve end results. Course is delivered in four, 3-hour sessions over a 2 week period. **Audience:** Analysts, executive-level managers and financial professionals. **Principal Exhibits:** This highly interactive course helps you build more powerful and accurate forecasting models that fast-track decision making and improve end results. Course is delivered in four, 3-hour sessions over a 2 week period.

23704 ■ AMA Export/Import Procedures and Documentation (Onsite)

URL(s): www.amanet.org

Description: Covers export and import guidelines and regulations, business documentation practices, using foreign trade zones, and financial aspects of importing and exporting. **Audience:** Import/export managers, traffic managers, shipping department personnel, international marketing managers, customer service staff, credit managers, controllers, purchasing managers and directors of procurement or logistics. **Principal Exhibits:** Covers export and import guidelines and regulations, business documentation practices, using foreign trade zones, and financial aspects of importing and exporting. **Telecommunication Services:** customerservice@amanet.org.

23705 ■ AMA's Finance Workshop for Nonfinancial Executives (Onsite)

URL(s): www.amanet.org

Price: $2,745, Non-members; $2,495, Members AMA; $2,268, Members GSA. **Description:** Comprehensive four-day seminar covering all aspects of corporate finance. **Audience:** Experienced managers, general managers, directors, vice presidents and top executives in sales. **Principal Exhibits:** Comprehensive four-day seminar covering all aspects of corporate finance.

23706 ■ Corporate Cash Management (onsite)

Seminar Information Service Inc. (SIS)
250 El Camino Real., Ste. 112
Tustin, CA 92780
Ph: (714)508-0340
Free: 877-736-4636
Fax: (714)734-8027
Co. E-mail: info@seminarinformation.com
URL: http://www.seminarinformation.com
Contact: Catherine Bellizzi, President
URL(s): www.seminarinformation.com

Description: Introductory course that covers how money moves, how to accelerate cash receipts, how to select the right cash management bank, and how to make better use of excess funds through short-term investments. **Audience:** Industry professionals. **Principal Exhibits:** Introductory course that covers how money moves, how to accelerate cash receipts, how to select the right cash management bank, and how to make better use of excess funds through short-term investments.

23707 ■ Creative Ways to Cut and Control Costs

Fred Pryor Seminars & CareerTrack
5700 Broadmoor, Ste. 300
Mission, KS 66202
Free: 800-780-8476
Fax: (913)967-8849
Co. E-mail: customerservice@pryor.com
URL: http://www.pryor.com
Contact: Janet Turner, Contact
E-mail: dmca@pryor.com
URL(s): www.pryor.com/mkt_info/seminars/desc/CZ.asp

Description: Learn how to control business expenses to create an organization that is competitive, profitable, and growth focused. **Audience:** Business professionals. **Principal Exhibits:** Learn how to control business expenses to create an organization that is competitive, profitable, and growth focused.

23708 ■ The Essentials of Cash Flow Forecasting

Fred Pryor Seminars & CareerTrack
5700 Broadmoor, Ste. 300
Mission, KS 66202
Free: 800-780-8476
Fax: (913)967-8849
Co. E-mail: customerservice@pryor.com
URL: http://www.pryor.com
Contact: Janet Turner, Contact
E-mail: dmca@pryor.com
URL(s): www.pryor.com/mkt_info/seminars/desc/KF.asp

Description: Learn to make better budget decisions through proven strategies and techniques. **Audience:** Business professionals. **Principal Exhibits:** Learn to make better budget decisions through proven strategies and techniques.

23709 ■ Financial & Accounting Concepts, Statements & Terminology: 2 Day (Onsite)

Seminar Information Service Inc. (SIS)
250 El Camino Real., Ste. 112
Tustin, CA 92780
Ph: (714)508-0340
Free: 877-736-4636
Fax: (714)734-8027
Co. E-mail: info@seminarinformation.com
URL: http://www.seminarinformation.com
Contact: Catherine Bellizzi, President
URL(s): www.seminarinformation.com

Description: Financial and accounting training in plain English. **Audience:** Nonfinancial managers. **Principal Exhibits:** Financial and accounting training in plain English.

23710 ■ Financial Statement Analysis (Onsite)

Seminar Information Service Inc. (SIS)
250 El Camino Real., Ste. 112
Tustin, CA 92780
Ph: (714)508-0340
Free: 877-736-4636
Fax: (714)734-8027
Co. E-mail: info@seminarinformation.com
URL: http://www.seminarinformation.com
Contact: Catherine Bellizzi, President
URL(s): www.seminarinformation.com/details.cfm?qc=qqbqym

Description: Enhance your ability to read, analyze and use financial statements to manage, drive and stay on top of your company's growth, including how to understand the specialized language of finance and quickly scan a financial report and pick out the numbers that matter and detect variance while there's time to take corrective action. **Audience:** Financial managers, financial analysts. **Principal Exhibits:** Enhance your ability to read, analyze and use financial statements to manage, drive and stay on top of your company's growth, including how to understand the specialized language of finance and quickly scan a financial report and pick out the numbers that matter and detect variance while there's time to take corrective action.

23711 ■ Fred Pryor Seminars & CareerTrack Collections Law (Onsite)

URL(s): www.pryor.com

Description: Ensure your organization is legally compliant, including strategies and techniques to gain quicker results in collecting money. **Audience:** Managers, supervisors, vice-presidents and professionals. **Principal Exhibits:** Ensure your organization is legally compliant, including strategies and techniques to gain quicker results in collecting money.

23712 ■ How to Implement Effective Internal Controls

Fred Pryor Seminars & CareerTrack
5700 Broadmoor, Ste. 300
Mission, KS 66202
Free: 800-780-8476
Fax: (913)967-8849
Co. E-mail: customerservice@pryor.com
URL: http://www.pryor.com
Contact: Janet Turner, Contact
E-mail: dmca@pryor.com
URL(s): www.seminarinformation.com/qqbujz/how-to-implement-effective-internal-controls

Description: Learn to protect, maintain, and control your financial structure while streamlining your business. **Audience:** Financial professionals, business leaders, managers, and supervisors. **Principal Exhibits:** Learn to protect, maintain, and control your financial structure while streamlining your business.

23713 ■ How to Manage & Organize Accounts Payable

Fred Pryor Seminars & CareerTrack
5700 Broadmoor, Ste. 300
Mission, KS 66202
Free: 800-780-8476
Fax: (913)967-8849
Co. E-mail: customerservice@pryor.com
URL: http://www.pryor.com
Contact: Janet Turner, Contact
E-mail: dmca@pryor.com
URL(s): www.pryor.com/training-seminars/how-to-manage-organize-accounts-payable

Frequency: Irregular. **Description:** Learn how to organize your files, records, and workspace for maximum organization and flow. **Audience:** Financial management professionals. **Principal Exhibits:** Learn how to organize your files, records, and workspace for maximum organization and flow.

23714 ■ How to Read and Understand Financial Statements (Onsite)
URL(s): www.pryor.com/site/webinar-audio/how-to-read-and-understand-financial-statements
Description: Learn how to read financial statements, interpret their data, and put that information to positive use. **Audience:** Small business owners, mid- to upper-level managers, department heads, and nonfinancial professionals. **Principal Exhibits:** Learn how to read financial statements, interpret their data, and put that information to positive use.

23715 ■ The Nonfinancial Manager's Guide to Understanding Financial Statements (Onsite)
National Seminars Training L.L.C. (NST)
14502 W 105th St.
Lenexa, KS 66215
Free: 800-349-1935
Co. E-mail: info@findaseminar.com
URL: http://www.findaseminar.com/tpd/Padgett-Thompson-Seminars.asp
URL(s): www.findaseminar.com/event1.asp?eventID=3403
Description: Comprehensive, fast-paced, one-day seminars that covers all the essentials of understanding financial statements. **Audience:** Managers and professionals. **Principal Exhibits:** Comprehensive, fast-paced, one-day seminars that covers all the essentials of understanding financial statements.

23716 ■ Successful Inventory Management (Onsite)
URL(s): www.pryor.com
Description: Learn proven cost saving methods that improve inventory and cycle count accuracy. **Audience:** Professionals. **Principal Exhibits:** Learn proven cost saving methods that improve inventory and cycle count accuracy.

23717 ■ WBENC Lift Financial Center of Excellence
URL(s): www.wbenc.org/programs/wbenc-lift-financial-center-of-excellence
Frequency: Irregular. **Description:** Educational program to educate women entrepreneurs on financial business support and funding opportunities. **Principal Exhibits:** Educational program to educate women entrepreneurs on financial business support and funding opportunities.

REFERENCE WORKS

23718 ■ "4 Financing Options for Agriculture Business Owners" in FORA Financial (Jan. 30, 2020)
URL(s): www.forafinancial.com/blog/industries-we-serve/agriculture-business/
Released: January 30, 2020. **Description:** Discusses what an agribusiness is, the pros and cons of starting an agribusiness, and options for financing your agribusiness. **Availability:** Online.

23719 ■ "4 Things You Need To Know About Credit Scores: What Millennials Don't Know Can Hurt Their Finances" in Black Enterprise (Vol. 45, July-August 2014, No. 1, pp. 64)
Pub: Earl G. Graves Ltd.
Contact: Earl Graves, Jr., President
Released: December 12, 2018. **Description:** The Consumer Federation of America and VantageScore Solutions LLC report their fourth annual survey on consumers' understanding of credit scores. Six types of businesses using credit scores, include electric company, cell phone company, home insurer, landlord, mortgage lender, and credit card issuer. Age, payment history, debt, years of having credit, last credit application date, and type of credit all factor into scores.

23720 ■ "5 Things You Should Know If Your Bank Fails" in Black Enterprise (Vol. 41, December 2010, No. 5, pp. 29)
Pub: Earl G. Graves Ltd.
Contact: Earl Graves, Jr., President

Ed: John Simons. **Description:** The Federal Deposit Insurance Corporation announced that the number of banks in trouble has reached the highest level since March 1993. Advice from the FDIC is cited. Statistical data included. **Availability:** Online.

23721 ■ "113D Filings: Investors Report to the SEC" in Barron's (Vol. 88, March 24, 2008, No. 12, pp. M13)
Pub: Dow Jones & Company Inc.
Contact: Almar Latour, Chief Executive Officer
Released: April 02, 2016. **Description:** HealthCor Management called as problematic the plan of Magellan Health Services to use its high cash balances for acquisitions. Carlson Capital discussed with Energy Partners possible changes in the latter's board. Investor Carl Icahn suggested that Enzon Pharmaceuticals consider selling itself or divest some of its assets. **Availability:** Print; Online.

23722 ■ "A 16-Year Housing Slump? It Could Happen" in Barron's (Vol. 88, March 17, 2008, No. 11, pp. 27)
Pub: Dow Jones & Company Inc.
Contact: Almar Latour, Chief Executive Officer
Ed: Gene Epstein. **Description:** Housing remains a good protection against inflation but over very long periods. Inflation-adjusted stock prices did even better but have greater volatility. Commodities, on the other hand, underperformed both housing and stocks as inflation hedges. House prices tend to rise faster than the consumer price index is because land is inherently limited. **Availability:** Online.

23723 ■ "401(k) Keys to Stable Value" in Barron's (Vol. 88, March 10, 2008, No. 10, pp. 40)
Pub: Dow Jones & Company Inc.
Contact: Almar Latour, Chief Executive Officer
Ed: Tom Sullivan. **Description:** Stable-value funds offer investors stability in a period of volatility in financial markets, attracting $888 million in funds. The Securities and Exchange Commission approved the launch of actively managed exchange-traded funds. **Availability:** Online.

23724 ■ "529.com Wins Outstanding Achievement in Web Development" in Investment Weekly (November 14, 2009, pp. 152)
Pub: Investment Weekly News
Description: Web Marketing Association's 2009 WebAward for Financial Services Standard of Excellence and Investment Standard of Excellence was won by 529.com, the website from Upromise Investments, Inc., the leading administrator of 529 college savings plans. **Availability:** Online.

23725 ■ "Accrual vs. Cash Accounting, Explained" in Business Owner (Vol. 35, July-August 2011, No. 4, pp. 13)
Description: Cash method versus accrual accounting methods are examined, using hypothetical situations.

23726 ■ "Ag Firms Harvest Revenue Growth" in The Business Journal-Serving Metropolitan Kansas City (Vol. 26, July 18, 2008, No. 45, pp. 1)
Description: Five of the biggest agricultural companies in the Kansas City area, except one, reported multibillion-dollar revenue increases in 2007. The companies, which include Lansing Trade Group, posted a combined $9.5 billion revenue growth. The factors that affected the revenue increase in the area's agricultural companies, such as prices and high demand, are also examined. **Availability:** Print; Online.

23727 ■ "All Eyes On Iris" in Canadian Business (Vol. 81, July 22, 2008, No. 12-13, pp. 20)
Description: Provincial governments in Canada are believed to be awaiting Alberta Finance Minister Iris Evans' financial and investment policies as well as Evans' development of a new saving strategy. Alberta is the only Canadian province that is in position to invest in sovereign wealth funds after it eliminated its debt in 2005. **Availability:** Print; Online.

23728 ■ "America's Top 40 Wealth Management Firms" in Barron's (Vol. 92, September 17, 2012, No. 38, pp. 28)
Pub: Dow Jones & Company Inc.
Contact: Almar Latour, Chief Executive Officer
Description: The 40 largest wealth managers in the US are ranked according to client assets held in accounts worth $5 million or more as of June 30, 2012. Bank of America Global Wealth and Investment Management remained the largest, with $792 billion in assets under management. **Availability:** Online.

23729 ■ "American Apparel: When Dov Cries" in Canadian Business (Vol. 83, June 15, 2010, No. 10, pp. 71)
Pub: Rogers Media Inc.
Contact: Neil Spivak, Chief Executive Officer
Ed: Joe Castaldo. **Description:** American Apparel disclosed that they will have problems meeting one of its debt covenants which could trigger a chain reaction that could lead to bankruptcy. The prospects look bleak, but eccentric company founder Dov Charney, has always defied expectations. **Availability:** Online.

23730 ■ American Bar Association Legal Guide for Small Business: Everything You Need to Know About Small Business, from Start-up to Employment to Financing and Selling
Released: Second edition. **Description:** The American Bar Association provides insight into financial, health and family issues affecting small business, including start up issues, employment laws, financing a business, and selling a business.

23731 ■ "American Water's Ed Vallejo Chosen for 2012 Minority Business Leader Awards" in Manufacturing Close-Up (July 30, 2012)
Description: Ed Vallejo, vice presient of investor relations at American Water, has been awarded the 2012 Minority Business Leader Award from the Philadelphia Business Journal. Vallejo is responsible for developing investor relations strategies for the publicly traded water and wastewater utility firm. He also serves as the company's liaison with financial analyst and investor communities. **Availability:** Online.

23732 ■ "The Annual Entitlement Lecture Medicare Elephantiasis" in Barron's (March 31, 2008)
Pub: Dow Jones & Company Inc.
Contact: Almar Latour, Chief Executive Officer
Ed: Thomas G. Donlan. **Description:** Expenditures on Medicare hospital insurance and the revenues available to pay for it have led to a gap of capital valued at $38.6 trillion. Slashing the benefits or raising taxes will not solve the gap which exists unless the government saves the money and invests it in private markets. **Availability:** Online.

23733 ■ "Are You Micromanaging Your Company's Financial Tasks?" in allBusiness
Ed: Rieva Lesonsky. **Description:** Provides information on the benefits of utilizing technology and/or outsourcing certain business operation tasks so that you can concentrate on working on the business you've invested so much time and money into building. The article goes into detail about micromanaging payroll and how to best use your time. **Availability:** Online.

23734 ■ "Are You Ready for Dow 20,000?" in Barron's (Vol. 88, March 24, 2008, No. 12, pp. 26)
Pub: Dow Jones & Company Inc.
Contact: Almar Latour, Chief Executive Officer
Ed: Jonathan R. Laing. **Description:** Stock strategist James Finucane forecasts that the Dow Jones Industrial Average will rise from its 12,361 level to as

high as 20,000 from 2008 to 2009. He believes that stock liquidation and a buildup of cash provide the perfect conditions for a huge rally. **Availability:** Online.

23735 ■ *"Are You Ready To Do It Yourself? Discipline and Self-Study Can Help You Profit From Online Trading"* in Black Enterprise (February 1, 2008)
Pub: Earl G. Graves Ltd.
Contact: Earl Graves, Jr., President
Ed: Steve Garmhausen. **Description:** Steps to help individuals invest in stocks online is given by an expert broker. Discount brokerage houses can save money for online investors. **Availability:** Online.

23736 ■ *"Asia Breathes a Sigh of Relief"* in Business Week (September 22, 2008, No. 4100, pp. 32)
Description: Foreign bankers, such as those in Asia, that had been investing heavily in the United States began to worry as the housing crisis deepened and the impact on Freddie Mac and Fannie Mae became increasingly clear. Due to the government bailout, however, central banks will most likely continue to buy American debt. **Availability:** Print; Online.

23737 ■ *"Au Revoir Or Goodbye?"* in Barron's (Vol. 88, July 14, 2008, No. 28, pp. 5)
Pub: Dow Jones & Company Inc.
Contact: Almar Latour, Chief Executive Officer
Ed: Alan Abelson. **Description:** Former Senator Phil Gramm's opinion that the U.S. is a "nation of whiners" as they moan about recession is another example of the disconnection between Washington and Wall Street on one hand and the real world on the other. It would be a catastrophe for most of the world if Fannie Mae and Freddie Mac were to go under and take their trillions of mortgage debt with them. **Availability:** Online.

23738 ■ *"BABs in Bond Land"* in Barron's (Vol. 89, July 6, 2009, No. 27, pp. 14)
Pub: Dow Jones & Company Inc.
Contact: Almar Latour, Chief Executive Officer
Ed: Jim McTague. **Description:** American Recovery and Reinvestment Act has created taxable Build America Bonds (BAB) to finance new construction projects. The issuance of the two varieties of taxable BABs is expected to benefit the municipal bond market. **Availability:** Online.

23739 ■ *"Baby's Room Franchisee Files Bankruptcy"* in Crain's Detroit Business (Vol. 25, June 22, 2009, No. 25, pp. 15)
Pub: Crain Communications Inc.
Contact: Barry Asin, President
Ed: Gabe Nelson. **Description:** Emery L, a franchisee of USA Baby Inc. and ran the franchised Baby's Room Nursery Furniture stores in the area has filed for bankruptcy. Details of the bankruptcy are included. **Availability:** Print; Online.

23740 ■ *"Back In the Black, Maryland Zoo Upgrades"* in Baltimore Business Journal (Vol. 32, July 25, 2014, No. 12, pp. 4)
Pub: American City Business Journals, Inc.
Contact: Mike Olivieri, Executive Vice President
Released: Weekly. **Price:** $4, introductory 4-week offer(Digital only). **Description:** Maryland Zoo has stabilized its finances after several years of budgetary problems that nearly caused the zoo to lose its accreditation from the Association of Zoos and Aquariums. President Donald P. Hutchinson reveals the zoo has increased the number of private and corporate donors and is carrying out several upgrades, including new penguin and flamingo exhibits. **Availability:** Print; Online.

23741 ■ *"Back in the Race. New Fund Manager Has Whipped Sentinel International Equity Back into Shape"* in Barron's (Vol. 88, March 17, 2008, No. 11, pp. 43)
Pub: Dow Jones & Company Inc.
Contact: Almar Latour, Chief Executive Officer

Ed: Leslie P. Norton. **Description:** Katherine Schapiro was able to get Sentinel International Equity's Morningstar classification to blended fund from a value fund rating after joining Sentinel from her former jobs at Strong Overseas Fund. Schapiro aims to benefit from the global rebalancing as the U.S.'s share of the world economy shrinks. **Availability:** Online.

23742 ■ *"Back-Tested ETFs Draw Assets, Flub Returns"* in Barron's (Vol. 92, July 23, 2012, No. 30, pp. 26)
Pub: Dow Jones & Company Inc.
Contact: Almar Latour, Chief Executive Officer
Ed: Janet Paskin. **Description:** New exchange-traded funds are attracting investors by using 'back-tested' data offered by the indexes they track. Investors are substituting real performance for these hypothetical returns, which measure past performance of indexes had they been in existence. **Availability:** Online.

23743 ■ *"Bad Loans Start Piling Up"* in Crain's New York Business (Vol. 24, January 6, 2008, No. 1, pp. 2)
Pub: Crain Communications, Inc.
Contact: Jessica Botos, Manager, Marketing
E-mail: jessica.botos@crainsnewyork.com
Ed: Tom Fredrickson. **Description:** Problems in the subprime mortgage industry have extended to other lending activities as evidenced by bank charge-offs on bad commercial and industrial loans which have more than doubled in the third quarter.

23744 ■ *"Balancing Risk and Return in a Customer Portfolio"* in Journal of Marketing (Vol. 75, May 2011, No. 3, pp. 1)
Pub: American Marketing Association
Contact: Bennie F. Johnson, Chief Executive Officer
Ed: Crina O. Tarasi, Ruth N. Bolton, Michael D. Hutt, Beth A. Walker. **Released:** Volume: 75 issue: 3.
Description: A framework for reducing the vulnerability and volatility of cash flows in customer portfolios is presented. The efficient portfolios of firms are identified and tested against their current portfolios and hypothetical profit maximization portfolios. **Availability:** PDF.

23745 ■ *"Bank of America Fights To Keep Top Spot in Mobile Banking"* in Charlotte Business Journal (Vol. 27, June 15, 2012, No. 13, pp. 1)
Pub: American City Business Journals, Inc.
Contact: Mike Olivieri, Executive Vice President
Released: Weekly. **Price:** $20, Introductory 12-week offer(Digital & Print). **Description:** Bank of America has been fighting to maintain its lead in mobile banking services. Financial institutions, payment processors and e-commerce firms have started offering mobile banking services. **Availability:** Print; Online.

23746 ■ *"Bank On It: New Year, New Estate Plan"* in Hawaii Business (Vol. 53, February 2008, No. 8, pp. 54)
Pub: PacificBasin Communications
Contact: Chuck Tindle, Director
E-mail: chuckt@pacificbasin.net
Ed: Antony M. Orme. **Description:** Discusses the start of the new year which can be a time to revise wills and estate plans as failure to do so may create problems of unequal inheritance and increase in estate tax exemption, which could disinherit beneficiaries. Other circumstances that can prompt changes in wills and estate plans are presented. **Availability:** Print; Online.

23747 ■ *"Banking Sector To See Moderate Growth in 2014"* in Houston Business Journal (Vol. 44, January 3, 2014, No. 35, pp. 5)
Pub: American City Business Journals, Inc.
Contact: Mike Olivieri, Executive Vice President
Released: January 03, 2014. **Price:** $4, introductory 4-week offer(Digital only). **Description:** The Greater Houston Partnership reported that Houston, Texas' finance industry recovered 50.9 percent of the 5,500 jobs it lost compared to the nation's recovery rate of 34.4 percent. However, Houston's banking sector remains strong and deposits have almost doubled since 2008. The banks that established or expanded operations in Houston are also presented. **Availability:** Print; Online.

23748 ■ *"The Bankrate Double Play, Bankrate Is Having Its Best Quarter Yet"* in Barron's (Vol. 88, March 24, 2008, No. 12, pp. 27)
Pub: Dow Jones & Company Inc.
Contact: Almar Latour, Chief Executive Officer
Ed: Neil A. Martin. **Description:** Shares of Bankrate may rise as much as 25 percent from their level of $45.08 a share due to a strong cash flow and balance sheet. The company's Internet business remains strong despite weakness in the online advertising industry and is a potential takeover target. **Availability:** Online.

23749 ■ *Bankruptcy for Small Business*
Description: Bankruptcy laws can be used to save a small business, homes or other property. The book provides general information for small business owners regarding the reasons for money problems, types of bankruptcy available and their alternatives, myths about bankruptcy, and the do's and don'ts for filing for bankruptcy. **Availability:** E-book; Print.

23750 ■ *"Banks Continue March Out of Bad-Loan Numbers: Total Loans Up, Non-Performing Loans Decline"* in Memphis Business Journal (Vol. 34, August 24, 2012, No. 19, pp. 1)
Pub: Baltimore Business Journal
Contact: Rhonda Pringle, President
E-mail: rpringle@bizjournals.com
Description: Banks in Memphis, Tennessee continue to improve their capital status throughout the second quarter of 2012. The twenty-five banks observed showed improvements in total loan volume, as well as in non-performing loans and real estate. Total loans grew $723.26 million, while non-performing loans and real-estate-owned assets fell $322.4 million. **Availability:** Print; Online.

23751 ■ *"Banks, Retailers Squabble Over Fees"* in Baltimore Business Journal (Vol. 28, June 18, 2010, No. 6, pp. 1)
Pub: Baltimore Business Journal
Contact: Rhonda Pringle, President
E-mail: rpringle@bizjournals.com
Ed: Gary Haber. **Description:** How an amendment to the financial regulatory reform bill would affect the bankers' and retailers' conflict over interchange fees is discussed. Interchange fees are paid for by retailers every time consumers make purchases through debit cards. Industry estimates indicate that approximately $50 million in such fees are paid by retailers. **Availability:** Print; Online.

23752 ■ *"Bargain Hunting In Vietnam"* in Barron's (Vol. 88, July 14, 2008, No. 28, pp. M6)
Pub: Dow Jones & Company Inc.
Contact: Almar Latour, Chief Executive Officer
Ed: Elliot Wilson. **Description:** Vietnam's economy grew by just 6.5 percent for the first half of 2008 and its balance of payments ballooned to $14.4 billion. The falling stock prices in the country is a boon for bargain hunters and investing in the numerous domestic funds is one way of investing in the country. Some shares that investors are taking an interest in are also discussed. **Availability:** Online.

23753 ■ *"Baupost Group Pours Money into Charlotte Real Estate Projects"* in Charlotte Business Journal (Vol. 25, December 3, 2010, No. 37, pp. 1)
Pub: Charlotte Business Journal
Contact: Robert Morris, Editor
E-mail: rmorris@bizjournals.com
Ed: Will Boye. **Description:** Boston-based hedge fund Baupost Group has been financing real estate project in Charlotte, North Carolina including more than 80 acres just north of uptown. Aside from purchasing the $23.8 million note for the Rosewood Condominiums from Regions Financial Corporation,

the Baupost Group is also negotiating with Regions to buy the $93.9 million debt of the EipCentre real estate project. **Availability:** Print; Online.

23754 ■ *"BDC Launches New Online Business Advice Centre"* in *Marketwired (July 13, 2010)*
Pub: Comtex News Network Inc.
Contact: Kan Devnani, President
Description: The Business Development Bank of Canada (BDC) offers entrepreneurs the chance to use their new online BDC Advice Centre in order to seek advice regarding the challenges of entrepreneurship. Free online business tools and information to help both startups and established firms are also provided. **Availability:** Print; Online.

23755 ■ *"The Bear Stearns-JPMorgan Deal - Rhymes with Steal - Of A Lifetime"* in *Barron's (Vol. 88, March 24, 2008, No. 12, pp. 24)*
Pub: Dow Jones & Company Inc.
Contact: Almar Latour, Chief Executive Officer
Ed: Andrew Bary. **Description:** JPMorgan Chase's impending acquisition of Bear Stearns for $2.50 a share is a huge steal for the former. JPMorgan is set to acquire a company with a potential annual earnings of $1 billion while the Federal Reserve funds Bear's illiquid assets by providing $30 billion in non-recourse loans. **Availability:** Online.

23756 ■ *"The Bear's Back"* in *Barron's (Vol. 88, July 7, 2008, No. 27, pp. 17)*
Pub: Dow Jones & Company Inc.
Contact: Almar Latour, Chief Executive Officer
Ed: Randall W. Forsyth, Vito Racanelli. **Description:** US stock markets have formally entered the bear market after the Dow Jones Industrial Average dropped 20 percent from its high as of June 2008. Investors remain uncertain as to how long the bear market will persist, especially with the US economy on the edge of recession. **Availability:** Online.

23757 ■ *"Beat the Buck: Bartering Tips from In-The-Know Authors"* in *(June 23, 2010)*
Pub: The Telegraph
Contact: Don Cherry, District Manager
E-mail: dcherry@thetelegraph.com
Description: The Art of Barter is a new book to help small businesses learn this art form in order to expand customer base and reserve cash flow. **Availability:** Online.

23758 ■ *"Beaumont Outsources Purchasing as Route to Supply Cost Savings"* in *Crain's Detroit Business (Vol. 25, June 1, 2009, No. 22)*
Pub: Crain Communications Inc.
Contact: Barry Asin, President
Ed: Jay Greene. **Description:** William Beaumont Hospitals in Royal Oak have begun outsourcing the purchasing of supplies in order to cut costs. So far, Beaumont is the only hospital in southeast Michigan to outsource its purchasing department. Other hospitals employ their own purchasing supply workers. **Availability:** Online.

23759 ■ *"The Beauty of Banking's Big Ugly"* in *Barron's (Vol. 89, July 27, 2009, No. 30, pp. 31)*
Pub: Dow Jones & Company Inc.
Contact: Almar Latour, Chief Executive Officer
Ed: Andrew Bary. **Description:** Appeal of the shares of Citigroup comes from its sharp discount to its tangible book value and the company's positive attributes include a strong capital position, high loan-loss reserves, and their appealing global-consumer. The shares have the potential to generate nice profits and decent stock gains as the economy turns. **Availability:** Online.

23760 ■ *"Behind the Numbers: When It Comes to Earnings, Look for Quality, Not Just Quantity"* in *Black Enterprise (Vol. 38, July 2008, pp. 35)*
Pub: Earl G. Graves Ltd.
Contact: Earl Graves, Jr., President
Description: It is important for investors to examine the quality of a company's earnings rather than fixate on the quantity of those earnings. Advice is given regarding issues investors can look at when trying to determine the potential growth of a firm.

23761 ■ *"Bertha's Birth Stirs Juice"* in *Barron's (Vol. 88, July 14, 2008, No. 28, pp. M11)*
Pub: Dow Jones & Company Inc.
Contact: Almar Latour, Chief Executive Officer
Ed: Tom Sellen. **Description:** Price of frozen concentrated orange juice, which has risen to four-month highs of $1.3620 in July 2008 is due, in part, to the hurricane season that has come earlier than normal in the far eastern Atlantic thereby possibly harming the 2008-2009 Florida orange crop. Future tropical-storm development will affect the prices of this commodity. **Availability:** Online.

23762 ■ *"Best Cash Flow Generators"* in *Canadian Business (Vol. 82, Summer 2009, No. 8, pp. 40)*
Description: Agrium Inc. and FirstService Corporation are in the list of firms that are found to have the potential to be the best cash flow generators in Canada. The list also includes WestJet Airlines Ltd., which accounts for 385 flights each day. More than 80 percent of analysts rate the airline stocks a Buy. **Availability:** Print; Online.

23763 ■ *"The Best Five-Month Run Since 1938"* in *Barron's (Vol. 89, August 3, 2009, No. 31, pp. M3)*
Pub: Dow Jones & Company Inc.
Contact: Almar Latour, Chief Executive Officer
Ed: Kopin Tan, Andrew Bary. **Description:** US stock markets ended July 2009 registering the highest five-month rise since 1938. The shares of Cablevision could rise as the company simplifies its structure and spins off its Madison Square Garden unit. The shares of Potash Corp. could fall as the company faces lower earnings due to falling potash purchases. **Availability:** Online.

23764 ■ *"Best Turnaround Stocks"* in *Canadian Business (Vol. 81, Summer 2008, No. 9, pp. 65)*
Description: Share prices of Sierra Wireless Inc. and EXFO Electro Optical Engineering Inc. have fallen over the past year but have good chance at a rebound considering that the companies have free cash flow and no long-term debt. One-year stock performance analysis of the two companies is presented. **Availability:** Print; Online.

23765 ■ *"Best Value Stocks"* in *Canadian Business (Vol. 81, Summer 2008, No. 9, pp. 63)*
Description: Table showing the one-year performance of bargain or best-value stocks is presented. These stocks are undervalued compared to their North American peers, but it is projected that their five-year average return on equity is greater. **Availability:** Online.

23766 ■ *"Betsey Johnson Falls Out of Fashion"* in *Canadian Business (Vol. 85, June 11, 2012, No. 10, pp. 14)*
Ed: Sarah Barmak. **Description:** Fashion label Betsey Johnson LLC filed for Chapter 11 bankruptcy protection in April 2012 that would result in 350 layoffs and closure of most of its 63 stores. The company cited severe liquidity constraints and $4.1 million in outstanding unsecured obligations to creditors in its filing. **Availability:** Print; Online.

23767 ■ *"A Better Way to Tax U.S. Businesses"* in *(Vol. 90, July-August 2012, No. 7-8, pp. 134)*
Pub: Harvard Business Review Press
Contact: Moderna V. Pfizer, Contact
Ed: Mihir A. Desai. **Price:** $8.95, PDF and hardcover black and white. **Description:** Correcting the US corporate tax code will require ending the disconnect between earnings stated to investors and taxable income, implementing rate reductions, eliminating the taxing of overseas income, and securing an agreement by business leaders to acknowledge taxes as a responsibility. **Availability:** Print; PDF; Online.

23768 ■ *"Betting Big, Winning Big: Interview With Bruce Berkowitz, CEO of Fairholme Capital Management"* in *Barron's (Vol. 88, March 17, 2008, No. 11, pp. 49)*
Pub: Dow Jones & Company Inc.
Contact: Almar Latour, Chief Executive Officer
Ed: Lawrence C. Strauss. **Description:** Bruce Berkowitz explains that the reason that his portfolio is concentrated is because getting more positions makes the portfolio more average compared to putting the money into your 10th or 20th-best idea. Berkowitz' picks include Berkshire Hathaway, Well-Care Health Plus, Sears Holdings, and Mohawk Industries. **Availability:** Online.

23769 ■ *"Betting on a Happy Ending"* in *Barron's (Vol. 88, July 7, 2008, No. 27, pp. 14)*
Pub: Dow Jones & Company Inc.
Contact: Almar Latour, Chief Executive Officer
Ed: Dimitra DeFotis. **Description:** Shares of Time Warner, priced at $14.69 each, appear under-priced as financial analysts discount the value of the company. The company should be worth more than $20 a share as the company is spinning off Time Warner Cable. **Availability:** Online.

23770 ■ *"Betting On Volatile Materials"* in *Barron's (Vol. 88, July 14, 2008, No. 28, pp. M11)*
Pub: Dow Jones & Company Inc.
Contact: Almar Latour, Chief Executive Officer
Ed: John Marshall. **Description:** Economic slowdowns in the U.S., Europe and China could cause sharp short-term declines in the materials sector. The S&P Materials sector is vulnerable to shifts in the flow of funds. Statistical data included. **Availability:** Online.

23771 ■ *"Beware of Rotting Money"* in *Barron's (Vol. 89, July 13, 2009, No. 28, pp. 31)*
Pub: Dow Jones & Company Inc.
Contact: Almar Latour, Chief Executive Officer
Ed: Thomas G. Donlan. **Description:** Inflation can take hold of a country and do it great harm; it is caused by people, most particularly central bankers in charge of the world's reserve currency. Arrogant economists pushed the belief that the government can engineer the economy and it is argued that there is trouble ahead when the government tries to control the economy. **Availability:** Online.

23772 ■ *"Beyond Microsoft and Yahoo!: Some M&A Prospects"* in *Barron's (Vol. 88, March 17, 2008, No. 11, pp. 39)*
Pub: Dow Jones & Company Inc.
Contact: Almar Latour, Chief Executive Officer
Ed: Eric J. Savitz. **Description:** Weak quarterly earnings report for Yahoo! could pressure the company's board to cut a deal with Microsoft. Electronic Arts is expected to win its hostile $26-a-share bid for Take-Two Interactive Software. Potential targets and buyers for mergers and acquisitions are mentioned. **Availability:** Online.

23773 ■ *"The Big Idea: The Judgment Deficit"* in *Harvard Business Review (Vol. 88, September 2010, No. 9, pp. 44)*
Pub: Harvard Business Publishing
Contact: Diane Belcher, Managing Director
Ed: Amar Bhide. **Price:** $8.95. **Description:** The importance of individual, decentralized initiative and judgment in the capitalist system is outlined. While financial models have their use, they cannot always account appropriately for the inherent uncertainty in economic decision making. **Availability:** Online; PDF.

23774 ■ *"Big Trouble at Sony Ericsson"* in *Barron's (Vol. 88, March 24, 2008, No. 12, pp. M9)*
Pub: Dow Jones & Company Inc.
Contact: Almar Latour, Chief Executive Officer

Ed: Angelo Franchini. **Description:** Sony Ericsson is facing trouble as it warned that its sales and net income before taxes will fall by nearly half for the first quarter of 2008. The joint venture of Sony and Ericsson has a global mobile phone market share of nine percent as of 2007, fourth largest in the world. **Availability:** Online.

23775 ■ *"Bill to Roll Back Banking Regulations Faces Tough Odds"* in *San Antonio Business Journal (Vol. 28, April 18, 2014, No. 10, pp. 6)*
Pub: American City Business Journals, Inc.
Contact: Mike Olivieri, Executive Vice President
Released: Weekly. **Price:** $4, Introductory 4-week offer(Digital only). **Description:** U.S. Representative Henry Cuellar is co-sponsoring legislation that will ease some of the regulations governing community banks. The Community Lending Enhancement and Regulatory Relief Act has 129 co-sponsors in the House of Representatives. **Availability:** Print; Online.

23776 ■ *"Blackstone's Outlook Still Tough"* in *Barron's (Vol. 88, March 17, 2008, No. 11, pp. 19)*
Pub: Dow Jones & Company Inc.
Contact: Almar Latour, Chief Executive Officer
Ed: Andrew Bary. **Description:** Earnings for the Blackstone Group may not recover soon since the company's specialty in big leveraged buyouts is floundering and may not recover until 2009. The company earns lucrative incentive fees on its funds but those fees went negative in the fourth quarter of 2007 and there could be more fee reversals in the future. **Availability:** Online.

23777 ■ *"Bloody Monday for Bear?"* in *Barron's (Vol. 88, March 17, 2008, No. 11, pp. M14)*
Pub: Dow Jones & Company Inc.
Contact: Almar Latour, Chief Executive Officer
Ed: Steven M. Sears. **Description:** Shares of Bear Stearns could slip further at the start of the trading week unless the company is bought out or bolstered by some other development over the weekend. Prices of the company's shares in the options market suggests about a 30 percent chance that the stock falls below $20 before March expirations expire. **Availability:** Online.

23778 ■ *"BMW Revs Up for a Rebound"* in *Barron's (Vol. 89, July 13, 2009, No. 28, pp. M7)*
Pub: Dow Jones & Company Inc.
Contact: Almar Latour, Chief Executive Officer
Ed: Jonathan Buck. **Description:** Investors may like BMW's stocks because the company has maintained its balance sheet strength and has an impressive production line of new models that should boost sales in the next few years. The company's sales are also gaining traction, although their vehicle delivery was down 1.7 percent year on year on June 2009, this was still the best monthly sales figure for 2009. **Availability:** Online.

23779 ■ *"Boar Market: Penny-Wise Consumers Favoring Pork"* in *Crain's Chicago Business (Vol. 31, April 14, 2008, No. 15, pp. 4)*
Pub: Crain Communications Inc.
Contact: Barry Asin, President
Ed: Bruce Blythe. **Description:** Interview with Alan Cole who is the president of Cedar Hill Associates Inc. and who discusses ways in which his company is taking advantage of the record highs of oil and natural gas as well as his overall outlook on the market. **Availability:** Online.

23780 ■ *"BofA Goes for Small Business"* in *Austin Business Journal (Vol. 31, July 22, 2011, No. 20, pp. A1)*
Pub: Austin Business Journal
Contact: Rachel McGrath, Director
E-mail: rmcgrath@bizjournals.com

Ed: Christopher Calnan. **Description:** Bank of America is planning to target small businesses as new customers. The bank lost its number one market share in Austin, Texas in 2010. **Availability:** Print; Online.

23781 ■ *"BofA May Part With U.S. Trust"* in *Boston Business Journal (Vol. 31, May 20, 2011, No. 17, pp. 1)*
Pub: Boston Business Journal
Contact: Carolyn M. Jones, President
E-mail: cmjones@bizjournals.com
Ed: Tim McLaughlin. **Description:** Bank of America Corporation is willing to sell its U.S. Trust private banking division to improve its capital ratio. The unit remains to be the corporation's core asset and posted $696 million revenue in the first quarter 2010 in contract with Merrill Lynch Global Wealth Management's $3.5 billion. Analysts say that U.S. Trust would fetch more than $3 billion. **Availability:** Print; Online.

23782 ■ *"The Bogleheads' Guide to Investing"*
Pub: John Wiley & Sons, Inc.
Contact: Christina Van Tassell, Executive Vice President Chief Financial Officer
Released: Second edition. **Price:** $26.95, hardcover; $17.99, E-Book. **Description:** Advice that provides the first step to successful financial investments includes new information of backdoor Roth IRAs and ETFs as mainstream buy and hold investments, estate taxes and gifting, along with information on the changes in laws regarding Traditional and Roth IRAs and 401k and 403b retirement plans. The author teaches how to craft proven individual investment strategies. **Availability:** E-book; Print.

23783 ■ *"Bonds v. Stocks: Who's Right About Recession?"* in *Barron's (Vol. 90, August 23, 2010, No. 34, pp. M3)*
Pub: Barron's Editorial & Corporate Headquarters
Ed: Kopin Tan. **Description:** The future of treasury securities and stocks should the U.S. enter or avoid a recession are discussed. The back to school business climate and BHP Billiton's bid for Potash Corporation of Saskatchewan are also discussed. **Availability:** Online.

23784 ■ *"The Book On Indigo"* in *Canadian Business (Vol. 81, July 22, 2008, No. 12-13, pp. 29)*
Description: Indigo Books & Music Inc. reported record sales of $922 million resulting in a record net profit of $52.8 million for the 2008 fiscal year ended March 29, 2008. Earnings per share were $2.13, greater than Standard & Poor's expected $1.70 per share. Additional information concerning Indigo Books is presented.

23785 ■ *"Bookkeeping For Dummies"*
Pub: For Dummies
Released: 2nd edition. **Description:** Because accurate and concise bookkeeping is critical to any small business, information for managing finances to save money while growing your business is offered. The guide covers the basics of bookkeeping, from recording transactions to producing balance sheets and year-end reports. **Availability:** Print; Online.

23786 ■ *"Boomers' Spending Hurts Retirement"* in *Employee Benefit News (Vol. 25, November 1, 2011, No. 14, pp. 18)*
Pub: SourceMedia LLC
Contact: Gemma Postlethwaite, Chief Executive Officer
Ed: Ann Marsh. **Description:** Financial planners and employers need to educate clients and employees about retirement planning. Boomers are spending money that should be saved for their retirement.

23787 ■ *"Bottom-Fishing and Speed-Dating in India-How Investors Feel About the Indian Market"* in *Barron's (Vol. 88, March 24, 2008, No. 12, pp. M12)*
Pub: Dow Jones & Company Inc.
Contact: Almar Latour, Chief Executive Officer

Ed: Elliot Wilson. **Description:** Indian stocks have fallen hard in 2008, with Mumbai's Sensex 30 down 30 percent from its January 2008 peak of 21,000 to 14,995 in March. The India Private Equity Fair 2008 attracted 140 of the world's largest private equity firms and about 24 of India's fastest-growing corporations. Statistical data included. **Availability:** Online.

23788 ■ *"Bountiful Barrels: Where to Find $140 Trillion"* in *Barron's (Vol. 88, July 14, 2008, No. 28, pp. 40)*
Pub: Dow Jones & Company Inc.
Contact: Almar Latour, Chief Executive Officer
Ed: Andrew Bary. **Description:** Surge in oil prices has caused a large transfer of wealth to oil-producing countries thereby reshaping the global economy. Oil reserves of oil exporting countries are now valued at $140 trillion. Economist Stephen Jen believes that this wealth will be transformed into paper assets as these countries invest in global stocks and bonds. **Availability:** Online.

23789 ■ *"Bracing for a Bear of a Week"* in *Barron's (Vol. 88, March 17, 2008, No. 11, pp. 24)*
Pub: Dow Jones & Company Inc.
Contact: Almar Latour, Chief Executive Officer
Ed: Jacqueline Doherty. **Description:** JPMorgan Chase and the Federal Reserve Bank of New York's opening of a line of credit to Bear Stearns cut the stock price of Bear Stearns by 47 percent to 30 followed by speculation of an imminent sale. JP Morgan may be the only potential buyer for the firm and some investors say Bears could be sold at $20 to $30. Bears prime assets include its enormous asset base worth $395 billion. **Availability:** Online.

23790 ■ *"Building Fast-Growing Companies"* in *South Florida Business Journal (Vol. 35, September 19, 2014, No. 8, pp. 16)*
Pub: American City Business Journals, Inc.
Contact: Mike Olivieri, Executive Vice President
Description: Members of Florida's construction industry have registered continuous growth in 2014. Recovery from the economic crisis is driving the construction growth. Economic resilience and proper debt management have also contributed to the sector's growth. **Availability:** Online.

23791 ■ *"Building the Right Culture Can Add Huge Value"* in *South Florida Business Journal (Vol. 34, May 9, 2014, No. 42, pp. 20)*
Pub: American City Business Journals, Inc.
Contact: Mike Olivieri, Executive Vice President
Released: Weekly. **Price:** $8, Introductory 4-week offer(Digital & Print). **Description:** Corporate culture has become an afterthought in many companies and this might be the result of viewing operating results purely from a financial perspective. However, it is the people who work for the companies that create value and they would become more effective by defining the culture. The benefits of creating a positive culture are also discussed. **Availability:** Print; Online.

23792 ■ *"A Bull Market in Finger-Pointing"* in *Barron's (Vol. 88, March 10, 2008, No. 10, pp. 9)*
Pub: Dow Jones & Company Inc.
Contact: Almar Latour, Chief Executive Officer
Ed: Michael Santoli. **Description:** Discusses who is to blame for the financial crisis brought about by the credit crunch in the United States; the country's financial markets will eventually digest this crisis but will bottom out first before the situation improves. **Availability:** Online.

23793 ■ *Business Black Belt: Develop the Strength, Flexibility and Agility to Run Your Company*
Price: $15.99. **Description:** Manual offering insights that will enable anyone to become successful in small business. Seventy short chapters included topics such as attitude, management, marketing, selling, employees, money, MBAs, lawyers, consultants, and investors. **Availability:** Print.

23794 ■ *"Business Execs Await Walker's Tax Cut Plan"* in Business Journal-Milwaukee (Vol. 28, December 17, 2010, No. 11, pp. A1)
Pub: The Business Journal
Contact: Heather Ladage, President
E-mail: hladage@bizjournals.com
Ed: Rich Kirchen. **Description:** Wisconsin governor-elect Scott Walker has to tackle the state's projected $3.3 billion budget deficit, which became the subject of speculation among business groups and state politic watchers. Walker has pledged to reduce the state taxes without driving costs down to the local government and school district level. **Availability:** Print; Online.

23795 ■ *"Business Guide and Employment Role"*
Pub: AuthorHouse Inc.
Contact: William Elliott, President
Released: July 10, 2014. **Price:** $4.99, e-book; $15.18, softcover. **Description:** Financial expert discusses the importance of economic and business and their role in employment. The business and finance manager is crucial to any small business. The guide is an essential tool for any entrepreneur, the investor in business enterprise, the individual businessman, the human resources manager, and the business and finance professional to learn the merits to do business and play a role in employment. **Availability:** E-book; Print.

23796 ■ *Business Management for Tropical Dairy Farmers*
Pub: CSIRO Publishing
Contact: Dr. Stefan Doerr, Editor-in-Chief
E-mail: s.doerr@swansea.ac.uk
Ed: John Moran. **Description:** Business management skills required for dairy farmers are addressed, focusing on financial management and ways to improve cattle housing and feeding systems. **Availability:** Print; PDF; Download.

23797 ■ *"Candidates Won't Bash Fed; Rate Cuts Bash Savers"* in Barron's (Vol. 88, March 24, 2008, No. 12, pp. 31)
Pub: Dow Jones & Company Inc.
Contact: Almar Latour, Chief Executive Officer
Ed: Jim McTague. **Description:** Candidates in the 2008 US presidential election, like the current administration, do not and will not bash the Federal Reserve. The Federal Reserve's aggressive interest rate cuts hurt the incomes of people depending on their savings accounts. **Availability:** Online.

23798 ■ *"Capturing Generation Y: Ready, Set, Transform"* in Credit Union Times (Vol. 21, July 14, 2010, No. 27, pp. 20)
Ed: Senthil Kumar. **Description:** The financial services sector recognizes that Generation Y will have a definite impact on the way business is conducted in the future. The mindset of Generation Y is social and companies need to use networking tools such as Facebook in order to reach this demographic. **Availability:** Online.

23799 ■ *Cash In a Flash*
Released: December 28, 2010. **Price:** $13.68, hardcover; $22.50. **Description:** Proven, practical advice and techniques are given to help entrepreneurs make money quickly using skills and resources known to generate permanent and recurring income. **Availability:** E-book; Print; Audio; Online.

23800 ■ *"Catch Up To Your Dream Retirement"* in Canadian Business (Vol. 85, July 16, 2012, No. 11-12, pp. 46)
Ed: David Aston. **Description:** Tips on how to save for retirement during the early saving years, family years, and pre-retirement years are provided. Priority for those in their early saving years is to pay off debts first then consider employer pension plans and registered retirement savings plans. Those in their family years can save bonuses while those in pre-retirement should start by taking stock.

23801 ■ *"Cautions on Loans with Your Business"* in Business Owner (Vol. 35, July-August 2011, No. 4, pp. 5)
Description: Caution must be used when borrowing from or lending to any small business. Tax guidelines for the borrowing and lending practice are also included. **Availability:** Print; Online.

23802 ■ *"Cemex Paves a Global Road to Solid Growth"* in Barron's (Vol. 88, March 10, 2008, No. 10, pp. 24)
Pub: Dow Jones & Company Inc.
Contact: Almar Latour, Chief Executive Officer
Ed: Sandra Ward. **Description:** Shares of Cemex are expected to perform well with the company's expected strong performance despite fears of a US recession. The company has a diverse geographical reach and benefits from a strong worldwide demand for cement. **Availability:** Online.

23803 ■ *CFR: Title 13. Business Credit and Assistance*
Pub: U.S. Government Publishing Office
Ed: Department of Commerce Staff. **Released:** Annual; volume 14. **Description:** Title 13 covers regulations governing the activities of the Small Business Administration and the Department of Commerce. Book covers information on business credit, finance, and economic development. **Availability:** Print; PDF.

23804 ■ *"Chasing Credit"* in Canadian Business (Vol. 81, November 10, 2008, No. 19, pp. 59)
Pub: Rogers Media Inc.
Contact: Neil Spivak, Chief Executive Officer
Ed: Joe Castaldo. **Description:** Small and medium sized companies are dealing with tightening credit because they appear riskier than usual. Some of these businesses are turning to private investors, but this is not easy since many have invested everything in the stock market. The sector is expected to weaken with the broader Canadian market in the next six months from October 2008. **Availability:** Online.

23805 ■ *"Cheap Deposits Fuel Bank Profits"* in Boston Business Journal (Vol. 31, July 29, 2011, No. 27, pp. 1)
Pub: Boston Business Journal
Contact: Carolyn M. Jones, President
E-mail: cmjones@bizjournals.com
Ed: Tim McLaughlin. **Price:** $4, Introductory 4-Week Offer(Digital Only). **Description:** Massachusetts-are banks increased profits primarily due to inexpensive deposits. The cheaper deposits have provided profit stability and fuel loan growth in an environment of historically low interest rates and uncertain economic recovery. Details of the banks' move to shed the more expensive certificates of deposit in favor of money market accounts are discussed. **Availability:** Print; Online.

23806 ■ *"Chuck's Big Chance"* in Barron's (Vol. 89, July 13, 2009, No. 28, pp. L3)
Pub: Dow Jones & Company Inc.
Contact: Almar Latour, Chief Executive Officer
Ed: Leslie P. Norton. **Description:** Charles Schwab is cutting prices and rolling out new products to lure customers and the company is well positioned to benefit from Wall Street's misery. Their shares are trading at just 17 times earnings, which should be at least at a multiple of 20. **Availability:** Online.

23807 ■ *"Cincinnati Hospitals Feel Pain from Slow Economy"* in Business Courier (Vol. 27, September 3, 2010, No. 18, pp. 1)
Pub: Business Courier
Ed: James Ritchie. **Description:** Hospitals in Cincinnati, Ohio have suffered from decreased revenues owing to the economic crises. Declining patient volumes and bad debt have also adversely impacted hospitals. **Availability:** Print; Online.

23808 ■ *"Citadel Hires Three Lehman Execs"* in Chicago Tribune (October 2, 2008)
Description: Citadel Investment Group LLC, Chicago hedge-fund operator, has hired three former senior executives of bankrupt investment banker Lehman Brothers Holding Inc. Citadel believes that the company's hiring spree will help them to further expand the firm's capabilities in the global fixed income business. **Availability:** Online.

23809 ■ *"Citi Ruling Could Chill SEC, Street Legal Pacts"* in Wall Street Journal Eastern Edition (November 29, 2011, pp. C1)
Pub: Dow Jones & Company Inc.
Contact: Almar Latour, Chief Executive Officer
Ed: Jean Eaglesham, Chad Bray. **Description:** A $285 million settlement was reached between the Securities and Exchange Commission and Citigroup Inc. over allegations the bank misled investors over a mortgage-bond deal. Now, Judge Jed S. Rakoff has ruled against the settlement, a decision that will affect the future of such attempts to prosecute Wall Street fraud. Rakoff said that the settlement was "neither fair, nor reasonable, nor adequate, nor in the public interest." **Availability:** Online.

23810 ■ *"Clearwire Struggling, Banks on Deals with Competitors"* in Puget Sound Business Journal (Vol. 33, August 24, 2012, No. 18, pp. 1)
Pub: Baltimore Business Journal
Contact: Rhonda Pringle, President
E-mail: rpringle@bizjournals.com
Ed: Emily Parkhurst, Alyson Raletz. **Description:** Clearwire Corporation's chief executive, Erik Prusch, is planning to lease the wireless spectrum of the company to major mobile providers that run out of their own supply. At issue is whether the Bellevue, Washington-based telecommunication company can manage its $4 billion debt and maximize the value of its technology while managing its partners all at the same time. **Availability:** Print; Online.

23811 ■ *"Climbing the Wall of Worry, Two Steps at a Time"* in Barron's (Vol. 89, July 13, 2009, No. 28, pp. L16)
Pub: Dow Jones & Company Inc.
Contact: Almar Latour, Chief Executive Officer
Ed: Brian Blackstone. **Description:** Statistical table that shows the performance of different mutual funds for the second quarter of 2009 is presented. The data shows that on average, the 8,272 diversified equity funds gained 17 percent for this quarter. **Availability:** Online.

23812 ■ *"Clock Ticks On Columbia Sussex Debt"* in Business Courier (Vol. 27, July 30, 2010, No. 13, pp. 1)
Pub: Business Courier
Ed: Dan Monk. **Description:** Cincinnati, Ohio-based Columbia Sussex Corporation has made plans to restructure a $1 billion loan bundle that was scheduled to mature in October 2010. The privately held hotel has strived in a weak hotel market to keep pace with its $3 billion debt load. **Availability:** Print; Online.

23813 ■ *"Column: Want People to Save? Force Them"* in Harvard Business Review (Vol. 88, September 2010, No. 9, pp. 36)
Pub: Harvard Business Publishing
Contact: Diane Belcher, Managing Director
Ed: Dan Ariely. **Price:** $6, PDF. **Description:** Contrasts in U.S. attitudes towards savings and government regulation with those of Chile, where all employees are required to save 11 percent of their salary in a retirement account, are highlighted. **Availability:** Online; PDF.

23814 ■ *"Coming: Cheaper Oil and a Stronger Buck"* in Barron's (Vol. 88, March 24, 2008, No. 12, pp. 53)
Pub: Dow Jones & Company Inc.
Contact: Almar Latour, Chief Executive Officer
Ed: Lawrence C. Strauss. **Description:** Carl C. Weinberg, the chief economist of High Frequency Economics, forecasts that Chinese economic growth will slow down and that oil prices will drop to $80 a barrel in 2008. He also believes that the US dollar will start rising the moment the Federal Reserve stops cutting interest rates. **Availability:** Online.

GENERAL SMALL BUSINESS TOPICS

Financial Management ■ 23834

23815 ■ "Coming Soon: Bailouts of Fannie and Freddie" in Barron's (Vol. 88, July 14, 2008, No. 28, pp. 14)
Pub: Dow Jones & Company Inc.
Contact: Almar Latour, Chief Executive Officer
Ed: Jonathan R. Laing. Description: Assurances from the government that Fannie Mae and Freddie Mac are adequately capitalized and able to carry on their duties as guarantors or owners of over $5 trillion of U.S. home mortgages are designed to keep both entities afloat until they attempt to raise $10 billion in new equity. The government would assume any losses in a bailout and owners of the banks' papers would profit as yields drop. Availability: Online.

23816 ■ "Coming: The End of Fiat Money" in Barron's (Vol. 92, July 23, 2012, No. 30, pp. 32)
Pub: Dow Jones & Company Inc.
Contact: Almar Latour, Chief Executive Officer
Ed: Leslie P. Norton. Description: Stephanie Pomboy, founder of MicroMavens, discusses her views on the global financial system. She believes that the global fiat currency system may collapse within five years and be replaced by a gold-backed currency system. Availability: Online.

23817 ■ "A Comment on 'Balancing Risk and Return in a Customer Portfolio'" in Journal of Marketing (Vol. 75, May 2011, No. 3, pp. 18)
Description: Issues regarding the use of approaches to managing customer portfolios are described. These are related to assumptions in modern financial portfolio theory and return and risk. Availability: Online.

23818 ■ "Commodity Speculation: Over the Top?" in Barron's (Vol. 89, July 13, 2009, No. 28, pp. 22)
Pub: Dow Jones & Company Inc.
Contact: Almar Latour, Chief Executive Officer
Ed: Gene Epstein. Description: Commodity Futures Trading Commission is planning to impose position limits on speculators of oil and other commodities as energy costs rebound from their lows. These regulations make much sense and these position limits would greatly diminish the cash commitment of the commodity index traders if these were imposed on speculators and swaps dealers properly. Availability: Online.

23819 ■ "Compelling Opportunities for Investors in Emerging Markets" in Barron's (Vol. 88, March 10, 2008, No. 10, pp. 39)
Pub: Dow Jones & Company Inc.
Contact: Almar Latour, Chief Executive Officer
Ed: Neil A. Martin. Description: Michael L. Reynal, portfolio manager of Principal International Emerging Markets Fund, is bullish on the growth prospects of stocks in emerging markets. He is investing big on energy, steel, and transportation companies. Availability: Online.

23820 ■ "Consumer Contagion? A Bleak Earnings View" in Barron's (Vol. 88, March 10, 2008, No. 10, pp. 15)
Pub: Dow Jones & Company Inc.
Contact: Almar Latour, Chief Executive Officer
Ed: Robin Goldwyn Blumenthal. Description: Analysts expect consumer discretionary profits in the S&P 500 to drop 8.4 percent in the first quarter of 2008. A less confident consumer is expected to pull profits down, putting forecasts of earnings growth in the S&P 500 at risk. Statistical data included. Availability: Online.

23821 ■ "Consumers Are Still Wary; Here's How To Win Them. The Great Recession Has Left Consumers Worried About Their Financial Future. But the Right Strategies Can Engage Leery Spenders" in Gallup Business Journal (June 24, 2014)
Pub: Gallup, Inc.
Contact: Jon Clifton, Chief Executive Officer

Description: Because consumers are concerned about their financial futures, they are less likely to spend money. Strategies to increase sales while increasing consumer confidence are outlined. Availability: Online.

23822 ■ "Consumers Seek to Redo Rate Structure: Smaller Biz Paid Big Rates" in Crain's Detroit Business (Vol. 25, June 22, 2009)
Pub: Crain Communications Inc.
Contact: Barry Asin, President
Ed: Amy Lane. Description: Consumers Energy Company charged small business customers disproportionately higher rates on June 2009 electric bills than other consumers. Availability: Print; Online.

23823 ■ "Consumers Turned Off? Not at Best Buy" in Barron's (Vol. 88, March 24, 2008, No. 12, pp. 29)
Pub: Dow Jones & Company Inc.
Contact: Almar Latour, Chief Executive Officer
Ed: Sandra Ward. Description: Shares of Best Buy, trading at $42.41 each, are expected to rise to an average of $52 a share due to the company's solid fundamentals. The company's shares have fallen 20 percent from their 52-week high and are attractive given the company's bright prospects in the video game sector and high-definition video. Availability: Online.

23824 ■ "Conversation Starters for the Holiday" in Barron's (Vol. 89, July 6, 2009, No. 27, pp. 7)
Pub: Dow Jones & Company Inc.
Contact: Almar Latour, Chief Executive Officer
Ed: Michael Santoli. Description: Investors are concerned that the US will experience high inflation due to low interest rates and improved money supply. US consumer spending has increased to 70 percent of gross domestic product, brought by health-care spending increases, while savings rates have risen to 6.9 percent. Availability: Online.

23825 ■ "A Conversation With: Ron Gantner, Jones Lang LaSalle" in Crain's Detroit Business (Vol. 24, October 6, 2008, No. 40, pp. 9)
Pub: Crain Communications Inc.
Contact: Barry Asin, President
Description: Interview with Ron Gantner who is a corporate real estate adviser with the real estate company Jones Lang LaSalle as well as the company's executive vice president and part of the tenant advisory team; Gantner speaks about the impact that the Wall Street crisis is having on the commercial real estate market in Detroit. Availability: Print; Online.

23826 ■ "Copy Karachi?" in Barron's (Vol. 88, June 30, 2008, No. 26, pp. 5)
Pub: Dow Jones & Company Inc.
Contact: Almar Latour, Chief Executive Officer
Ed: Randall W. Forsyth. Description: Karachi bourse had a historic 8.6 percent one-day gain because the bourse banned short-selling for a month and announced a 30 billion rupee fund to stabilize the market. The shares of General Motors are trading within the same values that it had in 1974. The reasons for this decline are discussed. Availability: Online.

23827 ■ "Cornerstone Seeks Investors for Hedge Fund" in Baltimore Business Journal (Vol. 32, June 20, 2014, No. 7, pp. 10)
Pub: American City Business Journals, Inc.
Contact: Mike Olivieri, Executive Vice President
Description: Cornerstone Advisory LLP is looking for investors to create a hedge fund that ties returns to various indices, real estate or commodity prices. Cornerstone hopes to raise between $30 million to $50 million and are planning a fall launch for the fund. They have hired New York law firm Thompson Hine LLP to draft the subscription agreement and NebraskaEs Gimini Fund Services LLC to run as third party administrator. Availability: Print; Online.

23828 ■ "Corporate Responsibility" in Professional Services Close-Up (July 2, 2010)
Description: List of firms awarded the inaugural Best Corporate Citizens in Government Contracting by the Corporate Responsibility Magazine is presented. The list is based on the methodology of the Magazine's Best Corporate Citizen's List, with 324 data points of publicly-available information in seven categories which include: environment, climate change, human rights, philanthropy, employee relations, financial performance, and governance. Availability: Online.

23829 ■ "Corus Eases Off Ailing Condo Market" in Crain's Chicago Business (April 28, 2008)
Pub: Crain Communications Inc.
Contact: Barry Asin, President
Ed: H. Lee Murphy. Description: Corus Bankshares Inc., a specialist in lending for the condominium high-rise construction market, is diversifying its portfolio by making loans to office developers and expects to be investing in hotels through the rest of the year. Corus' $7.57 billion loan portfolio is also discussed in detail as well as the company's earnings and share price. Statistical data included. Availability: Online.

23830 ■ "Cost of Creating Health Insurance Exchange in Md. 'Largely Unknown'" in Baltimore Business Journal (Vol. 28, September 3, 2010, No. 17, pp. 1)
Pub: Baltimore Business Journal
Contact: Rhonda Pringle, President
E-mail: rpringle@bizjournals.com
Ed: Emily Mullin. Description: United States health reform is seen to result in increased health insurance prices in Maryland. However, health care reform advocates claim a new marketplace and increased competition will help keep costs down. Availability: Print.

23831 ■ "Cost of Md.'s Business Banking May Soon Go Up" in Baltimore Business Journal (Vol. 28, October 29, 2010, No. 25, pp. 1)
Pub: Baltimore Business Journal
Contact: Rhonda Pringle, President
E-mail: rpringle@bizjournals.com
Ed: Gary Haber. Released: Weekly. Description: Experts in the financial industry expect banks to charge credit card transactions, especially to small business owners and consumers to recover about $11 million in lost revenue annually. Banks are expected to charge old fees and new ones, including $5 to $10 a month for a checking account. Availability: Print; Online.

23832 ■ "Couple Hopes to Lead Schlotzsky's Twin Cities Revival" in Business Journal (Vol. 31, January 17, 2014, No. 34, pp. 4)
Pub: American City Business Journals, Inc.
Contact: Mike Olivieri, Executive Vice President
Description: Austin, Texas-based Schlotzky's announced plans to open six Minnesota locations as it tries to regain its national prominence. The bankruptcy in 2004 and the reduction of its restaurant count had wiped out eight Minnesota restaurants and left only the Edina location. Schlotzky's six-restaurant deal with the local franchisees is examined. Availability: Print; Online.

23833 ■ "Crain's Picks Top '08 Stocks" in Crain's New York Business (Vol. 24, January 6, 2008, No. 1, pp. 3)
Pub: Crain Communications, Inc.
Contact: Jessica Botos, Manager, Marketing
E-mail: jessica.botos@crainsnewyork.com
Ed: Aaron Elstein. Description: Listing of five stocks that Crain's believes can deliver solid gains for shareholders. Availability: Online.

23834 ■ "Crash Landing? Serious Signal Flashing" in Barron's (Vol. 88, July 7, 2008, No. 27, pp. 11)
Pub: Dow Jones & Company Inc.
Contact: Almar Latour, Chief Executive Officer

Description: Discusses the Hindenburg Omen, named after the airship disaster of May 1937, which is considered a predictor of market crashes and has appeared twice in June 2008. There is a 25 percent probability that the US stock market will suffer a crash in the July-October 2008 period. **Availability:** Online.

23835 ■ *Crash Proof 2.0: How to Profit From the Economic Collapse*
Pub: John Wiley & Sons, Inc.
Contact: Christina Van Tassell, Executive Vice President Chief Financial Officer
Ed: Peter D. Schiff, John Downes. **Released:** Second edition. **Price:** $16.95, paperback; $27.95, hardcover; $18.99, e-book; $18.99, E-book. **Description:** Factors that will affect financial stability in the coming years are explained. A three step plan to battle the current economic downturn is also included. **Availability:** E-book; Print.

23836 ■ *"Creative In-Sourcing Boosts Franchisee Performance" in Franchising World (Vol. 42, September 2010, No. 9, pp. 16)*
Pub: International Franchise Association
Contact: Matthew Haller, President
E-mail: mhaller@franchise.org
Ed: Daniel M. Murphy. **Released:** 2010. **Description:** Operational training and support is usually provided by franchisors. To be successful in this process it is important to balance the reality of limited financial and human resources. **Availability:** Online.

23837 ■ *"Credit Conditions Improve for Small Businesses" in Small Business Economic Trends (February 2008, pp. 12)*
Pub: National Federation of Independent Business
Contact: Brad Close, President
Ed: William C. Dunkelberg, Holly Wade. **Description:** Graphs and tables that present the credit conditions of small businesses in the U.S. are provided. The tables include figures on availability of loans, interest rates, and expected credit conditions. **Availability:** Print; PDF; Online.

23838 ■ *"The Credit Crisis Continues to Take Victims" in Barron's (Vol. 88, March 10, 2008, No. 10, pp. M12)*
Pub: Dow Jones & Company Inc.
Contact: Almar Latour, Chief Executive Officer
Ed: Randall W. Forsyth. **Description:** Short-term Treasury yields dropped to new cyclical lows in early March 2008, with the yield for the two-year Treasury note falling to 1.532 percent. Spreads of the mortgage-backed securities of Fannie Mae and Freddie Mac rose on suspicion of collapses in financing. **Availability:** Online.

23839 ■ *"Cummins Is a Engine of Growth" in Barron's (Vol. 88, July 14, 2008, No. 28, pp. 43)*
Pub: Dow Jones & Company Inc.
Contact: Almar Latour, Chief Executive Officer
Ed: Shirley A. Lazo. **Description:** Engine maker Cummins increased its quarterly common dividend by 40 percent to 17.5 cents per share from 12.5 cents. CVS Caremark's dividend saw a hike of 18.4 percent from 9.5 cents to 11.25 cents per share while its competitor Walgreen is continuing its 75th straight year of dividend distribution and its 33rd straight year of dividend hikes. **Availability:** Online.

23840 ■ *Currency Internationalization: Global Experiences and Implications for the Renminbi*
Pub: Palgrave Macmillan
Released: First edition. **Description:** A collection of academic studies relating to the potential internationalization of China's remninbi. It also discusses the increasing use of China's remninbi currency in international trade and finance.

23841 ■ *"Deal Braces Cramer for Growth Run" in The Business Journal-Serving Metropolitan Kansas City (Vol. 26, July 4, 2008, No. 43, pp. 1)*
Description: Gardner, Kansas-based Cramer Products Inc. bought 100 percent of the stocks of Louisville, Kentucky-based Active Ankle Inc. from 26 private investors increasing its revenue by 20 percent. The latter is the second largest vendor of Cramer. Other details of the merger are presented. **Availability:** Print; Online.

23842 ■ *"Dealers Leasing Changes Name, Hopes to Stoke National Growth" in Wichita Business Journal (Vol. 27, January 27, 2012, No. 4, pp. 1)*
Pub: Baltimore Business Journal
Contact: Rhonda Pringle, President
E-mail: rpringle@bizjournals.com
Description: Wichita, Kansas-based Dealers Financing has changed its name to Lease Finance Partners as part of its plans to expand the market it serves. The name change was designed to better reflect the kind of business the company does, which is financing the leasing of fleet vehicles and heavy equipment.

23843 ■ *Dictionary of Finance, Investment and Banking*
Pub: Palgrave Macmillan
Ed: Erik Banks. **Released:** First edition. **Description:** Comprehensive dictionary covering terms used in finance, investment and banking sectors.

23844 ■ *"Digging Deep for Gold: David Iben, Manager, Nuveen Tradewinds Value Opportunities Fund" in Barron's (Vol. 88, March 24, 2008, No. 12, pp. 49)*
Pub: Dow Jones & Company Inc.
Contact: Almar Latour, Chief Executive Officer
Ed: Suzanne McGee. **Description:** David Iben, manager of the Nuveen Tradewinds Value Opportunities Fund, looks for value in companies and industries where the consensus of analysts is negative. He started investing in gold stocks well before gold prices started to rise. **Availability:** Online.

23845 ■ *"Do-It-Yourself Portfolio Management" in Barron's (Vol. 89, July 13, 2009, No. 28, pp. 25)*
Pub: Dow Jones & Company Inc.
Contact: Almar Latour, Chief Executive Officer
Ed: Mike Hogan. **Description:** Services of several portfolio management web sites are presented. These web sites include MarketRiders E.Adviser, TD Ameritrade and E. **Availability:** Online.

23846 ■ *"The Dogs of TSX" in Canadian Business (Vol. 81, Summer 2008, No. 9, pp. 77)*
Description: Table showing the one-year stock performance of the ten highest dividend-yielding stocks on the S&P/TSX 60 Composite Index is presented. This technique is similar to the 'Dogs of the Dow' approach. The idea in this investment strategy is to buy equal amounts of stocks from these companies and selling them a year later, and then repeat the process. **Availability:** Online.

23847 ■ *"Don't Bet Against The House" in Barron's (Vol. 88, July 14, 2008, No. 28, pp. 20)*
Pub: Dow Jones & Company Inc.
Contact: Almar Latour, Chief Executive Officer
Ed: Sandra Ward. **Description:** Shares of Nasdaq OMX have lost more than 50 percent of their value from November 2007 to July 2008 but the value of these shares could climb 50 percent on the strength of world security exchanges. Only 15 percent of the company's revenues come from the U.S. and the shares are trading at 12.5 times the amount expected for 2008. **Availability:** Online.

23848 ■ *"Don't Hang Up On FairPoint" in Barron's (Vol. 88, July 7, 2008, No. 27, pp. M5)*
Description: Shares of FairPoint Communications, priced at $6.63 each, are undervalued and should be worth over $12 each. The company increased its size by more than five times by acquiring Verizon's local telephone operations in Vermont, New Hampshire, and Maine, but must switch customers in those areas into their system by the end of September 2007. **Availability:** Online.

23849 ■ *"Downtown Bank Got High Marks for Irwin Purchase, Is Looking For More" in Business Courier (Vol. 27, September 3, 2010, No. 18, pp. 1)*
Pub: Business Courier
Ed: Steve Watkins. **Price:** $4, Introductory 4-Week Offer(Digital & Print). **Description:** First Financial Bancorp is looking to acquire more troubled banks following its purchase of Irwin Union Bank. The bank has reported a $383 million bargain purchase gain during the third quarter of 2009. **Availability:** Print; Online.

23850 ■ *"Drilling Deep and Flying High" in Barron's (Vol. 88, June 30, 2008, No. 26, pp. 34)*
Pub: Dow Jones & Company Inc.
Contact: Almar Latour, Chief Executive Officer
Ed: Kenneth Rapoza. **Description:** Shares of Petrobras could rise another 25 percent if the three deepwater wells that the company has found proves as lucrative as some expect. Petrobras will become an oil giant if the reserves are proven. **Availability:** Online.

23851 ■ *"Drug, Seed Firms Offer Antidote For Inflation" in Crain's Chicago Business (Vol. 31, April 21, 2008, No. 16, pp. 4)*
Pub: Crain Communications Inc.
Contact: Barry Asin, President
Ed: Daniel Rome Levine. **Description:** Interview with Jerrold Senser, the CEO of Institutional Capital LLC in Chicago, in which he discusses the ways that the company is adjusting to the economic slowdown and rising inflation, his favorite firms for investment and his prediction of an economic turnaround; he also recommends five companies he feels are worth investing in. **Availability:** Online.

23852 ■ *"Ducking the New Health-Care Taxes" in Barron's (Vol. 92, September 15, 2012, No. 38, pp. 34)*
Pub: Dow Jones & Company Inc.
Contact: Almar Latour, Chief Executive Officer
Ed: Elizabeth Ody. **Description:** Strategies that investors can use to avoid paying higher taxes starting January 2013 are discussed. These include selling assets by December 2012, distributing dividends, purchasing private-placement life insurance and converting individual retirement accounts. **Availability:** Online.

23853 ■ *"Dumb Financial Mistakes Business Owners Make and How to Avoid Them" in Small Business Trends(February 20, 2023)*
URL(s): smallbiztrends.com/2023/02/financial-mis takes-business-owners-make.html
Released: February 20, 2023. **Description:** President of Business Ventures Corporation, Ruth King, discusses mistakes small business owners typically make and how to avoid them. **Availability:** Online.

23854 ■ *"Dynamic Duo: Payouts Rise at General Dynamics, Steel Dynamics" in Barron's (Vol. 88, March 10, 2008, No. 10, pp. 45)*
Pub: Dow Jones & Company Inc.
Contact: Almar Latour, Chief Executive Officer
Ed: Shirley A. Lazo. **Description:** General Dynamics, the world's sixth-largest military contractor, raised its dividend payout by 20.7 percent from 29 cents to 35 cents a share. Steel Dynamics, producer of structural steel and steel bar products, declared a 2-for-1 stock split and raised its quarterly dividend by 33 percent to a split-adjusted 10 cents a share. **Availability:** Online.

23855 ■ *"Easier Options Orders" in Barron's (Vol. 92, August 25, 2012, No. 35, pp. 28)*
Pub: Dow Jones & Company Inc.
Contact: Almar Latour, Chief Executive Officer
Ed: Theresa W. Carey. **Description:** Online brokerage optionsXpress introduced the Walk Limit, a service that allows traders to improve pricing for op-

tions and save money. Online brokerage TradeMonster introduced portfolio margining to qualified customers. **Availability:** Online.

23856 ■ *"Eastern Market's New Bite?" in Washington Business Journal (Vol. 33, August 8, 2014, No. 16, pp. 6)*
Pub: American City Business Journals, Inc.
Contact: Mike Olivieri, Executive Vice President
Price: $4, Introductory 4-Week Offer(Digital & Print).
Description: Eastern Market continues to operate despite allegations of financial mismanagement on the part of Washington DC auditors. Many of the market's vendors have been operating their stands with expired leases for more than five years. However, the Department of General Services has vowed to draw a new standard contract for renting and renegotiate new leases. **Availability:** Print; Online.

23857 ■ *"Economic Recovery Prognosis: Four More Years" in Barron's (Vol. 89, July 13, 2009, No. 28, pp. 11)*
Pub: Dow Jones & Company Inc.
Contact: Almar Latour, Chief Executive Officer
Ed: Karen Hube. **Description:** Loomis Sayles Bond Fund manager Dan Fuss believes that the economy is bottoming and that recovery will be long and drawn out. Fuss guesses that the next peak in 10-year Treasury yields will be about 6.25% in around 4 and a half or five years ahead of 2009. **Availability:** Online.

23858 ■ *"An Educated Play on China" in Barron's (Vol. 88, June 30, 2008, No. 26, pp. M6)*
Pub: Dow Jones & Company Inc.
Contact: Almar Latour, Chief Executive Officer
Ed: Mohammed Hadi. **Description:** New Oriental Education & Technology Group sells English-language courses to an increasingly competitive Chinese workforce that values education. The shares in this company have been weighed down by worries on the impact of the Beijing Olympics on enrollment and the Sichuan earthquake. These shares could be a great way to get exposure to the long-term growth in China. **Availability:** Online.

23859 ■ *"Egg Fight: The Yolk's on the Shorts" in Barron's (Vol. 88, July 7, 2008, No. 27, pp. 20)*
Pub: Dow Jones & Company Inc.
Contact: Almar Latour, Chief Executive Officer
Ed: Christopher C. Williams. **Description:** Shares of Cal-Maine Foods, the largest egg producer and distributor in the US, are due for a huge rise because of the increase in egg prices. Short sellers, however, continue betting that the stock, priced at $31.84 each, will eventually go down. **Availability:** Online.

23860 ■ *"Elder Care Costs Surge" in National Underwriter Life & Health (Vol. 114, November 8, 2020, No. 21, pp. 25)*
Ed: Trevor Thomas. **Description:** Nursing home and assisted living rates rose from 2009 to 2010, according to MetLife Mature Market Institute. Statistical data included. **Availability:** Online.

23861 ■ *"End of an Era" in Barron's (Vol. 88, July 7, 2008, No. 27, pp. 3)*
Ed: Alan Abelson. **Released:** January 01, 2016. **Description:** June 2008 was a very bad month for US stocks, with investors losing as much as 41.9 percent in the first half of 2008 signaling an end to the financial environment that prevailed around the world since the 1980's. The US job market lost 62,000 jobs in June 2008. **Availability:** Print; Online.

23862 ■ *"Energy MPLs: Pipeline to Profits" in Barron's (Vol. 89, July 27, 2009, No. 30, pp. 9)*
Pub: Dow Jones & Company Inc.
Contact: Almar Latour, Chief Executive Officer
Ed: Dimitra DeFotis. **Description:** Energy master limited partnership stocks are range-bound in the next few months from July 2009 but there are there are some opportunities that remain. These include Energy Transfer Equity, Enterprise GP holdings, NuStar GP Holdings, and Plains All American Pipeline. **Availability:** Online.

23863 ■ *Entrepreneurial Finance*
Pub: Pearson Education Inc.
Contact: Andy Bird, Chief Executive Officer
Ed: Philip J. Adelman, Alan M. Marks. **Released:** Sixth edition. **Description:** Financial aspects of running a small business are covered; topics include sole proprietorships, partnerships, limited liability companies, and private corporations. **Availability:** Print; Download; Online.

23864 ■ *Entrepreneurial Small Business*
Pub: McGraw-Hill Higher Education
Contact: Michael Ryan, President
Ed: Jerome A. Katz, Richard P. Green. **Released:** Seventh edition. **Price:** $57, e-book; $70, print. **Description:** Students are able to get a clear vision of small enterprise in today's business climate. The textbook helps focus on the goal of having personal independence with financial security as an entrepreneur. **Availability:** Print.

23865 ■ *The Entrepreneur's Edge: Finding Money, Making Money, Keeping Money*
Released: August 01, 2016. **Price:** $20.99, bound softcover; $3.99, e-book. **Description:** Advice for starting, running and growing a new business is given. **Availability:** E-book; Print.

23866 ■ *"Equal Weighting's Heavy Allure" in Barron's (Vol. 92, July 23, 2012, No. 30, pp. 27)*
Pub: Dow Jones & Company Inc.
Contact: Almar Latour, Chief Executive Officer
Ed: Brendan Conway. **Description:** Equal weight index exchange-traded funds are attracting investors due to their strong returns. This strategy gives investors a greater exposure to mid-capitalization companies and could provide strong returns over longer stretches. **Availability:** Online.

23867 ■ *"Essential Releases Record First Quarter Results" in Marketwired (May 14, 2007)*
Pub: Comtex News Network Inc.
Contact: Kan Devnani, President
Description: The first quarter of 2007 saw record financial performance despite numerous challenges for Essential Energy Services Trust. Statistical data included. **Availability:** Print; Online.

23868 ■ *"ETF Score Card" in Barron's (Vol. 89, July 13, 2009, No. 28, pp. 51)*
Pub: Dow Jones & Company Inc.
Contact: Almar Latour, Chief Executive Officer
Description: Statistical table is presented which shows the net assets of various exchange-traded funds are presented. The table also shows the total return of these funds up to a three-year time period. **Availability:** Online.

23869 ■ *"Everyone Out of the Pool" in Barron's (Vol. 89, July 20, 2009, No. 29, pp. 18)*
Pub: Dow Jones & Company Inc.
Contact: Almar Latour, Chief Executive Officer
Ed: Sandra Ward. **Description:** Shares of Pool Corp. could drop as continued weakness in the housing market weakens the market for swimming pool equipment. The company's shares are trading at $18.29, about 20 times projected 2009 earnings of $0.91 a share. **Availability:** Online.

23870 ■ *"Evolving from Practice to Enterprise" in Financial Advisor (November 1, 2019)*
URL(s): www.fa-mag.com/news/evolving-from-practice-to-enterprise-52345.html
Ed: Dawn Doebler, Michael Nathanson. **Released:** November 01, 2019. **Description:** A look at the financial advisory industry as smaller firms grow from a practice to a larger business and even to an enterprise. Gives definitions of each term and the qualifications each entity must possess. **Availability:** Online.

23871 ■ *"Extra Rehab Time Boosts M-B's Off-Lease Profits" in Automotive News (Vol. 86, October 31, 2011, No. 6488, pp. 22)*
Pub: Crain Communications Inc.
Contact: Barry Asin, President
Ed: Arlena Sawyers. **Description:** Mercedes-Benz Financial Services USA is holding on to off-lease vehicles in order to recondition them and the move is boosting profits for the company. **Availability:** Print; Online.

23872 ■ *"Falling Local Executive Pay Could Suggest a Trend" in Tampa Bay Business Journal (Vol. 30, January 15, 2010, No. 4, pp. 1)*
Pub: Tampa Bay Business Journal
Contact: Ian Anderson, President
E-mail: ianderson@bizjournals.com
Ed: Margie Manning. **Description:** Tampa Bay, Florida-based Raymond James Financial Inc. and MarineMax Inc.'s proxy statements have shown the decreasing compensation of the companies' highest paid executives. The falling trend in executive compensation was a result of intensified shareholder scrutiny and the economy. **Availability:** Print; Online.

23873 ■ *"Falling Markets' Nastiest Habit" in Barron's (Vol. 88, July 7, 2008, No. 27, pp. 7)*
Pub: Dow Jones & Company Inc.
Contact: Almar Latour, Chief Executive Officer
Ed: Michael Santoli. **Description:** US market conditions reflect a bear market, with the S&P 500 index falling 20 percent below its recent high as of June 2008. The bear market is expected to persist in the immediate future, although bear market rallies are likely to occur. **Availability:** Online.

23874 ■ *"The Fatal Bias" in Business Strategy Review (Vol. 25, Summer 2014, No. 2, pp. 34)*
Description: The prevailing managerial bias towards cost efficiency is harmful to corporate performance. Management's fatal bias is discussed. **Availability:** Online; PDF.

23875 ■ *"February Hot for Mutual Fund Sales" in Globe & Mail (March 3, 2006, pp. B10)*
Ed: Keith Damsell. **Description:** The details on Canadian mutual fund sector, which posted $4.7 billion for February 2005, are presented. **Availability:** Print; Online.

23876 ■ *"Fed Tackles Bear of a Crisis" in Barron's (Vol. 88, March 17, 2008, No. 11, pp. M10)*
Pub: Dow Jones & Company Inc.
Contact: Almar Latour, Chief Executive Officer
Ed: Randall W. Forsyth. **Description:** Emergency funding package for Bear Stearns from the Federal Reserve Bank of New York through JPMorgan Chase is one of the steps taken by the central bank shore up bank liquidity. Prior to the emergency funding, the central bank announced the Term Securities Lending Facility to allow dealers to borrow easily saleable Treasuries in exchange for less-liquid issues. **Availability:** Online.

23877 ■ *"Fees Come Down; Markets Come Down More" in Barron's (Vol. 89, July 13, 2009, No. 28, pp. L8)*
Pub: Dow Jones & Company Inc.
Contact: Almar Latour, Chief Executive Officer
Ed: J.R. Brandstrader. **Description:** Investors spent less on mutual fund fees in 2009 than they did in the last 25 years. These fees include administration, accounting, and legal expense. Despite the popularity of money market funds which has contributed to this decline, the short-term yields of these funds fell in the last year. **Availability:** Online.

23878 ■ "A Few Points of Contention" in Barron's (Vol. 88, July 14, 2008, No. 28, pp. 3)
Pub: Dow Jones & Company Inc.
Contact: Almar Latour, Chief Executive Officer
Ed: Michael Santoli. **Description:** Headline inflation tends to revert to the lower core inflation, which excludes food and energy in its calculation over long periods. Prominent private equity figures believe that regulators should allow more than the de facto 10 percent to 25 percent limit of commercial banks to hasten the refunding of the financial sector. **Availability:** Online.

23879 ■ "Fifth Third Spinoff Eyes More Space" in Business Courier (Vol. 27, July 16, 2010, No. 11, pp. 1)
Pub: Business Courier
Ed: Dan Monk, Steve Watkins. **Description:** Electronic-funds transfer company Fifth Third Solutions (FTPS), a spinoff of Fifth Third Bancorp, is seeking as much as 200,000 square feet of new office space in Ohio. The bank's sale of 51 percent ownership stake to Boston-based Advent International Corporation has paved the way for the growth of FTPS. How real estate brokers' plans have responded to FTPS' growth mode is discussed. **Availability:** Print; Online.

23880 ■ Finance & Accounting: How to Keep Your Books and Manage Your Finances with an MBA, a CPA, or a Ph.D

23881 ■ Financial Planning & Analysis and Performance Management
Ed: Jack Alexander. **Released:** June 13, 2018. **Price:** $46.24, Hardcover; $36.79, E-book. **Description:** Comprehensive reference guide about financial planning for financial analysts working for organizations. Discussion topics include budget and forecasting, analysis, performance management, financial communication, metrics, benchmarking, and many others. **Availability:** E-book; Print.

23882 ■ "Financial Stability: Fraud, Confidence, and the Wealth of Nations"
Pub: John Wiley & Sons, Inc.
Contact: Christina Van Tassell, Executive Vice President Chief Financial Officer
Released: September 2014. **Price:** $48.99, e-book; $75, hardcover. **Description:** Instruction is provided to help modern investors and finance professionals to learn from past successes and failures and to gauge future market threats. Insight into today's financial markets and the political economy will help craft a strategy that leads to financial stability. Topics covered include: capital; forecasting; political reaction; and past, present, and future applications within all areas of business. A companion Website offers additional data and research, providing a comprehensive resource for those wishing a better understanding of risk factors in investing. **Availability:** E-book; Print; Online; PDF.

23883 ■ "Fine Wine, Poor Returns" in Barron's (Vol. 92, September 17, 2012, No. 38, pp. 11)
Description: Investing in wines in not considered a good idea due to irrationally high wine prices. Wine collectors buying wines at very high prices are not expected to make money and are charged with a 28 percent 'collectibles' tax. **Availability:** Online.

23884 ■ "First Mariner Bank's New Ads No Passing Fancy" in Baltimore Business Journal (Vol. 29, September 16, 2011, No. 19, pp. 1)
Pub: Boston Business Journal
Contact: Carolyn M. Jones, President
E-mail: cmjones@bizjournals.com
Ed: Gary Haber. **Description:** Baltimore, Maryland-based First Mariner Bank replaced Ed Hale, the bank's CEO and founder, as the pitchman for its television ads with Ravens quarterback Joe Flacco. Hales' exit from the advertisements is the result of First Mariner's struggle to raise money for re-capitalization. **Availability:** Online.

23885 ■ "FirstMerit's Top Executive Turns Around Credit Quality" in Crain's Cleveland Business (Vol. 28, October 15, 2007, No. 41, pp. 3)
Pub: Crain Communications Inc.
Contact: K. C. Crain, President
Ed: Shawn A. Turner. **Description:** Discusses the ways in which chairman and CEO Paul Greig has been able to improve FirstMerit Corp.'s credit quality and profit margin. Strategies included selling more than $70 million in bad loans, hiring a new chief credit officer and redirecting its focus on cross-selling its wealth and investment services to its commercial customers. Statistical data included. **Availability:** Online.

23886 ■ "Fiscal Cliff Notes" in Barron's (Vol. 92, September 15, 2012, No. 38, pp. 27)
Pub: Dow Jones & Company Inc.
Contact: Almar Latour, Chief Executive Officer
Ed: Mike Hogan. **Description:** Websites and blogs dedicated to providing information on the economic effects of the 'fiscal cliff' are described. These sites discuss possible effects on the US economy, budget, and personal finances. **Availability:** Online.

23887 ■ The Flaw of Averages: Why We Underestimate Risk in the Face of Uncertainty
Pub: John Wiley & Sons, Inc.
Contact: Christina Van Tassell, Executive Vice President Chief Financial Officer
Ed: Sam L. Savage. **Released:** March 26, 2012. **Price:** $19.95, paperback; $27.95, hardcover; $12.99, E-Book. **Description:** Personal and business plans are based on uncertainties on a daily basis. The common avoidable mistake individuals make in assessing risk in the face of uncertainty is defined. The explains why plans based on average assumptions are wrong, on average, in areas as diverse as finance, healthcare, accounting, the war on terror, and climate change. **Availability:** E-book; Print.

23888 ■ "A Flawed Yardstick for Banks" in Barron's (Vol. 88, July 14, 2008, No. 28, pp. M6)
Pub: Dow Jones & Company Inc.
Contact: Almar Latour, Chief Executive Officer
Ed: Arindam Nag. **Description:** Return on equity is no longer the best measure for investors to judge banks by in a post-subprime-crises world. Investors should consider the proportion of a bank's total assets that are considered risky and look out for any write-downs of goodwill when judging a bank's financial health. **Availability:** Online.

23889 ■ "Florida's Housing Gloom May Add To Woes of National City" in Crain's Cleveland Business (Vol. 28, October 29, 2007, No. 43, pp. 1)
Pub: Crain Communications Inc.
Contact: K. C. Crain, President
Ed: Shawn A. Turner. **Description:** Already suffering by bad loans in the troubled mortgage market, National City Corp. is attempting to diversify its geographic presence beyond the slow-growth industrial Midwest by acquiring two Florida firms. Analysts worry that the acquisitions may end up making National City vulnerable to a takeover if the housing slump continues and credit quality becomes more of an issue for the bank. **Availability:** Online.

23890 ■ Fooling Some of the People All of the Time
Pub: John Wiley & Sons, Inc.
Contact: Christina Van Tassell, Executive Vice President Chief Financial Officer
Ed: David Einhorn. **Released:** January 2011. **Price:** $14.50, Paperback; $10.99, e-book. **Description:** A chronicle of the ongoing saga between author, David Einhorn's hedge fund, Greenlight Capital, and Allied Capital, a leader in the private finance industry. **Availability:** E-book; Print.

23891 ■ "For Buffett Fans, the Price Is Right" in Barron's (Vol. 89, July 13, 2009, No. 28, pp. 17)
Pub: Dow Jones & Company Inc.
Contact: Almar Latour, Chief Executive Officer
Ed: Andrew Bary. **Description:** Shares of Warren Buffett's Berkshire Hathaway have fallen to $85,000 and these are cheap since they are trading at just 1.2 times estimated book value and are well below its peak of $149,000. One fan of the stock expects it to top $110,000 in the next year from June 2009. **Availability:** Online.

23892 ■ "For Gilead, Growth Beyond AIDS" in Barron's (Vol. 88, June 30, 2008, No. 26, pp. 18)
Pub: Dow Jones & Company Inc.
Contact: Almar Latour, Chief Executive Officer
Ed: Jay Palmer. **Description:** First-quarter 2008 revenue for Gilead Sciences grew by 22 percent and an earnings gain of 19 percent thanks to their HIV-treatment drugs that comprised over two-thirds of the company's sales in 2007. An analyst has a 12-month target from June, 2008 of 65 per share. The factors behind the company's prospects are also discussed. **Availability:** Online.

23893 ■ "Ford: Down, Not Out, and Still a Buy" in Barron's (Vol. 92, July 23, 2012, No. 30, pp. 14)
Pub: Dow Jones & Company Inc.
Contact: Almar Latour, Chief Executive Officer
Ed: Vito J. Racanelli. **Description:** Stocks of Ford Motor Company could gain value as the company continues to improve its finances despite fears of slower global economic growth. The company's stock prices could double from $9.35 per share within three years. **Availability:** Online.

23894 ■ "Forward Motion" in Green Industry Pro (July 2011)
Ed: Gregg Wartgow. **Description:** Several landscape contractors have joined this publication's Working Smarter Training Challenge over the last year. This process is helping them develop ways to improve work processes, boost morale, drive out waste, reduce costs, improve customer service, and be more competitive. **Availability:** Print; Online.

23895 ■ "The Four Cheapest Plays in Emerging Markets" in Barron's (Vol. 89, July 27, 2009, No. 30, pp. 34)
Pub: Dow Jones & Company Inc.
Contact: Almar Latour, Chief Executive Officer
Ed: Lawrence C. Strauss. **Description:** Portfolio manager Arjun Divecha of the GMO Emerging Markets III Fund says that the main thing in investing in emerging markets is getting the country right since getting it wrong makes it harder to add value. Divecha says that the four countries that they are positive on are Turkey, Russia, South Korea, and Thailand. **Availability:** Online.

23896 ■ "Four Ways to Fix Banks: A Wall Street Veteran Suggests How To Cut Through the Industry's Complexity" in (Vol. 90, June 2012, No. 6, pp. 106)
Pub: Harvard Business Review Press
Contact: Moderna V. Pfizer, Contact
Ed: Sallie Krawcheck. **Description:** Despite new regulations in the post-global economic crisis of 2008, banks are sill too complex for effective management of their boards. Recommendations for improving governance include incorporating bank debt in executive compensation to increase their sensitivity to risk, and paying dividends as a percentage of company earnings to maintain capital.

23897 ■ "Four Ways Hospitals Can Reduce Patient Readmissions; Hospitals Have a Powerful Financial Incentive to Reduce Readmissions. Here Are the Most Effective Strategies" in Gallup Business Journal (July 2, 2014)
Pub: Gallup, Inc.
Contact: Jon Clifton, Chief Executive Officer

GENERAL SMALL BUSINESS TOPICS   Financial Management ■ 23918

Description: The Centers for Medicare and Medicaid Services (CMS) report readmissions as hospitalizations that occur within 30 days of discharge. Hospitals need to identify and implement the right strategies to reduce readmissions. **Availability:** Print.

23898 ■ *"Fuel Costs Curb Food Truck Trend" in Tampa Tribune (March 26, 2012)*
Ed: Jeff Houck. **Description:** Owner of Maggie on the Move food truck, Margaret Loflin, has had to raise the cost of drinks served in order to cover the increased cost of gasoline to run her business. She also added smaller, less costly items to her menu. Her husband has gone back to a part-time job in he hopes of keeping their food truck running. **Availability:** Print; Online.

23899 ■ *"Full-Court Press for Apple" in Barron's (Vol. 88, March 24, 2008, No. 12, pp. 47)*
Pub: Dow Jones & Company Inc.
Contact: Almar Latour, Chief Executive Officer
Ed: Mark Veverka. **Description:** Apple Inc. is facing more intellectual property lawsuits in 2008, with 30 patent lawsuits filed compared to 15 in 2007 and nine in 2006. The lawsuits, which involve products such as the iPod and the iPhone, present some concern for Apple's shareholders. **Availability:** Online.

23900 ■ *"Funds 'Friend' Facebook" in Barron's (Vol. 89, July 27, 2009, No. 30, pp. 30)*
Pub: Dow Jones & Company Inc.
Contact: Almar Latour, Chief Executive Officer
Ed: Leslie P. Norton. **Description:** Mutual-fund companies are the latest entrants to the "social media" space and several companies have already set up Facebook and Twitter pages. The use of this technology pose special challenges for compliance and regulators especially since the Financial Industry Regulatory Authority reminds companies that advertising, sales and literature are governed by regulations. **Availability:** Online.

23901 ■ *"Future of the Street" in Barron's (Vol. 88, June 30, 2008, No. 26, pp. 27)*
Pub: Dow Jones & Company Inc.
Contact: Almar Latour, Chief Executive Officer
Ed: Michael Santoli. **Description:** Prospects of the securities industry in terms of jobs and profit sources are discussed. Suggestions on what the industry needs with regards to its use of capital are also discussed. **Availability:** Online.

23902 ■ *"Futures Shock for the CME" in Crain's Chicago Business (Vol. 31, November 10, 2008, No. 45, pp. 8)*
Pub: Crain Communications Inc.
Contact: Barry Asin, President
Ed: Ann Saphir. **Description:** Chicago-based CME Group Inc., the largest futures exchange operator in the U.S., is facing a potentially radically altered regulatory landscape as Congress weighs sweeping reform of financial oversight. The possible merger of the CFTC and the Securities and Exchange Commission are among CME's concerns. Other details of possible regulatory measures are provided. **Availability:** Online.

23903 ■ *"Garden Bargains: Restaurant Cut Costs With Homegrown Foods" in Washington Business Journal (Vol. 33, August 22, 2014, No. 18, pp. 6)*
Pub: American City Business Journals, Inc.
Contact: Mike Olivieri, Executive Vice President
Released: Weekly. **Price:** $4, introductory 4-week offer(Digital & Print). **Description:** A number of chefs and restaurants in Washington DC are seeing the benefits of growing their own healthy kitchen gardens. The Urbana restaurant is saving $250 monthly in herbs since it started planting them in 2014 and chef, Ethan McKee expects to increase that savings to $75 monthly in 2015. **Availability:** Print; Online.

23904 ■ *"Generation Y - An Opportunity for a Fresh Financial Start" in (September 11, 2010, pp. 241)*
Pub: VerticalNews
Description: Eleanor Blayney, the consumer advocate for the Certified Financial Planner Board of Standards, offers a financial strategy for Generation Y individuals starting their financial planning. The first segment of the non-profit's Lifelong Financial Strategies initiative is called 'Starting Out', and focuses on ways Generation Y people can avoid pitfalls of earlier generations by making smart financial decisions. **Availability:** Print; Online.

23905 ■ *Get a Financial Life: Personal Finance in Your Twenties and Thirties*
Ed: Beth Kobliner. **Released:** March 21, 2017. **Price:** $10.27, Paperback; $12.99, E-book. **Description:** A guide for younger adults as they navigate the financial world and financial planning. **Availability:** E-book; Print.

23906 ■ *"Get Off The Rollercoaster" in Michigan Vue (Vol. 13, July-August 2008, No. 4, pp. 19)*
Description: Benefits of creating and implementing a solid financial plan during these rocky economic times are examined. Things to keep in mind before meeting with a financial planner include risk assessment, investment goals, the length of time required to meet those goals and the amount of money one has available to invest. **Availability:** Print; Online.

23907 ■ *"Getting In on the Ground Floor With World-Class Companies" in Barron's (Vol. 89, July 27, 2009, No. 30, pp. 32)*
Ed: Jacqueline Doherty. **Description:** Shares of AvalonBay Communities have fallen 61 percent in the past two and a half years to July 2009 but at $56, the stock is trading near the asset value. The shares could rise as the economy improves and if the recovery takes longer, investors will be rewarded with a yield of 3.5 percent. **Availability:** Online.

23908 ■ *"Getting More Out of Retirement" in Agency Sales Magazine (Vol. 39, November 2009, No. 10, pp. 48)*
Description: Overview of the Tax Increase Prevention and Reconciliation Act, which lets employees convert to a Roth IRA in 2010. The benefits of conversion depend on age and wealth and it is best to consult a tax advisor to determine the best strategy for retirement planners. **Availability:** Print; Online.

23909 ■ *"A Gift From Interactive Brokers" in Barron's (Vol. 92, July 23, 2012, No. 30, pp. M11)*
Pub: Dow Jones & Company Inc.
Contact: Almar Latour, Chief Executive Officer
Ed: Steven M. Sears. **Description:** Investors are advised to sell put options of Interactive Brokers stock in anticipation of lower share prices. This trade is also a hedge against a possible takeover but allows investors to buy into a company that pays regular dividends and is managed well. **Availability:** Online.

23910 ■ *"The Globe: Singapore Airlines' Balancing Act" in Harvard Business Review (Vol. 88, July-August 2010, No. 7-8, pp. 145)*
Pub: Harvard Business Publishing
Contact: Diane Belcher, Managing Director
Ed: Loizos Heracleous, Jochen Wirtz. **Price:** $8.95. **Description:** Singapore Airlines is used as an illustration of organizational effectiveness. The article includes the firm's 4-3-3 rule of spending, its promotion of centralized as well as decentralized innovation, use of technology, and strategic planning. **Availability:** Online; PDF.

23911 ■ *"A Good Book Is Worth a Thousand Blogs" in Barron's (Vol. 88, July 14, 2008, No. 28, pp. 42)*
Pub: Dow Jones & Company Inc.
Contact: Almar Latour, Chief Executive Officer
Ed: Gene Epstein. **Description:** Nine summer book suggestions on economics are presented. The list includes 'The Revolution' by Ron Paul, 'The Forgotten Man' by Amity Shales, 'The Commitments of Traders Bible' by Stephen Briese, and 'Economic Facts and Fallacies' by Thomas Sowell. **Availability:** Online.

23912 ■ *"Good Going, Partners" in Barron's (Vol. 89, July 27, 2009, No. 30, pp. M8)*
Pub: Dow Jones & Company Inc.
Contact: Almar Latour, Chief Executive Officer
Ed: Shirley A. Lazo. **Description:** Four master limited partnerships boosted their dividends. Sunoco Logistics raised theirs by 11.2 percent, El Paso Pipeline by 12 percent, Holly Energy upped their dividends by a penny, and Western Gas hiked their dividend to 31 cents per unit. **Availability:** Online.

23913 ■ *"A Good Step, But There's a Long Way to Go" in Business Week (September 22, 2008, No. 4100, pp. 10)*
Ed: James C. Cooper. **Description:** Despite the historic action by the U.S. government to nationalize the mortgage giants Freddie Mac and Fannie Mae, rising unemployment rates may prove to be an even bigger roadblock to bringing back the economy from its downward spiral. The takeover is meant to restore confidence in the credit markets and help with the mortgage crisis but the rising rate in unemployment may make many households unable to take advantage of any benefits which arise from the bailout. Statistical data included. **Availability:** Online.

23914 ■ *"Google's Next Stop: Below 350?" in Barron's (Vol. 88, March 10, 2008, No. 10, pp. 17)*
Pub: Dow Jones & Company Inc.
Contact: Almar Latour, Chief Executive Officer
Ed: Jacqueline Doherty. **Description:** Share prices of Google Inc. are expected to drop from their level of $433 each to below $350 per share. The company is expected to miss its earnings forecast for the first quarter of 2008, and its continued aggressive spending on non-core areas will eventually bring down earnings. **Availability:** Online.

23915 ■ *"Graduates to the TSX in 2008" in Canadian Business (Vol. 81, Summer 2008, No. 9, pp. 79)*
Description: Table showing the market capitalization and stock performance of the companies that jumped to the TSX Venture Exchange is presented. The 17 companies that made the leap to the list will have an easier time raising capital, although leeway must be made in investing since they are still new businesses.

23916 ■ *"The Great Fall: Here Comes The Humpty Dumpty Economy" in Barron's (Vol. 88, March 10, 2008, No. 10, pp. 5)*
Pub: Dow Jones & Company Inc.
Contact: Almar Latour, Chief Executive Officer
Ed: Alan Abelson. **Description:** Discusses the US economy is considered to be in a recession, with the effects of the credit crisis expected to intensify as a result. Inflation is estimated at 4.3 percent in January 2008, while 63,000 jobs were lost in February 2008. **Availability:** Online.

23917 ■ *"A Greenish Light for Financial-Sector Funds" in Barron's (Vol. 88, March 24, 2008, No. 12, pp. 52)*
Pub: Dow Jones & Company Inc.
Contact: Almar Latour, Chief Executive Officer
Ed: Tom Sullivan. **Description:** Financial sector funds have lost value in 2008 through 17 March, and investors are advised to reduce investments in the financial sector. Exchange-traded funds present a good way to own financial stocks. **Availability:** Online.

23918 ■ *"A Gripping Read: Bargains & Noble" in Barron's (Vol. 88, March 17, 2008, No. 11, pp. 20)*
Pub: Dow Jones & Company Inc.
Contact: Almar Latour, Chief Executive Officer
Ed: Jonathan R. Laing. **Description:** Barnes & Noble's earnings forecast for the fiscal year ending in January, 2008 to be $1.70 to $1.90 per share which is way lower than the $2.12 analyst consensus. The

company also said that sales at stores one-year old or older dropped 0.5 percent in the fourth quarter. However, the shares are now cheap at 4.9 times enterprise value with some analysts putting a price target of 41 per share. **Availability:** Online.

23919 ■ *"Growing Expectations"* **in Financial Advisor (November 1, 2019)**
URL(s): www.fa-mag.com/news/growing--expectations-52348.html
Ed: Christopher Robbins. **Released:** November 01, 2019. **Description:** During the National Association of Personal Financial Advisors' 2019 Fall Conference, the need to keep upgrading the clients' experiences with technology was one of the key takeaways of the event. With the majority of the current workforce part of the generations that grew up on modern tech, it is easy to see why they would want to have options beyond just phone calls and face-to-face meetings. **Availability:** Online.

23920 ■ *"Growth Back on CIBC's Agenda"* **in Globe & Mail (March 3, 2006, pp. B1)**
Ed: Sinclair Stewart. **Description:** The details on business growth of Canadian Imperial Bank of Commerce, which posted $547 million profit for first quarter 2006, are presented. **Availability:** Online.

23921 ■ *"Handleman Liquidation Leaves Questions For Shareholders"* **in Crain's Detroit Business (Vol. 24, October 6, 2008, No. 40, pp. 4)**
Pub: Crain Communications Inc.
Contact: Barry Asin, President
Ed: Nancy Kaffer. **Description:** Discusses Handleman Co., a Troy-based music distribution company, and their plan of liquidation and dissolution as well as how shareholders will be affected by the company's plan. Handleman filed its plan to liquidate and dissolve assets with the Securities and Exchange Commission in mid-August, following several quarters of dismal earnings. **Availability:** Online.

23922 ■ *"The Hard Thing About Hard Things: Building a Business When There Are No Easy Answers"*
Pub: HarperCollins Publishers L.L.C.
Contact: Brian Murray, President
Released: 2014. **Price:** $29.99, Hardcover; $14.99, E-book; $23.99, Digital Audiobook Unabridged. **Description:** Cofounder of Andreessen Horowitz and well-respected Silicon Valley entrepreneur, offers advice for building and running a startup small business. Horowitz analyzes issues confronting leaders daily and shares insights he gained from managing, selling, buying investing in, and supervising technology firms. **Availability:** E-book; Print; Download.

23923 ■ *"Has Microsoft Found a Way to Get at Yahoo?"* **in Advertising Age (Vol. 79, July 7, 2008, No. 26, pp. 4)**
Pub: Crain Communications, Inc.
Contact: Jessica Botos, Manager, Marketing
E-mail: jessica.botos@crainsnewyork.com
Ed: Abbey Klaassen. **Description:** Microsoft's attempt to acquire Yahoo's search business is discussed as is Yahoo's plans for the future at a time when the company's shares have fallen dangerously low. **Availability:** Print; Online.

23924 ■ *"Headwinds From the New Sod Slow Aer Lingus"* **in Barron's (Vol. 88, March 10, 2008, No. 10, pp. M6)**
Pub: Dow Jones & Company Inc.
Contact: Almar Latour, Chief Executive Officer
Ed: Sean Walters, Arindam Nag. **Description:** Aer Lingus faces a drop in its share prices with a falling US market, higher jet fuel prices, and lower long-haul passenger load factors. British media companies Johnston Press and Yell Group are suffering from weaker ad revenue and heavier debt payments due to the credit crunch. **Availability:** Online.

23925 ■ *"The Heat Is On"* **in Crain's Chicago Business (Vol. 31, April 28, 2008, No. 17, pp. 4)**
Pub: Crain Communications Inc.
Contact: Barry Asin, President

Ed: Steve Daniels. **Description:** Discusses Nicor Inc., a natural-gas utility serving 2 million customers in Chicago's suburbs, and its potential acquirers; shares of the company have dropped 17 percent this year making Nicor the second-worst among 31 utilities in an index tracked by Standrd & Poor's. Statistical data included.

23926 ■ *"Hedge Funds for the Average Joe"* **in Canadian Business (Vol. 85, August 13, 2012, No. 13, pp. 51)**
Ed: Bryan Borzykowski. **Description:** The benefits of the Horizons Morningstar Hedge Fund Index ETF over traditional hedge funds are examined. Retail investors should avoid buying hedge fund exchange-traded funds (ETFs) because they are not actually buying into a hedge fund, the fund is just trying to emulate strategies that popular hedge funds use with derivatives. **Availability:** Print; Online.

23927 ■ *"High-Yield Turns Into Road Kill"* **in Barron's (Vol. 88, July 7, 2008, No. 27, pp. M7)**
Pub: Dow Jones & Company Inc.
Contact: Almar Latour, Chief Executive Officer
Ed: Emily Barrett. **Description:** High-yield bonds have returned to the brink of collapse after profits have recovered from the shock brought about by the collapse of Bear Stearns. The high-yield bond market could decline again due to weakness in the automotive sector, particularly in Ford and General Motors. **Availability:** Online.

23928 ■ *"Higher Payouts Should Be In the Cards"* **in Barron's (Vol. 92, July 23, 2012, No. 30, pp. 14)**
Pub: Dow Jones & Company Inc.
Contact: Almar Latour, Chief Executive Officer
Ed: Michael Santoli. **Description:** Credit card companies Visa and MasterCard should be more generous to shareholders and pay higher dividends. Both have low dividend yields, with Visa paying $0.88/share a year and MasterCard paying $1.20/share annually. **Availability:** Online.

23929 ■ *"Hitting Bottom? Several Banks and Brokerages Are Ready to Pop Up for Air"* **in Barron's (Vol. 88, March 24, 2008, No. 12, pp. 21)**
Pub: Dow Jones & Company Inc.
Contact: Almar Latour, Chief Executive Officer
Ed: Jacqueline Doherty. **Description:** Brokerage houses and banks may stabilize in 2008 as a result of regulatory responses brought about by the near-collapse of Bear Stearns. Some of their shares may rise by as much as 20 percent from 2008 to 2009. **Availability:** Online.

23930 ■ *"Homebuilders Continue to be Our Nemesis"* **in Contractor (Vol. 56, July 2009, No. 7, pp. 50)**
Ed: Robert P. Mader. **Description:** Homebuilders rank high on the greed scale along with Wall Street brokers. There is this one instance when a builder gave copies of another contractor's quotes that have just been blackened out and another instance when one builder let other bidders visit a site while the current mechanical contractor is working. **Availability:** Print; Online.

23931 ■ *"Hong Kong's Boom in IPOs"* **in Barron's (Vol. 89, July 13, 2009, No. 28, pp. M7)**
Pub: Dow Jones & Company Inc.
Contact: Almar Latour, Chief Executive Officer
Ed: Nick Lord. **Description:** Hong Kong's IPO (initial public offering) market is booming with 13 Chinese IPOs already on the market for the year as July 2009. One of them is Bawang International which raised $214 million after generating $9 billion in order which makes it 42 times oversubscribed. **Availability:** Online.

23932 ■ *"Hospital Revenue Healthier in 2009"* **in Orlando Business Journal (Vol. 26, February 5, 2010, No. 36, pp. 1)**
Pub: Orlando Business Journal
Contact: Julie Swyers, Director

E-mail: jswyers@bizjournals.com
Ed: Melanie Stawicki Azam. **Description:** Orlando Health, Health Central and Adventist Health System are Florida-based hospital systems that generated the most profits in 2009. Orlando Health had the highest profit in 2009 at $73.3 million, contrary to about $31 million in losses in 2008. The increased profits are attributed to stock market recovery, cost-cutting initiatives, and rising patient volumes. **Availability:** Print; Online.

23933 ■ *"Hospitals Try to Buy Smarter"* **in Crain's Detroit Business (Vol. 25, June 1, 2009, No. 22, pp. M025)**
Pub: Crain Communications Inc.
Contact: Barry Asin, President
Ed: Jay Greene. **Description:** Hospitals in southeast Michigan are using bulk discount purchasing of medical and non-medical supplies through group purchasing organizations in order to cut costs. **Availability:** Online.

23934 ■ *"How to Avoid the Most Common and Costliest Mistakes in Retirement Portfolio Investing"* **in Barron's (Vol. 88, March 10, 2008, No. 10, pp. 30)**
Pub: Dow Jones & Company Inc.
Contact: Almar Latour, Chief Executive Officer
Ed: Karen Hube. **Description:** Investors, particularly those having retirement investments, are advised to diversify their investments, refrain from market timing, and minimize payments to maximize investment gains. An investor committing these mistakes could lose as much as $375,000 dollars over ten years. **Availability:** Online.

23935 ■ *"How to Beat the Pros"* **in Canadian Business (Vol. 81, Summer 2008, No. 9, pp. 59)**
Description: Table showing the results of the Investor 500 beat the S&P/TSX composite index is presented. The average total return, best performing stocks and total return of the 2007 stock screen are provided. **Availability:** Online.

23936 ■ *"How to Conduct a Financial Stress Test for Small Business Owners"* **in Legal Zoom (November 10, 2022)**
URL(s): www.legalzoom.com/articles/how-to-conduct-a-financial-stress-test-for-small-business-owners
Ed: Marcia Layton Turner. **Released:** November 10, 2022. **Description:** Provides details on how to perform a small business stress test to make sure your company will be able to survive tough financial situations. **Availability:** Online.

23937 ■ *"How High Can Soybeans Fly?"* **in Barron's (Vol. 88, March 10, 2008, No. 10, pp. M14)**
Pub: Dow Jones & Company Inc.
Contact: Almar Latour, Chief Executive Officer
Ed: Kenneth Rapoza. **Description:** Prices of soybeans have risen to $14.0875 a bushel, up 8.3 percent for the week. Increased demand, such as in China and in other developing economies, and the investment-driven commodities boom are boosting prices. **Availability:** Online.

23938 ■ *How to Make Big Money in Your Own Small Business: Unexpected Rules Every Small Business Owner Needs to Know*
Ed: Jeffrey J. Fox, Jeffrey J. Fox. **Released:** May 12, 2004. **Price:** $16.95; C$24.95; $16.95; C$24.95; $16.95; C$24.95. **Description:** Former sales and marketing pro offers advice on growing a small business. **Availability:** Print.

23939 ■ *"How Millionaire Mentor Cedric Nash Went from a $36,000 Salary to $90M in Annual Business Revenue"* **in Black Enterprise(February 7, 2023)**
URL(s): www.blackenterprise.com/how-millionaire-mentor-cedric-nash-man-went-from-a-36000-salary-to-90-million-in-annual-business-revenue/

GENERAL SMALL BUSINESS TOPICS

Financial Management ■ 23960

Ed: Anne-Lyse Wealth. **Released:** February 07, 2023. **Description:** Founder of The Black Wealth Summit, Cedric Nash, discusses his rise in the financial advice world. **Availability:** Online.

23940 ■ *"How Not to Raise Bank Capital"* in *Barron's (Vol. 88, June 30, 2008, No. 26, pp. M6)*
Pub: Dow Jones & Company Inc.
Contact: Almar Latour, Chief Executive Officer
Ed: Sean Walters. **Description:** French bank Natixis wants to raise 1 billion euros from cash provided by their two major owners. Natixis will reimburse Banque Populaire and Caisses d'Epargne with hybrid securities so this move will not benefit Natixis' core Tier 1 ratio. This has also given the impression that the company is afraid of a full rights issue which could shake investors' faith in the bank. **Availability:** Online.

23941 ■ *"How Our Picks Beat The Bear"* in *Barron's (Vol. 88, July 14, 2008, No. 28, pp. 18)*
Pub: Dow Jones & Company Inc.
Contact: Almar Latour, Chief Executive Officer
Ed: Andrew Bary. **Description:** Performance of the stocks that Barron's covered in the first half of 2008 is discussed; some of the worst picks and most rewarding pans have been in the financial sector while the best plays were in the energy, materials, and the transportation sectors. **Availability:** Online.

23942 ■ *"How to Retire: Do's and Don'ts"* in *Canadian Business (Vol. 79, July 17, 2006, No. 14-15, pp. 29)*
Pub: Rogers Media Inc.
Contact: Neil Spivak, Chief Executive Officer
Ed: Andy Holloway, Erin Pooley, Thomas Watson. **Description:** Strategic tips for planning systematic investments, in order to make life more enjoyable after retirement, are elucidated. **Availability:** Print; Online.

23943 ■ *"How to Save More and Worry Less at Tax Time"* in *Canadian Business (Vol. 85, August 13, 2012, No. 13, pp. 33)*
Description: The top-down approach and the bottom-up approach are two cash-management strategies that are proven to make a person richer. The top-down approach to saving is best suitable to an analytical, detail-oriented person while the bottom-up approach can be effective to people who are having difficulties in keeping track of their spending. **Availability:** Online.

23944 ■ *How to Start a Small Business in Canada: Your Road Map to Financial Freedom*
Pub: Self-Help Publishers
Ed: Tariq Nadeem. **Released:** 2nd edition. **Description:** Provides information for starting and managing a small business in Canada.

23945 ■ *"How Sweet It Will Be"* in *Barron's (Vol. 89, July 13, 2009, No. 28, pp. M13)*
Pub: Dow Jones & Company Inc.
Contact: Almar Latour, Chief Executive Officer
Ed: Debbie Carlson. **Description:** Raw sugar experienced a rally in the first half of 2009 and the long term outlook for sugar prices is still good. However, there is a likely near-term correction due to the onset of Brazilian harvest that could be 20.7 percent higher for 2009 as compared to the previous year and October contracts could fall to 15.61 cents per pound. **Availability:** Online.

23946 ■ *"How To: Manage Your Cash Better"* in *Inc. (Volume 32, December 2010, No. 10, pp. 69)*
Pub: Mansueto Ventures L.L.C.
Contact: Stephanie Mehta, Chief Executive Officer
Released: December 01, 2010. **Description:** A monthly guide to policies, procedures and practices for managing cash for a small business. **Availability:** Online.

23947 ■ *"How to Use the Internet to Advertise, Promote, and Market Your Business or Web Site: With Little or No Money*
Pub: Atlantic Publishing Co.
Contact: Dr. Heather L. Johnson, Contact
Ed: Bruce C. Brown. **Released:** Revised third edition. **Description:** Information is given to help build, promote, and make money from your Website or brick and mortar store using the Internet, with minimal costs.

23948 ■ *How to Write a Great Business Plan for Your Small Business in 60 Minutes or Less*
Pub: Atlantic Publishing Co.
Contact: Dr. Heather L. Johnson, Contact
Ed: Sharon L. Fullen. **Released:** 2013. **Description:** A good business plan outlines goals and works as a company's resume to obtain funding, credit from suppliers, management of the operations and finances, promotion and marketing, and more. **Availability:** CD-ROM; E-book; Print; Online.

23949 ■ *"Iconic Boise Skateboard Shop to Close"* in *Idaho Business Review (August 19, 2014)*
Pub: BridgeTower Media
Contact: Adam Reinebach, President
Description: Lori Wright and Lori Ambur have owned Newt & Harold's for over 30 years. The partners are closing the firm that sold skateboards and snowboards. Wright focused on the marketing and inventory aspects of the retail shop, while Ambur ran the organizational and financial end. Wright and Ambur say they are leaving retail because the industry has faced so many changes since they first opened, particularly competing with online stores.

23950 ■ *"Ideas at Work: The Reality of Costs"* in *Business Strategy Review (Vol. 21, Summer 2010, No. 2, pp. 40)*
Ed: Jules Goddard. **Released:** June 24, 2010. **Description:** If you think that cost cutting is the surest way to business success, the author wants to challenge every assumption you hold. Costs are an outcome of sound strategy, never the goal of strategy. He offers a new perspective on what counts when it comes to costs. **Availability:** Print; PDF; Online.

23951 ■ *"I'll Have What She's Having"* in *Canadian Business (Vol. 85, September 17, 2012, No. 14, pp. 17)*
Ed: Andrew Hallam. **Description:** Studies show that women have the higher tendency to follow responsible investing rules than men, earning more money in the process. Women were also found to perform better in bull markets as well as in the male-dominated hedge fund sector. **Availability:** Online.

23952 ■ *"In 2011, Wichita-Area Banks Cleaned Up Books, Grew Earnings"* in *Wichita Business Journal (Vol. 27, February 17, 2012, No. 7, pp. 1)*
Pub: Baltimore Business Journal
Contact: Rhonda Pringle, President
E-mail: rpringle@bizjournals.com
Description: Wichita, Kansas-based banks have reported smaller loan portfolios and higher loan-loss allowances at the end of 2011 compared to the previous year. The earnings of the 35 banks in the metro area also grew strongly both for the quarter and for the year, while their assets increased. How the banks managed to generate positive earnings results is also discussed. **Availability:** Print; Online.

23953 ■ *"In China, Railways to Riches"* in *Barron's (Vol. 88, July 7, 2008, No. 27, pp. M9)*
Pub: Dow Jones & Company Inc.
Contact: Almar Latour, Chief Executive Officer
Ed: Assif Shameen. **Description:** Shares of Chinese railway companies look to benefit from multimillion-dollar investments aimed at upgrading the Chinese railway network. Investment in the sector is expected to reach $210 billion for the 2006-2010 period. **Availability:** Online.

23954 ■ *"In the Hot Finance Jobs, Women Are Still Shut Out"* in *Harvard Business Review (Vol. 90, July-August 2012, No. 7-8, pp. 30)*
Pub: Harvard Business Review Press
Contact: Moderna V. Pfizer, Contact
Ed: Nori Gerardo Lietz. **Price:** $6, PDF and hardcover black and white. **Description:** Although women constitute a significant proportion of business school graduates, the percentage of senior investment professionals who are female remain in a single-digit figure. Active effort will be needed to change corporate culture and industry awareness to raise this figure. **Availability:** Print; PDF; Online.

23955 ■ *"In India, A Gold-Price Threat?"* in *Barron's (Vol. 88, June 30, 2008, No. 26, pp. M12)*
Pub: Dow Jones & Company Inc.
Contact: Almar Latour, Chief Executive Officer
Ed: Melanie Burton. **Description:** Gold purchases in India are falling as record prices take its toll on demand. Gold imports to India fell by 52 percent in May 2008 from the previous year and local prices are higher by one-third from the previous year to 12,540 rupees for 10 grams. **Availability:** Online.

23956 ■ *"In the Options Market, Financial-Sector Trading Is Moody and Paranoid"* in *Barron's (Vol. 88, March 10, 2008, No. 10, pp. M14)*
Pub: Dow Jones & Company Inc.
Contact: Almar Latour, Chief Executive Officer
Ed: Steven M. Sears. **Description:** Discusses the options market which remains liquid but is cautious of possible failures, especially for financial companies. Investors are in absolute fear when trading with options involving the financial sector. **Availability:** Online.

23957 ■ *"In Praise of How Not to Invest"* in *Barron's (Vol. 89, July 13, 2009, No. 28, pp. 11)*
Pub: Dow Jones & Company Inc.
Contact: Almar Latour, Chief Executive Officer
Ed: Vito J. Racanelli. **Description:** One research study found that the shares of companies that have growing market shares and expanding asset bases underperform. This is contrary to the widely held premise that stock prices for these companies rise. It is argued that this result is caused by these companies' tendency to sacrifice profitability to grab market share and this is reflected in their stock prices. **Availability:** Online.

23958 ■ *"In Surging Oil Industry, Good Fortune Comes In Stages"* in *Barron's (Vol. 88, July 7, 2008, No. 27, pp. 12)*
Pub: Dow Jones & Company Inc.
Contact: Almar Latour, Chief Executive Officer
Ed: Sandra Ward. **Description:** Shares of US land oil and gas driller Helmerich and Payne, priced at $69 each, are estimated to be at peak levels. The shares are trading at 17 times 2008 earnings and could be in for some profit taking. **Availability:** Online.

23959 ■ *"Inesoft Cash Organizer Desktop: A New Approach to Personal Accounts Bookkeeping"* in *America's Intelligence Wire (August 7, 2012)*
Description: Inesoft Cash Organizer Desktop application is offering a new product for financial management on a home PC and mobile devices. The program supports the classification of money transactions by category, sub-category, project, sub-project, budget planning, and world currencies (including current exchange rates), credit calculators, special reports, and more. Multiple users in the family can use the appllication. Details of the program are outlined. **Availability:** Online.

23960 ■ *"Infomercial King on TeleBrands, Going Broke, Making Millions"* in *Philadelphia Business Journal (Vol. 33, July 11, 2014, No. 22, pp. 3)*
Pub: American City Business Journals, Inc.
Contact: Mike Olivieri, Executive Vice President

Small Business Sourcebook • 42nd Edition

Released: Weekly. Price: $4, Introductory 4-week offer(Digital only). Description: Ajit "A.J." Khubani is CEO of TeleBrands, the Fairfield, New Jersey company that brings to the American mainstream market novelty products by using infomercials, including AmberVision sunglasses and PedEgg. Though the marketing/advertising firm is worth $1 billion, Khubani's entrepreneurship career has gone through ups and downs and he has been close to bankruptcy three times. Availability: Print; Online.

23961 ■ *"Inland Snaps Up Rival REITs" in Crain's Chicago Business (Vol. 31, November 17, 2008, No. 46, pp. 3)*
Pub: Crain Communications Inc.
Contact: Barry Asin, President
Ed: Alby Gallun. Description: Discusses Inland American Real Estate Trust Inc., a real estate investment trust that is napping up depressed shares of publicly traded competitors, a possible first step toward taking over these companies; however, with hotel and retail properties accounting for approximately 70 percent of its portfolio, the company could soon face its own difficulties. Availability: Online.

23962 ■ *"International ETFs: Your Passport to the World" in Barron's (Vol. 89, July 13, 2009, No. 28, pp. L10)*
Pub: Dow Jones & Company Inc.
Contact: Almar Latour, Chief Executive Officer
Ed: John Hintze. Description: International exchange traded funds give investors more choices in terms of investment plays and there are 174 U.S. ETF listings worth $141 billion as of July 2009. Suggestions on how to invest in these funds based on one's conviction on how the global economy will unfold are presented. Availability: Online.

23963 ■ *"Invest Like Harvard" in Barron's (Vol. 92, September 15, 2012, No. 38, pp. 32)*
Pub: Dow Jones & Company Inc.
Contact: Almar Latour, Chief Executive Officer
Ed: Andrew Bary. Description: Asset management firms are offering endowment-style investment services that allow investors to invest in funds in the same way as foundations and endowments. HighVista Strategies with $3.6 billion in assets under management, has produced a total return of 43.5 percent after fees from October 2005 to June 2012 using this strategy. Availability: Online.

23964 ■ *"Investment Funds: Friends with Money" in Canadian Business (Vol. 81, May 22, 2008, No. 9, pp. 22)*
Pub: Rogers Media Inc.
Contact: Neil Spivak, Chief Executive Officer
Ed: Jeff Stanford. Description: Two of the most well connected managers in Canadian capital markets Rob Farquharson and Brian Gibson will launch Panoply Capital Asset Management in June. The investment management company aims to raise a billion dollars from institutions and high-net worth individuals. Availability: Print; Online.

23965 ■ *"Is Fannie Mae the Next Government Bailout?" in Barron's (Vol. 88, March 10, 2008, No. 10, pp. 21)*
Pub: Dow Jones & Company Inc.
Contact: Almar Latour, Chief Executive Officer
Ed: Jonathan R. Laing. Description: Fannie Mae may need a government bailout as it faces huge hits brought about by the effects of the housing crisis. The shares of the government-sponsored enterprise have dropped 65 percent since the housing crisis began. Availability: Online.

23966 ■ *"Is It OK To Expense a Parking Ticket? Straight Answers To Some Common Expense Report Conundrums" in Canadian Business (Vol. 85, June 11, 2012, No. 10, pp. 70)*
Ed: Sarah Barmak. Description: Human resource experts Andrea Fraser of DAC Group and Fiorella Callocchia of Deloitte offer advice to employees on personal costs and when to charge the company for travel expenses. The experts say expense claims should be reasonable and should depend on the firm's culture. Availability: Online.

23967 ■ *"Is Raising CPP Premiums a Good Idea?" in Canadian Business (Vol. 83, July 20, 2010, No. 11-12, pp. 37)*
Description: Big labor is pushing for an increase in Canada Pension Plan premiums but pension consultants believe this system is not broken and that the government needs to focus on addressing the low rate of personal retirement savings. If the premiums go up, even those with high savings will be forced to pay more and it could block other plans that really address the real issue. Availability: Print; Online.

23968 ■ *"Is Fierce Competition Loosening Standards?" in Birmingham Business Journal (Vol. 31, February 14, 2014, No. 7, pp. 6)*
Pub: American City Business Journals, Inc.
Contact: Mike Olivieri, Executive Vice President
Released: Weekly. Price: $4, introductory 4-week offer(Digital only). Description: Bankers have been seeing an intense competition for business loans in the Birmingham, Alabama market because of the limited number of qualified borrowers. However, some bankers expressed concerns that the trend signals a return to pre-recession habits for lenders. Availability: Print; Online.

23969 ■ *"Is There a Doctor In the House?" in Black Enterprise (Vol. 41, December 2010, No. 5, pp. 42)*
Pub: Earl G. Graves Ltd.
Contact: Earl Graves, Jr., President
Ed: Renita Burns. Description: Health insurance premiums have increased between 15 percent and 20 percent for small business owners, making it one of the most expensive costs. Ways to evaluate a health plan's costs and effectiveness are examined. Availability: Online.

23970 ■ *"Is the VIX in Denial?" in Barron's (Vol. 88, July 7, 2008, No. 27, pp. M12)*
Pub: Dow Jones & Company Inc.
Contact: Almar Latour, Chief Executive Officer
Ed: Lawrence McMillan. Description: Volatility Index (VIX) of the Chicago Board Options Exchange did not rise significantly despite the drop in the US stock markets, rising to near 25. This market decline, however, will eventually result in investor panic and the rise of the VIX. Availability: Online.

23971 ■ *"It Could Be Worse" in Barron's (Vol. 89, July 27, 2009, No. 30, pp. 5)*
Pub: Dow Jones & Company Inc.
Contact: Almar Latour, Chief Executive Officer
Ed: Alan Abelson. Description: Media sources are being fooled by corporate America who is peddling an economic recovery rather than reality as shown by the report of a rise in existing home sales which boosted the stock market even if it was a seasonal phenomenon. The phrase "things could be worse" sums up the reigning investment philosophy in the U.S. and this has been stirring up the market. Availability: Online.

23972 ■ *"It May Be Cheaper to Manufacture At Home" in Harvard Business Review (Vol. 88, October 2010, No. 10, pp. 84)*
Pub: Harvard Business Publishing
Contact: Diane Belcher, Managing Director
Ed: Suzanne de Treville, Lenos Trigeorgis. Price: $8.95, PDF. Description: Using a real options framework rather than a discounted cash flow model to assess and value supply chain processes is examined. This enables companies to assess costs for a variety of situations, not just ideal or normal circumstances, which can make the difference between domestic and foreign manufacturing decisions. Availability: Online; PDF.

23973 ■ *"It's Good To Be a CEO: Top Execs Pull Millions In Raises for 2013" in Atlanta Business Chronicle (June 20, 2014, pp. 22A)*
Pub: American City Business Journals, Inc.
Contact: Mike Olivieri, Executive Vice President
Description: Discussion regarding the highest paid CEOs in Georgia in 2013, with an average of 8.8 percent increase from 2012. The largest increase went to Jeffrey C. Sprecher, chairman and CEO of Intercontinental Exchange Inc., followed by John F. Brock, chairman and CEO of Coca-Cola Enterprises Inc. Availability: Print; Online.

23974 ■ *"J.C. Evans Files for Ch. 11 Protection" in Austin Business Journal (Vol. 31, August 12, 2011, No. 23, pp. A1)*
Pub: Austin Business Journal
Contact: Rachel McGrath, Director
E-mail: rmcgrath@bizjournals.com
Ed: Vicky Garza. Description: J.C. Evans Construction Holdings Inc., as well as its affiliated companies, has filed for Chapter 11 bankruptcy following its continued financial breakdown which it blames on the tough economy. Details are included. Availability: Print; Online.

23975 ■ *"J.C. Penney Head Shops for Shares" in Barron's (Vol. 88, July 7, 2008, No. 27, pp. 29)*
Pub: Dow Jones & Company Inc.
Contact: Almar Latour, Chief Executive Officer
Ed: Teresa Rivas. Description: Myron Ullman III, chairman and chief executive officer of J.C. Penney, purchased $1 million worth of shares of the company. He now owns 393,140 shares of the company and an additional 1,282 on his 401(k) plan. Availability: Online.

23976 ■ *"JK Lasser's New Rules for Estate, Retirement, and Tax Planning"*
Pub: John Wiley & Sons, Inc.
Contact: Christina Van Tassell, Executive Vice President Chief Financial Officer
Released: 6th Edition. Price: $24.95, paperback; $16.99, E-book. Description: The authoritative guide to estate, retirement and tax planning is fully updated and reflects the new changes and legal updates. Estate planning section covers: planning, taxation, investing, wills, executors, trusts, life insurance, retirement planning, Social Security, business planning, succession, asset protection and family limited partnerships. Availability: E-book; Print.

23977 ■ *"Juiced on Energy" in Barron's (Vol. 88, July 14, 2008, No. 28, pp. 33)*
Pub: Dow Jones & Company Inc.
Contact: Almar Latour, Chief Executive Officer
Ed: Leslie P. Norton. Description: Brad Evans and his team at Heartland Value Plus were able to outperform their peers by significantly undercommitting to financials and overexposing themselves with energy stocks. Brad Evans believes that there is a lot of value left in energy stocks such as natural gas. Availability: Online.

23978 ■ *"Just Hang Up" in Barron's (Vol. 88, March 10, 2008, No. 10, pp. 45)*
Description: Sprint's shares are expected to continue falling while the company attempts to attract subscribers by cutting prices, cutting earnings in the process. The company faces tougher competition from better-financed AT&T and Verizon Communications.

23979 ■ *"Keeping the Faith in Fuel-Tech" in Barron's (Vol. 88, March 24, 2008, No. 12, pp. 20)*
Pub: Dow Jones & Company Inc.
Contact: Almar Latour, Chief Executive Officer
Ed: Christopher C. Williams. Description: Shares of air pollution control company Fuel-Tech remain on track to reach $40 each from their $19 level due to a continued influx of contracts. The stock has suffered from lower-than-expected quarterly earnings and tougher competition but stand to benefit from increased orders. Availability: Online.

23980 ■ *"The Latin Beat Goes On" in Barron's (Vol. 88, July 7, 2008, No. 27, pp. L5)*
Pub: Dow Jones & Company Inc.
Contact: Almar Latour, Chief Executive Officer

Ed: Tom Sullivan. **Description:** Latin American stocks have outperformed other regional markets due to rising commodities prices and favorable economic climate. Countries such as Brazil, Mexico, Chile, and Peru provide investment opportunities, while Argentina and Venezuela are tougher places to invest. **Availability:** Online.

23981 ■ *"Leaders and Lagards"* in *Barron's* (Vol. 89, July 13, 2009, No. 28, pp. 14)
Description: Statistical table that shows the returns of different mutual funds in different categories that include U.S. stock funds, sector funds, world equity funds, and mixed equity funds is presented. The data presented is for the second quarter of 2009. **Availability:** Print; Online.

23982 ■ *"Legg Mason Compensation Committee Chair Defends CEO Fetting's Pay"* in *Baltimore Business Journal* (Vol. 29, July 22, 2011, No. 11, pp. 1)
Pub: Boston Business Journal
Contact: Carolyn M. Jones, President
E-mail: cmjones@bizjournals.com
Ed: Gary Haber. **Description:** Legg Mason Inc. CEO Mark R. Fetting has been awarded $5.9 million pay package and he expects to receive questions regarding it in the coming shareholders meeting. However, Baltimore, Maryland-based RKTL Associates chairman emeritus Harold R. Adams believes Fetting has done a tremendous job in bringing Legg's through a tough market. **Availability:** Print; Online.

23983 ■ *"Less Malaise in Malaysia"* in *Barron's* (Vol. 88, March 17, 2008, No. 11, pp. M12)
Pub: Dow Jones & Company Inc.
Contact: Almar Latour, Chief Executive Officer
Ed: Assif Shameen. **Description:** Shares of Malaysia's Bursa have been in freefall while the Malaysia government prolongs its pitch to sell a 10 percent stake of the exchange to NYSE Euronext. Asian bourses had produced very good returns for five years and charge some of the highest fees for exchanges. A key growth driver for Asian bourses could be the derivatives markets and exchange-traded funds. **Availability:** Online.

23984 ■ *"Let's Make a Deal"* in *Pittsburgh Business Times* (Vol. 33, July 18, 2014, No. 53, pp. 10)
Pub: American City Business Journals, Inc.
Contact: Mike Olivieri, Executive Vice President
Released: February 26, 2015. **Description:** The low interest rate, combined with regulation have reduced fixed income trading for banks, thus reducing their profits and increasing the volatility of quarterly earnings. Banks are being forced to consider new ways to make money as the low rates are a function of a Federally-structured government yield curve, reflecting lower economic growth and inflation expectations. **Availability:** Print; Online.

23985 ■ *"Lifesavers"* in *Black Enterprise* (Vol. 41, December 2010, No. 5, pp. 38)
Pub: Earl G. Graves Ltd.
Contact: Earl Graves, Jr., President
Ed: Tamara E. Holmes. **Description:** Profile of Interventional Nephrology Specialists Access Center and founders Dr. Omar Davis and Dr. Natarsha Grant; the center generated $5.5 million in revenue for 2009. Details on how they run their successful center are included. **Availability:** Online.

23986 ■ *"Listen Up: There's a Revolution in the Cubicle"* in *Barron's* (Vol. 89, July 27, 2009, No. 30, pp. 18)
Pub: Dow Jones & Company Inc.
Contact: Almar Latour, Chief Executive Officer
Ed: Jay Palmer. **Description:** Plantronics will be among the first beneficiaries when the unified communications revolution arrives in the office. Plantronics' shares could rise to around 30 in 2009 from the 20s as of July 2009. Unified communications could create a huge new multimillion-dollar market for Plantronics. **Availability:** Online.

23987 ■ *"The Little Biotech that Could"* in *Barron's* (Vol. 89, July 27, 2009, No. 30, pp. 19)
Pub: Dow Jones & Company Inc.
Contact: Almar Latour, Chief Executive Officer
Ed: Christopher C. Williams. **Description:** OSI Pharmaceuticals' shares is a compelling investment bet among small biotech firms due to its Tarceva anticancer drug which has a 23 percent market share as well as their strong balance sheet. OSI is planning to expand the use of Tarceva which could re-ignite sales and one analyst expects the shares to trade in the 40s one year from July 2009. **Availability:** Online.

23988 ■ *"Littleton Firm Chips In On Security Solution"* in *Denver Business Journal* (Vol. 65, May 9, 2014, No. 52, pp. A6)
Pub: American City Business Journals, Inc.
Contact: Mike Olivieri, Executive Vice President
Released: Weekly. **Price:** $4, introductory 4-week offer(Digital & Print). **Description:** CPI Card Group of Littleton, Colorado has been preparing for the nationwide transition to computer chip cards to secure credit and debit cards in the U.S. Banks and merchants in the country need to make the switch by October 2015 or risk being financially liable for fraud if not using the chipped cards in their retail establishments. **Availability:** Print; Online.

23989 ■ *"Loonie Tunes: When Will the Dollar Rise Again?"* in *Canadian Business* (Vol. 81, November 10, 2008, No. 19, pp. 62)
Pub: Rogers Media Inc.
Contact: Neil Spivak, Chief Executive Officer
Ed: Joe Castaldo. **Description:** The Canadian dollar has weakened against the U.S. Dollar as the U.S. financial crisis rocked global markets. A currency strategist says that the strength of the U.S. dollar is not based on people's optimism on the U.S. economy but on a structural demand where U.S. non-financial corporations have been repatriating greenbacks from foreign subsidiaries. **Availability:** Print; Online.

23990 ■ *"Lotus Starts Slowly, Dodges Subprime Woes"* in *Crain's Detroit Business* (Vol. 24, April 14, 2008, No. 15, pp. 3)
Pub: Crain Communications Inc.
Contact: Barry Asin, President
Ed: Tom Henderson. **Description:** Discusses Lotus Bancorp Inc. and their business plan, which although is not yet on target due to the subprime mortgage meltdown, is in a much better position than its competitors due to the quality of their loans. **Availability:** Online.

23991 ■ *"Make Money in 2011: What to Invest In"* in *Small Business Opportunities* (January 2011)
Pub: Harris Publishing, Inc.
Contact: Janet Chase, Contact
Description: Top twenty ways to pick up extra cash, boost your income and generate new revenue. There has never been a better time to start a small business. **Availability:** Online.

23992 ■ *"Making Automated Royalty Payments Work for Your Franchise"* in *Franchising World* (Vol. 42, October 2010, No. 10, pp. 30)
Pub: International Franchise Association
Contact: Matthew Haller, President
E-mail: mhaller@franchise.org
Ed: J.P. O'Brien. **Released:** October 10, 2010. **Description:** In the past, royalty payments were sent by franchisees through regular postal mail and accompanied by a single slip of paper with handwritten notes indicating the month's revenue numbers and royalty amounts. **Availability:** PDF; Online.

23993 ■ *"Making It Click: Annual Ranking Of the Best Online Brokers"* in *Barron's* (Vol. 88, March 17, 2008, No. 11, pp. 31)
Pub: Dow Jones & Company Inc.
Contact: Almar Latour, Chief Executive Officer
Ed: Theresa W. Carey. **Description:** Listing of 23 online brokers that are evaluated based on their trade experience, usability, range of offerings, research amenities, customer service and access, and costs. TradeStation Securities takes the top spot followed by thinkorswim by just a fraction. **Availability:** Online.

23994 ■ *"Managing Your Innovation Portfolio: People Throughout Your Organization Are Energetically Pursuing the New. But Does All That Add Up To a Strategy?"* in *Harvard Business Review* (Vol. 90, May 2012, No. 5, pp. 66)
Pub: Harvard Business Review Press
Contact: Moderna V. Pfizer, Contact
Ed: Bansi Nagji, Geoff Tuff. **Price:** $8.95. **Description:** Returns on innovation are higher with transformational initiatives than with core or adjacent pursuits, but require unique management methods. These include establishing a diverse talent set, separating teams from daily operations, and obtaining funding from outside the regular budget cycle. **Availability:** Online; PDF.

23995 ■ *"M&T On the March?"* in *Baltimore Business Journal* (Vol. 28, November 12, 2010, No. 27, pp. 1)
Pub: Baltimore Business Journal
Contact: Rhonda Pringle, President
E-mail: rpringle@bizjournals.com
Ed: Gary Haber. **Description:** Information on the growth of M&T Bank, as well as its expansion plans are presented. M&T recently acquired Wilmington Trust and took over $500 million in deposits from the failed K Bank. Analysts believe that M&T would continue its expansion through Washington DC and Richmond, Virginia, especially after a bank executive acknowledged that the markets in those areas are attractive. **Availability:** Print; Online.

23996 ■ *"Many Roads Lead to Value Says David J. Williams, Manager of Excelsior Value & Restructuring Fund"* in *Barron's* (Vol. 88, March 10, 2008, No. 10, pp. 46)
Pub: Dow Jones & Company Inc.
Contact: Almar Latour, Chief Executive Officer
Ed: Lawrence C. Strauss. **Description:** David J. Williams, lead manager of Excelsior Value & Restructuring Fund, invests in struggling companies and those companies whose turnarounds show promise. Morgan Stanley, Lehman Brothers, and Petroleo Brasileiro are some of the companies he holds shares in, while he has unloaded shares of Citigroup, Freddie Mac, and Sallie Mae. **Availability:** Online.

23997 ■ *"Mapping the Gender Gap"* in *Business Journal Portland* (Vol. 31, April 25, 2014, No. 8, pp. 4)
Pub: American City Business Journals, Inc.
Contact: Mike Olivieri, Executive Vice President
Released: April 25, 2014. **Price:** $4, introductory 4-week offer(Digital & Print). **Description:** The level of gender equality in the health care, banking, technology and commercial real estate industries of Oregon is examined. Gender bias in the workplace is one significant reason behind the wage gap and the lack of women in leadership positions. **Availability:** Print; Mailing list; Online.

23998 ■ *"Market Watch"* in *Barron's* (Vol. 88, March 24, 2008, No. 12, pp. M18)
Ed: Ashraf Laidi, Marc Pado, David Kotok. **Released:** 2018. **Description:** Latest measures implemented by the Federal Reserve to address the credit crisis did not benefit the US dollar, with the Japanese yen and the euro recouping earlier losses against the dollar. Goldman Sachs reported earnings of $3.23 per share, claiming a stronger liquidity position. The US markets bottomed early on 22 January 2007, according to evidence. **Availability:** Print; Online.

23999 ■ *"Market Watch: A Sampling of Advisory Opinion"* in *Barron's* (Vol. 88, March 17, 2008, No. 11, pp. M10)
Pub: Dow Jones & Company Inc.
Contact: Almar Latour, Chief Executive Officer

Ed: Paul Schatz, William Gibson, Michael Darda, Peter Greene, Ian Wyatt, Stephanie Pomboy. **Released:** January 25, 2014. **Description:** S&P 500 bank stocks were down 46 percent from their 2007 peak while the peak to through fall in 1989-1990 was just over 50 percent. This suggests that the bottom on the bank stocks could be near. The Federal Reserve Board announced they will lend up to $200 billion to primary lenders in exchange other securities. **Availability:** Print; Online.

24000 ■ *"Market Watch: A Sampling of Advisory Opinion US Stock Price Trends, Economic Effects of Global Trade, Chinese Economic Trends"* in Barron's (Vol. 92, July 23, 2012, No. 30, pp. M14)
Ed: Richard M. Salsman, Jack Ablin, Francois Sicart. **Description:** US stocks are considered inexpensive due to their low price-earnings ratios compared to levels before the global financial crisis. The US economy is becoming more dependent on the rest of the worldas a result of global trade. The Chinese economy continues to have strong economic growth despite a slowdown. **Availability:** Online.

24001 ■ *"Markets Defy the Doomsayers"* in Barron's (Vol. 88, March 24, 2008, No. 12, pp. M5)
Pub: Dow Jones & Company Inc.
Contact: Almar Latour, Chief Executive Officer
Ed: Leslie P. Norton. **Description:** US stock markets registered strong gains, with the Dow Jones Industrial Average rising 3.43 percent on the week to close at 12,361.32, in a rally that may be seen as short-covering. Shares of Hansen Natural are poised for further drops with a slowdown in the energy drink market. **Availability:** Online.

24002 ■ *"Mary Kramer: Good Things Happen When We Buy Local"* in Crain's Detroit Business (Vol. 24, October 6, 2008, No. 40, pp. 7)
Pub: Crain Communications Inc.
Contact: Barry Asin, President
Description: Michigan is facing incredibly difficult economic times. One way in which each one of us can help the state and the businesses located here is by purchasing our goods and services from local vendors. The state Agriculture Department projected that if Michigan households earmarked $10 per week in their grocery purchases to made-in-Michigan products, this would generate $30 million a week in economic impact. **Availability:** Online.

24003 ■ *"A Matter of Interest: Payday Loans"* in Canadian Business (Vol. 79, July 17, 2006, No. 14-15, pp. 21)
Pub: Rogers Media Inc.
Contact: Neil Spivak, Chief Executive Officer
Ed: Jeff Sanford. **Description:** With the steady decrease in savings, the need for growth in Canada's payloan industry is discussed. Also emphasized are the challenges faced by payloan operators. **Availability:** Online.

24004 ■ *"McDonald's Loses Its Sizzle"* in Barron's (Vol. 88, March 17, 2008, No. 11, pp. 47)
Description: McDonald's has promised to return $15 billion to $17 billion to shareholders in 2007-2009 but headwinds are rising for the company. December, 2007 same-store sales were flat and the company's traffic growth in the U.S. is slowing. Its shares are likely to trade in tandem with the market until recession fears recede. **Availability:** Online.

24005 ■ *"Md. Banks Beef Up Deposits, But Lending Lags"* in Baltimore Business Journal (Vol. 28, October 29, 2010, No. 25, pp. 1)
Pub: Baltimore Business Journal
Contact: Rhonda Pringle, President
E-mail: rpringle@bizjournals.com
Ed: Gary Haber. **Description:** Bank deposits in the Greater Baltimore area have increased but commercial loans have not. Small business owners complain that banks do not help them expand their businesses, but banks argue that they want to lend but the borrowers have to meet standard qualifications. **Availability:** Print; Online.

24006 ■ *"Meet the Money Whisperer to the Super-Rich N.B.A. Elite"* in The New York Times (June 6, 2019)
URL(s): www.nytimes.com/2019/06/06/business/nba-wealth-manager-klay-thompson-joe-mclean.html
Ed: Devin Gordon. **Released:** June 06, 2019. **Description:** Profile of Joe McLean, a premier wealth manager for the NBA elite. Discusses his unusual strategies for managing wealth and how he earns the trust of his clients. **Availability:** Online.

24007 ■ *"Merrill Lynch in Talks to Buy BlackRock Stake"* in Globe & Mail (February 13, 2006, pp. B4)
Description: Financial services firm Merrill Lynch and Co. Inc. is planning to acquire money managing company BlackRock Inc. for 8 million dollars. Sources report that this deal would create 1-trillion dollar huge fund management venture. **Availability:** Online.

24008 ■ *"Micro-Finance Agencies and SMEs: Model of Explication of Tacit Knowledge"* in International Journal of Entrepreneurship and Small Business (Vol. 11, August 3, 2010)
Ed: Patricia A. Rowe, Michael J. Christie, Frank Hoy. **Description:** Institutional preparedness of economic development agencies for developing small and medium-sized enterprises (SMEs) is discussed. The cases presented illustrate variations in the micro-finance lender agency-enterprise development of processes for sharing vision and interdependence. **Availability:** Online.

24009 ■ *"Microsoft's Big Gamble"* in Canadian Business (Vol. 81, March 3, 2008, No. 3, pp. 13)
Description: Microsoft Corp. is taking a big risk in buying Yahoo, as it is expected to pay more than $31 a share to finalize the acquisition. The deal would be seven and a half times bigger than any other that Microsoft has entered before, an execution of such deal is also anticipated to become a challenge for Microsoft. Recommendations on how Microsoft should handle the integration of the two businesses are given. **Availability:** Print; Online.

24010 ■ *"Millennial Money: How Young Investors Can Build a Fortune"*
Pub: Palgrave Macmillan
Released: October 14, 2014. **Price:** $26, hardcover. **Description:** Because the millennial generation won't be able to depend on pensions or social security for their retirement security, it is stressed that they save and invest their money wisely. As a generation, though, they are skeptical of advice from their elders, but are committed to passing wealth to future generations. A strategy for wise investments to help overcome shortcomings is included. **Availability:** E-book; Print.

24011 ■ *"Millennial Spending Influences County Budget"* in Puget Sound Business Journal (Vol. 35, September 26, 2014, No. 23, pp. 6)
Pub: American City Business Journals, Inc.
Contact: Mike Olivieri, Executive Vice President
Description: Washington State's tax system has been blamed by King County executive Dow Constantine for its proposed 2015-16 budget that cuts 500 positions. The millennial generation's spending was also partially blamed for the drop in sales tax revenue because they don't buy houses and cars as frequently compared to previous generations. How the millennial generation spends their money is also discussed. **Availability:** Online.

24012 ■ *"Millions of Senior Citizens Swindled by Financial Fraud"* in Black Enterprise (Vol. 41, September 2010, No. 2, pp. 24)
Pub: Earl G. Graves Ltd.
Contact: Earl Graves, Jr., President
Description: One of every five citizens over the age of 65 have been victims of financial fraud. Statistical data included.

24013 ■ *Minding Her Own Business, 4th Ed.*
Released: 4th edition. **Description:** A guide to taxes and financial records for women entrepreneurs is presented. **Availability:** E-book; Print.

24014 ■ *"Mine Woes Could Rouse Zinc"* in Barron's (Vol. 88, July 7, 2008, No. 27, pp. M12)
Pub: Dow Jones & Company Inc.
Contact: Almar Latour, Chief Executive Officer
Ed: Andrea Hotter. **Description:** Prices of zinc could increase due to supply problems in producing countries such as Australia and China. London Metal Exchange prices for the metal have dropped about 36 percent in 2008. **Availability:** Online.

24015 ■ *"Mining Goldman for Insight"* in Barron's (Vol. 89, July 20, 2009, No. 29, pp. M8)
Pub: Dow Jones & Company Inc.
Contact: Almar Latour, Chief Executive Officer
Ed: Steven M. Sears. **Description:** Methods of investing in options for companies with earnings estimates from Goldman Sachs are discussed. These methods take advantage of increased volatility generated by earnings revisions. **Availability:** Online.

24016 ■ *"A Mixed-Bag Quarter"* in Barron's (Vol. 88, July 7, 2008, No. 27, pp. 19)
Description: Seven component companies of the Dow Jones Industrial Average increased their dividend payouts in the second quarter of 2008 despite the weak performance of the index. Five companies in the Dow Jones Transportation index and three in the Dow Jones Utilities also increased their dividends. **Availability:** Online.

24017 ■ *"Money Basics: How to Handle a Bank Error"* in Black Enterprise (Vol. 41, December 2010, No. 5)
Pub: Earl G. Graves Ltd.
Contact: Earl Graves, Jr., President
Ed: Sheiresa Ngo. **Description:** Contact your bank or financial institution immediately after discovering an error in your account. **Availability:** Online.

24018 ■ *"Key Challenges Dog International Banking in South Florida"* in South Florida Business Journal (Vol. 35, August 1, 2014, No. 1, pp. 4)
Pub: American City Business Journals, Inc.
Contact: Mike Olivieri, Executive Vice President
Released: Weekly. **Price:** $8, introductory 4-week offer(Digital only). **Description:** Florida International Bankers Association president, Roberto R. Munoz, discusses the challenges and opportunities in the South Florida international banking market. He explains the impact on international banks with the loss of the Export-Import Bank of the United States charter and the Base1 III rules and regulations regarding higher capital requirements. **Availability:** Print; Online.

24019 ■ *"MoneyGram Hopes Digital Push Will Click With Customers"* in Dallas Business Journal (Vol. 37, July 4, 2014, No. 43, pp. 17)
Pub: American City Business Journals, Inc.
Contact: Mike Olivieri, Executive Vice President
Released: Weekly. **Price:** $4, introductory 4-week offer(Digital only). **Description:** Reports on MoneyGram's recent release of a digital monitoring system, which will allow it to work more closely with customers, is profiled. This digital monitoring system will aggregate data from social media platforms and enable the company to identify customer needs and trends across the money transfer industry. It will help MoneyGram outshine its rivals in the money transfer business. **Availability:** Print; Online.

GENERAL SMALL BUSINESS TOPICS

24020 ■ *"More Gains in the Pipeline"* in *Barron's* (Vol. 89, August 3, 2009, No. 31, pp. M5)
Description: Shares of El Paso Corp. could recover as the company concludes a deal with a private-equity group to fund pipeline construction. The company's shares are trading at $10.06 and could move up to $12 as bad news has already been priced into the stock. **Availability:** Online.

24021 ■ *"Mover and Sheika"* in *Conde Nast Portfolio* (Vol. 2, June 2008, No. 6, pp. 104)
Ed: John Arlidge. **Description:** Profile of Princess Sheika Lubna who is the first female foreign trade minister in the Middle East, the United Arab Emirates biggest business envoy, paving the way for billions in new investment, and also a manufacturer of her own perfume line. **Availability:** Online.

24022 ■ *"My Favorite Tool for Managing Expenses"* in *Inc.* (Volume 32, December 2010, No. 10, pp. 60)
Pub: Inc. Magazine
Ed: J.J. McCorvey. **Description:** Web-based service called Expensify is outlined. The service allows companies to log expenses while away from the office using the service's iPhone application. **Availability:** Online.

24023 ■ *"A Neat SocialTrade"* in *Barron's* (Vol. 92, July 23, 2012, No. 30, pp. 23)
Pub: Dow Jones & Company Inc.
Contact: Almar Latour, Chief Executive Officer
Ed: Theresa W. Carey. **Description:** SocialTrade is a Website that allows users to exchange ideas and data with each other through video. Online broker DittoTrade launched a mobile applications that allows investors to connect to other traders and follow their trades. **Availability:** Online.

24024 ■ *"Needed: A Strategy; Banking In China"* in *The Economist* (Vol. 390, January 3, 2009, No. 8612, pp. 54)
Description: International banks are competing for a role in China but are finding obstacles in their paths such as a reduction in the credit their operations may receive from Chinese banks and the role they can play in the public capital markets which remain limited. **Availability:** Print; Online.

24025 ■ *"A New Approach to Funding Social Enterprises: Unbundling Societal Benefits and Financial Returns Can Dramatically Increase Investment"* in *Harvard Business Review* (Vol. 90, January-February 2012, No.1-2, pp. 118)
Pub: Harvard Business Review Press
Contact: Moderna V. Pfizer, Contact
Ed: Bruce Kogut, Antony Bugg-Levine, Nalin Kulatilaka. **Price:** $8.95, PDF and hardcover black and white. **Description:** Identification of a range of financing arrangements that can maximize benefits delivered by social organizations. These include equity, quasi-equity debt, charitable giving, convertible debt, and securitized debt. The claims on assets and types of return for each are defined. **Availability:** Print; PDF; Online.

24026 ■ *"A New Kid on the Block"* in *Barron's* (Vol. 88, March 17, 2008, No. 11, pp. 58)
Pub: Dow Jones & Company Inc.
Contact: Almar Latour, Chief Executive Officer
Ed: Thomas G. Donlan. **Description:** Discusses the Federal Reserve which has offered to lend $100 billion in cash to banks and $200 billion in Treasuries to Wall Street investment banks that have problems with liquidity. The reluctance of the banks to lend money to meet a margin call on securities that could still depreciate is the reason why the agency is going into the direct loan business. **Availability:** Online.

24027 ■ *"New Rule Rankles In Jersey"* in *Philadelphia Business Journal* (Vol. 30, September 16, 2011, No. 31, pp. 1)
Pub: Philadelphia Business Journal
Contact: Sierra Quinn, Director
E-mail: squinn@bizjournals.com
Ed: Jeff Blumenthal. **Description:** A new rule in New Jersey which taxes out-of-state companies that conduct business in the state earned the ire of several banks, mortgage lenders and credit card companies and prompted opponents to threaten to file lawsuits. The new rule is an amendment to New Jersey Division of Taxation's corporate business tax regulation and is retroactive to 2002. Details are given. **Availability:** Online.

24028 ■ *"A New Way to Tell When to Fold 'Em"* in *Barron's* (Vol. 88, July 7, 2008, No. 27, pp. 27)
Pub: Dow Jones & Company Inc.
Contact: Almar Latour, Chief Executive Officer
Ed: Theresa W. Carey. **Description:** Overview of the Online trading company SmartStops, a firm that aims to tell investors when to sell the shares of a particular company. The company's Web site categorizes stocks as moving up, down, or sideways, and calculates exit points for individual stocks based on an overall market trend. **Availability:** Online.

24029 ■ *"The Next Economic Disaster: Why It's Coming and How to Avoid It"*
Released: 2014. **Description:** Findings from a team of economists show that the financial crisis of 2008 was from the rapid growth of private rather than public debt. Credit expert, Richard Vague, also argues that economic collapse over history and other economic downturns around the world were all preceded by a rise in privately held debt. He predicts China may soon be facing economic disaster. If banks in the U.S. do not embrace a policy of debt restructuring, economic growth will suffer.

24030 ■ *"Nightmare on Wall Street"* in *Canadian Business* (Vol. 81, October 13, 2008, No. 17, pp. 9)
Description: Information on events that happened on Wall Street on the week that started September 15, 2008, as well on its effect on financial markets around the world, are presented. Lehman Brothers filed for bankruptcy on September 15, 2008 after negotiations with Barclays Group and Bank of America failed. Details on AIG and Morgan Stanley are also presented. **Availability:** Online.

24031 ■ *"No Assets for Retirement? Eh, Who Cares?"* in *Financial Advisor* (November, 2019)
URL(s): www.fa-mag.com/news/no-assets-for-retirement--eh--who-cares-52368.html?issue=323
Ed: Karen Demasters. **Released:** November 2019. **Description:** About half of Americans have savings for retirement and those who do not, do not seem to care. With many people trying to pay bills and support themselves through the day, it's no wonder that many do not have savings set aside for the distant future.

24032 ■ *"Nonprofits Pressured to Rein in Fundraising Events"* in *Crain's Detroit Business* (Vol. 25, June 15, 2009, No. 24, pp. 1)
Pub: Crain Communications Inc.
Contact: Barry Asin, President
Ed: Sherri Begin Welch. **Description:** Local corporations have asked nonprofits to limit fundraising events in order to cut costs during the recession. **Availability:** Online.

24033 ■ *"The Numbers Speak For Themselves"* in *Barron's* (Vol. 88, July 14, 2008, No. 28, pp. 16)
Pub: Dow Jones & Company Inc.
Contact: Almar Latour, Chief Executive Officer
Ed: Bill Alpert. **Description:** Discusses quant fund managers versus traditional long-short equity funds after quants outperformed traditional funds in the year 2000. Causes for the underperformance are outlined and statistical data is included. **Availability:** Online.

24034 ■ *"Nvidia Shares Clobbered After Gloomy Warning"* in *Barron's* (Vol. 88, July 7, 2008, No. 27, pp. 25)
Pub: Dow Jones & Company Inc.
Contact: Almar Latour, Chief Executive Officer
Ed: Eric J. Savitz. **Description:** Shares of graphics chip manufacturer Nvidia suffered a 30 percent drop in its share price after the company warned that revenue and gross margin forecasts for the quarter ending July 27, 2008 will be below expectations. Stan Glasgow, chief operating officer of Sony Electronics, believes the US economic slowdown will not affect demand for the company's products. Statistical data included. **Availability:** Online.

24035 ■ *"Nvidia's Picture Brighter Than Stock Price Indicates"* in *Barron's* (Vol. 88, March 24, 2008, No. 12, pp. 46)
Pub: Dow Jones & Company Inc.
Contact: Almar Latour, Chief Executive Officer
Ed: Eric J. Savitz. **Description:** Shares of graphics chip maker Nvidia, priced at $18.52 each, do not indicate the company's strong position in the graphics chip market. The company's shares have dropped due to fears of slower demand for PCs, but the company is not as exposed to broader economic forces. **Availability:** Online.

24036 ■ *"Nymex Dissidents Rattle Sabers"* in *Crain's Chicago Business* (Vol. 31, April 21, 2008, No. 16, pp. 2)
Pub: Crain Communications Inc.
Contact: Barry Asin, President
Ed: Ann Saphir. **Description:** Two groups of New York Mercantile Exchange members say they have more than enough votes to stop CME Group Inc.'s $10 billion deal to acquire the oil and metals exchange and they are threatening a proxy fight if the Chicago exchange doesn't raise its offer. **Availability:** Online.

24037 ■ *"October 2009: Recovery Plods Along"* in *Hispanic Business* (October 2009, pp. 10-11)
Description: Economist reports on a possible economic recovery which will not be allowed to rely on a strong domestic demand in order to sustain it. Consumers, looking to counterbalance years of leverage financing based on unrealistic, ever-increasing home and portfolio valuations, are saving rather than spending money.

24038 ■ *"Ohio Commerce Draws Closer to Profitability"* in *Crain's Cleveland Business* (Vol. 28, October 29, 2007, No. 43, pp. 14)
Pub: Crain Communications Inc.
Contact: K. C. Crain, President
Ed: Shawn A. Turner. **Description:** Overview of the business plan of Ohio Commerce Bank, a de novo, or startup bank that is close to turning the corner to profitability. The bank opened in November 2006 and focuses on dealing with small businesses totaling $5 million or less in annual revenues. **Availability:** Online.

24039 ■ *"Older, But Not Wiser"* in *Canadian Business* (Vol. 85, July 16, 2012, No. 11-12, pp. 54)
Ed: Matthew McClearn, Michael McCullough. **Description:** Data from Statistics Canada revealed that two-thirds of workers aged 55 and above have some form of debt from mortgage to credit card balance while its one-third among the retired. Some factors contributing to the trend are the decline in borrowing costs, real estate, and older Canadians' car purchasing behavior. **Availability:** Print; Online.

24040 ■ *"One-Time Area Trust Executive Finds Trouble in N.H."* in *The Business Journal-Serving Metropolitan Kansas City* (September 12, 2008)
Description: About 200 investors, some from Missouri's Kansas City area, claim that they had conducted business with Noble Trust Co. The trust company was placed under New Hampshire Banking Department's conservatorship after $15 million was discovered to be missing from its account. It is alleged that the money was lost in a Colorado Ponzi scheme. **Availability:** Print; Online.

24041 ■ "Opportunity Now Lies at Short End of the Market" in Barron's (Vol. 88, June 30, 2008, No. 26, pp. M9)
Pub: Dow Jones & Company Inc.
Contact: Almar Latour, Chief Executive Officer
Ed: Michael S. Derby. Description: Renewed credit concerns and the lesser chance of a Federal Reserve interest rate hike boosted the bond market. Some portfolio managers are more bullish on short-dated securities as they expect the market to adjust to a more appropriate outlook. Availability: Online.

24042 ■ "Oracle: No Profit of Doom" in Barron's (Vol. 88, March 31, 2008, No. 13, pp. 40)
Pub: Dow Jones & Company Inc.
Contact: Almar Latour, Chief Executive Officer
Ed: Mark Veverka. Description: Oracle's revenues grew by 21 percent but fell short of expectation and their profits came in at the low-end of expectations. The company's shares dropped 8 percent but investors are advised to pay more attention to the company's earnings expansion rather than revenue growth in a slow economy. Nokia's Rick Simonson points out that their markets in Asia and particularly India is growing so they are not as affected by the U.S. economic conditions. Availability: Online.

24043 ■ "Outlook In Other Industries" in Crain's Detroit Business (Vol. 30, January 6, 2014, No. 1, pp. 3)
Pub: Crain Communications Inc.
Contact: Barry Asin, President
Released: January 6, 2014. Description: Outlook for industries in the Detroit area are listed, including small business growth, restaurants, defense contracts, nonprofits, transportation, auto suppliers, healthcare, bankruptcy, and government. Availability: Print; PDF; Online.

24044 ■ "Over A Barrel" in Canadian Business (Vol. 81, July 21, 2008, No. 11, pp. 13)
Description: Analysts predict that the skyrocketing price of fuel will cause a crackdown in the market as purported in the peak oil theory. It is forecasted that the price of oil will reach $200 per barrel. Details of the effect of the increasing oil prices on the market are presented.

24045 ■ "Packaging Firm Wraps Up Remake: Overseas Plants Help Firm Fatten Margins" in Crain's New York Business (January 6, 2008)
Pub: Crain Communications, Inc.
Contact: Jessica Botos, Manager, Marketing
E-mail: jessica.botos@crainsnewyork.com
Description: Sealed Air Corp., a packaging manufacturer, has seen its share price fall nearly 20 percent over the past two years, making it one of the worst performers in the packaging sector. Availability: Online.

24046 ■ Paper Fortunes: Modern Wall Street: Where It's Been and Where It's Going
Ed: Roy C. Smith. Released: 2010. Description: Comprehensive history of Wall Street and lessons learned with insight into ways Wall Street will reinvent itself in this new economy. Availability: E-book.

24047 ■ "Paradise Banquet Hall of Toronto: Breaking Traditions Can Keep a Wedding Budget Intact" in Internet Wire (June 12, 2012)
Description: Average wedding costs can reach nearly $27,000 and that amount does not inclue honeymoon, wedding shower, engagement party, or bachelor/bachelorette parties. Paradise Banquet Hall of Toronto uses Donna Freedman's approach to planning a wedding on a budget. Details are included. Availability: Print; Online.

24048 ■ "Paying for the Recession: Rebalancing Economic Growth" in Montana Business Quarterly (Vol. 49, Spring 2011, No. 1, pp. 2)
Pub: University of Montana Bureau of Business and Economic Research
Contact: Patrick Barkey, Director
E-mail: patrick.barkey@business.umt.edu
Ed: Patrick M. Barkey. Released: Quarterly. Description: Four key issues required to address in order to rebalance economic growth in America are examined. They include: savings rates, global trade imbalances, government budgets and most importantly, housing price correction. Availability: Online.

24049 ■ "Perry Ellis and G-III Apparel--Out of Fashion, but Still in Style" in Barron's (Vol. 88, March 17, 2008, No. 11, pp. 48)
Pub: Dow Jones & Company Inc.
Contact: Almar Latour, Chief Executive Officer
Ed: Robin Goldwyn Blumenthal. Description: Shares of Perry Ellis International and G-III Apparel Group have taken some beating in the market despite good growth earnings prospects. Perry Ellis sees earnings growth of 8 to 11 percent for fiscal 2009, while G-III Apparel expects earnings growth of 25 percent. Availability: Online.

24050 ■ Personal Success and the Bottom Line
Description: Retired certified public accountant provides a primer for those wishing to achieve a balance between career and their personal life. Availability: Print.

24051 ■ "Peter Bynoe Trades Up" in Black Enterprise (Vol. 38, July 2008, No. 12, pp. 30)
Pub: Earl G. Graves Ltd.
Contact: Earl Graves, Jr., President
Description: Chicago-based Loop Capital Markets L.L.C. has named Peter Bynoe managing director of corporate finance. Bynoe was previously a senior partner at the law firm DLA Piper U.S. L.L.P., where he worked on stadium deals.

24052 ■ "PhotoMedex Bouncing Back from Brink of Bankruptcy" in Philadelphia Business Journal (Vol. 30, January 6, 2012, No. 47, pp. 1)
Pub: Baltimore Business Journal
Contact: Rhonda Pringle, President
E-mail: rpringle@bizjournals.com
Description: PhotoMedex Inc. has managed to avoid bankruptcy through reorganization. The company appointed Dennis McGrath as president and chief executive. Details of the business reorganization plans are covered. Availability: Print; Online.

24053 ■ "Pioneering Strategies for Entrepreneurial Success" in Business Horizons (Vol. 51, January-February 2008, No. 1, pp. 21)
Pub: Elsevier Advanced Technology Publications
Ed: Candida G. Brush. Price: $8.95, hardcopy black and white. Description: Entrepreneurs are known for new products, services, processes, markets and industries. In order to achieve success, they have to develop a clear vision, creatively manage finances, and use social skills to persuade others to commit to the venture. Pioneering strategies and their implementation are examined. Availability: Print; PDF; Online.

24054 ■ "Place Restrictions on Your Stock Shares" in Business Owner (Vol. 35, July-August 2011, No. 4, pp. 14)
Description: It is critical for any small business owner to be certain that the buyer or recipient of any part of the company represents that the stock is being acquired or given for investment purposes only. Availability: Online.

24055 ■ "PNC Begins Search for New Baltimore-Area Headquarters" in Baltimore Business Journal (Vol. 28, June 4, 2010, No. 4, pp. 1)
Pub: Baltimore Business Journal
Contact: Rhonda Pringle, President
E-mail: rpringle@bizjournals.com
Ed: Daniel J. Sernovitz. Description: PNC Financial Services Group Inc. is searching for a new headquarters building in Greater Baltimore, Maryland. The company is seeking about 150,000 square feet for its regional operations. However, PNC could also end up moving out of Baltimore for space in the surrounding suburbs. Availability: Print; Online.

24056 ■ "Private-Equity Firms Can Elevate ESG, Diversity — and Their Returns" in Crain's Chicago Business (October 15, 2021)
URL(s): www.chicagobusiness.com/equity/private-equity-firms-can-advance-diversity
Ed: Jose Maria Liberti. Released: October 15, 2021. Description: Discusses the impact Private Equity firms can have on diversity within their companies as they shift towards focusing on long-term goals. Availability: Online.

24057 ■ "Private Equity Struggles with Its Diversity Problem" in Crain's Chicago Business (October 15, 2021)
URL(s): www.chicagobusiness.com/equity/private-equity-struggles-its-diversity-problem
Ed: Steve Hendershot. Released: October 15, 2021. Description: Discusses the issues of low diversity rates within the C-suite of private equity firms.

24058 ■ Problems and Materials on Debtor and Creditor Law
Ed: Christopehr G. Bradley. Released: 2022. Description: Discusses bankruptcy cases and lien and collection of debts.

24059 ■ "Profits Without Prosperity: Stock Buybacks Manipulate the Market and Leave Most Americans Worse Off" in Harvard Business Review (Vol. 92, September 2014, No. 9, pp. 46)
Pub: Harvard Business Publishing
Contact: Diane Belcher, Managing Director
Price: $8.95. Description: While stock prices rise due to stock buybacks, the long-term effects of buybacks are job instability, sluggish growth, and income inequality. Firms should not be permitted to repurchase their shares, and restrictions should be placed on stock-based pay. Profits should be invested in innovation. Availability: Online; PDF.

24060 ■ Progress-Driven Entrepreneurs, Private Equity Finance and Regulatory Issues
Pub: Palgrave Macmillan
Ed: Zuhayr Mikdashi. Released: 2010. Description: Durable business performance is critically dependent on a stakeholder's strategy along with accessible entrepreneurial financing availability within macro-economic and economic regulatory environments. Availability: E-book; Print.

24061 ■ "Putting SogoTrade Through Its Paces" in Barron's (Vol. 89, July 27, 2009, No. 30, pp. 27)
Pub: Dow Jones & Company Inc.
Contact: Almar Latour, Chief Executive Officer
Ed: Theresa W. Carey. Description: SogoTrade options platform streams options quotes in real time and lets users place a trade in several ways. The site also features notable security tactics and is a reasonable choice for bargain-seekers. OptionsXpress' Xtend platform lets users place trades and get real time quotes. Availability: Online.

24062 ■ "Putting the World at Your Fingertips" in Barron's (Vol. 88, July 7, 2008, No. 27, pp. L13)
Pub: Dow Jones & Company Inc.
Contact: Almar Latour, Chief Executive Officer
Ed: Neil A. Martin. Description: Currency-traded exchange funds allow investors to diversify their assets and take advantage of investment opportunities such as speculation and hedging. Investors can use these funds to build positions in favor of or against the US dollar. Availability: Online.

24063 ■ "Q&A with Google's Patrick Pichette" in Canadian Business (Vol. 81, October 13, 2008, No. 17, pp. 6)
Description: Patrick Pichette finds challenge in taking over the finances of an Internet company that has a market cap of about $140 billion. He feels, however, that serving as Google's chief financial officer is noth-

ing compared to running Bell Canada Enterprises (BCE). Pichette's other views on Google and BCE are presented. **Availability:** Print; Online.

24064 ■ *"Q&A: The CAPP's Greg Stringham" in Canadian Business (Vol. 81, February 12, 2008, No. 3, pp. 8)*
Pub: Rogers Media Inc.
Contact: Neil Spivak, Chief Executive Officer
Ed: Michelle Magnan. **Description:** Canadian Association of Petroleum Producers' Greg Stringham thinks that the new royalty plan will result in companies pulling out their investments for Alberta's conventional oil and gas sector. Stringham adds that Alberta is losing its competitive advantage and companies must study their cost profiles to retrieve that advantage. The effects of the royalty system on Alberta's economy are examined further. **Availability:** Print; Online.

24065 ■ *The Quants*
Released: January 25, 2011. **Price:** $22.50, audiobook. **Description:** The story of four rich and powerful men, along with Jim Simons, the founder of the most successful hedge fund in history and how they felt and what they thought in the days and weeks during the crash of Wall Street. **Availability:** E-book; Print; Audio.

24066 ■ *"A Questionable Chemical Romance" in Barron's (Vol. 88, July 14, 2008, No. 28, pp. 28)*
Pub: Dow Jones & Company Inc.
Contact: Almar Latour, Chief Executive Officer
Ed: Andrew Bary. **Description:** Dow Chemical paid $78-a-share for the surprise takeover of Rohm & Haas. The acquisition is reducing Dow Chemical's financial flexibility at a time when chemical companies are being affected by high costs and a weak U.S. economy. **Availability:** Online.

24067 ■ *"Quick Earnings Revival Unlikely" in Barron's (Vol. 88, June 30, 2008, No. 26, pp. 31)*
Description: Analysts are pushing back their prediction of a U.S. economy turnaround to 2009. A recession in the first half of 2008 may not have happened but unemployment is rising and house prices continue to fall.

24068 ■ *"Quicken Starter Edition 2008" in Black Enterprise (Vol. 38, March 1, 2008, No. 8, pp. 54)*
Pub: Earl G. Graves Ltd.
Contact: Earl Graves, Jr., President
Ed: Dale Coachman. **Description:** Profile of Quicken Starter Edition 2008 offering programs that track spending; it will also categorize tax deductible expenses. **Availability:** Online.

24069 ■ *"Raytheon Stock Up, Will Pay New Quarterly Dividend" in Barron's (Vol. 88, March 31, 2008, No. 13)*
Pub: Dow Jones & Company Inc.
Contact: Almar Latour, Chief Executive Officer
Ed: Shirley A. Lazo. **Description:** Raytheon hiked their quarterly dividend to 28 cents per share from 25.5 cents. Aircastle slashed their quarterly common dividend by 64 percent for them to retain additional capital that can be used to increase their liquidity position. **Availability:** Online.

24070 ■ *"The RBC Dynasty Continues" in Globe & Mail (January 30, 2006, pp. B1)*
Description: The details on business growth of Royal Bank of Canada, under chief executive officer Gordon Nixon, are presented. **Availability:** Print; Online.

24071 ■ *Reading Financial Reports for Dummies*
Pub: John Wiley & Sons, Inc.
Contact: Christina Van Tassell, Executive Vice President Chief Financial Officer
URL(s): www.amazon.com/gp/product/1119871360/ref=as_li_tl?ie=UTF8&tag=wiley01-20

Ed: Lita Epstein. **Released:** 4th Edition. **Price:** $27.18, paperback; $18, e-book. **Description:** The fourth edition contains more new and updated information. This book is meant as a guide to help the reader interpret and understand financial reports, annual reports, balance sheets, income statements, statements of cash flow and consolidated statements. Real-world examples are given. . **Availability:** E-book; Print.

24072 ■ *"Ready for a Rally?" in The Economist (Vol. 390, January 3, 2009, No. 8612, pp. 54)*
Description: Analysts predict that the recession could end by 2010. The current economic crisis is presented in detail. **Availability:** Print; Online.

24073 ■ *"Recovery Starts to Set Roots in R.I." in Providence Business News (Vol. 28, January 20, 2014, No. 42, pp. 1)*
Pub: American City Business Journals, Inc.
Contact: Mike Olivieri, Executive Vice President
URL(s): pbn.com/recovery-starts-to-set-roots-in-ri94397
Ed: Patrick Anderson. **Released:** January 18, 2014. **Description:** The results of a survey indicate that 84 percent of businesses in Rhode Island are expecting the state's economy to improve in 2014. Businesspeople had doubted the state's ability to recover because of fiscal crises. The impact of local firms' strong financial results on the economic recovery are discussed. **Availability:** Print; Online. **Telecommunication Services:** Anderson@pbn.com.

24074 ■ *"Reflecting State Economy, Banks Less Profitable in 1Q" in Providence Business News (Vol. 29, July 14, 2014, No. 15, pp. 8)*
Pub: American City Business Journals, Inc.
Contact: Mike Olivieri, Executive Vice President
URL(s): pbn.com/reflecting-state-economy-banks-less-profitable-in-1q98467
Description: Rhode Island banks posted an aggregate return on assets (ROA) of 0.60 percent for the first quarter (1Q) of 2014, slightly lower than the 0.66 percent in the same quarter 2013, reflecting the downturn in the state's economy and its high unemployment rate. However, two Rhode Island banks, Union Federal Savings Bank and The Washington Trust Company, reported higher ROA for 1Q than the national average at 3.98 percent and 1.19 percent respectively.

24075 ■ *"Reforms Equal Smaller 401(k)s" in Employee Benefit News (Vol. 25, December 1, 2011, No. 15, pp. 19)*
Pub: SourceMedia LLC
Contact: Gemma Postlethwaite, Chief Executive Officer
Ed: Lisa V. Gillespie. **Description:** According to a new analysis by the Employee Benefit Research Institute, two recent proposals to change existing tax treatment of 401(k) retirement plans could cost workers because they would lower their account balances towards retirement.

24076 ■ *"Regulator Issues Warning On Reverse Mortgage Loans" in Retirement Advisor (Vol. 13, October 2012, No. 10, pp. 28)*
Description: Reverse mortgages were first introduced in 1961 and are becoming popular now with aging baby boomers. The new Consumer Financial Protection Bureau warns the public to look closing before entering a reverse mortgage contract. The National Ethics Association encourages financial advisors to use the same caution and offers advise for advisors to help educate their clients about reverse mortgages. **Availability:** Print; Online.

24077 ■ *"Reports of Banks' Revival were Greatly Exaggerated" in Barron's (Vol. 88, July 7, 2008, No. 27, pp. L14)*
Pub: Dow Jones & Company Inc.
Contact: Almar Latour, Chief Executive Officer

Ed: Jack Willoughby. **Description:** Performance of mutual funds improved for the second quarter of 2008 compared to the previous quarter, registering an average gain of 0.13 percent; funds focusing on natural resources rose the highest, their value rising by an average of 24.50 percent. **Availability:** Online.

24078 ■ *"Research Reports" in Barron's (Vol. 88, March 24, 2008, No. 12, pp. M10)*
Pub: Dow Jones & Company Inc.
Contact: Almar Latour, Chief Executive Officer
Ed: Anita Peltonen. **Description:** Investors are recommending purchasing shares of Ampco Pittsburgh due to an expected surge in earnings. Deteriorating credit quality presents problems for the shares of BankAtlantic Bancorp, whose price targets have been lowered from $7 to $5 each. Shares of Helicos Biosciences are expected to move sideways from their $6 level. Statistical data included.

24079 ■ *"Research Reports: How Analysts Size Up Companies" in Barron's (Vol. 88, June 30, 2008, No. 26, pp. M11)*
Availability: Online.

24080 ■ *"Retirement Plans in a Quandary" in Employee Benefit News (Vol. 25, December 1, 2011, No. 15, pp. 18)*
Pub: SourceMedia LLC
Contact: Gemma Postlethwaite, Chief Executive Officer
Ed: Terry Dunne. **Description:** Complex issues arise when employees don't cash their 401(k) balance checks. The US Department of Labor permits plans to cash out accounts of former employees with less than $1,000 to reduce the cost and time required to manage them.

24081 ■ *"Return to Wealth; Bank Strategy" in The Economist (Vol. 390, January 3, 2009, No. 8612, pp. 56)*
Description: UBS' strategy to survive these trying economic times is presented. Statistical data included. UBS has a stronger balance-sheet than most of its investment-banking peers and has reduced its portfolio. **Availability:** Print; Online.

24082 ■ *"Reviving Entrepreneurship: Policy Decisions in 12 Areas Could Nurture - Or Cripple - America's Greatest Asset" in Harvard Business Review (Vol. 90, March 2012, No. 3, pp. 116)*
Pub: Harvard Business Review Press
Contact: Moderna V. Pfizer, Contact
Ed: Josh Lerner, William A. Sahlman. **Price:** $8.95, hardcover. **Description:** Government policies should address entrepreneurship as a process, rather than an act. Several key areas for policymaking include basic and translational science, supply and quality of human capital, information availability, tax treatment of rewards and risks, intellectual property rights, workforce healthcare, and mobility of financial and human capital. **Availability:** PDF; Online.

24083 ■ *Rich Dad, Poor Dad: What the Rich Teach Their Kids About Money-That the Poor and Middle Class Do Not!*
Released: October 25, 2016. **Price:** $5.95, hardcover. **Description:** Personal finance expert shares his economic perspective through exposure to a pair of disparate influences: his own highly education but fiscally unstable father and the multimillionaire eighth-grade dropout father of his closest friend. **Availability:** Print.

24084 ■ *Rich Dad's Increase Your Financial IQ: Get Smarter with Your Money*
Ed: Robert T. Kiyosaki. **Released:** January 07, 2014. **Price:** $14.95, paperback; $12.88, e-book. **Description:** Author describes his five key principles of financial knowledge to help readers build wealth. **Availability:** E-book; Print.

24085 ■ *"The Right Time for REITs" in Barron's (Vol. 88, July 14, 2008, No. 28, pp. 32)*
Pub: Dow Jones & Company Inc.
Contact: Almar Latour, Chief Executive Officer

Ed: Mike Hogan. **Description:** Discusses the downturn in U.S. real estate investment trusts so these are worth considering for investment. Several Websites that are useful for learning about real estate investment trusts for investment purposes are presented. **Availability:** Online.

24086 ■ *"Risk and Reward" in Canadian Business* (Vol. 81, October 13, 2008, No. 17, pp. 21)

Description: Macro-economist and currency analyst Mark Venezia believes that stable financial institutions, free-market reforms, and the role of central banks in keeping inflation and exchange rates stable could make emerging-market bonds strong performers for better future returns. Venezia's other views on emerging-market bonds are discussed. **Availability:** Print; Online.

24087 ■ *"Ryder's Shock Absorbers Are In Place" in Barron's* (Vol. 88, March 24, 2008, No. 12, pp. 19)
Pub: Dow Jones & Company Inc.
Contact: Almar Latour, Chief Executive Officer

Ed: Christopher C. Williams. **Description:** Shares of Ryder System Inc. are expected to continue rising on the back of rising earnings, forecast at $5.20 a share for 2009. The shares of the truck freight company hit a 52-week high of $62.27 each and may reach $70 a share. **Availability:** Online.

24088 ■ *"Sacred Success: A Course in Financial Miracles"*
Pub: BenBella Books Inc.
Contact: Aida Herrera, Director
E-mail: aida@benbellabooks.com

Released: October 01, 2014. **Price:** $17.46, hardcover; $11.87, paperback; $12.99, e-book(MOBI); $12.99, e-book(PDF), plus shipping charge; $12.99, E-Book (EPUB); $12.99, e-book(electronic publishing). **Description:** A leading expert on women and money helps women to take control of the finances and lose their fear or ambivalence towards it. It is a tutorial for taking charge of a woman's life along with financial investing success. **Availability:** E-book; Print; Electronic publishing; PDF; Online.

24089 ■ *Safety Net*
Released: February 22, 2011. **Price:** $23, hardcover; $9.99, e-book. **Description:** Ways to build a financial investment strategy that protects you, while ensuring growth in a strong financial future are presented. **Availability:** E-book; Print.

24090 ■ *Save Your Small Business: 10 Crucial Strategies to Survive Hard Times or Close Down & Move On*
Pub: Nolo
Contact: Chris Braun, President

Ed: Ralph Warner, Bethany Laurence. **Description:** According to a study among 500 businesses, 44 percent used credit cards in order to meet their firm's needs in the previous six months. Written by a business owner, this book provides twelve strategies to protect personal assets from creditors and survive the current recession. **Availability:** Print.

24091 ■ *"SBA Can Improve Your Cash Flow" in Business Owner* (Vol. 35, September-October 2011, No. 5, pp. 3)

Description: Federal assistance available to small business is examined. The Small Business Administration loan guarantee program is designed to improve availability and attractiveness of small business loans. **Availability:** Print; Online.

24092 ■ *Schaum's Outline of Financial Management*
Pub: McGraw-Hill Professional

Ed: Jae K. Shim, Joel G. Siegel. **Released:** Third edition. **Description:** Rules and regulations governing corporate finance, including the Sarbanes-Oxley Act are discussed. **Availability:** E-book; Print; Download.

24093 ■ *"Score One for Barron's" in Barron's* (Vol. 89, July 13, 2009, No. 28, pp. 14)
Pub: Dow Jones & Company Inc.
Contact: Almar Latour, Chief Executive Officer

Ed: Andrew Bary. **Description:** 57 companies that were bullishly covered on 'Barron's' for the first half of 2009 were up an average of 20.4 percent compared to the 10.2 percent gain in the relevant market indexes. The bearish stock picks by 'Barron's' were down 3.4 percent compared to a 6.4 percent for the benchmarks. **Availability:** Online.

24094 ■ *"Screening for the Best Stock Screens" in Barron's* (Vol. 90, September 13, 2010, No. 37, pp. 36)
Pub: Barron's Editorial & Corporate Headquarters

Ed: Mike Hogan. **Description:** Pros and cons of the new and revised stock screening tools from Zack, Finviz.com, and GuruFocus are discussed. FinVix.com is more capable for screening through stocks and the service is free. **Availability:** Online.

24095 ■ *"SEC Report On Rating Agencies Falls Short" in Barron's* (Vol. 88, July 14, 2008, No. 28, pp. 35)
Pub: Dow Jones & Company Inc.
Contact: Almar Latour, Chief Executive Officer

Ed: Jack Willoughby. **Description:** The Securities and Exchange Commissions report on credit-rating firms should have drawn attention to the slipshod practices in the offerings of collateralized debt obligations. The report fell short of prescribing correctives for the flawed system of these agencies' relationship with their clients. **Availability:** Online.

24096 ■ *"SECU's Tax Preparation Services Net Members More Than $86 Million in Refunds" in Economics Week* (May 11, 2012)
Description: State Employees' Credit Union (SECU) helped nearly 65,000 North Carolina members file their income taxes in 2012. SECU reports $86 million in refunds and saving members more than $8 million in preparation fees. The credit union promotes its tax preparation services so members can avoid the high fees paid to tax preparers. **Availability:** Print; Online.

24097 ■ *"Sedentary Shoppers: Point, Click, Buy" in Barron's* (Vol. 90, September 6, 2010, No. 36, pp. 11)
Pub: Barron's Editorial & Corporate Headquarters

Ed: Vito J. Racanelli. **Description:** Non-travel online retail sales from January to July 2010 increased nine percent which indicates that online shopping for the coming holidays will be good. Online sales are outpacing traditional shopping, but pricing is still critical. **Availability:** Online.

24098 ■ *"Sentiment Split on Financials: Is the Worse Over or Still to Come?" in Barron's* (Vol. 88, March 24, 2008, No. 12, pp. M14)
Pub: Dow Jones & Company Inc.
Contact: Almar Latour, Chief Executive Officer

Ed: Steven M. Sears. **Description:** Experts in the financial sector are split as to whether or not the worst of the financial crisis brought on by the credit crunch is over. Some options traders are trading on are defensive puts, expecting the worst, while investors buying calls are considered as bullish. **Availability:** Online.

24099 ■ *"Should the Fed Regulate Wall Street?" in Barron's* (Vol. 88, March 24, 2008, No. 12, pp. M15)
Pub: Dow Jones & Company Inc.
Contact: Almar Latour, Chief Executive Officer

Ed: Randall W. Forsyth. **Description:** Greater regulation of the financial sector by the Federal Reserve is essential for it to survive the crisis it is experiencing. The resulting regulation could be in complete contrast with the deregulation the sector previously experienced. **Availability:** Online.

24100 ■ *"Should I or Shouldn't I?" in Indoor Comfort Marketing* (Vol. 70, February 2011, No. 2, pp. 30)

Description: Investment tips are shared for investing in futures options. **Availability:** Print; Online.

24101 ■ *"Should You Choose a Lump-Sum Pension Payout? Here's How Entrepreneur Ramona Harper Decided" in Black Enterprise* (Vol. 44, June 2014, No. 10, pp. 27)
Pub: Earl G. Graves Ltd.
Contact: Earl Graves, Jr., President

Description: Entrepreneur, Ramona Harper, chose a lump sum payout of her pension in order to start a new business. She used $110,000 to start her accessories boutique and put the remaining money into a small business 401(k), which helped her avoid a large tax. Tips to help individuals decide the best way to collect their pension are provided. **Availability:** Online.

24102 ■ *"Silver Standard Reports First Quarter 2007 Results" in Marketwired* (May 14, 2007)
Pub: Comtex News Network Inc.
Contact: Kan Devnani, President

Description: Silver Standard Resources Inc. reports a first quarter loss of $1.6 million compared with the first quarter of 2006 in which the loss was $1.1 million. Statistical data included. **Availability:** PDF; Online.

24103 ■ *The Simple Path to Wealth: Your Road Map to Financial Independence and a Rich, Free Life*

Ed: JL Collins. **Price:** $15.11, Paperback; $9.99, E-book. **Description:** A guide about thinking about money and wealth, with practical, and humor-filled, discussions about a variety of topics involving investing. **Availability:** E-book; Print.

24104 ■ *"Siri Creator SRI International Hopes Lola Cashes In, Too" in Silicon Valley/San Jose Business Journal* (Vol. 30, July 6, 2012, No. 15, pp. 1)
Pub: Baltimore Business Journal
Contact: Rhonda Pringle, President
E-mail: rpringle@bizjournals.com

Description: Software developer and SRI and BBVA have partnered to create virtual personal assistant Lola. The program assists customers with their banking needs. Program features and dimensions are also included. **Availability:** Print; Online.

24105 ■ *"Six Great Stock Funds for the Long Haul" in Barron's* (Vol. 89, July 13, 2009, No. 28, pp. L5)
Pub: Dow Jones & Company Inc.
Contact: Almar Latour, Chief Executive Officer

Ed: Lawrence C. Strauss, Tom Sullivan. **Description:** Six mutual funds that have solid long-term performance, transparency, savvy stock picking, and discipline are presented. The managers of these funds are also evaluated. These funds include the T. Rowe Price Emerging Market Stock Fund, Fairholme, and Dodge & Cox Stock. **Availability:** Online.

24106 ■ *"A Slice of Danish; Fixing Finance" in The Economist* (Vol. 390, January 3, 2009, No. 8612, pp. 55)

Description: Denmark's mortgage-holders and the county's lending system is presented. **Availability:** Print; Online.

24107 ■ *The Small Business Bible: Everything You Need to Know to Succeed in Your Small Business*
Pub: John Wiley & Sons, Inc.
Contact: Christina Van Tassell, Executive Vice President Chief Financial Officer

Ed: Steven D. Strauss. **Released:** Third edition. **Price:** $22.95, paperback; $14.99, E-book. **Description:** Comprehensive guide to starting and running a successful small business. Topics include bookkeeping and financial management, marketing, publicity, and advertising. **Availability:** E-book; Print.

24108 ■ *"Small Business Capital Outlays" in Small Business Economic Trends* (April 2008, pp. 16)
Pub: National Federation of Independent Business
Contact: Brad Close, President

Ed: William C. Dunkelberg, Holly Wade. **Description:** Graphs and tables that present the capital outlays of small businesses in the U.S. are provided. The tables include figures on planned and actual capital expenditures, and type and amount of capital expenditures. **Availability:** PDF.

24109 ■ *"Small Business Capital Outlays" in Small Business Economic Trends (July 2010, pp. 16)*
Pub: National Federation of Independent Business
Contact: Brad Close, President

Description: A graph representing actual and planned capital expenditures among small businesses surveyed in the U.S. from January 1986 to June 2010 is given. Tables showing actual capital expenditures, type of capital expenditures made, amount of capital expenditures made, and capital expenditure plans are also presented. **Availability:** Print; PDF; Online.

24110 ■ *Small Business for Dummies*
Pub: John Wiley & Sons, Inc.
Contact: Christina Van Tassell, Executive Vice President Chief Financial Officer

Ed: Eric Tyson, Jim Schell. **Released:** 5th Edition. **Price:** $24.99, paperback; $16.99, E-book. **Description:** Guidebook for anyone wanting to start or grow a small business; topics include information financing, budgeting, marketing, management and more. **Availability:** E-book; Print.

24111 ■ *"Small Business Economic Trends: Moderate Improvement but No Clear Direction" in Small Business Economic Trends (March 2008, pp. 3)*
Pub: National Federation of Independent Business
Contact: Brad Close, President

Ed: William C. Dunkelberg, Holly Wade. **Description:** Commentary on the economic trends for small businesses in the U.S. is presented. Analysis of the labor market and low interest rates is given. The effect of the Federal Reserve's policy announcement on small business owner optimism is also discussed. **Availability:** Print; Online.

24112 ■ *"The Smell of Fear: Is a Bottom Near?" in Barron's (Vol. 88, March 17, 2008, No. 11, pp. M3)*
Pub: Dow Jones & Company Inc.
Contact: Almar Latour, Chief Executive Officer

Ed: Kopin Tan. **Description:** Liquidity problems at Bear Stearns frightened investors in markets around the world due to the fear of the prospects of a big bank's failure. Shares of health maintenance organizations got battered led by WellPoint, and Humana but longer-term investors who could weather short-term volatility may find value here. The value of J. Crew shares is also discussed. **Availability:** Online.

24113 ■ *"A Socko Payout Menu: Rural Phone Carrier Plots to Supercharge Its Shares" in Barron's (Vol. 88, June 30, 2008, No. 26, pp. M5)*

Description: CenturyTel boosted its quarterly common payout to 70 cents from 6.75 cents per share die to its strong cash flows and solid balance sheet. Eastman Kodak's plan for a buyback will be partially funded by its $581 million tax refund. CME Group will buyback stocks through 2009 worth $1.1 billion. **Availability:** Online.

24114 ■ *"Some Relief Possible Following Painful Week" in Barron's (Vol. 88, July 14, 2008, No. 28, pp. M3)*
Pub: Dow Jones & Company Inc.
Contact: Almar Latour, Chief Executive Officer

Ed: Kopin Tan. **Description:** Dow Chemical is offering a 74 percent premium to acquire Rohm & Haas' coatings and electronics materials operations. Frontline amassed a 5.6 percent stake in rival Overseas Shipholding Group and a merger between the two would create a giant global fleet with pricing power. Highlights of the U.S. stock market during the week that ended in July 11, 2008 are discussed. Statistical data included. **Availability:** Online.

24115 ■ *"Spotlight on Pensions" in Business Horizons (Vol. 51, March-April 2008, No. 2, pp. 105)*
Pub: Elsevier Advanced Technology Publications

Ed: Laureen A. Maines. **Description:** Perceptions of pension burden and risk among financial statement users is likely to increase with changes in pension accounting. These perceptions might affect decisions on pension commitments and investments. **Availability:** Online.

24116 ■ *"Spreading Your Wings" in Canadian Business (Vol. 81, March 17, 2008, No. 4, pp. 31)*

Ed: Megan Harman. **Released:** February 09, 2017. **Description:** Financing from angel investors is one avenue that should be explored by startups. Angel investors are typically affluent individuals who invest their own money. Angel investors usually want at least 10 times their initial investment within eight years but they benefit the businesses through their help in decision-making and the industry expertise they provide. **Availability:** Download; Online.

24117 ■ *"Stand-Up Guy: From Bear Stearns to Bear Market" in Barron's (Vol. 88, July 7, 2008, No. 27, pp. L11)*
Pub: Dow Jones & Company Inc.
Contact: Almar Latour, Chief Executive Officer

Ed: Suzanne McGee. **Description:** James O'Shaughnessy, a mutual fund manager with O'Shaughnessy Asset Management, is bullish on both financial and energy stocks. He was formerly involved with Bear Stearns until he left the firm in March 2008. **Availability:** Online.

24118 ■ *"State of the States" in Barron's (Vol. 92, August 27, 2012, No. 38, pp. 23)*
Pub: Dow Jones & Company Inc.
Contact: Almar Latour, Chief Executive Officer

Ed: Andrew Bary. **Description:** The strength of finances of US states are ranked based on their debt ad unfunded pensions compared with their gross domestic products. South Dakota is considered to have the healthiest finances, while those of Connecticut are the weakest. **Availability:** Online.

24119 ■ *"Stock Car Racing" in Canadian Business (Vol. 81, September 15, 2008, No. 14-15, pp. 29)*

Description: Some analysts predict a Chapter 11-style tune-up making GM and Ford a speculative turnaround stock. However, the price of oil could make or break the shares of the Big Three U.S. automobile manufacturers and if oil goes up too high then a speculative stock to watch is an electric car company called Zenn Motor Co. **Availability:** Online.

24120 ■ *"Strategy Migration In a Changing Climate" in Harvard Business Review (Vol. 92, May 2014, No. 5, pp. 42)*
Pub: Harvard Business Publishing
Contact: Diane Belcher, Managing Director

Price: $6. **Description:** The CEO of World Wildlife Fund discusses the importance of ensuring reliable source supplies and mitigating reputational and financial risk in promoting corporate sustainability. Forging alliances to achieve goals is also key. **Availability:** Online; PDF.

24121 ■ *Streetwise Finance and Accounting for Entrepreneurs: Set Budgets, Manage Costs, Keep Your Business Profitable*
Description: Book offers a basic understanding of accounting and finance for small businesses, including financial statements, credits and debits, as well as establishing a budget. Strategies for small companies in financial distress are included.

24122 ■ *"Stressed Out: 7 St. Louis Banks Rated 'At Risks'" in Saint Louis Business Journal (Vol. 32, September 16, 2011, No. 3, pp. 1)*
Pub: Saint Louis Business Journal
Contact: Robert Bobroff, President
E-mail: rbobroff@bizjournals.com

Ed: Greg Edwards. **Description:** St. Louis, Missouri has seven banks that are well above the 100 percent level that is considered 'at risk' based on a risk measurement called the Texas ratio. The banks are the Sun Security bank, 1st Advantage Bank, Superior Bank, Truman Bank, Reliance Bank, St. Louis Bank and Meramec Valley Bank. **Availability:** Online.

24123 ■ *"Stretch Your Last Dollar Or Invest It?" in Business Owner (Vol. 35, November-December 2011, No. 6, pp. 4)*
Description: Should small business owners cut expenses or invest in a downturned economy? Difficult times can be an opportunity to build a business brad. **Availability:** Print; Online.

24124 ■ *"A Study in Diversity: What Women Want: There Are Fundamental Differences Between How Men and Women View Retirement Planning" in Senior Market Advisor (Vol. 13, October 2012, No. 10, pp. 36)*
Description: An overview of women's attitudes towards finances and retirement planning is provided. Contrasting views are even held by male and female financial advisors. **Availability:** Print; Online.

24125 ■ *"Sudden Shift Leaves Wells Fargo Vendor Scrambling" in Charlotte Business Journal (Vol. 25, July 9, 2010, No. 16, pp. 1)*
Pub: Charlotte Business Journal
Contact: Robert Morris, Editor
E-mail: rmorris@bizjournals.com

Ed: Adam O'Daniel. **Description:** Rubber stamps vendor Carolina Marking Devices is facing a 30 percent drop in business after banking firm Wells Fargo & Company decided to buy its rubber stamps from another vendor. Carolina Marking Devices had provided rubber to First Union Corporation and its successor Wachovia Corporation, which was eventually acquired by Wells Fargo. Other reactions from Carolina Marking Device owners are given. **Availability:** Print; Online.

24126 ■ *"Surprise Package" in Business Courier (Vol. 27, June 25, 2010, No. 8, pp. 1)*
Pub: Business Courier

Ed: Dan Monk, Jon Newberry, Steve Watkins. **Description:** More than 60 percent of the chief executive officers (CEOs) in Greater Cincinnati's 35 public companies took a salary cut in 2009, but stock grants resulted in large paper gains for the CEOs. The salary cuts show efforts of boards of directors to observe austerity. Statistics on increased values of stock awards for CEOs, median pay for CEOs, and median shareholder return are also presented. **Availability:** Online.

24127 ■ *"Surviving the Storm" in Canadian Business (Vol. 81, July 22, 2008, No. 12-13, pp. 50)*
Description: Investment adviser Harry Dent and finance professor Paul Marsh discuss their views and forecasts on the United States' economic condition. Dent believes advisors should concentrate on wealth preservation rather than on returns. Other views regarding U.S. economic conditions are also presented. **Availability:** Print; Online.

24128 ■ *"A Swifter, Better Marketplace" in Barron's (Vol. 89, July 13, 2009, No. 28, pp. M13)*
Pub: Dow Jones & Company Inc.
Contact: Almar Latour, Chief Executive Officer

Ed: Eric W. Noll. **Description:** Listed-derivatives market is moving towards greater trading through computerized systems with an emphasis on speed and innovation. The market for listed options is also being changed by new techniques from other markets such as algorithmic trading, dark pools, and new-order priority systems. **Availability:** Online.

24129 ■ *"Tackling Tuition Increases Head On" in Pittsburgh Business Times (Vol. 34, July 25, 2014, No. 1, pp. 6)*
Pub: American City Business Journals, Inc.
Contact: Mike Olivieri, Executive Vice President

Description: The University of Pittsburgh has tried to contain tuition increases after the state cut funding by about $70 million in the 2012 budget year. The measures include a one-time-only early retirement program offered in 2012, greater focus on sustainability and cutting energy costs, and streamlining operations and sharing services. **Availability:** Print; Online.

24130 ■ "Take Control of Your Company's Finances" in Green Industry Pro (Vol. 23, March 2011, No. 3, pp. 24)
Ed: Gregg Wartgow. **Description:** Understanding that when certain leading indicators that affect the outcome of certain lagging indicators are aligned, companies will be able to take control of their firm's finances. Ways to improve the processes that drive financial performance for landscape firms are outlined. **Availability:** Online.

24131 ■ "Take It to the Bank" in Barron's (Vol. 89, July 13, 2009, No. 28, pp. 20)
Pub: Dow Jones & Company Inc.
Contact: Almar Latour, Chief Executive Officer
Ed: Jim McTague. **Description:** Banks are one of the safest place to put one's principal due to the temporary increase in the Federal Deposit Insurance Corp.'s insurance of bank accounts up to $250,000 and also because of the Cdars (Certificates of Deposit Registry Service) program which spreads the deposit to several banks thereby making the account covered as if it the money was deposited at multiple banks. **Availability:** Online.

24132 ■ "Taking the Over-the-Counter Route to U.S." in Barron's (Vol. 88, July 7, 2008, No. 27, pp. 24)
Pub: Dow Jones & Company Inc.
Contact: Almar Latour, Chief Executive Officer
Ed: Eric Uhlfelder. **Description:** Many multinational companies have left the New York Stock Exchange and allowed their shares to trade over-the-counter. The companies have taken advantage of a 2007 SEC rule allowing publicly listed foreign companies to change trading venues if less than 5 percent of global trading volume in the past 12 months occurred in the US. **Availability:** Online.

24133 ■ "Tao of Downfall: the Failures of High-profile Entrepreneurs in the Chinese Economic Reform" in International Journal of Entrepreneurship and Small Business (Vol. 11, August 31, 2010, No. 2, pp. 121)
Ed: Wenxian Zhang, Ilan Alon. **Description:** Through historical reviews and case studies, this research seeks to understand why some initially successful entrepreneurs failed in the economic boom of past decades. Among various factors contributing to their downfall are a unique political and business environment, fragile financial systems, traditional cultural influences and personal characteristics. **Availability:** Online.

24134 ■ "That's About It for Quantitative Easing" in Barron's (Vol. 89, July 20, 2009, No. 29, pp. M11)
Pub: Dow Jones & Company Inc.
Contact: Almar Latour, Chief Executive Officer
Ed: Brian Blackstone. **Description:** US Federal Reserve appears to have decided to halt quantitative easing, causing bond prices to drop and yields to rise. The yield for the 1-year Treasury bond rose more than 0.3 percentage point to about 3.65 percent. **Availability:** Online.

24135 ■ "They've Fallen, But Can Senior-Housing Stocks Get Up" in Barron's (Vol. 88, March 10, 2008, No. 10, pp. 43)
Pub: Dow Jones & Company Inc.
Contact: Almar Latour, Chief Executive Officer
Ed: Kopin Tan. **Description:** Shares of senior housing companies present buying opportunities to investors because of their low prices. Companies such as Brookdale Senior Living are not as dependent on housing prices but have suffered declines in share prices. **Availability:** Online.

24136 ■ "Time to Leave the Party? Re-Evaluating Commodities" in Barron's (Vol. 88, March 24, 2008, No. 12, pp. M16)
Pub: Dow Jones & Company Inc.
Contact: Almar Latour, Chief Executive Officer
Ed: Andrea Hotter. **Description:** Prices of commodities such as gold, copper, crude oil, sugar, cocoa, and wheat have fallen from their all-time highs set in the middle of March 2008. Analysts, however, caution that this decline in prices may be temporary, and that a banking crisis may trigger new price rises in commodities. **Availability:** Online.

24137 ■ "Time for a Little Pruning?" in Barron's (Vol. 89, July 6, 2009, No. 27, pp. 13)
Pub: Dow Jones & Company Inc.
Contact: Almar Latour, Chief Executive Officer
Ed: Dimitra DeFotis. **Description:** Investors are advised to avoid the shares of Whole Foods, American Tower, T. Rowe Price, Iron Mountain, Intuitive Surgical, Salesforce.com, and Juniper Networks due to their high price to earnings ratios. The shares of Amazon.com, Broadcom, and Expeditors International of Washington remain attractive to investors despite their high price to earnings ratios due to their strong growth. **Availability:** Online.

24138 ■ "Time to Tweet: Banks and Fun, Benefits in Social Media" in Philadelphia Business Journal (Vol. 31, February 24, 2012, No. 2, pp. 1)
Pub: Baltimore Business Journal
Contact: Rhonda Pringle, President
E-mail: rpringle@bizjournals.com
Description: Pennsylvania-based banks have benefited from the use of social media to market their services. TD Bank used Twitter to respond to customer complaints. Citizens Bank uses Twitter to provide customers with financial tips. **Availability:** Print.

24139 ■ "Time Value of Money Rate of Return" in Business Owner (Vol. 35, September-October 2011, No. 5, pp. 8)
Description: Estimating value of an income-generating asset or group of assets requires the small business owner to consider concepts such as the time value of money, risk and required rate of return. A brief summary explaining this theory is presented. **Availability:** Print; Online.

24140 ■ "Too Much Information?" in Black Enterprise (Vol. 37, December 2006, No. 5, pp. 59)
Pub: Earl G. Graves Ltd.
Contact: Earl Graves, Jr., President
Ed: James C. Johnson. **Description:** African American business owners often face the dilemma of whether or not to divulge their minority status when soliciting new customers and financial institutions. The quality of the products or services is always the key factor and race should never define one's business; however, it is appropriate to market oneself as a minority- or women-owned business, especially if the company is in an industry where those clients are offered top-tier contracts. **Availability:** Online.

24141 ■ "Too Much Precaution About Biotech Corn" in Barron's (Vol. 88, March 17, 2008, No. 11, pp. 54)
Pub: Dow Jones & Company Inc.
Contact: Almar Latour, Chief Executive Officer
Ed: Mark I. Schwartz. **Description:** In the U.S., 90 percent of cultivated soybeans are biotech varietals as well as 60 percent of the corn. Farmers have significantly reduced their reliance on pesticides in the growing of biotech corn. Biotech cotton cultivation has brought hundreds of millions of dollars in net financial gains to farmers. The European Union has precluded the cultivation or sale of biotech crops within its border. **Availability:** Online.

24142 ■ "Top 10 Retirement Mistakes and How to Avoid Them" in Canadian Business (Vol. 83, July 20, 2010, No. 11-12, pp. 39)
Pub: Rogers Media Inc.
Contact: Neil Spivak, Chief Executive Officer
Ed: Jacqueline Nelson, Angelina Chapin. **Description:** Some of the top retirement mistakes are relying on selling one's house to find a retirement. Other mistakes are paying too much for investments and planning to work in retirement since no one can be sure that they will be healthy enough to accomplish this. Suggestions to avoid these pitfalls are discussed. **Availability:** Print; Online.

24143 ■ "Top 50 In Total Revenue" in Canadian Business (Vol. 81, Summer 2008, No. 9, pp. 119)
Description: Table showing the top 50 Canadian companies in terms of total revenue is presented. Manulife Financial Corp. topped the list with revenue of 34.5 billion. The financial services firm is the 6th largest provider of life insurance in the world and the second largest in North America. **Availability:** Print; Online.

24144 ■ "Top 100 Indy Advisors" in Barron's (Vol. 92, August 25, 2012, No. 38, pp. S2)
Pub: Dow Jones & Company Inc.
Contact: Almar Latour, Chief Executive Officer
Ed: Suzanne McGee. **Description:** Profiles of five independent financial advisors included the Barron's Top 100 independent financial advisor rankings for 2012 are included. Their investment strategies are also discussed. **Availability:** Online.

24145 ■ "Top Law Firms Join Forces" in Business Journal Portland (Vol. 27, December 3, 2010, No. 40, pp. 1)
Pub: Portland Business Journal
Contact: Andy Giegerich, Managing Editor
E-mail: agiegerich@bizjournals.com
Description: Law Firms Powell PC and Roberts Kaplan LLP will forge a collaboration, whereby 17 Roberts Kaplan attorneys will join the Portland, Oregon-based office of Lane Powell. The partnership is expected to strengthen the law firms' grip on Portland's banking clients. **Availability:** Print; Online.

24146 ■ "Top Pension Fund Sends a Warning" in Barron's (Vol. 92, July 23, 2012, No. 30, pp. M9)
Pub: Dow Jones & Company Inc.
Contact: Almar Latour, Chief Executive Officer
Ed: Michael Aneiro. **Description:** The California Public Employees' Retirement System reported a 1 percent return on investments for the fiscal year ended June 30, 2012. It lost 7.2 percent on stock investments, 11 percent on forest-land holdings and 2 percent on absolute-return assets, negating a 12.7 percent gain on its fixed-income investments. **Availability:** Online.

24147 ■ The Total Money Makeover: A Proven Plan For Financial Fitness
Pub: Nelson Education Ltd.
Contact: Steve Brown, President
Ed: Dave Ramsey. **Released:** Classic edition. **Price:** $20.29, hardcover, free shipping on all orders over $35 (continental U.S. only). **Description:** How to get rid of debt and build up your rainy-day reserves. **Availability:** E-book; Print.

24148 ■ "A Trader Gets a Better Deal From the IRS Than an Investor" in Barron's (Vol. 88, March 31, 2008, No. 13, pp. 56)
Pub: Dow Jones & Company Inc.
Contact: Almar Latour, Chief Executive Officer
Ed: Dan McGuire. **Description:** There is a $3,000 a year annual limit to deducting investor's losses and normal investment expenses are purportedly deductible as miscellaneous expenses on Schedule A only to the extent that they exceed two percent of adjusted gross income. Professional gamblers who can use Schedule C are unable deduct a net gaming loss against income from any other sources. **Availability:** Online.

24149 ■ "Traditional vs. Roth IRA" in Black Enterprise (Vol. 37, October 2006, No. 3, pp. 58)
Pub: Earl G. Graves Ltd.
Contact: Earl Graves, Jr., President

Ed: K. Parker, Carolyn M. Brown. **Description:** Government taxes the traditional IRAs different than it taxes Roth IRAs. **Availability:** Online.

24150 ■ *"A Trend Is His Friend" in Barron's (Vol. 89, July 27, 2009, No. 30, pp. 28)*
Pub: Dow Jones & Company Inc.
Contact: Almar Latour, Chief Executive Officer
Ed: Eric Uhlfelder. **Description:** Global Diversified Program fund under Quality Capital Management is managed through a trading system called the Advanced Resource Allocator which rebalances short-term tactical moves to gather quick profits. CEO Aref Karim's allocations are based on risk and he says their sentiments toward the market conditions are agnostic. **Availability:** Online.

24151 ■ *"Tuesday Morning's Corporate Clearance Rack" in Dallas Business Journal (Vol. 37, February 28, 2014, No. 25, pp. 4)*
Pub: American City Business Journals, Inc.
Contact: Mike Olivieri, Executive Vice President
Released: October 30, 2015. **Description:** Tuesday Morning CEO, Michael Rouleau, has been working to help the company recover from its financial problems. Rouleau has improved the shopping experience from garage sale to discount showroom. The company has also been hiring different executives in the past few years. **Availability:** Print; Online.

24152 ■ *"UB Program Offers Free Tax Preparation" in Buffalo News (January 29, 2012)*
Ed: Jonathan D. Epstein. **Description:** University of Buffalo's Schhol of Management in New York is offering free tax preparation for low-income individuals and families. The program is available on North and South campuses and is designed to help these people save money and collect all refunds in which they are eligible. **Availability:** Online.

24153 ■ *"The Unbanking of America"*
Ed: Lisa Servon. Released: January 10, 2017. **Price:** $15.99, hardcover; $9.99, e-book. **Description:** With nearly half of Americans living paycheck to paycheck, consumers are finding alternatives to traditional banking. Banks often have high monthly fees and overdraft charges are pushing more and more to seek out check-cashers, payday lenders, and even informal lending clubs. This book examines how middle class Americans are operating without banks. **Availability:** E-book; Print.

24154 ■ *"Unemployment Tax Surge Could Hit Businesses Hard" in Orlando Business Journal (Vol. 26, January 1, 2010, No. 31, pp. 1)*
Pub: Orlando Business Journal
Contact: Julie Swyers, Director
E-mail: jswyers@bizjournals.com
Ed: Christopher Boyd. **Description:** Consequences of the almost 1,100 percent increase in Florida's minimum unemployment compensation insurance tax to businesses in the state are discussed. Employers pay for the said tax, which is used to fund the state's unemployment claims. **Availability:** Print; Online.

24155 ■ *"An Unfair Knock on Nokia" in Barron's (Vol. 88, March 10, 2008, No. 10, pp. 36)*
Pub: Dow Jones & Company Inc.
Contact: Almar Latour, Chief Executive Officer
Ed: Mark Veverka. **Description:** Discusses the decision by the brokerage house Exane to recommend a Sell on Nokia shares, presumably due to higher inventories, which is unfounded. The news that the company's inventories are rising is not an indicator of falling demand for its products. The company is also benefiting from solid management and rising market share. **Availability:** Online.

24156 ■ *"Univest Charter Switch Signals Banking Trend" in Philadelphia Business Journal (Vol. 30, September 2, 2011, No. 29, pp. 1)*
Pub: Philadelphia Business Journal
Contact: Sierra Quinn, Director

E-mail: squinn@bizjournals.com
Ed: Jeff Blumenthal. **Description:** Univest Corporation of Pennsylvania changed from a federal to state charter because of cost savings and state agency has greater understanding of the intricacies of the local economy. The Pennsylvania Department of Banking has also received inquiries from seven other banks about doing the same this year. **Availability:** Online.

24157 ■ *"Unpleasant Surprise - When a Stock Distribution is Taxed as Dividend Income" in Barron's (Vol. 88, March 24, 2008, No. 12, pp. 60)*
Pub: Dow Jones & Company Inc.
Contact: Almar Latour, Chief Executive Officer
Ed: Shirley A. Lazo. **Description:** Discusses the $175 million that footwear company Genesco received in a settlement with Finish Line and UBS is considered as a stock distribution and is taxable as dividend income. Railroad company CSX raised its quarterly common payout from 15 cents to 18 cents. **Availability:** Online.

24158 ■ *"The Upside of Fear and Loathing" in Barron's (Vol. 88, March 24, 2008, No. 12, pp. 11)*
Pub: Dow Jones & Company Inc.
Contact: Almar Latour, Chief Executive Officer
Ed: Michael Santoli. **Description:** Fear and risk aversion prevalent among investors may actually serve to cushion the decline and spark a rally in US stock prices. Surveys of investors indicate rising levels of anxiety and bearishness, indicating a possible positive turnaround. **Availability:** Online.

24159 ■ *Using Other People's Money to Get Rich: Secrets, Techniques, and Strategies Investors Use Every Day Using OPM to Make Millions*
Pub: Atlantic Publishing Co.
Contact: Dr. Heather L. Johnson, Contact
Ed: Eric J. Leech. Released: 2010. **Price:** $22.34. **Description:** Discussion showing individuals how to invest using other people's money. **Availability:** Print; Online.

24160 ■ *"Valenti: Roots of Financial Crisis Go Back to 1998" in Crain's Detroit Business (Vol. 24, October 6, 2008, No. 40, pp. 25)*
Pub: Crain Communications Inc.
Contact: Barry Asin, President
Ed: Tom Henderson, Nathan Skid. **Description:** Interview with Sam Valenti III who is the chairman and CEO of Valenti Capital L.L.C., a wealth-management firm; Valenti discusses in detail the history that led up to the current economic crisis as well as his prediction for the future of the country. **Availability:** Print; Online.

24161 ■ *"Virtue and Vice" in Entrepreneur (September 2014)*
Pub: Entrepreneur Media Inc.
Contact: Dan Bova, Director
E-mail: dbova@entrepreneur.com
Description: Socially responsible investments (SRI) are rising in the U.S., but many claim that vice funds offer better returns. Vice fund proponents argue that any profitable company deserves a place in a good investment portfolio. SRI proponents emphasize investments that benefit the society. Analysts note that investors who restrict their investment landscape by selecting only vice funds or only SRI funds may lead to lower returns. Other specialized funds attract activist investors supporting advocacies like gender equality or a positive work environment. **Availability:** PDF; Online.

24162 ■ *"Virtus.com Wins 'Best of Industry' WebAward for Excellence in Financial Services" in Investment Weekly News (October 24, 2009, pp. 227)*
Pub: Investment Weekly News
Description: Web Marketing Association honored Virtus.com, the Website of Virtus Investment Partners, Inc., for Outstanding Achievement in Web Development and Acsys Interactive was awarded the Financial Services Standard of Excellence Award for developing the site. The site was part of a rebranding effort and is a one-stop portal for both financial advisors and their investors. **Availability:** Online.

24163 ■ *"Watchful Eye: Entrepreneur Protects Clients and His Bottom Line" in Black Enterprise (Vol. 38, March 1, 2008, No. 8, pp. 46)*
Pub: Earl G. Graves Ltd.
Contact: Earl Graves, Jr., President
Ed: Tennille M. Robinson. **Description:** Profile of Elijah Shaw, founder of Icon Services Corporation, a full service security and investigative service; Shaw shares his plans to protect clients while growing his business. **Availability:** Online.

24164 ■ *"Wealth Advisory Firms Are Merging, but What's in It for Clients?" in The New York Times (September 13, 2019)*
URL(s): www.nytimes.com/2019/09/13/your-money/wealth-advisers-mergers-clients.html
Ed: Paul Sullivan. Released: September 13, 2019. **Description:** Wealth management firms are being sold due to their high values to private equity firms looking to expand their inventory of profitable companies. But is this good for clients? Favorite and familiar advisers may be lost and getting used to a new replacement can lead to difficulties, plus other aspects of the move may not be seamless such using new platforms. But, clients dealing with smaller firms may actually benefit because this is an opportunity for more growth, which translates to bigger wealth. **Availability:** Online.

24165 ■ *"A Week of the Worst Kind of Selling" in Barron's (Vol. 88, June 30, 2008, No. 26, pp. M3)*
Pub: Dow Jones & Company Inc.
Contact: Almar Latour, Chief Executive Officer
Ed: Kopin Tan. **Description:** In the week that ended in June 27, 2008 the selloff in the U.S. stock market was brought on by mounting bank losses and the spread of economic slowdown on top of high oil prices. The 31 percent decrease in the share price of Ingersoll-Rand since October 2007 may have factored in most of its risks. The company has completed its acquisition of Trane to morph into a refrigeration-equipment company. **Availability:** Online.

24166 ■ *"Well-Timed Entrance" in Barron's (Vol. 92, July 23, 2012, No. 30, pp. 24)*
Pub: Dow Jones & Company Inc.
Contact: Almar Latour, Chief Executive Officer
Ed: Michael Aneiro. **Description:** Dan Ivascyn, portfolio manager of Pimco Income Fund, discusses the fund's investment bonds. The fund is heavily invested in mortgage-backed securities and is positioned for a low-interest-rate environment well into 2014 or 2015. **Availability:** Online.

24167 ■ *"Wenzel Downhole Tools Ltd. Announces First Quarter Results for 2007" in Marketwired (May 14, 2007)*
Pub: Comtex News Network Inc.
Contact: Kan Devnani, President
Description: Wenzel Downhole Tools Ltd., a manufacturer, renter, and seller of drilling tools used in gas and oil exploration, announced its financial results for the first quarter ended March 31, 2007 which includes achieved revenues of $14.5 million. Statistical data included. **Availability:** Print; Online.

24168 ■ *"Western & Southern to Trim Rich Retirement Plan" in Business Courier (Vol. 27, October 15, 2010, No. 24, pp. 1)*
Pub: Business Courier
Ed: Dan Monk. **Description:** Insurance firm Western & Southern Financial Group announced that it will reduce the pension benefits of its 4,000 associates by more than 30 percent starting January 1, 2011. The move is expected to reduce annual retirement payments by several thousand dollars per associate. Western is a Fortune 500 company and has $34 billion in total assets. **Availability:** Print; Online.

24169 ■ *"Weyerhaeuser's REIT Decision Shouldn't Scare Investors Away"* in *Barron's* (Vol. 88, June 30, 2008, No. 26, pp. 18)
Pub: Dow Jones & Company Inc.
Contact: Almar Latour, Chief Executive Officer
Ed: Christopher Williams. **Description:** Weyerhaeuser Co.'s management said that a conversion to a real estate investment trust was not likely in 2009 since the move is not tax-efficient as of the moment and would overload its non-timber assets with debt. The company's shares have fallen by 19.5 percent. However, the company remains an asset-rich outfit and its activist shareholder is pushing for change. **Availability:** Online.

24170 ■ *"What Has Sergey Wrought?"* in *Barron's* (Vol. 89, July 13, 2009, No. 28, pp. 8)
Pub: Dow Jones & Company Inc.
Contact: Almar Latour, Chief Executive Officer
Ed: Alan Abelson. **Description:** Sergey Aleynikov is a computer expert that once worked for Goldman Sachs but he was arrested after he left the company and charged with theft for bringing with him the code for the company's proprietary software for high-frequency trading. The stock market has been down for four straight weeks as of July 13, 2009 which reflects the reality of how the economy is still struggling. **Availability:** Online.

24171 ■ *"What Online Brokers Are Doing To Keep Their Customers' Accounts Safe"* in *Barron's* (Vol. 88, March 10, 2008, No. 10, pp. 37)
Pub: Dow Jones & Company Inc.
Contact: Almar Latour, Chief Executive Officer
Ed: Theresa W. Carey. **Description:** Online brokerage firms employ different methods to protect the accounts of their customers from theft. These methods include secure Internet connections, momentary passwords, and proprietary algorithms. **Availability:** Online.

24172 ■ *"Whatever Happened to TGIF? How Much Of the Recession Is Priced into Stocks?"* in *Barron's* (Vol. 88, March 10, 2008, No. 10, pp. M3)
Pub: Dow Jones & Company Inc.
Contact: Almar Latour, Chief Executive Officer
Ed: Kopin Tan. **Description:** US stock markets fell in early March 2008 to their lowest level in 18 months, venturing close to entering a bear market phase. The S&P 500 has dropped an average of 0.78 percent on Fridays for 2008. **Availability:** Online.

24173 ■ *"What's More Important: Stag or Flation?"* in *Barron's* (Vol. 88, July 14, 2008, No. 28, pp. M8)
Pub: Dow Jones & Company Inc.
Ed: Randall W. Forsyth. **Description:** Economists are divided on which part of stagflation, an economic situation in which inflation and economic stagnation occur simultaneously and remain unchecked for a period of time, is more important. Some economists say that the Federal government is focusing on controlling inflation while others see the central bank as extending its liquidity facilities to the financial sector. **Availability:** Online.

24174 ■ *"When R&D Spending Is Not Enough: The Critical Role of Culture When You Really Want to Innovate"* in *Human Resource Management* (Vol. 49, July-August 2010, No. 4, pp. 767-792)
Pub: John Wiley & Sons, Inc.
Contact: Christina Van Tassell, Executive Vice President Chief Financial Officer
Ed: Sheng Wang, Rebecca M. Guidice, Judith W. Tansky, Zhong-Ming Wang. **Released:** July 19, 2010. **Description:** A study was conducted to examine the effect of contextual contingencies on innovation. Findings indicate that Chinese manufacturers with cultures emphasizing innovation and teamwork more effectively utilize financial resources in the innovation process. Results also show that a culture emphasizing outcomes and stability leads to lower levels innovation irrespective of investments. **Availability:** Print; PDF; Online.

24175 ■ *"When to Roll Over"* in *Black Enterprise* (Vol. 37, November 2006, No. 4, pp. 50)
Pub: Earl G. Graves Ltd.
Contact: Earl Graves, Jr., President
Ed: Carolyn M. Brown. **Description:** Being proactive and rolling over your funds if you own stock of your former employee will give you more control over your money, especially if the company merges or is sold. **Availability:** Online.

24176 ■ *"Where the Money Is"* in *Conde Nast Portfolio* (Vol. 2, June 2008, No. 6, pp. 113)
Description: Revenue generated from treatments for common brain disorders that are currently on the market are listed. **Availability:** Online.

24177 ■ *"Where Small Biz Gets a 'Yes' More Often"* in *Denver Business Journal* (Vol. 65, February 28, 2014, No. 42, pp. A10)
Pub: American City Business Journals, Inc.
Contact: Mike Olivieri, Executive Vice President
Released: Weekly. **Price:** $4, Introductory 4-week offer(Digital & Print). **Description:** The Biz2Credit Small Business Lending Index has found that alternative lenders granted 66.9 percent of funding requests in Colorado compared to the 15.1 percent approval of loans requests by big banks. The big banks' low approval rates were attributed to their less aggressive lending efforts and the state's fewer restrictions on alternative lending. Other findings from the study are discussed. **Availability:** Print; Online.

24178 ■ *"Where to Stash Your Cash"* in *Barron's* (Vol. 88, March 17, 2008, No. 11, pp. 41)
Pub: Dow Jones & Company Inc.
Contact: Almar Latour, Chief Executive Officer
Ed: Mike Hogan. **Description:** Investors are putting their money in money-market mutual funds seeking fractionally better yields and a safe haven from the uncertainties that was brought about by subprime lending. These funds, however, are hovering near 3.20 percent which is less than the 4 percent inflation rate. **Availability:** Online.

24179 ■ *"Whistling Past the Graveyard? Higher Quality Stocks Beckon to Investors?"* in *Barron's* (Vol. 88, March 17, 2008, No. 11, pp. 15)
Pub: Dow Jones & Company Inc.
Contact: Almar Latour, Chief Executive Officer
Ed: Michael Santoli. **Description:** Discusses the Federal Reserve's move to provide $200 billion to the system which can be seen as an effort to avoid the liquidity problems that Bear Stearns suffered. The Federal Reserve's move seems to frighten investors rather than reassure them. **Availability:** Online.

24180 ■ *"Why Asset Allocation Is Important: Don't Only Focus On Your Client's Finances, Start With Their Goals"* in *Retirement Advisor* (Vol. 13, October 2012, No. 10, pp. 20)
Ed: Lloyd Lofton. **Description:** Asset allocation can help investors, particularly seniors, to manage risk when planning investments. Diversity means spreading assets into three major classes of stocks, bonds and fixed products. These investments should be reviewed annually. **Availability:** Print; Online.

24181 ■ *"Why Every Business Owner Needs a Trust"* in *Legal Zoom* (March 24, 2023)
URL(s): www.legalzoom.com/articles/why-every-business-owner-needs-a-trust
Ed: Candice Lapin. **Released:** March 24, 2023. **Description:** Discusses the financial security small business owners receive when creating a trust. **Availability:** Online.

24182 ■ *"Why Intel Should Dump Its Flash-Memory Business"* in *Barron's* (Vol. 88, March 10, 2008, No. 10, pp. 35)
Pub: Dow Jones & Company Inc.
Contact: Almar Latour, Chief Executive Officer
Ed: Eric J. Savitz. **Description:** Intel Corp. must sell its NAND flash-memory business as soon as it possibly can to the highest bidder to focus on its PC processor business and take advantage of other business opportunities. Apple should consider a buyback of 10 percent of the company's shares to lift its stock. **Availability:** Online.

24183 ■ *"Why the Rout in Financials Isn't Over"* in *Barron's* (Vol. 88, June 30, 2008, No. 26, pp. 23)
Pub: Dow Jones & Company Inc.
Contact: Almar Latour, Chief Executive Officer
Ed: Robin Goldwyn Blumenthal. **Description:** Top market technician Louise Yamada warns that the retreat in the shares of financial services is not yet over based on her analysis of stock charts. Yamada's analysis of the charts of Citigroup, Fifth Third Bancorp and Merrill Lynch are discussed together with the graphs for these shares. Statistical data included. **Availability:** Online.

24184 ■ *"Why This Investing Expert Is Bullish On the Energy Sector: William Heard Expects the Changing Landscape to Lead to Greater Opportunities"* in *Black Enterprise* (Vol. 45, July-August 2014, No. 1, pp. 25)
Pub: Earl G. Graves Ltd.
Contact: Earl Graves, Jr., President
Description: Profile of William Heard and his firm Heard Capital, LLC, the Chicago-based investment company that invests in telecommunications, media, technology, financials, industrials, and energy. Heard shares his investment philosophy and current investments.

24185 ■ *"Why Your Business Credit Score Matters"* in *Legal Zoom* (March 9, 2023)
URL(s): www.legalzoom.com/articles/why-your-business-credit-score-matters
Ed: Kylie Ora Lobell. **Released:** March 09, 2023. **Description:** Much like your personal credit score, your business credit score is used to help the business obtain financing, so be sure to set and maintain a good score. **Availability:** Online.

24186 ■ *"Wielding a Big Ax"* in *Barron's* (Vol. 89, July 13, 2009, No. 28, pp. 26)
Pub: Dow Jones & Company Inc.
Contact: Almar Latour, Chief Executive Officer
Ed: Shirley A. Lazo. **Description:** Weyerhaeuser cut their quarterly common payout by 80 percent from 25 cents to a nickel a share which they say will help them preserve their long-term value and improve their performance. Paccar also cut their quarterly dividend by half to nine cents a share. Walgreen however, boosted their quarterly dividend by 22.2 percent to 13.75 cents a share. **Availability:** Online.

24187 ■ *Wisdom From Rich Dad, Poor Dad*
Released: October 25, 2016. **Price:** $5.95, hardcover. **Description:** What the wealthy teach their children about money that others do not. **Availability:** Print.

24188 ■ *"A World of Opportunity: Foreign Markets Offer Diversity to Keen Investors"* in *Canadian Business* (Vol. 81, Summer 2008, No. 9)
Description: International Monetary Fund projected in its 'World Economy Outlook' that there is a 25 percent chance that a global recession will occur in 2008 and 2009. Global growth rate is forecasted at 3.7 percent in 2008. Inflation in Asia emerging markets and forecasts on stock price indexes are presented. **Availability:** Online.

24189 ■ *"World's Best CEOs"* in *Barron's* (Vol. 88, March 24, 2008, No. 12, pp. 33)
Pub: Dow Jones & Company Inc.
Contact: Almar Latour, Chief Executive Officer

Ed: Andrew Bary. **Description:** Listing of the 30 best chief executive officers worldwide which was compiled through interviews with investors and analysts, analysis of financial and stock market performance, and leadership and industry stature.

24190 ■ *"The Worst Lies Ahead for Wall Street: More Losses Certain; More Expensive Capital to Be Needed"* in *Crain's New York Business* (Vol. 24, January 20, 2008, No. 3, pp. 1)
Pub: Crain Communications, Inc.
Contact: Jessica Botos, Manager, Marketing
E-mail: jessica.botos@crainsnewyork.com

Ed: Aaron Elstein. **Description:** Due to the weakening economy, many financial institutions will face further massive losses forcing them to borrow more at higher interest rates and dragging down their earnings for years to come. The effects on commercial real estate and credit card loans are also discussed as well as the trend to investing in Asia and the Middle East. **Availability:** Online.

24191 ■ *"You Won't Go Broke Filling Up On The Stock"* in *Barron's* (Vol. 88, July 14, 2008, No. 28, pp. 38)
Pub: Dow Jones & Company Inc.
Contact: Almar Latour, Chief Executive Officer

Ed: Assif Shameen. **Description:** Due to high economic growth, pro-business policies and a consumption boom, the Middle East is a good place to look for equities. The best ways in which to gain exposure to this market include investing in the real estate industry and telecommunications markets as well as large banks that serve corporations and consumers. **Availability:** Online.

24192 ■ *"Young People Speak Out On Credit Union Board Involvement"* in *Credit Union Times* (Vol. 21, July 14, 2010, No. 27, pp. 20)
Ed: Myriam DiGiovanni. **Description:** Results of a Credit Union Times survey of Generation Y individuals about serving on Credit Union boards across the country are examined. **Availability:** Online.

24193 ■ *Your Complete Guide to a Successful & Secure Retirement*
Ed: Larry Swedroe, Kevin Grogan. **Released:** January 07, 2019. **Price:** $11.88, Paperback; $8.19, E-book. **Description:** A helpful guide for those financially preparing for retirement. Discusses social security, medicare, investing, portfolio management, and more. **Availability:** E-book; Print.

24194 ■ *"Your Exposure to Bear Stearns"* in *Barron's* (Vol. 88, March 17, 2008, No. 11, pp. 45)
Pub: Dow Jones & Company Inc.
Contact: Almar Latour, Chief Executive Officer

Ed: Tom Sullivan, Jack Willoughby. **Description:** Bear Stearns makes up 5.5 percent of Pioneer Independence's portfolio, 1.4 percent of Vanguard Windsor II's portfolio, 1.2 percent of Legg Mason Value Trust, about 1 percent of Van Kampen Equity & Income, and 0.79 percent of Putnam Fund for Growth & Income. Ginnie Mae securities are now trading at 1.78 percentage points over treasuries due to the mortgage crises. **Availability:** Online.

24195 ■ *Your Guide to Arranging Bank & Debt Financing for Your Own Business in Canada*
Pub: Productive Publications
Contact: Iain Williamson, Author Publisher

Ed: Iain Williamson. **Released:** 2022-2023 Edition. **Price:** C$99.95, softcover, Postage/handling $19.95 on first title, Add postage/handling of $3.50 per title thereafter. **Description:** Bank financing for small businesses in Canada is discussed. **Availability:** Print.

24196 ■ *Your Guide to Canadian Export Financing: Successful Techniques for Financing Your Exports from Canada*
Pub: Productive Publications
Contact: Iain Williamson, Author Publisher

Ed: Iain Williamson. **Released:** 2022-2023 Edition. **Price:** C$74.95, softcover, Postage/handling $19.95 on first title, Add postage/handling of $3.50 per title thereafter. **Description:** Canadian export financing is covered. **Availability:** Print.

24197 ■ *Your Guide to Preparing a Plan to Raise Money for Your Own Business*
Pub: Productive Publications
Contact: Iain Williamson, Author Publisher

Ed: Iain Williamson. **Released:** Revised edition. **Price:** C$68.95, softcover, Postage/handling $19.95 on first title, Add postage/handling of $3.50 per title thereafter. **Description:** A good business plan is essential for raising money for any small business. **Availability:** Print.

24198 ■ *"Zions Offers Step-by-Step Small Business Guidance"* in *Idaho Business Review* (September 1, 2014)
Pub: BridgeTower Media
Contact: Adam Reinebach, President

Description: Zions bank provides small business guidance to clients through its Zions Bank Idaho Business Resource Center. The program helps entrepreneurs learn the basic rules of running a small business. Free courses teach the essentials of finance, marketing and selling, .

VIDEO/AUDIO MEDIA

24199 ■ *Be a Profitable Badass Small Business Owner: Are You a Profitable Business Owner?*
URL(s): traffic.libsyn.com/secure/localsmallbusinessownercoach/611_profitable_badass_business_owner.mp3

Ed: Tammy Adams. **Released:** July 15, 2024. **Description:** Podcast discusses acting like a profitable business owner vs. running a business from a survival mindset.

24200 ■ *Be a Profitable Badass Small Business Owner: Two Calculations to Know in Your Small Business*
URL(s): traffic.libsyn.com/secure/localsmallbusinessownercoach/598_pod_two_calucations_to_know_in_your_business.mp3

Ed: Tammy Adams. **Released:** April 01, 2024. **Description:** Podcast discusses two calculations to make a small business more profitable.

24201 ■ *The Best Small Business Show: 4 Steps to Dramatically Increase Your Profits*
URL(s): richgee.libsyn.com/245-4-steps-to-dramatically-increase-your-profits

Ed: Rich Gee. **Released:** April 04, 2022. **Description:** Podcast explains how to increase profits even with inflation.

24202 ■ *The Best Small Business Show: Make Friends with Your Business Financials*
URL(s): richgee.libsyn.com/231-make-friends-with-your-business-financials

Ed: Rich Gee. **Released:** February 21, 2022. **Description:** Podcast outlines a few basic habits to strengthen financial standing.

24203 ■ *A Billion-Dollar CEO's #1 Fundraiisng Tip*
URL(s): theceoschool.co/a-billion-dollar-ceos-1-fundraising-tip

Ed: Suneera Madhani. **Released:** September 07, 2022. **Description:** Podcast offers tips on raising capital and getting the funding you need for your business.

24204 ■ *BS-Free Service Business Show: Making the Math "Math" for Your Service Business*
URL(s): bsfreebusiness.com/math-for-your-service-business

Ed: Maggie Patterson. **Released:** May 13, 2024. **Description:** Podcast offers financial management tips, including overcoming poor financial advice, becoming more comfortable with using your numbers as strategic tool, spotting trends, budgeting effectively, understanding your profit margin, and paying yourself. .

24205 ■ *BS-Free Service Business Show: Pricing Survival Guide for a Messed-Up Economy*
URL(s): bsfreebusiness.com/pricing-services

Ed: Maggie Patterson. **Released:** May 20, 2024. **Description:** Podcast discusses the importance of accurate pricing, how to respond if clients say they can't afford your services, and analyzing your pricing structure.

24206 ■ *BS-Free Service Business Show: The Real Cost of Creating an Agency*
Ed: Maggie Patterson. **Released:** February 19, 2024. **Description:** Podcast discusses the real cost of agency ownership, including the financial realities, client expectations, and the roller coaster of leadership.

24207 ■ *Common Financial Mistakes Entrepreneurs Make and Hot to Avoid Them*
URL(s): theceoschool.co/common-financial-mistakes-entrepreneurs-make-and-how-to-avoid-them

Ed: Suneera Madhani. **Released:** April 10, 2023. **Description:** Podcast offers strategies to improve your business's financial health, including budgeting, expense tracking, and cash flow analysis. Also discusses using debt responsibly, building an emergency fund, separating business and personal expenses, and implementing tax strategies.

24208 ■ *Elevated Entrepreneurship: Alan Stein Jr.: Improving Your Entrepreneurial Game*
URL(s): mikemichalowicz.com/podcast/podcast/alan-stein-jr

Ed: Mike Michalowiicz. **Released:** April 27, 2020. **Description:** Podcast offers simple strategies to improve entrepreneurial performance.

24209 ■ *Five CEO Tips for Succeeding through an Economic Bust*
URL(s): theceoschool.co/256-five-ceo-tips-for-succeeding-through-an-economic-bust

Ed: Suneera Madhani. **Released:** September 28, 2023. **Description:** Podcast offers tips and strategies for CEOs during challenging economic times, including diversifying your revenue stream, focusing on current customers, and embracing digital marketing.

24210 ■ *The How of Business: Financial Projections for Small Business Startup*
URL(s): www.thehowofbusiness.com/395-business-startup-financial-projections

Ed: Henry Lopez. **Released:** October 25, 2021. **Description:** Podcast explains how to create a financial projection and what it should include.

24211 ■ *How to Master the Financial Fundamentals with Adam Kroener*
URL(s): www.eofire.com/podcast/adamkroener

Ed: Jon Lee Dumas. **Released:** March 05, 2024. **Description:** Podcast discusses financing fundamentals and what most those who are struggling get wrong.

24212 ■ *How to Sustain Profitability in Uncertain Times with Paul Zelizer*
URL(s): www.awarepreneurs.com/podcast/322-sustainable-profitability

Ed: Paul Zelizer. **Released:** February 13, 2024. **Description:** Podcast offers tip for sustaining profitability, including strategic partnerships, diversifying revenue streams, and SEO optimization.

24213 ■ *Profit First Nation: Boost Your Business's Value and Maximize Profit*
URL(s): www.profitfirstnation.com/episodes/ep-132-boost-your-business-value-and-maximize-profit-4-strategies-to-amplify-profitability

Ed: Danielle Mulvey. **Released:** August 22, 2023. **Description:** Podcast offers four strategies to maximize profit and value.

24214 ■ *Profit First Nation: Mastering Profit First: A Comprehensive Guide to Allocating Funds for Financial Success*
URL(s): www.profitfirstnation.com/episodes/ep-130-mastering-profit-first-a-comprehensive-guide-to-allocating-funds-for-financial-success
Ed: Danielle Mulvey. **Released:** August 22, 2023. **Description:** Podcast describes the Profit First philosophy and accounting system.

24215 ■ *Profit First Nation: The Sum of All Things*
URL(s): www.profitfirstnation.com/episodes/ep-101-unlocking-business-success-the-five-stages-that-drive-profit
Ed: Danielle Mulvey. **Released:** March 17, 2022. **Description:** Podcast describes five profit-driving stages and strategies to increase effectiveness at each stage.

24216 ■ *Profit First Nation: Unlocking Intentional Growth: 6 Steps for Increased Profitability and Deliberate Expansion*
URL(s): www.profitfirstnation.com/episodes/ep-131-unlocking-intentional-growth-6-steps-for-increased-profitability-and-deliberate-expansion
Ed: Danielle Mulvey. **Released:** August 22, 2023. **Description:** Podcast outlines a process for increased profitability and expansion.

24217 ■ *Setting Yourself Up for Financial Success with Crystalynn Shelton*
URL(s): www.makinggoodpodcast.com/episodes/182
Ed: Lauren Tilden. **Released:** June 20, 2023. **Description:** Podcast discusses financial systems and process to aid your business's success, how to budget for a CPA, financial "fear factors", and how to automate your finances. .

24218 ■ *Small Biz 101: How to Keep Clients Coming Back: Insights from Alex Theis*
URL(s): scatteredtostreamlined.com/how-to-keep-clients-coming-back-insights-from-alex-theis-sb022
Ed: Connie Whitesell. **Released:** November 17, 2023. **Description:** Podcast explains how client retention can break through revenue plateaus.

24219 ■ *This Is Small Business: Detara Finds Funding for Her Business*
URL(s): www.smallbusiness.amazon/podcast-episodes/detara-finds-funding-for-her-business
Ed: Andrea Marquez. **Released:** February 21, 2023. **Description:** Podcast discusses funding your small business. Includes tips on bootstrapping, loans, and grants.

24220 ■ *This Is Small Business: How to Handle Your Cash Flow*
URL(s): www.smallbusiness.amazon/podcast-episodes/ep-39-how-to-handle-your-cash-flow
Ed: Andrea Marquez. **Released:** October 31, 2023. **Description:** Podcast explains why cash flow is vital for funding, key sections in a cash flow statement, and what those sections represent.

24221 ■ *Why Blockchain, Cryptocurrency and NFTs are Important for You to Understand with Joel Comm*
URL(s): www.eofire.com/podcast/joelcomm3
Ed: Jon Lee Dumas. **Released:** February 23, 2024. **Description:** Podcast offers an overview of blockchain technology, cryptocurrency, and NFTs.

TRADE SHOWS AND CONVENTIONS

24222 ■ **ABA Bank Marketing Conference**
American Bankers Association (ABA)
1120 Connecticut Ave. NW
Washington, DC 20036
Free: 800-226-5377
Co. E-mail: support@aba.com
URL: http://www.aba.com
Contact: Rob Nichols, President
URL(s): www.aba.com/training-events/conferences/bank-marketing-conference

Frequency: Irregular. **Description:** Marketing metrics, branch development, compliance, marketing trends, retail banking, customer profitability, branding, online marketing, employee retention, marketing research, and payments. **Audience:** Industry professionals. **Principal Exhibits:** Marketing metrics, branch development, compliance, marketing trends, retail banking, customer profitability, branding, online marketing, employee retention, marketing research, and payments. **Telecommunication Services:** reghousing@aba.com.

24223 ■ **ABA/BMA National Conference for Community Bankers**
Visa Inc.
900 Metro Center B
Foster City, CA 94404
Ph: (650)432-3200
Fax: (650)432-7436
URL: http://www.visa.com
Contact: Rajat Taneja, President
URL(s): www.aba.com/training-events/conferences/conference-for-community-bankers

Frequency: Annual. **Description:** Products and services related to investment management, customer service improvements, advertising, asset/liability management, bank management, electronic data interchange, employee recruitment/training, insurance, strategic planning models, including preparation for the 21st century, new revenue sourhttp://camsfdr.cams.cengage.info:8080/fdr/images/close.jpgces, cost control techniques, mainframe computers, market research, MCIF technology, minicomputers in community banking applications, software: platform, optical disk, and loan pricing, sweep accounts, and relationship banking for community bankers. **Audience:** Industry professionals. **Principal Exhibits:** Products and services related to investment management, customer service improvements, advertising, asset/liability management, bank management, electronic data interchange, employee recruitment/training, insurance, strategic planning models, including preparation for the 21st century, new revenue sourhttp://camsfdr.cams.cengage.info:8080/fdr/images/close.jpgces, cost control techniques, mainframe computers, market research, MCIF technology, minicomputers in community banking applications, software: platform, optical disk, and loan pricing, sweep accounts, and relationship banking for community bankers. Dates and Locations: 2025 Feb 16-18 JW Marriott Phoenix Desert Ridge, Phoenix, AZ. **Telecommunication Services:** reghousing@aba.com.

24224 ■ **AFA Annual Meeting**
American Finance Association (AFA)
1655 E Campus Center Dr.
Salt Lake City, UT 84112
Ph: (201)299-4719
Co. E-mail: membership@afajof.org
URL: http://afajof.org
Contact: Kathleen Weiss Hanley, Executive Secretary Treasurer
E-mail: kwh315@lehigh.edu
URL(s): afajof.org/annual-meeting

Frequency: Annual; held in January. **Description:** Study and promotion of knowledge about financial economics. **Audience:** Members. **Principal Exhibits:** Study and promotion of knowledge about financial economics. Dates and Locations: 2026 Jan 03-05 Philadelphia, PA; 2027 Jan 03-05 Washington, DC; 2028 Jan 07-09 Atlanta, GA; 2029 Jan 05-07 San Diego, CA. **Telecommunication Services:** annette.clark@afajof.org.

24225 ■ **AICPA Advanced Personal Financial Planning (PFP) Conference**
ADP Chile
Apoquindo Avenue N° 5400 - 16th Fl.
Las Condes, Chile
Ph: 56 2 2582 2352
Co. E-mail: soporte.chile@adp.com
URL: http://cl.adp.com
URL(s): www.aicpa-cima.com/cpe-learning/conference/personal-financial-planning-summit

Frequency: Annual. **Description:** Offers guidance for practitioners who specialize in providing estate, tax, retirement, risk management and investment planning advice. **Audience:** Financial planning professionals. **Principal Exhibits:** Offers guidance for practitioners who specialize in providing estate, tax, retirement, risk management and investment planning advice. **Telecommunication Services:** groupconference@aicpa-cima.com.

24226 ■ **Annual Conference & Solutions Expo**
National Association of Federal Credit Unions (NAFCU)
3138 10th St. N
Arlington, VA 22201-2149
Free: 800-336-4644
Co. E-mail: msc@nafcu.org
URL: http://www.nafcu.org
Contact: B. Dan Berger, President
URL(s): www.nafcu.org/engage?tab=0

Frequency: Annual. **Description:** Complete range of financial products and services. **Audience:** Credit union officials and professionals. **Principal Exhibits:** Complete range of financial products and services. **Telecommunication Services:** info@nafcu.org.

24227 ■ **Association for Financial Technology Spring Summit**
URL(s): aftsummit.org

Frequency: Annual. **Description:** Offers professional development for members within the financial technology industry. **Principal Exhibits:** Offers professional development for members within the financial technology industry.

24228 ■ **FMS Forum**
Financial Managers Society (FMS)
7918 Jones Branch Dr., 4th Fl.
McLean, VA 22102
Ph: (312)578-1300
Fax: (312)578-1308
Co. E-mail: info@fmsinc.org
URL: http://www.fmsinc.org
Contact: Alana Vartanian, President
E-mail: avartanian@fmsinc.org
URL(s): www.fmsinc.org/forum25-home.html

Frequency: Annual. **Description:** Offer exemplary teaching and training programs. **Audience:** Industry professionals. **Principal Exhibits:** Offer exemplary teaching and training programs. Dates and Locations: 2025 Jun 22-24 Omni Orlando Resort Champions-Gate, Orlando, FL. **Telecommunication Services:** info@fmsinc.org.

24229 ■ **National Agricultural Bankers Conference**
CHS Hedging, LLC
5500 Cenex Dr.
Inver Grove Heights, MN 55077
Free: 800-328-6530
Co. E-mail: support@chshedging.com
URL: http://chshedging.com
Contact: Nelson Neale, President
URL(s): www.aba.com/training-events/conferences/agricultural-bankers-conference

Frequency: Annual. **Description:** On topics related to latest developments in the agricultural lending business, as well as strategies for better market share, profitability, and customer service. Includes keynote speakers, workshops, and sessions. **Audience:** Industry professionals. **Principal Exhibits:** On topics related to latest developments in the agricultural lending business, as well as strategies for better market share, profitability, and customer service. Includes keynote speakers, workshops, and sessions. **Telecommunication Services:** mrogers@aba.com.

24230 ■ **Small Business Investor Alliance Northeast Private Equity Conference**
Small Business Investor Alliance (SBIA)
529 14th St., NW
Washington, DC 20045
Ph: (202)628-5055
Co. E-mail: info@sbia.org
URL: http://www.sbia.org
Contact: Brett Palmer, President

E-mail: bpalmer@nasbic.org
URL(s): members.sbia.org/events/Details/2024-northeast-private-equity-conference-952960?sourceTypeId=Hub
Frequency: Annual. **Description:** Features speakers, and networking opportunities. **Audience:** Fund managers, limited partners, investment bankers, and industry professionals. **Principal Exhibits:** Features speakers, and networking opportunities. **Telecommunication Services:** events@sbia.org.

24231 ■ Wealth Management and Trust Conference
Alpha Core
URL(s): www.aba.com/training-events/conferences/wealth-management-trust-conference
Frequency: Annual. **Description:** Events for the wealth management and trust banking community. **Audience:** Industry professionals. **Principal Exhibits:** Events for the wealth management and trust banking community. Dates and Locations: 2025 Feb 24-26 Manchester Grand Hyatt, San Diego, CA. **Telecommunication Services:** kchancy@aba.com.

CONSULTANTS

24232 ■ ADG Group (ADG)
5952 Peachtree Industrial Blvd. – Ste. 2
Norcross, GA 30071
Ph: (770)447-9308
Fax: (770)447-9368
Co. E-mail: info@atldesigngroup.com
URL: http://atldesigngroup.com
Facebook: www.facebook.com/atldesigngroup
Linkedin: www.linkedin.com/company/atlanta-design-group
Instagram: www.instagram.com/atlantadesigngroup
Description: Corporate finance advisory firm specializing in arranging venture capital financing for emerging companies. Assists with mergers, acquisitions and divestitures. Offers balance sheet restructuring services for bankrupt and financially troubled companies. Also offers independent due diligence investigations. **Scope:** Corporate finance advisory firm specializing in arranging venture capital financing for emerging companies. Assists with mergers, acquisitions and divestitures. Offers balance sheet restructuring services for bankrupt and financially troubled companies. Also offers independent due diligence investigations.

24233 ■ Aurora Management Partners Inc.
1201 Peachtree St., Ste. 1570
Atlanta, GA 30361
Ph: (704)377-6010
Co. E-mail: info@auroramp.com
URL: http://www.auroramp.com
Contact: David Baker, CTP, Managing Partner
Linkedin: www.linkedin.com/company/aurora-management-partners/about
Description: Specializes in turnaround management and reorganization consulting, the company develops strategic initiatives, organize and analyze solutions, deal with creditor issues, review organizational structures and develop time frames for decision making. **Founded:** 2000. **Publications:** "TMA Turnaround of the Year Award, Small Company, Honorable Mention," Nov, 2005; "Back From The Brink - Bland Farms," Progressive Farmer, Oct, 2004; "New Breed of Turnaround Managers," Catalyst Magazine, Aug, 2004; "Key Performance Drivers - Bland Farms," The Produce News, Apr, 2004; "Corporate Governance: Averting Crisis's Before They Happen," ABJ journal, Feb, 2004.

24234 ■ Be Cause Business Resources Inc.
Canterbury Park
1335 3rd Ave.
Longview, WA 98632
Ph: (360)200-5840
URL: http://becausebusiness.com
Contact: John E. Anderson, President
X (Twitter): x.com/becausebusiness
Description: Firm provides business valuation, executive coaching, facilitation, finance, growth management, marketing, organizational design and project management services. **Scope:** Firm provides business valuation, executive coaching, facilitation, finance, growth management, marketing, organizational design and project management services. **Founded:** 2003.

24235 ■ Beacon Management-Management Consultants
Pompano Beach, FL 33069
Co. E-mail: md@beaconmgmt.com
URL: http://www.beaconmgmt.com
Contact: Michael J. Donnelly, Consultant Managing Director Principal
Description: Provider of management consulting services such as strategic and business planning, market intelligence, decision support services, corporate finance, and much more. **Scope:** Provider of management consulting services such as strategic and business planning, market intelligence, decision support services, corporate finance, and much more. **Founded:** 1985. **Publications:** "Sun-Sentinel Article," Oct, 2012.

24236 ■ Business Benefits, Inc. (BBI)
2620 Regatta Dr., Ste. 102
Las Vegas, NV 89128
Ph: (702)252-0888
Fax: (702)252-0785
URL: http://bbblt.com
Contact: Tim deRosa, President
Facebook: www.facebook.com/BusinessBenefitsInc
Description: Firm provides professional and insurance services such as group benefits, individual, and commercial insurance coverage plans. **Scope:** Firm provides professional and insurance services such as group benefits, individual, and commercial insurance coverage plans. **Founded:** 1981. **Training:** Guardian Advantage product. **Special Services:** Guardian Advantage®; MyWave.

24237 ■ The Business Law Center on WestlawNext
1333 H St. NW
Washington, DC 20005
Ph: (202)898-6300
URL: http://ca.practicallaw.thomsonreuters.com/7-382-3628?transitionType=Default&contextData=(sc.Default)&firstPage=true
Description: Research organization specializing in the real time dissemination of vital corporate information released by the Securities and Exchange Commission and other government agencies that oversee the financial markets. Provides demand and subscription services to remain aware of the current securities markets. Also offers LIVEDGAR, a full text searching research tool that provides real time, desktop access to all EDGAR (electronic data gathering analysis and retrieval) files. Advanced search capabilities include full-text and progressive searching, Boolean logic and search by example for precedent research. **Scope:** Research organization specializing in the real time dissemination of vital corporate information released by the Securities and Exchange Commission and other government agencies that oversee the financial markets. Provides demand and subscription services to remain aware of the current securities markets. Also offers LIVEDGAR, a full text searching research tool that provides real time, desktop access to all EDGAR (electronic data gathering analysis and retrieval) files. Advanced search capabilities include full-text and progressive searching, Boolean logic and search by example for precedent research. **Founded:** 1988. **Special Services:** GSI®; LIVEDGAR®.

24238 ■ Business Valuation Inc. (BVI)
5210 Belfort Rd., Ste. 300
Jacksonville, FL 32256
Ph: (904)356-7600
Co. E-mail: info@bvijax.com
URL: http://www.businessvaluationinc.com
Contact: Don Wiggins, President
E-mail: dwiggins@bvijax.com
X (Twitter): x.com/bizvalinc
Description: Firm provides valuation, litigation support, advisory and value enhancement services. **Scope:** Firm provides valuation, litigation support, advisory and value enhancement services. **Founded:** 1989. **Publications:** "The Economic Impact of Taxes on S Corporation Valuations," Jun, 2000; "Matching Cash Flows and Discount Rates in Discounted Cash Flow Appraisals," Mar, 1999; "A Universal Valuation Model for Closely Held Businesses," Jun, 1996; "Revisiting Valuation of Real Estate Partial Interests Recent Case Study"; "Selling a Business Now May Make Economic Sense". **Training:** How to Value a Business.

24239 ■ CBIZ, Inc.
CBIZ, Inc.
5959 Rockside Woods Blvd. N, Ste. 600
Independence, OH 44131
Ph: (216)447-9000
Fax: (216)447-9007
Co. E-mail: cbizwomensadvantage@cbiz.com
URL: http://www.cbiz.com
Contact: Jerome P. Grisko, Jr., President
Facebook: facebook.com/cbizmhmcareers
Linkedin: www.linkedin.com/company/cbiz
X (Twitter): twitter.com/cbz
YouTube: www.youtube.com/user/CBIZSolutions
Description: Diversified services company is engaged in providing an array of professional business services which include accounting and tax, healthcare and health benefits consulting, financial advisory, valuation, risk and advisory services, payroll, property and casualty insurance, retirement planning, managed networking and hardware services primarily to small and medium-sized businesses, as well as individuals, government agencies, and not-for-profit enterprises. **Founded:** 1996. **Training:** Health Care - What the Future Holds; Consumer Driven Health Plans; Executive Plans; Health Savings Accounts; Healthy Wealthy and Wise; Legislative Update; Medicare Part D; Retirement Plans.

24240 ■ Charles A. Krueger
1908 Innsbrooke Dr.
Sun Prairie, WI 53590-3515
Contact: Charles A. Krueger, Contact
Description: Financial management consultant specializing in professional education programs for managers and executives. Programs include: Finance and accounting for nonfinancial executives, financial management for executives and developing and using financial information for decision making. Major industries served include manufacturing, service, healthcare and insurance. **Scope:** Financial management consultant specializing in professional education programs for managers and executives. Programs include: Finance and accounting for nonfinancial executives, financial management for executives and developing and using financial information for decision making. Major industries served include manufacturing, service, healthcare and insurance. **Publications:** "Monitoring Financial Results, chapter in Corporate Controllers Manual," Warren Gorham and Lamont. **Training:** Finance and Accounting for Nonfinancial Executives; Financial Management for Health Care Executives; Financial Management for Insurance Executives; Direct Costing; Flexible Budgeting; Contribution Reporting; Building Value and Driving Profits - A Business Simulation.

24241 ■ Chartered Management Co.
100 Saunders Rd., Ste. 150
Lake Forest, IL 60045
Contact: William B. Avellone, President
Description: Operations improvement consultants. Specializes in strategic planning, feasibility studies, management audits and reports, profit enhancement, start-up businesses, mergers and acquisitions, joint ventures, divestitures, interim management, crisis management, turnarounds, business process re-engineering, venture capital and due diligence. **Scope:** Operations improvement consultants. Specializes in strategic planning, feasibility studies, management audits and reports, profit enhancement, start-up businesses, mergers and acquisitions, joint ventures, divestitures, interim management, crisis management, turnarounds, business process re-engineering, venture capital and due diligence. **Founded:** 1985.

24242 ■ Corporate Consulting, Inc.
100 Fillmore St.
Denver, CO 80206
Contact: Devereux C. Josephs, Contact
Description: Engaged in feasibility studies, organizational development, small business management, mergers and acquisitions, joint ventures, divestitures, interim management, crisis management, turnarounds, financing, appraisals valuations and due diligence studies. **Scope:** Engaged in feasibility studies, organizational development, small business management, mergers and acquisitions, joint ventures, divestitures, interim management, crisis management, turnarounds, financing, appraisals valuations and due diligence studies.

24243 ■ Effective Compensation Inc. (ECI)
5856 S Lowell Blvd., Ste. 32 No 322
Littleton, CO 80123
Ph: (303)854-1000
Co. E-mail: eci@effectivecompensation.com
URL: http://www.effectivecompensation.com
Contact: Terry Isselhardt, President
Description: Independent compensation consulting firm specializing in working with clients on a collaborative basis to improve their organization's efficiency through competitive, focused total compensation processes. Helps organizations determine how to competitively pay their employees. Provides quality, culture sensitive, compensation consulting assistance to all types of employers. **Scope:** Independent compensation consulting firm specializing in working with clients on a collaborative basis to improve their organization's efficiency through competitive, focused total compensation processes. Helps organizations determine how to competitively pay their employees. Provides quality, culture sensitive, compensation consulting assistance to all types of employers. **Founded:** 1991. **Publications:** "Alternative Job Evaluation Approaches"; "Broad Banding: A Management Overview"; "Job Evaluation: Understanding the Issues"; "Industry Compensation Surveys"; "Skill Based Pay"; "Four Levels of Team Membership"; "Factors in Designing an Incentive Plan"; "Key Stock Allocation Issues"; "Stock Plans Primer". **Training:** Alternative Job Evaluation Approaches; Broad Banding: A Management Overview; Skill Based Pay; Job Evaluation: Understanding the Issues; Designing Compensation Programs that Motivate Employees; Master the Compensation Maze; Base Salary Administration Manual.

24244 ■ FinancialAdvisors.com (FA)
520 Ave., Pico, 3156
San Clemente, CA 92674
Free: 888-689-9650
Co. E-mail: info@financialadvisors.com
URL: http://www.financialadvisors.com
Contact: Jim Eckel, Chief Executive Officer
Facebook: www.facebook.com/FinancialAdvisorsDOTcom
Linkedin: www.linkedin.com/company/financialadvisors-com
X (Twitter): x.com/FinanAdvisors
Instagram: www.instagram.com/financialadvisorsupport
Description: Firm advises clients on important tax and financial decisions, the company offers a website where professional financial advisors can get advice, information, products, and services and help them to manage their business more effectively. **Scope:** Firm advises clients on important tax and financial decisions, the company offers a website where professional financial advisors can get advice, information, products, and services and help them to manage their business more effectively. **Publications:** "The Next Big Thing - Life time Income Benefits," Apr, 2006.

24245 ■ Global Technology Transfer L.L.C.
1500 Dixie Hwy.
Park Hills, KY 41011
Contact: Anthony R. Zembrodt, Sr., Member
Description: Firm specializes in product development, quality assurance, new product development, and total quality management focusing on household chemical specialties, especially air fresheners. Utilizes latest technology from global resources. Specializes in enhancement products for home and automobile. **Scope:** Firm specializes in product development, quality assurance, new product development, and total quality management focusing on household chemical specialties, especially air fresheners. Utilizes latest technology from global resources. Specializes in enhancement products for home and automobile.

24246 ■ Hewitt Development Enterprises (HDE)
1717 N Bayshore Dr., Ste. 2154
Miami, FL 33132
Ph: (305)372-0941
Fax: (305)372-0941
Co. E-mail: info@hewittdevelopment.com
URL: http://www.hewittdevelopment.com
Contact: Robert G. Hewitt, Contact
E-mail: bob@hewittdevelopment.com
Description: Firm specializes in strategic planning, profit enhancement, startup businesses, interim and crisis management, turnarounds, production planning, just-in-time inventory and project management, serves senior management and acquirers of distressed businesses. **Scope:** Firm specializes in strategic planning, profit enhancement, startup businesses, interim and crisis management, turnarounds, production planning, just-in-time inventory and project management, serves senior management and acquirers of distressed businesses. **Founded:** 1985.

24247 ■ Hollingsworth & Associates
395 Wellington Rd. S, Ste. 101
London, ON, Canada N6C 5Z6
Ph: (519)649-2001
URL: http://www.appointmentquest.com/scheduler/2140113024
Description: Firm offers consulting services include software selection and financial information systems, accounting and tax preparation. **Scope:** Firm offers consulting services include software selection and financial information systems, accounting and tax preparation. **Founded:** 1993.

24248 ■ Human Capital Research Corp. (HCRC)
3015 N Lincoln Ave.
Chicago, IL 60657
Ph: (847)475-7580
Co. E-mail: info@humancapital.com
URL: http://www.humancapital.com
Contact: Brian Zucker, President
Description: Firm engages in educational consulting including enrollment management, long-term strategic planning, program evaluation, institutional research and learning outcomes assessment. **Scope:** Firm engages in educational consulting including enrollment management, long-term strategic planning, program evaluation, institutional research and learning outcomes assessment. **Founded:** 1991.

24249 ■ Interminds & Federer Resources Inc.
PO Box 438
Pasadena, CA 91102
Ph: (512)261-0761
Co. E-mail: yesyoucan@interminds.com
URL: http://www.interminds.com
Description: Firm specializes in feasibility studies, startup businesses, small business management, mergers and acquisitions, joint ventures, divestitures, interim and crisis management, turnarounds, production planning, team building, appraisals, and valuations. **Scope:** Firm specializes in feasibility studies, startup businesses, small business management, mergers and acquisitions, joint ventures, divestitures, interim and crisis management, turnarounds, production planning, team building, appraisals, and valuations. **Founded:** 1985. **Publications:** "Yes You Can: How To Be A Success No Matter Who You Are Or Where You're From".

24250 ■ John Alan Cohan
16133 Ventura Blvd., NO.700
Encino, CA 91436
Ph: (310)278-0203
Co. E-mail: johnalancohan@aol.com
URL: http://cohanlawoffice.com
Contact: John Alan Cohan, Contact
E-mail: johnalancohan@aol.com
Description: Specializes in tax law, probate, and conservatorships. The company handles complex tax audits, prepares tax compliance and regulatory opinion letters for trade associations, tax-exempt organizations and individual clients. It also offers in-depth knowledge regarding livestock, horse, and agricultural matters. **Founded:** 1981.

24251 ■ Johnston Co.
78 Bedford St.
Lexington, MA 02420
Ph: (781)862-7595
Fax: (781)862-9066
Co. E-mail: info@johnstoncompany.com
URL: http://johnstoncompany.com
Contact: Jim Johnston, Chief Executive Officer
E-mail: jimj@johnstoncompany.com
Description: Firm provides consulting on environmental and workplace services such as LSRP service, property acquisition and redevelopment, engineering and site remediation. **Scope:** Firm provides consulting on environmental and workplace services such as LSRP service, property acquisition and redevelopment, engineering and site remediation. **Publications:** "Why are board meetings such a waste of time," Boston Business Journal, Apr, 2004.

24252 ■ LaCloche Manitoulin Business Assistance Corp. (LAMBAC)
30 Meredith St.
Gore Bay, ON, Canada P0P 1H0
Ph: (705)282-3215
Free: 800-461-5131
Fax: (705)282-2989
Co. E-mail: info@lambac.org
URL: http://www.lambac.org
Contact: Carolyn Dearing, Officer
E-mail: carolyn@lambac.org
Facebook: www.facebook.com/lambacgorebay
Linkedin: www.linkedin.com/company/lambac
X (Twitter): x.com/laclochemanitou
Description: Firm provides encourages a strong, vibrant, sustainable, environmentally-friendly, business community through financial investment and support services. **Scope:** Firm provides encourages a strong, vibrant, sustainable, environmentally-friendly, business community through financial investment and support services. **Founded:** 1986. **Publications:** "Packed Panniers on Manitoulin," Sep, 2005; "One Wind Farm Gains License, Another Proposes 60 Windmills," Jul, 2005; "The Great Spirit Circle Trail," Jan, 2005.

24253 ■ McGill Business Consulting Group (MBCG)
Ste. 182, 3420 Rue McTavish
Montreal, QC, Canada H3A 3L1
Ph: (438)388-2095
Co. E-mail: info@mbcg.com
URL: http://www.mbcg.com
Contact: Gustavo Pinzon Carrillo, Partner
Linkedin: www.linkedin.com/company/mcgillbusinessconsulting
Description: Project consultants with wide experience in financial services, information and communications technology, health services, sales and marketing. **Scope:** Project consultants with wide experience in financial services, information and communications technology, health services, sales and marketing. **Founded:** 1983. **Publications:** "Lofty ideas at bargain basement prices,"2004.

24254 ■ McShane Group L.L.C.
2119 E Franklin St.
Richmond, VA 23223
URL: http://www.mcshanegroup.com
Contact: Jim L. Huitt, Jr., Principal
E-mail: jhuitt@mcshanegroup.com
Description: Firm provides diligence services, interim management, strategic business realignments, marketing, and much more. **Scope:** Firm

provides diligence services, interim management, strategic business realignments, marketing, and much more. **Founded:** 1987.

24255 ■ Mefford, Knutson & Associates Inc. (MKA)
6437 Lyndale Ave. S
Richfield, MN 55423
Co. E-mail: info@mkcconsulting.com
URL: http://mkaconsulting.com
Contact: Jeanette Mefford, Co-Founder
Description: Provider of consulting services to home health and related sectors. **Scope:** Provider of consulting services to home health and related sectors. **Founded:** 1990.

24256 ■ Merrimac Associates Inc.
4801 S Broad St. Bldg. 100 Ste. 400
Philadelphia, PA 19112
Contact: Philip G. Hirsch, President
Description: Provides project management and system integration services primarily to the power transmission and distribution, industrial, energy, and clean coal and renewable technologies industries. In addition, the company offers digital instrumentation and computer-based control systems, programmable logic controllers and distributed control systems to high-tech manufacturers, marine transport operators and fossil and nuclear power generators. It also performs start-up services and provides manuals and training for turnkey projects. **Special Services:** XtremePM™.

24257 ■ Metro Accounting Services Inc.
167 Oxmoor Blvd.
Homewood, AL 35209
Ph: (205)916-0900
Co. E-mail: info@metroaccountingservice.com
URL: http://www.metroaccountingservice.com
Contact: Jim Waligora, Founder
E-mail: jim@metroaccountingservice.com
Facebook: www.facebook.com/MetroAccountingService
Linkedin: www.linkedin.com/in/metroaccountingservice
X (Twitter): x.com/metroaccounting
Description: Firm provides tax, business and individual services. **Founded:** 1982. **Training:** How to Win the Money Game; Using Mutual Funds for Financial Independence; IRA's, Keogh and Other Retirement Plans; How to Quit Paying Income Taxes. **Special Services:** IRS problem solving, Quick Books® installation and training.

24258 ■ Miller/Cook & Associates Inc.
Marco Island, FL 34145
Ph: (239)266-2761
URL: http://www.millercook.com
Contact: William B. Miller, President
E-mail: bill@millercook.com
Description: Firm is engaged in consulting services such as enrollment integration and operation, re-recruitment and retention, tuition discount and net revenue reviews, integrated communication training to colleges and universities. **Scope:** Firm is engaged in consulting services such as enrollment integration and operation, re-recruitment and retention, tuition discount and net revenue reviews, integrated communication training to colleges and universities. **Founded:** 1988. **Publications:** "Capital gains: Surviving in an increasingly for profit world"; "Making steps to a brighter future". **Training:** Admissions: An overview of a changing profession; Admission practices: Managing the admissions office; Admission practices: Internal operations often make the difference; Effective communication and the enrollment process; Telemarketing or Tele counseling: How to use the telephone to effectively enroll and re-enroll students; Graduate and professional program recruitment: An overview Re-Recruitment: What is it? Is it necessary?; The effective use of electronic mediums in the recruitment process; The use of alumni to support and sustain your recruiting efforts.

24259 ■ Mitchell and Titus L.L.P.
80 Pine St., 32th Fl.
New York, NY 10005
Ph: (212)709-4500
Fax: (212)709-4680
Co. E-mail: info@mitchelltitus.com
URL: http://www.mitchelltitus.com
Contact: Anthony S. Kendall, Chief Executive Officer
Facebook: www.facebook.com/mitchelltitusllp
Linkedin: www.linkedin.com/company/mitchell-&-titus-llp
X (Twitter): x.com/Mitchell_Titus
Description: Firm provides public accounting, auditing, tax preparation and management consulting. **Scope:** Firm provides assurance, advisory business services, transaction support and tax services. Specializes in auditing and accounting services, tax planning and preparation services management and business advisory services. **Founded:** 1974. **Publications:** "ITEM Club Budget preview report," 2010; "Year end personal planning," 2010; "Steering towards the future using the Pre Budget Report to help the UK rebound," 2009; "Be careful what you wish for," 2009; "Year end personal planning," 2009. **Training:** Budget Seminar 2010, Mar, 2010.

24260 ■ Novus Business Services Inc.
299 S Main, Ste. 1300
Salt Lake City, UT 84111
Ph: (801)534-4444
Fax: (801)340-0250
URL: http://novusbiz.com
Contact: Mike Whaley, Chief Executive Officer
URL(s): www.hayesnovus.com
Description: Provider of advisory, negotiation and financial management services. **Founded:** 2002.

24261 ■ PBC Advisors L.L.C.
903 Commerce Dr., Ste. 333
Oak Brook, IL 60523
Ph: (630)571-6770
Fax: (630)571-8810
Co. E-mail: info@pbcgroup.com
URL: http://www.pbcgroup.com
Contact: Steve Blohm, Partner
Facebook: www.facebook.com/PBC-Advisors-LLC-520676794749915
Description: Firm provides accounting, financial, retirement, estate and tax planning, employment agreements, pension profit sharing administration, practice management, surveys, mergers, acquisitions, sales, and liquidation. **Scope:** Firm provides accounting, financial, retirement, estate and tax planning, employment agreements, pension profit sharing administration, practice management, surveys, mergers, acquisitions, sales, and liquidation. **Founded:** 1986.

24262 ■ Penny & Associates Inc. (PA)
2748 Bur Oak Ave., Ste. 2
Markham, ON, Canada L6B 1K4
Ph: (416)907-7158
Free: 866-370-0703
Co. E-mail: info@pennyinc.com
URL: http://www.pennyinc.com
Contact: Betty Penny, Contact
Description: Firm is an accounting and management firm that offers accounting and business solutions. **Scope:** Firm is an accounting and management firm that offers accounting and business solutions. **Founded:** 1994. **Training:** Quick Books, Aug, 2001; How to Stand Up to People Without Being a Jerk; How to Build Influence and Rapport With Almost Anyone; Dealing With Dissatisfied, Different and Difficult People; Effective Public Speaking; How to Incorporate Yourself; Company Perks: Attracting & Retaining Good People; FIRST AID. **Special Services:** Quickbooks®.

24263 ■ Profit Motivators International (PMI)
2146 Linden Dr.
Boulder, CO 80304
Ph: (303)444-1311
Free: 800-848-1311
Fax: (303)444-8511
Co. E-mail: info@profitmotivatorsintl.com
URL: http://www.profitmotivatorsintl.com
Contact: Peter Henthorn, President
E-mail: peter.henthorn@profitmotivatorsintl.com
Description: Firm offers a variety of different services for clients seeking operational and service improvements to enhance their bottom line and services offered include staff management control, funds management, fee income and product pricing, non-interest expense control, fringe benefit review, mid-management and supervisory training, sales training, branch profitability evaluations. **Scope:** Firm offers a variety of different services for clients seeking operational and service improvements to enhance their bottom line and services offered include staff management control, funds management, fee income and product pricing, non-interest expense control, fringe benefit review, mid-management and supervisory training, sales training, branch profitability evaluations. **Founded:** 1980.

24264 ■ Qualified Financial Services Inc. (QFS)
3625 Dufferin St., Ste. 340
Toronto, ON, Canada M3K 1Z2
Ph: (416)630-4000
Free: 800-263-4570
Fax: (416)630-4022
Co. E-mail: qfs@qfscanada.com
URL: http://www.qfscanada.com
Contact: Fiona Cuddy, President
Facebook: www.facebook.com/qfscanada
Linkedin: www.linkedin.com/company/qfscanada
Description: Designs and implements a financial plan for the shareholders partners of small businesses. Services include investment management, tax planning risk management in the form of structuring and funding shareholders agreements estate planning and creditor protection. **Scope:** Designs and implements a financial plan for the shareholders partners of small businesses. Services include investment management, tax planning risk management in the form of structuring and funding shareholders agreements estate planning and creditor protection. **Founded:** 1997.

24265 ■ Queen's Business Consulting (QBC)
Queen's University
Stephen J. R. Smith School of Business
Goodes Hall, Rm. LL201
Kingston, ON, Canada K7L 3N6
Ph: (613)893-2327
Co. E-mail: sbc@queensu.ca
URL: http://smith.queensu.ca/index.php
Contact: Charlie Mignault, Director
E-mail: cem10@queensu.ca
Description: Provider of management consulting services such as strategy, sales, marketing, data analysis, and operational planning. **Scope:** Provider of management consulting services such as strategy, sales, marketing, data analysis, and operational planning. **Founded:** 1973. **Publications:** "Information technology, network structure and competitive action. Information Systems Research," 2010; "The role of dominance in the appeal of violent media depictions. Journal of Advertising," 2010; "Great expectations and broken promises: Misleading claims, product failure, expectancy disconfirmation and consumer distrust. Journal of the Academy of Marketing Science," 2010; "Development and psychometric properties of the Transformational Teaching Questionnaire. Journal of Health Psychology," 2010; ". Predicting workplace aggression: myths, realities, and remaining questions," 2009; "The Inconvenient Truth about Improving Vehicle Fuel Efficiency: An MultiAttribute Analysis of the Efficient Frontier of the U.S. Automobile Industry, Transportation Research-Part," 2009; "Fraud in Canadian Nonprofit Organizations as Seen through the Eyes of Canadian Newspapers," 2009; "Disentangling the Indirect Links between SES and Health: The Dynamic Roles of Work Stressors and Personal Contro," 2009; "The strong situation hypothesis. Personality and Social Psychology Review," 2009; " Planning Your Next Crisis Decisively and Effectively. Ivey Business Journal," 2009. **Training:** Enabling Innovation Discussion Highlights, 2011; Intellectual Capital, 2010; On the diffusion of knowledge inside the organization, 2010; A model of the tacit knowledge lifecycle for decision-making: From creation to utilization, 2010; Individual, group, and

24266 ■ Scannell and Kurz Inc.
Ruffalo Noel Levitz, LLC (RNL)
71-B Munroe Ave.
Pittsford, NY 14534
Ph: (319)362-7483
Free: 800-876-1117
Fax: (319)362-7457
Co. E-mail: softwaresupport@ruffalonl.com
URL: http://www.ruffalonl.com
Contact: James Scannell, Chief Executive Officer

Description: Provides pricing and financial aid strategies, admissions market analysis, enrollment management and retention strategies. **Scope:** Provides pricing and financial aid strategies, admissions market analysis, enrollment management and retention strategies. **Publications:** "Financial Aid Strategies in Tough Economic Times," Jan, 2010; "Financial Aid Trends in the Current Economy: Lessons for the Future," Dec, 2009; "Data-Driven Retention Strategies," Feb, 2009; "Enrollment Management 101," Mar, 2008; "Don't Get Distracted: Top Audit Issues in Financial Aid," Sep, 2007; "Financial Aid and the Business Office," Jul, 2007; "Understanding the Value of Transfers," May, 2007; "Financial Aid Appeal Pitfalls," Mar, 2007; "Is Affordability Really the Issue," Nov, 2006; "Building a Financial Fundraising Case," Jul, 2006; "Enrollment Management Grows Up," May, 2006; "Just One Stop, But Many Potential Pitfalls," Mar, 2006; "Bond Rating: Beyond the Balance," Jan, 2006; "Strategy and Operations in Financial Aid," Nov, 2005; "The Evolution of a Successful Admissions Director"; "Profile of an Effective Enrollment Manager". **Training:** 2009 Enrollment and Financial Aid Results: Lessons for the Future, Presidents Institute, Jan, 2010; The Bottom Line on Student Retention: Data-Driven Approaches that Work, Nov, 2009; Thriving Without Deep Pockets--Achieving Enrollment Success on an Uneven Playing Field, Feb, 2009.

24267 ■ Stillwater Insurance Group
6800 S point Pkwy, Ste. 700
Jacksonville, FL 32216
Free: 800-220-1351
Fax: (800)491-7683
Co. E-mail: ins@stillwater.com
URL: http://stillwaterinsurance.com
Contact: Mark Davey, President
Facebook: www.facebook.com/Stillwater.Insurance.Company
Linkedin: www.linkedin.com/company/stillwater-insurance-group

Description: Provides strategic planning, budget and financial management, process improvement, organizational design and assessment and college student services operations. **Scope:** Provides strategic planning, budget and financial management, process improvement, organizational design and assessment and college student services operations. **Founded:** 2000. **Publications:** "Integrated Resource Planning (Irp)," Business Officer Magazine, 2005; "The Economic Risk Conundrum," University Business Magazine; "Revenue Analysis and Tuition Strategy"; "Managing Advancement Services: Processes and Paper".

24268 ■ Swigert & Associates Inc.
29 Salem Ln.
Evanston, IL 60203
Ph: (847)864-4690
Fax: (847)864-0802
URL: http://www.swigert.biz
Contact: Tom Swigert, Contact
E-mail: tom@swigert.biz

Description: Firm provides tax preparation and financial services. **Founded:** 1970.

24269 ■ Synergistic Business Solutions Group L.L.C. (SBSG)
18 Park Ln.
Fair Haven, NJ 07704-3514
Co. E-mail: info@sbs-corp.com
URL: http://www.sbs-corp.com

Description: Provider of financial services including rent-a-CFO, accounting systems selection, tailoring, business formation services and more. **Scope:** Provider of financial services including rent-a-CFO, accounting systems selection, tailoring, business formation services and more.

24270 ■ Total Business Care, L.L.C. (TBC)
39500 Stevenson Pl., Ste. 210
Fremont, CA 94539
Ph: (510)797-8375
Fax: (510)797-9503
Co. E-mail: info@totalbizcare.com
URL: http://www.totalbizcare.com
Contact: Elise Berticevich, Office Manager
Facebook: www.facebook.com/totalbizcare
Linkedin: www.linkedin.com/company/totalbusinesscarellc

Description: Services: Management consulting, accounting, tax preparation, franchise development, marketing management, operational analysis, management training and more. **Scope:** Services: Management consulting, accounting, tax preparation, franchise development, marketing management, operational analysis, management training and more. **Founded:** 1985. **Special Services:** ProAdvisors®; QuickBooks®.

24271 ■ Value Creation Group Inc.
7820 Scotia Dr., Ste. 2000
Dallas, TX 75248-3115
Ph: (972)980-7407
Co. E-mail: assistyou@valuecreationgroup.com
URL: http://www.valuecreationgroup.com
Contact: John Antos, Contact
E-mail: assistyou@valuecreationgroup.com

Description: Consulting firm provides process management, continuous improvement, performance management, cost accounting, forecasting, budgeting and training services. **Scope:** Consulting firm provides process management, continuous improvement, performance management, cost accounting, forecasting, budgeting and training services. **Founded:** 1984. **Publications:** "Handbook of Process Management Based Predictive Accounting," AIcpa 2002; "Cost Management for Today's Manufacturing Environment and Activity Based Management for Service Environments, Government Entities and Nonprofit Organizations"; "Risks and Opportunities in International Finance and Treasury"; "Driving Value Using Activity Based Budgeting"; "Process Based Accounting Leveraging Processes to Predict Results"; "Handbook of Supply Chain Management"; "Economic Value Management Applications and Techniques"; "The Change Handbook": "Group Methods for Creating the Future"; "Why Value Management and Performance Measurement Through U.S. Binoculars," Journal of Strategic Performance Measurement; "Real Options, Intangibles Measurement and the Benefits of Human Capital Investment to Power the Organization," Journal of Strategic Performance Measurement. **Training:** Activity Based Management; Predictive Accounting; Performance measures; ABM for Manufacturing; ABM for Service Organizations; Finance and Accounting for Non-Financial Executives; Return on Investment/Capital Expenditure Evaluation; Planning and Cost Control; The Next Step Intermediate Finance and Accounting for Non-financial Managers; Activity-Based Budgeting; Friendly Finance for Fund Raisers; Strategic Outsourcing.

24272 ■ Verbit & Co.
152 Union Ave.
Bala Cynwyd, PA 19004
Contact: Alan C. Verbit, Owner

Description: Management consulting firm to assist executives and managers fulfill their mission and to assure that adequate planning of day-to-day operations occurs, that controls sufficient to safeguard valuable resources and that results of decisions reviewed in sufficient time to effect continuing action. **Scope:** Management consulting firm to assist executives and managers fulfill their mission and to assure that adequate planning of day-to-day operations occurs, that controls sufficient to safeguard valuable resources and that results of decisions reviewed in sufficient time to effect continuing action. **Training:** Integrating Manufacturing Management Systems with Business Systems; Negotiating Information Systems Agreements with Suppliers.

24273 ■ WestCap Partners Inc.
150 E 58th St., Fl. 17
New York, NY 10155
Contact: Charles J. Cernansky, Chief Executive Officer

Description: Business and financial consultants provide corporate finance and advisory services to emerging and medium-sized companies, investment and merchant banking, trade assistance, planning, strategy and financing and financial consulting. Also temporarily assist growing companies in operational roles. Offer troubled company assistance through work-outs and turnarounds. **Scope:** Business and financial consultants provide corporate finance and advisory services to emerging and medium-sized companies, investment and merchant banking, trade assistance, planning, strategy and financing and financial consulting. Also temporarily assist growing companies in operational roles. Offer troubled company assistance through work-outs and turnarounds. **Training:** Financial Negotiations for Mergers, Acquisitions and Projects.

24274 ■ Westlife Consultants and Advisors
4 Robert Speck Pkwy.
Mississauga, ON, Canada L4Z, CA
URL: http://www.westlifeconsultants.com
Contact: Syed N. Hussain, President
E-mail: shussain@westlifeconsultante.com
Linkedin: www.linkedin.com/company/westlife-consultants-&-advisors

Description: Provider of entrepreneurs and businesses with a highly commercial and global perspectives on the international business development ideas under consideration. **Scope:** Provider of entrepreneurs and businesses with a highly commercial and global perspectives on the international business development ideas under consideration. **Founded:** 1992. **Publications:** "Innovative Management"; "Team Building and Leadership"; "Financial Planning"; "Estate Planning"; "Risk Management"; "Export/Import Trade Finance Mechanics"; "Marketing and Sales Management"; "What Your Banker Needs to Know"; "Building A Successful Financial Plan".

PUBLICATIONS

24275 ■ Financial Concepts & Tools for Business Managers
826 Riviera Dr.
Mansfield, TX 76063
Free: 800-990-4273
URL: http://www.americancpe.com
Contact: Dennis Gatlin, President
URL(s): www.americancpe.com/CPE-Courses/24-Financial-Concepts---Tools-for-Business-Managers.html

Price: $79, for printed text; $20, for additional exams; $59, for download searchable text and exam for apple computers; $59, for Searchable Text and Exam. **Description:** Contains detailed training information covering basic financial concepts and their use in business management settings. **Availability:** Print; Download. **Type:** Full-text.

24276 ■ Small Business Finance Frequently Asked Questions
URL(s): advocacy.sba.gov/2022/02/15/frequently-asked-questions-about-small-business-2022

Released: Annual **Description:** Contains latest statistics about America's small business. **Availability:** PDF; Online.

COMPUTERIZED DATABASES

24277 ■ *Baseline Intelligence*
URL(s): www.baselineintel.com
Type: Full-text; Numeric.

24278 ■ *Vickers Weekly Insider Report*
Vickers Stock Research Corp.
61 Broadway
New York, NY 10006
Co. E-mail: clientservices@vickers-stock.com
URL: http://www.vickers-stock.com
Contact: Joseph Dorsey, Chief Executive Officer
URL(s): www.vickers-stock.com/account/about/winsider.asp
Availability: PDF. **Type:** Full-text; Numeric.

INTERNET DATABASES

24279 ■ *African Americans in Business and Entrepreneurship: A Resource Guide*
URL(s): guides.loc.gov/african-americans-in-business
Description: A guide providing key topics on the history of African Americans in various business industries. **Availability:** Online.

24280 ■ *Small Business Financing: A Resource Guide*
URL(s): guides.loc.gov/small-business-financing
Description: Provides links to online resources to conduct research on financing options for small businesses and entrepreneurs. Covers the following topics: types of financing, financing by situation, financial management, and avoiding scams. **Availability:** Online.

LIBRARIES

24281 ■ **Carnegie Library of Pittsburgh Downtown & Business**
612 Smithfield St.
 Pittsburgh, PA 15222
Ph: (412)281-7141
URL: http://www.carnegielibrary.org/clp_location/downtown-business
Contact: Andrew Medlar, President
Scope: Local history. **Services:** Library open to the public. **Founded:** 1924. **Holdings:** Books; magazines; CD-ROMs; videos.

24282 ■ **Nichols College - Conant Library**
121 Center Rd.
 Dudley, MA 01571
Ph: (508)213-2334
Co. E-mail: circulation@nichols.edu
URL: http://www.nichols.edu/offices/conant-library
Contact: Carrie Grimshaw, Director
E-mail: carrie.grimshaw@nichols.edu
Scope: Sports management and education. **Services:** Interlibrary loan; copying; information service to groups; document delivery; library open to Dudley and Webster residents. **Founded:** 1962. **Holdings:** Figures not available.

24283 ■ **Strategic Account Management Association (SAMA) - Library**
200 W Madison St.
 Ste. 1040
 Chicago, IL 60606
Ph: (312)251-3131
Fax: (312)251-3132
Co. E-mail: info@strategicaccounts.org
URL: http://www.strategicaccounts.org/en
Contact: Denise Freier, President
X (Twitter): x.com/samatweet
Description: Corporation sales executives concerned with strategic account sales. Holds seminars on strategic account management. Serves as an information provider on strategic customer-supplier relationship resources. **Scope:** Account management. **Founded:** 1964. **Holdings:** Figures not available. **Publications:** *Focus: Account Manager* (Semiannual); *Velocity* (Quarterly). **Educational Activities:** SAMA Annual Conference (Annual). **Geographic Preference:** Multinational.

24284 ■ **University of Kentucky - Business & Economics Information Center**
105 Main Bldg.
 Lexington, KY 40506-0132
URL: http://gatton.uky.edu
Description: Center that provides various programs involving business strategies and ideas about the economy. **Scope:** Business, economics, business management, marketing, finance, accounting. **Services:** Library open to the public for reference use only. **Founded:** 1993.

RESEARCH CENTERS

24285 ■ **University of Oklahoma - Price College of Business - Division of Finance - Center for Financial Studies (CFS)**
307 West Brooks, Adams Hall Rm. 3250
 Norman, OK 73019
Co. E-mail: spam@ou.edu
URL: http://www.ou.edu/price/finance/research/cfs
Contact: Dr. Chitru S. Fernando, Director
E-mail: cfernando@ou.edu
Description: Integral unit of University of Oklahoma. **Scope:** Finance. **Publications:** *Center for Financial Studies working paper series*. **Educational Activities:** CFS Seminar (Irregular).

Franchising

OFFICE OF PERSONNEL MANAGEMENT

24286 ■ **Office Evolution (OE)**
2121 Vista Pkwy.
West Palm Beach, FL 33411
Free: 877-475-6300
Co. E-mail: marketing@officeevolution.com
URL: http://www.officeevolution.com
Contact: Mark Hemmeter, Chief Executive Officer
Facebook: www.facebook.com/officeevolutionhq
Linkedin: www.linkedin.com/company/office-evolution
Instagram: www.instagram.com/office_evolution
Description: Offers office space rentals and tools including conference rooms, meeting rooms, office rentals, coworking and shared workspaces to startups and entrepreneurs. **Founded:** 2003.

START-UP INFORMATION

24287 ■ *"7 Easy Steps to Start a Tutoring Business"* in The Daily Egg (July 12, 2022)
URL(s): www.crazyegg.com/blog/how-to-start-a-tutoring-business/
Released: July 12, 2022. **Availability:** Online.

24288 ■ *"Become a Franchise Owner in 5 Easy Steps"* in Entrepreneur (June 19, 2020)
URL(s): www.entrepreneur.com/franchise/become-a-franchise-owner-in-5-easy-steps/351546
Ed: Desmond Lim. **Released:** June 19, 2020. **Description:** Being a franchise owner offers the benefit of instant name reconigition. This article provides five steps to becoming a franchise owner yourself. **Availability:** Online.

24289 ■ *"Biz Pays Tribute: Franchise Helps Owners Grieve and Honor Their Beloved Pets"* in Small Business Opportunities (November 2007)
Description: Paws and Remember is a franchise company that provides pet cremation and memorial products while assisting veterinary clinics and other pet specialists to help clients when they lose a pet.

24290 ■ *"Blaze Pizza Adds Nine Franchise Groups"* in FastCasual.com (September 2, 2014)
Pub: Networld Media Group
Contact: Kathy Doyle, President
E-mail: publisher@networldmediagroup.com
Description: Blaze Fast Fire'd Pizza has signed nine new San Diego area development agreements that will add 67 franchise restaurants to its firm. The company will also open 315 company-owned and franchised pizza restaurants in 33 states by the end of 2015. **Availability:** Online.

24291 ■ *"Chem-Dry Carpet Cleaning Franchise on Pace for 120 New Locations In 2014"* in Internet Wire (September 16, 2014)
Pub: Comtex News Network Inc.
Contact: Kan Devnani, President

Description: Chem-Dry carpet cleaning franchise is poised to record-setting growth for 2014 with 120 new franchisees. Entrepreneur Magazine named Chem-Dry as the No. 1 carpet cleaning franchise, as well as a top home-based business opportunity with low startup-costs. **Availability:** Online.

24292 ■ *"Fast-Growing Office Pride Franchise Targets Louisville For Expansion"* in Internet Wire (September 9, 2014)
Pub: Comtex News Network Inc.
Contact: Kan Devnani, President
Description: Office Pride is a commercial cleaning service that is built on principles that include: honesty, trustworthy service, excellence, and treating everyone with dignity and respect. The commercial cleaning franchise is seeking a developer to help expand its business in Louisville, Kentucky. **Availability:** Online.

24293 ■ *"Franchisee to Smash Way Into Orlando's Better Burger Race"* in Orlando Business Journal (Vol. 30, January 31, 2014, No. 32, pp. 3)
Pub: American City Business Journals, Inc.
Contact: Mike Olivieri, Executive Vice President
Released: Weekly. **Price:** $8, introductory 4-week offer(Digital & Print). **Description:** Palm Coast, Florida-based Two Spurs LLC, the new franchisee for Smashburger, has announced plans to put its first of 12 restaurants in Orlando in 2014. Two Spurs executives, Wellesley Broomfield and Ray Ruiz, have been touring potential sites in the area. Detailed requirements for owning a Smash Burger franchise are provided. **Availability:** Print; Online.

24294 ■ *"Home: Where the Money Is!"* in Small Business Opportunities (May 1, 2008)
Pub: Harris Publishing, Inc.
Contact: Janet Chase, Contact
Description: Profile of ComForcare, a franchise company that serves the senior population in America; a franchise can be started with one owner and add and build a team as it grows. **Availability:** Print; Online.

24295 ■ *"Making Money Is Child's Play With This Retailer"* in Small Business Opportunities (March 1, 2008)
Pub: Harris Publishing, Inc.
Contact: Janet Chase, Contact
Description: Proven system helps launch a successful child care business. **Availability:** Print; Online.

24296 ■ *"The Melting Pot Targets Calgary, Canada For Franchise Expansion"* in CNW Group (September 9, 2014)
Pub: Comtex News Network Inc.
Contact: Kan Devnani, President
Description: The Melting Pot, a premier fondue restaurant, is seeking franchisees in the Calgary, Canada region. The restaurants offer posh, casual interactive dining to their guests. The franchise is also offering franchise opportunities in the Vancouver and Greater Toronto areas. Details covering Melting Pot restaurants are included. **Availability:** Print; Online.

24297 ■ *Microfranchising: Creating Wealth at the Bottom of the Pyramid*
Pub: Edward Elgar Publishing Inc.
Contact: Edward Elgar, Founder Chairman
Released: 2007. **Description:** Ideas from researchers and social entrepreneurs discusses the movement that moves microfranchising into a mechanism for sustainable poverty reduction on a scale to match microfinance.

24298 ■ *"Pump Up the Profits"* in Small Business Opportunities (Summer 2010)
Pub: Harris Publishing, Inc.
Contact: Janet Chase, Contact
Description: New fitness franchise offers customized personal training at bargain rates. Profile of Alan Katz, president of EduFit, a concept that allows small groups of people to workout with customized training is provided.

24299 ■ *"Riches In Recreation"* in Small Business Opportunities (March 2011)
Pub: Harris Publishing, Inc.
Contact: Janet Chase, Contact
Description: Making money is child's play thanks to new gym concept that makes parents and franchisors happy. Profile of Great Play, the franchised children's gym is provided. **Availability:** Download; PDF; Online.

24300 ■ *"Sloan's Ice Cream Inks First Franchise Deal In San Diego"* in FastCasual.com (September 12, 2014)
Pub: Networld Media Group
Contact: Kathy Doyle, President
E-mail: publisher@networldmediagroup.com
Description: Sloan's Ice Cream announced that is has awarded the first franchise location outside of South Florida to Ali Hajisattari of San Diego, California. **Availability:** Online.

24301 ■ *Start Small, Finish Big*
Released: December 15, 2012. **Description:** Fred DeLuca is profiled; after founding the multi-billion dollar chain of Subway sandwich restaurants, DeLuca is committed to helping microentrepreneurs, people who start successful small businesses with less than $1,000. **Availability:** Print; Online.

24302 ■ *"Stepping Out"* in Small Business Opportunities (Get Rich At Home 2010)
Description: Earn $1 million a year selling flip flops? A Flip Flop Shop franchise will help individuals start their own business. **Availability:** Print; Online.

24303 ■ *"WIN Home Inspection Garners Recognition as 2012 Military Friendly Franchise by G.I. Jobs Magazine"* in Entertainment Close-Up (May 21, 2012)
Description: G.I. Jobs Magazine ranked WIN Home Inspection in the top ten franchises thoughout the United States on its 2012 Military Friendly Franchises.

Veterans represent 1/4 of the firm's franchisee base, offering realistic opportunities for vets to become successful. Details of the training and skills involved and what it takes to be selected to launch a WIN franchise are included. **Availability:** Print; Online.

ASSOCIATIONS AND OTHER ORGANIZATIONS

24304 ■ **American Franchisee Association (AFA)**
410 S Michigan Ave., Ste. 528
Chicago, IL 60605
Ph: (312)431-0545
Fax: (312)431-1469
Co. E-mail: infoafa@franchisee.org
URL: http://www.franchisee.org
Contact: Susan P. Kezios, President
E-mail: spkezios@franchisee.org
Description: Works to promote and enhance the economic interests of small business franchisees; promote the growth and development of members' enterprises; assist in the formation of independent franchisee associations; offer support, assistance, and legal referral services to members. **Scope:** Offers expertise to potential franchise business opportunity buyers. **Founded:** 1993. **Publications:** *E-news* (Monthly). **Geographic Preference:** National.

24305 ■ **Association Canadienne de la Franchise [Canadian Franchise Association (CFA)]**
116-5399 Eglinton Ave. W
Toronto, ON, Canada M9C 5K6
Ph: (416)695-2896
Free: 800-665-4232
Fax: (416)695-1950
Co. E-mail: info@cfa.ca
URL: http://cfa.ca
Contact: Sherry McNeil, President
E-mail: smcneil@cfa.ca
Facebook: www.facebook.com/canadianfranchiseassociation
X (Twitter): x.com/CFAFranchise
Instagram: www.instagram.com/cfafranchise
YouTube: www.youtube.com/channel/UCvc_k5MWTFjDEx0Jw50gMlw
Description: Represents the shared interests of businesses and professionals active in the Canadian franchise sector. Provides information and guidance to aspiring franchisees. **Publications:** *FranchiseCanada* (Bimonthly). **Educational Activities:** IFA Annual Convention (Annual). **Awards:** CFA Awards of Excellence in Traditional Franchising (Annual). **Geographic Preference:** National.

24306 ■ **Coalition of Franchisee Associations, Inc. (CFA)**
1750 K St. NW, Ste. 200
Washington, DC 20006
Ph: (202)416-0270
Fax: (202)416-0269
Co. E-mail: info@thecfainc.com
URL: http://www.thecfainc.com
Contact: John Motta, Chairman
E-mail: thutchison711@gmail.com
Facebook: www.facebook.com/cfainc
Linkedin: www.linkedin.com/company/the-coalition-of-franchisee-associations
X (Twitter): x.com/cfainc
Instagram: www.instagram.com/cfainc
Description: Provides a unified voice for franchisee associations. Serves as a platform for members to promote best practices and share ideas and knowledge that will benefit the entire franchisee community. **Founded:** 2007. **Geographic Preference:** National.

24307 ■ **The Entrepreneur Authority L.L.C.**
5700 Granite Pky., Ste. 200
Plano, TX 75024
Free: 866-246-2884
Co. E-mail: hq@eauth.com
URL: http://eauth.com
Contact: David Omholt, Chief Executive Officer
E-mail: domholt@eauth.com
Facebook: www.facebook.com/FranchiseBrokers
Description: International network of franchise advisors trained to create win-win business relationships between franchiser and franchisees offers franchise and self-employment counseling to prospective franchisees and matches qualified franchisees with the pre-screened franchiser. **Scope:** International network of franchise advisors trained to create win-win business relationships between franchiser and franchisees offers franchise and self-employment counseling to prospective franchisees and matches qualified franchisees with the pre-screened franchiser. **Founded:** 2002. **Training:** Make Fantastic Career Choices; Evaluate Franchise companies and understand the current industry trends; Understand basic Franchise terminology and relationships; Determine if self-employment is right for you; Conduct solid Due Diligence and Avoid the Top 10 Mistakes most Buyers make; Finance your Franchise purchase; Decide between purchasing a new Franchise or a Re-sale; Choose a good Franchise Attorney and other needed professional Advisors.

24308 ■ **Franchise Brokers Association (FBA)**
3751 Maguire Blvd., Ste. .,115
Orlando, FL 32803
Free: 866-515-8814
Fax: (407)856-0616
Co. E-mail: info@franchiseba.com
URL: http://www.franchiseba.com
Contact: Chris Wall, Officer
Facebook: www.facebook.com/franchiseba
Linkedin: www.linkedin.com/company/franchise-brokers-association
X (Twitter): x.com/franchiseba
Instagram: www.instagram.com/franchiseba
YouTube: www.youtube.com/franchiseba
Description: Provides access to brokers for prospective franchisees. **Founded:** 2008.

24309 ■ *FranchiseCanada*
116-5399 Eglinton Ave. W
Toronto, ON, Canada M9C 5K6
Ph: (416)695-2896
Free: 800-665-4232
Fax: (416)695-1950
Co. E-mail: info@cfa.ca
URL: http://cfa.ca
Contact: Sherry McNeil, President
E-mail: smcneil@cfa.ca
URL(s): cfa.ca/franchisecanada
Ed: Kenny Chan. **Released:** Bimonthly **Description:** Magazine featuring information on franchising. **Availability:** Print; Online.

24310 ■ **International Franchise Association (IFA) - Library**
1900 K St., NW, Ste. 700
Washington, DC 20006
Ph: (202)628-8000
Co. E-mail: info@franchise.org
URL: http://www.franchise.org
Contact: Matthew Haller, President
E-mail: mhaller@franchise.org
Facebook: www.facebook.com/IFA.DC
Linkedin: www.linkedin.com/company/international-franchise-association
X (Twitter): x.com/franchising411
Instagram: www.instagram.com/franchising411
YouTube: www.youtube.com/user/ifadc
Description: Firms in 100 countries utilizing the franchise method of distribution for goods and services in all industries. **Scope:** Franchise. **Founded:** 1960. **Holdings:** Figures not available. **Publications:** *Franchises Directory*; *Franchising World* (6/year; Annual); *International Franchise Association--Franchise Opportunities Guide* (Semiannual). **Educational Activities:** International Franchise Expo (IFE) (Annual); IFA Legal Symposium (Annual); IFA Annual Convention (Annual). **Awards:** Don Debolt Franchising Scholarship Program (Annual); Franchise Law Diversity Scholarship Awards (Annual); IFA Entrepreneur of the Year (Annual); Bonny LeVine Award (Annual); IFA Hall of Fame Award (Annual). **Geographic Preference:** Multinational.

24311 ■ **National Franchisee Association (NFA)**
1701 Barrett Lakes Blvd. NW, Ste. 180
Kennesaw, GA 30144
Ph: (678)797-5160
Co. E-mail: communications@nfabk.org
URL: http://www.nfabk.org
Contact: Christy Williams, Chief Executive Officer
Facebook: www.facebook.com/people/National-Franchisee-Association/100063765872064
X (Twitter): x.com/NFAfranchisee
Instagram: www.instagram.com/nfafranchisee
Description: Federation of associations representing owners of Burger King restaurant franchises. Promotes members' interests. **Geographic Preference:** National.

24312 ■ **VetFran**
1900 K St. NW, Ste. 700
Washington, DC 20006
Ph: (202)662-7781
Co. E-mail: vetfran@franchise.org
URL: http://www.vetfran.org
Contact: Ralph Yarusso, Chief Executive Officer
Facebook: www.facebook.com/VetFranIFA
Linkedin: www.linkedin.com/company/vetfranifa
X (Twitter): x.com/VetFranIFA
Description: Educates Veterans about the entrepreneurship opportunities of franchising and works with franchisors to help make effective Veterans recruitment and hiring a part of their values and strategies. **Founded:** 1991.

REFERENCE WORKS

24313 ■ *"5 Automotive Tool Franchises" in Small Business Trends (February 15, 2023)*
URL(s): smallbiztrends.com/2023/02/automotive-tool-franchises.html
Ed: Rob Starr. **Released:** February 15, 2023. **Description:** Discusses and provides links to five automotive tool franchises. **Availability:** Online.

24314 ■ *"5 Tips for Hiring a Franchise Business Coach" in Entrepreneur (Aug. 10, 2017)*
URL(s): www.entrepreneur.com/franchise/5-tips-for-hiring-a-franchise-business-coach/298343
Ed: Rick Grossmann. **Released:** August 10, 2017. **Description:** Executive-level business coaching has increased in popularity. This article details reasons why hiring a business coach or mentor for your franchise business. **Availability:** Online.

24315 ■ *"5 Ways a Franchise Can Grow Fast" in Entrepreneur (January 14, 2020)*
URL(s): www.entrepreneur.com/franchise/5-ways-a-franchise-can-grow-fast/344500
Released: January 14, 2020. **Availability:** Online.

24316 ■ *"The 6 Best Financing Options for Franchising a Business" in Entrepreneur (May 16, 2018)*
URL(s): www.entrepreneur.com/franchise/the-6-best-financing-options-for-franchising-a-business/312476
Ed: Jared Hecht. **Released:** May 16, 2018. **Description:** Opening a franchise requires significant capital. This article provides six financing options to consider as you open your franchise. **Availability:** Online.

24317 ■ *"6 Legalese Terms Every Franchisee Should Understand" in Entrepreneur (Aug. 3, 2017)*
URL(s): www.entrepreneur.com/franchise/6-legalese-terms-every-franchisee-should-understand/297645
Ed: Rick Grossmann. **Released:** August 03, 2017. **Description:** Discusses the complexities of franchise agreements and provides information on six legal terms that any franchisee should understand. **Availability:** Online.

24318 ■ "6 Risk Factors You Need to Consider Before Purchasing a Franchise" in *Entrepreneur (Jan. 9, 2019)*
URL(s): www.entrepreneur.com/franchise/6-risk-factors-you-need-to-consider-before-purchasing-a/323371
Ed: Mark Siebert. **Released:** January 09, 2019. **Description:** Details six potential risk factors to consider when looking to open a franchise. **Availability:** Online.

24319 ■ "7 Reasons to Hire a Franchise Consultant" in *allBusiness*
URL(s): www.allbusiness.com/7-reasons-hire-franchise-consultant-203156-1.html
Ed: Don Daszkowski. **Availability:** Online.

24320 ■ "7 Things You Need to Know Before Becoming a Franchise Owner" in *Entrepreneur (Nov. 22, 2017)*
URL(s): www.entrepreneur.com/franchise/7-things-you-need-to-know-before-becoming-a-franchise-owner/305010
Ed: Gordon Tredgold. **Released:** November 22, 2017. **Description:** Provides information on seven things to be aware of before diving into a franchise opportunity to ensure that it's the right thing for you. **Availability:** Online.

24321 ■ 7 Ways to Buy a Franchise When You're Short on Funds
URL(s): www.merchantmaverick.com/buy-franchise-no-money/
Ed: Erica Seppala. **Released:** February 26, 2020. **Description:** Explores 7 ways to purchase a franchise when you don't have the funds to do so. **Availability:** Online.

24322 ■ "10 Bubble Tea Franchise Opportunities in 2023" in *Small Business Trends (March 13, 2023)*
URL(s): smallbiztrends.com/2023/03/bubble-tea-franchise.html
Ed: Annie Pilon. **Released:** March 13, 2023. **Description:** Bubble tea (boba tea) is gaining popularity in the U.S. which means there are franchise opportunities available. This article outlines ten different bubble tea franchises for you to consider. **Availability:** Online.

24323 ■ "10 Carpet Cleaning Franchises" in *Small Business Trends (March 1, 2023)*
URL(s): smallbiztrends.com/2023/03/carpet-cleaning-franchises.html
Ed: Rob Starr. **Released:** March 01, 2023. **Description:** Discusses and gives links to ten different carpet cleaning franchises. **Availability:** Online.

24324 ■ "12 Franchises Under 10K You Can Start in 2023" in *Small Business Trends (February 2, 2023)*
URL(s): smallbiztrends.com/2023/02/franchises-under-10k.html
Ed: Annie Pilon. **Released:** February 02, 2023. **Description:** Discusses and lists links to twelve franchises that can be started for under $10,000. **Availability:** Online.

24325 ■ "20 Home Improvement Franchises" in *Small Business Trends (February 21, 2023)*
URL(s): smallbiztrends.com/2023/02/home-improvement-franchises.html
Ed: Rob Starr. **Released:** February 21, 2023. **Description:** Discusses and provides links to twenty different home improvement franchises. **Availability:** Online.

24326 ■ "23 Questions to Ask a Franchisor When You Meet Face to Face" in *Entrepreneur (Feb. 6, 2019)*
URL(s): www.entrepreneur.com/franchise/23-questions-to-ask-a-franchisor-when-you-meet-face-to-face/323423
Released: February 06, 2019. **Description:** Provides a list of questions to use as a starting point when you have your first face-to-face meeting with your franchisor. **Availability:** Online.

24327 ■ "145 Restaurant Franchise Opportunities" in *Small Business Trends (March 6, 2023)*
URL(s): smallbiztrends.com/2023/03/restaurant-franchise.html
Ed: Samantha Lile. **Released:** March 06, 2023. **Description:** Discusses and provides online links to restaurant franchise opportunities. **Availability:** Online.

24328 ■ "All Fired Up!" in *Small Business Opportunities (November 2008)*
Description: Profile of Brixx Wood Fired Pizza, which has launched a franchising program due to the amount of interest the company's founders received over the years; franchisees do not need experience in the food industry or pizza restaurant service business in order to open a franchise of their own because all franchisees receive comprehensive training in which they are educated on all of the necessary tools to effectively run the business. **Availability:** Print; Online.

24329 ■ "All Those Applications, and Phone Users Just Want to Talk" in *Advertising Age (Vol. 79, August 11, 2008, No. 31, pp. 18)*
Pub: Crain Communications, Inc.
Contact: Jessica Botos, Manager, Marketing
E-mail: jessica.botos@crainsnewyork.com
Ed: Mike Vorhaus. **Description:** Although consumers are slowly coming to text messaging and other data applications, a majority of those Americans surveyed stated that they simply want to use their cell phones to talk and do not care about other activities. Statistical data included. **Availability:** Online.

24330 ■ "Allied Brands Loses Baskin-Robbins Franchise Down Under" in *Ice Cream Reporter (Vol. 23, November 20, 2010, No. 12, pp. 2)*
Description: Dunkin Brands, worldwide franchisor of Baskin-Robbins, terminated the master franchise agreement for Australia held by the food marketer Allied Brands Services. **Availability:** Print; Online.

24331 ■ "Ampm Focus Has BP Working Overtime" in *Crain's Chicago Business (April 28, 2008)*
Pub: Crain Communications Inc.
Contact: Barry Asin, President
Ed: John T. Slania. **Description:** Britian's oil giant BP PLC is opening its ampm convenience stores in the Chicago market and has already begun converting most of its 78 Chicago-area gas stations to ampms. The company has also started to franchise the stores to independent operators. BP is promoting the brand with traditional and unconventional marketing techniques such s real or simulated 3D snacks embedded in bus shelter ads and an in-store Guitar Hero contest featuring finalists from a recent contest at the House of Blues. **Availability:** Online.

24332 ■ "Area Small Businesses Enjoy Benefits of Bartering Group" in *News-Herald (August 22, 2010)*
Pub: The News Herald
Contact: Tricia Ambrose, Executive Editor
E-mail: tambrose@news-herald.com
Ed: Brandon C. Baker. **Description:** ITEX is a publicly traded firm that spurs cashless, business-to-business transactions within its own marketplace. Details of the bartering of goods and services within the company are outlined. **Availability:** Online.

24333 ■ "Attracting Veteran-Franchisees To Your System" in *Franchising World (Vol. 42, November 2010, No. 11, pp. 53)*
Pub: International Franchise Association
Contact: Matthew Haller, President
E-mail: mhaller@franchise.org
Ed: Mary Kennedy Thompson. **Released:** November 01, 2010. **Description:** As military servicemen and women return home, the franchising industry expects an increase in veterans as franchise owners. The Veterans Transition Franchise Initiative, also known as VetFran, is described. **Availability:** Online.

24334 ■ "Baby's Room Franchisee Files Bankruptcy" in *Crain's Detroit Business (Vol. 25, June 22, 2009, No. 25, pp. 15)*
Pub: Crain Communications Inc.
Contact: Barry Asin, President
Ed: Gabe Nelson. **Description:** Emery L, a franchisee of USA Baby Inc. and ran the franchised Baby's Room Nursery Furniture stores in the area has filed for bankruptcy. Details of the bankruptcy are included. **Availability:** Print; Online.

24335 ■ "Bark Up The Right Tree" in *Small Business Opportunities (Winter 2009)*
Released: February 09, 2016. **Description:** Profile of Central Bark, a daycare company catering to pets that offers franchise opportunities and is expanding rapidly despite the economic downturn; the company's growth strategy is also discussed.

24336 ■ "Baskin-Robbins: New in U.S., Old in Japan" in *Ice Cream Reporter (Vol. 23, August 20, 2010, No. 9, pp. 2)*
Description: Baskin-Robbins is celebrating its first franchise in Japan. **Availability:** Print; Online.

24337 ■ "Best Practices: Developing a Rewards Program" in *Franchising World (Vol. 42, September 2010, No. 9, pp. 13)*
Pub: International Franchise Association
Contact: Matthew Haller, President
E-mail: mhaller@franchise.org
Ed: Leah Templeton. **Description:** Rewards for a job well done are examined in order to recognize franchisees for outstanding performance. Ways to customize a rewards program are outlined. **Availability:** Online.

24338 ■ "BK Menu Gives Casual Dining Reason to Worry" in *Advertising Age (Vol. 79, November 17, 2008, No. 43, pp. 12)*
Pub: Crain Communications, Inc.
Contact: Jessica Botos, Manager, Marketing
E-mail: jessica.botos@crainsnewyork.com
Ed: Emily Bryson York. **Description:** Burger King is beginning to compete with such casual dining restaurants as Applebees and the Cheesecake Factory with new premium menu items, including thicker burgers and ribs; statistical data regarding the casual dining segment which continues to fall and Burger King, whose sales continue to rise is included. **Availability:** Online.

24339 ■ "Black-Owned Company Signed $334 Million Deal with Houston's William P. Hobby Airport" in *Black Enterprise(February 10, 2023)*
Ed: Darryl Robertson. **Released:** February 10, 2023. **Description:** Black-owned Latrelle's Management signed a deal to operate over 17,000 square feet of the Hobby Airport's dining areas. **Availability:** Online.

24340 ■ "Blog Buzz Heralds Arrival of IPhone 2.0" in *Advertising Age (Vol. 79, June 9, 2008, No. 40, pp. 8)*
Pub: Crain Communications, Inc.
Contact: Jessica Botos, Manager, Marketing
E-mail: jessica.botos@crainsnewyork.com
Ed: Abbey Klaassen. **Description:** Predictions concerning the next version of the iPhone include a global-positioning-system technology as well as a configuration to run on a faster, 3G network. **Availability:** Online.

24341 ■ "Building an Estate Sale Business by Franchising a Name and Brand" in *The New York Times (May 4, 2016)*
URL(s): www.nytimes.com/2016/05/05/business/smallbusiness/building-an-estate-sale-business-with-franchises.html
Ed: Janet Morrissey. **Released:** May 04, 2016. **Description:** When it's time to hold an estate sale, it's often hard to choose an estate sale company because they are not required to be licensed and there are no regulations. Grasons Company Estate Sale Services is hoping to change this by building a stellar reputation within the industry and franchising the name. **Availability:** Online.

GENERAL SMALL BUSINESS TOPICS

Franchising ■ 24365

24342 ■ *"Carvel Offers Franchisee Discount"* in Ice Cream Reporter (Vol. 21, August 20, 2008, No. 9, pp. 2)
Description: Carvel Ice Cream is offering new franchise opportunities in Florida, New Jersey, and New York. The company will offer incentive for new franchise owners. **Availability:** Print; Online.

24343 ■ *"Common Franchisee Mistakes—and How to Avoid Them"* in FranchiseWire(July 28, 2020)
URL(s): www.franchisewire.com/common-franchisee-mistakes-and-how-to-avoid-them/
Ed: Johnny Francis. **Released:** July 28, 2020.
Description: Outlines common struggles and situations franchisees encounter along with the mistakes that are often made.

24344 ■ *"Community Commitment Safeguards Franchising Industry"* in Franchising World (Vol. 42, November 2010, No. 11, pp. 38)
Pub: International Franchise Association
Contact: Matthew Haller, President
E-mail: mhaller@franchise.org
Description: Individuals who are dedicated to committing time and resources to bring to the attention of legislators those laws and proposals affecting franchise small businesses are highlighted in a monthly format. **Availability:** Online.

24345 ■ *"Convention Budgeting Best Practices"* in Franchising World (Vol. 42, November 2010, No. 11, pp. 11)
Pub: International Franchise Association
Contact: Matthew Haller, President
E-mail: mhaller@franchise.org
Ed: Steve Friedman. **Description:** Franchise conventions can offer benefits to both franchisor and franchisee in terms of culture-building, professional education and networking. However, these conventions can be costly. Tips for planning a successful franchising convention on a budget are outlined. **Availability:** Online.

24346 ■ *"Corner Bakery Readies Its Recipes for Growth"* in Dallas Business Journal (Vol. 35, February 17, 2012, No. 23, pp. 1)
Pub: Baltimore Business Journal
Contact: Rhonda Pringle, President
E-mail: rpringle@bizjournals.com
Description: Corner Bakery Cafe is planning to add 10 corporate locations and 15-20 franchise locations in 2012. The company was acquired by Roark Capital. **Availability:** Print; Online.

24347 ■ *"Couple Hopes to Lead Schlotzsky's Twin Cities Revival"* in Business Journal (Vol. 31, January 17, 2014, No. 34, pp. 4)
Pub: American City Business Journals, Inc.
Contact: Mike Olivieri, Executive Vice President
Description: Austin, Texas-based Schlotzsky's announced plans to open six Minnesota locations as it tries to regain its national prominence. The bankruptcy in 2004 and the reduction of its restaurant count had wiped out eight Minnesota restaurants and left only the Edina location. Schlotzky's six-restaurant deal with the local franchisees is examined. **Availability:** Print; Online.

24348 ■ *"Creative In-Sourcing Boosts Franchisee Performance"* in Franchising World (Vol. 42, September 2010, No. 9, pp. 16)
Pub: International Franchise Association
Contact: Matthew Haller, President
E-mail: mhaller@franchise.org
Ed: Daniel M. Murphy. **Released:** 2010. **Description:** Operational training and support is usually provided by franchisors. To be successful in this process it is important to balance the reality of limited financial and human resources. **Availability:** Online.

24349 ■ *"Customer Loyalty: Making Your Program Excel"* in Franchising World (Vol. 42, August 2010, No. 8, pp. 47)
Pub: International Franchise Association
Contact: Matthew Haller, President
E-mail: mhaller@franchise.org
Ed: Steve Baxter. **Description:** Customer loyalty is key to any franchise operation's growth. Tips for identifying preferred customers are outlined. **Availability:** Online.

24350 ■ *"Ditch the Rental Car: A New Way to Arrive in Style"* in Inc. (Vol. 33, September 2011, No. 7, pp. 54)
Pub: Inc. Magazine
Ed: Matt Rist. **Description:** EagleRider is a franchise offering various two-wheeled rentals, including BMWs and Harley-Davidsons at more than 100 locations worldwide. **Availability:** Online.

24351 ■ *"Dollar Thrifty Adds Franchises"* in Journal Record (December 7, 2010)
Pub: Dolan Media Newswires
Ed: D. Ray Tuttle. **Description:** Dollar Thrifty Automotive Group Inc. opened 31 franchise locations in 2010 as part of its expansion plan in the U.S. **Availability:** Print; Online.

24352 ■ *Don't Hire a Franchise Consultant if You See These Warning Signs!*
URL(s): www.franchiselawsolutions.com/learn/franchise-your-business/dont-hire-a-franchise-consultant-if-you-see-these-warning-signs
Description: Provides four warning signs to look for when utilizing the services of a franchise consultant. **Availability:** Online.

24353 ■ *"Dunkin' Donuts Franchise Looking Possible for 2011"* in Messenger-Inquirer (January 2, 2010)
Description: Dunkin' Donuts has approved expansion of their franchises in the Owensboro, Kentucky region.

24354 ■ *"Economic Loss Rule and Franchise Attorneys"* in Franchise Law Journal (Vol. 27, Winter 2008, No. 3, pp. 192)
Ed: Christian C. Burden, Scott Trende. **Released:** Volume 27. **Description:** Economic loss rule prohibits recovery of damages in tort when the subject injury is unaccompanied by either property damage or personal injury.

24355 ■ *Entrepreneur Franchise 500 Ranking*
Pub: Entrepreneur Media Inc.
Contact: Dan Bova, Director
E-mail: dbova@entrepreneur.com
URL(s): www.entrepreneur.com/franchise500
Ed: Rieva Lesonsky. **Released:** Annual **Description:** Publication includes listing and ranking of top 500 franchises in the United States and Canada. **Entries include:** Company name, address, and, in tabular form, key statistics. **Arrangement:** Classified by industry and ranking. **Availability:** Print.

24356 ■ *Entrepreneur Magazine's Ultimate Guide to Buying or Selling a Business*
Released: Fourth edition. **Description:** Proven strategies to evaluate, negotiate, and buy or sell a small business. Franchise and family business succession planning is included.

24357 ■ *"Flurry of Activity from Restaurant Groups as Industry Strengthens"* in Wichita Business Journal (Vol. 27, February 17, 2012, No. 7, pp. 1)
Pub: Baltimore Business Journal
Contact: Rhonda Pringle, President
E-mail: rpringle@bizjournals.com
Description: Atlanta, Georgia-based Chick-fil-A chain is set to open two restaurants in Wichita, Kansas and those additions were highly anticipated. However, there were other local management groups and franchisees that are investing on new buildings and refurbishing stores. Insights on the increasing restaurant constructions are also given. **Availability:** Print; Online.

24358 ■ *Franchise Basics*
URL(s): www.franchise500.com/article/36328
Description: A guide to help you decide if franchising is right for you. **Availability:** Online.

24359 ■ *"Franchise vs. Startup: Which Way to Go"* in Investopedia (July 14, 2020)
URL(s): www.investopedia.com/articles/personal-finance/110215/franchise-vs-startup-which-way-go.asp
Ed: James McWhinney. **Released:** July 14, 2020.
Description: Guides entrepreneurs through the pros and cons of franchising vs. launching a startup. **Availability:** Online.

24360 ■ *"Franchisee to Add 10 New Applebee's"* in Memphis Business Journal (Vol. 34, June 8, 2012, No. 8, pp. 1)
Pub: Baltimore Business Journal
Contact: Rhonda Pringle, President
E-mail: rpringle@bizjournals.com
Ed: Andy Ashby. **Description:** Apple Investor Group LLC seeks to open 10 more Applebee's restaurants in Memphis over the next two years. The franchisee purchased the 70-county market from DineEquity for $23 million in early 2012. The group is upgrading 17 Mid-South Applbee's units. **Availability:** Print; Online.

24361 ■ *The Franchisee Handbook*
URL(s): shop.aer.io/EntrepreneurBooks/p/title/9781599186399-2045
Ed: Mark Siebert. **Released:** January 22, 2019.
Price: $21.99. **Description:** Walks readers through the process of vetting and buying a franchise, helps you ask the right questions of franchisors and yourself, and gives you the resources you need to decide if franchising is right for you. **Availability:** E-book; Print.

24362 ■ *"Franchises with an Eye on Chicago"* in Crain's Chicago Business (Vol. 34, March 14, 2011, No. 11, pp. 20)
Pub: Crain Communications Inc.
Contact: Barry Asin, President
Ed: Kevin McKeough. **Description:** Profiles of franchise companies seeking franchisees for the Chicago area include: Extreme Pita, a sandwich shop; Hand and Stone, offering massage, facial and waxing services; Molly Maid, home-cleaning service; Primrose Schools, private accredited schools for children 6 months to 6 hears and after-school programs; Protect Painters, residential and light-commercial painting contractor; and Wingstop, a restaurant offering chicken wings in nine flavors, fries and side dishes. **Availability:** Online.

24363 ■ *"Franchising: The Importance Of Great Systems within the System"* in Small Business Trends (November 25, 2013)
URL(s): smallbiztrends.com/2013/11/franchise-systems-within-the-system.html
Ed: Joel Libava. **Released:** December 29, 2018.
Description: Discusses the processes and systems the owners of franchises are expected to provide and keep in good working order for those who purchase a franchise. **Availability:** Online.

24364 ■ *"GM's Decision to Boot Dealer Prompts Sale"* in Baltimore Business Journal (Vol. 27, November 6, 2009, No. 26, pp. 1)
Pub: Baltimore Business Journal
Contact: Rhonda Pringle, President
E-mail: rpringle@bizjournals.com
Ed: Daniel J. Sernovitz. **Description:** General Motors Corporation's (GM) decision to strip Baltimore's Anderson Automotive Group Inc. of its GM franchise has prompted the owner, Bruce Mortimer, to close the automotive dealership and sell the land to a developer. The new project could make way for new homes, a shopping center and supermarket. **Availability:** Print; Online.

24365 ■ *"Golden Spoon Accelerates Expansion Here and Abroad"* in Ice Cream Reporter (Vol. 22, December 20, 2008, No. 1, pp. 2)
Description: Golden Spoon frozen yogurt franchise chain is developing 35 more locations in the Phoenix, Arizona area along with plans to open a store in Japan. **Availability:** Print; Online.

24366 ■ *"Haagen-Dazs Recruits Shop Owners through Facebook"* in *Ice Cream Reporter* (Vol. 23, November 20, 2010, No. 12, pp. 1)
Description: Haagen-Dazs Shoppe Company is using Facebook, the leading social media, to recruit new franchises. **Availability:** Print; Online.

24367 ■ *"Happy Trails: RV Franchiser Gives Road Traveling Enthusiasts a Lift"* in *Black Enterprise* (Vol. 38, July 2008, No. 12, pp. 47)
Pub: Earl G. Graves Ltd.
Contact: Earl Graves, Jr., President
Ed: Tamara E. Holmes. **Description:** Overview of Bates International Motor Home Rental Systems Inc., a growing franchise that gives RV owners the chance to rent out their big-ticket purchases to others when they are not using them; Sandra Williams Bate launched the company as a franchise in July 1997 and now has a fleet of 30 franchises across the country. She expects the company to reach 2.2 million for 2008 due to a marketing initiative that will expand the company's presence.

24368 ■ *"Home Improvement Service Chain Had to Fix Its Own House"* in *Crain's Detroit Business* (Vol. 30, October 13, 2014, No. 41, pp. 15)
Pub: Crain Communications Inc.
Contact: Barry Asin, President
Description: Mr. Handyman International LLC is the franchising arm for the Mr. Handyman home improvement service chain. The franchises provide smaller home repair and improvement projects, mostly residential with only 15 percent of the jobs being commercial. Statistical data included. **Availability:** Online.

24369 ■ *"How BBQ Can Be Birmingham's Secret Sauce"* in *Birmingham Business Journal* (Vol. 31, May 9, 2014, No. 19, pp. 4)
Pub: American City Business Journals, Inc.
Contact: Mike Olivieri, Executive Vice President
Released: Weekly. **Price:** $4, introductory 4-week offer(Digital only). **Description:** Local barbecue joints in Birmingham, Alabama are branching out to new markets and extending distinct barbecue brand of the city through franchises and corporate expansions across the U.S. Experts say this trend is contributing to more brand awareness and tourists for Birmingham. **Availability:** Print; Online.

24370 ■ *"How to Find the Best CRM for Your Franchise"* in *Entrepreneur* (Oct. 25, 2019)
URL(s): www.entrepreneur.com/franchise/how-to-find-the-best-crm-for-your-franchise/339976
Ed: Hayden Field. **Released:** October 25, 2019. **Description:** Provides information on and describes the importance of finding the best customer relationship management software for your franchise. **Availability:** Online.

24371 ■ *"How to Franchise a Professional Service Business"* in *Chron*
URL(s): smallbusiness.chron.com/franchise-professional-service-business-14979.html
Ed: Tammi Metzler. **Description:** Seven steps to franchising your professional service business. **Availability:** Online.

24372 ■ *"How to Franchise a Startup: 5 Tips for Success"* in *Business News Daily* (Dec. 30, 2020)
URL(s): www.businessnewsdaily.com/5657-how-to-franchise.html
Ed: Sammi Caramela. **Released:** December 30, 2020. **Description:** Presents information on how to franchise your startup business. **Availability:** Online.

24373 ■ *"How to Franchise Your Business"* in *Small Business Trends* (October 18, 2022)
URL(s): smallbiztrends.com/2022/10/how-to-franchise-your-business.html
Ed: Kevin Ocasio. **Released:** October 18, 2022. **Description:** Details the steps you need to take if you want to franchise your own small business. **Availability:** Online.

24374 ■ *"How to Franchise Your Business: 7 Steps for Small Businesses"*
URL(s): www.legalzoom.com/articles/how-to-franchise-your-business-7-steps-for-small-businesses
Released: January 26, 2022. **Description:** Discusses the steps to take to scale your small business via franchising. **Availability:** Online.

24375 ■ *"How to Vet Franchisors and Predict Your ROI on a Franchise Business"* in *Entrepreneur* (Jan. 30, 2019)
URL(s): www.entrepreneur.com/franchise/how-to-vet-franchisors-and-predict-your-roi-on-a-franchise/323374
Ed: Mark Siebert. **Released:** January 30, 2019. **Description:** Explores how to ensure that you are investing in the best franchise opportunity for you so that you can make reasonable profits. **Availability:** Online.

24376 ■ *"Hyannis Mercedes Franchise Sold"* in *Cape Cod Times* (December 2, 2010)
Pub: Cape Cod Times
Contact: Anne Brennan, Executive Editor
E-mail: abrennan@capecodonline.com
Ed: Sarah Shemkus. **Description:** Trans-Atlantic Motors franchise has been sold to Mercedes-Benz of Westwood. **Availability:** Print; Online.

24377 ■ *"Integrating Your Compliance Program"* in *Franchising World* (Vol. 42, November 2010, No. 11, pp. 49)
Pub: International Franchise Association
Contact: Matthew Haller, President
E-mail: mhaller@franchise.org
Ed: Melanie Bergeron. **Description:** Compliance is integral to every part of any business operation and it is necessary for a company to make standards and compliance to those standards a priority. **Availability:** Online.

24378 ■ *International Franchise Association--Franchise Opportunities Guide*
Pub: International Franchise Association
Contact: Matthew Haller, President
E-mail: mhaller@franchise.org
URL(s): www.franchise.org/faqs/where-can-i-find-the-best-franchise-opportunities
Released: Semiannual **Description:** Covers companies offering franchises. **Entries include:** Company name, address, phone, type of business, contact, number of franchised and company-owned outlets, years in business, qualifications expected of prospective franchisees, investment required, training & support provided. **Arrangement:** Classified. **Availability:** Print; Online.

24379 ■ *"It's Good To Be King"* in *South Florida Business Journal* (Vol. 35, August 29, 2014, No. 5, pp. 12)
Released: December 01, 2013. **Description:** The $11.4 billion deal that will create a new holding company for Burger King Worldwide and Tim Hortons will be based in Oakville, Ontario, Canada and was met with public outrage. Burger King declares that the merger with the Canadian coffee and doughnut franchise chain was about global growth, not a strategy to avoid millions of dollars in corporate income tax payments to the U.S. government. **Availability:** Print; Online.

24380 ■ *"Joel Libava on Looking for the Perfect Franchise Opportunity"* in *Small Business Trends*(October 31, 2022)
URL(s): smallbiztrends.com/2022/10/joel-libava-looking-for-perfect-franchise-opportunity.html
Ed: Holly Chavez. **Released:** October 31, 2022. **Description:** Joel Libava is interviewed about the latest franchising trends. **Availability:** Online.

24381 ■ *"KFC Franchises Getting Rid of Popcorn Chicken"* in *Small Business Trends*(February 17, 2023)
URL(s): smallbiztrends.com/2023/02/kfc-is-getting-rid-of-popcorn-chicken.html
Released: February 17, 2023. **Description:** KFC franchises are discontinuing the popular popcorn chicken along with other items. **Availability:** Online.

24382 ■ *"Learn New Ideas from Experienced Menu Makers"* in *Nation's Restaurant News* (Vol. 45, June 27, 2011, No. 13, pp. 82)
Pub: Informa USA, Inc.
Contact: Stephen A. Carter, Chief Executive Officer
Ed: Nancy Kruse. **Released:** June 27, 2011. **Description:** National Restaurant Association Restaurant, Hotel-Motel Show featured the Food Truck Spot, a firm committed to all aspects of mobile catering, foodtruck manufacturers, leasers of fully equipped truck and a food-truck franchising group.

24383 ■ *"Local Firm Snaps up 91 Area Pizza Huts"* in *Orlando Business Journal* (Vol. 26, January 8, 2010, No. 32, pp. 1)
Pub: Orlando Business Journal
Contact: Julie Swyers, Director
E-mail: jswyers@bizjournals.com
Ed: Alexis Muellner, Anjali Fluker. **Description:** Orlando, Florida-based CFL Pizza LLC bought the 91 Orlando-area Pizza Hut restaurants for $35 million from parent company Yum! Brands Inc. CFL Pizza plans to distribute parts of the business to Central Florida vendors and the first business up for grabs is the advertising budget. **Availability:** Print; Online.

24384 ■ *"Magellan Companies Establishes Century 21 Beachhead in Boise"* in *Idaho Business Review* (September 15, 2014)
Pub: BridgeTower Media
Contact: Adam Reinebach, President
Description: New Jersey-based Century 21, the largest real estate franchise worldwide, has entered the Idaho market under the name Century 21 Magellan Realty with five agents. Wesley Flacker, builder, home renovator, broker, and property manager purchased the franchise and expects to have 60 agents by 2015.

24385 ■ *"Making Automated Royalty Payments Work for Your Franchise"* in *Franchising World* (Vol. 42, October 2010, No. 10, pp. 30)
Pub: International Franchise Association
Contact: Matthew Haller, President
E-mail: mhaller@franchise.org
Ed: J.P. O'Brien. **Released:** October 10, 2010. **Description:** In the past, royalty payments were sent by franchisees through regular postal mail and accompanied by a single slip of paper with handwritten notes indicating the month's revenue numbers and royalty amounts. **Availability:** PDF; Online.

24386 ■ *"Marketers Push for Mobile Tuesday as the New Black Friday"* in *Advertising Age* (Vol. 79, December 1, 2008, No. 44, pp. 21)
Pub: Crain Communications, Inc.
Contact: Jessica Botos, Manager, Marketing
E-mail: jessica.botos@crainsnewyork.com
Ed: Natalie Zmuda. **Description:** Marketers are using an innovative approach in an attempt to stimulate business on the Tuesday following Thanksgiving by utilizing consumer's cell phones to alert them of sales or present them with coupons for this typically slow retail business day; with this campaign both advertisers and retailers are hoping to start Mobile Tuesday, another profitable shopping day in line with Black Friday and Cyber Monday. **Availability:** Online.

24387 ■ *"Maximize Your Marketing Results In a Down Economy"* in *Franchising World* (Vol. 42, November 2010, No. 11, pp. 45)
Pub: International Franchise Association
Contact: Matthew Haller, President
E-mail: mhaller@franchise.org
Ed: Loren Rakich. **Description:** Strategies to help any franchisee to maximize their marketing efforts in a slow economy are outlined. **Availability:** Online.

24388 ■ "McDonald's Loses Its Sizzle" in Barron's (Vol. 88, March 17, 2008, No. 11, pp. 47)

Description: McDonald's has promised to return $15 billion to $17 billion to shareholders in 2007-2009 but headwinds are rising for the company. December, 2007 same-store sales were flat and the company's traffic growth in the U.S. is slowing. Its shares are likely to trade in tandem with the market until recession fears recede. **Availability:** Online.

24389 ■ "Menchie's Tops Restaurant Business' Future 50 List" in Ice Cream Reporter (Vol. 23, August 20, 2010, No. 9, pp. 4)

Description: Menchie's, frozen yogurt shop, announced it placed first in the Restaurant Business Magazine's Future 50, ranking the franchise the fastest-growing in the food industry. **Availability:** Print; Online.

24390 ■ "Mount Laurel Woman Launches Venture Into Children's Used Clothing" in Philadelphia Inquirer (September 17, 2010)
Pub: The Philadelphia Inquirer
Contact: Elizabeth H. Hughes, Chief Executive Officer

Ed: Maria Panaritis. **Description:** Profile of Jennifer Frisch, stay-at-home mom turned entrepreneur. Frisch started a used-clothing store Once Upon a Child after opening her franchised Plato's Closet, selling unwanted and used baby clothing and accessories at her new shop, while offering used merchandise to teens at Plato's Closet.

24391 ■ "Never Buy a Franchise Without Researching These 5 Sources" in Entrepreneur (Jan. 16, 2019)
URL(s): www.entrepreneur.com/franchise/never-buy-a-franchise-without-researching-these-5-sources/323372

Ed: Mark Siebert. **Released:** January 16, 2019. **Description:** Provides methods of research to complete when you have narrowed your choices for potential franchises to see if they are a good fit. **Availability:** Online.

24392 ■ "NexCen Brands Sells Chains and Will Liquidate" in Ice Cream Reporter (Vol. 23, August 20, 2010, No. 9, pp. 1)

Description: NexCen Brands is closing the sale of its franchise businesses, which include the frozen dessert chains MaggieMoo's and Marbel Slab Creamery, to Global Franchise Group. **Availability:** Print; Online.

24393 ■ "Ohio Franchisee Buys 21 Jacksonville-Area Papa John's" in Florida Times-Union (December 20, 2010)
Pub: Florida Times-Union

Ed: Mark Basch. **Description:** Ohio-based Papa John's pizza franchise acquired 21 of the restaurants in Duval, Clay and St. Johns counties in Jacksonville, Florida. **Availability:** Online.

24394 ■ "Open Price Agreements: Good Faith Pricing in the Franchise Relationship" in Franchise Law Journal (Vol. 27, Summer 2007, No. 1, pp. 45)
Pub: American Bar Association
Contact: Mary L. Smith, President

Ed: Douglas C. Berry, David M. Byers, Daniel Oates. **Description:** Open price term contracts are important to franchise businesses. Details of open price contracts are examined.

24395 ■ "Opening and Operating a Franchise" in Legal Zoom (March 27, 2023)
URL(s): www.legalzoom.com/articles/opening-and-operating-a-franchise

Ed: Stephanie Morrow. **Released:** March 27, 2023. **Description:** Defines what a franchise is and gives some general tips on opening one in your area. **Availability:** Online.

24396 ■ "Opportunity Knocks" in Small Business Opportunities (September 2008)

Description: Profile of YourOffice USA, a franchise that provides home-based and small businesses cost-effective and efficient support through "virtual" offices that are available as much or as little as the client needs it; they also supply necessary tools such as a professional business address, private mailbox service, personalized telephone answering and more that supports clients who want to look, act and operate with an advanced business image. **Availability:** Online.

24397 ■ "Panera Breadwinner Tries on Tattu Designer Jeans" in Houston Business Journal (Vol. 40, December 18, 2009, No. 32, pp. 1)
Pub: Houston Business Journal
Contact: Bob Charlet, President
E-mail: bcharlet@bizjournals.com

Ed: Allison Wollam. **Description:** Chuck Cain, the franchisee who introduced Panera Bread to Houston, Texas has partnered with tax accountant Jim Jacobsen to introduce custom-make Tattu Jeans. As more Tattu Jeans outlets are being planned, Cain is using entrepreneurial lessons learned from Panera Bread in the new venture. Both Panera Bread and Tattu Jeans were opened by Cain during economic downturns. **Availability:** Print; Online.

24398 ■ "Pizza or Beer? Why Kalil Made Right Call" in Business Journal (Vol. 31, January 31, 2014, No. 36, pp. 6)
Pub: American City Business Journals, Inc.
Contact: Mike Olivieri, Executive Vice President

Released: January 31, 2014. **Price:** $4, Introductory 4-week offer(Digital & Print). **Description:** Businessman, Matt Kalil, purchased the Pieology franchise rights for Minnesota. Kalil will open his first locations in Maple Grove and Saint Paul's Highland Park. The restaurant franchise is expected to have six locations by the end of 2014. **Availability:** Print; Online.

24399 ■ "Pizza Chain Enters Boston" in Boston Business Journal (Vol. 34, April 25, 2014, No. 12, pp. 3)
Pub: American City Business Journals, Inc.
Contact: Mike Olivieri, Executive Vice President

Released: April 25, 2014. **Description:** Mitch Roberts and David Peterman have decided to sign a franchise agreement with Blaze Pizza. The two restaurateurs will bring the California-based restaurant chain to Boston, Massachusetts.

24400 ■ "Potbelly Sandwich Shop Inks Multi-Unit Development Deal to Open Restaurants in Macy's Stores" in Franchising.com (October 9, 2019)
URL(s): www.franchising.com/news/20191009_potbelly_sandwich_shop_inks_multiunit_development_.html

Released: October 09, 2019. **Description:** The Potbelly Sandwich Shop has announced that it has signed a multi-unit franchise agreement to open up shops in Macy's department stores. Four units are planned, with three of them being located in California and the other one in New York. **Availability:** Online.

24401 ■ "Q&A With Devin Ringling: Franchise's Services Go Beyond Elder Care" in Gazette (October 2, 2010)
Pub: The Gazette
Contact: Vicki Cederholm, Director, Operations
E-mail: vicki.cederholm@gazette.com

Ed: Bill Radford. **Description:** Profile of franchise, Interim HealthCare, in Colorado Springs, Colorado; the company offers home care services that include wound care and specialized feedings to shopping and light housekeeping. It also runs a medical staffing company that provides nurses, therapists and other health care workers to hospitals, prisons, schools and other facilities. **Availability:** Online.

24402 ■ "Report: McD's Pepsi Score Best With Young Hispanics" in Brandweek (Vol. 49, April 21, 2008, No. 16, pp. 8)

Description: According to a new report, in order to reach Hispanic Gen Yers, marketing strategists need to understand this demographic's "bi-dentity," something which has proved an elusive task to many marketers. Another trend is the emergence of Latinas who have careers, as opposed to just jobs. There is an opportunity to tap this new, young and empowered female market with innovative messaging. Statistical data included. **Availability:** Online.

24403 ■ "Right at Home China Celebrates 1 Year Anniversary as U.S. In-Home Senior Care Master Franchise" in Professional Service Close-Up (June 24, 2012)

Description: Franchisor, Right at Home International Inc., provides in-home senior care and assistance and has experienced a one year franchise license agreement in China. Right at Home China predicts growth because China has 200 million adults over 65 years of age. **Availability:** Print; Online.

24404 ■ "The Rise of Franchise Consultants as a Result of the Pandemic" in Forbes (Aug. 25, 2021)
URL(s): www.forbes.com/sites/forbesbusinesscouncil/2021/08/25/the-rise-of-franchise-consultants-as-a-result-of-the-pandemic/?sh=3ea666461cd2

Ed: Don Daszkowski. **Released:** August 25, 2021. **Description:** Discusses the growth of the franchise consulting business. **Availability:** Online.

24405 ■ "Salad Creations To Open 2nd Location" in Crain's Detroit Business (Vol. 24, March 3, 2008, No. 9, pp. 26)

Description: Salad Creations, a franchise restaurant that allows customers to create their own salads and also offers soups and sandwiches; Salad Creations plans to open a total of five locations by the end of 2008. **Availability:** Online.

24406 ■ "Seasonal Franchises: Strategies to Advance" in Franchising World (Vol. 42, August 2010, No. 8, pp. 50)
Pub: International Franchise Association
Contact: Matthew Haller, President
E-mail: mhaller@franchise.org

Ed: Jennifery Lemcke. **Price:** $5.99. **Description:** Seasonal franchises, such as tax businesses can be slow during the summer months. Restaurants are slow during the months of January and February. The various challenges faced by seasonal franchises are examined. **Availability:** Online.

24407 ■ "Serious Growth Ahead for Tokyo Joe's" in Denver Business Journal (Vol. 65, April 4, 2014, No. 47, pp. A9)
Pub: American City Business Journals, Inc.
Contact: Mike Olivieri, Executive Vice President

Released: Weekly. **Price:** $4, introductory 4-week offer(Digital only). **Description:** Tokyo Joe's founder and chief innovation officer, Larry Leith, shares his perspective on the franchising and expansion of the Colorado-based Asian fast food chain. Leith describes the fast-casual chain market in Denver and considers the possibility of going public in the future. **Availability:** Print; Online.

24408 ■ Service Based Franchising: What Franchisors Want
URL(s): www.franchising.com/guides/services_what_franchisors_want.html

Ed: Eddy Goldberg. **Description:** Presents information on service-based franchising. **Availability:** Online.

24409 ■ "Setting Out on Your Own? Think Franchises" in Crain's Cleveland Business (Vol. 28, October 8, 2007, No. 40, pp. 20)
Pub: Crain Communications Inc.
Contact: K. C. Crain, President

Description: Franchisers are targeting baby boomers due to their willingness to put up some of their own money to open their own business. According to local franchising expert, Joel Libava, entrepreneurs should expect to pay about 15 to 30 percent of the total cost of starting the franchise out of their own pocket. **Availability:** Online.

24410 ■ *Should You Buy a Small Business Franchise?*
URL(s): www.wolterskluwer.com/en/expert-insights/should-you-buy-a-small-business-franchise
Released: December 13, 2020. **Description:** Discusses special considerations to think about when buying a small business franchise instead of buying an existing business or starting a new one from scratch. Includes advantages and disadvantages of franchising. **Availability:** Online.

24411 ■ *"Silver Dollars" in Small Business Opportunities (September 2008)*
Description: Profile of Always Best Care Senior Services, a franchise created by Michael Newman, which offers non-medical In-Home Care, Personal Emergency Response Systems, and Assisted Living Placement Services to seniors; the company offers franchisees the opportunity to fill what is oftentimes a void for the seniors and their families in the community. **Availability:** Online.

24412 ■ *"Smart Tips for Successfully Navigating the Initial Franchisor-Franchisee Interview" in Entrepreneur (Jan. 23, 2019)*
URL(s): www.entrepreneur.com/franchise/smart-tips-for-successfully-navigating-the-initial/323373
Ed: Mark Siebert. **Released:** January 23, 2019. **Description:** Once you have a few franchises in mind, you'll be talking to a franchise rep from each company. This article provides information on how to prepare for and navigate the initial phone calls with potential franchisors. **Availability:** Online.

24413 ■ *"Steering Toward Profitability" in Black Enterprise (Vol. 41, December 2010, No. 5, pp. 72)*
Pub: Earl G. Graves Ltd.
Contact: Earl Graves, Jr., President
Ed: Alan Hughes. **Description:** Systems Electro Coating LLC had to make quick adjustments when auto manufacturers were in a slump. The minority father-daughter team discuss their strategies during the auto industry collapse.

24414 ■ *:Subway Closings Accerlerate as Cold-Cuts Fail to Draw in Diners" in Bloomberg (March 28, 2019)*
URL(s): www.bloomberg.com/news/articles/2019-0 3-28/subway-closings-accelerate-as-cold-cut-subs-don-t-draw-in-diners
Ed: Leslie Patton. **Released:** March 28, 2019. **Description:** Subway Restaurants are closing stores at a faster pace than years past, due to slumping sales. Americans are not buying Subway as much as they used to, which resulted in 1,100 shops closing in 2018 and 800 in 2017. **Availability:** Online.

24415 ■ *"Subway Franchise Locations Celebrating National Potato Chip Day with Unique Menu Item" in Small Business Trends (March 9, 2023)*
Ed: Joshua Sophy. **Released:** March 09, 2023. **Description:** Subway has come up a new offer to celebrate National Potato Chip Day. The new sandwich uses potato chips as a topping. **Availability:** Online.

24416 ■ *"Subway Launches Expanded Cafes, Drive-Thru Window Locations" in South Florida Business Journal (Vol. 33, August 10, 2012, No. 2, pp. 1)*
Pub: Baltimore Business Journal
Contact: Rhonda Pringle, President
E-mail: rpringle@bizjournals.com
Description: Subway launched its larger cafe concept at Florida Atlantic University and plans to open more drive-thru restaurants in South Florida. This could change preferred leasing locations to Subway franchisees, which are also moving into nontraditional locations. Site selection issues are covered. **Availability:** Print; Online.

24417 ■ *"Sweet Tea From McDonald's: A Marketing 50 Case Study" in Advertising Age (Vol. 79, November 17, 2008, No. 43, pp. 4)*
Pub: Crain Communications, Inc.
Contact: Jessica Botos, Manager, Marketing
E-mail: jessica.botos@crainsnewyork.com
Ed: Emily Bryson York. **Description:** McDonald's launch of iced coffee and sweat tea, which were promoted via price cuts over the summer, helped to boost sales at the fast-food chain. **Availability:** Online.

24418 ■ *"Tasti D-Lite Has Franchise Agreement for Australia" in Ice Cream Reporter (Vol. 23, November 20, 2010, No. 12, pp. 3)*
Description: Tasti D-Lite signed an international master franchise agreement with Friezer Australia Pty. Ltd. and will open 30 units throughout Australia over the next five years. **Availability:** Print; Online.

24419 ■ *"Thinking Strategically About Technology" in Franchising World (Vol. 42, August 2010, No. 8, pp. 9)*
Pub: International Franchise Association
Contact: Matthew Haller, President
E-mail: mhaller@franchise.org
Ed: Bruce Franson. **Released:** 2010. **Description:** Nearly 25 percent of companies waste money from their technology budget. Most of the budget is spent on non-strategic software. Ways to spend money on technology for any franchise are examined. **Availability:** Online.

24420 ■ *"This Legendary New York Bagel Shop is Finally Going National" in Eat This, Not That (October 10, 2021)*
Ed: Krissy Gasbarre. **Released:** October 10, 2021. **Description:** A famous New York City bagel shop, H&H Bagels, is heading out of its comfort zone and announcing franchise opportunities, as it tries to branch out into other states. **Availability:** Download.

24421 ■ *"Thriving DFW Big Target for Franchisors" in Dallas Business Journal (Vol. 35, March 30, 2012, No. 29, pp. 1)*
Description: Dallas-Fort Worth Metropolitan Area has attracted outside franchisors looking to expand as Texas continues to fare better than other states during the recession. The Internation Franchising Association estimates that there will be 21,772 franchise establishments in DFW in 2012. **Availability:** Print; Online.

24422 ■ *"Training: an Investment in Performance Improvement" in Franchising World (Vol. 42, September 2010, No. 9, pp. 22)*
Pub: International Franchise Association
Contact: Matthew Haller, President
E-mail: mhaller@franchise.org
Ed: Catherine Monson. **Released:** 2010. **Description:** Advantages of training provided by franchisors that are available to franchisees and their employees are discussed. **Availability:** Online.

24423 ■ *"Types of Franchises" in Small Business Trends (February 22, 2023)*
URL(s): smallbiztrends.com/2023/02/types-of-franchises.html
Ed: Rob Starr. **Released:** February 22, 2023. **Description:** Discusses the five different types of franchises. **Availability:** Online.

24424 ■ *"U-Swirl Added to SBA's Franchise Registry" in Ice Cream Reporter (Vol. 23, September 20, 2010, No. 10, pp. 1)*
Description: Healthy Fast Food Inc., parent to the U-SWIRL Frozen Yogurt cafe chain announced that the U.S. Small Business Administration listed U-SWIRL Frozen Yogurt on its official franchise registry. This move will allow U-SWIRL the benefits of a streamlined review process for SBA financing. **Availability:** Print; Online.

24425 ■ *"U-Swirl To Open in Salt Lake City Metro Market" in Ice Cream Reporter (Vol. 23, November 20, 2010, No. 12, pp. 4)*
Description: Healthy Fast Food Inc., parent company to U-SWIRL International Inc., the owner and franchisor of U-SWIRL Frozen Yogurt cafes signed a franchising area development agreement for the Salt Lake City metropolitan area with Regents Management and will open 5 cafes over a five year period. **Availability:** Print; Online.

24426 ■ *"Ultimate Guide to Business Franchising" in Business News Daily (Dec. 17, 2021)*
URL(s): www.businessnewsdaily.com/15778-business-franchising-guide.html
Ed: Marisa Sanfilippo. **Released:** December 17, 2021. **Description:** Discusses the benefits of opening a franchise, the difference between a franchise and a chain, and how to buy a franchise. **Availability:** Online.

24427 ■ *The Ultimate Guide to Franchise Consultants, Franchise Brokers, and Franchise Coaches*
URL(s): www.thefranchiseking.com/what-everybody-ought-to-know-about-franchise-consultants
Ed: Joe Libava. **Description:** Comprehensive article covering everything you need to know about franchise consultants and franchise consulting services. The intended audience of this article is for prospective franchise buyers. **Availability:** Online.

24428 ■ *"Valuation of Intangible Assets in Franchise Companies and Multinational Groups: A Current Issue" in Franchise Law Journal (Vol. 27, No. 3, Winter 2008)*
Ed: Bruce D. Schaeffer, Susan J. Robins. **Released:** Volume 27. **Description:** Intangible assets, also known as intellectual properties are the most valuable assets for companies today. Legal intellectual property issues faced by franchises firms are discussed.

24429 ■ *"Want Leverage? Multi-Unit Franchisees Deliver Substantial Savings" in Franchising World (Vol. 42, October 2010, No. 10, pp. 39)*
Pub: International Franchise Association
Contact: Matthew Haller, President
E-mail: mhaller@franchise.org
Ed: Aziz Hashim. **Description:** Many retail franchises selling the same product are able to buy in bulk. Volume-buying can save money for any franchise. **Availability:** Online.

24430 ■ *"What Franchises Need From an Accountant" in Entrepreneur (May 5, 2020)*
URL(s): www.entrepreneur.com/franchise/what-franchises-need-from-an-accountant/348616
Ed: Hayden Field. **Released:** May 05, 2020. **Description:** Provides a checklist for franchisors to follow when looking for an account for their business. **Availability:** Online.

24431 ■ *What Is the Difference Between a Small Business and a Franchise?*
URL(s): 1851franchise.com/what-is-the-difference-between-a-small-business-and-a-franchise-271649 1#stories
Ed: Lauren Garcia. **Released:** August 23, 2021. **Description:** Discusses the differences between starting a small business and buying a franchise. **Availability:** Online.

24432 ■ *What Is a Franchise Consultant and What Do They Do?*
URL(s): regionaltoglobal.com/blog/2022/03/17/what-is-a-franchise-consultant-and-what-do-they-do/
Released: March 17, 2022. **Description:** Franchise consultants advise people who are interested in buying a franchise. This article provides information on the services offered by franchise consultants and why they are valuable. **Availability:** Online.

**24433 ■ "What Is a Franchise Consultant??"
in The Entrepreneur's Source**
URL(s): www.ifpg.org/franchise-consultant-training/
what-is-a-franchise-consultantentrepreneurssource
.com/what-is-a-franchise-consultant/
Description: Details what a certified franchise consultant does and provides information on how a franchise consultant can help guide you through the franchise selection, evaluation, and buying process. **Availability:** Online.

24434 ■ What to Know Before Buying a Gas Station Franchise
Ed: Bruce Hakutizwi. **Description:** With gas stations ranking as one of the most popular and profitable franchises, purchasing a gas station franchise can eliminate some of the startup costs and headaches that come with opening a new station. This article provides key factors to keep in mind if you are exploring the idea of purchasing a franchise. **Availability:** Online.

**24435 ■ "What the Popeyes Chicken Sandwich Feeding Frenzy Means for Rivals"
in Barron's (September 10, 2019)**
URL(s): www.barrons.com/articles/popeyes-chicken
-sandwich-frenzy-spells-bad-news-for-rivals-51568
109600
Ed: Connor Smith. **Released:** September 10, 2019. **Description:** The summer of 2019 produced one of the biggest debuts in the fast food business: the Popeyes chicken sandwich. Due to a Twitter war between Chick-Fil-A and Wendy's, Popeye's emerged with their own sandwich resulting in long lines and shortages at their restaurants. The company needed to step in and remove the item from its menu in order to regroup. However, the popular sandwich will be back. **Availability:** Online.

24436 ■ "What Should Franchises Look for in a Law Firm?" Entrepreneur (Dec. 10, 2019)
URL(s): www.entrepreneur.com/franchise/what-shoul
d-franchises-look-for-in-a-law-firm/341821
Ed: Hayden Field. **Released:** December 10, 2019. **Description:** Discusses the benefits of hiring a lawyer with franchising expertise for your new franchise to help with review of disclosure documents and with negotiation of changes to franchise agreements. **Availability:** Online.

24437 ■ "When Are Sales Representatives Also Franchisees?" in Franchise Law Journal (Vol. 27, Winter 2008, No. 3, pp. 151)
Ed: John R.F. Baer, David A. Beyer, Scott P. Weber. **Released:** Volume 27. **Description:** Review of the traditional definitions of sales representatives along with information on how these distribution models could fit into various legal tests for a franchise.

24438 ■ "Which Franchise Is Right For You? Follow These Steps" in Entrepreneur (Jan. 15, 2019)
URL(s): www.entrepreneur.com/franchise/which-fran
chise-is-right-for-you-follow-these-steps/325915
Ed: Mark Siebert. **Released:** January 15, 2019. **Description:** Presents information on how to develop a list of franchise candidates that will be the best fit for you. **Availability:** Online.

24439 ■ "Why These 3 Advisors Paid to Say 'No' Are Your Best Allies When Buying a Franchise" in Entrepreneur (Feb. 13, 2019)
URL(s): www.entrepreneur.com/franchise/why-these
-3-advisors-paid-to-say-no-are-your-best-allies/
323425
Ed: Mark Siebert. **Released:** February 13, 2019. **Description:** Explores the three advisors (banker, accountant, and attorney) needed to help you as you investigate buying a franchise. Their expertise and willingness to tell you when to say "no" are imperative before handing over your hard-earned cash for a franchise business. **Availability:** Online.

24440 ■ "Why Work with a Franchise Consultant?" in FranchiseWire (May 3, 2021)
URL(s): www.franchisewire.com/why-work-with-a
-franchise-consultant/
Ed: Mark Pasma. **Released:** May 03, 2021. **Description:** Details the benefits of utilizing a franchise consultant to help you navigate the franchise discovery process and potentially save you from making a mistake. **Availability:** Online.

24441 ■ "Worth His Salt" in Hawaii Business (Vol. 53, January 2008, No. 7, pp. 45)
Pub: PacificBasin Communications
Contact: Chuck Tindle, Director
E-mail: chuckt@pacificbasin.net
Ed: Jolyn Okimoto Rosa. **Description:** Bryan Zada owns three PretzelMaker franchises, whose total loss amounted to $40,000 in 2003. Zada believes that listening to employees was one of the key steps in turning the business around. The efforts made to improve the franchises' products are also given. **Availability:** Online.

24442 ■ "Wyndham Program Targeting Women Hotel Owners Signs 30 Franchisees in First Year" in Bizwomen (March 24, 2023)
URL(s): www.bizjournals.com/bizwomen/news/lates
t-news/2023/03/wyndham-program-for-women-hotel
-owners-signs-30-fr.html
Ed: Anne Stych. **Released:** 24, 2023. **Description:** A program that targets women's advancement in hotel ownership signed on 30 hotel franchises. Noted in the article that about 50 percent of these hotels are new constructions projects that will now be headed by women. **Availability:** Online.

24443 ■ "Yogun Fruz Adds First Location in Southern New York State" in Ice Cream Reporter (Vol. 23, September 20, 2010, No. 10, pp. 2)
Description: Yogen Fruz signed a master franchise agreement to expand into the southern counties of New York State. The firm offers a healthy and beneficial option to fast food and typical dessert choices. **Availability:** Print; Online.

STATISTICAL SOURCES

24444 ■ Laundromat Franchises Industry in the US - Market Research Report
URL(s): www.ibisworld.com/united-states/market-re
search-reports/laundromat-franchises-industry/
Price: $545. **Description:** On demand report that analyzes current and future trends in the laundromat franchise industry. **Availability:** On Demand.

TRADE PERIODICALS

24445 ■ Franchising World
Pub: International Franchise Association
Contact: Matthew Haller, President
E-mail: mhaller@franchise.org
URL(s): www.franchise.org/franchise-information/
franchising-world/franchising-world-digital-edition
-2024
Released: 6/year; online.; Annual; print. **Description:** Trade magazine covering topics of interest to franchise company executives and the business world. **Availability:** Print; Online.

VIDEO/AUDIO MEDIA

24446 ■ Car Wash to Cash Flow with Sean Oatney
URL(s): www.eofire.com/podcast/seanoatney
Ed: Jon Lee Dumas. **Released:** March 26, 2024. **Description:** Podcast discusses pros and cons of franchising but explains how it offers a unique chance to achieve success more quickly.

24447 ■ Franchises on Fire with Lance Graulich
URL(s): www.eofire.com/podcast/lancegraulich
Ed: Jon Lee Dumas. **Released:** November 21, 2023. **Description:** Podcast explains the pros and cons of buying into a franchise, discusses the realities of what it costs, and highlights some of the trending franchises.

24448 ■ Franchising 101: Buy It or Build It with Josh Minturn
URL(s): www.eofire.com/podcast/joshminturn
Ed: Jon Lee Dumas. **Released:** August 08, 2024. **Description:** Podcast discusses the fundamentals of franchising.

24449 ■ Franchising - The Better Path to Business Ownershp with Jon Ostenson
URL(s): www.eofire.com/podcast/jonostenson8
Ed: Jon Lee Dumas. **Released:** June 11, 2024. **Description:** Podcast discusses the advantages of (and trends in) franchising.

24450 ■ Great Opportunities in Non-Food Franchising with Jon Ostenson: An EOFire Classic from 2021
URL(s): www.eofire.com/podcast/jonostenson2
Ed: Jon Lee Dumas. **Released:** October 26, 2024.

24451 ■ The How of Business: Earsa Jackson - Franchise Attorney
URL(s): www.thehowofbusiness.com/franchising
-episodes/episode-006-earsa-jackson
Released: May 02, 2016. **Description:** Podcast shares tips on franchising.

24452 ■ The How of Business: Giuseppe Grammatico - Small Business Franchises
URL(s): www.thehowofbusisess.com/episode
-365-giuseppe-grammatico
Ed: Henry Lopez. **Released:** April 12, 2021. **Description:** Podcast explains why a franchise can be a good option for someone transitioning from a corporate career to business ownership.

24453 ■ The How of Business: Nick Neonakis - Franchises
URL(s): www.thehowofbusiness.com/franchising
-episodes/episode-023-nick-neonakis
Ed: Henry Lopez. **Released:** July 04, 2016. **Description:** Podcast discusses franchises as a business investment to help you understand whether owning one is right for you.

24454 ■ The How of Business: Sara Waskow - Franchising
URL(s): www.thehowofbusiness.com/franchising
-episodes/episode-018-sara-waskow
Ed: Henry Lopez. **Released:** June 13, 2016. **Description:** Podcast offers tips on finding the right franchise.

24455 ■ The How of Business: Starting a Franchise Business
URL(s): www.thehowofbusiness.com/episode-332-e
ddie-unbazo
Ed: Henry Lopez. **Released:** September 28, 2020. **Description:** Podcast discusses starting a franchise business.

24456 ■ The How of Business: Three Benefits of Franchising
URL(s): www.thehowofbusiness.com/franchising
-episodes/episode-016-3-benefits-of-franchising
Ed: Henry Lopez. **Released:** June 16, 2016. **Description:** Podcasts discusses the benefits to consider when finding a franchise that's right for you.

24457 ■ How to Franchise Your Small Business with Dr. Tom DuFore
URL(s): www.eofire.com/podcast/tomdufore
Ed: John Lee Dumas. **Released:** May 29, 2023. **Description:** Podcast offers tips on franchising your small business.

24458 ■ Nurture Small Business: A Guide to Buying and Maintaining a Franchise
URL(s): nurturesmallbusiness.buzzsprout.com/900
445/13219386-a-guide-to-buying-and-maintaining-a
-franchise
Ed: Denise Cagan. **Released:** July 24, 2023. **Description:** Podcast discusses running a franchise. Includes the structured phases of the sales processes, the importance of accurately estimating the financial runway and time commitment, and the differ-

ence between franchises and license agreements. Also touches on the increase on female-owned franchises and what it means for women in business.

24459 ■ *Responsible Franchising for Entrepreneurs with Aaron Harper*
URL(s): www.eofire.com/podcast/aaronharper
Ed: Jon Lee Dumas. **Released:** June 25, 2024. **Description:** Podcast discusses core issues for responsible franchising: expectations, capital adequacy, the right franchise, and sustainable growth.

24460 ■ *The Small Business School Podcast: Franchising and Tutus with Genevieve Weeks*
URL(s): podcasts.apple.com/us/podcast/franchising-and-tutus-with-genevieve-weeks/id1695210366?i=1000652716327
Released: April 17, 2024. **Description:** Podcast discusses the decision to franchise and how to nurture it.

24461 ■ *Starting a Franchise Restaurant Business*
URL(s): www.thehowofbusiness.com/episode-254-lauren-dowdus
Ed: Henry Lopez. **Released:** June 10, 2019. **Description:** Podcast explores selecting a restaurant franchise, facing a variety of challenges, planning for growth, and hiring/retaining employees.

24462 ■ *Think Business: Franchise Pitfalls and Prosperity - Giuseppe Grammatico*
URL(s): thinktyler.com/podcast_episode/franchise-giuseppe-grammatico
Ed: Tyler Martin. **Released:** December 11, 2023. **Description:** Podcast considers the difference between starting from scratch and buying into a franchise, why franchising may not be for everyone, and common franchise mistakes.

24463 ■ *Top Non-Food Franchise Opportunities for 2024 with Jon Ostenson*
URL(s): www.eofire.com/podcast/jonostenson7
Ed: Jon Lee Dumas. **Released:** January 08, 2024. **Description:** Podcast discusses non-food franchising, including custom orthotics and pavement striping.

24464 ■ *Transitioning from Small Business to a Franchisor with Bryan Appell*
URL(s): www.eofire.com/podcast/bryanappell
Ed: Jon Lee Dumas. **Released:** April 08, 2024. **Description:** Podcast explains that if you have hands-off day-to-day operations and stable systems, becoming a franchisor could be the next step.

TRADE SHOWS AND CONVENTIONS

24465 ■ **ABM Continuing Education Conference and Vendor Showcase**
URL(s): www.abm.com/abm-franchising-group
Frequency: Annual. **Description:** Conference dedicated to providing network opportunities for franchise owners and leading facility service providers. **Principal Exhibits:** Conference dedicated to providing network opportunities for franchise owners and leading facility service providers.

24466 ■ **Association of Kentucky Fried Chicken Franchisees Annual Convention**
URL(s): akfcf.com
Frequency: Annual. **Description:** Annual convention with talks about current events and trending topics for franchise owners. **Principal Exhibits:** Annual convention with talks about current events and trending topics for franchise owners.

24467 ■ **The Franchise Show**
URL(s): www.franchiseshowinfo.com/newyork/visitor
Description: Provides seminars, speakers, and vendors for those interested in starting a franchise business. **Audience:** Those who want to start their own franchise business. **Principal Exhibits:** Provides seminars, speakers, and vendors for those interested in starting a franchise business.

24468 ■ **The Great American Franchise Expo**
URL(s): www.franexpousa.com/attend-Houston-franchise-expo-trade-show-2022
Description: Trade show for those starting a franchise business. Provides seminars on franchise law, growing the business, and financing. **Principal Exhibits:** Trade show for those starting a franchise business. Provides seminars on franchise law, growing the business, and financing.

24469 ■ **IFA Annual Convention**
Association Canadienne de la Franchise
116-5399 Eglinton Ave. W
Toronto, ON, Canada M9C 5K6
Ph: (416)695-2896
Free: 800-665-4232
Fax: (416)695-1950
Co. E-mail: info@cfa.ca
URL: http://cfa.ca
Contact: Sherry McNeil, President
E-mail: smcneil@cfa.ca
URL(s): web.cvent.com/event/4368698a-cc7b-4f3d-b810-e30e5c239625/summary?rp=514e025a-6b71-48e2-bede-d49be6d5f532
Frequency: Annual. **Description:** Targets franchisees, franchisors and the steadfast supplier partners that support the franchise industry. **Audience:** Franchise professionals. **Principal Exhibits:** Targets franchisees, franchisors and the steadfast supplier partners that support the franchise industry. **Telecommunication Services:** events@franchise.org.

24470 ■ **International Franchise Expo (IFE)**
MFV Expositions
210 Route 4 E, Ste. 204
Paramus, NJ 07652
Ph: (201)226-1130
Co. E-mail: mfv@mfvexpo.com
URL: http://www.mfvexpo.com
Contact: Thomas Portesy, President
E-mail: tportesy@mfvexpo.com
URL(s): www.franchiseexpo.com/ife
Facebook: www.facebook.com/InternationalFranchiseExpo
X (Twitter): twitter.com/MFVExpositions
Frequency: Annual. **Description:** Event includes speakers, exhibits, and networking opportunities. **Audience:** Entrepreneurs and business owners. **Principal Exhibits:** Event includes speakers, exhibits, and networking opportunities. Dates and Locations: 2025 May 29-31 Jacob K. Javits Convention Center, New York, NY. **Telecommunication Services:** dana.stein@comexposium.com.

CONSULTANTS

24471 ■ **Accurate Franchising**
2121 Vista Pky.
West Palm Beach, FL 33411
Free: 888-331-8195
Co. E-mail: info@accuratefranchising.com
URL: http://www.accuratefranchising.com
Contact: Ray Titus, Chief Executive Officer
Facebook: www.facebook.com/accuratefranchising
Linkedin: www.linkedin.com/company/accurate-franchising
X (Twitter): x.com/Afifranchising
Instagram: www.instagram.com/accuratefranchising
Description: Franchise consulting, development, sales and training company that consults in all areas of franchising, from companies in the early stages of exploring their franchise options to already existing franchisors looking to improve sales, marketing or operational procedures. **Founded:** 1986.

24472 ■ **Arch Franchise Consultants**
Wentzville, MO
Ph: (636)262-8317
Co. E-mail: info@archfranchises.com
URL: http://archfranchises.com
Contact: Robert Barclay, President
Facebook: www.facebook.com/ArchFranchiseConsultants
Linkedin: www.linkedin.com/company/arch-franchise-consultants/
Description: A franchise consulting company dedicated to matching you with an established franchise or business opportunity that best fits your goals and objectives.

24473 ■ **Arnold Business Advisors L.L.C.**
9541 Greenthread Dr.
Zionsville, IN 46077
Ph: (317)203-9541
Co. E-mail: chris@chrisarnold.org
URL: http://www.chrisarnold.org/the-productivity-loop
Contact: Chris Arnold, President
E-mail: chris@chrisarnold.org
Description: Firm provides dry cleaning, laundry, retail clothing, hair care franchises, real estate investments, and much more. **Scope:** Firm provides dry cleaning, laundry, retail clothing, hair care franchises, real estate investments, and much more.

24474 ■ **Franchise Architects**
16427 N Scottsdale Rd., Ste. 410
Scottsdale, AZ 85254
Ph: (480)980-1441
Co. E-mail: info@franchisecentral.com
URL: http://Www.franchisearchitects.com
Contact: Craig Slavin, President
Description: Creates and manages indirect channels of distribution, which include franchising, licensing, dealerships and distributorships. Development and consulting services include strategic planning, positioning, naming, creation or refinement of training programs, operational manuals, marketing strategies and collateral brochures; organizational surveys and development; and human resource assessment. Industries served: retail, transportation, food service, technology, service and communications. **Scope:** Creates and manages indirect channels of distribution, which include franchising, licensing, dealerships and distributorships. Development and consulting services include strategic planning, positioning, naming, creation or refinement of training programs, operational manuals, marketing strategies and collateral brochures; organizational surveys and development; and human resource assessment. Industries served: retail, transportation, food service, technology, service and communications. **Founded:** 1980. **Training:** Making the Transition from Entrepreneurial to a Professionally Managed Company; Franchising - Is It for You?; The Franchise Success System.

24475 ■ **Franchise Business Systems Inc. (FBS)**
2319 N Andrews Ave.
Fort Lauderdale, FL 33311
Free: 800-382-1040
URL: http://www.franchiseaccounting.com
Contact: Steven J. Weil, President
E-mail: steve@franchiseaccounting.com
Description: National business consulting and accounting firm provides accounting and financial systems development, support and training to franchisors for use by their franchisee, accounting, bookkeeping, tax, business consulting and SBA loan packaging services to franchisees. **Scope:** National business consulting and accounting firm provides accounting and financial systems development, support and training to franchisors for use by their franchisee, accounting, bookkeeping, tax, business consulting and SBA loan packaging services to franchisees. **Founded:** 1998. **Training:** Tax planning for business owners; The dos and don'ts of S-corporations; Don't let the tax tail wag the dog; Cash is king; Business budgeting and living your budget; Working with your spouse; Employee incentives, how to get what you pay for; Who to turn to when the IRS comes calling; How to protect your family assets in estate planning; Elder care: what is it and who needs it; Tax planning for seniors; When to run - not walk - away from a financial professional; Year-end tax planning; So you want to start a business; Wealth care for the new millennium.

GENERAL SMALL BUSINESS TOPICS

24476 ■ The Franchise Consulting Company (FCC)
3735 SW 8th St., Ste. 207
Miami, FL 33134
Free: 800-321-6072
Facebook: www.facebook.com/thefranchiseconsultingco
Linkedin: www.linkedin.com/company/the-franchise-consulting-company
Description: Consulting firm serving prospective franchisees. **Founded:** 2016.

24477 ■ Franchise Consulting Group (FCG)
1801 Century Pk. E, Ste. 2400
Los Angeles, CA 90067
Ph: (310)552-2901
URL: http://franchiseconsulting.com
Contact: Edward Kushell, President
Description: Firm provides consulting services in new business startup and company expansion programs and performs analysis, research, planning and development of product service distribution systems. **Founded:** 1978.

24478 ■ Franchise Developments Inc.
5840 Aylesboro Ave.
Pittsburgh, PA 15217
Description: Franchise consultants that offer clients full development services for the purpose of designing and implementing a total franchise program. **Publications:** "Franchising Your Business," May/Jun, 2003; "Female Entrepreneur," May/Jun, 2003; "Franchising World," May/Jun, 2003; "Canadian Business Franchise," Jul/Aug, 2000. **Training:** Has presented franchising seminars under auspices of American Management Association, Management Center Europe and International Franchise Association. Recent programs include Expanding Your Business by Franchising; Writing Effective Franchise Operations Manuals. Also has franchise seminar on Prodigy.

24479 ■ Franchise Marketing Systems
6110 McFarland Station Dr., Unit 105
Alpharetta, GA 30004
Free: 800-610-0292
Co. E-mail: info@franchisemarketingsystems.com
URL: http://www.fmsfranchise.com
Contact: Chris Conner, President
Facebook: www.facebook.com/FranchiseMarketingSystems
Linkedin: www.linkedin.com/company/fmsfranchise
X (Twitter): x.com/FranchiseMkting
Instagram: www.instagram.com/fmsfranchise
YouTube: www.youtube.com/user/FranchiseMarketing1/videos
Description: Full service franchise consulting agency offering marketing and sales support to its clients. **Scope:** Full service franchise consulting agency offering marketing and sales support to its clients.

24480 ■ Franchise Specialists
2988 Silver Springs Blvd., Unit. 209
Coquitlam, BC, Canada V3E 3R6
Ph: (604)941-4361
URL: http://www.franchisespecialists.com
Contact: Wayne Maillet, Consultant
E-mail: wmaillet@franchisespecialists.com
Description: Firm provides franchise development and management such as operation manuals, strategic planning, franchise recruitment, and business coaching. **Scope:** Firm provides franchise development and management such as operation manuals, strategic planning, franchise recruitment, and business coaching. **Founded:** 1997. **Publications:** "Do you have what it takes to succeed as a franchisee?"; "Intro to Franchising," Franchise Canada Magazine, Feb, 2008; "Franchise Tutorial," Franchise Canada Magazine, Apr, 2008; "Is My Business Franchisable," Canadian Business Franchise, 2003; "Understanding Franchising"; "Do you have what it takes".

24481 ■ FranNet (FN)
10302 Brookridge Village Blvd., Ste. 201
Louisville, KY 40291
Ph: (502)753-2380
Free: 800-372-6638
Co. E-mail: info@frannet.com
URL: http://frannet.com
Contact: Amanda Duplantis, Director
Facebook: www.facebook.com/FranNetTeam
Linkedin: www.linkedin.com/company/frannet
X (Twitter): x.com/FranNet_Team
Instagram: www.instagram.com/FranNet_Team
YouTube: www.youtube.com/user/FranNetTeam
Description: Firm provides management consulting services. **Founded:** 1987.

24482 ■ FranSource International Inc.
1001 S Main St. N
Canton, OH 44720
Free: 844-233-7911
Co. E-mail: info@fransource.com
URL: http://fransource.com
Contact: Stephen Vandergrift, President
Linkedin: www.linkedin.com/company/fransource-international
Description: A full-service franchise development and consulting company. Provides comprehensive assistance, advisement, and support with every aspect of the franchise development process. **Founded:** 1997.

24483 ■ Harold L. Kestenbaum P.C. (HLK)
3401 Merrick Rd., Ste. 4
Wantagh, NY 11793
Ph: (215)544-2972
Co. E-mail: hkestenbaum@spadealaw.com
Contact: Harold L. Kestenbaum, Contact
E-mail: hkestenbaum@spadealaw.com
Facebook: www.facebook.com/haroldlkestenbaum
Linkedin: www.linkedin.com/in/hkestenbaum
X (Twitter): x.com/Kestenbaum_Law
Description: Provider of consulting services for startup and existing franchisors, their services include feasibility studies, determination of franchise format, business plan development, capital resources, manual preparation and legal services, and practices franchise law and offers marketing services, and serves all types of industries. **Scope:** Provider of consulting services for startup and existing franchisors, their services include feasibility studies, determination of franchise format, business plan development, capital resources, manual preparation and legal services, and practices franchise law and offers marketing services, and serves all types of industries. **Publications:** "Four tips to starting a successful franchise".

24484 ■ Kennedy Franchise Consultants
Tampa, FL
Ph: (813)494-1729
Co. E-mail: mkennedy@yourfranchisepro.com
URL: http://kennedyfranchiseconsultants.com
Contact: Mariruth Kennedy, Owner
Facebook: www.facebook.com/kennedyfranchiseconsultants
Description: Helps prospective franchisees build successful careers. Offers complimentary franchise consulting services to help match you with companies who are looking for people with your skills, abilities, and talents. **Founded:** 2008.

24485 ■ "Know the Difference Between a Franchise Advisor, Consultant & Broker?" in The Franchise Maker website
URL(s): www.thefranchisemaker.com/learningcenter/what-is-the-difference-between-a-franchise-consultant-franchise-advisor-franchise-broker-franchise-developer/
Description: Breaks down players in the franchising industry that are often co-mingled and poorly defined. Describes franchise consultants, franchise advisors, franchise brokers, and franchise developers. **Availability:** Online.

24486 ■ Management Action Programs, Inc. (MAP)
5900 Sepulveda Blvd., Ste. 425
Sherman Oaks, CA 91411
Free: 888-834-3040
Co. E-mail: map@mapconsulting.com
URL: http://www.mapconsulting.com
Contact: Michael Caito, Chief Executive Officer
E-mail: mc@mapconsulting.com
Facebook: www.facebook.com/ManagementActionPrograms
Linkedin: www.linkedin.com/company/map
X (Twitter): x.com/mapconsulting
Instagram: www.instagram.com/managementactionprograms
Description: Provides management consulting services such as performance improvement and business planning. **Founded:** 1960. **Publications:** "Vital Factors," Oct, 2006. **Training:** How to Finance a Growing Business; Venture Capital for Growing Business; Franchise Relations for the Large Accounting Firm; Should You Franchise Your Business; The Pitfalls of TQM; Productivity in the Manufacturing Sector and Re-engineering to Get Results; Management Development Workshop. **Special Services:** Vital Factor®.

24487 ■ National Cooperative Bank, Corporate Banking Div. (NCB)
2011 Crystal Dr., Ste. 800
Arlington, VA 22202
Ph: (703)302-8000
Free: 800-955-9622
Fax: (703)647-3460
URL: http://www.ncb.coop
Contact: Casey Fannon, President
Facebook: www.facebook.com/NationalCooperativeBank
Linkedin: www.linkedin.com/company/national-cooperative-bank/about
X (Twitter): x.com/natlcoopbank
Instagram: www.instagram.com/nationalcooperativebank
YouTube: www.youtube.com/user/NationalCoopBank
Description: Provider of banking and financial services. **Scope:** Provider of banking and financial services.

24488 ■ National Franchise Associates, Inc. (NFA)
240 Lake View Ct.
Lavonia, GA 30553
Ph: (706)356-5637
Fax: (706)356-5180
URL: http://www.nationalfranchise.com
Contact: Stephen S. Raines, Consultant
Description: Full service consulting and developmental firm with expertise in feasibility studies, Franchise agreements and UFOC's, advertising and public relations campaigns, operations and training manuals, franchise sales programs, and ongoing franchise consulting. **Scope:** Firm provides franchise consulting services including feasibility studies, franchise plans, venture capital, franchise agreement, FTC disclosure document, state registration applications, operations manuals, training materials, advertising and public relations, computer software programs, sales and marketing of franchises for businesses, public and private sector. **Founded:** 1981. **Publications:** "Keys To Successful Franchising: Franchise Marketing Reflections Of A Franchise Consultant"; "Keys To A Successful Franchise Training"; "Keys To Successful Franchise Development: Will The Franchise Generate Sufficient Money? Reflections Of A Franchise Consultant"; "Focus on Operations Manuals & Marketing"; "Keys To Successful Franchising: Will Your Franchise Program Make Enough Money?"; "Keys To Successful Franchise Planning: Selecting The Right Franchisees"; "DePalma's expanding into Asia"; "Spirit Of Ingenuity"; "Why a Franchise Consultant Can Be Helpful". **Training:** Franchise Training Program.

24489 ■ National Franchise Sales (NFS)
1601 Dove St., Ste. 150
Newport Beach, CA 92660
Ph: (949)428-0480
Fax: (949)428-0490
Co. E-mail: nfs@nationalfranchisesales.com
URL: http://www.nationalfranchisesales.com/home
Contact: Jerome Thissen, President
E-mail: jt@nationalfranchisesales.com
Facebook: www.facebook.com/nfsresales
Linkedin: www.linkedin.com/company/nfsresales
X (Twitter): x.com/NFSresales

Description: Firm provides business services such as brokerage, asset recovery, and advisory services. **Founded:** 1978. **Publications:** "Franchise National Connection Franchise Sales". **Training:** Franchising - How to Start a Franchise; Franchising - How to Market Your Franchise.

24490 ■ Pinnacle Franchise Development
10302 Brookridge Village Blvd., Ste. 201
Louisville, KY 40291
Ph: (954)205-3855
Co. E-mail: lory@pinnaclefd.com
URL: http://www.pinnaclefd.com
Linkedin: www.linkedin.com/company/pinnacle-franchise-development
Description: Franchise development firm serving emerging brands as well as established brands. **Founded:** 2015.

24491 ■ Summa Franchise Consulting
15051 N Kierland Blvd., Ste. 300
Scottsdale, AZ 85254
Ph: (623)999-1727
Co. E-mail: info@summafranchise.com
URL: http://summafranchise.com
Contact: Robert Stidham, Chief Executive Officer
Facebook: www.facebook.com/SummaFranchise
X (Twitter): x.com/SummaFranchise
Instagram: www.instagram.com/summafranchise
Description: Franchise consulting company specializing in advising franchising companies of all types at every step along the process, from emerging concept to sustainable success.

24492 ■ Upside Group Franchise Consulting Corp.
11445 E Via Linda, Ste. 2-495
Scottsdale, AZ 85259
Free: 888-445-2882
Co. E-mail: info@upsidefc.com
URL: http://upsidefranchiseconsulting.com
Contact: Mario Altiery, President
Description: Firm engages in full franchise consulting sales development. **Founded:** 2000. **Training:** Yes.

24493 ■ Venture Marketing Associates L.L.C.
800 Palisade Ave., Ste. 907
Fort Lee, NJ 07024
Ph: (201)924-7455
Co. E-mail: venturemkt@aol.com
URL: http://www.venturemarketingassociates.com
Contact: Shep Altshuler, Contact
Description: Business development/franchise consultants. **Scope:** Firm provides business development services for startups or multi-unit operations. **Founded:** 1976. **Training:** Franchise Your Business; How to Research a Franchise Services.

FRANCHISES AND BUSINESS OPPORTUNITIES

24494 ■ Aloha Hotels and Resorts
PO Box 15341
Honolulu, HI 96830
Ph: (808)826-6244
Co. E-mail: wb@alohahotels.com
URL: http://www.alohahotels.com
Contact: Walter Bono, Contact
Description: Firm provides independent inn, hotel and resort owners with the ability to obtain new sources of revenue. **Training:** Provides training an support programs. There is one assigned management team member to your property that is available to answer any questions and take you through the steps to become an Aloha Hotel and Resort member. There are many training and support areas that are included in your membership.

24495 ■ Dorsey & Whitney L.L.P.
701 5th Ave., Ste. 6100
Seattle, WA 98104-7043
Ph: (206)903-8800
URL: http://www.dorsey.com
Contact: Aaron Goldstein, Partner
E-mail: goldstein.aaron@dorsey.com
Facebook: www.facebook.com/DorseyWhitneyLLP
Linkedin: www.linkedin.com/company/dorsey-&-whitney-llp
X (Twitter): x.com/DorseyWhitney
Instagram: www.instagram.com/dorseywhitneyllp
YouTube: www.youtube.com/user/DorseyWhitneyLLP
Description: It provides legal knowledge and skills with practical wisdom and a deep understanding of business and industry. **Founded:** 1912.

24496 ■ Franchise Development International
6278 N Federal Hwy., Ste. 382
Fort Lauderdale, FL 33308
Contact: Linda D. Biciocchi, President
Description: Franchise development and marketing. **Founded:** 1991.

24497 ■ Franchise Developments Inc.
5840 Aylesboro Ave.
Pittsburgh, PA 15217
Description: Franchise consultants that offer clients full development services for the purpose of designing and implementing a total franchise program. **Publications:** "Franchising Your Business," May/Jun, 2003; "Female Entrepreneur," May/Jun, 2003; "Franchising World," May/Jun, 2003; "Canadian Business Franchise," Jul/Aug, 2000. **Training:** Has presented franchising seminars under auspices of American Management Association, Management Center Europe and International Franchise Association. Recent programs include Expanding Your Business by Franchising; Writing Effective Franchise Operations Manuals. Also has franchise seminar on Prodigy.

24498 ■ Franchise Foundations (FF)
San Francisco, CA
Ph: (415)225-3010
Co. E-mail: franchise888@gmail.com
URL: http://www.franchisefoundations.com
Contact: Kevin B. Murphy, Contact
Facebook: www.facebook.com/franchisefoundations
Linkedin: www.linkedin.com/company/franchise-foundations
X (Twitter): x.com/KevinB_Murphy
Pinterest: www.pinterest.com/franchisefoundations
Description: Firm provides franchise consulting services. **Founded:** 1980.

24499 ■ Franchise Search Inc.
48 Burd St., Ste. 101
Nyack, NY 10960-3226
Contact: Douglas Todd Kushell, Chief Executive Officer
E-mail: dkushell@franchise-search.com
Description: International executive search firm for franchisers. **Scope:** An international search firm specializing in executive searching for franchisers. Works exclusively for franchise organizations that need experienced franchise specialists in President, CEO, COO, Sales, Operations, Training, Marketing and Advertising, Legal, Finance, Real Estate and Construction and International Development. **Founded:** 1982.

24500 ■ Franchise Specialists Inc.
801 E 2120 Greentree Rd.
Pittsburgh, PA 15220
Contact: William F. Repack, President
Description: Firm is engaged in professional franchise development and sales. **Founded:** 1978.

24501 ■ FranchiseMart
2121 Vista Pky.
West Palm Beach, FL 33411
URL: http://unitedfranchisegroup.com
Contact: A. J. Titus, President
Description: Provider of franchising information and consulting services. **Franchised:** 2007. **Financial Assistance:** Yes **Training:** Yes.

24502 ■ FranChoice Inc.
7500 Flying Cloud Dr., Ste. 600
Eden Prairie, MN 55344
Ph: (952)345-8400
Free: 888-307-1371
Co. E-mail: info@franchoice.com
URL: http://www.franchoice.com
Contact: Jeff Elgin, Chief Executive Officer
E-mail: jelgin@franchoice.com
Facebook: www.facebook.com/FranChoice
Linkedin: www.linkedin.com/company/franchoice
X (Twitter): x.com/FranChoiceHQ
Description: Provides consumers with free guidance and advice to help them select a franchise that matches their individual interests and financial qualifications. **Scope:** Firm provides franchise consulting services for individuals. **Founded:** 1999. **Publications:** "VYPE High School Sports Magazine". **Training:** How to Evaluate a Franchise.

24503 ■ The iFranchise Group Inc.
905 W 175th St., 2nd Fl.
Homewood, IL 60430
URL: http://www.ifranchisegroup.com
Contact: David E. Hood, President
Linkedin: www.linkedin.com/company/ifranchise-group
X (Twitter): x.com/ifranchisegroup
Instagram: www.instagram.com/ifranchisegroup
Description: Firm provides franchise consulting, development and marketing services. **Scope:** Firm provides franchise consulting, development and marketing services. **Founded:** 1998. **Publications:** "Is Your Business Franchisable?"; "The Right Marketing Materials". **Training:** Franchise Sales and Marketing Techniques; Minimizing Franchise Litigation; How to Franchise a Business; Developing and Maintaining Good Franchisee Relations.

24504 ■ Jones & Co.
67 Yonge St., Ste. 602
Toronto, ON, Canada M5E 1J8
Ph: (416)703-5716
Fax: (416)703-6180
URL: http://www.jonesco-law.ca
Contact: Paul D. Jones, Principal
E-mail: pjones@jonesco-law.ca
Description: Law firm provides legal advice to businesses regarding the protection and distribution of their goods and services.

24505 ■ Kanouse and Walker P.A.
6879 Giralda Cir.
Boca Raton, FL 33433
Ph: (561)451-8090
Fax: (561)451-8089
URL: http://www.kanouse.com
Contact: Susan Walker, Vice President
E-mail: swalker@kanouse.com
Description: Firm offers legal services in matters of real estate, leasing and security law. **Founded:** 1974.

24506 ■ Kaufman & Canoles, P.C.
150 W Main St.
Norfolk, VA 23514
Ph: (757)624-3000
Free: 888-360-9092
URL: http://www.kaufcan.com
Contact: Karen H. Burris, Manager
E-mail: khburris@kaufcan.com
Facebook: www.facebook.com/Kaufman-Canoles-PC-311214283886
Linkedin: www.linkedin.com/company/kaufman-&-canoles
X (Twitter): x.com/KaufCan
YouTube: www.youtube.com/user/KaufCan
Description: Firm provides litigation services. **Founded:** 1982.

24507 ■ L. Michael Schwartz, P.A. (LMSPA)
7631 Widmer
Lenexa, KS 66215
Contact: L. Michael Schwartz, Contact
Description: Franchise consulting and full legal services.

24508 ■ National Franchise Associates, Inc. (NFA)
240 Lake View Ct.
Lavonia, GA 30553
Ph: (706)356-5637
Fax: (706)356-5180
URL: http://www.nationalfranchise.com
Contact: Stephen S. Raines, Consultant

Description: Full service consulting and developmental firm with expertise in feasibility studies, Franchise agreements and UFOC's, advertising and public relations campaigns, operations and training manuals, franchise sales programs, and ongoing franchise consulting. **Scope:** Firm provides franchise consulting services including feasibility studies, franchise plans, venture capital, franchise agreement, FTC disclosure document, state registration applications, operations manuals, training materials, advertising and public relations, computer software programs, sales and marketing of franchises for businesses, public and private sector. **Founded:** 1981. **Publications:** "Keys To Successful Franchising: Franchise Marketing Reflections Of A Franchise Consultant"; "Keys To A Successful Franchise Training"; "Keys To Successful Franchise Development: Will The Franchise Generate Sufficient Money? Reflections Of A Franchise Consultant"; "Focus on Operations Manuals & Marketing"; "Keys To Successful Franchising: Will Your Franchise Program Make Enough Money?"; "Keys To Successful Franchise Planning: Selecting The Right Franchisees"; "DePalma's expanding into Asia"; "Spirit Of Ingenuity"; "Why a Franchise Consultant Can Be Helpful". **Training:** Franchise Training Program.

INTERNET DATABASES

24509 ■ *Business Franchise Guide*
701 Brazos St. - Ste. 720
Austin, TX 78701
Co. E-mail: info@wolterskluwer.com
URL: http://www.wolterskluwer.com/en-in
Contact: Kevin Entricken, Chief Financial Officer
URL(s): law-store.wolterskluwer.com/s/product/business-franchise-guide3mo-subvitallaw/0 1t0f00000NY7ZWAA1
Released: Monthly; three-month periods (online).
Description: Contains extensive legal and regulatory information related to all aspects of business franchising. **Availability:** Online. **Type:** Full-text; Numeric.

LIBRARIES

24510 ■ Alberta Securities Commission (ASC)
250-5th St. SW, Ste. 600
Calgary, AB, Canada T2P 0R4
Ph: (403)297-6454
Free: 877-355-0585
Fax: (403)297-6156
Co. E-mail: inquiries@asc.ca
URL: http://www.asc.ca
Contact: Stan Magidson, Chief Executive Officer
Facebook: www.facebook.com/ASCUpdates
Linkedin: www.linkedin.com/company/alberta-securities-commission_2
X (Twitter): x.com/ASCUpdates
Description: Aims to foster a fair and efficient capital market in Alberta. We've made it easy for you to find the information you need. **Founded:** 1955.

RESEARCH CENTERS

24511 ■ Nature Conservancy - New Jersey
200 Pottersville Rd.
Chester, NJ 07930
Ph: (908)879-7262
Co. E-mail: newjersey@tnc.org
URL: http://www.nature.org/en-us/about-us/where-we-work/united-states/new-jersey
Contact: Dr. Barbara Brummer, Director
E-mail: bbrummer@tnc.org
Facebook: www.facebook.com/NJConservancy
X (Twitter): x.com/nature_NJ
Description: Protects ecologically significant natural areas and the diversity of life they support. **Scope:** Identifies rare plants and animals and the lands where they live; protects land through acquisition by gift or purchase and managing it using staff and volunteer land stewards. Also uses innovative strategies involving community and corporate partnerships. **Founded:** 1951. **Publications:** *Nature Conservancy Magazine* (Quarterly); *The Oak Leaf*. **Educational Activities:** New Jersey Chapter Office Annual Members Meeting, Held each fall. **Geographic Preference:** State.

General Business

START-UP INFORMATION

24512 ■ *The 250 Questions Every Self-Employed Person Should Ask*
Ed: Mary Mihaly. **Released:** 2010. **Description:** Comprehensive information is given for anyone wishing to start their own business.

24513 ■ *"2007 Top Colleges for Entrepreneurs" in Entrepreneur (Vol. 35, November 2007, No. 11, pp. 82)*
Pub: Entrepreneur Media Inc.
Contact: Dan Bova, Director
E-mail: dbova@entrepreneur.com
Ed: Nichole L. Torres. **Description:** Education in entrepreneurship is being pursued by many students and it is important to understand what entrepreneurship program fits you. Aspiring entrepreneurs should also ask about the program's focus. Considerations searched for by students regarding the particular school they chose to study entrepreneurship are discussed. **Availability:** Online.

24514 ■ *"Ailing Economy Nibbling at Tech-Sector Jobs" in Puget Sound Business Journal (Vol. 29, November 7, 2008, No. 29, pp. 1)*
Description: Seattle-area tech start-up companies including Redfin, Zillow, WildTangent, Daptiv, Avelle, and Intrepid Learning Solutions have cut staff as the nation's economy staggers. The layoffs are reminiscent of the tech bubble era, but most startups these days have been more prudent about spending and hiring as compared to that period. **Availability:** Print; Online.

24515 ■ *"Alpharetta Seeding Startups To Encourage Job Growth" in Atlanta Business Chronicle(June 20, 2014, pp. 3A)*
Pub: American City Business Journals, Inc,
Contact: Mike Olivieri, Executive Vice President
Description: The City of Alpharetta is witnessing several incubators and accelerators that will create the physical and educational infrastructure to convert ideas into sustainable businesses. This will help startups develop a go-to-market strategy, prepare for FDA certification and insurance reimbursement as well as see that the company reaches a point where it can attract private equity or venture capital. **Availability:** Print; Online.

24516 ■ *American Bar Association Legal Guide for Small Business: Everything You Need to Know About Small Business, from Start-up to Employment to Financing and Selling*
Released: Second edition. **Description:** The American Bar Association provides insight into financial, health and family issues affecting small business, including start up issues, employment laws, financing a business, and selling a business.

24517 ■ *"Angel Investors Across Texas Collaborate" in Austin Business Journal (Vol. 31, May 20, 2011, No. 11, pp. 1)*
Pub: Austin Business Journal
Contact: Rachel McGrath, Director
E-mail: rmcgrath@bizjournals.com
Ed: Christopher Calnan. **Description:** Texas' twelve angel investing groups are going to launch the umbrella organization Alliance of Texas Angel Networks (ATAN) to support more syndicated deals and boost investments in Texas. In 2010, these investing groups infused more than $24 million to startups in 61 deals. **Availability:** Print; Online.

24518 ■ *"Austin Welcomes New Program for Entrepreneurs" in Austin Business JournalInc. (Vol. 29, February 12, 2010, No. 29, pp. 1)*
Pub: Austin Business Journal
Contact: Rachel McGrath, Director
E-mail: rmcgrath@bizjournals.com
Ed: Christopher Calnan. **Description:** Nonprofit group Economic Development Catalyst Organization (ECDO) is formalizing its BizLaunch mentoring program, which was stated in 2009. The program aims to offer support networks to entrepreneurs and assistance regarding early-stage venture capital. **Availability:** Print; Online.

24519 ■ *"Barriers to Small Business Creations in Canada" in International Journal of Entrepreneurship and Small Business*
Description: Studies of Hatala (2005) and Choo and Wong (2006) related to the barriers to new venture creations in Canada are examined. **Availability:** Print; Online.

24520 ■ *"BDC Launches New Online Business Advice Centre" in Marketwired (July 13, 2010)*
Pub: Comtex News Network Inc.
Contact: Kan Devnani, President
Description: The Business Development Bank of Canada (BDC) offers entrepreneurs the chance to use their new online BDC Advice Centre in order to seek advice regarding the challenges of entrepreneurship. Free online business tools and information to help both startups and established firms are also provided. **Availability:** Print; Online.

24521 ■ *Become Your Own Boss in 12 Months: A Month-by-Month Guide to a Business that Works*
Ed: Melinda F. Emerson. **Released:** Second edition. **Price:** $16.99, paperback; $19.99, audio download; $12.99, e-book. **Description:** Realistic planning guide to help would-be entrepreneurs transition from working for someone else to working for themselves is given. The key to successfully starting a new company lies in thoughtful preparation at least a year and a half before quitting a job. **Availability:** E-book; Print; Download.

24522 ■ *"Brand Storytelling Becomes a Booming Business" in Entrepreneur (April 2012)*
Pub: Entrepreneur Media Inc.
Contact: Dan Bova, Director
E-mail: dbova@entrepreneur.com
Ed: Paula Andruss. **Description:** San Francisco-based Story House Creative engages in helping small businesses connect with their audience in communicating their brand identity. Web content, bios and tag lines are some of the marketing materials Story House Creative creates for its clients. The company also does search engine optimization, video, design, and copywriting. The Brandery, another brand-building company, helps startups promote their business. Eight to ten Brandery mentors are assigned to assist each startup client. Meanwhile, Brand Journalists is a Tennessee-based company focusing on corporate storytelling. It offers Web and blog content, human stories reporting and ghostwriting services. **Availability:** Print; Online.

24523 ■ *Brewing Up a Business: Adventures in Beer from the Founder of Dogfish Head Craft Brewery*
Pub: John Wiley & Sons, Inc.
Contact: Christina Van Tassell, Executive Vice President Chief Financial Officer
Ed: Sam Calagione. **Released:** 2nd Edition. **Price:** $18.95, paperback; $12.99, E-book. **Description:** Author shares nontraditional success secrets. Calgione began his business with a home brewing kit and grew it into Dogfish Head Craft Beer, the leading craft brewery in the U.S. **Availability:** E-book; Print.

24524 ■ *Canadian Small Business Kit for Dummies*
Ed: Margaret Kerr, JoAnn Kurtz, Andrew Dagys. **Released:** 4th edition. **Price:** $26.60, paperback; $39.99, paperback. **Description:** Resources include information on changes to laws and taxes for small businesses in Canada. **Availability:** Print; Online.

24525 ■ *Careers for Self-Starters and Other Entrepreneurial Types*
Released: Second Edition. **Description:** Advice to entrepreneurs wishing to start their own small company. Tips for turning hobbies into job skills are included. **Availability:** Print.

24526 ■ *Coin Laundries - Road to Financial Independence: A Complete Guide to Starting and Operating Profitable Self-Service Laundries*
Released: Revised edition. **Description:** Guide to starting and operating a self-service laundry. **Availability:** Print.

24527 ■ *The Complete Idiot's Guide to Starting an eBay® Business*
Pub: Penguin Publishing Group
Released: April 03, 2012. **Price:** $19.95, paperback; $12.99, e-book. **Description:** Guide for starting an eBay business includes information on products to

sell, how to price merchandise, and details for working with services like PayPal, and how to organize fulfillment services. **Availability:** E-book; Print.

24528 ■ *The E-Myth Enterprise: How to Turn a Great Idea into a Thriving Business*
Pub: HarperCollins Publishers L.L.C.
Contact: Brian Murray, President
Ed: Michael E. Gerber. **Released:** August 03, 2010. **Price:** $14.99, trade pb. **Description:** This book explores the requirement needed to start and run a successful small business. **Availability:** CD-ROM; E-book; Print.

24529 ■ "Editorial: It's Not Perfect; But Illinois a Good Home for Business" in Crain's Chicago Business (Vol. 34, October 24, 2011, No. 42, pp. 18)
Pub: Crain Communications Inc.
Contact: Barry Asin, President
Description: Focusing on all factors that encompass Illinois' business environment, findings show that Illinois is a good place to start and grow a business. The study focused on corporate income tax rates and the fact that talent, access to capital and customers along with transportation connections are among the important factors the state has for small businesses. **Availability:** Print.

24530 ■ *The Entrepreneur's Edge: Finding Money, Making Money, Keeping Money*
Released: August 01, 2016. **Price:** $20.99, bound softcover; $3.99, e-book. **Description:** Advice for starting, running and growing a new business is given. **Availability:** E-book; Print.

24531 ■ "Entrepreneurs: Search Party" in Business Strategy Review (Vol. 21, Autumn 2010, No. 3, pp. 30)
Ed: Georgina Peters. **Released:** September 22, 2010. **Description:** Entrepreneurs tend to be fixated on coming up with a foolproof idea for a new business and then raising money to start it. Raising startup funds is difficult, but it doesn't have to be that way. Search funds offer an innovative alternative, and the results are often impressive. **Availability:** Electronic publishing; Online.

24532 ■ *Entrepreneurship: A Small Business Approach*
Pub: McGraw-Hill Higher Education
Contact: Michael Ryan, President
Ed: Charles E. Bamford, Garry D. Bruton. **Released:** Sixth edition. **Description:** This text takes a hands-on, problem-based learning approach that works through real problems faced by entrepreneurs and small business owners. **Availability:** Print.

24533 ■ *Entrepreneurship and the Creation of Small Firms: Empirical Studies of New Ventures*
Pub: Edward Elgar Publishing Inc.
Contact: Edward Elgar, Founder Chairman
Ed: Carin Holmquist, Johan Wiklund. **Released:** 2010. **Description:** Study focuses on the important issue of new venture creation. Using a variety of data sources, methods and theories, the authors demonstrate the factors that aid or hinder new venture creation in a number of settings.

24534 ■ *Entrepreneurship: Successfully Launching New Ventures*
Ed: Bruce Barringer, Duane Ireland. **Released:** July 20, 2019. **Price:** $230.20. **Description:** Guide to help any entrepreneur successfully launch a new venture. **Availability:** Print.

24535 ■ *Escape from Cubicle Nation: From Corporate Prisoner to Thriving Entrepreneur*
Pub: Berkley Books
Contact: Ivan Held, President
Ed: Pamela Slim. **Released:** April 30, 2009. **Price:** $18.50, Paperback. **Description:** Insight is offered to help anyone wishing to leave their corporate position and start their own small business. **Availability:** E-book; Print.

24536 ■ *How to Form Your Own California Corporation*
Pub: Nolo
Contact: Chris Braun, President
Ed: Anthony Mancuso. **Released:** 15th edition. **Price:** $31.99, book and e-book; $27.99, e-book (downloadable); $34.99, E-book. **Description:** Instructions and forms required to incorporate any business in the State of California. **Availability:** E-book; Print.

24537 ■ *How I Made It: 40 Successful Entrepreneurs Reveal How They Made Millions*
Pub: Kogan Page Ltd.
Contact: Christina Lindeholm, Manager, Sales
Ed: Rachel Bridge. **Released:** Second edition. **Description:** Inspiration is given to anyone wishing to become a successful entrepreneur. **Availability:** Print; Electronic publishing.

24538 ■ *How to Make Big Money in Your Own Small Business: Unexpected Rules Every Small Business Owner Needs to Know*
Ed: Jeffrey J. Fox, Jeffrey J. Fox. **Released:** May 12, 2004. **Price:** $16.95; C$24.95; $16.95; C$24.95; $16.95; C$24.95. **Description:** Former sales and marketing pro offers advice on growing a small business. **Availability:** Print.

24539 ■ *How to Start a Home-Based Mail Order Business*
Ed: Georganne Fiumara. **Released:** June 01, 2011. **Price:** Paperback. **Description:** Step-by-step guide for starting and growing a home-based mail order business. Information about equipment, pricing, online marketing, are included along with worksheets and checklists for planning. **Availability:** Print; Online.

24540 ■ *How to Start an Internet Sales Business Without Making the Government Mad*
Pub: Lulu Press Inc.
Ed: Dan Davis. **Released:** October 01, 2011. **Price:** $19.95, paperback; $14.38, PDF; $14.38, e-book. **Description:** Small business guide for launching an Internet sales company. Topics include business structure, licenses, and taxes. **Availability:** E-book; Print; PDF.

24541 ■ *How to Start, Operate and Market a Freelance Notary Signing Agent Business*
Released: Revised second edition. **Description:** Due to the changes in the 2001 Uniform Commercial Code allowing notary public agents to serve as a witness to mortgage loan closings (eliminating the 2-witness requirement under the old code), notaries are working directly for mortgage, title and signing companies as mobile notaries.

24542 ■ *How to Start and Run Your Own Corporation: S-Corporations For Small Business Owners*
Pub: HCM Publishing
Ed: Peter I. Hupalo. **Description:** Basics of corporate business structure are explained. Topics include discovering the best business structure for your company; how to decided between an S-Corporation and LLC; choosing the state in which to incorporate, how to form a corporation, angel investing, special issues for one-person corporations, the role of bylaws and corporate minutes, board of directors, taxes, workers' compensation issues, retirement plans, and more. **Availability:** Print.

24543 ■ *How to Start a Small Business in Canada: Your Road Map to Financial Freedom*
Pub: Self-Help Publishers
Ed: Tariq Nadeem. **Released:** 2nd edition. **Description:** Provides information for starting and managing a small business in Canada.

24544 ■ "The Innovator's Method: Bringing the Lean Start-up into Your Organization"
Pub: Harvard Business Review Press
Contact: Moderna V. Pfizer, Contact
Released: September 09, 2014. **Price:** $35, Hardcover/Hardcopy. **Description:** The innovator's method was developed using research inside corporations and successful startups to create, refine, and bring ideas and inventions to the marketplace. Advice is provided to test, validate and commercialize ideas with the lean, design, and agile techniques used by successful startups. **Availability:** E-book; Print.

24545 ■ *Kick Start Your Dream Business: Getting It Started and Keeping You Going*
Description: Comprehensive guide covering the start-up process for any new company. **Availability:** Online.

24546 ■ "Lean Branding"
Pub: O'Reilly Media Inc.
Contact: Tim O'Reilly, Chief Executive Officer
E-mail: tim@oreilly.com
Released: September 01, 2014. **Description:** Branding your startup is essential to any small business success. A toolkit is provided to help build dynamic brands that generate conversion. Over 100 do-it-yourself branding tactics and case studies as well as step-by-step instructions for building and measuring 25 essential brand strategy ingredients, from logo design to demonstration day pitches. **Availability:** E-book.

24547 ■ *Legal Guide for Starting & Running a Small Business*
Pub: Nolo
Contact: Chris Braun, President
Ed: Fred S. Steingold. **Released:** 18th Edition. **Price:** $27.99, e-book. **Description:** Legal issues any small business owner needs to know for starting and running a successful business are outlined. **Availability:** Handheld; E-book; Print; Electronic publishing; PDF.

24548 ■ "Live & Learn: Gordon Stollery" in Canadian Business (Vol. 81, December 19, 2007, No. 1, pp. 76)
Pub: Rogers Media Inc.
Contact: Neil Spivak, Chief Executive Officer
Ed: Michelle Magnan. **Description:** Gordon Stollery of Highpine Oil and Gas Ltd. talks about being a hard-rock geologist and his move to start his oil and gas business. Other aspects of his business career are discussed. **Availability:** Print; Online.

24549 ■ "Looking To Leap?" in Black Enterprise (Vol. 38, January 2008, No. 6, pp. 64)
Pub: Earl G. Graves Ltd.
Contact: Earl Graves, Jr., President
Ed: Tennille M. Robinson. **Description:** Websites and organizations providing resources for any young entrepreneur wishing to start a new business are outlined.

24550 ■ "Make Money in 2011: What to Invest In" in Small Business Opportunities (January 2011)
Pub: Harris Publishing, Inc.
Contact: Janet Chase, Contact
Description: Top twenty ways to pick up extra cash, boost your income and generate new revenue. There has never been a better time to start a small business. **Availability:** Online.

24551 ■ "Making Social Ventures Work" in Harvard Business Review (Vol. 88, September 2010, No. 9, pp. 66)
Pub: Harvard Business Publishing
Contact: Diane Belcher, Managing Director
Ed: James D. Thompson, Ian C. MacMillan. **Price:** $8.95. **Description:** Five steps are to define, examine the political aspects, focus on discovery-driven planning, develop an appropriate exit strategy, and anticipate unexpected consequences when starting a new social venture. **Availability:** Online; PDF.

GENERAL SMALL BUSINESS TOPICS

24552 ■ Mobile Office: The Essential Small Business Guide to Office Technology
Released: September 1, 2009. **Price:** $6.95. **Description:** Essential pocket guide for startup businesses and entrepreneurs which provides information to create a mobile office in order to maximize business potential while using current technologies.

24553 ■ New Venture Creation: Entrepreneurship for the 21st Century with Online Learning Center Access Card
Released: Tenth edition. **Price:** $169.06, hardcover,softcover. **Description:** A handbook for students that explores all the concepts necessary for successfully launching a new enterprise. **Availability:** Print.

24554 ■ Niche and Grow Rich
Description: Consultants share insight to entrepreneurs wishing to find a profitable niche market. Authors write that good niche businesses are easy to start and easy to defend from competitors. They also report that finding a successful niche can attract and maintain good customers who are willing to pay more for unique goods and services.

24555 ■ Partnership: Small Business Start-Up Kit
Released: Second edition. **Description:** Guidebook detailing partnership law by state covering the formation and use of partnerships as a business form. Information on filing requirements, property laws, legal liability, standards, and the new Revised Uniform Partnership Act is covered.

24556 ■ "Self-Employment: What To Know To Be Your Own Boss" in Occupational Outlook Quarterly (Vol. 58, Summer 2014, No. 2, pp. 2)
Pub: Government Publishing Office
Contact: Hugh Nathanial Halpern, Director
Description: Information is presented to help would-be entrepreneurs decide if self-employment is for them. The challenges, rewards, and fastest growth sectors are discussed. Whether to incorporate or not is examined, as well as the skills and knowledge to become a successful small business owner is explored. **Availability:** Print; Online.

24557 ■ "Slow-Down Startups Hot" in Austin Business JournalInc. (Vol. 28, September 12, 2008, No. 26, pp. 1)
Pub: Austin Business Journal
Contact: Rachel McGrath, Director
E-mail: rmcgrath@bizjournals.com
Ed: Sandra Zaragoza. **Description:** A number of entrepreneurs from Austin, Texas are starting their own small business despite the economic slowdown. The Small Business Development Program in Austin has seen a 50 percent increase in the demand for its services in 2008 as compared to demand in 2007. Other details about the entrepreneurship trend are discussed. **Availability:** Print; Online.

24558 ■ Small Business for Dummies
Pub: John Wiley & Sons, Inc.
Contact: Christina Van Tassell, Executive Vice President Chief Financial Officer
Ed: Eric Tyson, Jim Schell. **Released:** 5th Edition. **Price:** $24.99, paperback; $16.99, E-book. **Description:** Guidebook for anyone wanting to start or grow a small business; topics include information financing, budgeting, marketing, management and more. **Availability:** E-book; Print.

24559 ■ Small Business Entrepreneur: Launching a New Venture and Managing a Business on a Day-to-Day Basis
Released: February 2006. **Price:** $19.95. **Description:** Comprehensive guide examining the management skills required to launch and run a small business.

24560 ■ Small Business Management: Launching and Growing New Ventures
Pub: Nelson Education Ltd.
Contact: Steve Brown, President
Ed: Justin G. Longenecker. **Released:** 6th edition. **Price:** $133.95, paperback. **Description:** Tips for starting and running a successful new company are provided. **Availability:** E-book; Print.

24561 ■ The Small Business Start-Up Kit
Pub: Nolo
Contact: Chris Braun, President
Ed: Peri Pakroo. **Released:** 12th edition. **Price:** $20.99, E-book. **Description:** Entrepreneurial advice for launching a new business. Topics include compliance with state regulations, sole proprietorships, partnerships, corporations, limited liability companies, as well as accounting and tax information. **Availability:** E-book; Print; Electronic publishing; PDF.

24562 ■ The Small Business Start-Up Kit for California
Pub: Nolo
Contact: Chris Braun, President
Ed: Peri Pakroo. **Released:** 14th edition. **Price:** $20.99, E-book. **Description:** Handbook covering all aspects of starting a business in California, including information about necessary fees, forms, and taxes. **Availability:** E-book; Print; Download.

24563 ■ Small Business Survival Guide
Released: First edition. **Description:** Small business expert provides strategies to start a company and survive in the 21st Century. He shows small business owners how to succeed despite challenges that can defeat any firm. His advice covers suppliers; customers and contractors; competitors and creditors; spouses, family and friends; as well as the ways lawyers, accountants and other can steal an entrepreneur's success. Ennico also describes how startups can comply with local regulations. **Availability:** E-book; Print.

24564 ■ Small Time Operator: How to Start Your Own Business, Keep Your Books, Pay Your Taxes, and Stay Out of Trouble
Ed: Bernard B. Kamoroff. **Released:** 14th edition. **Price:** $18.95, paperback. **Description:** Comprehensive guide for starting any kind of business. **Availability:** Print.

24565 ■ Soul Proprietor: 101 Lessons from a Lifestyle Entrepreneur
Price: $9.95. **Description:** More than 100 tips and stores to inspire and guide any would-be entrepreneur to earn a living from a favorite hobby or passion. **Availability:** E-book; Online.

24566 ■ Start Business in California, 3E
Description: Information required for starting any business in California.

24567 ■ Start, Run, & Grow a Successful Small Business
Pub: Toolkit Media Group
Ed: John L. Duoba, Joel Handelsman, Alice H. Magos, Catherine Gordon. **Released:** Sixth edition. **Availability:** Print.

24568 ■ Start Your Own Business
Pub: Entrepreneur Media Inc.
Contact: Dan Bova, Director
E-mail: dbova@entrepreneur.com
Ed: Rieva Lesonsky. **Released:** Eighth edition. **Description:** Author and the staff of Entrepreneur Magazine provide business resources and information for starting a successful business. The book guides you through the first three years of ownership and provides work sheets and checklists.

24569 ■ Start Your Own Lawn Care or Landscaping Business: Your Step-by-Step Guide to Success
Pub: Entrepreneur Media Inc.
Contact: Dan Bova, Director
E-mail: dbova@entrepreneur.com
Ed: Ciree Linsenman. **Released:** Fourth edition. **Description:** Steps for starting and running a lawn care service.

24570 ■ Start Your Own Wedding Consultant Business
Pub: Entrepreneur Media Inc.
Contact: Dan Bova, Director
E-mail: dbova@entrepreneur.com
Ed: Eileen Figure Sandlin. **Released:** Third edition. **Description:** Advice for starting and running a wedding consulting business.

24571 ■ Starting a Successful Business in Canada
Pub: Self-Counsel Press Inc.
Contact: Diana Douglas, Governor
Ed: Jack D. James. **Released:** Updated 18th Edition. **Price:** C$12.99; C$12.99; C$24.95. **Description:** Provides a framework for entrepreneurs launching a new business in Canada. **Availability:** E-book; Print; Download; PDF; Electronic publishing.

24572 ■ StartingUp Now Facilitator Guide
Price: $29.95. **Description:** Guide for those teaching entrepreneurship using StartingUp Now; the guide provides 24 lesson plans for each of the 24 steps/chapters in the book. **Availability:** Print.

24573 ■ "Startup Activity Among Jobless Execs is the Highest Since 2009, Survey Says" in South Florida Business Journal (Vol. 34, February 21, 2014, No. 31, pp. 3)
Pub: American City Business Journals, Inc.
Contact: Mike Olivieri, Executive Vice President
Released: Weekly. **Price:** $8, Introductory 4-week offer(Digital & Print). **Description:** The percentage of startup activity among former managers and executives in the U.S. increased 31 percent in 2013 according to consulting firm Challenger, Gray & Christmas. According to the survey, 5.5 percent of job-seeking executive launched their own business during each quarter in 2013, compared with 4.2 percent in 2012 and 3.2 percent in 2011. **Availability:** Print; Online.

24574 ■ "Startup Communities: Building an Entrepreneurial Ecosystem in Your City"
Pub: John Wiley & Sons, Inc.
Contact: Christina Van Tassell, Executive Vice President Chief Financial Officer
Released: September 2012. **Price:** $17.99, e-book; $26.95, hardcover. **Description:** A guide for building supportive entrepreneurial communities that drive innovation and small business energy. Brad Feld, entrepreneur turned-venture capitalist describes what it takes to create an entrepreneurial community in any city, at any time. He details the four critical principles required to form a sustainable startup community. **Availability:** O-book; E-book; Print; Online; PDF.

24575 ■ "Think of Start-Ups as Shots On Goal" in (Vol. 90, June 2012, No. 6, pp. 38)
Pub: Harvard Business Review Press
Contact: Moderna V. Pfizer, Contact
Ed: Robert E. Litan. **Price:** $6. **Description:** The importance of start-up businesses to the nation's economic recovery is emphasized. Comprehensive legislation is necessary to improve start-up access to opportunity and talent. **Availability:** PDF; Online.

24576 ■ The Toilet Paper Entrepreneur: The Tell-It-Like-It-Is Guide to Cleaning Up In Business, Even If You Are At the End of Your Roll
Pub: Obsidian Launch L.L.C.
Contact: Kelsey Ayres, President
Ed: Mike Michalowicz. **Description:** The founder of three multimillion-dollar companies, including Obsidian Launch, a company that partners with first-time entrepreneurs to grow their concepts into industry leaders. **Availability:** Print; Online.

24577 ■ "Troy Patent Law Firm Launches Rent-Free Tech Incubator" in Crain's Detroit Business (Vol. 25, June 8, 2009, No. 23, pp. 4)
Pub: Crain Communications Inc.
Contact: Barry Asin, President
Ed: Tom Henderson. **Description:** Young Basile Hanlon MacFarlane & Helmholdt PC, a patent law firm located in Troy, Michigan has created a small, rent-

free technology incubator on site. The incubator will be called North Woodward Tech Incubator and has room for four or five startups. The incubator is for the earliest or pre-seed stage for entrepreneurs who have not yet gotten significant investment capital. **Availability:** Online.

24578 ■ *"University of Texas Deans Serious about Biz" in Austin Business Journal (Vol. 31, May 20, 2011, No. 11, pp. 1)*
Pub: Austin Business Journal
Contact: Rachel McGrath, Director
E-mail: rmcgrath@bizjournals.com
Ed: Sandra Zaragoza. **Description:** Dean Thomas Gilligan of the University of Texas, McCombs School of Business and engineering school Dean Gregory Fenves have partnered to develop a joint engineering and business degree. Their partnership has resulted in an undergraduate course on initiating startups. **Availability:** Print; Online.

24579 ■ *Up and Running: Opening a Chiropractic Office*
Description: Tips for starting a chiropractic business. **Availability:** Print.

24580 ■ *"USM Focuses on Turning Science Into New Companies, Cash" in Boston Business Journal (Vol. 29, July 1, 2011, No. 8, pp. 1)*
Pub: Boston Business Journal
Contact: Carolyn M. Jones, President
E-mail: cmjones@bizjournals.com
Ed: Alexander Jackson. **Description:** University System of Maryland gears up to push for its plan for commercializing its scientific discoveries which by 2020 could create 325 companies and double the $1.4 billion the system's eleven schools garner in yearly research grants. It is talking with University of Utah and University Maryland, Baltimore to explore ways to make this plan a reality. **Availability:** Print; Online.

24581 ■ *Valuing Early Stage and Venture Backed Companies*
Pub: John Wiley & Sons, Inc.
Contact: Christina Van Tassell, Executive Vice President Chief Financial Officer
Ed: Neil J. Beaton. **Released:** March 2010. **Price:** $110, hardcover; $71.99, e-book; $71.99, e-book. **Description:** Valuation techniques that can be used to value early stage companies with complex capital structures are examined. **Availability:** O-book; E-book; Print; PDF.

24582 ■ *You Can Do It Too: The 20 Essential Things Every Budding Entrepreneur Should Know*
Pub: Kogan Page Ltd.
Contact: Christina Lindeholm, Manager, Sales
Ed: Rachel Bridge. **Released:** April 03, 2010. **Price:** $23.67, paperback / softback. **Description:** Collective wisdom of successful entrepreneurs in the form of twenty essential elements to focus on when starting a new company is illustrated by real-life entrepreneurial stories. **Availability:** E-book; Print; Online.

24583 ■ *Your Million-Dollar Idea: From Concept to Marketplace*
Description: Self-taught entrepreneur provides a 12-step plan to make a new product or service a profitable reality.

24584 ■ *"Zero to One: Notes on Startups, or How to Build the Future"*
Released: September 16, 2014. **Price:** $28, hardcover; $14.99, e-book; $30, CD; $15, audiobook download. **Description:** Entrepreneur and investor, Peter Thiel, covers new frontiers and new inventions yet to be discovered. Progress can be achieved in more industries than information technology, but thinking for one's self is critical to any entrepreneur in order to start and build a new venture. Tomorrow's leaders will avoid competition and create a unique business that will stand on its own. **Availability:** E-book; Print; Download; Audio.

ASSOCIATIONS AND OTHER ORGANIZATIONS

24585 ■ **Association for Enterprise Information (AFEI)**
2101 Wilson Blvd., Ste. 700
Arlington, VA 22201
URL: http://www.ndia.org/afei
Description: Strives to advance enterprise integration and electronic business practices for industries and governments. Represents corporate, government agencies, academic institutions, non-profit organizations, government employees, and individuals. Establishes opportunities for collaboration on enterprise information issues among government, business, and academia. **Founded:** 1998. **Geographic Preference:** National.

24586 ■ **BC Innovation Council (BCIC)**
Ste. 900, 1188 W Georgia St.
Vancouver, BC, Canada V6E 4A2
Ph: (604)757-1069
Free: 800-665-7222
Co. E-mail: info@innovatebc.ca
URL: http://www.innovatebc.ca
Contact: Raghwa Gopal, President
Facebook: www.facebook.com/innovatebc
Linkedin: www.linkedin.com/company/innovatebc
X (Twitter): x.com/innovate_bc
YouTube: www.youtube.com/user/bcinnovationcouncil
Description: Provides support and access to companies and institutions by using research results, development projects and programs to further enhance in creating innovations. **Founded:** 2005. **Geographic Preference:** State.

24587 ■ *Business Barometer*
401-4141 Yonge St.
Toronto, ON, Canada M2P 2A6
Co. E-mail: cfib@cfib.ca
URL: http://www.cfib-fcei.ca/en
Contact: Dan Kelly, President
URL(s): www.cfib-fcei.ca/en/research-economic-analysis/business-barometer
Released: Monthly **Availability:** Print; PDF.

24588 ■ **Canadian Federation of Independent Business (CFIB) - Research Library**
401-4141 Yonge St.
Toronto, ON, Canada M2P 2A6
Co. E-mail: cfib@cfib.ca
URL: http://www.cfib-fcei.ca/en
Contact: Dan Kelly, President
Facebook: www.facebook.com/CFIB
Linkedin: www.linkedin.com/company/canadian-federation-of-independent-business
X (Twitter): x.com/CFIBNews
Instagram: www.instagram.com/cfib_fcei
YouTube: www.youtube.com/user/cfibdotca
Description: Promotes economic well-being of members and seeks to maintain a healthy domestic business climate. **Scope:** Business. **Founded:** 1971. **Holdings:** Figures not available. **Publications:** *Mandate* (Quarterly); *Business Barometer* (Monthly). **Geographic Preference:** National.

24589 ■ **International Council for Small Business (ICSB)**
2201 G St. NW Funger Hall, Ste. 315
Washington, DC 20052
Ph: (202)994-0704
Fax: (202)994-4930
Co. E-mail: info@icsb.org
URL: http://icsb.org
Contact: Dr. Ayman El Tarabishy, President
E-mail: ayman@gwu.edu
Facebook: www.facebook.com/icsb.org
Linkedin: www.linkedin.com/company/international-council-for-small-business-icsb-
X (Twitter): x.com/icsb
Instagram: www.instagram.com/icsbglobal
YouTube: www.youtube.com/channel/UCvWy8wfz5nMk9a6yr5ZS0hQ
Description: Promotes and supports the interests and advancement of small businesses globally. **Founded:** 1955. **Publications:** *Journal of Small Business Management (JSBM)* (6/year). **Geographic Preference:** Multinational.

24590 ■ **National Small Business Association (NSBA)**
1156 15th St. NW, Ste. 502
Washington, DC 20005
Free: 800-345-6728
Co. E-mail: info@nsba.biz
URL: http://www.nsba.biz
Contact: Todd McCracken, President
Facebook: www.facebook.com/NSBAAdvocate
Linkedin: www.linkedin.com/company/2061777
X (Twitter): x.com/NSBAAdvocate
Description: Small businesses including manufacturing, wholesale, retail, service, and other firms. Works to advocate at the federal level on behalf of smaller businesses. **Founded:** 1937. **Educational Activities:** Small Business Meetup Day. **Awards:** Lewis A. Shattuck Small Business Advocate of the Year Award (Annual). **Geographic Preference:** National.

24591 ■ **SCORE [Score Association]**
712 H St. NE
Washington, DC 20002
Free: 800-634-0245
Co. E-mail: help@score.org
URL: http://www.score.org
Contact: Bridget Weston, Chief Executive Officer
Facebook: www.facebook.com/SCOREMentors
Linkedin: www.linkedin.com/company/score-mentors
X (Twitter): x.com/SCOREMentors
YouTube: www.youtube.com/user/SCORESmallBusiness
Pinterest: www.pinterest.com/scorementors
Description: Provides free business counseling to regarding the start-up of a small business, problems with their business, or expanding their business. Offers free one-on-one and online counseling as well as low cost workshops on a variety of business topics. **Founded:** 1964. **Publications:** *SCORE eNews*; *SCORE Today*. **Awards:** SCORE Chapter of the Year Award (Annual); SCORE Outstanding Woman-Owned Small Business Award (Annual). **Geographic Preference:** National.

24592 ■ **Small Business Investor Alliance (SBIA)**
529 14th St., NW
Washington, DC 20045
Ph: (202)628-5055
Co. E-mail: info@sbia.org
URL: http://www.sbia.org
Contact: Brett Palmer, President
E-mail: bpalmer@nasbic.org
Linkedin: www.linkedin.com/company/small-business-investor-alliance
X (Twitter): x.com/smallbusinesspe
Description: Firms licensed as Small Business Investment Companies (SBICs) under the Small Business Investment Act of 1958. **Founded:** 1958. **Publications:** *NASBIC News* (Quarterly); *Today's SBICs: Investing in America's Future*; *Venture Capital: Where to Find It* (Annual). **Educational Activities:** Venture Capital Institute for Entrepreneurs (Annual); Small Business Investor Alliance Northeast Private Equity Conference (Annual). **Geographic Preference:** National.

24593 ■ **United States Association for Small Business and Entrepreneurship (USASBE)**
100 N Merchant St.
Decatur, IL 62523
Ph: (262)472-1449
URL: http://www.usasbe.org
Contact: Julienne Shields, President
Facebook: www.facebook.com/usasbeHQ
Linkedin: www.linkedin.com/company/united-states-association-for-small-business-and-entrepreneurship
X (Twitter): x.com/usasbe
YouTube: www.youtube.com/channel/UCaH-glvHCx10TwUCj7AS5kQ

24594 ■ General Business

Description: Fosters business development through entrepreneurship education and research. Improves management knowledge, techniques and skills of small business owners and entrepreneurs. Develops an understanding of small businesses and entrepreneurship to promote a continuing exchange of expertise. **Founded:** 1981. **Educational Activities:** USASBE National Conference (Annual). **Awards:** Entrepreneurship Educator of the Year Award (Annual); Justin G. Longenecker Fellows (Annual); USASBE Model Program Award (Annual); Max S. Wortman Jr. Award for Lifetime Achievement in Entrepreneurship (Annual); USASBE Corporate Entrepreneur of the Year (Annual); John E. Hughes Award for Entrepreneurial Achievement (Periodic); USASBE Entrepreneurship Educator of the Year Award (Annual); USASBE Woman/Minority Entrepreneur of the Year (Annual); USASBE Outstanding Specialty Entrepreneurship Program Award (Annual); USASBE Model Emerging Program Award (Annual); USASBE Outstanding Entrepreneurship Program Abroad Award (Annual). **Geographic Preference:** National.

24594 ■ Veterans and Military Business Owners Association (VAMBOA)
4545 Industrial St., Ste. 5M
Simi Valley, CA 93063
Co. E-mail: info@vamboa.org
URL: http://vamboa.org
Contact: Debbie Gregory, Chief Executive Officer
Facebook: www.facebook.com/vamboa
X (Twitter): x.com/VAMBOA
Description: Business trade association that promotes and assists veteran business owners, service disabled veteran-owned businesses (SDVOB), and military business owners.

PROCUREMENT ASSISTANCE PROGRAMS

24595 ■ Handbook of Research on Virtual Workplaces and the New Nature of Business Practices
701 E Chocolate Ave.
Hershey, PA 17033
Ph: (717)533-8845
Free: 866-342-6657
Fax: (717)533-8661
Co. E-mail: cust@igi-global.com
URL: http://www.igi-global.com
Contact: Jan Travers, Director
URL(s): www.igi-global.com/book/handbook-research-virtual-workplaces-new/516
Released: Latest edition April 2008. **Price:** $245, for hardcover; $245, for eBook + hardcover; $245, for e-book; $37.50, for on demand. **Description:** Published by the Business Science Reference division of IGI Global. Compiles authoritative research from 51 scholars from 17 countries, covering the issues surrounding the influx of information technology to the office environment, from choice and effective use of technologies to necessary participants in the virtual workplace. **Availability:** Print; PDF; Online.

REFERENCE WORKS

24596 ■ "50 Best Companies for Diversity" in Black Enterprise (Vol. 38, July 2008, No. 12, pp. 12)
Pub: Earl G. Graves Ltd.
Contact: Earl Graves, Jr., President
Description: Maintaining excellence in a company's diversity efforts requires critical challenges such as recruiting, retaining and developing talent in the executive pipeline. Top young and diverse emerging executives in corporate America are featured. **Availability:** Online.

24597 ■ 101 Secrets to Building a Winning Business
Pub: Allen and Unwin Proprietary Ltd.
Ed: Andrew Griffiths. **Description:** Provides expert information for running and growing a small business. **Availability:** Print.

24598 ■ "2010 Book of Lists" in Business Courier (Vol. 26, December 26, 2009, No. 36, pp. 1)
Price: $49.95. **Description:** Rankings of companies and organizations within the business services, education, finance, health care, hospitality and tourism, real estate, and technology industries in the Cincinnati, Ohio-Northern Kentucky area are presented. Rankings are based on sales, business size, or other statistics. **Availability:** PDF; Online.

24599 ■ "Abaddon Acquires Pukaskwa Uranium Properties in NW Ontario" in Canadian Corporate News (May 16, 2007)
Description: Rubicon Minerals Corp. has entered into an Option Agreement with Consolidated Abaddon Resources Inc. for the acquisition of Pukaskwa uranium properties and plans to conduct an extensive exploration program to prove out the resource and geological potential of the area. Statistical data included. **Availability:** Online.

24600 ■ "Alberta: Help Wanted, Badly" in Globe & Mail (March 11, 2006, pp. B5)
Ed: Patrick Brethour, Dawn Walton. **Description:** The issue of unemployment rate, which fell by 3.1 percent in Alberta, is discussed. **Availability:** Print; Online.

24601 ■ "All In The Family: Weston Undergoes a Shakeup" in Canadian Business (Vol. 79, September 22, 2006, No. 19, pp. 75)
Pub: Rogers Media Inc.
Contact: Neil Spivak, Chief Executive Officer
Ed: Zena Olijnyk. **Description:** Continuing ownership of Weston dynasty on Canada's largest chain Loblaw Co. is discussed. **Availability:** Online.

24602 ■ "Are You Rich? How Much of a Nest Egg Do You Need to Join the True Elite" in Barron's (Vol. 88, March 10, 2008, No. 10, pp. 27)
Pub: Dow Jones & Company Inc.
Contact: Almar Latour, Chief Executive Officer
Ed: Tom Sullivan. **Description:** Discusses the minimum net worth of people considered as rich in America is now at $25 million. There are about 125,000 households in America that meet this threshold, while 49,000 households have a net worth between $25 million and $500 million, and about 1,400 US households have a net worth over $500 million. **Availability:** Online.

24603 ■ "The Art of War for Women" in Hawaii Business (Vol. 54, July 2008, No. 1, pp. 23)
Pub: PacificBasin Communications
Contact: Chuck Tindle, Director
E-mail: chuckt@pacificbasin.net
Ed: Chin-Ning Chu. **Description:** Business consultant Chi-Ning Chu talks about her new book 'The Art of War for Women: Sun Tzu's Ancient Strategies and Wisdom for Winning at Work', which discusses how women can more effectively win in business. She also shares her thoughts about the advantages that women have, which they can use in businesses decisions.

24604 ■ "Bank On It: New Year, New Estate Plan" in Hawaii Business (Vol. 53, February 2008, No. 8, pp. 54)
Pub: PacificBasin Communications
Contact: Chuck Tindle, Director
E-mail: chuckt@pacificbasin.net
Ed: Antony M. Orme. **Description:** Discusses the start of the new year which can be a time to revise wills and estate plans as failure to do so may create problems of unequal inheritance and increase in estate tax exemption, which could disinherit beneficiaries. Other circumstances that can prompt changes in wills and estate plans are presented. **Availability:** Print; Online.

24605 ■ "Bankruptcies" in Crain's Detroit Business (Vol. 24, March 24, 2008, No. 12, pp. 6)
Pub: Crain Communications Inc.
Contact: Barry Asin, President
Description: Current list of business that filed for Chapter 7 or 11 protection in U.S. Bankruptcy Court in Detroit include a construction company, a medical care company, a physical therapy firm and a communications firm. **Availability:** Online.

24606 ■ Bankruptcy for Small Business
Description: Bankruptcy laws can be used to save a small business, homes or other property. The book provides general information for small business owners regarding the reasons for money problems, types of bankruptcy available and their alternatives, myths about bankruptcy, and the do's and don'ts for filing for bankruptcy. **Availability:** E-book; Print.

24607 ■ "The Big Idea: No, Management Is Not a Profession" in Harvard Business Review (Vol. 88, July-August 2010, No. 7-8, pp. 52)
Pub: Harvard Business Publishing
Contact: Diane Belcher, Managing Director
Ed: Richard Barker. **Price:** $8.95, PDF. **Description:** An argument is presented that management is not a profession, as it is less focused on mastering a given body of knowledge than it is on obtaining integration and collaboration skills. Implications for teaching this new approach are also examined. **Availability:** Online; PDF.

24608 ■ "The Big Idea: The Case for Professional Boards" in Harvard Business Review (Vol. 88, December 2010, No. 12, pp. 50)
Pub: Harvard Business Publishing
Contact: Diane Belcher, Managing Director
Ed: Robert C. Pozen. **Price:** $8.95, PDF. **Description:** A professional directorship model can be applied to corporate governance. Suggestions for this include the reduction of board size to seven members in order to improve the effectiveness of decision making, along with the requirement that directors have industry expertise. **Availability:** Online; PDF.

24609 ■ "Billion-Dollar Impact: Nonprofit Sector is Economic Powerhouse" in Business First Buffalo (November 12, 2007, pp. 1)
Pub: Business First
Contact: John Tebeau, Publisher
E-mail: jtebeau@bizjournals.com
Ed: Tracey Drury. **Description:** Western New York has thousands of nonprofit organizations, 240 of which have collective revenue of $1.74 billion based on federal tax returns for the 2005 and 2006 fiscal years. The nonprofit sector has a large impact on WNY's economy, but it is not highly recognized. The financial performance of notable nonprofit organizations is given.

24610 ■ The Board Book: An Insider's Guide for Directors and Trustees
Pub: W.W. Norton & Company Ltd.
Contact: Stanley Kubrick, Director
Ed: William G. Bowen. **Released:** May 06, 2008. **Price:** $16.95, paperback; $26.95, hardcover. **Description:** A primer for all directors and trustees that provides suggestions for getting back to good-governance basics in business. **Availability:** Print.

24611 ■ "Bombardier Wins Chinese Rail Deal" in Globe & Mail (March 20, 2006, pp. B1)
Ed: Geoffrey York. **Description:** Bombardier Inc. has won a $68 million (U.S) contract to provide railway cars for rapid transit-link between Beijing and its international airport for 2008 Olympics in China. Details of the contract are presented. **Availability:** Print; Online.

24612 ■ "Bryan Berg, Target Corp., Senior Vice President, Region 1" in Hawaii Business (Vol. 53, March 2008, No. 9, pp. 28)
Pub: PacificBasin Communications
Contact: Chuck Tindle, Director

E-mail: chuckt@pacificbasin.net

Ed: David K. Choo. **Description:** Bryan Berg, senior vice president at Target Corp.'s Region 1, shares his thoughts about entering the Hawaiian market and Target representatives bringing malasadas when visiting a business in the state. Berg finds the state's aloha spirit interesting and feels that it is important to be respectful of the Hawaiian culture and traditions in doing their business there. **Availability:** Online.

24613 ■ *Built to Last: Successful Habits of Visionary Companies*
Pub: HarperCollins Publishers L.L.C.
Contact: Brian Murray, President
Ed: James C. Collins, Jerry I. Porras. **Released:** August 30, 2011. **Price:** $14.99, e-book; $18.99, paperback; $32.50, hardcover; $29.95, audiobook CD abridged. **Availability:** audiobook; E-book; Print.

24614 ■ *"Business Diary" in Crain's Detroit Business (Vol. 24, October 6, 2008, No. 40, pp. 23)*
Pub: Crain Communications Inc.
Contact: Barry Asin, President
Description: Detailed listing of acquisitions, expansions, new products, new services, business contracts and startups from the Detroit area is provided. **Availability:** Print; Online.

24615 ■ *Business Fairy Tales*
Ed: Cecil W. Jackson. **Description:** The seven most-common business schemes are uncovered.

24616 ■ *Business Freedom Index*
URL(s): www.heritage.org/index/business-freedom
Description: Presents scores from various factors concerning the ease of starting, running, and closing a business in terms of government regulations. **Availability:** Download.

24617 ■ *Business Know-How: An Operational Guide for Home-Based and Micro-Sized Businesses with Limited Budgets*

24618 ■ *"Business Looks for Results in Congress" in Baltimore Business Journal (Vol. 28, November 5, 2010, No. 26, pp. 1)*
Pub: Baltimore Business Journal
Contact: Rhonda Pringle, President
E-mail: rpringle@bizjournals.com
Ed: Kent Hoover. **Description:** Republican candidates in the 2010 Congressional elections were overwhelmingly supported by the business community. Republican John Boehner, who will be the next Speaker of the House, says that the party's victory would end economic uncertainty and would assist small businesses to rehire workers. **Availability:** Print; Online.

24619 ■ *Business, Occupations, Professions, & Vocations in the Bible*
Pub: ABC Book Publishing
Ed: Rich Brott. **Price:** $19.99, softcover. **Description:** The important role small business has played in all societies and cultures throughout history is examined. The ingenuity of individuals and their ability to design, craft, manufacture and harvest has kept countries and kingdoms prosperous. **Availability:** Print.

24620 ■ *Business Plans Kit for Dummies*
Pub: John Wiley & Sons, Inc.
Contact: Christina Van Tassell, Executive Vice President Chief Financial Officer
Ed: Steven D. Peterson, Peter E. Jaret, Barbara Findlay Schenck. **Released:** Fifth edition. **Price:** $34.99, paperback; $22.99, e-book. **Availability:** E-book; Print.

24621 ■ *Business Plans That Work: A Guide for Small Business*
Released: Second Edition. **Description:** Guide for preparing a small business plan along with an analysis of potential business opportunities. **Availability:** Print; Online.

24622 ■ *"Business Travel Can be a Trip if Structured Right" in Globe & Mail (February 3, 2007, pp. B11)*
Description: The importance of arranging a proper business trip for executives by employers, in order to achieve good benefits for the company, is discussed. **Availability:** Online.

24623 ■ *Business Warrior: Strategy for Entrepreneurs*
Price: $9.99. **Description:** Advice to help entrepreneurs understand competitive strategies in order to succeed, focusing on sales, marketing, and personnel management. **Availability:** Print; Download; PDF.

24624 ■ *"Can We Talk?" in Canadian Business (Vol. 79, September 11, 2006, No. 18, pp. 131)*
Ed: Sarah B. Hood. **Released:** September 08, 2015. **Description:** The importance of informal communications and steps to build strong social networks within the organizations are discussed. **Availability:** Online.

24625 ■ *"Canada Tops Again in G7: Study" in Globe & Mail (March 22, 2006, pp. B8)*
Description: Canada is still the cheapest place to do business among G7 countries, even though the rising dollar has eroded some of its advantages over the United States. The survey is detailed. **Availability:** Online.

24626 ■ *Canadian Small Business Kit for Dummies*
Ed: Margaret Kerr, JoAnn Kurtz, Andrew Dagys. **Released:** 4th edition. **Price:** $26.60, paperback; $39.99, paperback. **Description:** Resources include information on changes to laws and taxes for small businesses in Canada. **Availability:** Print; Online.

24627 ■ *"Capitol Ideas: Regions to Lansing: Focus on Taxes, Reform, Keeping Talent" in Crain's Detroit Business (Vol. 24, October 6, 2008)*
Pub: Crain Communications Inc.
Contact: Barry Asin, President
Ed: Amy Lane. **Description:** Michigan must make bold and dramatic changes in public policy regarding business legislation. The tax structure, unemployment issues and attracting and retaining talent are among the issues the state must confront, especially in this tough economic climate. **Availability:** Online.

24628 ■ *"Cashing In: Gleaning an Education from Our Economic State" in Agency Sales Magazine (Vol. 39, August 2009, No. 8, pp. 22)*
Description: Businesses have learned that cutting price can kill business and being tough is normal. The recession has also taught that getting the right vision and gaining the confidence and trust of consumers are important. **Availability:** Online.

24629 ■ *"Centerra Caught in Kyrgyzstan Dispute" in Globe & Mail (April 19, 2007, pp. B5)*
Ed: Andy Hoffman. **Description:** The details of the demonstrations carried against government proposal to nationalize Centerra Gold Inc.'s assets are presented. **Availability:** Online.

24630 ■ *CFR: Title 13. Business Credit and Assistance*
Pub: U.S. Government Publishing Office
Ed: Department of Commerce Staff. **Released:** Annual; volume 14. **Description:** Title 13 covers regulations governing the activities of the Small Business Administration and the Department of Commerce. Book covers information on business credit, finance, and economic development. **Availability:** Print; PDF.

24631 ■ *"The China Syndrome" in Canadian Business (Vol. 79, July 17, 2006, No. 14-15, pp. 25)*
Pub: Rogers Media Inc.
Contact: Neil Spivak, Chief Executive Officer

Ed: Peter Diekmeyer. **Description:** Contrasting pace of growth in China and India are presented. Reasons for the slow pace of growth of Canadian companies like CAE Inc. and Magna in India are also discussed. **Availability:** Online.

24632 ■ *China's Rational Entrepreneurs: The Development of the New Private Business Sector*
Pub: Routledge, Taylor & Francis Group
Ed: Barbara Krug. **Released:** First edition. **Description:** Difficulties faced by entrepreneurs in China are discussed, including analysis for understanding their behavior and relations with local governments in order to secure long-term business success.

24633 ■ *Cities from the Arabian Desert: The Building of Jubail and Yambu in Saudi Arabia*
Ed: Andrea H. Pampanini. **Description:** An overview of Saudi Arabia's government to take control of the nation's natural resources and change the government, educational system, and its culture by evolving into a modern industrial society. **Availability:** Print.

24634 ■ *"The Classless Workplace: The Digerati and the New Spirit of Technocapitalism" in WorkingUSA (Vol. 11, June 2008, No. 2, pp. 181)*
Description: Article argues the formation of a new type of economic actor at the intersection of a new capitalism and a new technology: The Dierati. The discourse in based on the analysis of the popular magazine Wired, which registers the culture of contemporary technocapitalism. The suggestion that the new persona of the digerati is constructed as a rejection of the ethics, which dominated the Fordist workplace and Fordist society: Hierarchy and differentiation between workers, on the one hand and capitalists and managers, on the other hand. The transformation of these two categories, workers and capitalists into the digerati worker and the digerati entrepreneur, is described. Set within the context of the structural transformations of capitalism from Fordism to post-Fordism, the article shows the ideological fit of the new ethics of the digerati to the new working arrangements of post-Fordist capitalism, characterized by more privatizes, flexible, and precarious working arrangements. **Availability:** Print; Online.

24635 ■ *"Column: Redefining Failure" in Harvard Business Review (Vol. 88, September 2010, No. 9, pp. 34)*
Pub: Harvard Business Publishing
Contact: Diane Belcher, Managing Director
Ed: Seth Godin. **Price:** $6, PDF. **Description:** Specific forms of failure, including design failure, failure of priorities, failure of opportunity, and failure to quit are examined. The negative implications of maintaining the status quo are discussed. **Availability:** Online; PDF.

24636 ■ *"Column: To Win, Create What's Scarce" in Harvard Business Review (Vol. 88, November 2010, No. 11, pp. 46)*
Pub: Harvard Business Publishing
Contact: Diane Belcher, Managing Director
Ed: Seth Godin. **Price:** $6, PDF. **Description:** It is recommended to identify what is scarce yet valuable and applying this principle to business in order to be successful. **Availability:** Online; PDF.

24637 ■ *"Commentary. Economic Trends for Small Business" in Small Business Economic Trends (April 2008, pp. 3)*
Description: Commentary on the economic trends for small businesses in the U.S. is presented. Analysis of recession possibilities is given. Reports indicate that the number of business owners citing inflation as their number one problem is at its highest point since 1982.

24638 ■ *"Companies Must Set Goals for Diversity" in Crain's Detroit Business (Vol. 24, April 14, 2008, No. 15, pp. 16)*
Pub: Crain Communications Inc.
Contact: Barry Asin, President

Ed: Laura Weiner. **Description:** Diversity programs should start with a plan that takes into account exactly what the company wants to accomplish; this may include wanting to increase the bottom line with new contracts or wanting a staff that is more innovative in their ideas due to their varied backgrounds. **Availability:** Online.

24639 ■ *"The Companies We Love" in Canadian Business (Vol. 85, September 17, 2012, No. 14, pp. 43)*
Description: The 2012 annual survey of the brands Canadians trust and respect the most revealed that only six of the top 60 international brands are based in Canada. Sony was the number one favorite brand of Canadians, while the highest-ranked Canadian Brand, Tim Hortons, is in the number 29 spot. **Availability:** Online.

24640 ■ *Corporate Affiliations*
Pub: LexisNexis
Contact: Mark Kelsey, Chief Executive Officer
URL(s): www.corporateaffiliations.comwww.lexisnexis.com/community/insights/professional/b/solutions/posts/6-kinds-of-datasets-
Ed: Tom Bachmann. **Released:** Annual **Description:** Covers business and financial information on approximately 3,800 U.S. parent companies and 44,500 subsidiaries, divisions, and affiliates worldwide, as well as 140,000 key executives. **Entries include:** Sales, assets, liabilities, ownership percentage. **Arrangement:** Alphabetical within each volume. **Indexes:** Each volume includes company name index; separate Master Index volumes list all company names in the set in one alphabetic sequence in five indexes including private, public, international, alphabetical, geographical, brand name, SIC, and corporate responsibilities. **Availability:** Print; Online.

24641 ■ *"Corporate Canada Eyes Retiree Health Benefit Cuts" in Globe & Mail (March 8, 2006, pp. B3)*
Ed: Virginia Galt. **Description:** A survey on Canadian companies reveals that due to rising health care costs and increasing number of baby boomer retirements, these companies are to cut down on health benefits they are providing to these retired employees. **Availability:** Online.

24642 ■ *Corporate Entrepreneurship & Innovation*
Ed: Michael H. Morris, Donald F. Kuratko, Jeffrey G. Covin. **Released:** 3rd edition. **Price:** $22.49, e-book; $279.95, hardcover. **Description:** Innovation is the key to running a successful small business. The book helps entrepreneurs to develop the skills and business savvy to sustain a competitive edge. **Availability:** E-book; Print.

24643 ■ *Corporate Radar: Tracking the Forces That Are Shaping Your Business*
Description: Ways for a business to assess the forces operating in the external environment that can affect the business and solutions to protect from outside threats. **Availability:** Print.

24644 ■ *"Culture Club: Effective Corporate Cultures" in Canadian Business (Vol. 79, October 9, 2006, No. 20, pp. 115)*
Pub: Rogers Media Inc.
Contact: Neil Spivak, Chief Executive Officer
Ed: Calvin Leung. **Description:** Positive impacts of an effective corporate culture on the employees' productivity and the performance of the business are discussed. **Availability:** Online.

24645 ■ *"Cutting Credit Card Processing Costs for Your Small Business" in Hawaii Business (Vol. 53, March 2008, No. 9, pp. 56)*
Ed: Robert K.O. Lum. **Description:** Accepting credit card payments offers businesses with profits from the discount rate. The discount rate includes processing fee, VISA & MasterCard assessment and interchange. Details regarding merchant service cost and discount rate portions are discussed. Statistical data included. **Availability:** Online.

24646 ■ *Dead on Arrival: How the Anti-Business Backlash is Destroying Entrepreneurship in America and What We Can Still Do About It!*
Released: August 01, 2017. **Price:** $26.99, hardcover; $9.99, e-book; $24.99, digital audiobook unabridged; $15.99, paperback. **Description:** Bernie Marcus, Home Depot leader, addresses regulations hurting small businesses in America. **Availability:** E-book; Print.

24647 ■ *"Dedge Rejects Inflation Concerns" in Globe & Mail (January 26, 2007, pp. B3)*
Ed: Heather Scoffield. **Description:** The rejection of concern over inflation by Governor of the Bank of Canada David Dodge and his views on checking inflation in Alberta are discussed. **Availability:** Print; Online.

24648 ■ *Delivering Knock Your Socks Off Service*
Pub: American Management Association
Contact: Manny Avramidis, President
Availability: Print.

24649 ■ *Divine Wisdom at Work: 10 Universal Principles for Enlightened Entrepreneurs*
Description: Entrepreneurial advice for managing a small enterprise is given using inspiration, anecdotes and exercises. **Availability:** Print.

24650 ■ *"Dodge Frets Over Flood of Fast Money" in Globe & Mail (May 2, 2007, pp. B1)*
Ed: Heather Scoffield. **Description:** The concern of governor of Bank of Canada, David Dodge, over the increase in global liquidity due to growth in the business of private equity, is discussed. **Availability:** Online.

24651 ■ *"Don't Quit When The Road Gets Bumpy" in Women Entrepreneur (November 25, 2008)*
Description: Discusses techniques four women entrepreneurs are utilizing to keep their businesses successful despite the credit crunch and the economic downturn.

24652 ■ *"Down a 'Peg" in Canadian Business (Vol. 79, September 25, 2006, No. 19, pp. 41)*
Description: Economic development in Canada's Winnipeg city is evaluated. **Availability:** Online.

24653 ■ *The Dynamic Small Business Manager*
Ed: Frank Vickers. **Released:** February 11, 2011. **Price:** $19.95, e-book, plus shipping charges; $39.91, paperback, plus shipping charges. **Description:** Practical advice is given to help small business owners successfully manage their company. **Availability:** E-book; Print.

24654 ■ *The Economics of Integrity: From Dairy Farmers to Toyota, How Wealth Is Built on Trust and What That Means for Our Future*
Ed: Anna Bernasek. **Released:** February 23, 2010. **Price:** $3.99. **Description:** Integrity is built over time and the importance of trust in starting and building business relationships is stressed. **Availability:** E-book.

24655 ■ *Encyclopedia of Small Business*
Ed: Arsen Darnay, Monique D. Magee, Kevin Hillstrom. **Released:** 5th edition. **Price:** $881. **Description:** Concise encyclopedia of small business information. **Availability:** E-book; Print.

24656 ■ *"Energy Slide Slows 4th-Quarter Profits" in Globe & Mail (April 13, 2007, pp. B9)*
Ed: Angela Barnes. **Description:** The decrease in the fourth quarter profits of several companies across various industries in Canada, including mining and manufacturing, due to global decrease in oil prices, is discussed.

24657 ■ *Enterprise and Small Business: Principles, Practice and Policy*
Pub: Pearson Education Inc.
Contact: Andy Bird, Chief Executive Officer
Ed: Sara Carter, Dylan Jones-Evans. **Released:** 3rd edition. **Description:** Introduction to small business, challenges of a changing environment, and the nature of entrepreneurship are among the issues covered. **Availability:** E-book; Print; Online; Download.

24658 ■ *The Entrepreneur Next Door: Discover the Secrets to Financial Independence*
Description: Traits required to become a successful entrepreneur are highlighted.

24659 ■ *Entrepreneurial Small Business*
Pub: McGraw-Hill Higher Education
Contact: Michael Ryan, President
Ed: Jerome A. Katz, Richard P. Green. **Released:** Seventh edition. **Price:** $57, e-book; $70, print. **Description:** Students are able to get a clear vision of small enterprise in today's business climate. The textbook helps focus on the goal of having personal independence with financial security as an entrepreneur. **Availability:** Print.

24660 ■ *Entrepreneurship: A Process Perspective*
Ed: Robert A. Baron, Scott A. Shane. **Released:** 2nd Edition. **Description:** Entrepreneurial process covering team building, finances, business plan, legal issues, marketing, growth and exit strategies. **Availability:** Print.

24661 ■ *Entrepreneurship and Small Business Development in the Former Soviet Bloc*
Description: Examination of entrepreneurship and small business in Russia and other key countries of Eastern Europe, showing how far small businesses have developed in the region. **Availability:** Online; PDF.

24662 ■ *Entrepreneurship: Theory, Process, and Practice*
Ed: Donald F. Kuratko. **Released:** Ninth edition. **Price:** $22.99, e-book; $44.49, rental,wholesale price $210,retail $279.95 . **Description:** Understanding the process of entrepreneurship. **Availability:** E-book; Print.

24663 ■ *"Even Money on Recession" in Barron's (Vol. 88, March 10, 2008, No. 10, pp. M9)*
Pub: Dow Jones & Company Inc.
Contact: Almar Latour, Chief Executive Officer
Ed: Gene Epstein. **Description:** Discusses the US unemployment rate which was steady in February 2008 at 4.8 percent, while nonfarm payroll employment decreased by 63,000 in the same month, with the private sector losing 101,000 jobs. The economic indicators showed mixed signals on whether or not the US economy is in a recession. **Availability:** Online.

24664 ■ *Falling Behind: How Rising Inequality Harms the Middle Class*
Ed: Robert H. Frank. **Released:** First edition. **Description:** Economist argues that though middle-class American families aren't earning much more than they were a few decades ago, they are spending considerably more, a pattern attributed primarily to the context of seeing and emulating the spending habits of the rich.

24665 ■ *Forbes Small Giants: 25 Companies that-believe-smaller-is-better*
Pub: Forbes Media LLC
URL(s): www.forbes.com/sites/maneetahuja/2020/05/12/forbes-small-giants-25-companies-that-believe-smaller-is-better
Ed: Steve Kichen. **Released:** Annual **Description:** Publication includes list of 200 small companies judged to be high quality and fast-growing on the basis of 5-year return on equity and other qualitative measurements. Also includes a list of the 100 best

small companies outside the U.S. Note: Issue does not carry address or CEO information for the foreign companies. **Entries include:** Company name, shareholdings data on chief executive officer; financial data. **Arrangement:** Alphabetical. **Indexes:** Ranking. **Availability:** Print.

24666 ■ *"The Future of Work" in Black Enterprise (Vol. 41, August 2010, No. 1, pp. 65)*
Pub: Earl G. Graves Ltd.
Contact: Earl Graves, Jr., President
Ed: Annya M. Lott. **Description:** Technology, globalization, and outsourcing will continue to shape the future of work. Social media is a means for small companies to market goods and services. **Availability:** Online.

24667 ■ *"The Future of Work" in Business Strategy Review (Vol. 21, Autumn 2010, No. 3, pp. 16)*
Pub: Wiley-Blackwell
Ed: Lynda Gratton. **Released:** August 28, 2017. **Description:** Work is universal. But how, why, where and when we work has never been so open to individual interpretation. The certainties of the past have been replaced by ambiguity, questions and the steady hum of technology. Now, in a groundbreaking research project covering 21 global companies and more than 200 executives, the author is making sense of the future of work. **Availability:** Print; PDF; Online.

24668 ■ *Get Your Business to Work!: 7 Steps to Earning More, Working Less and Living the Life You Want*
Pub: BenBella Books Inc.
Contact: Aida Herrera, Director
E-mail: aida@benbellabooks.com
Ed: George Hedley. **Released:** May 01, 2014. **Price:** $17.95, paperback; $9.99, E-Book (EPUB). **Description:** Complete step-by-step guide for the small business owner to realize profits, wealth and freedom. **Availability:** E-book; Print.

24669 ■ *The Go-Giver: A Little Story About a Powerful Business Idea*
Pub: Penguin Publishing Group
Ed: Bob Burg, John David Mann. **Released:** October 20, 2015. **Price:** $16.95, hardcover; $17.99; 11.95, audio. **Description:** Story of an ambitious young man named Joe who yearns for success. The book is a heartwarming tale that brings new relevance to the old proverb, "Give and you shall receive". **Availability:** E-book.

24670 ■ *Going to Extremes: How Like Minds Unite and Divide*
Ed: Cass R. Sustein. **Released:** July 09, 2009. **Description:** Solutions to marketplace problems are examined.

24671 ■ *Goventure: Live the Life of an Entrepreneur*
Description: Challenges of operating a small business are presented with more than 6,000 graphics, audio, and interactive video. **Availability:** CD-ROM.

24672 ■ *"Grand Action Makes Grand Changes in Grand Rapids" in Crain's Detroit Business (Vol. 25, June 1, 2009, No. 22, pp. M012)*
Pub: Crain Communications Inc.
Contact: Barry Asin, President
Ed: Amy Lane. **Description:** Businessman Dick DeVos believes that governments are not always the best to lead certain initiatives. That's why, in 1991, he gathered 50 west Michigan community leaders and volunteers to look consider the construction of an arena and expanding or renovating local convention operations. Grand Action has undertaken four major projects in the city. **Availability:** Online.

24673 ■ *The Gridlock Economy: How Too Much Ownership Wrecks Markets, Stops Innovation, and Costs Lives*
Ed: Michael Heller. **Released:** February 23, 2010. **Price:** $11.99, paperback; C$14.99. **Description:** While private ownership generally creates wealth, the author believes that economic gridlock results when too many people own pieces of one thing, which results in too many people being able to block each other from creating or using a scarce source. **Availability:** E-book; Print.

24674 ■ *"A Growing Concern" in Canadian Business (Vol. 79, October 9, 2006, No. 20, pp. 90)*
Description: With rich dividends being harvested by companies producing ethanol, after ethanol became a petrol additive, is discussed. **Availability:** Online.

24675 ■ *A Guide to the Project Management Body of Knowledge*
Pub: Project Management Institute
Contact: Pierre Le Manh, President
Released: Seventh edition. **Description:** A guide for project management using standard language, with new data flow diagrams; the Identify Stakeholders and Collect Requirements processes defined; and with greater attention placed on how knowledge areas integrate in the context of initiating, planning, executing, monitoring and controlling, and closing process groups. **Availability:** Print; Download.

24676 ■ *Happy About Joint-Venturing: The 8 Key Critical Factors of Success*
Pub: Happy About
Contact: Ric Vatner, Chief Executive Officer
Ed: Valerie Orsoni-Vauthey. **Price:** $19.95, paperback,(with 15% discount only ($16.96); $14.95, eBook,(with 20% discount only $11.95). **Description:** An overview of joint venturing is presented. **Availability:** E-book; Print; PDF.

24677 ■ *"Heavy Duty: The Case Against Packing Lightly" in Crain's Chicago Business (Vol. 31, April 21, 2008, No. 16, pp. 29)*
Pub: Crain Communications Inc.
Contact: Barry Asin, President
Ed: Sarah A. Klein. **Description:** Penelope Biggs, a Northern Trust executive who manages sales teams in North America, Europe and Asia gives advice on traveling abroad for business including time management skills, handling time-zone hops and avoiding jet-lag. **Availability:** Online.

24678 ■ *"Hire Education: An Emerging Cohort" in Canadian Business (Vol. 79, September 11, 2006, No. 18, pp. 114)*
Pub: LNRS Data Services Limited
Contact: Mark Vickers Kelsey, Director
Ed: Erin Pooley. **Description:** Study results showing the perceptions of students while considering full-time employment and the attributes they look for in their future employers are presented. **Availability:** Online.

24679 ■ *Hoover's Vision*
Released: 1st edition. **Description:** Founder of Bookstop Inc. and Hoover's Inc. provides a plan to turn an enterprise into a success by showing entrepreneurs how to address inputs with an open mind in order to see more than what other's envision. Hoover pushes business owners to create and feed a clear and consistent vision by recognizing the importance of history and trends, then helps them find the essential qualities of entrepreneurial leadership. **Availability:** Print.

24680 ■ *"How Innovative Is Michigan? Index Aims To Keep Track" in Crain's Detroit Business (Vol. 24, February 4, 2008, No. 5, pp. 1)*
Pub: Crain Communications Inc.
Contact: Barry Asin, President
Ed: Chad Halcom. **Description:** Profile of the newly created "Innovation Index", released by the University of Michigan-Dearborn. The report showed a combination of indicators that gauged innovation activity in the state slightly lower for second quarter 2007, but ahead of most levels for most of 2006. Statistical data included. **Availability:** Print; Online.

24681 ■ *How to Make Big Money in Your Own Small Business: Unexpected Rules Every Small Business Owner Needs to Know*
Ed: Jeffrey J. Fox, Jeffrey J. Fox. **Released:** May 12, 2004. **Price:** $16.95; C$24.95; $16.95; C$24.95; $16.95; C$24.95. **Description:** Former sales and marketing pro offers advice on growing a small business. **Availability:** Print.

24682 ■ *How to Run Your Business Like a Girl: Successful Strategies from Entrepreneurial Women Who Made It Happen*
Description: Tour of three women entrepreneurs and their successful companies.

24683 ■ *How to Succeed As a Lifestyle Entrepreneur*
Availability: Print; Online.

24684 ■ *"How To Live To Be 100: John E. Green Co. Grows Through Diversification" in Crain's Detroit Business (February 18, 2008)*
Pub: Crain Communications Inc.
Contact: Barry Asin, President
Ed: Chad Halcom. **Description:** Continuity, name recognition, and inventiveness are keys to continuing growth for Highland Park, Michigan's John E. Green Company, designer of pipe systems and mechanical contractor. **Availability:** Online.

24685 ■ *How: Why How We Do Anything Means Everything*
Pub: John Wiley & Sons, Inc.
Contact: Christina Van Tassell, Executive Vice President Chief Financial Officer
Ed: Dov L. Seidman. **Released:** Expanded edition. **Price:** $27.95, hardcover; $18.99, E-book. **Description:** Author shares his unique approach to building successful companies using case studies, anecdotes, research, and interviews to help entrepreneurs succeed in the 21st Century. **Availability:** E-book; Print.

24686 ■ *How to Write a Business Plan*
Pub: Nolo
Contact: Chris Braun, President
Ed: Mike McKeever. **Released:** November 2018. **Price:** E-Book. **Description:** Author, teacher and financial manager shows how to write an effective business plan. Examples and worksheets are included. **Availability:** E-book; Print.

24687 ■ *How to Write a Great Business Plan for Your Small Business in 60 Minutes or Less*
Pub: Atlantic Publishing Co.
Contact: Dr. Heather L. Johnson, Contact
Ed: Sharon L. Fullen. **Released:** 2013. **Description:** A good business plan outlines goals and works as a company's resume to obtain funding, credit from suppliers, management of the operations and finances, promotion and marketing, and more. **Availability:** CD-ROM; E-book; Print; Online.

24688 ■ *"The Human Factor" in Canadian Business (Vol. 80, October 8, 2007, No. 20, pp. 22)*
Description: David Foot, a demographer and an economics professor at the University of Toronto, talks about Canada's future, including economic and demographic trends. He discusses activities that should be done by businessmen in order to prepare for the future. He also addresses the role of the Canadian government in economic development. **Availability:** Print; Online.

24689 ■ *Inc.--The Inc. 500 Issue*
Contact: John Koten, Editor-in-Chief
URL(s): www.inc.com/inc5000www.inc.com
Released: Annual; Latest edition 2010. **Price:** $3.50, postpaid. **Description:** Publication includes list of 500 fastest-growing privately held companies based on percentage increase in sales over the five year period prior to compilation of current year's list.

Entries include: Company name, headquarters city, description of business, year founded, number of employees, sales five years earlier and currently, profitability range, and growth statistics. **Arrangement:** Ranked by sales growth. **Availability:** Print; Online.

24690 ■ *"Is the Sun Setting on Oil Sector's Heydey?"* in *Globe & Mail (January 25, 2007, pp. B3)*

Description: The effects of fuel efficiency management policies of the United States on Canadian petroleum industry are discussed. Canada is the largest exporter of crude oil to America after the Middle East. **Availability:** Online.

24691 ■ *"Is That the Best You Can Do?"* in *Entrepreneur (Vol. 37, October 2009, No. 10, pp. 85)*

Description: Small business owners can deal with hagglers better by setting parameters in advance. They should convince hagglers by offering the best value and separating this from price. **Availability:** Print; Online.

24692 ■ *"Is Your Company Ready to Succeed?"* in *Business Strategy Review (Vol. 21, Spring 2010, No. 1, pp. 68)*

Ed: Srikumar Rao. **Released:** February 09, 2010. **Description:** The author asked thousands of students about the ideal company of the future, the kind of place where they would want to spend their lives. **Availability:** Print; PDF; Online.

24693 ■ *"Is Your Supply Chain Sustainable?"* in *Harvard Business Review (Vol. 88, October 2010, No. 10, pp. 74)*
Pub: Harvard Business Publishing
Contact: Diane Belcher, Managing Director

Price: $8.95, PDF. **Description:** Charts and models are presented to help a firm assess its sustainability. **Availability:** Online; PDF.

24694 ■ *It's Not Just Who You Know: Transform Your Life (and Your Organization) by Turning Colleagues and Contacts into Lasting Relationships*

Released: August 10, 2010. **Price:** $11.99, hardcover; $29.57, paperback. **Description:** Tommy Spaulding teaches the reader how to reach out to others in order to create lasting relationships that go beyond superficial contacts. **Availability:** audiobook; E-book; Print.

24695 ■ *"Keith Crain: Business Must Stand Up And Be Counted"* in *Crain's Detroit Business (Vol. 24, October 6, 2008, No. 40, pp. 6)*
Pub: Crain Communications Inc.
Contact: Barry Asin, President

Description: Discusses the challenges that the new mayor of Detroit faces concerning business, the state of the economy and the exceptionally tight budget the city is running on, which includes a lot of red ink. It is very likely that the city is going to see tax revenues fall substantially in the next few months and business leaders may find it in their favor to lend their support to the new mayor as well as provide him with the executive talent necessary to overcome some of these crucial issues. **Availability:** Online.

24696 ■ *"Kinross Holds Firm on Offer for Bema"* in *Globe & Mail (January 20, 2007, pp. B5)*

Ed: Andy Hoffman. **Description:** The acquisition of Bema Gold Corp. by Kinross Gold Corp. is discussed. **Availability:** Online.

24697 ■ *"The Last Word Dirty Work Required"* in *Workforce Management (Vol. 88, November 16, 2009, No. 12, pp. 34)*
Pub: Crain Communications Inc.
Contact: Barry Asin, President

Ed: John Hollon. **Description:** Due to salary freezes, pay cuts, layoffs, buyouts and a number of other stress factors brought about by the recession, employee engagement has been difficult to maintain by managers. **Availability:** Online.

24698 ■ *"Leave It Behind"* in *Crain's Chicago Business (Vol. 31, April 21, 2008, No. 16, pp. 32)*
Pub: Crain Communications Inc.
Contact: Barry Asin, President

Ed: Sarah A. Klein. **Description:** Patrick Brady who investigates possible violations of the Foreign Corrupt Practices Act has a novel approach when traveling to frequent destinations which allows him to travel with only a carry-on piece of luggage: he leaves suits at dry cleaners in the places he visits most often and since he mainly stays at the same hotels, he also leaves sets of workout clothes and running shoes with hotel staff. **Availability:** Online.

24699 ■ *"Donald Tarlton"* in *Canadian Business (Vol. 80, March 26, 2007, No. 7, pp. 70)*
Pub: Rogers Media Inc.
Contact: Neil Spivak, Chief Executive Officer

Ed: Andy Holloway. **Description:** Donald Tarlton, owner of Donald K Donald Entertainment Group, shares few things about his childhood and career. **Availability:** Print; Online.

24700 ■ *"Live & Learn: Ian Delaney"* in *Canadian Business (Vol. 81, Summer 2008, No. 9, pp. 168)*
Pub: Rogers Media Inc.
Contact: Neil Spivak, Chief Executive Officer

Ed: Joe Castaldo. **Description:** Interview with Ian Delaney who is the executive chairman of chemical company Sherritt International Corp.; Delaney previously worked as chief executive for a holding company owned by Peter Munk. Details of his beliefs, profession and family life are discussed. **Availability:** Online.

24701 ■ *"Laurent Beaudoin"* in *Canadian Business (Vol. 80, April 9, 2007, No. 8, pp. 68)*
Pub: Rogers Media Inc.
Contact: Neil Spivak, Chief Executive Officer

Ed: Thomas Watson. **Description:** Chief executive officer of Bombardier Inc., Laurent Beaudoin, talks about his personal life and career. **Availability:** Print; Online.

24702 ■ *"Live & Learn: Philip Kives, Founder and CEO of K-Tel"* in *Canadian Business (Vol. 79, October 23, 2006, No. 21, pp. 160)*
Pub: Rogers Media Inc.
Contact: Neil Spivak, Chief Executive Officer

Ed: Joe Castaldo. **Description:** Philip Kives, founder and chief executive officer of K-Tel International Inc. discusses his professional achievements. **Availability:** Online.

24703 ■ *"Look Before You Lease"* in *Women Entrepreneur (February 3, 2009)*

Description: Top issues to consider before leasing an office space are discussed including: additional charges that may be expected on top of the basic rental price; determining both short- and long-term goals; the cost of improvements to the space; the cost of upkeep; and the conditions of the lease. **Availability:** Online.

24704 ■ *"Magna Banks on Big Cash Hoard"* in *Globe & Mail (March 1, 2006, pp. B3)*

Ed: Greg Keenan. **Description:** The details on Magna International Inc., which posted decline in profits at $639 million for 2005, are presented. **Availability:** Online.

24705 ■ *"Many Sectors Lost Jobs In Detroit Area, State"* in *Crain's Detroit Business (Vol. 24, February 11, 2008, No. 6, pp. 3)*
Pub: Crain Communications Inc.
Contact: Barry Asin, President

Ed: Amy Lane. **Description:** Southeast Michigan reported its highest jobless rate since 1992 in fourth quarter 2007. Statistical data included. **Availability:** Print; Online.

24706 ■ *"Mary Kramer: Good Things Happen When We Buy Local"* in *Crain's Detroit Business (Vol. 24, October 6, 2008, No. 40, pp. 7)*
Pub: Crain Communications Inc.
Contact: Barry Asin, President

Description: Michigan is facing incredibly difficult economic times. One way in which each one of us can help the state and the businesses located here is by purchasing our goods and services from local vendors. The state Agriculture Department projected that if Michigan households earmarked $10 per week in their grocery purchases to made-in-Michigan products, this would generate $30 million a week in economic impact. **Availability:** Online.

24707 ■ *"MBT Add-On: Gone by 2012?"* in *Crain's Detroit Business (Vol. 24, October 6, 2008, No. 40, pp. 1)*
Pub: Crain Communications Inc.
Contact: Barry Asin, President

Ed: Amy Lane. **Description:** Discusses the Michigan Business Tax (MBT), which has angered many businesses in the state due to the addition of a 21.99 percent surcharge. Although the tax policy will cut taxes on 63 percent of businesses in the state and represent no tax liability change for another nine percent of firms, other businesses will see increases of 100 percent or more. This increase means that many business owners will be forced to relocate or close their establishment and others will have to eliminate jobs. Lawmakers are attempting to find a solution to this problem. **Availability:** Print; Online.

24708 ■ *"More Than a Feeling"* in *Entrepreneur (Vol. 36, April 2008, No. 4, pp. 10)*

Description: It is said that emotion has no place when it comes to business matters, but it may not be the case as entrepreneurs and other people in business feel passionate about what they do. Emotions can help bring out a positive outlook in them. Other details on the topic are discussed. **Availability:** Online.

24709 ■ *"Most See Gloomy Year For Michigan Business"* in *Crain's Detroit Business (Vol. 24, October 6, 2008, No. 40, pp. 4)*
Pub: Crain Communications Inc.
Contact: Barry Asin, President

Ed: Amy Lane. **Description:** Michigan residents are extremely concerned about the economic climate and business conditions in the state. According to the latest quarterly State of the State Survey, conducted by Michigan State University's Institute for Public Policy and Social Research, 63.9 percent of those surveyed anticipate bad times for Michigan businesses over the next year. Additional findings from the survey are also included. **Availability:** Online.

24710 ■ *"A New Era for Raiders"* in *Harvard Business Review (Vol. 88, November 2010, No. 11, pp. 34)*
Pub: Harvard Business Publishing
Contact: Diane Belcher, Managing Director

Ed: Guhan Subramanian. **Price:** $6, PDF. **Description:** The article presents evidence that Section 203 is vulnerable, and a new wave of corporate takeovers may develop. The authors suggest that since no bidders have able to use the 85 percent stipulation over the last 19 years, it does not present a meaningful opportunity for success. **Availability:** Online; PDF.

24711 ■ *No Man's Land: What to Do When Your Company Is Too Big to Be Small but Too Small to Be Big*

Description: Insight to help fast-growing companies navigate the fatal trap of no-man's land, a perilous zone where they have outgrown the habits and practices that fueled their early growth but have not yet adopted new practices and resources in order to cope with new situations and challenges. **Availability:** E-book; Print.

24712 ■ *"O'Malley, Ehrlich Court Business Vote" in Baltimore Business Journal (Vol. 28, October 1, 2010, No. 21, pp. 1)*
Pub: Baltimore Business Journal
Contact: Rhonda Pringle, President
E-mail: rpringle@bizjournals.com
Ed: Scott Dance. **Description:** Maryland Governor Martin O'Malley and former Governor Robert Ehrlich reveal their business plans and platforms as they court business-minded votes in the state. Ehrlich, a Republican and O'Malley, a Democrat have both initiated programs that helped small businesses, but both have also introduced programs that made it more expensive and difficult to do business in the state. **Availability:** Print.

24713 ■ *"One Hundred Years of Excellence in Business Education: What Have We Learned?" in Business Horizons (January-February 2008)*
Pub: Elsevier Advanced Technology Publications
Ed: Frank Acito, Patricia M. McDougall, Daniel C. Smith. **Description:** Business schools have to be more innovative, efficient and nimble, so that the quality of the next generation of business leaders is improved. The Kelley School of Business, Indiana University has long been a leader in business education. The trends that influence the future of business education and useful success principles are discussed. **Availability:** PDF; Online.

24714 ■ *Organizations Alive!: Six Things That Challenge - Seven That Bring Success*
Pub: Yuill & Associates
Ed: Jan Yuill. **Price:** C$18.95, paperback. **Description:** New insight into understanding how organizations function as individuals is presented by an international consultant. Customer service, resource management, outsourcing, and management are among the issues covered.

24715 ■ *Outliers: The Story of Success*
Pub: Little, Brown and Company
Contact: Judy Clain, Editor-in-Chief
Ed: Malcolm Gladwell. **Released:** November 18, 2008. **Price:** $18.99, trade paper. **Description:** The book explores reasons for individual success. **Availability:** Large print; CD-ROM; E-book; Print; Download; Audio.

24716 ■ *The Platinum Rule for Small Business Success*
Description: Rules for running a successful and profitable small business are shared. **Availability:** E-book.

24717 ■ *PPC's Guide to Compensation Planning for Small Business*
Released: Annual. **Price:** $190, book volume 1; $215, online; $180. **Description:** Technical guide for developing a compensation system for small business. Forms and letters included. **Availability:** Online.

24718 ■ *"The Preparation Gap: Teacher Education for Middle School Mathematics in Six Countries" in Hawaii Business (Vol. 53, February 2008, No. 8, pp. 37)*
Pub: PacificBasin Communications
Contact: Chuck Tindle, Director
E-mail: chuckt@pacificbasin.net
Ed: Ashley Hamershock. **Description:** Discussion of the educational gap in Hawaii's workforce is being addressed by educational workshops that aim to improve students' knowledge in science, technology, math, and engineering, and prepare them for their entry into the workforce. Education beyond high school is required for jobs to be filled in the coming years. **Availability:** PDF; Online.

24719 ■ *Prescriptive Entrepreneurship*
Pub: Edward Elgar Publishing Inc.
Contact: Edward Elgar, Founder Chairman
Ed: James O. Fiet. **Released:** 2008. **Description:** In the only known program of prescriptive entrepreneurship, the author provides a marked contrast to the standard descriptive focus of entrepreneurship studies.

24720 ■ *"Priority: In Memoriam" in Inc. (December 2007, pp. 25-26, 28, 30)*
Ed: Ryan McCarthy. **Description:** Profiles of entrepreneurs who died in 2007; these individuals helped to create some major business trends in the last fifty years, from the advent of socially responsible business to development of quality manufacturing. **Availability:** Online.

24721 ■ *Re-Imagine! Business Excellence in a Disruptive Age*
Description: Examination of today's business order. Peters urges business owners to re-imagine business. **Availability:** Print; PDF.

24722 ■ *"The Real Job of Boards" in Business Strategy Review (Vol. 21, Autumn 2010, No. 3, pp. 36)*
Ed: Harry Korine, Marcus Alexander, Pierre-Yves Gomez. **Released:** September 29, 2010. **Description:** Widely seen as the key for ensuring quality in corporate governance, the board of directors has been a particular focal point for reform. The authors believe that more leadership at board level could avert many corporate crises in the future. **Availability:** Print; PDF; Online.

24723 ■ *Reality Check: The Irreverent Guide to Outsmarting, Outmanaging, and Outmarketing Your Competition*
Pub: Penguin Publishing Group
Ed: Guy Kawasaki. **Released:** February 22, 2011. **Price:** $13.34, paperback; $4.99, e-book; $19.89, hardcover; $20.43, audio. **Description:** Marketing guru and entrepreneur, Guy Kawasaki, provides a compilation of his blog posts on all aspects of starting and operating a business. **Availability:** E-book; Print.

24724 ■ *"Region and City Need Influx of Youth" in Crain's Detroit Business (Vol. 24, April 14, 2008, No. 15, pp. 8)*
Pub: Crain Communications Inc.
Contact: Barry Asin, President
Description: Discusses an upcoming report from Michigan Future Inc. which finds that young professionals, including those with children, are interested in living in an active urban environment. It also states that because many of those young professionals are entrepreneurial in nature, oftentimes businesses follow. **Availability:** Print; Online.

24725 ■ *"Relocation, Relocation, Relocation" in Conde Nast Portfolio (Vol. 2, June 2008, No. 6, pp. 36)*
Pub: American City Business Journals, Inc.
Contact: Mike Olivieri, Executive Vice President
Ed: Michelle Leder. **Description:** Perks regarding executive relocation are discussed. **Availability:** Print; Online.

24726 ■ *Resource and Environmental Management in Canada*
Ed: Bruce Mitchell. **Released:** Third edition. **Description:** Discusses resource management in Canada, focusing on business and industry, environmental groups, First Nations, the public, local communities with resource-based economies.

24727 ■ *The Road from Ruin: How to Revive Capitalism and Put America Back on Top*
Ed: Matthew Bishop, Michael Green. **Released:** 2011. **Description:** Authors show why American companies must respond to the economic crisis with long term vision and a renewed emphasis on values. **Availability:** E-book; Print.

24728 ■ *"Sage Advice" in Canadian Business (Vol. 80, October 22, 2007, No. 21, pp. 70)*
Description: Seymour Schulich, one of Canada's richest men and generous philanthropist, wrote the book, "Get Smarter: Life and Business Lessons". The business book sold more than 50,000 copies and now sits on Canada's bestseller's list. Its popularity is attributed to the marketing efforts of the entrepreneur and author. **Availability:** Print; Online.

24729 ■ *Save Your Small Business: 10 Crucial Strategies to Survive Hard Times or Close Down & Move On*
Pub: Nolo
Contact: Chris Braun, President
Ed: Ralph Warner, Bethany Laurence. **Description:** According to a study among 500 businesses, 44 percent used credit cards in order to meet their firm's needs in the previous six months. Written by a business owner, this book provides twelve strategies to protect personal assets from creditors and survive the current recession. **Availability:** Print.

24730 ■ *"The Search for Big Oil" in Canadian Business (Vol. 80, April 9, 2007, No. 8, pp. 10)*
Description: The continuing effort of Canmex Minerals Corp. to explore for oil in Somalia despite the failure of several other companies is discussed. **Availability:** Print; Online.

24731 ■ *"Secrets To Trade Show Success" in Women Entrepreneur (September 12, 2008)*
Description: Trade shows require an enormous amount of work, but they are an investment that can pay off handsomely because they allow a business to get their product or service in front of their target market. Advice regarding trade shows is given including selecting the correct venue, researching the affair and following up on leads obtained at the event. **Availability:** Online.

24732 ■ *Shop Class as Soulcraft*
Pub: Penguin Publishing Group
Ed: Matthew B. Crawford. **Released:** April 27, 2010. **Price:** $19.93, hardcover; $13.31, paperback; $14.99, audio. **Description:** A philosopher and mechanic argues for the satisfaction and challenges of manual work. **Availability:** E-book; Print.

24733 ■ *Simplified Incorporation Kit*
Released: 1st edition. **Description:** Kit includes all the forms, instructions, and information necessary for incorporating any small business in any state (CD-ROM included).

24734 ■ *"Single Most Important Problem" in Small Business Economic Trends (February 2008, pp. 18)*
Pub: National Federation of Independent Business
Contact: Brad Close, President
Ed: William C. Dunkelberg, Holly Wade. **Description:** Two graphs and a table representing the economic problems encountered by small businesses in the U.S. are presented. The figures presented in the graphs include data from 1974 to 2008. **Availability:** Print; Online; PDF.

24735 ■ *"A Skimmer's Guide to the Latest Business Books" in Inc. (Volume 32, December 2010, No. 10, pp. 34)*
Pub: Inc. Magazine
Description: A list of new books published covering all aspects of small business is offered. **Availability:** Online.

24736 ■ *Small Business: An Entrepreneur's Plan*
Pub: Nelson Education Ltd.
Contact: Steve Brown, President
Ed: Ronald A. Knowles. **Released:** 7th Canadian edition. **Price:** $111.95, paperback; $67.95, e-book. **Description:** Entrepreneur's guide to planning a small business. **Availability:** E-book; Print.

24737 ■ *The Small Business Bible: Everything You Need to Know to Succeed in Your Small Business*
Pub: John Wiley & Sons, Inc.
Contact: Christina Van Tassell, Executive Vice President Chief Financial Officer

Ed: Steven D. Strauss. **Released:** Third edition. **Price:** $22.95, paperback; $14.99, E-book. **Description:** Comprehensive guide to starting and running a successful small business. Topics include bookkeeping and financial management, marketing, publicity, and advertising. **Availability:** E-book; Print.

24738 ■ *"Small Business Compensation" in Small Business Economic Trends (February 2008, pp. 10)*

Pub: National Federation of Independent Business
Contact: Brad Close, President

Ed: William C. Dunkelberg, Holly Wade. **Description:** Graphs and tables that present compensation plans and compensation changes of small businesses in the U.S. are provided. The figures include data from 1974 to 2008.

24739 ■ *Small Business Encyclopedia*
URL(s): www.entrepreneur.com/encyclopedia

Description: An online encyclopedia from Entrepreneur that allows users to click on categories to pull up small-business terms to learn their definitions. **Availability:** Online.

24740 ■ *Small Business Sourcebook*

Released: 38th edition. **Price:** $1,001. **Description:** Two-volume guide to more than 27,300 listings of live and print sources for small business startups as well as small business growth and development. Over 30,500 topics are included. **Availability:** E-book; Print.

24741 ■ *Small Business Survival Guide*

Released: First edition. **Description:** Small business expert provides strategies to start a company and survive in the 21st Century. He shows small business owners how to succeed despite challenges that can defeat any firm. His advice covers suppliers; customers and contractors; competitors and creditors; spouses, family and friends; as well as the ways lawyers, accountants and other can steal an entrepreneur's success. Ennico also describes how startups can comply with local regulations. **Availability:** E-book; Print.

24742 ■ *Small Business Turnaround*

Price: $17.95 paperback. **Availability:** Print.

24743 ■ *"Smart Businesses See Value, and Profit, in Promoting Women" in Crain's Chicago Business (Vol. 30, February 2007, No. 6, pp. 30)*

Description: Despite U.S. corporations making little progress in advancing women to leadership positions over the past ten years, enlightened corporate decision makers understand that gender diversity is good business as the highest percentages of women officers yielded, on average, a 34 percent higher total return to shareholders and a 35.1 percent higher return on equity than those firms with the lowest percentages of women officers, according to a 2004 Catalyst study of Fortune 500 companies. **Availability:** Online.

24744 ■ *"Star Power Versus (Somewhat) Green Power" in Globe & Mail (January 18, 2007, pp. B2)*

Ed: Konrad Yakabuski. **Description:** The views of the Canadian actor Roy Dupuis on the trends of energy consumption by Quebeckers are presented, along with statistics of energy consumption in the Quebec region. **Availability:** Online.

24745 ■ *"Step Up to Help Regionalism Step Forward" in Crain's Cleveland Business (Vol. 28, November 12, 2007, No. 45, pp. 10)*

Pub: Crain Communications Inc.
Contact: K. C. Crain, President

Ed: Rob Briggs, William Currin. **Description:** Discusses the importance of regionalism for Northeast Ohio as being a broad, collaborative approach to spur economic development.

24746 ■ *Streetwise Small Business Book of Lists: Hundreds of Lists to Help You Reduce Costs, Increase Revenues, and Boost Your Profits!*

Price: Paperback. **Description:** Strategies to help small business owners locate services, increase sales, and lower expenses. **Availability:** Print.

24747 ■ *"Success Fees: A Word of Warning" in Canadian Business (Vol. 80, March 12, 2007, No. 6)*

Description: Legal issues regarding payment of lawyer fees termed 'fair fee' in Canada are discussed with an instance of Inmet Mining Corp.'s dealing with lawyer Irwin Nathanson. **Availability:** Online.

24748 ■ *Successful Proposal Strategies for Small Businesses: Using Knowledge Management to Win Government, Private-Sector, and International Contracts*

Pub: Artech House Inc.
Contact: Ed Waltz, Editor

Ed: Robert S. Frey. **Released:** Sixth edition. **Price:** $153, print; $153, e-book, CD-ROM included; $39, hardback; $76.50, digital download and online; $80. **Description:** Front-end proposal planning and storyboarding, focusing on the customer mission in proposals, along with the development of grant proposals. **Availability:** E-book; Print; Online; Download.

24749 ■ *"Survey Profile" in Small Business Economic Trends (September 2010, pp. 19)*

Pub: National Federation of Independent Business
Contact: Brad Close, President

Ed: William C. Dunkelberg, Holly Wade. **Description:** Two graphs and a table presenting the profile of small businesses that participated in the National Federation of Independent Business (NFIB) survey are provided. The actual number of firms, their industry types, and the number of full and part-time employees are presented. **Availability:** Print; PDF; Online.

24750 ■ *"Surviving the Storm" in Canadian Business (Vol. 81, July 22, 2008, No. 12-13, pp. 50)*

Description: Investment adviser Harry Dent and finance professor Paul Marsh discuss their views and forecasts on the United States' economic condition. Dent believes advisors should concentrate on wealth preservation rather than on returns. Other views regarding U.S. economic conditions are also presented. **Availability:** Print; Online.

24751 ■ *"Ten Ways to Save on Business Travel" in Women Entrepreneur (November 21, 2008)*

Description: Advice regarding ways in which to save money when traveling for business is given. **Availability:** Online.

24752 ■ *"Top 49ers Alphabetical Listing with Five Years Rank and Revenue" in Alaska Business Monthly (Vol. 27, October 2011, No. 10, pp. 100)*

Pub: Alaska Business Publishing Company Inc.
Contact: Charles Bell, Vice President, Sales and Marketing
E-mail: cbell@akbizmag.com

Description: A listing of Alaska's top 49 performing companies ranked by revenue for years 2010 and 2011. **Availability:** Print; Online.

24753 ■ *"Trimming Costs, But Not Looking It" in Crain's Chicago Business (Vol. 31, November 17, 2008, No. 46, pp. 35)*

Pub: Crain Communications Inc.
Contact: Barry Asin, President

Ed: Shia Kapos. **Description:** Advice is given concerning ways in which to keep up appearances of success during these troubled financial times. **Availability:** Online.

24754 ■ *"The Trouble With $150,000 Wine" in Barron's (Vol. 88, July 7, 2008, No. 27, pp. 33)*

Pub: Dow Jones & Company Inc.
Contact: Almar Latour, Chief Executive Officer

Ed: Jay Palmer. **Description:** Review of the book, "The Billionaire's Vinegar: The Mystery of the World's Most Expensive Bottle of Wine," which discusses vintners along with the marketing and distribution of wine as well as the winemaking industry as a whole. **Availability:** Online.

24755 ■ *"A Turn in the South" in The Economist (Vol. 390, January 3, 2009, No. 8612, pp. 34)*

Description: Overview of Charleston, South Carolina, a region that lost its navy base in 1996, which had provided work for more than 22,000 people; the city developed a plan called Noisette in order to redevelop the area and today the economy is healthier and more diversified than it was a decade ago. Charleston was described as among the best cities for doing business by Inc. Magazine and seems to be handling the downturn of the economy fairly well. Statistical data regarding growth, business and population is included. **Availability:** Print; Online.

24756 ■ *"Under Pressure" in Canadian Business (Vol. 81, July 21, 2008, No. 11, pp. 18)*

Description: According to a survey conducted by COMPASS Inc., meeting revenue targets is the main cause of job stress for chief executive officers. Staffing and keeping expenditures lower also contribute to the workplace stress experienced by business executives. Other results of the survey are presented. **Availability:** Online.

24757 ■ *"Unemployment Rates" in The Economist (Vol. 390, January 3, 2009, No. 8612, pp. 75)*

Description: Countries that are being impacted the worst by rising unemployment rates are those that have also been suffering from the housing market crisis. Spain has been the hardest hit followed by Ireland. America and Britain are also seeing levels of unemployment that indicate too much slack in the economy. **Availability:** Print; Online.

24758 ■ *"Unveiling the Secrets Behind Hispanic Business' 100 Fastest-Growing Companies" in Hispanic Business (Vol. 30, July-August 2008, No. 7-8, pp. 22)*

Ed: Michael Bowker. **Description:** CEO's of the five fastest growing Hispanic-owned companies discuss the success of their companies; most of them attribute their success to proper investment and diversification, effective innovations and seeing growth opportunities where others see roadblocks. **Availability:** Online.

24759 ■ *"The Upside of Fear and Loathing" in Barron's (Vol. 88, March 24, 2008, No. 12, pp. 11)*

Pub: Dow Jones & Company Inc.
Contact: Almar Latour, Chief Executive Officer

Ed: Michael Santoli. **Description:** Fear and risk aversion prevalent among investors may actually serve to cushion the decline and spark a rally in US stock prices. Surveys of investors indicate rising levels of anxiety and bearishness, indicating a possible positive turnaround. **Availability:** Online.

24760 ■ *"Valenti: Roots of Financial Crisis Go Back to 1998" in Crain's Detroit Business (Vol. 24, October 6, 2008, No. 40, pp. 25)*

Pub: Crain Communications Inc.
Contact: Barry Asin, President

Ed: Tom Henderson, Nathan Skid. **Description:** Interview with Sam Valenti III who is the chairman and CEO of Valenti Capital L.L.C., a wealth-management firm; Valenti discusses in detail the history that led up to the current economic crisis as well as his prediction for the future of the country. **Availability:** Print; Online.

GENERAL SMALL BUSINESS TOPICS

24761 ■ *"Valuation: Confusing and Misunderstood"* in *Business Owner* (Vol. 35, July-August 2011, No. 4, pp. 10)
Description: Business valuation is explained to help small business owners realize the value of their company. **Availability:** Print; Online.

24762 ■ *"Walker Seeks More Business Participation"* in *Business Journal-Milwaukee* (Vol. 28, December 10, 2010, No. 10, pp. A1)
Pub: The Business Journal
Contact: Heather Ladage, President
E-mail: hladage@bizjournals.com
Ed: Rich Kirchen. **Description:** Wisconsin governor Scott Walker is seeking the aid of Milwaukee business leaders to participate in resolving the challenges posed by the economic crisis. Walker is aiming to create 250,000 jobs. He is also planning to call a special session of the legislature to enact strategies to jumpstart the economy. **Availability:** Print; Online.

24763 ■ *Ward's Business Directory of U.S. Private and Public Companies*
Pub: Gale, part of Cengage Group
Contact: Paul Gazzolo, General Manager Senior Vice President
URL(s): www.gale.com/ebooks/9781414453064/wards-business-directory-of-u.s.-private-and-public-companies
Description: Covers approximately 112,000 companies, 90% of which are privately owned, representing all industries. **Entries include:** Company name, address, phone, fax, toll-free, e-mail, URL, names and titles of up to five officers, up to four Standard Industrial Classification (SIC) codes, NAICS code, revenue figure, number of employees, year founded, ticker symbol, stock exchange, immediate parent, fiscal year end, import/export, type of company (public, private, subsidiary, etc.). In Vol. 4, lists of top 1,000 privately held companies ranked by sales vol., top 1,000 publicly held companies ranked by sales volume, and top 1,000 employers ranked by number of employees; analyses of public and private companies by state, revenue per employee for top 1,000 companies, public and private companies by SIC code and NAICS code. In volume 5, national Standard Industrial Classification (SIC) code rankings are listed, while volumes 6 and 7 lists Standard Industrial Classification (SIC) code rankings by state. In all volumes, guide to abbreviations, codes, and symbols; explanation of classification system; numerical and alphabetical listings of SIC and NAICS codes. In volume 8, NAICS rankings. In the supplement, 10,000 new listings not contained in the main edition are included. **Arrangement:** Volumes 1, 2, and 3, alphabetical; volume 4 is geographical by state, then ascending zip; volume 5 is classified by 4-digit SIC code, then ranked by sales; volumes 6 and 7 are classified by Standard Industrial Classification (SIC) code within state; volume 8 classified by NAICS, then ranked; supplement arranged alphabetical and Standard Industrial Classification (SIC) code. **Indexes:** Company name index in volumes 5, 7, and 8. **Availability:** E-book; Print; Download. **Type:** Directory; Numeric.

24764 ■ *What Works: Success in Stressful Times*
Ed: Hamish McRae. **Released:** August 04, 2011. **Price:** $14.95, paperback; $5.99, e-book. **Description:** Exploration of success stories from across the glove, and what Michelle Obama referred to as 'the flimsy difference between success and failure.' Why do some initiatives take off while others flounder? How have communities managed to achieve so much while others struggle? What distinguishes the good companies from the bad? What lessons can be learned from the well-ordered Mumbai community made famous by 'Slumdog Millionaire'? Why have Canadian manners helped Whistler become the most popular ski resort in North America?. **Availability:** E-book; Print.

24765 ■ *"When Profit Is Not the Incentive"* in *Business North Carolina* (Vol. 28, February 2008, No. 2, pp. 42)
Pub: Business North Carolina
Contact: Peggy Knaack, Manager
E-mail: pknaack@businessnc.com
Ed: Amamda Parry. **Description:** Novant Health is North Carolina's fifth-largest private-sector employer and one of the largest nonprofit companies. Nonprofits grew 35 percent in North Carolina from 1995 to 2003. **Availability:** Online.

24766 ■ *"Where Are They Now?"* in *Canadian Business* (Vol. 79, October 9, 2006, No. 20, pp. 71)
Ed: Jeff Sanford, Zena Olijnyk, Andrew Wahl, Andy Holloway, John Gray. **Description:** The profile of the top chief executive officers of Canada for the year 2005 is discussed. **Availability:** Online.

24767 ■ *Who's Got Your Back*
Pub: Broadway Books
Contact: Sally McPherson, Editor Publisher Manager, Sales
Ed: Keith Ferrazzi. **Released:** 1st edition. **Description:** Achieving goals by building close relationships with a small circle of trusted individuals.

24768 ■ *"Why Entrepreneurs Will Save the World"* in *Women In Business* (Vol. 61, December 2009, No. 6, pp. 12)
Pub: American Business Women's Association
Contact: Rene Street, Executive Director
Ed: Leigh Elmore. **Released:** May 27, 2012. **Description:** American economic growth is attributed to small businesses but more than one-third of these businesses have had to cut jobs in 2009, while only five percent have increased workforces. This trend motivated organizations, such as the Ewing Marion Kauffman Foundation, to bring together entrepreneurs and assist them in having greater participation in public dialogues about America's economy. **Availability:** Print; Online.

24769 ■ *"Why LinkedIn is the Social Network that Will Never Die"* in *Advertising Age* (Vol. 81, December 6, 2010, No. 43, pp. 2)
Pub: Crain Communications, Inc.
Contact: Jessica Botos, Manager, Marketing
E-mail: jessica.botos@crainsnewyork.com
Ed: Irina Slutsky. **Description:** Despite the popularity of Facebook, LinkedIn in will always be a source for professionals who wish to network. **Availability:** Online.

24770 ■ *"Why Oil Fell, and How It May Rise"* in *Globe & Mail* (January 18, 2007, pp. B2)
Ed: Eric Reguly. **Description:** The causes of the decline in oil prices in Canada are discussed, along with prospects of an increase in the same. **Availability:** Print; Online.

24771 ■ *Wikinomics: How Mass Collaboration Changes Everything*
Pub: Penguin Publishing Group
Ed: Don Tapscott, Anthony D. Williams, Anthony D. Williams. **Released:** September 28, 2010. **Price:** $16.93, paperback; $8.99, e-book; $12.77, audio; $17, paperback; $13.99. **Description:** Research and information about the every changing world of the Internet is provided to help small businesses. **Availability:** E-book; Print; Electronic publishing.

24772 ■ *"Will Focus on Maryland Businesses Continue?"* in *Baltimore Business Journal* (Vol. 28, November 5, 2010, No. 26, pp. 1)
Pub: Baltimore Business Journal
Contact: Rhonda Pringle, President
E-mail: rpringle@bizjournals.com
Ed: Scott Dance. **Description:** The 2010 election may call for new efforts to teach new lawmakers to assure that the viewpoints of businesses are considered and accurately delivered. The Greater Baltimore Committee and similar groups have gathered reports on the competitiveness of Maryland and are planning to use them to make a case of keeping business a top priority. **Availability:** Print; Online.

24773 ■ *"Work Less, Earn More"* in *Canadian Business* (Vol. 80, March 12, 2007, No. 6, pp. 30)
Description: Expert advice on ways to work efficiently to complete the job instead of extending work hours is presented. **Availability:** Online.

24774 ■ *Working Together: Why Great Partnerships Succeed*
Pub: Harper Business
Contact: Hollis Heimbouch, Senior Vice President Publisher
Ed: Michael D. Eisner, Aaron Cohen. **Released:** September 14, 2010. **Price:** $13.59, trade paperback. **Description:** Michael D. Eisner, former CEO of the Walt Disney Company interviews corporate partners from various industries, including Bill and Melinda Gates and Warren Buffet and Charlie Munger. Why certain business partnerships succeed in the corporate world is discussed. **Availability:** E-book; Print; Download; Audio.

TRADE PERIODICALS

24775 ■ *Alliance of Area Business Publications--Membership Directory*
Pub: Alliance of Area Business Publishers
Contact: Cate Sanderson, Executive Director
E-mail: cate@sandersonmgt.com
URL(s): bizpubs.org/membership-directory
Description: Covers over 70 local, state, and regional member business publications in the United States, Canada, Australia and Puerto Rico. **Entries include:** Publication title, publisher name, address, phone; names of editor, advertising director, and manager; frequency, format, circulation; audit firm; full-page advertising rates; selected reader demographics, deadline information. **Arrangement:** Alphabetical. **Indexes:** Geographical. **Availability:** Print.

24776 ■ *Forbes*
Pub: Forbes Media LLC
URL(s): www.forbes.com/?sh=7099d3672254
Facebook: www.facebook.com/forbes
X (Twitter): x.com/Forbes
Instagram: www.instagram.com/forbes
Ed: Randall Lane. **Released:** 6/year **Price:** $12.99, for monthly; $145, for two year; $74.99, for 1 year; $1.50, for weekly. **Description:** Magazine reporting on industry, business and finance management. **Availability:** Print; Online. **Type:** Full-text.

24777 ■ *Fortune*
Pub: Fortune Media IP Limited
Contact: Alan Murray, Chief Executive Officer
E-mail: alan.murray@fortune.com
URL(s): fortune.com/section/magazine
Facebook: www.facebook.com/FortuneMagazine
Linkedin: www.linkedin.com/company/fortune-magazine
X (Twitter): twitter.com/FortuneMagazine
Instagram: www.instagram.com/fortunemag
Pinterest: www.pinterest.com/fortunemagazine
Ed: Adam Lashinsky. **Released:** Monthly **Price:** $1, for per month; $7.95, for one year; $10.95, for one year. **Description:** Multinational business magazine published for top executives and upper-level managers. **Availability:** Print; Online.

24778 ■ *IFMA's World Workplace Conference & Expo*
URL(s): worldworkplace.ifma.org/about
Frequency: Annual. **Description:** Includes discussions on facility management, and technology discoveries. **Audience:** Professionals, including facility managers, property owners, construction managers, consultants, engineers, architects, security professionals, human resources professionals, and IT professionals. **Principal Exhibits:** Includes discussions on facility management, and technology discoveries. Dates and Locations: 2025 Sep 17-19 Minneapolis, MN; 2026 Nov 18-20 Anaheim, CA; 2027. **Telecommunication Services:** registrations@ifma.org.

24779 ■ *Inc. Magazine: The Magazine for Growing Companies*
Contact: John Koten, Editor-in-Chief
URL(s): www.inc.com
Facebook: www.facebook.com/Inc
X (Twitter): twitter.com/Inc
Released: Monthly **Price:** $12.99, for 10 issue price; $5.99, for cover price. **Description:** Business and finance magazine for business owners and managers. **Availability:** Print; Online.

24780 ■ *Review of Business Information Systems (RBIS)*
Pub: The Clute Institute for Academic Research
URL(s): clutejournals.com/index.php/RBIS
Released: Semiannual; June and December. **Description:** Accounting Information Systems magazine. **Availability:** Print; PDF; Online.

VIDEO/AUDIO MEDIA

24781 ■ *10 Books That Changed My Business (+ Life)*
URL(s): www.makinggoodpodcast.com/episodes/234
Ed: Lauren Tilden. **Released:** April 30, 2024. **Description:** Podcast lists ten books than can change your business.

24782 ■ *10 Productivity Hacks that Actually Work*
URL(s): www.makinggoodpodcast.com/episodes/243
Ed: Lauren Tilden. **Released:** June 18, 2024. **Description:** Podcast offers tools and strategies to try that make a difference when it comes to getting stuff done.

24783 ■ *The Best Small Business Podcast: Decision Velocity - How to Make Tough Decisions*
URL(s): richgee.libsyn.com/295-decision-velocity-how-to-make-tough-decisions
Ed: Rich Gee. **Released:** May 15, 2023. **Description:** Podcast discusses the use of data to rapidly make decisions.

24784 ■ *The Best Small Business Show: 4 Easy Ways to Stand Out*
URL(s): richgee.libsyn.com/245-4-easy-ways-to-stand-out
Released: May 30, 2022. **Description:** Offers tips on how to make your small business stand out from the competition.

24785 ■ *The Best Small Business Show: Business Fears - What Do You Do If You Lose Your Biggest Client?*
URL(s): richgee.libsyn.com/233-business-fears-what-do-you-do-if-you-lose-your-biggest-client
Ed: Rich Gee. **Released:** March 14, 2022. **Description:** Podcast discusses how to navigate the loss of a crucial client.

24786 ■ *The Best Small Business Show: Business Fears - What Happens If You Get Sick?*
URL(s): richgee.libsyn.com/232-business-fears-what-happens-if-you-get-sick
Ed: Rich Gee. **Released:** February 28, 2022. **Description:** Podcast discusses how to keep your business healthy even when you're not.

24787 ■ *The Best Small Business Show: Business Fears - What If Your Industry Is Slowly Going Out of Business?*
URL(s): richgee.libsyn.com/235-business-fears-what-if-your-industry-is-slowly-going-out-of-business
Ed: Rich Gee. **Released:** March 21, 2022. **Description:** Podcast discusses how to navigate an obsolete industry.

24788 ■ *The Best Small Business Show: Choose the Right Product Mix to Get the Best Clients*
URL(s): richgee.libsyn.com/226-choose-the-right-product-mix-to-get-the-best-clients
Ed: Rich Gee. **Released:** January 17, 2022. **Description:** Podcasts discusses how to evaluate your product/service offerings.

24789 ■ *The Best Small Business Show: Finding Your Best Clients*
URL(s): richgee.libsyn.com/307-finding-your-best-clients
Released: August 07, 2023. **Description:** Podcast discusses how to find the best clients.

24790 ■ *The Best Small Business Show: Go Back 10 Years - What Would You Do Differently?*
URL(s): richgee.libsyn.com/269-go-back-10-years-what-would-you-do-differently
Released: November 14, 2022. **Description:** Podcast asks what small businesses would do differently if they could.

24791 ■ *The Best Small Business Show: How to Better Communicate with Your Audience*
Released: January 31, 2022. **Description:** Podcast discusses better communication--whether it's with clients, customers, or your chamber of commerce.

24792 ■ *The Best Small Business Show: Is Your Business Becoming Obsolete?*
URL(s): richgee.libsyn.com/313-is-your-business-becoming-obsolete
Ed: rich Gee. **Released:** September 18, 2023. **Description:** Podcast explains how to know when your business is outmoded in the fast-paced world of technology.

24793 ■ *The Best Small Business Show: Keeping a Watchful Eye on Your Vendors*
URL(s): richgee.libsyn.com/302-keeping-a-watchful-eye-on-your-vendors
Ed: Rich Gee. **Released:** July 03, 2023. **Description:** Podcast discusses monitoring your vendors.

24794 ■ *The Best Small Business Show: Organize Your Business with SDR Methods*
URL(s): richgee.libsyn.com/244-organize-your-business-with-sdr-methods
Released: May 23, 2022. **Description:** Podcast offers tips on using SDR to organize your business.

24795 ■ *The Best Small Business Show: The Best Ways to Network and Grow Your Business*
URL(s): richgee.libsyn.com/288-the-best-ways-to-network-grow-your-business
Ed: Rich Gee. **Released:** March 27, 2023. **Description:** Podcast discusses the importance of networking in growing your business.

24796 ■ *The Best Small Business Show: Top 4 Business Books You Should Be Reading*
URL(s): richgee.libsyn.com/276-top-4-business-books-you-should-be-reading
Released: January 02, 2023.

24797 ■ *The Best Small Business Show: Top 4 Business Tools You Should Be Using*
URL(s): richgee.libsyn.com/275-top-4-business-tools-you-should-be-using
Ed: Rich Gee. **Released:** December 26, 2022. **Description:** Highlights four important business tools.

24798 ■ *The Best Small Business Show: We All Can Fail - It's What You Do After*
URL(s): richgee.libsyn.com/304-we-all-can-fail-its-what-you-do-after
Ed: Rich Gee. **Released:** July 17, 2023. **Description:** Podcast discusses how to bounce back after business failure.

24799 ■ *The Best Small Business Show: When Major Shifts Need to Happen in Your Business*
URL(s): richgee.libsyn.com/265-when-major-shifts-need-to-happen-in-your-business
Ed: rich Gee. **Released:** September 26, 2022. **Description:** Podcast outlines when it's time to shift in your business.

24800 ■ *The Best Small Business Show: Why Did You Lose that Client?*
URL(s): richgee.libsyn.com/312-why-did-you-lose-that-client
Ed: Rich Gee. **Released:** September 11, 2023. **Description:** Pocast explains why small businesses may have lost clients.

24801 ■ *The Best Small Business Show: Why Getting Started Is More Important than Succeeding*
URL(s): richgee.libsyn.com/127-why-getting-started-is-more-important-than-succeeding
Ed: Rich Gee. **Released:** February 24, 2020. **Description:** Podcast offers tips on avoiding analysis paralysis.

24802 ■ *Breaking the Hustle-to-Burnout Pipeline with Doreen Vanderhart*
URL(s): www.makinggoodpodcast.com/episodes/225
Ed: Lauren Tilden. **Released:** March 12, 2024. **Description:** Podcast discusses taking the pressure off and trust yourself.

24803 ■ *BS-Free Service Business Show: Exits and Evolutions: Change Is the Only Constant*
URL(s): bsfreebusiness.com/change-management
Ed: Maggie Patterson. **Released:** April 29, 2024. **Description:** Podcast discusses the 4 Cs of change management. Also highlights changes to avoid and explains why you don't want to chase trends.

24804 ■ *Do You Have a Marketing Problem?*
URL(s): bizchix.com/570-do-you-have-a-marketing-problem
Ed: Natalie Eckdahl. **Released:** April 06, 2023. **Description:** Podcast discusses why most new clients cite marketing as their biggest problem, when it's actually something else: a desire for more control and stability. .

24805 ■ *Do You Have Too Many Services or Offers?*
URL(s): bizchix.com/527-do-you-have-too-many-services-of-offers
Released: June 09, 2022. **Description:** Podcasts discusses how too many offers may stall your business growth, confuse potential clients, and cause decision fatigue.

24806 ■ *Entrepreneurial Thought Leaders: The Biodesign Innovation Process*
URL(s): ecorner.stanford.edu/podcasts/the-biodesign-innovation-process
Ed: Ravi Belani. **Released:** June 01, 2022. **Description:** Podcast explains that innovation can be learned, improved, and deployed to solve specific problems.

24807 ■ *Entrepreneurial Thought Leaders: Weathering a Storm*
URL(s): ecorner.stanford.edu/podcasts/weathering-a-storm
Ed: Ravi Belani. **Released:** February 17, 2021. **Description:** Podcast discusses how to navigate controversy with the CEO of Robinhood.

24808 ■ *Evolving and Pivoting Your Business with Kathleen Shannon*
URL(s): beingboss.club/podcast/evolving-and-pivoting-your-business
Ed: Emily Thompson. **Released:** March 28, 2023. **Description:** Podcast discusses the differences between evolving and pivoting, along with how and when to make a shift.

24809 ■ *From Idea to Exit: Lessons from a Podcast Host with Chris Hutchins*
URL(s): www.eofire.com/podcast/chrishutchins
Ed: John Lee Dumas. **Released:** August 03, 2023. **Description:** Podcast discusses the business lifecycle.

24810 ■ *How to Build a Gentle Business*
URL(s): www.makinggoodpodcast.com/episodes/166

Ed: Lauren Tilden. **Released:** March 14, 2023. **Description:** Podcast discusses how to build a gentle business and how to move through self-sabotage. .

24811 ■ *The How of Business: Overcoming Decision Paralysis*
URL(s): www.thehowofbusiness.com/423-overcoming-decision-paralysis
Ed: Henry Lopez. **Released:** May 23, 2022. **Description:** Podcast offers ways to avoid decision paralysis, including using financial projections, setting end dates, and hiring a business coach.

24812 ■ *How to Finish (Part 3 of 3)*
URL(s): www.makinggoodpodcast.com/episodes/224
Ed: Lauren Tilden. **Released:** March 05, 2024. **Description:** Podcast discusses how to push past perfectionism and perfectionism to finish strong.

24813 ■ *How to Get Started (Part 1 of 3)*
URL(s): www.makinggoodpodcast.com/episodes/217
Ed: Lauren Tilden. **Released:** January 2024. **Description:** Podcast disusses the difficulty of getting started.

24814 ■ *How to Keep Going (Part 2 of 3)*
URL(s): www.makinggoodpodcast.com/episodes/222
Ed: Lauren Tilden. **Released:** February 20, 2024. **Description:** Podcast discusses the importance of being consistent in achieving goals.

24815 ■ *iDigress: 90 Percent of Business Ideas Fail. Here's How to Be Part of the 10 Percent that Will Succeed.*
URL(s): idigress.show/episodes/89-90-percent-of-business-ideas-will-fail-heres-how-to-be-part-of-the-10-percent-that-will-succeed
Released: June 28, 2023. **Description:** Podcast explains that most business ideas fail because they fail to transfer and idea into a tangible product or service that solves a big enough problem to be in demand.

24816 ■ *Intro to Launching (What, Why + How)*
URL(s): www.makinggoodpodcast.com/episodes/194
Ed: Lauren Tilden. **Released:** September 05, 2023. **Description:** Podcast explains how launching is a strategy that actually works.

24817 ■ *Local Networking + LinkedIn = Ideal Clients*
URL(s): bizchiz.com/541-local-networking-linkedin-ideal-clients
Released: September 15, 2022. **Description:** Discusses how to leverage LinkedIn and create a pipeline of clients by taking offline relationships online.

24818 ■ *Marketplace: A Yacht Broker Turned Her Love of Sailing into a Career Where There's "Only Room for Growth"*
URL(s): www.marketplace.org/2023/07/13/yacht-broker-turned-her-love-of-sailing-into-a-career-where-theres-only-room-for-growth
Ed: Sarah Leeson. **Released:** July 13, 2023. **Description:** Podcast explains how someone can turn a love of sailing into a yacht brokerage.

24819 ■ *Nurture Small Business: A CEO's Guide to Triumph*
URL(s): nurturesmallbusiness.buzzsprout.com/900445/episodes/14459185-transforming-failures-a-ceos-guide-to-triumph
Ed: Denise Cagan. **Released:** February 12, 2024. **Description:** Podcast discusses the notion of failure as an opportunity to learn and grow.

24820 ■ *Planet Money Summer School: MBA 5: Tech and the Innovator's Dilemma*
URL(s): www.npr.org/2023/08/09/1192922557/summer-school-technology-innovators-dilemma-distruption
Ed: Robert Smith. **Released:** August 09, 2023. **Description:** Explains how to use new technology to dream big, how new technology gets adopted, and what stops new technology from taking off.

24821 ■ *Planet Money Summer School: MBA 6: Operations and 25,000 Roses*
URL(s): www.npr.org/2023/08/16/1194256512/mba-6-operations-and-25-000-roses
Ed: Robert Smith. **Released:** August 16, 2023. **Description:** Discusses operations management: planning, modeling, and weighing the cost of messing up vs. missing out.

24822 ■ *Planet Money Summer School: MBA 7: Negotiating and the Empathetic Nibble*
URL(s): www.npr.org/2023/08/23/1195428142/summer-school-negotiations-price-salary-benefits
Ed: Robert Smith. **Released:** August 23, 2023. **Description:** Discusses how to negotiate tactically.

24823 ■ *Planet Money Summer School: MBA 8: Graduation and the Guppy Tank*
URL(s): www.npr.org/2023/08/30/1196895815/summer-school-graduation-guppy-tank
Released: August 30, 2023. **Description:** Offers insights into making your ptich to investors.

24824 ■ *Scale Like a Pro*
URL(s): omny.fm/shows/startup-hustle/scale-like-a-pro
Ed: Lauren Conaway. **Released:** August 24, 2023. **Description:** Podcast discusses scaling and exiting multiple businesses with Alexa D'Agostino, CEO of Thynk Consulting.

24825 ■ *Startups for the Rest of Us: Equipping Sales & Support with Critical Product Knowledge as You Grow*
URL(s): www.startupsfortherestofus.com/episodes/episode-647-equipping-sales-support-with-critical-product-knowldege-as-you-grow
Ed: Rob Walling. **Released:** February 07, 2023. **Description:** Podcast discusses how to equip sales/support with product knowledge as you grow and how to communicate all aspects of your product, including features, benefits, and use cases.

24826 ■ *Systems and Strategies for Business Growth*
URL(s): beingboss.club/podcast/systems-and-strategies-for-business-growth
Released: February 14, 2023. **Description:** Podcast discusses updating processes and systems and furthering company growth through marketing tactics to bridge the online and in-person shopping experience.

24827 ■ *Think Business with Tyler: Sustainable Business Practices with Jonathan Orpin*
URL(s): thinktyler.com/podcast_episode/sustainable-business-jonathan-orpin
Ed: Tyler Martin. **Released:** August 05, 2024. **Description:** Podcast explains how open communication, financial oversight, and aligning company values with employee well-being can drive company success.

24828 ■ *This Is Small Business: Chevalo and Monique Search for a Product Supplier*
URL(s): www.smallbusiness.amazon/podcast-episodes/ep-19-chevalo-and-monique-search-for-a-product-supplier
Released: March 21, 2023. **Description:** Podcast discusses finding product suppliers, as well as shipping and fulfillment considerations.

24829 ■ *This Is Small Business: How to Differentiate Your Product*
URL(s): www.smallbusiness.amazon/podcast-episodes/ep-35-how-to-differentiate-your-product
Ed: Andrea Marquez. **Released:** October 03, 2023. **Description:** Podcast offers tips on understanding what's important to your customer.

24830 ■ *This Is Small Business: Leslie Adds a New Product to Her Lineup*
URL(s): www.smallbusiness.amazon/podcast-episodes/ep-25-leslie-adds-a-new-product-to-her-lineup
Ed: Andrea Marquez. **Released:** May 02, 2023. **Description:** Podcast discusses product iteration and how to determine when it's time to offer additional products.

24831 ■ *When to Take Business Personally and When to Let Go with Kathleen Shannon*
URL(s): beingboss.club/podcast/when-to-take-business-personally-and-when-to-let-go
Ed: Emily Thompson. **Released:** May 09, 2023. **Description:** Podcast discusses the difference between taking things personally and seriously and offers practical examples (particularly for creative business owners) of when it's important to separate personal feelings from business decisions.

24832 ■ *Your Business Values in Action*
URL(s): beingboss.club/podcast/your-business-values-in-action
Ed: Emily Thompson. **Released:** March 27, 2023. **Description:** Podcast discusses practical ways to infuse your values into all aspects of your business.

TRADE SHOWS AND CONVENTIONS

24833 ■ **ABA Annual Convention**
Metrostudy
1501 S Mopac Expy., Ste. 220
Austin, TX 78746
Contact: Jeffrey Meyers, President
URL(s): www.aba.com/training-events/conferences/annual-convention

Frequency: Annual. **Description:** Includes various sessions, and discussions, annual business meeting and elections, and closing reception. **Audience:** Industry professionals. **Principal Exhibits:** Includes various sessions, and discussions, annual business meeting and elections, and closing reception. **Telecommunication Services:** reghousing@aba.com.

24834 ■ **APPA Business & Financial Conference**
Baker Tilly US, LLP
205 N Michigan Ave., 28th Fl.
Chicago, IL 60601-5927
Ph: (312)729-8000
URL: http://www.bakertilly.com
Contact: Jeffrey L. Ferro, Chief Executive Officer
URL(s): my.publicpower.org/s/community-event?id=a1Y6g000001xb1KEAQ

Frequency: Annual. **Description:** Products and services related to business and financial matters. **Audience:** Public power professionals. **Principal Exhibits:** Products and services related to business and financial matters. **Telecommunication Services:** registration@publicpower.org.

24835 ■ **APPA Customer Connections Conference**
National Information Solutions Cooperative Inc. (NISC)
One Innovation Cir.
Lake Saint Louis, MO 63367
Free: 866-999-6472
Co. E-mail: infosec@nisc.coop
URL: http://www.nisc.coop
Contact: Dan Wilbanks, President
URL(s): my.publicpower.org/s/community-event?id=a1Y6g000006IuIBEAQ#/Home

Frequency: Annual. **Description:** With concurrent sessions and many networking opportunities, including roundtable discussions, continental breakfasts, and evening receptions. **Audience:** Professional and management levels in the fields of customer service, energy services, key accounts and public communications. **Principal Exhibits:** With concurrent sessions and many networking opportunities, including roundtable discussions, continental breakfasts, and evening receptions. Dates and Locations: 2025 Nov 02-05 Salt Lake City, UT; 2026 Oct 25-28 Nashville, TN. **Telecommunication Services:** registration@publicpower.org.

24836 ■ Business Council of New York State Conference
Business Council
111 Washington Ave., Ste. 400
Albany, NY 12210
Ph: (518)465-7511
Free: 800-358-1202
Co. E-mail: customerservice@bcnys.org
URL: http://www.bcnys.org
Contact: Heather C. Briccetti, Esq., President
URL(s): www.bcnys.org/event/2021-renewable-energy-conference
Frequency: Annual. **Description:** Businesses (4800) and Chambers of Commerce (200). **Audience:** Business professionals and members. **Principal Exhibits:** Businesses (4800) and Chambers of Commerce (200).

24837 ■ Business History Conference Meeting
Business History Conference (BHC)
c/o Hagley Museum and Library
PO Box 3630
Wilmington, DE 19807-0630
Ph: (302)658-2400
Fax: (302)655-3188
Co. E-mail: clockman@hagley.org
URL: http://www.thebhc.org
Contact: Roger Horowitz, Director
URL(s): thebhc.org/2024-bhc-meeting
Frequency: Annual. **Description:** Offer exemplary teaching and training programs. **Audience:** Overseas scholars and business historians. **Principal Exhibits:** Offer exemplary teaching and training programs. Dates and Locations: 2025 Mar 13-15 Crowne Plaza Midtown, Atlanta, GA. **Telecommunication Services:** programcommittee@thebhc.org.

24838 ■ Business Opportunity Fair
National Minority Supplier Development Council (NMSDC)
1359 Broadway, 10th Fl., Ste. 1000
New York, NY 10018
Ph: (212)944-2430
URL: http://nmsdc.org
Contact: Adrienne Trimble, Chief Executive Officer
URL(s): nmsdc.org/business-opportunity-fair
Frequency: Annual. **Audience:** Corporate executives, procurement professionals and Asian, Black, Hispanic and Native American business owners.

24839 ■ HMSDC Business Expo
BP p.l.c.
1 St. James's Sq.
London SW1Y 4PD, United Kingdom
Ph: 44 207-496-4000
Fax: 44 207-496-4630
URL: http://www.bp.com
Contact: Murray Auchincloss, Chief Executive Officer
URL(s): hmsdc.lead2rev.com/portal/events/53
Frequency: Annual. **Description:** Includes workshops, keynote speakers, awards, and reception. **Audience:** Business owners, and industry professionals. **Principal Exhibits:** Includes workshops, keynote speakers, awards, and reception. **Telecommunication Services:** expo_help@hmsdc.org.

24840 ■ International Association of Administrative Professionals Summit
URL(s): iaap-summit.org
Frequency: Annual. **Description:** Provides education and networking for Strategic Business Professionals. **Audience:** Administrative professionals. **Principal Exhibits:** Provides education and networking for Strategic Business Professionals.

24841 ■ National Association of Housing Cooperatives Annual Conference
National Cooperative Business Association (NCBA)
1775 Eye St. NW, 8th Fl.
Washington, DC 20006
Ph: (202)638-6222
Fax: (202)638-1374
Co. E-mail: info@ncba.coop
URL: http://www.ncba.coop
Contact: Doug O'Brien, President
URL(s): ncba.coop/our-events/calendar-of-events
Frequency: Annual. **Description:** Exhibits relating to cooperative business. **Audience:** Industry professionals. **Principal Exhibits:** Exhibits relating to cooperative business.

24842 ■ National Business Coalition on Health Conference
National Alliance of Healthcare Purchaser Coalitions
1015 18th St. NW, Ste. 705
Washington, DC 20036
Ph: (202)775-9300
Fax: (202)775-1569
URL: http://www.nationalalliancehealth.org
URL(s): www.nationalalliancehealth.org
Frequency: Annual. **Description:** With interactive sessions, educational discussions, demonstrations, and exhibit. **Audience:** Business leaders, human resources professionals, benefit managers, wellness managers, health care executives, consultants and strategists. **Principal Exhibits:** With interactive sessions, educational discussions, demonstrations, and exhibit.

24843 ■ NHAR Fall Business and Education Conference
New Hampshire Association of Realtors (NHAR)
11 S Main St., Ste. 301
Concord, NH 03301
Ph: (603)225-5549
Co. E-mail: info@nhar.org
URL: http://www.nhar.org
Contact: Adam Gaudet, President
URL(s): www.nhar.com
Description: Realtors. **Audience:** Members and policymakers. **Principal Exhibits:** Realtors.

24844 ■ Office Business Center Association International Annual Convention
Description: Exhibits relating to office business and management. **Audience:** Industry professionals, including operations, sales, marketing, technology, and human resources. **Principal Exhibits:** Exhibits relating to office business and management. **Telecommunication Services:** rmeyers@obcai.com.

24845 ■ Payments Conference
Transactis
150 5th Ave.
New York, NY 10011
Ph: (347)474-7342
Co. E-mail: info@transactis.com
URL: http://www.transactis.com
Contact: Joe Proto, Chief Executive Officer
URL(s): payments.nacha.org/contact-us
Frequency: Annual. **Description:** With networking opportunity and educational programs. **Audience:** Industry professionals. **Principal Exhibits:** With networking opportunity and educational programs. **Telecommunication Services:** meetings@nacha.org.

24846 ■ Reservation Economic Summit (RES)
National Center for American Indian Enterprise Development (NCAIED)
953 E Juanita Ave.
Mesa, AZ 85204
Ph: (602)325-8554
Free: 888-962-2433
Co. E-mail: info@ncaied.org
URL: http://www.ncaied.org
Contact: Chris James, President
URL(s): res.ncaied.org/Home
Frequency: Annual. **Description:** Exhibits relating to Native American economics and trade. **Audience:** General public and trade professionals. **Principal Exhibits:** Exhibits relating to Native American economics and trade. **Telecommunication Services:** ncaied@eventpowersupport.com.

24847 ■ Sensors Expo & Conference
Berkeley Sensor and Actuator Center (BSAC)
University of California, Berkeley, 656 Sutardja Dai Hall
No. 1764
Berkeley, CA 94720-1764
Ph: (510)643-6690
Co. E-mail: bsac@berkeley.edu
URL: http://bsac.berkeley.edu
Contact: Dalene Schwartz Corey, Executive Director
E-mail: dalene@berkeley.edu
URL(s): www.sensorsexpo.com
Facebook: www.facebook.com/sensorsexpo?ref=nf&_ga=2.244946053.1255746641.1535098890-1747231955.1535098890
X (Twitter): twitter.com/SensorsExpo
Frequency: Annual. **Description:** Share design ideas, present today's sensing challenges, and find tomorrow's sensor solutions. **Audience:** Industry professionals. **Principal Exhibits:** Share design ideas, present today's sensing challenges, and find tomorrow's sensor solutions.

24848 ■ SMPS Build Business
Deltek Norge A.S.
Grundingen 6
'0250 Oslo, Norway
Ph: 47 22 0138-00
URL: http://www.deltek.com/nb-no
Contact: Mike Corkery, President
URL(s): my.smps.org/events/event-description?CalendarEventKey=8277813a-ea93-4905-af12-e0683f5400c2&Home=%2Fhome
X (Twitter): twitter.com/SMPSHQ
Frequency: Annual. **Description:** New business development equipment, supplies, and services. **Audience:** Marketers, business developers. **Principal Exhibits:** New business development equipment, supplies, and services.

CONSULTANTS

24849 ■ C.S. Simons Consulting L.L.C.
44 Island Pond Rd.
Atkinson, NH 03811
URL: http://cssimonsconsulting.com
Description: Provider of business consultancy services and business strategy services to clients that includes strategic business planning, workforce development, profitability assessments, audit functions, budgeting cycle and market study reports. **Scope:** Provider of business consultancy services and business strategy services to clients that includes strategic business planning, workforce development, profitability assessments, audit functions, budgeting cycle and market study reports.

24850 ■ Value Creation Group Inc.
7820 Scotia Dr., Ste. 2000
Dallas, TX 75248-3115
Ph: (972)980-7407
Co. E-mail: assistyou@valuecreationgroup.com
URL: http://www.valuecreationgroup.com
Contact: John Antos, Contact
E-mail: assistyou@valuecreationgroup.com
Description: Consulting firm provides process management, continuous improvement, performance management, cost accounting, forecasting, budgeting and training services. **Scope:** Consulting firm provides process management, continuous improvement, performance management, cost accounting, forecasting, budgeting and training services. **Founded:** 1984. **Publications:** "Handbook of Process Management Based Predictive Accounting," Alcpa 2002; "Cost Management for Today's Manufacturing Environment and Activity Based Management for Service Environments, Government Entities and Nonprofit Organizations"; "Risks and Opportunities in International Finance and Treasury"; "Driving Value Using Activity Based Budgeting"; "Process Based Accounting Leveraging Processes to Predict Results"; "Handbook of Supply Chain Management"; "Economic Value Management Applications and Techniques"; "The Change Handbook": "Group Methods for Creating the Future"; "Why Value Management and Performance Measurement Through U.S. Binoculars," Journal of Strategic Performance Measurement; "Real Options, Intangibles Measurement and the Benefits of Human Capital Investment to Power the Organization," Journal of Strategic Performance Measurement. **Training:** Activity Based Management; Predictive Accounting; Performance measures; ABM for Manufacturing; ABM for Service Organizations;

Finance and Accounting for Non-Financial Executives; Return on Investment/Capital Expenditure Evaluation; Planning and Cost Control; The Next Step Intermediate Finance and Accounting for Non-financial Managers; Activity-Based Budgeting; Friendly Finance for Fund Raisers; Strategic Outsourcing.

PUBLICATIONS

24851 ■ American Journal of Economics and Business Administration
Office 207, P Flr Bldg 07
Vails Gate, NY 12584
Co. E-mail: support@scipub.org
URL: http://thescipub.com
Contact: Hongtao Lu, Vice President
URL(s): thescipub.com/ajeba

Released: Continuous **Price:** $1,600, Single issue for print subscription. **Description:** Peer-reviewed journal containing studies representing the intersection of economics as a scientific discipline and the professional practice of business management. **Availability:** Print; PDF; Download; Online.

24852 ■ American Research Journal of Business and Management (ARJBM)
8770 W Bryn Mawr Ave., Ste. 1300
Chicago, IL 60631
Ph: (773)649-9077
Co. E-mail: info@arjonline.org
URL: http://www.arjonline.org
Contact: Dr. Hironobu Ihn, Vice President
URL(s): arjonline.org/american-research-journal-of-business-and-management

Released: Last Volume 9. **Description:** Open access journal containing research papers in the fields of business, management, marketing, finance, economics, human resource management, and relevant subjects. **Availability:** Print; PDF; Download; Online.

24853 ■ Arabian Journal of Business and Management Review (AJBMR)
2360 Corporate Cir., No. 400
Henderson, NV 89074
Ph: (650)618-9889
Fax: (650)618-1414
Co. E-mail: contact.omics@omicsonline.org
URL: http://www.omicsonline.org
URL(s): www.hilarispublisher.com/arabian-journal-business-management-review.html

Released: Monthly; latest volume 14, Issue 2, 2024. **Description:** Open access journal covering business, management, and related fields. **Availability:** Print; Online; PDF.

24854 ■ Basic Business Essentials: Concepts and Tools
826 Riviera Dr.
Mansfield, TX 76063
Free: 800-990-4273
URL: http://www.americancpe.com
Contact: Dennis Gatlin, President
URL(s): www.americancpe.com/CPE-Courses/24-Basic-Business-Essentials--Concepts---Tools.html

Price: $79, for download searchable text and exam; $79, for download searchable text and exam for apple computers; $94, for searchable CD-ROM; $99, for printed text; $40, for additional exams. **Description:** Contains detailed training information covering fundamental topics in business and business management. **Availability:** CD-ROM; Print; Download; Online. **Type:** Full-text.

24855 ■ Business and Economic Review
155 Adams Administration Building
Troy, AL 36082
Ph: (334)670-3124
Free: 800-414-5756
Fax: (334)670-3885
URL: http://www.troy.edu
Contact: Jack Hawkins, Jr., Chancellor
URL(s): www.troy.edu/academics/catalogs/undergraduate-catalog/general-information.html

Availability: Print.

24856 ■ Business History
530 Walnut St., Ste. 850
Philadelphia, PA 19106
Ph: (215)625-8900
Fax: (215)207-0050
URL: http://taylorandfrancis.com/journals
Contact: Annie Callanan, Chief Executive Officer
URL(s): www.tandfonline.com/journals/fbsh20
X (Twitter): x.com/BH__journal

Ed: Ray Stokes. **Released:** 8/year **Price:** $2,718, Institutions for print and online; $2,229, Institutions for online only; $273, Individuals for print only. **Description:** Business publication. **Availability:** Print; Download; PDF; Online.

24857 ■ Business History Review
Soldiers Field Rd.
Boston, MA 02163
Ph: (617)495-1003
Co. E-mail: admissions@hbs.edu
URL: http://www.hbs.edu/Pages/default.aspx
Contact: Jana Kierstead, Executive Director
URL(s): www.library.hbs.edu/citations/business-history-review

Ed: Geoffrey Jones, Walter A. Friedman. **Released:** Quarterly **Description:** A scholarly journal that seeks to publish articles with rigorous primary research that addresses major topics of debate, offers comparative perspectives, and contributes to the broadening of the subject. **Availability:** Print; PDF; Online.

24858 ■ Business Horizons
50 High St., Ste. 21
North Andover, MA 01845
Free: 866-344-2088
Co. E-mail: customercare@elsevier.com
URL: http://www.elsevier.com
URL(s): www.sciencedirect.com/journal/business-horizons

Ed: Gregory C. Fisher. **Released:** 6/year **Price:** $822, Institutions for print us, Canada; $167, Individuals for print us, Canada. **Description:** Business management journal covering a wide range of topical areas within the general field of business, with a focus on identifying important business issues or problems and recommending solutions. **Availability:** Print; Download; PDF; Online.

24859 ■ Business Information Review (BIR)
2455 Teller Rd.
Thousand Oaks, CA 91320
Contact: Tracey Ozmina, President
URL(s): journals.sagepub.com/home/bir
X (Twitter): x.com/BIRJournal

Ed: Claire Laybats, Luke Tredinnick. **Released:** Quarterly **Price:** $3,220, Institutions for print + online; $2,488, Institutions for online only; $50, Individuals for single print issue; $789, Institutions for single print issue; $2,868, Institutions for print and online; $2,927, Institutions for print + online; $153, Individuals for print only; $2,781, Institutions for print only; $3,176, Institutions for online. **Description:** Journal focused on information provision and management within organizations. **Availability:** Print; PDF; Download; Online.

24860 ■ Business & Society
2455 Teller Rd.
Thousand Oaks, CA 91320
Contact: Tracey Ozmina, President
URL(s): journals.sagepub.com/home/BAS
X (Twitter): x.com/BASeditors

Ed: Colin Higgins, Hari Bapuji, Andrew Crane. **Released:** 8/year **Price:** $1,493, Institutions for backfile lease, e-access plus backfile (all online content); $1,729, Institutions for print and online (backfile lease, combined plus backfile); $3,590, Institutions for backfile purchase, e-access (content through 1998); $212, Institutions for single print issue; $31, Individuals for single print issue; $1,572, Institutions for print and online; $1,336, Institutions for online only; $1,541, Institutions for print only; $191, Individuals for print only. **Description:** Peer-reviewed, scholarly journal focused on the intersection of business and society. Sponsored by the International Association for Business and Society (founded at Roosevelt University). **Availability:** Print; PDF; Download; Online.

24861 ■ Business Today (Princeton, New Jersey)
48 University Pl., Ste. 305
Princeton, NJ 08544
Co. E-mail: admin@businesstoday.org
URL: http://www.businesstoday.org
Contact: Sowon Lee, President
Linkedin: www.linkedin.com/company/business-today_2

Released: Semiannual **Description:** Provides articles on careers, university campuses, and opinions of students. Includes employment listings. **Availability:** Print.

24862 ■ The Cooperative Business Journal
1775 Eye St. NW, 8th Fl.
Washington, DC 20006
Ph: (202)638-6222
Fax: (202)638-1374
Co. E-mail: info@ncba.coop
URL: http://www.ncba.coop
Contact: Doug O'Brien, President
URL(s): ncbaclusa.coop/journal

Released: Quarterly; spring, summer, fall, winter. **Description:** Trade magazine covering business. **Availability:** PDF; Online.

24863 ■ Enterprise & Society: The International Journal of Business History
c/o Hagley Museum and Library
PO Box 3630
Wilmington, DE 19807-0630
Ph: (302)658-2400
Fax: (302)655-3188
Co. E-mail: clockman@hagley.org
URL: http://www.thebhc.org
Contact: Roger Horowitz, Director
URL(s): thebhc.org/enterprise-societywww.cambridge.org/core/journals/enterprise-and-society
X (Twitter): x.com/EntandSoc

Ed: Andrew Popp. **Released:** Quarterly **Price:** $302, Institutions for online only; $464, Institutions for bundle USD. **Description:** Journal covering scholarly research on the historical relations between businesses and their larger political, cultural, institutional, social, and economic contexts. **Availability:** Print; PDF; Download; Online. **Type:** Full-text.

24864 ■ Harvard Business Review (HBR)
20 Guest St., Ste. 700
Brighton, MA 02135
Free: 800-795-5200
Co. E-mail: corporate@harvardbusiness.org
URL: http://www.harvardbusiness.org
Contact: Diane Belcher, Managing Director
URL(s): hbr.org
Facebook: www.facebook.com/HBR
Linkedin: www.linkedin.com/company/harvard-business-review
X (Twitter): x.com/HarvardBiz
Instagram: www.instagram.com/harvard_business_review

Ed: Amy Bernstein, Maureen Hoch. **Released:** 6/year **Price:** $19.95, for current issue. **Description:** Magazine for business executives. **Availability:** Print; Online. **Type:** Bibliographic; Full-text.

24865 ■ IBIMA Business Review (IBIMABR)
630 Freedom Business Ctr. Dr., 3rd Fl.
King of Prussia, PA 19406
Fax: (215)867-9992
Co. E-mail: contact@ibimapublishing.com
URL: http://www.ibimapublishing.com
URL(s): ibimapublishing.com/journals/ibima-business-review

Released: Continuous **Description:** Peer-reviewed journal publishing case studies for business organizations. **Availability:** Print; Online; PDF.

24866 ■ International Journal of Business Analytics (IJBAN)
701 E Chocolate Ave.
Hershey, PA 17033

Ph: (717)533-8845
Free: 866-342-6657
Fax: (717)533-8661
Co. E-mail: cust@igi-global.com
URL: http://www.igi-global.com
Contact: Jan Travers, Director
URL(s): www.igi-global.com/journal/international-journal-business-analytics/67141

Released: Continuous **Description:** Multidisciplinary, peer-reviewed, open access journal covering all aspects of business analytics. **Availability:** Print; PDF; Online; Download.

24867 ▪ International Journal of Business and Industrial Marketing
1521 Concord Pke., Ste. 301
Wilmington, DE 19803
Ph: (910)795-1115
Co. E-mail: service@aascit.org
URL: http://www.aascit.org
URL(s): www.aascit.org/journal/ijbim

Released: Irregular; last edition Vol. 4, Issue 1, Mar. 2021. **Description:** Contains research articles, case analyses, conceptual arguments, and industry reviews in business and industrial marketing. **Availability:** Print; Download; PDF; Online.

24868 ▪ International Journal of Business Intelligence Research (IJBIR)
701 E Chocolate Ave.
Hershey, PA 17033
Ph: (717)533-8845
Free: 866-342-6657
Fax: (717)533-8661
Co. E-mail: cust@igi-global.com
URL: http://www.igi-global.com
Contact: Jan Travers, Director
URL(s): www.igi-global.com/journal/international-journal-business-intelligence-research/1168

Released: Continuous **Description:** Peer-reviewed journal covering research on business intelligence and analytics. **Availability:** Print; PDF; Download; Online.

24869 ▪ International Journal of Business Management and Information Technology
NY
Co. E-mail: editor@acascipub.com
URL: http://acascipub.com
URL(s): acascipub.com/International%20Journal%20of%20Business%20Management%20and%20Information%20Technology/International%20Journal%20of%20Business%20Management%20and%20Information%20Technology.php

Released: Monthly; 12 issues per year. **Description:** Open access journal containing full-length research articles, short communications, review papers, and case studies in all areas of business management and information technology. **Availability:** Print; Online; Download.

24870 ▪ International Journal of Business Strategy (IJBS)
10940 Trinity Pky., Ste. C-185
Stockton, CA 95219
Ph: (702)490-0016
Co. E-mail: admin@iabe.org
URL: http://iabe.org/iabeX/Default.aspx
Contact: Dr. Cheick Wague, President
URL(s): ejbr-journal.org/EJBR-JOURNAL/Default.aspx

Released: Annual **Description:** Peer-reviewed journal that publishes research/conceptual work or applied research/applications on topics related to research, practice, and teaching in all subject areas of Business, Economics, E-Business/E-Commerce. **Availability:** Print; Online.

24871 ▪ Jindal Journal of Business Research (JJBR)
2455 Teller Rd.
Thousand Oaks, CA 91320
Contact: Tracey Ozmina, President
URL(s): journals.sagepub.com/home/BRJ
Facebook: www.facebook.com/SAGEBRJ

Released: Semiannual **Price:** $240, Institutions for single print issue; $68, Individuals for single print issue; $445, Institutions for print and online; $378, Institutions for online only; $104, Individuals for print only; $436, Institutions for print only. **Description:** Peer-reviewed business/management journal focused on advancing the understanding of management in a global context. Published in association between SAGE and the O. P. Jindal Global University. **Availability:** Print; PDF; Download; Online.

24872 ▪ Journal Academy of Business and Economics (JABE)
10940 Trinity Pky., Ste. C-185
Stockton, CA 95219
Ph: (702)490-0016
Co. E-mail: admin@iabe.org
URL: http://iabe.org/iabeX/Default.aspx
Contact: Dr. Cheick Wague, President
URL(s): jabe-journal.org/JABE-JOURNAL/Default.aspx

Released: Quarterly; March, June, October and December. **Price:** $700, for individual price. **Description:** Peer-reviewed journal that publishes research/conceptual work or applied research/applications on topics related to research, practice, and teaching in all subject areas of Business, Economics, E-Business/E-Commerce. **Availability:** Print; Online.

24873 ▪ Journal of Applied Business Research (JABR)
8119 Shaffer Pky. A10
Littleton, CO 80127
Ph: (303)904-4750
URL: http://www.cluteinstitute.com
URL(s): clutejournals.com/index.php/JABR

Released: Quarterly; January, April, July, and October. **Description:** Journal covering business and economic research. **Availability:** Print; Download; PDF; Online.

24874 ▪ Journal of Behavioral Studies in Business (JBSB)
PO Box 350997
Jacksonville, FL 32099-0997
URL: http://www.aabri.com
Contact: Russell Baker, Executive Director
URL(s): www.aabri.com/jbsb.html

Ed: Dr. Michael Adams. **Released:** Latest Volume 14. **Description:** Journal containing manuscripts of behavioral studies in business related disciplines. **Availability:** Print; PDF; Online.

24875 ▪ Journal of Business Case Studies (JBCS)
8119 Shaffer Pky. A10
Littleton, CO 80127
Ph: (303)904-4750
URL: http://www.cluteinstitute.com
URL(s): clutejournals.com/index.php/JBCS

Released: Quarterly; January, April, July, and October. **Description:** Journal containing case studies for use in business and economics courses. **Availability:** Print; PDF; Download; Online.

24876 ▪ Journal of Business & Economic Research (JBER)
8119 Shaffer Pky. A10
Littleton, CO 80127
Ph: (303)904-4750
URL: http://www.cluteinstitute.com
URL(s): clutejournals.com/index.php/JBER

Released: Quarterly; January, April, July and October. **Description:** Refereed academic journal covering business and economics. **Availability:** Print; PDF; Online.

24877 ▪ Journal of Business and Economics
228 E 45th St., Ground Fl.
New York, NY 10017
Ph: (347)566-2153
Fax: (347)426-1986
Co. E-mail: service@academicstar.us
URL: http://www.academicstar.us
URL(s): www.academicstar.us/journalsshow.asp?ArtID=371

Released: Monthly **Description:** Open access journal containing articles on all functional areas of business (marketing, management, finance, accounting, decision sciences, operations research, and economics) as well as other disciplines that are business or economics oriented. **Availability:** Print; Download; PDF; Online.

24878 ▪ Journal of Business Logistics (JBL)
111 River St.
Hoboken, NJ 07030-5774
Ph: (201)748-6000
Fax: (201)748-6088
Co. E-mail: creditriskdept@wiley.com
URL: http://www.wiley.com/en-in
Contact: Brian Napack, Chief Executive Officer
URL(s): cscmp.org/CSCMP/CSCMP/Develop/Research/Journal_of_Business_Logistics.aspxonlinelibrary.wiley.com/journal/21581592
Linkedin: www.linkedin.com/company/journal-of-business-logisticss
X (Twitter): x.com/jbizlogistics

Ed: Robert Richey, Jr., Beth Davis-Sramek. **Released:** Quarterly; latest edition: volume 45, issue 3. **Price:** $373, Institutions for online only US, Canada, India; $96, Individuals for online only US, Canada, India. **Description:** Contains information on logistics operations and management. **Availability:** Print; Online; PDF; Download.

24879 ▪ Journal of Business & Management (JBM)
10685-B Hazelhurst Dr.Ste. No. 16258
Houston, TX 77043
Ph: (281)407-7509
Fax: (281)754-4941
Co. E-mail: info@centreofexcellence.net
URL: http://centreofexcellence.net
Contact: Farhat Tabbasum, Contact
URL(s): centreofexcellence.net/index.php/JBM

Released: Quarterly **Description:** Open access journal containing original research in all disciplines of business and management. **Availability:** Print; PDF; Online.

24880 ▪ Journal of Business and Psychology (JBP)
233 Spring St.
New York, NY 10013
Free: 866-839-0194
Fax: (212)460-1700
Co. E-mail: customerservice@springernature.com
URL: http://www.springer.com
Contact: Derk Haank, Chief Executive Officer
URL(s): link.springer.com/journal/10869

Released: 6/year; February, April, June, August, October, December. **Description:** Journal covering all aspects of psychology that apply to the business segment. Includes topics such as personnel selection and training, organizational assessment and development, risk management and loss control, marketing, and consumer behavior research. **Availability:** Print; PDF; Download; Online.

24881 ▪ Journal of Business Research (JBR)
50 High St., Ste. 21
North Andover, MA 01845
Free: 866-344-2088
Co. E-mail: customercare@elsevier.com
URL: http://www.elsevier.com
URL(s): www.sciencedirect.com/journal/journal-of-business-research

Released: 16/year. **Price:** $6,788, Institutions for print us, India and Canada. **Description:** Journal focused on business decisions, processes, and activities within the actual business setting. **Availability:** Print; PDF; Download; Online.

24882 ▪ Journal of Business Strategies
1821 Ave. I
Huntsville, TX 77340
Ph: (963)294-1254
Fax: (936)294-3612
URL: http://www.shsu.edu/centers/cbed
Contact: Christian Raschke, Director

GENERAL SMALL BUSINESS TOPICS

URL(s): www.shsu.edu/academics/business-administration/cbed/journal/index.htmljbs-ojs-shsu.tdl.org/jbs/index.php/jbs
Ed: William Green. **Released:** Semiannual; Spring and Fall. **Description:** Periodical covering issues in business. **Availability:** Print; Download; PDF; Online.

24883 ■ Journal of Business Venturing: A Journal Dedicated to Entrepreneurship
50 High St., Ste. 21
North Andover, MA 01845
Free: 866-344-2088
Co. E-mail: customercare@elsevier.com
URL: http://www.elsevier.com
URL(s): www.sciencedirect.com/journal/journal-of-business-venturing
Released: 6/year; January, March, May, July, September, November. **Price:** $237, Individuals for print us Canada, India; $2,197, Institutions for print us Canada, India. **Description:** Multidisciplinary journal providing a scholarly platform for the exchange of information and ideas on various aspects of entrepreneurship. **Availability:** Print; Download; PDF; Online.

24884 ■ Journal of Economics and Business
Alter Hall
Fox School of Business & Management
1801 Liacouras Walk
Philadelphia, PA 19122-6083
Ph: (215)204-7676
Fax: (215)204-5698
Co. E-mail: foxinfo@temple.edu
URL: http://www.fox.temple.edu
Contact: Richard Flanagan, Program Director
E-mail: richard.flanagan@temple.edu
URL(s): liberalarts.temple.edu/academics/departments-and-programs/economics/research
Released: 5/year **Price:** $140, Individuals for print 1 year India, US, CA; $1,167, Institutions for print 1 year India, US, CA. **Availability:** Print; PDF; Online; Download.

24885 ■ Journal of Global Academic Institute Business & Economics (JGAIBE)
1732 1st Ave., Ste. 25613
New York, NY 10128
Free: 877-300-4134
Co. E-mail: staff@globalacademicinstitute.com
URL: http://www.globalacademicinstitute.com
Contact: David Mayer, Chairman Editor-in-Chief
URL(s): www.globalacademicinstitute.com/publications/journal-of-global-academic-institute-business-economics-vol1-no1
Released: Quarterly **Description:** Open access journal containing articles in all areas of business and economics research. **Availability:** Online.

24886 ■ Journal of Innovation and Business Best Practices (JIBBP)
630 Freedom Business Ctr. Dr., 3rd Fl.
King of Prussia, PA 19406
Fax: (215)867-9992
Co. E-mail: contact@ibimapublishing.com
URL: http://www.ibimapublishing.com
URL(s): ibimapublishing.com/journals/journal-of-innovation-and-business-best-practice
Released: Volume 2024. **Description:** Peer-reviewed journal focusing on business innovation and best practices. **Availability:** Print; Online; PDF; Download.

24887 ■ Knowledge Management Strategies for Business Development
701 E Chocolate Ave.
Hershey, PA 17033
Ph: (717)533-8845
Free: 866-342-6657
Fax: (717)533-8661
Co. E-mail: cust@igi-global.com
URL: http://www.igi-global.com
Contact: Jan Travers, Director
URL(s): www.igi-global.com/book/knowledge-management-strategies-business-development/683
Price: $180, for hardcover; $180, for E-book; $37.50, for on demand; $215, for hardcover + e-book.
Description: Published by IGI Global. Addresses the relevance of knowledge management strategies for the advancement of organizations worldwide. Supplies business practitioners, academicians, and researchers with comprehensive tools to systematically guide through a process that focuses on data gathering, analysis, and decision making. **Availability:** E-book; Print.

24888 ■ Latin American Business Review
711 3rd Ave.
New York, NY 10017
URL: http://www.taylorandfrancis.com
Contact: Annie Callanan, Chief Executive Officer
URL(s): www.tandfonline.com/journals/wlab20
Ed: Sergio S. Olavarrieta, Denise Dimon, Luis Antonio Dib, Marcelo Cabús Klötzle, Carlos Heitor Campani. **Released:** Quarterly; volume 25, Issue 2. **Price:** $845, Institutions for print & online; $255, Individuals for print&online; $223, Individuals for online only; $693, Institutions for online only. **Description:** Peer-reviewed professional journal covering international business and economics. **Availability:** Print; Download; PDF; Online.

24889 ■ Panoptic Enterprises
6055 Ridge Ford Dr.
Burke, VA 22015
Ph: (703)451-5953
URL: http://www.fedgovcontracts.com
Description: Publishes news and insights for federal contractors through its timely dispatches, newsletters, and reference materials, the company offers government contract information, guidance, advice, including fast-changing rules and regulations, policies, and people. **Founded:** 1982. **Publications:** "Getting Started in Federal Contracting"; "Proposals That Win Federal Contracts"; " "The Federal Protest Package";"The Federal Procurement Process";"Providing Foreign Products to the Federal Government"; "Small Business Set-Asides and Preference Programs"; "The Defense Priorities and Allocations System"; "The History of Federal Procurement"; " Federal Profit Policy"; "Facilities Capital Cost of Money";"Getting Started in Federal Contracting"; "Proposals That Win Federal Contracts"; "The Federal Protest Package". **Training:** Basics of Federal Contracting; Writing Successful Proposals for Federal Contracts.

24890 ■ Regent Journal of Business and Technology (RJBT)
1200 Rosemead Blvd., Ste. D No. 105
El Monte, CA 91731
Co. E-mail: editor@sapub.org
URL: http://www.sapub.org/journal/index.aspx
URL(s): www.sapub.org/Journal/articles.aspx?journalid=1149
Released: Continuous **Price:** $60, for hardcopy. **Description:** International, peer-reviewed, open access journal focused on recent advancements in the study of business, science, and technology. **Availability:** PDF; Download; Online.

24891 ■ Review of Business
8000 Utopia Pky.
Queens, NY 11439
Ph: (718)990-2000
Co. E-mail: admhelp@stjohns.edu
URL: http://www.stjohns.edu/academics/schools-and-colleges/peter-j-tobin-college-business
Contact: Dr. Victoria Shoaf, Dean
E-mail: shoafv@stjohns.edu
URL(s): www.stjohns.edu/academics/schools/peter-j-tobin-college-business/departments-centers-and-faculty-research/review-business
Released: Semiannual; January, June. **Description:** Publication covering business. **Availability:** Print; PDF.

24892 ■ Review of Business Research (RBR)
10940 Trinity Pky., Ste. C-185
Stockton, CA 95219
Ph: (702)490-0016
Co. E-mail: admin@iabe.org
URL: http://iabe.org/iabeX/Default.aspx
Contact: Dr. Cheick Wague, President
URL(s): rbr-journal.org/RBR-JOURNAL/Default.aspx

Released: Annual; 1 issues per year. **Price:** $700, for one year. **Description:** Peer-reviewed journal that publishes research/conceptual work or applied research/applications on topics related to research, practice, and teaching in all subject areas of Business, Economics, E-Business/E-Commerce. **Availability:** Print; Online.

24893 ■ Stanford Business
Knight Management Ctr.
655 Knight Way
Stanford, CA 94305-7298
Ph: (650)723-4046
Fax: (650)723-5151
URL: http://www.gsb.stanford.edu
Contact: Jonathan Levin, Dean
URL(s): www.gsb.stanford.edu/magazine
Ed: Steve Hawk. **Released:** Semiannual **Description:** Magazine for business school alumni. **Availability:** Print; Online; PDF.

24894 ■ STERNbusiness
44 W 4th St.
New York, NY 10012
Ph: (212)998-0100
Co. E-mail: sternmba@stern.nyu.edu
URL: http://www.stern.nyu.edu
Contact: Al Lieberman, Executive Director
URL(s): www.stern.nyu.edu/portal-partners/alumni/alumni-news-profiles/sternbusiness-magazine
Ed: Marilyn Harris. **Released:** Annual **Description:** Magazine for alumni of New York University's Leonard N. Stern School of Business. **Availability:** Print; Online.

24895 ■ Strategize Magazine: Tomorrow's Ideas for Today's Business
1 S Dearborn St. 20th Fl.
Chicago, IL 60603
Ph: (872)212-3500
Co. E-mail: contact@avenirpublishing.com
URL: http://www.avenirpublishing.com
URL(s): strategizemagazine.com
Released: Quarterly; latest issue Spring 2016 edition. **Description:** Magazine for business improvement and innovation. **Availability:** Print; PDF; Online.

24896 ■ Taking Care of Business
4797 Hayes Rd., Ste. 202
Madison, WI 53704
Ph: (608)249-8588
Fax: (608)249-3163
Co. E-mail: wasbo@wasbo.com
URL: http://www.wasbo.com
Contact: Mike Barry, Executive Director
E-mail: mike.barry@wasbo.com
URL(s): wasbo.com/newsletter
Ed: Woody Wiedenhoeft. **Released:** Quarterly **Availability:** Print; Online.

24897 ■ Taking Care of Business
4797 Hayes Rd., Ste. 202
Madison, WI 53704
Ph: (608)249-8588
Fax: (608)249-3163
Co. E-mail: wasbo@wasbo.com
URL: http://www.wasbo.com
Contact: Mike Barry, Executive Director
E-mail: mike.barry@wasbo.com
URL(s): www.wasbo.com/WASBO/WASBO/Professional_Development/Publications/Taking_Care_of_Business.aspx
Released: Quarterly **Availability:** Print; Online.

24898 ■ Valuations Businesses Securities and Real Estate
826 Riviera Dr.
Mansfield, TX 76063
Free: 800-990-4273
URL: http://www.americancpe.com
Contact: Dennis Gatlin, President
URL(s): www.americancpe.com/CPE-Courses/24-Valuations-Businesses-Securities-and-Real-Estate.html
Price: $39, for download for searchable text and exam; $39, for download for searchable text and exam for apple computers; $54, for searchable CD-

ROM; $59, for printed text. **Description:** Contains detailed training information covering the valuation of businesses and other instruments and property related to businesses, including bonds, securities, preferred and common stock, and real estate. **Availability:** CD-ROM; Print; Download. **Type:** Full-text.

24899 ■ *Vision: The Journal of Business Perspective*
2455 Teller Rd.
  Thousand Oaks, CA 91320
Contact: Tracey Ozmina, President
URL(s): journals.sagepub.com/home/vis
Ed: Sajal Ghosh. **Released:** 5/year **Price:** $568, Institutions for subscription & backfile lease, combined plus backfile (current volume print & all online content); $491, Institutions for subscription & backfile lease, e-access plus backfile (all online content); $439, Institutions for backfile purchase, e-access (content through 1998); $111, Institutions for single print issue; $28, Individuals for single print issue; $106, Individuals for print and online; $516, Institutions for print and online; $439, Institutions for online only; $506, Institutions for print only. **Description:** Peer-reviewed journal covering all functional areas of management, including economics and business environments. Published in association between SAGE and the Management Development Institute, Gurugram. **Availability:** Print; PDF; Online.

24900 ■ *Ward's Business Directory of Private and Public Companies in Mexico and Canada*
27555 Executive Dr., Ste. 270
  Farmington Hills, MI 48331
Free: 800-877-4253
Co. E-mail: gale.customerservice@cengage.com
URL: http://www.gale.com
Contact: Paul Gazzolo, General Manager Senior Vice President
URL(s): www.gale.com/ebooks/9780028670867/wards-business-directory-of-private-and-public-companies-in-mexico-and-canada
Released: Latest 13 Edition. **Description:** Covers more than 20,000 private and publicly held companies in Canada and Mexico with an emphasis on small to mid-sized privately held businesses. **Entries include:** Company name, address, phone, fax, rankings and analysis, sales ranking (in $US) within NAICS codes, and evaluations of industry activity. **Arrangement:** Volume 1 is alphabetical by company name; Volume 2 is geographical. **Availability:** E-book; Download.

COMPUTERIZED DATABASES

24901 ■ *Academic OneFile*
URL(s): www.cengage.com/search/productOverview.do?Ntt=Academic+OneFile%7C%7C12966369221947093073113233006364471419 8&N=197&Nr=197&Ntk=APG%7C%7CP_EPI&Ntx=mode+matchallpartialwww.gale.com/c/academic-onefile
Availability: PDF; Online. **Type:** Full-text.

24902 ■ *Business Periodicals Index Retrospective™: 1913-1982*
EBSCO Information Services
  10 Estes St.
  Ipswich, MA 01938
Ph: (978)356-6500
Free: 800-653-2726
Co. E-mail: information@ebsco.com
URL: http://www.ebsco.com
Contact: Tim Collins, Chief Executive Officer
URL(s): www.ebsco.com/products/digital-archives/retrospective-indexes/business-periodicals-index-retrospective
Description: Contains citations to more than 2.5 million articles and book reviews in more than 1000 general business periodicals and trade journals. **Availability:** Online. **Type:** Bibliographic; Full-text.

24903 ■ *Business Source® Alumni Edition*
EBSCO Information Services
  10 Estes St.
  Ipswich, MA 01938
Ph: (978)356-6500
Free: 800-653-2726
Co. E-mail: information@ebsco.com
URL: http://www.ebsco.com
Contact: Tim Collins, Chief Executive Officer
URL(s): www.ebsco.com/products/research-databases/business-source-alumni-edition
Released: Monthly **Database covers:** Marketing, Management, Management Information Systems, Production and Operations Management, Accounting, Finance, Econometrics and Economics. **Availability:** Print; Online. **Type:** Full-text.

24904 ■ *Gale Business: Entrepreneurship (GB:E)*
Gale, part of Cengage Group
27555 Executive Dr., Ste. 270
  Farmington Hills, MI 48331
Free: 800-877-4253
Co. E-mail: gale.customerservice@cengage.com
URL: http://www.gale.com
Contact: Paul Gazzolo, General Manager Senior Vice President
URL(s): www.gale.com/c/business-entrepreneurship
Description: Covers all major areas of starting and operating a business including financing, management, marketing, human resources, franchising, accounting and taxes. **Availability:** Database; E-book; PDF; Online. **Type:** Full-text.

24905 ■ *Small Business: Internet Resources*
URL(s): www.loc.gov/rr/business/beonline/subjects.php?SubjectID=10
Description: An online database providing links to resources useful to small business owners. **Availability:** Online.

24906 ■ *Vente et Gestion*
EBSCO Information Services
  10 Estes St.
  Ipswich, MA 01938
Ph: (978)356-6500
Free: 800-653-2726
Co. E-mail: information@ebsco.com
URL: http://www.ebsco.com
Contact: Tim Collins, Chief Executive Officer
URL(s): www.ebsco.com/products/research-databases/vente-et-gestion
Released: Daily **Database covers:** Accounting and tax, administration, industry and manufacturing, logistics, marketing and technology. **Availability:** Online. **Type:** Full-text.

LIBRARIES

24907 ■ **Broome County Public Library - J. Donald Ahearn Business Resource Center**
Broome County Library
  Rm. 138, 185 Court St.
  Binghamton, NY 13901-3503
URL: http://www.bclibrary.info/content/ahearn-business-center
Scope: Business. **Services:** Center open to the public. **Holdings:** 1000 records; books; DVDs.

24908 ■ **Charles Darwin University - Palmerston Campus Library**
University Ave.
  Palmerston, NT 0830, Australia
Ph: 61 8 8946 7016
Co. E-mail: askthelibrary@cdu.edu.au
URL: http://www.cdu.edu.au/library
Contact: Kate Elder, Director, Library Services
E-mail: kate.elder@cdu.edu.au
Facebook: www.facebook.com/CDUniLibrary
X (Twitter): x.com/CDUniLibrary
Instagram: www.instagram.com/cdulibrary
YouTube: www.youtube.com/user/CDUniLibrary/featured
Scope: Hospitality; tourism. **Services:** Printing; photocopying; scanning. **Holdings:** Print; audio visual; online materials.

24909 ■ **College of William and Mary - Mason School of Business - McLeod Business Library**
101 Ukrop Way
  Williamsburg, VA 23185
Ph: (757)221-2916
Fax: (757)221-7428
Co. E-mail: mcleodlibrary@wm.edu
URL: http://mason.wm.edu/library
Contact: Anna Milholland, Head
E-mail: anna.milholland@mason.wm.edu
Scope: Business research. **Services:** Interlibrary loan. **Founded:** 1985. **Holdings:** Audio cassettes; videocassettes; periodicals and serials; reserve materials.

24910 ■ **Community Futures Development Corporation of Greater Trail - Kootenay Regional Business Library**
825 Spokane St.
  Trail, BC, Canada V1R 3W4
Ph: (250)364-2595
Fax: (250)364-2728
Co. E-mail: info@communityfutures.com
URL: http://communityfutures.com/cms
Contact: Erik Kalacis, Executive Director
E-mail: erik@communityfutures.com
Facebook: www.facebook.com/communityfuturesgt
X (Twitter): twitter.com/cfgreatertrail
Instagram: www.instagram.com/communityfuturesgt
YouTube: www.youtube.com/channel/UC5yOcHwYtNACkKEqmDGAMwQ
Description: Fosters local entrepreneurs through all phases of business from the pre-startup phase to the expansion of existing business. **Scope:** Business. **Services:** Library open to the public. **Founded:** 1994. **Holdings:** 700 business specific titles.

24911 ■ **East Baton Rouge Parish Library (EBRPL)**
7711 Goodwood Blvd.
  Baton Rouge, LA 70806
Ph: (225)231-3750
Co. E-mail: eref@ebrpl.com
URL: http://www.ebrpl.com
Contact: Jason Jacob, President
Facebook: www.facebook.com/ebrpl
X (Twitter): x.com/ebrpl
Instagram: www.instagram.com/ebrpl
YouTube: www.youtube.com/c/EastBatonRougeParishLibrary
Pinterest: www.pinterest.com/ebrpl
Description: The library is comprised of newspapers, books, DVDs, magazines, and online resources. **Scope:** Information, resources, materials, and technology. **Services:** Interlibrary loan; printing. **Founded:** 1939. **Holdings:** 2 million items; books.

24912 ■ **Florida State University - Panama Branch Library**
4750 Collegiate Dr.
  Panama City, FL 32405
URL: http://guides.lib.fsu.edu/panamacampus/research
URL(s): fsupanamabranch.library.site; fsupanamabranch.library.site/searchlist?type=Basic&keyword=%20Florida%20State%20University&searchin=&exact=false&location=31709
Scope: Business; computer science; engineering; environmental studies; information science; international affairs; Latin America and Caribbean studies; mathematics. **Services:** Interlibrary loan; copying. **Holdings:** Figures not available.

24913 ■ **NHTI, Concord's Community College - Library**
31 College Dr.
  Concord, NH 03301
Ph: (603)230-4001
Free: 800-247-0179
Co. E-mail: nhtiadm@ccsnh.edu
URL: http://www.nhti.edu
Contact: Christie Cho, Coordinator
Facebook: www.facebook.com/nhtilynx
Linkedin: www.linkedin.com/company/nhti-concord-community-college
X (Twitter): x.com/NHTI
YouTube: www.youtube.com/user/nhtilynx
Description: Offers higher education programs related to engineering and technology. **Scope:** Business; education; engineering; health; legal studies;

architecture; autism; nursing; dental assisting; anthropology; film studies; gaming; sports management. **Services:** Interlibrary loan; open to the public with restrictions. **Founded:** 1965. **Holdings:** 50,000+ print books, 600,000+ eBooks.

24914 ■ Oxford Brookes University - Wheatley Library
Wheatley Campus, Wheatley
Oxford OX33 1HX, United Kingdom
Ph: 44 1865 485870
Co. E-mail: whlibenquiries@brookes.ac.uk
URL: http://www.brookes.ac.uk/library/access-and-accessibility/locations-and-opening-hours/wheatley-library

Scope: Computing; engineering; mathematics. **Holdings:** Books; exam papers; dissertations.

24915 ■ Southern Methodist University - Cox School of Business Library
6100 Hillcrest Ave., Lower Level of Hamon Arts Library
Dallas, TX 75205
URL: http://www.smu.edu/libraries/business
Contact: Sandy Miller, Director
E-mail: slmiller@smu.edu

Scope: Business. **Founded:** 1987. **Holdings:** Figures not available.

24916 ■ Texas Southern University - Robert James Terry Library - Business Library
3100 Cleburne St.
Houston, TX 77004
Ph: (713)313-7402
URL: http://www.tsu.edu/academics/library/index-new.html

Scope: Accounting; business and economics. **Founded:** 1927. **Holdings:** 63,000 articles ; 52,500 volumes ; 300 serials; e-books ;newspapers ;reports; journals.

24917 ■ Touro College - Boro Park Library
1273 53rd St.
Brooklyn, NY 11219
Fax: (718)686-7071
URL: http://www.tourolib.org
Contact: Lisa Herman, Librarian
E-mail: lisa.herman3@touro.edu

Description: Supports research and academic goals, the Libraries partner with faculty and administrative staff to advance Touro College's mission to become a center of religious and secular scholarship. **Scope:** Education; psychology; Judaica. **Holdings:** Books; diskettes; audio and video tapes; CD-ROMs; DVDs; microfiche.

24918 ■ Touro College Brighton Beach Library
360 Neptune Ave., Rm. 412
Brooklyn, NY 11235
Ph: (718)885-8546
Co. E-mail: bella.reytblat@touro.edu
URL: http://www.tourolib.org/about/libraries/brighton-beach
Contact: Bashe Simon, Director
E-mail: bashe.simon@touro.edu

Description: Supports research and academic goals, the Libraries partner with faculty and administrative staff to advance Touro College's mission to become a center of religious and secular scholarship. **Scope:** Business; computer science; human services; esl. **Services:** Research and reference; copying; computer access; library open to college students, staff and affiliates. **Founded:** 1960. **Holdings:** Figures not available.

24919 ■ Touro College Cross River Campus Library
202 W 43rd St., Fl., 3
New York, NY 10036
Ph: (212)463-0400
Fax: (212)627-3696
URL: http://www.tourolib.org/about/libraries/midtown
Contact: Sara Tabaei, Director
E-mail: sara.tabaei@touro.edu

Description: Serves the New York School of Career and Applied Studies, the School of Health Sciences, the Graduate School of Education, the Graduate School of Jewish Studies, the Graduate School of Psychology, the Graduate School of Social Work, and the Graduate School of Technology. **Scope:** Business, education, ethnic studies, Jewish studies, psychology, pre-clinical and clinical medicine, and profession specific literature for physician assistant, physical therapy, and occupational therapy. **Holdings:** Figures not available.

24920 ■ Touro College Forest Hills Library
71-02 113th St.
Forest Hills, NY 11375
Ph: (718)520-5107
Fax: (718)793-3610
URL: http://www.tourolib.org/about/libraries/forest-hills
Contact: Dora Isakova, Library Assistant
E-mail: dorai@touro.edu

Description: Serves the New York School of Career and Applied Studies and supports the core curriculum. It has ESL materials and specializes in business, computer science, and human services. **Scope:** Core curriculum; business, computer science, and the human services; esl . **Services:** Copying; computer access for research purposes; library not open to public. **Founded:** 1970. **Holdings:** Books; journals; eBooks.

24921 ■ Touro College Lander College of Liberal Arts & Sciences Midwood Library
1602 Ave. J
Brooklyn, NY 11230
Ph: (718)252-7800
Fax: (718)338-7732
URL: http://www.tourolib.org/about/libraries/midwood
Contact: Bashe Simon, Director
E-mail: bashe.simon@touro.edu

Scope: Liberal Arts and Sciences; Psychology; business; computer science; education; human services; neurosciences; political science; psychology; speech pathology, and Judaica. **Services:** Copying; research services; library open to student and staff only. **Holdings:** Figures not available.

24922 ■ Touro College Lander College for Men Library
75-31 150th St.
Kew Gardens Hills, NY 11367
Ph: (718)820-4894
URL: http://www.tourolib.org/about/libraries/kew-gardens-hills
Contact: Yeshaya Metal, Librarian
E-mail: yeshaya.metal@touro.edu

Scope: Biology; business; computer science; management information science; political science; psychology; social sciences; Judaic. **Services:** Interlibrary loan; copying; library open to college staff and students. **Holdings:** Books; audio and video tapes; CD-ROMs; DVDs; microfiche.

24923 ■ Touro College Starrett City Library
1344 Pennsylvania Ave.
Brooklyn, NY 11239
Ph: (718)642-6562
Fax: (718)642-6807
URL: http://www.tourolib.org/about/libraries/starett-city
Contact: Emma Larson-Whittaker, Library Assistant
E-mail: elarson@touro.edu

Scope: Business; computer science; human services; esl. **Services:** Interlibrary loan; computer access for research use; library not open to public. **Holdings:** Figures not available.

24924 ■ Touro College - Sunset Park Library
475 53rd St.
Brooklyn, NY 11220
Ph: (718)748-2776
Fax: (718)492-9031
URL: http://www.nyslittree.org/index.cfm/fuseaction/DB.EntityDetail/EntityPK/1794.cfm
URL(s): www.tourolib.org/about/libraries/sunset-park

Scope: Business; computer science; human services; ESL. **Services:** Interlibrary loan; library open to college students and staff. **Founded:** 1960. **Subscriptions:** e-journals Books; diskettes; audio and video tapes; CD-ROMs; DVDs; microfiche.

24925 ■ University of Nevada - Reno - Mathewson-IGT Knowledge Center
85 W Stadium Way
Reno, NV 89512
Ph: (775)682-5625
Fax: (775)327-5385
URL: http://www.unr.edu/around-campus/mathewson-igt-knowledge-center

Description: Serves the School for Lifelong Education. It supports the core curriculum and specializes in education, psychology, and Judaica. **Scope:** Business; education. **Holdings:** Figures not available.

24926 ■ University of Northampton - Park Campus Library
Waterside Campus University Drive
Northampton NN1 5PH, United Kingdom
URL: http://www.northampton.ac.uk/about-us/services-and-facilities/library

Scope: Education. **Services:** Interlibrary loan. **Holdings:** Figures not available. **Subscriptions:** 15,000 journals and other serials.

24927 ■ University of Nottingham - Business Library
Top Fl., Business School S, Jubilee Campus
Wollaton Rd.
Nottingham NG8 1BB, United Kingdom
Co. E-mail: library-helpline@nottingham.ac.uk
URL: http://www.nottingham.ac.uk/library/using/libraries/business/business.aspx

Description: University of Nottighm library. **Scope:** Business. **Services:** Copying; scanning; laptop; printing and tablet loan. **Founded:** 1881. **Holdings:** Journals; monographs; periodicals; Books.

24928 ■ University of the West of Scotland - Ayr Campus Library
University Ave.
Ayr KA8 0SX, United Kingdom
Ph: 44 1292 886 000
URL: http://www.uws.ac.uk/university-life/campuses/ayr-campus

Description: Academic library. **Scope:** Education materials; sports. **Services:** Library open to the public. **Founded:** 2011. **Holdings:** Books; journals; videos.

24929 ■ Winthrop University - Small Business Development Center Library
118 Thurmond Bldg.
Rock Hill, SC 29733
Ph: (803)323-2283
Fax: (803)323-4281
Co. E-mail: winthropregionalsbdc@gmail.com
URL: http://www.winthropregionalsbdc.org
Facebook: www.facebook.com/SCSBDC
X (Twitter): x.com/scsbdc
Instagram: www.instagram.com/winthropsbdc

Scope: Business; software. **Services:** Performs searches on fee basis. **Holdings:** Books; audio/visual items.

Government Assistance

START-UP INFORMATION

24930 ■ *"Austin Welcomes New Program for Entrepreneurs"* in **Austin Business JournalInc. (Vol. 29, February 12, 2010, No. 29, pp. 1)**
Pub: Austin Business Journal
Contact: Rachel McGrath, Director
E-mail: rmcgrath@bizjournals.com
Ed: Christopher Calnan. **Description:** Nonprofit group Economic Development Catalyst Organization (ECDO) is formalizing its BizLaunch mentoring program, which was stated in 2009. The program aims to offer support networks to entrepreneurs and assistance regarding early-stage venture capital. **Availability:** Print; Online.

24931 ■ *"Military Vet Uses SBA Program to Help Fund His Business"* in **Philadelphia Business Journal (Vol. 33, May 9, 2014, No. 13, pp. 6)**
Pub: American City Business Journals, Inc.
Contact: Mike Olivieri, Executive Vice President
Released: Weekly. **Description:** Colonel Richard Elam and his wife Kimberly, both with the Florida Army National Guard, secured funding through the Small Business Administration's (SBA's) Veterans Advantage program to launch iPlay, which rents mobile entertainment equipment such as rock walls and laser-tag setups for group events. The capital access initiative, launched in January 2014, waives the origination fee for SBA Express loans to qualified veteran entrepreneurs. **Availability:** Print; Online.

24932 ■ *"SBA Program Helped New Company Survive As It Built Company Base"* in **Philadelphia Business Journal (Vol. 33, May 9, 2014, No. 13, pp. 4)**
Pub: American City Business Journals, Inc.
Contact: Mike Olivieri, Executive Vice President
Released: Weekly. **Description:** The Small Business Administration (SBA) Indiana District Business Office helped Netwise Resources set up its information technology (IT) consulting business with a six-month SBA-backed loan and the 8(a) Business Development Program for small disadvantaged businesses. Owner, Mark Gibson, attributes Netwise Resources' success to its focus on branding, recruiting skilled staff, and establishing relationships with clients within the target market. **Availability:** Print; Online.

24933 ■ *"Should State Invest in Startups?"* in **Providence Business News (Vol. 28, March 3, 2014, No. 48, pp. 1)**
Pub: American City Business Journals, Inc.
Contact: Mike Olivieri, Executive Vice President
Released: March 01, 2014. **Description:** The U.S. Treasury Department is investigating whether Rhode Island violated Federal rules when it used funds from the State Small Business Credit Initiative (SSBCI) to invest in Betaspring, a startup accelerator program for technology and design entrepreneurs ready to launch their businesses. The Lyon Park audit claims that Rhode Island violated SSBCI rules because a large portion of the money went to the business accelerator's operating expenses and not to the startups themselves. **Availability:** Print; Online.

24934 ■ *"Slow-Down Startups Hot"* in **Austin Business JournalInc. (Vol. 28, September 12, 2008, No. 26, pp. 1)**
Pub: Austin Business Journal
Contact: Rachel McGrath, Director
E-mail: rmcgrath@bizjournals.com
Ed: Sandra Zaragoza. **Description:** A number of entrepreneurs from Austin, Texas are starting their own small business despite the economic slowdown. The Small Business Development Program in Austin has seen a 50 percent increase in the demand for its services in 2008 as compared to demand in 2007. Other details about the entrepreneurship trend are discussed. **Availability:** Print; Online.

ASSOCIATIONS AND OTHER ORGANIZATIONS

24935 ■ **National Association of Government Guaranteed Lenders (NAGGL)**
11330 Legacy Dr., Ste. 304
Frisco, TX 75033
Ph: (469)293-9229
Co. E-mail: info@naggl.org
URL: http://www.naggl.org
Contact: Anthony R. Wilkinson, President
Facebook: www.facebook.com/naggl7a
Linkedin: www.linkedin.com/company/naggl
X (Twitter): x.com/naggl7a
YouTube: www.youtube.com/user/sbalendingnaggl
Description: Aims to serve the needs and represents the interests of the small business lending community who utilize the Small Business Administrations and other government guaranteed loan programs. **Founded:** 1984. **Educational Activities:** SBA Lending Technical Conference. **Geographic Preference:** National.

24936 ■ **Small Business Association for International Companies (SBAIC)**
2001 L St., NW, Ste. 500
Washington, DC 20040
Ph: (202)421-8995
Co. E-mail: memberservices@sbaic.org
URL: http://sbaic.org
Contact: Adm. (Ret.) Anita Campion, Secretary
Facebook: www.facebook.com/SmBsAsInCm
Linkedin: www.linkedin.com/company/sbaic
X (Twitter): x.com/SBAIC
Description: Membership organization working to promote the meaningful utilization of U.S. small businesses at U.S. government agencies providing foreign assistance. **Founded:** 2000.

REFERENCE WORKS

24937 ■ *"7 Best Small Business Grants in 2022"* in **Fit Small Business (Jan. 17, 2022)**
URL(s): fitsmallbusiness.com/best-small-business-grants/
Released: January 17, 2022. **Description:** Details seven grants that small businesses can utilize. **Availability:** Online.

24938 ■ *"63 Grants, Loans and Programs to Benefit Your Small Business"* in **CO - U.S. Chamber of Commerce (October 13, 2022)**
URL(s): www.uschamber.com/co/run/business-financing/government-small-business-grant-programs
Released: October 13, 2022. **Description:** Provides financing tips for small businesses, including information on grants and funding. **Availability:** Online.

24939 ■ *"$353 Million in SSBCI Funds Going to Small Businesses in 4 States"* in **Small Business Trends(March 1, 2023)**
URL(s): smallbiztrends.com/2023/03/ssbci-funds-for-small-businesses-in-4-states.html
Ed: Gabrielle Pickard-Whitehead. **Released:** March 01, 2023. **Description:** The State Small Business Credit Initiative is releasing four additional state plans, totaling up to $353.4 million. **Availability:** Online.

24940 ■ *"Action: Huge Film Incentive Boost Eyed in Virginia"* in **Washington Business Journal (Vol. 32, January 3, 2014, No. 38, pp. 5)**
Pub: American City Business Journals, Inc.
Contact: Mike Olivieri, Executive Vice President
Description: Senator John Watkins of Midlothian, Virginia is introducing a bill that would increase the film incentive program of the state from the existing 15 percent level to 20-25 percent and boost the credit fund from $5 million to $25 million every two years. The 15.7 percent increase in film industry employment in 2013 was credited by Governor Bob McDonnell to the government incentive program. **Availability:** Online.

24941 ■ *"Advantage Capital Partners Awarded $60 Million Allocation in New Markets Tax Credit Program"* in **Economics & Business Week (June 28, 2014, pp. 7)**
Pub: NewsRX LLC.
Contact: Kalani Rosell, Contact
Description: Leading venture capital and small business finance firm, Advantage Capital Partners, was awarded a $60 million allocation in competitive federal New Markets Tax Credit (NMTC) program. This allocation brings the firm's total awards since the program's start in 2002 to $659 million, and maintains the investment firm's leadership role as a top program participant across the nation.

24942 ■ *"Analysis of the U.S. Residential Solar Power Market"* in **PR Newswire (September 19, 2012)**
Pub: PR Newswire Association LLC.
Description: Analysis of the residential solar power market in the United States is presented. Solar PV is the fastest growing technology in the energy sector

for the nation during the last three years due to rising energy prices, volatile fuel costs, and government incentives for renewable energy.

24943 ■ "The Annual Entitlement Lecture Medicare Elephantiasis" in Barron's (March 31, 2008)
Pub: Dow Jones & Company Inc.
Contact: Almar Latour, Chief Executive Officer
Ed: Thomas G. Donlan. **Description:** Expenditures on Medicare hospital insurance and the revenues available to pay for it have led to a gap of capital valued at $38.6 trillion. Slashing the benefits or raising taxes will not solve the gap which exists unless the government saves the money and invests it in private markets. **Availability:** Online.

24944 ■ "BABs in Bond Land" in Barron's (Vol. 89, July 6, 2009, No. 27, pp. 14)
Pub: Dow Jones & Company Inc.
Contact: Almar Latour, Chief Executive Officer
Ed: Jim McTague. **Description:** American Recovery and Reinvestment Act has created taxable Build America Bonds (BAB) to finance new construction projects. The issuance of the two varieties of taxable BABs is expected to benefit the municipal bond market. **Availability:** Online.

24945 ■ "Baltimore Eyeing Tax Breaks for New Arena" in Boston Business Journal (Vol. 29, June 3, 2011, No. 4, pp. 1)
Pub: Boston Business Journal
Contact: Carolyn M. Jones, President
E-mail: cmjones@bizjournals.com
Ed: Daniel J. Sernovitz. **Description:** Baltimore City is opting to give millions of dollars in tax breaks and construction loans to a group of private investors led by William Hackerman who is proposing to build a new arena and hotel at the Baltimore Convention Center. The project will cost $500 million with the state putting up another $400 million for the center's expansion.

24946 ■ "Baltimore's Businesses: Equipment Tax Breaks Help, But Money Still Tight: Weighing the Write-Off" in Baltimore Business Journal (Vol. 28, September 10, 2010, No. 18, pp. 1)
Pub: Baltimore Business Journal
Contact: Rhonda Pringle, President
E-mail: rpringle@bizjournals.com
Ed: Daniel J. Sernovitz. **Description:** President Barrack Obama has proposed to let business write off their investments in plant and equipment upgrades under a plan aimed at getting the economy going. The plan would allow a company to write off 100 percent of the depreciation for their new investments at one time instead of over several years. **Availability:** Print.

24947 ■ "Barshop Leading 'Paradigm Shift' In Aging Research" in San Antonio Business Journal (Vol. 28, September 12, 2014, No. 31, pp. 4)
Pub: American City Business Journals, Inc.
Contact: Mike Olivieri, Executive Vice President
Released: September 12, 2014. **Price:** $4, Introductory 4-week offer(Digital & Print). **Description:** The National Institute of Health has given a $7.5 million five-year grant to University of Texas Health Science at San Antonio's Barshop Insitute for Longevity and Aging Studies. The funding was awarded to help researchers accelerate the discoveries of commercial drugs that slow the aging process. **Availability:** Print; Mailing list; Online.

24948 ■ "The Best Small Business Government Grants in 2022" in Business News Daily (Dec. 20, 2021)
URL(s): www.businessnewsdaily.com/15758-government-grants-for-small-businesses.html
Released: December 20, 2021. **Description:** Provides information for new or existing small business owners who want to secure a government grant to help them launch or grow their business. **Availability:** Online.

24949 ■ "BETC Backers Plot Future" in Business Journal Portland (Vol. 27, December 10, 2010, No. 41, pp. 1)
Pub: Portland Business Journal
Contact: Andy Giegerich, Managing Editor
E-mail: agiegerich@bizjournals.com
Ed: Erik Siemers. **Description:** A coalition of clean energy groups and industrial manufacturers have spearheaded a campaign aimed at persuading Oregon legislators that the state's Business Energy Tax Credit (BETC) is vital in job creation. Oregon's BETC grants tax credits for 50 percent of an eligible renewable or clean energy project's cost. However, some legislators propose BETC's abolition. **Availability:** Print; Online.

24950 ■ "Birmingham's Turf War" in Birmingham Business Journal (Vol. 31, January 24, 2014, No. 4, pp. 4)
Pub: American City Business Journals, Inc.
Contact: Mike Olivieri, Executive Vice President
Description: Metropolitan Birmingham, Alabama area incentive battles have been a mainstay for years and smaller cities were forced to compete against cities with larger cash reserves. The fight often means paying up to protect their turf and tax revenue. The rising trend among local municipalities to use incentives to lure companies is discussed. **Availability:** Print; Online.

24951 ■ "Boeing Partnership to Preserve Thousands of Acres of Threatened Wetlands in South Carolina" in Ecology, Environment & Conservation Business (August 2, 2014, pp. 3)
Pub: NewsRX LLC.
Contact: Kalani Rosell, Contact
Description: U.S. Army Corps of Engineers approved Boeing's comprehensive wetlands mitigation plan to preserve about 4,000 acres of land, including more than 2,000 acres of wetlands near the Francis Marion National Forest in South Carolina Lowcountry. Boeing worked in partnership with federal, state and local agencies and conservation organizations to identify the tracts for preservation in order to achieve conservation goals of regional and national significance. **Availability:** Online.

24952 ■ Bold Endeavors: How Our Government Built America, and Why It Must Rebuild Now
Pub: Simon & Schuster, Inc.
Contact: Jonathan Karp, President
Ed: Felix G. Rohatyn. **Released:** May 2011. **Price:** $17.99, paperback. **Description:** The federal government built the nation by investing in initiatives like the Erie Canal and the G.I. Bill and why it should do the same at this point in history is examined. **Availability:** E-book; Print.

24953 ■ "Building a Workforce" in Business Journal Milwaukee (Vol. 29, July 27, 2012, No. 44, pp. 1)
Pub: American City Business Journals, Inc.
Contact: Mike Olivieri, Executive Vice President
Ed: Rich Kirchen. **Description:** Governor Scott Walker's 'Wisconsin Working' initiative head Tim Sullivan announced that he will recommend the encouragement of immigration to meet current and future employment needs of the state. Sullivan believes immigration could help address the worker skills shortage that affected many southeaster Wisconsin businesses. **Availability:** Print; Online.

24954 ■ "Business Looks for Results in Congress" in Baltimore Business Journal (Vol. 28, November 5, 2010, No. 26, pp. 1)
Pub: Baltimore Business Journal
Contact: Rhonda Pringle, President
E-mail: rpringle@bizjournals.com
Ed: Kent Hoover. **Description:** Republican candidates in the 2010 Congressional elections were overwhelmingly supported by the business community. Republican John Boehner, who will be the next Speaker of the House, says that the party's victory would end economic uncertainty and would assist small businesses to rehire workers. **Availability:** Print; Online.

24955 ■ "Cash for Appliances Targets HVAC Products, Water Heaters" in Contractor (Vol. 56, October 2009, No. 10, pp. 1)
Ed: Candace Roulo. **Description:** States and territories would need to submit a full application that specifies their implementation plans if they are interested by joining the Cash for Appliances program funded by the American Recovery and Reinvestment Act. The Department of Energy urges states to focus on heating and cooling equipment, appliances and water heaters since these offer the greatest energy savings potential. **Availability:** Print; Online.

24956 ■ CFR: Title 13. Business Credit and Assistance
Pub: U.S. Government Publishing Office
Ed: Department of Commerce Staff. **Released:** Annual; volume 14. **Description:** Title 13 covers regulations governing the activities of the Small Business Administration and the Department of Commerce. Book covers information on business credit, finance, and economic development. **Availability:** Print; PDF.

24957 ■ "Cincinnati Hospitals Wage War on 'Bounce-Backs'" in Business Courier (Vol. 27, July 30, 2010, No. 13, pp. 1)
Pub: Business Courier
Ed: James Ritchie. **Description:** Health care organizations in Greater Cincinnati area have tried a number of care and follow up programs, primarily focused on congestive heart failure to prevent readmissions to hospitals. Hospital administrators have made the averting of bounce-backs a priority due to new federal government plans on reimbursement. **Availability:** Print; Online.

24958 ■ "Cleanup to Polish Plating Company's Bottom Line" in Crain's Cleveland Business (Vol. 28, October 29, 2007, No. 43, pp. 4)
Pub: Crain Communications Inc.
Contact: K. C. Crain, President
Ed: Jay Miller. **Description:** Barker Products Co, a manufacturer of nuts and bolts, is upgrading its aging facility which will allow them to operate at capacity and will save the company several hundred thousand dollars a year in operating costs. The new owners secured a construction loan from the county's new Commercial Redevelopment Fund which will allow them to upgrade the building which was hampered by years of neglect. **Availability:** Online.

24959 ■ "Colorado Companies Adjust as Drought Boosts Food Prices" in Denver Business Journal (Vol. 64, August 17, 2012, No. 13, pp. 1)
Pub: Baltimore Business Journal
Contact: Rhonda Pringle, President
E-mail: rpringle@bizjournals.com
Description: The drought engulfing most of the US has led some Colorado companies to modify product offerings and declare that food prices will be raised by four percent next year. The federal government has already declared all of Colorado and half of the nation's counties as disaster areas, making them accessible for federal aid. **Availability:** Print; Online.

24960 ■ "Colorado's Hollywood Wager" in Denver Business Journal (Vol. 65, April 25, 2014, No. 50, pp. A4)
Pub: American City Business Journals, Inc.
Contact: Mike Olivieri, Executive Vice President
Released: Weekly. **Price:** $4, introductory 4-week offer(Digital & Print). **Description:** The successes and controversies surrounding the film incentives program of Colorado are explored. Some critics question the incentive have been directed to people who paid for the lobbying of House Bill 1286, while others ask if incentives are a proper use of public funds. **Availability:** Print; Online.

24961 ■ "Coming Soon: Bailouts of Fannie and Freddie" in Barron's (Vol. 88, July 14, 2008, No. 28, pp. 14)
Pub: Dow Jones & Company Inc.
Contact: Almar Latour, Chief Executive Officer

Ed: Jonathan R. Laing. **Description:** Assurances from the government that Fannie Mae and Freddie Mac are adequately capitalized and able to carry on their duties as guarantors or owners of over $5 trillion of U.S. home mortgages are designed to keep both entities afloat until they attempt to raise $10 billion in new equity. The government would assume any losses in a bailout and owners of the banks' papers would profit as yields drop. **Availability:** Online.

24962 ■ *"Companies Press Ottawa to End CN Labor Dispute" in Globe & Mail (April 16, 2007, pp. B1)*
Ed: Brent Jang. **Description:** The plea of several industries to the Canadian parliament to end the labor dispute at the Canadian National Railway Co. is discussed. **Availability:** Online.

24963 ■ *"Condos Becoming FHA No-Lending Zones" in Providence Business News (Vol. 29, June 2, 2014, No. 9, pp. 7)*
Pub: American City Business Journals, Inc.
Contact: Mike Olivieri, Executive Vice President
Description: Federal policy changes and decisions by condominium boards of directors have made the condominium development ineligible for Federal Housing Administration (FHA) loans, making several communities prohibited lending zones. As a result, the number of condo developments approved for FHA funding has fallen by more than half, presenting a growing problem for first-time buyers, those with modest down payment cash, and senior citizens using a reverse mortgage. **Availability:** Online.

24964 ■ *"Congress Ponders Annuity Trusts" in National Underwriter Life & Health (Vol. 114, June 21, 2010, No. 12, pp. 10)*
Ed: Arthur D. Postal. **Description:** Congress is looking over several bills, including the Small Business Jobs Tax Relief Act that would significantly narrow the advantages of using grantor-retained annuity trusts (GRATs) to avoid estate and gift taxes. **Availability:** Online.

24965 ■ *"Corporate Responsibility" in Professional Services Close-Up (July 2, 2010)*
Description: List of firms awarded the inaugural Best Corporate Citizens in Government Contracting by the Corporate Responsibility Magazine is presented. The list is based on the methodology of the Magazine's Best Corporate Citizen's List, with 324 data points of publicly-available information in seven categories which include: environment, climate change, human rights, philanthropy, employee relations, financial performance, and governance. **Availability:** Online.

24966 ■ *"COVID-19 Small Business Resources & Federal Government Programs" by SBE Council (Jan. 23, 2022)*
URL(s): sbecouncil.org/2022/01/23/protecting-your-business-in-the-coronavirus-economy/
Released: January 23, 2022. **Description:** Includes resources and information from the private sector and government agencies on COVID-19 related programs and relief for small businesses. **Availability:** Online.

24967 ■ *"CR Magazine Taps ITT As a 'Best Corporate Citizen' in Government Contracting" in Profesisonal Services Close-Up (July 30, 2010)*
Description: ITT Corporation was named by Corporate Responsibility Magazine as a Best Corporate Citizen in Government Contracting. The list recognizes publicly-traded companies that exemplify transparency and accountability while serving the U.S. government. **Availability:** Print.

24968 ■ *"The Cudgel of Samson: How the Government Once Used 'Jawboning' to Fight Inflation" in Barron's (Vol. 88, March 24, 2008, No. 12, pp. 62)*
Pub: Dow Jones & Company Inc.
Contact: Almar Latour, Chief Executive Officer
Ed: Thomas G. Donlan. **Description:** Discusses the Federal Reserve is jawboning businesses against inflation while inflation is starting to rise because of the abundance of cheap money. The practice of jawboning has been used by the administrations of past US presidents with limited effect. **Availability:** Online.

24969 ■ *"Defense Budget Ax May Not Come Down So Hard on Maryland" in Baltimore Business Journal (Vol. 28, August 20, 2010, No. 15, pp. 1)*
Pub: Baltimore Business Journal
Contact: Rhonda Pringle, President
E-mail: rpringle@bizjournals.com
Ed: Daniel J. Sernovitz. **Description:** U.S. Defense Secretary Robert M. Gates' planned budget cuts are having little effect on Maryland's defense industry. Gates will reduce spending on intelligence service contracts by 10 percent. **Availability:** Print; Online.

24970 ■ *"Detroit Residential Market Slows; Bright Spots Emerge" in Crain's Detroit Business (Vol. 24, October 6, 2008, No. 40, pp. 11)*
Pub: Crain Communications Inc.
Contact: Barry Asin, President
Ed: Daniel Duggan. **Description:** Discusses the state of the residential real estate market in Detroit; although condominium projects receive the most attention, deals for single-family homes are taking place in greater numbers due to financing issues. Buyers can purchase a single family home with a 3.5 percent down payment compared to 20 percent for some condo deals because of the number of first-time homebuyer programs under the Federal Housing Administration.

24971 ■ *"Developers Tout Benefits of Federal Tax Breaks" in Business First of Buffalo (Vol. 30, March 14, 2014, No. 26, pp. 4)*
Pub: American City Business Journals, Inc.
Contact: Mike Olivieri, Executive Vice President
Released: Weekly. **Price:** $140, Digital & Print; $115, Digital only. **Description:** President Obama has included a Federal tax credit program in the 2015 Federal budget that provides some relief to the local development community. Congressman Mark Higgins promised to support the program that offers tax breaks to urban developers who rehabilitate older buildings with new investments. The tax credit's economic benefits are also discussed. **Availability:** Print; Online.

24972 ■ *"Down the Tracks, a Whistle Is a-Blowin" in Barron's (Vol. 89, July 27, 2009, No. 30, pp. 36)*
Pub: Dow Jones & Company Inc.
Contact: Almar Latour, Chief Executive Officer
Ed: Jim McTague. **Description:** Higher numbers of freight-rail carloads is a sign that the economy is improving and it is no stretch to imagine that this is aided by the American Recovery and Reinvestment Act. It is also predicted that 2009 municipal bond issuance will be above $373 billion with at least $55 billion of it made up of Buy America Bonds that are subsidized by the federal government. **Availability:** Online.

24973 ■ *"Dox Choice Joins Growing Medical Records Industry" in Memphis Business Journal (Vol. 34, April 13, 2012, No. 53, pp. 1)*
Pub: Baltimore Business Journal
Contact: Rhonda Pringle, President
E-mail: rpringle@bizjournals.com
Description: A profile of electronic health records provider Dox Choice LLC is presented. The company has received an incentive from the Center for Medicare and Medicaid Services. **Availability:** Print; Online.

24974 ■ *"Dream On" in Barron's (Vol. 89, July 27, 2009, No. 30, pp. 21)*
Pub: Dow Jones & Company Inc.
Contact: Almar Latour, Chief Executive Officer
Ed: Jonathan R. Laing. **Description:** California's budget agreement which purports to eliminate a $26 billion deficit is discussed. The frequent budgetary dustups in the state calls for several reforms including a rainy day fund of 15 percent of any budget and a constitutional convention. Other reform suggestions are discussed.

24975 ■ *"Employer Jobless Tax Could Rise" in Sacramento Business Journal (Vol. 28, May 27, 2011, No. 13, pp. 1)*
Pub: Sacramento Business Journal
Contact: Stephanie Fretwell, Director
E-mail: sfretwell@bizjournals.com
Ed: Kathy Robertson. **Description:** The government of California is facing an estimated $16 billion deficit in its unemployment insurance fund. Unemployment insurance spending has exceeded employer contributions to the fund. Statistics on unemployment insurance is included. **Availability:** Online.

24976 ■ *"Encouraging Study in Critical Languages" in Occupational Outlook Quarterly (Vol. 55, Summer 2011, No. 2, pp. 23)*
Description: Proficiency in particular foreign languages is vital to the defense, diplomacy, and security of the United States. Several federal programs provide scholarships and other funding to encourage high school and college students to learn languages of the Middle East, China, and Russia. **Availability:** Print; Online.

24977 ■ *"ETF Process May be Tweaked" in Austin Business JournalInc. (Vol. 28, December 26, 2008, No. 41, pp. 3)*
Description: Some government officials are proposing for an adjustment of the Texas Emerging Technology Fund's (ETF) policies. The ETF was created to get startup companies capital to get off the ground. Reports show that the global recession had made it more difficult for startup companies to garner investment. **Availability:** Online.

24978 ■ *"Evolve Bank Ramps Up Staff for SBA Lending" in Memphis Business Journal (Vol. 33, February 24, 2012, No. 46, pp. 1)*
Pub: Baltimore Business Journal
Contact: Rhonda Pringle, President
E-mail: rpringle@bizjournals.com
Ed: Christopher Sheffield. **Description:** Memphis, Tennessee-based Evolve Bank has hired Marty Ferguson and Tre Luckett to handle its national and local Small Business Administration (SBA) lending operations. The two are long-time leaders in SBA lending. **Availability:** Print; Online.

24979 ■ *"The Fed Still Has Ammunition" in Barron's (Vol. 90, August 30, 2010, No. 35, pp. M9)*
Pub: Barron's Editorial & Corporate Headquarters
Ed: Randall W. Forsyth. **Description:** Federal Reserve chairman Ben Bernanke said the agency still has tools to combat deflation and a second downturn but these strategies are not needed at this time. The prospects of the Federal Open Market Committee's purchasing of treasuries are also discussed. **Availability:** Online.

24980 ■ *"Fed Tackles Bear of a Crisis" in Barron's (Vol. 88, March 17, 2008, No. 11, pp. M10)*
Pub: Dow Jones & Company Inc.
Contact: Almar Latour, Chief Executive Officer
Ed: Randall W. Forsyth. **Description:** Emergency funding package for Bear Stearns from the Federal Reserve Bank of New York through JPMorgan Chase is one of the steps taken by the central bank shore up bank liquidity. Prior to the emergency funding, the central bank announced the Term Securities Lending Facility to allow dealers to borrow easily saleable Treasuries in exchange for less-liquid issues. **Availability:** Online.

24981 ■ *"Federal Bailout, Three Years Later" in Business Owner (Vol. 35, September-October 2011, No. 5, pp. 6)*
Description: State of the economy and small business sector three years after the government stimulus and bailout programs were instituted. **Availability:** Print; Online.

GENERAL SMALL BUSINESS TOPICS　　　　　　　　　　　　　　　　　　　　　　　　　　　　　　Government Assistance ■ 25001

24982 ■ *"Federal Financial Assistance for Small Businesses"* on Benefits.gov (Mar 31, 2021)
URL(s): www.benefits.gov/news/article/421
Released: March 31, 2021. **Description:** Provides information on small business funding options, small business grants, and provides links to resources to small business owners who need help with challenges that the pandemic has brought. **Availability:** Online.

24983 ■ *"Federal Support for Small Business Owners and Independent Contractors Impacted by COVID-19"* by The American Speech-Language-Hearing Association (Apr 2, 2021)
URL(s): www.asha.org/advocacy/federal-support-for-small-business-owners-and-independent-contractors-impacted-by-covid-19/
Released: April 02, 2021. **Description:** Provides information for small businesses, private practices, and independent contractors who may qualify for emergency issues due to the COVID-19 pandemic. **Availability:** Online.

24984 ■ *"Feds to Pay University Hospital $20M"* in Business Courier (Vol. 27, July 23, 2010, No. 12, pp. 3)
Pub: Business Courier
Ed: James Ritchie. **Description:** The U.S. government is set to pay University Hospital and medical residents who trained there $20 million as part of a tax dispute settlement. Around 1,000 former residents are to receive tax refunds. But the hospital must provide the U.S. Internal Revenue Service with extensive documentation. **Availability:** Print; Mailing list; Online.

24985 ■ *"A Few Points of Contention"* in Barron's (Vol. 88, July 14, 2008, No. 28, pp. 3)
Pub: Dow Jones & Company Inc.
Contact: Almar Latour, Chief Executive Officer
Ed: Michael Santoli. **Description:** Headline inflation tends to revert to the lower core inflation, which excludes food and energy in its calculation over long periods. Prominent private equity figures believe that regulators should allow more than the de facto 10 percent to 25 percent limit of commercial banks to hasten the refunding of the financial sector. **Availability:** Online.

24986 ■ *"Five Area Businesses Win State Tax Breaks"* in Crain's Detroit Business (Vol. 25, June 22, 2009, No. 25, pp. 9)
Pub: Crain Communications Inc.
Contact: Barry Asin, President
Ed: Amy Lane. **Description:** Michigan Economic Growth Authority approved tax breaks for five area businesses among 15 across the state. Details of the tax credits are provided. **Availability:** Print; Online.

24987 ■ *"Five New Scientists Bring Danforth Center $16 Million"* in Saint Louis Business Journal (Vol. 32, October 7, 2011, No. 6, pp. 1)
Pub: Saint Louis Business Journal
Contact: Robert Bobroff, President
E-mail: rbobroff@bizjournals.com
Ed: E.B. Solomont. **Description:** Donald Danforth Plant Science Center's appointment of five new lead scientists has increased its federal funding by $16 million. Cornell University scientist Tom Brutnell is one of the five new appointees. **Availability:** Print; Online.

24988 ■ *"Free File Alliance & IRS Launch 10th Year of Free Online Tax Preparation Services for Millions of Americans"* in Economics Week (February 3, 2012, pp. 82)
Pub: PR Newswire Association LLC.
Description: A coalition of tax software companies have partnered with the Internal Revenue Service to offer the 212 IRS Free File progam. The Free File Alliance offers low-to-moderate income taxpayers free access to online commercial tax preparation software. Details of the program are included. **Availability:** Online.

24989 ■ *"Geico and the USO of Metropolitan Washington Have Teamed Up to Provide Military Troops with a New 'Home Away From Home'"* in Best's Review (Vol. 113, September 2012, No. 5, pp. 13)
Description: Geico and the USO of Metropolitan Washington have partnered to provide military troops and their families an area in the USO airport lounge at Ronald Reagan Washington National Airport with wireless Internet access, seating area with large-screen TV, assistance with travel-related questions, and a snack bar. **Availability:** Online.

24990 ■ *"Georgia Looking to Expand Film Industry Tax Credits"* in Atlanta Business Chronicle (June 27, 2014, pp. 3A)
Pub: American City Business Journals, Inc.
Contact: Mike Olivieri, Executive Vice President
Released: Weekly. **Price:** $4, introductory 4-week offer(Digital only). **Description:** The lawmakers of the State of Georgia are looking to expand film tax incentives at a time when many states are eliminating or scaling back their film industry tax credits. A recently created legislative study committee will begin meeting to consider proposals to expand Georgia's film tax credit program to encourage an already rapidly growing industry. **Availability:** Print; Online.

24991 ■ *"A Good Step, But There's a Long Way to Go"* in Business Week (September 22, 2008, No. 4100, pp. 10)
Ed: James C. Cooper. **Description:** Despite the historic action by the U.S. government to nationalize the mortgage giants Freddie Mac and Fannie Mae, rising unemployment rates may prove to be an even bigger roadblock to bringing back the economy from its downward spiral. The takeover is meant to restore confidence in the credit markets and help with the mortgage crisis but the rising rate in unemployment may make many households unable to take advantage of any benefits which arise from the bailout. Statistical data included. **Availability:** Online.

24992 ■ *"Government Assistance in Business"* in Chron (July 28, 2020)
URL(s): smallbusiness.chron.com/government-assistance-business-3033.html
Released: July 28, 2020. **Description:** Discusses how the government may help to build your small business from the ground up. Includes information on the history of government assistance, types of government assistance, as well as the impact of the pandemic. **Availability:** Online.

24993 ■ *"Grant Could Help Schools Harness Wind"* in Dallas Business Journal (Vol. 37, April 11, 2014, No. 31, pp. 8)
Pub: American City Business Journals, Inc.
Contact: Mike Olivieri, Executive Vice President
Released: Weekly. **Price:** $4, introductory 4-week offer(Digital only); $4, introductory 4-week offer(Digital & Print). **Description:** Five universities led by Texas A&M have received a $2.2 million grant from the Texas Emerging Technologies Fund for use in wind technology research. The research will focus on turbines that feature bigger blades to capture more wind. Technology developed by the universities will eventually be handed to the state. **Availability:** Print; Online.

24994 ■ *"Green Rules To Drive Innovation: Charging for Carbon Can Inspire Conservation, Fuel Competition, and Enhance Competitiveness"* in Harvard Business Review (Vol. 90, March 2012, No. 3, pp. 120)
Pub: Harvard Business Review Press
Contact: Moderna V. Pfizer, Contact
Ed: Daniel C. Esty, Steve Charnovitz. **Price:** $8.95. **Description:** Along with carbon emissions charges, other green policy recommendations include expanding domestic renewable power and the use of natural gas, increasing federal funding of clean-energy research, utilizing incentive-based approaches to encourage the adoption of renewable energy, and implementing the World Trade Organization's Doha negotiations on sustainable development. **Availability:** Online; PDF.

24995 ■ *"Grocers Fight Food Stamp Plan"* in Philadelphia Business Journal (Vol. 30, January 20, 2012, No. 49, pp. 1)
Pub: Baltimore Business Journal
Contact: Rhonda Pringle, President
E-mail: rpringle@bizjournals.com
Description: Grocers in Philadelphia, Pennsylvania have opposed the state's plan to eliminate food stamps for individuals and families with more than $2,000 in savings and other assets. About one-third of Philadelphia's population is eligible for food stamps. **Availability:** Print; Online.

24996 ■ *"Growing Field"* in Crain's Detroit Business (Vol. 26, January 11, 2010, No. 2, pp. 3)
Pub: Crain Communications Inc.
Contact: Barry Asin, President
Description: Detroit's TechTown was awarded a combination loan and grant of $4.1 million from the U.S. Department of Housing and Urban Development to build a 15,000-square-foot stem cell center, a collection of laboratories that will be available to both for-profit companies and university researchers. **Availability:** Online.

24997 ■ *"Half a World Away"* in Tampa Bay Business Journal (Vol. 30, December 4, 2009, No. 50, pp. 1)
Description: Enterprise Florida has offered four trade grants for Florida's marine industry businesses to give them a chance to tap into the Middle East market at the Dubai International Boat Show on March 9 to 13, 2010. The grants pay for 50 percent of the exhibition costs for the qualifying business. **Availability:** Online.

24998 ■ *"Health Care of the Future"* in Business Journal Serving Greater Tampa Bay (Vol. 30, November 19, 2010, No. 48, pp. 1)
Pub: Tampa Bay Business Journal
Contact: Ian Anderson, President
E-mail: ianderson@bizjournals.com
Description: Information about accountable care organizations (ACO), which are integrated care systems with doctors and hospitals working closely together to handle patient care, is provided. The Patient Protection and Affordable Care Act paved the way for ACOs as Medicare demonstration projects. **Availability:** Online.

24999 ■ *"Health Centers Plan Expansion: $3M from D.C. Expected; Uninsured a Target"* in Crain's Detroit Business (Vol. 25, June 15, 2009, No. 24, pp. 3)
Pub: Crain Communications Inc.
Contact: Barry Asin, President
Ed: Jay Greene. **Description:** Detroit has five federally qualified health centers that plan to receive over $3 million in federal stimulus money that will be used to expand projects that will care for uninsured patients. **Availability:** Print; Online.

25000 ■ *"Heart Hospitals Ranked for Mortality Rates"* in Philadelphia Business Journal (Vol. 30, September 2, 2011, No. 29, pp. 1)
Pub: Philadelphia Business Journal
Contact: Sierra Quinn, Director
E-mail: squinn@bizjournals.com
Ed: John George. **Description:** Centers for Medicare and Medicaid Services (CMS) released updated data on mortality rates for heart attack patients as hospitals in Pennsylvania. Doylestown Hospital posted the lowest mortality rates with 10.9 percent, tying the fourth best in the entire nation. Other details on the CMS data are presented. **Availability:** Online.

25001 ■ *"Help Wanted: 100 Hospital IT Workers"* in Business Courier (Vol. 27, October 8, 2010, No. 23, pp. 1)
Pub: Business Courier

Ed: James Ritchie. **Description:** Hospitals in the Greater Cincinnati area are expected to hire more than 100 information technology (IT) workers to help digitize medical records. Financial incentives from the health care reform bill encouraged investments in electronic medical record systems, increasing the demand for IT workers that would help make information exchange across the healthcare system easier. **Availability:** Print; Online.

25002 ■ *"His Record, Not Polls, Is What Matters"* in Bangor Daily News (October 13, 2010)
Pub: Bangor Daily News
Contact: David M. Austin, Contact
Ed: Nick Sambides, Jr. **Description:** The Small Business Jobs Tax Relief Act could spur investment in small businesses by increasing capital gains tax cuts for investors in small business in 2010 and increase to $20,000 from $5,000 the deduction for start-up businesses. **Availability:** Print; Online.

25003 ■ *"Hopkins, University of Maryland, Baltimore Worry Reduced NIH Budget Will Impact Research"* in Baltimore Business Journal (Vol. 29, August 19, 2011, No. 15, pp. 1)
Pub: Boston Business Journal
Contact: Carolyn M. Jones, President
E-mail: cmjones@bizjournals.com
Ed: Scott Dance. **Description:** The budget for the National Institutes of Health (NIH) is slated to be cut by at least 7.9 percent to $2.5 billion in 2013. This will have a big negative effect on medical and biotech research in Maryland, especially Johns Hopkins University and University of Maryland, Baltimore which could face stiffer completion for grants from the NIH. **Availability:** Online.

25004 ■ *"How Baltimore's Largest Private Companies Weathered the Recession's Punch; Top Private Companies"* in Baltimore Business Journal (Vol. 28, August 27, 2010, No. 16, pp. 1)
Pub: Baltimore Business Journal
Contact: Rhonda Pringle, President
E-mail: rpringle@bizjournals.com
Ed: Gary Haber. **Description:** The combined revenue of the 100 largest private firms in Maryland's Baltimore region dropped from about $22.7 billion in 2008 to $21 billion in 2009, an annual decrease of more than 7 percent. To survive the recession's impact, these firms resorted to strategies such as government contracting and overseas expansion. How these strategies affected the revenue of some firms is described. **Availability:** Print; Online.

25005 ■ *"How Green Is The Valley?"* in Barron's (Vol. 88, July 4, 2008, No. 28, pp. 13)
Description: San Jose, California has made a good start towards becoming a leader in alternative energy technology through the establishment of United Laboratories' own lab in the city. The certification process for photovoltaic cells will be dramatically shortened with this endeavor. **Availability:** Print.

25006 ■ *"In the News: Hundreds of Millions of Dollars Available to Small Businesses from SSBCI"* in Small Business Trends(March 3, 2023)
URL(s): smallbiztrends.com/2023/03/weeklsmall-business-news-roundup-march-3-2023.html
Released: March 03, 2023. **Description:** Small businesses can apply for funding through the State Small Business Credit Initiative in order to provide help for their long-term survival. **Availability:** Online.

25007 ■ *"In the SBA's Face"* in American Small Business League (December 2010)
Ed: Richard Larsen. **Description:** Lloyd Chapman uses the American Small Business League to champion small business. Statistical data included.

25008 ■ *"Incentives In Play for Astronautics"* in Business Journal-Milwaukee (Vol. 28, November 5, 2010, No. 5, pp. A1)
Pub: The Business Journal
Contact: Heather Ladage, President

E-mail: hladage@bizjournals.com
Ed: Sean Ryan. **Description:** Astronautics Corporation was offered incentives by local government officials in Milwaukee, Wisconsin and by Brewery Project LLC to move into a building in The Brewery in the city. The company's officials remain indecisive over the offers and incentives. **Availability:** Print; Online.

25009 ■ *"Income Tax Credit for Business Pushes the Job Creation Button"* in Idaho Business Review (August 27, 2014)
Pub: BridgeTower Media
Contact: Adam Reinebach, President
Description: Idaho's new Reimbursement Incentive Act program creates a tax credit for businesses with a qualifying project that will add new jobs that are paid at or above the average wage for work performed. Legislation and technical requirements for small businesses to quality are outlined.

25010 ■ *"Infographic: Social Spending by Country: How Bloated is European Social Spending?"* in Canadian Business (Vol. 85, August 13, 2012, No. 13, pp. 66)
Ed: James Cowan. **Description:** A study conducted by the World Bank found that social spending in Europe is higher than the rest of the world combined. A chart is presented which illustrates government spending on social protection in European countries and in other countries. **Availability:** Print; Online.

25011 ■ *"Is Fannie Mae the Next Government Bailout?"* in Barron's (Vol. 88, March 10, 2008, No. 10, pp. 21)
Pub: Dow Jones & Company Inc.
Contact: Almar Latour, Chief Executive Officer
Ed: Jonathan R. Laing. **Description:** Fannie Mae may need a government bailout as it faces huge hits brought about by the effects of the housing crisis. The shares of the government-sponsored enterprise have dropped 65 percent since the housing crisis began. **Availability:** Online.

25012 ■ *"Is Mulcair Good for Business?"* in Canadian Business (Vol. 85, June 11, 2012, No. 10, pp. 20)
Ed: Sarah Barmak. **Description:** Some of the pronouncements made by New Democratic Party leader Thomas Mulcair suggest that he may be both a friend and an enemy of the Canadian business community. He expressed supportto the energy sector and endorsed lower taxes but also commented on the negative effect of oilsands development. **Availability:** Online.

25013 ■ *"It's Time To Swim"* in Canadian Business (Vol. 81, March 3, 2008, No. 3, pp. 37)
Description: Canadian manufacturers should consider Asian markets such as India and the United Arab Emirates as the U.S. economic downturn continues. Canada's shortage in skilled labor is also expected to negatively affect manufacturing industries. Ontario's plans to assist manufacturers are also presented. **Availability:** Print; PDF; Download; Online.

25014 ■ *"KC Incentives Debate Rages on Unabated"* in The Business Journal-Serving Metropolitan Kansas City (Vol. 26, September 5, 2008, No. 52)
Pub: American City Business Journals, Inc.
Contact: Mike Olivieri, Executive Vice President
Ed: Rob Roberts. **Description:** Debate on the new economic development and incentives policy adopted by the Kansas City Council is still on. The city's Planned Industrial Expansion Authority has rejected a standard property tax abatement proposal. The real estate development community has opposed the rejection of proposed the tax incentives policy. **Availability:** Online.

25015 ■ *"Lawmakers, Execs Launch Effort to Save Rural Hospitals"* in Atlanta Business Chronicle (June 13, 2014, pp. 7A)
Pub: American City Business Journals, Inc.
Contact: Mike Olivieri, Executive Vice President

Description: Governor Nathan Deal has appointed a committee of Georgia lawmakers and healthcare executives to launch an effort to save the state's financially burdened rural hospitals. In addition, he plans to allow rural hospitals that have closed or are on the verge of closing, to scale back their operations, under a new rule approved by the Georgia Board of Community Health. **Availability:** Print; Online.

25016 ■ *"Local Film Industry Stands To Lose Jobs, Millions of Dollars Unless Florida Expands"* in Orlando Business Journal (Vol. 30, March 14, 2014, No. 38, pp. 4)
Pub: American City Business Journals, Inc.
Contact: Mike Olivieri, Executive Vice President
Released: Weekly. Price: $8, introductory 4-week offer(Digital & Print). **Description:** Central Florida's motion picture and TV production industries are in need of more government incentives. Many TV programs have been cancelled due to lack of this funding. Meanwhile, members of the sectors are set to lobby legislature to pass a $1.2 billion incentive package. **Availability:** Print; Online.

25017 ■ *"Market Watch"* in Barron's (Vol. 88, March 24, 2008, No. 12, pp. M18)
Ed: Ashraf Laidi, Marc Pado, David Kotok. **Released:** 2018. **Description:** Latest measures implemented by the Federal Reserve to address the credit crisis did not benefit the US dollar, with the Japanese yen and the euro recouping earlier losses against the dollar. Goldman Sachs reported earnings of $3.23 per share, claiming a stronger liquidity position. The US markets bottomed early on 22 January 2007, according to evidence. **Availability:** Print; Online.

25018 ■ *"Maryland May Avoid Congress on Medicare Waiver"* in Baltimore Business Journal (Vol. 30, June 15, 2012, No. 6, pp. 1)
Pub: American City Business Journals, Inc.
Contact: Mike Olivieri, Executive Vice President
Ed: Sarah Gantz. **Description:** Maryland leaders may not seek the US Congress' help to avoid losing a Medicare waiver. The waiver has standardized Medicare reimbursement rates for all hospitals. Comments from officials included. **Availability:** Online.

25019 ■ *"Md. Bankers Say 'Devil Is In the Details' of New $30B Loan Fund"* in Baltimore Business Journal (Vol. 28, October 8, 2010, No. 22)
Pub: Baltimore Business Journal
Contact: Rhonda Pringle, President
E-mail: rpringle@bizjournals.com
Ed: Gary Haber. **Description:** Maryland community bankers have expressed doubts over a new federal loan program for small business. The new law will also earmark $80 billion for community banks. Comments from executives also given. **Availability:** Print.

25020 ■ *"Md. Housing Leaders Race to Stem Rising Tide of Foreclosures: Neighborhood Watch"* in Baltimore Business Journal (Vol. 28, July 23, 2010, No. 11, pp. 1)
Pub: Baltimore Business Journal
Contact: Rhonda Pringle, President
E-mail: rpringle@bizjournals.com
Ed: Daniel J. Sernovitz. **Description:** Maryland government and housing leaders are set to spend $100 million in federal funding to stem the increase in foreclosures in the area. The federal funding is seen as inadequate to resolve the problem of foreclosures. **Availability:** Print.

25021 ■ *"Md.'s Film Industry Professionals have to Leave the State to Find Work: Exiting Stage Left"* in Baltimore Business Journal (Vol. 28, June 18, 2010, No. 6, pp. 1)
Pub: Baltimore Business Journal
Contact: Rhonda Pringle, President
E-mail: rpringle@bizjournals.com
Ed: Scott Dance. **Released:** Weekly. **Description:** Film professionals including crew members and actors have been leaving Maryland to find work in other states such as Michigan, Louisiana, and Georgia

GENERAL SMALL BUSINESS TOPICS

where bigger budgets and film production incentives are given. Other consequences of this trend in local TV and film production are discussed. **Availability:** Print.

25022 ■ *"Mercy Parent Nets Almost $1B in 2011" in Sacramento Business Journal (Vol. 28, September 30, 2011, No. 31, pp. 1)*
Pub: Sacramento Business Journal
Contact: Stephanie Fretwell, Director
E-mail: sfretwell@bizjournals.com
Ed: Kathy Robertson. **Price:** $4, Print & Digital introductory 4-week offer; $4, Digital introductory 4-week offer. **Description:** Catholic Healthcare West has reported almost $1 billion in profits for 2010. The company has reported a profit margin of 8.7 percent. It also absorbed more than $1 billion in costs from charity care and government programs. **Availability:** Print; Online.

25023 ■ *"Michaud Touts Small-Business Credentials" in Bangor Daily News (September 10, 2010)*
Pub: Bangor Daily News
Contact: David M. Austin, Contact
Ed: Nick Sambides, Jr. **Description:** Mike Michaud, Democrat, is running against a Republican challenger in the 2nd District and states he will support the Small Business Jobs Tax Relief Act if reelected. **Availability:** Print; Online.

25024 ■ *"Michigan Means Growth: Sustaining Growth Through Thick and Thin: Michigan Companies Sustain Growth with Well-Timed Access to Capital" in Inc. (Vol. 36, September 2014, No. 7, pp. 164)*
Pub: Mansueto Ventures L.L.C.
Contact: Stephanie Mehta, Chief Executive Officer
Description: Successful companies possess flexibility, foresight and resources to turn adversity into opportunity. The small businesses in Michigan who have sustained experienced sales growth despite the recession of 2007. The Michigan Economic Development Corporation has introduced three initiatives to help Michigan businesses grow, including venture capital, collateral support and loan participation through the State Small Business Credit Initiative, and cash incentives for businesses looking to invest in urban communities or grow jobs. **Availability:** Print; Online.

25025 ■ *"Microlending Seen as Having a Major Impact" in Business Journal Serving Greater Tampa Bay (Vol. 30, November 26, 2010, No. 49, pp. 1)*
Pub: Tampa Bay Business Journal
Contact: Ian Anderson, President
E-mail: ianderson@bizjournals.com
Ed: Margie Manning. **Description:** There are several organizations that are planning to offer microlending services in Tampa Bay, Florida. These include the Children's Board of Hillsborough County, and OUR Microlending Florida LLC. Organizations that are already offering these services in the area include the Small Business Administration and the Tampa Bay Black Business Investment Corp. **Availability:** Print; Online.

25026 ■ *"Minnesota ABC Event Looks at Government Contracting" in Finance and Commerce Daily Newspaper (November 23, 2010)*
Ed: Brian Johnson. **Description:** Minnesota Associated Builders and Contractors hosted an event focusing on doing business with government agencies. Topics included bidding work, awarding jobs, paperwork, guidelines, certifications and upcoming projects. **Availability:** Online.

25027 ■ *"Minority Auto Suppliers Get Help Diversifying" in Crain's Detroit Business (Vol. 26, January 11, 2010, No. 2, pp. 3)*
Pub: Crain Communications Inc.
Contact: Barry Asin, President
Ed: Sherri Welch. **Description:** Displaced minority auto suppliers are being given assistance by the Kauffman's Foundation Urban Entrepreneur Partnership Detroit program, a three-year effort to assist 150 of the region's suppliers into more diversified businesses. **Availability:** Online.

25028 ■ *"More Corporate Welfare?" in Canadian Business (Vol. 80, February 12, 2007, No. 4, pp. 96)*
Description: The burden on Canadian taxpayers by governmental efforts to finance loss-making companies in the name of corporate welfare is discussed. **Availability:** Online.

25029 ■ *"Multifamily Banks on Fannie, Freddie" in Memphis Business Journal (Vol. 33, February 24, 2012, No. 46, pp. 1)*
Pub: Baltimore Business Journal
Contact: Rhonda Pringle, President
E-mail: rpringle@bizjournals.com
Ed: Andy Ashby. **Description:** The possible demise of Fannie Mae and Freddie Mac is seen to adversely impact the multifamily apartment market of Memphis, Tennessee. The apartment market relies on federal loans for funding. **Availability:** Print; Online.

25030 ■ *Navigating Your Way to Business Success: An Entrepreneur's Journey*
Ed: Kathryn B. Freeland. **Released:** January 01, 2010. **Price:** $24.95, hardcover. **Description:** Learn first-hand from a successful entrepreneur about assessing skills and talent, envisioning your company, planning a path to success, and then tapping into available government agencies to make your business become a reality. **Availability:** Print.

25031 ■ *"New Apartments To Rise Downtown" in Memphis Business Journal (Vol. 33, January 27, 2012, No. 42, pp. 1)*
Pub: Baltimore Business Journal
Contact: Rhonda Pringle, President
E-mail: rpringle@bizjournals.com
Ed: Andy Ashby. **Description:** TOV Virginia LP is planning to build an apartment complex in Memphis, Tennessee. The construction project is estimated to cost around $10.5 million. The development wll be focused on affordable housing and will use local and federal incentives. **Availability:** Print; Online.

25032 ■ *"A New Kid on the Block" in Barron's (Vol. 88, March 17, 2008, No. 11, pp. 58)*
Pub: Dow Jones & Company Inc.
Contact: Almar Latour, Chief Executive Officer
Ed: Thomas G. Donlan. **Description:** Discusses the Federal Reserve which has offered to lend $100 billion in cash to banks and $200 billion in Treasuries to Wall Street investment banks that have problems with liquidity. The reluctance of the banks to lend money to meet a margin call on securities that could still depreciate is the reason why the agency is going into the direct loan business. **Availability:** Online.

25033 ■ *"New Ways to Finance Solar Power Projects Expected to Lower Cost of Capital, Cut Electricity Rates, Boost Profits, and Expand Investor Pool" in PR Newswire (September 28, 2012)*
Pub: PR Newswire Association LLC.
Description: Renewable energy companies are examining new ways to finance solar power projects. One such strategy includes the use of the REIT structure as a means to lowering costs of capital, lower the cost of generating solar power by nearly 20 percent. Investors would be more interested in the easy and liquid means in which to own a part of the fast growing solar market. Statistical details included.

25034 ■ *"No End to the Nightmare; America's Car Industry" in The Economist (Vol. 390, January 3, 2009, No. 8612, pp. 46)*
Description: Detroit's struggling auto industry and the government loan package is discussed as well as the United Auto Worker union, which is loathed by Senate Republicans. **Availability:** Print; Online.

Government Assistance ■ 25041

25035 ■ *"NYPA Grants Aid Area Companies" in Business First of Buffalo (Vol. 30, January 10, 2014, No. 17, pp. 6)*
Pub: American City Business Journals, Inc.
Contact: Mike Olivieri, Executive Vice President
Released: Weekly. **Price:** $140, One-Year Print & Digital; $115, One-Year Digital. **Description:** New York Power Authority (NYPA) trustees have approved more than $3.5 million in financial aid to Western New York enterprises. The NYPA and Empire State Development have also funded a package that includes low cost hydropower and $7 million in capital grants and tax credits. The Western New York area manufacturers that were granted aid are also presented. **Availability:** Print; Online.

25036 ■ *"Organic Food Industry Goes to College" in USA Today (April 9, 2012)*
Ed: Chuck Raasch. **Description:** With the organic food industry growing the US Department of Agriculture is has pumped $117 million into organic research in the last three years. According to a recent report by the Organic Farming Research Foundation (OFRF), the number of states committing land for organic research has nearly doubled from 2003 to 2011. Universities offering academic programs in organic farming rose from none to nine. The OFRF supports organic farmers and producers. **Availability:** Online.

25037 ■ *"Pennsylvania DEP To Conduct Natural Gas Vehicle Seminar" in Travel & Leisure Close-Up (October 8, 2012)*
Description: Pennsylvania Department of Environmental Protection is holding a Natural Gas Vehicle seminar at the Bayfront Convention Center in Erie, PA, as well as other locations throughout the state. The seminars will help municipal and commercial fleet owners make better informed decisions when converting fleets from compressed natural gas and liquefied natural gas. **Availability:** Print; Online.

25038 ■ *"The People Puzzle; Re-Training America's Workers" in The Economist (Vol. 390, January 3, 2009, No. 8612, pp. 32)*
Description: With thousands of workers losing their jobs, America is now facing the task of getting them back to work. With an overall unemployment rate of 6.7 percent, the federal government has three main ways for leading workers back to employment: training them for new jobs, providing unemployment insurance in order to replace lost wages during the period of job-hunting; and matching employers who desire a skill with workers who have that skill. Specialized staffing agencies provide employers and potential employees with the help necessary to find a job in some of the more niche markets. **Availability:** Online.

25039 ■ *"Political Environments and Business Strategy: Implications for Managers" in Business Horizons (Vol. 51, January-February 2008)*
Pub: Elsevier Advanced Technology Publications
Ed: Gerald D. Keim, Amy J. Hillman. **Description:** Various government bodies and business organizations work together in shaping new business opportunities and policies that arise from globalization. Presented is framework of public policy considerations for business managers. The framework is based on Nobel laureate Douglas North's work. **Availability:** PDF; Online.

25040 ■ *"The Price of Citizenship" in Canadian Business (Vol. 79, August 14, 2006, No. 16-17, pp. 13)*
Description: Safety and insurance benefits provided by the Canadian government to Canadian passport holders returning from Lebanon, is discussed. **Availability:** Print; Online.

25041 ■ *"Providers Ride First Wave of eHealth Dollars" in Boston Business Journal (Vol. 31, June 10, 2011, No. 20, pp. 1)*
Pub: Boston Business Journal
Contact: Carolyn M. Jones, President
E-mail: cmjones@bizjournals.com

Ed: Julie M. Donnelly. **Released:** Weekly. **Description:** Health care providers in Massachusetts implementing electronic medical records technology started receiving federal stimulus funds. Beth Israel Deaconess Medical Center was the first hospital to qualify for the funds. **Availability:** Print.

25042 ■ *"Public Health Care Funding and the Montana Economy"* in *Montana Business Quarterly (Vol. 49, Spring 2011, No. 1, pp. 23)*
Pub: University of Montana Bureau of Business and Economic Research
Contact: Patrick Barkey, Director
E-mail: patrick.barkey@business.umt.edu
Ed: Gregg Davis. **Released:** Quarterly. **Description:** Montana has more baby boomers and veterans per capita than any other state in the nation. The role of public health in the state is a crucial part of the state's economy. **Availability:** Online.

25043 ■ *"The Quest for a Smart Prosthetic"* in *Canadian Business (Vol. 83, October 12, 2010, No. 17, pp. 26)*
Pub: Rogers Media Inc.
Contact: Neil Spivak, Chief Executive Officer
Ed: Jacqueline Nelson. **Description:** Information about a two-year research project led by Southern Methodist University (SMU) and funded by the Defense Advance Research Projects Agency (DARPA) is provided. The agency aims to create a 'smart prosthetic' which will improve the lives of military amputees. The planned prosthetic will use a sensor that can carry nerve signals through synthetic channels. **Availability:** Print; Online.

25044 ■ *"Rawlings-Blake Unveils Business Plan for Next Four Years"* in *Baltimore Business Journal (Vol. 29, September 16, 2011, No. 19, pp. 1)*
Pub: Boston Business Journal
Contact: Carolyn M. Jones, President
E-mail: cmjones@bizjournals.com
Ed: Gary Haber. **Description:** Mayor Stephanie Rawlings-Blake of Baltimore, Maryland unveiled her plan to push the economy forward. Her key objectives include giving more support for the city's technology companies and refocusing the Baltimore Development Corporation on job creation and retention. **Availability:** Online.

25045 ■ *"Ready for Our Ships to Come In"* in *Philadelphia Business Journal (Vol. 33, April 11, 2014, No. 9, pp. 4)*
Pub: American City Business Journals, Inc.
Contact: Mike Olivieri, Executive Vice President
Description: Philadelphia Regional Port Authority planned the construction of the Southport Marine Terminal in South Philadelphia at a cost of $300 million to capitalize on changes in the shipping industry. The Tioga Marine Terminal in Port Richmond is also being improved using a mix of public and private money. The growing competition among the East Coast ports is also discussed. **Availability:** Online.

25046 ■ *"Region to Be Named Innovation Hub"* in *Business Courier (Vol. 27, July 2, 2010, No. 9, pp. 1)*
Pub: Business Courier
Ed: Dan Monk. **Description:** The selection of Cincinnati's consumer-marketing cluster as a 'Hub of Innovation' by the Ohio Department of Development could boost Cincinnati's chances of receiving $100 million in grants from Ohio's Third Frontier program and other funding sources. Implications of the University of Cincinnati's designation as a Center of Excellence in Advanced Transportation and Aerospace are also discussed. **Availability:** Print; Online.

25047 ■ *"R.I. Lags in Solar Incentives"* in *Providence Business News (Vol. 29, May 26, 2014, No. 8, pp. 1)*
Pub: American City Business Journals, Inc.
Contact: Mike Olivieri, Executive Vice President
Released: May 24, 2014. **Description:** The state of Rhode Island has offered less in government renewable energy incentives than its neighboring states and has yet to experience the growth of residential solar energy projects. The Rhode Island Renewable Energy Fund allocated $800,000 to the small scale solar program in 2014. **Availability:** Print; Online.

25048 ■ *"Rich or Poor, Hospitals Must Work Together"* in *Crain's Chicago Business (Vol. 31, April 28, 2008, No. 17, pp. 22)*
Pub: Crain Communications Inc.
Contact: Barry Asin, President
Description: Chicago-area safety-net hospitals that serve the poor, uninsured and underinsured are struggling to stay open while wealthier areas compete to build advanced facilities for the expensive surgical procedures their privately insured patients can afford. If these safety-net hospitals close, their patients, many of them in ambulances, will show up at the remaining hospitals resulting in a strain that will test the ability of hospitals across the region to care for all of their patients. Hospitals need to address the threats to the local health care system before it slips into crisis since the current every-hospital-for-itself approach that pays off big for some will eventually will make losers of everyone. **Availability:** Online.

25049 ■ *"Ride-Share Programs Seem to Fit San Antonio's Future"* in *San Antonio Business Journal (Vol. 28, May 9, 2014, No. 13, pp. 6)*
Pub: American City Business Journals, Inc.
Contact: Mike Olivieri, Executive Vice President
Price: $4, Introductory 4-Week Offer(Digital & Print). **Description:** San Antonio, Texas Mayor Julian Castro has been promoting the SA2020 plan that calls for an increase in downtown living and expanded public transit options. Castro made positive comments regarding the ride sharing services, even if they include a few disqualifications. The potential benefits of the ride sharing services into the city's plan are examined. **Availability:** Print; Online.

25050 ■ *"RIM Reinforces Claim as Top Dog by Expanding BlackBerry Service"* in *Globe & Mail (March 11, 2006, pp. B3)*
Ed: Simon Avery. **Description:** The plans of Research In Motion Ltd. to enhance the features of BlackBerry, through acquisition of Ascendent Systems, are presented. **Availability:** Online.

25051 ■ *"Rosewood Site Faces Big Cleanup Before Stevenson Can Expand"* in *Baltimore Business Journal (Vol. 27, February 6, 2010, No. 40, pp. 1)*
Pub: Baltimore Business Journal
Contact: Rhonda Pringle, President
E-mail: rpringle@bizjournals.com
Ed: Daniel J. Sernovitz. **Description:** Environmental assessment report states that Maryland's Rosewood Center for the Developmentally Disabled has significant amounts of toxic chemicals, which could impact Stevenson University's decision to purchase the property. Senator Robert A. Zirkin believes that the state should pay for the cleanup, which is expected to cost millions. **Availability:** Print; Online.

25052 ■ *"RT Seeking Ways to Finance Expansion"* in *Sacramento Business Journal (Vol. 28, July 29, 2011, No. 22, pp. 1)*
Pub: Sacramento Business Journal
Contact: Stephanie Fretwell, Director
E-mail: sfretwell@bizjournals.com
Ed: Melanie Turner. **Description:** Sacramento Regional Transit District is considering ways to finance all its capital projects outlined in a 30-year transit master plan which would cost more than $7 billion to complete. Current funding sources include developer fees and state and federal assistance and fares. Part of the master plan is a light-rail line to Sacramento International Airport. **Availability:** Print.

25053 ■ *"Ryan Gilbert Wants SBA To Mean Speedy Business Administration"* in *Philadelphia Business Journal (Vol. 33, May 9, 2014, No. 13, pp. 8)*
Pub: American City Business Journals, Inc.
Contact: Mike Olivieri, Executive Vice President
Released: May 23, 2014. **Description:** Ryan Gilbert, CEO of San Francisco, California-based Better Finance explains that his company uses its financial technology, SmartBiz, to help banks expedite Small Business Administration (SBA) loans. Better Finance, formerly known as BillFloat, helps small business owners receive SBA 7(a) loans between $5,000 and $150,000 within five business days instead of several week, offering easy online access to SBA loans at low interest rates. **Availability:** Print; Online.

25054 ■ *"A Safety Net in Need of Repair"* in *The Economist (Vol. 390, January 3, 2009, No. 8612, pp. 33)*
Description: America's unemployment-insurance scheme is outdated and skimpy compared to other industrialized countries despite the fact that Americans tend to work harder at returning to the job market; the benefits are lower and available for a smaller amount of time and less unemployed workers are even able to collect these benefits. Statistical data included.

25055 ■ *"Salmon's Gem Air Wants Grant For Year-round Boise Flight"* in *Idaho Business Review (September 3, 2014)*
Pub: BridgeTower Media
Contact: Adam Reinebach, President
Description: Gem Air offers four flights between Salmon and Boise, for both tourists and businesspeople including doctors and architects. The airline is requesting a $250,000 federal grant in order to compete with larger airlines and hopes to attract more business travelers with a direct flight between Boise and Atlanta.

25056 ■ *"SBA Can Improve Your Cash Flow"* in *Business Owner (Vol. 35, September-October 2011, No. 5, pp. 3)*
Description: Federal assistance available to small business is examined. The Small Business Administration loan guarantee program is designed to improve availability and attractiveness of small business loans. **Availability:** Print; Online.

25057 ■ *"SBA Lending Hits Record"* in *Saint Louis Business Journal (Vol. 32, September 30, 2011, No. 5, pp. 1)*
Pub: Saint Louis Business Journal
Contact: Robert Bobroff, President
E-mail: rbobroff@bizjournals.com
Ed: Rick Desloge. **Description:** US Small Business Administration loans have reached a record high of $200 million in 2011. The agency decreased the usual loan fees. **Availability:** Print; Online.

25058 ■ *"Science Museum, Theater Seeking State Loans"* in *Sacramento Business Journal (Vol. 31, May 30, 2014, No. 14, pp. 4)*
Pub: American City Business Journals, Inc.
Contact: Mike Olivieri, Executive Vice President
Released: Weekly. **Price:** $4, Introductory 4-week offer(Digital & Print). **Description:** The Powerhouse Science Center and B Street Theatre in Sacramento, California are hoping to secure loans from the California Infrastructure and Economic Development Bank. Both nonprofit organizations are planning to start their own construction projects as soon as loans are received. **Availability:** Print; Online.

25059 ■ *"A Second Chance at Road Dollars"* in *Orlando Business Journal (Vol. 26, February 5, 2010, No. 36, pp. 1)*
Pub: Orlando Business Journal
Contact: Julie Swyers, Director
E-mail: jswyers@bizjournals.com
Description: Nearly $10 million worth of construction projects in Central Florida would give construction companies that missed the initial round of federal stimulus-funded local road building projects another opportunity. Cost savings in the initial round of road projects enabled Orange, Osceola, and Seminole Counties to secure additional projects. **Availability:** Print; Online.

25060 ■ *"Second to None"* **in Crain's Detroit Business (Vol. 26, January 18, 2010, No. 3, pp. 9)**
Pub: Crain Communications Inc.
Contact: Barry Asin, President
Ed: Nancy Kaffer. Description: Second-stage companies are beginning to attract more attention from government entities and the business community alike, due in part to their ability to create jobs more rapidly than their counterparts both smaller and larger. Second-stage companies have between 10-99 employees and consistently have supplied the most jobs, despite overall job declines in recent years. Availability: Online.

25061 ■ *"Sharp Restarts Toner Manufacturing: Production Moved from Japan to Serve China Market"* **in Memphis Business Journal (Vol. 34, May 11, 2012, No. 4, pp. 1)**
Pub: Baltimore Business Journal
Contact: Rhonda Pringle, President
E-mail: rpringle@bizjournals.com
Ed: Michael Sheffield. Description: Sharp Manufacturing Company of America has decided to reopen its ink toner production plant in Memphis, Tennessee because of cheaper material, labor and freight costs. The company's move was also attributed to local economic growth and the government support they received after a 2008 tornado hit the area surrounding the area. Availability: Print; Online.

25062 ■ *"Shining a Light on Entrepreneurial Opportunities"* **in San Antonio Business Journal (Vol. 28, July 11, 2014, No. 22, pp. 4)**
Pub: American City Business Journals, Inc.
Contact: Mike Olivieri, Executive Vice President
Released: Weekly. Price: $4, Introductory 4-week offer(Digital & Print). Description: Café Commerce is a small business and entrepreneurship development program launched by the City of San Antonio in partnership with microlender Accion Texas. The goal of the new resource center is to make entrepreneurship easier by complementing existing programs and serving as a platform to introduce new ones to the business community. Availability: Print; Online.

25063 ■ *"Should the Fed Regulate Wall Street?"* **in Barron's (Vol. 88, March 24, 2008, No. 12, pp. M15)**
Pub: Dow Jones & Company Inc.
Contact: Almar Latour, Chief Executive Officer
Ed: Randall W. Forsyth. Description: Greater regulation of the financial sector by the Federal Reserve is essential for it to survive the crisis it is experiencing. The resulting regulation could be in complete contrast with the deregulation the sector previously experienced. Availability: Online.

25064 ■ *"Sky Harvest Windpower Corp. - Operational Update"* **in Investment Weekly News (March 10, 2012, pp. 744)**
Pub: PR Newswire Association LLC.
Description: Sky Harvest Windpower Corporation is rebranding its focus on gas and power activities both nationally and internationally. The firm's Canadian projects are outlined as well as its commitment to purse the Green Options Partners Program in 2012. Availability: Online.

25065 ■ *"Small Bank Has Big Lending Plans, New Hire"* **in Silicon Valley/San Jose Business Journal (Vol. 30, September 21, 2012, No. 26, pp. 1)**
Pub: Baltimore Business Journal
Contact: Rhonda Pringle, President
E-mail: rpringle@bizjournals.com
Description: Santa Cruz County Bank has hired government-backed loans specialist Sat Kanwar in addition to Susan Chandler, Jorge Reguerin and Daljit Bains to boost the bank's Small Business Administration lending department. According to Chandler, the bank will take on loans ranging from $25,000 to several million dollars. Availability: Print; Online.

25066 ■ *"Small Business Grants: Free Money for Your Business"* **in Nav (Jan. 28, 2022)**
URL(s): www.nav.com/resource/small-business-grants/
Released: January 28, 2022. Description: Discusses the benefits and types of small business grants as well as how to apply for a small business grant. Availability: Online.

25067 ■ *"Small Business Grants: Here Are 32 You Can Apply for in 2022"* **in digital.com (Jan. 28, 2022)**
URL(s): digital.com/small-business-grants/
Released: January 28, 2022. Description: Provides information on 32 small business grants that your company may be able to apply for. Availability: Online.

25068 ■ *"Small-Business Grants: Where to Find Free Money"* **in NerdWallet (Nov. 3, 2021)**
URL(s): www.nerdwallet.com/article/small-business/small-business-grants
Ed: Steve Nicastro. Released: November 03, 2021. Description: Provides a list of resources in which small business owners can find information on small business grants. Availability: Online.

25069 ■ *Small Business Grants: Where to Find Funds*
URL(s): www.lendingtree.com/business/grant/
Description: Provides information on small business grants that can provide needed capital without putting your company in debt. Availability: Online.

25070 ■ *"Small Wind Power Market to Double by 2015 at $634 Million"* **in Western Farm Press (September 30, 2011)**
Description: Small wind power provides cost-effective electricity on a highly localized level, in both remote settings as well as in conjunction with power from the utility grid. Government incentives are spurring new growth in the industry. Availability: Online.

25071 ■ *"Spin Zone: Where Hawaii's Leaders Face Off, Have High-Tech Tax Credits Helped or Hurt Hawaii?"* **in Hawaii Business (Vol. 53, December 2007, No. 6, pp. 28)**
Pub: PacificBasin Communications
Contact: Chuck Tindle, Director
E-mail: chuckt@pacificbasin.net
Description: Presents the opinons of Channel Capital LLC's Walter R. Roth and Hawaii Venture Capital Association's Bill Spencer concerning the impacts of tax credits. Roth thinks that Act 221 appeals to investors who can earn despite business failure while Spencer thinks that the legislation promotes investments in innovative technology firms. The need to support tax credits is also discussed. Availability: Print; Online.

25072 ■ *"State Investment Goes Sour"* **in Business Journal Portland (Vol. 26, December 4, 2009, No. 39, pp. 1)**
Pub: Portland Business Journal
Contact: Andy Giegerich, Managing Editor
E-mail: agiegerich@bizjournals.com
Ed: Erik Siemers. Description: Oregon might recoup only $500,000 of a $20 million loan to Vancouver-based Cascade Grain Products LLC. Cascade Grain's ethanol plant in Clatskanie, OR will be put into auction under the supervision of a bankruptcy court. Availability: Print; Online.

25073 ■ *"State Moves to Improve Child Care"* **in Providence Business News (Vol. 29, April 7, 2014, No. 1, pp. 1)**
Pub: American City Business Journals, Inc.
Contact: Mike Olivieri, Executive Vice President
URL(s): pbn.com/state-moves-to-improve-child-care96248
Description: Rhode Island Department of Human Services has been helping to administer BrightStars contracts to child care centers, home-based providers and educational programs to help ensure the availability of high quality child care to the workforce. Part of the BrightStars funding came from the $50 million Race to the Top grant. Insights on BrightStars rating systems are also given.

25074 ■ *"The Surplus Shell Game"* **in Canadian Business (Vol. 80, March 12, 2007, No. 6, pp. 72)**
Description: The effort of successive federal governments in Canada to ensure budget surpluses and its impact on the economy are discussed. Availability: Online.

25075 ■ *"Survey: Don't Expect Big Results From Stimulus"* **in Crain's Detroit Business (Vol. 25, June 1, 2009, No. 22)**
Pub: Crain Communications Inc.
Contact: Barry Asin, President
Ed: Nancy Kaffer, Chad Halcom. Description: In a recent survey, Michigan business owners, operators or managers showed that 48 percent of respondents oppose the President's stimulus package and believe it will have little or no effect on the economy. Availability: Print.

25076 ■ *"Tackling Tuition Increases Head On"* **in Pittsburgh Business Times (Vol. 34, July 25, 2014, No. 1, pp. 6)**
Pub: American City Business Journals, Inc.
Contact: Mike Olivieri, Executive Vice President
Description: The University of Pittsburgh has tried to contain tuition increases after the state cut funding by about $70 million in the 2012 budget year. The measures include a one-time-only early retirement program offered in 2012, greater focus on sustainability and cutting energy costs, and streamlining operations and sharing services. Availability: Print; Online.

25077 ■ *"Tattooed Bellwethers of Economic Development"* **in Austin Business Journal (Vol. 34, May 2, 2014, No. 11, pp. A4)**
Pub: American City Business Journals, Inc.
Contact: Mike Olivieri, Executive Vice President
Released: Weekly. Price: $4, Introductory 4-week offer(Digital & Print). Description: The creative community's art-centered business have helped Austin, Texas' growth by moving into transitional areas with low rents. Their kind of pioneering spirit primes the area for later commercial and residential development. The city's assistance programs for creative enterprises are also presented. Availability: Print; Online.

25078 ■ *"Tax Breaks Favor Outsiders, Business Owners Object"* **in Business Review Albany (Vol. 41, August 22, 2014, No. 22, pp. 7)**
Pub: American City Business Journals, Inc.
Contact: Mike Olivieri, Executive Vice President
Released: Weekly. Price: $4, introductory 4-week offer(Digital only). Description: New York business owners have criticized Governor Andrew Cuomo's Start-Up NY tax-break program. They argue that the existing companies are essentially ignored and they are concerned whether the companies receiving the tax breaks stay longer than ten years. Insights on the Start-Up NY program are included. Availability: Print; Online.

25079 ■ *"A Taxi Service for the Homeless"* **in Forest Park Review (April 16, 2019)**
URL(s): www.forestparkreview.com/News/Articles/4-16-2019/A-taxi-service-for-the-homeless-/
Ed: Tom Holmes. Released: April 16, 2019. Description: Forest Park resident John Netherly has been using his own car to transport homeless people to shelters or to receive treatment or help for the last two years. Creating a taxicab for the homeless, this social worker is willing to fill the gap that government agencies do not address. Availability: Online.

25080 ■ *"Taylor Tests Land Grant Program"* **in Austin Business Journal (Vol. 31, June 3, 2011, No. 13, pp. 1)**
Pub: Austin Business Journal
Contact: Rachel McGrath, Director
E-mail: rmcgrath@bizjournals.com

25081 ■ Government Assistance

Ed: Vicky Garza. **Description:** Taylor Economic Development Corporation implemented a land grant program called Build On Our Lot to lure businesses to Taylor City, Austin, Texas. They are targeting small businesses, especially those in the renewable energy, advanced manufacturing, technical services and food products. Program details are included. **Availability:** Print; Online.

25081 ■ *"This Just In. State House Introduces Film-Industry Stimulus Bills"* in *Crain's Detroit Business* (Vol. 24, March 3, 2008, No. 9)
Pub: Crain Communications Inc.
Contact: Barry Asin, President
Description: House Bills 5841-5856 would give Michigan the most competitive incentives in the U.S. to encourage projects by film industry. Provisions of the bill are outlined. **Availability:** Online.

25082 ■ *"This Just In: TechTown, Partners Get $1M to Start Tech Exchange"* in *Crain's Detroit Business* (Vol. 25, June 1, 2009, No. 22, pp. 1)
Pub: Crain Communications Inc.
Contact: Barry Asin, President
Ed: Daniel Duggan. **Description:** Three veterans of the auto industry have partnered to create, Revitalizing Michigan, a nonprofit dedicated to help manufacturers improve their processes. The firm is seeking federal, state and private grants to fund the mission. **Availability:** Print; Online.

25083 ■ *"TMC Development Closes $1.1 Million Real Estate Purchase for Mansa, LLC Using SBA 504 Real Estate Financing"* in *Marketwired* (September 17, 2009)
Pub: Comtex News Network Inc.
Contact: Kan Devnani, President
Description: TMC Development announced the closing of a $1.1 million real estate purchase for Mansa, LLC dba Kwikee Mart, a Napa-based convenience store; TMC helped the company secure a Small Business Administration 504 loan in order to purchase the acquisition of a 3,464 square foot building. SBA created the 504 loan program to provide financing for growing small and medium-sized businesses. **Availability:** Online.

25084 ■ *"Today's Business Sale Climate"* in *Business Owner* (Vol. 35, September-October 2011, No. 5, pp. 10)
Description: Despite the weak economy, there is a surplus of individuals wanting to purchase a small business. The Small Business Administration loan guarantees program helps with its loans for purchase/sale of business assistance. **Availability:** Print; Online.

25085 ■ *"Triad, Fortune Dump TARP Cut Costs, Boost Lending"* in *Saint Louis Business Journal* (Vol. 32, October 7, 2011, No. 6, pp. 1)
Pub: Saint Louis Business Journal
Contact: Robert Bobroff, President
E-mail: rbobroff@bizjournals.com
Ed: Greg Edwards. **Description:** St. Louis, Missouri-based Triad Bank and Fortune Bank have been using an alternative federal loan program to pay back financing from the Troubled Asset Relief Program. Triad got a $5 million loan at one percent interest rate from the US Small Business Lending Fund. **Availability:** Print; Online.

25086 ■ *"U-Swirl Added to SBA's Franchise Registry"* in *Ice Cream Reporter* (Vol. 23, September 20, 2010, No. 10, pp. 1)
Description: Healthy Fast Food Inc., parent to the U-SWIRL Frozen Yogurt cafe chain announced that the U.S. Small Business Administration listed U-SWIRL Frozen Yogurt on its official franchise registry. This move will allow U-SWIRL the benefits of a streamlined review process for SBA financing. **Availability:** Print; Online.

25087 ■ *"Union, Heal Thyself"* in *Canadian Business* (Vol. 81, July 21, 2008, No. 11, pp. 9)
Description: General Motors Corp. was offered by the federal government a $250 million fund after the company declared plans to close its facility in Ontario. The government move is geared towards supporting the workers who have refused to support the automotive company. Details of the labor contract between General Motors and the Canadian Auto Workers are presented. **Availability:** Print; Online.

25088 ■ *"Unions Pony Up $1 Million for McBride Stimulus"* in *Saint Louis Business Journal* (Vol. 31, July 29, 2011, No. 49, pp. 1)
Pub: Saint Louis Business Journal
Contact: Robert Bobroff, President
E-mail: rbobroff@bizjournals.com
Ed: Evan Binns. **Description:** Carpenters District Council of Greater St. Louis and International Brotherhood of Electrical Workers Local 1 were among the nine unions that agreed to split the cost of nearly $1 million in incentives for homebuyers who purchase homes in McBride communities. McBride & Son has spent over $100,000 to promote the incentive program. **Availability:** Print; Online.

25089 ■ *"UTSA Entrepreneur Program Receives Federal Designation"* in *San Antonio Business Journal* (Vol. 28, June 6, 2014, No. 17, pp. 7)
Pub: American City Business Journals, Inc.
Contact: Mike Olivieri, Executive Vice President
Released: Weekly. **Price:** $4, Introductory 4-week offer(Digital & Print). **Description:** The National Science Foundation has designated the University of Texas at San Antonio (UTSA) as an Innovation Corps Site because of its strong entrepreneurial system through the Center for Innovation and Technology Entrepreneurship. The UTSA expects to see an increase in entrepreneurial activity and successful technology commercialization with such designation. **Availability:** Print; Online.

25090 ■ *"VA Exceeds Government-Wide Goal for Veteran-Owned Business Procurement"* in *Benzinga.com* (July 3, 2012)
Pub: Benzinga.com
Contact: Jason Raznick, Founder
Ed: Aaron Wise. **Description:** Department of Veterans Affairs has surpassed its goal of government procurements of the Small Business Adminstration by more than six times. The VA's committment to the success of veteran-owned small businesses is covered.

25091 ■ *"Valenti: Roots of Financial Crisis Go Back to 1998"* in *Crain's Detroit Business* (Vol. 24, October 6, 2008, No. 40, pp. 25)
Pub: Crain Communications Inc.
Contact: Barry Asin, President
Ed: Tom Henderson, Nathan Skid. **Description:** Interview with Sam Valenti III who is the chairman and CEO of Valenti Capital L.L.C., a wealth-management firm; Valenti discusses in detail the history that led up to the current economic crisis as well as his prediction for the future of the country. **Availability:** Print; Online.

25092 ■ *"VPA to Pay $9.5 Million to Settle Whistle-Blower Lawsuits"* in *Crain's Detroit Business* (Vol. 26, January 11, 2010, No. 2, pp. 13)
Pub: Crain Communications Inc.
Contact: Barry Asin, President
Ed: Jay Greene. **Description:** According to Terrence Berg, first assistant with the U.S. Attorney's Office in Detroit, Voluntary Physicians Association, a local home health care company, has agreed to pay $9.5 million to settle four whistle-blower lawsuits; the agreement settles allegations that VPA submitted claims to TriCare, the Michigan Medicaid program and Medicare for unnecessary home visits, tests and procedures. **Availability:** Online.

25093 ■ *"Walker Seeks More Business Participation"* in *Business Journal-Milwaukee* (Vol. 28, December 10, 2010, No. 10, pp. A1)
Pub: The Business Journal
Contact: Heather Ladage, President
E-mail: hladage@bizjournals.com
Ed: Rich Kirchen. **Description:** Wisconsin governor Scott Walker is seeking the aid of Milwaukee business leaders to participate in resolving the challenges posed by the economic crisis. Walker is aiming to create 250,000 jobs. He is also planning to call a special session of the legislature to enact strategies to jumpstart the economy. **Availability:** Print; Online.

25094 ■ *"What's Ahead for Fannie and Fred?"* in *Barron's* (Vol. 90, August 30, 2010, No. 35, pp. 26)
Pub: Barron's Editorial & Corporate Headquarters
Ed: Jonathan R. Laing. **Description:** A meeting presided by Treasury Secretary Timothy Geithner discussed the future of Fannie Mae and Freddie Mac. The two government sponsored enterprises were mismanaged and reforming these two agencies is critical. **Availability:** Online.

25095 ■ *"Whistling in the Dark"* in *Canadian Business* (Vol. 79, September 25, 2006, No. 19, pp. 17)
Description: Increasing subsidies for research projects in Canada is discussed. **Availability:** Online.

25096 ■ *"Whistling Past the Graveyard? Higher Quality Stocks Beckon to Investors?"* in *Barron's* (Vol. 88, March 17, 2008, No. 11, pp. 15)
Pub: Dow Jones & Company Inc.
Contact: Almar Latour, Chief Executive Officer
Ed: Michael Santoli. **Description:** Discusses the Federal Reserve's move to provide $200 billion to the system which can be seen as an effort to avoid the liquidity problems that Bear Stearns suffered. The Federal Reserve's move seems to frighten investors rather than reassure them. **Availability:** Online.

25097 ■ *"Will Focus on Maryland Businesses Continue?"* in *Baltimore Business Journal* (Vol. 28, November 5, 2010, No. 26, pp. 1)
Pub: Baltimore Business Journal
Contact: Rhonda Pringle, President
E-mail: rpringle@bizjournals.com
Ed: Scott Dance. **Description:** The 2010 election may call for new efforts to teach new lawmakers to assure that the viewpoints of businesses are considered and accurately delivered. The Greater Baltimore Committee and similar groups have gathered reports on the competitiveness of Maryland and are planning to use them to make a case of keeping business a top priority. **Availability:** Print; Online.

RESEARCH CENTERS

25098 ■ **Center for International Private Enterprise (CIPE) [Centre International pour l'Entreprise Privée]**
1211 Connecticut Ave. NW Ste. 700
Washington, DC 20036
Ph: (202)721-9200
Fax: (202)280-1000
URL: http://www.cipe.org
Contact: Andrew Wilson, Executive Director
Linkedin: www.linkedin.com/company/center-for-international-private-enterprise
X (Twitter): x.com/CIPEglobal

YouTube: www.youtube.com/channel/UCXdHlaCXrThhX3H63QUz_2w
Description: Encourages the growth of voluntary business organizations and private enterprise systems abroad, such as chambers of commerce, trade associations, employers' organizations, and business-oriented research groups, particularly in developing countries. Helps business communities abroad strengthen their organizational capabilities; creates exchanges among business leaders and institutions to strengthen the international private enterprise system; encourages development of active business participation in the political process. **Scope:** Worldwide democracy through the promotion of private enterprise, market-oriented reform, and legal, regulatory and business institutions, including supporting strategies and techniques that address market-based democratic development and working with indigenous organizations in emerging democracies. Provides matching funds to a variety of developing country institutions for political and economic development. **Founded:** 1983. **Publications:** *Economic Reform Feature Service*. **Geographic Preference:** National.

Government Procurement

START-UP INFORMATION

25099 ■ *"No. 407: What I Learned in the Military, and What I Had to Unlearn"* in *Inc. (Vol. 36, September 2014, No. 7, pp. 80)*
Pub: Mansueto Ventures L.L.C.
Contact: Stephanie Mehta, Chief Executive Officer
Released: September 2014. **Description:** Profile of William Bailey, who served in the U.S. Army as information manager at the U.S. Military Academy at West Point. Bailey discusses his startup firm, Rapier Solutions, a government contractor providing IT, logistics, and social-work expertise. The firm has developed a new survivor outreach system for the U.S. Army. **Availability:** Print; Online.

25100 ■ *"Should State Invest in Startups?"* in *Providence Business News (Vol. 28, March 3, 2014, No. 48, pp. 1)*
Pub: American City Business Journals, Inc.
Contact: Mike Olivieri, Executive Vice President
Released: March 01, 2014. **Description:** The U.S. Treasury Department is investigating whether Rhode Island violated Federal rules when it used funds from the State Small Business Credit Initiative (SSBCI) to invest in Betaspring, a startup accelerator program for technology and design entrepreneurs ready to launch their businesses. The Lyon Park audit claims that Rhode Island violated SSBCI rules because a large portion of the money went to the business accelerator's operating expenses and not to the startups themselves. **Availability:** Print; Online.

ASSOCIATIONS AND OTHER ORGANIZATIONS

25101 ■ **Coalition for Government Procurement (CGP)**
1990 M St. NW, Ste. 450
Washington, DC 20036
Ph: (202)331-0975
Fax: (202)521-3533
URL: http://thecgp.org
Contact: Roger Waldron, President
E-mail: rwaldron@thecgp.org
Linkedin: www.linkedin.com/company/875140
X (Twitter): x.com/TheCGPOrg

Description: Represents large and small businesses interested in commercial product procurement issues. Works to help protect the interests of federal government commercial product suppliers; to monitor commercial product legislation, policies, regulations and procurement trends of federal agencies. Provides members with current information, changes and developments in procurement policies and their impact. Conducts phone consultations. **Founded:** 1979. **Publications:** *Off the Shelf* (Monthly). **Awards:** CGP Excellence in Partnership Award - Lifetime Acquisition Excellence Award (Annual); CGP Excellence in Partnership Award - Myth-Busters Award (Annual); CGP Excellence in Partnership Award - Best Veteran Hiring Award (Annual); CGP Excellence in Partnership Award - Green Excellence in Partnership Award (Irregular); CGP Excellence in Partnership Award - Government Savings Award (Annual). **Geographic Preference:** National.

25102 ■ **National Contract Management Association (NCMA)**
21740 Beaumeade Cir., Ste. 125
Ashburn, VA 20147
Ph: (571)382-0082
Free: 800-344-8096
Fax: (703)448-0939
Co. E-mail: ncma@ncmahq.org
URL: http://www.ncmahq.org
Contact: Amanda Christian, President
Facebook: www.facebook.com/NCMAHQ
Linkedin: www.linkedin.com/company/ncma
X (Twitter): x.com/ncma
YouTube: www.youtube.com/user/NCMAHQ
Description: Professional individuals concerned with administration, procurement, acquisition, negotiation and management of contracts and subcontracts. Works for the education, improvement and professional development of members and nonmembers through national and chapter programs, symposia and educational materials. Offers certification in Contract Management (CPCM, CFCM, and CCCM) designations as well as a credential program. Operates speaker's bureau. **Founded:** 1959. **Publications:** *Journal of Contract Management* (Annual); *National Contract Management Journal* (Annual); *Contract Management* (Monthly). **Awards:** James E. Cravens Membership Award (Annual); NCMA Outstanding Fellow Award (Irregular). **Geographic Preference:** National.

EDUCATIONAL PROGRAMS

25103 ■ **Advanced Writing and Editing for Government Proposals**
URL(s): www.eeicom.com
Description: Developed for anyone who regularly writes, edits, or manages government proposals to explore proposal-specific writing and editing challenges, including how to ensure consistent voice no matter how many writers are involved. **Audience:** Professionals, administrative. **Principal Exhibits:** Developed for anyone who regularly writes, edits, or manages government proposals to explore proposal-specific writing and editing challenges, including how to ensure consistent voice no matter how many writers are involved.

25104 ■ **Basics of Government Contract Administration (Onsite)**
Seminar Information Service Inc. (SIS)
250 El Camino Real., Ste. 112
Tustin, CA 92780
Ph: (714)508-0340
Free: 877-736-4636
Fax: (714)734-8027
Co. E-mail: info@seminarinformation.com
URL: http://www.seminarinformation.com
Contact: Catherine Bellizzi, President
URL(s): www.seminarinformation.com
Description: Designed to show you how to fill out the most common standard forms, where the forms are found, and how proper forms preparation avoids administration pitfalls. **Audience:** General public. **Principal Exhibits:** Designed to show you how to fill out the most common standard forms, where the forms are found, and how proper forms preparation avoids administration pitfalls.

25105 ■ **Government Contract Accounting (Onsite)**
Seminar Information Service Inc. (SIS)
250 El Camino Real., Ste. 112
Tustin, CA 92780
Ph: (714)508-0340
Free: 877-736-4636
Fax: (714)734-8027
Co. E-mail: info@seminarinformation.com
URL: http://www.seminarinformation.com
Contact: Catherine Bellizzi, President
URL(s): www.seminarinformation.com
Description: Accounting principles as they relate to procurement activities with the Federal Government, with focus on Government forms and formats, direct and indirect cost rate submissions, cost principles, dealing with Government auditors, changes and delay claims and terminations. **Audience:** Purchasing professionals. **Principal Exhibits:** Accounting principles as they relate to procurement activities with the Federal Government, with focus on Government forms and formats, direct and indirect cost rate submissions, cost principles, dealing with Government auditors, changes and delay claims and terminations.

25106 ■ **Government Proposal Writing Basics**
URL(s): www.eeicom.com
Description: Designed for proposal novices at any level of writing ability, this course explains the unique features of government proposals and the government procurement process. **Audience:** Administrative professionals. **Principal Exhibits:** Designed for proposal novices at any level of writing ability, this course explains the unique features of government proposals and the government procurement process.

25107 ■ **Grow Your Business Through Government Contracting**
URL(s): cwewbc.ecenterdirect.com/events/977308
Description: This online meeting offered by the Center for Women and Enterprise provides information for Veteran business owners to grow their business and discusses helpful verifications and certifications. **Audience:** Small business owners, women, veterens. **Principal Exhibits:** This online meeting offered by the Center for Women and Enterprise provides information for Veteran business owners to grow their business and discusses helpful verifications and certifications.

REFERENCE WORKS

25108 ■ *"$161.9M 'Pit Stop' Fix-Up Will Create About 1,600 Jobs"* in *Orlando Business Journal (Vol. 26, January 22, 2010, No. 34, pp. 1)*
Pub: Orlando Business Journal
Contact: Julie Swyers, Director

GENERAL SMALL BUSINESS TOPICS

Government Procurement ■ 25128

E-mail: jswyers@bizjournals.com
Ed: Anjali Fluker. **Description:** State of Florida will be providing $161.9 million to renovate eight service plazas starting November 2010. The project is expected to create 1,600 jobs across the state and is expected to be completed by 2012. Details on bid advertisements and facilities slated for improvement are discussed. **Availability:** Print; Online.

25109 ■ "2012 Department of Homeland Security Small Business Achievement Award Given to Compass for Outstanding Performance" in Information Technology Business (May 1, 2012, pp. 16)
Description: Compass Systems Consulting Inc. was presented with the 2012 Department of Homeland Security (DHS) Small Business Achievement Award for outstanding work in support of the DHS mission. Compass is a management consulting company specializing in Performance Improvement, Program & Project Management, Acquisition Management and Audit, and Freedom of InformationACT (FOIA). **Availability:** Online.

25110 ■ "AG Warns Slots MBE Plan Risky" in Boston Business Journal (Vol. 29, May 27, 2011, No. 3, pp. 1)
Description: Attorney General Doug Gansler states that the law extending the minority business program on slots parlors contracting through 2018 could be open to lawsuits. He recommended that the state should conduct a study proving that minority- and women-owned businesses do not get a fair share in the gaming industry before it signs the bill to avoid lawsuits from majority-owned firms. **Availability:** Print; Online.

25111 ■ "Airmall Mulls I-95 Travel Plazas Bid" in Baltimore Business Journal (Vol. 29, September 2, 2011, No. 17, pp. 3)
Pub: Boston Business Journal
Contact: Carolyn M. Jones, President
E-mail: cmjones@bizjournals.com
Ed: Alexander Jackson. **Description:** Airmall USA is planning to move its food courts from the Baltimore/Washington International Thurgood Marshall Airport to the new travel plazas on Interstate 95. The plazas are up for bid. **Availability:** Online.

25112 ■ "Annapolis Seeks City Market Vendors" in Boston Business Journal (Vol. 29, June 10, 2011, No. 5, pp. 3)
Pub: Boston Business Journal
Contact: Carolyn M. Jones, President
E-mail: cmjones@bizjournals.com
Ed: Daniel J. Sernovitz. **Price:** $350. **Description:** The city of Annapolis, Maryland is planning to revive the historical landmark Market House and it is now accepting bids from vendors until June 10, 2011. The city hopes to reopen the facility by July 2011 for a six-month period after which it will undergo renovations. **Availability:** Print; Online.

25113 ■ "App Maker Thinks He Has the Ticket: But Denver Is Balking At Alternative To Parking Fines" in Denver Business Journal (Vol. 65, April 25, 2014, No. 50, pp. A10)
Pub: American City Business Journals, Inc.
Contact: Mike Olivieri, Executive Vice President
Released: Weekly. **Price:** $4, introductory 4-week offer(Digital & Print). **Description:** Taylor Linnell started Ticket Cricket LLC with partner, Jeff Valdez, to make parking tickets obsolete in Denver, Colorado by using two smartphone applications, One, Ticket Cricket and 5 for 5. The Department of Public Works rejected Linnell's proposal; he was encouraged to try it with the city's parking system technology vendor, Xerox. **Availability:** Print; Online.

25114 ■ "Apples, Decoded: WSU Scientist Unraveling the Fruit's Genetics" in Puget Sound Business Journal (Vol. 29, September 5, 2008, No. 20)
Description: Washington State University researcher is working to map the apple's genome in order to gain information about how the fruit grows, looks and tastes. His work, funded by a research grant from the US Department of Agriculture and the Washington Apple Commission is crucial to improving the state's position as an apple-producing region. **Availability:** Print; Online.

25115 ■ "Auto Bankruptcies Could Weaken Defense" in Crain's Detroit Business (Vol. 25, June 8, 2009, No. 23, pp. 1)
Pub: Crain Communications Inc.
Contact: Barry Asin, President
Ed: Chad Halcom. **Description:** Bankruptcy and supplier consolidation of General Motors Corporation and Chrysler LLC could interfere with the supply chains of some defense contractors, particularly makers of trucks and smaller vehicles. **Availability:** Print; Online.

25116 ■ "Aviat Networks Partners With AT&T Government Solutions for Department of Homeland Security Business" in Entertainment Close-Up August 13, 2012
Description: Aviat Networks Inc. will provide US Department of Homeland Security and other federal agencies withh the capability to acquire microwave radio communication equipment, engineering, design, installation and maintenace services. Aviat is a subcontractor on the AT&T Government Solutions' team. Aviat has a history of partnerships in federal technology space. **Availability:** Print; PDF; Online.

25117 ■ "Bloomington Police to Buy 24-Hour Electronic Kiosk With Federal Grant" in Herald-Times (September 5, 2012)
Ed: Abby Tonsing. **Description:** Bloomington, Indiana police department will purchase two electronic kiosks with money from a federal grant. The kiosks will operate 24 hours a day and provide the public with the ability to communicate with the police, obtain forms and permits, as well as other police-related activities. **Availability:** Print; Online.

25118 ■ "Bombardier Deja Vu" in Canadian Business (Vol. 83, August 17, 2010, No. 13-14, pp. 28)
Pub: Rogers Media Inc.
Contact: Neil Spivak, Chief Executive Officer
Ed: Laura Cameron. **Description:** Foreign competitors have accused the Quebec government and the Societe de transport de Montreal of giving Bombardier preferential treatment when it bids for contract to replace Montreal metro's rail cars. Bombardier was in a similar situation in 1974 when it won the contract to build the metro's second generation rail cars. **Availability:** Print; Online.

25119 ■ "Canada Seeks Collection Agency To Pursue $129M In Fines" in PaymentsSource (August 21, 2012)
Description: Canada's federal government has posted a letter of interest seeking a collection agency to recover about $129 million in unpaid fines. Details of the program are covered. **Availability:** Print; Online.

25120 ■ "Capital Metro May Soon Seek Contractor" in Austin Business Journal (Vol. 31, June 10, 2011, No. 14, pp. 1)
Pub: Austin Business Journal
Contact: Rachel McGrath, Director
E-mail: rmcgrath@bizjournals.com
Ed: Vicky Garza. **Description:** Capital Metropolitan Transportation Authority may be forced to contract out its bus services provided by StarTran Inc. as early as September 2012 following legislation approved by the Texas legislature. The bill originates in a report by the Sunset Advisory Commission. Details are included. **Availability:** Print; Online.

25121 ■ "Centerra Caught in Kyrgyzstan Dispute" in Globe & Mail (April 19, 2007, pp. B5)
Ed: Andy Hoffman. **Description:** The details of the demonstrations carried against government proposal to nationalize Centerra Gold Inc.'s assets are presented. **Availability:** Online.

25122 ■ "CEO Forecast: With Cloudy Economy, Executives Turn to Government Contracting" in Hispanic Business (January-February 2009, pp. 34, 36)
Ed: Jessica Haro, Richard Kaplan. **Description:** As economic uncertainty fogs the future, executives turn to government contracts in order to boost business. Revenue sources, health care challenges, environmental consulting and remediation services, as well as technological strides are discussed. **Availability:** Print; Online.

25123 ■ "Chesapeake Firm Regains Veteran-Owned Status" in Virginian-Pilot (August 21, 2012)
Pub: McClatchy Tribune Information Services
Contact: Patrick J. Talamantes, President
Ed: Philip Walzer. **Description:** Syncon LLC has regained status as a "veteran-owned" business. Mark Lilly, the president of Syncon is a retired Navy SEAL master chief who was wounded in combat in Afghanistan. Over-regulation by the US Department of Vetrans Affairs in order to stop fraud in the veteran certification program was responsible for the mistake. **Availability:** Print; Online.

25124 ■ "City Seeks More Minorities" in Austin Business Journal Inc. (Vol. 28, November 7, 2008, No. 34, pp. A1)
Pub: Austin Business Journal
Contact: Rachel McGrath, Director
E-mail: rmcgrath@bizjournals.com
Ed: Jean Kwon. **Description:** Austin, Texas is planning to increase the participation of minority- and women-owned businesses in government contracts. Contractors are required to show 'good faith' to comply with the specified goals. The city is planning to effect the changes in the construction and professional services sector. **Availability:** Print; Online.

25125 ■ "A Civilian Cybersecurity Center for D.C.?" in Washington Business Journal (Vol. 32, March 7, 2014, No. 47, pp. 5)
Pub: American City Business Journals, Inc.
Contact: Mike Olivieri, Executive Vice President
Description: The U.S. General Services Administration (GSA) is investigating the possibility for a civilian cybersecurity center in Washington DC to encourage further collaboration between government agencies. The GSA is seeking $35 million in the proposed 2015 federal budget for the project's design. **Availability:** Print; Online.

25126 ■ "Communications and Power Industries Awarded $6 Million to Support Apache Helicopter" in Defense & Aerospace Business (August 13, 2014, pp. 11)
Pub: NewsRX LLC.
Contact: Kalani Rosell, Contact
Description: Communications and Power Industries LLC procured an order totaling $6 million from Lockheed Martin Missiles and Fire Control for manufacturing tactical common data links. These links will be installed on the AH-64E Guardian variant of the Apache helicopter used to support U.S. warfighters. **Availability:** Online.

25127 ■ "Complete Discovery Source, Inc. (CDS) Receives Minority Owned Business Certification" in Marketwired (December 14, 2010)
Pub: Comtex News Network Inc.
Contact: Kan Devnani, President
Description: Complete Discovery Source Inc. (CDS) was granted Minority-Owned Business Enterprise status by the New York State Department of Economic Development. The certification provides CDS, an end-to-end eDiscovery services provider, with access to contracting opportunities with 130 government agencies throughout New York state. **Availability:** Print; Online.

25128 ■ "Contractor Backlog Dip Signals New Uncertainty" in Washington Business Journal (Vol. 31, August 3, 2012, No. 15, pp. 1)
Pub: Baltimore Business Journal
Contact: Rhonda Pringle, President

E-mail: rpringle@bizjournals.com
Description: Expected revenue from government awarded contracts may decline, US government contractors have reported. Budget uncertainties are seen to drive the development. **Availability:** Print; Online.

25129 ■ "Decorated Marine Sues Contractor" in Wall Street Journal Eastern Edition (November 29, 2011, pp. A4)
Pub: Dow Jones & Company Inc.
Contact: Almar Latour, Chief Executive Officer
Ed: Julian E. Barnes. **Description:** Marine Devon Maylie, who was awarded the Congressional Medal of Honor for bravery, has filed a lawsuit against defense contractor BAE Systems PLC claiming that the company prevented his hiring by another firm by saying he has a mental condition and a drinking problem. Maylie says that this was in retaliation for his objections to the company's plan to sell the Pakistani military high-tech sniper scopes. **Availability:** Online.

25130 ■ "DEM Says River Needs Cleanup" in Providence Business News (Vol. 28, January 6, 2014, No. 40, pp. 1)
Pub: American City Business Journals, Inc.
Contact: Mike Olivieri, Executive Vice President
Released: January 04, 2014. **Description:** Rhode Island's Department of Environmental Management (DEM) called a meeting to gather information for its Ten Mile River water-quality-restoration plan. DEM announced the failure of the Ten Mile River and its impoundments to meet state water quality standards. The government grant received by Attleboro for the cleanup efforts is examined. **Availability:** Print; Online.

25131 ■ "DIA Contract Sets a Record for Denver Minority, Woman-Owned Business" in Denver Business Journal (Vol. 65, February 21, 2014, No. 41)
Pub: American City Business Journals, Inc.
Contact: Mike Olivieri, Executive Vice President
Released: Weekly. **Description:** The City of Denver, Colorado has awarded a $39.6 million contract to Burgess Services Inc. to construct a transit and hotel project near the Denver International Airport. Burgess Services is owned by Denise Burgess. This is the largest public contract awarded to a woman0 or minority-owned business in the city's history. **Availability:** Print; Online.

25132 ■ "EOTech Product Improves Holographic Gun Sights" in Crain's Detroit Business (Vol. 24, February 4, 2008, No. 5, pp. 9)
Pub: Crain Communications Inc.
Contact: Barry Asin, President
Ed: Chad Halcom. **Description:** L-3 Communications EOTech Inc. procured new business contracts to fulfill military and law enforcement's demand for improved holographic sites used on handheld weapons. **Availability:** Online.

25133 ■ "France Telecom Takes Minitel Offline" in Canadian Business (Vol. 85, August 13, 2012, No. 13, pp. 12)
Ed: Matthew McClearn. **Description:** The Minitel online service was developed to reduce the costs of printing phone directories in the French postal and telecommunications ministry in 1978 and became popular in Paris in 1982. With its user-based halved annually and services declining in its waning years, France Telecom opted to terminate the service on June 30, 2012. **Availability:** Print; Online.

25134 ■ "General Dynamics Secures U.S. Navy Contract" in Travel & Leisure Close-Up (October 8, 2012)
Description: General Dynamics Electric Boat was awarded a $100.4 million contract modification by the U.S. Navy. Electric Boat will provide lead-yard services for Virginia-class nuclear-powered attack submarines. Details of the government procured contract are included. **Availability:** Online.

25135 ■ Getting Started in Federal Contracting: A Guide through the Federal Procurement Maze
Pub: Panoptic Enterprises
URL(s): www.fedgovcontracts.comwww.fedgovcontracts.com/bookstor.htm#book1
Released: Irregular **Price:** $39.95, Single issue for print. **Description:** Publication includes lists of 26 offices of small and disadvantaged business utilization; 10 Department of Labor regional offices, 11 General Services Administration business service centers, and 11 Small Business Administration regional offices, plus 14 Government resource offices; 35 commercial resources; training; books; newsletters; and associations. These agencies are of use to those privately-owned businesses wishing to sell their products and services to the federal government. Plus 26 Federal Acquisition Computer Network (FACNET) Certified Value Added Networks (VANS). **Entries include:** Agency name, address, phone, geographical territory covered. Principal content is discussion of current procurement regulations and information on how to submit proposals. **Arrangement:** Classified by agency represented; type of resource. **Indexes:** Organization name. **Availability:** Print.

25136 ■ "Goldbelt Inc.: Targeting Shareholder Development" in Alaska Business Monthly (Vol. 27, October 2011, No. 10, pp. 108)
Pub: Alaska Business Publishing Company Inc.
Contact: Charles Bell, Vice President, Sales and Marketing
E-mail: cbell@akbizmag.com
Ed: Tracy Kalytiak. **Description:** Profile of Goldbelt Inc., the company that has changed its original focus of timber to real estate to tourism and then to government contracting opportunities. **Availability:** Print; Online.

25137 ■ "Grant Program Boosting Biomedical Research" in Providence Business News (Vol. 28, February 24, 2014, No. 47, pp. 3)
Pub: American City Business Journals, Inc.
Contact: Mike Olivieri, Executive Vice President
Released: February 22, 2014. **Description:** The role played by the Institutional Development Award Network of Biomedical Research Excellence (INBRE) is boosting biomedical research in Rhode Island. According to researcher, Niall G. Howlett, procuring startup funding through INBRE led to receiving other grants and working with graduate students who have the potential to become part of the biomedical workforce. **Availability:** Print; Online.

25138 ■ "Half a World Away" in Tampa Bay Business Journal (Vol. 30, December 4, 2009, No. 50, pp. 1)
Description: Enterprise Florida has offered four trade grants for Florida's marine industry businesses to give them a chance to tap into the Middle East market at the Dubai International Boat Show on March 9 to 13, 2010. The grants pay for 50 percent of the exhibition costs for the qualifying business. **Availability:** Online.

25139 ■ "High-Tech Job-Apalooza!" in Orlando Business Journal (Vol. 26, January 15, 2010, No. 33, pp. 1)
Pub: Orlando Business Journal
Contact: Julie Swyers, Director
E-mail: jswyers@bizjournals.com
Ed: Christopher Boyd. **Description:** Science Applications International Corporation, Saab Training USA LLC, CAE USA, and Pelliconi &C.SPA attempt to obtain $939,000 in tax incentives to generate 222 technology and defense-related jobs in Orange County, Florida. Each job will provide an average salary of $67,000. Future plans of each technology and defense firm are also presented. **Availability:** Print; Online.

25140 ■ How to Pay Zero Taxes: Your Guide to Every Tax Break the IRS Allows
Released: 2020-2021 edition. **Price:** $12.96, e-book; $24, paperback. **Description:** Simple strategies to save your small business money in taxes, while following the government's tax regulations are covered, for this year and years beyond. The guide covers deductions organized into six categories: exclusions, general deductions, below the line deductions, traditional tax shelters, and super tax shelters. **Availability:** E-book; Print.

25141 ■ "Indiana Town Reports Success With Collection Agency" in PaymentsSource (August 20, 2012)
Description: Capital Recovery Systems has collected nearly $80,000 in unpaid parking fines in Bloomington, Indiana. The city's agreement with the collection agency allows them to pursue an unlimited amount of unpaid parking tickets at least 30 days late. **Availability:** Print; Online.

25142 ■ "Infusion Device Gets $1.47 Million Army Grant" in Memphis Business Journal (Vol. 33, January 20, 2012, No. 41, pp. 1)
Pub: Baltimore Business Journal
Contact: Rhonda Pringle, President
E-mail: rpringle@bizjournals.com
Ed: Michael Sheffield. **Description:** Infusense has procured a $1.47 million grant from the US Army to develop an automated delivery system for the anesthesia Propofol. The drug is used in more than 70 million surgeries and procedures in the country. The medical device would allow for the administration of the anesthesia to wounded soldiers by medics in the field. **Availability:** Print; Online.

25143 ■ "iRobot Appoints Former BAE Systems Vice President, Frank Wilson to Lead Defense & Security Business Unit" in News Bites US (August 9, 2012)
Description: Frank Wilson will serve as senior vice president and general manager of iRobot's Defense & Security business unit. He will focus on strategic business development and product development in order for the firm to meet military, civil defense, and security needs. Tim Trainer, previous acting interim general manager, will remain vice president of programs. **Availability:** Print; Online.

25144 ■ "Job Corps Center Remains Vacant After Operator is Booted" in Tampa Bay Business Journal (Vol. 30, January 15, 2010, No. 4, pp. 1)
Pub: Tampa Bay Business Journal
Contact: Ian Anderson, President
E-mail: ianderson@bizjournals.com
Ed: Jane Meinhardt. **Description:** Pinellas County, Florida Job Corps Center has remained vacant due to a conflict over the $16 million contract awarded to Res-Care Inc. by the US Department of Labor (DOL) The DOL has ordered Res-Care to stop operation at the center and it is uncertain when it will open or what company will operate it. **Availability:** Print; Online.

25145 ■ "Lancaster Firm Helps Tidy Navy Aircraft Carriers" in Business First of Buffalo (Vol. 30, February 7, 2014, No. 21, pp. 4)
Pub: American City Business Journals, Inc.
Contact: Mike Olivieri, Executive Vice President
Released: February 7, 2014. **Price:** $140, Digital & Print; $115, Digital only. **Description:** Performance Advantage Company sells aluminum took racking systems for use by fire trucks, SWAT teams and departments of public works. The Lancaster, New York-based firm also manufactures clamps and racks for the U.S. Navy, which uses them in aircraft carriers. **Availability:** Print; Online.

25146 ■ "Local Companies Land Federal Securities Pacts" in Sacramento Business Journal (Vol. 31, March 7, 2014, No. 2, pp. 6)
Pub: American City Business Journals, Inc.
Contact: Mike Olivieri, Executive Vice President
Description: Three companies in Sacramento, California have received Federal security contracts in 2014. Capitol Digital Document Solutions has a five-year contract with the U.S. Department of Homeland Security, while Hewlett-Packard signed a deal with

the same government agency. Stratovan Corporation secured two contracts from the U.S. Transportation Security Board. **Availability:** Online.

25147 ■ *"Local Company Seeks Patent For Armored Trucks"* in *Crain's Detroit Business (Vol. 24, February 4, 2008, No. 5, pp. 10)*
Pub: Crain Communications Inc.
Contact: Barry Asin, President
Description: Profile of James LeBlanc Sr., mechanical engineer and defense contractor, discusses his eleven utility patents pending for a set of vehicles and subsystems that would work as countermeasures to explosively formed projectiles. **Availability:** Print; Online.

25148 ■ *"Maryland Nonprofits May Lose Minority Business Enterprise Status"* in *Baltimore Business Journal (Vol. 29, September 2, 2011, No. 17, pp. 1)*
Pub: Boston Business Journal
Contact: Carolyn M. Jones, President
E-mail: cmjones@bizjournals.com
Ed: Scott Dance. **Description:** A business group has been pushing to bar nonprofits from Maryland's Minority Business program. Nonprofits have been found to take a large portion of state contracts intended for women- and minority-owned businesses. The group is also crafting proposed legislation to remove nonprofits from the program. **Availability:** Online.

25149 ■ *"Maryland Ready to Defend Slots Minority Policy"* in *Boston Business Journal (Vol. 29, July 8, 2011, No. 9, pp. 3)*
Pub: Boston Business Journal
Contact: Carolyn M. Jones, President
E-mail: cmjones@bizjournals.com
Ed: Scott Dance. **Description:** The legality of Maryland's minority inclusion policy may be put under scrutiny once the lawsuit filed by rejected slots developer Baltimore City Entertainment Group on July 5, 2011 is heard in court. The lawsuit aims to stop the bidding process on a proposed casino in Baltimore because the minority policy amounts to reverse discrimination. **Availability:** Print; Online.

25150 ■ *"Montgomery & Barnes: a Service-Disabled, Veteran-Owned Small Business"* in *Underground Construction (Vol. 65, October 2010, No. 10)*
Description: Gary Montgomery, chairman of Montgomery and Barnes announced that President Wendell (Buddy) Barnes is now majority owner, thus making the Houston-based civil engineering and consulting services firm, eligible to quality as a Service-Disabled Veteran-Owned Small Business (SDVOSB). **Availability:** Online.

25151 ■ *"North Carolina Town Hires Collection Agency"* in *PaymentsSource (April 24, 2012)*
Description: Selma, North Carolina hired TekCollect to collect about $500,000 in unpaid utility bills. The collection agency will be paid $13,000 up frnt for guaranteed collections on 500 of the 1,200 accounts. **Availability:** Online.

25152 ■ *"Not in Your Backyard?"* in *Canadian Business (Vol. 80, March 12, 2007, No. 6, pp. 44)*
Description: The threat of losing residential property rights of persons whose land has rightful stakes from miners due to availability of minerals at the place is discussed. **Availability:** Print; Online.

25153 ■ *"Outlook In Other Industries"* in *Crain's Detroit Business (Vol. 30, January 6, 2014, No. 1, pp. 3)*
Pub: Crain Communications Inc.
Contact: Barry Asin, President
Released: January 6, 2014. **Description:** Outlook for industries in the Detroit area are listed, including small business growth, restaurants, defense contracts, nonprofits, transportation, auto suppliers, healthcare, bankruptcy, and government. **Availability:** Print; PDF; Online.

25154 ■ *"Pentagon Awards $17.6B Contract for EB-Built Subs Through 2018"* in *Providence Business News (Vol. 29, April 28, 2014, No. 4)*
Pub: American City Business Journals, Inc.
Contact: Mike Olivieri, Executive Vice President
URL(s): pbn.com/pentagon-awards-176b-contract-for-eb-built-subs-through-20189678
Description: The U.S. Navy has signed a $17.6 billion contract with Newport News Shipbuilding and General Dynamics Corporation for construction of 10 new naval submarines. The deal will help employment at General Dynamics' Quonset Business Park Electric Boat production site. The submarines are scheduled to be built between 2014-2018. Electric Boat expects to hire 650 additional workers.

25155 ■ *"Private Health-Care Services Growing in Canada"* in *Canadian Business (Vol. 85, June 11, 2012, No. 10, pp. 10)*
Ed: Laura Cameron. **Description:** Some public-private partnerships in Canada include the acquisition of clinics by Centric Health Corporation and the partnership between Westbank First National and Johns Hopkins Hospital. Private healthcare providers have operated by dividing their funding among government contracts, clients not covered by Medicare and patients paying out of pocket and non-insured services. **Availability:** Print; Online.

25156 ■ *"The Quest for a Smart Prosthetic"* in *Canadian Business (Vol. 83, October 12, 2010, No. 17, pp. 26)*
Pub: Rogers Media Inc.
Contact: Neil Spivak, Chief Executive Officer
Ed: Jacqueline Nelson. **Description:** Information about a two-year research project led by Southern Methodist University (SMU) and funded by the Defense Advance Research Projects Agency (DARPA) is provided. The agency aims to create a 'smart prosthetic' which will improve the lives of military amputees. The planned prosthetic will use a sensor that can carry nerve signals through synthetic channels. **Availability:** Print; Online.

25157 ■ *"SAIC To Be Honored For Supporting Veteran-Owned Businesses"* in *News Bites US (June 13, 2012)*
Description: Science Applications International Corporation (SAIC) was recognized by the National Veteran Small Business Coalition at the Veteran Entrepreneur Training Symposium (VETS2012) 'Champions of Veteran Enterprise' luncheon held in Reno, Nevada in June. SAIC is honored for its work with veteran-owned and service-disabled veteran owned small businesses. Statistical data included. **Availability:** Print; Online.

25158 ■ *"A Second Chance at Road Dollars"* in *Orlando Business Journal (Vol. 26, February 5, 2010, No. 36, pp. 1)*
Pub: Orlando Business Journal
Contact: Julie Swyers, Director
E-mail: jswyers@bizjournals.com
Description: Nearly $10 million worth of construction projects in Central Florida would give construction companies that missed the initial round of federal stimulus-funded local road building projects another opportunity. Cost savings in the initial round of road projects enabled Orange, Osceola, and Seminole Counties to secure additional projects. **Availability:** Print; Online.

25159 ■ *"Six Arkansas Construction Projects Get LEED Certification"* in *Arkansas Business (Vol. 29, July 23, 2012, No. 30, pp. 19)*
Pub: Arkansas Business Publishing Group
Contact: Mitch Bettis, President
Ed: Lance Turner. **Description:** State of Arkansas has bestowed its Leadership in Energy and Environmental Design certification on 55 projects throughout the state. Six projects are identified and described. A list of all projects is included. **Availability:** Online.

25160 ■ *"Slater Progress Stalled"* in *Providence Business News (Vol. 28, March 10, 2014, No. 49, pp. 1)*
Pub: American City Business Journals, Inc.
Contact: Mike Olivieri, Executive Vice President
URL(s): pbn.com/slater-progress-stalled95603
Description: Slater Technology Fund has received only $1.9 million of the $9 million in expected federal funds. However, the venture capital firm decided to invest in some promising technology companies in Providence, Rhode Island. Slater senior managing director, Richard Horan, reveals that uncertainties with respect to grants have delayed private fundraising. **Availability:** Online.

25161 ■ *"Special Events Pro Mary Tribble Reveals Secrets of Winning Bids for Political Convention Business"* in *Special Events Magazine (May 30, 2012)*
Ed: Lisa Hurley. **Description:** Mary Tribble, successful event planner, offers tips for winning bids for political conventions. Tribble serves as chief of event planning for the "Charlotte in 2012" convention for the Democratic National Convention.

25162 ■ *"Taking Off"* in *Puget Sound Business Journal (Vol. 34, January 31, 2014, No. 42, pp. 4)*
Pub: American City Business Journals, Inc.
Contact: Mike Olivieri, Executive Vice President
Description: Washington State is at the forefront of the U.S. space flight industry, as the federal government shrinks its role and entrepreneurs are filling the gap. The region is becoming a leader in the space sector because of its high-tech aerospace skills, software intellectuals, and investors willing to fund these enterprises. **Availability:** Online.

25163 ■ *"TIA Wrestles with Procurement Issues"* in *Business Journal Serving Greater Tampa Bay (Vol. 30, November 12, 2010, No. 47, pp. 1)*
Pub: Tampa Bay Business Journal
Contact: Ian Anderson, President
E-mail: ianderson@bizjournals.com
Ed: Mark Holan. **Description:** Tampa International Airport (TIA) has been caught in conflict of interest and procurement policy issues after the Hillsborough County Aviation Authority learned of the spousal relationship of an employee with his wife's firm, Gresham Smith and Partners. Gresham already won contracts with TIA and was ahead of other firms in a new contract. **Availability:** Print; Online.

25164 ■ *"U-Swirl Added to SBA's Franchise Registry"* in *Ice Cream Reporter (Vol. 23, September 20, 2010, No. 10, pp. 1)*
Description: Healthy Fast Food Inc., parent to the U-SWIRL Frozen Yogurt cafe chain announced that the U.S. Small Business Administration listed U-SWIRL Frozen Yogurt on its official franchise registry. This move will allow U-SWIRL the benefits of a streamlined review process for SBA financing. **Availability:** Print; Online.

25165 ■ *"UW Wary of WSU's Wish for Spokane Medical School"* in *Puget Sound Business Journal (Vol. 35, May 9, 2014, No. 3, pp. 9)*
Pub: American City Business Journals, Inc.
Contact: Mike Olivieri, Executive Vice President
Description: University of Washington leaders believe that opening a medical school in Washington State University's (WSU) Spokane Campus will create more competition for state funding. However, WSU officials claim that the demand for new doctors demonstrates the need for a second school. **Availability:** Online.

25166 ■ *"VA Exceeds Government-Wide Goal for Veteran-Owned Business Procurement"* in *Benzinga.com (July 3, 2012)*
Pub: Benzinga.com
Contact: Jason Raznick, Founder

Ed: Aaron Wise. **Description:** Department of Veterans Affairs has surpassed its goal of government procurements of the Small Business Adminstration by more than six times. The VA's committment to the success of veteran-owned small businesses is covered.

25167 ■ *"Veteran-Owned Firm Enlists Street" in Traders (Vol. 25, May 1, 2012, No. 337)*
Description: Academy Securities discusses its vision to give US military veterans a chance at a career on Wall Street. Academy is a veteran owned investment brokerage firm and is pursuing Wall Street professionals willing to mentor veterans. The firm is dedicated to giving back to the veterans who have served the nation and is a certified Service Disabled Veteran Owned Business. **Availability:** Print; Online.

25168 ■ *"Wi-Fi Finds Its Way Despite Nixed Plan for Free System" in Crain's Cleveland Business (Vol. 28, November 12, 2007, No. 45, pp. 3)*
Pub: Crain Communications Inc.
Contact: K. C. Crain, President
Ed: Jay Miller. **Description:** Discusses the issues facing Cleveland and Northeast Ohio concerning their proposal to offer citizens wireless Internet services for free or a small fee. **Availability:** Online.

25169 ■ *Win Government Contracts for Your Small Business*
Pub: DTI
Ed: John DiGiacomo. **Released:** Fifth edition. **Price:** $6.29; $7.09, paperback. **Description:** Techniques to help small companies negotiate and win government contracts.

TRADE PERIODICALS

25170 ■ *Inside Missile Defense*
Pub: Inside Washington Publishers
Contact: Robert Woolard, Contact
URL(s): insidedefense.com/services2/missile-defense-news
Released: Biweekly **Price:** $795, U.S. and Canada; $845, Elsewhere for one year. **Description:** Reports on U.S. missile defense programs, procurement, and policymaking. **Availability:** Print.

VIDEO/AUDIO MEDIA

25171 ■ *The How of Business: Kizzy Parks - Government Contracts*
URL(s): www.thehowofbusiness.com/386-kizzy-parks-government-contracts
Ed: Henry Lopez. **Released:** August 23, 2021. **Description:** Podcast offers tips on securing and managing government contracts.

COMPUTERIZED DATABASES

25172 ■ *FedBizOpps*
URL(s): www.cbd-net.com
Availability: Online. **Type:** Full-text; Directory.

LIBRARIES

25173 ■ **Georgia State University - J. Mack Robinson College of Business - Small Business Development Center (SBDC) - Reference Collection [University of Georgia Small Business Development Center at Georgia State University; University of Georgia - Small Business Development Center - Atlanta Office]**
75 Piedmont Ave., Ste. 700
Atlanta, GA 30303
Ph: (404)413-7830
Fax: (404)413-7832
Co. E-mail: atlanta@georgiasbdc.org
URL: http://sbdc.robinson.gsu.edu
Contact: Alicia Johnson, Coordinator
E-mail: ajohnson@georgiasbdc.org
URL(s): www.georgiasbdc.org/atlanta-office
Facebook: www.facebook.com/ugasbdcgsu
Linkedin: www.linkedin.com/company/ugasbdcgsu
X (Twitter): x.com/ugasbdcgsu
Instagram: www.instagram.com/ugasbdcgsu
Description: Integral unit of Georgia State University. **Scope:** Small business, marketing, finance, international business, and government procurement. **Services:** Counseling; Center open to the public for reference use only. **Founded:** 1977. **Holdings:** Business directories; government publications and journals, periodicals, training manuals and videotapes. **Subscriptions:** 11 journals and other serials. **Geographic Preference:** Local.

25174 ■ **NIGP: The Institute for Public Procurement - Document Library**
13800 Coppermine Rd, 1st Fl.
Herndon, VA 20171
Ph: (703)736-8900
Free: 800-367-6447
Fax: (703)736-9644
Co. E-mail: customercare@nigp.org
URL: http://www.nigp.org
Contact: Fareshta Touhami, Director, Marketing
E-mail: ftouhami@nigp.org
Facebook: www.facebook.com/OfficialNIGP
Linkedin: www.linkedin.com/company/national-institute-of-governmental-purchasing
X (Twitter): x.com/OfficialNIGP
YouTube: www.youtube.com/user/NIGP1
Description: Administers certification program for the Universal Public Purchasing Certification Council (UPPCC) for Certified Professional Public Buyer (CPPB) and Certified Public Purchasing Officer (CPPO); offers audit consulting services and cost-saving programs and tools for governmental agencies, including product commodity code to online specifications library. **Scope:** Provides services to the International procurement community. Develops standards and specifications for governmental buying; promotes uniform purchasing laws and procedures; conducts specialized education and research programs. **Founded:** 1944. **Holdings:** 1,000 templates, publications. **Publications:** *NIGP BuyWeekly* (Semimonthly); *The NIGP Source* (Quarterly); *The Procurement Professional* (Bimonthly); *The Public Purchaser* (Bimonthly). **Educational Activities:** NIGP Annual Forum & Products Exposition (Annual). **Awards:** NIGP Distinguished Service Awards (DSA) (Annual); Albert H. Hall Memorial Award (Annual); NIGP Chapter of the Year Award (Annual); Procurement Specialist of the Year Award (Annual); NIGP Manager of the Year Award (Annual); NIGP Outstanding Agency Accreditation Achievement (Annual). **Geographic Preference:** National.

Government Regulations

START-UP INFORMATION

25175 ■ *"Breaking Barriers"* in *Baltimore Business Journal (Vol. 30, June 29, 2012, No. 8, pp. 1)*

Ed: Jack Lambert. **Description:** Many Hispanic entrepreneurs have been struggling to start businesses in Baltimore, Maryland. Many necessary documents are available only in English. Hispanic businesses are seen to spark future economic growth in Baltimore. **Availability:** Print; Online.

25176 ■ *"JOBS Act Spurring Bio IPOs"* in *Philadelphia Business Journal (Vol. 33, May 2, 2014, No. 12, pp. 4)*

Pub: American City Business Journals, Inc.
Contact: Mike Olivieri, Executive Vice President

Released: Weekly. **Price:** $4, Introductory 4-week offer(Digital only). **Description:** The Jumpstart Our Business Startups Act has important provisions that are helping many early-stage biotechnology companies in their initial public offerings. Trevena Inc. of King of Prussia, Pennsylvania benefited from the extra time to educate the investment community and from the exemptions on the regulatory requirements. **Availability:** Print; Online.

25177 ■ *The Small Business Start-Up Kit*
Pub: Nolo
Contact: Chris Braun, President

Ed: Peri Pakroo. **Released:** 12th edition. **Price:** $20.99, E-book. **Description:** Entrepreneurial advice for launching a new business. Topics include compliance with state regulations, sole proprietorships, partnerships, corporations, limited liability companies, as well as accounting and tax information. **Availability:** E-book; Print; Electronic publishing; PDF.

25178 ■ *Small Business Survival Guide*

Released: First edition. **Description:** Small business expert provides strategies to start a company and survive in the 21st Century. He shows small business owners how to succeed despite challenges that can defeat any firm. His advice covers suppliers; customers and contractors; competitors and creditors; spouses, family and friends; as well as the ways lawyers, accountants and other can steal an entrepreneur's success. Ennico also describes how startups can comply with local regulations. **Availability:** E-book; Print.

25179 ■ *"So What Is Crowdfunding Anyway? New Legislation by Obama and Congress Relaxes Solicitation by Startups"* in *Accounting Today (August 6, 2012)*

Ed: Jim Brendel. **Description:** An introduction to crowdfunding provides a concise description to the process in which a group of investors partner to fund small business and startups. Rules from the SEC regarding crowdfunding are expected to be in place by the end of the year. **Availability:** Print; Online.

25180 ■ *"StartX Med Prescribed for Innovation"* in *Silicon Valley/San Jose Business Journal (Vol. 30, June 8, 2012, No. 11, pp. 1)*
Pub: Baltimore Business Journal
Contact: Rhonda Pringle, President
E-mail: rpringle@bizjournals.com

Description: StartX Med is a program started by entrepreneur Divya Nag along with Stanford student-led nonprofit StartX to help medical startups. Under the program, entrepreneurs will have access to wet and dry laboratory space, animal testing and information related to US Food and Drug Adminstration regulations. **Availability:** Print; Online.

ASSOCIATIONS AND OTHER ORGANIZATIONS

25181 ■ **Small Business Council of America (SBCA)**
2751 Centerville Rd., Ste. 401
Wilmington, DE 19808
Ph: (302)691-7222
URL: http://www.sbca.net
Contact: Gary Kushner, President

Description: Small business and professional organizations. Goals are to keep federal tax and employee benefit legislation from becoming burdensome, and to support legislation. **Founded:** 1979. **Publications:** *News Flashes*; *SBCA Member and Congressional Directory* (Annual); *Tax Report* (Monthly); *Small Business Council of America--Alert* (Quarterly). **Educational Activities:** SBCA Congressional Awards Ceremony. **Awards:** SBCA Connie Murdoch Award (Annual); The Mort Harris Small Business Person of the Year Award (Annual); The SBCA Humanitarian of the Year Awards (Annual). **Geographic Preference:** National.

25182 ■ **Small Business Legislative Council (SBLC)**
4800 Hampden Ln., 6th Fl.
Bethesda, MD 20814
Ph: (301)652-8302
Co. E-mail: email@sblc.org
URL: http://sblc.org
Contact: Paula Calimafde, President

Description: Serves as an independent coalition of trade and professional associations that share a common commitment to the future of small business. Represents the interests of small businesses in such diverse economic sectors as manufacturing, retailing, distribution, professional and technical services, construction, transportation, and agriculture. **Founded:** 1976. **Geographic Preference:** National.

EDUCATIONAL PROGRAMS

25183 ■ **Adobe Acrobat Section 508 Accessibility (Onsite)**
URL(s): www.eeicom.com

Description: Covers the regulations by the Federal Government's Section 508 accessibility and the features of Adobe Acrobat software designed to meet the regulations, including definition of accessibility, authoring for accessibility, working with existing PDF files, forms, and scanned documents, using the accessibility checker, and tags palette, and testing your PDF files for accessibility. **Audience:** Industry professionals. **Principal Exhibits:** Covers the regulations by the Federal Government's Section 508 accessibility and the features of Adobe Acrobat software designed to meet the regulations, including definition of accessibility, authoring for accessibility, working with existing PDF files, forms, and scanned documents, using the accessibility checker, and tags palette, and testing your PDF files for accessibility.

25184 ■ **ASTM Phase I & Phase II Environmental Site Assessment Processes (Onsite)**
Seminar Information Service Inc. (SIS)
250 El Camino Real., Ste. 112
Tustin, CA 92780
Ph: (714)508-0340
Free: 877-736-4636
Fax: (714)734-8027
Co. E-mail: info@seminarinformation.com
URL: http://www.seminarinformation.com
Contact: Catherine Bellizzi, President
URL(s): www.seminarinformation.com/qqbrwl/astm-phase-i-and-phase-ii-environmental-site-assessment

Description: Gain an understanding how to use the standards and how the standards affect the way you do business. The 'Innocent Landowner Defense' under the Comprehensive Environmental Response, Compensation and Liability Act (CERCLA) and why due diligence is necessary will be covered. **Audience:** Industry professionals. **Principal Exhibits:** Gain an understanding how to use the standards and how the standards affect the way you do business. The 'Innocent Landowner Defense' under the Comprehensive Environmental Response, Compensation and Liability Act (CERCLA) and why due diligence is necessary will be covered.

25185 ■ **Automotive Glazing Materials (Onsite)**
Seminar Information Service Inc. (SIS)
250 El Camino Real., Ste. 112
Tustin, CA 92780
Ph: (714)508-0340
Free: 877-736-4636
Fax: (714)734-8027
Co. E-mail: info@seminarinformation.com
URL: http://www.seminarinformation.com
Contact: Catherine Bellizzi, President
URL(s): www.seminarinformation.com

Description: An overview of the different automotive glazing materials, past, present and future, including the laws that govern their use, and manufacture, installation, usage, testing, safety aspects and how they affect automotive performance. Topics include the chemical, physical and design issues of annealed, laminated, tempered, glass-plastic and plastic glazing materials. **Audience:** Industry professionals. **Principal Exhibits:** An overview of the different automotive glazing materials, past, present and future, including the laws that govern their use, and manufacture, installation, usage, testing, safety aspects and how they affect automotive performance. Topics include the chemical, physical and design issues of annealed, laminated, tempered, glass-plastic and plastic glazing materials.

25186 ■ Automotive Lighting (Onsite)
Seminar Information Service Inc. (SIS)
  250 El Camino Real., Ste. 112
  Tustin, CA 92780
Ph: (714)508-0340
Free: 877-736-4636
Fax: (714)734-8027
Co. E-mail: info@seminarinformation.com
URL: http://www.seminarinformation.com
Contact: Catherine Bellizzi, President
URL(s): www.seminarinformation.com

Description: Provides broad information about automotive lighting systems with emphasis on lighting functions, effectiveness, and technologies, including the legal aspects and implications related to automotive lighting and examine safety measurements used with lighting functions and human factors costs. **Audience:** Industry professionals. **Principal Exhibits:** Provides broad information about automotive lighting systems with emphasis on lighting functions, effectiveness, and technologies, including the legal aspects and implications related to automotive lighting and examine safety measurements used with lighting functions and human factors costs.

25187 ■ DOT Hazardous Materials Training (Onsite)
Seminar Information Service Inc. (SIS)
  250 El Camino Real., Ste. 112
  Tustin, CA 92780
Ph: (714)508-0340
Free: 877-736-4636
Fax: (714)734-8027
Co. E-mail: info@seminarinformation.com
URL: http://www.seminarinformation.com
Contact: Catherine Bellizzi, President
URL(s): www.seminarinformation.com/details.cfm?qc=qqaubm

Description: DOT is changing virtually all of the rules for hazardous materials containers, labeling, shipping papers, placards, and shipping names. Learn how to comply with the regulations. **Audience:** Shipping supervisors, purchasing managers, traffic managers, plant managers, shipping clerks, dispatchers, purchasing agents, drivers, and compliance managers. **Principal Exhibits:** DOT is changing virtually all of the rules for hazardous materials containers, labeling, shipping papers, placards, and shipping names. Learn how to comply with the regulations.

25188 ■ Fred Pryor Seminars & CareerTrack Collections Law (Onsite)
URL(s): www.pryor.com

Description: Ensure your organization is legally compliant, including strategies and techniques to gain quicker results in collecting money. **Audience:** Managers, supervisors, vice-presidents and professionals. **Principal Exhibits:** Ensure your organization is legally compliant, including strategies and techniques to gain quicker results in collecting money.

25189 ■ Fred Pryor Seminars & CareerTrack Records Retention and Destruction (Onsite)
URL(s): www.pryor.com

Description: Gain valuable information for successfully organizing, storing, archiving and destroying your organization's critical business documents while eliminating risk and ensuring compliance with the latest legal requirements. **Audience:** Controllers, accountants, medical records professionals, legal professionals, administrators, information technology staff, financial professionals, human resource managers and staff. **Principal Exhibits:** Gain valuable information for successfully organizing, storing, archiving and destroying your organization's critical business documents while eliminating risk and ensuring compliance with the latest legal requirements.

25190 ■ Hazardous Waste Management: The Complete Course
Seminar Information Service Inc. (SIS)
  250 El Camino Real., Ste. 112
  Tustin, CA 92780
Ph: (714)508-0340
Free: 877-736-4636
Fax: (714)734-8027
Co. E-mail: info@seminarinformation.com
URL: http://www.seminarinformation.com
Contact: Catherine Bellizzi, President
URL(s): www.seminarinformation.com/qqajxq/hazardous-waste-management-the-complete-course

Description: Covers how to meet your annual training requirement and learn a systematic approach to understanding and complying with the latest state and federal regulations. **Audience:** Environmental coordinators, hazardous waste managers and plant managers. **Principal Exhibits:** Covers how to meet your annual training requirement and learn a systematic approach to understanding and complying with the latest state and federal regulations.

25191 ■ Hazardous Waste Management: The Complete Course (Onsite)
Seminar Information Service Inc. (SIS)
  250 El Camino Real., Ste. 112
  Tustin, CA 92780
Ph: (714)508-0340
Free: 877-736-4636
Fax: (714)734-8027
Co. E-mail: info@seminarinformation.com
URL: http://www.seminarinformation.com
Contact: Catherine Bellizzi, President
URL(s): www.seminarinformation.com/qqajxq/hazardous-waste-management-the-complete-course

Description: Learn a systematic approach to understanding and complying with the latest state and federal regulations. **Audience:** Environmental coordinators, hazardous waste managers and plant managers. **Principal Exhibits:** Learn a systematic approach to understanding and complying with the latest state and federal regulations.

25192 ■ SARA Title III Workshop (Onsite)
Seminar Information Service Inc. (SIS)
  250 El Camino Real., Ste. 112
  Tustin, CA 92780
Ph: (714)508-0340
Free: 877-736-4636
Fax: (714)734-8027
Co. E-mail: info@seminarinformation.com
URL: http://www.seminarinformation.com
Contact: Catherine Bellizzi, President
URL(s): www.seminarinformation.com/details.cfm?qc=qqakcg

Description: Step-by-step procedures for compliance with Title III of the Superfund Amendments. **Audience:** Safety coordinators, plant managers and training directors. **Principal Exhibits:** Step-by-step procedures for compliance with Title III of the Superfund Amendments.

25193 ■ Storm Water Management: How to Comply with Federal and State Regulations (Onsite)
Seminar Information Service Inc. (SIS)
  250 El Camino Real., Ste. 112
  Tustin, CA 92780
Ph: (714)508-0340
Free: 877-736-4636
Fax: (714)734-8027
Co. E-mail: info@seminarinformation.com
URL: http://www.seminarinformation.com
Contact: Catherine Bellizzi, President
URL(s): www.seminarinformation.com/qqakep/storm-water-management-how-to-comply-with-federal-and

Description: Learn what discharges must be permitted, how to apply for a permit, and requirements for maintaining permit compliance. **Audience:** Environmental coordinators, safety coordinators, plant managers, and hazardous waste managers. **Principal Exhibits:** Learn what discharges must be permitted, how to apply for a permit, and requirements for maintaining permit compliance.

25194 ■ Workers' Compensation
Fred Pryor Seminars & CareerTrack
  5700 Broadmoor, Ste. 300
  Mission, KS 66202
Free: 800-780-8476
Fax: (913)967-8849
Co. E-mail: customerservice@pryor.com
URL: http://www.pryor.com
Contact: Janet Turner, Contact
E-mail: dmca@pryor.com
URL(s): www.pryor.com/training-seminars/workers-compensation

Frequency: Irregular. **Description:** Learn strategies, insider tips, tools, and more to help manage entire workers' compensation plan more effectively, including how workers' compensation, FMLA, and ADA regulations can overlap. **Audience:** Professionals. **Principal Exhibits:** Learn strategies, insider tips, tools, and more to help manage entire workers' compensation plan more effectively, including how workers' compensation, FMLA, and ADA regulations can overlap.

REFERENCE WORKS

25195 ■ "5 Things You Should Know If Your Bank Fails" in Black Enterprise (Vol. 41, December 2010, No. 5, pp. 29)
Pub: Earl G. Graves Ltd.
Contact: Earl Graves, Jr., President
Ed: John Simons. **Description:** The Federal Deposit Insurance Corporation announced that the number of banks in trouble has reached the highest level since March 1993. Advice from the FDIC is cited. Statistical data included. **Availability:** Online.

25196 ■ "11th Circuit: Don't Break the Law to Comply with It" in Miami Daily Business Review (October 21, 2009)
Pub: Incisive Media Inc.
Contact: Jonathon Whiteley, Chief Executive Officer
Ed: Janet L. Conley. **Description:** Niagara Credit Solutions argued with a three-judge panel that the company broke the rule saying debt collectors must identify themselves so that they could comply with a rule barring debt collectors from communicating about a debt with third parties. **Availability:** Print; Online.

25197 ■ "401(k) Keys to Stable Value" in Barron's (Vol. 88, March 10, 2008, No. 10, pp. 40)
Pub: Dow Jones & Company Inc.
Contact: Almar Latour, Chief Executive Officer
Ed: Tom Sullivan. **Description:** Stable-value funds offer investors stability in a period of volatility in financial markets, attracting $888 million in funds. The Securities and Exchange Commission approved the launch of actively managed exchange-traded funds. **Availability:** Online.

25198 ■ "2015 Corporate Counsel Legal Pricing Guide - Mergers & Acquisitions" in Economics & Business Week (August 16, 2014, pp. 3)
Pub: NewsRX LLC.
Contact: Kalani Rosell, Contact
Description: Research and Markets has added the 2015 Corporate Counsel Legal Pricing Guide - Mergers & Acquisitions to its report. The guide details how the mergers and acquisitions market for law firms has increased since the downturn in 2008-2009 due mostly to an improved economy, increased corporate liquidity and sometimes corporate tax policies of certain countries. **Availability:** Print; Online.

25199 ■ "AG Warns Slots MBE Plan Risky" in Boston Business Journal (Vol. 29, May 27, 2011, No. 3, pp. 1)
Description: Attorney General Doug Gansler states that the law extending the minority business program on slots parlors contracting through 2018 could be open to lawsuits. He recommended that the state

should conduct a study proving that minority- and women-owned businesses do not get a fair share in the gaming industry before it signs the bill to avoid lawsuits from majority-owned firms. **Availability:** Print; Online.

25200 ■ *"Alberta Carbon Capture Strategy Falters: Alberta's Favoured Emissions-Control Plan is Falling Apart" in Canadian Business (Vol. 85, June 11, 2012, No. 10, pp. 13)*
Ed: Matthew McClearn. **Description:** The emissions-control plan of Alberta suffered a major setback following cancellations of major carbon capture and storage (CCS) pilot projects. Project Pioneer was cancelled because the saving did not justify the operating costs while discontinuation of Heartland Area Redwater Project was due to the uncertainty surrounding the province's changing CCS rules. **Availability:** Print; Online.

25201 ■ *"Alberta Star Begins Phase 2 Drilling On Its Eldorado & Contact Lake IOCG & Uranium Projects" in Canadian Corporate News (May 16, 2007)*
Description: Profile of Alberta Star Development Corp., a Canadian mineral exploration company that identifies, acquires, and finances advanced stage exploration projects in Canada, and its current undertaking of its 2007 drill program in which the company intends to begin accelerating its uranium and poly-metallic exploration and drilling activities on all of its drill targets for 2007 now that it has been granted its permits. **Availability:** Online.

25202 ■ *"All Eyes On Iris" in Canadian Business (Vol. 81, July 22, 2008, No. 12-13, pp. 20)*
Description: Provincial governments in Canada are believed to be awaiting Alberta Finance Minister Iris Evans' financial and investment policies as well as Evans' development of a new saving strategy. Alberta is the only Canadian province that is in position to invest in sovereign wealth funds after it eliminated its debt in 2005. **Availability:** Print; Online.

25203 ■ *"All-Star Execs: Top CEO: Gordon Nixon" in Canadian Business (Vol. 80, November 24, 2008, No. 22, pp. 9)*
Pub: Rogers Media Inc.
Contact: Neil Spivak, Chief Executive Officer
Ed: Jeff Sanford. **Description:** Royal Bank of Canada (RBC) CEO, Gordon Nixon, believes the Canadian financial services segment is heavily regulated. Nixon also feels that it has become difficult for local banks to enter the market since foreign banks can easily come in and compete with them. His views on RBC's success are provided. **Availability:** Print; Online.

25204 ■ *"Alpharetta Seeding Startups To Encourage Job Growth" in Atlanta Business Chronicle(June 20, 2014, pp. 3A)*
Pub: American City Business Journals, Inc.
Contact: Mike Olivieri, Executive Vice President
Description: The City of Alpharetta is witnessing several incubators and accelerators that will create the physical and educational infrastructure to convert ideas into sustainable businesses. This will help startups develop a go-to-market strategy, prepare for FDA certification and insurance reimbursement as well as see that the company reaches a point where it can attract private equity or venture capital. **Availability:** Print; Online.

25205 ■ *"American Chemistry Council Launches Flagship Blog" in Ecology,Environment & Conservation Business (October 29, 2011, pp. 5)*
Pub: PR Newswire Association LLC.
Description: American Chemistry Council (ACC) launched its blog, American Chemistry Matters, where interactive space allows bloggers to respond to news coverage and to discuss policy issues and their impact on innovation, competitiveness, job creation and safety. **Availability:** Online.

25206 ■ *"Arkansas Attorney General Sues Collection Agency" in PaymentsSource (July 18, 2012)*
Description: National Credit Adjusters is being sued by Arkansas Attorney General Dustin McDaniel's office. The lawsuit alleges that the collection agency violated the Arkansas Deceptive Trade Practices Act while attempting to collect debts from payday and high-interest installment loan debts. **Availability:** Print; Online.

25207 ■ *"Au Revoir Or Goodbye?" in Barron's (Vol. 88, July 14, 2008, No. 28, pp. 5)*
Pub: Dow Jones & Company Inc.
Contact: Almar Latour, Chief Executive Officer
Ed: Alan Abelson. **Description:** Former Senator Phil Gramm's opinion that the U.S. is a "nation of whiners" as they moan about recession is another example of the disconnection between Washington and Wall Street on one hand and the real world on the other. It would be a catastrophe for most of the world if Fannie Mae and Freddie Mac were to go under and take their trillions of mortgage debt with them. **Availability:** Online.

25208 ■ *"Auditing the Auditors" in Barron's (Vol. 92, September 17, 2012, No. 38, pp. 16)*
Description: The Public Company Accounting Oversight Board banned Michael T. Studer, president of the accounting firm Studer Group, because he failed to comply with auditing standards in his audits involving hinese reverse mergers. **Availability:** Online.

25209 ■ *"Austin Ponders Annexing Formula One Racetrack" in Austin Business Journal (Vol. 31, July 8, 2011, No. 18, pp. 1)*
Pub: Austin Business Journal
Contact: Rachel McGrath, Director
E-mail: rmcgrath@bizjournals.com
Ed: Vicky Garza. **Description:** City planners in Austin, Texas are studying the feasibility of annexing the land under and around the Circuit of the Americas Formula One Racetrack being constructed east of the city. The annexation could generate at least $13 million in financial gain over 25 years from property taxes alone. **Availability:** Print; Online.

25210 ■ *"Austin on Verge of Losing 7,500 Jobs" in Austin Business Journal (Vol. 31, May 6, 2011, No. 9, pp. 1)*
Pub: Austin Business Journal
Contact: Rachel McGrath, Director
E-mail: rmcgrath@bizjournals.com
Ed: Jacob Dirr. **Description:** Proposed state budget cuts are seen to result in the loss of as many as 7,500 public and private sector jobs in Austin, Texas, with the private sector losing the majority of workers. Comments from analysts are included. **Availability:** Print; Online.

25211 ■ *"Azaya Therapeutics Taking Big Steps" in San Antonio Business Journal (Vol. 28, March 28, 2014, No. 7, pp. 8)*
Pub: American City Business Journals, Inc.
Contact: Mike Olivieri, Executive Vice President
Released: Weekly. **Price:** $4, Introductory 4-week offer(Digital only). **Description:** Azaya Therapeutics believes that its $5 million funding round will be completed in 2014. The convertible-note bridge funding was initiated in October 2013. The company, which plans to pursue regulatory approval for its cancer medications, is also focusing on expanding the business. **Availability:** Print; Online.

25212 ■ *"Back Off on ABM Legislation, Banks Warn MPs" in Globe & Mail (April 20, 2007, pp. B1)*
Ed: Steven Chase. **Description:** The efforts of banks to prevent legislation by the Canadian government on the automated banking machine levies charged from customers of other institutions are described. **Availability:** Online.

25213 ■ *"Bad Paper" in Canadian Business (Vol. 80, November 19, 2007, No. 23, pp. 34)*
Description: The Canadian government froze the market for non-bank asset-backed commercial paper (ABCP) August 2007, which means holders will be unable to withdraw investments. The crisis and value of ABCP are discussed. **Availability:** Print; Online.

25214 ■ *"Ballpark Sales Tax Extension Could Fund New Arena" in Milwaukee Business Journal (Vol. 27, January 29, 2010, No. 18, pp. A1)*
Pub: The Business Journal
Contact: Heather Ladage, President
E-mail: hladage@bizjournals.com
Ed: Mark Kass. **Description:** Milwaukee, Wisconsin-area business executives believe the extension of the Miller Park 0.1 percent sales tax could help fund a new basketball arena to replace the 21-year-old Bradley Center in downtown Milwaukee. However, any sales tax expansion that includes the new basketball arena would need approval by Wisconsin's legislature. **Availability:** Print; Online.

25215 ■ *"Baltimore Businesses Put Cash Behind Bernstein" in Baltimore Business Journal (Vol. 28, August 20, 2010, No. 15, pp. 1)*
Pub: Baltimore Business Journal
Contact: Rhonda Pringle, President
E-mail: rpringle@bizjournals.com
Ed: Scott Dance. **Description:** Baltimore, Maryland-based businesses have invested $40,000 to support lawyer Gregg L. Bernstein in the 2010 State Attorney election. The election campaign is being fueled by fear of a crime surge. Many businesses have been dealing with crimes such as muggings, shootings, and car break-ins. **Availability:** Print.

25216 ■ *"Baltimore Rejects Plans for Waxter Site" in Baltimore Business Journal (Vol. 30, May 25, 2012, No. 3, pp. 1)*
Pub: American City Business Journals, Inc.
Contact: Mike Olivieri, Executive Vice President
Ed: James Briggs. **Description:** The City of Baltimore, Maryland has turned down a proposal for a mixed-use development project at the Waxter Center in Mount Vernon. The project is estimated to cost up to $70 million. **Availability:** Print; Online.

25217 ■ *"Ban Threatens Soda Fountain: Mayor's Size Limit Could Crimp Sales, Change Bottling" in Crain's New York Business (Vol. 28, July 30, 2012, No. 31, pp. 6)*
Pub: Crain Communications, Inc.
Contact: Jessica Botos, Manager, Marketing
E-mail: jessica.botos@crainsnewyork.com
Ed: Lisa Fickenscher. **Description:** New York City's Mayor is threatening to limit bottles and cups of soda and other sweetened beverages to 16 ounces. That means that the 20 ounce and 32 ounce drinks will be banned from the city. Details and the ban and responses from soft drink companies are included. **Availability:** Print; Online.

25218 ■ *"Banks, Retailers Squabble Over Fees" in Baltimore Business Journal (Vol. 28, June 18, 2010, No. 6, pp. 1)*
Pub: Baltimore Business Journal
Contact: Rhonda Pringle, President
E-mail: rpringle@bizjournals.com
Ed: Gary Haber. **Description:** How an amendment to the financial regulatory reform bill would affect the bankers' and retailers' conflict over interchange fees is discussed. Interchange fees are paid for by retailers every time consumers make purchases through debit cards. Industry estimates indicate that approximately $50 million in such fees are paid by retailers. **Availability:** Print; Online.

25219 ■ *"Bee Mindful: NY Lawmakers Want to Preserve, Relocate Pesky Hives" in TimesUnion (October 10, 2019)*
URL(s): www.timesunion.com/news/article/Bee-min dful-State-lawmakers-want-to-preserve-and-145039 33.php

Ed: Cayla Harris. **Released:** October 10, 2019. **Description:** A new bill is being proposed to help preserve honey bee colonies in New York. This bill would require people to contact the state's Division of Plant Industry about pesky bee colonies so they be removed and relocated, inside of destroyed. **Availability:** Online.

25220 ■ *"Bernier Open to Telecom Changes" in Globe & Mail (March 22, 2006, pp. B1)*
Ed: Simon Tuck. **Description:** Federal Industry Minister Maxime Bernier of Canada says that he is open to scrapping restrictions on foreign ownership in telecommunications. His views on telecom industry are detailed. **Availability:** Online.

25221 ■ *"BETC Backers Plot Future" in Business Journal Portland (Vol. 27, December 10, 2010, No. 41, pp. 1)*
Pub: Portland Business Journal
Contact: Andy Giegerich, Managing Editor
E-mail: agiegerich@bizjournals.com
Ed: Erik Siemers. **Description:** A coalition of clean energy groups and industrial manufacturers have spearheaded a campaign aimed at persuading Oregon legislators that the state's Business Energy Tax Credit (BETC) is vital in job creation. Oregon's BETC grants tax credits for 50 percent of an eligible renewable or clean energy project's cost. However, some legislators propose BETC's abolition. **Availability:** Print; Online.

25222 ■ *"Beware of E15 Gasoline" in Rental Product News (Vol. 33, October 2011)*
Ed: Curt Bennink. **Description:** Environmental Protection Agency (EPA) set a new regulation that grants partial waivers to allow gasoline containing up to 15 percent ethanol (E15) to be introduced into commerce for use in model year 2001 and newer light-duty motor vehicles, subject to certain conditions. **Availability:** Online.

25223 ■ *"Beware of Rotting Money" in Barron's (Vol. 89, July 13, 2009, No. 28, pp. 31)*
Pub: Dow Jones & Company Inc.
Contact: Almar Latour, Chief Executive Officer
Ed: Thomas G. Donlan. **Description:** Inflation can take hold of a country and do it great harm; it is caused by people, most particularly central bankers in charge of the world's reserve currency. Arrogant economists pushed the belief that the government can engineer the economy and it is argued that there is trouble ahead when the government tries to control the economy. **Availability:** Online.

25224 ■ *"Bill to Roll Back Banking Regulations Faces Tough Odds" in San Antonio Business Journal (Vol. 28, April 18, 2014, No. 10, pp. 6)*
Pub: American City Business Journals, Inc.
Contact: Mike Olivieri, Executive Vice President
Released: Weekly. **Price:** $4, Introductory 4-week offer(Digital only). **Description:** U.S. Representative Henry Cuellar is co-sponsoring legislation that will ease some of the regulations governing community banks. The Community Lending Enhancement and Regulatory Relief Act has 129 co-sponsors in the House of Representatives. **Availability:** Print; Online.

25225 ■ *"Bills Raise Blues Debate: An Unfair Edge or Level Playing Field?" in Crain's Detroit Business (Vol. 24, January 21, 2008, No. 3)*
Pub: Crain Communications Inc.
Contact: Barry Asin, President
Ed: Sherri Begin. **Description:** Changes in Michigan state law would change the way health insurance can be sold to individuals. Michigan Blue Cross Blue Shield is working to keep its tax-exempt status while staying competitive against for-profit insurers and nonprofit HMOs. **Availability:** Print; Online.

25226 ■ *"Bills Would Regulate Mortgage Loan Officers" in Crain's Detroit Business (Vol. 24, February 25, 2008, No. 8, pp. 9)*
Pub: Crain Communications Inc.
Contact: Barry Asin, President
Ed: Amy Lane. **Description:** New legislation in Michigan, if passed, would create a registration process for mortgage loan officers in the state in order to address the mortgage loan crisis. **Availability:** Print; Online.

25227 ■ *"Bloomington Police to Buy 24-Hour Electronic Kiosk With Federal Grant" in Herald-Times (September 5, 2012)*
Ed: Abby Tonsing. **Description:** Bloomington, Indiana police department will purchase two electronic kiosks with money from a federal grant. The kiosks will operate 24 hours a day and provide the public with the ability to communicate with the police, obtain forms and permits, as well as other police-related activities. **Availability:** Print; Online.

25228 ■ *"Boatyard Expansion 8-Year Odyssey" in Providence Business News (Vol. 28, March 31, 2014, No. 52, p. 1)*
Pub: American City Business Journals, Inc.
Contact: Mike Olivieri, Executive Vice President
Released: March 29, 2014. **Description:** Bristol Marine owner, Andy Tyska, has found it challenging to operate and improve the boatyard due to lack of available coastal land and restrictive environmental regulations. Tyska made a large investment in plans for expanding the property he purchased in 1998. Tyska discusses the challenges faced while trying to improve his boatyard. **Availability:** Print; Online.

25229 ■ *Bold Endeavors: How Our Government Built America, and Why It Must Rebuild Now*
Pub: Simon & Schuster, Inc.
Contact: Jonathan Karp, President
Ed: Felix G. Rohatyn. **Released:** May 2011. **Price:** $17.99, paperback. **Description:** The federal government built the nation by investing in initiatives like the Erie Canal and the G.I. Bill and why it should do the same at this point in history is examined. **Availability:** E-book; Print.

25230 ■ *"Bringing Manufacturing Concerns to Springfield" in Crain's Chicago Business (Vol. 31, March 31, 2008, No. 13, pp. 6)*
Pub: Crain Communications Inc.
Contact: Barry Asin, President
Ed: Paul Merrion. **Description:** Profile of the new executive vice-president of Tooling & Manufacturing Assn., Paul Merrion, a man who plans to grow TMA's membership with an aggressive legislative agenda in Springfield. **Availability:** Online.

25231 ■ *"Builders Aim to Cut Costs: Pushing Changes to Regain Share of Residential Market; Seek Council's Help" in Crain's New York Business*
Pub: Crain Communications, Inc.
Contact: Jessica Botos, Manager, Marketing
E-mail: jessica.botos@crainsnewyork.com
Ed: Erik Engquist. **Description:** Union contractors and workers are worried about a decline in their market share for housing so they intend to ask the City Council to impose new safety and benefit standards on all contractors to avoid being undercut by nonunion competitors. **Availability:** Print; Online.

25232 ■ *"Building Targeted for Marriott in Violation" in Business Journal-Milwaukee (Vol. 28, December 24, 2010, No. 12, pp. A1)*
Pub: The Business Journal
Contact: Heather Ladage, President
E-mail: hladage@bizjournals.com
Ed: Sean Ryan. **Description:** Milwaukee, Wisconsin's Department of Neighborhood Services has ordered structural improvements and safeguards for the Pioneer Building after three violations from structural failures were found. Pioneer was among the five buildings wanted by Jackson Street Management LLC to demolish for the new Marriott Hotel. **Availability:** Print; Online.

25233 ■ *"Bullied Into Legislation" in Philadelphia Business Journal (Vol. 33, February 21, 2014, No. 2, pp. 4)*
Pub: American City Business Journals, Inc.
Contact: Mike Olivieri, Executive Vice President
Released: Weekly. **Price:** $4, introductory 4-week offer(Digital & Print). **Description:** The results of a study indicate that 35 percent of workers in the U.S. experience bullying firsthand. Because of this, Pennsylvania and other states have considered enacting anti-workplace bullying legislation. Many of these states use some version of the Healthy Workplace Act for their bills. **Availability:** Print; Online.

25234 ■ *"Business Looks for Results in Congress" in Baltimore Business Journal (Vol. 28, November 5, 2010, No. 26, pp. 1)*
Pub: Baltimore Business Journal
Contact: Rhonda Pringle, President
E-mail: rpringle@bizjournals.com
Ed: Kent Hoover. **Description:** Republican candidates in the 2010 Congressional elections were overwhelmingly supported by the business community. Republican John Boehner, who will be the next Speaker of the House, says that the party's victory would end economic uncertainty and would assist small businesses to rehire workers. **Availability:** Print; Online.

25235 ■ *"The Business of Medicine: Maintaining a Healthy Bottom Line" in Black Enterprise (Vol. 41, October 2010, No. 3, pp. 60)*
Released: January 10, 2010. **Description:** Sustainable government reform requires reconstruction in the areas of financing and delivery of services in the field of medicine. **Availability:** Online.

25236 ■ *"Business Sidestepped Trouble" in Denver Business Journal (Vol. 65, May 9, 2014, No. 52, pp. A8)*
Pub: American City Business Journals, Inc.
Contact: Mike Olivieri, Executive Vice President
Released: May 09, 2014. **Description:** A number of business-friendly laws were adopted during the 2014 legislative session Colorado. the legislators passed 11 tax breaks, including the personal property tax break proposal. **Availability:** Print; Online.

25237 ■ *"Business Tax Complaints Prompt Action" in Sacramento Business Journal (Vol. 28, July 29, 2011, No. 22, pp. 1)*
Pub: Sacramento Business Journal
Contact: Stephanie Fretwell, Director
E-mail: sfretwell@bizjournals.com
Ed: Michael Shaw. **Description:** California's Board of Equalization has amended a program to collect taxes from businesses for out-of-state purchases due to a flood of complaints from owners who find the paperwork costly and time consuming. The program was created in 2009 and fell short of expectations as it only brought in $56 million in the first two years against the projected $264 million. **Availability:** Online.

25238 ■ *"Business Without Borders: All For One, None for All?" in Canadian Business (Vol. 83, October 12, 2010, No. 17, pp. 60)*
Pub: Rogers Media Inc.
Contact: Neil Spivak, Chief Executive Officer
Ed: Michael McCullogh. **Description:** The effect of the growth of Canada's overseas provincial trade offices on Canadian trade is discussed. Economic development commissions in the country have devised a single 'Consider Canada' campaign to pitch foreign investors. It is hoped that large cities will gain from banding together rather than competing against one another. **Availability:** Print; Online.

25239 ■ *"California Forces Pet Stores to Sell Only Dogs and Cats from Shelters" in The New York Times (January 2, 2019)*
URL(s): www.nytimes.com/2019/01/02/us/california-pet-store-rescue-law.html

Ed: Christine Hauser. **Released:** January 02, 2019. **Description:** A new law in California has required all pet stores to sell only dogs, cats, and rabbits from animal shelters instead of obtaining animals from breeding mills, which have a history of very poor conditions. Stores who do not comply will be subjected to a $500 per animal fine. **Availability:** Online.

25240 ■ *"The California Fur Ban and What It Means for You"* **in The New York Times (October 14, 2019)**
URL(s): www.nytimes.com/2019/10/14/style/fur-ban-california.html?action=click&module=RelatedCoverage&pgtype=Article&region=Footer

Ed: Vanessa Friedman. **Released:** October 14, 2019. **Description:** California has become the first state to ban fur, meaning only the sale of new clothing and accessories are actually banned. The wearing of fur is still legal and any old fur still in circulation is acceptable as is any religious, traditional, or cultural fur. This is all due to a growing trend of people not purchasing fur due to animal welfare concerns and changing tastes in fashion with the younger generations. **Availability:** Online.

25241 ■ *"California vs. Freelance Writers"* **in National Review (October 22, 2019)**
URL(s): www.nationalreview.com/corner/new-california-labor-law-hits-freelance-writers-hard/

Ed: Robert Verbruggen. **Released:** October 22, 2019. **Description:** Freelancers in California are gearing up for major changes to their work when a new law takes effect that will force all companies to treat freelancers as regular employees. **Availability:** Online.

25242 ■ *"Call for Superblock Jobs Tie-In Lacks Baltimore Backing"* **in Baltimore Business Journal (Vol. 30, June 1, 2012, No. 4, pp. 1)**
Pub: American City Business Journals, Inc.
Contact: Mike Olivieri, Executive Vice President

Ed: James Briggs. **Description:** Officials of Baltimore, Maryland are seen to turn down the proposal to mandate local hiring rules for Lexington Square Partners. The plan is in line with the company's push for tax breaks on its superblock project. **Availability:** Print; Online.

25243 ■ *"Canada Joins TPP Free Trade Talks"* **in Canadian Business (Vol. 85, August 13, 2012, No. 13, pp. 7)**

Ed: Tim Shufelt. **Description:** The decision of the Canadian government to join the Trans-Pacific Partnership (TPP) has potential economic benefits in terms of trading with China and the U.S.Failure of the World Trade Ogranization's Doha Round and the admission of the U.S. to the TPP prompted Canada to join the trade agreement. **Availability:** Print; Online.

25244 ■ *"Canada Nears European Trade Treaty"* **in Globe & Mail (February 5, 2007, pp. B1)**

Ed: Steven Chase. **Description:** The probable establishment of a treaty by Canada with Norway, Switzerland and Iceland for free-trade is discussed. The treaty will allow an annual business of $11 billion to take place in Canada. **Availability:** Print; Online.

25245 ■ *"Canada Seeks Collection Agency To Pursue $129M In Fines"* **in PaymentsSource (August 21, 2012)**

Description: Canada's federal government has posted a letter of interest seeking a collection agency to recover about $129 million in unpaid fines. Details of the program are covered. **Availability:** Print; Online.

25246 ■ *"Canada's New Government Introduces Amendments to Deny Work Permits to Foreign Strippers"* **in Marketwired (May 16, 2007)**
Pub: Comtex News Network Inc.
Contact: Kan Devnani, President

Description: Honourable Diane Finley, Minister of Citizenship and Immigration, introduced amendments to the Immigration and Refugee Protection Act (IRPA) to help prevent the exploitation and abuse of vulnerable foreign workers, such as strippers. **Availability:** Print.

25247 ■ *"Canadian Wine to Ship Across Provincial Borders: Let the Wine Flow Freely. Feds To Allow Shipments Inside Canada"* **in Canadian Business (Vol. 85, August 13, 2012, No. 13, pp. 8)**

Ed: Sarah Barmak. **Description:** The passage of federal Bill C-311 is anticipated to remove restriction on interprovincial wine trade imposed under the Importation of Intoxicating Liquors Act of 1928. There are claims that legalizing direct-to-consumer selling will not affect liquor store sales. **Availability:** Print; Online.

25248 ■ *"Candidates Won't Bash Fed; Rate Cuts Bash Savers"* **in Barron's (Vol. 88, March 24, 2008, No. 12, pp. 31)**
Pub: Dow Jones & Company Inc.
Contact: Almar Latour, Chief Executive Officer

Ed: Jim McTague. **Description:** Candidates in the 2008 US presidential election, like the current administration, do not and will not bash the Federal Reserve. The Federal Reserve's aggressive interest rate cuts hurt the incomes of people depending on their savings accounts. **Availability:** Online.

25249 ■ *"CanWEA Unveils WindVision for BC: 5,250 MW of Wind Energy by 2025"* **in CNW Group (October 4, 2011)**
Pub: CNW Group Ltd.

Description: Wind industry leaders are asking British Columbia, Canada policy makers to created conditions to further develop and integrate wind energy in accordance with greenhouse gas emission targets and projected economic growth. Statistical data included. **Availability:** PDF; Online.

25250 ■ *"Capital Metro May Soon Seek Contractor"* **in Austin Business Journal (Vol. 31, June 10, 2011, No. 14, pp. 1)**
Pub: Austin Business Journal
Contact: Rachel McGrath, Director
E-mail: rmcgrath@bizjournals.com

Ed: Vicky Garza. **Description:** Capital Metropolitan Transportation Authority may be forced to contract out its bus services provided by StarTran Inc. as early as September 2012 following legislation approved by the Texas legislature. The bill originates in a report by the Sunset Advisory Commission. Details are included. **Availability:** Print; Online.

25251 ■ *"Capitol Ideas: Regions to Lansing: Focus on Taxes, Reform, Keeping Talent"* **in Crain's Detroit Business (Vol. 24, October 6, 2008)**
Pub: Crain Communications Inc.
Contact: Barry Asin, President

Ed: Amy Lane. **Description:** Michigan must make bold and dramatic changes in public policy regarding business legislation. The tax structure, unemployment issues and attracting and retaining talent are among the issues the state must confront, especially in this tough economic climate. **Availability:** Online.

25252 ■ *"Carbon Capture and Storage: Grave Concerns"* **in Canadian Business (Vol. 81, July 21 2008, No. 11, pp. 25)**

Ed: Andrew Nikiforuk. **Released:** January 01, 2017. **Description:** Air pollution control regulations to reduce greenhouse gasses have been implemented by the Canadian government. The federal government is planning to construct a carbon funeral industry that will store the global warming gases, however the expenditure for the project will be shifted to the taxpayers. Details of the Bruce Peachy's initiative on how to reduce GHGs are presented. **Availability:** Print; Online.

25253 ■ *"Case IH Announces Strategy to Meet 2014 Clean Air Standards"* **in Farm Industry News (September 15, 2011)**
Pub: Informa Business Media, Inc.
Contact: Charlie McCurdy, President

Ed: Jodie Wehrspann. **Description:** Case IH will meet EPA's stringent engine emissions limits imposed in 2014, called Tier 4. The limits call for a 90 percent reduction in particulate matter and nitrogen oxides (NOx) over the Tier 3 requirements from a few years ago. **Availability:** Print; Online.

25254 ■ *"The Case for Treating the Sex Trade As an Industry"* **in Canadian Business (Vol. 83, October 12, 2010, No. 17, pp. 9)**
Pub: Rogers Media Inc.
Contact: Neil Spivak, Chief Executive Officer

Ed: Steve Maich. **Description:** It is believed that the worst aspects of prostitution in Canada are exacerbated by the fact that it must take place in secret. The laws that deal with the market for sex have led to an unsafe working environment. Prostitutes believe their industry needs to be sanctioned and regulated rather than ignored and reviled. **Availability:** Online.

25255 ■ *"The CEO Poll: Fuel for Thought II Canadian Business Leaders on Energy Policy"* **in Canadian Business (Vol. 81, September 15, 2008, No. 14-15, pp. 12)**
Pub: Rogers Media Inc.
Contact: Neil Spivak, Chief Executive Officer

Ed: Joe Castaldo. **Description:** Most Canadian business leaders worry about the unreliability of the oil supply but feel that Canada is in a better position to benefit from the energy supply crisis than other countries. Many respondents also highlighted the need to invest in renewable energy sources. **Availability:** Online.

25256 ■ *"The CEO Poll: Potash Sale Must Be Blocked"* **in Canadian Business (Vol. 83, October 12, 2010, No. 17, pp. 24)**
Pub: Rogers Media Inc.
Contact: Neil Spivak, Chief Executive Officer

Ed: Kasey Coholan. **Description:** Chief executive officers (CEOs) and corporate leaders in Canada are concerned about the possible sale of Potash Corporation to foreign buyers. A Compas Inc. poll recently asked CEOs whether the Canadian Government should step in to block the sale of the country's largest fertilizer firm. **Availability:** Print; Online.

25257 ■ *"The CEO Poll: Split on Migrant Workers"* **in Canadian Business (Vol. 83, September 14, 2010, No. 15, pp. 23)**
Pub: Rogers Media Inc.
Contact: Neil Spivak, Chief Executive Officer

Ed: Jacqueline Nelson. **Description:** A survey of Canadian CEOs shows that 49 percent of the respondents believe it was wrong to suspend the immigration programs and companies should be allowed to hire the most skilled workers regardless of citizenship. However, 42 percent believe the suspension was right because employment of Canadians must take precedence. **Availability:** Print; Online.

25258 ■ **CFR: Title 13. Business Credit and Assistance**
Pub: U.S. Government Publishing Office

Ed: Department of Commerce Staff. **Released:** Annual; volume 14. **Description:** Title 13 covers regulations governing the activities of the Small Business Administration and the Department of Commerce. Book covers information on business credit, finance, and economic development. **Availability:** Print; PDF.

25259 ■ *"Chafee Eyes Tax On Travel Sites"* **in Providence Business News (Vol. 28, March 24, 2014, No. 51, pp. 1)**
Pub: American City Business Journals, Inc.
Contact: Mike Olivieri, Executive Vice President
URL(s): pbn.com/chafee-eyes-tax-on-travel-sites95903

Description: Rhode Island Governor, Lincoln D. Chafee's 2015 budget will include new tax rules for travel Websites. State officials claim the new regulations will deal with a loophole that has allowed travel Websites to pay less in taxes. Many hotels enter into partnerships with travel Websites in order to sell rooms in bulk. **Availability:** Online. **Telecommunication Services:** Anderson@pbn.com.

25260 ■ *"Changes Sought to Health Law"* in *Baltimore Business Journal (Vol. 28, July 30, 2010, No. 12, pp. 1)*
Pub: Baltimore Business Journal
Contact: Rhonda Pringle, President
E-mail: rpringle@bizjournals.com
Ed: Kent Hoover. **Description:** Business groups that opposed health care reform are working to undo parts of the new laws even before they go into effect. Business groups are gaining support for one legislative fix, which is repealing the law's provision that requires all businesses to file 1099 forms with the IRS any time they pay more than $600 a year to another business. **Availability:** Print; Online.

25261 ■ *"Changing the Rules of the Accounting Game"* in *Canadian Business (Vol. 81, December 8, 2008, No. 21, pp. 19)*
Description: Interference from world politicians in developing accounting standards is believed to have resulted in untested rules that are inferior to current standards. European lawmakers have recently asked to change International Financial Reporting Standards. **Availability:** Online.

25262 ■ *"Cheap Tubing Risk to Local Jobs, Execs Caution"* in *Pittsburgh Business Times (Vol. 33, May 23, 2014, No. 45, pp. 4)*
Pub: American City Business Journals, Inc.
Contact: Mike Olivieri, Executive Vice President
Released: Weekly. **Price:** $4, introductory 4-week offer(Digital only). **Description:** U.S. Steel Corporation requests the U.S. Department of Commerce to take action against unfairly traded steel imports in the market because thousands of jobs are at risk. At least 26,400 jobs in Pennsylvania may be affected by the unfair trading practices of foreign exporters according to the office of Governor Tom Corbett. **Availability:** Print; Online.

25263 ■ *"Chesapeake Firm Regains Veteran-Owned Status"* in *Virginian-Pilot (August 21, 2012)*
Pub: McClatchy Tribune Information Services
Contact: Patrick J. Talamantes, President
Ed: Philip Walzer. **Description:** Syncon LLC has regained status as a "veteran-owned" business. Mark Lilly, the president of Syncon is a retired Navy SEAL master chief who was wounded in combat in Afghanistan. Over-regulation by the US Department of Vetrans Affairs in order to stop fraud in the veteran certification program was responsible for the mistake. **Availability:** Print; Online.

25264 ■ *"China Vs the World: Whose Technology Is It?"* in *Harvard Business Review (Vol. 88, December 2010, No. 12, pp. 94)*
Pub: Harvard Business Publishing
Contact: Diane Belcher, Managing Director
Ed: Thomas M. Hout, Pankaj Ghemawat. **Price:** $8.95, PDF. **Description:** Examination of the regulation the Chinese government is implementing that require foreign corporations wishing to do business in the country to give up their new technologies. These regulations avoid World Trade Organization technology transfer provisions and complicate the convergence of socialism and capitalism. **Availability:** Online; PDF.

25265 ■ *"China's Transition to Green Energy Systems: The Economics of Home Solar Water Heaters and Their Popularization in Dezhou City"* in *Energy Policy (Vol. 39, October 2011, No. 10, pp. 5909-5919)*
Ed: Wei Li, Guojun Song, Melanie Beresford, Ben Ma. **Released:** 2011. **Description:** The economics of home solar water heaters and their growing popularity in Dezhous City, China is discussed. **Availability:** PDF; Online.

25266 ■ *"Christmas Trees Keep Giving in St. Louis Area"* in *St. Louis Post-Dispatch (January 11, 2012)*
Pub: Tribune News Service
Contact: Jack Barry, Vice President, Operations
E-mail: jbarry@tribpub.com
Ed: Jonah Newman. **Description:** Missouri state law prohibiting disposing of Christmas trees into area lakes has forced citizens to find new ways to use their old trees. Saint Louis and other municipalities offers ways to recycle Christmas trees while creating a good habitat for fish. Cities have sunk a portion of the trees, then created mulch and is offered free to residents. **Availability:** Online.

25267 ■ *"Cincinnati Business Committee's Tom Williams: Future is Now"* in *Business Courier (Vol. 27, August 13, 2010, No. 15, pp. 1)*
Pub: Business Courier
Ed: Lucy May. **Description:** Tom Williams, chairman of the Cincinnati Business Committee (CBC), maintains that politicians and business leaders must cooperate to ensure the competitiveness of the city for the 21st Century. Under Williams' leadership, the CBC has put emphasis on initiatives related to government efficiency, economic development, and public education. Williams' views on a proposed inland port are given. **Availability:** Print; Online.

25268 ■ *"Cincinnati Consults Executives on Police Chief Hire"* in *Business Courier (Vol. 27, August 27, 2010, No. 17, pp. 1)*
Pub: Business Courier
Ed: Dan Monk, Lucy May. **Description:** The City of Cincinnati, Ohio has begun a selection process for the new police chief by consulting the city's business executives. The city charter amendment known as Issue 5 has removed civil service protection from the chief's post and enables City Manager Milton Dohoney to hire a chief from outside the department. **Availability:** Print; Online.

25269 ■ *"Cincinnati Hospitals Wage War on 'Bounce-Backs"* in *Business Courier (Vol. 27, July 30, 2010, No. 13, pp. 1)*
Pub: Business Courier
Ed: James Ritchie. **Description:** Health care organizations in Greater Cincinnati area have tried a number of care and follow up programs, primarily focused on congestive heart failure to prevent readmissions to hospitals. Hospital administrators have made the averting of bounce-backs a priority due to new federal government plans on reimbursement. **Availability:** Print; Online.

25270 ■ *Cities from the Arabian Desert: The Building of Jubail and Yambu in Saudi Arabia*
Ed: Andrea H. Pampanini. **Description:** An overview of Saudi Arabia's government to take control of the nation's natural resources and change the government, educational system, and its culture by evolving into a modern industrial society. **Availability:** Print.

25271 ■ *"City Board Tweaks Internet Cafe Ordinance"* in *Ocala Star-Banner (July 19, 2011)*
Pub: Ocala Star-Banner
Contact: Austin L. Miller, Officer
E-mail: austin.miller@starbanner.com
Ed: Susan Latham Carr. **Description:** Ocala Planning and Zoning Commission revised the proposed draft of the Internet Cafe ordinance by eliminating the cap on the number of locations allowed, but keeping fees and number of devices the same. **Availability:** Online.

25272 ■ *"City May Aid Pop-Up Stores Downtown"* in *Austin Business Journal (Vol. 31, August 19, 2011, No. 24, pp. A1)*
Pub: Austin Business Journal
Contact: Rachel McGrath, Director
E-mail: rmcgrath@bizjournals.com
Ed: Vicky Garza. **Description:** Temporary retail stores may soon become common in Austin as City Council has urged the city manager to look into the possibility of amending the city codes to permit businesses to temporarily fill the vacant spaces downtown. **Availability:** Print; Online.

25273 ■ *"Clarence Firm Gets OK To Make Tobacco Products"* in *Business First of Buffalo (Vol. 30, March 14, 2014, No. 26, pp. 3)*
Pub: American City Business Journals, Inc.
Contact: Mike Olivieri, Executive Vice President
Released: March 14, 2014. **Price:** $4, Introductory 4-Week Offer(Digital & Print). **Description:** Clarence, New York-based 22nd Century Group Inc.'s subsidiary Goodrich Tobacco Company, has received approval from the Alcohol and Tobacco Tax Trade Bureau to produce tobacco products. The approval came after 22nd Century purchased the assets of North Carolina-based Nasco Products LLC, which holds a similar permit. Details of the deal are included. **Availability:** Print; Online.

25274 ■ *"The Clash of the Cultures: Investment vs. Speculation"*
Pub: John Wiley & Sons, Inc.
Contact: Christina Van Tassell, Executive Vice President Chief Financial Officer
Released: August 05, 2012. **Price:** $29.95, hardcover; $19.99, e-book. **Description:** Founder of Vanguard Group urges a return to the common sense principles of long-term investing. John C. Bogle draws on his sixty-years of experience in the mutual fund industry to discuss his views on the changing culture in mutual fund investing, how speculation has invaded our national retirement system, the failure of institutional money managers to effectively participate in corporate governance, and the need for a federal standard of fiduciary duty. Bogle also discusses the history of the index mutual fund and how he created it. **Availability:** E-book; Print.

25275 ■ *"Clusters Last Stand?"* in *Canadian Electronics (Vol. 23, February 2008, No. 1, pp. 6)*
Description: Survival of technology clusters was the focus of Strategic Microelectronics Council's conference entitled, "The Power of Community: Building Technology Clusters in Canada". Clusters can help foster growth in the microelectronics sector, and it was recognized that government intervention is needed to maintain these clusters. **Availability:** Download; PDF; Online.

25276 ■ *"Collateral Damage"* in *Business Courier (Vol. 26, October 16, 2009, No. 25, pp. 1)*
Pub: American City Business Journals, Inc.
Contact: Mike Olivieri, Executive Vice President
Ed: Jon Newberry. **Description:** Non-union construction firms representing Ohio Valley Associated Builders and Contractors Inc. have filed cases against unionized shops claiming violations of wage law in Ohio. Defendants say the violations are minor, however, they believe they are caught in the middle of the group's campaign to change the state's wage law. **Availability:** Print; Online.

25277 ■ *"Collection Agency Issues Whitepaper on Legal and Ethical Methods of Collecting on Overdue Accounts"* in *Marketwired (July 20, 2009)*
Pub: Comtex News Network Inc.
Contact: Kan Devnani, President
Description: American Profit Recovery, a collection agency based in Massachusetts and Michigan, has updated and reissued a whitepaper on what businesses can and cannot do regarding conversing with their customers in an attempt to collect on overdue accounts and payments. A detailed summary on the federal laws associated with collecting on overdue accounts is outlined in such a way that any business owner, manager, or responsible party can easily understand. **Availability:** Print; Online.

25278 ■ *"Colorado Could Set Record for Oil Production"* in *Denver Business Journal (Vol. 64, August 24, 2012, No. 14, pp. 1)*
Pub: Baltimore Business Journal
Contact: Rhonda Pringle, President

E-mail: rpringle@bizjournals.com

Description: Colorado's oil production is expected to set a record for 2012. This is due to the robust investment and drilling activities at the Niobrara rock formation. On the other hand, the efforts of several counties and city governments to introduce new regulations on drilling locations and processes threaten to limit the steady rise of oil production and investments in the area.

25279 ■ *"Colorado Statehouse Races Key for Business"* in *Denver Business Journal (Vol. 64, August 31, 2012, No. 15, pp. 1)*

Pub: Baltimore Business Journal
Contact: Rhonda Pringle, President
E-mail: rpringle@bizjournals.com

Description: The elections for Colorado's Senate and House of Representatives can have a great impact on the state's economy. Republicans are focusing on regulatory-reform measures, while Democrats are pushing for bidding priorities given to companies that buy and hire locally. Experts state that Republican and Democratic candidates seem to agree on job-creation proposals. **Availability:** Print; Online.

25280 ■ *"Column: Want People to Save? Force Them"* in *Harvard Business Review (Vol. 88, September 2010, No. 9, pp. 36)*

Pub: Harvard Business Publishing
Contact: Diane Belcher, Managing Director

Ed: Dan Ariely. **Price:** $6, PDF. **Description:** Contrasts in U.S. attitudes towards savings and government regulation with those of Chile, where all employees are required to save 11 percent of their salary in a retirement account, are highlighted. **Availability:** Online; PDF.

25281 ■ *"Coming Soon: Bailouts of Fannie and Freddie"* in *Barron's (Vol. 88, July 14, 2008, No. 28, pp. 14)*

Pub: Dow Jones & Company Inc.
Contact: Almar Latour, Chief Executive Officer

Ed: Jonathan R. Laing. **Description:** Assurances from the government that Fannie Mae and Freddie Mac are adequately capitalized and able to carry on their duties as guarantors or owners of over $5 trillion of U.S. home mortgages are designed to keep both entities afloat until they attempt to raise $10 billion in new equity. The government would assume any losses in a bailout and owners of the banks' papers would profit as yields drop. **Availability:** Online.

25282 ■ *"Commodity Speculation: Over the Top?"* in *Barron's (Vol. 89, July 13, 2009, No. 28, pp. 22)*

Pub: Dow Jones & Company Inc.
Contact: Almar Latour, Chief Executive Officer

Ed: Gene Epstein. **Description:** Commodity Futures Trading Commission is planning to impose position limits on speculators of oil and other commodities as energy costs rebound from their lows. These regulations make much sense and these position limits would greatly diminish the cash commitment of the commodity index traders if these were imposed on speculators and swaps dealers properly. **Availability:** Online.

25283 ■ *"Complete Discovery Source, Inc. (CDS) Receives Minority Owned Business Certification"* in *Marketwired (December 14, 2010)*

Pub: Comtex News Network Inc.
Contact: Kan Devnani, President

Description: Complete Discovery Source Inc. (CDS) was granted Minority-Owned Business Enterprise status by the New York State Department of Economic Development. The certification provides CDS, an end-to-end eDiscovery services provider, with access to contracting opportunities with 130 government agencies throughout New York state. **Availability:** Print; Online.

25284 ■ *"Condos Becoming FHA No-Lending Zones"* in *Providence Business News (Vol. 29, June 2, 2014, No. 9, pp. 7)*

Pub: American City Business Journals, Inc.
Contact: Mike Olivieri, Executive Vice President

Description: Federal policy changes and decisions by condominium boards of directors have made the condominium development ineligible for Federal Housing Administration (FHA) loans, making several communities prohibited lending zones. As a result, the number of condo developments approved for FHA funding has fallen by more than half, presenting a growing problem for first-time buyers, those with modest down payment cash, and senior citizens using a reverse mortgage. **Availability:** Online.

25285 ■ *"Congress Targets Online Ad Tracking"* in *Inc. (Vol. 33, November 2011, No. 9, pp. 30)*

Pub: Inc. Magazine

Ed: Issie Lapowsky. **Description:** Congressional bills dealing with behavioral tracking whereby advertising networks monitor people's online behavior and use the date to tailor ads to people's interest propose Do Not Track measures which would allow consumers to turn off online behavior tracking by clicking a button. **Availability:** Online.

25286 ■ *"Contractors Must be Lead Certified"* in *Contractor (Vol. 57, February 2010, No. 2, pp. 3)*

Description: Contractors should be trained and certified to comply with the U.S. Environmental Protection Agency's Lead Renovation, Repair, and Painting regulation if they work on housing built before 1978 by April 2010. Contractors with previous lead abatement training must be trained and certified under this new program. **Availability:** Print; Online.

25287 ■ *"Controversial Bill Could Raise Rates for Homeowners"* in *Orlando Business Journal (Vol. 26, January 22, 2010, No. 34, pp. 1)*

Pub: Orlando Business Journal
Contact: Julie Swyers, Director
E-mail: jswyers@bizjournals.com

Ed: Oscar Pedro Musibay, Christopher Boyd. **Description:** Florida Senate Bill 876 and its companion House Bill 447 are pushing for the deregulation of rates in the state's home insurance market. The bill is being opposed by consumer advocates as it could mean higher rates for homeowner insurance policies. **Availability:** Print; Online.

25288 ■ *"Convergence Collaboration: Revising Revenue Recognition"* in *Management Accounting Quarterly (Vol. 12, Spring 2011, No. 3, pp. 18)*

Pub: Management Accounting Quarterly
Contact: Mike DePrisco, President

Ed: Jack T. Ciesielski, Thomas R. Weirich. **Description:** While revenue recognition is critical, regulations have been developed on an ad hoc basis until now. The joint FASB/IASB proposed accounting standard on revenue recognition is a meaningful convergence of standards that will require a major adjustment for financial statement preparers. The proposal is a radical departure from the way revenue has been recognized by the U.S. GAAP. For industries such as consulting, engineering, construction, and technology, it could dramatically change revenue recognition, impacting the top line. The new proposed standard, its potential impact, and the critical role that contracts play is examined thoroughly. **Availability:** PDF; Online.

25289 ■ *"Convictions Under the Fisheries Act"* in *Marketwired (May 16, 2007)*

Pub: Comtex News Network Inc.
Contact: Kan Devnani, President

Description: Fisheries and Oceans Canada is mandated to protect and conserve marine resources and thus released a list of fishers fined for various offences under the Fisheries Act in March and April. **Availability:** Print; Online.

25290 ■ *"Credit Unions Seek to Raise Lending for Small Business"* in *Denver Business Journal (Vol. 64, September 28, 2012, No. 64, pp. 1)*

Pub: Baltimore Business Journal
Contact: Rhonda Pringle, President
E-mail: rpringle@bizjournals.com

Description: United States Senator Mark Udall has introduced the Small Business Lending Enhancement Act, which aims to increase the commercial lending authority of credit unions. The bill's supporters claim that small business owners are still experiencing problems getting credit, and that the legislation will increase small business lending by $13 milliion within its first year of enactment. **Availability:** Print; Online.

25291 ■ *"Crowd Control"* in *Washington Business Journal (Vol. 33, August 15, 2014, No. 17, pp. 8)*

Pub: American City Business Journals, Inc.
Contact: Mike Olivieri, Executive Vice President

Description: Washington DC's Department of Insurance, Securities and Banking issued a proposal that would create the legal framework by which companies can raise cash through crowdfunding. The DC proposal would allow District-based businesses to crowdfund from District-based backers. The advantages and drawbacks to the plan are examined. **Availability:** Online.

25292 ■ *"CrowdFunding Made Simple Conference at University of Utah Ignites Ecosystem of Entrepreneurs and Investors"* in *Economics Week (June 29, 2012)*

Description: The first national conference on crowdfunding was held at the University of Utah Guest House and Conference Center May 31 through June 1, 2012. The event, CrowdFunding Made Simple, gathered entrepreneurs, business owners, professional service providers, investors, government officials and students to provide understanding and potential of crowdfunding, including information on the Jumpstart Our Business Startups (JOBS) Act. **Availability:** Print; Online.

25293 ■ *"CTV's CHUM Proposal Gets Chilly Reception"* in *Globe & Mail (May 1, 2007, pp. B1)*

Ed: Grant Robertson. **Description:** The possible violation of broadcast regulations in case of acquisition of CHUM Ltd. by CTV Inc. for $1.4 billion is discussed. **Availability:** Online.

25294 ■ *"The Cudgel of Samson: How the Government Once Used 'Jawboning' to Fight Inflation"* in *Barron's (Vol. 88, March 24, 2008, No. 12, pp. 62)*

Pub: Dow Jones & Company Inc.
Contact: Almar Latour, Chief Executive Officer

Ed: Thomas G. Donlan. **Description:** Discusses the Federal Reserve is jawboning businesses against inflation while inflation is starting to rise because of the abundance of cheap money. The practice of jawboning has been used by the administrations of past US presidents with limited effect. **Availability:** Online.

25295 ■ *"Curbing the Debt Collector"* in *Business Journal-Portland (Vol. 24, October 5, 2007, No. 32, pp. 1)*

Pub: Portland Business Journal
Contact: Andy Giegerich, Managing Editor
E-mail: agiegerich@bizjournals.com

Ed: Andy Giergerich. **Description:** Republican representative Sal Esquivel, who had a bad personal experience with a Houston collector, is developing legislation that would give the state attorney general's office enforcement powers over debt collecting agencies. The existing Oregon legislation concerning the debt collection industry is also discussed. **Availability:** Print; Online.

25296 ■ *"The Danger of Doing Nothing"* in *Harvard Business Review (Vol. 90, April 2012, No. 4, pp. 38)*

Pub: Harvard Business Review Press
Contact: Moderna V. Pfizer, Contact

Ed: Erskine Bowles. **Price:** $6. **Description:** Solving the US economic crisis will require a blend of revenue increases, spending cuts, and bipartisan cooperation in Congress. The National Commission on Fiscal Responsibility and Reform, also known as Simpson-Bowles, has proposed a plan intended to make America competitive again. **Availability:** PDF; Online.

25297 ■ *Dead on Arrival: How the Anti-Business Backlash is Destroying Entrepreneurship in America and What We Can Still Do About It!*

Released: August 01, 2017. **Price:** $26.99, hardcover; $9.99, e-book; $24.99, digital audiobook unabridged; $15.99, paperback. **Description:** Bernie Marcus, Home Depot leader, addresses regulations hurting small businesses in America. **Availability:** E-book; Print.

25298 ■ *"Death Spiral" in Business Journal Serving Greater Tampa Bay (Vol. 30, October 29, 2010, No. 45, pp. 1)*

Pub: Tampa Bay Business Journal
Contact: Ian Anderson, President
E-mail: ianderson@bizjournals.com

Description: Bay Cities Bank has started working on the loan portfolio of its acquisition, Progress Bank of Florida. Regulators closed Progress Bank in October 2010 after capital collapsed due to charge-offs and increases in the provision for future loan losses. **Availability:** Print; Online.

25299 ■ *"Defend Your Research: People Often Trust Eloquence More Than Honesty" in Harvard Business Review (Vol. 88, November 2010, No. 11, pp. 36)*

Pub: Harvard Business Publishing
Contact: Diane Belcher, Managing Director

Ed: Todd Rogers, Michael I. Norton. **Price:** $6, PDF. **Description:** The article shows how deftly side-stepping a question in an eloquent manner generates a more positive response in an audience than does a direct answer that is ineffectively delivered. Implications for both politics and business are discussed. **Availability:** Online; PDF.

25300 ■ *"Defense Budget Ax May Not Come Down So Hard on Maryland" in Baltimore Business Journal (Vol. 28, August 20, 2010, No. 15, pp. 1)*

Pub: Baltimore Business Journal
Contact: Rhonda Pringle, President
E-mail: rpringle@bizjournals.com

Ed: Daniel J. Sernovitz. **Description:** U.S. Defense Secretary Robert M. Gates' planned budget cuts are having little effect on Maryland's defense industry. Gates will reduce spending on intelligence service contracts by 10 percent. **Availability:** Print; Online.

25301 ■ *"DEM Says River Needs Cleanup" in Providence Business News (Vol. 28, January 6, 2014, No. 40, pp. 1)*

Pub: American City Business Journals, Inc.
Contact: Mike Olivieri, Executive Vice President

Released: January 04, 2014. **Description:** Rhode Island's Department of Environmental Management (DEM) called a meeting to gather information for its Ten Mile River water-quality-restoration plan. DEM announced the failure of the Ten Mile River and its impoundments to meet state water quality standards. The government grant received by Attleboro for the cleanup efforts is examined. **Availability:** Print; Online.

25302 ■ *"Directors May Revise HCA Collection Agency Regulations" in Standard-Speaker (May 20, 2012)*

Pub: McClatchy Tribune Information Services
Contact: Patrick J. Talamantes, President

Ed: Sam Galski. **Description:** Hazelton, Pennsylvania authorities are thinking about changing ts 42-year-old regulations, thus having a collection agency pursue payment of outstanding water and trash fees. Details of the plan are included. **Availability:** Online.

25303 ■ *The Diversity Code: Unlock the Secrets to Making Differences Work in the Real World*

Pub: HarperCollins Leadership
Contact: Donald Miller, Chief Executive Officer

Ed: Michelle T. Johnson. **Released:** January 24, 2019. **Description:** The most diligent compliance with laws and regulations can't foster true work place diversity. The best organizations have become genuine cross-cultural communities that believe equality in reconciling difference and valuing them. The book promotes understanding by answering many of the toughest questions that professionals and their employers are afraid to ask. **Availability:** Print.

25304 ■ *"Doctor: J & J Alerted in '06 to Procedure Risks" in Pittsburgh Business Times (Vol. 33, June 6, 2014, No. 47, pp. 4)*

Pub: American City Business Journals, Inc.
Contact: Mike Olivieri, Executive Vice President

Released: Weekly. **Price:** $4, introductory 4-week offer(Digital & Print). **Description:** Dr. Robert Lamparter, then pathologist at Lewisburg's Evangelical Community Hospital, states that he had alerted Johnson and Johnson (J and J) in 2006 of the potential risk of spreading undetected cancer following the use of its power morcellator during hysterectomy procedures. J and J suspended worldwide sales of the device in April 2014 after the laboratory warning, and days after a US Food and Drug Administration advisory discouraging doctors from using it, but doctors are still divided over the morcellation procedure. **Availability:** Print; Online.

25305 ■ *"Doctor Shortage Continues to Plague Region" in Business First of Buffalo (Vol. 30, April 11, 2014, No. 30, pp. 6)*

Pub: American City Business Journals, Inc.
Contact: Mike Olivieri, Executive Vice President

Released: April 11, 2014. **Price:** $140, Digital & Print; $115, Digital only. **Description:** New York hospitals need at least 1,000 additional physicians, particularly primary care doctors, as they try to meet the criteria set by Federal health reform's Affordable Care Act. The Western New York region gained only 421 new physicians, while losing 544 in 2013. **Availability:** Print; Online.

25306 ■ *"Does Your Home or Building Need Radon Testing?" in U.S. News & World Report (February 24, 2016)*

URL(s): health.usnews.com/health-news/patient-advice/articles/2016-02-24/does-your-home-or-building-need-radon-testing

Ed: Lisa Esposito. **Released:** February 24, 2016. **Description:** Details the dangers of radon in our homes and who is susceptible to falling sick from exposure. Short-term testing is available, but long-term testing is recommended because radon levels can fluctuate which will give a better sample. DIY testing kits are also available for a low price. **Availability:** Online.

25307 ■ *"Dog Days and Stimulus Fatigue" in Barron's (Vol. 92, August 25, 2012, No. 38, pp. M10)*

Pub: Dow Jones & Company Inc.
Contact: Almar Latour, Chief Executive Officer

Ed: Michael Aneiro. **Description:** Credit market movements in August 2012 have been influenced by small news and speculation. US Federal Reserve Chairman Ben Bernanke has been more transparent, yet this transparency can also confound investors. **Availability:** Online.

25308 ■ *"DOL Stiffens Child Labor Penalties" in HR Specialist (Vol. 8, September 2010, No. 9, pp. 2)*

Pub: Capitol Information Group Inc.
Contact: Allie Ash, Chief Executive Officer

Description: U.S. Department of Labor (DOL) will impose new penalties for employers that violate U.S. child labor laws. Details of the new law are included.

25309 ■ *"Down the Tracks, a Whistle Is a-Blowin" in Barron's (Vol. 89, July 27, 2009, No. 30, pp. 36)*

Pub: Dow Jones & Company Inc.
Contact: Almar Latour, Chief Executive Officer

Ed: Jim McTague. **Description:** Higher numbers of freight-rail carloads are a sign that the economy is improving and it is no stretch to imagine that this is aided by the American Recovery and Reinvestment Act. It is also predicted that 2009 municipal bond issuance will be above $373 billion with at least $55 billion of it made up of Buy America Bonds that are subsidized by the federal government. **Availability:** Online.

25310 ■ *"Duro Bag to Expand, Add 130 Jobs" in Business Courier (Vol. 27, August 6, 2010, No. 14, pp. 1)*

Pub: Business Courier

Ed: Jon Newberry. **Description:** Duro Bag Manufacturing Company will expand capacity at its Florence, Kentucky plant and will add around 130 jobs over the next few years. The state of Kentucky has given preliminary approval for up to $1 million in tax incentives over 10 years, tied to the creation of new jobs. The company's investment will include new production and packaging equipment and building improvements. **Availability:** Print; Online.

25311 ■ *"Economists Warn Against Smart Cap" in Orlando Business Journal (Vol. 29, September 21, 2012, No. 14, pp. 1)*

Pub: Baltimore Business Journal
Contact: Rhonda Pringle, President
E-mail: rpringle@bizjournals.com

Ed: Abraham Aboraya, Richard Bilbao. **Description:** Opponents to the proposed amendment to the Florida State Revenue Limitations warn about the economic impact of the plan to cap state government spending. Under the proposal, the amount of taxes that the state should spend each year will be capped and a rainy day fund will be created where excess revenue collected will be placed. **Availability:** Print; Online.

25312 ■ *"EEOC Issues Enforcement Guidance Addressing Pregnancy-Related Disabilities" in Idaho Business Review (August 18, 2014)*

Pub: BridgeTower Media
Contact: Adam Reinebach, President

Description: An overview of the Pregnancy Discrimination Act (PDA) is presented. The EEOC is finally addressing this prohibited form of discrimination again pregnant women in the workplace. Requirements that link pregnancy-related disabilities with duties imposed by the Americans With Disabilities Act are covered.

25313 ■ *"Elanco Challenges Bayer's Advantage, K9 Advantix Ad Claims" in Pet Product News (Vol. 64, November 2010, No. 11, pp. 11)*

Description: Elanco Animal Health has disputed Bayer Animal Health's print and Web advertising claims involving its flea, tick, and mosquito control products Advantage and K9 Advantix. The National Advertising Division of the Council of Better Business Bureaus recommended the discontinuation of ads, while Bayer Animal Health reiterated its commitment to self-regulation. **Availability:** Online.

25314 ■ *"Elder Care, Rx Drug Reforms Top Zoeller's Agenda" in Times (December 21, 2010)*

Pub: The Times

Ed: Sarah Tompkins. **Description:** Indiana Attorney General Greg Zoeller is hoping to develop a program in the state that will help regulate care for the elderly; freeze medical licenses for doctors involved in criminal investigations; address illegal drug use; and to establish a program to help individuals dispose of old prescription medications easily at pharmacies. **Availability:** Online.

GENERAL SMALL BUSINESS TOPICS

Government Regulations ■ 25334

25315 ■ *"Election Futures are a Smart Idea"* in Canadian Business (Vol. 85, June 11, 2012, No. 10, pp. 18)
Ed: Mike Moffatt. **Description:** The decision of the U.S. Commodity Futures Trading Commission to ban political-event derivatives contracts was criticized along with the idea that such products could cause a systemic financial collapse. Political derivatives can be used as tools to help reduce risk and predict future political events. **Availability:** Print; Online.

25316 ■ *"Emissions: Cloudy Skies"* in Canadian Business (Vol. 81, October 27, 2008, No. 18, pp. 101)
Pub: Rogers Media Inc.
Contact: Neil Spivak, Chief Executive Officer
Ed: Andrew Wahl. **Description:** Canada's federal government is expected to implement its regulations on greenhouse-gas emissions by January 1, 2010, but companies are worried because the plan took so long and some details are yet to be revealed. Corporate Canada wants a firm, long-range plan similar to the European Union Emissions Trading Scheme in dealing with greenhouse-gas emissions. **Availability:** Online.

25317 ■ *"Empty Lots Could Be Full of Promise"* in San Francisco Business Times (Vol. 28, March 14, 2014, No. 34, pp. 4)
Pub: American City Business Journals, Inc.
Contact: Mike Olivieri, Executive Vice President
Price: $4, Introductory 4-Week Offer(Digital Only).
Description: San Francisco, California officials are looking at the city's own landholdings in order to start constructing new homes. However, the use of city-owned land does not ensure that the home permit process will be trouble-free. **Availability:** Print; Online.

25318 ■ *"End of the Beginning"* in Canadian Business (Vol. 81, November 10, 2008, No. 19, pp. 17)
Ed: David Wolf. **Released:** September 30, 2016. **Description:** The freeze in the money markets and historic decline in equity markets around the world finally forced governments into aggressive coordinated action. The asset price inflation brought on by cheap credit will now work in reverse and the tightening of credit will be difficult economically. Canada is exposed to the fallout everywhere, given that the U.S, the U.K. and Japan buy 30 percent of Canada's output. **Availability:** Print; Online.

25319 ■ *"The End of Clock-Punching"* in Canadian Business (Vol. 83, September 14, 2010, No. 15, pp. 96)
Pub: Rogers Media Inc.
Contact: Neil Spivak, Chief Executive Officer
Ed: Lyndsie Bourgon. **Description:** Workplace consultant Peter Hadwen is pushing for the transformation of Canada's government departments into results-only work environments (ROWE). ROWE does not require employees to show up to work at a certain time as long as they are meeting goals and achieving results in their jobs. Details of studies regarding ROWE in US companies are examined. **Availability:** Online.

25320 ■ *"Energy Efficiency Ordinance Softened"* in Austin Business JournalInc. (Vol. 28, October 3, 2008, No. 29)
Pub: Austin Business Journal
Contact: Rachel McGrath, Director
E-mail: rmcgrath@bizjournals.com
Ed: Jean Kwon. **Description:** City of Austin has eliminated mandatory energy efficiency upgrades to single-family housing as a condition for selling or renting homes or buildings. The new law proposes that an energy performance audit be conducted on single-family homes before being sold and the results of the audit disclosed to perspectives buyers. **Availability:** Print; Online.

25321 ■ *"Energy Firms Face Stricter Definitions"* in Globe & Mail (March 26, 2007, pp. B3)
Ed: David Ebner. **Description:** The Alberta Securities Commission has imposed strict securities regulations on oil and gas industries. Energy industries will have to submit revenue details to stake holders. **Availability:** Online.

25322 ■ *"EPA Grants E15 Waiver for 2001-2006 Vehicles"* in Farm Industry News (January 21, 2011)
Pub: Informa Business Media, Inc.
Contact: Charlie McCurdy, President
Ed: Lynn Grooms. **Description:** U.S. Environmental Protection Agency waived a limitation on selling gasoline that contains more than 10 percent ethanol for model year 2001-2006 cars and light trucks, allowing fuel to contain up to 15 percent ethanol (E15) for these vehicles. **Availability:** Online.

25323 ■ *"EPA Removes New York Scrap Dealer from Superfund List"* in Waste Today (October 30, 2019)
URL(s): www.wastetodaymagazine.com/article/ellenville-scrap-iron-and-metal-cleanup/
Ed: Kelly Maile. **Released:** October 30, 2019. **Description:** Ellenville Scrap Iron and Metal was on the EPA's list of hazardous sites in need of cleanup, and after extensive work was completed on the property, the once contaminated land is now a safe and productive site. **Availability:** Online.

25324 ■ *"EPA Removes Strasburg Landfill from National Priorities List"* in Waste Today (September 6, 2019)
URL(s): www.wastetodaymagazine.com/article/epa-removes-strasburg-landfill-superfund-site-national-priorities-list/
Ed: Theresa Cottom. **Released:** September 06, 2019. **Description:** The Strasburg Landfill Superfund Site in Pennsylvania was removed from the EPA's National Priorities List after nearly 30 years of cleanup. Moving forward, the site will only need to be monitored as all cleanup goals have now been met. **Availability:** Online.

25325 ■ *"Equity 'Crowdfunding' Platform, RelayFund, Launched by Michigan Investor Group"* in Economics Week (July 20, 2012)
Description: RelayFund was launched by a group of Michigan venture capitalists, entrepreneurs, and investment bankers to link small investors with startup firms under the new JOBS (Jumpstart Our Business Startups) Act. Crowdfunding is money raised for charities, projects or pre-selling products or services and allows online micro investments for startup companies.

25326 ■ *"Evaluating the 1996-2006 Employment Projections"* in Montly Labor Review (Vol. 133, September 2010, No. 9, pp. 33)
Pub: U.S. Department of Labor Bureau of Labor Statistics
Contact: Amrit Kohli, Director
E-mail: kohli.amrit@bls.gov
Description: Bureau of Labor Statistics employment projections outperformed alternative naive models, but not projecting the housing bubble or the rise in oil prices caused some inaccuracies in the projects. These projections are used by policymakers, economists, and students. **Availability:** PDF; Online.

25327 ■ *"Executive Compensation: Both Eyes on the Prize"* in Canadian Business (Vol. 83, September 14, 2010, No. 15, pp. 42)
Pub: Rogers Media Inc.
Contact: Neil Spivak, Chief Executive Officer
Ed: Jacqueline Nelson. **Description:** North American executive compensation has fundamentally shifted partly due to pressure from the US government and recent adjustments in the way CEO pay packages are structured. The changes have also become common practice in Canada and helped in scrutinizing the executive pay. **Availability:** Online.

25328 ■ *"Expect Action on Health Care and the Economy"* in Contractor (Vol. 57, January 2010, No. 1, pp. 30)
Ed: Kevin Schwalb. **Description:** The Plumbing-Heating-Cooling Contractors National Association is working to solidify its standing in the public policy arena as the legislative agenda will focus on health care reform, estate tax and immigration reform, all of which will impact the industries. **Availability:** Print; Online.

25329 ■ *"Extortion: How Politicians Extract Your Money, Buy Votes, and Line Their Own Pockets"*
Pub: Mariner Books
Released: October 22, 2013. **Price:** $12.79, Paperback. **Description:** Politicians and lawmakers have developed a new set of legislative tactics designed to extort wealthy industries and donors into huge contributions. This money is then funneled into the pockets of their friends and family members. Schweizer reveals the secret 'fees' each political party charges politicians for top committee assignments; how fourteen members of Congress received hundreds of thousands of dollars using a self-loan loophole; how PAC money is used to bankroll their lavish lifestyles; and more. The first time these unethical issues have been reported to the public. **Availability:** E-book; Print.

25330 ■ *"Family Child Care Record-Keeping Guide, Ninth Edition (Redleaf Business Series)"*
Pub: Redleaf Press
Contact: Barbara Yates, President
Released: 9th edition. **Price:** $21.95, soft bound. **Description:** Writer, trainer, lawyer, and consultant provides concise information for home-based family child care (day care) providers. The book covers tracking expenses, being profitable, filing taxes, and meeting government regulations. This resources covers the process of accurate bookkeeping and record-keeping to take advantage of all allowable tax deductions. Changes in depreciation rules, adjustments to food and mileage rates, and clarifications on how to calculate the Time-Space percentage are defined. **Availability:** Print.

25331 ■ *"The Favorite In the Casino, Racino Race"* in Business Review Albany (Vol. 41, July 25, 2014, No. 18, pp. 7)
Released: 2014. **Description:** The New York Government's plan to license four casinos could adversely impact the earnings of racinos. Racinos combine harness racing with video slot machines. The planned casinos are expected to attract racino customers creating competition. **Availability:** Print; Online.

25332 ■ *"FCC Adopts New Media Ownership Rules"* in Black Enterprise (Vol. 38, March 1, 2008, No. 8, pp. 26)
Pub: Earl G. Graves Ltd.
Contact: Earl Graves, Jr., President
Ed: Joyce Jones. **Description:** Federal Communications Commission approved a ruling that lifts a ban on newspaper and/or broadcast cross ownership. Because of declining sales in newspaper advertising and readership the ban will allow companies to share local news gathering costs across multiple media platforms. **Availability:** Online.

25333 ■ *"The FCC Has Fined Robocallers $208 Million. It's Collected $6,790"* in The Wall Street Journal (March 28, 2019)
URL(s): www.wsj.com/articles/the-fcc-has-fined-robocallers-208-million-its-collected-6-790-11553770803
Ed: Sarah Krouse. **Released:** March 28, 2019. **Description:** Since 2015 the FCC has ordered violators of the Telephone Consumer Protection Act to pay $208.4 million, but has only managed to collect $6,790 of that amount. Collecting these fines is difficult because illegal operations close up shop quickly and change their names. Others are based overseas making it almost impossible to seize assets. **Availability:** Online.

25334 ■ *"Feds Finalize I-9 Form Rules Allowing Electronic Storage"* in HR Specialist (Vol. 8, September 2010, No. 9, pp. 5)
Pub: Capitol Information Group Inc.
Contact: Allie Ash, Chief Executive Officer

25335 ■ Government Regulations

GENERAL SMALL BUSINESS TOPICS

Description: U.S. Department of Homeland Security issued regulations that give employers more flexibility to electronically sing and store I-9 employee verification forms. **Availability:** Print; PDF; Online.

25335 ■ *"A Few Points of Contention"* **in Barron's (Vol. 88, July 14, 2008, No. 28, pp. 3)**
Pub: Dow Jones & Company Inc.
Contact: Almar Latour, Chief Executive Officer
Ed: Michael Santoli. **Description:** Headline inflation tends to revert to the lower core inflation, which excludes food and energy in its calculation over long periods. Prominent private equity figures believe that regulators should allow more than the de facto 10 percent to 25 percent limit of commercial banks to hasten the refunding of the financial sector. **Availability:** Online.

25336 ■ *"Finally! Windsor Gets a New Bridge"* **in Canadian Business (Vol. 85, August 21, 2012, No. 14, pp. 20)**
Ed: Tim Shufelt. **Description:** Canadian Prime Minister Stephen Harper agreed to loan Michigan $550 million to build its new highway interchange and customs plaza linking Windsor, Ontario and Detroit, Michigan. Billionaire Manuel Maroun, owner of the Ambassador Bridge, has initiated a signature campaign for a referendum on any new border crossings. **Availability:** Print; Online.

25337 ■ *"Firm Restricts Cellphone Use While Driving"* **in Globe & Mail (January 30, 2006, pp. B3)**
Description: The details on AMEC Plc, which adopted cellphone-free driving policy, are presented. **Availability:** Online.

25338 ■ *"First Sustainability Standard for Household Portable and Floor Care Appliances Developed to Identify Environmentally Responsible Products"* **in Ecology, Environment & Conservation Business (September 13, 2014, pp. 39)**
Pub: NewsRX LLC.
Contact: Kalani Rosell, Contact
Description: the Association of Home Appliance Manufacturers (AHAM), CSA Group, and the UL Environment released the AHAM 7002-2014/CSA SPE-7002-14/UL 7002, Sustainability Standard for Household Portable and Floor Care Appliances. This is the first voluntary sustainability standards for these appliances and is the third in a unit of product sustainability standards under development by the group. These standards are intended for use by manufacturers, governments, retailers, and others to identify products conforming to these standards in six key areas: materials, manufacturing and operations, energy consumption during use, end-of-life, consumables, and innovation. **Availability:** Online.

25339 ■ *"First-Time Landlord: Your Guide to Renting Out a Single-Family Home"*
Pub: Nolo
Contact: Chris Braun, President
Released: 6th Edition. **Price:** $17.49, e-book (downloadable); $19.99, book and e-book. **Description:** The basics for becoming an landlord for anyone wishing to start an entrepreneurial pursuit in home rentals are outlined. Concise information for renting out a single-family home includes, how to determine whether the property will turn a profit, landlord business basics, finding the right tenants, preparing and signing a lead, handling repairs, complying with state rental laws, dealing with problem tenants, and preparing for the sale of the property. **Availability:** E-book.

25340 ■ *The Flaw of Averages: Why We Underestimate Risk in the Face of Uncertainty*
Pub: John Wiley & Sons, Inc.
Contact: Christina Van Tassell, Executive Vice President Chief Financial Officer
Ed: Sam L. Savage. **Released:** March 26, 2012. **Price:** $19.95, paperback; $27.95, hardcover; $12.99, E-Book. **Description:** Personal and business plans are based on uncertainties on a daily basis. The common avoidable mistake individuals make in assessing risk in the face of uncertainty is defined. The explains why plans based on average assumptions are wrong, on average, in areas as diverse as finance, healthcare, accounting, the war on terror, and climate change. **Availability:** E-book; Print.

25341 ■ *"'Focusing On the Moment"* **in Dallas Business Journal (Vol. 37, June 27, 2014, No. 42, pp. 4)**
Pub: American City Business Journals, Inc.
Contact: Mike Olivieri, Executive Vice President
Description: Southwest Airlines chairman, president, and CEO Gary Kelly, believes the key to the carrier's growth in 2014 will be to 'focus on the moment' and ensure that new projects are launched and strategies implemented successfully. Kelly discusses the potential impact of the repeal of the Wright Amendment on October 13, as well as Southwest's merger with AirTran and the launch of nonstop flights from New York and Washington DC. **Availability:** Print; Online.

25342 ■ *"Food Truck Group Backs Proposed Regulations"* **in Buffalo News (January 18, 2012)**
Ed: Aaron Besecker. **Description:** Food truck operators in the city of Buffalo, New York have accepted the newly created rules governing their operations in the city, despite the higher-than-expected $1,000 permit fee. An attorney for the Western New York Food Truck Association stated that the proposed rules would be acceptable to the membership. **Availability:** Print; Online.

25343 ■ *"Former Prov. Mayor Sees Potential in Newport Grand"* **in Providence Business News (Vol. 29, July 21, 2014, No. 16, pp. 4)**
Pub: American City Business Journals, Inc.
Contact: Mike Olivieri, Executive Vice President
URL(s): pbn.com/former-prov-mayor-sees-potential-in-newport-grand98638
Description: Joseph R. Paolino, Jr., managing partner at Paolino Properties and former Providence Mayor, believes introducing table games to Newport Grand can help the gambling casino generate needed revenues. Paolino notes that if voters approve a ballot referendum to authorize table games in November, he and his partners will acquire and renovate Newport Grand as an entertainment center. **Telecommunication Services:** Daddona@pbn.com.

25344 ■ *"Four Ways to Fix Banks: A Wall Street Veteran Suggests How To Cut Through the Industry's Complexity"* **in (Vol. 90, June 2012, No. 6, pp. 106)**
Pub: Harvard Business Review Press
Contact: Moderna V. Pfizer, Contact
Ed: Sallie Krawcheck. **Description:** Despite new regulations in the post-global economic crisis of 2008, banks are sill too complex for effective management of their boards. Recommendations for improving governance include incorporating bank debt in executive compensation to increase their sensitivity to risk, and paying dividends as a percentage of company earnings to maintain capital.

25345 ■ *"Free Speech Vs. Privacy in Data Mining"* **in Information Today (Vol. 28, September 2011, No. 8, pp. 22)**
Pub: Information Today Inc.
Contact: Thomas H. Hogan, President
Ed: George H. Pike. **Description:** The U.S. Constitution does not explicitly guarantee the right of privacy. Organizations and businesses that require obtaining and disseminating information can be caught in the middle of privacy rights. The long-term impact on data mining, Internet marketing, and Internet privacy issues are examined.

25346 ■ *"Fresh Off its IPO, HomeStreet Bank is Now the No. 2 Mortgage Lender in King County"* **in Puget Sound Business Journal (Vol. 33, June 15, 2012, No. 8, pp. 3)**
Pub: Baltimore Business Journal
Contact: Rhonda Pringle, President
E-mail: rpringle@bizjournals.com
Ed: Greg Lamm. **Description:** HomeStreet Bank has hired 300 new workers to work in its mortgage lending business and plans to open 13 new loan centers. Such moves has positioned the bank as King County's top two mortgage lenders. Federal regulators ordered HomeStreet Banki three years ago to raise additional capital of tens of millions.

25347 ■ *"Full Speed Ahead?"* **in San Antonio Business Journal (Vol. 28, May 9, 2014, No. 13, pp. 4)**
Pub: American City Business Journals, Inc.
Contact: Mike Olivieri, Executive Vice President
Released: May 09, 2014. **Price:** $4, Introductory 4-Week Offer(Digital & Print). **Description:** Lyft and Uber Technologies Inc. have launched ride-sharing services in San Antonio, Texas without the city's permission and the objections of taxi and limousine industries. The ride-sharing service issues were brought into court and to the City Council, while the San Antonio Police Department issued a cease-and-desist order to the ride-sharing companies. The complaints against Lyft and Uber are outlined. **Availability:** Print; Online.

25348 ■ *"Funders Fuel Explosion of Biotech Activity"* **in Puget Sound Business Journal (Vol. 35, July 11, 2014, No. 12, pp. 3A)**
Pub: American City Business Journals, Inc.
Contact: Mike Olivieri, Executive Vice President
Description: Washington's life sciences industry is experiencing problems due to a lack of support from state lawmakers, but the industry is receiving capital through initial public offerings, partnerships and venture equity. Joel Marcus of Alexandria Real Estate Equities claims that capital flows are at their highest levels since the dot-com bubble. **Availability:** Online.

25349 ■ *"Funds "Friend" Facebook"* **in Barron's (Vol. 89, July 27, 2009, No. 30, pp. 30)**
Pub: Dow Jones & Company Inc.
Contact: Almar Latour, Chief Executive Officer
Ed: Leslie P. Norton. **Description:** Mutual-fund companies are the latest entrants to the "social media" space and several companies have already set up Facebook and Twitter pages. The use of this technology pose special challenges for compliance and regulators especially since the Financial Industry Regulatory Authority reminds companies that advertising, sales and literature are governed by regulations. **Availability:** Online.

25350 ■ *"Fur Helped Build the City. Now Its Sale May Be Banned."* **in The New York Times (May 16, 2019)**
URL(s): www.nytimes.com/2019/05/16/nyregion/newyorktoday/nyc-news-fur-ban.html
Ed: Corey Kilgannon. **Description:** The New York City Council has a proposed bill that would ban fur sales, introduced by Corey Johnson. Although the fur industry has declined in the city, it still exists and has the largest retail fur market in the country. **Availability:** Online.

25351 ■ *"Future Fuzzy at Former Pemco Plant"* **in Baltimore Business Journal (Vol. 32, July 25, 2014, No. 12, pp. 10)**
Pub: American City Business Journals, Inc.
Contact: Mike Olivieri, Executive Vice President
Released: Weekly. **Price:** $4, introductory 4-week offer(Digital only). **Description:** The abandoned Pemco Corporation site on Eastern Avenue in Southeast Baltimore faces an uncertain future as new owner, MCB Real Estate LLC, fails to specify its prospective development plans for the property. City Councilman, James B. Kraft, wants to restrict the amount of retail space to be built at the Pemco and might even delay filing legislation on the space until MCB provides more details for the 20-acre property. **Availability:** Print; Online.

25352 ■ *"Futures Shock for the CME"* **in Crain's Chicago Business (Vol. 31, November 10, 2008, No. 45, pp. 8)**
Pub: Crain Communications Inc.
Contact: Barry Asin, President

Ed: Ann Saphir. **Description:** Chicago-based CME Group Inc., the largest futures exchange operator in the U.S., is facing a potentially radically altered regulatory landscape as Congress weighs sweeping reform of financial oversight. The possible merger of the CFTC and the Securities and Exchange Commission are among CME's concerns. Other details of possible regulatory measures are provided. **Availability:** Online.

25353 ■ *"Gay Gordon-Byrne on Protecting the Right to Repair" in Small Business Trends (September 27, 2022)*
URL(s): smallbiztrends.com/2022/09/right-to-repair-2.html
Ed: Holly Chavez. **Released:** September 27, 2022. **Description:** An interview with Gay Gordon-Byrne discussing the Right to Repair legislation that is being debated within the U.S. House. **Availability:** Online.

25354 ■ *"German Win Through Sharing" in Canadian Business (Vol. 83, September 14, 2010, No. 15, pp. 16)*
Pub: Rogers Media Inc.
Contact: Neil Spivak, Chief Executive Officer
Ed: Jordan Timm. **Released:** September 14, 2010. **Description:** German economic historian Eckhard Hoffner has a two-volume work showing how German's relaxed attitude toward copyright and intellectual property helped it catch up to industrialized United Kingdom. Hoffner's research was in response to his interest in the usefulness of software patents. Information on the debate regarding Canada's copyright laws is given. **Availability:** Print; Online.

25355 ■ *"Get Prepared for New Employee Free Choice Act" in HRMagazine (Vol. 53, December 2008, No. 12, pp. 22)*
Description: According to the director of global labor and employee relations with Ingersoll Rand Company, unions may have started having employees signing authorization cards in anticipation of the Employee Free Choice Act. Once signed, the cards are good for one year and employers would have only ten days in which to prepare for bargaining with unions over the first labor contract. The Act also requires these negotiations be subject to mandatory arbitration if a contract is not reached within 120 days of negotiations with unions, resulting in employers' wage rates, health insurance, retirement benefits and key language about flexibility would be determined by an arbitrator with no vested interest in the success of the company. **Availability:** Print; Online.

25356 ■ *"Getting Rid of Global Glitches: Choosing Software For Trade Compliance" in Black Enterprise (Vol. 41, September 2010, No. 2, pp. 48)*
Pub: Earl G. Graves Ltd.
Contact: Earl Graves, Jr., President
Ed: Marcia Wade Talbert. **Description:** Compliance software for trading with foreign companies must be compatible with the U.S. Census Bureau's Automated Export System (www.aesdirect.gov). It has to be current with regulatory requirements for any country in the world. Whether owners handle their own compliance or hire a logistics company, they need to be familiar with this software in order to access reports and improve transparency and efficiency of theft supply chain. **Availability:** Online.

25357 ■ *"The Gig's Up for Freelancers" in The Wall Street Journal (October 27, 2019)*
URL(s): www.wsj.com/articles/the-gigs-up-for-freelancers-11572208945
Ed: Andy Kessler. **Released:** October 27, 2019. **Description:** Assembly Bill 5 is set to take effect, meaning that most independent contractors will now be considered full-time employees in California. While it could mean that more contract workers receive sick leave and health care but more than likely, contractors will find their livelihoods taken away as employers will stop hiring freelancers from California. **Availability:** Online.

25358 ■ *"GM's Volt Woes Cast Shadow on E-Cars" in Wall Street Journal Eastern Edition (November 28, 2011, pp. B1)*
Pub: Dow Jones & Company Inc.
Contact: Almar Latour, Chief Executive Officer
Ed: Sharon Terlep. **Description:** The future of electric cars is darkened with the government investigation by the National Highway Traffic Safety Administration into General Motor Company's Chevy Volt after two instances of the car's battery packs catching fire during crash tests conducted by the Agency. **Availability:** Online.

25359 ■ *"A Good Step, But There's a Long Way to Go" in Business Week (September 22, 2008, No. 4100, pp. 10)*
Ed: James C. Cooper. **Description:** Despite the historic action by the U.S. government to nationalize the mortgage giants Freddie Mac and Fannie Mae, rising unemployment rates may prove to be an even bigger roadblock to bringing back the economy from its downward spiral. The takeover is meant to restore confidence in the credit markets and help with the mortgage crisis but the rising rate in unemployment may make many households unable to take advantage of any benefits which arise from the bailout. Statistical data included. **Availability:** Online.

25360 ■ *"Governor Candidates Differ on Oregon's Green Streak" in Business Journal Portland (Vol. 27, October 22, 2010, No. 34, pp. 1)*
Pub: Portland Business Journal
Contact: Andy Giegerich, Managing Editor
E-mail: agiegerich@bizjournals.com
Ed: Andy Giegerich. **Description:** The views of Oregon gubernatorial candidates Chris Dudley and John Kitzhaber on the state's economy and on environmental policies are presented. Both Dudley, who is a Republican, and his Democratic challenger believe that biomass could help drive the state's economy. Both candidates also pledged changes in Oregon's business energy tax credit (BETC) program.

25361 ■ *"The Great Deformation: The Corruption of Capitalism in America"*
Pub: PublicAffairs
Contact: Jaime Leifer, Director
Released: April 02, 2013. **Price:** $24.99, paperback; $14.99, E-book. **Description:** Washington's response to the recent financial crises and fiscal mismanagement is covered. The author provides a catalogue of economic corrupters and defenders of sound money, fiscal rectitude, and free markets. The book covers the history of political statesmen who championed balanced budgets and financial market discipline. The threat to free market prosperity and American political democracy are examined. **Availability:** E-book; Print.

25362 ■ *"Green Rules To Drive Innovation: Charging for Carbon Can Inspire Conservation, Fuel Competition, and Enhance Competitiveness" in Harvard Business Review (Vol. 90, March 2012, No. 3, pp. 120)*
Pub: Harvard Business Review Press
Contact: Moderna V. Pfizer, Contact
Ed: Daniel C. Esty, Steve Charnovitz. **Price:** $8.95. **Description:** Along with carbon emissions charges, other green policy recommendations include expanding domestic renewable power and the use of natural gas, increasing federal funding of clean-energy research, utilizing incentive-based approaches to encourage the adoption of renewable energy, and implementing the World Trade Organization's Doha negotiations on sustainable development. **Availability:** Online; PDF.

25363 ■ *"'Gregory Cunningham on Taking on Farm Credit of Florida" in South Florida Business Journal (Vol. 34, July 18, 2014, No. 52, pp. 11)*
Pub: American City Business Journals, Inc.
Contact: Mike Olivieri, Executive Vice President

Released: Weekly. **Price:** $8, introductory 4-week offer(Digital only). **Description:** Gregory Cunningham, president and CEO of Farm Credit of Florida, shares the lessons he learned from his military background that he applies to managing a company. He explains why he decided to take on the challenge of helping the agricultural credit group deal with its regulatory order. **Availability:** Print; Online.

25364 ■ *"Has Daylight Savings Time Fuelled Gasoline Consumption?" in Globe & Mail (April 18, 2007, pp. B1)*
Ed: Shawn McCarthy. **Description:** The prospects of the acquisition of BCE Inc, by Canadian pension funds are discussed. The effect of the growth of these pension funds on the Canadian economy is described. **Availability:** Online.

25365 ■ *"HBR Case Study: Setting Up Shop in a Political Hot Spot" in Harvard Business Review (Vol. 88, October 2010, No. 10, pp. 141)*
Pub: Harvard Business Publishing
Contact: Diane Belcher, Managing Director
Ed: Patrick Chun, John Coleman, Nabil El-Hage. **Price:** $8.95, PDF. **Description:** A fictitious foreign operations scenario is presented, with contributors providing comments and advice. The scenario involves a politically charged North Korean-South Korean business venture; suggestions range from ensuring financial flexibility in case of adverse events to avoiding any business venture until political stability is achieved. **Availability:** Online; PDF.

25366 ■ *"Health Care of the Future" in Business Journal Serving Greater Tampa Bay (Vol. 30, November 19, 2010, No. 48, pp. 1)*
Pub: Tampa Bay Business Journal
Contact: Ian Anderson, President
E-mail: ianderson@bizjournals.com
Description: Information about accountable care organizations (ACO), which are integrated care systems with doctors and hospitals working closely together to handle patient care, is provided. The Patient Protection and Affordable Care Act paved the way for ACOs as Medicare demonstration projects. **Availability:** Online.

25367 ■ *"Health IT Regulations Generate Static Among Providers" in Philadelphia Business Journal (Vol. 28, January 29, 2010, No. 50, pp. 1)*
Pub: Philadelphia Business Journal
Contact: Sierra Quinn, Director
E-mail: squinn@bizjournals.com
Ed: John George. **Description:** US Centers for Medicaid and Medicare Services and the Office of the National Coordinator for Health Information Technology have proposed rules regarding the meaningful use of electronic health records. The rules must be complied with by hospitals and physicians to qualify for federal stimulus funds. **Availability:** Online.

25368 ■ *"Health Reform Could Expand HSA-Based Plans" in Workforce Management (Vol. 88, December 14, 2009, No. 13, pp. 6)*
Description: HSA-qualified plans are the cheapest insurance plans on the market as they have a higher deductible but cost less upfront. If health care reform passes, HSA-qualified plans should benefit greatly. **Availability:** Print; Online.

25369 ■ *"Health Reform: How to Make it Cheaper" in Business Courier (Vol. 26, December 11, 2009, No. 33, pp. 1)*
Description: Greater Cincinnati health care leaders shared views about the health care reform bill. Respondents included the Cincinnati Visiting Nurse's Wallen Falberg, healthcare consultant Hirsch Cohen, Greater Cincinnati Health Council's Coleen O'Toole, Employer Health Care Alliance's Sharron DiMario, Legal Aid Society of Greater Cincinnati's Col Owens, Christ Hospital's Susan Croushore, and Humana of Ohio's Tim Cappel. **Availability:** Online.

25370 ■ Government Regulations

25370 ■ "Higher-Ed Finally in Session" in Business Journal Portland (Vol. 30, February 7, 2014, No. 49, pp. 4)
Pub: American City Business Journals, Inc.
Contact: Mike Olivieri, Executive Vice President
Released: February 07, 2014. Price: $4, Introductory 4-Week Offer(Digital & Print). Description: Oregon lawmakers and voters are set to consider several proposals on how higher education is funded, including free community college and free college for a percentage of future earnings. State Treasurer, Ted Wheeler, is proposing a large endowment that would pay for scholarships and vocational training. Availability: Print; Online.

25371 ■ "Hike in Md.'s Alcohol Tax May Be Hard For Lawmakers to Swallow" in Baltimore Business Journal (Vol. 28, November 19, 2010, No. 28)
Pub: Baltimore Business Journal
Contact: Rhonda Pringle, President
E-mail: rpringle@bizjournals.com
Ed: Emily Mullin. Description: Maryland's General Assembly has been reluctant to support a dime-per-drink increase in alcohol tax that was drafted in the 2009 bill if the tax revenue goes into a separate fund. The alcohol tax increase is considered unnecessary by some lawmakers and business leaders due to impending federal spending boosts. Availability: Print; Online.

25372 ■ "Hiring Unpaid Interns: Failing To Comply With Labor Laws Can Lead to Legal Trouble" in Black Enterprise (Vol. 44, June 2014, No. 10, pp. 22)
Pub: Earl G. Graves Ltd.
Contact: Earl Graves, Jr., President
Description: Before hiring an intern for a small business it is critical to study the Department of Labor's legal criteria, determine whether the internship should be paid or unpaid, weigh the pros and cons, focus on the training aspect, and work with local colleges.

25373 ■ "Hispanic Business 100 Influentials" in Hispanic Business (October 2009, pp. 22)
Description: Profiles of the top one hundred influential Hispanics in business and government are presented. Availability: Online.

25374 ■ "Historic Is Hot, But Challenging, in Bham" in Birmingham Business Journal (Vol. 31, August 1, 2014, No. 31, pp. 10)
Pub: American City Business Journals, Inc.
Contact: Mike Olivieri, Executive Vice President
Description: Birmingham, Alabama is witnessing a growing trend of restoring old and historic buildings for modern office spaces, driven by the new state credit for the projects. However, developers state that renovation projects present numerous challenges, including complying with current building codes and the use of energy-efficient innovation. Availability: Print; Online.

25375 ■ "A History of Neglect: Health Care for Blacks and Mill Workers in the Twentieth-Century South" in Canadian Business (Vol. 79, September 11, 2006, No. 18, pp. 21)
Description: Faulty practices being followed by auditors and regulators of Canada are discussed. The need for appropriate steps to protect investors against these frauds are emphasized. Availability: PDF.

25376 ■ "Hitting Bottom? Several Banks and Brokerages Are Ready to Pop Up for Air" in Barron's (Vol. 88, March 24, 2008, No. 12, pp. 21)
Pub: Dow Jones & Company Inc.
Contact: Almar Latour, Chief Executive Officer
Ed: Jacqueline Doherty. Description: Brokerage houses and banks may stabilize in 2008 as a result of regulatory responses brought about by the near-collapse of Bear Stearns. Some of their shares may rise by as much as 20 percent from 2008 to 2009. Availability: Online.

25377 ■ "Home, Sweet Shipping Container" in Washington Business Journal (Vol. 33, July 18, 2014, No. 13, pp. 4)
Pub: American City Business Journals, Inc.
Contact: Mike Olivieri, Executive Vice President
Description: Brookland Equity Group LLC is converting a single-family hom ein Brookland into a three-story, four-unit shipping container apartment building in Washington DC. According to the Department of Consumer Regulatory Affairs, the application was reviewed for lighting, ventilation, insulation, and other construction standards. Discussion on the new micro small living spaces trend is presented. Availability: Print; Online.

25378 ■ "Horse Racing Industry Cries Foul Over Budget Switch" in Philadelphia Business Journal (Vol. 31, March 23, 2012, No. 6, pp. 1)
Pub: Baltimore Business Journal
Contact: Rhonda Pringle, President
E-mail: rpringle@bizjournals.com
Price: Introductory 4-Week Offer(Digital & Print); $4, Introductory 4-Week Offer(Digital Only). Description: Pennsylvania Governor Tom Corbett's proposal to slash $72 million from the Horse Racing Development Fund is seen to adversely impact the sector. The plan has been criticized by track operators, trainers, owners and horse breeders. Availability: Print; Online.

25379 ■ "Hospitals Say Medicaid Expansion is Critical" in Dallas Business Journal (Vol. 35, August 3, 2012, No. 47, pp. 1)
Pub: Baltimore Business Journal
Contact: Rhonda Pringle, President
E-mail: rpringle@bizjournals.com
Ed: Bill Hethcock, Matt Joyce. Description: Governor Rick Perry's rejection of the Texas expansion of Medicaid is met with disapproval by health organizations such as the Methodist Health System. The federal government has extended $70 billion in financing to help more Texans become eligible for primary health care. Expansion supporters argue that Medicaid is critical in lowering insurance osts for those who need it. Availability: Print; Online.

25380 ■ "How To: Manage Your Cash Better" in Inc. (Volume 32, December 2010, No. 10, pp. 69)
Pub: Mansueto Ventures L.L.C.
Contact: Stephanie Mehta, Chief Executive Officer
Released: December 01, 2010. Description: A monthly guide to policies, procedures and practices for managing cash for a small business. Availability: Online.

25381 ■ "How To Reduce the Risk of Discrimination" in Idaho Business Review (September 11, 2014)
Pub: BridgeTower Media
Contact: Adam Reinebach, President
Description: Human resource departments in small businesses in Boise are aware of the city's discrimination ordinance making it unlawful to use sexual orientation and gender identity/expression in any consideration of hiring or terminating an employee, or for any other issue. The impact of the ordinance is yet to be determined.

25382 ■ "How To Spark Up a Medical Marijuana Firm in Florida - and Not Get Burned in the Process" in Orlando Business Journal (Vol. 30, March 21, 2014, No. 39, pp. 6)
Pub: American City Business Journals, Inc.
Contact: Mike Olivieri, Executive Vice President
Released: Weekly. Price: $8, introductory 4-week offer(Digital & Print). Description: Colorado business owners and experts offer tips on starting a medical marijuana business in Florida. Andy Williams recalls that he was filled with fear he would wake up in Federal prison and not see his family again when he started Medicine Man. Jerald Bovine of GreenZipp.

com advises those interested in entering the medical marijuana field to know the details of regulation of facilities and labs. Availability: Print; Online.

25383 ■ "How To Win the Fed's New Game" in Barron's (Vol. 92, September 17, 2012, No. 38, pp. M10)
Description: Options trading strategies designed to take advantage of the US Federal Reserve's third quantitative easing program are discussed. Options traders are advised to invest in short-term options to maximize gains. Availability: Print; Online.

25384 ■ "Huge Fight Over Tiny Apartments" in Puget Sound Business Journal (Vol. 35, September 12, 2014, No. 21, pp. 8)
Pub: American City Business Journals, Inc.
Contact: Mike Olivieri, Executive Vice President
Description: Smart Growth Seattle director, Roger Valdez and Seattle City Council member, Mike O'Brien, share their views about the proposed new rules and regulations governing micro-apartment buildings. Valdes says O'Brien's proposal would eliminate a choice for many people and force them to pay more or live elsewhere. O'Brien says the bill aims to apply existing construction rules to micro-housing in a fair way. Availability: Online.

25385 ■ "The Human Factor" in Canadian Business (Vol. 80, October 8, 2007, No. 20, pp. 22)
Description: David Foot, a demographer and an economics professor at the University of Toronto, talks about Canada's future, including economic and demographic trends. He discusses activities that should be done by businessmen in order to prepare for the future. He also addresses the role of the Canadian government in economic development. Availability: Print; Online.

25386 ■ "Illinois Regulators Revoke Collection Agency's License" in Collections & Credit Risk (Vol. 15, August 1, 2010, No. 7, pp. 13)
Pub: SourceMedia LLC
Contact: Gemma Postlethwaite, Chief Executive Officer
Description: Creditors Service Bureau of Springfield, Illinois had its license revoked by a state regulatory agency and was fined $55,000 because the owner and president, Craig W. Lewis, did not turn over portions of collected funds to clients. Availability: Print; Online.

25387 ■ "Immigration: Give Us Your Skilled" in Canadian Business (Vol. 80, October 8, 2007, No. 20, pp. 78)
Pub: Rogers Media Inc.
Contact: Neil Spivak, Chief Executive Officer
Ed: Zena Olijnyk. Description: Demand for skilled workers in Canada is discussed. Despite a strong demand, as evidenced by shortages in both skilled and unskilled labor, the country's immigration policy is affecting the recruitment process. Peter Veress, founder and president of Vermax Group, believes the country is wasting opportunities to take advantage of its attractiveness as a destination for foreign workers. Availability: Online.

25388 ■ "In the SBA's Face" in American Small Business League (December 2010)
Ed: Richard Larsen. Description: Lloyd Chapman uses the American Small Business League to champion small business. Statistical data included.

25389 ■ "Inco Takeover Faces Foreign Hurdles" in Globe & Mail (February 13, 2006, pp. B1)
Ed: Paul Waldie. Description: The issues that impact Inco Ltd.'s acquisition of Falconbridge Ltd., for $12.5 billion, are presented. Inco Ltd. is awaiting foreign regulatory approval in the United States and Europe. Availability: Print; Online.

GENERAL SMALL BUSINESS TOPICS

Government Regulations ■ 25410

25390 ■ *Incorporate Your Business: A Legal Guide to Forming a Corporation in Your State*
Pub: Nolo
Contact: Chris Braun, President
Ed: Anthony Mancuso. **Released:** 11th edition. **Price:** $34.99, e-book; $39.99, book and e-book; $34.99, e-book. **Description:** Legal guide to incorporating a business in the U.S., covering all 50 states. **Availability:** E-book; Print.

25391 ■ *"Inco's Takeover Offer Extended Four Months" in Globe & Mail (February 22, 2006, pp. B1)*
Description: United States and Europe competition authorities wanted more time to investigate Inco Ltd.'s takeover of Falconbridge Ltd. and compelling Inco to extend its $12.5 billion offer for the third time. **Availability:** Online.

25392 ■ *"Indiana Town Reports Success With Collection Agency" in PaymentsSource (August 20, 2012)*
Description: Capital Recovery Systems has collected nearly $80,000 in unpaid parking fines in Bloomington, Indiana. The city's agreement with the collection agency allows them to pursue an unlimited amount of unpaid parking tickets at least 30 days late. **Availability:** Print; Online.

25393 ■ *"Industry Associations Seek Clarity of CFPB's Large Collection Agency Definition" in PaymentsSource (May 24, 2012)*
Description: ACA International and DBA International are questioning the Consumer Financial Protection Bureau's definition of a large collection agency. The ACA has filed comments arguing that the threshold needs to be raised to $250 million, rather than the $10 million or more in annual receipts or money recovered as its definition. Details are provided. **Availability:** Print; Online.

25394 ■ *"Industry Escalates Lobbying Efforts For Loan Program" in Crain's Detroit Business (Vol. 24, September 22, 2008, No. 38, pp. 22)*
Pub: Crain Communications Inc.
Contact: Barry Asin, President
Ed: Jay Greene, Ryan Beene, Harry Stoffer. **Description:** Auto suppliers such as Lear Corp., which is best known for vehicle seating, also supplies high-voltage wiring for Ford hybrids and is developing other hybrid components. These suppliers are joining automakers in lobbying for the loan program which would promote the accelerated development of fuel-efficient vehicles. **Availability:** Print; PDF; Online.

25395 ■ *"Infrastructure: Things Fall Apart" in Canadian Business (Vol. 80, October 8, 2007, No. 20, pp. 187)*
Pub: Rogers Media Inc.
Contact: Neil Spivak, Chief Executive Officer
Ed: Jeff Sanford. **Description:** Infrastructure crisis in Canada and in other countries in North America is examined. Incidents that demonstrate this crisis, such as the collapse of a bridge in Minneapolis and the collapse of an overpass in Quebec, Canada are presented. It is estimated that the reconstruction in the country will cost between C$44 billion and C$200 billion. **Availability:** Print; Online.

25396 ■ *"Inking the Deal" in Slate (October 1, 2014)*
URL(s): slate.com/business/2014/10/tattoo-parlors-a-surprisingly-great-small-business-bet.html
Ed: Jesse Dorris. **Released:** October 01, 2014. **Description:** Discusses how tattoo parlors are often a good bet when it comes to opening a small business. Tattoos have been gaining in popularity with the Instagram crowd and their reputations are much higher than they used to be because so many people have tattoos that they have gone mainstream. Local governments are also surprisingly friendly to the industry, making it easier on owners. **Availability:** Online.

25397 ■ *"Innovation Central: Tech, Tweets, and Trolls" in Inc. (Vol. 36, September 2014, No. 7, pp. 102)*
Pub: Mansueto Ventures L.L.C.
Contact: Stephanie Mehta, Chief Executive Officer
Description: Results of a survey regarding the ways small business is using technology to grow their businesses is presented. Information covers social media applications, government software patents, trends impacting small business, and the most innovative technology companies. **Availability:** Print; Online.

25398 ■ *"Insurance Roars Back Into Style" in Barron's (Vol. 92, September 17, 2012, No. 38, pp. 11)*
Description: The US Federal Reserve's decision to implement a mortgage-buying policy is seen by the stock market as an insurance policy. The Federal Reserve will buy mortgage-backed securities worth $40 billion each month, a move which could bolster stock prices. **Availability:** Online.

25399 ■ *"Insurers Enter Ridesharing Dispute" in Sacramento Business Journal (Vol. 31, June 6, 2014, No. 15, pp. 8)*
Pub: American City Business Journals, Inc.
Contact: Mike Olivieri, Executive Vice President
Released: Weekly. **Price:** $4, Introductory 4-week offer(Digital & Print). **Description:** Insurance companies have been lobbying the California Assembly to pass legislation requiring ridesharing drivers to carry commercial liability insurance. Ridesharing companies provide drivers with liability coverage as a backup when an accident is not covered by personal insurance. The passage of such a bill would boost ridesharing companies' revenues. **Availability:** Print; Online.

25400 ■ *"International Waters: Hawaii Aquarium Legislation Dead...Or Is It?" in Pet Product News (Vol. 66, September 2012, No. 9, pp. 76)*
Ed: John Dawes. **Description:** SB 580 is deemed as one of the Hawaiin Senate bills that would lead to prohibition of, or heavy restrictions to, the collection of marine reef fish for home aquaria. Implications of these Senate bill on marine life conservation and stakeholder submissions are discussed. **Availability:** Online.

25401 ■ *"Internet Cafe Logging in to Chardon Plaza?" in News-Herald (July 16, 2011)*
Ed: Betsy Scott. **Description:** Pearl's High Rollers Inc. applied for an Internet sweepstakes cafe license that would reside in a vacant space in Chardon Plaza. City officials have created regulations for such businesses and Pearl's applied for a license and is awaiting approval. **Availability:** Online.

25402 ■ *"Investment In Israel Is Investment in the Future of Georgia" in Atlanta Business Chronicle (May 30, 2014, pp. 22A)*
Pub: American City Business Journals, Inc.
Contact: Mike Olivieri, Executive Vice President
Description: Georgia Governor Nathan Deal will travel to Israel to lead an economic and trade mission and consolidate Georgia's trade ties with Israel. Israel and the State of Georgia are already collaborating in the fields of health information technology, agrotechnology, homeland security, defense, aerospace and cybersecurity, and microelectronics and nanotechnology. The proposed visit by the Governor will build on this particular partnership from which both parties will benefit. **Availability:** Print; Online.

25403 ■ *"IP Transition Is Unlikely To Make Waves In R.I." in Providence Business News (Vol. 28, January 13, 2014, No. 41, pp. 1)*
Pub: American City Business Journals, Inc.
Contact: Mike Olivieri, Executive Vice President
Released: January 13, 2014. **Description:** The transition from copper and circuit switches to fiber and Internet Protocol is changing the telecommunications landscape across the U.S. The Rhode Island General Assembly passed a bill that deregulates wireless communications systems, which means that the growth of wireless in the area previously held by landlines will not change its status for now. **Availability:** Print; Online.

25404 ■ *"IPOs: Can You Keep a Secret?" in Silicon Valley/San Jose Business Journal (Vol. 30, August 31, 2012, No. 23, pp. 1)*
Pub: Baltimore Business Journal
Contact: Rhonda Pringle, President
E-mail: rpringle@bizjournals.com
Description: Many business enterprises have been keeping their initial public offering (IPO) filings confidential through a new rule under the JOBS Act. The rule permits companies with less than $1 billion in revenue to keep their IPO filings confidential until 21 days before going public. As keeping IPO filings secret offer many advantages, drawbacks of this action are also discussed. **Availability:** Print; Online.

25405 ■ *"IRS Announces New Standards for Tax Preparers" in Bellingham Business Journal (Vol. February 2010, pp. 9)*
Pub: Sound Publishing Inc.
Contact: Josh O'Connor, President
Ed: Isaac Bonnell. **Description:** A new oversight plan was announced by the Internal Revenue Services (IRS) that will require tax professionals to pass a competency test and register with the government in order to ensure greater accountability in the industry.

25406 ■ *"Ivernia Mine Closing Could Boost Lead" in Globe & Mail (April 4, 2007, pp. B5)*
Ed: Andy Hoffman. **Description:** The closing of Ivernia Inc.'s mine in view of government investigation into alleged lead contamination at the port of Esperance is discussed. The likely increase in the price of lead is also discussed. **Availability:** Print; Online.

25407 ■ *"Kaboom!" in Canadian Business (Vol. 81, November 10, 2008, No. 19, pp. 18)*
Description: International Financial Reporting Standards (IFRS) is a good idea in theory but was implemented in a hurry and had poor quality standards from the beginning. **Availability:** Print; Online.

25408 ■ *"KC Incentives Debate Rages on Unabated" in The Business Journal-Serving Metropolitan Kansas City (Vol. 26, September 5, 2008, No. 52)*
Pub: American City Business Journals, Inc.
Contact: Mike Olivieri, Executive Vice President
Ed: Rob Roberts. **Description:** Debate on the new economic development and incentives policy adopted by the Kansas City Council is still on. The city's Planned Industrial Expansion Authority has rejected a standard property tax abatement proposal. The real estate development community has opposed the rejection of proposed the tax incentives policy. **Availability:** Online.

25409 ■ *"Keith Crain: Business Must Stand Up And Be Counted" in Crain's Detroit Business (Vol. 24, October 6, 2008, No. 40, pp. 6)*
Pub: Crain Communications Inc.
Contact: Barry Asin, President
Description: Discusses the challenges that the new mayor of Detroit faces concerning business, the state of the economy and the exceptionally tight budget the city is running on, which includes a lot of red ink. It is very likely that the city is going to see tax revenues fall substantially in the next few months and business leaders may find it in their favor to lend their support to the new mayor as well as provide him with the executive talent necessary to overcome some of these crucial issues. **Availability:** Online.

25410 ■ *"Keltic Gets Nod to Build N.S. Petrochemical Plant" in Globe & Mail (March 15, 2007, pp. B9)*
Ed: Shawn McCarthy. **Description:** The government of Nova Scotia has awarded clearance to Keltic Inc. for the construction of new petrochemical plant in Goldboro region. Complete details in this context are discussed. **Availability:** Online.

25411 ■ "LA Passes HET Ordinance, California Greens Code" in Contractor (Vol. 56, September 2009, No. 9, pp. 1)
Ed: Candace Roulo. Description: Los Angeles City Council has passed a Water Efficiency Requirements ordinance. The law mandates lower low-flow plumbing requirements for plumbing fixtures installed in new buildings and retrofits. Under the ordinance, a toilet's maximum flush volume may not exceed 1.28-gpf. Availability: Print; Online.

25412 ■ "Land Swap Key to Ending Royal Oak Project Impasse" in Crain's Detroit Business (Vol. 25, June 8, 2009, No. 23, pp. 20)
Pub: Crain Communications Inc.
Contact: Barry Asin, President
Ed: Chad Halcom. Description: Details of the new construction of the LA Fitness health club near Woodward and Washington Avenues in Royal Oak, Michigan are discussed. Availability: Online.

25413 ■ "The Latest on E-Verify" in Contractor (Vol. 56, September 2009, No. 9, pp. 58)
Ed: Susan McGreevy. Description: United States government has required federal contractors to use its E-Verify program to verify the eligibility of incoming and existent employees. The use of the program is seen to eliminate Social Security mismatches. Availability: Print; Online.

25414 ■ "Law Firms Cash In On Alcohol" in Business Journal Portland (Vol. 27, November 19, 2010, No. 38, pp. 1)
Pub: Portland Business Journal
Contact: Andy Giegerich, Managing Editor
E-mail: agiegerich@bizjournals.com
Ed: Andy Giegerich. Description: Oregon-based law firms have continued to corner big business on the state's growing alcohol industry as demand for their services increased. Lawyers, who represent wine, beer and liquor distillery interests, have seen their workload increased by 20 to 30 percent in 2009. Availability: Print; Online.

25415 ■ "Lawmakers, Execs Launch Effort to Save Rural Hospitals" in Atlanta Business Chronicle (June 13, 2014, pp. 7A)
Pub: American City Business Journals, Inc.
Contact: Mike Olivieri, Executive Vice President
Description: Governor Nathan Deal has appointed a committee of Georgia lawmakers and healthcare executives to launch an effort to save the state's financially burdened rural hospitals. In addition, he plans to allow rural hospitals that have closed or are on the verge of closing, to scale back their operations, under a new rule approved by the Georgia Board of Community Health. Availability: Print; Online.

25416 ■ "Lawsuit Seeks To Shut Down Illinois Collection Agency" in PaymentsSource (January 12, 2012)
Pub: SourceMedia LLC
Contact: Gemma Postlethwaite, Chief Executive Officer
Description: PN Financial is facing charges by the Illinois State Attorney General's Office, alleging that the company used abusive and threatening actions against consumers. Details of the lawsuit are covered. Availability: Online.

25417 ■ "Lawsuits Claim Coke Sent Illegal Ad Texts" in Atlanta Business Chronicle (June 13, 2014, pp. 4A)
Pub: American City Business Journals, Inc.
Contact: Mike Olivieri, Executive Vice President
Description: Coca-Cola Company is facing lawsuits in San Diego and California from consumers who claim to have received unsolicited ads to their wireless phones, thus putting Coke in violation of the Federal law, called the Telephone Consumer Protection Act. The plaintiff of the California lawsuit is seeking damages amounting to $1,500 for each text message sent. Availability: Print; Online.

25418 ■ "LCB Puts a Cork in Kiosk Wine Sales" in Times Leader (December 22, 2010)
Ed: Andrew M. Seder. Description: The Pennsylvania Liquor Control Board closed down thirty Pronto Wine Kiosks located in supermarkets throughout the state. The Board cited mechanical and technological issues such as products not dispensing. Availability: Online.

25419 ■ "Lead-Free Products must Meet Requirements" in Contractor (Vol. 56, September 2009, No. 9, pp. 30)
Ed: Robert Gottermeier. Description: United States Environmental Protection Agency's adoption of the Safe Drinking Water Act is aimed at lowering lead extraction levels from plumbing products. Manufacturers have since deleaded brass and bronze potable water products. Meanwhile, California and Vermont have passed a law limiting lead content for potable water conveying plumbing products. Availability: Print; Online.

25420 ■ "Legislating the Cloud" in Information Today (Vol. 28, October 2011, No. 9, pp. 1)
Pub: Information Today Inc.
Contact: Thomas H. Hogan, President
Ed: Kurt Schiller. Description: Internet and telecommunications industry leaders are asking for legislation to address the emerging market in cloud computing. Existing communications laws do not adequately govern the modern Internet.

25421 ■ "Legislative Changes Providing Boost to San Antonio Distillers" in San Antonio Business Journal (Vol. 28, March 7, 2014, No. 4, pp. 4)
Pub: American City Business Journals, Inc.
Contact: Mike Olivieri, Executive Vice President
Released: Weekly. Price: $4, Introductory 4-week offer(Digital only). Description: Lawmakers in Texas have implemented legislative changes that will provide financial flexibility to brew pubs and breweries. Distilleries in the state are now allowed to sell their products directly to food companies. The growth in San Antonio, Texas' craft spirits industry is also discussed. Availability: Print; Online.

25422 ■ "Legislators Must Cut Cost of Government" in Crain's Detroit Business (Vol. 24, October 6, 2008, No. 40, pp. 6)
Pub: Crain Communications Inc.
Contact: Barry Asin, President
Description: Southeast and West Michigan business leaders are setting aside their differences and have proposed clear agendas, ranging from eliminating the Michigan Business Tax to overhauling public employee and retiree benefits and pensions. Lawmakers must also come together to find solutions for the state's economy and discover an entirely new vision for the future of Michigan business. Availability: Print; Online.

25423 ■ "Less Malaise in Malaysia" in Barron's (Vol. 88, March 17, 2008, No. 11, pp. M12)
Pub: Dow Jones & Company Inc.
Contact: Almar Latour, Chief Executive Officer
Ed: Assif Shameen. Description: Shares of Malaysia's Bursa have been in freefall while the Malaysia government prolongs its pitch to sell a 10 percent stake of the exchange to NYSE Euronext. Asian bourses had produced very good returns for five years and charge some of the highest fees for exchanges. A key growth driver for Asian bourses could be the derivatives markets and exchange-traded funds. Availability: Online.

25424 ■ "Let Markets Decide?" in Canadian Business (Vol. 80, October 8, 2007, No. 20, pp. 67)
Description: Need to protect Canadian companies that could help boost the country's economy is discussed. It is expected that free markets alone will solve economic problems. Suggested policies that will discourage the takeover of major companies in the country, such as the organization of capitalization with multiple voting shares, are also presented. Availability: Print; Online.

25425 ■ "Let's Make a Deal" in Pittsburgh Business Times (Vol. 33, July 18, 2014, No. 53, pp. 10)
Pub: American City Business Journals, Inc.
Contact: Mike Olivieri, Executive Vice President
Released: February 26, 2015. Description: The low interest rate, combined with regulation have reduced fixed income trading for banks, thus reducing their profits and increasing the volatility of quarterly earnings. Banks are being forced to consider new ways to make money as the low rates are a function of a Federally-structured government yield curve, reflecting lower economic growth and inflation expectations. Availability: Print; Online.

25426 ■ "Lindbergh Receives Kiosks to Expedite Travel Through Customs: Vetting Process 'Pre-Screens' Low-Risk Travelers" in San Diego Business Journal (Vol. 33, August 20, 2012, No. 34, pp. 8)
Pub: CBJ L.P.
Contact: Terri Cunningham, Contact
Ed: Mike Allen. Description: Lindbergh Field airport in California installed two automated kiosks to help international travelers pass through customs in minutes. Global Entry verifies identification and allows declaration of items and is used for low risk passsengers. Availability: Online.

25427 ■ "Liquor-Sales Issue in Kansas Creates Strange Bedfellows" in Wichita Business Journal (Vol. 27, February 10, 2012, No. 6, pp. 1)
Pub: Baltimore Business Journal
Contact: Rhonda Pringle, President
E-mail: rpringle@bizjournals.com
Description: How the business community in Kansas has reacted to House Bill 2532, a legislation that would alter the way liquor is sold in the state, is presented. Under the legislation, groceries and convenience stores would be allowed to get licenses to sell liquor, wine and full-strength beer. On the other hand, liquor stores would be permitted to sell other products on the premises. Availability: Print; Online.

25428 ■ "Liquor Stores Feeling Financial Impact Six Months after Grocery Stores Allowed to Sell Wine on Sundays" in wsmv.com (June 26, 2019)
URL(s): www.wsmv.com/news/liquor-stores-feeling-financial-impact-six-months-after-grocery-stores/article_bb9c13f36-987f-11e9-bb72-8f7b70b01ee4.html
Ed: Cameron Taylor. Released: June 26, 2019. Description: Six months after a new Tennessee law went info effect allowing grocery stores to sell liquor on Sundays, local liquor stores noticed they are losing profits. Since it's easier to pick up alcohol while doing grocery shopping, there is no longer an incentive to visit the liquor store and make a purchase. Availability: Online.

25429 ■ "Live & Learn: Thomas D'Aquino" in Canadian Business (Vol. 80, November 19, 2007, No. 23, pp. 92)
Pub: Rogers Media Inc.
Contact: Neil Spivak, Chief Executive Officer
Ed: Calvin Leung. Description: Thomas D'Aquino is the CEO and president of the Canadian Council of Chief Executives since 1981. D'Aquino thinks he has the best job in Canada because he can change the way policies are made and the way people think. Details of his career as a lawyer and CEO and his views on Canada's economy are provided. Availability: Print; Online.

25430 ■ "Living in a 'Goldfish Bowl'" in WorkingUSA (Vol. 11, June 2008, No. 2, pp. 277)
Description: Recent changes in laws, regulations and even the reporting format of labor organization annual financial reports in both the U.S. and Australia have received surprisingly little attention, yet they have significantly increased the amount of informa-

tion available both to union members and the public in general, as reports in both countries are available via government Websites. While such financial reporting laws are extremely rare in European countries, with the exception of the UK and Ireland, the U.S. and Australian reporting systems have become among the most detailed in the world. After reviewing these changes in financial reporting and the availability of these reports, as well as comparing and contrasting the specific reporting requirements of each country, this paper then examines the cost-benefit impact of more detailed financial reporting. **Availability:** Print; Online.

25431 ■ *"Local Couple Pushes for Change to Waco Beekeeping Ordinance" in Waco Tribune-Herald (May 31, 2019)*
URL(s): www.wacotrib.com/news/government/local-couple-pushes-for-change-to-waco-beekeeping-ordinance/article_d8e9559e-13dc-5634-92ab-d22fcd898aec.html
Released: May 31, 2019. **Description:** Due to an ordinance that requires beekeepers to obtain permission from everyone who lives in a 300-foot radius of the hive, a local beekeeper had to give up her hives. This spurned the beekeeper into action, hoping to get the ordinance changed so that more people can easily keep bees and help the ecosystem. **Availability:** Online.

25432 ■ *"Locals Eager for $785M Medical Marijuana Business" in Orlando Business Journal (Vol. 30, March 21, 2014, No. 39, pp. 4)*
Pub: American City Business Journals, Inc.
Contact: Mike Olivieri, Executive Vice President
Released: Weekly. **Price:** $8, introductory 4-week offer(Digital & Print). **Description:** A number of local companies in Central Florida are preparing for a ballot initiative to legalize medical marijuana in November 2014. The National Cannabis Association estimates the medical marijuana market in Florida at $785 million, with about 260,000 patients, while Orlando's share is estimated at $89.1 million, with 29,518 potential patients. **Availability:** Print; Online.

25433 ■ *"A Long Road to Recovery" in Barron's (Vol. 89, July 27, 2009, No. 30, pp. 37)*
Ed: Henry Kaufman. **Released:** November 01, 2016. **Description:** United States' economy remains hobbled by some underlying constraint and real recovery remains ephemeral. Much of the financial problems could have been avoided if t he Federal Reserve was effectively guarding the financial system. **Availability:** Print; Online.

25434 ■ *"Looking To Hire Young? Be Careful" in Boston Business Journal (Vol. 30, November 19, 2010, No. 43, pp. 1)*
Pub: Boston Business Journal
Contact: Carolyn M. Jones, President
E-mail: cmjones@bizjournals.com
Ed: Lisa van der Pool. **Released:** Weekly. **Description:** The Massachusetts Commission Against Discrimination (MCAD) has been using undercover job applicants to expose discrimination. Cabot's Ice Cream and Restaurant has been accused of denying older workers equal employment opportunities. MCAD has discovered unfair hiring practices such as hiring high school and college students. **Availability:** Print; Online.

25435 ■ *"Lower Prices No Shoo-In as Telcos Near Deregulation" in Globe & Mail (March 28, 2007, pp. B1)*
Ed: Catherine McLean. **Description:** The fall in market share and low quality of service among other issues that may disallow telecommunication industries in Canada from setting their phone rates is discussed. **Availability:** Online.

25436 ■ *"Managerial Ties with Local Firms and Governments: an Analysis of Japanese Firms In China" in International Journal of Business and Emerging Markets (Vol. 4, July 11, 2012, No. 3, pp. 181)*
Pub: Inderscience Publishers

Ed: Naoki Ando, Daniel Z. Ding. **Description:** This study explores how managerial ties between foreign firms and local firms and those between foreign firms and local government officials affect the performance of firms operating in transition economies. Using survey data collected from Japanese firms operating in China, this study finds that managerial ties between foreign firms and local firms and local government officials are positively associated with the performance of Japanese firms in China. **Availability:** Print; PDF; Online.

25437 ■ *"Managing the Federal HOME Program: Past and Future" in Real Estate Review (Vol. 41, Spring 2012, No. 1, pp. 29)*
Released: Spring 2012. **Description:** The US Department of Housing and Urban Development's Home Investment Partnerships Program (HOME) is discussed. The program is allocated to eligible state and local governments, with the goal of increasing affordable housing. HOME has been criticized for idling home construction projects.

25438 ■ *"Market Takes Shape for Emissions Credits" in Globe & Mail (April 16, 2007, pp. B3)*
Ed: Shawn McCarthy. **Description:** The effort of Canadian companies to prepare for emissions trading after the government imposes climate change regulations is discussed. **Availability:** Online.

25439 ■ *"Market Watch" in Barron's (Vol. 88, March 24, 2008, No. 12, pp. M18)*
Ed: Ashraf Laidi, Marc Pado, David Kotok. **Released:** 2018. **Description:** Latest measures implemented by the Federal Reserve to address the credit crisis did not benefit the US dollar, with the Japanese yen and the euro recouping earlier losses against the dollar. Goldman Sachs reported earnings of $3.23 per share, claiming a stronger liquidity position. The US markets bottomed early on 22 January 2007, according to evidence. **Availability:** Print; Online.

25440 ■ *"Maryland Nonprofits May Lose Minority Business Enterprise Status" in Baltimore Business Journal (Vol. 29, September 2, 2011, No. 17, pp. 1)*
Pub: Boston Business Journal
Contact: Carolyn M. Jones, President
E-mail: cmjones@bizjournals.com
Ed: Scott Dance. **Description:** A business group has been pushing to bar nonprofits from Maryland's Minority Business program. Nonprofits have been found to take a large portion of state contracts intended for women- and minority-owned businesses. The group is also crafting proposed legislation to remove nonprofits from the program. **Availability:** Online.

25441 ■ *"Maryland Ready to Defend Slots Minority Policy" in Boston Business Journal (Vol. 29, July 8, 2011, No. 9, pp. 3)*
Pub: Boston Business Journal
Contact: Carolyn M. Jones, President
E-mail: cmjones@bizjournals.com
Ed: Scott Dance. **Description:** The legality of Maryland's minority inclusion policy may be put under scrutiny once the lawsuit filed by rejected slots developer Baltimore City Entertainment Group on July 5, 2011 is heard in court. The lawsuit aims to stop the bidding process on a proposed casino in Baltimore because the minority policy amounts to reverse discrimination. **Availability:** Print; Online.

25442 ■ *"A Matter of Perspective" in Business Journal-Portland (Vol. 24, November 2, 2007, No. 35, pp. 1)*
Pub: Portland Business Journal
Contact: Andy Giegerich, Managing Editor
E-mail: agiegerich@bizjournals.com
Ed: Andy Giegerich. **Description:** Oregon Governor Ted Kulongoski assembled the Mortgage Lending Work Group, made up of members of the mortgage industry and consumer groups, to recommend possible bills for the Oregon Senate and House to consider. How its members try to balance philosophical differences in mortgage lending rules is discussed. **Availability:** Online.

25443 ■ *"MBT Add-On: Gone by 2012?" in Crain's Detroit Business (Vol. 24, October 6, 2008, No. 40, pp. 1)*
Pub: Crain Communications Inc.
Contact: Barry Asin, President
Ed: Amy Lane. **Description:** Discusses the Michigan Business Tax (MBT), which has angered many businesses in the state due to the addition of a 21.99 percent surcharge. Although the tax policy will cut taxes on 63 percent of businesses in the state and represent no tax liability change for another nine percent of firms, other businesses will see increases of 100 percent or more. This increase means that many business owners will be forced to relocate or close their establishment and others will have to eliminate jobs. Lawmakers are attempting to find a solution to this problem. **Availability:** Print; Online.

25444 ■ *"Md. Faces Daunting Task of Educating Masses About Health Reform Law" in Baltimore Business Journal (Vol. 28, October 15, 2010, No. 23, pp. 1)*
Pub: Baltimore Business Journal
Contact: Rhonda Pringle, President
E-mail: rpringle@bizjournals.com
Ed: Emily Mullin. **Description:** The Henry J. Kaiser Family Foundation's survey shows nearly 53 percent of Americans remain confused about health care reform and it was up to the states to educate the people. However, Maryland is still trying to figure out how to conduct the campaign without guidance or funding from the Federal government. **Availability:** Print.

25445 ■ *"Meals on Wheels; Chicago Puts the Brakes on Upwardly Mobile Food Truck Operators" in Wall Street Journal (August 7, 2012, pp. A12)*
Pub: Dow Jones & Company Inc.
Contact: Almar Latour, Chief Executive Officer
Description: Details on the City of Chicago's move to regulate mobile food truck operators is presented. **Availability:** Online.

25446 ■ *"Medical Collection Agency Refutes Allegations In AG's Report" in PaymentsSource (May 1, 2012)*
Description: Accretive Health Inc. denies allegations by the Minnesota State Attorney General's Office that the firm used heavy-handed tactics pressuring patients to pay for services before receiving treatment. The medical collection agency's report states 'inaccuracies, innuendo and unfounded speculation' in the charges. **Availability:** Print; Online.

25447 ■ *"Medical Pot Backers Say Industry Will Survive" in Sacramento Business Journal (Vol. 28, October 14, 2011, No. 33, pp. 1)*
Pub: Sacramento Business Journal
Contact: Stephanie Fretwell, Director
E-mail: sfretwell@bizjournals.com
Ed: Melanie Turner. **Description:** Medical marijuana supporters have expected the industry to decline but will survive the federal restriction on growers and dispensaries across California. California Cannabis Association and National Cannabis Industry Association believe that some of the dispensaries will remain and the shakeout will lead to stronger state regulations. **Availability:** Online.

25448 ■ *"Medicare Fraudsters Turn to Pharmacies" in South Florida Business Journal (Vol. 32, June 15, 2012, No. 47, pp. 1)*
Pub: Baltimore Business Journal
Contact: Rhonda Pringle, President
E-mail: rpringle@bizjournals.com
Description: U.S. Department of Health and Human Services, Office of Inspector General reports indicate that 2,637 retail pharmacies, or 4.4 percent of all pharmacies, had dubious Part D practices in 2009.

25449 ■ Government Regulations

However, the Miami area led the nation with 19.4 percent of its retail pharmacies submitting dubious claims as unethical frauds turn them in. **Availability:** Print; Online.

25449 ■ "Merger Expected to Bring New Player to TV Market" in Providence Business News (Vol. 28, March 31, 2014, No. 52, pp. 1)
Pub: American City Business Journals, Inc.
Contact: Mike Olivieri, Executive Vice President
URL(s): pbn.com/merger-expected-to-bring-new-player-to-tv-market96073
Description: The proposed merger of Media General and Providence, Rhode Island-based LIN Media LLC has the potential to change the TV landscape in the state. The two media companies' TV stations overlap in five markets and ownership at one of the stations is expected to change due to federal regulations regarding TV station ownership. The two TV stations are outlined.

25450 ■ "Key Challenges Dog International Banking in South Florida" in South Florida Business Journal (Vol. 35, August 1, 2014, No. 1, pp. 4)
Pub: American City Business Journals, Inc.
Contact: Mike Olivieri, Executive Vice President
Released: Weekly. **Price:** $8, introductory 4-week offer(Digital only). **Description:** Florida International Bankers Association president, Roberto R. Munoz, discusses the challenges and opportunities in the South Florida international banking market. He explains the impact on international banks with the loss of the Export-Import Bank of the United States charter and the Base1 III rules and regulations regarding higher capital requirements. **Availability:** Print; Online.

25451 ■ "Monsanto's Next Single-Bag Refuge Product Approved" in Farm Industry News (December 5, 2011)
Pub: Informa Business Media, Inc.
Contact: Charlie McCurdy, President
Description: Monsanto's refuge-in-a-bag (RIB) product was approved for commercialization in 2012. The Genuity VT Double Pro RIB Complete is a blend of 95 percent Genuity VT Double Pro and 5 percent refuge (non-Bt) seed and provides above-ground pest control and not corn rootworm protection. **Availability:** Print; Online.

25452 ■ "More SouthPark Shopping for Charlotte" in Charlotte Business Journal (Vol. 25, July 16, 2010, No. 17, pp. 1)
Pub: Charlotte Business Journal
Contact: Robert Morris, Editor
E-mail: rmorris@bizjournals.com
Ed: Will Boye. **Description:** Charlotte, North Carolina-based Bissel Companies has announced plans to expand its retail presence at the Siskey and Sharon properties in SouthPark. Bissel Companies has requested a rezoning to a mixed-use development classification so that it can utilize the entire ground floor of the Siskey building for restaurant and retail uses. **Availability:** Print; Online.

25453 ■ "MyWireless.org Commends Arizona Congressman Trent Franks for Committing to Wireless Tax Relief for American Consumers and Businesses" in PR Newswire (September 21, 2012)
Pub: PR Newswire Association LLC.
Description: MyWireless.org presented Congressman Trent Franks from Arizona with the 2012 Wireless Consumer Hero Award for his work on wireless tax relief for American consumers and businesses. Franks' 'Wireless Tax Fairness Act' (HR 1002) promotes access to wireless networks as a key ingredient of millions of Americans' livelihoods, whether phone, broadband Internet necessary to run a small business. **Availability:** Print; Online.

25454 ■ "A New Era for Raiders" in Harvard Business Review (Vol. 88, November 2010, No. 11, pp. 34)
Pub: Harvard Business Publishing
Contact: Diane Belcher, Managing Director
Ed: Guhan Subramanian. **Price:** $6, PDF. **Description:** The article presents evidence that Section 203 is vulnerable, and a new wave of corporate takeovers may develop. The authors suggest that since no bidders have able to use the 85 percent stipulation over the last 19 years, it does not present a meaningful opportunity for success. **Availability:** Online; PDF.

25455 ■ "New Government Tool Opens Window into Nursing-Home Abuse" in The Wall Street Journal (November 19, 2019)
URL(s): www.wsj.com/articles/new-government-tool-opens-window-into-nursing-home-abuse-11574159400
Ed: Yuka Hayashi. **Released:** November 19, 2019. **Description:** The government database, Nursing Home Compare, has a new feature that marks facilities cited for abuse or neglect with a small red icon. So far, 760 facilities have been indicated, and the symbols are updated monthly. **Availability:** Online.

25456 ■ "New Jersey Enacts Strict Opioid Prescribing Law" in Pharmacy Times (February 21, 2017)
URL(s): www.pharmacytimes.com/contributor/timothy-o-shea/2017/02/new-jersey-enacts-strict-opioid-prescribing-law
Ed: Timothy O'Shea. **Released:** February 21, 2017. **Description:** Governor Chris Christie of New Jersey signed legislation to help curb the opioid addiction running through the state. With the new legislation, initial opioid prescriptions can only be for a 5-day supply. **Availability:** Online.

25457 ■ "New Push for Mainers to Test for Radon in Homes" in News Center Maine (January 28, 2019)
URL(s): www.newscentermaine.com/article/news/new-push-for-mainers-to-test-for-radon-in-homes/97-d24c0b79-a28f-4ed8-8dc7-42fed9462654
Ed: Lindsey Mills. **Released:** January 28, 2019. **Description:** Maine CDC director Dr. Bruce Bates is urging everyone in Maine to have their homes tested for radon after 12 of their 16 counties were found to have have high radon amounts. If radon is detected, there are various measures residents can take, with the simplest being opening the windows to ventilate the house. **Availability:** Online.

25458 ■ "New Rule Rankles In Jersey" in Philadelphia Business Journal (Vol. 30, September 16, 2011, No. 31, pp. 1)
Pub: Philadelphia Business Journal
Contact: Sierra Quinn, Director
E-mail: squinn@bizjournals.com
Ed: Jeff Blumenthal. **Description:** A new rule in New Jersey which taxes out-of-state companies that conduct business in the state earned the ire of several banks, mortgage lenders and credit card companies and prompted opponents to threaten to file lawsuits. The new rule is an amendment to New Jersey Division of Taxation's corporate business tax regulation and is retroactive to 2002. Details are given. **Availability:** Online.

25459 ■ "New State Rules Require Cranes and Operators to be Certified" in Bellingham Business Journal (Vol. February 2010, pp. 11)
Pub: Sound Publishing Inc.
Contact: Josh O'Connor, President
Ed: Isaac Bonnell. **Description:** All construction cranes in Washington state must be inspected annually to be certified for use. The move is part of a larger L&I crane safety program that also requires crane operators to pass a written exam and a skill test.

25460 ■ "The Next Step in Patent Reform" in Information Today (Vol. 28, November 2011, No. 10, pp. 1)
Pub: Information Today Inc.
Contact: Thomas H. Hogan, President
Ed: George H. Pike. **Description:** The Leahy-Smith America Invents Act was signed into law in September 2011. The new act reformed the previous US patent system. Information involving the new patent law process is discussed.

GENERAL SMALL BUSINESS TOPICS

25461 ■ "The Next Wave" in Hawaii Business (Vol. 53, January 2008, No. 7, pp. 27)
Pub: PacificBasin Communications
Contact: Chuck Tindle, Director
E-mail: chuckt@pacificbasin.net
Ed: Cathy S. Cruz-George. **Description:** Only 40,000 Koreans took a visit to Hawaii in 2007, a decline from the pre-September averages of 123,000 visits. The number of Korean visitors in Hawaii could increase if the visa waiver proposal is passed. Efforts to improve Hawaiian tourism are presented. **Availability:** Print; Online.

25462 ■ "Nixon Assails Insurance Rules" in Globe & Mail (March 4, 2006, pp. B5)
Ed: Sinclair Stewart. **Description:** The opinions of chief executive officer Gordon Nixon of Royal Bank of Canada on the need to amend banking regulations, in order to provide insurance services, are presented. **Availability:** Print; Online.

25463 ■ "No End to the Nightmare; America's Car Industry" in The Economist (Vol. 390, January 3, 2009, No. 8612, pp. 46)
Description: Detroit's struggling auto industry and the government loan package is discussed as well as the United Auto Worker union, which is loathed by Senate Republicans. **Availability:** Print; Online.

25464 ■ "No Shortage of Challenges for Cross-Border Trade" in Canadian Sailings (June 30, 2008)
Description: Pros and cons of the North American Free Trade Agreement are examined. The agreement between the U.S. and Canada concerning trade was an essential step toward securing economic growth for Canadian citizens. Two-way trade between the counties has tripled since the agreement and accounts for 7.1 million American and 3 million Canadian jobs. **Availability:** Print; Online; PDF.

25465 ■ Non-Standard Employment under Globalization: Flexible Work and Social Security in the Newly Industrializing Countries
Pub: Palgrave Macmillan
Ed: Koichi Usami. **Released:** First edition. **Description:** Expansion of non-standard employment under globalization is being recognized in all of the newly industrialized countries. The book examines deregulation of labor markets, social protection for nonstandard workers, and social security reforms in accordance with the transformation of employment.

25466 ■ "Norway to Ban Fur Farms as Fox and Mink Go Out of Fashion" in Business of Fashion (January 15, 2018)
URL(s): www.businessoffashion.com/articles/news-analysis/norway-to-ban-fur-farms-as-fox-and-mink-go-out-of-fashion
Released: January 15, 2018. **Description:** Norway is planning to phase out fur farms by 2025. Animal rights group Noah is celebrating this victory for animal rights, but on the other side of the debate are the 200 fur farms that employ 400 people, and the industry already adhered to strict rules for animal welfare. **Availability:** Online.

25467 ■ "Not In Our Backyard" in Canadian Business (Vol. 80, October 22, 2007, No. 21, pp. 76)
Description: Alberta Energy and Utilities Board's proposed construction of electric transmission line has let to protests by landowners. The electric utility was also accused of spying on ordinary citizens and violating impartiality rules. Details of the case between Lavesta Area Group and the Board are discussed. **Availability:** Online.

25468 ■ "Nude Maid Service Could Face Fines" in UPI NewsTrack (April 10, 2012)
Pub: United Press International Inc.
Contact: Nicholas Chiaia, President
Description: Lubbock Fantasy Maid Service, located in Texas, is facing fines because it is operating without a permit. The cleaning service provides maids dresses in lingerie, topless or nude. Without the

permit, the firm could face fines of $2,000 daily. The company reports it is doing nothing illegally. **Availability:** Online.

25469 ■ *"Obama Orders Contractors To Raise Minimum Wage" in Atlanta Business Chronicle (June 20, 2014, pp. 9A)*
Pub: American City Business Journals, Inc.
Contact: Mike Olivieri, Executive Vice President

Description: Discussion of the new rules set out by President Obama, which includes the minimum wage of employees and discrimination against employees doing business with the Federal government is presented. The minimum wage law will increase to $10 per hour from $7.25 per hour; and discrimination against employees on the basis of sexual orientation or gender identity will not be tolerated. **Availability:** Print; Online.

25470 ■ *"Observers See Different Messages if Voters Reject Ambassador Tax Rebate" in Wichita Business Journal (Vol. 27, February 17, 2012, No. 7, pp. 1)*
Pub: Baltimore Business Journal
Contact: Rhonda Pringle, President
E-mail: rpringle@bizjournals.com

Description: Ambassador Hotel's room tax rebate has been put on a referendum in Wichita,Kansas and the rejection is expected to affect future downtown projects. However, the observers differ on the messages of a no vote would send to real estate investors. Insights on the ongoing debate on economic development policy are also given. **Availability:** Print; Online.

25471 ■ *"Ohio Regulator Sues Collection Agency" in PaymentsSource (September 21, 2012)*
Pub: SourceMedia LLC
Contact: Gemma Postlethwaite, Chief Executive Officer

Description: Mike DeWine, Ohio Attorney General, is suing Royal Oak Financial Services, a collection agency doing business as Collection and Recovery Bureau. The suit alleges that the firm used collection tactics banned by federal law and also attempting to collect unverified debts.

25472 ■ *"O'Malley, Ehrlich Court Business Vote" in Baltimore Business Journal (Vol. 28, October 1, 2010, No. 21, pp. 1)*
Pub: Baltimore Business Journal
Contact: Rhonda Pringle, President
E-mail: rpringle@bizjournals.com

Ed: Scott Dance. **Description:** Maryland Governor Martin O'Malley and former Governor Robert Ehrlich reveal their business plans and platforms as they court business-minded votes in the state. Ehrlich, a Republican and O'Malley, a Democrat have both initiated programs that helped small businesses, but both have also introduced programs that made it more expensive and difficult to do business in the state. **Availability:** Print.

25473 ■ *"On the Horizon" in Advertising Age (Vol. 83, October 1, 2012, No. 35, pp. 5)*
Released: Quarterly. **Description:** Federal Trade Commission is revising rules regarding online marketing aimed at children due to the growth of the Web and innovations like mobile applications. The current Children's Online Privacy Protection Act went into effect in 1998. **Availability:** Print; Online.

25474 ■ *"On the U.S. Election: Shaky on Free Trade" in Canadian Business (Vol. 81, December 19, 2007, No. 1, pp. 29)*
Pub: Rogers Media Inc.
Contact: Neil Spivak, Chief Executive Officer

Ed: Rachel Pulfer. **Description:** Rhetoric at the U.S. presidential elections seems to be pointing toward a weaker free trade consensus, with Democratic candidates being against the renewal of free trade deals, while Republican candidates seem to be for free trade. **Availability:** Online.

25475 ■ *"Opinion: Prison Farms are Closing, but the Manure Remains" in Canadian Business (Vol. 83, August 17, 2010, No. 13-14, pp. 9)*
Pub: Rogers Media Inc.
Contact: Neil Spivak, Chief Executive Officer

Ed: Steve Maich. **Description:** The explanation given by Canada's government ministers on planned closure of the prison farms and scrapping of the long form census are designed by mixing of spin, argument and transparent justification. The defense should have been plausible but the ministers could not handle the simple questions about statistics and prison job training with pretense. **Availability:** Online.

25476 ■ *"Orange County's Paid Sick Leave Initiative Draws Ire of Businesses" in Orlando Business Journal (Vol. 29, August 24, 2012, No. 10, pp. 1)*
Pub: Baltimore Business Journal
Contact: Rhonda Pringle, President
E-mail: rpringle@bizjournals.com

Ed: Anjali Fluker. **Description:** A proposed sick leave initiative has been opposed by businesses in Orange County, Florida. The regulation will require businesses with more than than 15 employees to provide workers with paid sick leave benefits. **Availability:** Print; Online.

25477 ■ *"OSC Eyes New Tack on Litigation" in Globe & Mail (April 9, 2007, pp. B1)*
Ed: Janet McFarland. **Description:** The efforts of the Ontario Securities Commission to set up a tribunal for the investigation and control of securities fraud are described. The rate of the conviction of corporate officials in cases heard by the courts is discussed. **Availability:** Online.

25478 ■ *"The Overlicensed Society" in Harvard Business Review (Vol. 90, April 2012, No. 4, pp. 38)*
Pub: Harvard Business Review Press
Contact: Moderna V. Pfizer, Contact

Ed: Robert E. Litan. **Price:** $6, hardcover. **Description:** The author argues that certification and licensing requirements are hindering professionals who might otherwise be able to find positions and provide services inexpensively. To key areas are healthcare and law. Federal mutual recognition agreements may be one method of addressing both practice and consumer protection issues. **Availability:** PDF; Online.

25479 ■ *"An Overview of Energy Consumption of the Globalized World Economy" in Energy Policy (Vol. 39, October 2011, No. 10, pp. 5920-2928)*
Ed: Z. M. Chen, G. Q. Chen. **Released:** October 01, 2011. **Description:** Energy consumption and its impact on the global world economy is examined. **Availability:** Print; Online.

25480 ■ *"Pa. Pushes for Collection of Online Sales Tax" in Philadelphia Business Journal (Vol. 31, March 2, 2012, No. 3, pp. 1)*
Pub: Baltimore Business Journal
Contact: Rhonda Pringle, President
E-mail: rpringle@bizjournals.com

Description: The government of Pennsylvania is seeking to increase taxes from e-sales. The government estimates that it could lose $380 million in uncollected online sales and use tax to the e-commerce retail sector in 2012. It has also introduced tax forms that instruct taxpayers to report and remit use tax. **Availability:** Print; Online.

25481 ■ *"Paid Petsitting in Homes Is Illegal in New York. That's News to Some Sitters" in The New York Times (July 21, 2017)*
URL(s): www.nytimes.com/2017/07/21/nyregion/dogsitting-new-york-illegal.html
Ed: Sarah Maslin Nir. **Released:** July 21, 2017. **Description:** People running petsitting services in NYC where shocked to discover that their businesses were not legal, since they must be licensed to board animals and in a permitted kennel, which is not allowed in the city. However, the rules for this are rarely enforced, unless a complaint is filed. This is starting to change with the advent of large, app-based petcare businesses and law makers are cracking down on these services. The app owners are not backing down. **Availability:** Online.

25482 ■ *"Panel to Call for Reduced Restraints on Telecom Sector" in Globe & Mail (March 17, 2006, pp. B1)*
Ed: Simon Tuck. **Description:** A federal panel called to adopt a more market-friendly approach to the lucrative telecommunications sector in Canada. Details of the report are presented. **Availability:** Online.

25483 ■ *"Panel Calls for 'Fundamental' Change to Telecom Regulation" in Globe & Mail (March 23, 2006, pp. B1)*
Ed: Catherine McLean. **Description:** A federal panel review at Ottawa called for a shakeup of regulations and policies that govern telecommunications companies to contend with sweeping technological changes. Details of the panel review are presented. **Availability:** Print; Online.

25484 ■ *"Partisan Vote in House for Export-Import Bank Measure" in U.S. News & World Report (November 15, 2019)*
URL(s): www.usnews.com/news/business/articles/2019-11-15/partisan-vote-likely-for-export-import-bank
Released: November 15, 2019. **Description:** The Democratic-controlled House passed a measure renewing the charter for the Export-Import Bank. The U.S. agency provides loans to foreign buyers of U.S. exports. However, the White House issued a veto threat and the legislation died when it arrived in the GOP-controlled Senate. **Availability:** Online.

25485 ■ *"Pay Heed to 'Smack Stack" in Puget Sound Business Journal (Vol. 35, May 16, 2014, No. 4, pp. 6)*
Pub: American City Business Journals, Inc.
Contact: Mike Olivieri, Executive Vice President

Description: Technology consultant, Geoffrey Moore, discloses the topics he plans to discuss at the annual State of Technology Luncheon held in Washington on May 19, 2014. He will explore the impact of technology and business trends on public-policy making and regulations. **Availability:** Online.

25486 ■ *"Paying for the Recession: Rebalancing Economic Growth" in Montana Business Quarterly (Vol. 49, Spring 2011, No. 1, pp. 2)*
Pub: University of Montana Bureau of Business and Economic Research
Contact: Patrick Barkey, Director
E-mail: patrick.barkey@business.umt.edu

Ed: Patrick M. Barkey. **Released:** Quarterly. **Description:** Four key issues required to address in order to rebalance economic growth in America are examined. They include: savings rates, global trade imbalances, government budgets and most importantly, housing price correction. **Availability:** Online.

25487 ■ *"Pep Boys to Pay $3.7M for Illegally Disposing of Hazardous Waste" in Waste Today (October 1, 2019)*
URL(s): www.wastetodaymagazine.com/article/pep-boys-hazardous-waste-lawsuit/
Ed: Adam Redling. **Released:** October 01, 2019. **Description:** After disposing toxic waste from automotive fluids into municipal landfills, Pep Boys must pay a $3.7 million settlement. This is based off of undercover inspections and charges were brought forth by the Alameda County District Attorney's Office Environmental Protection Unit. **Availability:** Online.

25488 ■ *"Philadelphia's Largest Employers Will Fill 6,000 Jobs Within 6 Months" in Philadelphia Business Journal (Vol. 28, February 5, 2010, No. 51, pp. 1)*
Pub: Philadelphia Business Journal
Contact: Sierra Quinn, Director
E-mail: squinn@bizjournals.com

Ed: Peter Van Allen. **Description:** Philadelphia, Pennsylvania's largest employers have openings for at least 6,000 jobs. But businesses remain cautious and are selective in hiring or waiting to see what happens to federal policy changes. **Availability:** Online.

25489 ■ *"Physicians Hail New York's Surprise Billing Law as a Success"* in *RevCycle Intelligence (September 30, 2019)*
URL(s): revcycleintelligence.com/news/physicians-hail-new-yorks-surprise-billing-law-as-a-success
Ed: Jacqueline LaPointe. **Released:** September 30, 2019. **Description:** A surprise billing law that was passed several years ago has been deemed a success according to New York's Department of Financial Services. In total, it's saved over $400 million from 2015 to 2018 for healthcare consumers and relieving the burden of a surprise bill. **Availability:** Online.

25490 ■ *"Pipeline Dreams"* in *Canadian Business (Vol. 80, October 22, 2007, No. 21, pp. 19)*
Description: Northwest Mackenzie Valley Pipeline has been under review by the National Energy Board since 2004. Hearings on the construction of the gas pipeline will wrap up in 2008. Pius Rolheiser, the spokesman of Imperial Oil Company Inc. believes the change of government in the area will not affect the negotiations on the pipeline construction. **Availability:** Print; Online.

25491 ■ *"Planned CO2 Regulations Could Hit Region Hard"* in *Pittsburgh Business Times (Vol. 33, June 6, 2014, No. 47, pp. 9)*
Pub: American City Business Journals, Inc.
Contact: Mike Olivieri, Executive Vice President
Released: Weekly. **Price:** $4, introductory 4-week offer(Digital only). **Description:** The U.S. Environmental Protection Agency's (EPA's) proposed rules to cut carbon dioxide (CO2) emissions by 30 percent over 16 years could have an adverse impact on southwestern Pennsylvania. The draft regulations, announced June 2, 2014, will affect the Pennsylvania region's power-generation sector as well as its coal industry, thereby impacting the regional economy. **Availability:** Print; Online.

25492 ■ *"Playfair Receives Drill Permit for Risby, Yukon Tungsten Deposit"* in *Marketwired (May 16, 2007)*
Pub: Comtex News Network Inc.
Contact: Kan Devnani, President
Description: Playfair Mining announced that it has received a 5 year Class III land use permit from the Mineral Resources Branch, Yukon which will allow the company to carry out a drill program during the upcoming drill season on the company-owned Risby, Yukon tungsten deposit. Statistical data included. **Availability:** Online.

25493 ■ *"Political Environments and Business Strategy: Implications for Managers"* in *Business Horizons (Vol. 51, January-February 2008)*
Pub: Elsevier Advanced Technology Publications
Ed: Gerald D. Keim, Amy J. Hillman. **Description:** Various government bodies and business organizations work together in shaping new business opportunities and policies that arise from globalization. Presented is framework of public policy considerations for business managers. The framework is based on Nobel laureate Douglas North's work. **Availability:** PDF; Online.

25494 ■ *"The Power Brokers"* in *Crain's Chicago Business (Vol. 31, April 28, 2008, No. 17, pp. 41)*
Pub: Crain Communications Inc.
Contact: Barry Asin, President
Ed: Samantha Stainburn. **Description:** Profile of BlueStar Energy Services Inc., one of the first suppliers to cash in on the deregulation f the electricity market by the Illinois Legislature; last year BlueStar's revenue was $171.1 million, up from $600,000 in 2002, the year the company was founded. **Availability:** Online.

25495 ■ *"Privacy Concern: Are 'Group' Time Sheets Legal?"* in *HR Specialist (Vol. 8, September 2010, No. 9, pp. 4)*
Pub: Capitol Information Group Inc.
Contact: Allie Ash, Chief Executive Officer
Description: Under the Fair Labor Standards Act (FLSA) employers are required to maintain and preserve payroll or other records, including the number of hours worked, but it does not prescribe a particular order or form in which these records must be kept. **Availability:** PDF; Online.

25496 ■ *"Provinces Tackle E-Waste Problem"* in *Canadian Electronics (Vol. 23, June-July 2008, No. 4, pp. 1)*
Pub: Action Communication Inc.
Ed: Ken Manchen. **Description:** Canadian provinces are implementing measures concerning the safe and environmentally friendly disposal of electronic waste. Alberta, British Columbia, Nova Scotia, and Saskatchewan impose an e-waste recycling fee on electronic equipment purchases. **Availability:** Online.

25497 ■ *"PSC Approves $130M TECO Solar Project"* in *Tampa Bay Business Journal (Vol. 30, December 18, 2009, No. 52, pp. 1)*
Pub: Tampa Bay Business Journal
Contact: Ian Anderson, President
E-mail: ianderson@bizjournals.com
Ed: Michael Hinman. **Description:** Florida's Public Service Commission has endorsed Tampa Electric Company's plan to add 25 megawatts of solar energy to its portfolio. TECO's plan needed the approval by PSC to defray additional costs for the project through ratepayers. **Availability:** Print; Online.

25498 ■ *"Publisher Steve Forbes: Small Business Can Flourish in Boise"* in *Idaho Business Review (August 19, 2014)*
Pub: BridgeTower Media
Contact: Adam Reinebach, President
Price: $99, Digital & Mobile Only(1 Year); $11.99, Print, Digital & Mobile(1 Month); $149, Print, Digital & Mobile(1 Year); $99, Digital & Mobile Only(For 1 Year); $11.99, Print, Digital & Mobile (For 1 Month Intro Rate); $149, Print, Digital & Mobile (For 1 Year).
Description: Steve Forbes spoke at the Zions Bank Small Business Conference in Boise, Idaho. He explored the opportunities for small firms in the area in regards to the global economy. Forbes also addressed taxation and government regulations. **Availability:** Print; Online.

25499 ■ *"Putting Down Roots"* in *Entrepreneur (August 2014)*
Released: October 28, 2016. **Description:** Entrepreneur Justin Hartfield and partner Doug Francis created Weedmaps.com, an online portal for marijuana dispensaries, after California legalized the sale of medical marijuana. Hartfield is looking forward to a billion-dollar business once the federal prohibition of marijuana is ended. Local dispensaries pay a monthly subscription of $420 to appear on the site while doctors pay $295 to be featured on the site. Harfield is seeking partnerships with laboratories that will provide marijuana testing and other services. **Availability:** Online.

25500 ■ *"Q&A: RBC's Gordon Nixon"* in *Canadian Business (Vol. 80, May 31, 2011, No. 22, pp. 9)*
Pub: Rogers Media Inc.
Contact: Neil Spivak, Chief Executive Officer
Ed: Rachel Pulfer. **Description:** Royal Bank of Canada (RBC) chief executive officer Gordon Nixon believes that the Canadian financial services segment is heavily regulated. Nixon also feels that it has become difficult for local banks to enter the market since foreign banks can easily come in and compete with Canadian banks. His views on RBC's success are provided. **Availability:** Online.

25501 ■ *"Q&A: The CAPP's Greg Stringham"* in *Canadian Business (Vol. 81, February 12, 2008, No. 3, pp. 8)*
Pub: Rogers Media Inc.
Contact: Neil Spivak, Chief Executive Officer
Ed: Michelle Magnan. **Description:** Canadian Association of Petroleum Producers' Greg Stringham thinks that the new royalty plan will result in companies pulling out their investments for Alberta's conventional oil and gas sector. Stringham adds that Alberta is losing its competitive advantage and companies must study their cost profiles to retrieve that advantage. The effects of the royalty system on Alberta's economy are examined further. **Availability:** Print; Online.

25502 ■ *"Questions Abound in Voluminous Health Care Reform Law"* in *Memphis Business Journal (Vol. 34, July 6, 2012, No. 12, pp. 1)*
Pub: Baltimore Business Journal
Contact: Rhonda Pringle, President
E-mail: rpringle@bizjournals.com
Ed: Cole Epley. **Description:** US Supreme Court has upheld the health care reform legislation, also known as Obamacare, as thelaw of the land. However, key questions remain and conjecture surrounding which direction states and insurance providers will pursue abounds. Insights on possible impact of health care providers of TennCare are also given. **Availability:** Print; Online.

25503 ■ *"The Rabbi Trust: How to Earn It Now, But Defer the Tax to the Future"* in *Barron's (Vol. 88, March 24, 2008, No. 12, pp. 55)*
Pub: Dow Jones & Company Inc.
Contact: Almar Latour, Chief Executive Officer
Ed: Joseph F. Gelband. **Description:** Discusses a rabbi trust which is a method of deferring taxes on compensation allowed by the Internal Revenue Service. Funding of the trust is not considered taxable. Other regulations concerning tax deferment are also discussed. **Availability:** Online.

25504 ■ *"The Race Is On For High-Stakes Casino Gambling in Florida"* in *South Florida Business Journal (Vol. 34, January 10, 2014, No. 25, pp. 12)*
Pub: American City Business Journals, Inc.
Contact: Mike Olivieri, Executive Vice President
Released: Weekly. **Price:** $8, Introductory 4-week offer(Digital & Print). **Description:** The Florida Senate is considering the possibility of expanding the limits of gambling in the state by establishing destination casinos. However, Professor Bob Jarvis believes that placing limits on the gambling sector could hinder economic development. **Availability:** Print; Online.

25505 ■ *Reading Financial Reports for Dummies*
Pub: John Wiley & Sons, Inc.
Contact: Christina Van Tassell, Executive Vice President Chief Financial Officer
URL(s): www.amazon.com/gp/product/1119871360/ref=as_li_tl?ie=UTF8&tag=wiley01-20
Ed: Lita Epstein. **Released:** 4th Edition. **Price:** $27.18, paperback; $18, e-book. **Description:** The fourth edition contains more new and updated information. This book is meant as a guide to help the reader interpret and understand financial reports, annual reports, balance sheets, income statements, statements of cash flow and consolidated statements. Real-world examples are given. . **Availability:** E-book; Print.

25506 ■ *"Reagan HQ In Limbo"* in *Austin Business Journal (Vol. 32, April 6, 2012, No. 5, pp. A1)*
Pub: American City Business Journals, Inc.
Contact: Mike Olivieri, Executive Vice President
Ed: Vicky Garza. **Description:** Reagan National Advertising has been awaiting the Austin City Council decision on whether it would be allowed to build a new headquarters that was on the drawing board for more than five years. However, approval of Reagan's plan would cut down several trees and that would violate the Heritage tree ordinance. **Availability:** Online.

GENERAL SMALL BUSINESS TOPICS

Government Regulations ∎ 25526

25507 ∎ *"Refiners, Producers are at Odds in Debate Over U.S. Oil Exports"* in *San Antonio Business Journal* (Vol. 27, January 17, 2014, No. 50, pp. 4)
Pub: American City Business Journals, Inc.
Contact: Mike Olivieri, Executive Vice President
Released: Weekly. **Price:** $4, Introductory 4-week offer(Digital & Print). **Description:** The American Petroleum Institute has been lobbying for the elimination of the decades-old ban on oil exports to open new markets for U.S. crude. Refiners such as San Antonio-based Valero Energy Corporation and Tesoro Corporation are against lifting the ban because it would drive the price of crude and tighten margins. Insights into the debate over U.S. oil exports are provided. **Availability:** Print; Online.

25508 ∎ *"Reforms Equal Smaller 401(k)s"* in *Employee Benefit News* (Vol. 25, December 1, 2011, No. 15, pp. 19)
Pub: SourceMedia LLC
Contact: Gemma Postlethwaite, Chief Executive Officer
Ed: Lisa V. Gillespie. **Description:** According to a new analysis by the Employee Benefit Research Institute, two recent proposals to change existing tax treatment of 401(k) retirement plans could cost workers because they would lower their account balances towards retirement.

25509 ∎ *"Regulator Issues Warning On Reverse Mortgage Loans"* in *Retirement Advisor* (Vol. 13, October 2012, No. 10, pp. 28)
Description: Reverse mortgages were first introduced in 1961 and are becoming popular now with aging baby boomers. The new Consumer Financial Protection Bureau warns the public to look closing before entering a reverse mortgage contract. The National Ethics Association encourages financial advisors to use the same caution and offers advise for advisors to help educate their clients about reverse mortgages. **Availability:** Print; Online.

25510 ∎ *"REITs Decry Foreign Limits on Investment"* in *Globe & Mail* (March 29, 2007, pp. B4)
Ed: Elizabeth Church. **Description:** The planned legislation by Canadian government for regulation foreign investments by real estate investment trusts is discussed. **Availability:** Online.

25511 ∎ *"Renewable Energy Adoption in an Ageing Population: Heterogeneity in Preferences for Micro-Generation Technology Adoption"* in *Energy Policy* (Vol. 39, October 2011, No. 10, pp. 6021-6029)
Ed: Ken Willis, Riccardo Scarpa, Rose Gilroy, Neveen Hamza. **Released:** October 01, 2011. **Description:** Attitudes and impacts of renewable energy adoption on an aging population is examined. **Availability:** Print; Online.

25512 ∎ *"Rent Laws' Impact: Tenant Paradise or Return of the 'Bronx is Burning'?"* in *The New York Times* (June 17, 2019)
URL(s): www.nytimes.com/2019/06/17/nyregion/rent-regulation-nyc.html
Released: June 17, 2019. **Description:** New York's new rent laws are having an impact in the New York City real estate market by establishing new rules from rent increases to security deposits to evictions. The Bronx is being affected the most since they have the highest number of rent-regulated apartments, which residents are cheering on, but the real estate industry is having doubts about the changes. **Availability:** Online.

25513 ∎ *"Retirement Plan Disclosures: Prepare Now for Fiduciary Rules"* in *Employee Benefit News* (Vol. 25, November 1, 2011, No. 14, pp. 24)
Pub: SourceMedia LLC
Contact: Gemma Postlethwaite, Chief Executive Officer

Ed: Brian M. Pinheiro, Kurt R. Anderson. **Description:** Department of Labor has delayed the deadlines on new affirmative obligations for fiduciaries of retirement plans subject to the Employee Retirement Income Security Act. Details included. **Availability:** Online; PDF; Download.

25514 ∎ *"Retirement Plans in a Quandary"* in *Employee Benefit News* (Vol. 25, December 1, 2011, No. 15, pp. 18)
Pub: SourceMedia LLC
Contact: Gemma Postlethwaite, Chief Executive Officer
Ed: Terry Dunne. **Description:** Complex issues arise when employees don't cash their 401(k) balance checks. The US Department of Labor permits plans to cash out accounts of former employees with less than $1,000 to reduce the cost and time required to manage them.

25515 ∎ *"ReVenture Plan Appears Close to Landing Key N.C. Legislative Deal"* in *Charlotte Business Journal* (Vol. 25, July 9, 2010, No. 16, pp. 1)
Pub: Charlotte Business Journal
Contact: Robert Morris, Editor
E-mail: rmorris@bizjournals.com
Ed: John Downey. **Description:** North Carolina lawmakers acted on special legislation that would boost development of Forsite Development 667-acre ReVenture Energy Park. The legislation could also improve chances that Duke Energy Carolinas will contract to purchase the power from the planned 50-megawatt biomass power plant located at the park. How utilities would benefit from the legislation is also discussed. **Availability:** Print; Online.

25516 ∎ *"Reversal of Fortune"* in *Canadian Business* (Vol. 85, June 11, 2012, No. 10, pp. 32)
Ed: Matthew McClearn. **Description:** First Quantum Minerals of Vancouver, British Columbia contested the decisio of the Democratic Republic of Congo to revoke their mining license in the Kolwezi Tailings by means of political pressure and international law. Eurasian National Resources Corporation agreed to pay First Quantum $1.25 billion in return for uncontested title to Congo mines and a ceasefire in January 2012. **Availability:** Print; Online.

25517 ∎ *"Reviving Entrepreneurship: Policy Decisions in 12 Areas Could Nurture - Or Cripple - America's Greatest Asset"* in *Harvard Business Review* (Vol. 90, March 2012, No. 3, pp. 116)
Pub: Harvard Business Review Press
Contact: Moderna V. Pfizer, Contact
Ed: Josh Lerner, William A. Sahlman. **Price:** $8.95, hardcover. **Description:** Government policies should address entrepreneurship as a process, rather than an act. Several key areas for policymaking include basic and translational science, supply and quality of human capital, information availability, tax treatment of rewards and risks, intellectual property rights, workforce healthcare, and mobility of financial and human capital. **Availability:** PDF; Online.

25518 ∎ *"Ride-Share Field Has New Player"* in *Providence Business News* (Vol. 29, April 21, 2014, No. 3, pp. 1)
Pub: American City Business Journals, Inc.
Contact: Mike Olivieri, Executive Vice President
URL(s): pbn.com/ride-share-field-has-new-player96580
Description: Lyft is Providence, Rhode Island's newest ride-sharing service. State officials continue to look for ways to regulate Internet vehicle services, taxis and limousines. Nearly all of Lyft's drivers are part-time employees using their own personal vehicles.

25519 ∎ *"Riding the Export Wave: How To Find a Good Distributor Overseas"* in *Inc.* (January 2008, pp. 49)
Ed: Sarah Goldstein. **Description:** Small companies should contact the U.S. embassy in foreign companies in order to connect with the U.S. Commercial Service's Gold Key program that is designed to work with small and midsize exporters. **Availability:** Online.

25520 ∎ *"Riding Herd on Health Care"* in *Business Journal Portland* (Vol. 30, February 7, 2014, No. 49, pp. 8)
Pub: American City Business Journals, Inc.
Contact: Mike Olivieri, Executive Vice President
Released: February 07, 2014. **Description:** Singing rancher and aspiring gubernatorial candidate, Jon Justesen, explains his views on universal healthcare. He expresses support for health care reform and Cover Oregon and he is looking at his options after dropping his Republican primary bid. **Availability:** Print; Online.

25521 ∎ *"Rising Above Flood-Insurance Costs"* in *Providence Business News* (Vol. 28, February 3, 2014, No. 44, pp. 1)
Pub: American City Business Journals, Inc.
Contact: Mike Olivieri, Executive Vice President
Released: February 01, 2014. **Description:** Businesses are advised to examine flood insurance costs when rebuilding or expanding their facilities. Some firms choose to elevate their buildings in response to the redrawing of Federal Emergency Management Agency flood maps and regulations. The process for getting a flood-elevation survey is also explored. **Availability:** Print; Online.

25522 ∎ *"Russia: Uncle Volodya's Flagging Christmas Spirit"* in *The Economist* (Vol. 390, January 3, 2009, No. 8612, pp. 22)
Description: Overview of Russia's struggling economy as well as unpopular government decisions such as raising import duties on used foreign vehicles so as to protect Russian carmakers. **Availability:** Print; Online.

25523 ∎ *"S.A. Officials Hunting for Prospects in California"* in *San Antonio Business Journal* (Vol. 26, August 17, 2012, No. 29, pp. 1)
Released: August 17, 2012. **Description:** Officials of the San Antonio Economic Development Foundation in Texas will meet with 15 or more companies in Los Angeles, California in a bid to convince these businesses to relocated some of their operations to Alamo City. Officials are hoping the companies will recognize the advantages of San Antonio as they face pressures due to increased taxes and added government regulations in California.

25524 ∎ *"Sacramento Businesses Must Cut Water Use 20 Percent"* in *Sacramento Business Journal* (Vol. 30, January 17, 2014, No. 47, pp. 5)
Pub: American City Business Journals, Inc.
Contact: Mike Olivieri, Executive Vice President
Released: Weekly. **Price:** $4, introductory 4-week offer(Digital & Print). **Description:** The Sacramento, California City, California Council's decision to reduce water use by 20 percent could have a big impact on businesses. Hotels and restaurants are among the biggest commercial users of water, while golf courses generally use well water. The need for businesses to purchase more efficient fixtures is also discussed. **Availability:** Print; Online.

25525 ∎ *"San Marcos May Ban Smoking"* in *Austin Business Journal* (Vol. 31, June 17, 2011, No. 15, pp. 1)
Pub: Austin Business Journal
Contact: Rachel McGrath, Director
E-mail: rmcgrath@bizjournals.com
Ed: Vicky Garza. **Description:** The City Council of San Marcos, Texas will hold a public hearing regarding a proposed citywide smoking ban. The city is moving towards the smoking ban because it appears a statewide ban may be enacted. **Availability:** Print; Online.

25526 ∎ *"Santa Clara Wineries at Odds with County Over Regulations"* in *Silicon Valley/San Jose Business Journal* (Vol. 30, September 7, 2012, No. 24, pp. 1)
Pub: Baltimore Business Journal
Contact: Rhonda Pringle, President

E-mail: rpringle@bizjournals.com
Description: A proposed ordinance in Santa Clara County, California will change existing winery regulations and implement a sliding fee system for event permits. Officials believe that the government ordinance will improve agricultural tourism, but winery owners claim that it would force them to choose between canceling events and footing the bill for certain costs. **Availability:** Print; Online.

25527 ■ *"Santander 'Redlining' Suit is a Crass and Opportunistic Shakedown" in Boston Business Journal (Vol. 34, June 6, 2014, No. 18, pp. 7)*
Pub: American City Business Journals, Inc.
Contact: Mike Olivieri, Executive Vice President
Released: Weekly. **Description:** Santander Bank's residential mortgage lending to minorities in Providence, Massachusetts has declined by 34 percent in recent years. The development is a violation of the US Fair Housing Act and the Equal Credit Opportunity Act. The city has sued Santander over the issue. **Availability:** Print; Online.

25528 ■ *"SCPA Members Seek Senate Support for H.R. 872" in Farm Industry News (May 26, 2011)*
Pub: Informa Business Media, Inc.
Contact: Charlie McCurdy, President
Ed: Forrest Laws. **Description:** U.S. House of Representatives passed legislation, H.R. 872 the Reducing Regulatory Burdens Act that frees pesticide applicators from having to obtain NPDES permits for applications over or near water. **Availability:** Online.

25529 ■ *"S.E.C. Adopts New Broker Rules That Consumer Advocates Say Are Toothless" in The New York Times (June 5, 2019)*
URL(s): www.nytimes.com/2019/06/05/your-money/sec-investment-brokers-fiduciary-duty.html
Ed: Tara Siegel Bernard. **Released:** June 05, 2019. **Description:** The SEC voted to pass the Regulation Best Interest, which should help Main Street investors. However, consumer advocates say it does little for its customers. **Availability:** Online.

25530 ■ *"SEC Decide if Austin Ventures is VC Firm" in Austin Business Journal (Vol. 31, June 17, 2011, No. 15, pp. 1)*
Pub: Austin Business Journal
Contact: Rachel McGrath, Director
E-mail: rmcgrath@bizjournals.com
Ed: Christopher Calnan. **Description:** Investment firm Austin Ventures could lose its classification as a venture capital firm under a new definition of venture capital by the Securities and Exchange Commission. The reclassification could result in additional expenses for Austin Ventures, which has two-thirds of its investments in growth equity transactions. **Availability:** Print; Online.

25531 ■ *"SEC FAQs About Crowdfunding Intermediaries" in Mondaq Business Briefing (June 11, 2012)*
Pub: Mondaq Ltd.
Contact: Tim Harty, Chief Executive Officer
Ed: Yelena Barychev, Christin R. Cerullo, Francis E. Dehel, Melissa Palat Murawsky, Michael E. Plunkett. **Description:** Guide for implementing crowdfunding intermediary provisions of Title III of the JOBS Act is provided. Operating restrictions and legal obligations are outlined. **Availability:** Print; Online.

25532 ■ *"SEC, NASAA Tell Small Businesses: Wait To Join the 'Crowd': Crowdfunding Is 'Not Yet Legal Until the Commission Appoints Rules', Says SEC's Kim" in Investment Advisor (Vol. 3, August 2012, No. 8, pp. 13)*
Ed: Melanie Waddell. **Description:** Securities and Exchange Commission along with state regulators have advised small businesses and entrepreneurs to wait until the SEC has produced rules governing crowdfunding practices. Until that happens, federal and state securities laws prohibit publicly accessible Internet securities offerings. An overview of crowdfunding and the JOBS Act is included. **Availability:** Online.

25533 ■ *"SEC Report On Rating Agencies Falls Short" in Barron's (Vol. 88, July 14, 2008, No. 28, pp. 35)*
Pub: Dow Jones & Company Inc.
Contact: Almar Latour, Chief Executive Officer
Ed: Jack Willoughby. **Description:** The Securities and Exchange Commissions report on credit-rating firms should have drawn attention to the slipshod practices in the offerings of collateralized debt obligations. The report fell short of prescribing correctives for the flawed system of these agencies' relationship with their clients. **Availability:** Online.

25534 ■ *"Seed-Count Labeling" in Farm Industry News (October 20, 2010)*
Pub: Informa Business Media, Inc.
Contact: Charlie McCurdy, President
Ed: Mark Moore. **Price:** $4, Print and Online; Special Offers only for 4 weeks. **Description:** National Conference on Weights and Measures voted to standardize testing methods and procedures that will verify seed-count labeling. **Availability:** Print; Online.

25535 ■ *"Seminar on Crowdfunding Set for Aug. 1" in Gazette (July 25, 2012)*
URL(s): gazette.com/seminar-on-crowdfunding-set-for-aug.-1/article/142192#!
Description: Senator Michael Bennet is co-hosting a seminar with Epicentral Coworking on crowdfunding featuring two panels with local entrepreneurs and business owners, legal experts, and representatives from investment firms. The seminar will be held August 1, 2012. **Availability:** Print; Online.

25536 ■ *"Senate Approval Adds Steam to Port of Savannah Project" in Atlanta Business Chronicle (May 30, 2014, pp. 18A)*
Pub: American City Business Journals, Inc.
Contact: Mike Olivieri, Executive Vice President
Description: U.S. Senate approved a budget for the long pending Savannah Harbor dredging project. The Senate approved $652 million for the dredging of the Savannah Harbor from 42 feet to 47 feet to enhance the port's ability to serve the new generation of supersized containerized cargo ships. **Availability:** Print; Online.

25537 ■ *"Senator Grills Collection Agency, Health System Executives" in Collections & Credit Risk (May 31, 2012)*
Pub: SourceMedia LLC
Contact: Gemma Postlethwaite, Chief Executive Officer
Description: Accretive Health Inc. and Fairview Health Services executives were questioned by Senator Al Franken about its debt collection practices. The suit was initiated after unencrypted private information on 23,500 patients was stolen from an Acrretive employee's vehicle. Details of the lawsuit are outlined.

25538 ■ *"Shattering the Myths About U.S. Trade Policy: Stop Blaming China and India. A More Active Trade Policy Can Lead to a Stronger U.S. Economy" in Harvard Business Review (Vol. 90, March 2012, No. 3, pp. 149)*
Pub: Harvard Business Review Press
Contact: Moderna V. Pfizer, Contact
Ed: Robert Z. Lawrence, Lawrence Edwards. **Price:** $8.95, hardcopy black and white. **Description:** Myths debunked include the belief that the US open trade policy has caused job losses, and that living standards are falling due to export market competition. American must leverage China's need for global economic engagement and secure an open domestic market in China. It must also persuade the World Trade Organization to improve market access. **Availability:** Print; PDF; Online.

25539 ■ *"Should the Fed Regulate Wall Street?" in Barron's (Vol. 88, March 24, 2008, No. 12, pp. M15)*
Pub: Dow Jones & Company Inc.
Contact: Almar Latour, Chief Executive Officer
Ed: Randall W. Forsyth. **Description:** Greater regulation of the financial sector by the Federal Reserve is essential for it to survive the crisis it is experiencing. The resulting regulation could be in complete contrast with the deregulation the sector previously experienced. **Availability:** Online.

25540 ■ *"Should State Invest in Startups?" in Providence Business News (Vol. 28, March 3, 2014, No. 48, pp. 1)*
Pub: American City Business Journals, Inc.
Contact: Mike Olivieri, Executive Vice President
Released: March 01, 2014. **Description:** The U.S. Treasury Department is investigating whether Rhode Island violated Federal rules when it used funds from the State Small Business Credit Initiative (SSBCI) to invest in Betaspring, a startup accelerator program for technology and design entrepreneurs ready to launch their businesses. The Lyon Park audit claims that Rhode Island violated SSBCI rules because a large portion of the money went to the business accelerator's operating expenses and not to the startups themselves. **Availability:** Print; Online.

25541 ■ *"A Simple Old Reg that Needs Dusting Off" in Barron's (Vol. 88, June 30, 2008, No. 26, pp. 35)*
Pub: Dow Jones & Company Inc.
Contact: Almar Latour, Chief Executive Officer
Ed: Gene Epstein. **Description:** Senator Joe Lieberman has a point when he accused speculators of inflating the prices of food and fuel futures but introducing legislation to address speculation has an alternative. The senator's committee should instead demand that the Commodity Futures Trading Commission enforce position limits on the maximum number of contracts in a given market per speculative entity. **Availability:** Online.

25542 ■ *"Small Business Economic Trends: Moderate Improvement but No Clear Direction" in Small Business Economic Trends (March 2008, pp. 3)*
Pub: National Federation of Independent Business
Contact: Brad Close, President
Ed: William C. Dunkelberg, Holly Wade. **Description:** Commentary on the economic trends for small businesses in the U.S. is presented. Analysis of the labor market and low interest rates is given. The effect of the Federal Reserve's policy announcement on small business owner optimism is also discussed. **Availability:** Print; Online.

25543 ■ *"Small, But Mighty" in Employee Benefit News (Vol. 25, November 1, 2011, No. 14, pp. 32)*
Pub: SourceMedia LLC
Contact: Gemma Postlethwaite, Chief Executive Officer
Ed: Andrea Davis. **Description:** Three consulting firms are facing the challenge of helping clients understand the new health care reform in a tight economy. **Availability:** Print; PDF; Online.

25544 ■ *"Small Firms Punch Ticket for Growth" in Houston Business Journal (Vol. 40, January 29, 2010, No. 38, pp. 1)*
Pub: Houston Business Journal
Contact: Bob Charlet, President
E-mail: bcharlet@bizjournals.com
Ed: Allison Wollam. **Description:** Independent ticket agencies anticipate growth as American and Canadian authorities approved a merger between Ticketmaster and concert promoter Live Nation. Expansion of service offerings and acquisition of venues have also been done by independent ticket agencies in light of the merger. Details of the merger are included. **Availability:** Print; Online.

25545 ■ *"Soldiers as Consumers: Predatory and Unfair Business Practices Harming the Military Community"*
Pub: CreateSpace
Released: October 05, 2014. Price: $9.81, paperback. Description: Soldiers, airmen, sailors, and marines are young consumers and are appealing targets for unscrupulous businesses. There are lending organizations that prey upon our military offering products to help them bridge financial problems. Unethical elements of these loans includes higher interest rates and/or high fees or waivers of certain rights in fine print of contracts. A Federal Law called the Military Lending Act is supposed to protect service members from this kind of abuse, but the law only covers loans with terms of six months or less. Availability: Print.

25546 ■ *"Some Homeowners Caught in Tax-Code Limbo"* in Providence Business News (Vol. 29, June 23, 2014, No. 12, pp. 9)
Pub: American City Business Journals, Inc.
Contact: Mike Olivieri, Executive Vice President
Released: June 22, 2014. Description: The Mortgage Forgiveness Debt Relief Act expired on December 31, 2013 and Congress delayed reauthorizing the tax code, thus impacting homeowners looking for short sales in 2014. Short sellers are unsure whether they will avoid taxation on their forgiven mortgage debt or if the lack of reauthorization by Congress, retroactive to January 1, will lead to large income tax payouts in 2015. Availability: Print; Online.

25547 ■ *"Spin Zone: Where Hawaii's Leaders Face Off, Have High-Tech Tax Credits Helped or Hurt Hawaii?"* in Hawaii Business (Vol. 53, December 2007, No. 6, pp. 28)
Pub: PacificBasin Communications
Contact: Chuck Tindle, Director
E-mail: chuckt@pacificbasin.net
Description: Presents the opinons of Channel Capital LLC's Walter R. Roth and Hawaii Venture Capital Association's Bill Spencer concerning the impacts of tax credits. Roth thinks that Act 221 appeals to investors who can earn despite business failure while Spencer thinks that the legislation promotes investments in innovative technology firms. The need to support tax credits is also discussed. Availability: Print; Online.

25548 ■ *"Stakes Rising on Business Cyber Security"* in Denver Business Journal (Vol. 63, May 18, 2012, No. 52, pp. A1)
Pub: Baltimore Business Journal
Contact: Rhonda Pringle, President
E-mail: rpringle@bizjournals.com
Ed: Greg Avery. Description: Congress and federal regulators are seeking to tighten rules for companies in infrastructure industries amid a series of high profile cyber attacks. The federal legislation might give the US Department of Homeland Security a role in ensuring they are not left vulnerable to cyber warfare and foreign Internet spies. Availability: Print; Online.

25549 ■ *"Stan Chesley Fighting Kentucky Disbarment"* in Business Courier (Vol. 27, September 10, 2010, No. 19, pp. 1)
Pub: Business Courier
Ed: Jon Newberry. Description: Stan Chesley, a Cincinnati attorney, has been accused of making false statements to the courts and bar officials, self-dealing in violation of the bar's conflict of interest rules, and failing to adequately inform clients. Kentucky Bar Association officials will seek to have Chesley permanently disbarred. Availability: Print; Online.

25550 ■ *"State Accuses Eight Companies of Making Sales Calls to People Who Signed up to Stop Them"* in WTVA.com (September 4, 2019)
URL(s): www.wtva.com/content/news/State-accuses-eight-companies-of-violating-the-law-concerning-telemarketing-calls-559422281.html

Ed: Craig Ford. Released: September 04, 2019. Description: The Mississippi Pubic Service Commission is charging eight companies with breaking the law by making telemarketing calls to people who specifically signed up to not receive such calls. They face $5,000 per illegal call. Availability: Online.

25551 ■ *"State Democrats Push for Changes to Plant Security Law"* in Chemical Week (Vol. 172, July 19, 2010, No. 17, pp. 8)
Description: Legislation has been introduced to revise the existing U.S. Chemical Facility Anti-Terrorism Standards (CFATS) that would include a requirement for facilities to use inherently safer technology (IST). The bill would eliminate the current law's exemption of water treatment plants and certain port facilities and preserve the states' authority to establish stronger security standards. Availability: PDF; Online.

25552 ■ *"State Pressure Keeps Rates Low"* in Sacramento Business Journal (Vol. 31, August 8, 2014, No. 24, pp. 4)
Pub: American City Business Journals, Inc.
Contact: Mike Olivieri, Executive Vice President
Description: The proposed California Covered rate increases are likely to hit an average 4.2 percent in 2015, with the average increase in Sacramento expected at 3.7 percent. The health insurance exchange was set up to be an active purchaser so that it differs with the proposed exchange in other states, which range from 8 percent to 20 percent. Insights on the advantages of Covered California are presented. Availability: Print; Online.

25553 ■ *"State Regulators Reject AEP Ohio's Plans to Build 400MW of Solar Funded by Ratepayers"* in Greentech Media (November 21, 2019)
URL(s): www.greentechmedia.com/articles/read/ohio-regulators-reject-aep-ohios-solar-plans
Ed: Emma Foehringer Merchant. Released: November 21, 2019. Description: Arguing that the power isn't needed, Ohio regulators rejected plans from American Electric Power's Ohio subsidiary to charge ratepayers to build a new solar project. Availability: Online.

25554 ■ *"State Reverses Food Truck Order"* in Cape Cod Times (May 15, 2012)
Ed: Patrick Cassidy. Description: Massachusetts Department of Transportation is developing a plan that will allow food truck owners to operate under a new pilot program. Owners must obtain a license to operate through the Transportation Department's legal division. License requirements will be modeled on present license applications and some modifications may be necessary. Insurance issues must be addressed. Availability: Online.

25555 ■ *"State VC Fund To Get At Least $7.5 Million"* in Crain's Detroit Business (Vol. 24, February 25, 2008, No. 8, pp. 14)
Pub: Crain Communications Inc.
Contact: Barry Asin, President
Ed: Tom Henderson. Description: Michigan's 21st Century Investment Fund is expected to receive $7.5 million, financed by tobacco-settlement money. The Michigan Strategic Fund Board will determine which firms will receive venture capital, which is mandated by legislation to invest the fund within three years. Availability: Online.

25556 ■ *"State Wants to Add Escape Clause to Leases"* in Sacramento Business Journal (Vol. 28, October 14, 2011, No. 33, pp. 1)
Pub: Sacramento Business Journal
Contact: Stephanie Fretwell, Director
E-mail: sfretwell@bizjournals.com
Ed: Michael Shaw. Description: California Governor Jerry Brown's administration has decided to add escape clauses to new lease agreements, which created new worry for building owners and brokers in Sacramento, California. Real estate brokers believe the appropriation of funds clauses have been making the lenders nervous and would result in less competition. Availability: Online.

25557 ■ *"Sumitomo Invests in Desert Sunlight Solar Farm, the Largest PV Project Approved for Federal Land"* in PR Newswire (October 2, 2012)
Pub: PR Newswire Association LLC.
Description: The Desert Sunlight Solar Farm, 550MW solar power project being constructed in the California desert area east of Palm Springs, is the largest solar photovoltaic (PV) facility approved for US public land. Sumitomo Corporation of America is investing in the project and plans to expand its renewable energy portfolio across the US.

25558 ■ *"The Sunday Newspaper (est. 1891): the Death of Three Postmedia Sunday Papers Leaves Few Remaining"* in Canadian Business (Vol. 85, July 16, 2012, No. 11-12, pp. 14)
Ed: Conan Tobias. Description: Postmedia Network Canada Corporation announced the cancellation of the Sunday editions of three of its newspapers, namely 'Calgary Herald', Edmonton Journal', and 'Ottawa Citizen', in order to focus on digital distribution. The first newspaper in Canada to publish a Sunday edition was 'The World' on May 24, 1891 but law required it to be delivered on Saturday. Availability: Print; Online.

25559 ■ *"A Supply-Side Solution for Health Care"* in Barron's (Vol. 92, July 23, 2012, No. 30, pp. 30)
Pub: Dow Jones & Company Inc.
Contact: Almar Latour, Chief Executive Officer
Ed: H. Woody Brock. Description: The United States should increase the supply of new doctors, nurses and other health care professionals to improve the American health care system by increasing supply. Health care reform proposals in the US Congress fail to address the supply side of the problem. Availability: Online.

25560 ■ *"Taking the Jump Off the Fiscal Cliff"* in Barron's (Vol. 92, August 25, 2012, No. 35, pp. 47)
Pub: Dow Jones & Company Inc.
Contact: Almar Latour, Chief Executive Officer
Ed: Thomas G. Donlan. Description: The arrival of tax increases and spending cuts by the end of 2012 should help the United States reduce its budget deficit. Policy prescriptions advocating looser monetary and fiscal policies are not going to help the country solve its budget problems. Availability: Online.

25561 ■ *"Tao of Downfall: the Failures of High-profile Entrepreneurs in the Chinese Economic Reform"* in International Journal of Entrepreneurship and Small Business (Vol. 11, August 31, 2010, No. 2, pp. 121)
Ed: Wenxian Zhang, Ilan Alon. Description: Through historical reviews and case studies, this research seeks to understand why some initially successful entrepreneurs failed in the economic boom of past decades. Among various factors contributing to their downfall are a unique political and business environment, fragile financial systems, traditional cultural influences and personal characteristics. Availability: Online.

25562 ■ *"Tax Breaks Favor Outsiders, Business Owners Object"* in Business Review Albany (Vol. 41, August 22, 2014, No. 22, pp. 7)
Pub: American City Business Journals, Inc.
Contact: Mike Olivieri, Executive Vice President
Released: Weekly. Price: $4, introductory 4-week offer(Digital only). Description: New York business owners have criticized Governor Andrew Cuomo's Start-Up NY tax-break program. They argue that the existing companies are essentially ignored and they are concerned whether the companies receiving the tax breaks stay longer than ten years. Insights on the Start-Up NY program are included. Availability: Print; Online.

25563 ■ Government Regulations

25563 ■ *"Tax Credits for Renewables Get Another Shot in Congress"* in Greentech Media (November 19, 2019)
URL(s): www.greentechmedia.com/articles/read/renewable-tax-credits-get-another-shot-in-congress
Ed: Emma Foehringer Merchant. **Released:** November 19, 2019. **Description:** The U.S. House Ways and Means Committee drafted legislation that will extend tax credits for renewable technologies. It also includes incentives for energy storage, electric vehicles, and environmental justice programs at colleges and universities. **Availability:** Online.

25564 ■ *"Texas Legislature Green-Lights Bigger Liquor Chains, but Still Excludes the Biggest Retailer, Walmart"* in Dallas News (May 28, 2019)
URL(s): www.dallasnews.com/business/retail/2019/05/28/texas-legislature-green-lights-bigger-liquor-chains-but-still-excludes-the-biggest-retailer-walmart/
Ed: Maria Halkias. **Released:** May 28, 2019. **Description:** A new bill in Texas is closing some liquor law loopholes, but is still denying publicly traded companies like Walmart, Costco, Walgreens, and Kroger from selling liquor in Texas. **Availability:** Online.

25565 ■ *"Three Trails Blazes Tax Credit Deal"* in The Business Journal-Serving Metropolitan Kansas City (Vol. 27, November 7, 2008, No. 9)
Description: Three Trails Redevelopment LLC plans to redevelop the Bannister Mall area. The Missouri Development Finance Board is expected to approve $30 million in tax credits for the project. A verbal agreement on the terms and conditions has already been reached according to the agency's executive director.

25566 ■ *"TIA Wrestles with Procurement Issues"* in Business Journal Serving Greater Tampa Bay (Vol. 30, November 12, 2010, No. 47, pp. 1)
Pub: Tampa Bay Business Journal
Contact: Ian Anderson, President
E-mail: ianderson@bizjournals.com
Ed: Mark Holan. **Description:** Tampa International Airport (TIA) has been caught in conflict of interest and procurement policy issues after the Hillsborough County Aviation Authority learned of the spousal relationship of an employee with his wife's firm, Gresham Smith and Partners. Gresham already won contracts with TIA and was ahead of other firms in a new contract. **Availability:** Print; Online.

25567 ■ *"UEDs Would Light Up Street with News, Ads"* in Philadelphia Business Journal (Vol. 33, April 11, 2014, No. 9, pp. 8)
Pub: American City Business Journals, Inc.
Contact: Mike Olivieri, Executive Vice President
Description: Catalyst Outdoor head, Thaddeus Bartkowski, has been working on legislation to create a digital district that would permit urban experiential displays (UEDs) in a well-defined area in Center City. UEDs, which would communicate advertising and news, are being considered as a potential revenue stream for the city. The challenges in the installation of UEDs are also presented. **Availability:** Online.

25568 ■ *"Union, Heal Thyself"* in Canadian Business (Vol. 81, July 21, 2008, No. 11, pp. 9)
Description: General Motors Corp. was offered by the federal government a $250 million fund after the company declared plans to close its facility in Ontario. The government move is geared towards supporting the workers who have refused to support the automotive company. Details of the labor contract between General Motors and the Canadian Auto Workers are presented. **Availability:** Print; Online.

25569 ■ United Nations Security Council Reform
URL(s): www.mofa.go.jp/files/100059111.pdf
Released: March 2022. **Description:** Outlines the world issues that call for a reform of the UN Security Council and the steps needed in order to achieve reform. **Availability:** PDF.

25570 ■ *"U.S. Primaries: An Amazing Race"* in Canadian Business (Vol. 81, February 12, 2008, No. 3, pp. 25)
Pub: Rogers Media Inc.
Contact: Neil Spivak, Chief Executive Officer
Ed: Rachel Pulfer. **Description:** U.S. presidential candidates Barack Obama and Hilary Clinton lead the Democratic Part primaries while John McCain is a frontrunner at the Republican Party. These leading candidates have different plans for the U.S. economy which will affect Canada's own economy particularly concerning trade policies. The presidential candidates' proposals and the impacts of U.S. economic downturn on Canada are examined. **Availability:** Print; Online.

25571 ■ *"United's Next Hurdle: Costly Repairs"* in Crain's Chicago Business (Vol. 31, April 14, 2008, No. 15, pp. 1)
Pub: Crain Communications Inc.
Contact: Barry Asin, President
Ed: John Pletz. **Description:** Discusses the recent crackdown by aviation regulators concerning airline safety at United Airlines as well as other carriers. Maintenance costs at United for the upkeep on the company's older planes is severely affecting its bottom line which is already sagging under heavy fuel costs. **Availability:** Online.

25572 ■ *"Univest Charter Switch Signals Banking Trend"* in Philadelphia Business Journal (Vol. 30, September 2, 2011, No. 29, pp. 1)
Pub: Philadelphia Business Journal
Contact: Sierra Quinn, Director
E-mail: squinn@bizjournals.com
Ed: Jeff Blumenthal. **Description:** Univest Corporation of Pennsylvania changed from a federal to state charter because of cost savings and state agency has greater understanding of the intricacies of the local economy. The Pennsylvania Department of Banking has also received inquiries from seven other banks about doing the same this year. **Availability:** Online.

25573 ■ *"Unlicensed Utah Collection Agency Settles with State Finance Department"* in Idaho Business Review, Boise (July 15, 2010)
Pub: Idaho Business Review
Contact: Autumn Kersey, Sales Executive
E-mail: akersey@idahobusinessreview.com
Description: Federal Recovery Acceptance Inc., doing business as Paramount Acceptance in Utah, agreed to pay penalties and expenses after the firm was investigated by the state for improprieties. The firm was charged with conducting unlicensed collection activity. **Availability:** Print; Online.

25574 ■ *"Up On The Farm"* in Canadian Business (Vol. 81, March 31, 2008, No. 5, pp. 23)
Description: Agricultural products have outperformed both energy and metal and even the prospect of a global economic slowdown does not seem to hinder its prospects. The Organization for Economic Cooperation and Development sees prices above historic equilibrium levels during the next ten years given that fuel and fertilizers remain high and greater demand from India and China remain steady. **Availability:** Print; Online.

25575 ■ *"Up To Code? Website Eases Compliance Burden for Entrepreneurs"* in Black Enterprise (Vol. 38, March 1, 2008, No. 8, pp. 48)
Pub: Earl G. Graves Ltd.
Contact: Earl Graves, Jr., President
Ed: Robin White-Goode. **Description:** Business.gov is a presidential E-government project created to help small businesses easily find, understand, and comply with laws and regulations pertaining to a particular industry. **Availability:** Online.

25576 ■ *"Utah Collection Agency Settles File-Sharing Charges"* in PaymentsSource (June 11, 2012)
Pub: SourceMedia LLC
Contact: Gemma Postlethwaite, Chief Executive Officer
Ed: Darren Waggoner. **Description:** EPN Inc., doing business as Checknet Inc., settled charges filed by the Federal Trade Commission that it exposed sensitive information on its computers and networks creating a potential security risk to the consumer information it stored. Details of the suit are provided.

25577 ■ *"Utah Liquor Stores to Pour Cases of Beer Down the Drain"* in U.S. News & World Report (October 24, 2019)
URL(s): www.usnews.com/news/best-states/utah/articles/2019-10-24/utah-liquor-stores-to-pour-cases-of-beer-down-the-drain
Released: October 24, 2019. **Description:** Due to a new law in Utah where beer must be 4% alcohol by volume (ABV) or less, liquor stores announced plans to pour any beer higher than that down the drain if they don't sell by October 31. **Availability:** Online.

25578 ■ *"Valenti: Roots of Financial Crisis Go Back to 1998"* in Crain's Detroit Business (Vol. 24, October 6, 2008, No. 40, pp. 25)
Pub: Crain Communications Inc.
Contact: Barry Asin, President
Ed: Tom Henderson, Nathan Skid. **Description:** Interview with Sam Valenti III who is the chairman and CEO of Valenti Capital L.L.C., a wealth-management firm; Valenti discusses in detail the history that led up to the current economic crisis as well as his prediction for the future of the country. **Availability:** Print; Online.

25579 ■ *"Vape, Smoke Shops on Edge as Santa Maria Mulls Ban of Flavored Tobacco Products"* in Santa Maria Times (November 17, 2019)
URL(s): santamariatimes.com/news/local/govt-and-politics/vape-smoke-shops-on-edge-as-santa-maria-mulls-ban/article_60b3d1ca-ba4a-5580-b851-f9d51ff2c940.html
Ed: Razi Syed. **Released:** November 17, 2019. **Description:** After dozens of municipalities across California have moved to ban the sale of flavored tobacco and vaping products, the city of Santa Maria is considering it as well. If passed, the ordinance would also require that tobacco retailers become licensed with the city. **Availability:** Online.

25580 ■ *"The View from the Field: Six Leaders Offer Their Perspectives On Sales Success"* in (Vol. 90, July-August 2012, No. 7-8, pp. 101)
Pub: Harvard Business Review Press
Contact: Moderna V. Pfizer, Contact
Ed: Jim Koch, James Farley, Susan Silbermann, Duncan Mac Naughton, Phil Guido, Suresh Goklaney. **Price:** $8.95. **Description:** Six business leaders provide their perspectives on successful selling. Common themes include engaging customers and seeking their input, personalizing their services, ensuring accountability, implementing community outreach, being mindful of cultural and regulatory issues, providing unique offerings, incorporating experiential learning, and properly identifying a customer's needs. **Availability:** Online; PDF.

25581 ■ *"Volunteers Needed"* in Canadian Business (Vol. 81, October 27, 2008, No. 18, pp. 60)
Description: Emissions-targeting regulations focus on the biggest polluters, missing out on other companies that leave carbon footprints in things such as shipping and travel. Some companies in Canada have initiated programs to offset their carbon emissions. Critics claim that offsetting does not reduce emissions and the programs merely justify pollution.

25582 ■ *"Waiting for the Sunset on Taxes"* in Memphis Business Journal (Vol. 34, September 28, 2012, No. 24, pp. 1)
Pub: Baltimore Business Journal
Contact: Rhonda Pringle, President

E-mail: rpringle@bizjournals.com
Description: The implementation of the Tax Relief, Unemployment Reauthorization and Job Creation Act of 2010 will end on December 31, 2012. The exemption threshold will fall to $1 million, and the tax rate on transfers above that limit will be at 55 percent. The effect of political uncertainty on tax planning is also discussed. **Availability:** Print; Online.

25583 ■ *"Wal-Mart China Woes Add Up"* in *Wall Street Journal Eastern Edition (October 17, 2011, pp. B3)*
Pub: Dow Jones & Company Inc.
Contact: Almar Latour, Chief Executive Officer
Ed: Laurie Burkitt. **Description:** Woes for Wal-Mart Inc.'s subsidiary in China are adding up as Wal-Mart China president and chief executive Ed Chan stepped down, as well as the company's senior vice president for human resources, Clara Wong. The company has been charged by regulators with mislabeling pork products, the result which has forced stores to close. Sales in China have been slow at the retail stores. **Availability:** Online.

25584 ■ *"Walker Seeks More Business Participation"* in *Business Journal-Milwaukee (Vol. 28, December 10, 2010, No. 10, pp. A1)*
Pub: The Business Journal
Contact: Heather Ladage, President
E-mail: hladage@bizjournals.com
Ed: Rich Kirchen. **Description:** Wisconsin governor Scott Walker is seeking the aid of Milwaukee business leaders to participate in resolving the challenges posed by the economic crisis. Walker is aiming to create 250,000 jobs. He is also planning to call a special session of the legislature to enact strategies to jumpstart the economy. **Availability:** Print; Online.

25585 ■ *"Watchdogs for Health Care"* in *Money (Vol. 41, October 2012, No. 9, pp. 63)*
Description: Bonnie Burns, California Health Advocates' policy specialist, discusses issues facity seniors regarding their health care. **Availability:** Print; Online.

25586 ■ *"Water Efficiency Bills Move Through Congress"* in *Contractor (Vol. 56, July 2009, No. 7, pp. 20)*
Ed: Kevin Schwalb. **Description:** National Association, a plumbing-heating-cooling contractor, was instrumental in drafting the Water Advanced Technologies for Efficient Resource Use Act of 2009 and they are also backing the Water Accountability Tax Efficiency Reinvestment Act. The first bill promotes WaterSense-labeled products while the other promotes water conservation through tax credits. **Availability:** Print; Online.

25587 ■ *"Wealth and Jobs: the Broken Link"* in *Harvard Business Review (Vol. 88, November 2010, No. 11, pp. 44)*
Pub: Harvard Business Publishing
Contact: Diane Belcher, Managing Director
Ed: Nitin Nohria. **Price:** $6, PDF. **Description:** Rebuilding the link between business and job creation to shore up the middle class is advocated. A blend of government policies and business strategies that foster entrepreneurship and innovation are essential. **Availability:** Online; PDF.

25588 ■ *"We're Drowning In Fine Print"* in *Canadian Business (Vol. 87, July 2014, No. 7, pp. 30)*
Description: The implications of mandatory disclosure rules for Canadian businesses and consumers are discussed. Businesses are advised to pay more attention to costs and benefits rather than force their customers to claim they have read and agree with the terms and conditions of lengthy and complex disclosures and privacy agreements. **Availability:** Print; Online.

25589 ■ *"What Can Michael Brown Do For Biz?"* in *Washington Business Journal (Vol. 31, June 15, 2012, No. 8, pp. 1)*
Pub: Baltimore Business Journal
Contact: Rhonda Pringle, President

E-mail: rpringle@bizjournals.com
Description: Michael Brown, Washington DC's new economic development point man, aims to ease business regulation, speed up retail development, and create opportunities for local contractors. He is also expected to deal with oversight of all housing and economic development issues and agencies within the state. **Availability:** Print; Online.

25590 ■ *"What Do Your ISO Procedures Say?"* in *Modern Machine Shop (Vol. 84, September 2011, No. 4, pp. 34)*
Pub: Gardner Business Media Inc.
Contact: Rick Kline, Jr., President
E-mail: rkline2@gardnerweb.com
Ed: Wayne Chaneski. **Released:** August 24, 2011. **Description:** ISO 9000 certification can be time-consuming and costly, but it is a necessary step in developing a quality management system that meets both current and potential customer needs. **Availability:** Print; Online.

25591 ■ *"What the Future Holds for Consumers"* in *Black Enterprise (Vol. 41, August 2010, No. 1, pp. 47)*
Pub: Earl G. Graves Ltd.
Contact: Earl Graves, Jr., President
Ed: Sheiresa Ngo. **Description:** The way people purchase goods and service has changed with technology. With an increased focus on security (as well as privacy and fairness) the U.S. Congress began regulating the credit card industry with the Fair Credit Reporting Act of 1970 and the Credit Card Accountability, Responsibility, and Disclosure (CARD) Act of 2009. **Availability:** Online.

25592 ■ *"What Happens in Vegas Could Happen in Baltimore, Too"* in *Boston Business Journal (Vol. 29, June 17, 2011, No. 6, pp. 1)*
Pub: Boston Business Journal
Contact: Carolyn M. Jones, President
E-mail: cmjones@bizjournals.com
Ed: Daniel J. Sernovitz. **Description:** At least 36 companies expressed their interest in developing a casino in South Baltimore following the state commission's announcement for bids. Developers have until July 28, 2011 to submit their proposals. Baltimore's strong economy is the major factor for the interest, yet the fact that blackjack and poker are outlawed in Maryland could be a drawback. **Availability:** Print; Online.

25593 ■ *"What Keeps Global Leaders Up at Night"* in *Harvard Business Review (Vol. 90, April 2012, No. 4, pp. 32)*
Pub: Harvard Business Review Press
Contact: Moderna V. Pfizer, Contact
Price: $6. **Description:** A chart uses colored squares to portray economic, environmental, geopolitical, societal, and technological concerns of industry leaders, and ranks them according to likelihood and impact. **Availability:** PDF; Online.

25594 ■ *"What's Ahead for Fannie and Fred?"* in *Barron's (Vol. 90, August 30, 2010, No. 35, pp. 26)*
Pub: Barron's Editorial & Corporate Headquarters
Ed: Jonathan R. Laing. **Description:** A meeting presided by Treasury Secretary Timothy Geithner discussed the future of Fannie Mae and Freddie Mac. The two government sponsored enterprises were mismanaged and reforming these two agencies is critical. **Availability:** Online.

25595 ■ *"What's More Important: Stag or Flation?"* in *Barron's (Vol. 88, July 14, 2008, No. 28, pp. M8)*
Pub: Dow Jones & Company Inc.
Contact: Almar Latour, Chief Executive Officer
Ed: Randall W. Forsyth. **Description:** Economists are divided on which part of stagflation, an economic situation in which inflation and economic stagnation occur simultaneously and remain unchecked for a period of time, is more important. Some economists say that the Federal government is focusing on controlling inflation while others see the central bank as extending its liquidity facilities to the financial sector. **Availability:** Online.

25596 ■ *"Whistling Past the Graveyard? Higher Quality Stocks Beckon to Investors?"* in *Barron's (Vol. 88, March 17, 2008, No. 11, pp. 15)*
Pub: Dow Jones & Company Inc.
Contact: Almar Latour, Chief Executive Officer
Ed: Michael Santoli. **Description:** Discusses the Federal Reserve's move to provide $200 billion to the system which can be seen as an effort to avoid the liquidity problems that Bear Stearns suffered. The Federal Reserve's move seems to frighten investors rather than reassure them. **Availability:** Online.

25597 ■ *"Why Change?"* in *Canadian Business (Vol. 80, October 8, 2007, No. 20, pp. 9)*
Description: The need for economic change in Canada is discussed. Despite the country's economic growth and low unemployment rate, economic reform is needed in order to maximize its economic potential in the future. Other reasons for the need to further develop its economy, such as the rise of manufacturing and service industries in Asia and the emergence of regional trade pacts in South America are also tackled.

25598 ■ *"Why Japan Is So Interested In Alabama"* in *Birmingham Business Journal (Vol. 31, August 1, 2014, No. 31, pp. 11)*
Pub: American City Business Journals, Inc.
Contact: Mike Olivieri, Executive Vice President
Description: Kazuo Sunaga, Consul General of Japan in Atlanta, Georgia lists several reasons why Alabama presents several opportunities for Japanese companies, including fewer labor laws, low tax rates and the availability of trained workers. The state's relationship with Japan will be further enhanced when Birmingham hosts the Southeast U.S./Japan Association meeting in 2015, which will be attended by leaders from the business, political, and nonprofit sectors. **Availability:** Print; Online.

25599 ■ *"Why Optimism Over Europe Won't Last"* in *Barron's (Vol. 92, August 25, 2012, No. 38, pp. M6)*
Pub: Dow Jones & Company Inc.
Contact: Almar Latour, Chief Executive Officer
Ed: Jonathan Buck. **Description:** European markets could experience losses in the second half of 2012 as uncertainty over political events could wipe out market gains. Greece has to abide by the terms of ts agreements with creditors to receive bailout funds. The stock prices of BG Group could gain as much as 20 percent in 2013 due to its strong lifquified natural gas business. **Availability:** Online.

25600 ■ *"Why Seattle Children's Appealed"* in *Puget Sound Business Journal (Vol. 35, May 30, 2014, No. 6, pp. 6)*
Pub: American City Business Journals, Inc.
Contact: Mike Olivieri, Executive Vice President
Description: Seattle Children's Hospital filed an appeal against the Washing State Office of the Insurance Commissioner for approving several health exchange plans that excluded the hospital. Children's argues that it offers unique services and treatments only available through their medical facility and health insurance plans excluding them is putting children at risk. **Availability:** Online.

25601 ■ *"Will Bush Cuts Survive? Tax Thriller in D.C."* in *Barron's (Vol. 90, August 30, 2010, No. 35, pp. 17)*
Pub: Barron's Editorial & Corporate Headquarters
Ed: Jim McTague. **Description:** There are speculations on how Senator Harry Reid can push his bill to raise taxes on the wealthy while retaining the George W. Bush tax rates for the rest. Reid's challenge is to get the 60 votes needed to pass the bill. **Availability:** Online.

25602 ■ "Will Focus on Maryland Businesses Continue?" in Baltimore Business Journal (Vol. 28, November 5, 2010, No. 26, pp. 1)
Pub: Baltimore Business Journal
Contact: Rhonda Pringle, President
E-mail: rpringle@bizjournals.com

Ed: Scott Dance. **Description:** The 2010 election may call for new efforts to teach new lawmakers to assure that the viewpoints of businesses are considered and accurately delivered. The Greater Baltimore Committee and similar groups have gathered reports on the competitiveness of Maryland and are planning to use them to make a case of keeping business a top priority. **Availability:** Print; Online.

25603 ■ "With Mine Approval, Crystallex's Value as Target Seen on Rise" in Globe & Mail (March 28, 2006, pp. B3)

Ed: Wendy Stueck. **Description:** Crystallex International Corp. obtains Venezuelan Ministry of Basic Industry and Mining's authorization on Las Cristinas mining project. The impact of the approval, which posted rise in shares by 21 percent for the company, is discussed.

25604 ■ "Wood Increasingly Used in School Construction" in Arkansas Business (Vol. 29, July 23, 2012, No. 30, pp. 11)
Pub: Arkansas Business Publishing Group
Contact: Mitch Bettis, President

Ed: Jan Cottingham. **Description:** Arkansas state guidelines have increased the use of wood in school building construction. Wood is believed to provide strength and durability along with cost effectiveness and environmental benefits. **Availability:** Online.

25605 ■ "A Word With Connie Runia of Collection Bureau" in Idaho Business Review (September 8, 2014)
Pub: BridgeTower Media
Contact: Adam Reinebach, President

Description: Connie Runia, attorney and general counsel for Collection Bureau, located in Nampa, Idaho, joined the firm four years ago. These collection bureaus are licensed by the Department of Finance and regulated by the Federal Trade Commission. The Consumer Financial Protection Bureau is developing new rules for collection agencies. Statistical data included. **Availability:** Online.

25606 ■ "WQA Develops Certification Program" in Contractor (Vol. 57, January 2010, No. 1, pp. 56)

Ed: Dennis Sowards. **Description:** Water Quality Association is now offering a new certification program for companies that may be affected by California's law that prohibits any products intended to convey or dispense water for human consumption that is not lead-free. All pipe or plumbing fixtures must be certified by a third party certification body. **Availability:** Print; Online.

25607 ■ "WQA's Leadership Conference Tackles Industry Issues" in Contractor (Vol. 56, October 2009, No. 10, pp. 3)

Ed: Candace Roulo. **Description:** Water Quality Association's Mid-Year Leadership Conference held in Bloomingdale, Illinois in September 2009 tackled lead regulation, water softeners, and product efficiency. The possibility of a WQA green seal was discussed by the Water Sciences Committee and the Government Relations Committee meeting. **Availability:** Online.

25608 ■ "Yield Vanishes, Inflation Lurks" in Barron's (Vol. 92, September 17, 2012, No. 38, pp. M12)

Description: The US Federal Reserve's announcement of a third round of quantitative easing resulted in lower yields for bonds. Investors are becoming concerned with the probability of a rise in inflation after th quantitative easing program expires. **Availability:** Online.

25609 ■ "You Won't Go Broke Filling Up On The Stock" in Barron's (Vol. 88, July 14, 2008, No. 28, pp. 38)
Pub: Dow Jones & Company Inc.
Contact: Almar Latour, Chief Executive Officer

Ed: Assif Shameen. **Description:** Due to high economic growth, pro-business policies and a consumption boom, the Middle East is a good place to look for equities. The best ways in which to gain exposure to this market include investing in the real estate industry and telecommunications markets as well as large banks that serve corporations and consumers. **Availability:** Online.

TRADE PERIODICALS

25610 ■ *Dickinson's FDA Review*
Pub: Ferdic Inc.
Contact: James G. Dickinson, Founder
URL(s): www.fdareview.com

Released: Weekly **Description:** Recurring features include interviews, news of research, a calendar of events, reports of meetings, and notices of publications available. **Availability:** Print.

25611 ■ *FDA Week*
Pub: Inside Washington Publishers
Contact: Robert Woolard, Contact
URL(s): insidehealthpolicy.com/fda-week/daily-news

Released: Weekly **Price:** $705, U.S. and Canada for per year; $755, Elsewhere for per year. **Description:** Reports on Food and Drug Administration policy, regulation, and enforcement. **Availability:** Online.

25612 ■ *Water Policy Report*
Pub: Inside Washington Publishers
Contact: Robert Woolard, Contact
URL(s): iwpnews.com/index.html#products

Released: Biweekly **Price:** $730, U.S. for per year; $730, Canada for per year; $780, Elsewhere for per year. **Description:** Reports on federal water quality programs and policies. Covers topics such as drinking water, toxics, enforcement, monitoring, and state/EPA relations. **Availability:** Online.

VIDEO/AUDIO MEDIA

25613 ■ *Unraveling ESG: Understanding Enviornmental, Social, and Governance Factors in Business - Part 1*
URL(s): podcast.imanet.org/224

Released: May 22, 2023. **Description:** Podcast discusses the complexities of ESG (Environmental, Social, and Governance) with a panel of experts.

25614 ■ *Unraveling ESG: Understanding Enviornmental, Social, and Governance Factors in Business - Part 2*
URL(s): podcast.imanet.org/225

Description: Podcast discusses the complexities of ESG (Environmental, Social, and Governance) with a panel of experts.

TRADE SHOWS AND CONVENTIONS

25615 ■ IECA Annual Conference and Expo
URL(s): https://www.ieca.org//IECA

Price: $750, Members Full conference pass. **Frequency:** Annual. **Description:** Educational programs and sessions engaged in the erosion and sediment control industry. The expo portion hosts products and services vendors. **Principal Exhibits:** Educational programs and sessions engaged in the erosion and sediment control industry. The expo portion hosts products and services vendors.

CONSULTANTS

25616 ■ ARDITO Information and Research Inc.
910 Foulk Rd., Ste. 200
Wilmington, DE 19803

Description: A full-service information and research firm. Provides information in areas of financial data, published research, demographic data, industry-specific publications, competitor data, marketing and sales trends, new product developments, government relations, bibliographies. Industries served are pharmaceutical, health, publishing and environment and business. **Scope:** A full-service information and research firm. Provides information in areas of financial data, published research, demographic data, industry-specific publications, competitor data, marketing and sales trends, new product developments, government relations, bibliographies. Industries served are pharmaceutical, health, publishing and environment and business. **Publications:** "The Swine flu pandemic: Authoritative information versus community gossip," Searcher, Oct, 2009; "The Medical blogosphere: How social networking platforms are changing medical searching," Searcher, May, 2009; "Social Networking and Video Web Sites: MySpace and YouTube Meet the Copyright Cops," Searcher, May, 2007; "Copyright Clearance Center raises transactional fees," Information Today, Jul, 2004.

25617 ■ Capitol Services
3609 Bradshaw Rd., Ste. H 343
Sacramento, CA 95827
Free: 866-443-0657
Fax: (916)443-1908
Co. E-mail: info@cutredtape.com
URL: http://cutredtape.com
Contact: Shauna Krause, Consultant Principal

Description: Firm provides the registered agent, corporate and uniform commercial code services. **Scope:** Offers assistance to out-of-state businesses wishing to relocate or expand into California and to existing businesses within the State. Specific activities include helping construction trade firms secure a California contractors license, research and assistance in obtaining state and local government permits and licenses, assisting lawyers with public document search and retrieval and public policy analysis. Also helps with contractors licensing in California, Arizona and Nevada. **Founded:** 1978. **Publications:** "Handyman and CSLB Publications," Apr,2010; "Unlicensed Penalties, Suspensions and LLC's," Jan, 2010; "What every Contractor Should Know".

25618 ■ Compliance Consultants
1151 Hope St.
Stamford, CT 06907
Ph: (203)329-2700
Fax: (203)329-2345
Co. E-mail: rkeen@fda-complianceconsultants.com
URL: http://www.fda-complianceconsultants.com

Description: Provider of consulting services with an expertise in regulatory engineering, product development, and medical devices, the firm advises manufacturers in regulatory requirements and submits detailed engineering facts and marketing reports to obtain market approvals, and serves domestic and foreign clients. **Scope:** Provider of consulting services with an expertise in regulatory engineering, product development, and medical devices, the firm advises manufacturers in regulatory requirements and submits detailed engineering facts and marketing reports to obtain market approvals, and serves domestic and foreign clients. **Founded:** 1988.

25619 ■ Daniel Bloom and Associates Inc. (DBAI)
11517 128th Ave. N
Largo, FL 33778
Ph: (727)581-6216
URL: http://dbaiconsulting.com
Contact: Daniel T. Bloom, Chief Executive Officer

Description: Human resources management consultant with a specialization in corporate relocation. Offers clients a turn key service aimed at meeting the unique relocation needs of their employees. Develops and implements training programs within the relocation industry. **Scope:** Human resources management consultant with a specialization in corporate relocation. Offers clients a turn key service aimed at meeting the unique relocation needs of their employees. Develops and implements training programs within the relocation industry. **Founded:** 1980. **Publications:** "Where Have All the Elders Gone," Aug, 2002; "Recoup Your Hiring Investment," Brainbuzz.com, Aug, 2000; "Managing Your Lump Sum Program," Brainbuzz.com, Jun, 2000; "Buyer Value Options," Brainbuzz.com, Apr, 2000; "Just Get Me There". **Training:** Chaos in the Workplace: Multiple Generational Interactions; Training Effectiveness: Is the Cost Justified?; Human Capital Resource Management: A Six-Sigma Based Approach to Paving Your Way to the Table; Welcome to My World.

25620 ■ Envar Services Inc.
505 Milltown Rd.
 North Brunswick, NJ 08902
Ph: (732)296-9601
Fax: (732)296-9602
Co. E-mail: mail@envarservices.com
URL: http://www.envarservices.com
Contact: John Shultis, President
Description: Provider of consulting services such as engineering design and construction, environmental compliance, civil and municipal engineers and planners, construction management services for the erection or renovation of office, laboratory, warehouse, and manufacturing space. **Scope:** Provider of consulting services such as engineering design and construction, environmental compliance, civil and municipal engineers and planners, construction management services for the erection or renovation of office, laboratory, warehouse, and manufacturing space. **Founded:** 1960. **Publications:** "Method of Detoxification and Stabilization of Soils Contaminated with Chromium Ore Waste".

25621 ■ Environmental Assessment Services Inc.
201 E 5th St. 2500 Central Trust Ctr.
 Cincinnati, OH 45202
Contact: Larry H. McMillin, Contact
Description: Offers environmental and health and safety services in compliance auditing, program management and implementation, field services and real estate assessment. **Scope:** Offers environmental and health and safety services in compliance auditing, program management and implementation, field services and real estate assessment.

25622 ■ Environmental Management Consultants, Inc. (EMC)
427 Main St.
 Evansville, IN 47708
Ph: (812)424-7768
Free: 800-280-7768
Fax: (812)424-7797
Co. E-mail: info@emcevv.com
URL: http://www.emcevv.com
Contact: Roger Cohen, Director
Facebook: www.facebook.com/EnvironmentalManagementConsultants
Linkedin: www.linkedin.com/company/environmental-management-consultants-inc
X (Twitter): x.com/EMCEVV
Description: Firm provides environmental consulting in air and water quality monitoring, environmental site assessments, training, underground and aboveground storage tanks, industrial regulatory compliance, and hazardous materials cleanups. **Scope:** Firm provides environmental consulting in air and water quality monitoring, environmental site assessments, training, underground and above-ground storage tanks, industrial regulatory compliance, and hazardous materials cleanups. **Founded:** 1988.

25623 ■ Environmental Monitoring Inc. (EMI)
5730 Industrial Pk. Rd.
 Norton, VA 24273
Ph: (276)679-6544
Fax: (276)679-6549
URL: http://www.emilab.com
Contact: R. J. Porter, President
E-mail: rjporter@emilab.com
Facebook: www.facebook.com/pages/category/Environmental-Consultant/Environmental-Monitoring-Inc-1514044468841406
Linkedin: www.linkedin.com/company/environmental-monitoring-inc
Description: Firm provides environmental and analytical services for industry, government, individuals, and other related services. **Scope:** Firm provides environmental and analytical services for industry, government, individuals, and other related services. **Founded:** 1983.

25624 ■ Environmental Support Network Inc. (ESN)
PO Box 36448
 Canton, OH 44735
Ph: (330)494-0905
URL: http://www.environmental-support.com
Contact: William Racine, Contact
Description: Provides environmental, health and safety consulting and project management services. These include compliance auditing and remediation specifications concerning air, groundwater and soil quality. Also offers health and safety reviews, asbestos and lead-based paint handling, noise sampling, industrial permitting and UST management. Industries served: education, finance, industry and government. **Scope:** Provides environmental, health and safety consulting and project management services. These include compliance auditing and remediation specifications concerning air, groundwater and soil quality. Also offers health and safety reviews, asbestos and lead-based paint handling, noise sampling, industrial permitting and UST management. Industries served: education, finance, industry and government. **Founded:** 1989. **Training:** Environmental Health and Safety Management in Ohio; Managing Compliance in Ohio; Environmental Site Remediation in Ohio and Surrounding States; Conducting ESAs by ASTM Standards; Health and Safety Management in the Medical Setting; Exposure Monitoring in Schools and Public Buildings.

25625 ■ International Business - Government Counsellors Inc. (IBC)
818 Connecticut Ave. NW, 12th Fl.
 Washington, DC 20006-2702
URL: http://www.ibgc.com
Contact: Melissa San Miguel, President
Description: Firm provides international government, business relations counseling services for multinational companies in areas such as trade, investment, and political risk analysis, and much more. **Scope:** Firm provides international government, business relations counseling services for multinational companies in areas such as trade, investment, and political risk analysis, and much more. **Founded:** 1972.

25626 ■ Safety Management Services (SMS)
1847 W 9000 S, Ste. 205
 West Jordan, UT 84088
Ph: (801)567-0456
Fax: (801)567-0457
URL: http://smsenergetics.com
Contact: Robert Ford, President
Facebook: www.facebook.com/safetymanagementservices
Linkedin: www.linkedin.com/company/safety-management-services-inc
Description: Provider of safety consulting services including evaluating safety policies and procedures to determine degree of effectiveness, advises on compliance with OSHA standards and provides safety programs for managers, supervisors, and workers. **Scope:** Provider of safety consulting services including evaluating safety policies and procedures to determine degree of effectiveness, advises on compliance with OSHA standards and provides safety programs for managers, supervisors, and workers. **Founded:** 1998. **Publications:** "What Can Go Wrong?," International Cranes magazine, Apr, 1994. **Training:** Federal OSHA Construction Safety and Health Course for Trainers, University of California, San Diego; OSHA 10-Hour Construction Safety Course; 90-Hour Construction Safety Management Certificate Course - 1991 to 1993; Fall Protection; Confined Space Standards; Cranes and Rigging; Scaffold or Trenching and Excavation; and Safe Construction Work Practices.

PUBLICATIONS

25627 ■ *Regulation: Cato Review of Business & Government*
1000 Massachusetts Ave. NW
 Washington, DC 20001-5403
Ph: (202)842-0200
Co. E-mail: pr@cato.org
URL: http://www.cato.org
Contact: Peter Goettler, President
E-mail: pgoettler@cato.org
URL(s): www.cato.org/regulation/about
Ed: Peter Van Doren. **Released:** Quarterly **Price:** $20, Individuals for one year; $35, Individuals for two year; $50, Individuals for 3 year; $40, Institutions for one year library; $70, Institutions for 2 year library; $100, Institutions for 3 year library. **Description:** Magazine publishing articles on government regulation. **Availability:** Print; PDF.

COMPUTERIZED DATABASES

25628 ■ *CCH ProSystem fx Tax*™
Wolters Kluwer
 90 Sheppard Ave. E, Ste. 300
 Toronto, ON, Canada M2N 6X1
Ph: (416)224-2248
URL: http://www.wolterskluwer.com/en-in
Contact: Kevin Entricken, Chief Financial Officer
URL(s): www.wolterskluwer.com/en/solutions/cch-prosystem-fx/tax
Availability: PDF; Download; Online. **Type:** Bulletin board.

LIBRARIES

25629 ■ Bryan Cave L.L.P., Law Library
1155 F St. NW, Ste. 700
 Washington, DC 20004-1357
URL: http://www.bclplaw.com/en-US/people/pedro-j-martinez-fraga.html
Scope: Government and politics; law - commercial, corporate, environmental, intellectual property, taxation. **Services:** Interlibrary loan; copying; faxing; library open to the public with restrictions. **Founded:** 1978. **Holdings:** 11,000 volumes.

RESEARCH CENTERS

25630 ■ American Enterprise Institute (AEI)
1789 Massachusetts Ave. NW
 Washington, DC 20036
Ph: (202)862-5800
Fax: (202)862-7177
Co. E-mail: mediaservices@aei.org
URL: http://www.aei.org
Contact: Robert Doar, President
E-mail: robert.doar@aei.org
Facebook: www.facebook.com/aei
Linkedin: www.linkedin.com/company/american-enterprise-institute
X (Twitter): x.com/AEI
Instagram: www.instagram.com/aei
YouTube: www.youtube.com/user/AEIVideos
Description: Private research group which seeks to preserve and improve: open and competitive enterprise; limited and public-oriented government; defense and foreign policies; cultural and political values. Conducts research on domestic and international economic policy; foreign and defense policy; social and political studies. Conducts educational programs. **Scope:** Economic policy, including domestic taxing, spending, and regulatory programs, and international trade and competitiveness; foreign and defense policy, including the spread of democracy and free enterprise, and the development of stable international security arrangements; social and political studies, including U.S. politics and public opinion, the Constitution and legal policy, and social welfare, educational and cultural issues. **Founded:** 1938. **Publications:** *AEI Newsletter* (Monthly); *The American Enterprise* (8/year); *The American* (Bimonthly); *The American Enterprise: A National Magazine of*

Politics, Business, and Culture. **Awards:** American Enterprise Institute National Research Initiative Fellowships (NRI) (Annual). **Geographic Preference:** National.

25631 ■ Washington Policy Center (WPC)
9 S Washington St Ste. 212
Spokane, WA 99201
Ph: (206)937-9691
Fax: (206)624-8038
Co. E-mail: wpc@washingtonpolicy.org
URL: http://www.washingtonpolicy.org
Contact: Liv Finne, Director
E-mail: lfinne@washingtonpolicy.org
Facebook: www.facebook.com/washington.policy.center
Linkedin: www.linkedin.com/company/washington-policy-center
X (Twitter): x.com/WAPolicyCenter
YouTube: www.youtube.com/channel/UCTljIqVt94OrqtCyNkRIRqg
Description: Independent, nonprofit think tank. **Scope:** Free-market economic policy issues at the local, state, and national level. **Founded:** 1986. **Publications:** *Policy briefs*; *Environmental Watch* (Monthly); *Policy notes*. **Educational Activities:** WPC Forums. **Awards:** WPC Internships.

Healthcare and Social Assistance

START-UP INFORMATION

25632 ■ *"An Insurer Stretches Out" in Business Journal Portland (Vol. 30, February 21, 2014, No. 51, pp. 4)*
Pub: American City Business Journals, Inc.
Contact: Mike Olivieri, Executive Vice President
Released: Weekly. **Price:** $4, Introductory 4-week offer(Digital & Print). **Description:** The diversification strategy of Cambia Health Solutions has led to investments in several health care startups. The company earned $5.8 billion in revenue from insurance premiums in 2012 and posted a profit margin of about 2 percent for its net income of $173 million. **Availability:** Print; Online.

25633 ■ *"Katharine Grayson: Three Questions with John Brownlee, CEO of Vidscrip.com" in Business Journal (Vol. 32, June 27, 2014, No. 5, pp. 6)*
Pub: American City Business Journals, Inc.
Contact: Mike Olivieri, Executive Vice President
Description: John Brownlee, CEO of vidscrip.com, discusses the Minneapolis, Minnesota startup's deal with Partners HealthCare and what it means for the business. Partners HealthCare is using the vidscrip technology to create educational videos for patients. **Availability:** Print; Online.

25634 ■ *"Made@Mayo: Mayo Professor Doubles As Founder of Text Tech Company" in Business Journal (Vol. 32, June 6, 2014, No. 2, pp. 10)*
Pub: American City Business Journals, Inc.
Contact: Mike Olivieri, Executive Vice President
Description: Rochester, Minnesota-based Mayo Clinic Ventures has managed the licensing of Mayo Clinic technologies and invests in startups. Mayo Clinic Ventures has a $100 million growth fund for investing in startups and two smaller funds worth about $500,000 combined. Insights on the stories of Mayo researchers leading startups are also provided. **Availability:** Online.

25635 ■ *"No. 407: What I Learned in the Military, and What I Had to Unlearn" in Inc. (Vol. 36, September 2014, No. 7, pp. 80)*
Pub: Mansueto Ventures L.L.C.
Contact: Stephanie Mehta, Chief Executive Officer
Released: September 2014. **Description:** Profile of William Bailey, who served in the U.S. Army as information manager at the U.S. Military Academy at West Point. Bailey discusses his startup firm, Rapier Solutions, a government contractor providing IT, logistics, and social-work expertise. The firm has developed a new survivor outreach system for the U.S. Army. **Availability:** Print; Online.

25636 ■ *"One of the Best Ways to Build Wealth...Is to Take Equity In a Company" in Business Journal (Vol. 31, May 2, 2014, No. 49, pp. 9)*
Pub: American City Business Journals, Inc.
Contact: Mike Olivieri, Executive Vice President

Released: Weekly. **Price:** $4, introductory 4-week offer(Digital only). **Description:** Entrepreneur Abir Sen reveals that he was not planning to start a business after selling Bloom Health, but he soon discovered that he wanted to do something productive. He believes that the traditional model of employer-paid health care insurance is dying. His opinion on health care entrepreneurial activity in Minnesota is also examined. **Availability:** Print; Online.

25637 ■ *"Pot Watch: Magic Butter Delivers THC-infused Food Truck" in Puget Sound Business Journal (Vol. 35, May 30, 2014, No. 6, pp. 10)*
Pub: American City Business Journals, Inc.
Contact: Mike Olivieri, Executive Vice President
Description: Magical Butter is a startup in Seattle, Washington that sells a botanical extractor for infusing herbs into food ingredients like the active ingredient in marijuana known as THC into butter or oil. Career chef, Jeremy Cooper, has perfected the peanut butter and jelly sandwich with THC and sells them from the company's food truck business in Denver, Colorado. **Availability:** Online.

25638 ■ *Up and Running: Opening a Chiropractic Office*
Description: Tips for starting a chiropractic business. **Availability:** Print.

ASSOCIATIONS AND OTHER ORGANIZATIONS

25639 ■ **AcademyHealth**
1666 K St. NW Ste. 1100
Washington, DC 20006
Ph: (202)292-6700
Fax: (202)292-6800
Co. E-mail: info@academyhealth.org
URL: http://academyhealth.org
Contact: Dr. Lisa Simpson, President
Facebook: www.facebook.com/AcademyHealth
Linkedin: www.linkedin.com/groups/academyhealth-3771534
X (Twitter): x.com/academyhealth
YouTube: www.youtube.com/user/AcademyHealth
Description: Promotes interaction across the health research and policy arenas by bringing together a broad spectrum of players to share their perspectives, learn from each other and strengthen their working relationships. Convenes national scientific and health policy conferences; helps public and private policymakers transform research and policy into workable programs; educates policymakers, researchers, government officials, and business leaders; disseminates vital information through research syntheses, special report findings, newsletters and website; and conducts major programs that serve the research community, health policy leaders, and business and government decision-makers. **Founded:** 2000. **Publications:** *AcademyHealth Reports* (Quarterly); *eGEMs: The Journal for Electronic Health Data and Methods (GEMs)* (Continuous). **Awards:** Reinhardt Distinguished Career Award (Annual); Alice S. Hersh New Investigator Award (Annual). **Geographic Preference:** National.

25640 ■ **American College of Clinical Pharmacy (ACCP)**
13000 W 87th St., Pky.
Lenexa, KS 66215
Ph: (913)492-3311
URL: http://www.accp.com
Contact: Jimmi Hatton Kolpek, President
Facebook: www.facebook.com/ClinicalPharm
Linkedin: www.linkedin.com/company/american-college-of-clinical-pharmacy
X (Twitter): x.com/accp
Description: Clinical pharmacists dedicated to: promoting rational use of drugs in society; advancing the practice of clinical pharmacy and interdisciplinary health care; assuring high quality clinical pharmacy by establishing and maintaining standards in education and training at advanced levels. Encourages research and recognizes excellence in clinical pharmacy. Offers educational programs, symposia, research forums, fellowship training, and college-funded grants through competitions. Maintains placement service. **Founded:** 1979. **Publications:** *Journal of the American College of Clinical Pharmacy (JACCP)* (Monthly); *ACCP Report*; *Pharmacotherapy* (Monthly); *Residency and Fellowship Programs Offered by ACCP Members*. **Educational Activities:** ACCP Annual Meeting (Annual). **Awards:** ACCP Education Award (Annual); Paul F. Parker Medal for Distinguished Service to the Profession of Pharmacy (Annual); Russell R. Miller Award (Annual); Robert M. Elenbaas Service Award (Occasionally); ACCP Therapeutic Frontiers Lecture Award (Annual); ACCP New Investigator Award (Annual); ACCP Clinical Practice Award (Annual). **Geographic Preference:** National.

25641 ■ **American Health Care Association (AHCA)**
1201 L St. NW
Washington, DC 20005
Ph: (202)842-4444
Fax: (202)842-3860
Co. E-mail: help@ltctrendtracker.com
URL: http://www.ahcancal.org/Pages/default.aspx
Contact: Mark Parkinson, President
Facebook: www.facebook.com/ahcancal
X (Twitter): x.com/ahcancal
YouTube: www.youtube.com/user/ahcancalstream
Description: Federation of state associations of long-term health care facilities. Promotes standards for professionals in long-term health care delivery and quality care for patients and residents in a safe environment. Focuses on issues of availability, quality, affordability, and fair payment. Operates as liaison with governmental agencies, Congress, and professional associations. Compiles statistics. American Health Care Association is an association of long term and post-acute care providers and advocates for quality care and services for frail, elderly and disabled Americans. **Founded:** 1949. **Publications:**

Focus (Weekly); Provider--LTC Buyers' Guide Issue (Annual); American Health Care Association: Provider (Monthly); Choosing a Nursing Home Pamphlet; Choosing An Assisted Living Residence: A Consumer's Guide; Having Your Say: Advance Directives Fact Sheet; Understanding Long Term Care Insurance Fact Sheet; Assisted Living State Regulatory Review (Annual); NCAL Connections (Weekly); Resident Assistant Newsletter; Assessing Your Needs: Consumer Guides to Nursing and Assisted Living Facilities; Caring for Someone with Alzheimer's Fact Sheet; Living in a Nursing Home: Myths and Realities Fact Sheet; Tips on Visiting Friends and Relatives Fact Sheet; Family Questions: The First Thirty Days Fact Sheet; Moving Into an Assisted Living Residence: Making a Successful Transition Fact Sheet; Making the Transition to Nursing Facility Life Fact Sheet; Paying for Long Term Care Pamphlet; Glossary of Terms Pamphlet; Advice for Families Pamphlet; Advance Preparation: Having the Conversation About Long Term Care Pamphlet; Coping with the Transition Pamphlet; Talking To Your Loved Ones About Their Care Pamphlet; Capitol Connection Newsletter (Biweekly); NCAL Focus Newsletter (Monthly); AHCA Notes (Monthly); Provider: For Long Term Care Professionals (Monthly). **Educational Activities:** American Health Care Association Annual Convention and Exposition (Annual). **Awards:** AHCA/NCAL National Quality Award - Bronze Level (Annual); AHCA/NCAL Adult Volunteer of the Year (Annual); AHCA Group Volunteer of the Year (Annual); AHCA/NCAL Young Adult Volunteer of the Year Award (Annual); AHCA/NCAL National Quality Award - Silver Level (Annual); AHCA/NCAL National Quality Award - Gold Level (Annual). **Geographic Preference:** National.

25642 ■ American Psychological Association (APA) - Arthur W. Melton Library
750 1st St. NE
Washington, DC 20002-4242
Ph: (202)336-5500
Free: 800-374-2721
Co. E-mail: order@apa.org
URL: http://www.apa.org
Contact: Dr. Cynthia de las Fuentes, President
E-mail: cdelasfuentes@apaboard.org
Facebook: www.facebook.com/AmericanPsychologicalAssociation
Linkedin: www.linkedin.com/company/american-psychological-association
X (Twitter): x.com/apa
Instagram: www.instagram.com/apa_org
YouTube: www.youtube.com/theapavideo

Description: Scientific and professional society of psychologists; students participate as affiliates. Advances psychology as a science, a profession, and as a means of promoting health, education and the human welfare. **Scope:** Psychology. **Founded:** 1892. **Holdings:** 3,000 books; photographs; films; journals; records. **Publications:** Division Digest (Semimonthly); Clinical Psychology (Annual); Psychological Methods (Bimonthly); PsycINFO® (Semiweekly); APA Monitor (Semimonthly); Monitor on Psychology (8/year); Global Insights Newsletter (Quarterly); PsycINFO News (Quarterly); Communique Newsletter; Graduate Study in Psychology; PsycSCAN: Behavior Analysis & Therapy (Quarterly); Health Psychology (Monthly); Neuropsychology (8/year); Journal of Psychopathology and Clinical Science (8/year); Journal of Applied Psychology (Monthly); Consulting Psychology Journal: Practice and Research (Quarterly); Dreaming (Quarterly); History of Psychology (Quarterly); International Journal of Stress Management (IJSM) (Quarterly); Journal of Comparative Psychology (Quarterly); Journal of Experimental Psychology: Applied (Quarterly); Journal of Experimental Psychology: General (Monthly); Psychoanalytic Psychology (Quarterly); Psychological Services (Quarterly); Psychotherapy (Quarterly); Rehabilitation Psychology (Quarterly); PracticeUpdate Newsletter (Semimonthly); Psychology & AIDS Exchange Newsletter (Annual); The Addictions Newsletter (3/year); The General Psychologist; The Experimental Psychology Bulletin; The Behavioral Neuroscientist and Comparative Psychology Newsletter (3/year); Developmental Psychology Newsletter (Semiannual); The Forward Newsletter (3/year); The Consulting Psychologist Newsletter, Newsletter for Educational Psychologists (3/year); The School Psychologist Newsletter (TSP) (3/year); Public Service Psychology Newsletter (3/year); The Military Psychologist Newsletter (3/year); Adult Development & Aging News; The Community Psychologist Newsletter (TCP) (Quarterly); Psychopharmacology and Substance Abuse Newsletter (3/year); Psychotherapy Bulletin (Quarterly); Psychological Hypnosis Newsletter (Periodic); Newsletter Co-op; Society for Humanistic Psychology Newsletter (3/year); Psychology in Intellectual and Developmental Disabilities/Autism Spectrum Disorders (Semiannual); Environmental, Population & Conservation Psychology Bulletin (3/year); Feminist Psychologist Newsletter (Periodic); Society for the Psychology of Religion and Spirituality Newsletter (3/year); The Advocate (3/year); The Health Psychologist; Psychologist-Psychoanalyst: Division 39 Newsletter, Society for Clinical Neuropsychology Newsletter 40 (Semiannual); AP-LS Newsletter (Monthly); The Independent Practitioner (Quarterly); Family Psychologist: Division 43 Newsletter (3/year); Focus: Division 45 Newsletter (Semiannual); The Amplifier Magazine (Semiannual); SPSMM Bulletin: Division 51 Newsletter, Behavioral Neuroscience (Bimonthly); Computer Use in Psychology: A Directory of Software; Directory of Ethnic Minority Professionals in Psychology; Review of General Psychology (Quarterly); Psychology in Intellectual and Developmental Disabilities / Autism Spectrum Disorder (Semiannual); The Score (Quarterly); Psychological Abstracts; APA Membership Directory; PsycSCAN: Applied Psychology, Journal of Consulting and Clinical Psychology (Monthly); PsycSCAN: Clinical Psychology (Monthly); PsycSCAN: Learning Disabilities and Mental Retardation; Neuropsychology Abstracts (Quarterly); Law and Human Behavior (Bimonthly); Clinician's Research Digest: Adult Populations (Monthly); Contemporary Psychology (Monthly); Journal of Counseling Psychology (6/year); APA PsycArticles® (Biweekly); APA PsycBooksS® (Monthly); PsycCRITIQUES®; APA PsycExtra® (Biweekly); APA Division Digest Newsletter (Semimonthly); Journal of Family Psychology (JFP) (8/year); Journal of Educational Psychology (8/year); Journal of Experimental Psychology: Animal Learning and Cognition (Quarterly); Journal of Experimental Psychology: Human Perception and Performance (Monthly); Journal of Experimental Psychology: Learning, Memory, and Cognition (Monthly); Journal of Personality and Social Psychology (Monthly); American Psychologist (9/year); Monitor on Psychology (8/year); Cultural Diversity & Ethnic Minority Psychology (Quarterly); Emotion (8/year); Experimental and Clinical Psychopharmacology (Bimonthly); Group Dynamics: Theory, Research, and Practice (Quarterly); Journal of Occupational Health Psychology (Bimonthly); Psychological Methods (Bimonthly); Psychology of Men & Masculinity (Quarterly); Psychology, Public Policy, and Law (Quarterly); Review of General Psychology (Quarterly); Canadian Journal of Experimental Psychology (Quarterly); International Journal of Play Therapy (Quarterly); Journal of Diversity in Higher Education (Bimonthly); Psychology of Violence (Bimonthly); School Psychology (Bimonthly); Families, Systems & Health® (Quarterly); PsycTESTS®; Graduate Study in Psychology; APAGS Newsletter, gradPSYCH Newsletter (Quarterly); Aging Issues Newsletter (Semiannual); CYF News; CoA Update (Quarterly); In the Public Interest Newsletter (Semimonthly); PsychMarketer Newsletter (Quarterly); Psychology Giving Newsletter (Periodic); Psychology Teacher Network Newsletter (PTN) (Quarterly); APA Science Policy News (ASPN) (Monthly); Spotlight on Disability Newsletter, Synapse Newsletter, The Educator Newsletter (Semiannual); The Pipeline Newsletter, The SES Indicator (3/year); Variability Newsletter (Annual); Women's Psych-E Newsletter, APA Guide to Research Support; Journal of Psychotherapy Integration (Quarterly); Psychology of Addictive Behaviors (8/year); Professional Psychology: Research and Practice (Bimonthly); Psychological Abstracts; Psychological Bulletin (Monthly); Psychological Review (6/year); Psychological Assessment (Monthly); Psychology and Aging (8/year); PsycSCAN: Applied Experimental & Engineering Psychology (Quarterly); PsycCRITIQUES: APA Review of Books (Weekly); Developmental Psychology (Monthly); Journals in Psychology: A Resource Listing for Authors; Latin American Psychology: A Guide to Research and Training; Psychology of Religion and Spirituality (Quarterly). **Educational Activities:** APA Annual Convention (Annual). **Geographic Preference:** National.

25643 ■ Associated Medical Services (AMS)
162 Cumberland Ste. 228
Toronto, ON, Canada M5R 3N5
Co. E-mail: info@amshealthcare.ca
URL: http://www.ams-inc.on.ca
Contact: Anne Avery, Director, Operations Director, Communications
E-mail: anne.avery@ams-inc.on.ca
Linkedin: www.linkedin.com/company/ams-healthcare
X (Twitter): x.com/AMSHealthcare
YouTube: www.youtube.com/channel/UC-LSdsxmL7s9cYhsjeEn9qg

Description: Promotes increased availability of quality health care. Facilitates communication and cooperation among members. **Founded:** 1937. **Publications:** Corporate Report (Biennial). **Awards:** Hannah Senior General Scholarships; Jason A. Hannah Medal; Hannah Junior General Scholarships; Hannah Independent Scholar Grant (Annual); Hannah Junior General Scholarship (Annual); Hannah Post-doctoral Fellowship (Annual). **Geographic Preference:** National.

25644 ■ Association for Behavioral Health and Wellness (ABHW)
700 12th St. NW, Ste. 700
Washington, DC 20005
Ph: (202)449-7660
Co. E-mail: info@abhw.org
URL: http://abhw.org
Contact: Pamela Greenberg, President
X (Twitter): x.com/ABHWorg

Description: Managed behavioral healthcare organizations. Works to advance the value of managed behavioral healthcare and promotes the inclusion of mental illnesses and addiction disorders in benefit coverage. **Founded:** 1994. **Publications:** Catalog of Special Reports. **Geographic Preference:** National.

25645 ■ Association of Black Social Workers (ABSW)
190 Victoria Rd. Ste. 204
Dartmouth, NS, Canada B3A 1W5
Ph: (902)407-8809
Free: 855-732-1253
Co. E-mail: offfice@nsabsw.ca
URL: http://www.nsabsw.ca
Contact: Rachelle Sweeting, President
Facebook: www.facebook.com/abswoffice
Instagram: www.instagram.com/absw_ns

Description: A volunteer charitable organization made up of Black social workers and human service workers. **Founded:** 1977.

25646 ■ Association of Black Women Physicians (ABWP)
4712 Admiralty Way, Ste. No. 175
Marina del Rey, CA 90292
Ph: (424)443-9454
Co. E-mail: abwpcorrespondence@gmail.com
URL: http://www.blackwomenphysicians.org
Contact: Latanya Hines, President
Facebook: www.facebook.com/Blackfemaledoctors
X (Twitter): x.com/ABWP_Drs
Instagram: www.instagram.com/blackwomenphysicians
YouTube: www.youtube.com/channel/UCbUPOVe4K7BRx8zz5hROPmw

Description: Black female physicians committed to the improvement of public health and welfare through the advancement of knowledge concerning women and the health of the black community. Provides an ongoing forum for support, social networking, mentorship, community education, health advocacy, and scholarships to deserving medical students. **Founded:** 1982. **Awards:** Rebecca Lee Crumpler, M.D. Scholarship (Annual).

GENERAL SMALL BUSINESS TOPICS | Healthcare and Social Assistance ■ 25655

25647 ■ Association Canadienne de la Medecine du Travail et de l'Environnement (OEMAC) [Occupational and Environmental Medical Association of Canada]
386 Broadway, Ste. 503
Winnipeg, MB, Canada R3C 3R6
Free: 888-223-3808
Fax: (877)947-9767
Co. E-mail: info@oemac.org
URL: http://www.oemac.org
Contact: Itua Iriogbe, President
Description: Health care professionals with an active interest in occupational and environmental medicine. **Founded:** 1985. **Publications:** Liaison Newsletter (Quarterly). **Awards:** Meritorious Service Award (Annual). **Geographic Preference:** National.

25648 ■ Association Medicale Canadienne (AMC) [Canadian Medical Association]
1410 Blair Towers Pl., Ste. 500
Ottawa, ON, Canada K1J 9B9
Free: 888-855-2555
URL: http://www.cma.ca/fr
Contact: Dr. Suzanne Strasberg, Chairman
Facebook: www.facebook.com/Associationme
 dicalecanadienne
X (Twitter): x.com/amc_sante
YouTube: www.youtube.com/channel/UCHz
 6DECOocsjIbDJtpK0zvw
Description: Seeks to improve medical care for persons living in Canada. **Publications:** Strategy: The Financial Digest for Physicians (Monthly); Humane Medicine (Quarterly); Mediscan (3/year); Canadian Medical Association Journal (CMAJ) (Annual); Journal of Psychiatry and Neuroscience (JPN) (Bimonthly); CMA News (Biweekly); Canadian Association of Radiologists Journal (Quarterly). **Geographic Preference:** National.

25649 ■ Canadian Academy of Periodontology (CAP) [Academie Canadienne de Parodontologie]
No. 201 - 1815 Alta Vista Dr.
Ottawa, ON, Canada K1G 3Y6
Ph: (613)523-9800
Fax: (613)523-1968
Co. E-mail: info@cap-acp.ca
URL: http://www.cap-acp.ca/en/home.html
Contact: Dr. Omid Kiarash, President
E-mail: president@cap-acp.ca
Description: Promotes advancement in the practice and teaching of periodontology. Conducts continuing professional education courses for members. Maintains speakers' bureau. **Founded:** 1955. **Publications:** CAPsule. **Geographic Preference:** National.

25650 ■ Canadian Association of Gerontology (CAG) [Association canadienne de gerontologie]
c/o Dept of Occupational Science & Occupational
 Therapy
University of Toronto
500 University Ave.
Toronto, ON, Canada M5G 1V7
Co. E-mail: contact@cagacg.ca
URL: http://cagacg.ca
Contact: Brad A. Meisner, President
E-mail: meisnerb@yorku.ca
Facebook: www.facebook.com/CdnAssocGero
Linkedin: www.linkedin.com/company/canadian
 -association-on-gerontology
X (Twitter): x.com/cagacg
YouTube: www.youtube.com/channel/UC_Gv
 4_8uRuM0Rk3crZg4epg
Description: An interdisciplinary scientific and educational association principally engaged in the collection and dissemination of research and information regarding aging. The organization's members comprise health care professionals, researchers, academics, administrators, governmental representatives, national organization executives, students, and seniors. **Founded:** 1971. **Publications:** CAG Newsletter (Quarterly); Canadian Journal on Aging (CJA) (Quarterly). **Educational Activities:** Canadian Association on Gerontology Annual Scientific and Educational Meeting. **Awards:** Recognition Award for Excellence in Student Mentoring: In Honour of Evelyn Shapiro (Biennial); Recognition Award for Excellence in Longitudinal Research: In Honour of Betty Havens (Biennial); Schlegel-UW RIA Scholarship (Annual); Donald Menzies Bursary Award (Annual); Margery Boyce Bursary Award (Irregular); CAG Award for Contribution to Gerontology (Annual); CAG Distinguished Member Award (Annual); CAG Honorary Member (Annual); Margery Boyce Bursary (Irregular); CAG Award for Contribution to Gerontology (Irregular); CAG Distinguished Member Award (Annual); CAG Honorary Member (Annual); Margery Boyce Bursary (Irregular). **Geographic Preference:** National.

25651 ■ Canadian Cardiovascular Society (CCS) [Societe Canadienne de Cardiologie]
150 Elgin St., Ste. 1000
Ottawa, ON, Canada K2P 1L4
Ph: (613)569-3407
Free: 877-569-3407
Co. E-mail: info@ccs.ca
URL: http://ccs.ca
Contact: Dr. Carolyn Pullen, Chief Executive Officer
E-mail: pullen@ccs.ca
Facebook: www.facebook.com/SCC.CCS.ca
Linkedin: www.linkedin.com/company/canadian-car
 diovascular-society
X (Twitter): x.com/SCC_CCS
YouTube: www.youtube.com/user/CdnCardioSociety
Description: Physicians, surgeons, and scientists practicing or conducting research in cardiology and related fields. Works to advance the cardiovascular health and care of Canadians through leadership on professional development, advocacy, and the promotion, dissemination of research. **Founded:** 1947. **Publications:** The Canadian Journal of Cardiology: The Official Journal of the Canadian Cardiovascular Society (CJC) (Monthly); The Canadian Journal of Cardiology (Monthly); CCS News. **Educational Activities:** Canadian Cardiovascular Congress (Annual). **Awards:** Research Achievement (Annual); Dr. Harold N. Segall Award of Merit (Annual); Dr. Robert E. Beamish Award (Annual); Research Achievement Award (Annual); CCS Achievement Award (Annual); CCS Distinguished Teacher Award (Annual); Dr. Harold N. Segall Award of Merit (Annual); CCS Trainee Research Award (TRA) (Annual); CCS Trainee Excellence in Education Award (Annual); CCS Young Investigator Award (YIA) (Annual). **Geographic Preference:** National.

25652 ■ Canadian College of Health Leaders (CCHL) - Library [College Canadien des Leaders en Sante]
150 Isabella, Ste. 1102
Ottawa, ON, Canada K1S 1V7
Ph: (613)235-7218
Free: 800-363-9056
Fax: (613)235-5451
Co. E-mail: info@cchl-ccls.ca
URL: http://www.cchl-ccls.ca
Contact: Alain Doucet, President
E-mail: adoucet@cchl-ccls.ca
Facebook: www.facebook.com/CCHL.National
Linkedin: www.linkedin.com/company/canadian-col
 lege-of-health-leaders
X (Twitter): x.com/CCHL_CCLS
YouTube: www.youtube.com/user/HealthLea
 dersCanada
Description: Serves health service executives in Canada. Offers a forum for the exchange of ideas and information, a career network, and professional development opportunities. **Scope:** Leadership. **Founded:** 1970. **Holdings:** Figures not available. **Publications:** Healthcare Management Forum (HMF) (Bimonthly); Healthcare Management Forum (Bimonthly). **Educational Activities:** Canada West Health Leaders Conference (Annual). **Awards:** Robert Zed Young Health Leader Award (Annual); CCHL-CCLS Quality of Life Award (Annual); Robert Wood Johnson Award (Annual); CCHL/CCLS 3M Health Care Quality Team Awards (Annual). **Geographic Preference:** National.

25653 ■ Canadian Dermatology Association (CDA) [Association Canadienne de Dermatologie (ACD)]
320 March Rd., Ste. 400
Ottawa, ON, Canada K2K 2E3
Ph: (613)738-1748
Free: 800-267-3376
Fax: (613)738-4695
Co. E-mail: info@dermatology.ca
URL: http://www.dermatology.ca
Contact: Dr. Jennifer Beecker, President
Facebook: www.facebook.com/CdnDermatology
Linkedin: www.linkedin.com/company/canadian
 -dermatology-association
X (Twitter): x.com/cdndermatology
Instagram: www.instagram.com/canadianderma
 tologyassociation
YouTube: www.youtube.com/user/canadianderma
 tology
Description: Promotes continuing education programs in dermatology. Provides public education program on skin cancer prevention. Holds an annual National Sun Awareness Week. **Founded:** 1925. **Publications:** Journal of Cutaneous Medicine and Surgery (JCMS) (Bimonthly); Membership and Corporate Directory (Annual). **Educational Activities:** CDA Annual Conference (Annual). **Awards:** Barney Usher Award (Annual); CDA Award of Merit (Annual); Barney Usher Research Award in Dermatology; CDA President's Cup (Annual); CDA Young Dermatologists' Volunteer Award (Annual); CDA Award of Honour (Annual); CDA Public Education Awards (Annual). **Geographic Preference:** National.

25654 ■ *Canadian Family Physician (CFP)*
2630 Skymark Ave.
Mississauga, ON, Canada L4W 5A4
Ph: (905)629-0900
Free: 800-387-6197
Fax: (905)629-0893
Co. E-mail: education@cfpc.ca
URL: http://www.cfp.ca/content/AboutCollege
Contact: Dr. Paul Sawchuk, President
URL(s): www.cfp.ca
Linkedin: www.linkedin.com/showcase/canadian
 -family-physician
Instagram: www.instagram.com/cfpjournal
Ed: Nicholas Pimlott. **Released:** Monthly; 12X per year. **Price:** $20, U.S.; $25, Other countries; C$412, Institutions, Canada for 2 yr.; C$15, Canada for single issue; C$229, Institutions, Canada for per yr.; C$165, Individuals for per yr.; $229, Individuals for United States & Mexico per yr.; $269, Institutions for United States & Mexico per yr.; $726, Institutions for United States & Mexico 3 years; $618, Individuals for United States & Mexico 3 yr.; C$110, Individuals for Canadian physician per yr.; C$198, Individuals for Canadian physician 2 yr.; C$297, Individuals for Canadian physician 3 yr.; C$445, Individuals for Canada (other) 3 yr.; $412, Individuals for US & Mexico 2 yr.; $484, Institutions for US & Mexico 2 yr.; $269, Individuals for Overseas per yr.; $299, Institutions for Overseas 1 years; $538, Institutions for Overseas 2 years; $484, Individuals for Overseas 2 yr.; $726, Individuals for Overseas 3 yr.; C$618, Institutions, Canada for Canada 3 yr.; $807, Institutions, other countries for per 3 years. **Description:** Peer-reviewed journal of family medicine (English and French). **Availability:** Print; PDF; Online.

25655 ■ *Canadian Journal on Aging (CJA)*
c/o Dept of Occupational Science & Occupational
 Therapy
University of Toronto
500 University Ave.
Toronto, ON, Canada M5G 1V7
Co. E-mail: contact@cagacg.ca
URL: http://cagacg.ca
Contact: Brad A. Meisner, President
E-mail: meisnerb@yorku.ca
URL(s): cagacg.ca/cjawww.cambridge.org/core/
 journals/canadian-journal-on-aging-la-revue-cana
 dienne-du-vieillissement#
X (Twitter): x.com/cjarcv

Small Business Sourcebook • 42nd Edition

Released: Quarterly **Price:** $303, Institutions for online only US. **Description:** Features manuscripts on aging concerned with biology, educational gerontology, health sciences, psychology and social policy. **Availability:** Print; PDF; Download; Online.

25656 ■ The Canadian Journal of Cardiology
150 Elgin St., Ste. 1000
Ottawa, ON, Canada K2P 1L4
Ph: (613)569-3407
Free: 877-569-3407
Co. E-mail: info@ccs.ca
URL: http://ccs.ca
Contact: Dr. Carolyn Pullen, Chief Executive Officer
E-mail: pullen@ccs.ca
URL(s): onlinecjc.ca
X (Twitter): twitter.com/CJCJournals
Released: Monthly **Price:** $361, for online international; $356, U.S. for online only Us; $306, Canada for online Canada. **Availability:** Print; Download; PDF; Online.

25657 ■ The Canadian Journal of Psychiatry (CJP)
2455 Teller Rd.
Thousand Oaks, CA 91320
Contact: Tracey Ozmina, President
URL(s): www.cpa-apc.org/clinical-resources/the-canadian-journal-of-psychiatryjournals.sagepub.com/home/CPA
Released: Monthly **Price:** $370, Institutions for institutional backfile purchase, e-access; $367, Institutions for subscription, e-access; $329, Individuals for print and online; $432, Institutions for print & e-access; $475, Institutions for print and online; $36, Individuals for print single; $39, Institutions for print single; $410, Institutions for online only; $423, Institutions for print only. **Description:** Peer-reviewed journal reporting on clinical developments in the field of psychiatry. Published in association between SAGE and the Canadian Psychiatric Association. **Availability:** Print; PDF; Download; Online.

25658 ■ Canadian Medical Protective Association (CMPA) [Association Canadienne de Protection Medicale]
875 Carling Ave.
Ottawa, ON, Canada K1S 5P1
Ph: (613)725-2000
Free: 877-763-1300
Fax: (613)725-1300
Co. E-mail: inquiries@cmpa.org
URL: http://www.cmpa-acpm.ca/en/home
Contact: Jean-Hugues Brossard, President
E-mail: jbrossard@cmpa.org
X (Twitter): x.com/CMPAmembers
YouTube: www.youtube.com/user/cmpamembers
Description: Defense organization for physicians practicing in Canada. **Founded:** 1901. **Geographic Preference:** National.

25659 ■ Canadian Mental Health Association (CMHA)
250 Dundas St. W Ste. 500
Toronto, ON, Canada M5T 2Z5
Ph: (416)646-5557
Co. E-mail: info@cmha.ca
URL: http://cmha.ca
Contact: Margaret Eaton, Chief Executive Officer
Facebook: www.facebook.com/CMHA.ACSM.National
Linkedin: www.linkedin.com/company/canadian-mental-health-association
X (Twitter): twitter.com/CMHA_NTL
Instagram: www.instagram.com/cmhanational
YouTube: www.youtube.com/user/cmhanational
Description: Serves as a social advocate to encourage public action to strengthen community mental health services. Organizes and operates grass roots programs to help people whose mental health is at risk to make use of the services available to them. **Founded:** 1918. **Awards:** CMHA Workplace Excellence Award (Annual). **Geographic Preference:** National.

25660 ■ Canadian Paediatric Society (CPS) [Societe canadienne de pediatrie]
2305 St. Laurent Blvd., Ste. 100
Ottawa, ON, Canada K1G 4J8
Ph: (613)526-9397
Fax: (613)526-3332
Co. E-mail: info@cps.ca
URL: http://cps.ca
Contact: Mark Feldman, President
Facebook: www.facebook.com/CanPaedSociety
X (Twitter): x.com/canpaedsociety
YouTube: www.youtube.com/user/CanPaedSociety
Description: Professional organization of pediatricians serving on committees and sections focusing on adolescent medicine, bioethics, drug therapy, hazardous substances, fetus and newborns, Indian and Inuit health, infectious disease and immunization, injury prevention, pediatric practice, nutrition, and psychological pediatrics. **Founded:** 1922. **Publications:** Clinical Practice Guidelines (Periodic); Paediatrics & Child Health (8/year); CPS News (Semiannual). **Awards:** Noni MacDonald Award (Annual); Alan Ross Award (Annual); Alan Ross Award (Annual); Geoffrey C. Robinson Award (Biennial); Career Research Award (Biennial). **Geographic Preference:** National.

25661 ■ Canadian Pain Society (CPS)
Ste., 800 234 - 5149 Country Hills Boulevard N.W.
Calgary, AB, Canada L3R 9X9
Ph: (365)873-2320
Fax: (905)415-0071
Co. E-mail: office@canadianpainsociety.ca
URL: http://www.canadianpainsociety.ca
Contact: Dr. John Xavier Pereira, President
Facebook: www.facebook.com/CanadianPain
Linkedin: www.linkedin.com/check
X (Twitter): x.com/CanadianPain
Instagram: www.instagram.com/canadianpainsociety
Description: Health care professionals and medical and pharmaceutical researchers with an interest in pain and its alleviation. Fosters research on the causes of pain; seeks improved methods of pain management. Facilitates communication and cooperation among pain researchers and clinicians; sponsors educational and research programs. **Founded:** 1982. **Publications:** Canadian Journal of Pain (Annual); CPS Newsletter (Quarterly); Pain Research and Management. **Awards:** Canadian Pain Society Post-Doctoral Fellowship Awards; CPS Excellence in Interprofessional Pain Education Awards (Annual); CPS Interprofessional Nursing Project Awards (Annual); CPS Knowledge Translation Research Awards (Annual); CPS Nursing Excellence in Pain Management Awards (Annual); CPS Nursing Research and Education Awards (Annual); CPS Outstanding Pain Mentorship Award (Annual); CPS Trainee Research Awards (Annual). **Geographic Preference:** National.

25662 ■ Canadian Psychiatric Association (CPA)
141 Laurier Ave. W, Ste. 701
Ottawa, ON, Canada K1P 5J3
Ph: (613)234-2815
Free: 800-267-1555
Fax: (613)234-9857
Co. E-mail: cpa@cpa-apc.org
URL: http://www.cpa-apc.org
Contact: Dr. Pamela Forsythe, Chairman
Facebook: www.facebook.com/cpa.apc
Linkedin: www.linkedin.com/company/canadian-psychiatric-association
X (Twitter): x.com/CPA_APC
Description: Works to improve mental health and psychiatric care delivery systems in Canada. Fosters high standards among Canadian psychiatrists; promotes continuing education of members; encourages and participates in educational programs for patient care providers; promotes research into psychiatric disorders; advocates for mental health system reforms and on related issues affecting the practice of psychiatry. **Founded:** 1951. **Publications:** The Canadian Journal of Psychiatry (CJP) (Monthly). **Educational Activities:** Canadian Psychiatric Association Annual Conference (Annual). **Awards:** Paul Patterson Education Leadership Award (Annual); C.A. Roberts Award for Clinical Leadership (Annual); J.M. Cleghorn Award for Excellence and Leadership in Clinical Research (Annual); Paul Patterson Innovation in Education Leadership Award (Annual); CPA President's Commendation (Annual); CPA Special Recognition Awards (Irregular); CPA Honorary Members (Periodic); Fellows of the Canadian Psychiatric Association (FCPA) (Annual); Alex Leighton CPA-CAPE Award in Psychiatric Epidemiology (Annual); Joint CPA-COPCE Award for the Most Outstanding Continuing Education Activity in Psychiatry in Canada (Annual); R.O. Jones Awards for Best Papers (Annual); CPA Awards for Best Posters (Annual). **Geographic Preference:** National.

25663 ■ Canadian Public Health Association (CPHA) [Association Canadienne de Sante Publique]
404-1525 Carling Ave.
Ottawa, ON, Canada K1Z 8R9
Ph: (613)725-3769
Co. E-mail: info@cpha.ca
URL: http://www.cpha.ca
Contact: Ian Culbert, Executive Director
E-mail: iculbert@cpha.ca
Facebook: www.facebook.com/cpha.acsp
Linkedin: www.linkedin.com/company/cpha-acsp
X (Twitter): x.com/CPHA_ACSP
Instagram: www.instagram.com/cpha_acsp
YouTube: www.youtube.com/channel/UC_SDgqaCLW1YKWKYqlO4evg
Description: Advises decision-makers about public health system reform in Canada. Promotes health equity and social justice. Raises awareness of growing public health issues. **Founded:** 1910. **Publications:** CPHA Health Digest (Quarterly); Canadian Journal of Public Health (Bimonthly). **Educational Activities:** Public Health (Annual). **Awards:** CPHA National Public Health Hero Award (Annual); R.D. Defries Award (Annual); R.D. Defries Award (Annual); CPHA Honorary Life Membership (Annual); CPHA Certificate of Merit (Annual); Ron Draper Health Promotion Award (Annual); CPHA International Award (Irregular); Dr. John Hastings Student Award (Annual). **Geographic Preference:** National.

25664 ■ Catholic Health Alliance (CHAC) - Library
96 Empress Ave.
Ottawa, ON, Canada K1R 7G3
Ph: (613)567-1200
URL: http://www.chac.ca/en
Contact: Sara John Fowler, Chairman
Description: Represents the interests of Catholic Hospitals and nursing homes in Canada. Works to administer Christian principles within the Canadian healthcare system. Fosters competent and efficient health care services. **Scope:** Healthcare; ethics; medicine; pastoral care. **Services:** Library not open to the public. **Founded:** 1939. **Holdings:** 6,000 books; periodicals. **Publications:** Catholic Health Association of Canada--Membership Directory; CHAC Info Newsletter (Quarterly). **Geographic Preference:** National.

25665 ■ Clinical and Investigative Medicine (CIM)
114 Cheyenne Way
Ottawa, ON, Canada K2J 0E9
Free: 877-968-9449
Fax: (613)491-0073
Co. E-mail: info@csci-scrc.ca
URL: http://csci-scrc.ca
Contact: Dr. Nicola L. Jones, President
URL(s): utpjournals.press/loi/cim
Ed: Dr. Jonathan Angel. **Released:** Quarterly; vol 47 no.1 2024. **Price:** $250, Institutions for online one year; $525, Institutions for online volume 47; $5,831.04, Institutions for online only; $7,236.69, Institutions for print and online. **Description:** Journal covering the field of basic and applied clinical research. Official publication of the Canadian Society for Clinical Investigation (English and French). **Availability:** Print; PDF; Online.

GENERAL SMALL BUSINESS TOPICS

25666 ■ Coalition Canadienne de la Santé [Canadian Health Coalition (CHC)]
116 Albert St., Ste. 300
 Ottawa, ON, Canada K1P 5G3
Ph: (613)699-9898
Co. E-mail: hello@healthcoalition.ca
URL: http://www.healthcoalition.ca
Contact: Rita Morbia, Treasurer
Facebook: www.facebook.com/CanadianHealthCoalition
X (Twitter): x.com/healthcoalition
Description: Individuals and organizations with an interest in health care. Promotes increased availability and quality of health services. Monitors the performance of health care facilities and services and makes recommendations for their improvement. **Founded:** 1979. **Geographic Preference:** National.

25667 ■ College of Family Physicians of Canada - Ontario Chapter (CFPC) [College des Medecins de Famille du Canada]
400 University Ave., Ste. 2100
 Toronto, ON, Canada M5G 1S5
Ph: (416)867-9646
Free: 800-670-6237
Fax: (416)867-9990
URL: http://www.ontariofamilyphysicians.ca
Contact: Dr. Liz Muggah, President
URL(s): www.cfpc.ca/en/provincial-chapters
Linkedin: www.linkedin.com/company/ocfp
X (Twitter): x.com/OntarioCollege
Description: National medical association of family physicians and general practitioners. **Founded:** 1954. **Publications:** *CFPC-Liaison Newsletter* (Quarterly); *Self-Evaluation*. **Geographic Preference:** National.

25668 ■ Consumer Healthcare Products Association (CHPA)
1625 Eye St. NW, Ste. 600
 Washington, DC 20006
Ph: (202)429-9260
Fax: (202)223-6835
URL: http://www.chpa.org
Contact: Scott Melville, President
E-mail: melville@chpa.org
Linkedin: www.linkedin.com/company/chpa
X (Twitter): x.com/CHPA
YouTube: www.youtube.com/channel/UCfDdgJ8Vzfr8Ovt_V6Rsb-A
Description: Marketers of nonprescription medicines and dietary supplements, which are packaged and available over-the-counter; associate members include suppliers, consultants, research and testing laboratories, advertising agencies and media. Obtains and disseminates business, legislative, regulatory and scientific information; conducts voluntary labeling review service to assist members in complying with laws and regulations. **Founded:** 1881. **Publications:** *OTC Connections* (Quarterly); *CHPA State Legislative News Bulletin* (Periodic). **Geographic Preference:** National.

25669 ■ *CPS News*
2305 St. Laurent Blvd., Ste. 100
 Ottawa, ON, Canada K1G 4J8
Ph: (613)526-9397
Fax: (613)526-3332
Co. E-mail: info@cps.ca
URL: http://cps.ca
Contact: Mark Feldman, President
URL(s): cps.ca/en/publications/cps-news
Released: Semiannual; Spring/Summer and Fall/Winter. **Description:** Provides news of society activities and advocacy efforts, news of members, and news from provincial paediatric associations. Offers section and liaison reports and information on upcoming meetings. **Availability:** Print; PDF; Online.

25670 ■ Epilepsy Canada (EC) - Library [Epilepsie Canada]
3250 Bloor St. W, E Tower, Ste. 600
 Toronto, ON, Canada M8X 2X9
Ph: (647)775-1611
Free: 877-734-0873
Co. E-mail: epilepsy@epilepsy.ca
URL: http://www.epilepsy.ca

Contact: Gary Collins, Chief Executive Officer
E-mail: garycollins@epilepsy.ca
Facebook: www.facebook.com/EpilepsyCanada
Instagram: www.instagram.com/epilepsycanada
Description: Seeks to improve the quality of life of people affected by epilepsy through promotion and support of research. **Scope:** Epilepsy. **Founded:** 1966. **Holdings:** Figures not available. **Publications:** *Lumina* (Semiannual); *Lumina Newsletter* (Semiannual). **Awards:** Epilepsy Canada Postdoctoral Research Award (Annual). **Geographic Preference:** National.

25671 ■ Foundation of the National Student Nurses Association (FNSNA)
45 Main St., Ste. 606
 Brooklyn, NY 11201
Ph: (718)210-0705
Fax: (718)797-1186
Co. E-mail: fnsna@forevernursing.org
URL: http://www.forevernursing.org
Contact: Carol Toussie Weingarten, President
Facebook: www.facebook.com/FNSNA
X (Twitter): x.com/forevernursing
Instagram: www.instagram.com/nsnainc
Description: Association for the national student nurses. **Founded:** 1969. **Awards:** Career Mobility Scholarships (Annual); Breakthrough to Nursing Scholarships (Annual).

25672 ■ Health Information Resource Center (HIRC)
328 W Lincoln Ave., Ste. 10
 Libertyville, IL 60048-2725
Ph: (847)816-8660
Free: 800-828-8225
Fax: (847)816-8662
Co. E-mail: info@healthawards.com
URL: http://healthawards.com/dha/aboutus.html
Description: Clearinghouse for consumer health information. Provides information and referral services to many organizations that use or produce consumer health information materials. Conducts market research. **Founded:** 1993. **Publications:** *Health and Medical Media: The Comprehensive Sourcebook of Media Contacts for Healthcare Professionals* (Biennial). **Awards:** HIRC National Health Information Awards (Annual); HIRC Digital Health Awards (Annual). **Geographic Preference:** National.

25673 ■ *Healthcare Management Forum*
150 Isabella, Ste. 1102
 Ottawa, ON, Canada K1S 1V7
Ph: (613)235-7218
Free: 800-363-9056
Fax: (613)235-5451
Co. E-mail: info@cchl-ccls.ca
URL: http://www.cchl-ccls.ca
Contact: Alain Doucet, President
E-mail: adoucet@cchl-ccls.ca
URL(s): cchl-ccls.ca/resource/healthcare-management-forum-may-editionjournals.sagepub.com/home/hmf
Ed: David Persaud. **Released:** Bimonthly; current volume: 37 issue: 4. **Price:** $290, Institutions for back file purchase, e-access (content through 1998); $108, Individuals for e-access; $290, Institutions for e-access. **Description:** Contains articles on innovations in health services. **Availability:** Print; PDF; Online.

25674 ■ HealthCareCAN
17 York St., Ste. 100
 Ottawa, ON, Canada K1N 5S7
Ph: (613)241-8005
Free: 855-236-0213
Fax: (613)241-5055
Co. E-mail: info@healthcarecan.ca
URL: http://www.healthcarecan.ca
Contact: Jessica Schierbeck, Director
E-mail: jschierbeck@healthcarecan.ca
Facebook: www.facebook.com/healthcarecan.soinssantecan
Linkedin: www.linkedin.com/company/healthcarecan
X (Twitter): x.com/HealthCareCAN

Description: Foster informed and continuous, results-oriented discovery and innovation across the continuum of healthcare. **Publications:** *Guide to Canadian Healthcare Facilities* (Annual); *CHA Guide to Canadian Healthcare Facilities*; *Leadership in Health Services* (Bimonthly). **Awards:** Marion Stephenson Award (Annual). **Geographic Preference:** National.

25675 ■ Independent Visually Impaired Entrepreneurs (IVIE)
2121 Scott Rd., Ste. 105
 Burbank, CA 91504
Ph: (818)238-9321
Co. E-mail: abazyn@bazyncommunications.com
URL: http://ivie-acb.org
Contact: Ardis Bazyn, President
E-mail: abazyn@bazyncommunications.com
Description: Blind and visually impaired people who own or operate small businesses. Seeks to: broaden vocational opportunities in business for the blind and visually impaired; improve rehabilitational facilities for all types of business enterprises; publicize capabilities of the blind and visually impaired. Maintains speakers' bureau. **Founded:** 1980. **Publications:** *IVIE Motivator* (Quarterly). **Educational Activities:** Independent Visually Impaired Enterprisers Convention (Annual). **Geographic Preference:** National.

25676 ■ Infection Prevention and Control Canada (IPAC) [Prévention et contrôle des Infections Canada (PCI)]
67 Bergman Cres.
 Winnipeg, MB, Canada R3R 1Y9
Ph: (204)897-5990
Free: 866-999-7111
Fax: (204)895-9595
Co. E-mail: info@ipac-canada.org
URL: http://ipac-canada.org
Contact: Zahir Hirji, President
Facebook: www.facebook.com/IPACCanada
Linkedin: www.linkedin.com/company/ipac-canada
X (Twitter): twitter.com/IPACCanada
YouTube: www.youtube.com/c/IPACCanadaVideos
Description: Seeks to improve the health of Canadians by promoting excellence in the practice of infection prevention and control. Serves as a clearinghouse on infection control standards and practices; conducts continuing professional education programs for members. **Founded:** 1976. **Publications:** *Canadian Journal of Infection Control* (Quarterly). **Educational Activities:** National Education Conference (Annual). **Geographic Preference:** National.

25677 ■ Infirmieres et Infirmiers en Santé Communautaire du Canada (IISCC) [Community Health Nurses Association of Canada (CHNC)]
632 Hugel Ave.
 Midland, ON, Canada L4R 1W7
Ph: (705)527-1014
Co. E-mail: info@chnc.ca
URL: http://www.chnc.ca/en
Contact: Donna Jepsen, President
Linkedin: www.linkedin.com/company/chnc-iiscc
X (Twitter): x.com/chnc_iiscc
Instagram: www.instagram.com/chnc_iiscc
YouTube: www.youtube.com/channel/UCFvfhKz2oU_xkjV-tYhVVJg
Description: Seeks to advance the practice of community health nursing and enhance members' professional status. **Founded:** 1987. **Geographic Preference:** National.

25678 ■ *International Perspectives in Public Health*
292 Dupont
 Toronto, ON, Canada M5R 0A2
Ph: (647)931-0513
URL: http://concernforhealth.org
Contact: Dr. Marion Odell, President
Released: Annual **Availability:** Print.

25679 ■ *Journal of Cutaneous Medicine and Surgery (JCMS)*
320 March Rd., Ste. 400
 Ottawa, ON, Canada K2K 2E3

Ph: (613)738-1748
Free: 800-267-3376
Fax: (613)738-4695
Co. E-mail: info@dermatology.ca
URL: http://www.dermatology.ca
Contact: Dr. Jennifer Beecker, President
URL(s): dermatology.ca/public-patients/resources/ jcmsjournals.sagepub.com/home/cms
Released: Bimonthly **Price:** $164, Institutions for Single print Issue; $83, Individuals for Single print Issue; $331, Individuals for subscription, e-access; $381, Individuals for subscription, print only; $389, Individuals for subscription, combined (print & e-access); $772, Institutions for back file purchase, e-access (content through 1998); $774, Institutions for subscription, e-access; $893, Institutions for subscription, print only; $865, Institutions for subscription & back file lease, e-access plus back file (all online content); $911, Institutions for subscription, combined (print & e-access); $1,002, Institutions for subscription & back file lease, combined plus back file (current volume print & all online content). **Description:** Provides original scientific writings, as well as a complete critical review of the dermatology literature for clinicians, trainees, and academicians. **Availability:** Print; Download; PDF; Online.

25680 ■ Louisiana Public Health Association (LPHA)
7515 Jefferson Hwy. 161
Baton Rouge, LA 70806
Ph: (225)324-6989
Co. E-mail: busmgr.lpha@yahoo.com
URL: http://lpha.org
Contact: Knesha Rose-Davison, President
Facebook: www.facebook.com/lahealthfan
X (Twitter): x.com/lahealthfan
Instagram: www.instagram.com/lahealthfan
Description: Aims to promote health in the state of Louisiana. Fosters acquaintances and mutual understanding among persons interested in public health. Supports and sponsoring movements and policies tending to raise personnel standards, secure adequate income of workers and promote security and tenure. **Founded:** 1948. **Awards:** LPHA Scholarships (Annual); LPHA Founders Award (Annual); Louise McFarland Award for Excellence in Public Health Communication (Annual); LPHA Members Award (Annual); LPHA Meritorious Award (Annual); LPHA Public Service Award (Annual). **Geographic Preference:** State.

25681 ■ National Association of Social Workers (NASW) - Library
750 1st St. NE, Ste. 800
Washington, DC 20002
Free: 800-742-4089
Fax: (202)336-8313
Co. E-mail: membership@socialworkers.org
URL: http://www.socialworkers.org
Contact: Dr. Anthony Estreet, Chief Executive Officer
Facebook: www.facebook.com/nawsocialworkers
X (Twitter): x.com/nasw
Instagram: www.instagram.com/nawsocialworkers
YouTube: www.youtube.com/user/socialworkers
Description: Regular members are persons who hold a minimum of a baccalaureate degree in social work. Associate members are persons engaged in social work who have a baccalaureate degree in another field. Student members are persons enrolled in accredited (by the Council on Social Work Education) graduate or undergraduate social work programs. Works to create professional standards for social work practice; advocate sound public social policies through political and legislative action; provide a wide range of membership services, including continuing education opportunities and an extensive professional program. Operates National Center for Social Policy and Practice. Conducts research; compiles statistics. **Scope:** Social work. **Founded:** 1955. **Holdings:** Figures not available. **Publications:** Disabilities; Pain; Health & Social Work: A Journal of the National Association of Social Workers (Quarterly); Social Work: Journal of the National Association of Social Workers (Quarterly); Children & Schools: A Journal of the National Association of Social Workers (Quarterly); Social Work Research (Quarterly); Choices: Careers in Social Work Pamphlet; Your New Career in Social Work: You've Got the Power!; Gangs and Youth: A Guide for Social Workers; School Social Workers: Enhancing School Success for Students; Starting a Private Practice; There Are Many Doors to Recovery: Social Workers Can Be the Key; Gerontological Social Workers: Helping Older Adults Maximize Their Dignity, Health, and Independence; Making a Critical Difference: Social Workers in Child Welfare; Baccalaureate Social Workers: Equipped with Skills, Knowledge, and Values Essential in Social Work Practice; If You're Right for the Job, It's the Best Job in the World Pamphlet; Youth Bullying...How Social Workers Can Help; Clinical Social Workers in Private Practice: A Reference Guide; Retiring or Closing a Private Practice?: Tips to Help You Along the Way; Gerontological Social Work: Aging in a New Age; Social Work and International Development: A Global Role for Social Workers; Children & Schools (Quarterly); NASW News (Monthly); Social Work Abstracts (SWAB) (Quarterly); International Social Work Fact Sheet; Social Justice Fact Sheet; School Social Work Fact Sheet; Aging Fact Sheet; Children and Families Fact Sheet; Poverty Fact Sheet; Advocacy and Organizing Fact Sheet; Mind and Spirit; Mind and Spirit: Addictions; Mind and Spirit: About Addictions; Mind and Spirit: Alcohol and Addiction Trends; Addiction Tip Sheet--Addiction and Weight Loss Surgery: A Social Worker's Perspective; Addiction Tip Sheet: Six Skills for Families and Significant Others Who Are affected by Someone Who Abuses Substances Fact Sheet; Addictions Tip Sheet: What To Do If Your Partner Is Alcoholic; Addictions Tip Sheet: Understanding Tobacco Addiction; Addictions Tip Sheet: Quitting Tobacco: Where to Get Help; Gambling Risks; Mind and Spirit: Anxiety; Anxiety Tip Sheet: Disaster Mental Health; Anxiety Tip Sheet: When Terrorism Strikes--What Parents Can Do; Anxiety Tip Sheet: About Anxiety Attacks; Anxiety Tip Sheet: The Value of Self Talk; Mind and Spirit: Attention Deficit and Hyperactivity Disorder Fact Sheet; Attention-Deficit Hyperactivity Disorder Tip Sheet for Parents; Mind and Spirit: Depression Fact Sheet; Depression Tip Sheet: Depression--Your Options: Women, Depression and Cognitive Therapy; Depression--Tip Sheet: Manage Your Depression With a Self-Help Kit; Depression Tip Sheet: Why You Might Have Trouble Sleeping; Depression Tip Sheet--The Various Types and Symptoms of Depression; Depression Tip Sheet--The Symptoms of Bipolar Disorder; Mind and Spirit: Eating Disorders; Eating Disorders Tip Sheet--Taking Better Care of Your Body; Mind and Spirit: Grief and Loss Fact Sheet; Grief and Loss Tip Sheet: Loss After Loss: Dealing With the Death of Someone for Whom You Have Provided Care; Grief and Loss Tip Sheet: Sudden Death in Disasters and Accidents; Grief and Loss Tip Sheet: Understanding Adolescents' and Children's Responses to the Loss; Grief and Loss Tip Sheet: Understanding Professional Grief; Grief and Loss Tip Sheet: Understanding Acute Grief; Grief and Loss Tip Sheet: Writing a Child's Obituary: What Do I Say?; Grief and Loss--Tips on Coping With Grief; Grief and Loss Tip Sheet: Supporting Children Through Grief; Grief and Loss Tip Sheet: Recovering from High Profile Traumatic Events; Obsessions and Compulsions; Obsessions and Compulsions--Tip Sheet: Buy Now and Pay Later: The Hidden Problem of Compulsive Shopping; Obsessions and Compulsions Tip Sheet; Relationships; Relationship Tip Sheet: Couples Therapy for Lesbians and Gay Men: The Basics; Relationship Tip Sheet: How Infertility Affects Couples; Relationship Tip Sheet: Healing from Infidelity; Relationship Tip Sheet: Choosing a Marital Therapist; Relationship Tip Sheet: How Couples Can Keep Their Relationship Together After Their Child Is Diagnosed with a Serious Illness; Stress Management; Stress Management Tip Sheet: Forgiving Ourselves and Others: An Essential Part of Good Stress Management; Stress Management Tip Sheet: Dealing with Stress; Stress Management Tip Sheet: The ABCs of Stress; Stress Management Tip Sheet: Calling a Crisis Hotline in Times of Disaster or Emergencies; Schizophrenia; Schizophrenia Tip Sheet: Symptoms of Schizophrenia; Schizophrenia Tip Sheet: Facts About Schizophrenia; Suicide Prevention; Suicide Prevention Tip Sheet: Suicide Warning Signs and Prevention Tips; Suicide Prevention Tip Sheet: Spotting the Warning Signs of Teen Suicide; Kids and Families; Adoptions and Foster Care Tip Sheet: Helping Children Find Permanence; Adoptions and Foster Care Tip Sheet; Early Childhood Development; Early Childhood Development Tip Sheet: How to Discipline an Angry Child; Early Childhood Development Tip Sheet: What's So Terrible About Being Two?; Early Childhood Development Tip Sheet: Fetal Alcohol Syndrome: What Everyone Should Know; Early Childhood Development Tip Sheet: Tips and Resources for Families Who Have a Child with a Congenital Heart Defect; Family Safety; Family Safety Tip Sheet: Recognizing the Signs of Domestic Violence; Family Safety Tip Sheet: Helping Children Cope with Traumatic Events; Healthy Parenting; Healthy Parenting Tip Sheet: Evaluating a Child Care Center; Healthy Parenting Tip Sheet: Parenting Adolescents: What Works; Healthy Parenting Tip Sheet: Helping Your Child Break Bad Habits; Healthy Parenting Tip Sheet: Preventing Teen Substance Use Disorders; Healthy Parenting Tip Sheet: The Importance of Being a Good Role Model: Parenting in Native Alaskan Villages; Schools and Communities; Schools and Communities Tip Sheet: Are You Anxious About Going Back to School?; Schools and Communities Tip Sheet: Teaching Children Financial Literacy; Schools and Communities Tip Sheet: Making Homework Manageable; Schools and Communities Tip Sheet: Tips for Parents Dealing with Bullying; Youth Development; Youth Development Tip Sheet: Tips for Families; Health and Wellness Fact Sheet; Understanding Cancer Fact Sheet; Cancer Tip Sheet: Chemobrain Cognitive Problems after Chemotherapy; Cancer Tip Sheet: Doctor, Can We Talk About Chemobrain?; Cancer Tip Sheet: Steel Magnolias and Cancer: How Women Survive the Crisis; Cancer Tip Sheet: Glossary of Terms and Definitions; Cancer Tip Sheet: Talking to Your Children About Cancer; Getting Through the Holidays: Tips for Cancer Survivors; Cancer Tip Sheet: Ask Tough Questions; About Family Genetics; When Is Genetic Testing Recommended?; NASW Register of Clinical Social Workers (Biennial); Encyclopedia of Social Work; The Family Acceptance Project's Studies of LGBT Youth; Helping Pre-Teens and Teens Navigate Their Social World; Risk Factors and Intervention Strategies for LGBT Youth; Understanding Teen Cliques; Adolescents and Depression; The Indian Child Welfare Act (ICWA) (ICWA); How Social Workers Help Struggling Teens; Youth Development Resources; Youth Development Services; Youth Development Current Trends; Veterans and Combat Stress; Spending Time in Foster Care: A Guide for Children; Help for Spouses of Combat Veterans With Post Traumatic Stress Disorder From People Who Know Fact Sheet; Options for Adoptions and Foster Care; Health Fact Sheet; Mental Health, SOW Fact Sheet; Diversity and Cultural Competence; Family Genetics Real Life Story--In Fighting Disorder, Family Stays Vigilant Fact Sheet; Early Childhood Development--How Social Workers Help Children With Emotional/Behavioral Problems; Early Childhood Development Resources; Early Childhood Development--How Do I Know if My Child Is Transgender?; Tantrums Getting the Better of You?; About Family Safety; About Domestic Homicide and Murder-Suicide; Parent-Youth Safe Driving Contract; Interpersonal Violence in the LGBTQ Community; What to Expect from a Self-Defense Class; Unprovoked Shootings, Violence and Possible Explanations; Violence Against Women in the United States; Violence in the American Workplace; Five Most Common Parenting Mistakes and Their Fixes; Healthy Parenting--How Social Workers Help Struggling Teens; Children and Divorce; Dealing With the Holiday Blues: A Note to Single Parents; Managing Children's Anger About Divorce or Separation; Practical Tips for LGBTQIA Parents Raising Teenagers; Pregnancy Loss: Healing the Invisible Loss; Slowing it Down: Parenting in an Age of Anxiety; Teaching Kids Patience; Three Questions About Troubled Teens; Raising Confident and Secure Children; Does Your Teen Need Counseling?; Helping Children of Prisoners; Theories About Insightful Parents and Secure Children; Parenting a Child With

GENERAL SMALL BUSINESS TOPICS

Special Needs: Understanding and Addressing the Emotional Dynamics; "Me-Time" for Moms and Fun Time for Kids; Preparing for In Vitro Fertilization: Emotional Considerations; Healthy Parenting Tip Sheet--How to Take a Breath and Raise a Kid with Confidence and Heart; Responsible Parenting Guidelines for Families in Transition; Tips To Help Single Moms Live Well on a Budget; Healthy Parenting Tip Sheet--Who Gets Custody of the School Play? Stepfamily Issues; Three Questions About Sending Your Child to Summer Camp; Teaching Kids Honesty; The Lost Art of Play; The Miscarriage Dilemma for Couples Today; Healthy Parenting Tip Sheet--Tips for Divorcing Parents Regarding Their Children; Tips for Single Parents; Cruelty Online: The Growing Problem of Cyberbullying; Helping Latino Immigrant Students Adjust: The Bienvenido Program; Schools and Communities--Current Trends in Social Work; Schools and Communities Real Life Story--Malicious Deeds: It Doesn't Take Physical Contact to Leave Scars Fact Sheet; Veterans Affairs Resources; Sleep Deprivation Affects Performance at School and Work; Death and Dying; Death and Dying Tip Sheet: Ask Tough Questions; Death and Dying Tip Sheet: Planning Your End of Life Care; Death and Dying Tip Sheet: A Positive Dying Experience; Death and Dying Tip Sheet: Advance Care Planning Tips; Disabilities Tip Sheet: An Uncommon Challenge: Tips for Parents; Disabilities Tip Sheet: Communicating With Disabled Individuals; Healthy Lifestyles; Healthy Lifestyles Tip Sheet: Five Ways to Get Moving: Fifty Ways to Keep Moving; Healthly Lifestyles Tip Sheet: Understanding Tobacco Addiction; Healthy Lifestyle Tip Sheet: Quitting Smoking: Where To Get Help; HIV/AIDS; HIV/AIDS Tip Sheet: Good Communication Is Good For Your Health; Living with Illness; Living with Illness Tip Sheet: How Couples Can Keep Their Relationship Together After Their Child Is Diagnosed with a Serious Illness; Living with Illness Tip Sheet: Talking With Children About a Parent's Serious Illness; Pain Tip Sheet: Arthritis, Exercise, and Treatment; Seniors and Aging; Advance Care Planning; Advance Care Planning Tip Sheet: Important Documentation; Alzheimer's Disease/Dementia; Alzheimer's Disease/Dementia Tip Sheet; Caregiving; Caregiving Tip Sheet: What to Consider in the Beginning; Residential Long-Term Care; Long Term Care Tip Sheet: How to Make Your Own Long-Term Care Decisions; Lifespan Planning; Lifespan Planning Tip Sheet; Vital Aging Real Life Story: Depression Is Common Among Elderly, Treatable Fact Sheet; Vital Aging Tip Sheet: Questions and Answers About Depression in Older Adults; Vital Aging Tip Sheet: Wise Use of Medications. **Educational Activities:** Delegate Assembly (Triennial). **Awards:** Jane B. Aron Doctoral Fellowship (Annual); Eileen Blackey Doctoral Fellowship (Annual); Consuelo W. Gosnell Memorial MSW Scholarship (Annual); Verne LaMarr Lyons Memorial Scholarship (Annual); NASW Lifetime Achievement Award (Biennial); NASW Public Citizen of the Year (Annual); NASW Social Worker of the Year (Annual). **Geographic Preference:** National.

25682 ■ North Carolina Association of Health Care Recruitment (NCAHCR)
520 Weycroft Grant Dr.
Cary, NC 27519
URL: http://ncahcr.org
Contact: Ram Upadhyaya, President
E-mail: ramesh.upadhyaya@ncdps.gov
Linkedin: www.linkedin.com/company/north-carolina-association-of-health-care-recruiters-ncahcr-
Description: Statewide professional association of healthcare recruiters and human resources professionals who support information sharing, education and networking. **Awards:** North Carolina Association of Health Care Recruiters Scholarship. **Geographic Preference:** National.

25683 ■ *Occupational Medicine*
2 St Andrews Pl.
London NW1 4LB, United Kingdom
Ph: 44 20 39104531
URL: http://www.som.org.uk
Contact: Nick Pahl, Chief Executive Officer
E-mail: nick.pahl@som.org.uk
URL(s): academic.oup.com/occmed
X (Twitter): x.com/journal_occmed
Instagram: www.instagram.com/journal.occmed
YouTube: www.youtube.com/channel/UCG2H2ymjNRpWddRkPywEEew
Ed: S. Thomas Nimmo. **Released:** 9 / year. **Price:** $137, Members for online Australasian Faculty of Occupational and Environmental Medicine; $167, Members for print Australasian Faculty of Occupational and Environmental Medicine; $137, Members for online American College of Occupational and Environmental Medicine; $190, Members for print American College of Occupational and Environmental Medicine; $137, Members for online International Commission on Occupational Health,; $335, for corporate print single issue; $2,621, for corporate online +print; $18, Members for print single issue; $269, Institutions for print single issue; $94, Individuals for print single issue; $1,876, for corporate online; $2,415, for corporate print; $2,057, Institutions for print + online; $1,500, Institutions for online; $1,932, Institutions for print; $681, Individuals for print. **Description:** Provides vital information for the promotion of workplace health and safety. **Availability:** Print; PDF; Online.

25684 ■ Operation Eyesight Universal (OEU)
4 Parkdale Cres. NW, Ste. 200
Calgary, AB, Canada T2N 3T8
Ph: (403)283-6323
Free: 800-585-8265
Fax: (403)270-1899
Co. E-mail: info@operationeyesight.com
URL: http://operationeyesight.com
Contact: Kashinath Bhoosnurmath, President
E-mail: bhoosnurmathk@operationeyesight.com
Facebook: www.facebook.com/OperationEyesightUniversal
X (Twitter): x.com/opeyesight
YouTube: www.youtube.com/user/OpEyesightUniversal
Description: Provides medical and educational assistance to needy individuals. Assists in the establishment of: special programs to combat blindness due to malnutrition. **Founded:** 1963. **Publications:** Sightlines (Quarterly); Sightlines Newsletter (3/year). **Educational Activities:** Operation Eyesight Universal General Assembly (Annual). **Geographic Preference:** Multinational.

25685 ■ Osteoporosis Canada
201 - 250 Ferrand Dr.
Toronto, ON, Canada M3C 3G8
Ph: (416)696-2663
Free: 800-463-6842
Fax: (416)696-2673
Co. E-mail: info@osteoporosis.ca
URL: http://osteoporosis.ca
Contact: Dr. Famida Jiwa, President
Facebook: www.facebook.com/osteoporosiscanada
X (Twitter): x.com/OsteoporosisCA
Instagram: www.instagram.com/osteoporosis_canada
YouTube: www.youtube.com/user/OsteoporosisCA
Description: Individuals and organizations interested in the prevention, diagnosis, and treatment of osteoporosis. Supports research programs that seek to improve the quality of life for women with osteoporosis. Promotes education about osteoporosis among professional health practitioners. Disseminates informational materials to individuals with osteoporosis, physicians, and the public. **Founded:** 1982. **Publications:** Osteoblast Newsletter; Osteoblast (Quarterly); Osteoporosis Update (Quarterly). **Geographic Preference:** National; Local.

25686 ■ *Paediatrics & Child Health*
2305 St. Laurent Blvd., Ste. 100
Ottawa, ON, Canada K1G 4J8
Ph: (613)526-9397
Fax: (613)526-3332
Co. E-mail: info@cps.ca
URL: http://cps.ca
Contact: Mark Feldman, President
URL(s): cps.ca/pchacademic.oup.com/pch
X (Twitter): x.com/CanPaedsJournal

Healthcare and Social Assistance ■ 25690

Released: 8/year **Price:** $652, Institutions for print; $534, Institutions for online only access; $708, Institutions for print and online; $415, Individuals for print. **Availability:** Print; PDF; Online.

25687 ■ Parachute [SecuriJeunes Canada]
150 Eglinton Ave., E Ste., 300
Toronto, ON, Canada M4P 1E8
Ph: (647)776-5100
Free: 888-537-7777
Co. E-mail: info@parachute.ca
URL: http://www.parachutecanada.org/en
Contact: Pamela Fuselli, President
E-mail: pfuselli@parachutecanada.org
Facebook: www.facebook.com/parachutecanada
Linkedin: www.linkedin.com/company/parachute---leaders-in-injury-prevention
X (Twitter): x.com/parachutecanada
Instagram: www.instagram.com/parachutecanada
YouTube: www.youtube.com/parachutecanada
Description: Works to reduce the number of injuries in Canada. Sponsors campaigns to raise public awareness of preventable causes of injury in all aspects of daily life. **Scope:** Injury prevention. **Founded:** 2012. **Holdings:** Figures not available. **Publications:** Heads Up (Monthly); Will It Float. **Geographic Preference:** National.

25688 ■ Physicians Committee for Responsible Medicine (PCRM)
5100 Wisconsin Ave. NW, Ste. 400
Washington, DC 20016
Ph: (202)686-2210
Fax: (202)686-2216
URL: http://www.pcrm.org
Contact: Neal D. Barnard, President
Facebook: www.facebook.com/PCRM.org
X (Twitter): x.com/PCRM
YouTube: www.youtube.com/user/PCRM
Description: Supports research into U.S. agricultural and public health policies. Promotes the New Four Food Groups, a no-cholesterol, low-fat alternative to U.S.D.A. dietary recommendations. Maintains the Gold Plan program, which includes information on low-fat, cholesterol-free entrees and nutrition for institutional food services. **Founded:** 1985. **Publications:** GOOD MEDICINE (Quarterly). **Geographic Preference:** National.

25689 ■ *Sightlines*
4 Parkdale Cres. NW, Ste. 200
Calgary, AB, Canada T2N 3T8
Ph: (403)283-6323
Free: 800-585-8265
Fax: (403)270-1899
Co. E-mail: info@operationeyesight.com
URL: http://operationeyesight.com
Contact: Kashinath Bhoosnurmath, President
E-mail: bhoosnurmathk@operationeyesight.com
URL(s): operationeyesight.com/about/newsletter-and-social-media
Released: Quarterly; summer, spring, winter and fall. **Description:** Inspirational stories about people whose sight has been restored and their lives forever changed. **Availability:** PDF; Online.

25690 ■ Société Canadienne du Cancer (CCS) - Bibliotheque [Canadian Cancer Society (CCS)]
55 St. Clair Ave. W, Ste. 500
Toronto, ON, Canada M4V 2Y7
Free: 888-939-3333
Fax: (416)488-2872
Co. E-mail: connect@cancer.ca
URL: http://cancer.ca/en
Contact: Andrea Seale, Chief Executive Officer
Facebook: www.facebook.com/CanadianCancerSociety
Linkedin: www.linkedin.com/company/canadian-cancer-society
X (Twitter): x.com/cancersociety
Instagram: www.instagram.com/cancersociety
YouTube: www.youtube.com/user/CDNCancerSociety
Description: Community-based volunteers. Promotes research into the causes, detection, and cure of cancer; seeks to improve the quality of life of

people with cancer. Conducts fundraising activities benefiting cancer research; sponsors volunteer training programs; makes available educational courses. **Scope:** Cancer treatment and prevention. **Founded:** 1938. **Holdings:** Figures not available. **Geographic Preference:** National.

25691 ■ Société Canadienne de Recherches Cliniques (SCRC) [Canadian Society for Clinical Investigation]
114 Cheyenne Way
Ottawa, ON, Canada K2J 0E9
Free: 877-968-9449
Fax: (613)491-0073
Co. E-mail: info@csci-scrc.ca
URL: http://csci-scrc.ca
Contact: Dr. Nicola L. Jones, President
Description: Canadian clinical investigators working in the field of human health. Represents members' interests. **Founded:** 1951. **Publications:** *Clinical and Investigative Medicine (CIM)* (Quarterly). **Awards:** CSCI Distinguished Scientist Lectures and Awards (Annual); Henry Friesen Awards and Lecture (Annual); Distinguished Scientist Lecture and Award (Annual); Dr. Mel Silverman Distinguished Service Award (Annual). **Geographic Preference:** National.

25692 ■ Society for the Psychological Study of Social Issues (SPSSI) - Reference Collection
700 7th St. SE
Washington, DC 20003
Ph: (202)675-6956
Free: 877-310-7778
Fax: (202)675-6902
Co. E-mail: spssi@spssi.org
URL: http://www.spssi.org
Contact: Anila Balkissoon, Executive Director
E-mail: abalkissoon@spssi.org
Facebook: www.facebook.com/spssi
Linkedin: www.linkedin.com/company/society-for-the-psychological-study-of-social-issues
X (Twitter): x.com/spssi
YouTube: www.youtube.com/channel/UCLJcyTbZTJzzduYF9wCLm3g
Description: Psychologists, sociologists, anthropologists, psychiatrists, political scientists, and social workers. Works to: obtain and disseminate to the public scientific knowledge about social change and other social processes; promote psychological research on significant theoretical and practical questions of social issues; encourage application of findings to problems of society. **Scope:** Psychological study of social issues, focusing on theoretical and practical questions about social life and change. **Founded:** 1936. **Publications:** *Journal of Social Issues: A Journal of the Society for the Psychological Study of Social Issues (JSI)* (Quarterly); *Research Methods in Social Relations* (Quarterly); *SPSSI Newsletter Forward* (3/year); *Analyses of Social Issues and Public Policy Newsletter (ASAP)* (Annual); *Forward* (3/year); *SPSSI Newsletter* (3/year); *Journal of Social Issues* (Quarterly); *Analyses of Social Issues and Public Policy (ASAP)* (3/year). **Educational Activities:** Social Justice: Research, Action & Policy (Biennial); SPSSI Conferences (Annual). **Awards:** Applied Social Issues Internship Program (Annual); Dalmas A. Taylor Summer Minority Policy Fellowship (Annual); The James Marshall Public Policy Postdoctoral Fellowship (Annual); The Michele Alexander Early Career Award for Scholarship and Service (Annual); SPSSI Action Grants for Experienced Scholars (SAGES) (Annual); The Clara Mayo Grants (Annual); The Gordon Allport Intergroup Relations Prize (Annual); Grants-in-aid (Semiannual); SPSSI Grants-In-Aid Program (Semiannual); Grants-In-Aid Program (Semiannual); The Otto Klineberg Intercultural and International Relations Award (Annual); Outstanding Teaching and Mentoring Awards (Annual); SAGES Grant Program (Annual); The Gordon Allport Intergroup Relations Prize (Annual); The Social Issues Dissertation Award (Annual); Otto Klineberg Award (Annual); The Louise Kidder Early Career Award (Annual); The Michele Alexander Early Career Award For Scholarship and Service (Annual); Awards for Outstanding Teaching and Mentoring (Annual); The Kurt Lewin Award (Annual). **Geographic Preference:** National; Regional.

25693 ■ Society for the Study of Social Problems (SSSP)
901 McClung Twr., University of Tennessee
Knoxville, TN 37996-0490
Ph: (865)689-1531
Fax: (865)689-1534
Co. E-mail: sssp@utk.edu
URL: http://www.sssp1.org
Facebook: www.facebook.com/SSSP1org
X (Twitter): x.com/SSSP1org
Description: An interdisciplinary community of scholars, activists, practitioners, and students endeavoring to create greater social justice through social research. Members are often social scientists working in colleges and universities, in non-profit organizations and in other applied and policy settings. **Scope:** Global problems; institutional ethnography; community research and development; crime and juvenile delinquency; drinking and drugs; racial and ethnic minorities; conflict, social action, and change; family; poverty, class, and inequality; social problems theory; mental health; teaching social problems; sociology and social welfare; youth, aging, and the life course; educational problems; environment and technology; labor studies; sexual behavior, politics and communities; law and society; health, health policy and health services; disabilities; sport, leisure, and the body. **Founded:** 1951. **Publications:** *SSSP Newsletters*; *Social Problems* (Quarterly); *SSSP Social Problems* (Quarterly). **Educational Activities:** SSSP Annual Meetings (Annual); SSSP Symposia. **Awards:** Erwin O. Smigel Award (Annual); Lee Scholar Support Fund (Annual); Lee Student Support Fund (Annual); Thomas C. Hood Social Action Award (Annual); C. Wright Mills Award (Annual); Lee Founders Award (Annual); SSSP Joseph B. Gittler Award (Irregular); SSSP Racial/Ethnic Minority Graduate Fellowship (Annual). **Geographic Preference:** National.

25694 ■ Society for Women's Health Research (SWHR)
1025 Connecticut Ave. NW Ste. 1104
Washington, DC 20036
Ph: (202)223-8224
Co. E-mail: info@swhr.org
URL: http://swhr.org
Contact: Kathryn G. Schubert, President
E-mail: kathryn@swhr.org
Facebook: www.facebook.com/SocietyForWomensHealthResearch
Linkedin: www.linkedin.com/company/society-for-women's-health-research-swhr
X (Twitter): x.com/SWHR
YouTube: www.youtube.com/user/womenshealth
Description: Seeks to improve the health of women by promoting equity in research. Advocates policies which promotes the inclusion of women in clinical trials; informs government agencies and private industry of issues affecting women's health and sex-based biology; educates women consumers on conditions that affect women; promotes funding for women's health research. **Founded:** 1990. **Publications:** *Artherosclerosis Newsletter*; *Sex Differences in Autoimmune Disease Fact Sheet*; *Sex Differences in the Brain Fact Sheet*; *Sex Differences in Cancer Fact Sheet*; *Sex Differences in Cardio/Cerebrovascular Diseases Fact Sheet*; *Sex Differences in Diabetes Fact Sheet*; *Sex Differences in Response to Pharmaceuticals, Tobacco, Alcohol and Illicit Drugs Fact Sheet*; *Sex Differences in HIV/AIDS Fact Sheet*; *Sex Differences in Mental Health Fact Sheet*; *Sex Differences in Musculoskeletal Health Fact Sheet*; *Sex Differences in Obesity Fact Sheet*; *Asthma and Allergies Fact Sheet*; *Autoimmune Diseases Fact Sheet*; *Brain and Degenerative Disorders Fact Sheet*; *Cancer Fact Sheet, WHR*; *Cardiovascular Disease Fact Sheet (CVD)*; *Diabetes, WHR Fact Sheet*; *Diet, Obesity and Eating Disorders Fact Sheet*; *Eye Health Fact Sheet*; *SWHR Journal of Women's Health* (Monthly); *Sexx Matters* (Quarterly); *Hearing Fact Sheet*; *Menopause/Hormone Therapy Fact Sheet*; *Mental Health, WHR Fact Sheet*; *Musculoskeletal Health Fact Sheet*; *Oral Health, WHR Fact Sheet*; *Pain, WHR Fact Sheet*; *Pharmaceuticals Fact Sheet*; *Preventing Birth Defects Fact Sheet*; *Sleep Fact Sheet*; *STDs and HIV/AIDS Fact Sheet*; *Urinary Tract Health/Incontinence Fact Sheet*. **Educational Activities:** Scientific Advisory Meeting: Update on Women's Health. **Geographic Preference:** National.

25695 ■ Texas Counseling Association (TCA)
PO Box 2566
San Antonio, TX 78299
Ph: (512)472-3403
Fax: (512)472-3756
Co. E-mail: info@txca.org
URL: http://www.txca.org
Contact: Jan Friese, Chief Executive Officer
E-mail: jan@txca.org
Facebook: www.facebook.com/TexasCounselingAssociation
Linkedin: www.linkedin.com/company/texas-counseling-association
X (Twitter): x.com/TxCAtweets
Description: Educates others about, and advocates for the understanding and delivery of effective counseling to all Texans. **Publications:** *TCA Guidelines* (Quarterly). **Educational Activities:** Annual TCA Professional Growth Conference (Annual). **Awards:** TCA Outstanding Graduate Student Award (Annual); TCA Layperson Exemplary Service Award (Annual); Molly Gerold Human Rights Award (Periodic); Outstanding TCA Chapter Award (Annual); Outstanding TCA Division Award (Annual). **Geographic Preference:** State.

25696 ■ United Methodist Association of Health and Welfare Ministries (UMA)
5285 Westview Dr., Ste. 200
Frederick, MD 21703
Ph: (301)556-1340
Co. E-mail: askuma@ouruma.org
URL: http://www.ouruma.org
Contact: Mary Kemper, President
E-mail: mkemper@ouruma.org
Facebook: www.facebook.com/OurUMA
Linkedin: www.linkedin.com/company/united-methodist-association-of-health-and-welfare-ministries
X (Twitter): x.com/umassociation
Description: Offers communications and church relations guidance. Provides leadership development training for health and human service professionals in United Methodist-related organizations and agencies. Develops ethical and theological statements on institutional care. Operates Educational Assessment Guidelines Leading Toward Excellence (EAGLE), a self-assessment and peer review accreditation program. Operates a Field Consultation Program; members may access skilled professionals to assist with governance questions. Offers audiovisual services to members. Administers the Order of Good Shepherds program designed to recognize ministry in the workplace by employees at member organizations. Maintains speakers' bureau; compiles statistics. **Founded:** 1940. **Publications:** *National Directory of all United Methodist Related Health and Welfare Ministries* (Annual); *National Directory of Healthcare and Human Service Ministries* (Annual). **Geographic Preference:** National.

25697 ■ Womenpalante
15800 Crabbs Branch Way No. 323
Rockville, MD 20855
Ph: (202)495-1915
Co. E-mail: info@womenpalante.org
URL: http://womenpalante.org
Contact: Patricia Skillin, President
Facebook: www.facebook.com/Womenpalante
Linkedin: www.linkedin.com/company/women-palante
X (Twitter): x.com/womenpalante
Instagram: www.instagram.com/womenpalante
YouTube: www.youtube.com/channel/UCDZuQ1CnzCTc_5ROGx49AfQ
Description: Firm provides healthcare services. Woman-owned, Hispanic American-owned. **Founded:** 2019.

GENERAL SMALL BUSINESS TOPICS

INCUBATORS/RESEARCH AND TECHNOLOGY PARKS

25698 ■ The Health Lab
Co. E-mail: info@thehealthlab.com
URL: http://thehealthlab.com
Description: Collaborates with innovators and entrepreneurs to create sustainable, commercially viable businesses that solve health-related problems. **Founded:** 2014.

25699 ■ Plug and Play - Health
440 N Wolfe Rd.
Sunnyvale, CA 94085
URL: http://www.plugandplaytechcenter.com
Description: An accelerator for startups in the health tech industry. Provides support with venture and angel partners, mentorship, a data center, office space, and networking opportunities. This program focuses on hospital workflow, AI and big data analytics, medication adherence, sensors and wearables, telemedicine and care management, chronic disease management, mental health, VR/AR, and diagnostics. **Founded:** 2015.

EDUCATIONAL PROGRAMS

25700 ■ WBENC Industry Spotlight
URL(s): www.wbenc.org/programs/industry-spotlight-series
Frequency: Irregular. **Description:** A series of webinars and resources for women business owners in order to learn about new trends, innovations, and sources of support in the automotive, food & beverage, utilities, healthcare, energy, financial services, and manufacturing sectors. **Principal Exhibits:** A series of webinars and resources for women business owners in order to learn about new trends, innovations, and sources of support in the automotive, food & beverage, utilities, healthcare, energy, financial services, and manufacturing sectors.

REFERENCE WORKS

25701 ■ "113D Filings: Investors Report to the SEC" in Barron's (Vol. 88, March 24, 2008, No. 12, pp. M13)
Pub: Dow Jones & Company Inc.
Contact: Almar Latour, Chief Executive Officer
Released: April 02, 2016. **Description:** HealthCor Management called as problematic the plan of Magellan Health Services to use its high cash balances for acquisitions. Carlson Capital discussed with Energy Partners possible changes in the latter's board. Investor Carl Icahn suggested that Enzon Pharmaceuticals consider selling itself or divest some of its assets. **Availability:** Print; Online.

25702 ■ "26 Things Holding Canadians Back" in Canadian Business (Vol. 85, August 13, 2012, No. 13, pp. 27)
Description: A list of the problems that Canada needs to address in order to succeed as an economic superpower is presented. Some of these barriers include declining fertility rate, rising percentage of overweight and obese, and obsolete copyright laws. **Availability:** Print; Online.

25703 ■ "2010 Book of Lists" in Business Courier (Vol. 26, December 26, 2009, No. 36, pp. 1)
Price: $49.95. **Description:** Rankings of companies and organizations within the business services, education, finance, health care, hospitality and tourism, real estate, and technology industries in the Cincinnati, Ohio-Northern Kentucky area are presented. Rankings are based on sales, business size, or other statistics. **Availability:** PDF; Online.

25704 ■ "Acsys Interactive Announces Crowdsourcing Comes to the Hospital Industry" in Marketwired (August 23, 2010)
Pub: Comtex News Network Inc.
Contact: Kan Devnani, President
Description: Hospital marketers are obtaining data through crowdsourcing as strategy to gain ideas and feedback. The Hospital Industry Crowdsourced Survey of Digital, Integrated and Emerging Marketing is the first initiative among hospitals. **Availability:** Print; Online.

25705 ■ Adoption Resource Book
Pub: HarperCollins Publishers L.L.C.
Contact: Brian Murray, President
URL(s): www.harpercollins.com/products/the-adoption-resource-book-4th-edition-lois-gilman?variant=32117479079970
Price: $19.99, Individuals for paperback. **Description:** Publication includes list of public and private adoption agencies, support groups, and services. **Entries include:** Agency name, address, phone, special requirements. Principal content of the publication is a discussion of adoption procedures and requirements, including adoption of foreign children and open adoption. **Arrangement:** Geographical. **Availability:** Print.

25706 ■ "Ambitious Horse Center Is In the Works for Southeastern Idaho" in Idaho Business Review (August 25, 2014)
Pub: BridgeTower Media
Contact: Adam Reinebach, President
Price: $99, Digital & Mobile Only(1 Year); $11.99, Print, Digital & Mobile(1 Month); $149, Print, Digital & Mobile(1 Year); $99, Digital & Mobile Only(For 1 Year); $11.99, Print, Digital & Mobile (For 1 Month Intro Rate); $149, Print, Digital & Mobile (For 1 Year). **Description:** Ernest Bleinberger is planning to develop a 167-acre mixed-use project called Horse Station and will be located in Cache Valley, Idaho. Horse Station will include stables for about 250 horses and an arena, along with medical facilities, a hotel, retail shopping center, and a farmers market. **Availability:** Print; Online.

25707 ■ "The Annual Entitlement Lecture Medicare Elephantiasis" in Barron's (March 31, 2008)
Pub: Dow Jones & Company Inc.
Contact: Almar Latour, Chief Executive Officer
Ed: Thomas G. Donlan. **Description:** Expenditures on Medicare hospital insurance and the revenues available to pay for it have led to a gap of capital valued at $38.6 trillion. Slashing the benefits or raising taxes will not solve the gap which exists unless the government saves the money and invests it in private markets. **Availability:** Online.

25708 ■ "Anthem Becomes First to Penalize Small-Business Employees for Smoking" in Denver Business Journal (Vol. 64, August 17, 2012, No. 13, pp. 1)
Pub: Baltimore Business Journal
Contact: Rhonda Pringle, President
E-mail: rpringle@bizjournals.com
Description: Health insurance companies Anthem Blue Cross and Blue Shield of Colorado are first to impose higher premiums on employee smokers who are under their small-group policies. The premiums may increase up to 15 percent starting September, to be paid by the smoking employees or the company. The law aims to help reduce tobacco-related health problems, as well as health care costs.

25709 ■ "Audit: Bad Billing System Costs Glens Falls Hospital $38 Million in Revenue" in The Post Star (March 7, 2019)
URL(s): poststar.com/news/local/audit-bad-billing-system-costs-glens-falls-hospital-million-in/article_4b430f4f-859f-59ba-bac0-5e886c8b9d85.html
Ed: Kathleen Moore. **Released:** March 07, 2019. **Description:** Glens Falls Hospital instituted a new billing system, which malfunctioned in 2017 and ended up costing the hospital $38 million. The mistake costs many employees their jobs in order to help make up the difference. **Availability:** Online.

25710 ■ "Avoid the Stress of Traffic and Pollution with House Call Doctor Los Angeles" in Ecology, Environment & Conservation Business (May 24, 2014)
Pub: NewsRX LLC.
Contact: Kalani Rosell, Contact

Healthcare and Social Assistance ■ 25716

Description: Record levels of air pollution in the Los Angeles, California area pose serious risks to those suffering from illness or injury. Michael Farzam and his team at House Call Doctor Los Angeles provides telephone medicine for those unable or unwilling to visit a physician in person. The mobile doctor in Los Angeles offers individuals throughout the area with concierge care without leaving home. **Availability:** Online.

25711 ■ "Baby Boomers Look to Senior Concierge Services to Raise Income" in The New York Times (May 19, 2017)
URL(s): www.nytimes.com/2017/05/19/business/retirement/boomers-retiring-concierge.html
Ed: Liz Moyer. **Released:** May 19, 2017. **Description:** Elder concierge is a growing industry of mostly part-time workers who assist older clients with living independently. They help out around the house, drive clients to appointments, run small errands, and are often an extra set of eyes and ears. Organizations are looking for workers and it's often ideal for stay-at-home parents looking for some extra income, or a retired person. **Availability:** Online.

25712 ■ "Backtalk with Terrie M. Williams" in Black Enterprise (Vol. 38, December 2007, No. 5, pp. 204)
Pub: Earl G. Graves Ltd.
Contact: Earl Graves, Jr., President
Ed: Tennille M. Robinson. **Description:** Profile of Terrie M. Williams, president of a public relations agency as well as founder of a youth empowerment organization called Stay Strong Foundation. Williams reflects on her bouts with depression and how the disease impacts sufferers and talks about her book that will inspire others dealing with depression. **Availability:** Online.

25713 ■ "Baltimore-Area Hospital Tower Projects Could Add Hundreds of New Jobs" in Baltimore Business Journal (Vol. 28, June 25, 2010, No. 7, pp. 1)
Pub: Baltimore Business Journal
Contact: Rhonda Pringle, President
E-mail: rpringle@bizjournals.com
Ed: Scott Graham. **Description:** Greater Baltimore, Maryland has four hospitals that are in the middle of transforming their campuses with new facilities for treating various patients. Construction at Mercy Medical Center, Johns Hopkins Hospital, Franklin Square Hospital and Anne Rundle Hospital has helped bring the construction industry back to life. Insights into the hiring plans of these hospitals are also included.

25714 ■ "Banking on Cord Blood" in Business Journal-Serving Phoenix & the Valley of the Sun (Vol. 31, September 10, 2010, No. 1, pp. 1)
Description: Celebration Stem Cell Centre obtained contracts from Mercy Gilbert Medical Center and its two sister hospitals, St. Joseph Hospital and Medical Center in Phoenix, Arizona and Chandler Regional Medical Center. The contract will facilitate the donation of unused umbilical cord blood for research. **Availability:** PDF; Online.

25715 ■ "Bankruptcies" in Crain's Detroit Business (Vol. 24, March 24, 2008, No. 12, pp. 6)
Pub: Crain Communications Inc.
Contact: Barry Asin, President
Description: Current list of business that filed for Chapter 7 or 11 protection in U.S. Bankruptcy Court in Detroit include a construction company, a medical care company, a physical therapy firm and a communications firm. **Availability:** Online.

25716 ■ "Baptist Hatching Health Care Plan" in Memphis Business Journal (Vol. 34, June 15, 2012, No. 9, pp. 1)
Pub: Baltimore Business Journal
Contact: Rhonda Pringle, President
E-mail: rpringle@bizjournals.com
Ed: Cole Epley. **Description:** Baptist Memorial Health Care Corporation is planning to launch its Select Health Alliance initiative. The program will

focus on the improvement of care quality and efficiency through the measurement and tracking of quality standards. **Availability:** Print; Online.

25717 ■ *"Baptist Health System Plans to Expand Stone Oak-Area Hospital: $32 Million Project Will Add Two Floors, 100 Beds"* in *San Antonio Business Journal (Vol. 26, May 25, 2012, No. 17, pp. 1)*
Pub: Baltimore Business Journal
Contact: Rhonda Pringle, President
E-mail: rpringle@bizjournals.com
Price: $4, introductory 4-week offer(Digital & Print).
Description: Baptist Health System is planning to start the $32 million expansion of the North Central Baptist Hospital in San Antonio, Texas that will include the addition of two floors and 100 beds. An estimate of hiring 200 new health care workers will be created by the expansion. **Availability:** Print; Online.

25718 ■ *"Baylor Turns Around Carrollton Hospital"* in *Dallas Business Journal (Vol. 35, June 15, 2012, No. 40, pp. 1)*
Pub: Baltimore Business Journal
Contact: Rhonda Pringle, President
E-mail: rpringle@bizjournals.com
Ed: Bill Hethcock. **Description:** Baylor Health Care System has boosted the service performance of Trinity Medical Center in Carrollton, Texas. Trinity was the worst performing hospital in the area in terms of mortality rates and patient satisfaction. **Availability:** Print; Online.

25719 ■ *"Beyond Repair"* in *Business First Buffalo (Vol. 28, March 23, 2012, No. 27, pp. 1)*
Pub: American City Business Journals, Inc.
Contact: Mike Olivieri, Executive Vice President
Released: Weekly. **Price:** $140, one year subscription (Print & Digital); $115, one year subscription (Digital Only). **Description:** Episcopal Church Home and Affiliates once ran a thriving senior care community on a Rhode Island Street property located nearthe Peace Bridge entrance in Buffalo, New York. However, a proposed bridge expansion that would run across the campus has led to the phased shutdown that began seven years ago. Insights on the $14 million liens on the property are also given. **Availability:** Print; Online.

25720 ■ *"Biotechnology Wants a Lead Role"* in *Business North Carolina (Vol. 28, March 2008, No. 3, pp. 14)*
Description: According to experts, North Carolina is poised as a leader in the biotechnology sector. Highlights of a recent roundtable discussion sponsored by the North Carolina Biotechnology Center in Research Triangle Park are presented. **Availability:** Online.

25721 ■ *"Blue Cross to Put Kiosk in Mall"* in *News & Observer (November 9, 2010)*
Pub: News and Observer
Contact: Bill Church, Editor
Ed: Alan M. Wolf. **Description:** Blue Cross and Blue Shield of North Carolina has placed a kiosk in Durham's Streets of Southpoint in order to market its health insurance. **Availability:** Online.

25722 ■ *"Breast Surgery Breakthrough Propels Palo Alto Startup AirXpanders"* in *Silicon Valley/San Jose Business Journal (Vol. 30, June 22, 2012, No. 13, pp. 1)*
Pub: Baltimore Business Journal
Contact: Rhonda Pringle, President
E-mail: rpringle@bizjournals.com
Description: Palo Alto, California-based AirXpanders Inc. has designed and started the testing of the Aero-Form tissue expander, a medical device to help women undergoing reconstructive surgery. The device helps in expanding tissue to accommodate reconstruction of a woman's breast following a mastectomy. The extent to which this device would succeed in the market is discussed. **Availability:** Print; Online.

25723 ■ *"Brisk Activity in North Fulton Office Market"* in *Atlanta Business Chronicle (July 11, 2014, pp. 2B)*
Description: Activity appears to have pickup up briskly in the North Fulton office market during the first six months of 2014, mainly due to the high profile deals involving major players in the technology and health care sectors. **Availability:** Print; Online.

25724 ■ *"The Business of Medicine: Maintaining a Healthy Bottom Line"* in *Black Enterprise (Vol. 41, October 2010, No. 3, pp. 60)*
Released: January 10, 2010. **Description:** Sustainable government reform requires reconstruction in the areas of financing and delivery of services in the field of medicine. **Availability:** Online.

25725 ■ *"California has a Plan B for Enacting Health Care Reform"* in *Sacramento Business Journal (Vol. 29, May 18, 2012, No. 12, pp. 1)*
Pub: Baltimore Business Journal
Contact: Rhonda Pringle, President
E-mail: rpringle@bizjournals.com
Description: California lawmakers are pushing for a bill that would implement health care reform in the state. The bill is in anticipation of the US Supreme Court's ruling on the Federal Affordable Healthcare Act. **Availability:** Print; Online.

25726 ■ *"Campbell Clinic in Expansion Mode: Plans to Triple Size of Surgery Center, Add Employees"* in *Memphis Business Journal (Vol. 34, August 24, 2012, No. 19, pp. 1)*
Pub: Baltimore Business Journal
Contact: Rhonda Pringle, President
E-mail: rpringle@bizjournals.com
Description: The Campbell Clinic Inc. is pushing forward with its plan to expand and hire new employees. The clinic has filed a Certificate of Need with the Tennessee Health Services Development Agency worth $13 million. Expansion projects include the enlargement of the surgery center, which handles 700 cases a month, a figure which is expected to rise to 750 in August 2012. **Availability:** Print; Online.

25727 ■ *"Canadian Patients Give Detroit Hospitals a Boost"* in *Crain's Detroit Business (Vol. 24, April 14, 2008, No. 15, pp. 10)*
Pub: Crain Communications Inc.
Contact: Barry Asin, President
Ed: Jay Greene. **Description:** Each year thousands of Canadians travel to Detroit area hospitals seeking quicker solutions to medical problems or access to services that are limited or unavailable in Canada. **Availability:** Online.

25728 ■ *"Canadian Wind Farm Sued Due to Negative Health Effects"* in *PC Magazine Online (September 22, 2011)*
Pub: PC Magazine
Contact: Dan Costa, Editor-in-Chief
E-mail: dan_costa@pcmag.com
Ed: Andrew Webster. **Description:** Suncor Energy is being sued by a family in Ontario, Canada. The family claims that Suncor's wind turbines have created health problems for them, ranging from vertigo and sleep disturbance to depression and suicidal thoughts. The family's home is over 1,000 meters from the eight wind turbines, and according to Ontario officials, wind turbines must be a minimum of 550 meters from existing homes. **Availability:** Online.

25729 ■ *"Cancer Genome Project Will Put San Antonio In Research Spotlight"* in *San Antonio Business Journal (Vol. 25, January 27, 2012, No. 53, pp. 1)*
Pub: Baltimore Business Journal
Contact: Rhonda Pringle, President
E-mail: rpringle@bizjournals.com
Description: San Antonio, Texas-based South Texas Accelerated Research Therapeutics has been spearheading the development of a new cancer research effort. The San Antonio 1000 Cancer Genome Project will use the genome sequencing process to examine and compare the difference between normal tissue and tissue from some 1,000 tumors. **Availability:** Print; Online.

25730 ■ *"Cancer Survivor Becomes Marathoner, Author"* in *Business Journal-Serving Phoenix & the Valley of the Sun (Vol. 30, August 20, 2010, No. 50, pp. 1)*
Pub: Phoenix Business Journal
Contact: Alex McAlister, Director
E-mail: amcalister@bizjournals.com
Ed: Angela Gonzales. **Description:** Cancer survivor Helene Neville has finished a record-breaking 2,520-mile run in 93 days and then celebrated her 50th birthday despite being diagnosed with Hodgkins' lymphoma in 1991. Neveille, who is also a Phoenix area registered nurse, made stops along the way to promote her book, 'Nurses in Shape'. Neville also discusses how she fought her cancer through running. **Availability:** Print; Online.

25731 ■ *CARES Directory: Social and Health Services in the Greater New York Area*
Contact: Raquel Dasilva, Contact
E-mail: rdasilva@uwnyc.org
URL(s): www.unitedwaynyc.org/?id=65
Released: Biennial **Description:** Covers over 2,469 nonprofit social service agencies in the greater New York area. **Entries include:** Name, address, phone, names and titles of key personnel, agency mission, programs offered, eligibility requirements, fees, application procedure, geographic area served, other locations, site director name and title, accessibility to the handicapped, hours open, languages spoken, transportation facilities. **Arrangement:** Alphabetical by agency name. **Indexes:** Program, Keyword/Target Group. **Availability:** Print; Online.

25732 ■ *"Celebrate Innovation, No Matter Where It Occurs"* in *Harvard Business Review (Vol. 90, April 2012, No. 4, pp. 36)*
Pub: Harvard Business Review Press
Contact: Moderna V. Pfizer, Contact
Ed: Nitin Nohria. **Price:** $6, hardcover. **Description:** Yoga is used to illustrate the global success of a given concept not originally construed as a product or service. Although yoga emerged in ancient India, it is now practiced worldwide and is at the center of many businesses and disciplines, from the health care industry to clothing and accessories. **Availability:** PDF; Online.

25733 ■ *"CEO Forecast: With Cloudy Economy, Executives Turn to Government Contracting"* in *Hispanic Business (January-February 2009, pp. 34, 36)*
Ed: Jessica Haro, Richard Kaplan. **Description:** As economic uncertainty fogs the future, executives turn to government contracts in order to boost business. Revenue sources, health care challenges, environmental consulting and remediation services, as well as technological strides are discussed. **Availability:** Print; Online.

25734 ■ *"The Change Foundation Awards Northumberland Community Partnership $3 Million Project To Improve Seniors' Healthcare Transitions and Use Patient Input to Drive Redesign"* in *CNW Group (June 5, 2012)*
Pub: Comtex News Network Inc.
Contact: Kan Devnani, President
Description: The Change Foundation has awarded the Northumberland Community Partnership with its $3 million project PATH-Partners Advancing Transitions in Healthcare for Ontario patients. The program brings together 12 health and social care organizations with patients and caregivers to identify healthcare transition issues in Central East Ontario, Canada. It will work with service providers to redesign care and to improve experiences. **Availability:** Online.

25735 ■ "Changes Sought to Health Law" in Baltimore Business Journal (Vol. 28, July 30, 2010, No. 12, pp. 1)
Pub: Baltimore Business Journal
Contact: Rhonda Pringle, President
E-mail: rpringle@bizjournals.com
Ed: Kent Hoover. Description: Business groups that opposed health care reform are working to undo parts of the new laws even before they go into effect. Business groups are gaining support for one legislative fix, which is repealing the law's provision that requires all businesses to file 1099 forms with the IRS any time they pay more than $600 a year to another business. Availability: Print; Online.

25736 ■ "Chicago Senior Care Acquires The Clare at Water Tower" in Investment Weekly News (April 29, 2012, pp. 168)
Pub: PR Newswire Association LLC.
Description: Senior Care Development LLC, Fundamental Advisors LP, and Life Care Companies LLC partnered to create Chicago Senior Care LLC (CSC) and won the bid for purchasing The Clare at Water Tower, a senior housing community. Availability: Online.

25737 ■ "Children's Hospital to Grow" in Austin Business Journal (Vol. 31, July 22, 2011, No. 20, pp. A1)
Pub: Austin Business Journal
Contact: Rachel McGrath, Director
E-mail: rmcgrath@bizjournals.com
Ed: Sandra Zaragoza. Description: Austin, Texas-based Dell Children's Medical Center is set to embark on a tower expansion. The plan will accommodate more patients and make room for the hospital's growing specialty program. Availability: Print; Online.

25738 ■ "Cincinnati Hospitals Feel Pain from Slow Economy" in Business Courier (Vol. 27, September 3, 2010, No. 18, pp. 1)
Pub: Business Courier
Ed: James Ritchie. Description: Hospitals in Cincinnati, Ohio have suffered from decreased revenues owing to the economic crises. Declining patient volumes and bad debt have also adversely impacted hospitals. Availability: Print; Online.

25739 ■ "Cincinnati Hospitals Mandate Flu Shots" in Business Courier (Vol. 27, November 19, 2010, No. 29, pp. 1)
Pub: Business Courier
Ed: James Ritchie. Description: TriHealth has mandated that employees who refuse to get the vaccination shot for 2010 could be penalized with unpaid administrative leave. Other hospital employers, such as University Hospital and Cincinnati Children's Hospital and Medical Center have fired employees for forgoing flu shots. Vaccination rates among hospital employees are given. Availability: Print; Mailing list; Online.

25740 ■ "Cincinnati Hospitals Wage War on 'Bounce-Backs'" in Business Courier (Vol. 27, July 30, 2010, No. 13, pp. 1)
Pub: Business Courier
Ed: James Ritchie. Description: Health care organizations in Greater Cincinnati area have tried a number of care and follow up programs, primarily focused on congestive heart failure to prevent readmissions to hospitals. Hospital administrators have made the averting of bounce-backs a priority due to new federal government plans on reimbursement. Availability: Print; Online.

25741 ■ "Clash of the Titans" in San Francisco Business Times (Vol. 28, February 7, 2014, No. 29, pp. 4)
Pub: American City Business Journals, Inc.
Contact: Mike Olivieri, Executive Vice President
Released: September 01, 2017. Description: University of California, San Francisco (UCSF) Medical Center and Stanford Hospital and Clinics have been competing for dominance for San Francisco Bay Area's health care. Both medical centers are competing to affiliate with more doctors, gain more patients, and accomplish more fundraising. Ways the UCSF and Stanford plan to pursue their expansion and integration are also discussed. Availability: Print; Online.

25742 ■ "Commercial Builders Take It on the Chin" in Crain's Chicago Business (Vol. 31, April 28, 2008, No. 17, pp. 16)
Pub: Crain Communications Inc.
Contact: Barry Asin, President
Ed: Alby Gallun. Description: Although the health care development sector has seen growth, the rest of Chicago's local commercial building industry has seen steep declines in the first quarter of this year. According to McGraw-Hill Construction, Chicago-area non-residential construction starts totaled $731 million in the quarter, a 60 percent drop from the year-earlier period. Volume in the retail, office and hotel markets fell by nearly 70 percent. Availability: Online.

25743 ■ "Competition Is Fierce For Hospital Rankings" in Dallas Business Journal (Vol. 35, July 20, 2012, No. 45, pp. 1)
Pub: Baltimore Business Journal
Contact: Rhonda Pringle, President
E-mail: rpringle@bizjournals.com
Ed: Bill Hethcock. Description: U.S. News and World Report has released its ranking of Best Hospitals and triggering press releases in the highly competitive North Texas health care market. The press releases are being taken seriously by the hospitals since they learn from each other. Availability: Print; Online.

25744 ■ "Complementary Strengths Fuel Research Duo's Success" in Providence Business News (Vol. 29, June 2, 2014, No. 9, pp. 22)
Pub: American City Business Journals, Inc.
Contact: Mike Olivieri, Executive Vice President
URL(s): pbn.com/complementary-strengths-fuel-research-duos-success96239
Description: Johnna A. Pezzullo and Lynne A. Haughey achieved success with Omega Medical Research through their complementary strengths. The company has been successful and works with pharmaceutical companies like Pfizer and GlaxoSmithKline. Telecommunication Services: Daddona@pbn.com.

25745 ■ "Con Roundup: Novi Eyed for $11 Million, 100-Bed Medilodge" in Crain's Detroit Business (Vol. 25, June 1, 2009, No. 22, pp. M032)
Pub: Crain Communications Inc.
Contact: Barry Asin, President
Description: Novi, Michigan is one of the cities being considered for construction of a new 110-bed skilled nursing facility. Details of the project are included. Availability: Online.

25746 ■ "Consulting Firm Goes Shopping" in Crain's Chicago Business (Vol. 31, April 28, 2008, No. 17, pp. 45)
Pub: Crain Communications Inc.
Contact: Barry Asin, President
Ed: Phuong Ly. Description: Clark & Wamberg LLC was created last year after the merger of Clark Inc. to a Dutch insurance conglomerate. Clark Inc. was a life insurance and benefits consultancy which had been on a downslide, returning just 5.6 percent a year to shareholders. In contrast Clark & Wamberg posted first-year revenue of $106.8 million, fueled by business from its executive compensation and health care clients. Availability: Online.

25747 ■ "Conversation Starters for the Holiday" in Barron's (Vol. 89, July 6, 2009, No. 27, pp. 7)
Pub: Dow Jones & Company Inc.
Contact: Almar Latour, Chief Executive Officer
Ed: Michael Santoli. Description: Investors are concerned that the US will experience high inflation due to low interest rates and improved money supply. US consumer spending has increased to 70 percent of gross domestic product, brought by health-care spending increases, while savings rates have risen to 6.9 percent. Availability: Online.

25748 ■ "Corporate Canada Eyes Retiree Health Benefit Cuts" in Globe & Mail (March 8, 2006, pp. B3)
Ed: Virginia Galt. Description: A survey on Canadian companies reveals that due to rising health care costs and increasing number of baby boomer retirements, these companies are to cut down on health benefits they are providing to these retired employees. Availability: Online.

25749 ■ "Corrales Site of New Senior Living/Care Complex" in America's Intelligence Wire (August 13, 2012)
Description: David Dronet, developer of Corrales Senior Living LLC, has chosen Corrales, New Mexico as its newest site to construct a continuum of care for senior citizens. The project entails a $60 million complex of private homes and health care units with amenities like a restaurant, fitness areas, and gardens. Availability: Print; Online.

25750 ■ "Cost of Creating Health Insurance Exchange in Md. 'Largely Unknown'" in Baltimore Business Journal (Vol. 28, September 3, 2010, No. 17, pp. 1)
Pub: Baltimore Business Journal
Contact: Rhonda Pringle, President
E-mail: rpringle@bizjournals.com
Ed: Emily Mullin. Description: United States health reform is seen to result in increased health insurance prices in Maryland. However, health care reform advocates claim a new marketplace and increased competition will help keep costs down. Availability: Print.

25751 ■ "Could UNC Charlotte Be Home to Future Med School?" in Charlotte Business Journal (Vol. 25, July 23, 2010, No. 18, pp. 1)
Pub: Charlotte Business Journal
Contact: Robert Morris, Editor
E-mail: rmorris@bizjournals.com
Ed: Jennifer Thomas. Description: University of North Carolina, Charlotte chancellor Phil Dubois is proposing that a medical school be established at the campus. The idea began in 2007 and Dubois' plan is for students to spend all four years in Charlotte and train at the Carolinas Medical Center. Availability: Print; Online.

25752 ■ "Covered California Adds Dental Benefits" in Sacramento Business Journal (Vol. 31, August 29, 2014, No. 27, pp. 8)
Pub: American City Business Journals, Inc.
Contact: Mike Olivieri, Executive Vice President
Released: Weekly. Price: $4, introductory 4-week offer(Digital only). Description: Health benefit exchange, Covered California, is introducing stand-alone family dental benefits for consumers who enroll in health insurance coverage for 2015. The Governor has yet to sign a bill that would establish a separate vision care marketplace linked to Covered California's Website. Availability: Print; Online.

25753 ■ "Creating Health-Tech Opportunity" in Providence Business News (Vol. 29, April 14, 2014, No. 2, pp. 1)
Pub: American City Business Journals, Inc.
Contact: Mike Olivieri, Executive Vice President
Released: April 12, 2014. Description: MedMates has officially launched, in April 2013, as Rhode Island's first group for networking and advocacy in health technology. MedMates now have 410 members that span every sector of health technology and its membership is not exclusive to the private sector. Insights into MedMates' first year success are also presented. Availability: Print; Online.

25754 ■ "Day Care Directors Are Playing Doctor, and Parents Suffer" in The New York Times (September 16, 2019)
URL(s): www.nytimes.com/2019/09/16/upshot/day-care-pink-eye-parents.html

25755 ■ Healthcare and Social Assistance

Ed: Aaron E. Carroll. **Released:** September 16, 2019. **Description:** Discusses how day cares, in an effort to protect the health of all children within the facility, may actually be doing more harm than good. With strict policies in place for minor childhood illnesses needing to be fully treated before the child can be readmitted, this has put a large burden on working parents, their bank accounts, and the health of the sick child who may be receiving antibiotics with limited effects. **Availability:** Online.

25755 ■ *"Deals Dip In Florida Amid Squabbles Over Price"* **in South Florida Business Journal (Vol. 34, May 30, 2014, No. 45, pp. 4)**
Pub: American City Business Journals, Inc.
Contact: Mike Olivieri, Executive Vice President
Released: Weekly. **Price:** $8, introductory 4-week offer(Digital only). **Description:** Private equity firm investments in local companies in Florida dropped from 146 in 2012 to 135 in 2013. James Cassel of Cassel, Salpeter and Company, says companies in the information technology and health care sectors have been acquired because of strong multiples of their book value. **Availability:** Print; Online.

25756 ■ *"Death by 1,000 Clicks: Where Electronic Health Records Went Wrong"* **in Kaiser Health News (March 18, 2019)**
URL(s): khn.org/news/death-by-a-thousand-clicks/
Ed: Fred Schulte, Erika Fry. **Released:** March 18, 2019. **Description:** Troubling evidence of health practices that use electronic coding and billing, which has caused issues to patient safety and it's also used to overcharge insurance companies and patients. **Availability:** Online.

25757 ■ *"Design Challenge Seeks to Expand Access"* **in Philadelphia Business Journal (Vol. 33, April 25, 2014, No. 11, pp. 7)**
Pub: American City Business Journals, Inc.
Contact: Mike Olivieri, Executive Vice President
Description: The Thomas Scattergood Behavioral Health Foundation sponsored the 2014 design challenge on making mental healthcare education, access and services available at retail clinics. The winner was the mental health screening tool, 'Wellness at Your Fingertips', submitted by the Philadelphia Department of Behavioral Health and Intellectual Disability Services in Pennsylvania. **Availability:** Online.

25758 ■ *"Despite FDA Approval, Heart Test No Boom for BG Medical"* **in Boston Business Journal (Vol. 31, June 17, 2011, No. 21, pp. 1)**
Pub: Boston Business Journal
Contact: Carolyn M. Jones, President
E-mail: cmjones@bizjournals.com
Ed: Julie M. Donnelly. **Description:** The Galectin-3 test failed to boost stock prices of its manufacturer, BG Medicine, which has fallen to $6.06/share. The company hopes that its revenue will be boosted by widespread adoption of an automated and faster version of the test, which diagnoses for heart failure. **Availability:** Online.

25759 ■ *"Developer To Use New Owasso Senior Care Center as Template for More Services, Expansion"* **in Journal Record (May 23, 2012)**
Description: A new $7.5 million senior care and rehabilitation center will be built in Owasso, Oklahoma. The builder, Steve Cox, is using his Senior Suites of Owasso as his model. JRJ Construction of Weatherford, Texas will complete the 105-bed private-suite facility by spring 2013. **Availability:** Print; Online.

25760 ■ *"Discovery Communications: Don't Sell, But Don't Buy"* **in Workforce Management (Vol. 88, December 14, 2009, No. 13, pp. 17)**
Pub: Crain Communications Inc.
Contact: Barry Asin, President
Ed: Jeremy Smerd. **Description:** Discovery Communications provides its employees a wealth of free health services via a comprehensive work-site medical clinic that is available to its employees and their dependents. Overview of the company's innovative approach to healthcare is presented. **Availability:** Online.

25761 ■ *"Dispelling Rocky Mountain Myths Key to Wellness"* **in Employee Benefit News (Vol. 25, November 1, 2011, No. 14, pp. 12)**
Pub: SourceMedia LLC
Contact: Gemma Postlethwaite, Chief Executive Officer
Ed: Andrea Davis. **Description:** Andrew Sykes, chairman of Health at Work Wellness Actuaries, states that it is a myth that Colorado is ranked as the healthiest state in America. Sykes helped implement a wellness programs at Brighton School District in the Denver area.

25762 ■ *"Docs Might Hold Cure for Baltimore-Area Real Estate, Banks"* **in Baltimore Business Journal (Vol. 28, November 5, 2010, No. 26, pp. 1)**
Pub: Baltimore Business Journal
Contact: Rhonda Pringle, President
E-mail: rpringle@bizjournals.com
Ed: Gary Haber. **Description:** Health care providers, including physicians are purchasing their office space instead of renting it as banks lower interest rates to 6 percent on mortgages for medical offices. The rise in demand offers relief to the commercial real estate market. It has also resulted in a boom in building new medical offices. **Availability:** Print; Online.

25763 ■ *"Doctor: J & J Alerted in '06 to Procedure Risks"* **in Pittsburgh Business Times (Vol. 33, June 6, 2014, No. 47, pp. 4)**
Pub: American City Business Journals, Inc.
Contact: Mike Olivieri, Executive Vice President
Released: Weekly. **Price:** $4, introductory 4-week offer(Digital & Print). **Description:** Dr. Robert Lamparter, then pathologist at Lewisburg's Evangelical Community Hospital, states that he had alerted Johnson and Johnson (J and J) in 2006 of the potential risk of spreading undetected cancer following the use of its power morcellator during hysterectomy procedures. J and J suspended worldwide sales of the device in April 2014 after the laboratory warning, and days after a US Food and Drug Administration advisory discouraging doctors from using it, but doctors are still divided over the morcellation procedure. **Availability:** Print; Online.

25764 ■ *"Doctor Shortage Continues to Plague Region"* **in Business First of Buffalo (Vol. 30, April 11, 2014, No. 30, pp. 6)**
Pub: American City Business Journals, Inc.
Contact: Mike Olivieri, Executive Vice President
Released: April 11, 2014. **Price:** $140, Digital & Print; $115, Digital only. **Description:** New York hospitals need at least 1,000 additional physicians, particularly primary care doctors, as they try to meet the criteria set by Federal health reform's Affordable Care Act. The Western New York region gained only 421 new physicians, while losing 544 in 2013. **Availability:** Print; Online.

25765 ■ *"Doctors Try 1st CRISPR Editing in the Body for Blindness"* **in Associated Press (March 4, 2020)**
Pub: Associated Press
Contact: Daisy Veerasingham, President
URL(s): https://apnews.com/17fcd6ae57d39d06b72ca40fe7cee461
Description: Staff at the Oregon Health & Science University performed the first-ever in vivo CRISPR gene edit procedure on a patient who had an inherited form of blindness. **Availability:** Online.

25766 ■ *"DT Interpreting VideoHub Service Expanding"* **in Internet Wire (March 26, 2012)**
Pub: Comtex News Network Inc.
Contact: Kan Devnani, President
Description: Profile of the Deaf-Talk Inc. has launched its new DTViedeoHub, to improve and expand its interpreting services to healthcare facilities. Details of the new program are included. **Availability:** Online.

25767 ■ *"Ducking the New Health-Care Taxes"* **in Barron's (Vol. 92, September 15, 2012, No. 38, pp. 34)**
Pub: Dow Jones & Company Inc.
Contact: Almar Latour, Chief Executive Officer
Ed: Elizabeth Ody. **Description:** Strategies that investors can use to avoid paying higher taxes starting January 2013 are discussed. These include selling assets by December 2012, distributing dividends, purchasing private-placement life insurance and converting individual retirement accounts. **Availability:** Online.

25768 ■ *"E-Medical Records Save Money, Time in Ann Arbor"* **in Crain's Detroit Business (Vol. 24, January 21, 2008, No. 3, pp. 6)**
Pub: Crain Communications Inc.
Contact: Barry Asin, President
Ed: Jay Greene. **Description:** Ann Arbor Area Health Information Exchange is improving patient outcomes by sharing clinical and administrative data in electronic medical record systems. **Availability:** Online.

25769 ■ *"Easing the Global (and Costly) Problem of Workplace Stress; Stress Is Reportedly the Leading Cause of Long-Term Sickness for Workers Around the World. But Relief Is In Sight"* **in Gallup Business Journal (March 27, 2014)**
Pub: Gallup, Inc.
Contact: Jon Clifton, Chief Executive Officer
Description: Stress is considered the leading cause of long-term illness for workers globally. According to an employee engagement survey, workplace stress can be reduced through engagement. **Availability:** Online.

25770 ■ *"Employers See Workers' Comp Rates Rising"* **in Sacramento Business Journal (Vol. 28, April 8, 2011, No. 6, pp. 1)**
Pub: Sacramento Business Journal
Contact: Stephanie Fretwell, Director
E-mail: sfretwell@bizjournals.com
Ed: Kelly Johnson. **Released:** Weekly. **Price:** $4. **Description:** Employers in California are facing higher workers compensation costs. Increased medical costs and litigation are seen to drive the trend. **Availability:** Online.

25771 ■ *"Everett Hospice Planned"* **in Puget Sound Business Journal (Vol. 29, September 26, 2008, No. 23, pp. 1)**
Description: Providence Senior and Community Services is pursuing a purchase-and-sales agreement for land in Everett to build a $9.7 million 20-bed hospice facility. The organization plans to break ground on the new facility in 2009. **Availability:** Print; Online.

25772 ■ *"Executive Summary: Codeines and Coding"* **in Business Strategy Review (Vol. 23, Spring 2012, No. 1, pp. 82)**
Description: Adam Powell, Sergei Savin, and Nicos Savva, 'Physician Workload and Hospital Reimbursement: Overworked Servers Generate Lower Income', working paper, August 2011 is examined. **Availability:** Online.

25773 ■ *"Expect Action on Health Care and the Economy"* **in Contractor (Vol. 57, January 2010, No. 1, pp. 30)**
Ed: Kevin Schwalb. **Description:** The Plumbing-Heating-Cooling Contractors National Association is working to solidify its standing in the public policy arena as the legislative agenda will focus on health care reform, estate tax and immigration reform, all of which will impact the industries. **Availability:** Print; Online.

25774 ■ *"Experts Sound Off On Top Legal Trends"* **in Birmingham Business Journal (Vol. 31, January 17, 2014, No. 3, pp. 4)**
Pub: American City Business Journals, Inc.
Contact: Mike Olivieri, Executive Vice President

Released: Weekly. **Price:** $4, introductory 4-week offer(Digital & Print). **Description:** Lawyers' views on potential legal trends in Birmingham, Alabama for 2014 are presented, with the Affordable Care Act leading the agenda. One attorney addressed the challenges associated with the use of social media. **Availability:** Print; Online.

25775 ■ *"Falling Through the Cracks of Vision Care"* in U.S. News & World Report (May 15, 2018)
URL(s): www.usnews.com/news/healthiest-communities/articles/2018-05-15/falling-through-the-insurance-gaps-for-vision-care
Released: May 15, 2018. **Description:** Discusses how lack of vision insurance has created medical concerns for 16 million Americans. While not often life-threatening, having vision issues can impact learning, jobs, and just everyday life, but most medical insurance plans do not cover vision. **Availability:** Online.

25776 ■ *"Family Takes Wind Turbine Companies to Court Over Gag Clauses on Health Effects of Turbines"* in CNW Group (September 12, 2011)
Pub: CNW Group Ltd.
Description: Shawn and Trisha Drennan are concerned about the negative experiences other have had with wind turbines close to their homes, including adverse health effects. The couple's home will be approximately 650 meters from the Kingsbridge II wind farm project in Ontario, Canada. **Availability:** Online.

25777 ■ *"Feds to Pay University Hospital $20M"* in Business Courier (Vol. 27, July 23, 2010, No. 12, pp. 3)
Pub: Business Courier
Ed: James Ritchie. **Description:** The U.S. government is set to pay University Hospital and medical residents who trained there $20 million as part of a tax dispute settlement. Around 1,000 former residents are to receive tax refunds. But the hospital must provide the U.S. Internal Revenue Service with extensive documentation. **Availability:** Print; Mailing list; Online.

25778 ■ *"Firms Bet On Games To Hike Wellness"* in Business Journal (Vol. 30, June 1, 2012, No. 1, pp. 1)
Pub: American City Business Journals, Inc.
Contact: Mike Olivieri, Executive Vice President
Ed: Katharine Grayson. **Released:** Weekly. **Price:** $4, introductory 4-week offer(Digital only). **Description:** Twin Cities-based firms providing corporate wellness services are integrating games into these programs. These games include friendly competitions between work teams or high-tech smartphone applications. **Availability:** Print; Online.

25779 ■ *The Flaw of Averages: Why We Underestimate Risk in the Face of Uncertainty*
Pub: John Wiley & Sons, Inc.
Contact: Christina Van Tassell, Executive Vice President Chief Financial Officer
Ed: Sam L. Savage. **Released:** March 26, 2012. **Price:** $19.95, paperback; $27.95, hardcover; $12.99, E-Book. **Description:** Personal and business plans are based on uncertainties on a daily basis. The common avoidable mistake individuals make in assessing risk in the face of uncertainty is defined. The explains why plans based on average assumptions are wrong, on average, in areas as diverse as finance, healthcare, accounting, the war on terror, and climate change. **Availability:** E-book; Print.

25780 ■ *"Florida Hospital Planning $104.1M in Expansions"* in Orlando Business Journal (Vol. 29, June 8, 2012, No. 53, pp. 1)
Pub: Baltimore Business Journal
Contact: Rhonda Pringle, President
E-mail: rpringle@bizjournals.com
Description: Florida Hospital is planning $104.1 million in expansion projects that will create about 140 new permanent health care jobs and 576 temporary contruction jobs. The projects include an emergency department and medical office space in Winter Garden, an expanded emergency department at Florida Hospital East Orlando and additional floors in Ginsburg Tower at Florida Hospital Orlando. **Availability:** Print; Online.

25781 ■ *"Florida Hospital, UCF Affiliation in Danger?"* in Orlando Business Journal (Vol. 29, September 21, 2012, No. 29, pp. 1)
Pub: Baltimore Business Journal
Contact: Rhonda Pringle, President
E-mail: rpringle@bizjournals.com
Description: Florida Hospital is said to be considering the possibility of terminating its affiliation agreement with the University of Central Florida's (UCF) College of Medicine that ends June 30, 2018. Two of the reasons for the move include UCF's plans for a teaching hospital and a new graduate medical education program that could place Florida Hospital into competition with UCF. **Availability:** Print; Online.

25782 ■ *"For Gilead, Growth Beyond AIDS"* in Barron's (Vol. 88, June 30, 2008, No. 26, pp. 18)
Pub: Dow Jones & Company Inc.
Contact: Almar Latour, Chief Executive Officer
Ed: Jay Palmer. **Description:** First-quarter 2008 revenue for Gilead Sciences grew by 22 percent and an earnings gain of 19 percent thanks to their HIV-treatment drugs that comprised over two-thirds of the company's sales in 2007. An analyst has a 12-month target from June, 2008 of 65 per share. The factors behind the company's prospects are also discussed. **Availability:** Online.

25783 ■ *"For-Profit Medical School Ramping Up for Business"* in Sacramento Business Journal (Vol. 30, February 21, 2014, No. 52, pp. 6)
Pub: American City Business Journals, Inc.
Contact: Mike Olivieri, Executive Vice President
Description: California Northstate University got full accreditation for the College of Pharmacy at Elk Grove in summer 2013 and hopes to start classes in August or September 2014. The university is in talks to acquire a second building in the area worth $15 million. **Availability:** Online.

25784 ■ *"Forest Park Medical Center to Double Operations"* in Dallas Business Journal (Vol. 35, April 13, 2012, No. 31, pp. 1)
Pub: Baltimore Business Journal
Contact: Rhonda Pringle, President
E-mail: rpringle@bizjournals.com
Description: Dallas, Texas-based Neal Richards Group launched a growth plan for the Forest Park Medical Center System called '12 by 12' that will more than double its hospital count in the next two years. The group wants to have 12 Forest Park facilities open or in various levels of development by the end of 2012. Forest Park is a physician-owned system. **Availability:** Print; Online.

25785 ■ *"Four Ways Hospitals Can Reduce Patient Readmissions; Hospitals Have a Powerful Financial Incentive to Reduce Readmissions. Here Are the Most Effective Strategies"* in Gallup Business Journal (July 2, 2014)
Pub: Gallup, Inc.
Contact: Jon Clifton, Chief Executive Officer
Description: The Centers for Medicare and Medicaid Services (CMS) report readmissions as hospitalizations that occur within 30 days of discharge. Hospitals need to identify and implement the right strategies to reduce readmissions. **Availability:** Print.

25786 ■ *"Generation Y: Engaging the Invincibles"* in Employee Benefit News (Vol. 25, November 1, 2011, No. 14, pp. 22)
Pub: SourceMedia LLC
Contact: Gemma Postlethwaite, Chief Executive Officer
Ed: Brenna Shebel, Dannel Dan. **Description:** Employers will need to engage younger workers about healthcare decisions and lifestyle improvement as they become the majority worker as boomers retire. **Availability:** Online.

25787 ■ *"Genetic Counselor"* in Occupational Outlook Quarterly (Vol. 55, Summer 2011, No. 2, pp. 34)
Pub: U.S. Department of Labor Bureau of Labor Statistics
Contact: Amrit Kohli, Director
E-mail: kohli.amrit@bls.gov
Ed: John Mullins. **Description:** Genetic counseling involves the practice of informing clients about genetic disorders and to help them understand and manage a disorder. There are approximately 2,400 certified genetic counselors in the U.S. and earn a median annual salary of about $63,000, according to the American Board of Genetic Counseling. The US Bureau of Labor Statistics does not have data on employment or wages for genetic counselors. **Availability:** PDF; Online.

25788 ■ *"Giving Biotech Startups a Hand"* in Philadelphia Business Journal (Vol. 28, January 8, 2010, No. 47, pp. 1)
Pub: Philadelphia Business Journal
Contact: Sierra Quinn, Director
E-mail: squinn@bizjournals.com
Ed: John George. **Description:** Elkins Park, Pennsylvania-based BioStrategy Partners is a virtual life sciences incubator that is seeking to improve the dull ranking of Philadelphia in the small business vitality index of life sciences. BioStrategy provides technology and business development services to startup life sciences companies and university-based research projects. **Availability:** Online.

25789 ■ *"Glossary of Health Benefit Terms"* in HRMagazine (Vol. 53, August 2008, No. 8, pp. 78)
Pub: Society for Human Resource Management
Contact: Johnny C. Taylor, Jr., President
E-mail: shrmceo@shrm.org
Description: Glossary of health benefit terms is presented to help when choosing a health benefits package. **Availability:** Print; Online.

25790 ■ *"Good for Business: Houston is a Hot Spot for Economic Growth"* in Black Enterprise (Vol. 37, October 2006, No. 3, pp. 216)
Pub: Earl G. Graves Ltd.
Contact: Earl Graves, Jr., President
Ed: Jeanette Valentine. **Description:** Fast-growing sectors in the biotechnology and healthcare industries are among the driving forces of Houston's economic growth. More than 76,000 small businesses in the area employ about one in four area workers, according to the Small Business Administration. Housing and business costs are 26 and 11 percent below the national average, respectively, garnering the attention of corporate giants.

25791 ■ *"Halls Give Hospital Drive $11 Million Infusion"* in The Business Journal-Serving Metropolitan Kansas City (Vol. 26, July 18, 2008)
Description: Don Hall, chairman of Hallmark Cards Inc., and eight family members have announced that they will give $11 million to Children's Mercy Hospitals and Clinics for its $800 million expansion plan. Hall Family Foundation president Bill Hall that contributions such as that for Children's Mercy reflect the charitable interests of the foundation's board and founders. The possible impacts of the Hall's donation are analyzed.

25792 ■ *"Healing Power from Medical Waste"* in Memphis Business Journal (Vol. 33, March 30, 2012, No. 51, pp. 1)
Pub: Baltimore Business Journal
Contact: Rhonda Pringle, President
E-mail: rpringle@bizjournals.com

Description: Tennessee-based BioD LLC has been using amniotic fluid in placenta from cesarian section births, which was considered as biomedical waste, to make various compounds that are used to develop stem cell-based healing products. BioD has sales of $3 million in 2011 and it expects sales of $6 million in 2012. **Availability:** Print; Online.

25793 ■ *"Health Care Briefs: Survey Says Most Approve of Donating Used Pacemakers to Medically Underserved"* in *Crain's Detroit Business (Vol. 25, June 1, 2009)*
Pub: Crain Communications Inc.
Contact: Barry Asin, President
Description: According to a survey conducted by University of Michigan Cardiovascular Center, 87 percent of those with pacemakers and 71 percent of the general population would donate the device to patients in underserved nations.

25794 ■ *"Health Care of the Future"* in *Business Journal Serving Greater Tampa Bay (Vol. 30, November 19, 2010, No. 48, pp. 1)*
Pub: Tampa Bay Business Journal
Contact: Ian Anderson, President
E-mail: ianderson@bizjournals.com
Description: Information about accountable care organizations (ACO), which are integrated care systems with doctors and hospitals working closely together to handle patient care, is provided. The Patient Protection and Affordable Care Act paved the way for ACOs as Medicare demonstration projects. **Availability:** Online.

25795 ■ *"Health-Care Highway"* in *Saint Louis Business Journal (Vol. 32, October 14, 2011, No. 7, pp. 1)*
Pub: Saint Louis Business Journal
Contact: Robert Bobroff, President
E-mail: rbobroff@bizjournals.com
Ed: Angela Mueller. **Description:** Around $2.6 billion will be invested in health care facilities along the Highway 64/40 corridor in St. Louis, Missouri. Mercy Hospital is planning to invest $19 million in a virtual care center. St. Elizabeth's Hospital on the other hand, will purchase 105 acres in the corridor. **Availability:** Print; Online.

25796 ■ *"Health care: Medicare Inc."* in *Canadian Business (Vol. 80, October 8, 2007, No. 20, pp. 160)*
Pub: Rogers Media Inc.
Contact: Neil Spivak, Chief Executive Officer
Ed: Erin Pooley. **Description:** State of Canada's health care system is discussed. A report by the Fraser Institute in Vancouver predicts that public health spending in six of ten provinces in the country will use more than half the revenues from all sources by 2020. Experts believe competition in the health care industry will help solve the current problems in the sector. **Availability:** Print; Online.

25797 ■ *"Health Centers Plan Expansion: $3M from D.C. Expected; Uninsured a Target"* in *Crain's Detroit Business (Vol. 25, June 15, 2009, No. 24, pp. 3)*
Pub: Crain Communications Inc.
Contact: Barry Asin, President
Ed: Jay Greene. **Description:** Detroit has five federally qualified health centers that plan to receive over $3 million in federal stimulus money that will be used to expand projects that will care for uninsured patients. **Availability:** Print; Online.

25798 ■ *"Health Clinic Expansion Fuels Debate Over Care In Massachusetts"* in *Boston Business Journal (Vol. 34, June 27, 2014, No. 21, pp. 9)*
Pub: American City Business Journals, Inc.
Contact: Mike Olivieri, Executive Vice President
Released: Weekly. **Description:** The announcement of expansion by several retail health clinics has fueled debate over their quality and competiveness. AFC Doctors Express, a fast-growing chain of retail health clinics, announced its plan to open two new locations in Massachusetts in 2014 and CVS's MinuteClinic announced its intention to open nine additional locations. Concerns are being raised about the cost and quality of this type of healthcare, with a medical society expressing concern that this is fragmented care, not comprehensive care. **Availability:** Print; Online.

25799 ■ *"Health Giants Throw Support Behind Sports Centers"* in *Pittsburgh Business Times (Vol. 34, July 25, 2014, No. 1, pp. 8)*
Pub: American City Business Journals, Inc.
Contact: Mike Olivieri, Executive Vice President
Released: Weekly. **Price:** $4, introductory 4-week offer(Digital & Print). **Description:** Allegheny Health Network will provide health services for the $19 million Cool Springs Sports Complex being constructed in two phases in Bethel Park. Meanwhile, UPMC is developing the $70 UPMC Lemieux Sports Complex in Cranberry Township, which will include a center for sports medicine together with two ice rinks that will be used as a practice facility for the Pittsburgh Penguins as well as by high school teams and figure skaters. **Availability:** Print; Online.

25800 ■ *"Health IT Regulations Generate Static Among Providers"* in *Philadelphia Business Journal (Vol. 28, January 29, 2010, No. 50, pp. 1)*
Pub: Philadelphia Business Journal
Contact: Sierra Quinn, Director
E-mail: squinn@bizjournals.com
Ed: John George. **Description:** US Centers for Medicaid and Medicare Services and the Office of the National Coordinator for Health Information Technology have proposed rules regarding the meaningful use of electronic health records. The rules must be complied with by hospitals and physicians to qualify for federal stimulus funds. **Availability:** Online.

25801 ■ *"Health Reform Could Expand HSA-Based Plans"* in *Workforce Management (Vol. 88, December 14, 2009, No. 13, pp. 6)*
Description: HSA-qualified plans are the cheapest insurance plans on the market as they have a higher deductible but cost less upfront. If health care reform passes, HSA-qualified plans should benefit greatly. **Availability:** Print; Online.

25802 ■ *"Health Reform: How to Make it Cheaper"* in *Business Courier (Vol. 26, December 11, 2009, No. 33, pp. 1)*
Description: Greater Cincinnati health care leaders shared views about the health care reform bill. Respondents included the Cincinnati Visiting Nurse's Wallen Falberg, healthcare consultant Hirsch Cohen, Greater Cincinnati Health Council's Coleen O'Toole, Employer Health Care Alliance's Sharron DiMario, Legal Aid Society of Greater Cincinnati's Col Owens, Christ Hospital's Susan Croushore, and Humana of Ohio's Tim Cappel. **Availability:** Online.

25803 ■ *"Health Science Center's Capital Campaign Will Boost Local Research"* in *San Antonio Business Journal (Vol. 28, March 14, 2014, No. 5, pp. 8)*
Pub: American City Business Journals, Inc.
Contact: Mike Olivieri, Executive Vice President
Description: The University of Texas Health Science Center at San Antonio's Campaign for the Future of fundraising project has been completed. The Health Science Center is expected to use the money to support research at the South Texas Medical Center. The capital campaign will allow the Health Science Center to become one of the most prominent universities in the U.S. **Availability:** Print; Online.

25804 ■ *"Healthcare Facilities Increasingly Embracing Dynamic Glass to Benefit Patients"* in *Ecology, Environment & Conservation Business (May 24, 2014)*
Pub: NewsRX LLC.
Contact: Kalani Rosell, Contact
Description: According to research, optimizing natural daylight and outdoor views in healthcare facilities helps to improve outcomes and shorter recovery times for patients. Therefore, a growing number of healthcare facilities are incorporating SageGlass(R) dynamic glass, a product of Saint-Gobain, into their new construction and remodeling/renovation designs. **Availability:** Online.

25805 ■ *"Healthy Dose of New Vitality"* in *Business Courier (Vol. 24, February 28, 2008, No. 47, pp. 1)*
Pub: American City Business Journals, Inc.
Contact: Mike Olivieri, Executive Vice President
Ed: Dan Monk. **Description:** Healthy Advice plans to become a leading consumer brand and expand to pharmacies and hospitals. The growth opportunities for healthy Advice are discussed. **Availability:** Online.

25806 ■ *"Healthy Start for Medical Kiosks; Lions Kick in $20K"* in *Crain's Detroit Business (Vol. 28, June 11, 2012, No. 24, pp. 18)*
Pub: Crain Communications Inc.
Contact: Barry Asin, President
Ed: Jay Greene. **Description:** Detroit Lions Charities has given Henry Ford Health System's school-based and community health program money to purchase nine interactive health kiosks. These kiosks will be provided by Medical Imagineering LLC, a spinoff of Henry Ford's Innovation Institute and installed in elementary and middle schools in Detroit. **Availability:** Print; Online.

25807 ■ *"Hearing Damage Leads to Settlement"* in *Register-Guard (August 13, 2011)*
Description: Cynergy Pest Control lost a court battle when a rural Cottage Grove man was granted a $37,000 settlement after his hearing was damaged by the pest control companies method to eradicate gophers, using blasts in his neighbor's yard. **Availability:** Print; Online.

25808 ■ *"The Heart of Health Village: innovation Is Key, and to Get It, Florida Hospital Is Wooing Disruptors, Millenials"* in *Orlando Business Journal (Vol. 30, May 16, 2014, No. 47, pp. 4)*
Pub: American City Business Journals, Inc.
Contact: Mike Olivieri, Executive Vice President
Released: May 16, 2014. **Description:** The economic impact of Florida Hospital's planned Health Village in downtown Orlando is explored. The 172-acre development aims to bring together business people, scientists for research, and early and mid-stage companies to combine co-working activities in its Medical Innovation Laboratory. **Availability:** Print; Online.

25809 ■ *"Heart Hospitals Ranked for Mortality Rates"* in *Philadelphia Business Journal (Vol. 30, September 2, 2011, No. 29, pp. 1)*
Pub: Philadelphia Business Journal
Contact: Sierra Quinn, Director
E-mail: squinn@bizjournals.com
Ed: John George. **Description:** Centers for Medicare and Medicaid Services (CMS) released updated data on mortality rates for heart attack patients as hospitals in Pennsylvania. Doylestown Hospital posted the lowest mortality rates with 10.9 percent, tying the fourth best in the entire nation. Other details on the CMS data are presented. **Availability:** Online.

25810 ■ *"Help Wanted: 100 Hospital IT Workers"* in *Business Courier (Vol. 27, October 8, 2010, No. 23, pp. 1)*
Pub: Business Courier
Ed: James Ritchie. **Description:** Hospitals in the Greater Cincinnati area are expected to hire more than 100 information technology (IT) workers to help digitize medical records. Financial incentives from the health care reform bill encouraged investments in electronic medical record systems, increasing the demand for IT workers that would help make information exchange across the healthcare system easier. **Availability:** Print; Online.

25811 ■ "Home Instead Senior Care Introduces Post-Discharge Care Initiative; Aims to Reduce Hospital Readmissions Among Seniors" in Benzinga.com (September 18, 2012)
Pub: Benzinga.com
Contact: Jason Raznick, Founder
Released: September 18, 2012. **Description:** Home Instead Senior Care(R) launched its new, much-needed health program that provides care and support services, mostly for seniors, after being discharged from the hospital. The service is aimed at reducing the number of unnecessary hospital readmissions. **Availability:** Online.

25812 ■ "Home Instead Senior Care of Seacoast and Southern New Hampshire" inNew Hampshire Business Review (Vol. 34, April 6, 2012, No. 7, pp. 45)
Description: Portsmouth, New Hampshire-based Home Instead Senior Care of Seacoast and Southern New Hampshire launched a specialized training program for professional and family caregivers designed to help them improve the quality of life for those living with dementia and the families who support them. **Availability:** Online.

25813 ■ "Hopkins, University of Maryland, Baltimore Worry Reduced NIH Budget Will Impact Research" in Baltimore Business Journal (Vol. 29, August 19, 2011, No. 15, pp. 1)
Pub: Boston Business Journal
Contact: Carolyn M. Jones, President
E-mail: cmjones@bizjournals.com
Ed: Scott Dance. **Description:** The budget for the National Institutes of Health (NIH) is slated to be cut by at least 7.9 percent to $2.5 billion in 2013. This will have a big negative effect on medical and biotech research in Maryland, especially Johns Hopkins University and University of Maryland, Baltimore which could face stiffer completion for grants from the NIH. **Availability:** Online.

25814 ■ "Hospital Communication Goes Mobile" in Providence Business News (Vol. 29, July 7, 2014, No. 14, pp. 12)
Pub: American City Business Journals, Inc.
Contact: Mike Olivieri, Executive Vice President
Released: July 05, 2014. **Description:** Software company, Care Thread, has designed a mobile health records application that allows providers to share patient e-medical records over a secure network. Care Thread signed a contract for the system with Eastern Connecticut Health Network and Boston's Brigham and Women's Hospital as well as a deal with health care management firm Beacon Partners Inc. to sell and implement the app across the U.S. **Availability:** Print; Online.

25815 ■ "Hospital Revenue Healthier in 2009" in Orlando Business Journal (Vol. 26, February 5, 2010, No. 36, pp. 1)
Pub: Orlando Business Journal
Contact: Julie Swyers, Director
E-mail: jswyers@bizjournals.com
Ed: Melanie Stawicki Azam. **Description:** Orlando Health, Health Central and Adventist Health System are Florida-based hospital systems that generated the most profits in 2009. Orlando Health had the highest profit in 2009 at $73.3 million, contrary to about $31 million in losses in 2008. The increased profits are attributed to stock market recovery, cost-cutting initiatives, and rising patient volumes. **Availability:** Print; Online.

25816 ■ "Hospitals Say Medicaid Expansion is Critical" in Dallas Business Journal (Vol. 35, August 3, 2012, No. 47, pp. 1)
Pub: Baltimore Business Journal
Contact: Rhonda Pringle, President
E-mail: rpringle@bizjournals.com
Ed: Bill Hethcock, Matt Joyce. **Description:** Governor Rick Perry's rejection of the Texas expansion of Medicaid is met with disapproval by health organizations such as the Methodist Health System. The federal government has extended $70 billion in financing to help more Texans become eligible for primary health care. Expansion supporters argue that Medicaid is critical in lowering insurance osts for those who need it. **Availability:** Print; Online.

25817 ■ "Hospitals Singing OB Blues" in Philadelphia Business Journal (Vol. 31, April 6, 2012, No. 8, pp. 1)
Pub: Baltimore Business Journal
Contact: Rhonda Pringle, President
E-mail: rpringle@bizjournals.com
Description: Pennsylvania hospitals are seen to receive lower payments for normal born births involving women covered by medical assistance. The Pennsylvania Department of Welfare has proposed to eliminate separate payments for infant care for normal deliveries. **Availability:** Print; Online.

25818 ■ "Hospitals Try to Buy Smarter" in Crain's Detroit Business (Vol. 25, June 1, 2009, No. 22, pp. M025)
Pub: Crain Communications Inc.
Contact: Barry Asin, President
Ed: Jay Greene. **Description:** Hospitals in southeast Michigan are using bulk discount purchasing of medical and non-medical supplies through group purchasing organizations in order to cut costs. **Availability:** Online.

25819 ■ "Hospitals Vying to Buy Physician Associates LLC" in Orlando Business Journal (Vol. 29, August 31, 2012, No. 11, pp. 1)
Pub: Baltimore Business Journal
Contact: Rhonda Pringle, President
E-mail: rpringle@bizjournals.com
Description: Hospitals is battling it out on who gets to buy Physician Associates LLC, the largest multi-specialty practice in Central Florida. The most likely candidates to purchase the practice are Orlando Health and Florida Hospital. The deal could be worth $20 million to $60 million and it could also hike health care costs since Physician Asociates serves 19 percent of Central Florida's uninsured population. **Availability:** Print; Online.

25820 ■ "Houston Doctors Buy In to Medical Timeshares" in Houston Business Journal (Vol. 40, December 11, 2009, No. 31, pp. 1)
Pub: Houston Business Journal
Contact: Bob Charlet, President
E-mail: bcharlet@bizjournals.com
Ed: Mary Ann Azevedo. **Description:** Memorial Hermann Hospital System has leased to doctors three examination rooms and medical office space in the Memorial Hermann Medical Plaza in line with its new timeshare concept. The concept was designed to bring primary care physicians to its Texas Medical Center campus. **Availability:** Print; Online.

25821 ■ "How to Conduct a Functional Magnetic Resonance (fMRI) Study in Social Science Research" in MIS Quarterly (Vol. 36, September 2012, No. 3, pp. 811)
Pub: University of Minnesota Carlson School of Management Management Information Systems Research Center
Ed: Angelika Dimoka. **Description:** A set of guidelines for conducting functional magnetic resonance imaging studies in social sciences and information systems research is provided. **Availability:** PDF; Online.

25822 ■ "How to Get a Workplace Wellness Program for Your Office" in Entrepreneurs (June 2014)
Pub: Entrepreneur Media Inc.
Contact: Dan Bova, Director
E-mail: dbova@entrepreneur.com
Description: Workplace wellness programs can be started by checking with insurers who may provide program and activity suggestions promotional materials or other resources. Teaming up with others is encouraged. For instance, employees from various departments or nearby companies can get flu shots or blood pressure screening. Management should also get involved in these programs, because it will then be known among employees that wellness is taken seriously. It is also important that workplace wellness programs are kept safe and legally sound. **Availability:** Online.

25823 ■ "How Healthcare Managers Can Improve Outcomes and Patient Care; They Can Start With These Five Steps for Turning their Organization's Employee Engagement Results Into Clinical Improvements" in Gallup Business Journal (August 7, 2014)
Pub: Gallup, Inc.
Contact: Jon Clifton, Chief Executive Officer
Description: Health care managers can improve outcomes and patient care by following the five steps outlined in this article. **Availability:** Print; Online.

25824 ■ "How Healthcare Organizations Can Help Improve Social Risk Interventions" in RevCycle Intelligence (February 6, 2023)
URL(s): revcycleintelligence.com/news/how-heal thcare-organizations-can-help-improve-social-risk-in terventions
Ed: Victoria Bailey. **Released:** February 06, 2023. **Description:** Patients who check into hospitals often face social determinants, which often lead to poor outcomes in health care outcomes. Discusses pros and cons of adding collaborative social services within the healthcare sector. **Availability:** Online.

25825 ■ "How to Open a Private Medical Practice, Step by Step" in Business News Daily (February 28, 2023)
URL(s): www.businessnewsdaily.com/8910-opening-a-medical-practice.html
Ed: Max Freedman. **Released:** February 28, 2023. **Description:** Opening a private medical office could be a good choice for certain healthcare professionals. Included is a discussion on how to do that and certain operations that should be considered. **Availability:** Online.

25826 ■ "How Quitting Tobacco Reshaped CVS: Q&A with CEO Larry Merlo" in USA Today (September 14, 2019)
URL(s): www.usatoday.com/story/money/2019/09/03/cvs-pharmacy-tobacco-sales-ceo-larry-merlo/2151148001/
Description: In September 2014, CVS quit selling tobacco products. CEO Larry Merlo discusses the impact that decision has made on its stores and the health of the American people. **Availability:** Online.

25827 ■ "Handling New Health Insurance Regulations" in Baltimore Business Journal (Vol. 31, April 25, 2014, No. 52, pp. 25)
Pub: American City Business Journals, Inc.
Contact: Mike Olivieri, Executive Vice President
Released: March 13, 2014. **Description:** Research and consulting firm, Mercer, surveyed businesses in January 2014 to examine their employer-sponsored health plans following enrollment in the Affordable Care Act-created exchanges. The survey found employers were taking advantage of a delay to a key regulation in the Act on offering insurance to employees who work at least 30 hours a week. **Availability:** Print; Online.

25828 ■ How to Start a Home-Based Senior Care Business
Ed: James L. Ferry. **Released:** 2nd edition. **Price:** Paperback,softback; Electronic Book. **Description:** Information is provided to start a home-based senior care business. **Availability:** E-book; Print.

25829 ■ "How To Spark Up a Medical Marijuana Firm in Florida - and Not Get Burned in the Process" in Orlando Business Journal (Vol. 30, March 21, 2014, No. 39, pp. 6)
Pub: American City Business Journals, Inc.
Contact: Mike Olivieri, Executive Vice President
Released: Weekly. **Price:** $8, introductory 4-week offer(Digital & Print). **Description:** Colorado business owners and experts offer tips on starting a medical marijuana business in Florida. Andy Williams recalls that he was filled with fear he would wake up in

25830 ■ **Healthcare and Social Assistance**

Federal prison and not see his family again when he started Medicine Man. Jerald Bovine of GreenZipp.com advises those interested in entering the medical marijuana field to know the details of regulation of facilities and labs. **Availability:** Print; Online.

25830 ■ *"Humana Seeks Higher Stake in Memphis Market"* in *Memphis Business Journal (Vol. 33, February 17, 2012, No. 45, pp. 1)*
Pub: Baltimore Business Journal
Contact: Rhonda Pringle, President
E-mail: rpringle@bizjournals.com

Ed: Christopher Sheffield. **Description:** Humana of Tennessee has been hoping to get a bigger share of the West Tennessee insurance market through its new three-year contract with Baptist Memorial Health Care Corporation. Louisville, Kentucky-based Humana Inc. has a business relationship with Baptist that stretches back more than two decades. **Availability:** Print; Online.

25831 ■ *"Hunhu Healthcare Gets Some Mayo Help"* in *Business Journal (Vol. 32, August 29, 2014, No. 14, pp. 4)*
Pub: American City Business Journals, Inc.
Contact: Mike Olivieri, Executive Vice President

Description: Hunhu Healthcare Inc. has signed a licensing agreement with Mayo Clinic to develop mobile and Web applications that will enable patients to communicate with the company's network using social networking tools. The firm is expected to charge a monthly fee for the service. **Availability:** Print; Online.

25832 ■ *"I Hate My Hearing Aids. What Do I Do?"* in *Healthy Hearing (November 12, 2019)*
URL(s): www.healthyhearing.com/report/53024-I-hate-my-hearing-aids

Ed: Debbie Clason. **Released:** November 12, 2019. **Description:** A guide to how to like your new hearing aids. Most people who first receive hearing aids, are not used to them and find them to be uncomfortable. Learning to adjust to these devices is key, because your brain is not used to hearing particular sounds and must relearn them. **Availability:** Online.

25833 ■ *"In Chesterfield: Paletta's Operations Raise Competitors' Blood Pressure"* in *St. Louis Business Journal (Vol. 33, August 17, 2012, No. 52, pp. 1)*
Pub: Baltimore Business Journal
Contact: Rhonda Pringle, President
E-mail: rpringle@bizjournals.com

Description: The proposed relocation of Doctor George Paletta Jr.'s Orthopedic Center of Saint Louis to a new 62,000-square-foot facility was met with opposition by local hospital officials and the Missouri Hospital Association. Officials state the facility must be licensed as a hospital in order to provide overnight post-operative care as planned by Paletta.

25834 ■ *"In the Raw: Karyn Calabrese Brings Healthy Dining to a New Sophisticated Level"* in *Black Enterprise (Vol. 41, September 2010)*
Pub: Earl G. Graves Ltd.
Contact: Earl Graves, Jr., President

Ed: Sonia Alleyne. **Description:** Profile of Karyn Calabrese whose businesses are based in Chicago, Illinois. Calabrese has launched a complete line of products (vitamins and beauty items), services (spa, chiropractic, and acupuncture treatments), and restaurants to bring health dining and lifestyles to a better level. **Availability:** Online.

25835 ■ *"Independence Blue Cross Reverses Membership Slide"* in *Philadelphia Business Journal (Vol. 30, September 23, 2011, No. 32, pp. 1)*
Pub: Philadelphia Business Journal
Contact: Sierra Quinn, Director
E-mail: squinn@bizjournals.com

Ed: John George. **Description:** Health insurer Independence Blue Cross (IBC) added more than 40,000 members across all product lines since the start of 2011. It has 2.2 million members in Pennsylvania's Philadelphia region and 3.1 million members across the U.S. Services and other growth-related plans of IBC are covered. **Availability:** Online.

25836 ■ *"Infographic: Social Spending by Country: How Bloated is European Social Spending?"* in *Canadian Business (Vol. 85, August 13, 2012, No. 13, pp. 66)*

Ed: James Cowan. **Description:** A study conducted by the World Bank found that social spending in Europe is higher than the rest of the world combined. A chart is presented which illustrates government spending on social protection in European countries and in other countries. **Availability:** Print; Online.

25837 ■ *"Infusion Device Gets $1.47 Million Army Grant"* in *Memphis Business Journal (Vol. 33, January 20, 2012, No. 41, pp. 1)*
Pub: Baltimore Business Journal
Contact: Rhonda Pringle, President
E-mail: rpringle@bizjournals.com

Ed: Michael Sheffield. **Description:** Infusense has procured a $1.47 million grant from the US Army to develop an automated delivery system for the anesthesia Propofol. The drug is used in more than 70 million surgeries and procedures in the country. The medical device would allow for the administration of the anesthesia to wounded soldiers by medics in the field. **Availability:** Print; Online.

25838 ■ *"Innovation: A Blood Test on a Chip"* in *Inc. (Vol. 33, November 2011, No. 9, pp. 42)*
Pub: Inc. Magazine

Ed: Christine Chafkin-Lagorio. **Description:** Harvard University researchers have developed a device called the mChip that produces accurate blood tests in about 10 minutes. Plans to apply for FDA approval for the mChip in the US should happen in 2012. **Availability:** Online.

25839 ■ *"Innovative Trauma Care Sets Up U.S. HQ in San Antonio"* in *San Antonio Business Journal (Vol. 26, August 31, 2012, No. 31, pp. 1)*
Pub: Baltimore Business Journal
Contact: Rhonda Pringle, President
E-mail: rpringle@bizjournals.com

Description: Canadian biotech firm Innovative Trauma Care (ITC) has selected San Antonio, Texas as the location of its new US headquarters. The selection could boost the reputation of San Antonio region as a hub for medical technology and trauma-related expertise. **Availability:** Print; Online.

25840 ■ *"Inventive Doctor New Venture Partner"* in *Houston Business Journal (Vol. 40, January 29, 2010, No. 38, pp. A2)*
Pub: Houston Business Journal
Contact: Bob Charlet, President
E-mail: bcharlet@bizjournals.com

Ed: Ford Gunter. **Description:** Dr. Billy Cohn, a surgeon from Houston, Texas has been named as venture partner for venture firm Sante Ventures LLC of Austin, Texas. Cohn will be responsible for seeing marketable developing technologies in the medical industry. The motivation for Cohn's naming as venture partner is his development of a minimally invasive therapy for end-stage renal disease. **Availability:** Print; Online.

25841 ■ *"Investing In Employee Health, Wellness"* in *South Florida Business Journal (Vol. 34, June 6, 2014, No. 46, pp. 28)*
Pub: American City Business Journals, Inc.
Contact: Mike Olivieri, Executive Vice President

Released: Weekly. **Price:** $8, introductory 4-week offer(Digital & Print). **Description:** Companies are investing in employee wellness programs as an employee benefit because health issues within the organization can lead to absenteeism and unproductive employees. The results of a study indicate that losses from absenteeism across all professions could reach $84 billion. **Availability:** Print; Online.

GENERAL SMALL BUSINESS TOPICS

25842 ■ *"Investment In Israel Is Investment in the Future of Georgia"* in *Atlanta Business Chronicle (May 30, 2014, pp. 22A)*
Pub: American City Business Journals, Inc.
Contact: Mike Olivieri, Executive Vice President

Description: Georgia Governor Nathan Deal will travel to Israel to lead an economic and trade mission and consolidate Georgia's trade ties with Israel. Israel and the State of Georgia are already collaborating in the fields of health information technology, agrotechnology, homeland security, defense, aerospace and cybersecurity, and microelectronics and nanotechnology. The proposed visit by the Governor will build on this particular partnership from which both parties will benefit. **Availability:** Print; Online.

25843 ■ *"Is Your Employees' BMI Your Business?"* in *Canadian Business (Vol. 83, September 14, 2010, No. 15, pp. 98)*
Pub: Rogers Media Inc.
Contact: Neil Spivak, Chief Executive Officer

Ed: Jacqueline Nelson. **Description:** Canada's Public Health Agency's research shows that there is a solid business case for companies to promote active living to their employees. However, employers must toe the line between being helpful and being invasive. Insights into the issues faces by companies when introducing health programs are discussed. **Availability:** Online.

25844 ■ *"I've Always Been an Entrepreneur"* in *South Florida Business Journal (Vol. 34, June 13, 2014, No. 47, pp. 11)*
Pub: American City Business Journals, Inc.
Contact: Mike Olivieri, Executive Vice President

Released: June 13, 2014. **Price:** $4, Introductory 4-Week Offer(Digital & Print). **Description:** Modernizing Medicine CEO, Daniel Cane, says he started doing business at age six when he opened a lemonade stand. His firm helps physicians increase efficiencies in their practices while improving both business and treatment outcomes. He surrounds himself with talented people, which is what he likes most about his job. Cane added that dividing time between work and family is difficult for entrepreneurs. **Availability:** Print; Online.

25845 ■ *"Kaiser Permanente's Innovation on the Front Lines"* in *Harvard Business Review (Vol. 88, September 2010, No. 9, pp. 92)*
Pub: Harvard Business Publishing
Contact: Diane Belcher, Managing Director

Ed: Lew McCreary. **Price:** $8.95. **Description:** Kaiser Permanente's human-centered model for organizational effectiveness emphasizes the roles of patients and providers as collaborators driving quality improvement and innovation. **Availability:** Online; PDF.

25846 ■ *"Kaiser Says Hospital Room Service Saves Money"* in *Pacific Business News (Vol. 26, August 22, 2014, No. 26, pp. 10)*
Pub: American City Business Journals, Inc.
Contact: Mike Olivieri, Executive Vice President

Released: Weekly. **Price:** $4, Introductory 4-week offer(Digital & Print). **Description:** Kaiser Permanente Hawaii's Moanalua Medical Center reveals that it has save nearly $1.5 million annually in food costs since it introduced in-house meal preparation and room service for patients two years ago. The hospital, which previous outsourced meal preparation to Aramark, finds that the new policy avoids waste by allowing patients to choose their own food as well as their mealtime. **Availability:** Print; Online.

25847 ■ *"KCET Takes On Elder-Care With Robust Your Turn To Care Website"* in *PR Newswire (July 31, 2012)*
Pub: PR Newswire Association LLC.

Description: Your Turn To Care is a new Website created by KCET, the nation's largest independent public television station. The network, serving southern and central California, offers the Website to serve as a resource for families, caregivers and seniors in te US facing the challenges of caring for an ailing or aging loved one. The Website also covers issues involved in aging.

25848 ■ *"The Keeper of Records"* in *Black Enterprise (Vol. 41, December 2010, No. 5, pp. 54)*
Pub: Earl G. Graves Ltd.
Contact: Earl Graves, Jr., President
Ed: Denise A. Campbell. **Description:** Medical billing and coding, submission of claims to health insurance companies and Medicare or Medicaid for payment is one of the fastest growing disciplines in healthcare. **Availability:** Online.

25849 ■ *"Kids in Crisis"* in *Employee Benefit News (Vol. 25, November 1, 2011, No. 14, pp. 26)*
Pub: Comtex News Network Inc.
Contact: Kan Devnani, President
Ed: Lisa V. Gillespie. **Description:** Employers and vendor are taking more aggressive steps to help battle childhood obesity. **Availability:** Print; Online.

25850 ■ *"King of the Crib: How Good Samaritan Became Ohio's Baby HQ"* in *Business Courier (Vol. 27, June 18, 2010, No. 7, pp. 1)*
Pub: Business Courier
Ed: James Ritchie. **Description:** Cincinnati's Good Samaritan hospital had 6,875 live births in 2009, which is more than any other hospital in Ohio. They specialize in the highest-risk pregnancies and deliveries and other hospitals are trying to grab Good Samaritan's share in this niche. **Availability:** Print; Online.

25851 ■ *"Lawmakers, Execs Launch Effort to Save Rural Hospitals"* in *Atlanta Business Chronicle (June 13, 2014, pp. 7A)*
Pub: American City Business Journals, Inc.
Contact: Mike Olivieri, Executive Vice President
Description: Governor Nathan Deal has appointed a committee of Georgia lawmakers and healthcare executives to launch an effort to save the state's financially burdened rural hospitals. In addition, he plans to allow rural hospitals that have closed or are on the verge of closing, to scale back their operations, under a new rule approved by the Georgia Board of Community Health. **Availability:** Print; Online.

25852 ■ *"Lean Machine: Health Care Follows Auto's Lead, Gears Up for Efficiency"* in *Crain's Detroit Business (Vol. 26, Jan. 11, 2010)*
Pub: Crain Communications Inc.
Contact: Barry Asin, President
Ed: Jay Greene. **Description:** Reducing waste and becoming more efficient is a goal of many businesses involved in the health care industry. These firms are looking to the local manufacturing sector, comparing themselves in specifically to the auto industry, for ways in which to become more efficient. **Availability:** Print; Online.

25853 ■ *"Life's Work: Oliver Sacks"* in *Harvard Business Review (Vol. 88, November 2010, No. 11, pp. 152)*
Pub: Harvard Business Publishing
Contact: Diane Belcher, Managing Director
Ed: Lisa Burrell. **Price:** $8.95, PDF. **Description:** Neurologist and author Oliver Sacks discusses whether different types of minds tend toward certain skills, physician-patient communication, and his own perspectives from being a patient himself. **Availability:** Online; PDF.

25854 ■ *"Lifesavers"* in *Black Enterprise (Vol. 41, December 2010, No. 5, pp. 38)*
Pub: Earl G. Graves Ltd.
Contact: Earl Graves, Jr., President
Ed: Tamara E. Holmes. **Description:** Profile of Interventional Nephrology Specialists Access Center and founders Dr. Omar Davis and Dr. Natarsha Grant; the center generated $5.5 million in revenue for 2009. Details on how they run their successful center are included. **Availability:** Online.

25855 ■ *"The List: Top South Florida Diagnostic Centers"* in *South Florida Business Journal (Vol. 34, April 18, 2014, No. 39, pp. 12)*
Pub: American City Business Journals, Inc.
Contact: Mike Olivieri, Executive Vice President
Released: Weekly. **Description:** Rankings of medical diagnostic centers in South Florida are presented. Rankings were based on the number of patients each laboratory or medical facility saw in 2013. **Availability:** Print; Online.

25856 ■ *"The Little Biotech that Could"* in *Barron's (Vol. 89, July 27, 2009, No. 30, pp. 19)*
Pub: Dow Jones & Company Inc.
Contact: Almar Latour, Chief Executive Officer
Ed: Christopher C. Williams. **Description:** OSI Pharmaceuticals' shares is a compelling investment bet among small biotech firms due to its Tarceva anticancer drug which has a 23 percent market share as well as their strong balance sheet. OSI is planning to expand the use of Tarceva which could re-ignite sales and one analyst expects the shares to trade in the 40s one year from July 2009. **Availability:** Online.

25857 ■ *"Locals Eager for $785M Medical Marijuana Business"* in *Orlando Business Journal (Vol. 30, March 21, 2014, No. 39, pp. 4)*
Pub: American City Business Journals, Inc.
Contact: Mike Olivieri, Executive Vice President
Released: Weekly. **Price:** $8, introductory 4-week offer(Digital & Print). **Description:** A number of local companies in Central Florida are preparing for a ballot initiative to legalize medical marijuana in November 2014. The National Cannabis Association estimates the medical marijuana market in Florida at $785 million, with about 260,000 patients, while Orlando's share is estimated at $89.1 million, with 29,518 potential patients. **Availability:** Print; Online.

25858 ■ *"Los Angeles Jewish Home to Expand to Westside With New Senior Care Community and In-Home Services"* in *PR Newswire (September 12, 2012)*
Pub: PR Newswire Association LLC.
Description: Los Angeles Jewish Home plans to develop a senior care community at The Village at Playa Vista on the west side of Los Angeles, California. They will serve residential, healthcare and in-home care for seniors living on the west side of LA. Gonda Healthy Aging Westside Campus, donated by Leslie and Susan Gonda (Goldschmied) Foundation, will be part of the Jewish Home's mission to serve seniors in the area. Statistical data included.

25859 ■ *"Lower Unemployment Hasn't Offset Total Losses"* in *Sacramento Business Journal (Vol. 31, May 23, 2014, No. 13, pp. 6)*
Pub: American City Business Journals, Inc.
Contact: Mike Olivieri, Executive Vice President
Released: Weekly. **Price:** $4, Introductory 4-week offer(Digital & Print). **Description:** The decline in Sacramento, California's unemployment rate has not reduced the city's economic losses. Unemployment in the area has decreased by 7.5 percent in April 2014. Meanwhile, educational and health services are expected to be the job growth sectors in the next 12 months. **Availability:** Print; Online.

25860 ■ *"Macroeconomic Policy and U.S. Competitiveness: A Reformed Fiscal Policy Is Vital To Renewing America's Productivity"* in *Harvard Business Review (Vol. 90, March 2012, No. 3, pp. 112)*
Pub: Harvard Business Review Press
Contact: Moderna V. Pfizer, Contact
Ed: Matthew Weinzierl, Richard H.K. Vietor. **Description:** Improving productivity requires increasing physical capital (such as equipment or technology), raising human capital, or using both of these types of capital more efficiently. The authors promote a plan that blends cuts in defense and health care spending, adjustments to Social Security, and carbon and gas taxes.

25861 ■ *"Mapping the Gender Gap"* in *Business Journal Portland (Vol. 31, April 25, 2014, No. 8, pp. 4)*
Pub: American City Business Journals, Inc.
Contact: Mike Olivieri, Executive Vice President
Released: April 25, 2014. **Price:** $4, introductory 4-week offer(Digital & Print). **Description:** The level of gender equality in the health care, banking, technology and commercial real estate industries of Oregon is examined. Gender bias in the workplace is one significant reason behind the wage gap and the lack of women in leadership positions. **Availability:** Print; Mailing list; Online.

25862 ■ *"Maryland Hospitals Cope with Rare Drop in Patient Admissions"* in *Baltimore Business Journal (Vol. 29, September 23, 2011, No. 20, pp. 1)*
Pub: Boston Business Journal
Contact: Carolyn M. Jones, President
E-mail: cmjones@bizjournals.com
Ed: Scott Dance. **Description:** Admissions to Maryland hospitals have dropped to less than 700,000 in fiscal year 2010 and initial figures for fiscal 2011 show in-patient admissions are now nearing 660,000. The decline can be partly attributed to new ways health insurers are paying hospitals for care and to the financial reward hospitals get for cutting back on admissions. **Availability:** Online.

25863 ■ *"Maryland May Avoid Congress on Medicare Waiver"* in *Baltimore Business Journal (Vol. 30, June 15, 2012, No. 6, pp. 1)*
Pub: American City Business Journals, Inc.
Contact: Mike Olivieri, Executive Vice President
Ed: Sarah Gantz. **Description:** Maryland leaders may not seek the US Congress' help to avoid losing a Medicare waiver. The waiver has standardized Medicare reimbursement rates for all hospitals. Comments from officials included. **Availability:** Online.

25864 ■ *"The Massachusetts Mess"* in *Barron's (Vol. 89, July 27, 2009, No. 30, pp. 39)*
Pub: Dow Jones & Company Inc.
Contact: Almar Latour, Chief Executive Officer
Ed: Thomas G. Donlan. **Description:** Massachusetts' mandatory health insurance has produced the highest rate of insurance coverage among the states but the state is now unable to afford its dream of universal coverage just three years after they enacted it. This supposed model for federal health-care reform is turning out to be a joke. **Availability:** Online.

25865 ■ *"Md. Faces Daunting Task of Educating Masses About Health Reform Law"* in *Baltimore Business Journal (Vol. 28, October 15, 2010, No. 23, pp. 1)*
Pub: Baltimore Business Journal
Contact: Rhonda Pringle, President
E-mail: rpringle@bizjournals.com
Ed: Emily Mullin. **Description:** The Henry J. Kaiser Family Foundation's survey shows nearly 53 percent of Americans remain confused about health care reform and it was up to the states to educate the people. However, Maryland is still trying to figure out how to conduct the campaign without guidance or funding from the Federal government. **Availability:** Print.

25866 ■ *"Medical Collection Agency Refutes Allegations In AG's Report"* in *PaymentsSource (May 1, 2012)*
Description: Accretive Health Inc. denies allegations by the Minnesota State Attorney General's Office that the firm used heavy-handed tactics pressuring patients to pay for services before receiving treatment. The medical collection agency's report states 'inaccuracies, innuendo and unfounded speculation' in the charges. **Availability:** Print; Online.

25867 ■ *"Medical Pot Backers Say Industry Will Survive"* in *Sacramento Business Journal* (Vol. 28, October 14, 2011, No. 33, pp. 1)
Pub: Sacramento Business Journal
Contact: Stephanie Fretwell, Director
E-mail: sfretwell@bizjournals.com

Ed: Melanie Turner. **Description:** Medical marijuana supporters have expected the industry to decline but will survive the federal restriction on growers and dispensaries across California. California Cannabis Association and National Cannabis Industry Association believe that some of the dispensaries will remain and the shakeout will lead to stronger state regulations. **Availability:** Online.

25868 ■ *"Medical Tech Jobs Take More Than a Month To Fill"* in *Austin Business Journal* (Vol. 34, July 11, 2014, No. 21, pp. 10)
Pub: American City Business Journals, Inc.
Contact: Mike Olivieri, Executive Vice President

Released: July 11, 2014. **Price:** $4, introductory 4-week offer(Digital only). **Description:** A report by Brookings Institute has revealed that nearly half of Austin's jobs require STEM - science, technology, engineering and mathematical skills. However, these jobs generally take more than a month to fill. **Availability:** Print; Online.

25869 ■ *"Medicare Plans Step Up Battle for Subscribers"* in *Sacramento Business Journal* (Vol. 28, October 21, 2011, No. 34, pp. 1)
Pub: Sacramento Business Journal
Contact: Stephanie Fretwell, Director
E-mail: sfretwell@bizjournals.com

Ed: Kathy Robertson. **Description:** California's market for health plans have become increasingly competitive as more than 313,000 seniors try to figure out the best plans to meet their needs for 2012. Health plans are rated on Medicare materials to help consumers distinguish among the Medicare health maintenance organizations (HMOs). **Availability:** Online.

25870 ■ *Medicare & You Handbook*
Pub: U.S. Department of Health & Human Service Centers for Medicare & Medicaid Services
URL(s): www.cms.gov/newsroom/mediareleasedatabase/press-releases/2014-press-releases-items/2014-10-15-2.html

Released: Irregular; Latest Edition 2016. **Description:** Publication includes lists of Medicare carriers in individual states. Principal content includes discussion of what Medicare is, what its various options are, and what new benefits have been added recently. **Availability:** Print; Online.

25871 ■ *"Mercy Parent Nets Almost $1B in 2011"* in *Sacramento Business Journal* (Vol. 28, September 30, 2011, No. 31, pp. 1)
Pub: Sacramento Business Journal
Contact: Stephanie Fretwell, Director
E-mail: sfretwell@bizjournals.com

Ed: Kathy Robertson. **Price:** $4, Print & Digital introductory 4-week offer; $4, Digital introductory 4-week offer. **Description:** Catholic Healthcare West has reported almost $1 billion in profits for 2010. The company has reported a profit margin of 8.7 percent. It also absorbed more than $1 billion in costs from charity care and government programs. **Availability:** Print; Online.

25872 ■ *"Methodist Plans Richardson Hospital"* in *Dallas Business Journal* (Vol. 35, June 29, 2012, No. 42, pp. 1)
Pub: Baltimore Business Journal
Contact: Rhonda Pringle, President
E-mail: rpringle@bizjournals.com

Ed: Bill Hethcock. **Description:** Methodist Health System is planning to build a hospital in Richardson, Texas. The hospital will have a capacity of 125 beds and employ around 900 people. Comments from executives are included. **Availability:** Print; Online.

25873 ■ *"Methodist Sees Dwindling Transplant Organs"* in *Memphis Business Journal* (Vol. 34, June 29, 2012, No. 11, pp. 1)
Pub: Baltimore Business Journal
Contact: Rhonda Pringle, President
E-mail: rpringle@bizjournals.com

Ed: Cole Epley. **Description:** The Methodist University Hospital Transplant Institute opposes the national organ policies established by the United Network for Organ Sharing as it would impact their liver transplant program negatively. Mid-South Transplant Foundation refuses to go forward with a merger with Tennessee Donor Services as favored by the Methodist program. **Availability:** Print; Online.

25874 ■ *"MMRGlobal Home Health and Senior Care Programs to Be Showcased at Visiting Nurse Associations of America's Annual Meeting"* in *Marketwired* (April 12, 2012)
Pub: Comtex News Network Inc.
Contact: Kan Devnani, President

Description: MMR Global Inc. will highlight its storage and solutions and electronic document management and imaging systems for healthcare professionals at the Visiting Nurse Associations of America (VNAA) 30th Annual Meeting in Phoenix, Arizona. Personal Health Records (PHRs), MyEsafeDepositBox and other programs are profiled. **Availability:** Print; Online.

25875 ■ *"More Small Businesses in Baltimore Willing to Fund Employees' Health Benefits"* in *Baltimore Business Journal* (Vol. 28, June 18, 2010, No. 6, pp. 1)
Pub: Baltimore Business Journal
Contact: Rhonda Pringle, President
E-mail: rpringle@bizjournals.com

Ed: Scott Graham. **Description:** An increasing number of small businesses in Maryland are tapping into potentially cheaper self-funded health plans instead of providing fully insured benefits to employees through traditional health plans. Self-funded health plans charge employers for health care up to a specified level. Economic implications of self-funded plans to small businesses are discussed.

25876 ■ *National Wellness Institute--Membership Directory* (Online only)
Pub: National Wellness Institute
URL(s): members.nationalwellness.org/page/Benefits_GW4W

Description: Covers more than 1,600 health and wellness promotion professionals in corporations, hospitals, colleges, government agencies, universities, community organizations, schools (K-12), and consulting firms, and managed care. **Entries include:** Member name, address, and phone, fax, email. **Arrangement:** Same information given in alphabetical, and geographical and work setting arrangements. **Availability:** Print.

25877 ■ *"New Book Takes Alternate View on Ontario's Wind Industry"* in *CNW Group* (September 19, 2011)
Pub: CNW Group Ltd.

Description: Dirty Business: The Reality Behind Ontario's Rush to Wind Power, was written by editor and health care writer Jane Wilson of Ottawa, Ontario, Canada along with contributing editor Parker Gallant. The book contains articles and papers on the wind business, including information on illnesses caused from the environmental noise. **Availability:** Print; Online.

25878 ■ *"A New Cloud-Based Phone System Is Installed Remotely for North Carolina Senior Care Council"* in *Information Technology Business* (June 19, 2012)

Description: North Carolina Senior Care Council (NcSCC) has partnered with VoxNet to provide long-term care for Cloud-based PBX to help NcSCC manage their system that assists seniors. **Availability:** Online.

25879 ■ *"New Health Care Payment Model Coming to Boise"* in *Idaho Business Review* (August 20, 2014)
Pub: BridgeTower Media
Contact: Adam Reinebach, President

Description: Direct primary care is coming to the Boise, Idaho area. The process offers patients a range of treatment options, including most wellness and acute care but not hospital visits or some pharmaceuticals, for a monthly membership fee. This trend does not allow health insurance or health savings accounts to pay the monthly fees. Proponents believe direct primary care benefits doctors, patients and the overall health system in many ways.

25880 ■ *"New Jersey Enacts Strict Opioid Prescribing Law"* in *Pharmacy Times* (February 21, 2017)
URL(s): www.pharmacytimes.com/contributor/timothy-o-shea/2017/02/new-jersey-enacts-strict-opioid-prescribing-law

Ed: Timothy O'Shea. **Released:** February 21, 2017. **Description:** Governor Chris Christie of New Jersey signed legislation to help curb the opioid addiction running through the state. With the new legislation, initial opioid prescriptions can only be for a 5-day supply. **Availability:** Online.

25881 ■ *"New Stem Cell Research Awareness Org Launched in Austin"* in *Austin Business Journal* (Vol. 31, June 3, 2011, No. 13, pp. 1)
Pub: Austin Business Journal
Contact: Rachel McGrath, Director
E-mail: rmcgrath@bizjournals.com

Ed: Sandra Zaragoza. **Description:** MedRebels Foundation was launched in February 2011 with the goal of providing millions of dollars for research funding, education and advocacy for adult stem cell-focused medicine. The foundation, whose major contributor is SpineSmith LP, is a collaboration of other adult stem cell-related companies and nonprofit partners. It hopes to raise $200,000 by the end of 2011. **Availability:** Print; Online.

25882 ■ *"Newton Robotics Company Bets on Rehab Robots for Growth"* in *Boston Business Journal* (Vol. 34, April 4, 2014, No. 9, pp. 6)
Pub: American City Business Journals, Inc.
Contact: Mike Olivieri, Executive Vice President

Description: Robotics firm Barrett Technology is transforming into a health care company by developing rehabilitation robots. The business is expected to generate 80 percent of its revenue from its health care clients over the next five years. The possibility of hiring new employees is also discussed. **Availability:** Print; Online.

25883 ■ *"Non-Users Still Inhale Nicotine From E-Cigarettes"* in *Business First of Buffalo* (Vol. 30, February 7, 2014, No. 21, pp. 6)
Pub: American City Business Journals, Inc.
Contact: Mike Olivieri, Executive Vice President

Released: Weekly. **Price:** $140, Digital & Print; $115, Digital only. **Description:** A group of researchers at Roswell Park Cancer Institute's Department of Health Behavior, led by Maciej Goniewicz, found traces of some potentially dangerous chemical in the vapor of electronic cigarettes. Although smoking e-cigarettes is less harmful than regular cigarettes, non-users are still exposed to nicotine in the same way as second-hand smoke. **Availability:** Print; Online.

25884 ■ *"Notes on Current Labor Statistics"* in *Montly Labor Review* (Vol. 133, September 2010, No. 9, pp. 75)
Pub: U.S. Department of Labor Bureau of Labor Statistics
Contact: Amrit Kohli, Director
E-mail: kohli.amrit@bls.gov

Description: Principal statistics and calculated by the Bureau of Labor Statistics are presented. The series includes statistics on labor force; employment; unemployment; labor compensation; consumer, producer, and international prices; productivity; international comparisons; and injury and illness statistics. **Availability:** Online; PDF.

25885 ■ *"Number-Cruncher Gets 'Pushback'" in Philadelphia Business Journal (Vol. 33, August 22, 2014, No. 28, pp. 10)*
Pub: American City Business Journals, Inc.
Contact: Mike Olivieri, Executive Vice President
Released: Weekly. **Price:** $4, introductory 4-week offer(Digital only). **Description:** Bryan Wellen, senior director of clinical informatics for Continuum Health Alliance (CHA), asserts that while some physicians are receptive to patient information, others respond with an element of 'pushback' and criticism of the data. CHA and Horizon Blue Cross Blue Shield of New Jersey are using data analysis to create strategies that improve health care and reduce costs. **Availability:** Print; Online.

25886 ■ *"Oberg Industries' Initiative Offers Many Paths Down Wellness Road" in Pittsburgh Business Times (Vol. 33, June 6, 2014, No. 47, pp. 12)*
Pub: American City Business Journals, Inc.
Contact: Mike Olivieri, Executive Vice President
Released: Weekly. **Price:** $4, introductory 4-week offer(Digital only). **Description:** Oberg Industries, Category Winner in the 500 to 1,999 employee group in Healthiest Employers of Western Pennsylvania 2014, offers several awareness programs to help employees adopt a healthier lifestyle. Initiatives to increase employee participation in wellness programs include the National Walk at Lunch Day and providing free blood work services. **Availability:** Print; Online.

25887 ■ *"Of Paper Towels and Health Insurance" in Philadelphia Business Journal (Vol. 28, May 11, 2012, No. 13, pp. 1)*
Pub: Baltimore Business Journal
Contact: Rhonda Pringle, President
E-mail: rpringle@bizjournals.com
Description: Health insurance companies are using different strategies to take advantage of the demand growth in health coverage in markets such as Philadelphia. Horizon Blue Cross lue Shield of New Jersey, for example, is creating a retail center where customers can get information from specially trained staff about insurance, health and wellness. IBC, on the other hand, has partnered with AAA Mid-Atlantic to market its plan option to AAA members. **Availability:** Print; Online.

25888 ■ *"On the Use of Neurophysiological Tools In IS Research: Developing a Research Agenda for NeuroIS" in MIS Quarterly (Vol. 36, September 2012, No. 3, pp. 679)*
Pub: University of Minnesota Carlson School of Management Management Information Systems Research Center
Ed: Angelika Dimoka. **Price:** $15. **Description:** The role of neurophysiological tools and neuroimaging tools in information systems research is discussed. Promising application areas and research questions regarding the use of neurophysiological data to benefit information systems researchers are identified. **Availability:** PDF.

25889 ■ *"One Personal Trainer's Fitness Goal: Help Cancer Patients Feel Better During and After Treatment" in America's Intelligence Wire (February 1, 2012)*
Description: Laura Rosencrantz quit her job as a fitness instructor to develop a specialized training program to help cancer patients remain stronger while in treatment, stronger in recovery, or to help them feel better in their final months. She watched her grandfather grow weak during his cancer treatment and she knew she could help others during this time. **Availability:** Print; Online.

25890 ■ *"The One Thing That's Holding Back Your Wellness Program" in Employee Benefit News (Vol. 25, December 1, 2011, No. 15, pp. 8)*
Pub: SourceMedia LLC
Contact: Gemma Postlethwaite, Chief Executive Officer
Description: A 13-year study shows that women who sat for more than six hours a day were 94 percent more likely to die during the study period. Most women sit at their desks an average of 7.7 hours while at work.

25891 ■ *"Open Enrollment: Staying Healthy During Enrollment Season" in Employee Benefit News (Vol. 25, November 1, 2011, No. 14, pp. 41)*
Pub: SourceMedia LLC
Contact: Gemma Postlethwaite, Chief Executive Officer
Ed: Shana Sweeney. **Description:** Tips for staying healthy during your benefit open enrollment period are outlined.

25892 ■ *"Open Enrollment: What Small Businesses Need to Know About the Affordable Care Act" in Business News Daily (February 21, 2023)*
URL(s): www.businessnewsdaily.com/8535-open-enrollment-tips.html
Ed: Marisa Sanfilippo. **Released:** February 21, 2023. **Description:** Get the information you need to put together a benefits package for your employees using the Affordable Care Act. **Availability:** Online.

25893 ■ *"Orlando Health to Build $24M Proton Therapy Facility" in Orlando Business Journal (Vol. 26, January 22, 2010, No. 34, pp. 1)*
Pub: Orlando Business Journal
Contact: Julie Swyers, Director
E-mail: jswyers@bizjournals.com
Ed: Melanie Stawicki Azam. **Description:** Orlando Health is planning to construct a $24 million proton therapy facility at its MD Anderson Cancer Center Orlando in Florida. The facility, which aims for a 2011 opening, will be using radiation for more accurate targeting of tumors and avoiding the damage to surrounding tissues and organs. **Availability:** Print; Online.

25894 ■ *"Other Players Want In On Ellis-St. Peter's Deal" in Business Review Albany (Vol. 41, July 4, 2014, No. 15, pp. 9)*
Pub: American City Business Journals, Inc.
Contact: Mike Olivieri, Executive Vice President
Released: Weekly. **Price:** $4, introductory 4-week offer(Digital only). **Description:** Other hospital systems and smaller health care providers expressed interest in joining the partnership between Ellis Medicine and St. Peter's Health Partners in Albany, New York. The partnership aims to transform a scattered health care industry into regional networks while allowing companies to maintain independent operations. **Availability:** Print; Online.

25895 ■ *"Outlook In Other Industries" in Crain's Detroit Business (Vol. 30, January 6, 2014, No. 1, pp. 3)*
Pub: Crain Communications Inc.
Contact: Barry Asin, President
Released: January 6, 2014. **Description:** Outlook for industries in the Detroit area are listed, including small business growth, restaurants, defense contracts, nonprofits, transportation, auto suppliers, healthcare, bankruptcy, and government. **Availability:** Print; PDF; Online.

25896 ■ *"The Overlicensed Society" in Harvard Business Review (Vol. 90, April 2012, No. 4, pp. 38)*
Pub: Harvard Business Review Press
Contact: Moderna V. Pfizer, Contact
Ed: Robert E. Litan. **Price:** $6, hardcover. **Description:** The author argues that certification and licensing requirements are hindering professionals who might otherwise be able to find positions and provide services inexpensively. To key areas are healthcare and law. Federal mutual recognition agreements may be one method of addressing both practice and consumer protection issues. **Availability:** PDF; Online.

25897 ■ *"Patients to Elect to Cut Care" in The Business Journal-Serving Metropolitan Kansas City (Vol. 27, November 21, 2008, No. 11, pp. 1)*
Pub: American City Business Journals, Inc.
Contact: Mike Olivieri, Executive Vice President
Ed: Rob Roberts. **Description:** Patients in Kansas City, Missouri are cutting down on health care services due to the economic crisis. A decline in diagnostic procedures has been observed at Northland Cardiology. Elective reconstructive procedures have also been reduced by 25 percent. Additional information and statistics regarding the healthcare sector is included. **Availability:** Online.

25898 ■ *"Pet Store Fish Provide Clue to How Alzheimer's Disease May Start" in Marketwired (July 9, 2012)*
Pub: Comtex News Network Inc.
Contact: Kan Devnani, President
Released: August 07, 2012. **Description:** Western University of Health Sciences in Pomona, California researchers report that studies with zebrafish provided an important clue to understanding how Alzheimer's disease starts. Details of the study are included. **Availability:** Print; Online.

25899 ■ *"Faster To Dissolve, Faster To Work" in Philadelphia Business Journal (Vol. 33, March 14, 2014, No. 5, pp. 8)*
Pub: American City Business Journals, Inc.
Contact: Mike Olivieri, Executive Vice President
Released: Weekly. **Price:** $4, introductory 4-week offer(Digital & Print). **Description:** The U.S. Food and Drug Administration approved Iroko Pharmaceutical's anti-inflammatory drug Tivorbex. The company's technology reformulates a braded drug's active ingredient as submicron particles 20 times smaller than their original size. Iroko also applies the technology to drugs used in oncology. **Availability:** Print; Online.

25900 ■ *"Physicians Development Groupn Kicks Off $13M Skilled Nursing Facility in NE Wichita" in Wichita Business Journal (Vol. 27, January 20, 2012, No. 3, pp. 1)*
Pub: Baltimore Business Journal
Contact: Rhonda Pringle, President
E-mail: rpringle@bizjournals.com
Description: Physicians Development Group has started construction of a skilled nursing facility in Wichita, Kansas. The 80-bed nursing facility is estimated to cost around $13 million. **Availability:** Print; Online.

25901 ■ *"Physics for Females" in Occupational Outlook Quarterly (Vol. 55, Summer 2011, No. 2, pp. 22)*
Description: Free resources to help females investigate careers in medical physics and health physics are available from the American Physical Society. The booklet is designed for girls in middle and high school and describes the work of 15 women who use physics to solve medical mysteries, discover planets, research new materials, and more. **Availability:** Print; Online.

25902 ■ *"Presidential Address: Innovation in Retrospect and Prospect" in Canadian Journal of Electronics (Vol. 43, November 2010, No. 4)*
Pub: Journal of the Canadian Economics Association
Ed: James A. Brander. **Description:** Has innovation slowed in recent decades? While there has been progress in information and communications technology, the recent record of innovation in agriculture, energy, transportation and healthcare sectors is cause for concern. **Availability:** PDF; Online.

25903 ■ "Private Health-Care Services Growing in Canada" in Canadian Business (Vol. 85, June 11, 2012, No. 10, pp. 10)
Ed: Laura Cameron. Description: Some public-private partnerships in Canada include the acquisition of clinics by Centric Health Corporation and the partnership between Westbank First National and Johns Hopkins Hospital. Private healthcare providers have operated by dividing their funding among government contracts, clients not covered by Medicare and patients paying out of pocket and non-insured services. Availability: Print; Online.

25904 ■ "The Problem of Private Ambulances Services" in Current Affairs (August 30, 2018)
URL(s): www.currentaffairs.org/2018/08/the-problem-of-private-ambulance-services
Ed: David Anderson. Released: August 30, 2018. Description: Burnout, fatigue, poor health, and low pay are rampant in the private EMS industry, which is discussed in detail along with the monopoly that American Medical Response holds in the US. The high-cost to keep the private ambulance system going is compared to what it would cost to have it fully funded through public taxes. Availability: Print; Online.

25905 ■ "Professor: More Will Follow CVS Ban on Tobacco" in Philadelphia Business Journal (Vol. 33, February 14, 2014, No. 1, pp. 6)
Pub: American City Business Journals, Inc.
Contact: Mike Olivieri, Executive Vice President
Released: Weekly. Price: $4, introductory 4-week offer(Digital & Print). Description: Professor Daniel A. Hussar believes that CVS Caremark's decision to discontinue the sale of tobacco products reflects the company's concern for the health of consumers. He thinks that other drugstores will follow suit. The need for CVS Caremark to emphasize the importance of pharmacists' services is also examined. Availability: Print; Online.

25906 ■ "Providence Exec Explains Why the Deal with Boeing is the Way of the Future" in Puget Sound Business Journal (Vol. 35, June 27, 2014, No. 10, pp. 6)
Pub: American City Business Journals, Inc.
Contact: Mike Olivieri, Executive Vice President
Description: Providence-Swedish Accountable Care Organization CEO, Joe Gifford, shares his views on the deal to provide health care to Boeing employees. Gifford says there is opportunity to grow the business if public image spreads showing they offer great quality and service in providing unique healthcare and benefits at a lower cost. Gifford believes meeting directly with the employer customer they create a direct loop of process improvement. Availability: Online.

25907 ■ "Providers Ride First Wave of eHealth Dollars" in Boston Business Journal (Vol. 31, June 10, 2011, No. 20, pp. 1)
Pub: Boston Business Journal
Contact: Carolyn M. Jones, President
E-mail: cmjones@bizjournals.com
Ed: Julie M. Donnelly. Released: Weekly. Description: Health care providers in Massachusetts implementing electronic medical records technology started receiving federal stimulus funds. Beth Israel Deaconess Medical Center was the first hospital to qualify for the funds. Availability: Print.

25908 ■ "Public Health Care Funding and the Montana Economy" in Montana Business Quarterly (Vol. 49, Spring 2011, No. 1, pp. 23)
Pub: University of Montana Bureau of Business and Economic Research
Contact: Patrick Barkey, Director
E-mail: patrick.barkey@business.umt.edu
Ed: Gregg Davis. Released: Quarterly. Description: Montana has more baby boomers and veterans per capita than any other state in the nation. The role of public health in the state is a crucial part of the state's economy. Availability: Online.

25909 ■ "Put the Good, the Bad and the Ugly on the Table" in South Florida Business Journal (Vol. 35, September 19, 2014, No. 8, pp. 13)
Pub: American City Business Journals, Inc.
Contact: Mike Olivieri, Executive Vice President
Description: United Way of Broward County chief executive, Kathleen Cannon, says the creation of a macropractice for social work is the most rewarding part of her job. She also said teaching people how to give back is the most challenging part of her role.

25910 ■ "Putting Down Roots" in Entrepreneur (August 2014)
Released: October 28, 2016. Description: Entrepreneur Justin Hartfield and partner Doug Francis created Weedmaps.com, an online portal for marijuana dispensaries, after California legalized the sale of medical marijuana. Hartfield is looking forward to a billion-dollar business once the federal prohibition of marijuana is ended. Local dispensaries pay a monthly subscription of $420 to appear on the site while doctors pay $295 to be featured on the site. Harfield is seeking partnerships with laboratories that will provide marijuana testing and other services. Availability: Online.

25911 ■ "Q&A With Devin Ringling: Franchise's Services Go Beyond Elder Care" in Gazette (October 2, 2010)
Pub: The Gazette
Contact: Vicki Cederholm, Director, Operations
E-mail: vicki.cederholm@gazette.com
Ed: Bill Radford. Description: Profile of franchise, Interim HealthCare, in Colorado Springs, Colorado; the company offers home care services that include wound care and specialized feedings to shopping and light housekeeping. It also runs a medical staffing company that provides nurses, therapists and other health care workers to hospitals, prisons, schools and other facilities. Availability: Online.

25912 ■ "The Quest for a Smart Prosthetic" in Canadian Business (Vol. 83, October 12, 2010, No. 17, pp. 26)
Pub: Rogers Media Inc.
Contact: Neil Spivak, Chief Executive Officer
Ed: Jacqueline Nelson. Description: Information about a two-year research project led by Southern Methodist University (SMU) and funded by the Defense Advance Research Projects Agency (DARPA) is provided. The agency aims to create a 'smart prosthetic' which will improve the lives of military amputees. The planned prosthetic will use a sensor that can carry nerve signals through synthetic channels. Availability: Print; Online.

25913 ■ "Questions Abound in Voluminous Health Care Reform Law" in Memphis Business Journal (Vol. 34, July 6, 2012, No. 12, pp. 1)
Pub: Baltimore Business Journal
Contact: Rhonda Pringle, President
E-mail: rpringle@bizjournals.com
Ed: Cole Epley. Description: US Supreme Court has upheld the health care reform legislation, also known as Obamacare, as thelaw of the land. However, key questions remain and conjecture surrounding which direction states and insurance providers will pursue abounds. Insights on possible impact of health care providers of TennCare are also given. Availability: Print; Online.

25914 ■ "Quincy Veterinarian Advises That Pets as 'Young' as Seven Years Need Senior Care" in Benzinga.com (September 9, 2012)
Pub: Comtex News Network Inc.
Contact: Kan Devnani, President
Released: September 09, 2012. Description: Veterinarian advises pet owners to have their pets over seven years of age seen for regular senior office visits. That age in animals is equal to middle age of humans. At age 10, a pet is considered geriatric. Health conditions after age seven can include arthritis, heart disease, liver or kidney problems, and thyroid problems. Availability: Online.

25915 ■ "Recovery on Tap for 2010?" in Orlando Business Journal (Vol. 26, January 1, 2010, No. 31, pp. 1)
Pub: Orlando Business Journal
Contact: Julie Swyers, Director
E-mail: jswyers@bizjournals.com
Ed: Melanie Stawicki Azam, Richard Bilbao, Christopher Boyd, Anjali Fluker. Description: Economic forecasts for Central Florida's leading business sectors in 2010 are presented. These sectors include housing, film and TV, sports business, law, restaurants, aviation, tourism and hospitality, banking and finance, commercial real estate, retail, health care, insurance, higher education, and manufacturing. According to some local executives, Central Florida's economy will slowly recover in 2010. Availability: Online.

25916 ■ "Region Wins as GE Puts Plants Close to R&D" in Business Review Albany (Vol. 41, July 4, 2014, No. 15, pp. 8)
Pub: American City Business Journals, Inc.
Contact: Mike Olivieri, Executive Vice President
Description: General Electric Company (GE) invested over $400 million into the expansion of its health care, battery and renewable energy businesses in the Albany, New York region. The company's local growth secured about 7,000 private-sector jobs in the area and strengthened the relationship between GE research and manufacturing. Availability: Print; Online.

25917 ■ "Renal Solutions Move Not a Sign of the Times" in Pittsburgh Business Times (Vol. 33, February 14, 2014, No. 31, pp. 5)
Pub: American City Business Journals, Inc.
Contact: Mike Olivieri, Executive Vice President
Released: Weekly. Price: $4, Introductory 4-week offer(Digital only). Description: Renal Solutions, a Pittsburgh, Pennsylvania-based company, has decided to relocate to California. Company founder, Pete DeComo, believes that the firm's move should not be a cause for concern within the city's business community. Renal Solutions was acquired by Fresenius Medical Care North America in 2007. Availability: Print; Online.

25918 ■ "Report Card Gives Employees Health Grade" in Pittsburgh Business Times (Vol. 33, June 6, 2014, No. 47, pp. 7)
Pub: American City Business Journals, Inc.
Contact: Mike Olivieri, Executive Vice President
Released: Weekly. Price: $4, introductory 4-week offer(Digital only). Description: Excela Health, Category Winner in the 1,200 to 4,999 employees group in Healthiest Employers of Western Pennsylvania 2014, offered employees a report card giving a letter grade summary of their biometric screening results and forwarded same to primary care doctors within 30 minutes of the test. The initiative was extended to spouses and partners and also carried a financial incentive to participate. Availability: Print; Online.

25919 ■ "Research, Treatment to Expand" in Philadelphia Business Journal (Vol. 28, June 22, 2012, No. 19, pp. 1)
Pub: Baltimore Business Journal
Contact: Rhonda Pringle, President
E-mail: rpringle@bizjournals.com
Description: Fox Chase Cancer Center and Temple University Health System have been planning several projects once their merger is completed. Their plans include the construction of a unit for cancer patients on the third floor of the Founder's Building at Jeanes Hospital and a granting mechanism to fund research collaborations. Availability: Print; Online.

25920 ■ "Retailers, Your Will, and More" in Agency Sales Magazine (Vol. 39, July 2009, No. 7, pp. 46)
Description: IRS audit guide for small retail businesses is presented. Tips on how to make a will with multiple beneficiaries are discussed together with medical expenses that cannot be deducted.

25921 ■ "Reviving Entrepreneurship: Policy Decisions in 12 Areas Could Nurture - Or Cripple - America's Greatest Asset" in Harvard Business Review (Vol. 90, March 2012, No. 3, pp. 116)
Pub: Harvard Business Review Press
Contact: Moderna V. Pfizer, Contact

Ed: Josh Lerner, William A. Sahlman. Price: $8.95, hardcover. Description: Government policies should address entrepreneurship as a process, rather than an act. Several key areas for policymaking include basic and translational science, supply and quality of human capital, information availability, tax treatment of rewards and risks, intellectual property rights, workforce healthcare, and mobility of financial and human capital. Availability: PDF; Online.

25922 ■ "RF Technologies Celebrates 25th Anniversary of Keeping Patients and Senior Care Residents Safe and Secure" in PR Newswire (August 1, 2012)
Pub: PR Newswire Association LLC.

Description: RF Technologies has entered into the senior care market by offering wireless wandering managemnt systems and transmitters to help reduce the risk of resident elopements. RF is a leading provider of customized radio frequency identification (RFID) healthcare safety and security solutions for the healthcare sector.

25923 ■ "Rich or Poor, Hospitals Must Work Together" in Crain's Chicago Business (Vol. 31, April 28, 2008, No. 17, pp. 22)
Pub: Crain Communications Inc.
Contact: Barry Asin, President

Description: Chicago-area safety-net hospitals that serve the poor, uninsured and underinsured are struggling to stay open while wealthier areas compete to build advanced facilities for the expensive surgical procedures their privately insured patients can afford. If these safety-net hospitals close, their patients, many of them in ambulances, will show up at the remaining hospitals resulting in a strain that will test the ability of hospitals across the region to care for all of their patients. Hospitals need to address the threats to the local health care system before it slips into crisis since the current every-hospital-for-itself approach that pays off big for some will eventually will make losers of everyone. Availability: Online.

25924 ■ "Riding Herd on Health Care" in Business Journal Portland (Vol. 30, February 7, 2014, No. 49, pp. 8)
Pub: American City Business Journals, Inc.
Contact: Mike Olivieri, Executive Vice President

Released: February 07, 2014. Description: Singing rancher and aspiring gubernatorial candidate, Jon Justesen, explains his views on universal healthcare. He expresses support for health care reform and Cover Oregon and he is looking at his options after dropping his Republican primary bid. Availability: Print; Online.

25925 ■ "Riding the Wave: Past Trends and Future Directions for Health IT Research" in MIS Quarterly (Vol. 36, September 2012, No. 3, pp. III)
Pub: University of Minnesota Carlson School of Management Management Information Systems Research Center

Description: Trends in healthcare information technologies, also known as health informatics, are discussed. Availability: Download.

25926 ■ "The Right Remedy: Entrepreneur's Success Is a Matter of Life and Death" in Black Enterprise (Vol. 38, February 2008, No. 7, pp. 46)
Pub: Earl G. Graves Ltd.
Contact: Earl Graves, Jr., President

Ed: Tamara E. Holmes. Description: Profile of Leah Brown, whose company conducts clinical trials to determine if specific drugs will relieve particular symptoms. Her company will also visit physician's offices to make certain doctors are following proper protocol for a clinical trial or will collect data from patients. Availability: Online.

25927 ■ "St. Luke's Gets Shot in the Arm From Outpatient Services" in Saint Louis Business Journal (Vol. 31, August 19, 2011, No. 52, pp. 1)
Pub: Saint Louis Business Journal
Contact: Robert Bobroff, President
E-mail: rbobroff@bizjournals.com

Ed: Angela Mueller, E.B. Solomont. Description: St. Louis, Missouri-based St. Luke's Hospital benefited from investing in outpatient services as contained in its latest bond offering. Fitch Ratings gave the bond issuance an A rating. Availability: Print; Online.

25928 ■ "San Antonio Researchers Develop New Laser-Based Imaging System" in San Antonio Business Journal (Vol. 26, August 24, 2012, No. 30, pp. 1)
Pub: Baltimore Business Journal
Contact: Rhonda Pringle, President
E-mail: rpringle@bizjournals.com

Description: Researchers at the University of Texas Health Science Center at San Antonio in Texas have developed an optical sensor-dependent medical imaging system, which is ready for commercialization. The laser-based imaging system is expected to improve non-invasive imaging for medical diagnostics. Availability: Print; Online.

25929 ■ Selling the Invisible: A Field Guide to Modern Marketing
Ed: Harry Beckwith. Released: March 20, 2012. Price: $16, paperback, ($21.00 in canada); $13.98, audiobook abridged library($16.99 in canada); $16.98, audiobook abridged($19.75 in canada); $9.98, audiobook abridged($12.98 in canada); $9.99, electronic book($9.99 in canada). Description: Tips for marketing and selling intangibles such as health care, entertainment, tourism, legal services, and more are provided. Availability: audiobook; E-book; Print.

25930 ■ "Senator Grills Collection Agency, Health System Executives" in Collections & Credit Risk (May 31, 2012)
Pub: SourceMedia LLC
Contact: Gemma Postlethwaite, Chief Executive Officer

Description: Accretive Health Inc. and Fairview Health Services executives were questioned by Senator Al Franken about its debt collection practices. The suit was initiated after unencrypted private information on 23,500 patients was stolen from an Acrretive employee's vehicle. Details of the lawsuit are outlined.

25931 ■ "Seton Grows Heart Institute" in Austin Business Journal (Vol. 31, July 15, 2011, No. 19, pp. A1)
Pub: Austin Business Journal
Contact: Rachel McGrath, Director
E-mail: rmcgrath@bizjournals.com

Ed: Sandra Zaragoza. Description: Seton Heart Institute experienced significant growth in the last six months. The organization added physicians, specialists and outreach offices across Central Texas. Availability: Print; Online.

25932 ■ "Seven Things Great Employers Do (That Others Don't); Unusual, Innovative, and Proven Tactics To Create Productive and Profitable Working Environments" in Gallup Business Journal (April 15, 2014)
Pub: Gallup, Inc.
Contact: Jon Clifton, Chief Executive Officer

Price: $8.95. Description: Seven unusual, innovative, and proven tactics that create productive and profitable working environments are examined through researching 32 companies. These firms represented many industries, including healthcare, financial services, hospitality, manufacturing, and retail throughout the world. Availability: Print; PDF; Online.

25933 ■ "A Shave, a Haircut — and a Blood Pressure Check" in U.S. News & World Report (April 15, 2019)
URL(s): www.usnews.com/news/healthiest-communities/articles/2019-04-15/battling-high-blood-pressure-at-the-barber

Ed: Joseph P. Williams. Released: April 15, 2019. Description: More than 50 barbershops in the Los Angeles County area are participating in a program that allows customers to check their blood pressure and to receive follow up training and care from an on-site pharmacist. The goal is to successfully treat men, especially African American men, who may not know they are suffering from this condition. So far, the results have been positive and more programs like it are being introduced around the country. Availability: Online.

25934 ■ "Shop Happy: Harvesting Happiness Announces Grassroots Crowdfunding Site for HH4Heroes" in Marketwired (July 2, 2012)
Pub: Comtex News Network Inc.
Contact: Kan Devnani, President

Description: Shop Happy online store has created a fundraising aspect to their customers' shopping experience. Shoppers can assist in helping to heal post combat veterans suffering from PTSD, TBI, MST, andMSA who have served as combat warriors in Operations Iraqi and Enduring Freedom. Lisa Cypers Kamen, founder of Harvesting Happiness believes this program will help both veterans and customers to empower themselves and our veterans in a positive way (HH4Heroes.org).

25935 ■ "Sinai Doctor's Research May Lead to Rival Plavix Drug" in Baltimore Business Journal (Vol. 28, July 16, 2010, No. 10, pp. 1)
Pub: Baltimore Business Journal
Contact: Rhonda Pringle, President
E-mail: rpringle@bizjournals.com

Ed: Emily Mullin. Description: Paul Gurbel, Sinai Hospital Center for Thrombosis Research director, is seeking an FDA approval of Brilinta, a drug which he helped create and test. Gurbel says that the approval could bring the drug to market as early as December 2010. The drug is expected to rival Bristol-Myers' Plavix, which generated almost $6.2 billion in 2009. Availability: Print; Online.

25936 ■ "Sleep Apnea Pill Nears Human Tests" in Philadelphia Business Journal (Vol. 33, May 9, 2014, No. 13, pp. 8)
Pub: American City Business Journals, Inc.
Contact: Mike Olivieri, Executive Vice President

Released: Weekly. Price: $4, Introductory 4-week offer(Digital & Print). Description: Galleon Pharmaceuticals is set to begin human testing of its experimental therapy GAL-160, an oral medicine for sleep apnea, and has already started human testing of GAL-021, an intravenous drug to treat respiratory complications in patients receiving anesthetics and opiate pain medication. Galleon CEO, James C. Mannion, hopes that both drugs pass the proof-of-concept stage and move to mid-stage clinical testing in humans by mid-2015. Availability: Print; Online.

25937 ■ "SLU, Des Peres Hospitals Face Unions" in St. Louis Business Journal (Vol. 32, June 1, 2012, No. 41, pp. 1)
Pub: Baltimore Business Journal
Contact: Rhonda Pringle, President
E-mail: rpringle@bizjournals.com

Description: Executives at St. Louis University (SLU) Hospital and Des Peres Hospital are watching efforts by labor unions to organize workers at the hospitals. The simultaneous campaigns are being led by the California Nurses Association/National Nurses Organizing Committee and SEIU Healthcare. SLU Hospital nurses will vote on union representation on June 7, 2012. Availability: Print; Online.

25938 ■ "Small Biz Owners Are Tapping Into Health Savings Plans" in Small Business Opportunities (Fall 2007)

Description: Health savings accounts were developed by Golden Rule, a United Healthcare company.

Today, more than 40 percent of the company's customers are covered by health savings account plans.

25939 ■ "Small, But Mighty" in Employee Benefit News (Vol. 25, November 1, 2011, No. 14, pp. 32)
Pub: SourceMedia LLC
Contact: Gemma Postlethwaite, Chief Executive Officer
Ed: Andrea Davis. Description: Three consulting firms are facing the challenge of helping clients understand the new health care reform in a tight economy. Availability: Print; PDF; Online.

25940 ■ "The Smell of Fear: Is a Bottom Near?" in Barron's (Vol. 88, March 17, 2008, No. 11, pp. M3)
Pub: Dow Jones & Company Inc.
Contact: Almar Latour, Chief Executive Officer
Ed: Kopin Tan. Description: Liquidity problems at Bear Stearns frightened investors in markets around the world due to the fear of the prospects of a big bank's failure. Shares of health maintenance organizations got battered led by WellPoint, and Humana but longer-term investors who could weather short-term volatility may find value here. The value of J. Crew shares is also discussed. Availability: Online.

25941 ■ "A Social Context Model of Envy and Social Undermining" in Academy of Management Journal (Vol. 55, June 1, 2012, No. 3, pp. 643)
Pub: Academy of Management
Contact: Sharon Alvarez, President
Ed: Michelle K. Duffy, Kristin L. Scott, Jason D. Shaw, Bennett J. Tepper, Karl Aquino. Description: The relationship between envy and social undermining is investigated using the case of hospital employees. Results show that the impact of envy on social undermining through moral disengagement is higher when social identification ith coworkers is low. The indirect effect of envy is also greater in teams with high team undermining norms and low team identification. Availability: Electronic publishing; Download; PDF; Online.

25942 ■ "Spinout Success: New Leadership Steps In At UW's C4C" in Puget Sound Business Journal (Vol. 35, June 27, 2014, No. 10, pp. 11)
Pub: American City Business Journals, Inc.
Contact: Mike Olivieri, Executive Vice President
Description: University of Washington's Center for Commercialization vice provost, Vikram Jandhyala, talks about his new position with the school. Jandhyala says he plans to build more synergy between the medical school and engineering and between social sciences and computer science. He also says the medical and software industry need to grow to accommodate the volume of data crossing and stored within the Internet. Availability: Online.

25943 ■ "Spouses, Health Coaching Added to Mix" in Pittsburgh Business Times (Vol. 33, June 6, 2014, No. 47, pp. 5)
Pub: American City Business Journals, Inc.
Contact: Mike Olivieri, Executive Vice President
Released: Weekly. Price: $4, introductory 4-week offer (Digital & Print). Description: Hospital giant, UPMC, was the Category Winner in the 5,000+ employees group of Healthiest Employers in Western Pennsylvania, for its initiative in expanding its health assessment and wellness programs to the spouses and partners of all its employees, regardless of their health insurance carrier. In addition, UPMC Health Plan expanded its individual health coaching option for members as well as corporate clients. Availability: Print; Online.

25944 ■ "Spouses Plan for the Return of the Company Doctor" in Philadelphia Business Journal (Vol. 33, May 2, 2014, No. 12, pp. 4)
Pub: American City Business Journals, Inc.
Contact: Mike Olivieri, Executive Vice President

Released: Weekly. Price: $4, introductory 4-week offer(Digital only). Description: Nephrologist, Scott Bralow and primary care physician, Vick Bralow, started a company called Affordable Care Options in Philadelphia, Pennsylvania. The couple's company will provide physicians to the workplace to monitor the health of employees for a monthly fee. Availability: Print; Online.

25945 ■ "Startup Osteosphere Formed to Develop Laboratory Discovery" in Houston Business Journal (Vol. 40, January 8, 2010, No. 35, pp. 1)
Pub: Houston Business Journal
Contact: Bob Charlet, President
E-mail: bcharlet@bizjournals.com
Ed: Casey Wooten. Description: Biotech startup company Osteosphere in Houston, Texas aims to market a technology in which laboratory-grown bone tissues can be processed to appear like a real human bone tissue. The technology was developed by a co-founder of the startup and it can be applied to bone disease and injury treatment. Osteophere's future plans, such as the search for possible investors, is also outlined. Availability: Print; Online.

25946 ■ "Strategic Issue Management as Change Catalyst" in Strategy and Leadership (Vol. 39, September-October 2011, No. 5, pp. 20-29)
Pub: Emerald Group Publishing Limited
Contact: Erika Valenti, President
Ed: Bruce E. Perrott. Description: A study analyzes the case of a well-known Australian healthcare organization to examine how a company's periodic planning cycle is supplemented with a dynamic, real-time, strategic-issue-management system under high turbulence conditions. Findings highlight the eight steps that a company's management can use in its strategic issue management (SIM) process to track, monitor and manage strategic issues so as to ensure that the corporate, strategy, and capability are aligned with one another in turbulent times. Availability: Download; PDF; Online.

25947 ■ "SunLink Health Systems Subsidiaries Open Senior Behavioral Care Units in Dahlonega, GA and Fulton, MO" in Mental Health Weekly Digest (July 16, 2012, pp. 326)
Pub: NewsRX LLC.
Contact: Kalani Rosell, Contact
Description: SunLink Health Systems Inc. opened Changing Seasons, a 10-bed geriatric psychiatric unit in Dahlonega, Georgia and Kingdom Senior Solutions opened a 19-bed geriatric psychiatric unit in Fulton, Georgia. Details of the new facilities are defined.

25948 ■ "Surgical Center Relocating to St. Joseph Campus" in Business First of Buffalo (Vol. 30, January 24, 2014, No. 19, pp. 3)
Pub: American City Business Journals, Inc.
Contact: Mike Olivieri, Executive Vice President
Released: Weekly. Price: $140, One-Year Print & Digital; $115, One-Year Digital. Description: The Sisters of Charity Hospital is relocating its off-site ambulatory surgery center to its St. Joseph campus in Buffalo, New York. the moves makes better use of available space, reduces costs and allows for ongoing redevelopment of the Cheektowaga campus, according to vice president of operations, Marty Boryszak. Availability: Print; Online.

25949 ■ "Sutter Court Win is Part of Trend" in Sacramento Business Journal (Vol. 31, July 25, 2014, No. 22, pp. 3)
Pub: American City Business Journals, Inc.
Contact: Mike Olivieri, Executive Vice President
Released: July 25, 2014. Description: The Third District Court of Appeals dismissed 13 coordinated data-breach lawsuits filed against Sutter Health of Sacramento, California. The plaintiffs claim $4 billion in damages over theft of patient data from a local Sutter Health office in October 2011.

25950 ■ "The Swedish Solution" in San Francisco Business Times (Vol. 28, May 2, 2014, No. 41, pp. 4)
Pub: American City Business Journals, Inc.
Contact: Mike Olivieri, Executive Vice President
Description: Seattle, Washington's Swedish Health Services decided to cut prices for outpatient procedures by about 35 percent. Some patients are hoping that the San Francisco Bay Area in California will see Swedish Health do the same, but observers think the region will have a hard time implementing price reductions. Availability: Print; Online.

25951 ■ "Technology: Elder Care Enters the Digital Age: Wireless Companies Devise Ways to Aid Home Health, Let People Stay in Homes" in Atlanta Journal-Constitution (April 29, 2012, pp. D1)
Description: Mobile phone industry is actually helping families keep aging loved one in their homes. The home healthcare industry is adding technology, telecommunications, smartphone applications and other devices to make it easier for seniors to remain in their homes. Details on this growing industry are included along with statistical data. Availability: Online.

25952 ■ "Tenant Demands Broaden Medical Office Landscape" in San Antonio Business Journal (Vol. 28, September 12, 2014, No. 31, pp. 8)
Pub: American City Business Journals, Inc.
Contact: Mike Olivieri, Executive Vice President
Description: The NAI REOC San Antonio report has shown a demand among health care firms for real estate in San Antonio, Texas. However, the slight decline in absorption of space in the medical office market highlight the changing demand among medical users to facilities other than medical office buildings. The thriving healthcare industry in San Antonio is also discussed. Availability: Online.

25953 ■ "This Is Your Brain on Crafting" in CNN.com (January 5, 2015)
URL(s): www.cnn.com/2014/03/25/health/brain-crafting-benefits/index.html
Ed: Jacque Wilson. Released: January 05, 2015. Description: A report on how participating in crafting can ease anxiety, depression, and even chronic pain. Availability: Online.

25954 ■ "Ticketmaster Unveils Pink Tickets to Support Breast Cancer Awareness Month" in Travel & Leisure Close-Up (October 8, 2012)
Description: National Football League is helping to raise awareness for the National Breast Cancer Awareness Month by issuing all tickets purchased through Ticketmaster be pink. A portion of every NFL ticket sold on Ticketmaster and on NFL Ticket Exchange will go toward the American Cancer Society's fight against breast cancer. Availability: Print; Online.

25955 ■ "Today's Rx: Solo Physician Practice Loses Appeal" in Dallas Business Journal (Vol. 35, July 13, 2012, No. 44, pp. 1)
Pub: Baltimore Business Journal
Contact: Rhonda Pringle, President
E-mail: rpringle@bizjournals.com
Ed: Bill Hethcock. Description: The national statistics has shown a trend toward doctors increasingly choosing to work for hospitals, clinics and physician groups. Irving, Texas-based Merritt Hawkins has found in a survey that solo physicians accounted for just one percent of all the firm's searches. Survey details are included. Availability: Print; Online.

25956 ■ "Top 10 Retirement Mistakes and How to Avoid Them" in Canadian Business (Vol. 83, July 20, 2010, No. 11-12, pp. 39)
Pub: Rogers Media Inc.
Contact: Neil Spivak, Chief Executive Officer
Ed: Jacqueline Nelson, Angelina Chapin. Description: Some of the top retirement mistakes are relying on selling one's house to find a retirement. Other

mistakes are paying too much for investments and planning to work in retirement since no one can be sure that they will be healthy enough to accomplish this. Suggestions to avoid these pitfalls are discussed. **Availability:** Print; Online.

25957 ■ *"UIC Medical Ethicist Faces Life-and-Death Decisions Daily"* in *Crain's Chicago Business* (Vol. 34, October 24, 2011, No. 42, pp. 31)
Pub: Crain Communications Inc.
Contact: Barry Asin, President
Ed: Lisa Bertagnoli. **Description:** Technology has enabled doctors to provide more and better methods for helping patients, however end of life issues faced by medical ethicists are discussed. **Availability:** Print.

25958 ■ *"U.S. Combined Life and Health Writers--Industry's Reported Admitted Assets of $5.7 Trillion"* in *Best's Review* (Vol. 113, September 2012, No. 5, pp. 33)
Description: U.S. Combined Life and Health Writers--Industry's Reported Admitted Assets of $5.7 Trillion report is presented. Companies/Groups are ranked in 2011 by admitted assets. **Availability:** Print; Online.

25959 ■ *"UPMC Aims to Profit From Billing Angst"* in *Pittsburgh Business Times* (Vol. 33, Jun3 27, 2014, No. 50, pp. 8)
Pub: American City Business Journals, Inc.
Contact: Mike Olivieri, Executive Vice President
Released: Weekly. **Price:** $4, introductory 4-week offer(Digital only). **Description:** Hospital network UPMC has created a wholly owned, for-profit subsidiary named Ovation Revenue Cycle Solutions that helps medical providers with the complex new Medicare billing codes that take effect October 2015. The service provides revenue-cycle tools designed to help medical groups enhance efficiency, cut rejection rates and reduce time between billing and payment. **Availability:** Print; Online.

25960 ■ *"UPMC Develops Own Billing Solutions"* in *Pittsburgh Business Times* (Vol. 33, January 17, 2014, No. 27, pp. 6)
Pub: American City Business Journals, Inc.
Contact: Mike Olivieri, Executive Vice President
Description: How University of Pittsburgh Medical Center (UPMC) Health System transformed its accounts payable department by passing its process to a subsidiary, Prodigo Solutions, is discussed. UPMC moved suppliers and purchasers to a shared electronic platform and created a digital marketplace. The system's no purchase order, no pay policy has reduced the number of rogue purchases. **Availability:** Online.

25961 ■ *"UW Wary of WSU's Wish for Spokane Medical School"* in *Puget Sound Business Journal* (Vol. 35, May 9, 2014, No. 3, pp. 9)
Pub: American City Business Journals, Inc.
Contact: Mike Olivieri, Executive Vice President
Description: University of Washington leaders believe that opening a medical school in Washington State University's (WSU) Spokane Campus will create more competition for state funding. However, WSU officials claim that the demand for new doctors demonstrates the need for a second school. **Availability:** Online.

25962 ■ *"VA Seeking Bidders for Fort Howard"* in *Baltimore Business Journal* (Vol. 28, June 25, 2010, No. 7, pp. 1)
Pub: Baltimore Business Journal
Contact: Rhonda Pringle, President
E-mail: rpringle@bizjournals.com
Ed: Daniel J. Servnoitz. **Description:** The Veterans Affairs Maryland Health Care Systems has requested proposals from developers to build a retirement community at Fort Howard in Baltimore County. The historic site, which has about 36 mostly vacant buildings, could become the home to hundreds of war veterans. Details of the proposed development are discussed. **Availability:** Print; Online.

25963 ■ *"VC Round Will Pay for 'Sham' Surgery Trial"* in *Business Journal* (Vol. 31, April 11, 2014, No. 46, pp. 6)
Pub: American City Business Journals, Inc.
Contact: Mike Olivieri, Executive Vice President
Released: April 11, 2014. **Price:** $4, Introductory 4-week offer(Digital & Print). **Description:** Holaira Inc. is preparing for a clinical trial of its technology for treating lung disease after raising $42 million in venture capital. The clinical trial will take place in Europe and will involve about 170 patients. **Availability:** Print; Online.

25964 ■ *"Victory Healthcare Moves Into Dallas-Fort Worth Market"* in *Dallas Business Journal* (Vol. 35, May 18, 2012, No. 36, pp. 1)
Pub: Baltimore Business Journal
Contact: Rhonda Pringle, President
E-mail: rpringle@bizjournals.com
Ed: Bill Hethcock. **Description:** Victory Healthcare Holdings is to open Victory Medical Center in Plano, Texas. The company is also planning two more health facilities in the Dallas-Fort Worth area. Victory Medical will provide rehabilitative care as well as spinal and orthopedic surgery, which both have high demands. **Availability:** Print; Online.

25965 ■ *"VPA to Pay $9.5 Million to Settle Whistle-Blower Lawsuits"* in *Crain's Detroit Business* (Vol. 26, January 11, 2010, No. 2, pp. 13)
Pub: Crain Communications Inc.
Contact: Barry Asin, President
Ed: Jay Greene. **Description:** According to Terrence Berg, first assistant with the U.S. Attorney's Office in Detroit, Voluntary Physicians Association, a local home health care company, has agreed to pay $9.5 million to settle four whistle-blower lawsuits; the agreement settles allegations that VPA submitted claims to TriCare, the Michigan Medicaid program and Medicare for unnecessary home visits, tests and procedures. **Availability:** Online.

25966 ■ *"Walgreens Turns to Robots to Fill Prescriptions, as Pharmacists Take on More Responsibilities"* in *CNBC.com* (March 30, 2022)
URL(s): www.cnbc.com/2022/03/30/walgreens-turns-to-robots-to-fill-prescriptions-as-pharmacists-take-on-more-responsibilities.html
Ed: Melissa Repko. **Description:** Pharmacy jobs are adjusting and pharmacists are taking on different responsibilities. In order to keep serving customers, robot-powered fulfillment centers are being built to keep up with, and even exceed, demand.

25967 ■ *"Walk-In Retail Clinics Enjoying Robust Health"* in *Memphis Business Journal* (Vol. 34, April 27, 2012, No. 2, pp. 1)
Pub: Baltimore Business Journal
Contact: Rhonda Pringle, President
E-mail: rpringle@bizjournals.com
Description: Walk-in clinics in Memphis, Tennessee have reported increased profits in 2012. Such clinics offer consumers immediate care while retail shopping. **Availability:** Print; Online.

25968 ■ *"Want To Increase Hospital Revenues? Engage Your Physicians. When Doctors Are Frustrated, Patient Care and Hospital Revenues Suffer. Here's How to Boost Physicians' Engagement -- and the Bottom Line"* in *Gallup Business Journal* (June 5, 2014)
Pub: Gallup, Inc.
Contact: Jon Clifton, Chief Executive Officer
Description: Hospitals need to engage their doctors in order to be successful for both patient care and the bottom line. Four key practices to drive physician engagement are outlined. **Availability:** Print.

25969 ■ *"Watchdogs for Health Care"* in *Money* (Vol. 41, October 2012, No. 9, pp. 63)
Description: Bonnie Burns, California Health Advocates' policy specialist, discusses issues facity seniors regarding their health care. **Availability:** Print; Online.

25970 ■ *"Waukesha Firm Hit for $8.9M for Junk Faxes"* in *Business Journal Milwaukee* (Vol. 29, August 3, 2012, No. 45, pp. 1)
Pub: American City Business Journals, Inc.
Contact: Mike Olivieri, Executive Vice President
Ed: Stacy Vogel Davis. **Released:** Weekly. **Price:** $4, introductory 4-week offer(Digital & Print). **Description:** Waukesha County, Wisconsin-based Easy PC Solutions LLC has been facing an $8.9 million settlement for sending unsolicited faxes to 7,000 health care providers. However, the company won't have to pay since the plaintiffs are expected to go after its insurance company. **Availability:** Print; Online.

25971 ■ *"Wayne, Oakland Counties Create Own 'Medical Corridor"'* in *Crain's Detroit Business* (Vol. 24, October 6, 2008, No. 40, pp. 8)
Pub: Crain Communications Inc.
Contact: Barry Asin, President
Ed: Jay Greene. **Description:** Woodward Medical Corridor that runs along Woodward Avenue and currently encompasses twelve hospitals and is rapidly growing with additional physician offices, advanced oncology centers and new hospitals. Beaumont Hospital is building a $160 million proton-beam therapy cancer center on its Royal Oak campus in a joint venture with Procure Treatment Centers of Bloomington Ind. That is expected to open in 2010 and will employ approximately 145 new workers. **Availability:** Online.

25972 ■ *"Week on the Web"* in *Crain's Detroit Business* (Vol. 25, June 22, 2009, No. 25, pp. 19)
Pub: Crain Communications Inc.
Contact: Barry Asin, President
Description: Blue Cross Blue Shield of Michigan, in a class-action lawsuit, will pay about 100 families whose children were either denied coverage for autism treatment or paid for treatment out of pocket. The settlement is worth about $ million. **Availability:** Print; Online.

25973 ■ *"A Well-Crafted Employee Handbook Can Make Work Run More Smoothly"* in *Idaho Business Review* (September 17, 2014)
Pub: BridgeTower Media
Contact: Adam Reinebach, President
Description: An employee handbook will provide a complaint process, provide company management flexibility and clarity and keep a company out of legal problems. Training, compensation, benefits, security, health, performance appraisals, and safety issues must be covered. Human resource managers and other mangers should cover basics to help communicate with workers.

25974 ■ *"What Business Schools Can Learn From the Medical Profession"* in *Harvard Business Review* (Vol. 90, January-February 2012, No.1-2, pp. 38)
Pub: Harvard Business Review Press
Contact: Moderna V. Pfizer, Contact
Ed: Nitin Nohria. **Price:** $6. **Description:** The author recommends closing the knowing-doing gap by applying health care feedback methods to business school instruction. Hospital residents receive feedback after making their rounds; so too should business school students and faculty assemble on a regular basis so that they can discuss what they are learning. **Availability:** Online; PDF.

25975 ■ *"What Choice Did I Have?"* in *Entrepreneur* (Vol. 37, October 2009, No. 10, pp. 88)
Pub: Entrepreneur Media Inc.
Contact: Dan Bova, Director
E-mail: dbova@entrepreneur.com
Ed: Craig Matsuda. **Description:** Profile of a worker at a financial services company who acquired firsthand knowledge concerning the relationship between health insurance costs and coverage. The worker's son got severely ill, forcing the worker to spend above what is covered by health insurance. **Availability:** Print; Online.

25976 ■ *"What Your Workplace Wellness Programs are Missing; Companies Can Benefit From Taking a Holistic Approach To Their Employees. Here's How"* in *Gallup Business Journal (July 7, 2014)*
Pub: Gallup, Inc.
Contact: Jon Clifton, Chief Executive Officer
Description: Companies should take a holistic approach to their employees' well being when addressing physical wellness in their workforce. Although employers are working to improve the physical wellness of workers, including weight loss, smoking cessation, and stress management, five essential elements: purpose, social, financial, community and physical issues would round out a good program. **Availability:** Print.

25977 ■ *"Wheel Genius"* in *Entrepreneur (June 2014)*
Pub: Entrepreneur Media Inc.
Contact: Dan Bova, Director
E-mail: dbova@entrepreneur.com
Description: Electric car startup, Kenguru, has developed a hatchback that aims to improve mobility for wheelchair users, who enter the vehicle using a rear-opening tailgate and automatic ramp. The Kenguru, which is Hungarian for kangaroo, uses motorcycle-style handlebars instead of steering wheels. The 1,000-pound car has an estimated range of 60 miles and can travel up to 35 miles per hour. The Kenguru could sell for about $25,000. Founder Stacy Zoern partnered with Budapest, Hungary-based Istvan Kissaroslaki in developing the new car. **Availability:** Print; Online.

25978 ■ *"Where the Money Is"* in *Conde Nast Portfolio (Vol. 2, June 2008, No. 6, pp. 113)*
Description: Revenue generated from treatments for common brain disorders that are currently on the market are listed. **Availability:** Online.

25979 ■ *"Why Seattle Children's Appealed"* in *Puget Sound Business Journal (Vol. 35, May 30, 2014, No. 6, pp. 6)*
Pub: American City Business Journals, Inc.
Contact: Mike Olivieri, Executive Vice President
Description: Seattle Children's Hospital filed an appeal against the Washing State Office of the Insurance Commissioner for approving several health exchange plans that excluded the hospital. Children's argues that it offers unique services and treatments only available through their medical facility and health insurance plans excluding them is putting children at risk. **Availability:** Online.

25980 ■ *Wisconsin Medical Directory*
Pub: Jola Publications
Contact: Jeremiah J. Schapiro, Contact
URL(s): www.jolapub.com/index_med_home_t.html
Description: Covers approximately 15,000 doctors, hospitals, clinics, nursing homes, and other selected health care providers in Wisconsin. **Entries include:** Doctor or facility name, address, phone, fax, doctors' UPINS. **Arrangement:** Classified by type of facility or care provided. **Indexes:** Name, product/service, subject. **Availability:** Print.

25981 ■ *Women's Health Concerns Sourcebook*
Pub: Omnigraphics Inc.
Contact: Kevin Hayes, Contact
Ed: Sandra J. Judd, Siva Ganesh Maharaja. **Description:** Publication includes resources on women's health issues. **Entries include:** Publication name, address. Principal content of publication is articles on specific health issues, definitions, symptoms, risks, treatment, and answers to frequently asked questions. **Arrangement:** Topic. **Indexes:** subject index/alpha. **Availability:** E-book.

TRADE PERIODICALS

25982 ■ *Abbeyfield Houses Society of Canada Newsletter*
Pub: Abbeyfield Houses Society of Canada
Contact: Denis Laframboise, President
URL(s): abbeyfield.ca/start-a-house
Description: Reports on news of Abbeyfield Houses Society of Canada, a provider of care and companionship for the elderly. Also features articles related to aging, housing, and lifestyle in Canada and internationally. Recurring features include letters to the editor, and columns titled News of Local Societies and Bits 'n Bites. **Availability:** PDF; Download.

25983 ■ *Academic Emergency Medicine: A Global Journal of Emergency Care (AEM)*
Pub: Wiley-Blackwell
URL(s): onlinelibrary.wiley.com/journal/15532712
X (Twitter): x.com/AcademicEmerMed
Released: Monthly **Price:** $199, Individuals for online only India , Japan; $504, Institutions for online only India , Japan; $199, Individuals for online only US, Canada; $490, Institutions for online only US, Canada. **Description:** Journal covering the practice, educational advancements, and investigation of emergency medicine. Published by Wiley on behalf of the Society for Academic Emergency Medicine (SAEM). **Availability:** Print; PDF; Download; Online.

25984 ■ *AHA News: American Hospital Association News*
Contact: Gary Luggiero, Managing Editor
E-mail: gluggiero@aha.org
URL(s): www.ahanews.com
Description: Tabloid for healthcare industry professionals covering related business issues, legislative policies, and hospital management issues. **Availability:** Print; Online.

25985 ■ *Air Medical Journal (AMJ)*
Pub: National EMS Pilots Association
Contact: Miles Dunagan, President
E-mail: miles.dunagan@nemspa.org
URL(s): www.airmedicaljournal.com
Ed: Jacqueline C. Stocking, PhD, Eric R. Swanson, MD. **Released:** 6/year **Price:** $292, Individuals for print + online 1 year international; $241, Individuals for print and online 1 year US; $205, Individuals for online only Us , Canada; $217, Individuals for online international; $310, Individuals for print and online US. **Description:** Journal for air medical transport professionals. Official Journal of the Air & Surface Transport Nurses Association, Air Medical Physician Association, Association of Air Medical Services, International Association of Flight and Critical Care Paramedics, and National EMS Pilots Association. **Availability:** Print; Download; PDF; Online.

25986 ■ *Alive*
Pub: Alive Publishing Group Inc.
Contact: Scott Yavis, Creative Director
URL(s): apg.alive.com/about/our-company
Ed: Vanessa Annand, Colleen Grant. **Released:** Monthly **Description:** Magazine promoting healthy living, alternative health, and nutrition. **Availability:** Print.

25987 ■ *American Journal of Infection Control (AJIC) (AJIC)*
Pub: Elsevier Inc.
URL(s): www.ajicjournal.orgwww.sciencedirect.com/journal/american-journal-of-infection-control
Released: Monthly; Annual; volume 49, issue 12 December 2021. **Description:** Peer-reviewed journal covering important topics and issues in infection control and epidemiology. Official publication of the Association for Professionals in Infection Control and Epidemiology (APIC). **Availability:** Print; Download; PDF; Online. **Type:** Full-text.

25988 ■ *APTA Magazine*
Pub: American Physical Therapy Association
Contact: Roger Herr, President
URL(s): www.apta.org/apta-magazine
Released: 11/year **Description:** Magazine for physical therapy professionals. **Availability:** Online.

25989 ■ *The Arc News*
Pub: The Arc Carroll County
Contact: Corynne Courpas, President
URL(s): arccarroll.org/membership
Released: Monthly **Description:** Spotlights issues concerning the mentally and physically disabled. Discusses rehabilitation, safety, housing, and centers. **Availability:** Online.

25990 ■ *Archives of Environmental & Occupational Health: An International Journal*
Pub: Taylor & Francis Group (Journals)
Contact: Annie Callanan, Chief Executive Officer
URL(s): www.tandfonline.com/journals/vaeh20
Released: 10/year **Price:** $1,428, Institutions for online; $1,741, Institutions for print & online only; $1,136, Individuals for print & online only. **Description:** Journal providing objective documentation of the effects of environmental agents on human health. Official publication of the Society for Occupational and Environmental Health. **Availability:** Print; Download; PDF; Online.

25991 ■ *Business Insurance*
Pub: Crain Communications Inc.
Contact: Barry Asin, President
URL(s): www.businessinsurance.com
Facebook: www.facebook.com/BusInsMagazine
Linkedin: www.linkedin.com/company/business-insurance
X (Twitter): x.com/BusInsMagazine
Released: Biweekly **Description:** International newsweekly reporting on corporate risk and employee benefit management news. **Availability:** Print; Online. **Type:** Full-text.

25992 ■ *Cambridge Quarterly of Healthcare Ethics*
Pub: Cambridge University Press
Contact: Peter Phillips, Chief Executive Officer
URL(s): www.cambridge.org/core/journals/cambridge-quarterly-of-healthcare-ethics
Ed: Steve Heilig, Thomasine Kushner. **Released:** Quarterly; January, April, July, October. **Price:** $527, Institutions for online. **Description:** Journal focusing on ethics as applied to medicine. **Availability:** Print; Download; PDF; Online.

25993 ■ *Canadian Journal of Dietetic Practice and Research*
Pub: Dietitians of Canada
Contact: Alexis Williams, Chief Executive Officer
URL(s): dcjournal.ca/journal/cjdpr
Ed: Dawna Royall. **Released:** Quarterly **Price:** $62, Individuals for one year online only; $340, Institutions for one year online only. **Description:** Peer-reviewed professional journal for dietitians and nutritionists in Canada (English and French). **Availability:** Print; PDF; Online.

25994 ■ *Canadian Journal of Public Health*
Pub: Springer Nature Limited
Contact: Frank Vrancken Peeters, Chief Executive Officer
URL(s): link.springer.com/journal/41997
Facebook: www.facebook.com/CJPH.RCSP
X (Twitter): x.com/CJPH_RCSP
Released: Bimonthly **Description:** Journal featuring peer-reviewed scientific articles on all aspects of public health, including health promotion, disease prevention, and healthy public policy. A publication of The Canadian Public Health Association. **Availability:** Print; PDF; Download; Online.

25995 ■ *Child and Youth Services*
Pub: Taylor And Francis Group
Contact: Annie Callanan, Chief Executive Officer
URL(s): www.tandfonline.com/journals/wcys20
Ed: Kiaras Gharabaghi, Doug Magnuson, Doug Magnuson, PhD, Jerome Beker. **Released:** Quarterly; volume 45, issue 2, 2024. **Price:** $204, Individuals for online only; $1,032, Institutions for online only. **Description:** Journal on youth services. **Availability:** Print; Download; PDF; Online.

25996 ■ *Children's Voice*
Pub: Child Welfare League of America
Contact: Ray Bierria, Chief Financial Officer
E-mail: rbierria@cwla.org
URL(s): www.cwla.org/childrens-voice

Ed: Jennifer Michael. **Released:** Volume 33, number 1. **Price:** $5.95, Single issue for pdf. **Description:** Magazine providing information on child welfare programs and policy developments. **Availability:** PDF.

25997 ■ Clinical Laboratory News
Pub: Association for Diagnostics & Laboratory Medicine
Contact: Anthony Killeen, President
URL(s): www.myadlm.org/cln

Released: Bimonthly **Price:** $103, U.S. for per year; $146, Other countries for per year; $11, Single issue. **Description:** Scholarly magazine providing current news in the field of clinical laboratory science. **Availability:** Print; PDF; Online.

25998 ■ Evaluation & the Health Professions
Pub: SAGE Publications
Contact: Tracey Ozmina, President
URL(s): journals.sagepub.com/home/ehpa

Ed: Steven Yale Sussman, PhD. **Released:** Quarterly **Price:** $1,626, Institutions for backfile lease, combined plus backfile (current volume print & all online content); $1,404, Institutions for backfile lease, e-access plus backfile (all online content); $2,242, Institutions for backfile purchase, e-access (content through 1998); $398, Institutions for single print issue; $70, Individuals for single print issue; $1,478, Institutions for print and online; $220, Individuals for print and online; $1,256, Institutions for online only; $1,448, Institutions for print only; $215, Individuals for print only; $187, Individuals for e-access. **Description:** Multidisciplinary, peer-reviewed journal providing information relating to research and practice in health settings. **Availability:** Print; PDF; Online.

25999 ■ FDA Week
Pub: Inside Washington Publishers
Contact: Robert Woolard, Contact
URL(s): insidehealthpolicy.com/fda-week/daily-news

Released: Weekly **Price:** $705, U.S. and Canada for per year; $755, Elsewhere for per year. **Description:** Reports on Food and Drug Administration policy, regulation, and enforcement. **Availability:** Online.

26000 ■ Fertility Weekly
Pub: Keith Key
URL(s): www.fertilityweekly.com

Released: Weekly **Price:** $659, U.S. and other countries online; $699, Individuals print; $739, Individuals print and online; $799, Other countries print; $839, Other countries print and online. **Description:** Discusses information pertaining to fertility. Recurring features include news of research, a calendar of events, reports of meetings, and a column titled Periodical Review. **Availability:** Print; PDF.

26001 ■ Focus on Autism and Other Developmental Disabilities
Pub: SAGE Publications
Contact: Tracey Ozmina, President
URL(s): journals.sagepub.com/home/foab

Ed: K. Alisa Lowrey, Kevin M. Ayres. **Released:** Quarterly **Price:** $97, Institutions for single print issue; us.sagepub.com/en-us/nam/journal/focus-autism-and-other-developmental-disabilities; $394, Institutions for backfile lease, combined plus backfile (current volume print & all online content); $340, Institutions for backfile lease, e-access plus backfile (all online content); $335, Institutions for backfile purchase, e-access (content through 1998); $30, Individuals for single print issue; $358, Institutions for print and online; $92, Individuals for print and online; $304, Institutions for online only; $351, Institutions for print only. **Description:** Journal focused on practical educational and treatment suggestions for teachers, trainers, and parents of persons with autism or other pervasive developmental disabilities. Published by the Hammill Institute on Disabilities and SAGE in association with The Division on Autism and Developmental Disabilities of The Council for Exceptional Children. **Availability:** Print; PDF; Download; Online.

26002 ■ Frontiers of Health Services Management
Pub: American College of Healthcare Executives
Contact: Deborah J. Bowen, President
URL(s): www.ache.org/learning-center/publications/journalshop.lww.com/Frontiers-of-Health-Services-Management/p/0748-8157

Released: Quarterly **Price:** $164, Individuals for print + online US 1 year; $135, Individuals for print + online Canada/Mexico, international, UK/Australia 1 year; $185, Individuals for print and online International UK/Australia; $641, Institutions for print only Canada/Mexico; $654, Institutions for print only international UK/Australia. **Description:** Journal publishing articles and commentaries on evolving trends in health services management. Each issue is dedicated to a single timely topic in the field. **Availability:** Print; Online.

26003 ■ Government Recreation and Fitness
Pub: Executive Business Media Inc.
Contact: Gregory Parisi, Art Director
E-mail: greg@productionebm.com
URL(s): www.ebmpubs.com/GRF/grf_media.asp

Released: 9/year **Price:** $35, U.S. for one year; $65, U.S. for two years; $5, Single issue. **Description:** Government administration magazine concentrating on fitness centers, recreation concepts, and facilities. **Availability:** Print; Online.

26004 ■ Health Affairs
Pub: Project HOPE
Contact: Rabih Torbay, President
URL(s): www.healthaffairs.org
Facebook: www.facebook.com/HealthAffairs
Linkedin: www.linkedin.com/company/health-affairs
X (Twitter): x.com/Health_Affairs
Instagram: www.instagram.com/health_affairs_org
YouTube: www.youtube.com/user/HealthAffairsJournal

Ed: Jane Hiebert-White, John K. Iglehart, Donald E. Metz. **Released:** Monthly **Price:** $26, Individuals for online (Unlimited); $15, Individuals for insider-only; $14, Individuals for online. **Description:** Peer-reviewed journal featuring health policy and health services research. **Availability:** Print; PDF; Online.

26005 ■ Health Care for Women International: Official Journal of the International Council on Women's Health Issues
Pub: Routledge, Taylor & Francis Group
URL(s): www.tandfonline.com/journals/uhcw20

Ed: Carole Anne McKenzie, PhD. **Released:** Monthly; 12 issues per year. **Price:** $2,519, Institutions for online; $3,072, Institutions for print + online; $676, Individuals for print + online. **Description:** Interdisciplinary journal on women's health care. Covers cultural differences, psychological challenges, alternative lifestyles, aging, wife abuse, childbearing and ethical issues. **Availability:** Print; Download; PDF; Online.

26006 ■ Health Progress
Pub: Catholic Health Association of the United States
Contact: Mary Haddad, President
URL(s): www.chausa.org/publications/health-progress/current-issue

Ed: Betsy Taylor. **Released:** Quarterly; Winter, Spring, Summer, Fall. **Price:** $29, Nonmembers for Foreign & Canada, US; $10, Nonmembers for back issue. **Description:** Magazine for administrative-level and other managerial personnel in Catholic healthcare and related organizations. Featured are articles on management concepts, legislative and regulatory trends, and theological, sociological, ethical, legal, and technical issues. **Availability:** Print; PDF; Online.

26007 ■ Health and Safety Science Abstracts
URL(s): www.csa.com/

Released: Monthly **Description:** Health and Safety Science Abstracts provides coverage of world literature on general safety, environmental and ecological safety, industrial hygiene and occupational safety, transportation safety, aviation and aerospace safety, and medical safety. It is available as a quarterly print journal, through magnetic tape lease, online, on CD-ROM, and via the Internet through the Internet Database Service. **Availability:** Print; Online.

26008 ■ Health Science: Living Well Into the Future
Pub: National Health Association
Contact: Mark Huberman, President
URL(s): www.healthscience.org/health-science

Ed: Cathy Fisher. **Released:** Quarterly **Price:** $8.95, Single issue. **Description:** Health and natural hygiene magazine, for members of ANHS. **Availability:** Online.

26009 ■ Healthcare Executive
Pub: American College of Healthcare Executives
Contact: Deborah J. Bowen, President
URL(s): healthcareexecutive.org

Released: Bimonthly **Description:** Provides in-depth analysis of emerging trends in healthcare management and includes strategies for confronting healthcare management issues. **Availability:** Print; PDF; Online.

26010 ■ Heart and Lung: The Journal of Cardiopulmonary and Acute Care
Pub: Elsevier Inc.
URL(s): www.heartandlung.org

Ed: Nancy S. Redeker, PhD. **Description:** Peer-reviewed journal covering original research on techniques, advances, investigations, and observations related to the care of patients with acute and critical illness and patients with chronic cardiac or pulmonary disorders. Official publication of The American Association of Heart Failure Nurses. **Availability:** Print; Download; PDF; Online.

26011 ■ HIMSS Annual Conference & Exhibition (HIMSS)
URL(s): www.himssconference.com/about-the-conference

Frequency: Annual. **Description:** Health care information systems, telecommunications, consulting firms, hardware, software, and service providers. **Audience:** Industry professionals. **Principal Exhibits:** Health care information systems, telecommunications, consulting firms, hardware, software, and service providers. Dates and Locations: 2025 Mar 03-6 The Venetian Convention & Expo Center, Caesars Forum, and Wynn Las Vegas, Las Vegas, NV. **Telecommunication Services:** eventregistration@himss.org.

26012 ■ Home Health Care Management & Practice (HHCMP)
Pub: SAGE Publications
Contact: Tracey Ozmina, President
URL(s): journals.sagepub.com/home/hhc

Released: Quarterly **Price:** $1,130, Institutions for back file lease, combined plus back file (current volume print & all online content); $976, Institutions for back file lease, e-access plus back file (all online content); $969, Institutions for back file purchase, e-access (content through 1998); $277, Institutions for single print issue; $81, Individuals for single print issue; $1,027, Institutions for print and online; $253, Individuals for print and online; $215, Individuals for online only; $873, Institutions for online only; $1,006, Institutions for print only; $248, Individuals for print only. **Description:** Peer-reviewed journal covering all aspects of home health care practice and management. **Availability:** Print; PDF; Download; Online.

26013 ■ Home Health Care Services Quarterly
Pub: Taylor And Francis Group
Contact: Annie Callanan, Chief Executive Officer
URL(s): www.tandfonline.com/journals/whhc20

Ed: Hongdao Meng. **Released:** Quarterly **Price:** $1,767, Institutions for print and online; $257, Individuals for print and online; $1,449, Institutions for online only; $237, Individuals for online only. **Description:** Professional journal. **Availability:** Print; Download; PDF; Online.

26014 ■ Hospital Topics
Pub: Routledge, Taylor & Francis Group

URL(s): www.tandfonline.com/journals/vhos20
Released: Quarterly; volume 102, issue 2. **Price:** $200, Individuals for print and online; $595, Institutions for print and online; $488, Institutions for online only. **Description:** Journal for upper and middle management in the changing hospital and health care industry. **Availability:** Print; Download; PDF; Online.

26015 ■ *International Journal of Health Planning and Management*
Pub: John Wiley & Sons Ltd.
Contact: Matthew Kissner, Chief Executive Officer
URL(s): onlinelibrary.wiley.com/journal/10991751
Released: Quarterly **Price:** $4,638, Institutions for print&online; $4,129, Institutions for online only; $4,307, Institutions for print only. **Description:** International, multidisciplinary journal seeking to provide a forum for publications related to major issues in health policy, planning, and management. **Availability:** Print; PDF; Download; Online.

26016 ■ *International Journal of Technology Assessment in Health Care*
Pub: Cambridge University Press
Contact: Peter Phillips, Chief Executive Officer
URL(s): www.cambridge.org/core/journals/international-journal-of-technology-assessment-in-health-care
X (Twitter): x.com/ijtahc
Ed: Prof. Egon Jonsson. **Released:** Annual **Description:** Journal covering advancements in health care technology. **Availability:** Print; Download; PDF; Online.

26017 ■ *The Joint Commission Journal on Quality and Patient Safety*
Pub: Joint Commission Resources
Contact: Dr. Jonathan B. Perlin, President
URL(s): store.jcrinc.com/the-joint-commission-journal-on-quality-and-patient-safetywww.sciencedirect.com/journal/the-joint-commission-journal-on-quality-and-patient-safety
Released: Monthly **Price:** $1,147, Individuals for print + online Canada; $450, Individuals for print + online Canada; $810, Individuals for print + online Canada; $1,114, Individuals for print + online India; $437, Individuals for print + online India; $786, Individuals for print + online India; $1,083, Individuals for print + online US; $425, Individuals for print + online US; $765, Individuals for print + online US. **Description:** Magazine directed to health care providers and administrators quality assurance/improvement managers and researchers concerned with the quality of health care; specifically quality improvement, CQI/TQM, and risk management. **Availability:** Print; Download; PDF; Online.

26018 ■ *Journal of Agromedicine*
Pub: Taylor And Francis Group
Contact: Annie Callanan, Chief Executive Officer
URL(s): www.tandfonline.com/journals/wagr20
Ed: Matthew C. Keifer, MD. **Released:** Quarterly **Price:** $256, Individuals for print and online; $596, Institutions for print and online; $2,214, Individuals for online only; $489, Institutions for Online only. **Description:** Journal on the health effects of agricultural operations on workers and their families, consumers, and the environment. **Availability:** Print; Download; PDF; Online.

26019 ■ *Journal of the American Board of Family Medicine (JABFM)*
Pub: American Board of Family Medicine
Contact: Dr. Warren Newton, President
URL(s): www.jabfm.org
X (Twitter): x.com/JAmBoardFamMed
YouTube: www.youtube.com/@jabfmjabfm7563
Ed: Anne Victoria Neale, PhD, Marjorie A. Bowman. **Released:** Bimonthly; January, March, May, July, September, and November. **Description:** Peer-reviewed journal publishing information on advancement of family medicine research and clinical practice. **Availability:** Print; Download; PDF; Online.

26020 ■ *Journal of American College Health*
Pub: Routledge, Taylor & Francis Group
URL(s): www.acha.org/ACHA/Resources/Publications/Journal/ACHA/Resources/JACH.aspxwww.tandfonline.com/journals/vach20
Released: 9/year **Price:** $1,156, Institutions for print & online; $371, Individuals for print&online; $948, Institutions for online only. **Description:** Journal covering developments and research in the college healthcare field. **Availability:** Print; PDF; Download; Online.

26021 ■ *Journal of the Association of Nurses in AIDS Care (JANAC)*
Pub: Lippincott Williams & Wilkins
URL(s): journals.lww.com/janac/pages/default.aspx
Facebook: www.facebook.com/ANACJournal
X (Twitter): x.com/ANACJournal
Released: Bimonthly **Price:** $194, Individuals for online us, international; $2,240, Institutions for print us, Canada/Mexico 2 years; $3,360, Institutions for print us, Canada/Mexico 3 years; $278, Individuals for print and online international and UK/Australia; $1,212, Institutions for print international, UK/australia1 year; $264, Individuals for print and online Canada/Mexico 1 year; $1,198, Institutions for print US, Canada/Mexico 1 year; $210, Individuals for print and online, US 1 year. **Description:** Peer-reviewed, international nursing journal that covers all aspects of the global HIV epidemic, with an emphasis on prevention, evidence-based care management, interprofessional clinical care, epidemiology, research, advocacy and education, policies, social determinants of health, and program development. **Availability:** Print; PDF; Online.

26022 ■ *Journal of Behavioral Health Services & Research*
Pub: Springer US
Contact: Derk Haank, Chief Executive Officer
URL(s): link.springer.com/journal/11414
X (Twitter): x.com/TheJBHSR
Released: Quarterly **Description:** Peer-reviewed journal on the organization, financing, delivery, and outcome of behavioral health services. **Availability:** Print; Download; PDF.

26023 ■ *Journal of Ethnic & Cultural Diversity in Social Work: Innovations in Theory, Research & Practice*
Pub: Taylor And Francis Group
Contact: Annie Callanan, Chief Executive Officer
URL(s): www.tandfonline.com/journals/wecd20
Ed: Mo Yee Lee, Mo Yee Lee, PhD. **Released:** Quarterly **Price:** $1,480, Institutions for print & online; $357, Individuals for print & online; $1,214, Institutions for online only; $309, Individuals for online only. **Description:** Journal examines multicultural social issues related to social work policy, research, theory, and practice. **Availability:** Print; PDF; Download; Online.

26024 ■ *Journal of Health Care Chaplaincy*
Pub: Association of Professional Chaplains
Contact: Dr. Jeffery T. Garland, President
URL(s): www.tandfonline.com/journals/whcc20
Released: Quarterly; vol.30, 2024. **Price:** $728, Institutions for print and online; $129, Individuals for online & print; $597, Institutions for online only; $112, Individuals for online. **Description:** Journal on chaplaincy in health care institutions. **Availability:** Print; Download; PDF; Online.

26025 ■ *Journal of Health Care for the Poor and Underserved (JHCPU)*
Pub: Association of Clinicians for the Underserved
URL(s): www.press.jhu.edu/journals/journal-health-care-poor-and-underservedclinicians.org/acu-membership/journal-of-health-care-for-the-poor-and-underserved
Ed: Virginia M. Brennan. **Released:** Quarterly; February, May, August, and November. **Price:** $85, Individuals for print 1 year 4 issue; $90, Individuals for 1 year online; $162, Institutions for 2 year online; $153, Individuals for 2 year 8 issue print; $970, Institutions for 2 year 8 issue print; $485, Institutions for 1 year 4 issue. **Description:** Peer-reviewed journal focusing on contemporary health care issues of medically underserved communities. **Availability:** Print; Online.

26026 ■ *Journal of Health and Social Behavior (JHSB)*
Pub: SAGE Publications
Contact: Tracey Ozmina, President
URL(s): journals.sagepub.com/home/hsbwww.sagepub.com/journals/Journal201971
X (Twitter): x.com/asr_journal
Ed: Deborah Carr. **Released:** Quarterly; March, June, September, December. **Price:** $576, Institutions for online only; $663, Institutions for print only; $677, Institutions for print and online; $182, Institutions for single print issue; $92, /issue for institutions. **Description:** Medical sociology journal covering empirical and theoretical research that applies sociological concepts and methods to the understanding of health and illness and the organization of medicine and health care. Published in association between SAGE and the American Sociological Association. **Availability:** Print; Download; PDF; Online. **Telecommunication Services:** Email: info@sagepub.com .

26027 ■ *Journal for Healthcare Quality*
Pub: National Association for Healthcare Quality
Contact: Stephanie Mercado, Chief Executive Officer
E-mail: ceo@nahq.org
URL(s): nahq.org/nahq-intelligence/journal-members-only
Released: Bimonthly **Description:** Professional publication that explores safe, cost-effective, quality healthcare. **Availability:** Print; Online.

26028 ■ *Journal of Intensive Care Medicine (JIC)*
Pub: SAGE Publications
Contact: Tracey Ozmina, President
URL(s): journals.sagepub.com/home/jic
Ed: Nicholas Smyrnios, MD, James M. Rippe, MD. **Released:** Monthly **Price:** $2,338, Institutions for backfile lease, combined plus backfile (current volume print & all online content); $2,019, Institutions for backfile lease, e-access plus backfile (all online content); $1,629, Institutions for backfile purchase, e-access (content through 1998); $191, Institutions for single print issue; $49, Individuals for single print issue; $2,125, Institutions for print and online; $1,806, Institutions for online only; $2,083, Institutions for print only; $448, Individuals for print only. **Description:** Peer-reviewed, multidisciplinary journal covering all aspects of intensive/critical/coronary care. **Availability:** Print; PDF; Download; Online.

26029 ■ *Journal of School Health (JOSH)*
Pub: Wiley-Blackwell
URL(s): www.ashaweb.org/journal-of-school-healthonlinelibrary.wiley.com/journal/17461561
Ed: Michael J. Mann. **Released:** Monthly **Price:** $678, Institutions for online only US and Canada; $845, Institutions for online India and Japan. **Description:** Journal covering practice, theory, and research related to the health and well-being of school-aged youth. Published by Wiley on behalf of the American School Health Association. **Availability:** Print; Download; PDF; Online.

26030 ■ *Journal of Social Service Research*
Pub: Taylor And Francis Group
Contact: Annie Callanan, Chief Executive Officer
URL(s): www.tandfonline.com/journals/wssr20
Ed: Sophia F. Dziegielewski, Sophia F. Dziegielewski, PhD. **Released:** 6/year; volume 50, issue 3. **Price:** $2,066, Institutions for print and online; $269, Individuals for print and online; $236, Individuals for online only; $1,694, Institutions for online. **Description:** Devoted to empirical research and its application to the design, delivery, and management of the new social services. **Availability:** Print; PDF; Download; Online.

26031 ■ *Managed Healthcare Executive: The News Magazine for Health Care Costs and Quality*
Pub: MJH Life Sciences
Contact: Mike Hennessy, Jr., President
E-mail: mjhennessy@mjhassoc.com
URL(s): www.managedhealthcareexecutive.com

Facebook: www.facebook.com/ManagedHeal
thcareExecutive
Linkedin: www.linkedin.com/company/managed-heal
thcare-executive
X (Twitter): twitter.com/MHExecutive
Description: Professional magazine reporting news and information pertinent to healthcare purchasing decisions made in the managed care industry. Topics include quality assurance, technology, disease management, and trends in integrated health systems. **Availability:** Print.

26032 ■ Massage Therapy Journal (MTJ)
Pub: American Massage Therapy Association
Contact: Steve Albertson, President
URL(s): www.amtamassage.org/publications/
massage-therapy-journal
Released: Quarterly; Summer, spring, Winter, Fall. **Description:** Contains scholarly articles on massage therapy. **Availability:** Print; Online.

26033 ■ Medicine on the Net
Pub: COR Healthcare Resources
URL(s): www.hcpro.com/services/corhealth/index.cfm
Released: Monthly **Price:** $229, Individuals. **Description:** Spotlights developing issues in the use of the Internet by medical professionals. Recurring features include letters to the editor, interviews, news of research, and book reviews. **Availability:** Print; PDF.

26034 ■ Morbidity and Mortality Weekly Report (MMWR)
Pub: U.S. Department of Health and Human Services Centers for Disease Control and Prevention
Contact: Reginald R. Mebane, Director
URL(s): www.cdc.gov/mmwr/index.html
Ed: Ron Moolenaar, MD. **Released:** Weekly **Description:** Magazine focusing on public health problems and diseases. **Availability:** Print; PDF; Online.

26035 ■ The Nation's Health
Pub: American Public Health Association
Contact: Ella Greene-Moton, President
URL(s): www.apha.org/Publications/The-Nations
-Healthwww.thenationshealth.org
X (Twitter): x.com/nationshealth
Released: 10/year **Price:** $11, Single issue for print per copy US; $12, for international; $8, Single issue; $81, U.S. for 1 year print Canada; $103, Individuals for 1 year print only US/Canada; $167, Institutions for print and online US/Canada; $103, Individuals for 1 year online US/Canada and International; $135, Institutions for 1 year online US/Canada and International; $98, for 1 year print only international; $130, Individuals for 1 year print + online international; $185, Institutions for 1 year print + online international. **Description:** Newspaper covering public health news and other information for public health professionals, legislators, and decision-makers. **Availability:** Print; PDF; Online.

26036 ■ The Neurodiagnostic Journal
Pub: ASET - The Neurodiagnostic Society
Contact: Kevin Helm, Executive Director
E-mail: kevin@aset.org
URL(s): www.aset.org/the-neurodiagnostic
-journalwww.tandfonline.com/journals/utnj20
Released: Quarterly **Price:** $491, Institutions for online only; $249, Individuals for print only; $599, Institutions for print and online only. **Description:** Professional Journal. **Availability:** Print; PDF; Online.

26037 ■ Nursing Education Perspectives (NEP)
Pub: National League for Nursing
Contact: Beverly Malone, Chief Executive Officer
E-mail: oceo@nln.org
URL(s): www.nln.org/news/publications/publica
tionsjournals.lww.com/neponline/pages/default.aspx
Ed: Joyce Fitzpatrick. **Released:** Bimonthly **Price:** $223, Individuals for print and online international, uk/Australia; $615, Institutions for print international, uk/Australia; $203, Individuals for print and online Canada/Mexico; $124, Individuals for online US, international; $595, Institutions for print US, Canada/Mexico; $158, Institutions for print and online US.

Description: Professional journal for nurses. Includes articles on health policy, social and economic issues affecting health care, and nursing education and practice. **Availability:** Print; Download; PDF; Online.

26038 ■ Nutrition & Foodservice Edge Magazine
Pub: Association of Nutrition and Foodservice Professionals
Contact: Joyce Gilbert, President
URL(s): www.anfponline.org/news-resources/nutrition
-and-foodservice-magazine
Ed: Diane Everett. **Released:** 6/year **Description:** Professional magazine focusing on nutrition and management issues encountered by dietary managers in non-commercial food service. **Availability:** Print; PDF; Online.

26039 ■ Nutrition Today
Pub: Lippincott Williams & Wilkins
URL(s): journals.lww.com/nutritiontodayonline/pages/
default.aspx
Facebook: www.facebook.com/100033470302155
X (Twitter): x.com/Ntjournalonline
Ed: Johanna Dwyer. **Released:** 6/year; volume 59 - issue 3. **Price:** $82, for print online training one year USA & Canada/Mexico; $98, for print online international & UK/Australia one year in training; $72, for online intraning international & USA one year; $1,028, Institutions for print international & UK /Australia one year; $122, Individuals for online USA & international one year; $166, Individuals for print online Canada/Mexico one year; $300, Individuals for international print online one year; $257, Institutions for print online UK/Australia one year; $757, for print one year Canada/Mexico; $144, Individuals for print+ online USA one year; $1,012, Institutions for print USA one year. **Description:** Health science journal. **Availability:** Print; PDF; Online.

26040 ■ Occupational Therapy in Health Care: A Journal of Contemporary Practice
Pub: Taylor & Francis Group (Journals)
Contact: Annie Callanan, Chief Executive Officer
URL(s): www.tandfonline.com/journals/iohc20
Ed: Anne Elizabeth Dickerson, PhD. **Released:** Quarterly **Price:** $1,520, Institutions for print and online; $1,246, Institutions for online only. **Description:** Journal covering contemporary practice in occupational therapy. **Availability:** Print; Download; PDF; Online.

26041 ■ Osteoporosis International: with other metabolic bone diseases
Pub: Springer London
URL(s): link.springer.com/journal/198
Released: Monthly **Description:** Journal covering the diagnosis, prevention, treatment, and management of osteoporosis and other metabolic bone diseases. **Availability:** Print; PDF; Download; Online.

26042 ■ Peritoneal Dialysis International (PDI)
Pub: SAGE Publications
Contact: Tracey Ozmina, President
URL(s): journals.sagepub.com/home/ptda
Released: Bimonthly **Price:** $1,519, Institutions for backfile lease, combined plus backfile (current volume print & all online content); $1,312, Institutions for backfile lease, e-access plus backfile (all online content); $248, Institutions for single print issue; $1,176, for back file purchase; $550, Individuals for print and online; $1,381, Institutions for print + online; $117, Individuals for single issues; $468, Individuals for online only; $1,174, Institutions for e access; $1,353, Institutions for print; $539, Individuals for print. **Description:** International journal focused on peritoneal dialysis. Official journal of the International Society for Peritoneal Dialysis (ISPD). **Availability:** Print; PDF; Online.

26043 ■ Physical & Occupational Therapy In Pediatrics: A Quarterly Journal of Developmental Therapy (POTP)
Pub: Taylor & Francis Group (Journals)
Contact: Annie Callanan, Chief Executive Officer
URL(s): www.tandfonline.com/journals/ipop20

Ed: Robert J. Palisano, Annette Majnemer. **Released:** 6/year; volume 44, issue 4 2024. **Price:** $3,222, Institutions for print and online.; $2,642, Institutions for online only. **Description:** Journal for therapists involved in developmental and physical rehabilitation of infants and children. **Availability:** Print; Download; PDF; Online.

26044 ■ Physician Executive
Pub: American Association for Physician Leadership
Contact: Peter B. Angood, President
URL(s): www.physicianleaders.org/about
Released: Bimonthly **Description:** Focuses on health care management and medical management for physician executives. **Availability:** Print.

26045 ■ Provider: For Long Term Care Professionals
Pub: American Health Care Association
Contact: Mark Parkinson, President
URL(s): www.providermagazine.com/Pages/defaul
t.aspx
Ed: Joanne Erickson. **Released:** Monthly **Description:** Includes buyers' guide, news reports, advertisers' index, a listing of new products and services, and calendar of events. **Availability:** Print; Online.

26046 ■ Psychoanalytic Social Work
Pub: Taylor And Francis Group
Contact: Annie Callanan, Chief Executive Officer
URL(s): www.www.tandfonline.com/journals/wpsw20
Released: Semiannual; vol.31, issue 1, 2024. **Price:** $1,149, Institutions for print and online; $231, Individuals for print + online; $203, Individuals for online only; $942, Institutions for online only. **Availability:** Print; Download; PDF; Online.

26047 ■ Qualitative Health Research (QHR)
Pub: SAGE Publications
Contact: Tracey Ozmina, President
URL(s): journals.sagepub.com/home/qhra
Ed: Prof. Julianne Cheek. **Released:** 14/year. **Price:** $220, Institutions for single print issue; us.sagepub.com/en-us/nam/journal/qualitative-health-research; $2,720, Institutions for backfile lease, e-access plus backfile (all online content); $2,302, Institutions for backfile purchase, e-access (content through 1998); $2,863, Institutions for combined (print & e-access); $31, Individuals for single print issue; $3,149, Institutions for print and online; $2,434, Institutions for online only; $290, Individuals for online only; $2,806, Institutions for print only; $337, Individuals for print only. **Description:** International, interdisciplinary, peer-reviewed journal focused on furthering the development and understanding of qualitative research in health and social service settings. **Availability:** Print; PDF; Download; Online.

26048 ■ Revista Panamericana de Salud Pública/Pan American Journal (RPSP/PAJPH)
Pub: World Health Organization
Contact: Jane Ellison, Executive Director
URL(s): journal.paho.org/en
Facebook: www.facebook.com/PAHOWHO
Linkedin: www.linkedin.com/company/pan-american
-health-organization
X (Twitter): x.com/rpsp_pajph
YouTube: www.youtube.com/pahopin
Released: Monthly **Description:** Open access, peer-reviewed multilingual public health journal providing information on medical and health progress in America. **Availability:** Print; PDF; Online.

26049 ■ Seizure: European Journal of Epilepsy
Pub: Elsevier B.V.
Contact: Kumsal Bayazit, Chief Executive Officer
URL(s): www.seizure-journal.comwww.sciencedirec
t.com/journal/seizure-european-journal-of-epilepsy
Facebook: www.facebook.com/seizure.journal
X (Twitter): x.com/SeizureJournal
Released: 10/year **Price:** $609, for print and online US, International; $518, for online US, International; $1,964, Institutions for 1 year print US, Canada; $609, Individuals for 1 year print US, Canada.

Description: International journal covering all topics related to epilepsy and seizure disorders. **Availability:** Print; PDF; Download; Online.

26050 ■ *Share*
Pub: SHARE
URL(s): www.sharecancersupport.org
Released: Monthly **Description:** Acts as a forum for information, meetings, resources, and support groups for women with breast or ovarian cancer. **Availability:** Online.

26051 ■ *Sleep*
Pub: Sleep Research Society
URL(s): www.sleepmeeting.org/abstract-supplementsacademic.oup.com/sleep
Released: Monthly **Price:** $305, Individuals for online only; $614, Institutions for online only; $305, Individuals for online; $614, Institutions for online. **Description:** Peer-reviewed journal covering findings on sleep and circadian rhythms. **Availability:** Print; PDF; Online.

26052 ■ *Social Work with Groups: A Journal of Community and Clinical Practice*
Pub: Taylor And Francis Group
Contact: Annie Callanan, Chief Executive Officer
URL(s): www.tandfonline.com/journals/wswg20
Ed: Catherine P. Papell, Beulah Rothman. **Released:** Quarterly; latest edition: volume 47, issue 3. **Price:** $1,629, Institutions for print and online; $269, Individuals for print and online; $1,336, Institutions for online; $237, Individuals for online. **Description:** Offers readers fresh examples of evidence-guided group work with diverse populations in multiple settings through a combination of vivid practice illustrations and sound theoretical concepts. **Availability:** Print; Download; PDF; Online.

26053 ■ *Social Work in Health Care: A Quarterly Journal Adopted by the Society for Social Work Leadership in Health Care*
Pub: Taylor And Francis Group
Contact: Annie Callanan, Chief Executive Officer
URL(s): www.tandfonline.com/journals/wshc20
Ed: Ji Seon Lee, Gary Rosenberg, PhD. **Released:** 10/year **Price:** $680, Individuals for print and online; $595, Individuals for online only. **Description:** Gives the tools to improve your practice while keeping you up-to-date with the latest crucial information. **Availability:** Print; PDF; Download; Online.

26054 ■ *Social Work in Public Health*
Pub: Taylor And Francis Group
Contact: Annie Callanan, Chief Executive Officer
URL(s): www.tandfonline.com/journals/whsp20
Ed: Marvin D. Feit, PhD, Stanley F. Battle, PhD. **Released:** 8/year **Price:** $2,022, Institutions for print and online; $307, Individuals for print and online; $1,658, Institutions for online; $268, Individuals for online. **Description:** Journal for people interested in health and social policy issues. **Availability:** Print; Download; PDF; Online.

26055 ■ *Therapeutic Recreation Journal*
Pub: Sagamore Publishing L.L.C.
Contact: Peter Bannon, Manager
URL(s): js.sagamorepub.com/index.php/trj
Released: Quarterly **Price:** $242, Individuals for print & online international; $681, Institutions for print & online international; $72, Members for atra online only; $72, Members for ctra online only; $72, for ctrs online only; $72, Members for tro online only; $195, Individuals for print & online; $628, Institutions for print & online; $137, Individuals for online; $595, Institutions for online. **Description:** Journal providing forum for research and discussion of therapeutic recreation for persons with disabilities. **Availability:** Print; Online; Download; PDF.

26056 ■ *Topics in Clinical Nutrition (TICN)*
Pub: Lippincott Williams & Wilkins
URL(s): journals.lww.com/topicsinclinicalnutrition/pages/default.aspx
Facebook: www.facebook.com/100028714222254/wall#!/pages/Topics-in-Clinical-Nutrition/124938497585061
X (Twitter): x.com/TCN_online
Released: Quarterly **Price:** $1,258, Institutions for print international, up/Australia 1 year; $144, Individuals for online 1 year US International; $288, Individuals for online 2 year US International; $432, Individuals for online 3 year US International; $142, for online 2 year In Training US; $213, for online 3 year In Training US; $71, for online 1 year In Training US; $1,231, Institutions for print 1 year Canada/Mexico; $1,357, Institutions for print 1 year International; $2,462, Institutions for print 2 year Canada/Mexico; $2,714, Institutions for print 2 year International; $3,693, Institutions for print 3 year Canada/Mexico; $4,071, Institutions for print 3 year International; $1,357, Institutions for print 1 year UK/Australia; $2,714, Institutions for print 2 year UK/Australia; $4,071, Institutions for print 3 year UK/Australia; $1,097, Institutions for print 1 year US; $2,194, Institutions for print 2 year US; $3,291, Institutions for print 3 year US. **Description:** Peer-reviewed journal addressing the challenges and problems of dietitians and others involved in dietary care in a health care setting. **Availability:** Print; PDF; Online.

26057 ■ *Women and Health: A Multi Disciplinary Journal of Women's Health Issues*
Pub: Taylor And Francis Group
Contact: Annie Callanan, Chief Executive Officer
URL(s): www.tandfonline.com/journals/wwah20
Released: 10/year **Price:** $628, Institutions for print and online; $4,039, Institutions for print & online; $3,312, Institutions for online only; $567, Individuals for online only. **Description:** Multidisciplinary journal on health for women. **Availability:** Print; Download; PDF; Online.

VIDEO/AUDIO MEDIA

26058 ■ *How I Built My Small Business: How to Start and Run an Osteopathic Practice with All Words Health with Dr. Arlene Dijamco*
URL(s): www.annemcginty.com/transcripts/arlenedijamco
Ed: Anne McGinty. **Released:** February 20, 2024. **Description:** Podcast features a conversation with the founder of an osteopathic practice in Georgia.

26059 ■ *Midwest Moxie: Providing Virtual, Pediatric Mental Health Service: Monika Roots*
URL(s): www.wuwm.com/podcast/midwest-moxie/2023-12-06/providing-virtual-pediatric-mental-health-services-monika-roots
Ed: Kathleen Gallagher. **Released:** December 06, 2023. **Description:** Podcast discusses health start-ups implementing a unique model for services in a youth mental health crisis.

TRADE SHOWS AND CONVENTIONS

26060 ■ AACPDM Annual Meeting
American Academy for Cerebral Palsy and Developmental Medicine (AACPDM)
555 E Wells St., Ste. 1100
Milwaukee, WI 53202
Ph: (414)918-3014
Fax: (414)276-2146
Co. E-mail: info@aacpdm.org
URL: http://www.aacpdm.org
Contact: Tom F. Novacheck, President
URL(s): www.aacpdm.org/events/2024
Frequency: Annual. **Description:** Disseminate information on new developments in applied and translational sciences, prevention, diagnosis, treatment, and technology. **Audience:** Developmental and other pediatricians, neurologists, psychologists, physiatrists, orthopedic and neuro-surgeons, physical and occupational therapists, speech and language pathologists, orthotists, rehab engineers, kinesiologists, nurses, nutritionists, special educators, administrators, researchers, and all others concerned with the care of people with cerebral palsy and other childhood-onset disabilities. **Principal Exhibits:** Disseminate information on new developments in applied and translational sciences, prevention, diagnosis, treatment, and technology. Dates and Locations: 2025 Oct 15-18 New Orleans Marriott, New Orleans, LA; 2026 Sep 27-30 Philadelphia Marriott Downtown, Philadelphia, PA; 2027 Sep 22-25 Sheraton Denver Downtown, Denver, CO. **Telecommunication Services:** meetings@aacpdm.org.

26061 ■ AAD Annual Meeting
American Academy of Dermatology (AAD)
9500 W Bryn Mawr Ave., Ste. 500
Rosemont, IL 60018-5216
Ph: (847)240-1280
Fax: (847)240-1859
Co. E-mail: mrc@aad.org
URL: http://www.aad.org
Contact: Mark D. Kaufmann, President
URL(s): www.aad.org/member/meetings-education/am25
Frequency: Annual. **Description:** Annual meeting for members of dermatologists. **Audience:** Industry professionals. **Principal Exhibits:** Annual meeting for members of dermatologists. Dates and Locations: 2025 Mar 07-11 Orlando, FL; 2026 Mar 27-31 Denver, CO. **Telecommunication Services:** exhibits@aad.org.

26062 ■ AAFP Family Medicine Experience (FMX)
American Academy of Family Physicians (AAFP)
11400 Tomahawk Creek Pky.
Leawood, KS 66211-2680
Ph: (913)906-6000
Free: 800-274-2237
Fax: (913)906-6075
Co. E-mail: aafp@aafp.org
URL: http://www.aafp.org/home.html
Contact: Steven P. Furr, President
URL(s): www.aafp.org/events/fmx.html
Frequency: Annual. **Description:** Pharmaceuticals, diagnostic products, medical equipment and devices, computer software, physician placement, and publishers. **Audience:** Physicians. **Principal Exhibits:** Pharmaceuticals, diagnostic products, medical equipment and devices, computer software, physician placement, and publishers. Dates and Locations: 2025 Oct 05-09 Anaheim, CA; 2026 Oct 20-24 Nashville, TN; 2027 Sep 20-24 San Diego, CA; 2028 Oct 10-14 Chicago, IL; 2029 Oct 16-20 New Orleans, LA; 2030 Oct 15-19 Salt Lake City, UT; 2031 Oct 26-30 Nashville, TN; 2032 Sep 21-25 Washington, DC. **Telecommunication Services:** aafp@aafp.org.

26063 ■ American Organization of Nurse Executives Annual Meeting and Exposition (AONE)
American Organization for Nursing Leadership (AONE)
155 N Wacker Dr., Ste. 400
Chicago, IL 60606
URL: http://www.aonl.org
Contact: Erik Martin, President
URL(s): www.aonl.org/news/voice/may-2024
Frequency: Annual. **Audience:** Nursing professionals.

26064 ■ American Public Health Association Public Health Expo
American Public Health Association (APHA)
800 I St. NW
Washington, DC 20001
Ph: (202)777-2742
Fax: (202)777-2534
Co. E-mail: membership.mail@apha.org
URL: http://www.apha.org
Contact: Ella Greene-Moton, President
URL(s): www.apha.org/Events-and-Meetings/Annual/Program/Public-Health-Expo
Frequency: Annual. **Description:** Share ideas, network and learn about a range of public health topics. Event will be in-person and will host a digital version of the expo a week later. **Audience:** Public health professionals, physicians, nurses, and health administrators. **Principal Exhibits:** Share ideas, network and learn about a range of public health top-

ics. Event will be in-person and will host a digital version of the expo a week later. **Telecommunication Services:** annualmeeting@apha.org.

26065 ▪ American School Health Association National School Health Conference
American School Health Association (ASHA)
501 N Morton St., Ste. 111
Bloomington, IN 47404
Ph: (202)854-1721
Co. E-mail: info@ashaweb.org
URL: http://www.ashaweb.org
Contact: Meagan Shipley, President
URL(s): www.ashaweb.org
X (Twitter): twitter.com/ASHAnews

Frequency: Annual. **Description:** Publications, pharmaceuticals, clinical and medical equipment and supplies, information on health organizations, and health education methods and materials. **Audience:** School nurses, health educators, physicians, teachers, school administrators, dentists, school counselors, physical educators, and school health coordinators. **Principal Exhibits:** Publications, pharmaceuticals, clinical and medical equipment and supplies, information on health organizations, and health education methods and materials.

26066 ▪ American Society for Healthcare Risk Management Convention
URL(s): www.ashrm.org/annual-conference/index.dhtml

Frequency: Annual. **Audience:** Healthcare professionals. **Telecommunication Services:** ashrm@aha.org.

26067 ▪ Annual ARNOVA Conference
Association for Research on Nonprofit Organizations and Voluntary Action (ARNOVA)
1100 W 42nd St., Ste. 140
Indianapolis, IN 46208
Ph: (317)684-2120
Co. E-mail: conference@arnova.org
URL: http://www.arnova.org
Contact: Emily Barman, President
URL(s): web.cvent.com/event/fabe347c-475b-40e4-9f57-1e1af84d01f7/websitePage:6bc04e53-f251-446f-8190-74a468298cce?locale=en

Frequency: Annual. **Description:** Creates a public conversation on, as well as opportunities for presenting research about, pressing issues and vital opportunities facing the voluntary or nonprofit sector. **Audience:** Industry professionals. **Principal Exhibits:** Creates a public conversation on, as well as opportunities for presenting research about, pressing issues and vital opportunities facing the voluntary or nonprofit sector. Dates and Locations: 2025 Nov 20-22 Indianapolis Marriott Downtown, Indianapolis, IN. **Telecommunication Services:** conference@arnova.org.

26068 ▪ Florida Health Care Association Conference
Bouchard Insurance
URL(s): fhcaconference.org

Frequency: Annual. **Audience:** Health care industry professionals. Dates and Locations: 2025 Jul 13-17 Hyatt Regency, Orlando, FL; 2026 Jul 26-30 Rosen Shingle Creek, Orlando, FL; 2027 Jul 25-29 Marriott World Center, Orlando, FL; 2028 Jul 23-27 Marriott World Center, Orlando, FL. **Telecommunication Services:** jearly@fhca.org.

26069 ▪ IAHCSMM Annual Conference & Expo
International Association of Healthcare Central Service Materiel Management (IAHCSMM)
55 W Wacker Dr., Ste. 501
Chicago, IL 60601
Ph: (312)440-0078
Free: 800-962-8274
Fax: (312)440-9474
Co. E-mail: mailbox@iahcsmm.org
URL: http://myhspa.org
Contact: Susan Adams, Executive Director
E-mail: susan@iahcsmm.org
URL(s): s6.goeshow.com/hspa/annual/2025

Frequency: Annual. **Description:** Exhibits related to medical devices, packaging, sterilization, infection control, and medical supplies. **Audience:** Central service professionals and members. **Principal Exhibits:** Exhibits related to medical devices, packaging, sterilization, infection control, and medical supplies. Dates and Locations: 2025 Apr 26-29 Kentucky International Convention Center, Louisville, KY; 2026 Apr 25-28 Baltimore, MD; 2027 Apr 24-27 Columbus, OH. **Telecommunication Services:** conference@iahcsmm.org.

26070 ▪ National Conference on Correctional Health Care
National Commission on Correctional Health Care (NCCHC)
1145 W Diversey Pky.
Chicago, IL 60614
Ph: (773)880-1460
Fax: (773)880-2424
Co. E-mail: info@ncchc.org
URL: http://www.ncchc.org
Contact: Edwin Megargee, Vice Chairman of the Board
URL(s): events.ncchc.org/national-conference

Frequency: Annual. **Audience:** Physicians, nurses, psychologists, social workers and related professionals. **Telecommunication Services:** sales@ncchc.org.

26071 ▪ National Rural Health Association Annual Rural Health Conference
National Clearinghouse for Primary Care Information
8201 Greensboro Dr.
McLean, VA 22201
URL(s): www.ruralhealthweb.org/events/schedule-of-nrha-events

Frequency: Annual. **Description:** Equipment, supplies, services, and programs for persons interested or involved in rural health issues and rural healthcare delivery. **Audience:** Rural health practitioners, hospital administrators, clinic directors and lay health workers, social workers, state and federal health employees, academics, and community members. **Principal Exhibits:** Equipment, supplies, services, and programs for persons interested or involved in rural health issues and rural healthcare delivery.

26072 ▪ National Teaching Institute & Critical Care Exposition (NTI)
American Association of Critical-Care Nurses (AACN)
27071 Aliso Creek Rd.
Aliso Viejo, CA 92656-3399
Ph: (949)362-2000
Fax: (949)362-2020
Co. E-mail: info@aacn.org
URL: http://www.aacn.org
Contact: Beth Wathen, President
URL(s): www.aacn.org/conferences-and-events/nti?tab=NTI%20Virtual

Frequency: Annual. **Description:** Healthcare supplies, devices, products and pharmaceuticals; career opportunity/recruiting; publications and educational materials; market research and related non-profit organizations. **Audience:** High-acuity and critical care nurses. **Principal Exhibits:** Healthcare supplies, devices, products and pharmaceuticals; career opportunity/recruiting; publications and educational materials; market research and related non-profit organizations. Dates and Locations: 2025 May 18-21 New Orleans, LA; 2026 May 17-20 San Diego, CA. **Telecommunication Services:** randy.bauler@aacn.org.

26073 ▪ NCRA Annual Educational Conference
National Cancer Registrars Association (NCRA)
1330 Braddock Pl., Ste. 520
Alexandria, VA 22314
Ph: (703)299-6640
Fax: (703)299-6620
Co. E-mail: info@ncra-usa.org
URL: http://www.ncra-usa.org
Contact: Karen Anne Mason, President
URL(s): www.ncra-usa.org/Conference/2025-NCRA-Annual-Conference/2025-Conference-Information

Frequency: Annual. **Description:** Computer hardware and software, consultants, publications publishers and insurance programs. **Audience:** Cancer registry professionals, researchers, healthcare providers, and public health officials. **Principal Exhibits:** Computer hardware and software, consultants, publications publishers and insurance programs. Dates and Locations: 2025 May 03-06 Renaissance Orlando at SeaWorld, Orlando, FL. **Telecommunication Services:** registration@ncra-usa.org.

26074 ▪ NCSA Annual Meeting
American Society of Anesthesiologists (ASA)
1061 American Ln.
Schaumburg, IL 60173-4973
Ph: (847)825-5586
Fax: (847)825-1692
Co. E-mail: info@asahq.org
URL: http://www.asahq.org
Contact: Adamina G. Podraza, President
E-mail: adaminapod@gmail.com
URL(s): www.ncsanet.org/annual-meeting

Frequency: Annual. **Description:** Discuss clinical and operational strategies for promoting patient safety. **Audience:** Industry professionals. **Principal Exhibits:** Discuss clinical and operational strategies for promoting patient safety. **Telecommunication Services:** ncsa@paragonme.net.

26075 ▪ OHCA Convention & Expo
Ohio Health Care Association (OHCA)
55 Green Meadows Dr. S
Lewis Center, OH 43035
Ph: (614)436-4154
Fax: (614)436-0939
Co. E-mail: ohca@ohca.org
URL: http://www.ohca.org
Contact: Jill Herron, President
URL(s): www.ohca.org/convention

Frequency: Annual. **Description:** Nursing home supplies and services. **Audience:** Industry professionals. **Principal Exhibits:** Nursing home supplies and services. **Telecommunication Services:** lobrien@ohca.org.

26076 ▪ SHSMD Connections
Society for Healthcare Strategy and Market Development (SHSMD)
155 N Wacker Dr.
Chicago, IL 60606
Ph: (312)422-3888
Co. E-mail: shsmd@aha.org
URL: http://www.shsmd.org
Contact: Lisa Schiller, President
URL(s): www.shsmd.org/education/annualconference

Frequency: Annual. **Description:** Equipment, supplies, and services for healthcare marketing, business development, managed care, and communications executives. **Audience:** Healthcare professionals in the areas of public relations, marketing, business, development, and strategic planning. **Principal Exhibits:** Equipment, supplies, and services for healthcare marketing, business development, managed care, and communications executives. Dates and Locations: 2025 Oct 12-15 Dallas, TX. **Telecommunication Services:** shsmd@aha.org.

26077 ▪ Southeastern Psychological Association Meeting
Southeastern Psychological Association (SEPA)
c/o The Citadel Psychology Department
171 Moultrie St.
Charleston, SC 29409
Co. E-mail: sepa@citadel.edu
URL: http://www.sepaonline.com
Contact: John N. Bohannon, President
E-mail: j.n.bohannon3@gmail.com
URL(s): sepaonline.com/event/72nd-annual-meeting

Frequency: Annual. **Description:** Computers, textbooks, and mental health services. **Audience:** Doctors of psychology and related fields. **Principal Exhibits:** Computers, textbooks, and mental health services. Dates and Locations: 2025 Apr 09-12 Crown Plaza Ravinia of Dunwoody, Atlanta, GA; 2026 Mar 25-28 The Sheraton New Orleans, New Orleans, LA.

26078 ■ Virginia Health Care Association Annual Convention and Trade Show
Virginia Health Care Association (VHCA)
2112 W Laburnum Ave., Ste. 206
Richmond, VA 23227
Ph: (804)353-9101
Fax: (804)353-3098
Co. E-mail: info@vhca.org
URL: http://www.vhca.org
Contact: Keith Hare, President
E-mail: keith.hare@vhca.org
URL(s): 2024tradeshow.vhca.org

Frequency: Annual. **Description:** Equipment, supplies, and services for nursing home operations, including food, medical supplies, furniture, computer systems, linen, medical equipment, insurance, pharmaceuticals, optometrists, psychologists, and transportation. **Audience:** Health care professionals and general public. **Principal Exhibits:** Equipment, supplies, and services for nursing home operations, including food, medical supplies, furniture, computer systems, linen, medical equipment, insurance, pharmaceuticals, optometrists, psychologists, and transportation. **Telecommunication Services:** doran.hutchinson@vhca.org.

26079 ■ Yankee Dental Congress
Vermont State Dental Society (VSDS)
1 Kennedy Dr., Ste. L-3
South Burlington, VT 05403
Ph: (802)864-0115
Co. E-mail: info@vsds.org
URL: http://www.vsds.org
Contact: Dr. Rebekah Lucier Pryles, President
URL(s): www.yankeedental.com

Frequency: Annual; held on January. **Description:** Dental products, equipment, and services. **Audience:** Industrial Professionals. **Principal Exhibits:** Dental products, equipment, and services. Dates and Locations: 2025 Jan 29-Feb 01 Boston Convention & Exhibition Center, Boston, MA; 2026 Jan 30-31 Boston Convention & Exhibition Center, Boston, MA; 2027 Jan 28-30; 2028 Jan 27-29. **Telecommunication Services:** yankeedental@massdental.org.

CONSULTANTS

26080 ■ Alternative Services Inc. (ASI)
32625 W 7 Mile Rd., Ste. 11
Livonia, MI 48152
Ph: (248)471-4880
URL: http://www.asi-mi.org
Contact: Jenny Bhaskaran, Executive Director
E-mail: jbhaskaran@asi-mi.org

Description: Services: Developmental disabilities training. **Scope:** Services: Developmental disabilities training. **Founded:** 1978.

26081 ■ Anesthesia Business Consultants L.L.C. (ABC)
255 W Michigan Ave.
Jackson, MI 49201
Free: 800-242-1131
Co. E-mail: customer.service@anesthesiallc.com
URL: http://www.anesthesiallc.com
Facebook: www.facebook.com/anesthesiallc
Linkedin: www.linkedin.com/company/anesthesia-business-consultants
X (Twitter): x.com/anesthesiallc

Description: Firm specializes in the practice of anesthesia and pain management provides compliance review and development of compliance programs, and much more. **Scope:** Firm specializes in the practice of anesthesia and pain management provides compliance review and development of compliance programs, and much more. **Founded:** 1979. **Publications:** "Assessing the Impact of the Recession on Anesthesia"; "Navigating the Recession Through Knowledge and Elbow Grease"; "The Anesthesia Community Must Be Prepared for Increased Audit Activity by RACS and Others"; "Out Of Network Penalties: How Your Patients Can Help You Receive Payment In Full"; "Healthcarare Marketing: Navigating the Regulatory Landscape"; "The Billing Nuances of Post-Op Pain". **Training:** Billing for Anesthesia Services; Interpretation of the Centers for Medicare and Medicaid Services Rules and Regulations; Pain Management Billing; Audits and Compliance Issues; The New Environment For Fraud & Abuse Enforcement For Anesthesia & Pain Management, Aug, 2009. **Special Services:** F1RSTAnesthesia™.

26082 ■ BioSciCon, Inc. [Biomedical Science Consulting Company, Inc.]
14905 Forest Landing Cir.
Rockville, MD 20850
Ph: (301)610-9130
Fax: (301)610-7662
Co. E-mail: info@bioscicon.com
URL: http://www.bioscicon.com
Contact: Dr. Nenad Markovic, President

Description: Provider of biomedical science consulting and also a developer of biotechnology products. **Scope:** Provider of biomedical science consulting and also a developer of biotechnology products. **Founded:** 1996. **Publications:** "Cervical Acid Phosphates: A Biomarker of Cervical Dysplasia and Potential Surrogate Endpoint for Colposcopy," 2004; "Enhancing Pap test with a new biological marker of cervical dysplasia," 2004; "A cytoplasmic biomarker for liquid-based Pap," The FACEB Journal Experimental Biology, 2004; "Pap test and new biomarker-based technology for enhancing visibility of abnormal cells," 2004. **Special Services:** MarkPap®; PreservCyt®.

26083 ■ Center for Lifestyle Enhancement-Columbia Medical Center of Plano
3901 West 15th St
Plano, TX 75075
Ph: (972)596-6800
Fax: (972)519-1299
URL: http://medicalcityplano.com
Contact: Erol R. Akdamar, President
Facebook: www.facebook.com/medicalcityplano
X (Twitter): twitter.com/MedCityPlano

Description: Firm provides professional health counseling in the areas of general nutrition for weight management, eating disorders, diabetic education, cholesterol reduction and adolescent weight management. Offers work site health promotion and preventive services. Also coordinates speaker's bureau, cooking classes and physician referrals. **Scope:** Firm provides professional health counseling in the areas of general nutrition for weight management, eating disorders, diabetic education, cholesterol reduction and adolescent weight management. Offers work site health promotion and preventive services. Also coordinates speaker's bureau, cooking classes and physician referrals. **Founded:** 1975. **Training:** Rx Diet and Exercise; Smoking Cessation; Stress Management; Health Fairs; Fitness Screenings; Body Composition; Nutrition Analysis; Exercise Classes; Prenatal Nutrition; SHAPEDOWN; Successfully Managing Diabetes; Gourmet Foods for Your Heart; The Aging Heart; Heart Smart Saturday featuring Day of Dance; Weight-Loss Management Seminars; The Right Stroke for Men; Peripheral Artery Disease Screening; Menstruation: The Cycle Begins; Boot Camp for New Dads; Grand parenting 101: Caring for Kids Today; Teddy Bear C New Baby Day C Safe Sitter Babysitting Class.

26084 ■ Children's Psychological Health Center, Inc. (CPHC)
2105 Divisadero St.
San Francisco, CA 94115
Ph: (415)292-7119
Fax: (415)749-2802
URL: http://www.childrenspsychologicalhealthcenter.org
Contact: Jessie Rios, Executive Director
E-mail: jessie.rios@expertchildpsychiatry.org
Linkedin: www.linkedin.com/in/childrenspsychological

Description: Treats those with psychological trauma claimed from stressors including institutional negligence, vehicular and aviation accidents, wrongful death in the family, rape, molestation, fire, explosion, flood, earthquake, loss of parents, terrorism, kidnapping, disfiguring events, emotional damage from social work, medical malpractice or defective products. **Scope:** Treats those with psychological trauma claimed from stressors including institutional negligence, vehicular and aviation accidents, wrongful death in the family, rape, molestation, fire, explosion, flood, earthquake, loss of parents, terrorism, kidnapping, disfiguring events, emotional damage from social work, medical malpractice or defective products. **Founded:** 1992. **Publications:** "My Personal Story About Tropical Storm Stan," Feb, 2006; "My Personal Story About Hurricanes Katrina and Rita: A guided activity workbook to help coping, learning and Healthy expression," Sep, 2005; "Helping Patients and their Families Cope in a National Disaster," Jan, 2002; "The practice of behavioral treatment in the acute rehabilitation setting".

26085 ■ Diversified Health Resources Inc.
1209 N Astor St., No. 2N
Chicago, IL 60610-2655
Contact: Andrea Rice Rozran, President

Description: Offers health care consulting for hospitals, nursing homes including homes for the aged and other health related facilities and companies. Specializes in planning and marketing. Also conducts executive searches for top level health care administrative positions. Serves private industries as well as government agencies. **Scope:** Offers health care consulting for hospitals, nursing homes including homes for the aged and other health related facilities and companies. Specializes in planning and marketing. Also conducts executive searches for top level health care administrative positions. Serves private industries as well as government agencies. **Publications:** "City Finance".

26086 ■ Doctors Management L.L.C. (DM)
Doctors Management L.L.C. (DM)
10401 Kingston Pke.
Knoxville, TN 37922
Ph: (865)531-0176
Free: 800-635-4040
Fax: (865)531-0722
Co. E-mail: info@drsmgmt.com
URL: http://www.doctorsmanagement.com
Contact: Paul King, President
Facebook: www.facebook.com/DoctorsManagement
Linkedin: www.linkedin.com/company/doctorsmanagement
X (Twitter): x.com/drsmanagement
YouTube: www.youtube.com/user/DoctorsManagement

Description: Firm provides medical, dental practice and healthcare consulting services such as consulting, operations, and compliance. **Scope:** Firm provides medical, dental practice and healthcare consulting services such as consulting, operations, and compliance. **Founded:** 1956. **Training:** Coding, OSHA compliance, customer service, Human Resources School, School of Practice Management; CLIA compliance, HIPAA.

26087 ■ Family Resource Center on Disabilities (FRCD)
11 E Adams St., Ste. 1002
Chicago, IL 60603
Ph: (312)939-3513
Fax: (312)854-8980
Co. E-mail: info@frcd.org
URL: http://frcd.org
Contact: Michelle Phillips, Contact
X (Twitter): x.com/FRCDPTI
YouTube: www.youtube.com/user/frcd1231
Pinterest: www.pinterest.com/frcdpti

Description: Parents, professionals, and volunteers seeking to improve services for all children with disabilities. Organized as a result of the 1969 Illinois law mandating the education of all children with disabilities and operates as a coalition to inform and activate parents. Provides information and referral services, individualized support services for low-income Chicago families, transition services, and special education rights training. **Scope:** Provider of consulting services to advocacy groups and individuals seeking support for children with disabilities. **Founded:** 1969. **Publications:** "How to Get Services

By Being Assertive"; "How to Organize an Effective Parent/Advocacy Group and Move Bureaucracies"; "Main roads Travel to Tomorrow - a Road Map for the Future"; "Does Your Child Have Special Education Needs"; "How to Prepare for a Successful Due Process Hearing"; "How to Participate Effectively in Your Child's IEP Meeting"; "Tax Guide for Parents". **Training:** How to Support Parents as Effective Advocates; How to Get Services by Being Assertive; How to Develop an Awareness Program for Nondisabled Children; How to Organize a Parent Support Group; How to Move Bureaucratic Mountains; How to Raise Money Painlessly through Publishing; How to Use Humor in Public Presentations. **Geographic Preference:** National.

26088 ■ Medical Business Associates Inc. (MBA)
580 Oakmont Ln.
Westmont, IL 60559
URL: http://mbaaudit.com
Description: Provider of healthcare consulting, auditing and forensic services. **Scope:** Provider of healthcare consulting, auditing and forensic services. **Founded:** 1991. **Publications:** "Healthcare Reform & the Fraud Problem: New Rules, New Defenses," White-Collar Crime Fighter, Jan, 2010; "Workers Comp-The Latest in Fraud Analysis and Detection," Sep, 2009; "Health care Reform and the New Opportunities for the Ethically Challenged," Jul, 2009; "Advanced Topics Health care Fraud," Apr, 2009; "Medical Identity Theft," Apr, 2009; "EMR-Fraud Challenges and Implications for Investigators," Apr, 2009; "The Auditigators Role in Finding Trigger Points for Fraud," Apr, 2009; "Emerging Trends in Medicaid Pharmacy," Mar, 2009; "Medicare Legislation Changes - Medical Severity DRG's The Biggest Change in Medical Billing in 25 Years," Mar, 2009; "New Fraud Trends on How to Break the Claims Adjudication System & Take Your Money," Mar, 2009; "Medicare & General Case Evaluations, Chapter 12 Volume II," Jan, 2009; "Advanced Two Day Health Care Fraud Course," Oct, 2008; "Health care Fraud: Audit & Detection Guidebook," Wiley & Sons Publications, Oct, 2007; "Fraud Casebook: Lessons from the Bad Side of Business," Wiley & Sons Publications, Jul, 2007; "Health-care fraud and 'PHI' Employers protecting employees & bottom line," Fraud Magazine, Nov-Dec, 2005; "Coping with Intermittent Explosive Disorder with Diffusing Techniques," Oct, 2005. **Training:** Advanced Two Day Health Care Fraud Course, Oct, 2008; Health care Fraud and the Medical Record, Louisville, Nov, 2006; Workers' Comp Fraud: Screening for the Ethically Challenged, Las Vegas, Nov, 2006; HIPAA health care Privacy Issues; Developing Internal Audit Programs; Employee Training Programs; Medical Record Documentation from a financial, legal, and risk management perspective; Risk Management; Health Care Waste Fraud and Abuse; Understanding Reimbursement Methodologies.

26089 ■ Medical Business Consultants Inc.
6800 Pk. Ten Blvd., Ste. 115N
San Antonio, TX 78213
Contact: David R. Vela, President
Description: It is A dynamic and evolving medical healthcare services organization located in San Antonio. Started as medical billing company now they also provide Medical staffing and Medical readiness services to both government and united states military. **Scope:** It is A dynamic and evolving medical healthcare services organization located in San Antonio. Started as medical billing company now they also provide Medical staffing and Medical readiness services to both government and united states military. **Training:** Billing and Collections to Medical Schools Graduating Residents.

26090 ■ Medical Dental Business Consultants LLC
7405 University Ave., Ste. 2
Clive, IA 50325
Ph: (515)223-8803
Fax: (515)309-9001
URL: http://www.medicaldentalbusinessconsultants.com

Contact: Laura R. Luetje, Contact
Description: Firm provides consulting and accounting services for healthcare industry. **Scope:** Firm provides consulting and accounting services for healthcare industry. **Founded:** 1991.

26091 ■ Occupational & Environmental Health Consulting Services Inc. (OEHCS)
6877 Bonillo Dr.
Las Vegas, NV 89103
Ph: (630)325-2083
URL: http://www.oehcs.com
Description: Provider of consulting services such as regulatory, safety, industrial hygiene and environmental engineering, and much more. **Scope:** Provider of consulting services such as regulatory, safety, industrial hygiene and environmental engineering, and much more. **Founded:** 1984. **Publications:** "Worldwide Exposure Standards for Mold and Bacteria"; "Global Occupational Exposure Limits for Over 5000 Specific Chemicals"; "Post-Remediation Verification and Clearance Testing for Mold and Bacteria Risk Based Levels of Cleanliness". **Training:** Right-To-Know Compliance; Setting Internal Exposure Standards; Hospital Right-to-Know and Contingency Response; Ethylene Oxide Control; Industrial Hygiene Training; Asbestos Worker Training; Biosafety; Asbestos Operations and Maintenance. **Special Services:** Safety Software Program, Audiogram Analysis, First Report of Injury Form, Human Resources Database; Material Safety Data Sheet (MSDS); NPDES Monthly Reports; Lockout/Tagout (LOTO) Procedure Software; VOC Usage Tracking and Reporting Software, Medical Department Patient Records Database, Pictorial Labels for Chemical Containers, TIER II Hazardous Material Inventory Form & Database.

FRANCHISES AND BUSINESS OPPORTUNITIES

26092 ■ CPR Services
22 Stoneybrook Dr.
Ashland, MA 01721
Ph: (508)881-5107
URL: http://www.cpr-services.com
Contact: Anne Ferrari-Greenberg, Owner
E-mail: anne@cpr-services.com
Description: Provider of health education courses and programs. **Founded:** 1985. **Financial Assistance:** No **Training:** Yes.

26093 ■ The Dentist's Choice, Inc. (TDC)
246 W Shaw Ave.
Fresno, CA 93704
Contact: Steven Paganetti, Contact
Description: Provider of dental hand piece rebuilt, repair and maintenance services and also retailer of dental hand piece models. **Founded:** 1994. **Financial Assistance:** Yes **Training:** Provides 1 week at headquarters and ongoing support.

26094 ■ Interim HealthCare Inc.
1551 Sawgrass Corporate Pky., Ste. 230
Sunrise, FL 33323
Free: 800-338-7786
Co. E-mail: tsc@interimhealthcare.com
URL: http://www.interimhealthcare.com
Contact: Chrissy Kaupie, President
Facebook: www.facebook.com/interimhealthcare
Linkedin: www.linkedin.com/company/interim-healthcare
X (Twitter): x.com/InterimHealth
Instagram: www.instagram.com/interimhealthcare
YouTube: www.youtube.com/interimhealthcare
Description: Provides health care and home care services. **No. of Franchise Units:** 530. **Founded:** 1966. **Equity Capital Needed:** Healthcare: $100,000 - $200,000; HealthCare Hospice: $389,250-$477,000. **Franchise Fee:** Healthcare: $48,000; HealthCare Hospice: $60,000. **Financial Assistance:** No

26095 ■ Superior Senior Care (SSC)
620 Ouachita Ave.
Hot Springs, AR 71901
Ph: (501)321-1743

Free: 800-951-9792
Fax: (501)623-7853
Co. E-mail: info@superiorseniorcare.com
URL: http://www.superiorseniorcare.com
Contact: Rita Hurst, Owner
Description: Provider of light housekeeping and home management, meal preparation, shopping, transportation and companionship. **Founded:** 1985. **Training:** Yes.

PUBLICATIONS

26096 ■ AAID Business Bite
211 E Chicago Ave., Ste. 1100
Chicago, IL 60611
Ph: (312)335-1550
Free: 877-335-2243
Fax: (312)335-9090
Co. E-mail: info@aaid.com
URL: http://www.aaid.com
Contact: Bernee Dunson, President
URL(s): www.aaid.com/enewsletters
Released: Monthly **Description:** AAID's monthly electronic newsletter providing practical practice management information for those involved in implant dentistry. **Availability:** Print.

PUBLISHERS

26097 ■ "A Supply-Side Solution for Health Care" in Barron's (Vol. 92, July 23, 2012, No. 30, pp. 30)
Dow Jones & Company Inc.
1211 Avenue of the Americas
New York, NY 10036
Free: 800-568-7625
Co. E-mail: support@dowjones.com
URL: http://dowjones.com
Contact: Almar Latour, Chief Executive Officer
Ed: H. Woody Brock. **Description:** The United States should increase the supply of new doctors, nurses and other health care professionals to improve the American health care system by increasing supply. Health care reform proposals in the US Congress fail to address the supply side of the problem. **Availability:** Online.

COMPUTERIZED DATABASES

26098 ■ GrantSelect™
Schoolhouse Partners L.L.C.
1281 Win Hentschel Blvd.
West Lafayette, IN 47906
Ph: (765)237-3390
Fax: (765)594-4302
URL: http://www.schoolhousepartners.net
Contact: Louis S. Schafer, Chief Executive Officer
URL(s): www.grantselect.com
Facebook: www.facebook.com/GrantSelect
X (Twitter): twitter.com/GrantSelect
Price: $495, Individuals for per year professional-annual; $150, Individuals for per year standard-quarter. **Availability:** Print; Download; Online. **Type:** Directory; Numeric.

26099 ■ Health & Wellness InSite
Type: Full-text.

LIBRARIES

26100 ■ Citygate Network - Wooley Library
2153 Chuckwagon Rd.
Colorado Springs, CO 80919
Ph: (719)266-8300
Free: 800-473-7283
Fax: (719)266-8600
Co. E-mail: info@agrm.org
URL: http://www.citygatenetwork.org/agrm/default.asp
Contact: John Ashmen, President
E-mail: jashmen@citygatenetwork.org
Facebook: www.facebook.com/CitygateSocial

26101 ■ Healthcare and Social Assistance

Description: Rescue ministry executives and staff, and concerned individuals in 6 countries. Promotes rescue mission work for all persons experiencing crisis. Aims to sponsor coffee-houses for youths, emergency shelters for men and women, women with children, and families, day camps, resident camps, and wilderness camps for inner-city children, cafeterias for low-income persons. Serves meals and provide sleeping space to individuals in need. Sponsors long-term residential programs offering addiction recovery, education and employment services, and assistance to the elderly and mentally ill. **Scope:** Crisis shelters; life-transformation centers. **Holdings:** Figures not available. **Publications:** *Rescue Magazine* (Bimonthly); *How to Have a Better Board of Directors*; *Membership and Resource Directory*; *RESCUE Happenings* (Bimonthly); *Rescue Mission Salary Survey* (Annual); *Sample Staff Policy Manual*; *Association of Gospel Rescue Missions Directory and Resource Book* (Biennial). **Educational Activities:** Annual Conference and Exposition (Annual). **Awards:** AGRM Rescuer Award. **Geographic Preference:** National.

26101 ■ National Families in Action (NFIA) - Library
PO Box 133136
Atlanta, GA 30333-3136
Contact: Sue Rusche, Chief Executive Officer

Description: Parents and other adults concerned about preventing drug abuse. Seeks to: educate parents, children, and the community about the use of drugs; counteract social pressures that condone and promote drug use; stop drug use. Worked for passage of statewide drug paraphernalia statutes. **Scope:** Drug abuse. **Founded:** 1977. **Holdings:** Figures not available. **Publications:** *Drug Abuse Update* (Quarterly); *Crack Update*. **Educational Activities:** Parent Leader Certification. **Geographic Preference:** National.

RESEARCH CENTERS

26102 ■ American College of Apothecaries Research & Education Foundation - Research & Education Resource Center
2830 Summer Oaks Dr.
Bartlett, TN 38134
URL: http://acainfo.org/about-aca
Contact: Shara Rudner, President

Description: Public foundation operating as a part of the Research and Education Foundation, American College of Apothecaries. **Scope:** Three-fold objective of the Foundation is to promote public welfare through development of services in institutions providing health care, encourage and conduct research to improve health care and education, and encourage health care practitioners to improve the quality and availability of their services. **Founded:** 1998.

26103 ■ Amref Health Africa, USA - Library
224 W 35th St., Ste. 500 No.237
New York, NY 10001
Ph: (212)768-2440
Co. E-mail: info@amrefusa.org
URL: http://amrefusa.org
Contact: Robert Kelty, Chief Executive Officer
Facebook: www.facebook.com/amrefusa
X (Twitter): x.com/AMREFUSA
Instagram: www.instagram.com/amrefusa
YouTube: www.youtube.com/user/amrefusa

Description: Provides medical services to aid and augment health programs in developing nations and in rural areas of East Africa. Attempts to reach isolated peoples and outlying medical facilities through a network of two-way radios, clinic-equipped mobile units, and a Flying Doctor Service. **Scope:** Strengthens health systems and train African health workers to respond to the continent's most critical health challenges: maternal health, child health, HIV/AIDS, TB, malaria, the lack of access to water and sanitation, and the lack of access to quality diagnostic, and surgical services. **Founded:** 1957. **Holdings:** Figures not available. **Publications:** *AMREFocus* (Annual). **Geographic Preference:** National.

26104 ■ Baylor College of Medicine - Center for Medical Ethics and Health Policy
1 Baylor Plz., Ste. 310D
Houston, TX 77030-3411
Ph: (713)798-3500
Fax: (713)798-5678
URL: http://www.bcm.edu/academic-centers/medical-ethics-and-health-policy
Contact: Dr. Amy Lynn McGuire, Director
E-mail: amcguire@bcm.edu
Facebook: www.facebook.com/BCMEthics
X (Twitter): twitter.com/bcmethics

Description: Primarily affiliated with, supported by and controlled by Baylor College of Medicine, but also sponsored by Rice University. Offers consultation services. **Scope:** Priorities for health care services, methods of funding health care services, and social controls on health care service, including studies on ethics in clinical decision making and value issues in controlling the cost of medicine. **Founded:** 1982. **Publications:** *News Bulletin* (Semimonthly).

26105 ■ Benaroya Research Institute at Virginia Mason (BRI)
1201 Ninth Ave.
Seattle, WA 98101-2795
Ph: (206)342-6500
Co. E-mail: info@benaroyaresearch.org
URL: http://www.benaroyaresearch.org
Contact: Dr. Jane Buckner, Officer
E-mail: jbuckner@benaroyaresearch.org
Facebook: www.facebook.com/BenaroyaResearch
Linkedin: www.linkedin.com/company/benaroya-research-institute
Instagram: www.instagram.com/benaroyaresearch
YouTube: www.youtube.com/user/BenaroyaResearch

Description: Independent, nonprofit research organization affiliated with Virginia Mason Hospital and Virginia Mason Clinic. Offers educational opportunities through high school programs and postdoctoral training. **Scope:** Research center carries out research in the following areas; Immunology, diabetes and clinical research. **Founded:** 1956. **Publications:** *Bulletin of the Virginia Mason Clinic*.

26106 ■ Blanton-Peale Institute and Counseling Center - Library
7 West 30th St., 9th & 10th Fl.
New York, NY 10001
Ph: (212)725-7850
Co. E-mail: info@blantonpeale.org
URL: http://www.blantonpeale.org
Contact: Dr. Shari K. Brink, President
Facebook: www.facebook.com/BlantonPeale
Linkedin: www.linkedin.com/school/blanton-peale-institute
X (Twitter): twitter.com/blantonpeale

Description: Research center and library located in Manhattan. **Scope:** Policy studies related to psychoanalysis, marriage and family therapy, pastoral care, and the dialogue between theology and psychology. **Services:** Interlibrary loan; library not open to the public. **Founded:** 1937. **Holdings:** 5,000 books; 4 VF drawers of reports; pamphlets; dissertations. **Subscriptions:** 23 journals and other serials. **Publications:** *Journal of Religion and Health* (Quarterly); *Labyrinth Newsletter*.

26107 ■ Brandeis University - Schneider Institutes for Health Policy (SIHP)
415 South St., MS 035
Waltham, MA 02453
Ph: (781)736-3964
Co. E-mail: sihp@brandeis.edu
URL: http://heller.brandeis.edu/sihp
Contact: Dr. Stuart H. Altman, Director
E-mail: altman@brandeis.edu

Description: Integral unit of Heller Graduate School at Brandeis University. **Scope:** Health care, focusing on the intersection of health behavior and systems of care, including policy studies in the areas of financing organization, value of health services, quality, high cost and high risk populations, and technology. **Founded:** 1978. **Publications:** *Background Reports*; *Heller Highlights* (3/year); *Major Issue Papers*; *Program Analyses*; *Publication Catalogue*.

26108 ■ Brown University - Watson Institute for International Studies
111 Thayer St.
Providence, RI 02912
Ph: (401)863-2809
Fax: (401)863-1270
Co. E-mail: watson_institute@brown.edu
URL: http://watson.brown.edu
Contact: Michael Kennedy, Professor
E-mail: michael_kennedy@brown.edu
Facebook: www.facebook.com/WatsonInstitute
Linkedin: www.linkedin.com/school/watson-institute-brown
X (Twitter): x.com/WatsonInstitute
Instagram: www.instagram.com/watsoninstitute
YouTube: www.youtube.com/c/WatsonInstituteforInternationalandPublicAffairs

Description: Integral unit of Brown University. Extensive outreach activities for community and policy makers available. **Scope:** Contemporary global problems and challenges in security, economy, ecology, identity and culture. **Founded:** 1986. **Publications:** *Watson Institute for International Studies Annual Report*; *Blogs*; *Conference Reports*; *Documentaries*; *Watson Institute for International Studies Newsletters* (Semiannual); *Streaming video*; *Studies in Comparative International Development (SCID)* (Quarterly). **Educational Activities:** Development studies undergraduate major; Watson Institute for International Studies Seminars (Irregular); Undergraduate Thesis Conference.

26109 ■ California State University, Los Angeles - Edmund G. Brown Institute for Public Affairs
5151 State University Dr., GE Rm. 224
Los Angeles, CA 90032-8261
Ph: (323)343-3770
Co. E-mail: pbi@calstatela.edu
URL: http://calstatela.patbrowninstitute.org
Contact: Dr. Raphael J. Sonenshein, Executive Director
E-mail: raphael.sonenshein@calstatela.edu

Description: Integral unit of California State University, Los Angeles, operating under its own board of advisors. Offers technical assistance and consulting on policy issues. **Scope:** Applied research and analysis of public policy issues of California and greater Los Angeles area, including ethnic community participation in politics, futures planning, the environment, mental health, law and justice, water, the homeless, history, infrastructure, the judicial system, healthcare, education, transportation, and emergency disaster management. **Founded:** 1987. **Awards:** Edmund G. "Pat" Brown Institute of Public Affairs.

26110 ■ Center for the Study of Social Policy (CSSP)
1575 Eye St. NW Ste. 500
Washington, DC 20005
Ph: (202)371-1565
Fax: (202)371-1472
Co. E-mail: info@cssp.org
URL: http://cssp.org
Contact: Annie E. Casey, Director
Facebook: www.facebook.com/CtrSocialPolicy
Linkedin: www.linkedin.com/company/center-for-the-study-of-social-policy
X (Twitter): x.com/ctrsocialpolicy
YouTube: www.youtube.com/channel/UCgw_slCsjgt4FqOiouYjD4g

Description: Provides analyses on the effects of contemporary policy issues on states, communities, families, and individuals for federal, state, and local decision makers. **Scope:** Promotes public policies that strengthen families and protect and lift children from poverty. **Founded:** 1978. **Publications:** *Building Community Ownership in Neighborhood Revitalization*. **Geographic Preference:** National.

26111 ■ Centre de Recherches pour le Développement International (CRDI) - Library [International Development Research Centre]
45 O'Connor St.
Ottawa, ON, Canada K1G 3H9
Ph: (613)236-6163

Co. E-mail: info@idrc.ca
URL: http://idrc-crdi.ca/en
Contact: Julie Delahanty, President
Facebook: www.facebook.com/IDRC.CRDI
Linkedin: www.linkedin.com/company/idrc
X (Twitter): x.com/Idrc_crdi
YouTube: www.youtube.com/user/IDRCCRDI
Description: Supports and promotes research on international development and related issues. Gathers and disseminates information on research activities in developing countries; conducts fund raising activities; sponsors research programs in developing countries. **Scope:** Supports scientific and technical research projects identified and carried out by research institutions in developing countries. IDRC maintains the following program initiative areas: strategies and policies for healthy societies; sustainable employment; equity in natural resources management; biodiversity conservation; food security; information and communication; peace building and reconstruction. Research activities focus on integrating environmental, social, and economic policies; technology and the environment; information and communication for development; health and the environment; and biodiversity. Supports research that is essential to sustainable and equitable development through three areas of enquiry: social and economic equity; environmental and natural resource management; and information and communication technologies for development. Research activities focus areas include water resource management, ecosystem management, biodiversity control, governance, delivery of public services (health, education, social security), small enterprise and livelihoods, information access, information capacity-building, macroeconomic policy, regional integration, and global threats to health (social instability, AIDS, malnutrition, tobacco use). **Services:** Document delivery; library open to the public with restrictions. **Founded:** 1970. **Holdings:** 333 books. **Subscriptions:** journals. **Publications:** *IDRC* (Annual); *IDRC Reports*; *Searching Series*. **Awards:** IDRC Sabbatical Awards (Periodic); IDRC Awards for International Development Journalism (Periodic); IDRC Research Awards (Annual); Bentley Research Fellowship (Biennial); John G. Bene Fellowship (Annual); IDRC International Fellowships. **Geographic Preference:** Multinational.

26112 ■ Dalhousie University - Faculty of Medicine - Department of Community Health and Epidemiology - Health Data Nova Scotia (HDNS)
5790 University Avenue Centre for Clinical
  Research, Rm 420
  Halifax, NS, Canada B3H 1V7
Co. E-mail: hdns@dal.ca
URL: http://medicine.dal.ca/departments/departmen
  t-sites/community-health/research/hdns.html
Contact: Dr. Samuel Stewart, Director
E-mail: sam.stewart@dal.ca
Description: Integral unit of the Department of Community Health and Epidemiology, Dalhousie University. **Scope:** Health and social sciences, particularly population health, health services utilization and their interrelationships.

26113 ■ Dartmouth College - Geisel School of Medicine - Dartmouth Institute for Health Policy and Clinical Practice
1 Medical Center Dr., WTRB5
  Lebanon, NH 03756
Ph: (603)646-5678
URL: http://geiselmed.dartmouth.edu/tdi
Contact: Dr. Elliott S. Fisher, Contact
E-mail: elliott.s.fisher@dartmouth.edu
Linkedin: www.linkedin.com/school/dartmou
  thpublichealth
X (Twitter): x.com/DartmouthInst
Description: Integral unit of Geisel School of Medicine at Dartmouth College. Offers fellowships to physicians, administrators, and health policy makers. **Scope:** Evaluative clinical science and health care delivery, including medical care epidemiology, health policy, health behavior, efficacy of medical procedures, quality of medical and surgical care, distribution of health care resources, medical interventions and consequences for patients, care at the end of life, distribution of health care resources across hospital market areas, geriatric health, and sociology of medical organizations. **Founded:** 1988. **Publications:** *The Dartmouth Atlas of Health Care*.

26114 ■ Forum for State Health Policy Leadership
444 N Capital St. NW, Ste. 515
  Washington, DC 20001
Ph: (202)624-5400
Fax: (202)737-1069
URL: http://www.ncsl.org/research/health/state-health
  -systems-innovations.aspx
Contact: Donna Folkemer, Director
E-mail: donna.folkemer@ncsl.org
Description: Department within the National Conference of State Legislatures. Offers assistance on particular issues and research projects; legislative and state clearinghouses. Maintains a network of health policy correspondents: in each of the fifty states who keep the project abreast of significant developments in the states; state legislative tracking service. **Scope:** Health laws and programs of the states, including research in such areas as alternatives to institutional care, state healthcare reform, managing and funding healthcare programs, preventive health services for children, state Medicaid programs, state comprehensive and catastrophic health insurance programs, Medicaid cost containment, state health promotion and disease prevention initiatives, AIDS, and private health insurance benefits for alcoholism, drug abuse, and mental illness. **Founded:** 1977. **Publications:** *Primary Care News*; *Reports on long-term care, primary care, and children's health*; *State Health Notes*; *State Health Notes Newsletter* (Biweekly).

26115 ■ Freedom Foundation
PO Box 552
  Olympia, WA 98507
Ph: (360)956-3482
Co. E-mail: info@freedomfoundation.com
URL: http://www.freedomfoundation.com
Contact: Brian Minnich, Executive Vice President
E-mail: bminnich@freedomfoundation.com
Facebook: www.facebook.com/FreedomFounda
  tionUSA
Linkedin: www.linkedin.com/company/freedom-foun
  dation
X (Twitter): x.com/FreedomFdtn
Instagram: www.instagram.com/freedomfounda
  tionusa
YouTube: www.youtube.com/user/EvergreenFF
Description: Works to advance individual liberty, free enterprise and limited, accountable government. **Scope:** Healthcare, budget, taxes, education, welfare reform, citizenship and governance issues, with emphasis on limited, accountable, representative government, and working partnerships between governing bodies and the private sector. **Founded:** 1991. **Publications:** *In-Briefs*; *EFF Newsletter* (Monthly); *Policy Highlighters*. **Geographic Preference:** National.

26116 ■ George Washington University - Milken Institute School of Public Health - Jacobs Institute of Women's Health (JIWH)
950 New Hampshire Ave. NW 6th Fl.
  Washington, DC 20052
Ph: (202)994-0034
URL: http://jiwh.publichealth.gwu.edu
Contact: Dr. Susan F. Wood, Executive Director
E-mail: sfwood@gwu.edu
Description: Independent, nonprofit organization. **Scope:** Women's health care services and policy issues, focusing on the interaction of medical and social systems. **Founded:** 1990. **Publications:** *Women's Health Issues (WHI)* (Bimonthly). **Educational Activities:** JIWH Seminars; JIWH Symposia. **Awards:** Charles E. Gibbs MD Leadership Prize (Annual).

26117 ■ Georgia State University - Center for Risk Management and Insurance Research
35 Broad St. NW, 11th Fl.
  Atlanta, GA 30302-4050
URL: http://robinson.gsu.edu/academic-departments/
  risk-management-and-insurance
Contact: Stephen Shore, Department Chairman
E-mail: sshore@gsu.edu
Description: Integral unit of J. Mack Robinson College of Business, Georgia State University. Offers consultation; develops technical and professional materials; Issues working papers; responds to proposal requests. **Scope:** Provides technical materials and policy research in the areas of health care financing, international issues, law and regulation, corporate finance, retirement financing, risk, risk management, insurance, finance, economics. **Founded:** 1953. **Publications:** *Reprint series*; *Research report series*; *Working paper series*.

26118 ■ Health Research and Educational Trust (HRET)
155 N Wacker, Ste. 400
  Chicago, IL 60606
URL: http://www.aha.org/center/hret
Contact: Russell R. Gronewold, President
Description: Research and education affiliate of the American Hospital Association. Advances ideas and practices beneficial to health care practitioners, institutions, consumers and society at large. **Scope:** Improvement in the delivery of hospital and health care. **Founded:** 1944. **Publications:** *HSR* (Bimonthly); *Health Services Research* (Bimonthly). **Educational Activities:** HRET Conference. **Geographic Preference:** National.

26119 ■ Health Research and Educational Trust of New Jersey (HRET)
760 Alexander Rd.
  Princeton, NJ 08543
Co. E-mail: info@accme.org
URL: http://www.accme.org/find-cme-provider/health
  -research-and-educational-trust-new-jersey-hret
Contact: Victoria Brogan, Contact
Description: Integral unit of the New Jersey Hospital Association, but with its own board of control. Offers continuing education courses. **Scope:** Health services in New Jersey. Topics explored include access to primary healthcare, parenting education, breast cancer, newborn screening. **Founded:** 1964. **Publications:** *Shaping Healthier Tomorrows*. **Educational Activities:** HRET Annual Meeting (Annual). **Awards:** HRET Community Outreach Awards (Annual); NJHA Health Careers Scholarships (Annual).

26120 ■ Heartland Institute (HI) - Michael Parry Mazur Memorial Library
3939 N Wilke Rd.
  Arlington Heights, IL 60004
Ph: (312)377-4000
Fax: (312)275-7942
Co. E-mail: database@heartland.org
URL: http://heartland.org
Contact: Wanda L. Davis, Director, Administration
E-mail: wdavis@heartland.org
Facebook: www.facebook.com/HeartlandInstitute
X (Twitter): x.com/heartlandinst
YouTube: www.youtube.com/user/HeartlandTube
Description: Privatization, deregulation, tax reform, education reform, healthcare policy, environmental policy, and telecommunications. Seeks alternatives to government-provided services at the national, state, and local levels. **Scope:** Privatization, deregulation, tax reform, education reform, healthcare policy, environmental policy, and telecommunications. Seeks alternatives to government-provided services at the national, state, and local levels. **Services:** Library open to the public by appointment; copying. **Founded:** 1984. **Holdings:** 20,000 books; journals. **Publications:** Privatization, deregulation, tax reform, education reform, healthcare policy, environmental policy, and telecommunications. Seeks alternatives to government-provided services at the national, state, and local levels. **Awards:** Heartland Liberty Prize (Irregular). **Geographic Preference:** National.

26121 ■ Indiana University-Purdue University at Indianapolis - William S. and Christine S. Hall Center for Law and Health
530 W New York St.
Indianapolis, IN 46202
URL: http://mckinneylaw.iu.edu/health-law
Description: Integral unit of Indiana University-Purdue University at Indianapolis. **Scope:** All issues related to health law and policy. **Founded:** 1987. **Publications:** *Hall Centre Newsletter*.

26122 ■ Institute for Women's Policy Research (IWPR)
1200 18th St. NW Ste. 301
Washington, DC 20036
Ph: (202)785-5100
Fax: (202)833-4362
Co. E-mail: iwpr@iwpr.org
URL: http://iwpr.org
Contact: Ariane Hegewisch, Officer
Facebook: www.facebook.com/iwpresearch
Linkedin: www.linkedin.com/company/institute-for-women's-policy-research
X (Twitter): x.com/IWPResearch
Instagram: www.instagram.com/iwpresearch
YouTube: www.youtube.com/channel/UCEXv3ypWhnReEXJlQSKXh6A
Description: Those concerned with economic and social justice for women and families. Designs, executes, and disseminates research findings that illuminate policy issues affecting women and families. Addresses complex issues engendered by race, ethnicity, and class. Focuses on survival issues such as welfare reform, family and medical leave, childcare, pay equity and the wage gap, the glass ceiling, labor law reform, and equal opportunity for women of all race and ethnic backgrounds. Builds a network of individuals and organizations that conduct and use women-oriented policy research. **Scope:** Causes and consequences of women's poverty, particularly of minority women; costs and benefits of family and work policies; pay equity; wages and employment opportunities; impact of tax policy on women and families; and access to and costs of healthcare. Specific issues include the impact of the Pregnancy Discrimination Act, the costs and benefits of family and medical leave, pay equity in 20 state civil service systems, the wage gap between women of color and white women, low-wage work, welfare reform, microenterprise, women and labor unions (labor law reform), and women's economic agendas. **Founded:** 1987. **Publications:** *Research News Reporter* (Monthly). **Educational Activities:** IWPR Workshops, Offer exemplary teaching and training programs. **Awards:** IWPR Summer Internships. **Geographic Preference:** National.

26123 ■ Johns Hopkins University Bloomberg School of Public Health - Center for Health Services and Outcomes Research (CHSOR)
Hampton House, 6th Fl.
624 N Broadway
Baltimore, MD 21205-1901
URL: http://publichealth.jhu.edu/center-for-health-services-outcomes-research
Contact: Dr. Albert Wu, Director
E-mail: awu@jhsph.edu
Description: Integral unit of School of Public Health at Johns Hopkins University. Offers technical assistance for local and national groups. **Scope:** Health services, including determinants of health outcomes; the impacts of alternative health care systems on cost and quality; effective strategies for health promotion and disease prevention; and methods of meeting the needs of high risk populations such as the poor, older persons, disabled persons, children, and people with mental health challenges. **Founded:** 1969.

26124 ■ Johns Hopkins University - Bloomberg School of Public Health Department of Health Policy and Management - Center for Hospital Finance and Management
615 N Wolfe St.
Baltimore, MD 21205
URL: http://publichealth.jhu.edu/johns-hopkins-drug-access-and-affordability-initiative/our-project-team
Contact: Gerard F. Amderson, Director
Description: Component of Johns Hopkins Medical Institution. Offers Congressional testimony. **Scope:** Hospital finance and management, technology assessment, reform of cost containment and payment, policies, clinical education, managed care, and medical effectiveness. **Founded:** 1979.

26125 ■ Kaiser Permanente Center for Health Research (CHR)
3800 N Interstate Ave.
Portland, OR 97227-1098
Ph: (503)335-2400
Co. E-mail: information@kpchr.org
URL: http://research.kpchr.org
Contact: John Ogden, Director
E-mail: john.r.ogden@kpchr.org
Linkedin: www.linkedin.com/company/kpchr
X (Twitter): x.com/KPCHR
Description: Integral unit of Kaiser Foundation Hospitals, Inc. **Scope:** Organization, financing, costs and quality of medical care in an HMO; mental health; medical informatics; patient safety; health behavior interventions; epidemiology; effectiveness of alternative therapies and services; nutrition; genetics; dental research; and biometry and research methods. **Founded:** 1964. **Educational Activities:** CHR Annual Saward Lecture (Annual).

26126 ■ Kaiser Permanente - Division of Research
2000 Broadway
Oakland, CA 94612
Ph: (510)891-3400
Free: 866-454-8855
Co. E-mail: dor-communications@kp.org
URL: http://divisionofresearch.kaiserpermanente.org
Contact: Dr. Tracy A. Lieu, Director
E-mail: tracy.lieu@kp.org
X (Twitter): x.com/kpdor
Description: Integral unit of Permanente Medical Group, Inc. and Kaiser Permanente Medical Care Program, California Region. Staff teaches at local universities and performs editorial and review services for scientific and medical journals. **Scope:** Epidemiology, biometrics and biostatistics, technology assessment, health services research, and health education research and evaluation. Supports clinical research in medical centers. **Founded:** 1961. **Awards:** Kaiser Permanente Northern California Delivery Science Fellowship Program (Annual).

26127 ■ Marshall University Research Corp. (MURC)
1676 3rd Ave., Arthur Weisberg Family Applied engineering Complex, 4th Fl.
Huntington, WV 25703
Ph: (304)696-6271
Fax: (304)697-2770
Co. E-mail: itservicedesk@marshall.edu
URL: http://www.marshall.edu/murc
Contact: Dr. John Maher, Executive Director
E-mail: maherj@marshall.edu
Description: Integral unit of Marshall University. Offers counseling and referral services; technical and research assistance. **Scope:** Provides technical and research assistance to West Virginia businesses and governments, focusing on business and industry, including business and job development, marketing research, and feasibility studies; community and government, including housing, zoning, recreation, criminology, traffic safety, transportation, personnel administration, and finance; education, including basic teaching skills, educational financing, and extended training for primary and secondary instructors; arts and culture, including developing, coordinating, and promoting cultural activities, and assisting local arts and cultural organizations in obtaining funding; health, including basic and applied research, and mechanisms for continuing growth of health care services and education; family and consumer, including problems of families in transition, support of displaced workers, housing norms, retirement preparation and adjustment, and consumer issues. **Educational Activities:** MURC Educational seminars, workshops, and lectures; MURC Graduate cooperative education programs.

26128 ■ Medical Technology and Practice Patterns Institute (MTPPI)
4800 Hampden Ln. 2nd Flr.
Bethesda, MD 20814
Ph: (301)652-4005
Fax: (301)652-8335
Co. E-mail: info@mtppi.org
URL: http://www.mtppi.org
Contact: Dennis Cotter, President
Linkedin: www.linkedin.com/company/medical-technology-and-practice-patterns-institute
X (Twitter): x.com/MTPPI
Description: Independent, nonprofit corporation. Offers consulting for public and private organizations. **Scope:** New and emerging health-care technologies and their implications for local, national, and international policy. **Founded:** 1986. **Publications:** *Diagnostic Imaging and Child Abuse*; *Direct and Indirect Costs of Diabetes* (Occasionally); *Implications of NAFTA for Trade in Health Care Technology*; *Rational Use of Health Technologies*; *Reports on various health technologies*.

26129 ■ Methodist Research Institute (MRI)
1701 N Senate Blvd.
Indianapolis, IN 46202
URL: http://iuhealth.org/for-researchers/our-regional-locations/iu-health-methodist-clinical-research
Contact: Dr. Cary N. Mariash, Medical Director
Description: Integral unit of Methodist Hospital and Clarian Health Partners. Offers statistical analysis, abstract and manuscript preparation, and grant proposal writing. **Scope:** Pharmaceutical and device clinical trials, experimental cell research, cell signaling, ion channel physiology, immunology, nutrition angiogenesis, cancer, shock. Other research involves heart, kidney, lung, pancreas, and liver transplants; biliary and renal extracorporeal shock wave lithotripsy; and clot lysis programs. **Founded:** 1956. **Educational Activities:** Summer Student Research Program.

26130 ■ Michigan Family Forum (MFF)
120 N Washington Sq., Ste. 240
Lansing, MI 48933
Ph: (517)374-1171
Fax: (517)374-6112
Co. E-mail: info@michiganfamily.org
URL: http://www.michiganfamily.org
Contact: Jeff Hewson, Executive Director
Description: Research and education organization that focuses on family issues in the Michigan Legislature. **Scope:** Public policy issues and responsible citizenship, focusing on strengthening families. Areas of study include education, sex education, educational choice, educational curriculum, divorce, adoption, euthanasia, marriage and marriage protection, welfare reform, and healthcare. **Founded:** 1989. **Publications:** *Michigan Voter Guide* (Periodic); *Forum Online* (Weekly). **Educational Activities:** MFF Choose Freedom Peer Abstinence Network. **Geographic Preference:** State.

26131 ■ New Mexico Clinical Research and Osteoporosis Center
300 Oak St. NE
Albuquerque, NM 87106
Ph: (505)855-5505
Fax: (505)855-5506
URL: http://www.nmbonecare.com
Contact: Dr. E. Michael Lewiecki, Director
Description: Provide the highest level of service for our patients, with special interest in clinical research, osteoporosis care, and bone density testing. **Scope:** Health care quality, health promotion, clinical research, and continuing medical education. **Founded:** 1987. **Publications:** *New Mexico Clinical Research and Osteoporosis Center Newsletter* (Periodic; Periodic).

26132 ■ The New School - Center for New York City Affairs
72 Fifth Ave., 6th Fl.
New York, NY 10011
Ph: (212)229-5400
Fax: (212)229-5335
Co. E-mail: centernyc@newschool.edu
URL: http://www.centernyc.org
Contact: Kristin Morse, Executive Director
E-mail: morsek@newschool.edu
Facebook: www.facebook.com/centernyc
X (Twitter): x.com/CenterNYC
Instagram: www.instagram.com/centernyc
Description: Integral unit of New School University. Offers conferences, lectures, short courses, and seminars. **Scope:** Applied research and journalism on public policy in urban centers, including children and families, immigrant communities, poverty and politics. **Founded:** 1964. **Publications:** *Child Welfare Watch* (Semiannual); *Developmental Disabilities Watch* (Annual); *Center for New York City Affairs Working papers* (Occasionally).

26133 ■ Pacific Health Research and Education Institute (PHREI)
3375 Koapaka St., Ste. I 540
Honolulu, HI 96819
Ph: (808)524-4411
Fax: (808)524-5559
Co. E-mail: info@phrei.org
URL: http://www.phrei.org
Contact: Douglas D. Wilson, Treasurer
Description: Independent, public, charitable, non-profit organization. **Scope:** Health services and clinical research, including breast cancer, hypertension, osteoporosis, diabetes, heart attacks, drug studies, effects of chemical exposure, and cost-effectiveness analysis. Specific studies focus on risk factors associated with breast cancer, methods of delaying or preventing postmenopausal osteoporosis, isolated systolic hypertension among the elderly, outcomes research, leprosy, interactive videodiscs, geriatrics, and prostate, lung, colorectal, and ovarian cancer screening. Participates in a statewide consortium of hospitals to address quality and cost of care. Hawaii MEDTEP (Medical Treatment Effectiveness Program) Research Center, outcomes research with a focus on minority populations. **Founded:** 1960.

26134 ■ Pacific Research Institute for Public Policy (PRI)
2110 K St., Ste. 28
Sacramento, CA 95816
Ph: (916)389-9774
URL: http://www.pacificresearch.org
Contact: Sally C. Pipes, President
Description: Aims to inform the public about issues that affect the free enterprise system and the rights of individuals. Studies public policy issues, including education, environment, technology, economics, health and welfare. **Scope:** Public policy issues. Administers a publishing program focusing on health care, environment, education, technology, and privatization, with an outreach program of breakfasts, luncheons, conferences, briefings, and opinion editorials. **Founded:** 1979. **Publications:** *Capital Ideas*; *The Contrarian*; *PRI Newsletter* (Quarterly); *Policy Briefings*; *Studies* (Irregular). **Educational Activities:** Privatization Competition (Annual). **Geographic Preference:** National.

26135 ■ Portland VA Research Foundation (PVARF)
3710 SW US Veterans Hospital Rd., Building 104
Rm. G218 & 219
Portland, OR 97239
Ph: (503)273-5228
Fax: (503)402-2866
URL: http://www.pvarf.org
Linkedin: www.linkedin.com/company/portland-va-research-foundation
Description: Independent, nonprofit organization, affiliated with the Portland VA Medical Center. **Scope:** Medicine and medical research. **Founded:** 1989.

26136 ■ Public Citizen Health Research Group (PCHRG)
1600 20th St. NW
Washington, DC 20009
URL: http://www.citizen.org/about/person/michael-abrams
Contact: Michael Abrams, Officer
E-mail: mabrams@citizen.org
Description: Works on issues of health care delivery, workplace safety and health, drug regulation, food additives, medical device safety, and environmental influences on health. **Scope:** Conducts consumer advocacy and lobbying on health matters and monitors the enforcement of health and safety legislation. **Founded:** 1971. **Publications:** *PCHRG Health Letter* (Monthly); *Health Research Group Publications* (Annual); *Worst Pills, Best Pills* (Monthly). **Geographic Preference:** National.

26137 ■ Regenstrief Institute (RI)
1101 W 10th St.
Indianapolis, IN 46202
Ph: (317)274-9000
Co. E-mail: prteam@regenstrief.org
URL: http://www.regenstrief.org
Contact: Marjorie Rallins, Director
Facebook: www.facebook.com/regenstriefinstitute
Linkedin: www.linkedin.com/company/regenstrief-institute
X (Twitter): x.com/Regenstrief
Description: Separately incorporated research affiliated with Indiana University-Purdue University at Indianapolis, School of Medicine. **Scope:** Health care, including use of computers in health care delivery, and use of engineering and computer techniques to improve medical diagnosis and therapy. **Founded:** 1969.

26138 ■ RTI International [Research Triangle Institute]
3040 East Cornwallis Rd.
Research Triangle Park, NC 27709-2194
Ph: (919)541-6000
Co. E-mail: nidilrrapr@rti.org
URL: http://www.rti.org
Contact: Tim J. Gabel, President
Facebook: www.facebook.com/rti.international
Linkedin: www.linkedin.com/company/rti-international
X (Twitter): x.com/RTI_Intl
Instagram: www.instagram.com/rti_intl
YouTube: www.youtube.com/c/rtiinternational
Description: Provides research, development, and technical services to government and commercial clients worldwide. **Scope:** Performs interdisciplinary research and development and provides technical services in social and economic systems and human resources, statistical sciences and survey research, chemistry and life sciences and toxicology, energy and environmental sciences, and electronics and engineered systems. Industries served health care products, electronics, chemicals, oil and gas, manufacturing, government agencies, and electric utilities. **Services:** Library not open to the public. **Founded:** 1958. **Holdings:** 100 books; 50 videotapes. **Publications:** "Differences in contraceptive use across generations of migration among women of Mexican origin," Sep, 2009; "Peer effects in adolescent overweight," Sep, 2008; "South Africa: Access Before Quality, and What to Do Now," 2006; "Assistive Technology Data Collection Project," Oct, 2003; "Automated Testing of the Census Cfu Instrument"; "Challenges of Designing and Implementing Multi mode Instruments: Fedcasic"; "Research and Development in Audio-Recorded Interviewing"; "Web-Based Meta data Tracking System Designed for the National Survey on Drug Use and Health". **Training:** Whither SA's education investment? A rights and skills agenda, Investment Choices for Education In Africa, Sep, 2006; Family and early childhood; Elementary and secondary education; Postsecondary education; International education policy and systems; Disability policy and programs. **Educational Activities:** Peace Corps Connect (Annual). **Special Services:** SUDAAN, ExhibitAR, AVATALK-Survey, Geode.

26139 ■ Rutgers, The State University of New Jersey - Institute for Health, Health Care Policy and Aging Research
112 Paterson St.
New Brunswick, NJ 08901-1293
Ph: (848)932-8413
Fax: (732)932-1253
Co. E-mail: community@ifh.rutgers.edu
URL: http://ifh.rutgers.edu
Contact: Stacey Pacheco, Officer
E-mail: spacheco@ifh.rutgers.edu
Facebook: www.facebook.com/RutgersIFH
Linkedin: www.linkedin.com/company/rutgersifh
X (Twitter): x.com/rutgersifh
YouTube: www.youtube.com/channel/UCHQLOS1tXo2VGNCjEmHQuDg
Description: Integral unit of Rutgers University. **Scope:** Research divisions include and focus on the following activities: the Division of Health studies the impact of stress on emotional states and health and risk behaviors and how these latter factors influence the immune system and morbidity and mortality, and studies how stress and emotional states affect symptom appraisal and the decision to use health care; the Division of Health Care Policy analyzes the health and cost outcomes of the current allocation of health resources, with emphasis on preventive care and chronic illnesses; analyzes the evolution of managed care and its impact on patient outcomes, medical professions and utilization of services; examines trust relationships among consumers and physicians and managed care organizations; the Division on Aging measures income inequality, investigates the role of instrumental and social support as buffers against stress and chronic illness, and identifies predictors of poor self-assessments of health among the elderly and assesses treatments and outcomes in long term care; the AIDS Policy Research Group measures health care utilization and cost among patients with HIV illness; the Center for Mental Health Services and Criminal Justice Research Division conducts research on improving care and treatment of persons with mental illness in the criminal justice systems; the Center for the Study of Health Beliefs and Behavior targets the relationships among cognitions, emotions, personality, social relationships and health and health behavior. Investigators are developing models to improve communications among practitioners, clients and families to facilitate quality health outcomes; the Center for Obesity Research and Intervention investigates the treatment of obesity; the Center for Health Services Research on Pharmacotherapy, Chronic Disease Management and Outcomes fosters collaborative research on pharmacotherapy for persons with chronic illness, including more effective use of drugs, the impact of policy changes and sociocultural influences on utilization; the Center for State Health Policy analyzes and researches state health policy; the Center for Education and Research in Therapeutics studies the use of antidepressant and antipsychotic medications among children and adolescents, psychotropic drug use among adults and the frail elderly, and the outcomes of pharmaceutical care. **Founded:** 1986. **Publications:** *Peer-reviewed articles*. **Educational Activities:** Brown Bag Seminar Series, Topics on health, mental health and health policy.

26140 ■ Rutgers University - Institute for Health, Health Care Policy, and Aging Research - Division on Aging - AIDS Policy Research Group (ARG)
112 Paterson St.
New Brunswick, NJ 08901-1293
Co. E-mail: community@ifh.rutgers.edu
URL: http://ifh.rutgers.edu/aids-research-group
Contact: Dr. Stephen Crystal, Director
E-mail: scrystal@ifh.rutgers.edu
Description: Integral unit of Institute for Health, Health Care Policy, and Aging Research, Rutgers University. **Scope:** AIDS, and gerontology, focusing on policy issues and applying social science methodology to the planning and evaluation of programs and policies designed to meet public health objectives. Specific areas of research include HIV health services, long-term care, social networks, mental health

programs, the social context of health-related behavior in Hispanic and black subcultures, health cognition and health belief systems, legal aspects of serving endangered and high-risk populations, and cost of care and services utilization studies. Special areas of emphasis include quality of life and long-term care for the elderly, intervention-focused behavioral science research, increasing patient-provider communication, furthering methods of research in the health services field, adherence and access to prescription drugs and medical care, social and behavioral AIDS research, and mental health issues in relation to previous areas listed. **Founded:** 1968. **Publications:** *ARG Annual report* (Annual); *State health policy reports*; *White papers*.

26141 ■ Seton Hall University College of Arts and Sciences - Center for Public Service
400 S Orange Ave.
South Orange, NJ 07079
URL: http://www.shu.edu/public-service
Contact: Dr. Naomi Bailin Wish, Director

Description: Research unit of College of Arts and Sciences, Seton Hall University. Offers technical assistance and training. **Scope:** Nonprofit management education; health policy issues, finance, and management; nonprofit information technology; service learning; strategic planning; etc. **Founded:** 1989. **Educational Activities:** Distinguished Lecture Series in Philanthropy; Center for Public Service Master's program, In public and healthcare administration. **Awards:** Goya Scholarships; Thomas J. Stanton, Jr. Scholarships (Annual); Partial Scholarships for Nonprofit Management Courses Scholarship.

26142 ■ Society for the Study of Social Problems (SSSP)
901 McClung Twr., University of Tennessee
Knoxville, TN 37996-0490
Ph: (865)689-1531
Fax: (865)689-1534
Co. E-mail: sssp@utk.edu
URL: http://www.sssp1.org
Facebook: www.facebook.com/SSSP1org
X (Twitter): x.com/SSSP1org

Description: An interdisciplinary community of scholars, activists, practitioners, and students endeavoring to create greater social justice through social research. Members are often social scientists working in colleges and universities, in non-profit organizations and in other applied and policy settings. **Scope:** Global problems; institutional ethnography; community research and development; crime and juvenile delinquency; drinking and drugs; racial and ethnic minorities; conflict, social action, and change; family; poverty, class, and inequality; social problems theory; mental health; teaching social problems; sociology and social welfare; youth, aging, and the life course; educational problems; environment and technology; labor studies; sexual behavior, politics and communities; law and society; health, health policy and health services; disabilities; sport, leisure, and the body. **Founded:** 1951. **Publications:** *SSSP Newsletters*; *Social Problems* (Quarterly); *SSSP Social Problems* (Quarterly). **Educational Activities:** SSSP Annual Meetings (Annual); SSSP Symposia. **Awards:** Erwin O. Smigel Award (Annual); Lee Scholar Support Fund (Annual); Lee Student Support Fund (Annual); Thomas C. Hood Social Action Award (Annual); C. Wright Mills Award (Annual); Lee Founders Award (Annual); SSSP Joseph B. Gittler Award (Irregular); SSSP Racial/Ethnic Minority Graduate Fellowship (Annual). **Geographic Preference:** National.

26143 ■ Southern Illinois University at Carbondale School of Medicine - Center for Rural Health and Social Service Development (CRHSSD)
975 S Normal Ave., MC 6892
Carbondale, IL 62901
Ph: (618)453-1262
Fax: (618)453-0253
Co. E-mail: circulation@siumed.edu
URL: http://www.siumed.edu/orp/crhssd/contact-us.html
URL(s): www.siumed.edu/about-center-rural-health-and-social-service-development.html

Description: Integral unit of School of Medicine, Southern Illinois University at Carbondale. Offers community needs assessments, project development and management. **Scope:** Health care and social service issues that impact the lives and productivity of the citizens in Illinois and the nation, including alternative service delivery systems and policy alternatives. Studies include rural health care, rural safety, rural medical transportation mental, health and substance use, violence prevention, tobacco initiatives, and obesity prevention. **Founded:** 1989. **Publications:** *Center Briefs*. **Educational Activities:** Training, curriculum development.

26144 ■ Texas A&M University - Bush School of Government and Public Service - Institute for Science, Technology and Public Policy (ISTPP)
2115 Allen Bldg.
College Station, TX 77843-4220
Co. E-mail: bushschoolistpp@tamu.edu
URL: http://bush.tamu.edu/istpp

Description: Integral unit of Bush School of Government and Public Service, Texas A&M University. **Scope:** Social and policy implications of emerging science and technology research. Specific research areas include public policy issues related to the environment and natural resources, emerging technologies such as nanotechnology and biotechnology, infrastructure and the built environment, and health. **Founded:** 2000. **Publications:** *Articles in scholarly, peer-reviewed journals*; *ISTPP Reports* (Occasionally).

26145 ■ Texas Tech University - Rawls College of Business - Center for Healthcare Innovation, Education and Research (CHIER)
703 Flint Ave.
Lubbock, TX 79409
URL: http://www.depts.ttu.edu/rawlsbusiness/about/hom/chier
Contact: Dr. Jeffrey Burkhardt, Contact
E-mail: jeffrey.burkhardt@ttu.edu

Description: Integral unit of of College Administration at Texas Tech University. **Scope:** Interdisciplinary approaches to studying healthcare safety issues and addition of electronic medical records. **Founded:** 1997. **Publications:** *Advances in Health Care Management* (Annual). **Educational Activities:** John A. Buesseler Lecture Series (Semiannual).

26146 ■ Texas Tech University - Rawls College of Business - Institute for Leadership Research (ILR)
703 Flint Ave.
Lubbock, TX 79409
URL: http://www.depts.ttu.edu/rawlsbusiness/about/management/leadershipinstitute.php
Contact: Dr. Michael R. Ryan, Executive Director
E-mail: michael.r.ryan@ttu.edu

Description: Integral unit of Rawls College of Business, Texas Tech University. **Scope:** Develops and tests state of the art leadership theory. Applies theory to leaders at all organizational levels. Incorporates effective existing and emerging leadership practice into the development of new theory for managerial leaders. **Founded:** 1988. **Publications:** *Journal of Management Inquiry* (Quarterly); *ILR Monographs*. **Educational Activities:** ILR Distinguished lecturer and panel discussions; ILR Forums for chief executive officers; ILR Leadership Development Series, Series of workshop offered to the regional business community to enhance leadership development in the business and community sectors.

26147 ■ Thomas Jefferson University - Center for Research in Medical Education and Health Care (CRMEHC)
1015 Walnut St., Curtis Bldg., Ste. 319
Philadelphia, PA 19107
Ph: (215)955-0731
Fax: (215)923-6939
URL: http://www.jefferson.edu/academics/colleges-schools-institutes/skmc/research/research-medical-education/team.html
Contact: Dr. Charles A. Pohl, Director
E-mail: charles.pohl@jefferson.edu
URL(s): jdc.jefferson.edu/jmc-crmehc

Description: Integral unit of Jefferson Medical College of Thomas Jefferson University. Offers consultation and technical services. **Scope:** Medical education research focuses on the following areas: measurement of physician competence; long-term follow-up study of graduates; program evaluation; specialty choice; and refinement of evaluation methods. **Founded:** 1983. **Publications:** *ABSTRACTS: Longitudinal Study of Medical Students and Graduates*; *Center for Research in Medical Education and Health Care Annual report* (Annual).

26148 ■ University of Alabama at Birmingham School of Public Health - Lister Hill Center for Health Policy (LHC)
Ryals Public Health Bldg., Ste. 514., 1665 University Blvd.
Birmingham, AL 35294
Ph: (205)934-6553
Co. E-mail: lhc@uab.edu
URL: http://sites.uab.edu/listerhillcenter
Contact: Dr. Suzanne Judd, Director
Facebook: www.facebook.com/UABLHC
X (Twitter): x.com/uablhc
Instagram: www.instagram.com/uablhc

Description: Integral unit of University of Alabama at Birmingham School of Public Health. **Scope:** Health policy research, focusing on health care markets and managed care, maternal and child health, management in public health organizations, aging policy, and outcomes research. **Founded:** 1987. **Publications:** *Health Policy Abstract*. **Educational Activities:** Methods Workshops; Lister Hill Center for Health Policy Research Seminars (Irregular). **Awards:** UAB Lister Hill Center Intramural Grant Program (Annual); UAB Health Policy Fellowship (Annual).

26149 ■ University of Arizona - Native American Research and Training Center (NARTC)
1642 E Helen St.
Tucson, AZ 85719
Ph: (520)621-5560
Fax: (520)621-9802
URL: http://wassajacenter.arizona.edu
Contact: Christina Bell Andrews, Executive Director
E-mail: christinaandrews@arizona.edu

Description: Research and training unit of University of Arizona. **Scope:** Health and rehabilitation of disabled and chronically ill Native Americans. Core areas include the following: needs assessment, service delivery, and evaluation as determined by or in cooperation with the tribal community and empowerment that is sensitive to Indian values and needs. Also studies the impact of government policy on the delivery of health care. Promotes self determination and parity among Native Americans in health and rehabilitation. Serve as a national resource for all North American tribes and Alaska natives. **Founded:** 1983. **Publications:** *NARTC Books*; *Dual track videotapes*; *NARTC Reports*. **Educational Activities:** NARTC Conferences and workshops; Training programs for indigenous trainers and direct-service providers.

26150 ■ University of California, Berkeley - Center for Labor Research and Education [The Labor Center - Institute for Research on Labor and Employment]
2521 Channing Way No.5555
Berkeley, CA 94720
Ph: (510)642-0323
Fax: (510)643-4673
Co. E-mail: laborcenter@berkeley.edu
URL: http://laborcenter.berkeley.edu
Contact: Jenifer MacGillvary, Coordinator
E-mail: jmacgill@berkeley.edu
Facebook: www.facebook.com/ucberkeleylaborcenter
X (Twitter): x.com/ucblaborcenter

Instagram: www.instagram.com/
ucberkeleylaborcenter
YouTube: www.youtube.com/user/ucblaborcenter
Description: Works to develop educational programs to meet the needs of unions. Conducts research concerning organized labor and the workforce; offers management training courses; holds computer training workshops; sponsors multi-union conferences on labor issues. Maintains speakers' bureau. **Scope:** Labor standards: job quality, living wages, healthcare. Organizing models: human services, immigrant workers, young workers, Black workers, workers in the global economy. **Founded:** 1964. **Publications:** *Labor Center Reporter* (Quarterly); *California Workers Rights, and various pamphlets*; *Eyes on the Fries*; *Falling Apart: Declining Job-Based Health Coverage for Working Families in California and the United States*; *Hidden Costs of Wal-Mart Jobs*; *Hidden Public Costs of Low Wage Work*; *Kids at Risk: Declining Employer-Based Health Coverage in California and the U.S.*; *Organize to Improve the Quality of Jobs in the Black Community*; *The State of Labor Education in the U.S.*; *Trade Secrets*; *The Weingarten Decision and the Right to Representation on the Job*; *Winning at Work*. **Educational Activities:** California Lead Organizers Institute; California Union Leadership School; C.L. Dellums African American Leadership School; Latino American Leadership School; Media Skills Workshop; Strategic Campaigns Workshop (Annual); Strategic Research Workshop; Center for Labor Research and Education Board meeting. **Geographic Preference:** National.

26151 ■ University of California, San Francisco - Philip R. Lee Institute for Health Policy Studies (PRL-IHPS)
490 Illinois St., Fl. 7
San Francisco, CA 94158
Ph: (415)476-4921
Co. E-mail: ihps@ucsf.edu
URL: http://healthpolicy.ucsf.edu/philip-r-lee-institute-health-policy-studies
Contact: Caldwell B. Esselstyn, Chairman of the Board
Facebook: www.facebook.com/UCSF.HealthPolicy
X (Twitter): x.com/ucsf_ihps
YouTube: www.youtube.com/user/UCSFIHPS
Description: Integral unit of University of California, San Francisco. **Scope:** Health policy and health services research, from individual clinics to hospital and healthcare systems; drugs and pharmaceuticals; population health. **Founded:** 1972.

26152 ■ University of Colorado at Denver School of Medicine - Division of Health Care Policy and Research (HCPR)
13199 East Montview Blvd. 1st Fl.
Aurora, CO 80045
Ph: (303)724-2400
URL: http://medschool.cuanschutz.edu/health-care-policy-and-research
Contact: Eric Coleman, Professor Head
E-mail: eric.coleman@ucdenver.edu
Description: Integral unit of University of Colorado-Denver. **Scope:** Health services and health policies at the federal and state levels, emphasizing Medicare and Medicaid quality assurance and reimbursement for long-term care providers, including home health agencies, subacute care facilities, swing-bed hospitals, and traditional nursing homes. **Founded:** 1977.

26153 ■ University of Connecticut - School of Medicine - Department of Public Health Sciences - Center for International Community Health Studies (CICHS)
263 Farmington Ave.
Farmington, CT 06030-6325
Co. E-mail: schensul@uchc.edu
URL: http://health.uconn.edu/complementary-integrative/faculty-and-staff
Contact: Dr. Stephen L. Schensul, Director
E-mail: schensul@uchc.edu
Description: Integral unit of Department of Community Medicine and Health Care, School of Medicine, University of Connecticut Health Center. **Scope:** The health of underprivileged people in the U.S. and abroad, emphasizing international primary health care and community health, including international health policy, urban health in developing and developed countries, maternal and child health. **Founded:** 1971. **Publications:** *Annual Training Program Catalogue*; *CICHS Connections Newsletter*. **Educational Activities:** Language training programs, short-term research, evaluation, curriculum design, and management training programs, Global health-related training and educational exhibits.

26154 ■ University of Manitoba - Manitoba Centre for Nursing and Health Research (MCNHR)
Helen Glass Centre for Nursing
89 Curry Pl., University of Manitoba
Winnipeg, MB, Canada R3T 2N2
Ph: (204)474-9080
Free: 800-432-1960
Fax: (204)474-7683
Co. E-mail: mcnhr@umanitoba.ca
URL: http://umanitoba.ca/nursing/research/manitoba-centre-nursing-and-health-research-mcnhr
Contact: Dr. Susan McClement, Associate Dean Professor
E-mail: susan.mcclement@umanitoba.ca
Description: Integral unit of Faculty of Nursing, University of Manitoba, with its own advisory committee. Offers consultation for faculty, graduate students and community nurses; research support for research grant applications and knowledge translation activities. **Scope:** Quality assurance for nursing education & nursing and health care research. **Publications:** *MCNHR Annual reports* (Annual); *Research activity reports*. **Educational Activities:** Research Seminars, Workshops and Training. **Awards:** Fort Garry Branch Royal Canadian Legion Poppy Trust Fund Research Grant (Annual); MCNHR Research Grant (Annual).

26155 ■ University of Maryland at College Park - Center on Aging
4200 Valley Dr., Ste. 2242
College Park, MD 20742-2611
URL: http://sph.umd.edu/research-impact/research-centers/center-aging
Description: Integral unit of University of Maryland at College Park. Offers curriculum development. **Scope:** Gerontology, including senior service and volunteerism, long-term care financing, service credit banking, informal caregiving, aging and disabilities, productive aging, lifelong learning and engagement, health care delivery systems and cost containment. Conducts health assessment and longitudinal data base projects on aging, lifelong learning and civil engagement. **Founded:** 1974. **Publications:** *Community Gerontology*. **Educational Activities:** Legacy Leadership Institutes.

26156 ■ University of Minnesota School of Public Health - Health Policy & Management Division (HPM)
420 Delaware St SE
Minneapolis, MN 55455
Ph: (612)624-6151
URL: http://www.sph.umn.edu/academics/divisions/hpm
Contact: Ira Moscovice, Director
E-mail: mosco001@umn.edu
Description: Division within the School of Public Health, University of Minnesota. Designed to function as interdisciplinary unit of the University, the Institute links the health sciences with other disciplines such as public affairs, economics, businesses, administration, and sociology. **Scope:** Involves in long-term care, health insurance, managed health care, patient care outcomes, rural health services, and health policy analysis. **Founded:** 1978. **Publications:** *Institute News* (3/year); *Research Brief*. **Educational Activities:** Minnesota Health Services Research Conference (Annual).

26157 ■ University of Pennsylvania - Leonard Davis Institute of Health Economics (LDI)
Colonial Penn Ctr., 3641 Locust Walk
Philadelphia, PA 19104-6218
Ph: (215)898-5611
Fax: (215)898-0229
Co. E-mail: pennldi-info@wharton.upenn.edu
URL: http://ldi.upenn.edu
Contact: Rachel M. Werner, MD, PhD, Executive Director
E-mail: rwerner@upenn.edu
Linkedin: www.linkedin.com/company/leonard-davis-institute-of-health-economics
X (Twitter): x.com/PennLDI
Description: Integral unit of University of Pennsylvania. **Scope:** Health economics; health care financing; systems design, organization, and management; evaluation of medical practices; and related policy issues that address the efficient allocation of health resources, the appropriate use of health services, the development of innovative health care delivery systems, and changing patient and provider behavior. Areas of concern include evaluation and optimization of clinical care and new technologies; access to health care; payment/reimbursement mechanisms and insurance; and institutional structure, management, and governance. **Founded:** 1967. **Publications:** *LDI Brochures*; *Issue briefs*. **Educational Activities:** LDI Advanced management education programs, To senior health care executives and other health care professionals.; LDI Health Policy Seminar Series; LDI Research Conference; LDI Research Seminar Series.

26158 ■ University of South Florida - Louis de la Parte Florida Mental Health Institute College of Behavioral and Community Sciences - Center for HIV Education and Research
4202 E Fowler Ave.
Tampa, FL 33612
URL: http://www.usf.edu/cbcs/fmhi/research
Description: Integral unit of College of Behavioral and Community Sciences, Louis de la Parte Florida Mental Health Institute, University of South Florida. Offers consulting to hospitals, clinics, public health centers, community health centers, and substance abuse centers. **Scope:** Diagnosis, treatment, and care of persons infected with HIV, study of HIV risk factors, and HIV/AIDS prevention. **Founded:** 1988. **Publications:** *HIV/AIDS Primary Care Guide*; *HIV Carelink Newsletter*; *Pocket Treatment Cards*. **Educational Activities:** Florida/Caribbean AIDS Education and Training Center (Annual); HIV Conference, Designed to increase the knowledge and skills of HIV healthcare providers.; Perinatal Transmission Prevention Program; Center for HIV Education and Research Workshops, On topics related to and on clinical management for public health and correctional medical personnel specifically addressing HIV/AIDS.

26159 ■ University of Wisconsin--Madison - Center for Health System Research and Analysis (CHSRA)
333 Bascom Hall 500 Lincoln Dr.
Madison, WI 53706
URL: http://research.wisc.edu/centers-cores/more-uw-research-centers-and-programs
Description: Integral unit of University of Wisconsin—Madison but operating under its own board of control. **Scope:** Five major research areas: quality assessment and improvement, long term care, public health policy and program evaluation, consumer decision making, and patient education and support. **Founded:** 1973.

26160 ■ Vanderbilt University - Vanderbilt Institute for Public Policy Studies (VIPPS)
230 Appleton Pl. PMB 0505
Nashville, TN 37203-5721
Ph: (615)322-6789
URL: http://as.vanderbilt.edu/public-policy-studies
Contact: Dr. Christopher Carpenter, Director
E-mail: christopher.s.carpenter@vanderbilt.edu
Description: Research, educational, and public service unit of Vanderbilt University. **Scope:** Strives to provide a bridge between academic research on child and family policy options and the worlds of state and local policy makers. Fosters collaboration among faculty members at the University by operating research centers. **Founded:** 1975. **Publications:** *VIPPS Annual Report*; *Semiannual Newsletter*.

Educational Activities: VIPPS Conferences; VIPPS Faculty discussion groups; Freshman Tennessee Legislator Issue Workshop.

26161 ■ Welfare Research, Inc. (WRI)
14 Columbia Cir., Ste., 104
Albany, NY 12203
Ph: (518)713-4726
Fax: (518)608-5435
Co. E-mail: info@welfareresearch.org
URL: http://www.wrisolutions.org
Contact: Ellen Conklin, President
Facebook: www.facebook.com/wrisolutions
Linkedin: www.linkedin.com/company/wri-solutions
X (Twitter): x.com/WRI_NY
Description: Seeks to improve social service agencies operations and services. Provides research, evaluation, training, and technical and management assistance to the human services community. Conducts policy studies in child welfare, adolescent health, teen pregnancy, employment for welfare recipients, and service needs of refugees. **Scope:** Child welfare, AIDS, human services, health services, mental hygiene, nutrition assistance, public housing, employment and training, and nonprofit organization management. **Founded:** 1967. **Publications:** *WRI Annual Report* (Annual); *Adoption Recruitment Brochure*; *Congregate Care Health Services Manual*; *Foster Care Team Manual for Niagara County*; *New York State Foster Parent Manual*; *When Your Child is in Foster Care: A Handbook for Parents*. **Educational Activities:** WRI Communication and public information programs. **Geographic Preference:** National.

High-Tech Business

START-UP INFORMATION

26162 ■ *"Adventure Capital"* in Austin Business Journal (Vol. 34, June 20, 2014, No. 18, pp. 4)
Pub: American City Business Journals, Inc.
Contact: Mike Olivieri, Executive Vice President
Description: Several startup companies in the Austin, Texas area have raised millions of dollars from venture capital firms over several years, without reaching profitability or becoming self-funded. However, while this strategy has been successful for startups such as hologram technology developer Zebra Imaging Inc., others like solar panel maker Helio Volt Corporation and low-power chip maker Calxeda Inc. have been forced to shut down despite receiving substantial amounts of investment capital. **Availability:** Online.

26163 ■ *"After $4M Funding, ThisClicks CEO Talks What's Next"* in Business Journal (Vol. 31, January 10, 2014, No. 33, pp. 7)
Pub: American City Business Journals, Inc.
Contact: Mike Olivieri, Executive Vice President
Released: Weekly. **Price:** $4, Introductory 4-week offer(Digital & Print). **Description:** Chad Halvorson, CEO of technology startup ThisClicks, describes the fundraising process for the Roseville, Minnesota-based company. He discusses the factors driving the startup's growth and the firm's new products. **Availability:** Print; Online.

26164 ■ *"Ailing Economy Nibbling at Tech-Sector Jobs"* in Puget Sound Business Journal (Vol. 29, November 7, 2008, No. 29, pp. 1)
Description: Seattle-area tech start-up companies including Redfin, Zillow, WildTangent, Daptiv, Avelle, and Intrepid Learning Solutions have cut staff as the nation's economy staggers. The layoffs are reminiscent of the tech bubble era, but most startups these days have been more prudent about spending and hiring as compared to that period. **Availability:** Print; Online.

26165 ■ *"Do Cool Sh*t: Quit Your Day Job, Start Your Own Business, and Live Happily Ever After"*
Pub: Harper Business
Contact: Hollis Heimbouch, Senior Vice President Publisher
Released: January 20, 2015. **Price:** $16.61, hardcover; $11.97, paperback; $11.49, e-book; $3.13, kindle; $0.05, hardcover(99 used from $0.05); $8, hardcover(44 new from $8.00); $2, paperback(76 used from $2.00); $5.47, paperback(64 new from $5.47). **Description:** Serial social entrepreneur, angel investor, and woman business leader, Miki Agrawal, teaches how to start and run a successful new business. She covers all issues from brainstorming, to raising money to getting press without any connections, and still have time to enjoy life. She created WILD, a farm-to-table pizzeria in New York City and Las Vegas. She also partnered in a children's multimedia company called Super Sprowtz--a story-driven nutrition program for children, and she launched a patented high-tech underware business called THINX. Agrawal also discusses the growth in her businesses. **Availability:** E-book; Print.

26166 ■ *"ETF Process May be Tweaked"* in Austin Business JournalInc. (Vol. 28, December 26, 2008, No. 41, pp. 3)
Description: Some government officials are proposing for an adjustment of the Texas Emerging Technology Fund's (ETF) policies. The ETF was created to get startup companies capital to get off the ground. Reports show that the global recession had made it more difficult for startup companies to garner investment. **Availability:** Online.

26167 ■ *"'Find a Customer To Validate Your Idea"* in South Florida Business Journal (Vol. 34, May 2, 2014, No. 41, pp. 15)
Pub: American City Business Journals, Inc.
Contact: Mike Olivieri, Executive Vice President
Released: Weekly. **Price:** $8, Introductory 4-week offer(Digital only). **Description:** Venture Hive founder, Susan Amat, share her views on her mission to nurture the entrepreneurial ecosystem from South Florida to the Americas. Amat says Venture Hive is a safe space where world-class technologists can learn to scale their businesses. Amat is a 40 Under 40 honoree, a White House Champion of Change, chair of Startup Florida, an Emerging Leader and a Woman to Watch. **Availability:** Print; Online.

26168 ■ *"GeoEye CEO Sees Investors In His Future: Matt O'Connell Eyeing Intel Startup Post-Sale"* in Washington Business Journal (Vol. 31, September 14, 2012, No. 21, pp. 1)
Pub: Baltimore Business Journal
Contact: Rhonda Pringle, President
E-mail: rpringle@bizjournals.com
Description: GeoEye Inc. chief executive officer, Matt O'Connell, plans to start a new technology venture in Northern Virginia like the one that supports intelligence gathering once DigitalGlobe Inc. has completed the acquisition of his company in 2013. He will work in an advisory role for DigitalGlobal following the acquisition and will not be involved in satellite imagery security for competitive reasons. **Availability:** Print; Online.

26169 ■ *"Giving Biotech Startups a Hand"* in Philadelphia Business Journal (Vol. 28, January 8, 2010, No. 47, pp. 1)
Pub: Philadelphia Business Journal
Contact: Sierra Quinn, Director
E-mail: squinn@bizjournals.com
Ed: John George. **Description:** Elkins Park, Pennsylvania-based BioStrategy Partners is a virtual life sciences incubator that is seeking to improve the dull ranking of Philadelphia in the small business vitality index of life sciences. BioStrategy provides technology and business development services to startup life sciences companies and university-based research projects. **Availability:** Online.

26170 ■ *"JOBS Act Spurring Bio IPOs"* in Philadelphia Business Journal (Vol. 33, May 2, 2014, No. 12, pp. 4)
Pub: American City Business Journals, Inc.
Contact: Mike Olivieri, Executive Vice President
Released: Weekly. **Price:** $4, Introductory 4-week offer(Digital only). **Description:** The Jumpstart Our Business Startups Act has important provisions that are helping many early-stage biotechnology companies in their initial public offerings. Trevena Inc. of King of Prussia, Pennsylvania benefited from the extra time to educate the investment community and from the exemptions on the regulatory requirements. **Availability:** Print; Online.

26171 ■ *"Leading Digital: Turning Technology into Business Transformation"*
Pub: Harvard Business Review Press
Contact: Moderna V. Pfizer, Contact
Released: October 14, 2014. **Price:** $32, Hardcover/Hardcopy. **Description:** Mobile technology, analytics, social media, sensors, and cloud computing have changed the entire business environment in every industry. A guide to help any small startup business in any industry gain strategic advantage using digital, including where to invest in digital technologies and how to lead the transformation. The guide teaches how to engage better with customers, digitally enhance operations, create a digital vision, and govern digital activities. **Availability:** E-book; Print.

26172 ■ *"Made@Mayo: Mayo Professor Doubles As Founder of Text Tech Company"* in Business Journal (Vol. 32, June 6, 2014, No. 2, pp. 10)
Pub: American City Business Journals, Inc.
Contact: Mike Olivieri, Executive Vice President
Description: Rochester, Minnesota-based Mayo Clinic Ventures has managed the licensing of Mayo Clinic technologies and invests in startups. Mayo Clinic Ventures has a $100 million growth fund for investing in startups and two smaller funds worth about $500,000 combined. Insights on the stories of Mayo researchers leading startups are also provided. **Availability:** Online.

26173 ■ *"No. 407: What I Learned in the Military, and What I Had to Unlearn"* in Inc. (Vol. 36, September 2014, No. 7, pp. 80)
Pub: Mansueto Ventures L.L.C.
Contact: Stephanie Mehta, Chief Executive Officer
Released: September 2014. **Description:** Profile of William Bailey, who served in the U.S. Army as information manager at the U.S. Military Academy at West Point. Bailey discusses his startup firm, Rapier Solutions, a government contractor providing IT, logistics, and social-work expertise. The firm has developed a new survivor outreach system for the U.S. Army. **Availability:** Print; Online.

26174 ■ *"Red McCombs, Partner Rolling Out New Venture Capital Fund"* in San Antonio Business Journal (Vol. 26, April 20, 2012, No. 12, pp. 1)
Pub: Baltimore Business Journal
Contact: Rhonda Pringle, President

E-mail: rpringle@bizjournals.com

Description: Entrepreneur Red McCombs has partnered with businessman Chase Fraser to create a new venture capital fund. This new fund will focus on technology startups in the automotive sector. **Availability:** Print; Online.

26175 ■ *"SBA Program Helped New Company Survive As It Built Company Base" in Philadelphia Business Journal (Vol. 33, May 9, 2014, No. 13, pp. 4)*

Pub: American City Business Journals, Inc.
Contact: Mike Olivieri, Executive Vice President

Released: Weekly. **Description:** The Small Business Administration (SBA) Indiana District Business Office helped Netwise Resources set up its information technology (IT) consulting business with a six-month SBA-backed loan and the 8(a) Business Development Program for small disadvantaged businesses. Owner, Mark Gibson, attributes Netwise Resources' success to its focus on branding, recruiting skilled staff, and establishing relationships with clients within the target market. **Availability:** Print; Online.

26176 ■ *Seed-Stage Venture Investing: An Insider's Guide to Start-Ups for Scientists, Engineers, and Investors*

Ed: William L. Robbins, Jonathan Lasch. **Released:** 2011. **Description:** Ideas for starting, funding, and managing technology-based firms, also known as, venture capitalists, are featured.

26177 ■ *"Should State Invest In Startups?" in Providence Business News (Vol. 28, March 3, 2014, No. 48, pp. 1)*

Pub: American City Business Journals, Inc.
Contact: Mike Olivieri, Executive Vice President

Released: March 01, 2014. **Description:** The U.S. Treasury Department is investigating whether Rhode Island violated Federal rules when it used funds from the State Small Business Credit Initiative (SSBCI) to invest in Betaspring, a startup accelerator program for technology and design entrepreneurs ready to launch their businesses. The Lyon Park audit claims that Rhode Island violated SSBCI rules because a large portion of the money went to the business accelerator's operating expenses and not to the startups themselves. **Availability:** Print; Online.

26178 ■ *"Start-Up! So You Want to Be an Entrepreneur. So You Want to Be Rich"*

Released: September 25, 2014. **Price:** $14.99. **Description:** Entrepreneur offers a guide for startups. Jim Lewis shares the innovative thinking that helped him launch, grow and sell two successful high-tech companies.

26179 ■ *"Starting Up All Over Again: Alex Bogusky Backs Bootcamp for Advertising Startup" in Denver Business Journal (Vol. 65, February 7, 2014, No. 39, pp. 8)*

Pub: American City Business Journals, Inc.
Contact: Mike Olivieri, Executive Vice President

Released: February 7, 2014. **Description:** Once called the Elvis of advertising, Alex Bogusky is now launching a new startup named 'Boomtown' with an aim to cultivate a new generation of advertising, marketing, design, and media related tech companies. The end goal of boomtown will be to figure out the trend in which media as well as the relationship between brands and people is going.

26180 ■ *"Tale of Two Tech Facilities" in Business Journal Portland (Vol. 30, January 3, 2014, No. 44, pp. 12)*

Pub: American City Business Journals, Inc.
Contact: Mike Olivieri, Executive Vice President

Released: January 3, 2014. **Description:** The cities of Pittsburgh, Pennsylvania and Portland, Oregon share similarities when it comes to supporting technology startups. Both have been collaborating with the startup community. Portland has the capability to build strong companies due to its local talent pool.

26181 ■ *Technology Ventures: From Idea to Enterprise*

Pub: McGraw-Hill Higher Education
Contact: Michael Ryan, President

Ed: Richard C. Dorf, Thomas H. Byers, Andrew Nelson. **Released:** Fifth edition. **Price:** $130.66; $80. **Description:** Textbook examining technology entrepreneurship on a global basis; technology management theories are explored. **Availability:** E-book; Print.

26182 ■ *"Texas State Seeks Startups" in Austin Business Journal (Vol. 32, April 20, 2012, No. 7, pp. 1)*

Pub: American City Business Journals, Inc.
Contact: Mike Olivieri, Executive Vice President

Ed: Sandra Zaragoza. **Description:** Texas State University is set to open a new business incubator for technology startups. The incubator will have secure wet labs, clean rooms and office space. **Availability:** Online.

26183 ■ *"Troy Patent Law Firm Launches Rent-Free Tech Incubator" in Crain's Detroit Business (Vol. 25, June 8, 2009, No. 23, pp. 4)*

Pub: Crain Communications Inc.
Contact: Barry Asin, President

Ed: Tom Henderson. **Description:** Young Basile Hanlon MacFarlane & Helmholdt PC, a patent law firm located in Troy, Michigan has created a small, rent-free technology incubator on site. The incubator will be called North Woodward Tech Incubator and has room for four or five startups. The incubator is for the earliest or pre-seed stage for entrepreneurs who have not yet gotten significant investment capital. **Availability:** Online.

EDUCATIONAL PROGRAMS

26184 ■ **Application Systems Development Audit and Security**
Seminar Information Service Inc. (SIS)
250 El Camino Real., Ste. 112
Tustin, CA 92780
Ph: (714)508-0340
Free: 877-736-4636
Fax: (714)734-8027
Co. E-mail: info@seminarinformation.com
URL: http://www.seminarinformation.com
Contact: Catherine Bellizzi, President
URL(s): www.seminarinformation.com

Description: Learn an end-to-end approach for ensuring the design, security, integrity, and performance of your application system. **Audience:** Financial, operational, business applications, information technology professionals and external auditors. **Principal Exhibits:** Learn an end-to-end approach for ensuring the design, security, integrity, and performance of your application system.

26185 ■ **Auditing Business Application Systems (Onsite)**
Seminar Information Service Inc. (SIS)
250 El Camino Real., Ste. 112
Tustin, CA 92780
Ph: (714)508-0340
Free: 877-736-4636
Fax: (714)734-8027
Co. E-mail: info@seminarinformation.com
URL: http://www.seminarinformation.com
Contact: Catherine Bellizzi, President
URL(s): www.seminarinformation.com

Description: Three-day seminar attendees will learn how to audit and how to develop controls for complex automated applications which use online/real-time, distributed processing, and/or database technologies, including an opportunity to actually prepare an audit plan for a complex application system. **Audience:** Information technology, financial, operations, and business applications auditors and audit managers. **Principal Exhibits:** Three-day seminar attendees will learn how to audit and how to develop controls for complex automated applications which use online/real-time, distributed processing, and/or database technologies, including an opportunity to actually prepare an audit plan for a complex application system.

26186 ■ **Auditing Networked Computers (Onsite)**
Seminar Information Service Inc. (SIS)
250 El Camino Real., Ste. 112
Tustin, CA 92780
Ph: (714)508-0340
Free: 877-736-4636
Fax: (714)734-8027
Co. E-mail: info@seminarinformation.com
URL: http://www.seminarinformation.com
Contact: Catherine Bellizzi, President
URL(s): www.seminarinformation.com

Description: Seminar designed as a first look at LANs, WANs, workstations, and servers where you will focus on understanding the technology, evaluating the risks, and establishing n audit approach. **Audience:** Business industry professionals. **Principal Exhibits:** Seminar designed as a first look at LANs, WANs, workstations, and servers where you will focus on understanding the technology, evaluating the risks, and establishing n audit approach.

26187 ■ **Auditing and Securing Oracle Databases (Onsite)**
Seminar Information Service Inc. (SIS)
250 El Camino Real., Ste. 112
Tustin, CA 92780
Ph: (714)508-0340
Free: 877-736-4636
Fax: (714)734-8027
Co. E-mail: info@seminarinformation.com
URL: http://www.seminarinformation.com
Contact: Catherine Bellizzi, President
URL(s): www.seminarinformation.com

Description: Learn Oracle's database facilities and terminology along with the commands you need to know to provide security, audit and query controls for Oracle and Oracle-controlled data. **Audience:** Experienced IT auditors, auditors. **Principal Exhibits:** Learn Oracle's database facilities and terminology along with the commands you need to know to provide security, audit and query controls for Oracle and Oracle-controlled data.

26188 ■ **BGP - Configuring BGP on Cisco Routers (Onsite)**
Seminar Information Service Inc. (SIS)
250 El Camino Real., Ste. 112
Tustin, CA 92780
Ph: (714)508-0340
Free: 877-736-4636
Fax: (714)734-8027
Co. E-mail: info@seminarinformation.com
URL: http://www.seminarinformation.com
Contact: Catherine Bellizzi, President
URL(s): www.seminarinformation.com/qqbmsa/bgp-configuring-bgp-on-cisco-routers

Description: Comprehensive five-day course explores the theory of BGP, configuration of BGP on Cisco IOS routers, and detailed troubleshooting information. **Audience:** Internet service providers, and networking professionals. **Principal Exhibits:** Comprehensive five-day course explores the theory of BGP, configuration of BGP on Cisco IOS routers, and detailed troubleshooting information.

26189 ■ **Computer Forensics and Incident Response: Hands-On - Analyzing Windows-Based Systems (Onsite)**
Seminar Information Service Inc. (SIS)
250 El Camino Real., Ste. 112
Tustin, CA 92780
Ph: (714)508-0340
Free: 877-736-4636
Fax: (714)734-8027
Co. E-mail: info@seminarinformation.com
URL: http://www.seminarinformation.com
Contact: Catherine Bellizzi, President
URL(s): www.seminarinformation.com

Description: Learn how to: Implement a computer forensics incident-response strategy; Lead a successful investigation from the initial response to completion; Conduct disk-based analysis and recover deleted files; Identify information-hiding techniques; Reconstruct user activity from e-mail, temporary Internet files and cached data; Assess the integrity of system memory and process architecture to reveal malicious code. **Audience:** Industry professionals. **Principal Exhibits:** Learn how to: Implement a computer forensics incident-response strategy; Lead a successful investigation from the initial response to completion; Conduct disk-based analysis and recover deleted files; Identify information-hiding techniques; Reconstruct user activity from e-mail, temporary Internet files and cached data; Assess the integrity of system memory and process architecture to reveal malicious code.

26190 ■ Deploying Intrusion Detection Systems: Hands-On (Onsite)
Seminar Information Service Inc. (SIS)
  250 El Camino Real., Ste. 112
  Tustin, CA 92780
Ph: (714)508-0340
Free: 877-736-4636
Fax: (714)734-8027
Co. E-mail: info@seminarinformation.com
URL: http://www.seminarinformation.com
Contact: Catherine Bellizzi, President
URL(s): www.seminarinformation.com

Description: Learn how to: Detect and respond to network- and host-based intruder attacks; Integrate intrusion detection systems (IDS) into your current network topology; Analyze IDS alerts using the latest tools and techniques; Identify methods hackers use to attack systems; Recognize detection avoidance schemes; Stop attackers with Intrusion Prevention Systems (IPSs). **Audience:** Industry professionals. **Principal Exhibits:** Learn how to: Detect and respond to network- and host-based intruder attacks; Integrate intrusion detection systems (IDS) into your current network topology; Analyze IDS alerts using the latest tools and techniques; Identify methods hackers use to attack systems; Recognize detection avoidance schemes; Stop attackers with Intrusion Prevention Systems (IPSs).

26191 ■ Deterring Social Engineering Attacks: Resisting Human Deception (Onsite)
Seminar Information Service Inc. (SIS)
  250 El Camino Real., Ste. 112
  Tustin, CA 92780
Ph: (714)508-0340
Free: 877-736-4636
Fax: (714)734-8027
Co. E-mail: info@seminarinformation.com
URL: http://www.seminarinformation.com
Contact: Catherine Bellizzi, President
URL(s): www.seminarinformation.com

Description: Learn how to: Help prevent social engineering exploits by heightening your security awareness; Decode the art of human deception; Identify the social engineering attack cycle; Define and help protect corporate and personal assets; Assess and quantify the impact of social engineering attacks; Integrate your corporate security policy into your professional responsibilities; Apply an employee social engineering defense checklist. **Audience:** Industry professionals and general public. **Principal Exhibits:** Learn how to: Help prevent social engineering exploits by heightening your security awareness; Decode the art of human deception; Identify the social engineering attack cycle; Define and help protect corporate and personal assets; Assess and quantify the impact of social engineering attacks; Integrate your corporate security policy into your professional responsibilities; Apply an employee social engineering defense checklist.

26192 ■ Developing High-Performance SQL Server Databases: Hands-On Onsite Meeting
Seminar Information Service Inc. (SIS)
  250 El Camino Real., Ste. 112
  Tustin, CA 92780
Ph: (714)508-0340
Free: 877-736-4636
Fax: (714)734-8027
Co. E-mail: info@seminarinformation.com
URL: http://www.seminarinformation.com
Contact: Catherine Bellizzi, President
URL(s): www.seminarinformation.com/qqbtlw/developing-high-performance-sql-server-databases-hands

Description: Learn how to design and implement high-performance databases for SQL Server 2005 and 2000; Create indexes that optimize different types of queries; Design transactions that maximize concurrency and minimize contention; Interpret the data access plans produced by the query optimizer; Minimize I/O by designing efficient physical data structures; Improve response time by introducing controlled redundancy; and analyze and cure performance problems using SQL Server's tools. **Audience:** Industry professionals. **Principal Exhibits:** Learn how to design and implement high-performance databases for SQL Server 2005 and 2000; Create indexes that optimize different types of queries; Design transactions that maximize concurrency and minimize contention; Interpret the data access plans produced by the query optimizer; Minimize I/O by designing efficient physical data structures; Improve response time by introducing controlled redundancy; and analyze and cure performance problems using SQL Server's tools.

26193 ■ Disaster Recovery Planning: Ensuring Business Continuity (Onsite)
Seminar Information Service Inc. (SIS)
  250 El Camino Real., Ste. 112
  Tustin, CA 92780
Ph: (714)508-0340
Free: 877-736-4636
Fax: (714)734-8027
Co. E-mail: info@seminarinformation.com
URL: http://www.seminarinformation.com
Contact: Catherine Bellizzi, President
URL(s): www.seminarinformation.com/qqbtkc/disaster-recovery-planning-ensuring-business-continuity

Description: Learn how to: Create, document and test continuity arrangements for your organization; Perform a risk assessment and Business Impact Assessment (BIA) to identify vulnerabilities; Select and deploy an alternate site for continuity of mission-critical activities; Identify appropriate strategies to recover the infrastructure and processes; Organize and manage recovery teams; Test and maintain an effective recovery plan in a rapidly changing technology environment. **Audience:** Industry professionals. **Principal Exhibits:** Learn how to: Create, document and test continuity arrangements for your organization; Perform a risk assessment and Business Impact Assessment (BIA) to identify vulnerabilities; Select and deploy an alternate site for continuity of mission-critical activities; Identify appropriate strategies to recover the infrastructure and processes; Organize and manage recovery teams; Test and maintain an effective recovery plan in a rapidly changing technology environment.

26194 ■ DSP: Digital Signal Processing (Onsite)
Seminar Information Service Inc. (SIS)
  250 El Camino Real., Ste. 112
  Tustin, CA 92780
Ph: (714)508-0340
Free: 877-736-4636
Fax: (714)734-8027
Co. E-mail: info@seminarinformation.com
URL: http://www.seminarinformation.com
Contact: Catherine Bellizzi, President
URL(s): www.seminarinformation.com/qqbftd/dsp-digital-signal-processing

Description: Introduction to DSP concepts and implementation, including a complete model of a DSP system from the input transducer through all the stages. **Audience:** Technicians and engineers. **Principal Exhibits:** Introduction to DSP concepts and implementation, including a complete model of a DSP system from the input transducer through all the stages.

26195 ■ EEI Communications Introduction to Soundtrack Pro
URL(s): www.eeicom.com

Description: Course includes an introduction to Soundtrack Pro Interface, basic audio editing, importing audio, post-production techniques with audio and video, producing podcasts with Soundtrack Pro, and exporting your audio projects. **Audience:** Industry professionals, public. **Principal Exhibits:** Course includes an introduction to Soundtrack Pro Interface, basic audio editing, importing audio, post-production techniques with audio and video, producing podcasts with Soundtrack Pro, and exporting your audio projects.

26196 ■ Ethical Hacking and Countermeasures: Hands-On - Preventing Network and System Breaches (Onsite)
Seminar Information Service Inc. (SIS)
  250 El Camino Real., Ste. 112
  Tustin, CA 92780
Ph: (714)508-0340
Free: 877-736-4636
Fax: (714)734-8027
Co. E-mail: info@seminarinformation.com
URL: http://www.seminarinformation.com
Contact: Catherine Bellizzi, President
URL(s): www.seminarinformation.com

Description: Learn how to deploy ethical hacking to expose weaknesses in your organization and select countermeasures; Gather intelligence by employing social engineering, published data and scanning tools; Probe and compromise your network using hacking tools to improve your security; Discover how malicious hackers exploit weaknesses to 'own' the network; Protect against privilege escalation to prevent intrusions; Defend against evasions of antivirus, firewalls and IDS. **Audience:** Industry professionals, IT. **Principal Exhibits:** Learn how to deploy ethical hacking to expose weaknesses in your organization and select countermeasures; Gather intelligence by employing social engineering, published data and scanning tools; Probe and compromise your network using hacking tools to improve your security; Discover how malicious hackers exploit weaknesses to 'own' the network; Protect against privilege escalation to prevent intrusions; Defend against evasions of antivirus, firewalls and IDS.

26197 ■ Fundamentals of Information Security (Onsite)
Seminar Information Service Inc. (SIS)
  250 El Camino Real., Ste. 112
  Tustin, CA 92780
Ph: (714)508-0340
Free: 877-736-4636
Fax: (714)734-8027
Co. E-mail: info@seminarinformation.com
URL: http://www.seminarinformation.com
Contact: Catherine Bellizzi, President
URL(s): www.seminarinformation.com

Description: Three-day seminar will guide you through the basics of information security in today's high-tech, business environment, including external threats, establishing effective security policies, contingency planning, and employee privacy rights. **Audience:** Industry professionals. **Principal Exhibits:** Three-day seminar will guide you through the basics of information security in today's high-tech, business environment, including external threats, establishing effective security policies, contingency planning, and employee privacy rights.

26198 ■ IT Auditing and Controls (Onsite)
Seminar Information Service Inc. (SIS)
  250 El Camino Real., Ste. 112
  Tustin, CA 92780
Ph: (714)508-0340
Free: 877-736-4636
Fax: (714)734-8027
Co. E-mail: info@seminarinformation.com
URL: http://www.seminarinformation.com
Contact: Catherine Bellizzi, President
URL(s): www.seminarinformation.com

Description: Three-day seminar outlines the concepts of information systems you need to know in order to understand the audit concerns in the IS environment. You will learn the necessary controls for application systems- the session pinpoints specific controls to evaluate when auditing currently installed system, new systems under development, and the various activities within the information systems department, as well as techniques for auditing automated systems. **Audience:** Financial, operational, business applications and external auditors, IT. **Principal Exhibits:** Three-day seminar outlines the concepts of information systems you need to know in order to understand the audit concerns in the IS environment. You will learn the necessary controls for application systems- the session pinpoints specific controls to evaluate when auditing currently installed system, new systems under development, and the various activities within the information systems department, as well as techniques for auditing automated systems.

26199 ■ A Practical Guide to Controls for IT Professionals (Onsite)
Seminar Information Service Inc. (SIS)
  250 El Camino Real., Ste. 112
  Tustin, CA 92780
Ph: (714)508-0340
Free: 877-736-4636
Fax: (714)734-8027
Co. E-mail: info@seminarinformation.com
URL: http://www.seminarinformation.com
Contact: Catherine Bellizzi, President
URL(s): www.seminarinformation.com

Description: Designed to provide all levels of IT personnel with an understanding of what controls are and why they are critical to safeguarding information assets. Discover why it is important to have a business-process view of IT controls and review the critical role they play in providing for a smooth running, efficiently manager IT environment. **Audience:** IT management and staff, other IT personnel and IT auditors. **Principal Exhibits:** Designed to provide all levels of IT personnel with an understanding of what controls are and why they are critical to safeguarding information assets. Discover why it is important to have a business-process view of IT controls and review the critical role they play in providing for a smooth running, efficiently manager IT environment.

REFERENCE WORKS

26200 ■ "2nd Watch Rides AWS Market Maturity to 400% Growth" in Computer Business Week (August 28, 2014, pp. 21)
Description: 2nd Watch reports record earnings for the second quarter of 2014. The firm helps companies develop and implement IT strategies that are based on Amazon Web Services (AWS). Details of the companies business strategies are outlined. **Availability:** Print; Online.

26201 ■ 5 Priorities for Hiring & Retaining Women in Tech
URL(s): www.kornferry.com/insights/featured-topics/diversity-equity-inclusion/five-priorities-for-hiring-and-retaining-women-in-tech
Released: May 12, 2022. **Description:** Outlines five things to keep in mind when hiring and retaining women in tech. **Availability:** Online.

26202 ■ "7 Trends Affecting the Security Technology Business" in IP SecurityWatch.com (March 2012)
Ed: Geoff Kohl. **Description:** Scott Harkins, president of Honeywell Security Products for the Americas, outlines the seven trends affecting the security technology business. He covers smart phones and tablets, home automation, interctive services, integration beyond security systems, cloud services, standards, and apps. **Availability:** Online.

26203 ■ "2010 Book of Lists" in Business Courier (Vol. 26, December 26, 2009, No. 36, pp. 1)
Price: $49.95. **Description:** Rankings of companies and organizations within the business services, education, finance, health care, hospitality and tourism, real estate, and technology industries in the Cincinnati, Ohio-Northern Kentucky area are presented. Rankings are based on sales, business size, or other statistics. **Availability:** PDF; Online.

26204 ■ "2014 Promises Tech IPO Frenzy" in San Francisco Business Times (Vol. 28, January 3, 2014, No. 24, pp. 6)
Pub: American City Business Journals, Inc.
Contact: Mike Olivieri, Executive Vice President
Released: Weekly. **Price:** $4, Introductory 4-week offer(Digital & Print). **Description:** Bay Area-based venture-backed technology companies are expected to fill 2014 with initial public offerings (IPOs) and fuel more venture capital funding in the region. The U.S. IPO market has recorded more than 220 pricings and was the strongest since the dot-com bubble of 2000. California-based technology companies that valued at $1 billion or more are also profiled. **Availability:** Print; Online.

26205 ■ Aging and Working in the New Economy: Changing Career Structures in Small IT Firms
Pub: Edward Elgar Publishing Inc.
Contact: Edward Elgar, Founder Chairman
Ed: Juliie Ann McMullin, Victor W. Marshall. **Released:** 2010. **Description:** Case studies and analyses provide insight into the structural features of small- and medium-sized firms in the information technology sector, and the implications of these features for the careers of people employed by them.

26206 ■ "Agricharts Launches New Mobile App for Ag Market" in Farm Industry News (December 1, 2011)
Pub: Informa Business Media, Inc.
Contact: Charlie McCurdy, President
Description: AgriCharts provides market data, agribusiness Website hosting and technology solutions for the agricultural industry. AgriCharts is a division of Barchart.com Inc. and announced the release of a new mobile applications that offers real-time or delayed platform for viewing quotes, charts and analysis of grains, livestock and other commodity markets. **Availability:** Print; Online.

26207 ■ Agritech Sprouts Start-Ups
URL(s): www.businesstoday.in/magazine/the-hub/story/agritech-sprouts-start-ups-117925-2018-12-10
Ed: K T P Radhika. **Released:** December 30, 2018. **Description:** Discusses the growing agri-tech business sector and how they are attracting investors. **Availability:** Online.

26208 ■ Agritech Startups, Innovations & Facts
URL(s): apiumhub.com/tech-blog-barcelona/agritech-startups-innovations-facts/
Ed: Ekaterina Novoseltseva. **Released:** September 19, 2019. **Description:** Discusses agri-tech innovations and eight agri-tech startups to follow. **Availability:** Online.

26209 ■ "All About The Benjamins" in Canadian Business (Vol. 81, September 29, 2008, No. 16, pp. 92)
Description: Discusses real estate developer Royal Indian Raj International Corp., a company that planned to build a $3 billion "smart city" near the Bangalore airport; to this day nothing has ever been built. The company was incorporated in 1999 by Manoj C. Benjamin one investor, Bill Zack, has been sued by the developer for libel due to his website that calls the company a scam. Benjamin has had a previous case of fraud issued against him as well as a string of liabilities and lawsuits. **Availability:** Online.

26210 ■ "All Those Applications, and Phone Users Just Want to Talk" in Advertising Age (Vol. 79, August 11, 2008, No. 31, pp. 18)
Pub: Crain Communications, Inc.
Contact: Jessica Botos, Manager, Marketing
E-mail: jessica.botos@crainsnewyork.com
Ed: Mike Vorhaus. **Description:** Although consumers are slowly coming to text messaging and other data applications, a majority of those Americans surveyed stated that they simply want to use their cell phones to talk and do not care about other activities. Statistical data included. **Availability:** Online.

26211 ■ "Analysts: Intel Site May Be Last Major U.S.-Built Fab" in Business Journal-Serving Phoenix and the Valley of the Sun (October 18, 2007)
Pub: Phoenix Business Journal
Contact: Alex McAlister, Director
E-mail: amcalister@bizjournals.com
Ed: Ty Young. **Description:** Intel's million-square-foot manufacturing facility, called Fab 32, is expected to open in 2007. The plant will mass-produce the 45-nanometer microchip. Industry analysts believe Fab 32 may be the last of its kind to be built in the U.S., as construction costs are higher in America than in other countries. Intel's future in Chandler is examined. **Availability:** Print; Online.

26212 ■ "Ann Arbor Google's Growth Dips: Few Worried about High-tech Firm's Future" in Crain's Detroit Business (Vol. 25, June 8, 2009, No. 23, pp. 3)
Pub: Crain Communications Inc.
Contact: Barry Asin, President
Ed: Bill Shea. **Description:** Global recession has slowed the growth of Google Inc. Three years ago, when Google moved to Ann Arbor, Michigan it estimated it would provide 1,000 new jobs within five years, so far the firm employs 250. **Availability:** Online; PDF.

26213 ■ "App Brings Real-Time Personal Security, Company Says" in Philadelphia Business Journal (Vol. 33, July 4, 2014, No. 21, pp. 11)
Pub: American City Business Journals, Inc.
Contact: Mike Olivieri, Executive Vice President
Released: Weekly. **Price:** $4, Introductory 4-week offer(Digital & Print). **Description:** EmergenSee, which is a mobile technology that transforms smartphones or tablets into personal security systems by downloading the app. It has the ability to stream live video and audio. **Availability:** Print; Online.

26214 ■ "App Maker Thinks He Has the Ticket: But Denver Is Balking At Alternative To Parking Fines" in Denver Business Journal (Vol. 65, April 25, 2014, No. 50, pp. A10)
Pub: American City Business Journals, Inc.
Contact: Mike Olivieri, Executive Vice President
Released: Weekly. **Price:** $4, introductory 4-week offer(Digital & Print). **Description:** Taylor Linnell started Ticket Cricket LLC with partner, Jeff Valdez, to make parking tickets obsolete in Denver, Colorado by using two smartphone applications, One, Ticket Cricket and 5 for 5. The Department of Public Works rejected Linnell's proposal; he was encouraged to try it with the city's parking system technology vendor, Xerox. **Availability:** Print; Online.

26215 ■ "Apps For Anybody With an Idea" in Advertising Age (Vol. 79, October 17, 2008, No. 39, pp. 29)
Pub: Crain Communications, Inc.
Contact: Jessica Botos, Manager, Marketing
E-mail: jessica.botos@crainsnewyork.com
Ed: Beth Snyder Bulik. **Description:** Apple's new online App Store is open to anyone with an idea and the ability to write code and many of these developers are not only finding a sense of community through this venue but are also making money since the sales are split with Apple, 30/70 in the developer's favor. **Availability:** Online.

26216 ■ "As Technology Changes, So Must African American Business" in Black Enterprise (Vol. 41, August 2010, No. 1, pp. 61)
Pub: Earl G. Graves Ltd.
Contact: Earl Graves, Jr., President

Ed: Sonya A. Donaldson. **Description:** Social media is essential to compete in today's business environment, especially for African American firms. **Availability:** Online.

26217 ■ *"As Windows 8 Looms, Tech Investors Hold Their Breath"* in *Barron's (Vol. 92, July 23, 2012, No. 30, pp. 22)*
Pub: Dow Jones & Company Inc.
Contact: Almar Latour, Chief Executive Officer
Ed: Tiernan Ray. **Description:** Launch of the Microsoft Windows 8 operating system could affect the stock prices of Microsoft and Intel. The effects of the software's introduction on the market share of personal computers remains uncertain. **Availability:** Online.

26218 ■ *"Aviat Networks Partners With AT&T Government Solutions for Department of Homeland Security Business"* in *Entertainment Close-Up August 13, 2012*
Description: Aviat Networks Inc. will provide US Department of Homeland Security and other federal agencies withh the capability to acquire microwave radio communication equipment, engineering, design, installation and maintenace services. Aviat is a subcontractor on the AT&T Government Solutions' team. Aviat has a history of partnerships in federal technology space. **Availability:** Print; PDF; Online.

26219 ■ *"Back Off on ABM Legislation, Banks Warn MPs"* in *Globe & Mail (April 20, 2007, pp. B1)*
Ed: Steven Chase. **Description:** The efforts of banks to prevent legislation by the Canadian government on the automated banking machine levies charged from customers of other institutions are described. **Availability:** Online.

26220 ■ *"The Bell Tolls for Thee"* in *Canadian Business (Vol. 81, March 3, 2008, No. 3, pp. 36)*
Description: Bell Canada has formed the Canadian Coalition for Tomorrow's IT Skills to solve the shortage of technology talent in the country. Canada's total workforce has only around 4%, or 600,000 people employed in information technology-related fields. The aims of the Bell-led coalition, which is supported by different industry associations and 30 corporations, are investigated. **Availability:** Print; Online.

26221 ■ *"Bernier Open to Telecom Changes"* in *Globe & Mail (March 22, 2006, pp. B1)*
Ed: Simon Tuck. **Description:** Federal Industry Minister Maxime Bernier of Canada says that he is open to scrapping restrictions on foreign ownership in telecommunications. His views on telecom industry are detailed. **Availability:** Online.

26222 ■ *"Beyond Microsoft and Yahoo!: Some M&A Prospects"* in *Barron's (Vol. 88, March 17, 2008, No. 11, pp. 39)*
Pub: Dow Jones & Company Inc.
Contact: Almar Latour, Chief Executive Officer
Ed: Eric J. Savitz. **Description:** Weak quarterly earnings report for Yahoo! could pressure the company's board to cut a deal with Microsoft. Electronic Arts is expected to win its hostile $26-a-share bid for Take-Two Interactive Software. Potential targets and buyers for mergers and acquisitions are mentioned. **Availability:** Online.

26223 ■ *The Big Switch: Rewiring the World, from Edison to Google*
Pub: W.W. Norton & Company Ltd.
Contact: Stanley Kubrick, Director
Ed: Nicholas Carr. **Released:** June 10, 2013. **Price:** $16.95, paperback; $26.95, hardcover. **Description:** Companies such as Google, Microsoft, and Amazon.com are building huge centers in order to create massive data centers. Together these centers form a giant computing grid that will deliver the digital universe to scientific labs, companies and homes in the future. This trend could bring about a new, darker phase for the Internet, one where these networks could operate as a fearsome entity that will dominate the lives of individuals worldwide. **Availability:** Print.

26224 ■ *"Biotech Reels In $120M for 1Q"* in *Philadelphia Business Journal (Vol. 31, March 30, 2012, No. 7, pp. 1)*
Pub: Baltimore Business Journal
Contact: Rhonda Pringle, President
E-mail: rpringle@bizjournals.com
Description: Philadelphia, Pennsylvania-based biotechnology firms have raised over $120 million in 2012 by selling stocks and debts. Discovery Laboratories has accounted for more than a third of the total funding. **Availability:** Print; Online.

26225 ■ *"Biotechnology Wants a Lead Role"* in *Business North Carolina (Vol. 28, March 2008, No. 3, pp. 14)*
Description: According to experts, North Carolina is poised as a leader in the biotechnology sector. Highlights of a recent roundtable discussion sponsored by the North Carolina Biotechnology Center in Research Triangle Park are presented. **Availability:** Online.

26226 ■ *"Biotechs Are Using Back Door to Go Public"* in *Boston Business Journal (Vol. 31, May 27, 2011, No. 18, pp. 1)*
Pub: Boston Business Journal
Contact: Carolyn M. Jones, President
E-mail: cmjones@bizjournals.com
Ed: Julie M. Donnelly. **Description:** Members of Massachusetts' biotechnology sector have been engaging in reverse mergers as an alternative to initial public offerings. Reverse mergers provide access to institutional investors and hedge funds. **Availability:** Print; Online.

26227 ■ *"Birmingham Tech Firms Eye Growth in 2014"* in *Birmingham Business Journal (Vol. 31, January 10, 2014, No. 2, pp. 4)*
Pub: American City Business Journals, Inc.
Contact: Mike Olivieri, Executive Vice President
Released: Weekly. **Price:** $4, introductory 4-week offer(Digital & Print). **Description:** Birmingham, Alabama-based high-tech firms, ProctorU and Chronicle Studio are planning to expand their work forces in 2014. ProctorU will add more than 50 employees, while Chronicle will add three more positions to their staff. **Availability:** Print; Online.

26228 ■ *"Bitcoin 'Killer App' Or the Currency of the Future?"* in *Providence Business News (Vol. 28, January 6, 2014, No. 40, pp. 1)*
Pub: American City Business Journals, Inc.
Contact: Mike Olivieri, Executive Vice President
URL(s): pbn.com/bitcoin-killer-app-or-the-currency-of-the-future94158
Description: The Providence Bitcoin Meetup has gathered several technology experts to discuss Bitcoin, the popular digital currency. However, software developers, engineers and entrepreneurs see Bitcoin as the next killer app for the Internet and is changing how information and data is stored, shared and verified. The Bitcoin's impact in Rhode Island is examined. **Availability:** Online. **Telecommunication Services:** Anderson@pbn.com.

26229 ■ *"Blog Buzz Heralds Arrival of IPhone 2.0"* in *Advertising Age (Vol. 79, June 9, 2008, No. 40, pp. 8)*
Pub: Crain Communications, Inc.
Contact: Jessica Botos, Manager, Marketing
E-mail: jessica.botos@crainsnewyork.com
Ed: Abbey Klaassen. **Description:** Predictions concerning the next version of the iPhone include a global-positioning-system technology as well as a configuration to run on a faster, 3G network. **Availability:** Online.

26230 ■ *"Boom has Tech Grads Mulling Their Options"* in *Globe & Mail (March 14, 2006, pp. B1)*
Ed: Grant Robertson. **Description:** Internet giant Google Inc. has stepped up its efforts to hire the talented people, in Canada, at Waterloo University in southern Ontario, to expand its operations. The details of the job market and increasing salaries are analyzed. **Availability:** Online.

26231 ■ *"Border Boletin: UA to Take Lie-Detector Kiosk to Poland"* in *Arizona Daily Star (September 14, 2010)*
Pub: Arizona Daily Star
Contact: John D'Orlando, President
E-mail: jdorlando@tucson.com
Ed: Brady McCombs. **Description:** University of Arizona's National Center for Border Security and Immigration Research will send a team to Warsaw, Poland to show border guards from 27 European Union countries the center's Avatar Kiosk. The Avatar technology is designed for use at border ports and airports to assist Customs officers detect individuals who are lying. **Availability:** Print; Online.

26232 ■ *"Branding Your Way"* in *Canadian Business (Vol. 80, February 12, 2007, No. 4, pp. 31)*
Description: The trend in involving consumers in brand marketing by seeking their views through contests or inviting them to produce and submit commercials through Internet is discussed. **Availability:** Online.

26233 ■ *"Breaking from Tradition Techstyle"* in *Providence Business News (Vol. 28, March 17, 2014, No. 50, pp. 1)*
Pub: American City Business Journals, Inc.
Contact: Mike Olivieri, Executive Vice President
Released: March 15, 2014. **Description:** Providence, Rhode Island's Techstyle Haus is being constructed by a group of students from Brown University. The textile house features a flexible exterior that uses high-performance materials and solar cells. Techstyle Haus is one of two entries from the U.S. competing in the Solar Decathlon Europe 2014. **Availability:** Print; Online.

26234 ■ *"Brisk Activity in North Fulton Office Market"* in *Atlanta Business Chronicle (July 11, 2014, pp. 2B)*
Description: Activity appears to have pickup up briskly in the North Fulton office market during the first six months of 2014, mainly due to the high profile deals involving major players in the technology and health care sectors. **Availability:** Print; Online.

26235 ■ *"Can Slow and Steady Win the Eco-Devo Race?"* in *Birmingham Business Journal (Vol. 31, June 6, 2014, No. 23, pp. 8)*
Pub: American City Business Journals, Inc.
Contact: Mike Olivieri, Executive Vice President
Released: Weekly. **Price:** $4, introductory 4-week offer(Digital & Print). **Description:** Evonik Corporation's expansion in Birmingham, Alabama reflects the city's economic development strategy. The company's creation of 25 jobs may be replicated by other companies. Birmingham is serious about becoming a biotechnology hub. **Availability:** Print; Online.

26236 ■ *"Can Tech Industry Share Wealth?"* in *Puget Sound Business Journal (Vol. 35, May 23, 2014, No. 5, pp. 10)*
Pub: American City Business Journals, Inc.
Contact: Mike Olivieri, Executive Vice President
Description: Nearly 700 local technology leaders gathered at the annual State of Technology event organized by Tech Alliance in Washington in May 2014. Trade show speaker, Geoffrey Moore, emphasized the role of the technology industry as a driver of local economies. **Availability:** Online.

26237 ■ *"Can You Hear Them Now?"* in *Hawaii Business (Vol. 54, August 2008, No. 2, pp. 48)*
Description: Coral Wireless LLC (dba Mobi PCS) is ranked 237 in Hawaii Business' list of the state's top 250 companies for 2008. The company is a local wireless phone provider, which has expanded its market to Oahu, Maui and the Big Island since opening in 2006, offering 13 phones and unlimited texts and calls. Details on the company's sales are provided. **Availability:** Print; Online.

26238 ■ *"Capital Coming Into City, but Local Money Lags"* in *Pittsburgh Business Times* **(Vol. 33, March 21, 2014, No. 36, pp. 4)**
Pub: American City Business Journals, Inc.
Contact: Mike Olivieri, Executive Vice President
Released: Weekly. **Price:** $4, Introductory 4-week offer(Digital & Print). **Description:** The strong investment market in Pittsburgh, Pennsylvania was fueled by capital from a combination of angel, venture, corporate and other sources, attracting $338 million in capital to finance 148 deals in 2013, but local money is lagging behind. Lynette Horrell of Ernst & Young notes that local money is not keeping up with the growth of technology companies in Pittsburgh. **Availability:** Print; Online.

26239 ■ *"Catch the Wind Announces Filing of Injunction Against Air Data Systems LLC and Philip Rogers"* in *CNW Group* **(September 30, 2011)**
Pub: CNW Group Ltd.
Description: Catch the Wind, providers of laser-based wind sensor products and technology, filed an injunction against Optical Air Data Systems (OADS) LLC and its former President and CEO Philip L. Rogers. The complaint seeks to have OADS and Rogers return tangible and intangible property owned by Catch the Wind, which the firm believes to be critical to the operations of their business. **Availability:** Online.

26240 ■ *"Catch the Wind to Hold Investor Update Conference Call on October 18, 2011"* in *CNW Group* **(October 4, 2011)**
Pub: CNW Group Ltd.
Description: Catch the Wind Ltd., providers of laser-based wind sensor products and technology, held a conference call for analysts and institutional investors. The high-growth technology firm is headquartered in Manassas, Virginia. **Availability:** Print; Online.

26241 ■ *"CBC Eyes Partners for TV Downloads"* in *Globe & Mail* **(February 9, 2006, pp. B1)**
Description: The details on Canadian Broadcasting Corp.'s distribution agreement with Google Inc. and Apple Computer Inc. are presented. **Availability:** Online.

26242 ■ *"CEO Forecast: With Cloudy Economy, Executives Turn to Government Contracting"* in *Hispanic Business* **(January-February 2009, pp. 34, 36)**
Ed: Jessica Haro, Richard Kaplan. **Description:** As economic uncertainty fogs the future, executives turn to government contracts in order to boost business. Revenue sources, health care challenges, environmental consulting and remediation services, as well as technological strides are discussed. **Availability:** Print; Online.

26243 ■ *"Certification Experts Germanischer Lloyd Wind Energy Assist NaiKun's Offshore Wind Project"* in *Marketwired* **(May 14, 2007)**
Pub: Comtex News Network Inc.
Contact: Kan Devnani, President
Description: Germanischer Lloyd Wind Energy (GL Wind) will examine, inspect, and provide quality management services for the engineering, design, and construction of the offshore wind project planned by NaiKun Wind Development Inc. in northwest British Columbia. **Availability:** Online.

26244 ■ *"China Vs the World: Whose Technology Is It?"* in *Harvard Business Review* **(Vol. 88, December 2010, No. 12, pp. 94)**
Pub: Harvard Business Publishing
Contact: Diane Belcher, Managing Director
Ed: Thomas M. Hout, Pankaj Ghemawat. **Price:** $8.95, PDF. **Description:** Examination of the regulation the Chinese government is implementing that require foreign corporations wishing to do business in the country to give up their new technologies. These regulations avoid World Trade Organization technology transfer provisions and complicate the convergence of socialism and capitalism. **Availability:** Online; PDF.

26245 ■ *"The Chips Are In"* in *Business Journal-Portland* **(Vol. 24, November 2, 2007, No. 35, pp. 1)**
Description: The $30 million funding round of Ambric Inc., which brings a total investment of $51 million, is about to close, and its clients are releasing over half-dozen products containing Ambric chips in January 2008. The features of Ambric's semiconductors, its market sectors and market positioning, as well as its investor relations, are discussed. **Availability:** Online.

26246 ■ *"Clash of the Titans"* in *Canadian Business* **(Vol. 80, March 12, 2007, No. 6, pp. 27)**
Description: The frequent allegations of Google Inc. and Microsoft Corp. against each other over copyright and other legal issues, with a view to taking away other's market share, is discussed. **Availability:** Print; Online.

26247 ■ *"Cloud City: An Industry - and a Region - On the Rise"* in *Puget Sound Business Journal* **(Vol. 34, February 28, 2014, No. 46, pp. 4)**
Pub: American City Business Journals, Inc.
Contact: Mike Olivieri, Executive Vice President
Description: Seattle, Washington is experiencing an influx of the world's most innovative cloud companies. Businesses are shifting their applications from in-house servers or private data center into public cloud infrastructure, which is less expensive than buying the servers and managing the data systems. Seattle software companies are taking advantage of this trend and developing products. **Availability:** Online.

26248 ■ *"Clusters Last Stand?"* in *Canadian Electronics* **(Vol. 23, February 2008, No. 1, pp. 6)**
Description: Survival of technology clusters was the focus of Strategic Microelectronics Council's conference entitled, "The Power of Community: Building Technology Clusters in Canada". Clusters can help foster growth in the microelectronics sector, and it was recognized that government intervention is needed to maintain these clusters. **Availability:** Download; PDF; Online.

26249 ■ *"CommScope and Comsearch to Showcase Innovative Wind Power Solutions at WINDPOWER 2012 in Atlanta"* in *Benzinga.com* **(May 31, 2012)**
Pub: Benzinga.com
Contact: Jason Raznick, Founder
Ed: Aaron Wise. **Description:** CommScope Inc. and its subsidiary CommScope will highlight their complete wind power solution products during the WIND-POWER 2012 Conference and Exhibition in Atlanta, Georgia this year. CommScope's wind power products include fiber optic cabling solutions, while Commsearch offers wind energy services that address the siting challenges resulting from complex telecommunications issues. **Availability:** Print; PDF; Online.

26250 ■ *"Conferencing Takes on High-Tech Futuristic Feel"* in *Crain's Cleveland Business* **(Vol. 28, October 29, 2007, No. 43, pp. 17)**
Pub: Crain Communications Inc.
Contact: K. C. Crain, President
Ed: Chuck Soder. **Description:** Overview of the newest technologies which are making local company's meetings more effective including: tele-presence, a videoconferencing technology, as well as virtual flip charts. **Availability:** Online.

26251 ■ *"Congestion Relief: The Land Use Alternative"* in *Canadian Business* **(Vol. 80, February 12, 2007, No. 4, pp. 31)**
Description: The development of a satellite-based system for traffic management including paying for parking fees by Skymeter Corp. is discussed. **Availability:** Download; PDF.

26252 ■ *"Consumers Turned Off? Not at Best Buy"* in *Barron's* **(Vol. 88, March 24, 2008, No. 12, pp. 29)**
Pub: Dow Jones & Company Inc.
Contact: Almar Latour, Chief Executive Officer
Ed: Sandra Ward. **Description:** Shares of Best Buy, trading at $42.41 each, are expected to rise to an average of $52 a share due to the company's solid fundamentals. The company's shares have fallen 20 percent from their 52-week high and are attractive given the company's bright prospects in the video game sector and high-definition video. **Availability:** Online.

26253 ■ *"Conversations Need to Yield Actions Measured in Dollars"* in *Advertising Age* **(Vol. 79, July 7, 2008, No. 26, pp. 18)**
Pub: Crain Communications, Inc.
Contact: Jessica Botos, Manager, Marketing
E-mail: jessica.botos@crainsnewyork.com
Ed: Jonathan Salem Baskin. **Description:** New ways in which to market to consumers are discussed. **Availability:** Online.

26254 ■ *"CradlePoint Is Adding Workers, Seeking More Space"* in *Idaho Business Review* **(September 3, 2014)**
Pub: BridgeTower Media
Contact: Adam Reinebach, President
Price: $11.99, Print, Digital & Mobile(1 Month); 149, Print, Digital & Mobile(1 Year); 99, Digital & Mobile Only(1 Year); $99, Digital & Mobile Only(For 1 Year); $9.95, Print, Digital & Mobile (For 1 Month Intro Rate); $149, Print, Digital & Mobile(For 1 Year). **Description:** CradlePoint makes networking routers and software, focusing on security for businesses. The firm is hiring new workers at a rate higher than predicted and is seeking new office space in downtown Boise, Idaho. CradlePoint is a major player in the growing wireless service and cloud platform market and is growing faster than its competitors. **Availability:** Print; Online.

26255 ■ *"Creating Health-Tech Opportunity"* in *Providence Business News* **(Vol. 29, April 14, 2014, No. 2, pp. 1)**
Pub: American City Business Journals, Inc.
Contact: Mike Olivieri, Executive Vice President
Released: April 12, 2014. **Description:** MedMates has officially launched, in April 2013, as Rhode Island's first group for networking and advocacy in health technology. MedMates now have 410 members that span every sector of health technology and its membership is not exclusive to the private sector. Insights into MedMates' first year success are also presented. **Availability:** Print; Online.

26256 ■ *Crossing the Chasm: Marketing and Selling Disruptive Products to Mainstream Customers*
Pub: HarperCollins Publishers L.L.C.
Contact: Brian Murray, President
Ed: Geoffrey A. Moore. **Released:** 3rd edition. **Price:** $21.99, paperback; $11.99, e-book. **Description:** A guide for marketing in high-technology industries, focusing on the Internet. **Availability:** E-book; Print.

26257 ■ *"Danaher to Acquire Tectronix for $2.8 Billion"* in *Canadian Electronics* **(Vol. 22, November-December 2007, No. 7, pp. 1)**
Description: Leading supplier of measurement, test and monitoring equipment Tektronix will be acquired by Danaher Corporation for $2.8 billion. Tektronix products are expected to complement Danaher's test equipment sector. The impacts of the deal on Tektronix shareholders and Danaher's operations are discussed. **Availability:** Print; Online.

26258 ■ *"Deals Dip In Florida Amid Squabbles Over Price"* in *South Florida Business Journal* **(Vol. 34, May 30, 2014, No. 45, pp. 4)**
Pub: American City Business Journals, Inc.
Contact: Mike Olivieri, Executive Vice President

Released: Weekly. **Price:** $8, introductory 4-week offer(Digital only). **Description:** Private equity firm investments in local companies in Florida dropped from 146 in 2012 to 135 in 2013. James Cassel of Cassel, Salpeter and Company, says companies in the information technology and health care sectors have been acquired because of strong multiples of their book value. **Availability:** Print; Online.

26259 ■ *"Detroit Hosts Conferences on Green Building, IT, Finance"* in Crain's Detroit Business (Vol. 25, June 1, 2009, No. 22, pp. 9)
Pub: Crain Communications Inc.
Contact: Barry Asin, President
Ed: Tom Henderson. **Description:** Detroit will host three conferences in June 2009, one features green technology, one information technology and the third will gather black bankers and financial experts from across the nation. **Availability:** Online.

26260 ■ *"Digital Duplication"* in Crain's Cleveland Business (Vol. 28, October 1, 2007, No. 39, pp. 3)
Pub: Crain Communications Inc.
Contact: K. C. Crain, President
Ed: David Bennett. **Description:** Profile of the business plan of eBlueprint Holdings LLC, a reprographics company that found success by converting customers' paper blueprints to an electronic format; the company plans to expand into other geographic markets by acquiring solid reprographics companies and converting their computer systems so that customers' blueprints can be managed electronically. **Availability:** Online.

26261 ■ *"Digital Marketing: Integrating Strategy and Tactics with Values, A Guidebook for Executives, Managers, and Students"*
Pub: Routledge, Taylor & Francis Group
Released: First edition. **Price:** $59.95, Paperback- $47.96; $190, Hardback - $152; $29.98, e-book. **Description:** Guidebook filled with information on the latest digital marketing tactics and strategic insights to help small businesses generate sustainable growth and achieve competitive advantage through digital integration. A five-step program: mindset, model, strategy, implementation, and sustainability is explained. **Availability:** E-book; Print.

26262 ■ *"Digital Power Management and the PMBus"* in Canadian Electronics (Vol. 23, June-July 2008, No. 4, pp. 8)
Pub: Annex Buisness Media
Contact: Mike Fredericks, President
Ed: Torbjorn Holmberg. **Description:** PMBus is an interface that can be applied to a variety of devices including power management devices. Information on digital power management products using this interface are also provided. **Availability:** Print; Online.

26263 ■ *"Dr. Melanie Brown"* in Women in Business (Vol. 65, Winter 2013, No. 3, pp. 40)
Description: Milestones in the career of Melanie Brown, PhD, are highlighted in light of her selection as the 2014 American Business Woman of American Business Women's Association (ABWA). An ABWA member since 2007, Dr. Brown is also the Information Technology Strategic and Analytics Manager at CenterPoint Energy. **Availability:** Print; Online.

26264 ■ *"Dougherty: AuthenTec Embedded Security Business Building Momentum"* in Benzinga.com (March 5, 2012)
Pub: Benzinga.com
Contact: Jason Raznick, Founder
Ed: Delores Land. **Description:** According to research conducted by Dougherty & Company, AuthenTec Inc.'s embedded security business is waiting for the fingerprint sensor businesss is completely developed. **Availability:** Online.

26265 ■ *"Downturn Tests HCL's Pledge to Employees"* in Workforce Management (Vol. 88, November 16, 2009, No. 12, pp. 23)
Pub: Crain Communications Inc.
Contact: Barry Asin, President

Ed: Ed Frauenheim. **Description:** HCL Technologies has kept its promise to keep from laying any employees off during the recession which served as a test for the tech firm's Employee First program, which seeks to give workers greater income security as well as a stronger voice in the firm. **Availability:** Online.

26266 ■ *"Economy: The Case for a Bright Future"* in Canadian Business (Vol. 83, July 20, 2010, No. 11-12, pp. 58)
Pub: Rogers Media Inc.
Contact: Neil Spivak, Chief Executive Officer
Ed: Andrew Potter. **Description:** Writer Matt Ridley argues that trade is the determinant of development and that it is the reason why humans got rich. Ridley believes that the important innovations are often low-tech and is often processes rather than products. **Availability:** Print; Online.

26267 ■ Electronic Commerce
Ed: Gary P. Schneider, Bryant Chrzan, Charles McCormick. **Released:** 12th edition. **Price:** $29.49, e-book. **Description:** E-commerce can open the door to more opportunities than ever before for small business. Packed with real-world examples and cases, the book delivers comprehensive coverage of emerging online technologies and trends and their influence on the electronic marketplace. It details how the landscape of online commerce is evolving, reflecting changes in the economy and how business and society are responding to those changes. Balancing technological issues with the strategic business aspects of successful e-commerce, the new edition includes expanded coverage of international issues, social networking, mobile commerce, Web 2.0 technologies, and updates on spam, phishing, and identity theft. **Availability:** Print.

26268 ■ *"Electronics Assembly"* in Canadian Electronics (Vol. 23, February 2008, No. 1, pp. 12)
Description: I&J Fisnar Inc. has launched a new system of bench top dispensing robots while Vitronics Soltec and KIC have introduced a new reflow soldering machine. Teknek, on the other hand, has announced a new product, called the CM10, which an be used in cleaning large format substrates. Other new products and their description are presented. **Availability:** Print; Online.

26269 ■ *"The End of RIM"* in Canadian Business (Vol. 85, August 13, 2012, No. 13, pp. 22)
Ed: Joe Castaldo. **Description:** The potential implications of the collapse of Research in Motion (RIM) on the Canadian technology sector are examined. The country is expected to lose its biggest training ground for technology talent without RIM, but the company's decline will not stop Canadians from trying to build and sustain multinational technolgy companies. **Availability:** Print; Online.

26270 ■ *"Energy Boom Spurring Manufacturing Growth"* in Pittsburgh Business Times (Vol. 33, May 2, 2014, No. 42, pp. 7)
Pub: American City Business Journals, Inc.
Contact: Mike Olivieri, Executive Vice President
Released: May 02, 2014. **Price:** $4, introductory 4-week offer(Digital only). **Description:** The manufacturing and energy technology sectors both showed strong growth, according to the Pittsburgh Technology Council in Pennsylvania. Data shows that the sectors added about 7,000 jobs as a result of the growth in the Marcellus Shale from 2010 to 2012. **Availability:** Print; Online.

26271 ■ *"EOTech Product Improves Holographic Gun Sights"* in Crain's Detroit Business (Vol. 24, February 4, 2008, No. 5, pp. 9)
Pub: Crain Communications Inc.
Contact: Barry Asin, President

Ed: Chad Halcom. **Description:** L-3 Communications EOTech Inc. procured new business contracts to fulfill military and law enforcement's demand for improved holographic sites used on handheld weapons. **Availability:** Online.

26272 ■ *"Executive Decision: XM Mulls Betting the Bank in Competitive Game of Subscriber Growth"* in Globe & Mail (March 18, 2006, pp. B3)
Ed: Grant Robertson. **Description:** Canadian Satellite Radio Inc., XM Canada, president and Chief Operating Officer Stephen Tapp feel that establishing a profile in satellite radio to attract subscribers is a very big challenge. His views on the Canadian radio market are detailed. **Availability:** Print; Online.

26273 ■ *"Far Out: Satellite Radio Finds New Way to Tally Listeners"* in Globe & Mail (March 14, 2007, pp. B14)
Description: The marketing strategy adopted by satellite radio broadcasting firm XM Satellite Radio Inc. in Canada for increasing its subscriber based is discussed. **Availability:** Online.

26274 ■ *"Firm Raises City's Largest VC Fund In 3 Years"* in Dallas Business Journal (Vol. 35, July 20, 2012, No. 45, pp. 1)
Pub: Baltimore Business Journal
Contact: Rhonda Pringle, President
E-mail: rpringle@bizjournals.com
Ed: Jeff Bounds. **Description:** Trailblazer Capital has raised $25 million in commitments for its second fund, the largest fund raised by a Dallas-Fort Worth Metropolitan Area-based ventury company since at least 2009. VC funding has been uncommon in the area since the technology and telecom bubble burst in 2000 and 2001. Insights into Trailblazer's approach to investing is provided. **Availability:** Print; Online.

26275 ■ *"First Impressions of Robotic Farming Systems"* in Farm Industry News (September 30, 2011)
Pub: Informa Business Media, Inc.
Contact: Charlie McCurdy, President
Ed: Jodie Wehrspann. **Description:** Farm Science Review featured tillage tools and land rollers, including John Deere's GPS system where a cart tractor is automatically controlled as well as a new line of Kinze's carts and a video of their robotic system for a driver-less cart tractor. **Availability:** Print; Online.

26276 ■ *"FIS-Metavante Deal Paying Off for Many"* in Business Journal-Milwaukee (Vol. 28, December 17, 2010, No. 11, pp. A1)
Pub: The Business Journal
Contact: Heather Ladage, President
E-mail: hladage@bizjournals.com
Ed: Rich Kirchen. **Description:** Jacksonville, Florida-based Fidelity National Information Services Inc., also known as FIS, has remained committed to Milwaukee, Wisconsin more than a year after purchasing Metavante Technologies Inc. FIS has transferred several operations into Metropolitan Milwaukee and has continued its contribution to charitable organizations in the area. **Availability:** Print; Online.

26277 ■ *"For Apple, It's Showtime Again"* in Barron's (Vol. 90, August 30, 2010, No. 35, pp. 29)
Pub: Barron's Editorial & Corporate Headquarters
Ed: Eric J. Savitz. **Description:** Speculations on what Apple Inc. will unveil at its product launch event are presented. These products include a possible new iPhone Nano, a new update to its Apple TV, and possibly a deal with the Beatles to distribute their songs over iTunes. **Availability:** Online.

26278 ■ *"'Frozen' Assets: Refrigeration Goes High Tech as Hussmann Invests $7 Million in Global Hub"* in St. Louis Business Journal (Vol. 33, September 21, 2012, No. 4, pp. 1)
Pub: Baltimore Business Journal
Contact: Rhonda Pringle, President
E-mail: rpringle@bizjournals.com

Description: Hussmann Corporation is spending $7 million to create a high-tech innovation and clients collaboration center that will be called Global Hub, a venue for grocery food retailers, industry trend setters and through leaders. The company is also focusing on tapping the potential of convenience marts and dollar-store retailers. **Availability:** Print.

26279 ■ *"Full-Court Press for Apple"* in *Barron's* (Vol. 88, March 24, 2008, No. 12, pp. 47)
Pub: Dow Jones & Company Inc.
Contact: Almar Latour, Chief Executive Officer
Ed: Mark Veverka. **Description:** Apple Inc. is facing more intellectual property lawsuits in 2008, with 30 patent lawsuits filed compared to 15 in 2007 and nine in 2006. The lawsuits, which involve products such as the iPod and the iPhone, present some concern for Apple's shareholders. **Availability:** Online.

26280 ■ *"Funders Fuel Explosion of Biotech Activity"* in *Puget Sound Business Journal* (Vol. 35, July 11, 2014, No. 12, pp. 3A)
Pub: American City Business Journals, Inc.
Contact: Mike Olivieri, Executive Vice President
Description: Washington's life sciences industry is experiencing problems due to a lack of support from state lawmakers, but the industry is receiving capital through initial public offerings, partnerships and venture equity. Joel Marcus of Alexandria Real Estate Equities claims that capital flows are at their highest levels since the dot-com bubble. **Availability:** Online.

26281 ■ *"Funds "Friend" Facebook"* in *Barron's* (Vol. 89, July 27, 2009, No. 30, pp. 30)
Pub: Dow Jones & Company Inc.
Contact: Almar Latour, Chief Executive Officer
Ed: Leslie P. Norton. **Description:** Mutual-fund companies are the latest entrants to the "social media" space and several companies have already set up Facebook and Twitter pages. The use of this technology pose special challenges for compliance and regulators especially since the Financial Industry Regulatory Authority reminds companies that advertising, sales and literature are governed by regulations. **Availability:** Online.

26282 ■ *"The Future of Work"* in *Black Enterprise* (Vol. 41, August 2010, No. 1, pp. 65)
Pub: Earl G. Graves Ltd.
Contact: Earl Graves, Jr., President
Ed: Annya M. Lott. **Description:** Technology, globalization, and outsourcing will continue to shape the future of work. Social media is a means for small companies to market goods and services. **Availability:** Online.

26283 ■ *"The Future of Work"* in *Business Strategy Review* (Vol. 21, Autumn 2010, No. 3, pp. 16)
Pub: Wiley-Blackwell
Ed: Lynda Gratton. **Released:** August 28, 2017. **Description:** Work is universal. But how, why, where and when we work has never been so open to individual interpretation. The certainties of the past have been replaced by ambiguity, questions and the steady hum of technology. Now, in a groundbreaking research project covering 21 global companies and more than 200 executives, the author is making sense of the future of work. **Availability:** Print; PDF; Online.

26284 ■ *"Gadget Makers Aim for New Chapter in Reading"* in *Crain's Cleveland Business* (Vol. 28, October 22, 2007, No. 42, pp. 20)
Pub: Crain Communications Inc.
Contact: K. C. Crain, President
Ed: Jennifer McKevitt. **Description:** Although e-books and e-audiobooks are becoming more popular, e-readers, devices that display digital books, still haven't caught on with the public. Experts feel that consumers, many of whom have to look at a computer screen all day for work, still like the feel of a real book in their hands. **Availability:** Online.

26285 ■ *"Game On: When Work Becomes Play"* in *Canadian Business* (Vol. 80, February 12, 2007, No. 4, pp. 15)
Description: The plan of president of TransGaming Vikas Gupta to create innovative software programs for games that can be played in different operating systems is discussed. **Availability:** Online.

26286 ■ *"Game Plan: The Business of Bingo"* in *Canadian Business* (Vol. 79, September 11, 2006, No. 18, pp. 50)
Ed: Joe Castaldo. **Released:** September 08, 2016. **Description:** Strategies adopted by gaming companies to revitalize their business and give a stimulus to their falling resources are presented. **Availability:** Print; Online.

26287 ■ *"Globalization: Canada Tomorrow"* in *Canadian Business* (Vol. 80, October 8, 2007, No. 20, pp. 14)
Description: An assessment of Canada's future in terms of its educational, social, and economic environment is presented. Concerns regarding the country's educational system such as the declining interest in science and technology and the possible lack of teachers in the future are discussed. In terms of its social and economic aspects, the need to support entrepreneurs and other qualified people is explained. **Availability:** Online.

26288 ■ *"The Globe: Singapore Airlines' Balancing Act"* in *Harvard Business Review* (Vol. 88, July-August 2010, No. 7-8, pp. 145)
Pub: Harvard Business Publishing
Contact: Diane Belcher, Managing Director
Ed: Loizos Heracleous, Jochen Wirtz. **Price:** $8.95. **Description:** Singapore Airlines is used as an illustration of organizational effectiveness. The article includes the firm's 4-3-3 rule of spending, its promotion of centralized as well as decentralized innovation, use of technology, and strategic planning. **Availability:** Online; PDF.

26289 ■ *A Golden Opportunity in Crisis? Decoding Agri-Tech Post Pandemic*
URL(s): economictimes.indiatimes.com/small-biz/star tups/newsbuzz/a-golden-opportunity-in-crisis-deco ding-agri-tech-post-pandemic/articleshow/75499858 .cms?from=mdr
Ed: Pankajj Ghode. **Released:** May 02, 2020. **Description:** Discusses the need for agribusiness to transition from traditional methods to incorporating technology to ensure healthy food production as well as continued revenue. **Availability:** Online.

26290 ■ *"Google Places a Call to Bargain Hunters"* in *Advertising Age* (Vol. 79, September 29, 2008, No. 36, pp. 13)
Pub: Crain Communications, Inc.
Contact: Jessica Botos, Manager, Marketing
E-mail: jessica.botos@crainsnewyork.com
Ed: Abbey Klaassen. **Description:** Google highlighted application developers who have created tools for its Android mobile phone in the device's unveiling; applications such as ShopSavvy and CompareEverywhere help shoppers to find bargains by allowing them to compare prices in their local areas and across the web. **Availability:** Online.

26291 ■ *"Google's Next Stop: Below 350?"* in *Barron's* (Vol. 88, March 10, 2008, No. 10, pp. 17)
Pub: Dow Jones & Company Inc.
Contact: Almar Latour, Chief Executive Officer
Ed: Jacqueline Doherty. **Description:** Share prices of Google Inc. are expected to drop from their level of $433 each to below $350 per share. The company is expected to miss its earnings forecast for the first quarter of 2008, and its continued aggressive spending on non-core areas will eventually bring down earnings. **Availability:** Online.

26292 ■ *"Grant Could Help Schools Harness Wind"* in *Dallas Business Journal* (Vol. 37, April 11, 2014, No. 31, pp. 8)
Pub: American City Business Journals, Inc.
Contact: Mike Olivieri, Executive Vice President
Released: Weekly. **Price:** $4, introductory 4-week offer(Digital only); $4, introductory 4-week offer(Digital & Print). **Description:** Five universities led by Texas A&M have received a $2.2 million grant from the Texas Emerging Technologies Fund for use in wind technology research. The research will focus on turbines that feature bigger blades to capture more wind. Technology developed by the universities will eventually be handed to the state. **Availability:** Print; Online.

26293 ■ *"Greg Lueck: Glass Blowing"* in *Inc.* (Volume 32, December 2010, No. 10, pp. 36)
Pub: Mansueto Ventures L.L.C.
Contact: Stephanie Mehta, Chief Executive Officer
Ed: April Joyner. **Description:** Profile of Greg Lueck, partner and COO of Centerstance, a tech consulting firm in Portland, Oregon. Lueck opened Firehouse Glass, a studio that provides workspace and equipment for glass blowers. He says glass blowing serves as a welcome counterbalance to the cerebral work he does at the office. **Availability:** Online.

26294 ■ *Groundswell: Winning in a World Transformed by Social Technologies*
Pub: Harvard Business Review Press
Contact: Moderna V. Pfizer, Contact
Ed: Charlene Li, Josh Bernoff. **Released:** June 09, 2011. **Price:** $22, paperback/softbound. **Description:** Individuals are using online social technologies such as blogs, social networking sites, YouTube, and podcasts to discuss products and companies, write their own news, and find their own deals. When consumers you've never met are rating your company's products in public forums with which you have no experience or influence, your company is vulnerable. This book teaches the tools and data necessary to turn this treat into an opportunity. **Availability:** E-book; Print.

26295 ■ *"The Hard Thing About Hard Things: Building a Business When There Are No Easy Answers"*
Pub: HarperCollins Publishers L.L.C.
Contact: Brian Murray, President
Released: 2014. **Price:** $29.99, Hardcover; $14.99, E-book; $23.99, Digital Audiobook Unabridged. **Description:** Cofounder of Andreessen Horowitz and well-respected Silicon Valley entrepreneur, offers advice for building and running a startup small business. Horowitz analyzes issues confronting leaders daily and shares insights he gained from managing, selling, buying investing in, and supervising technology firms. **Availability:** E-book; Print; Download.

26296 ■ *"Has Microsoft Found a Way to Get at Yahoo?"* in *Advertising Age* (Vol. 79, July 7, 2008, No. 26, pp. 4)
Pub: Crain Communications, Inc.
Contact: Jessica Botos, Manager, Marketing
E-mail: jessica.botos@crainsnewyork.com
Ed: Abbey Klaassen. **Description:** Microsoft's attempt to acquire Yahoo's search business is discussed as is Yahoo's plans for the future at a time when the company's shares have fallen dangerously low. **Availability:** Print; Online.

26297 ■ *"HBSDealer Stock Watch: In the FAST Lane"* in *Chain Store Age* (Vol. 85, November 2009, No. 11, pp. 44)
Ed: Samantha Murphy. **Description:** Quick Chek, which operates some 120 convenience stores in New Jersey and southern New York, is testing a new self-checkout system in order to examine how speed affects its in-store experience. **Availability:** Online.

26298 ■ *"High-Tech Job-Apalooza!"* in *Orlando Business Journal* (Vol. 26, January 15, 2010, No. 33, pp. 1)
Pub: Orlando Business Journal
Contact: Julie Swyers, Director
E-mail: jswyers@bizjournals.com
Ed: Christopher Boyd. **Description:** Science Applications International Corporation, Saab Training USA LLC, CAE USA, and Pelliconi &C.SPA attempt to obtain $939,000 in tax incentives to generate 222 technology and defense-related jobs in Orange

GENERAL SMALL BUSINESS TOPICS

County, Florida. Each job will provide an average salary of $67,000. Future plans of each technology and defense firm are also presented. **Availability:** Print; Online.

26299 ■ *"Hope Grows for a Muscular Dystrophy Drug"* in *Barron's (Vol. 92, August 25, 2012, No. 35, pp. 35)*
Pub: Dow Jones & Company Inc.
Contact: Almar Latour, Chief Executive Officer

Ed: Andrew Bary. **Description:** The stocks of biotechnology firm Sarepta Therapeutics could gain value if trials for eterpirsen, a drug being developed for Duchenne muscular dystrophy, are successful. The company's stock prices could rise from $10/share to as high as $26/share. **Availability:** Online.

26300 ■ *"Horse Race: Putting the App in Apple"* in *Inc. (Vol. 30, November 2008, No. 11)*
Pub: Mansueto Ventures L.L.C.
Contact: Stephanie Mehta, Chief Executive Officer

Ed: Nitasha Tiku. **Description:** Aftermarket companies are scrambling to develop games and widgets for Apple's iPhone. Apple launched a kit for developers interested in creating iPhone-specific software along with the App Store, and an iTunes spinoff. Profiles of various software programs that may be used on the iPhone are given. **Availability:** Online.

26301 ■ *"Houston Tech Company Eyes California for HQ Move"* in *Houston Business Journal (Vol. 45, July 18, 2014, No. 10, pp. 10A)*
Pub: American City Business Journals, Inc.
Contact: Mike Olivieri, Executive Vice President

Released: Weekly. **Price:** $4, Introductory 4-week offer(Digital & Print). **Description:** Ed Chipul, CEO of Tendenci, a longtime Houston technology company, has stated that they are looking for a headquarters move to California. The decision to move to Silicon Valley is mainly due to a lack of synergy within the venture capital community in Houston. **Availability:** Print; Online.

26302 ■ *"How Agritech Startups Are Boosting Agricultural Economy by Employing AI and Data Science - Expert Explains"* in *Zee Business (Nov. 12, 2021)*
URL(s): www.zeebiz.com/small-business/news-how-agritech-startups-are-boosting-agricultural-economy-by-employing-ai-and-data-science-expert-explains-170613

Ed: Prashant Singh. **Released:** November 12, 2021. **Description:** Explores the need for agritech startups to shift their operations from legacy structures to technology-driven solutions. **Availability:** Online.

26303 ■ *"How Church Street Exchange May Bring Retail, 350 Jobs"* in *Orlando Business Journal (Vol. 30, February 28, 2014, No. 36, pp. 10)*
Pub: American City Business Journals, Inc.
Contact: Mike Olivieri, Executive Vice President

Released: Weekly. **Price:** $8, introductory 4-week offer(Digital & Print). **Description:** Nonprofit organization, Canvs, is finalizing a lease for 14,069 square feet of technology-focused co-working space at Church Street Exchange in downtown Orlando, Florida. Jones Lang LaSalle is negotiating for more space than the 87,000-square-foot building has that could bring 300 to 350 high-tech jobs to the area. **Availability:** Print; Online.

26304 ■ *"How to Play the Tech Mergers"* in *Barron's (Vol. 90, August 30, 2010, No. 35, pp. 18)*
Pub: Barron's Editorial & Corporate Headquarters

Ed: Tiernan Ray. **Description:** The intense bidding by Hewlett-Packard and Dell for 3Par was foreseen in a previous Barron's cover story and 3Par's stock has nearly tripled since reported. Other possible acquisition targets in the tech industry include Brocade Communication Systems, NetApp, Xyratex, and Isilon Systems. **Availability:** Online.

26305 ■ *"IBM's Best-Kept Secret: It's Huge in Software Too"* in *Canadian Business (Vol. 79, September 25, 2006, No. 19, pp. 19)*
Description: The contribution of IBM vice-president Steve Mills in company's development is discussed. **Availability:** Print; Online.

26306 ■ *"Image Consultants"* in *Entrepreneur (June 2014)*
Pub: Entrepreneur Media Inc.
Contact: Dan Bova, Director
E-mail: dbova@entrepreneur.com

Description: The ASAP54 mobile application, created by a company of the same name, uses visual recognition technology to help users determine the name of the designer or retailer of a clothing item using photographs. The company has compiled a database consisting of more than 1 million products from its retail partners. It claims an average of 5 percent commission on purchases completed through the application. Other useful wearable gadgets include Nymi, which authenticates identities based on cardiac rhythms, and Netatmo, a bracelet that measures daily sun exposure. **Availability:** Online.

26307 ■ *"The Impact of Acquisitions On the Productivity of Inventors at Semiconductor Firms: A Synthesis of Knowledge-Based and Incentive-Based Perspective"* in *Academy of Management Journal (Vol. 50, No. 5, October 1, 2007, pp. 1133)*
Pub: Academy of Management
Contact: Sharon Alvarez, President

Ed: Rahul Kapoor, Kwanghui Lim. **Description:** Study examined the relation between knowledge-based and incentive-based outlook in explaining the impact of acquisitions on the productivity of inventors at acquired semiconductor firms. Results showed a definite relation between the two perspectives. **Availability:** Electronic publishing; Download; PDF; Online.

26308 ■ *"Incentives In Play for Astronautics"* in *Business Journal-Milwaukee (Vol. 28, November 5, 2010, No. 5, pp. A1)*
Pub: The Business Journal
Contact: Heather Ladage, President
E-mail: hladage@bizjournals.com

Ed: Sean Ryan. **Description:** Astronautics Corporation was offered incentives by local government officials in Milwaukee, Wisconsin and by Brewery Project LLC to move into a building in The Brewery in the city. The company's officials remain indecisive over the offers and incentives. **Availability:** Print; Online.

26309 ■ *"Information Technology Changes Roles, Highlights Hiring Needs"* in *South Florida Business Journal (Vol. 34, February 14, 2014, No. 30, pp. 3)*
Pub: American City Business Journals, Inc.
Contact: Mike Olivieri, Executive Vice President

Released: Weekly. **Price:** $8, Introductory 4-week offer(Digital & Print). **Description:** Results of the Steven Douglas Associates survey of 218 senior and mid-level information technology executives in South Florida are presented. About 75 percent of the respondents cited cloud services, mobile technologies, big data and enterprise reporting planning as having the most profound impact on their roles. The challenges they face with the expected hiring growth are also examined. **Availability:** Print; Online.

26310 ■ *Information Technology for the Small Business: How to Make IT Work For Your Company*
Description: Basics of information technology to help small companies maximize benefits are covered. Topics include pitfalls to avoid, email and Internet use, data backup, recovery and overall IT organization.

26311 ■ *"Ingrian and Channel Management International Sign Distribution Agreement"* in *Canadian Corporate News (May 16, 2007)*
Description: Channel Management International (CMI), a Canadian channel management and distribution company, and Ingrian Networks, Inc., the leading provider of data privacy solutions, announced a Canadian distribution agreement to resell Ingrian encryption solutions to the Canadian market. **Availability:** Online.

26312 ■ *"Innovation in 3D: NextFab"* in *Philadelphia Business Journal (Vol. 28, January 22, 2010, No. 49, pp. 1)*
Pub: Philadelphia Business Journal
Contact: Sierra Quinn, Director
E-mail: squinn@bizjournals.com

Ed: Peter Key. **Description:** NextFab Studio LLC is set to offer product development services using 3D technology. The company has developed a three-dimensional printer which fabricates objects usually made of plastic. **Availability:** Online.

26313 ■ *"Innovation Station"* in *Canadian Business (Vol. 80, October 8, 2007, No. 20, pp. 42)*
Description: Study and teaching of entrepreneurship at the University of Waterloo is discussed. Research projects in the university are expected to be influential in Canada's economic development. In spite of the success of these studies, financing is still a problem for the university, especially in technological innovations. **Availability:** Online.

26314 ■ *"Innovative Trauma Care Sets Up U.S. HQ in San Antonio"* in *San Antonio Business Journal (Vol. 26, August 31, 2012, No. 31, pp. 1)*
Pub: Baltimore Business Journal
Contact: Rhonda Pringle, President
E-mail: rpringle@bizjournals.com

Description: Canadian biotech firm Innovative Trauma Care (ITC) has selected San Antonio, Texas as the location of its new US headquarters. The selection could boost the reputation of San Antonio region as a hub for medical technology and trauma-related expertise. **Availability:** Print; Online.

26315 ■ *"Innovators Critical in Technical Economy"* in *Crain's Cleveland Business (Vol. 28, November 5, 2007, No. 44, pp. 10)*
Pub: Crain Communications Inc.
Contact: K. C. Crain, President

Ed: Peter Rea. **Description:** Discusses the importance to attract, develop and retain talented innovators on Ohio's economy. Also breaks down the four fronts on which the international battle for talent is being waged. **Availability:** Online.

26316 ■ *"Inside Waterloo's Quiet Tech Titan"* in *Canadian Business (Vol. 87, July 2014, No. 7, pp. 39)*
Description: OpenText chief executive officer Mark Barrenechea feels confident about the financial health of the Waterloo, Ontario-based software company. He adds that the company is exploring opportunities by the big data phenomenon. **Availability:** Online.

26317 ■ *"The Intel Trinity: How Robert Noyce, Gordon Moore, and Andy Grove Built the World's Most Important Company"*
Pub: Harper Business
Contact: Hollis Heimbouch, Senior Vice President Publisher

Released: July 15, 2014. **Price:** $34.99, hardcover; $11.74, e-book; $4.34, kindle; $19.42, hardcover; $4.30, hardcover(69 used from $4.30); $15.17, hardcover(56 new from $15.17); $19.99, hardcover(1 collectible from $19.99); $31.74, paperback; $22.95, paperback(10 used from $22.95); $19.13, paperback(4 new from $19.13). **Description:** A complete history of Intel Corporation, the essential company of the digital age, is presented. After over four decades Intel remains the most important company in the world, a defining company of the global digital economy. The inventors of the microprocessor that powers nearly every intelligent electronic device worldwide are profiled. These entrepreneurs made the personal computer, Internet, telecommunications, and personal electronics all possible. The challenges and successes of the company and its ability to maintain its dominance, its culture and its legacy are examined. **Availability:** E-book; Print; Online.

26318 ■ "Interactive Stores a Big Part of Borders' Turnaround Plan" in Crain's Detroit Business (Vol. 24, February 18, 2008, No. 7, pp. 4)
Pub: Crain Communications Inc.
Contact: Barry Asin, President

Ed: Nathan Skid. Description: Borders Group Inc. is using digital technology and interactive media as a part of the firm's turnaround plan. The digital store will allow shoppers to create CDs, download audio books, publish their own works, print photos and search family genealogy. Availability: Online.

26319 ■ "The Internet Of You" in Canadian Business (Vol. 87, July 2014, No. 7, pp. 43)
Description: Wearable computers like smart watches, fitness trackers, and bracelets like Nymi are starting to break down the barrier between human beings and the digital world. The Nymi is a wrist-worn device developed by Bionym that allows the wearer to be instantly recognizable to any wireless device. Availability: Online.

26320 ■ "Into the Groove: Fine-Tune Your Biz By Getting Into the Good Habit Groove" in Small Business Opportunities (Spring 2008)
Description: Profile of Ty Freyvogel and his consulting firm Freyvogel Communications. Freyvogel serves the telecommunications need of Fortune 500 and mid-sized businesses.

26321 ■ "Investment In Israel Is Investment in the Future of Georgia" in Atlanta Business Chronicle (May 30, 2014, pp. 22A)
Pub: American City Business Journals, Inc.
Contact: Mike Olivieri, Executive Vice President

Description: Georgia Governor Nathan Deal will travel to Israel to lead an economic and trade mission and consolidate Georgia's trade ties with Israel. Israel and the State of Georgia are already collaborating in the fields of health information technology, agrotechnology, homeland security, defense, aerospace and cybersecurity, and microelectronics and nanotechnology. The proposed visit by the Governor will build on this particular partnership from which both parties will benefit. Availability: Print; Online.

26322 ■ "Jacksonville Doing Well In Growing Economy" in Orlando Business Journal (Vol. 30, June 27, 2014, No. 53, pp. 8)
Pub: American City Business Journals, Inc.
Contact: Mike Olivieri, Executive Vice President

Released: June 27, 2014. Description: Jerry Mallot is the president of JaxUSA Partnership, the economic development arm of the Jax Chambers. According to Mallot, Northeast Florida's strongest selling points for business site or relocation there include advanced manufacturing, financial services, aviation and aerospace technology, life sciences, logistics and information technology.

26323 ■ "Keeping the Vehicle On the Road--A Survey On On-Road Lane Detection Systems" in ACM Computing Surveys (Vol. 46, Spring 2014, No. 1, pp. 2)
Pub: Association for Computing Machinery - University of Wyoming
Contact: Ed Seidel, President
E-mail: uwpres@uwyo.edu

Description: The development of wireless sensor networks, such as researchers Advanced Driver Assistance Systems (ADAS) requires the ability to analyze the road scene in the same as a human. Road scene analysis is an essential, complex, and challenging task and it consists of: road detection and obstacle detection. The detection of the road borders, the estimation of the road geometry, and the localization of the vehicle are essential tasks in this context since they are required for the lateral and longitudinal control of the vehicle. A comprehensive review of vision-based road detection systems vision in automobiles and trucks is examined. Availability: Online.

26324 ■ "Kineta Helps Grow Start Group of 5 Biotech Partners" in Puget Sound Business Journal (Vol. 35, June 13, 2014, No. 8, pp. 6)
Pub: American City Business Journals, Inc.
Contact: Mike Olivieri, Executive Vice President

Description: Kineta Inc is seeking new funding through its KPI Therapeutics. Kineta offers investors a return on their investments after three to five years. KPI Therapeutics is a new collaborative initiative between drug development firms and private investors. KPI's vision is to create a better way to develop early- and mid-stage therapies for patients and will act as an investment group and a strategic research hub. Availability: Print; Online.

26325 ■ "A League of Their Own" in St. Louis Business Journal (Vol. 32, May 4, 2012, No. 37, pp. 1)
Pub: Baltimore Business Journal
Contact: Rhonda Pringle, President
E-mail: rpringle@bizjournals.com

Description: Entrepreneurs Brian and Carol Matthews, Jim McKelvey and Rick Holton Jr. have partnered to create Cultivation Capital. The venture capital fund will target technology firms. Availability: Print; Online.

26326 ■ "Legislators Must Cut Cost of Government" in Crain's Detroit Business (Vol. 24, October 6, 2008, No. 40, pp. 6)
Pub: Crain Communications Inc.
Contact: Barry Asin, President

Description: Southeast and West Michigan business leaders are setting aside their differences and have proposed clear agendas, ranging from eliminating the Michigan Business Tax to overhauling public employee and retiree benefits and pensions. Lawmakers must also come together to find solutions for the state's economy and discover an entirely new vision for the future of Michigan business. Availability: Print; Online.

26327 ■ "Looks Like We Made It (In Philadelphia)" in Philadelphia Business Journal (Vol. 32, January 24, 2014, No. 50, pp. 4)
Pub: American City Business Journals, Inc.
Contact: Mike Olivieri, Executive Vice President

Released: Weekly. Price: $4, introductory 4-week offer(Digital & Print). Description: Philadelphia, Pennsylvania was once viewed as a manufacturing city, and its manufacturing workforce reached 365,000 in the early 1950s. The city is now focusing on advanced manufacturing that requires scientific and technical expertise. The decrease in the number of manufacturing jobs is also examined. Availability: Print; Online.

26328 ■ "Managing the Facebookers; Business" in The Economist (Vol. 390, January 3, 2009, No. 8612, pp. 10)
Pub: Economist Newspaper Ltd.
Contact: Lara Boro, Chief Executive Officer

Description: According to a report from PricewaterhouseCoopers, a business consultancy, workers from Generation Y, also known as the Net Generation, are more difficult to recruit and integrate into companies that practice traditional business acumen. 61 percent of chief executive managers say that they have trouble with younger employees who tend to be more narcissistic and more interested in personal fulfillment with a need for frequent feedback and an overprecise set of objectives on the path to promotion which can be hard for managers who are used to a different relationship with their subordinates. Older bosses should prepare to make some concessions to their younger talent since some of the issues that make them happy include cheaper online ways to communicate and additional coaching, both of which are good for business. Availability: Online.

26329 ■ "Many in Tech Look to Push More Community Involvement, But Not in Traditional Ways" in Boston Business Journal (Vol. 31, August 5, 2011, No. 28, pp. 1)
Pub: Boston Business Journal
Contact: Carolyn M. Jones, President

E-mail: cmjones@bizjournals.com
Ed: Mary Moore. Released: Weekly. Price: $4, Introductory 4-Week Offer(Digital Only). Description: Entrepreneurs and venture capitalists in Boston have launched Technology Underwriting Greater Good, the tech industry's answer to the criticism that they are not charitable. The foundation finances nonprofits that aid young people through entrepreneurship, education and life experience. Other tech firms in Boston doing charitable works are discussed. Availability: Print; Online.

26330 ■ "Mapping the Gender Gap" in Business Journal Portland (Vol. 31, April 25, 2014, No. 8, pp. 4)
Pub: American City Business Journals, Inc.
Contact: Mike Olivieri, Executive Vice President

Released: April 25, 2014. Price: $4, introductory 4-week offer(Digital & Print). Description: The level of gender equality in the health care, banking, technology and commercial real estate industries of Oregon is examined. Gender bias in the workplace is one significant reason behind the wage gap and the lack of women in leadership positions. Availability: Print; Mailing list; Online.

26331 ■ "Market and Technology Orientations for Service Delivery Innovation: the Link of Innovative Competence" in Journal of Business & Industrial Marketing (Vol. 29, July 2014, No. 6)
Pub: Emerald Group Publishing Limited
Contact: Erika Valenti, President

Description: A study to formulate an alternative method of predicting service delivery innovation based on market and technology orientations and innovative competence is examined. Five hypotheses were proposed and tested using the Partial Least Square (PLS) analysis. It was observed that proactive market orientation and technology orientation regulate exploratory and exploitative innovative competences, while exploitative competence influences service delivery innovation. Availability: Download; Online.

26332 ■ "Marketers Push for Mobile Tuesday as the New Black Friday" in Advertising Age (Vol. 79, December 1, 2008, No. 44, pp. 21)
Pub: Crain Communications, Inc.
Contact: Jessica Botos, Manager, Marketing
E-mail: jessica.botos@crainsnewyork.com

Ed: Natalie Zmuda. Description: Marketers are using an innovative approach in an attempt to stimulate business on the Tuesday following Thanksgiving by utilizing consumer's cell phones to alert them of sales or present them with coupons for this typically slow retail business day; with this campaign both advertisers and retailers are hoping to start Mobile Tuesday, another profitable shopping day in line with Black Friday and Cyber Monday. Availability: Online.

26333 ■ "Mass. STEM Approach and R.I. Model?" in Providence Business News (Vol. 28, March 10, 2014, No. 49, pp. 1)
Pub: American City Business Journals, Inc.
Contact: Mike Olivieri, Executive Vice President

Released: March 08, 2014. Description: Rhode Island is in the process of developing an educational system that prepares students to excel in science, technology, engineering and math (STEM). Educational services in the state are examining the Massachusetts educational program in order to generate ideas. Availability: Print; Online.

26334 ■ "MBlox, Which Sends Coupons to Phones and Tables, Raises $43.5M" in Atlanta Business Chronicle (July 11, 2014, pp. 12A)
Pub: American City Business Journals, Inc.
Contact: Mike Olivieri, Executive Vice President

Released: Weekly. Price: $4, introductory 4-week offer(Digital only). Description: mBlox, the mobile technology firm that sends coupons to hphones and tablets has managed to successfully raise $43.5 million to undertake global expansion. Availability: Print; Online.

26335 ■ "Med-Tech Vet's Trip From Heart to Sleeve" in Business Journal (Vol. 31, February 14, 2014, No. 38, pp. 8)
Pub: American City Business Journals, Inc.
Contact: Mike Olivieri, Executive Vice President
Released: February 14, 2014. Price: $4, Introductory 4-week offer(Digital & Print). Description: Conventus Orthopaedics CEO, Paul Buckman, describes the device which repairs wrist fractures. Buckman reveals plans to use the $17 million venture capital to continue research and development and to conduct clinical studies to justify use of the technology. Availability: Print; Online.

26336 ■ "Meet the Golden 100 List's Youngest Firm: Kavaliro" in Orlando Business Journal (Vol. 29, September 21, 2012, No. 14, pp. 1)
Pub: Baltimore Business Journal
Contact: Rhonda Pringle, President
E-mail: rpringle@bizjournals.com
Description: Technology and information technology staffing firm Kavaliro is the youngest company in the 2012 Golden 100 list of top privately held cmpanies in Central Florida ranked by the 'Orlando Business Journal'. Kavaliro provides 5-10 percent of the local staffing market and has 373 employees, with about 16 working in Central Florida. Availability: Print; Online.

26337 ■ "Meet the White-Label Cash Kings" in Globe & Mail (April 23, 2007, pp. B1)
Ed: Tara Perkins, Tavia Grant. Description: The services provided by the independent Canadian companies managing automated banking machines are described. The trends of ownership of automated banking machines in Canada are discussed. Availability: Online.

26338 ■ "Merkle Lands $75M Private-Equity Investment" in Baltimore Business Journal (Vol. 28, October 15, 2010, No. 23, pp. 1)
Pub: Baltimore Business Journal
Contact: Rhonda Pringle, President
E-mail: rpringle@bizjournals.com
Ed: Gary Haber. Description: Baltimore, Maryland-based Merkle has received a $75 million investment from Silicon Valley-based Technology Crossover Ventures. The private equity firm's cash infusion was considered the biggest stake made in a company in the region and provides a healthy sign for Greater Baltimore's company. Availability: Print; Online.

26339 ■ "Microsoft Goes Macrosoft" in Barron's (Vol. 89, July 27, 2009, No. 30, pp. 25)
Pub: Dow Jones & Company Inc.
Contact: Almar Latour, Chief Executive Officer
Ed: Mark Veverka. Description: Microsoft reported a weak quarter on the heels of a tech rally which suggests the economy has not turned around. Marc Andreesen describes his new venture-capital fund as focused on "classic tech" and that historical reference places him in the annals of the last millennium. Availability: Online.

26340 ■ "Microsoft's Big Gamble" in Canadian Business (Vol. 81, March 3, 2008, No. 3, pp. 13)
Description: Microsoft Corp. is taking a big risk in buying Yahoo, as it is expected to pay more than $31 a share to finalize the acquisition. The deal would be seven and a half times bigger than any other that Microsoft has entered before, an execution of such deal is also anticipated to become a challenge for Microsoft. Recommendations on how Microsoft should handle the integration of the two businesses are given. Availability: Print; Online.

26341 ■ "Microsoft's Diversity Program Clicks into High Speed" in Hispanic Business (Vol. 30, July-August 2008, No. 7-8, pp. 54)
Ed: Derek Reveron. Description: Microsoft's diversity hiring and vendor diversity program to capture more Hispanic consumer and business-to-business market is described. One of the main goals of these programs is to hire more Hispanic executives and managers who will help the company develop and market products and services that will appeal and benefit Hispanic consumers.

26342 ■ "MicroTech Is Fastest Growing Private Company in Washington Area on Deloitte Technology Fast 500" in Hispanic Business (July-August 2009, pp. 20, 22)
Ed: Suzanne Heibel. Description: Profile of Tony Jimenez, former lieutenant colonel in the Army and CEO and founder of Virginia-based information technology firm, Micro Tech LLC. Jimenez was named Latinos in Information Science and Technology Association's CEO of the Year for 2008.

26343 ■ "Miller's Crossroad" in Canadian Business (Vol. 83, September 14, 2010, No. 15, pp. 58)
Ed: Joe Castaldo. Released: September 14, 2010. Description: Future Electronics founder and billionaire Robert Miller shares the secret of Future's unique operating model, which is based on inventory and market research. Miller attributes much of the company's success to its privately held status that enables quick movement against competitors. Availability: Print; Online.

26344 ■ "Mobile Marketing Grows With Size of Cell Phone Screens" in Crain's Detroit Business (Vol. 24, January 14, 2008, No. 2, pp. 13)
Pub: Crain Communications Inc.
Contact: Barry Asin, President
Ed: Bill Shea. Description: Experts are predicting increased marketing for cell phones with the inception of larger screens and improved technology.

26345 ■ Mobile Office: The Essential Small Business Guide to Office Technology
Released: September 1, 2009. Price: $6.95. Description: Essential pocket guide for startup businesses and entrepreneurs which provides information to create a mobile office in order to maximize business potential while using current technologies.

26346 ■ "A Model Development" in Crain's Cleveland Business (Vol. 28, October 1, 2007, No. 39, pp. 12)
Pub: Crain Communications Inc.
Contact: K. C. Crain, President
Ed: Scott Suttell. Description: Profile a Forest City Enterprises Inc., a firm that is developing a project in New Mexico called Mesa del Sol. The Albuquerque development is being seen as the vanguard of master-planned communities with its high-tech economic development center which is expected to become the site of 60,000 jobs, 38,000 homes and a town center. Availability: PDF.

26347 ■ "Mosaid Grants First Wireless Patent License To Matsushita" in Canadian Electronics (Vol. 23, June-July 2008, No. 5, pp. 1)
Pub: Annex Buisness Media
Contact: Mike Fredericks, President
Description: Matsushita Electric Industrial Co. Ltd. has been granted a six-and-a-half-year license by Mosaid Technologies Inc. to manufacture the latter's products. The patent portfolio license agreement covers Mosaid's Wi-Fi, Wi-Max, CDMA-enabled notebook computers and other products.

26348 ■ "Motors and Motion Control" in Canadian Electronics (Vol. 23, February 2008, No. 1, pp. 23)
Description: A new version of MicroMo Electronics Inc.'s Smoovy Series 0303.B has been added to MicroMo's DC motor product line. United Electronic Industries, on the other hand, has introduced the new UEIPAC series of programmable automation controllers that can offer solutions to various applications such as unmanned vehicle controllers. Features and functions of other new motors and motion control devices are given.

26349 ■ "Nerd Alert on 3rd" in Philadelphia Business Journal (Vol. 28, August 17, 2012, No. 27, pp. 1)
Pub: Baltimore Business Journal
Contact: Rhonda Pringle, President
E-mail: rpringle@bizjournals.com
Description: The transformation of North 3rd Street in the neighborhood of Old City in Philadelphia, Pennsylvania into a cluster of technology businesses and workers, dubbed at N3rd (pronounced 'nerd'), is described. Some of the firms located in the area include the Web engineering company Jarv.us Innovations and the collaborative workspace Devnuts. Prospects of the cluster's growth are also discussed. Availability: Print; Online.

26350 ■ "NETGEAR Upgrades Small Business Security Line With Multiple Industry Firsts" in Benzinga.com (March 1, 2012)
Pub: PR Newswire Association LLC.
Description: Netgear's launched its new firmware that delivers affordable application firewall and redundant connectivity as well as extending virtually unlimited logging capacity.

26351 ■ "New Giants CEO Goes to Bat for Sponsorships" in Silicon Valley/San Jose Business Journal (Vol. 29, February 3, 2012, No. 45, pp. 1)
Pub: Baltimore Business Journal
Contact: Rhonda Pringle, President
E-mail: rpringle@bizjournals.com
Description: New San Jose Giants baseball team, chief executive Dan Orum, is planning to increase the team's sponsorship, advertising, and ticket revenue. Orum will target technology companies and other firms as prospective sponsors. Orum's career background and achievements are also outlined. Availability: Print; Online.

26352 ■ "New IPhone Also Brings New Way of Mobile Marketing" in Advertising Age (Vol. 79, June 16, 2008, No. 24, pp. 23)
Pub: Crain Communications, Inc.
Contact: Jessica Botos, Manager, Marketing
E-mail: jessica.botos@crainsnewyork.com
Ed: Abbey Klaassen. Description: Currently there are two kinds of applications for the iPhone and other mobile devices: native applications that allow for richer experiences and take advantage of features that are built into a phone and web applications, those that allow access to the web through specific platforms. Marketers are interested in creating useful experiences for customers and opening up the platforms which will allow them to do this. Availability: Online.

26353 ■ "New Jersey Bio Grows Despite Turbulent Times" in Philadelphia Business Journal (Vol. 28, August 17, 2012, No. 27, pp. 1)
Pub: Baltimore Business Journal
Contact: Rhonda Pringle, President
E-mail: rpringle@bizjournals.com
Description: The number of biotechnology firms with operations in New Jersey increased from about 300 to more than 340, while the number of employees working at those grew 9.3 percent from 15,000 in July 2012 to 16,400 in 2012. The growth has been realized despite issues that are said to affect the national and international economic situation. Calls to develop economic incentives are also examined. Availability: Print; Online.

26354 ■ "New Sony HD Ads Tout Digital" in Brandweek (Vol. 49, April 21, 2008, No. 16, pp. 5)
Description: Looking to promote Sony Electronics' digital imaging products, the company has launched another campaign effort known as HDNA, a play on the words high-definition and DNA; originally Sony focused the HDNA campaign on their televisions, the new ads will include still and video cameras as well and marketing efforts will consist of advertising in print, Online, television spots and publicity at various venues across the country. Availability: Online.

High-Tech Business

26355 ■ *"A New Way to Tell When to Fold 'Em"* in *Barron's* (Vol. 88, July 7, 2008, No. 27, pp. 27)
Pub: Dow Jones & Company Inc.
Contact: Almar Latour, Chief Executive Officer
Ed: Theresa W. Carey. **Description:** Overview of the Online trading company SmartStops, a firm that aims to tell investors when to sell the shares of a particular company. The company's Web site categorizes stocks as moving up, down, or sideways, and calculates exit points for individual stocks based on an overall market trend. **Availability:** Online.

26356 ■ *"Newton Robotics Company Bets on Rehab Robots for Growth"* in *Boston Business Journal* (Vol. 34, April 4, 2014, No. 9, pp. 6)
Pub: American City Business Journals, Inc.
Contact: Mike Olivieri, Executive Vice President
Description: Robotics firm Barrett Technology is transforming into a health care company by developing rehabilitation robots. The business is expected to generate 80 percent of its revenue from its health care clients over the next five years. The possibility of hiring new employees is also discussed. **Availability:** Print; Online.

26357 ■ *"No More Ivory Towers: Local Colleges and Universities are Here to Help Your Business"* in *Orlando Business Journal* (Vol. 30, February 28, 2014, No. 36, pp. 4)
Pub: American City Business Journals, Inc.
Contact: Mike Olivieri, Executive Vice President
Released: Weekly. **Price:** $8, Introductory 4-week offer(Digital & Print). **Description:** A number of school leaders in Central Florida share their views on partnering with the business community, boosting science and technology graduates, benefits of a private college, economic development efforts and fixing the higher education construction gridlock. Local universities and colleges have a combined economic impact of $15 billion each year. **Availability:** Print; Online.

26358 ■ *The Nokia Revolution: The Story of an Extraordinary Company That Transformed an Industry*
Description: Profile of Nokia, the world's largest wireless communications company. Nokia started in 1865 in rural Finland and merged its rubber company and a cabling firm to form the corporation around 1965. The firm's corporate strategy in the mobile communications industry is highlighted. **Availability:** E-book; Print.

26359 ■ *"Nortel Makes Customers Stars in New Campaign"* in *Brandweek* (Vol. 49, April 21, 2008, No. 16, pp. 8)
Description: Nortel has launched a new television advertising campaign in which the business-to-business communications technology provider cast senior executives in 30-second TV case studies that show how Nortel's technology helped their businesses innovate. **Availability:** Online.

26360 ■ *"Nortel Romances Chinese Rival Huawei"* in *Globe & Mail* (February 2, 2006, pp. B1)
Description: The reasons behind Nortel Networks Corp.'s joint venture with Huawei Technologies Company Ltd. are presented. **Availability:** Online.

26361 ■ *"Not Your Father's Whiteboard"* in *Inc.* (Vol. 33, November 2011, No. 9, pp. 50)
Pub: Inc. Magazine
Ed: Adam Baer. **Description:** Sharp's new interactive whiteboard is really a 70-inch touch screen monitor with software for importing presentations from any Windows 7 computer. **Availability:** Online.

26362 ■ *"No. 82: a Few Good Apps"* in *Inc.* (Vol. 36, September 2014, No. 7, pp. 103)
Pub: Mansueto Ventures L.L.C.
Contact: Stephanie Mehta, Chief Executive Officer
Description: Alan S. Knitowski, former U.S. Army Captain, and his Austin, Texas-based mobile-focused development company is profiled. Phunware, creates apps for clients like ESPN, Cisco, Noscar, WWE, and NBC Sports. The firm won awards for its MythBusters app. **Availability:** Online.

26363 ■ *"Nvidia Shares Clobbered After Gloomy Warning"* in *Barron's* (Vol. 88, July 7, 2008, No. 27, pp. 25)
Pub: Dow Jones & Company Inc.
Contact: Almar Latour, Chief Executive Officer
Ed: Eric J. Savitz. **Description:** Shares of graphics chip manufacturer Nvidia suffered a 30 percent drop in its share price after the company warned that revenue and gross margin forecasts for the quarter ending July 27, 2008 will be below expectations. Stan Glasgow, chief operating officer of Sony Electronics, believes the US economic slowdown will not affect demand for the company's products. Statistical data included. **Availability:** Online.

26364 ■ *"Nvidia's Picture Brighter Than Stock Price Indicates"* in *Barron's* (Vol. 88, March 24, 2008, No. 12, pp. 46)
Pub: Dow Jones & Company Inc.
Contact: Almar Latour, Chief Executive Officer
Ed: Eric J. Savitz. **Description:** Shares of graphics chip maker Nvidia, priced at $18.52 each, do not indicate the company's strong position in the graphics chip market. The company's shares have dropped due to fears of slower demand for PCs, but the company is not as exposed to broader economic forces. **Availability:** Online.

26365 ■ *"NYC Tops Hub in Tech VC Dollars"* in *Boston Business Journal* (Vol. 31, August 5, 2011, No. 28, pp. 1)
Pub: Boston Business Journal
Contact: Carolyn M. Jones, President
E-mail: cmjones@bizjournals.com
Ed: Kyle Alspach. **Description:** New York City has been outdoing Boston in terms of venture capital for technology firms since second quarter 2010. New York tech firms raised $865 million during the first two quarters of 2011 against Boston techs' $682 million. Boston has the edge, though, when it comes to hiring engineering talent as it is home to the Massachusetts Institute of Technology. **Availability:** Print; Online.

26366 ■ *"On Technology: The Web Gets Real"* in *Canadian Business* (Vol. 79, July 17, 2006, No. 14-15, pp. 19)
Pub: Rogers Media Inc.
Contact: Neil Spivak, Chief Executive Officer
Ed: Andrew Wahl. **Description:** Ron Lake's efforts of bringing the virtual and physical worlds more closely together by using Geographic Markup Language (GML) are presented. **Availability:** Print; PDF; Online.

26367 ■ *"Online Training Requires Tools, Accessories"* in *Contractor* (Vol. 56, September 2009, No. 9, pp. 67)
Ed: Larry Drake. **Description:** Importance of the right equipment and tools to members of the United States plumbing industry undergoing online training is discussed. Portable devices such as BlackBerrys and I-phones could be used for online training. The use of headphones makes listening easier for the trainee. **Availability:** Print; Online.

26368 ■ *"Optimal Awarded US $256 Thousand Contract to Conduct LiDAR Survey for a Major Electric Utility in the Southwest"* in *Canadian Corporate News*
Description: Optimal Geomatics, a company specializing in the science and technology of analyzing, gathering, interpreting, distributing, and using geographic information, was awarded a new contract from a long-standing electric utility customer in the Southwest to conduct a LiDAR survey for a part of the utility's overhead transmission line system. **Availability:** Print; Online.

26369 ■ *"Oracle: No Profit of Doom"* in *Barron's* (Vol. 88, March 31, 2008, No. 13, pp. 40)
Pub: Dow Jones & Company Inc.
Contact: Almar Latour, Chief Executive Officer

General Small Business Topics

Ed: Mark Veverka. **Description:** Oracle's revenues grew by 21 percent but fell short of expectation and their profits came in at the low-end of expectations. The company's shares dropped 8 percent but investors are advised to pay more attention to the company's earnings expansion rather than revenue growth in a slow economy. Nokia's Rick Simonson points out that their markets in Asia and particularly India is growing so they are not as affected by the U.S. economic conditions. **Availability:** Online.

26370 ■ *"Orlando Patents Forecast Biz Diversity and Growth"* in *Orlando Business Journal* (Vol. 30, April 18, 2014, No. 43, pp. 4)
Pub: American City Business Journals, Inc.
Contact: Mike Olivieri, Executive Vice President
Released: Weekly. **Price:** $8, introductory 4-week offer(Digital & Print). **Description:** Orlando, Florida ranked among cities in the state in terms of number of patents filed. Around 275 patents were issued to Orlando-based inventors and businesses in 2013. The increase in the number of high technology companies entering the city has contributed to this trend. **Availability:** Print; Online.

26371 ■ *"Our Gadget of the Week: Eye Candy From Dell"* in *Barron's* (Vol. 89, July 27, 2009, No. 30, pp. 26)
Description: Zeo Sleep Coach has a lightweight headband with built-in sensors which measures the user's brain waves and records their sleep patterns. The device details the time the users spends in deep sleep, light sleep and the restorative REM (rapid eye movement) sleep mode. Users can get lifestyle change recommendations from a website to improve their sleep. **Availability:** Online.

26372 ■ *"Paging Dr. Phil"* in *Canadian Business* (Vol. 79, September 25, 2006, No. 19, pp. 21)
Description: Increasing corporate crimes in software industry is discussed by focusing on recent case of Hewlett and Packard. **Availability:** Print; Mailing list; Online.

26373 ■ *"Panel to Call for Reduced Restraints on Telecom Sector"* in *Globe & Mail* (March 17, 2006, pp. B1)
Ed: Simon Tuck. **Description:** A federal panel called to adopt a more market-friendly approach to the lucrative telecommunications sector in Canada. Details of the report are presented. **Availability:** Online.

26374 ■ *"Panel Calls for 'Fundamental' Change to Telecom Regulation"* in *Globe & Mail* (March 23, 2006, pp. B1)
Ed: Catherine McLean. **Description:** A federal panel review at Ottawa called for a shakeup of regulations and policies that govern telecommunications companies to contend with sweeping technological changes. Details of the panel review are presented. **Availability:** Print; Online.

26375 ■ *"Paterson Plots Comeback With Internet IPO"* in *Globe & Mail* (February 20, 2006, pp. B1)
Ed: Grant Robertson. **Description:** The initial public offering plans of chief executive officer Scott Paterson of JumpTV.com are presented. **Availability:** Online.

26376 ■ *"Paul Hawken and Other Top Lumnaries to Participate in Green Business BASE CAMP in Los Angeles"* in *Benzinga.com* (April 19, 2012)
Pub: Benzinga.com
Contact: Jason Raznick, Founder
Ed: Aaron Wise. **Description:** Paul Hawken, environmentalist, entrepreneur and author, is one of many people participating in the Green Business BASE CAMP, a four-day workshop for green business and cleantech entrepreneurs. The event will be held in Los Angeles, California from May 31 through June 3, 2012. Insider guidance will be offered to early-stage entrepreneurs seeking to compete within this sector. **Availability:** Online.

26377 ■ "Pay Heed to 'Smack Stack" in Puget Sound Business Journal (Vol. 35, May 16, 2014, No. 4, pp. 6)
Pub: American City Business Journals, Inc.
Contact: Mike Olivieri, Executive Vice President
Description: Technology consultant, Geoffrey Moore, discloses the topics he plans to discuss at the annual State of Technology Luncheon held in Washington on May 19, 2014. He will explore the impact of technology and business trends on public-policy making and regulations. **Availability:** Online.

26378 ■ "PC Connection Acquires Cloud Software Provider" in New Hampshire Business Review (Vol. 33, March 25, 2011, No. 6, pp. 8)
Description: Merrimack-based PC Connection Inc. acquired ValCom Technology, a provider of cloud-based IT service management software. Details of the deal are included. **Availability:** Print; Online.

26379 ■ "Philanthropy Good For Business" in Crain's Detroit Business (Vol. 24, February 18, 2008, No. 7, pp. 14)
Pub: Crain Communications Inc.
Contact: Barry Asin, President
Ed: Sheena Harrison. **Description:** Profile of Burce McCully, founder of Dynamic Edge Inc., and his views on philanthropy as a key to any small company's success. The Ann Arbor, Michigan information technology firm has volunteered and raised funds for many causes since 1999 when the company was founded. **Availability:** Print; Online.

26380 ■ "Prepaid Phones Surge in Bad Economy" in Advertising Age (Vol. 79, November 17, 2008, No. 43, pp. 6)
Pub: Crain Communications, Inc.
Contact: Jessica Botos, Manager, Marketing
E-mail: jessica.botos@crainsnewyork.com
Ed: Rita Chang. **Description:** Prepay cell phone offerings are becoming increasingly competitive amid a greater choice of plans and handsets. In an economic environment in which many consumers are unable to pass the credit checks required for traditional cell phone plans, the prepay market is surging.

26381 ■ "Presidential Address: Innovation in Retrospect and Prospect" in Canadian Journal of Electronics (Vol. 43, November 2010, No. 4)
Pub: Journal of the Canadian Economics Association
Ed: James A. Brander. **Description:** Has innovation slowed in recent decades? While there has been progress in information and communications technology, the recent record of innovation in agriculture, energy, transportation and healthcare sectors is cause for concern. **Availability:** PDF; Online.

26382 ■ "The Promise of the Promised Land" in San Francisco Business Times (Vol. 28, January 3, 2014, No. 24, pp. 4)
Pub: American City Business Journals, Inc.
Contact: Mike Olivieri, Executive Vice President
Released: September 15, 2016. **Price:** $4, print. **Description:** San Francisco Bay Area in California has become the site selection for investment, technology and talent. The financing finding its way to the Bay Area has led to robust job creation, drawing people and increasing the population by 2.6 percent to 805,000. The impact of the Bay Area's technology boon in rents and home prices are also presented. **Availability:** Print; Online.

26383 ■ "Punta Gorda Interested in Wi-Fi Internet" in Charlotte Observer (February 1, 2007)
Description: Punta Gorda officials are developing plans to provide free wireless Internet services to businesses and residents. **Availability:** Online.

26384 ■ "Quantivo Empowers Online Media Companies to Immediately Expand Audiences and Grow Online Profits" in Marketwired (November 18, 2009)
Pub: Comtex News Network Inc.
Contact: Kan Devnani, President
Description: Quantivo, the leader in on-demand Behavioral Analytics, has launched a new solution that includes 22 of the most critical Internet audience behavior insights as out-of-the-box reports; Internet marketers need to understand their audience, what they want and how often to offer it to them in order to gain successful branding and campaigns online. **Availability:** Online.

26385 ■ "Racing to Beam Electricity to Devices Wirelessly" in San Francisco Business Times (Vol. 28, April 11, 2014, No. 38, pp. 6)
Pub: American City Business Journals, Inc.
Contact: Mike Olivieri, Executive Vice President
Description: Pleasanton, California-based Energous Corporation has developed a technology that safely converts radio waves into electrical current. The innovation makes it possible to charge multiple/cellular mobile phones or other electrical devices from a distance of 15 feet. The prototype of Energous founder, Michael Leabman's invention is also outlined. **Availability:** Print; Online.

26386 ■ "Radio Feels Heat from iPod Generation" in Globe & Mail (March 16, 2006, pp. B1)
Ed: Simon Tuck, Grant Robertson. **Description:** Conventional radio stations are losing the younger generation listeners to new technology such as MP3 players, satellite radio and music-playing cell phones. The report of Canadian Association of Broadcasters (CAB) is detailed. **Availability:** Online.

26387 ■ "Raptor Opens Austin Office" in Austin Business Journal (Vol. 31, July 8, 2011, No. 18, pp. 1)
Pub: Austin Business Journal
Contact: Rachel McGrath, Director
E-mail: rmcgrath@bizjournals.com
Ed: Christopher Calnan. **Description:** Boston hedge fund operator Raptor Group launched Raptor Accelerator, a consulting business providing sales and advisory services to early-stage companies in Central Texas. Aside from getting involved with the startups in which the Raptor Group invests, Raptor Accelerator will target firms operating in the sports, media, entertainment, and content technology sectors. **Availability:** Print; Online.

26388 ■ "RavenBrick Ready to Manufacture Its High-Tech Windows" in Denver Business Journal (Vol. 64, September 7, 2012, No. 16, pp. 1)
Pub: Baltimore Business Journal
Contact: Rhonda Pringle, President
E-mail: rpringle@bizjournals.com
Description: RavenBrick LLC is set to build a new manufacturing plant in Denver, Colorado. The company manufactures auto-darkening window films. RavenBrick has raised a total of $13.5 million in new investment capital. **Availability:** Print; Online.

26389 ■ "Rawlings-Blake Unveils Business Plan for Next Four Years" in Baltimore Business Journal (Vol. 29, September 16, 2011, No. 19, pp. 1)
Pub: Boston Business Journal
Contact: Carolyn M. Jones, President
E-mail: cmjones@bizjournals.com
Ed: Gary Haber. **Description:** Mayor Stephanie Rawlings-Blake of Baltimore, Maryland unveiled her plan to push the economy forward. Her key objectives include giving more support for the city's technology companies and refocusing the Baltimore Development Corporation on job creation and retention. **Availability:** Online.

26390 ■ "Raytheon Stock Up, Will Pay New Quarterly Dividend" in Barron's (Vol. 88, March 31, 2008, No. 13)
Pub: Dow Jones & Company Inc.
Contact: Almar Latour, Chief Executive Officer
Ed: Shirley A. Lazo. **Description:** Raytheon hiked their quarterly dividend to 28 cents per share from 25.5 cents. Aircastle slashed their quarterly common dividend by 64 percent for them to retain additional capital that can be used to increase their liquidity position. **Availability:** Online.

26391 ■ Reading Financial Reports for Dummies
Pub: John Wiley & Sons, Inc.
Contact: Christina Van Tassell, Executive Vice President Chief Financial Officer
URL(s): www.amazon.com/gp/product/1119871360/ref=as_li_tl?ie=UTF8&tag=wiley01-20
Ed: Lita Epstein. **Released:** 4th Edition. **Price:** $27.18, paperback; $18, e-book. **Description:** The fourth edition contains more new and updated information. This book is meant as a guide to help the reader interpret and understand financial reports, annual reports, balance sheets, income statements, statements of cash flow and consolidated statements. Real-world examples are given. . **Availability:** E-book; Print.

26392 ■ "Region to Be Named Innovation Hub" in Business Courier (Vol. 27, July 2, 2010, No. 9, pp. 1)
Pub: Business Courier
Ed: Dan Monk. **Description:** The selection of Cincinnati's consumer-marketing cluster as a 'Hub of Innovation' by the Ohio Department of Development could boost Cincinnati's chances of receiving $100 million in grants from Ohio's Third Frontier program and other funding sources. Implications of the University of Cincinnati's designation as a Center of Excellence in Advanced Transportation and Aerospace are also discussed. **Availability:** Print; Online.

26393 ■ "Reportlinker.com Adds Report: GeoWeb and Local Internet Markets: 2008 Edition" in Entertainment Close-Up (September 11, 2009)
Description: Reportlinker.com is adding a new market research report that is available in its catalogue: GeoWeb and Local Internet Markets - 2008 Edition; highlights include the outlook for consumer mapping services and an examination of monetizing services and an analysis the development outlook for geospacial Internet market, also referred to as the Geoweb. **Availability:** Online.

26394 ■ "Research and Market Adds Report: Endpoint Security for Business" in Wireless News (October 26, 2009)
Description: Summarizes Research and Markets Adds Report: Endpoint Security for Business: Desktops, Laptops & Mobile Devices 2009-2014; highlights include a detailed analysis of where the industry is at present and forecasts regarding how it will develop over the next five years.

26395 ■ "Research and Markets Adds Report: The U.S. Mobile Web Market" in Entertainment Close-Up (December 10, 2009)
Description: Highlights of the new Research and Markets report "The U.S. Mobile Web Market: Taking Advantage of the iPhone Phenomenon" include: mobile Internet marketing strategies; the growth of mobile web usage; the growth of revenue in the mobile web market; and a look at Internet business communications, social media and networking. **Availability:** Print; Online.

26396 ■ "Riding the Wave: Past Trends and Future Directions for Health IT Research" in MIS Quarterly (Vol. 36, September 2012, No. 3, pp. III)
Pub: University of Minnesota Carlson School of Management Management Information Systems Research Center
Description: Trends in healthcare information technologies, also known as health informatics, are discussed. **Availability:** Download.

26397 ■ "RIM Reinforces Claim as Top Dog by Expanding BlackBerry Service" in Globe & Mail (March 11, 2006, pp. B3)
Ed: Simon Avery. **Description:** The plans of Research In Motion Ltd. to enhance the features of BlackBerry, through acquisition of Ascendent Systems, are presented. **Availability:** Online.

High-Tech Business

26398 ■ *"Rising in the East; Research and Development"* in *The Economist* (Vol. 390, January 3, 2009, No. 8612, pp. 47)
Description: Impressive growth of the technological research and development in Asian countries is discussed. Statistical data included. **Availability:** Online.

26399 ■ *"Samsung's Metamorphosis in Austin"* in *Austin Business Journal* (Vol. 31, May 20, 2011, No. 11, pp. 1)
Pub: Austin Business Journal
Contact: Rachel McGrath, Director
E-mail: rmcgrath@bizjournals.com
Ed: Christopher Calnan. **Description:** Samsung Austin Semiconductor LP, a developer of semiconductors for smartphones and tablet computers, plans to diversify its offerings to include niche products: flash memory devices and microprocessing devices. In light of this strategy, Samsung Austin will be hiring 300 engineers as part of a $3.6 billion expansion of its plant. **Availability:** Print; Online.

26400 ■ *"San Jose Hopes to Build on Uptick in Manufacturing"* in *Silicon Valley/San Jose Business Journal* (Vol. 30, July 13, 2012, No. 16, pp. 1)
Pub: Baltimore Business Journal
Contact: Rhonda Pringle, President
E-mail: rpringle@bizjournals.com
Description: San Jose, California-based manufacturing companies that cater to high-technology companies and startups have been experiencing an uptick in business. The San Jose metropolitan area is the country's second-largest specialized manufacturing market and the city has rolled out its efforts to help support this growth. **Availability:** Print; Online.

26401 ■ *"Say Goodbye to Voicemail, Hello To Ribbit Mobile"* in *Agency Sales Magazine* (Vol. 39, November 2009, No. 10, pp. 3)
Description: Salespeople should think twice before leaving a voicemail. The emerging modern etiquette is to send a text message or to e-mail the customer or client. Communication suggestions for both salespeople and their principals are presented. **Availability:** Print; Online.

26402 ■ *"Scientific American Builds Novel Blog Network"* in *Information Today* (Vol. 28, September 2011, No. 8, pp. 12)
Pub: Information Today Inc.
Contact: Thomas H. Hogan, President
Ed: Kurt Schiller. **Description:** Scientific American launched a new blog network that joins a diverse lineup of bloggers cover various scientific topics under one banner. The blog network includes 60 bloggers providing insights into the ever-changing world of science and technology.

26403 ■ *"Search Engines: Image Conscious"* in *Canadian Business* (Vol. 81, February 26, 2008, No. 4, pp. 36)
Pub: Rogers Media Inc.
Contact: Neil Spivak, Chief Executive Officer
Ed: Andrew Wahl. **Description:** Idee Inc. is testing an Internet search engine for images that does not rely on tags but compares its visual data to a database of other images. The company was founded and managed by Leila Boujnane as an off-shoot of their risk-management software firm. Their software has already been used by image companies to track copyrighted images and to find images within their own archives. **Availability:** Online.

26404 ■ *"The Second Machine Age: Work, Progress, and Prosperity in a Time of Brilliant Technologies"*
Released: January 01, 2016. **Price:** $16.95, paperback; $26.95, hardcover. **Description:** Insights into ways digital technologies are transforming our economy in order to develop new business models, new technologies, and new policies to enhance human capabilities are provided. **Availability:** Print.

26405 ■ *"Sherwin-Williams Workers Forgo Travel for Virtual Trade Show"* in *Crain's Cleveland Business* (Vol. 28, October 15, 2007, No. 41, pp. 4)
Pub: Crain Communications Inc.
Contact: K. C. Crain, President
Ed: John Booth. **Description:** Overview of Cyber-Coating 2007, a cutting-edge virtual three-dimensional trade show that exhibitors such as Sherwin-Williams Co.'s Chemical Coatings Division will take part in by chatting verbally or via text messages in order to exchange information and listen to pitches just like they would on an actual trade show floor. **Availability:** Online.

26406 ■ *"The Skype's the Limit"* in *Canadian Business* (Vol. 80, February 12, 2007, No. 4, pp. 70)
Description: The increase in the market share of Skype Technologies S.A.'s Internet phone service to 171 million users is discussed. **Availability:** Print; Online.

26407 ■ *"Slater Progress Stalled"* in *Providence Business News* (Vol. 28, March 10, 2014, No. 49, pp. 1)
Pub: American City Business Journals, Inc.
Contact: Mike Olivieri, Executive Vice President
URL(s): pbn.com/slater-progress-stalled95603
Description: Slater Technology Fund has received only $1.9 million of the $9 million in expected federal funds. However, the venture capital firm decided to invest in some promising technology companies in Providence, Rhode Island. Slater senior managing director, Richard Horan, reveals that uncertainties with respect to grants have delayed private fundraising. **Availability:** Online.

26408 ■ *"Slow but Steady into the Future"* in *Barron's* (Vol. 88, July 7, 2008, No. 27, pp. M)
Pub: Dow Jones & Company Inc.
Contact: Almar Latour, Chief Executive Officer
Ed: Mark Veverka. **Description:** Investors are advised to maintain their watch on the shares of business software company NetSuite. The company's chief executive officer, Zach Nelson, claims that the company has a 10-year lead on its competitors with the development of software-as-a service. **Availability:** Online.

26409 ■ *"Social Media Conference NW 2010"* in *Bellingham Business Journal* (Vol. February 2010, pp. 3)
Pub: Sound Publishing Inc.
Contact: Josh O'Connor, President
Ed: Lance Henderson. **Description:** Center for Economic Vitality (CEV) and the Technology Alliance Group (TAG) will host the 2010 Social Media Conference at the McIntyre Hall Performing Arts & Conference Center in Mt. Vernon, Washington. The event will provide networking opportunities for attendees.

26410 ■ *"Sources"* in *Canadian Electronics* (Vol. 23, August 2008, No. 5, pp. 12)
Description: Directory of electronic manufacturers, distributors and representatives in Canada is provided. The list presents distributors and representatives under each manufacturer.

26411 ■ *"Spin Zone: Where Hawaii's Leaders Face Off, Have High-Tech Tax Credits Helped or Hurt Hawaii?"* in *Hawaii Business* (Vol. 53, December 2007, No. 6, pp. 28)
Pub: PacificBasin Communications
Contact: Chuck Tindle, Director
E-mail: chuckt@pacificbasin.net
Description: Presents the opinons of Channel Capital LLC's Walter R. Roth and Hawaii Venture Capital Association's Bill Spencer concerning the impacts of tax credits. Roth thinks that Act 221 appeals to investors who can earn despite business failure while Spencer thinks that the legislation promotes investments in innovative technology firms. The need to support tax credits is also discussed. **Availability:** Print; Online.

General Small Business Topics

26412 ■ *"Startup Osteosphere Formed to Develop Laboratory Discovery"* in *Houston Business Journal* (Vol. 40, January 8, 2010, No. 35, pp. 1)
Pub: Houston Business Journal
Contact: Bob Charlet, President
E-mail: bcharlet@bizjournals.com
Ed: Casey Wooten. **Description:** Biotech startup company Osteosphere in Houston, Texas aims to market a technology in which laboratory-grown bone tissues can be processed to appear like a real human bone tissue. The technology was developed by a co-founder of the startup and it can be applied to bone disease and injury treatment. Osteophere's future plans, such as the search for possible investors, is also outlined. **Availability:** Print; Online.

26413 ■ *"State of Play"* in *Canadian Business* (Vol. 79, June 19, 2006, No. 13, pp. 25)
Description: Top 100 information technology companies in Canada are ranked by their market capitalization as of June 1. The statistics that show the revenues of these companies are also presented. **Availability:** Print; Online.

26414 ■ *"Steelhead Makes High-Tech Tanks"* in *Denver Business Journal* (Vol. 65, March 28, 2014, No. 46, pp. A7)
Pub: American City Business Journals, Inc.
Contact: Mike Olivieri, Executive Vice President
Released: Weekly. **Price:** $4, introductory 4-week offer(Digital only). **Description:** Steelhead Composites LLC is known for its high-technology tanks that hold pressurized gases. The company, which was founded in October 2012, aimed to tackle problems associated with long delivery times. Reports show that the firm's supporters have invested more than $5 million into the business. **Availability:** Print; Online.

26415 ■ *"STMicroelectronics"* in *Canadian Electronics* (Vol. 23, February 2008, No. 1, pp. 1)
Description: STMicroelectronics, a semiconductor maker, revealed that it plans to acquire Genesis Microchip Inc. Genesis develops image and video processing systems. It was reported that the acquisition has been approved by Genesis' Board of Directors. It is expected that Genesis will enhance STMicroelectronics' technological capabilities. **Availability:** Online.

26416 ■ *"The Story Of Diane Greene"* in *Barron's* (Vol. 88, July 14, 2008, No. 28, pp. 31)
Pub: Dow Jones & Company Inc.
Contact: Almar Latour, Chief Executive Officer
Ed: Mark Veverka. **Description:** Discusses the ousting of Diane Greene as a chief executive of VMWare, a developer of virtualization software, after the firm went public; in this case Greene, a brilliant engineer, should not be negatively impacted by the decision because it is common for companies to bring in new executive leadership that is more operations oriented after the company goes public. **Availability:** Online.

26417 ■ *"Stuff that Works for You: In the Mobikey of Life"* in *Canadian Business* (Vol. 81, June 11, 2008, No. 11, pp. 42)
Pub: Rogers Media Inc.
Contact: Neil Spivak, Chief Executive Officer
Ed: John Gray. **Description:** Toronto-based Route1 has created a data security software system that allows employees to access files and programs stored in the head office without permanently transferring data to the actual computer being used. Mobikey technology is useful in protecting laptops of chief executive officers, which contain confidential financial and customer data. **Availability:** Online.

26418 ■ *"Suited for Success"* in *Retail Merchandiser* (Vol. 51, July-August 2011, No. 4, pp. 6)
Description: MyBestFit is a size-matching body scanner that helps consumers find the perfect size clothing for themselves, giving brick and mortar retailers an edge on ecommerce competitors. **Availability:** Online.

26419 ■ "The Superpower Dilemma" in Canadian Business (Vol. 83, August 17, 2010, No. 13-14, pp. 42)
Description: Canada has been an energy superpower partly because it controls the energy source and the production means, particularly of fossil fuels. However, Canada's status as superpower could diminish if it replaces petroleum exports with renewable technology for using sources of energy available globally. **Availability:** Online.

26420 ■ "A Swifter, Better Marketplace" in Barron's (Vol. 89, July 13, 2009, No. 28, pp. M13)
Pub: Dow Jones & Company Inc.
Contact: Almar Latour, Chief Executive Officer
Ed: Eric W. Noll. **Description:** Listed-derivatives market is moving towards greater trading through computerized systems with an emphasis on speed and innovation. The market for listed options is also being changed by new techniques from other markets such as algorithmic trading, dark pools, and new-order priority systems. **Availability:** Online.

26421 ■ "Symbility Solutions Joins Motion Computing Partner Program" in Marketwired (May 14, 2007)
Pub: Comtex News Network Inc.
Contact: Kan Devnani, President
Description: Symbility Solutions Inc., a wholly owned subsidiary of Automated Benefits Corp., announced an agreement with Alliance Partner of Motion Computing, a leader in wireless communications and mobile computing, in which both companies will invest in a sales and marketing strategy that focuses specifically on the insurance market. **Availability:** Print; Online.

26422 ■ "Taking on 911 - and Making a New Tech Biz In the Process" in Orlando Business Journal (Vol. 30, January 24, 2014, No. 31, pp. 3)
Pub: American City Business Journals, Inc.
Contact: Mike Olivieri, Executive Vice President
Released: Weekly. **Price:** $8, introductory 4-week offer(Digital & Print). **Description:** Central Florida-based TapShield LLC is on the path to growth. The firm has developed a mobile application that enables University of Florida students to coordinate with police. Meanwhile, TapShield is in negotiations with large companies for similar deals. **Availability:** Print; Online.

26423 ■ "Taking a Leap With Mobile Wi-Fi" in Austin Business Journal (Vol. 34, July 25, 2014, No. 23, pp. 10)
Pub: American City Business Journals, Inc.
Contact: Mike Olivieri, Executive Vice President
Released: July 25, 2014. **Price:** $4, introductory 4-week offer(Digital only). **Description:** Austin-based semi-conductor design company Nitero Inc.'s recent release of its Wi-Fi chip, Nietero's key rival Wilocity Ltd.'s acquisition by a tech giant, pushing demand for semiconductors; thus spurring growth for Nitero. It's Wi-Fi's system for mobile platforms will enable users to do more things on their Smartphones, thus converging more devices into one. **Availability:** Print; Online.

26424 ■ "Taking Off" in Puget Sound Business Journal (Vol. 34, January 31, 2014, No. 42, pp. 4)
Pub: American City Business Journals, Inc.
Contact: Mike Olivieri, Executive Vice President
Description: Washington State is at the forefront of the U.S. space flight industry, as the federal government shrinks its role and entrepreneurs are filling the gap. The region is becoming a leader in the space sector because of its high-tech aerospace skills, software intellectuals, and investors willing to fund these enterprises. **Availability:** Online.

26425 ■ "Tale of a Gun" in Canadian Business (Vol. 80, February 26, 2007, No. 5, pp. 37)
Description: The technology behind automated ballistic identification systems, which can be used to analyze fired ammunition components and link them to crime guns and suspects, developed by Canadian companies is presented. **Availability:** Online.

26426 ■ "Tale of the Tape: IPhone Vs. G1" in Advertising Age (Vol. 79, October 27, 2008, No. 40, pp. 6)
Pub: Crain Communications, Inc.
Contact: Jessica Botos, Manager, Marketing
E-mail: jessica.botos@crainsnewyork.com
Ed: Rita Chang. **Description:** T-Mobile's G1 has been positioned as the first serious competitor to Apple's iPhone. G1 is the first mobile phone to run on the Google-backed, open-source platform Android.

26427 ■ "Targeted Technology Raises More Than $40 Million" in San Antonio Business Journal (Vol. 28, September 5, 2014, No. 30, pp. 8)
Pub: American City Business Journals, Inc.
Contact: Mike Olivieri, Executive Vice President
Released: September 05, 2014. **Price:** $4, introductory 4-week offer(Digital & Print). **Description:** Targeted Technology has raised more than $40 million in venture capital funding for early-stage biotechnology companies in San Antonio, Texas through its Targeted Technology Fund II. Senior managing partner, Paul Castella, recognizes the lack of venture capital funds in the area and the role played by his organization to help these firms. **Availability:** Print; Online.

26428 ■ "Taylor Tests Land Grant Program" in Austin Business Journal (Vol. 31, June 3, 2011, No. 13, pp. 1)
Pub: Austin Business Journal
Contact: Rachel McGrath, Director
E-mail: rmcgrath@bizjournals.com
Ed: Vicky Garza. **Description:** Taylor Economic Development Corporation implemented a land grant program called Build On Our Lot to lure businesses to Taylor City, Austin, Texas. They are targeting small businesses, especially those in the renewable energy, advanced manufacturing, technical services and food products. Program details are included. **Availability:** Print; Online.

26429 ■ "The Tech 100" in Canadian Business (Vol. 81, July 21, 2008, No. 11, pp. 48)
Description: Absolute Software Corp. Day4 Energy Inc., Sandvine Corp., Norsat International Inc. and Call Genie Inc. are the five technology firms included in the annual ranking of top companies in Canada by market capitalization. The services and the one-year total return potential of the companies are presented. **Availability:** Online.

26430 ■ "Tech Coalition Warns Takeover Spree is Nigh" in Globe & Mail (February 6, 2007, pp. B1)
Ed: Steven Chase. **Description:** The declaration by an alliance of technology-rich companies, that the huge credits that these companies have to endure due to research and development activities may lead to company takeovers, is discussed. **Availability:** Online.

26431 ■ "Tech Data Launches Unified Communications and Network Security Specialized Business Units" in Wireless News (October 22,2009)
Description: Responding to the growing demand for unified communications and network security, Tech Data announced the formation of two new Specialized Business Units. **Availability:** Online.

26432 ■ "Tech Jobs Rebound from Downturn" in Denver Business Journal (Vol. 65, March 7, 2014, No. 43, pp. A9)
Pub: American City Business Journals, Inc.
Contact: Mike Olivieri, Executive Vice President
Released: Weekly. **Price:** $4, Introductory 4-week offer(Digital & Print). **Description:** Denver, Colorado's employment in core technology industries has returned from pre-Great Recession figures. The computer software industry's surging job growth and the slight increase in the broadcasts and telecommunications industry offset the job losses in biotechnology and private aerospace industry from 2008 through 2013. The growth in specific industries is also discussed. **Availability:** Print; Online.

26433 ■ "Technically Speaking" in Black Enterprise (Vol. 38, February 2008, No. 7, pp. 64)
Pub: Earl G. Graves Ltd.
Contact: Earl Graves, Jr., President
Ed: Sonia Alleyne. **Description:** Marketing manager for Texas Instruments discusses the Strategic Marketing of Technology Products course offered at the California Institute of Technology. The course helps turn products into profits.

26434 ■ "Technology Companies are Increasing Their Hiring" in Philadelphia Business Journal (Vol. 31, March 16, 2012, No. 5, pp. 1)
Pub: Baltimore Business Journal
Contact: Rhonda Pringle, President
E-mail: rpringle@bizjournals.com
Description: Technology firms in Pennsylvania have been expanding their work force. Online advertisements for computer and math science hiring have increased. **Availability:** Print; Online.

26435 ■ "Technology: Elder Care Enters the Digital Age: Wireless Companies Devise Ways to Aid Home Health, Let People Stay in Homes" in Atlanta Journal-Constitution (April 29, 2012, pp. D1)
Description: Mobile phone industry is actually helping families keep aging loved one in their homes. The home healthcare industry is adding technology, telecommunications, smartphone applications and other devices to make it easier for seniors to remain in their homes. Details on this growing industry are included along with statistical data. **Availability:** Online.

26436 ■ "Technology-Market Combinations and the Identification of Entrepreneurial Opportunities: an Investigation of the Opportunity-Individual Nexus" in Academy of Management Journal (Vol. 55, August 1, 2012, No. 4, pp. 753)
Pub: Academy of Management
Contact: Sharon Alvarez, President
Ed: Denis A. Gregoire, Dean A. Shepherd. **Description:** The effects of differences among opportunity ideas on entrepreneurs' opportunity beliefs are investigated. Results indicate that the formation of opportunity beliefs is influenced by the superficial and structural similarities of technology-market combinations and individual differences pay a significant role in moderating these relationships. **Availability:** Download; Electronic publishing; PDF; Online.

26437 ■ "Thinking Strategically About Technology" in Franchising World (Vol. 42, August 2010, No. 8, pp. 9)
Pub: International Franchise Association
Contact: Matthew Haller, President
E-mail: mhaller@franchise.org
Ed: Bruce Franson. **Released:** 2010. **Description:** Nearly 25 percent of companies waste money from their technology budget. Most of the budget is spent on non-strategic software. Ways to spend money on technology for any franchise are examined. **Availability:** Online.

26438 ■ "TiVo, Domino's Team to Offer Pizza Ordering by DVR" in Advertising Age (Vol. 79, November 17, 2008, No. 43, pp. 48)
Pub: Crain Communications, Inc.
Contact: Jessica Botos, Manager, Marketing
E-mail: jessica.botos@crainsnewyork.com
Ed: Brian Steinberg. **Description:** Domino's Pizza and TiVo are teaming up to make it possible for customers to order from the restaurant straight from their DVR. The companies see that this kind of interactive television and consumer experience will

only serve to generate more sales as the customer can be exposed to a fuller range of menu selections and will not have to interrupt their viewing, while workers can spend more time making the product. **Availability:** Online.

26439 ■ *"To Build for the Future, Reach Beyond the Skies" in Canadian Business (Vol. 83, June 15, 2010, No. 10, pp. 11)*
Pub: Rogers Media Inc.
Contact: Neil Spivak, Chief Executive Officer
Ed: Richard Branson. **Description:** Richard Branson says that tackling an engineering challenge or a scientific venture is a real adventure for an entrepreneur. Branson discusses Virgin's foray into the aviation business and states that at Virgin, they build for the future. **Availability:** Print; Online.

26440 ■ *"TomTom GO910: On the Road Again" in Black Enterprise (Vol. 37, January 2007, No. 6, pp. 52)*
Pub: Earl G. Graves Ltd.
Contact: Earl Graves, Jr., President
Ed: Stephanie Young. **Description:** TomTom GO 910 is a GPS navigator that offers detailed maps of the U.S., Canada, and Europe. Consumers view their routes by a customizable LCD screen showing everything from the quickest to the shortest routes available or how to avoid toll roads. Business travelers may find this product invaluable as it also functions as a cell phone and connects to a variety of other multi-media devices. **Availability:** Online.

26441 ■ *"Too Much Precaution About Biotech Corn" in Barron's (Vol. 88, March 17, 2008, No. 11, pp. 54)*
Pub: Dow Jones & Company Inc.
Contact: Almar Latour, Chief Executive Officer
Ed: Mark I. Schwartz. **Description:** In the U.S., 90 percent of cultivated soybeans are biotech varietals as well as 60 percent of the corn. Farmers have significantly reduced their reliance on pesticides in the growing of biotech corn. Biotech cotton cultivation has brought hundreds of millions of dollars in net financial gains to farmers. The European Union has precluded the cultivation or sale of biotech crops within its border. **Availability:** Online.

26442 ■ *"Top Architecture Firms" in South Florida Business Journal (Vol. 34, June 13, 2014, No. 47, pp. 13)*
Pub: American City Business Journals, Inc.
Contact: Mike Olivieri, Executive Vice President
Description: The top architectural firms in South Florida, as of June 13, 2014, ranked by gross billings are listed. AECOM Technology Corporation got the top spot, ADD Inc. ranked third. **Availability:** Print; Online.

26443 ■ *"Top Women In Tech: Whether It's Mobile or Engineering, These Mavens Are Making an Impact on Today's Tech Scene" in Black Enterprise (Vol. 44, February 2014, No. 6, pp. 29)*
Pub: Earl G. Graves Ltd.
Contact: Earl Graves, Jr., President
Description: There are fewer women than men in technology, science, engineering, and mathematics professions. As part of the magazine's Women of Power coverage, three successful minority women in their fields are profiled.

26444 ■ *"Transfusion" in Puget Sound Business Journal (Vol. 33, August 31, 2012, No. 19, pp. 1)*
Released: July 12, 2019. **Description:** Seattle, Washington-based nonprofit biotechnology companies have been hiring people with fundraising and scientific skills. The development is part of efforts to find new funding resources. **Availability:** Online.

26445 ■ *"The Transparent Supply Chain" in Harvard Business Review (Vol. 88, October 2010, No. 10, pp. 76)*
Pub: Harvard Business Publishing
Contact: Diane Belcher, Managing Director

Ed: Steve New. **Price:** $8.95, PDF. **Description:** Examination of the use of new technologies to create a transparent supply chain, such as next-generation 2D bar codes in clothing labels that can provide data on a garment's provenance. **Availability:** Online; PDF.

26446 ■ *"Turning Drivers Into Geeks; Auto Dealers Debate Need for Technology Specialists to Bring Buyers Up to Speed" in Crain's Detroit Business (Vol. 30, January 6, 2014, No. 1, pp. 3)*
Pub: Crain Communications Inc.
Contact: Barry Asin, President
Description: Dealers at the 2014 North American International Auto Show discuss the need for technology specialists to educate sales staff as well as customers on the new high-tech items manufactured on today's automobiles and trucks. **Availability:** Print; Online.

26447 ■ *"Two Local Firms Make Inc. List: Minority Business" in Indianapolis Business Journal (Vol. 31, August 30, 2010, No. 26, pp. 13A)*
Description: Smart IT staffing agency and Entap Inc., an IT outsourcing firm were among the top ten fastest growing black-owned businesses in the U.S. by Inc. magazine. **Availability:** Print; Online.

26448 ■ *"UIC Medical Ethicist Faces Life-and-Death Decisions Daily" in Crain's Chicago Business (Vol. 34, October 24, 2011, No. 42, pp. 31)*
Pub: Crain Communications Inc.
Contact: Barry Asin, President
Ed: Lisa Bertagnoli. **Description:** Technology has enabled doctors to provide more and better methods for helping patients, however end of life issues faced by medical ethicists are discussed. **Availability:** Print.

26449 ■ *"Unbreakable: Computer Software" in Canadian Business (Vol. 79, October 9, 2006, No. 20, pp. 111)*
Pub: Rogers Media Inc.
Contact: Neil Spivak, Chief Executive Officer
Ed: Robert Hercz. **Description:** The features and functions of Neutrino, an embedded operating system developed by QNX Software Systems are discussed. **Availability:** Online.

26450 ■ *"Understanding Geeks: A Field Guide To Your Tech Staff" in Inc. (December 2007, pp. 62-63)*
Ed: Adam Bluestein. **Description:** Guide to demystify managing the information technology staff of any small business is presented, including a list of do's and don'ts and a glossary of technical terms. **Availability:** Online.

26451 ■ *"UTM Appliances Protect Small Businesses/Hotspots/Branch Offices" in Product News Network (March 7, 2012)*
Pub: Thomas Publishing Company
Contact: Tony Uphoff, President
E-mail: tuphoff@thomaspublishing.com
Description: Five 1GbE ports, WatchGuard(R) XTM 25 and XTM 26 are profiled. All deliver intrusion prevention, spam-blocking, and gateway anti-virus functionality. Borth models profiled integrate VPN, HTTPS inspection and VoIP support along with options for Application Control and other WatchGuard security services already available. Details are included. **Availability:** Online.

26452 ■ *"UTSA Entrepreneur Program Receives Federal Designation" in San Antonio Business Journal (Vol. 28, June 6, 2014, No. 17, pp. 7)*
Pub: American City Business Journals, Inc.
Contact: Mike Olivieri, Executive Vice President
Released: Weekly. **Price:** $4, Introductory 4-week offer(Digital & Print). **Description:** The National Science Foundation has designated the University of Texas at San Antonio (UTSA) as an Innovation Corps Site because of its strong entrepreneurial system through the Center for Innovation and Technology Entrepreneurship. The UTSA expects to see an increase in entrepreneurial activity and successful technology commercialization with such designation. **Availability:** Print; Online.

26453 ■ *"Valenti: Roots of Financial Crisis Go Back to 1998" in Crain's Detroit Business (Vol. 24, October 6, 2008, No. 40, pp. 25)*
Pub: Crain Communications Inc.
Contact: Barry Asin, President
Ed: Tom Henderson, Nathan Skid. **Description:** Interview with Sam Valenti III who is the chairman and CEO of Valenti Capital L.L.C., a wealth-management firm; Valenti discusses in detail the history that led up to the current economic crisis as well as his prediction for the future of the country. **Availability:** Print; Online.

26454 ■ *"Venturing Into New Territory: Career Experiences of Corporate Venture Capital Managers and Practice Variation" in Academy of Management Journal (Vol. 55, June 1, 2012, No. 3, pp. 563)*
Pub: Academy of Management
Contact: Sharon Alvarez, President
Ed: Gina Dokko, Vibha Gaba. **Description:** The role of venture capital managers' experiences in information technology firms' practice variation is investigated. Findings reveal that firms with managers who have practice-specific experience invest more in diverse industries and early-stage startups. The firm's goal orientation also tend to change from financial to strategic when venture capital managers have firm-specific experience and engineering experience. **Availability:** Electronic publishing; Download; PDF; Online.

26455 ■ *"Verizon's Big Gamble Comes Down to the Wire" in Globe & Mail (February 3, 2007, pp. B1)*
Ed: Catherine McLean. **Description:** The launch of a new broadband service by Verizon Communications Inc. based on fiber optic cable technology is discussed. The company has spent $23 billion for introducing the new service. **Availability:** Online.

26456 ■ *"Virgin Mobile has Big Plans for Year Two" in Globe & Mail (March 6, 2006, pp. B5)*
Ed: Catherine McLean. **Description:** The business growth plans of Virgin Mobile Canada are presented. **Availability:** Online.

26457 ■ *"Watson May Study New Field" in Business Review Albany (Vol. 41, July 18, 2014, No. 17, pp. 10)*
Description: IBM Corporation has extended its Watson computer system's cognitive capacities to the Cloud. Rensselaer Polytechnic Institute has been training Watson to be a data advisor. It is also using the system to study human thought and cognition. **Availability:** Print; Online.

26458 ■ *"We're Ignoring the Only Industry We Can't Do Without" in Entrepreneur (Apr 11, 2019)*
URL(s): www.entrepreneur.com/article/331120
Ed: Kim Walsh. **Released:** April 11, 2019. **Description:** Discusses the need for agricultural practices to make significant advances to support growing agribusiness needs -- agritech. **Availability:** Online.

26459 ■ *"What Keeps Global Leaders Up at Night" in Harvard Business Review (Vol. 90, April 2012, No. 4, pp. 32)*
Pub: Harvard Business Review Press
Contact: Moderna V. Pfizer, Contact
Price: $6. **Description:** A chart uses colored squares to portray economic, environmental, geopolitical, societal, and technological concerns of industry leaders, and ranks them according to likelihood and impact. **Availability:** PDF; Online.

26460 ■ *"What Online Brokers Are Doing To Keep Their Customers' Accounts Safe" in Barron's (Vol. 88, March 10, 2008, No. 10, pp. 37)*
Pub: Dow Jones & Company Inc.
Contact: Almar Latour, Chief Executive Officer

Ed: Theresa W. Carey. **Description:** Online brokerage firms employ different methods to protect the accounts of their customers from theft. These methods include secure Internet connections, momentary passwords, and proprietary algorithms. **Availability:** Online.

26461 ■ *"What We Know - And What We Don't - About Apple TV"* in Barron's (Vol. 92, August 25, 2012, No. 38, pp. 27)
Pub: Dow Jones & Company Inc.
Contact: Almar Latour, Chief Executive Officer
Ed: Alexander Eule. **Description:** Apple Inc.'s entry into the television market is not likely to involve an introduction of disruptive technologies. Cable companies are the most likely partners of Apple as it seeks to enter the televisiion broadcasting market. **Availability:** Online.

26462 ■ *"What's Working Now: In Providing Jobs for North Carolinians"* in Business North Carolina (Vol. 28, February 2008, No. 2, pp. 16)
Pub: Business North Carolina
Contact: Peggy Knaack, Manager
E-mail: pknaack@businessnc.com
Ed: Edward Martin, Frank Maley. **Description:** Individuals previously employed in the furniture, tobacco, or textile manufacturing sectors have gone back to school to be trained in new sectors in the area such as life sciences, finances and other emerging sectors. **Availability:** Online.

26463 ■ *"Why Alabama's Aerospace Is Still Sitting Pretty After 777X"* in Birmingham Business Journal (Vol. 31, January 10, 2014, No. 2, pp. 3)
Pub: American City Business Journals, Inc.
Contact: Mike Olivieri, Executive Vice President
Released: Weekly. **Price:** $4, introductory 4-week offer(Digital & Print). **Description:** Alabama's aerospace sector can still benefit from Boeing despite the state's failure to attract the company's 777X project. Boeing is planning to do some of the project's engineering work in Huntsville, Alabama. The company plans to move about 400 engineering jobs to the state. **Availability:** Print; Online.

26464 ■ *"Why Intel Should Dump Its Flash-Memory Business"* in Barron's (Vol. 88, March 10, 2008, No. 10, pp. 35)
Pub: Dow Jones & Company Inc.
Contact: Almar Latour, Chief Executive Officer
Ed: Eric J. Savitz. **Description:** Intel Corp. must sell its NAND flash-memory business as soon as it possibly can to the highest bidder to focus on its PC processor business and take advantage of other business opportunities. Apple should consider a buyback of 10 percent of the company's shares to lift its stock. **Availability:** Online.

26465 ■ *"Why Life Science Needs Its Own Silicon Valley: Human Genomics Won't Reach Its Full Potential Until It Has a Sizable Industry Cluster"* in Harvard Business Review (Vol. 90, July-August 2012, No. 7-8, pp. 25)
Pub: Harvard Business Review Press
Contact: Moderna V. Pfizer, Contact
Ed: Fariborz Ghadar, John Sviokla, Dietrich A. Stephan. **Price:** $6, PDF and hardcover black and white. **Description:** The creation of an industry cluster will be key to advancing human genomics research. High degrees of specialization via multiple contributors will be needed to generate significant innovations; an accessible, coherent data source will also be necessary. **Availability:** Print; PDF; Online.

26466 ■ *"Wi-Fi Finds Its Way Despite Nixed Plan for Free System"* in Crain's Cleveland Business (Vol. 28, November 12, 2007, No. 45, pp. 3)
Pub: Crain Communications Inc.
Contact: K. C. Crain, President

Ed: Jay Miller. **Description:** Discusses the issues facing Cleveland and Northeast Ohio concerning their proposal to offer citizens wireless Internet services for free or a small fee. **Availability:** Online.

26467 ■ *"Winners & Losers"* in Canadian Business (Vol. 85, July 16, 2012, No. 11-12, pp. 22)
Description: Canadian Pacific Railway's 4,800 locomotive engineers and conductors walked out in protest of the proposed work rules and pension cuts. Shareholders rejected a $25-million bonus and retention payout to Astral Media chief executive officer Ian Greenburg. The Dragon spacecraft of Space Exploration Technologies delivered supplies and experiments to the International Space Station. **Availability:** Print.

26468 ■ *"Woodlands Tech Company Grapples With a Rapidly Changing Market"* in Houston Business Journal (Vol. 44, January 10, 2014, No. 36, pp. 6)
Pub: American City Business Journals, Inc.
Contact: Mike Olivieri, Executive Vice President
Released: Weekly. **Price:** $4, Introductory 4-week offer(Digital & Print). **Description:** Woodlands, Texas-based UniPixel Inc. has experienced some significant changes in 2013 that cause the company to experience rapid rises and falls. The resignation of the company's CEO, Reed Killion, from his position resulted in a drop in UniPixel shares from $11.80 on December 30 to $10.08 on December 31. The story behind the rise and fall of UniPixel's share prices is also presented. **Availability:** Print; Online.

26469 ■ *"The Yahoo Family Tree"* in Conde Nast Portfolio (Vol. 2, June 2008, No. 6, pp. 34)
Pub: Conde Nast Publications
Contact: Agnes Chu, President
Ed: Blaise Zerega. **Description:** Yahoo, founded in 1994 by Stanford students Jerry Yang and David Filo, is still an Internet powerhouse. The company's history is also outlined as well as the reasons in which Microsoft desperately wants to acquire the firm. **Availability:** Print.

VIDEO/AUDIO MEDIA

26470 ■ *Automotive Technology & Digital Retailing*
URL(s): www.startuphustlepodcast.com/automotive-technology-digital-retailing
Ed: Matt Watson. **Released:** February 27, 2024. **Description:** Podcast discusses automotive technology and online car-buying platforms.

26471 ■ *How I Built This: Advice Line with Leah Solivan of Taskrabbit*
URL(s): wondery.com/shows/how-i-built-this/episode/10386-advice-line-with-leah-solivan-of-taskrabbit
Ed: Guy Raz. **Released:** September 16, 2024. **Description:** Podcast offers advice for tech founders wanting to identify and grow their customer base. .

26472 ■ *Software QA Solutions*
URL(s): www.startuphustlepodcast.com/software-qa-solutions
Ed: Matthews Watson. **Released:** November 20, 2023. **Description:** Podcast discusses software QA solutions, optimal timing for QA processes, and debates manual vs. automated QA.

26473 ■ *What's New with ChatGPT and Scaling into Product Market Fit*
URL(s): www.startuphustlepodcast.com/whats-new-with-chatgpt-and-scaling-into-product-market-fit
Ed: Matthews Watson. **Released:** December 2023. **Description:** Podcast discusses the latest developments in ChatGPT, navigating the product-market fit, and the evolving landscape (and ethical considerations) of AI.

26474 ■ *Why Building Software Is Getting Easier*
Ed: Matt Watson. **Released:** January 10, 2024. **Description:** Podcast discusses software development for non-tech founders, the challenges of scaling, data transfer from legacy systems, and fragmented microservices.

RESEARCH CENTERS

26475 ■ **Georgia Institute of Technology - Advanced Technology Development Center (ATDC)**
Tech Sq.
75 5th St. NW Ste. 2000
Atlanta, GA 30308
Ph: (404)894-3575
Fax: (404)894-4545
Co. E-mail: ivy@atdc.org
URL: http://atdc.org
Contact: John Avery, Director
E-mail: john.avery@atdc.org
URL(s): catalog.gatech.edu/academics/research-support-facilities/advanced-technology-development-center
Facebook: www.facebook.com/atdcgt
Linkedin: www.linkedin.com/company/atdc
X (Twitter): x.com/atdc
Instagram: www.instagram.com/theatdc
YouTube: www.youtube.com/channel/UCX6GcHHK2E0_XlcSwkfOdrw
Description: A start-up accelerator helping technology entrepreneurs in Georgia. **Scope:** Promotes the development of advanced technology-based companies throughout Georgia. including firms involved in advanced structural materials, electronic equipment, biotechnology, health and medical products, artificial intelligence, environmental sciences, telecommunications, aerospace systems, instrumentation and test equipment, robotics, and related technologies. **Founded:** 1980. **Publications:** *Technology Partners* (Quarterly).

26476 ■ **National Center for Technology Planning (NCTP)**
PO Box 2393
Tupelo, MS 38803
Ph: (662)844-9630
Fax: (662)844-9630
URL: http://www.nctp.com
Contact: Dr. Larry S. Anderson, Director
E-mail: larry@nctp.com
Description: Independent, nonprofit research and education organization. Offers consulting services. **Scope:** Technology planning, with dissemination looking to guide those developing technology plans, working on unfinished technology plans, implementing new technology plans, or evaluating current plans. **Founded:** 1992. **Educational Activities:** NCTP Speeches and presentations; NCTP Workshops.

26477 ■ **Progress Corporate Park**
Progress Blvd.
Alachua, FL 32615
URL: http://progressparkfl.com
Contact: Sandy Burgess, Contact
E-mail: sandy@burgessms.com
Description: Research and technology park of the University of Florida developed in cooperation with and under primary control of Echelon International Corporation. Offers assistance in entrepreneurial development, commercialization of scientific and technological innovations, and international marketing. **Scope:** 200-acre research and technology park open to both public and private research and manufacturing organizations emphasizing high-technology development, including electronics, biotechnology, advanced materials, pharmacology, and agriculture. Center provides a link between University researchers and industry and transfers new technologies from the laboratory to the marketplace. **Founded:** 1984.

26478 ■ **University of California, Berkeley - Berkeley Roundtable on International Economy (BRIE)**
330 Sutardja Dai Hall
Berkeley, CA 94720
Co. E-mail: brie.dept@berkeley.edu
URL: http://brie.berkeley.edu
Contact: Stephen S. Cohen, Professor
Linkedin: www.linkedin.com/company/berkeleyroundtable
Description: Integral unit of University of California at Berkeley. **Scope:** Policy studies of the interaction of high technology development and the international economy. **Founded:** 1982. **Publications:** *BRIE Working Paper Series*.

www.ingramcontent.com/pod-product-compliance
Lightning Source LLC
Jackson TN
JSHW060747100425
82367JS00003B/56